THE NATIONAL REGISTER OF HISTORIC PLACES 1972

THE
NATIONAL
REGISTER
OF
HISTORIC
PLACES

1972

Statue of Liberty National Monument, New York, New York. *NPS*

This is the second publication in book form of THE NATIONAL
REGISTER OF HISTORIC PLACES. It was prepared in the Office of
Archeology and Historic Preservation (Robert M. Utley, Director) by
the staff of the National Register of Historic Places (William J.
Murtagh, Keeper of the National Register, Elizabeth A. Dippel, Editor).
All photographs in this book are by the National Park Service except
where otherwise specified.

Future listings in THE NATIONAL REGISTER OF HISTORIC PLACES will be
made through additions to the National Park Service by Acts of
Congress, designations as National Historic Landmarks by the
Secretary of the Interior and by nominations from the States and
Federal agencies.

Contents current through June 1971.

For sale by the Superintendent of Documents,
U.S. Government Printing Office, Washington, D.C. 20402
Price $7.80 domestic postpaid, or $7.25 GPO Bookstore
Stock Number 2405-0294

Foreword

The story of America has been, throughout, a story of accelerating growth and change. Securely settled into a tradition of taking, moving on, and not looking back, Americans since 1900 have been faced increasingly with the prospect of virtually destroying their natural and historical birthright in the name of progress.

The problem was recognized early by small groups of devoted conservationists, through whose efforts much landmark legislation has been passed. Of primary significance in the preservation of our historic past have been the Antiquities Act of 1906, which extended protection over antiquities on Federal property and empowered the President to set aside portions of the public domain as National Monuments; the Organic Act of 1916 creating the National Park Service; the Historic Sites Act of 1935, which provided for historical units of the National Park System and authorized a program for identifying and marking National Historic Landmarks; and the National Historic Preservation Act of 1966, which extended the policy of historic preservation to every Federal agency and acknowledged Federal concern for historical values important to the States and communities of the Nation.

On May 13, 1971, in an executive action without precedent, President Nixon issued Executive Order 11593, which further emphasized the Federal role in preserving, restoring, and maintaining the historical and cultural environment of the Nation. This pronouncement, stressing the responsibilities attached to Federal stewardship of historic properties, calls upon all Federal agencies to participate actively in the preservation of the Nation's patrimony. It recognizes that the American people will hold their government accountable for this stewardship in terms of how effectively that government has directed its policies, plans, and programs toward the enjoyment by future generations of those historic properties it now holds in trust.

The machinery has been set up by which Americans can identify those reminders of the past worth saving, and the weapons have been forged by which they can be defended against destruction without due process. The successful utilization of this machinery and these weapons is dependent on the continuing devotion of the American people to the cause of historic preservation.

Rogers CB Morton

Secretary of the Interior

Preface

In recent years the traditional role of the National Park Service has been greatly expanded. From guardianship of America's prime natural, historic, and prehistoric monuments, our task has grown to include new responsibilities in providing for the recreational and cultural needs of modern America. The National Historic Preservation Act of 1966 is a logical part of those new responsibilities.

Initially, the National Register of Historic Places included only properties that possessed national significance and were either units of the National Park System or qualified for status as National Historic Landmarks. Under the Historic Sites Act of 1935, National Park Service historians study and evaluate historic properties throughout the country. Acting upon their findings and the recommendations of the Advisory Board on National Parks, Historic Sites, Buildings, and Monuments, the Secretary of the Interior may declare the properties eligible for designation as National Historic Landmarks. The owner of such a property is offered a certificate and a bronze plaque designating it a National Historic Landmark. In return he agrees to preserve those significant historical values for which it was singled out.

The National Historic Preservation Act of 1966 called for the expansion of the National Register to include historic properties of State and local significance. It charged the States with the responsibility for carrying out the surveys necessary for this expansion, to be accomplished with the assistance of the Department of the Interior. The 50 States, the District of Columbia, the three territories, and the Commonwealth of Puerto Rico have each appointed a liaison officer to coordinate this multilevel program. The National Park Service

and the State Liaison Officers, working together in a close partnership to effect its provisions, have already expanded the National Register to some 3,500 entries, and it is still growing.

The historical surveys also contribute to the preparation of the State's historic preservation plan, the public document which projects within the national context the program for preserving that State's historic patrimony. National Park Service approval of a statewide historic preservation plan makes possible the application of Federal funds for individual historic preservation projects within that State. The National Historic Preservation Act authorizes matching grants-in-aid to the States and the National Trust to assist them in historic preservation. Grants may be allocated to the survey, acquisition, or preservation of State, locally, or privately owned properties. Grants-in-aid constitute a growing program which to date has provided the States slightly more than $5.1 million for conducting historical surveys and over $4.1 million for acquiring and restoring historic properties. In addition, the National Trust has received $2.5 million to fund its acquisition, preservation, and technical assistance programs. An Advisory Council on Historic Preservation composed of seven Federal officers of cabinet rank, the Chairman of the National Trust, the secretary of the Smithsonian Institution, the Administrator of the General Services Administration, and 10 citizens appointed by the President of the United States has been created under Title II of the Act, as amended. Their duty is to advise the President and the Congress on matters pertaining to historic preservation. The Council is the Federal Government's clearing house for historic preservation. It is a vigorous and creative body which has worked quite successfully in countering threats to the historical integrity of properties listed on the National Register.

The Advisory Council's strength and the National Register's defense is section 106 of the Act:

> Section 106. The head of any Federal agency having direct or indirect jurisdiction over a proposed Federal or federally assisted undertaking in any State and the head of any Federal department or independent agency having authority to license any undertaking shall, prior to the approval of the expenditure of any Federal funds on the undertaking or prior to the issuance of any license, as the case may be, take into account the effect of the undertaking on any district, site, building, structure, or object that is included in the National Register. The head of any such Federal agency shall afford the Advisory Council on Historic Preservation established under title II of this Act a reasonable opportunity to comment with regard to such undertaking.

In evaluating "effect" within the meaning of section 106, the Advisory Council is guided by the following criteria:

> A federally financed or licensed undertaking shall be considered to have an effect on a National Register listing (districts, sites, buildings, structures, and objects including their settings) when any condition of the undertaking creates a change in the quality of the historical, architectural, archeological, or cultural character that qualified the property under the National Register criteria for listing in the National Register.
>
> Generally, adverse effect occurs under conditions which include but are not limited to:
>
> a. destruction or alteration of all or part of a property;
> b. isolation from or alteration of its surrounding environment; or
> c. introduction of visual, audible, or atmospheric elements that are out of character with the property and its setting.

Of 192 cases which have arisen under section 106 during the past three years, only 21 have been referred to the Advisory Council. The remaining 171 cases were settled according to procedures of the Advisory Council by agreement among the agency involved, the State, and the National Park Service.

President Nixon, promulgating Executive Order 11593, charged the heads of Federal agencies with two basic tasks: first, the preservation of historic properties under their jurisdiction, and, second, nomination of such properties to the National Register. Nominations of these properties are to be submitted by July 1, 1973.

Responsibility for consulting the National Register in potential section 106 cases is placed upon the Federal agency carrying out, financing, or licensing the undertaking. If such an undertaking would affect any National Register property, the agency is also responsible for affording the Advisory Council an opportunity to comment.

The National Park Service is prepared to provide professional advice and assistance concerning National Register consultation, agency procedures, and potential section 106 issues with the view to resolving such issues by mutual agreement before it becomes necessary to refer them to the Council.

The National Park Service is pleased to present this second edition of the National Register. A mature society looks with respect upon its past and with confidence toward its future. It is our sincere hope that this volume will contribute to that outlook in our society as its awareness of our cultural patrimony grows.

Contents

Notes on Arrangement and Terminology of Entries

1. States and territories are listed alphabetically.
2. County
   a. In **States** with county subdivisions these divisions are used and counties appear in alphabetical order.
   b. In Louisiana the similar subdivisions are termed *parishes*.
   c. In Alaska the divisions used correspond to judicial districts except when a property is situated in one of the newly constituted boroughs and the borough name is used.
   d. Baltimore, St. Louis, and various other cities are designated *independent cities* because they are administratively independent of any county.
   e. Puerto Rico and the Virgin Islands have no comparable subdivisions.
3. Entries containing the name of a person are alphabetized according to surname; other entries follow a standard pattern of alphabetization.
4. Properties not within a municipality are listed under the nearest city or town followed by the word *vicinity*.
5. In the case of some historic districts boundaries are too detailed to be included in this book but are on file in the office of the National Register.
6. The historic districts originally recognized under the Historic Sites Act of 1935 often have no boundary designations. The Act provided no legal protection for these districts, and, at the time, such designations were not necessary. The National Park Service has already or is in the process of defining boundaries for all historic districts that have been designated National Historic Landmarks.
7. Date and Architect
   a. Whenever known the date of construction for a building, structure, or object is listed.
   b. Historic districts are dated according to the period or periods of the predominant architectural styles.
   c. Historic sites such as battlefields are dated according to the event for which the site is recognized.
   d. Archeological sites are dated according to the principal period of occupation.
   e. Unless otherwise specified all dates are A.D.
   f. Any significant secondary or associated dates are given in the text.
   g. The name following the date indicates the architectural firm, architect, or engineer who designed the structure. Carpenters, builders, commissioners, or owners, if significant, are noted in the text.

Following each entry is abbreviated information about ownership and accessibility to the public. Frequently the designations NHL, NPS, and/or HABS or HAER appear, and these are explained as follows:

1. NHL — A National Historic Landmark is a building, structure, site, object, or district of national importance not administered by the National Park Service; each entry has been declared eligible for recognition by the Secretary of the Interior under the provisions of the Historic Sites Act of 1935; National Landmarks may be in Federal, State, municipal, county, or private hands or any combination thereof.

2. NPS — Sites within the National Park system are administered by the Park Service or by **State** or

private organizations in cooperation with the Park Service. The total acreage of such Park Service areas, both Federal and non-Federal, is given, and if the land has been authorized for purchase by the Federal government but not yet acquired, it is so noted.

3. HABS – A HABS designation indicates that documentation by photographs, measured drawings, and/or data sheets has been made by the Historic American Buildings Survey of the National Park Service as evidence of a building's historical or architectural significance. Records are deposited at the Library of Congress.

4. HAER – A HAER designation means that a property has been recognized and recorded as an important example of American engineering. The Historic American Engineering Record is conducted by the National Park Service in cooperation with the American Society of Civil Engineers. Records are kept at the Library of Congress.

All properties are accessible unless otherwise noted.

TERMINOLOGY

1. Building – a structure created to shelter any form of human activity.
2. Structure – a work constructed by man.
3. Object – a material thing of functional, aesthetic, cultural, historical, or scientific value that is usually, by nature or design, movable.
4. Site – the location of an event, building, structure, or object.
5. District – a geographically definable area, urban or rural, possessing a significant concentration or linkage of sites, buildings, structures, or objects unified by past events or aesthetically by plan or physical development.

Exemptions

Section 107 of the National Historic Preservation Act of 1966 (P.L. 89–665) as amended states:

Nothing in this Act shall be construed to be applicable to the White House and its grounds, the Supreme Court building and its grounds, or the United States Capitol and its related buildings and grounds.

The following are the exempted historic properties in Washington, D.C., protected by other provisions of law, which would otherwise be eligible for inclusion in the National Register. Therefore, the entries for these nationally significant structures are here included for purposes of historical information and reference only.

LIBRARY OF CONGRESS

1st Street and Independence Avenue, S.E.
1886–1897, Smithmeyer and Pelz

The Library of Congress, established in 1800, contains over 43,000,000 items and is one of the world's largest libraries. Although founded primarily to serve the Congress, the Library has expanded its field of service to include government agencies, serious scholars, other libraries, and the general public. It has also become the office of copyright registry and deposit. Originally housed in the Capitol, the Library was moved to its present location in 1897. The French Rennaissance building is three stories high on a raised basement and was constructed of gray granite. This main building is now supplemented by the Library Annex.

Federal
NHL

SUPREME COURT BUILDING

1st and E. Capitol Streets, N.E.
1935, Cass Gilbert

The Supreme Court Building is an impressive marble structure of classical Roman temple design. Its massive rectangular center section is flanked by one-story wings. The entire structure rests on a raised basement approached by a wide flight of marble stairs. A double row of Corinthian columns topped by a sculptured pediment completes the facade. The pediment sculpture on the west facade incorporates real personages (Charles Evans Hughes, Cass Gilbert, Elihu Root, John Marshall, and William Howard Taft) into symbolic groupings, and on the east facade are representatives of Eastern lawgivers (Moses, Confucius, Solon). The interior courtroom is characterized by its symmetry and highlighted by bronze grillwork screens. Nine justices sit on the bench of the Supreme Court, which is the final court of appeal and decision for cases involving federal law, state law, and questions of constitutional interpretation.

Federal

UNITED STATES CAPITOL

Capitol Hill
1793–1802, Dr. William Thornton
1803–1817, Benjamin Henry Latrobe
1819–1829, Charles Bulfinch
1836–1851, Robert Mills
1851–1865, Thomas Ustick Walter

The United States Capitol, with only one brief exception, has housed the legislative chambers of Congress since 1800. In addition, the Supreme Court sat here from 1800 until 1935. Traditionally, presidential inaugurations are held on the east front. In the old basement Supreme Court room Samuel F. B. Morse tapped out the world's first telegraph message in 1844. Construction on the Capitol began on September 18, 1793, when President George Washington laid the cornerstone. All 16 states then in the Union are represented by the 16 columns in the rotunda of the north wing. Tobacco leaves, representing an important product of the young nation, form the Corinthian capitals of these columns. Much of the interior painting was executed by Constantino Brumidi, whose most monumental work is the fresco on the rotunda dome.

Federal
NHL; HABS

WHITE HOUSE

1600 Pennsylvania Avenue, N.W.
1800, James Hoban
1824, Benjamin Latrobe
1902, McKim, Mead, and White
1952, Lorenzo Winslow

The White House has been the residence of every President of the United States since John Adams. It was the first public building erected in the District of Columbia. Constructed of Virginia sandstone, the house was painted white after having been burned by the British in 1814. The exterior of the house remains essentially unaltered except for minor changes and additions. The interior, however, has undergone numerous alterations. A complete renovation and several additions were completed during the Truman administration (1948–1952) with extensive interior restoration and redecoration during the Kennedy administration.

Federal
NPS; 18.07 acres

Alabama

Oakleigh, Mobile, Alabama. *Thigpen Photography*

Statue of Booker T. Washington, Tuskegee Institute, Tuskegee, Alabama. *NPS*

Ordeman-Shaw Historic District, Montgomery, Alabama. *Frank L. Thiemonge III*

Barton Academy, Mobile, Alabama. *Roy Thigpen*

BALDWIN COUNTY
Gasque vicinity
FORT MORGAN
Western terminus of Ala. 180
1833–1834

Guarding the entrance to Mobile Bay, Fort Morgan was significant to Admiral David G. Farragut's naval battle of August 1864, which opened the bay to the Union Navy and sealed off the port to Confederate commercial and supply ships. It was surrendered by the Confederate commanding officer, Brigadier General Richard L. Page, August 23. The original ten-sided brick citadel, repaired by the Union forces after its capture, is still in excellent condition.
State
NHL

BARBOUR COUNTY
Eufaula
BRAY-BARRON HOME
N. Eufaula Avenue
19th century

This house, built prior to 1850 by Nathan Bray, is one of Alabama's better examples of a mid-19th-century middle-class town house. Representative of Greek Revival architecture, the one-story white frame dwelling is constructed with heavy hand-hewn sills, 56 feet long. The porch, which extends the length of the front facade, has six Doric columns connected by a banister railing. The double entrance doors are flanked by sidelights and topped by a fanlight. Interior plan is central hall. The original brick cook house in the rear yard is connected to the house by a gallery.
Private

BARBOUR COUNTY
Eufaula
CATO HOUSE
823 W. Barbour Street
1858

Lewis Llewellyn Cato, known as "the great secessionist," was a friend of secessionist William Lowndes Yancey's and an active member of the Eufaula Regency, probably the leading secessionist organization in the state. His home was the scene of many secessionist meetings during the late 1850's. When Alabama seceded from the Union, a great celebration was held at the Cato House. The five-bay, T-shaped frame dwelling is a Greek Revival style cottage. It has a square-piered gallery extending the length of the front facade, and the roof is surmounted by a balustraded peristyle.
Private

BARBOUR COUNTY
Eufaula
FENDALL HALL
Barbour Street
19th century

Fendall Hall is an Italianate, antebellum home built by Eufaula merchant and banker Edward Brown Young. The two-story frame structure is distinguished by a cupola and widow's walk atop the hip roof. Identical brackets support the cornices of the cupola and the main roof. Eight pairs of colonettes line the front porch with five more on each side. Carved wood scallops separate the pairs of colonettes. Inside, the central hall, with a floor of black and white Italian marble, runs the length of the house. Gold leaf medallions adorn the ceilings above the chandeliers in the dining and drawing rooms.
Private

BARBOUR COUNTY
Eufaula
McNAB BANK BUILDING
Broad Street
Mid–19th century

During its early history Alabama had a state monopoly on banking. A law, passed in 1850, allowed for the chartering of one free bank at each session of the legislature. Such banks provided a circulation medium for trade and funds for state use when other money was unavailable. The Eastern Bank of Alabama, one of the oldest standing bank buildings in the state, was one of these early free banks. It was chartered in 1858, and some time after 1864 the name was changed to the John McNab Bank. Stylistically the bank is Italian Renaissance Revival. Its facade is cast iron on the first floor and has cast iron decoration on the second. The second-floor overhanging balcony has a lacy grillwork balustrade. Iron shutters on the first floor pull down over the windows and can be locked. All ceilings inside the bank are plaster, and two original fireplaces survive. The bank operated until 1891.
Private

BARBOUR COUNTY
Eufaula
SHEPPARD COTTAGE
E. Barbour Street
1837

The oldest residence in Eufaula, Sheppard Cottage, is one of Alabama's better examples of a Southern adaptation of a Cape Cod cottage. It was constructed of clapboard, using wooden pegs and hand worked laths. The structure consists of a raised brick basement, a main floor, and an attic. The 17th-century style sloping roof has brick end chimneys. The raised basement of the cottage and its floor plan are distinctly Southern. Four sidelights and eight fanlights surround the double doors of the front entrance, which is approached by a stairway on either side.
Public

BARBOUR COUNTY
Eufaula
THE TAVERN (RIVER TAVERN)
105 Riverside Drive
1836

The Tavern was the first permanent structure erected in Irwinton (forerunner of Eufaula), an early 19th-century trading settlement on the Chattahoochee River. Built by Edward Williams as an inn, it served as a stopping place for steamboat passengers. The Tavern has also been a residence, an Episcopal church, and a hospital during the Civil War. There is a two-story gallery across the main facade which has square columns on the ground floor and round ones above. The upper gallery is enclosed by balusters. Both central doors have sidelights, and the large end chimneys were constructed of handmade brick. Pegs and square nails were used throughout, and the Tavern is one of a few pioneer buildings lacking a central hall.
Private
HABS

BLOUNT COUNTY
Oneonta vicinity
HORTON MILL COVERED BRIDGE
5 miles north of Oneonta on Route 3
1930's

Built as a replacement for a late 19th-century covered bridge, the Horton Mill Covered Bridge is a two-span structure with a Town truss. It measures 220 feet long, 14 feet wide, and 10.5 feet high. Spanning the Calvert prong of the Warrior River, the Horton Bridge is one of only 16 remaining in the state.
State

CALHOUN COUNTY
Jacksonville
FRANCIS, DR. J. C., OFFICE
100 Gayle Street
Early 1850's

Dr. Francis' Office is a typical doctor's office of the 1850's and the only surviving structure of its type in northeast Alabama. The office is frame, one story high, and pilasters mark the front corners and frame the entrance. The entrance has sidelights and a semielliptical fanlight. The unadorned roof pediment is supported by

four fluted Doric columns. Most of the building materials (ceiling, wall boards, exterior lap siding, wood trim on the portico, pilasters, columns, and windows) appear to be original, although the office has been altered. Dr. J. C. Francis came to Jacksonville from Tennessee and practiced medicine here for more than 50 years.
State

COLBERT COUNTY (also in Lauderdale County)
Florence vicinity
WILSON DAM
Tennessee River, on U.S. 72
1918–1925

The suitability of Muscle Shoals on the Tennessee River for a publicly owned hydroelectric plant was recognized as early as 1900. Not until World War I, however, when nitrate plants were required for the manufacture of war supplies, did Congress authorize the construction of Wilson Dam to provide the necessary power. The dam came under the administration of the Tennessee Valley Authority at its inception in 1933. It was the first hydroelectric operation in the system. Its generative capacity is the largest of any of the Tennessee Valley Authority facilities.
Federal
NHL

COLBERT COUNTY
Tuscumbia
IVY GREEN (HELEN KELLER BIRTHPLACE)
300 W. North Common
1820

Ivy Green was built as a one-and-one-half-story frame cottage fronted by a small porch. The main entrance has a rectangular transom and sidelights. Other buildings in the complex are the pumphouse and former office, now the birthplace cottage. Helen Keller was born here on June 27, 1880. At the age of two she became ill and, as a consequence, was left blind and deaf. Unable to communicate with those around her, she was, after great effort, introduced to the world of sight and sound by her teacher Anne Sullivan. Helen Keller developed into an intelligent and sensitive woman who wrote her autobiography *The Story of My Life* (1902) and graduated with honor from Radcliffe College in 1904. She died in 1968 after working all her life for the betterment of the handicapped.
Municipal

DEKALB COUNTY
Fort Payne
FORT PAYNE OPERA HOUSE
510 Gault Avenue, North
Late 19th century

Fort Payne was a boomtown which speculators expected to become a thriving manufacturing city by the late 1880's. Local deposits of coal and iron were to be the basis of the new prosperity. However, within ten years the venture failed. The opera house is one of the few structures remaining from the boomtown era. Its exterior walls are brick topped by a gable roof; inside there are two balconies and a ceiling of heavy oak. The entire opera house has been noticeably altered.
Public/private

ELMORE COUNTY
Wetumpka vicinity
FORT TOULOUSE
4 miles southwest of Wetumpka at confluence of the Coosa and Tallapoosa rivers
1717

Constructed by the French in 1717, Fort Toulouse served until the end of the French and Indian War as the eastern outpost of the Province of Louisiana. It protected settlements from Mobile Bay to New Orleans and formed the potential spearhead of the French drive in the Southeast. Andrew Jackson built Fort Jackson on the abandoned site in 1814. A six-acre tract presently contains the site of the fort, two monuments, and the remains of a probable powder magazine. Remains of an ancient Indian village stand nearby.
Multiple public/private
NHL

GREENE COUNTY
Eutaw
COLEMAN-BANKS HOUSE
430 Springfield Road
Mid–19th century

The Coleman-Banks House is an outstanding example of Greek Revival architecture in Alabama. There are four large, two-story, fluted Ionic columns on the main facade and an unusual second-story overhanging balcony of full veranda length. Both the upper and lower entrances have double doors, pilastered sidelights, and support full entablatures. An original kitchen and smokehouse still survive.
County
HABS

GREENE COUNTY
Eutaw
GREENE COUNTY COURTHOUSE
Courthouse Square
1869

The Greene County Courthouse was constructed on the foundations of its predecessor, a frame building which had burned. Architecturally the courthouse evidences the waning popularity of the Greek Revival style. Pilasters and cornices are its remaining hallmarks, but both are unobtrusive or even vie with the overall structural form. Iron balconies protrude at the second-floor level above all entrances. Built of brick and covered with stucco, the courthouse is two stories high. Both the Probate Office (1856) and the Grand Jury Building (1824) predate the courthouse.
County
HABS

GREENE COUNTY
Forkland vicinity
ROSEMOUNT
1 mile northwest of Forkland
1832–1839

Allen Glover constructed this Greek Revival antebellum mansion with the help of dozens of slaves. The 20-room house has a portico of six Ionic columns above which is a hip roof topped by a temple-like cupola and a widow's walk. This observatory served as a music conservatory and was reached from the second floor by a pulley-operated elevator. Noteworthy architectural features include the handsomely executed fluted columns, identical doorways on the entrances at each level, the woodwork of the four double doors in the large entrance vestibule, and the elaborate cupola. Restoration was undertaken in the 1950's.
Private
HABS

HALE COUNTY
Moundville vicinity
MOUNDVILLE SITE
1 mile west of Moundville on County Route 21
1000–1500

The Moundville Site is a well-preserved ceremonial temple mound site with approximately 20 extant mounds. It includes a small museum which displays artifacts from this site and two burial areas *in situ*. As a major Southern Cult center, it has produced a large quantity of ceremonial material. Excavations during the 1930's revealed that it represents a major period of Mississippian culture in the southern United States.
State
NHL

Bridgeport vicinity
RUSSELL CAVE NATIONAL
MONUMENT
  8 miles west of Bridgeport via U.S. 72
  and County Routes 91 and 75
  c. 7000 B.C. to early 19th-century
  A.D.

At Russell Cave hundreds of generations of prehistoric Americans lived a rigorous and demanding life. The first inhabitants, who occupied the area from about 7000 to 6500 B.C., camped on an irregular floor of rock slabs. For nearly 7000 years the peoples who made the cave a seasonal haven in fall and winter lived by hunting and gathering. Later inhabitants of the Woodland and Mississippian periods were far more advanced technologically. They made pottery and probably practiced primitive agriculture. Artifacts from all periods of occupation have been unearthed by several archeological explorations.
Federal
NPS; 310.45 acres

JEFFERSON COUNTY
Birmingham
ARLINGTON (MUDD-MUNGER
HOME)
  331 Cotton Avenue, S.W.
  19th century

Arlington is believed to be the oldest structure in Birmingham. The west wing of the present house was built about 1822 as a four-room home. A later owner, William Mudd, added the east wing in 1842, and the house assumed its present appearance at that time. Notable exterior features are the tapered, two-story, paneled piers which support the roof of the second-floor veranda. Entrances are also paneled and have side- and fanlights and full entablatures. The house itself is frame with a hip roof. A 20th-century owner was R. S. Munger.
Municipal
HABS

LAUDERDALE COUNTY
WILSON DAM
Reference—see Colbert County

LAUDERDALE COUNTY
Florence
KARSNER-CARROLL HOUSE

  303 N. Pine Street
  Early 19th century

The greatly altered exterior of the one-and-one-half-story brick Karsner-Carroll House conceals an interior notable for its fine Federal style woodwork. Probably built sometime before 1830, this structure is a rare example in the Tennessee valley of sophisticated adornment applied to a house of relatively modest proportions. This is evident in the stairway, the paneled wainscoting, and the elliptical fanlight over the entranceway. Major changes in the house since its construction have been the addition of a front porch and dormer windows and the removal of the south rear portion of the outer wall in order to enlarge the dining area.
Municipal; not accessible to the public

LOWNDES COUNTY
Hayneville
LOWNDES COUNTY COURTHOUSE
  Washington Street
  1856

The Lowndes County Courthouse is one of only four antebellum Alabama courthouses still in use. The two-story structure has a gable roof, low side wings, and a projecting three-bay entrance portico. Walls are brick (first floor) and frame covered with stucco. There were at one time roof pediments on all sides, but considerable alteration was effected about 1905 when the front portico was remodeled and partially enclosed and its roofline and pediment were lowered. Above the main roof is a cupola topped by a ribbed dome. There are double disengaged columns at each corner of the base, and the dome above is octagonal.
County

MACON COUNTY
Tuskegee vicinity
TUSKEGEE INSTITUTE
  1 mile northwest of Tuskegee on U.S.
  80
  1881

Tuskegee Institute, a pioneer Negro educational institution, was chartered by the State of Alabama in 1881. With Booker T. Washington as its first president, it became the core of effort to ameliorate economic handicaps of the Negro through vocational and industrial training. It operates today as a privately endowed college offering a wide educational program. Most of the existing buildings were constructed after 1900. Points of special historical interest include The Oaks, Washington's home; the Booker T. Washington monument; the graves of Washington and George Washington Carver; and the Carver Museum.
Private
NHL

MARENGO COUNTY
Demopolis
BLUFF HALL
  405 N. Commissioners Avenue
  1832–late 1840's

Bluff Hall, set high above the Tombigbee River on White Bluff, was the home of Francis Strother Lyon. The earliest portion of the house, the present main facade, was constructed in 1832, and the columns and west wing were added in the late 1840's. A combination of materials was used in building the Greek Revival house—brick covered with plaster and wood for the back half of the L-shaped north wing. The six front piers are thick, massive, and rather squat in relation to the rest of the house. Side panels and a fanlight transom surround the main entrance, and a similar doorway opens onto a second-floor balcony above. Lyon was a lawyer and cotton planter who served in both the U.S. and Confederate Congresses.
Private
HABS

MARENGO COUNTY
Demopolis
WHITE BLUFF
  Arch Street

White Bluff is a Selma chalk formation above the Tombigbee River in Demopolis. Here, in 1817, a group of French settlers—veterans of the Napoleonic Wars—led by General Charles Lefebvre Desnouettes, landed and founded Demopolis. After the battle of Waterloo a number of Napoleon's supporters were banished from France and fled to America. Gathering in Philadelphia, they petitioned Congress for a land grant and were awarded four contiguous townships near the confluence of the Tombigbee and Black Warrior rivers in Alabama Territory. White Bluff originally towered 70 or 80 feet above the river. Completion of the U.S. Lock and Dam in 1955 raised the water level 40 feet, and the bluff now rises only 20 to 40 feet above the river.
Municipal

MOBILE COUNTY
Mobile
BARTON ACADEMY
  504 Government Street
  1836

The Greek Revival Barton Academy has brick walls covered with stucco on the outside. On all four sides Doric pilasters run from the second floor to the roof cornice. The entrance portico projects slightly from the building's facade. Barton Academy was financed largely by private

funds, and it housed private and denominational schools from 1836 to 1851. In 1852 Mobile voters chose to establish a public school system using the Academy as its nucleus. Classes were held here until 1965. Presently the building houses the offices of the Board of School Commissioners of Mobile County.
County
HABS

MOBILE COUNTY
Mobile
BISHOP PORTIER HOME
307 Conti Street
19th century

The Bishop Portier Home, a one-and-one-half-story "Creole" cottage on a raised basement, served as a residence for ranking prelates of the Roman Catholic Church in Alabama from 1833 to 1914. Constructed of wood, the house has Federal detailing on the exterior—notably the sidelights, transom, engaged pilasters, and entablature of the front door and the segmented, semicircular pediments above the three dormer windows. Michael Portier, first bishop of Alabama (1829–1859), had jurisdiction over Alabama and Florida.
Private
HABS

MOBILE COUNTY
Mobile
FORT CONDÉ-CHARLOTTE
Church and Royal Streets
1717

Jean Baptiste le Moyne, Sieur de Bienville, governor of French Louisiana, built a wooden stockade on this site in 1711 and named it Fort Louis de la Mobile. In 1717 the fort was rebuilt with brick, and it was renamed Fort Condé de la Mobile in 1720. The Treaty of Paris (1763), ending the Seven Years War, ceded West Florida, including Fort Condé to the British. Major Robert Farmer, placed in command of the Mobile district, renamed the fort in honor of Queen Charlotte of England. Don Bernardo de Galvez, governor of Spanish Louisiana, attacked Mobile in 1780 and overwhelmed the British garrison. Political and military events resulted in Spanish acquisition of East and West Florida under a second Treaty of Paris (1783). Under Spanish rule the fort continued to be called Charlotte (Carlota). President James Madison directed American troops to take the fort in 1813, and the Spaniards surrendered without bloodshed. Five years later the sale of the fort and fort lands was authorized by Congress, and the transaction took place in 1820. The masonry fort measured 300 feet from tip to tip of the bastions. Archeological investigations

have revealed that the foundation of the fort was a 3-foot deep footing of burnt shell mortar and sandstone rocks leveled off with brick scraps. The walls of laid brick were placed on this level footing.
State

MOBILE COUNTY
Mobile
HORST, MARTIN, HOUSE
407 Conti Street
1867–1868

This two-story brick dwelling plus service wing is basically Italianate in style, although some Greek Revival detailing is visible. A balcony across the main facade has cast iron columns, and windows and doors are segmentally arched. The front windows are somewhat taller than those on other elevations, and all have cornices and sills of cast iron. The roof cornice is bracketed. A double gallery with wooden columns runs along the back of the house and the service wing. The interior plan is central hall. Martin Horst was a German immigrant who served as mayor of Mobile (1870–1871).
Private
HABS

MOBILE COUNTY
Mobile
MOBILE CITY HALL
111 S. Royal Street
Mid–19th century

The City Hall was completed in 1858 in an area which formerly contained an open-air municipal market. Business continued to be transacted in the various shops around the City Hall until the middle of the 20th century. The building itself served as a militia armory during the Civil War and today houses municipal offices. Italianate in style, the structure is brick covered with stucco. The central twin gabled portion is connected to two smaller outer wings by crenelated arcades.
Municipal
HABS

MOBILE COUNTY
Mobile
MOBILE CITY HOSPITAL (OLD CITY HOSPITAL)
900–950 St. Anthony Street
1830

The Old City Hospital served Mobile from 1831 until 1966, when a new hospital was opened. Brick and plaster are the principal building materials. The architecture is Greek Revival with some late Federal influence. The three-story facade is ornamented by a projecting central portico and giant order Doric columns supporting double roofs above the two-story open

galleries. End bays were added in 1907 and 1908.
Municipal
HABS

MOBILE COUNTY
Mobile
OAKLEIGH
350 Oakleigh Street
1831–1832

The T-plan upon which Oakleigh was built is indigenous to the southeastern United States. Such a plan afforded maximum light and ventilation in a humid climate. Basically it is a two-story raised frame cottage on a brick basement. Galleries with square pillars form a pedimented portico at the base of the "T" (on the main facade). Unique features are the use of a curved staircase to connect the ground and upper levels and the split and hinged panels beneath the windows at the second level. Oakleigh presently serves as headquarters for the Historic Mobile Preservation Society.
Municipal
HABS

MOBILE COUNTY
Mobile
SEMMES, RAPHAEL, HOUSE
804 Government Street
19th century

Raphael Semmes (1809–1879), a rear admiral of the Confederate Navy, lived in this house from 1871 until his death. The house is composed of two rectangles united at their corners. Upper and lower cast iron porches ornament the facade. Semmes retired to Mobile and practiced law there during the ten years preceding his death.
Private
HABS

MONTGOMERY COUNTY
Montgomery
ALABAMA STATE CAPITOL (FIRST CONFEDERATE CAPITOL)
Goat Hill, east end of Dexter Avenue
1851, George Nichols

The first State capitol on this site was destroyed by fire, and the present building, modeled after the original, was constructed in 1851. In February 1861, delegates from six Southern states met here to adopt the provisional constitution for the Confederacy. Here Jefferson Davis took his oath of office as the first President of the Confederacy on February 18, 1861, and the permanent constitution was adopted on March 11. The Confederate Congress met here until the capital was moved to Richmond, Virginia, in May. Originally square, the Greek Revival

building is now T-shaped, the rear wing having been added in 1885, the north and south wings in the early 20th century. The interior of the central portion is essentially unaltered from the Civil War era. The building still serves as the State capitol of Alabama.
State
NHL; HABS

MONTGOMERY COUNTY
Montgomery
ORDEMAN-SHAW HISTORIC DISTRICT
Bounded on the west by a line midway between McDonough and Hull Streets; on the north by Randolph Street; on the east by a line midway between Hull and Decatur Streets (to Jefferson Street) and by Decatur Street; and on the south by Madison Avenue
Mid–19th century

The Ordeman-Shaw Historic District is a complex containing the Ordeman-Shaw House, a slave quarters, the DeWolfe-Cooper Cottage, the Campbell-Holtzclaw Cottage, and laundry-necessary outbuildings. The Ordeman-Shaw House is a modified, two-story Italianate residence of brick covered with scored stucco. Outbuildings are also brick, although only the slave quarters is original. The Campbell-Holtzclaw Cottage, as yet unrestored, is a one-story dwelling with a Greek Revival front portico. The DeWolfe-Cooper Cottage, modified Gothic Revival, was moved to its present site in 1970. Charles Ordeman, architect and civil engineer, completed the Ordeman-Shaw House (which had been begun in 1842) and built the Campbell Cottage in 1852. He also put up the slave quarters and outbuildings. Restoration has been undertaken in an effort to recreate a building complex in a Southern town during the economic boom preceding the Civil War.
Multiple public/private

RUSSELL COUNTY
Holy Trinity vicinity
APALACHICOLA FORT
1.5 miles east of Holy Trinity on Chattahoochee River
1690

The northernmost Spanish outpost on the Chattahoochee River, Apalachicola Fort was built to prevent English inroads among the Lower Creek Indians. Archeological excavations and historical records agree that its palisade was rectangular with corner bastions and walls of wattle and daub reinforced by an exterior half-wall of clay. It was encircled by a moat which was in turn surrounded by an earthen embankment. In 1961 the structure was destroyed by the Spanish because of the English threat.
Private; not accessible to the public
NHL

TALLADEGA COUNTY
Talladega vicinity
CURRY, J. L. M., HOME
3 miles northeast of Talladega on Ala. 21
Early 19th century

J. L. M. Curry was a key figure in the development of public education and teacher training programs in the South during the latter part of the 19th century. He served as general agent for the George Peabody Education Fund (1881–1903) and the John F. Slater Fund for the Education of Negroes (1890–1903). In 1898 he helped to organize the Conference for Education in the South, which set up the Southern Educational Board to implement its programs for universal education. Curry was its supervising director until his death in 1903. He purchased this one-story frame house shortly after his marriage in 1847.
Private; not accessible to the public
NHL

TALLAPOOSA COUNTY
Dadeville vicinity
HORSESHOE BEND NATIONAL MILITARY PARK
Tallapoosa River, 12 miles north of Dadeville on Ala. 49
1814

On March 27, 1814, the forces of General Andrew Jackson defeated warriors of the Creek Indian Nation under Chief Menawa. This decisive victory broke the power of the southern Indians, opened the Old Southwest to white settlement, and established Jackson's reputation nationally as a military leader and Indian fighter. The battle derived its name from the barricades made by the Indians within the U-bend of the Tallapoosa River.
Federal
NPS; 2,040 acres

WASHINGTON COUNTY
St. Stephens vicinity
SITE OF OLD ST. STEPHENS
Northeast of St. Stephens and bounded on the north by cement excavations, on the east by the Tombigbee River, on the south by woodland, and on the west by woodland and pasture

St. Stephens was Alabama's territorial capital from 1817 to 1819. The Spanish had constructed a fort on the site in 1789 around which a town grew up. Spain conveyed the fort to the United States by treaty in 1795, and Americans began settling in large numbers a decade later. The first territorial legislature convened here in January, 1818, the first American court in Alabama met in 1804, the first Alabama school was chartered in 1811, and the first bank, in 1818. When the capital was moved to Huntsville, St. Stephens declined rapidly. By the 1820's it had practically ceased to exist, and by 1860 the site was overgrown with woods. A few graves of prominent residents, traces of former streets, foundation stones, and cellars are the only remaining visual evidence.
State

Alaska

Totem Pole, Old Kassan, Alaska. *Jane Wallen*

Totem Bight Historic Site Community House,
Ketchikan, Alaska. *William Lattin*

U.S. Courthouse, Eagle Historic District,
Eagle, Alaska.
Alaska Division of Parks

GATEWAY BOROUGH
Ketchikan
ALASKA TOTEMS
Between Park and Deermont
Avenues

Totem poles are the last salvable examples
of an ethnic art form which flourished
from British Columbia to Yakutat, Alaska,
from the mid–18th through the 19th centuries. The art form was indigenous to
only one part of the present United States
—Alaska. Totems were carved by Indians
and were the specific property of a family
or clan. There are memorial poles, story
poles, and family or clan poles. In the
summer of 1970 poles were retrieved from
their original locations at long-abandoned
village sites. After special treatment to
preserve them, the totems will be housed
in a building to be erected on this site.
Municipal

INTERIOR DISTRICT
City of Eagle and vicinity
EAGLE HISTORIC DISTRICT
19th and 20th centuries

Once a thriving town, the city of Eagle
served as military, judicial, communication, and transportation center for interior
Alaska. The Army established Fort Egbert, adjacent to the townsite, in 1899 and
later located headquarters of the District
of North Alaska at the post, which was
deactivated in 1925. In 1901 Eagle
became the first incorporated city in interior Alaska. The town was a major port
on the Yukon River, a stopover on the
Trans-Alaska Military Road, and northern
terminus of the Valdez-Eagle telegraph
line. Discovery of gold in Fairbanks and
the ascendancy of rail over water and
overland travel led to Eagle's decline.
Once a town of 3,000, it had a population
of only 28 in 1970. Buildings that survive
are the customshouse, the federal
courthouse, various commercial structures, and the remains of Fort Egbert.
These include quarters, stables, a granary,
and a hospital. More substantial buildings
were balloon frame similar to those
erected in the western United States at the
turn of the century.
Multiple public/private

INTERIOR DISTRICT
Flaxman Island
LEFFINGWELL CAMP
Arctic coast, 58 miles west of Barter
Island

In 1906 a geologist named Ernest de K.
Leffingwell landed on the coast of
northern Alaska at Flaxman Island. He
and Ejnar Mikkelsen, a Danish sea captain, were leaders of a small scientific expedition whose primary objective was to

investigate the possibility of land lying
north of Alaska's Arctic coast. Conveyed
to Flaxman Island on board a small schooner, the party wintered here until March,
1907. That summer the totally unseaworthy ship was dismantled and a
cabin built from her interior woodwork.
Most members of the expedition departed
southward on board the first passing vessel, but Leffingwell remained for seven
years carrying on scientific work. He
mapped the coastline from Point Barrow
to Demarcation Bay and studied the
topography and geology of the Sadlerochit
Mountains. He was the first man to study
permafrost, and many of his theories have
proved quite accurate. By 1967 Leffingwell's cabin, modified by later occupants,
had collapsed, but other features of his
camp (storage shed, ice cellar, two large
iron ship tanks) could be located.
State

NORTHWESTERN DISTRICT
Barrow vicinity
BIRNIRK SITE
5 miles northeast of Barrow
300–1000

The series of mounds at Birnirk Site contains material of Birnirk and western
Thule peoples. It provides materials by
which archeologists have been able to
describe the development of Eskimo culture in this area from about A.D. 600 to
the present. Two recently abandoned villages also furnish evidence for evaluation
of recent Point Barrow culture. The
mounds are located on old "stranded"
beach ridges which are now well back
from the present shoreline.
Federal
NHL

NORTHWESTERN DISTRICT
Cape Denbigh peninsula
IYATAYET SITE
Norton Sound
6000–4000 B.C.

One of the earliest yet found, Iyatayet Site
has given archeologists definite sequential
evidence of coastal occupation beginning
with the Denbigh flint industry. This was
followed by the Norton culture (500
B.C.–A.D. 300) and finally that of a slate
polishing Eskimo group (A.D. 800). The
elements of the earliest level relate
Alaskan archeology to a definite cir-
cumpolar series of early cultures and has
given substance to the assumption that the
first people in the Americas came south
from Alaska.
Federal
NHL

NORTHWESTERN DISTRICT
Cape Prince of Wales vicinity
WALES SITES
Adjacent to Cape Prince of Wales on
Seward Peninsula
600–800

The Wales Sites include sites dating from
early prehistoric times to a present
Eskimo community. They encompass the
American equivalent of Asian sites from
the time of the Birnirk people to the
present day. The mound, known as Ku-
rigitavik, was the first site in Alaska where
Thule culture was found. The small sand
burial mound north of Wales was the first
Birnirk site to be found south of Point
Barrow. The lowest levels of the beach
midden, which are older than the Ku-
rigitavik site, may contain old Bering Sea
material.
Federal
NHL

NORTHWESTERN DISTRICT
Nome vicinity
**ANVIL CREEK GOLD DISCOVERY
SITE**
4.25 miles north of Nome on Seward
Peninsula at Anvil Creek
1898

Alaska's great gold rush began when the
first large gold placer strike was made
here on September 20, 1898. By the latter
part of June, 1899, Nome (then called
Anvil City) had a population of approximately 1700 which increased to 12,488 by
June, 1900. In the next two years mining
activities spread to the entire peninsula.
The long-abandoned site of the original
gold discovery has reverted to a natural
state.
Private; not accessible to the public
NHL

NORTHWESTERN DISTRICT
Point Hope Peninsula
IPIUTAK SITE
Tip of Point Hope
300

The largest known Paleo-Eskimo community, Ipiutak Site has revealed a form of
prehistoric culture to which later Eskimo
groups belonged. The findings included a
burial cult comprised of multiple burials in
log tombs accompanied by grave offerings
and subsurface remains of houses. Art objects discovered are related to the Scytho-
Siberian style. The site consists of 600 to
800 house ruins and a cemetery in about
200 acres of tundra extending over a
stretch of terrain about four miles long.
Federal
NHL

NORTHWESTERN DISTRICT
St. Lawrence Island
GAMBELL SITES
Northwest Cape
c. 100

This series of house and village sites is located on the slope of a headland and on beach ridges that have formed successively during some 2000 years. The Gambell Sites were the first in the Greater Bering Strait region to be archeologically investigated. Archeologists have determined that cultural waves from the mainland of Asia produced a succession of art styles and practices distinguished as Okvik (pre-A.D. 100), Old Bering Sea (A.D. 100–500), Punuk (A.D. 500–1000), and the period from A.D. 1000. Within an area of about two square miles, there are a number of dwellings and three large mounds.
Federal
NHL

SOUTHCENTRAL DISTRICT
Dutch Harbor, Unalaska Island
CHURCH OF THE HOLY ASCENSION
Unalaska
1826, 1894

Russian fur traders established an outpost on the site of present-day Unalaska sometime between 1766 and 1770. Early in the 19th century the first church was constructed, and by 1824 Father Ivan Veniaminov, a missionary, had arrived. The cornerstone of a more permanent house of worship was laid in 1825. This church, consecrated on July 1, 1826, was incorporated into a larger structure built in 1894. The original church was two stories and square with a steeply pitched roof, octagonal cupola, and onion-shaped dome; the new church was cruciform in plan. Three low, one-story wings were attached to the sides and rear of the square. In front a three-story tower was constructed and also topped with an octagonal cupola and onion dome.
Private

SOUTHCENTRAL DISTRICT
Kenai
CHURCH OF THE ASSUMPTION OF THE VIRGIN MARY
East shore of Cook Inlet
c. 1894

Russians built the first log chapel at Kenai, then called Fort St. Nicholas, in 1841. Eight years later a church was constructed which stood until replaced by the present structure. Today the Kenai church is considered the best preserved example in Alaska of a 19th-century Russian Orthodox church with a quadrilateral ground plan. The main section is frame, two stories high with one-and-one-half-story extensions on either side. A two-story tower at the front is topped by an octagonal cupola and an onion-shaped dome. The church is covered by clapboard siding and is still in use.
Private
NHL

SOUTHCENTRAL DISTRICT
Kodiak, Kodiak Island
ERSKINE HOUSE (BARANOV WAREHOUSE)
Main and Mission Streets
1793–1794

Erected by Alexander Baranov as an office and fur warehouse, the Erskine House is the oldest Russian building standing in the United States. The walls, built of rough-hewn square logs, were covered with California red cedar siding. The original hip roof was changed to a gable roof, and a dormer window was added at the front in 1883. William J. Erskine purchased the building in 1911, enclosing a part of the front porch with glass and altering the interior for use as a residence. The frame house contains ten rooms on the first floor, five on the second, and a large attic.
State
NHL

SOUTHCENTRAL DISTRICT
Kodiak vicinity
FORT ABERCROMBIE STATE HISTORIC SITE
Kodiak Island, about 5 miles from Kodiak
20th century

Fort Abercrombie is a representative north Pacific coast defense installation of the type operative during the Second World War. Though never attacked by an enemy, the fort is situated close to the area which witnessed the struggle for control of the Aleutians. In November, 1941, the headquarters battery of the 250th Coast Artillery was established at Miller Point, and on December 7 a battalion observation post (evidently a radar surveillance site) began operating on the headland. By spring, 1942, two eight-inch naval guns were mounted. Named for Lieutenant William H. Abercrombie, a 19th-century explorer, the post remained active until 1945. Concrete beds for gun emplacements, fragments of exploded armaments, cavernous magazines, and building foundations are the only remnants of Fort Abercrombie. Little is known about the wartime appearance because it was a secret installation, but its location atop a high headland commanding a view of the straits and bays was obviously strategically important.
State

SOUTHCENTRAL DISTRICT
Nikolski vicinity
CHALUKA SITE
Umnak Island, Aleutian Islands
1800 B.C.

Chaluka Site appears to represent all periods of culture so far identified in this region. While recent archeological excavations have not been fully reported, Chaluka promises the first careful stratigraphic treatment of a single large Aleutian site. It consists of a village mound 700 feet long by 200 feet wide, with a depth of 21 feet in some places. Less than ten percent of the area has been excavated.
Federal
NHL

SOUTHCENTRAL DISTRICT
Pribilof Islands, St. Paul Island
FUR SEAL ROOKERIES
1787

The Pribilof Islands have lured Russian, British, French, Spanish, and American fur hunters since the 18th century. The seal herds have several times been threatened with extinction due to indiscriminate hunting, but the 1911 convenant between the United States, Great Britain, Russia, and Japan has provided them with international protection and management. Today's flourishing herds illustrate the international application of conservation principles. The beaches of St. Paul Island, the greatest single source of seal furs in the world, appear little changed since 1787.
Federal
NHL

SOUTHCENTRAL DISTRICT
Rip Rock vicinity, Hawkins Island
PALUGVIK SITE
3.75 miles east of Rip Rock on Prince William Sound
1200

Palugvik has given evidence of a long-established Eskimo occupation and culture on the Pacific bays and islands of southern Alaska. It marks the eastern range of Eskimo archeology in the south and clarifies the Eskimo's relationship to the Tlingit Indians, who also lived in this region. Excavations have revealed two middens a few hundred feet apart.
Federal
NHL

SOUTHCENTRAL DISTRICT
Yukon Island
YUKON ISLAND MAIN SITE
Kachemak Bay, Cook Inlet
c. 750 B.C.

The Yukon Island site is the oldest and most continuously occupied of the Cook Inlet group that collectively led to the definition of the Kachemak Bay culture. Although of a general Eskimo type, archeological excavation has shown that these people were also related to both the Salish Indians farther south and the Kamchatkans and Ainu of the Asian coast. The main site includes a shell heap and village midden.
Federal
NHL

SOUTHEASTERN DISTRICT
Ketchikan vicinity
TOTEM BIGHT STATE HISTORIC SITE (MUD BIGHT VILLAGE)
About 5 miles northwest of Ketchikan
19th century

The Totem Bight State Historic Site contains a replica of a 19th-century community house and 13 totem poles carved in the Haida and Tlingit styles. The house has a low oval entrance and elaborate hand carving on the main facade. A carved man wearing a spruce root hat rests cane in hand atop each front corner post. The carving of the stylized raven is unusual. Inside is a single large room with a central fire pit surrounded by a plank platform. Several families would have lived here and shared the fire. All but one of the totem poles are copies of 19th-century originals made in the 1940's.
State

SOUTHEASTERN DISTRICT
Sitka
AMERICAN FLAG RAISING SITE
Castle Hill
1867

At this site on October 18, 1867, the lowering of the Russian flag and the raising of the American flag symbolized the transfer of sovereignty over Alaska. At the time the United States purchase of the territory from Russia was ridiculed as "Seward's Folly." The place where the flagpole stood has been marked by a plaque, and six Russian cannon stand on the grass-covered site pointing out to sea.
State
NHL

SOUTHEASTERN DISTRICT
Sitka
RUSSIAN MISSION ORPHANAGE
Lincoln and Monastery Streets
1842

The Russian Mission Orphanage was erected as a mission building for Bishop Innocent Veniaminov of the Russian Orthodox Greek Catholic Church. This example of Russian architecture of the period contains the Bishop's Chapel or Church of the Annunciation. It has also served as a school for children of the Russian American Company and as a seminary. Today it is the residence of the Greek Orthodox Bishop of Alaska.
Private
NHL

SOUTHEASTERN DISTRICT
Sitka
ST. MICHAEL'S CATHEDRAL
Lincoln and Maksoutoff Streets
1848–1850

Built under the direction of Bishop Innocent Veniaminov, first Bishop of Alaska, St. Michael's Cathedral became the spiritual center of the Russian Church in Alaska. Until destroyed by fire on January 2, 1966, it was among the finest examples of Russian architecture in the United States. Constructed of logs covered with clapboard, the cathedral was laid out on the cruciform plan with the main altar in the center. The central portion of the church was covered by a large dome on top of which was a cupola and a second cross. The interior contained original icons, religious books, chalices, and decorated canvases. Plans are underway to rebuild the cathedral according to the original design.
Private
NHL; HABS

SOUTHEASTERN DISTRICT
Sitka, Baranof Island
SITKA NATIONAL MONUMENT

Sitka National Monument was created to protect a collection of Alaskan Indian totem poles and to preserve the history of Indian, Russian, and American occupation of the area. Within the area are 18 totem poles which were part of the Alaska exhibit at the St. Louis Exposition in 1904. Also included are the graves of seven Russians killed during the battle of Sitka in 1804 and the site of the Indian stockade where the Kit-Siti tribe made its last stand against the Russian settlers. Following the Russian victory, Alexander Baranov, first manager of the Russian American Company, authorized the construction of a blockhouse which has been reconstructed.
Federal
NPS; 54.33 acres

SOUTHEASTERN DISTRICT
Sitka vicinity, Baranof Island
OLD SITKA SITE
6 miles north of Sitka on Starrigavan Bay
1799

In an effort to circumvent American, British, and Spanish penetration of southeastern Alaska, Alexander Baranov and a party of Russian fur hunters founded a fortified trading post here on July 7, 1799. By 1800 Old Sitka, known as Redoubt St. Michael, contained one two-story building, a blacksmith shop, a house for Baranov, accommodations for officers and servants, a bath house, and a temporary kitchen. The burning of the settlement during a surprise attack by Tlingit Indians in June, 1802, frustrated Baranov's first effort to colonize the Alexander Archipelago. There are no surface remains.
State
NHL

SOUTHEASTERN DISTRICT
Skagway and vicinity
SKAGWAY HISTORIC DISTRICT AND WHITE PASS
Head of Taiya Inlet on Lynn Canal
1897

The town of Skagway grew up as a result of gold discoveries in the Upper Yukon Valley and the Klondike Region in the 1890's. Lying on a direct route into the gold-bearing region, it became the terminus for the White Pass and Yukon Route Railway. The approximately 100 buildings still standing form the largest existing example of an Alaskan frontier mining town. Among the buildings are the railroad depot and several hotels, saloons, and lodge halls. The old Federal Court Building is now a museum. Northeast of Skagway is White Pass, which is about 45 miles long with a maximum elevation of 2886 feet.
Multiple public
NHL

SOUTHEASTERN DISTRICT
Wrangell
CHIEF SHAKES STATE HISTORIC SITE
Shakes Island

Shakes Island, a traditional chieftain's campsite, is associated with a revered lineage in Alaskan Indian heritage. The Wrangell tribe defeated the Tsimpsians and won the right to use the Tsimpsian word "Shakes" (whale killer). A succession of

Wrangell leaders used the name until 1944, when the last Chief Shakes died. The Chief Shakes Site is dominated by a 1940 replica of an early 19th-century Tlingit community house which incorporates four ancient houseposts of Chief Shakes' Shark House as well as an original pair of Raven Clan houseposts. The house is surrounded by nine totem poles carved in 1940 as a Civilian Conservation Corps project.
Federal

St. Michael's Cathedral,
Sitka, Alaska. *NPS*

Restored Russian Blockhouse
and graves,
Sitka National Monument,
Alaska. *NPS*

Arizona

Tumacacori National Monument, Nogales vicinity, Arizona. *NPS*

San Xavier Del Bac Mission Church,
Tucson vicinity, Arizona. *HABS*

Roosevelt Dam,
Globe vicinity, Arizona.
NPS

APACHE COUNTY
Chinle
CANYON DE CHELLY NATIONAL MONUMENT
East side of Chinle
c. 300–1300

The prehistoric Pueblo Indian dwellings in Canyon de Chelly were built at the base of sheer red cliffs or in caves in the canyon walls. Within these ruins are preserved many perishable artifacts. The monument includes many individual sites in which remains have been preserved because of the arid climate. The significance of these findings is further enhanced because at other sites the majority of remains dating from earliest archeological periods have decayed beyond recognition. Several notable specific sites are Mummy Cave Ruin, White House, and Antelope House.
Federal
NPS; 83,840 acres

APACHE COUNTY
Ganado
HUBBELL TRADING POST NATIONAL HISTORIC SITE
West side of Ganado
1878

Under the guidance of its founder, Don Lorenzo Hubbell, the Hubbell Trading Post became the most important trade center on the Navajo Indian Reservation. Through its influence, rug weaving was revived and became an important means of livelihood among the Navajos. It has had an unbroken history of influence among the Navajos and is the oldest surviving post of its kind.
Federal
NPS; 156 acres

APACHE COUNTY
Springerville vicinity
CASA MALPAIS SITE
2 miles north of Springerville
1300

An unexcavated pueblo ruin of about 10 acres, Casa Malpais is an interesting example of communal efforts at building and defending a village site. The Indians filled numerous crevices in a fallen lava cliff, making a smooth area on which to build. They also cleared six acres for farming, built a ceremonial structure, and cleared a trail to the village across a deep chasm to a stairway up the cliff.
Private; not accessible to the public
NHL

COCHISE COUNTY
Bisbee
PHELPS DODGE GENERAL OFFICE BUILDING
Copper Queen Plaza, intersection of Main Street and Brewery Gulch
c. 1890

Bisbee is the center of one of the nation's richest copper producing areas. The Copper Queen Consolidated Mining Company was formed in 1880 when the Copper Queen merged with Phelps Dodge. This brick building was erected to provide general office space in the business center of Bisbee. Basically rectangular, it is two stories high with a gable roof. Windows and doors are topped by semicircular arches.
Private; not accessible to the public

COCHISE COUNTY
Bisbee vicinity
CORONADO NATIONAL MEMORIAL
30 miles southwest of Bisbee via Ariz. 92 and secondary road
1540–1542

Located on the boundary between the United States and Mexico, the Coronado National Memorial commemorates the exploration of what is now the United States by Francisco Vasquez de Coronado, 1540–1542. The area includes Coronado Peak, which affords a view of a portion of the route by which the Spanish expedition entered the present United States. The region they traversed extended from El Fuerte, Mexico, through the San Pedro Valley and thence into the present United States. The expedition was the first major exploration by Europeans into the American Southwest.
Federal
NPS; 2834.16 acres

COCHISE COUNTY
Bisbee vicinity
LEHNER MAMMOTH-KILL SITE
10 miles west of Bisbee
c. 11,000 B.C.

The Lehner site is one of the outstanding mammoth-kill sites in the New World. The stone butchering tools found with Clovis fluted spear points expand the variety of tools known to have been used by these nomadic hunters. Radiocarbon dates for the artifacts and bones serve as a control for several scientific studies, including the most intensively analyzed pollen chronology of any alluvial site in the Southwest. The site, which remains largely in a natural state, is well preserved.
Private
NHL

COCHISE COUNTY
Bowie vicinity
FORT BOWIE NATIONAL HISTORIC SITE
13 miles south of Bowie
1862

Established by California Volunteers during the Civil War, Fort Bowie controlled a key water source in strategic Apache Pass. Its garrison, situated in the homeland of the Chiricahua Apache Indians, was active during the 1860's, 1870's, and 1880's in the Chiricahua wars led by Cochise, Geronimo, and other Apache chieftains who spread terror throughout the Southwest. A major way point of cross-country travel in the Southwest, Apache Pass permitted crossing of the Chiricahua Mountains. It was considered the most dangerous point along the entire southern Overland Mail Route, which stretched from Tipton, Missouri, to San Francisco, California. Stone foundations and rock debris today mark the site of the Apache Pass Stage Station. The Butterfield Trail traverses the pass, and the natural historic setting remains intact. Stabilized adobe walls mark the fort site, which was abandoned by the Army in 1894.
Federal
NPS; 900 acres

COCHISE COUNTY
Douglas vicinity
DOUBLE ADOBE SITE
12 miles northwest of Douglas on the west bank of Whitewater Creek
5700 B.C.

The discovery of the Double Adobe Site in 1926 gave archeologists the first indication that in ancient times the climate and ecology of southern Arizona were quite different from the present and that prehistoric man hunted animals now extinct. It also provided the impetus that led to the defining of the pre-ceramic Cochise culture in the Southwest. The site contains the remains of peoples who lived by gathering wild plants, nuts, and seeds, as well as by hunting. Bones of certain extinct animals were also found. The site is preserved in its natural state.
Private; not accessible to the public
NHL

COCHISE COUNTY
Douglas vicinity
SAN BERNARDINO RANCH
17 miles east of Douglas on the international boundary
Early 1800's

The San Bernardino Ranch illustrates the continuity of Spanish-Mexican and American cattle ranching in the Southwest. The abundant springs at the ranch were a crossroads of travel for military expedi-

tions, stock drives, and emigration throughout the period of westward expansion. Because of numerous Apache Indian raids San Bernardino was abandoned at least twice during its history. The American phase began with John Slaughter's purchase of the ranch in 1884. The present Headquarters Complex, the buildings of which are still in use, dates from this period.
Private; not accessible to the public
NHL

COCHISE COUNTY
Fairbank vicinity
QUIBURI
North of Fairbank
Pre-Columbian

Valuable information about the prehistoric Sobaipuri Indians has been gained from excavation of this site. The earliest structures unearthed were small jacal houses dated from c. 1200 A.D. Sobaipuri villages occupied the site from 1692 to 1698, from 1706 to 1762, and from 1775 to 1780. The first village burned, and the second, smaller village was built atop the old foundations. During the third occupation the presidio of Santa Cruz de Terrenate was established here to guard Sonora from Apache attacks. The adobe fort, built on rock foundations, was never fully completed. An exterior wall, storerooms, living quarters, and a church were built of adobe bricks with roofs made of mesquite or oak topped with adobe soil. All that remains of those structures are a few sections of the church walls and the west fortification wall.
Private
HABS

COCHISE COUNTY
Tombstone
TOMBSTONE HISTORIC DISTRICT
1877

Tombstone, which surrounded the mining claim of Ed Schieffelin, was widely known in the southwestern mining frontier. The site of rich silver mines, it attracted miners, gamblers, and gunmen, attaining a population of 7,000 by 1881. Its unrivaled reputation for lawlessness and violence is evidenced by the Earp-Clanton feud which culminated in the gunfight at the OK Corral in 1881. The town declined as a mining center because of the entry of water into the mining shafts. Among the buildings illustrating the town's frontier flavor are the Bird Cage Theatre, the City Hall, and St. Paul's Episcopal Church.
Multiple public/private
NHL; HABS

COCONINO COUNTY
Flagstaff vicinity
LOWELL OBSERVATORY
1 mile west of Flagstaff on Mars Hill
1894

The broad program of astronomical research conducted by Lowell Observatory, founded by Dr. Percival Lowell, has contributed greatly to knowledge of the universe. Most significant of the observatory's discoveries was the first observable evidence of the expanding universe, made by Dr. V. M. Slipher in 1912. It is also noted for intensive studies of Mars, the discovery of Pluto, and researches in zodiacal light and sunspot phenomena. The 24-inch Lowell refracting telescope, installed in 1896, is in operation today in its original housing.
Private
NHL

COCONINO COUNTY
Flagstaff vicinity
MERRIAM, C. HART, BASE CAMP SITE
20 miles northwest of Flagstaff, at Little Springs, a private enclave in Coconino National Forest
1889

Operating from this camp, Dr. Clinton Hart Merriam (1855–1942) made the investigations that led to his formulation of the Life Zone concept, which was basic in the development of the science of ecology. Merriam concluded that forms of life are peculiar to certain climatic zones or regions which are determined by the combination of altitude, exposure, and latitude. His so-called "laws of temperature," delimiting life zones and life distribution, are fundamental to the Life Zone concept.
Private
NHL

COCONINO COUNTY
Flagstaff vicinity
WALNUT CANYON NATIONAL MONUMENT
8 miles east of Flagstaff via U.S. 66
c. 100–1200

Walnut Canyon National Monument preserves the remains of over 300 small cliff dwellings where prehistoric Indians built their one-room homes in recesses along canyon walls. Conditions in the area provided many inducements for choosing this site: sufficient water, protection from the elements and enemies, abundant fuel, and fertile soil. The inhabitants, who were farmers and pottery makers, were Stone Age people with no knowledge of metal. The site is important because it yielded in-

formation concerning population shifts after the eruption of Sunset Crater in 1065.
Federal
NPS; 1879.46 acres

COCONINO COUNTY
Winona vicinity
WINONA SITE
5 miles northeast of Winona on U.S. 66, Coconino National Forest
1065

Winona was one of the major Indian villages that developed immediately after the eruption of Sunset Crater. The site has yielded considerable detail on cultural developments in the Flagstaff area up to 1130. It shows the complex story of three groups coming together to form a pattern of life new to the Southwest. In a period of only two generations, occupants of this site learned to build surface masonry buildings. Ceramics and crafts also reflected new techniques and forms.
Federal
NHL

COCONINO COUNTY
Flagstaff vicinity
WUPATKI NATIONAL MONUMENT
30 miles north of Flagstaff off U.S. 89
c. 1000–1215

The red sandstone prehistoric pueblos of Wupatki were built by groups of farming Indians who settled here following a local environmental disturbance. These ruins constitute the tangible remains of an 11th-century Indian "land rush" that resulted from increased soil fertility caused by the eruption of Sunset Crater, a nearby volcano, in 1065. The area includes several large pueblos, a masonry and one other ball court, and an open-air amphitheatre. Nearly 800 sites are located within the monument boundaries.
Federal
NPS; 35,232.84 acres

GILA COUNTY (also in Maricopa County)
Globe vicinity
ROOSEVELT DAM
Salt River, 31 miles northwest of Globe on Ariz. 88
1906–1911

Roosevelt Dam was the first major project to be completed under the Reclamation Act of 1902. Its primary purpose was to provide adequate water storage for the Salt River Irrigation Complex, whose line of descent goes back to the ancient Hohokam irrigation projects, the historic Pima Indian projects, and the projects of 19th-century settlers in the area. The world's highest masonry dam, Roosevelt is

284 feet high and 1,125 feet long. Roosevelt Lake, which is impounded by the dam, irrigates over a quarter million acres of farmland.
Federal
NHL

GILA COUNTY
Globe vicinity
TONTO NATIONAL MONUMENT
28 miles northwest of Globe on Ariz. 88
14th century

Tonto National Monument comprises two of the most accessible and best preserved cliff dwellings of southern Arizona. The dwellings, constructed of masonry and topped with pole and mud roofs, were built with primitive wooden and stone tools by Indians who farmed in the Salt River Valley during the mid–1300's. The Lower Ruin has 16 or 17 ground-floor rooms with at least four second-story rooms. The Upper Ruin, with 32 ground-floor and 14 second-story rooms, is better preserved. That the Tonto cliff dwellers were excellent craftsmen is illustrated by artifacts found in the ruins. Decorated storage vessels with bold, complicated designs and plain utility vessels were the principal pottery forms. Also found were examples of textiles, jewelry, and weaponry. One of the largest collections of vegetal material in the Southwest was recovered from these ruins.
Federal
NPS; 1,120 acres

GILA COUNTY
Whiteriver vicinity
KINISHBA RUINS
15 miles west of Whiteriver via Ariz. 73 and secondary road
c. 1250–1350

A large pueblo consisting of two large and seven small masonry buildings, Kinishba Ruins could have housed perhaps up to 1000 Indians. The culture of the inhabitants represents the climax period in the White Mountain area, a blend of Mogollon and Anasazi ancestry. The people depended primarily on agriculture for subsistence; pottery was manufactured for storage, table, and ceremonial use. A large rectangular building on the east has two enclosed courtyards, an architectural plan typical of this mountain region during the late 1200's and early 1300's. The pueblo was abandoned about 1400.
Private
NHL

GRAHAM COUNTY
Bonita vicinity
SIERRA BONITA RANCH
Southwest of Bonita
1872

Founded by Colonel Henry C. Hooker, Sierra Bonita was the first permanent American cattle ranch in Arizona to survive the Apache Indian terror. With its establishment, American cattlemen succeeded to the lush grasslands of southeastern Arizona that had witnessed the rise and fall of an earlier Spanish-Mexican cattle empire. Hooker erected his ranch buildings on the site of an abandoned hacienda. His house is a large rectangular building with thick adobe walls and gunports in the parapets. It has been remodeled inside but still retains the fortress-like appearance of early days. The original adobe corrals, bunkhouses, and barns surround the ranch house.
Private; not accessible to the public
NHL

GRAHAM COUNTY
Morenci vicinity
POINT OF PINES SITES
30 miles northwest of Morenci, San Carlos Indian Reservation
2000 B.C.–A.D. 1400

The region of Point of Pines village contains a considerable number of ruins representing a long period of occupation. One excavated pueblo of about 800 rooms shows marked architectural variations within itself. Evidences of definite pottery and crop influences from the north suggest an influx of people from the Kayenta area in the late 1200's. Features such as large ceremonial structures and walk-in wells are indicative of the communal efforts of the inhabitants.
Private
NHL

MARICOPA COUNTY
Gila Bend vicinity
FORTALEZA
Gila Bend Indian Reservation
Pre-Columbian

The Fortaleza is located on one of six bluffs (starting from the south, the fifth escarpment sloping toward the west) oriented in a north-south line perpendicular to the Gila River. The excavated ruin consists of a village of approximately 50 stone houses. Archeological investigation has indicated that the Fortaleza was constructed during the 14th century and inhabited by Hohokam Indians. Two unique characteristics of the ruin are its fortified location (the Hohokam were a peaceful,

agricultural people), and the building material used. Usually the early Hohokam peoples built houses with adobe walls, often reinforced with posts set into the adobe, and sod roofs. The Fortaleza houses were built with walls of dry laid stone masonry and sod roofs.
Private

MARICOPA COUNTY
Gila Bend vicinity
GATLIN SITE
3 miles north of Gila Bend
1000–1150

The platform mound at Gatlin Site proved to be a ceremonial structure of the Hohokam culture area of southern Arizona. The mound—which underwent six periods of construction and modification—the adjacent cremation area and ball court, the assumed labor force required to build it, and the unusual post mold alignments all suggest that ceremonial functions were connected with the complex. The mound itself is thought to reflect a northern extension of the pyramid idea of Mexico. The trash mound, ball court, and mound surface are still visible.
Multiple public/private
NHL

MARICOPA COUNTY
ROOSEVELT DAM
Reference—see Gila County

MARICOPA COUNTY
Phoenix
HOHOKAM-PIMA IRRIGATION SITES
Park of the Four Waters
1200–1400

Spanish explorers first found the Pima Indians of the Gila River irrigating their crops from canals and ditches of complex construction in 1687. Later archeological excavations have shown that other irrigation works were originally constructed by peoples of the Hohokam culture. The systems, built as communal efforts with hand tools, formed great networks extending over thousands of acres of land. Some of the canals are still in use today, tied in with contemporary irrigation systems of Indians and whites who currently farm the valley. These sites illustrate that both ancient and modern man have made similar adjustments to the arid environment of the Southwest.
Multiple public/private
NHL

MARICOPA COUNTY
Phoenix
PUEBLO GRANDE RUIN
Washington Avenue, Pueblo Grande
City Park
900–1450

Pueblo Grande Ruin is one of the few remaining large Hohokam village sites in the area. Its major feature is a large house mound, standing some 20 feet above the desert floor, on and around which jacal and caliche-walled houses were located. The latter structures have been encroached upon by modern developments, but four prehistoric canals are visible across the existing irrigation canal in the "Park of Four Waters." The above-ground structures, with the exception of the ball court, represent the final phase of occupation (A.D. 1150–1450), during which the cultures of two distinct peoples were fused.
Municipal
NHL

MARICOPA COUNTY
Phoenix
ROSSON, DR. RONALD, HOUSE
139 N. 6th Street
1892–1893

The Rosson House is a rare example of a Victorian dwelling in the city of Phoenix. It was designed in the Eastlake mode. The veranda possesses lattice-like decoration of lathe worked posts and smaller spindles, and there is additional carved wood ornament in the pediment above the main entrance. This pediment is stepped out from the veranda and supported by two spindle posts on each side. Walls are brick masonry, except for a frame extension over the veranda roof which was made in the 20th century. The third story is a composite of dormers and "A" roofs, and its most outstanding feature is a hexagonal turret with shingled roof and elaborate lightning rod. Dr. Ronald Rosson was an Army physician at nearby Fort McDowell.
Private; not accessible to the public
HABS

MOHAVE COUNTY
Fredonia vicinity
PIPE SPRING NATIONAL MONUMENT
15 miles southwest of Fredonia
1871

Pipe Spring is a monument to the Mormon pioneers who were responsible for the exploration, settlement, and development of this region of the Southwest. Protected within the monument area is a well-preserved fort constructed by these pioneers in 1871 to protect themselves

from Indian attacks. The earliest well-documented visit to Pipe Spring was that of an 1858 exploratory party led by Jacob Hamblin. His report on the area's grasslands led to settlement by stockmen. By 1868 the property had been purchased by the Mormon Church, which held the land until 1875.
Federal
NPS; 40 acres

NAVAJO COUNTY
Kayenta vicinity
NAVAJO NATIONAL MONUMENT
30 miles southwest of Kayenta
1225–1300

Navajo National Monument has three of the largest cliff dwellings of the prehistoric Pueblo Indians still extant. Betatakin is 450 feet long, with a maximum depth of 150 feet. It once had almost 150 rooms, including dwellings, ceremonial rooms (kivas), courts, storage areas, and grinding rooms. Keet Seel, one of the largest cliff ruins in Arizona, was among the last in the area to be abandoned. Inscription House, the smallest of the three, is notable for the date of 1661 carved on the plastered wall of one of the rooms.
Federal
NPS; 360 acres

NAVAJO COUNTY
Keams Canyon vicinity
AWATOVI RUINS
8 miles south of Keams Canyon on Hopi Indian Reservation
17th century

In July, 1540, Francisco Vasquez de Coronado dispatched Pedro de Továr to investigate the Hopi Indian villages in the province called Tusayan by the Spanish. His expedition became the first European visit to the Hopi pueblos. Awatovi, one of the largest and most important of the villages, was the first to be reached by the Spanish. During the period of missionary activity (1628 until the Pueblo Rebellion of 1680), Awatovi showed the highest number of converts. The pueblo was destroyed in 1700 by neighboring villages who resented its supposed sympathy to Christianity. Excavation of the site has uncovered much of the pueblo and three churches. Most of the material recovered was aboriginal, with only a few fragments of porcelain, metal, and other Spanish materials.
Private
NHL

NAVAJO COUNTY
Oraibi vicinity
OLD ORAIBI
3 miles west of Oraibi on Ariz. 264, Hopi Indian Reservation
1300–present

Old Oraibi is probably the oldest continuously inhabited pueblo in the Southwest. The site consists of seven discontinuous north-south house rows with most houses three to four stories high. There are thirteen kivas and a number of enclosed courts. The Hopi Indians were the only prehistoric pueblo culture in Arizona to survive into historic times. Studies at this site have produced invaluable data for tree-ring dating in the Southwest. The site indicates one of the least changed Indian cultures in the United States as well as numerous early contacts between the Hopis and European explorers.
Private
NHL

PIMA COUNTY
Santa Rosa vicinity
VENTANA CAVE
11 miles west of Santa Rosa, Papago Indian Reservation
c. 11,000 B.C.–A.D. 20th century

Ventana Cave provided a history of continuous Indian occupation in Arizona extending over a period of about 5000 years. The earliest occupations were those of food-gathering peoples related in their way of life to inhabitants of southern California. The final occupation was by Indians who dwelt there in early historic times. The high, shallow cave lies at the base of a cliff on the southeast face of Castle Mountain.
Private
NHL

PIMA COUNTY
Tucson
FRÉMONT HOUSE
145–153 S. Main Street
19th century

Portions of this adobe dwelling may date from the late 1850's, and there was a house on the property by 1862. About 1880 extensive remodeling and alterations were undertaken. Despite recent changes and its adaptation as apartments, the Frémont House remains essentially an adobe residence of the type common in Tucson in the 1870's. Its "Zaguan" plan incorporates two distinct domestic areas joined by a drive leading to an interior courtyard. The one-story walls are adobe covered with stucco, and wooden detailing above the two west doors is noteworthy. The family of John C. Frémont, territorial

governor of Arizona, is reputed to have lived in the house.
State; not accessible to the public

PIMA COUNTY
Tucson
THE OLD ADOBE PATIO (CHARLES O. BROWN HOUSE)
40 W. Broadway
1868, 1876

The Charles O. Brown House is actually two dwellings, connected by a row of rooms, each representing a distinct style of adobe architecture. The Jackson Street house (believed to contain rooms dating from the 1850's) is the older of the two; remodeled in 1868 by Charles Brown, it has no covered porch and the walls are flush with the street and lack ornament. The newer section is an Anglo or territorial version of the Mexican adobe, distinguished by a covered porch having a sloping roof supported by wooden columns and curved wooden brackets. Both buildings have flat roofs, and the vigas and savinas are original.
State

PIMA COUNTY
Tucson vicinity
DESERT LABORATORY
West of Tucson off West Anklam Road on Tumamoc Hill
1903

As part of the Carnegie Institution of Washington, the Desert Laboratory is recognized as having initiated the study of the ecology of arid regions. Of the many studies conducted there, the most important were those dealing with the influence of arid conditions on the evolution of plants and on their migration from humid zones. Operation of the laboratory for ecological studies ended in the late 1930's. The United States Forest Service used the site as an experiment station until 1958 when it was acquired by the University of Arizona for its geochronology program. Three major buildings dating from the period of the Desert Laboratory are still in use.
State
NHL

PIMA COUNTY
Tucson vicinity
SAN XAVIER DEL BAC
9 miles south of Tucson via Mission Road
1700

Established by the Jesuit padre Eusebio Francisco Kino, the Mission of San Xavier del Bac is among the finest surviving Spanish Colonial churches in the United States. The center portion of the main facade is marked by a profusion of carved and molded ornament in the Churrigueresque style. Towers flank this center portion. Constructed of brick covered with stucco, the church has a cruciform plan; the nave, transepts and apse are covered by low brick domes. The richly ornamented interior is executed in the baroque style. After a period of Indian hostilities during which the mission was twice abandoned, the present church was completed and consecrated by Franciscans in 1797. It was again abandoned when the mission lands were secularized during the Mexican regime and reoccupied in 1859 after the territory had passed to the United States under the Gadsden Purchase. Extensively repaired by the Catholic Church in the early 20th century, San Xavier is now an active parish on the San Xavier Indian Reservation.
Private
NHL; HABS

PINAL COUNTY
Chandler vicinity
SNAKETOWN
12 miles southwest of Chandler, Gila River Indian Reservation
300 B.C.–A.D. 1200

Snaketown was one of the large Hohokam Indian "city states" of prehistoric Arizona. Excavations revealed that the Indians of southern Arizona were strongly influenced by the more highly developed cultures of Mexico. These cultures lifted the Indians into a pattern of living that contrasted sharply with the scattered rancherias of early Indian farmers in the region. The irrigation canal system and the large urban developments mark the highest achievement of Hohokam labor.
Private
NHL

PINAL COUNTY
Coolidge vicinity
CASA GRANDE RUINS NATIONAL MONUMENT
2 miles north of Coolidge on Ariz. 87
c. 1000–1450

Casa Grande or "Big House" is a four-story tower of packed earthen walls built over 600 years ago by Indian farmers of the Gila River Valley. This building and others with thick walls of unreinforced clay were built by a people accustomed to constructing multi-story dwellings. The site also contains Hohokam Indian remains dating from about A.D. 900. It served both as an observation tower and an apartment house. Early excavations of the Casa Grande ruins recovered ordinary cooking and storage vessels, sleeping mats, and fragments of textiles.
Federal
NPS; 472.50 acres

PINAL COUNTY
Florence vicinity
ADAMSVILLE RUIN
3.5 miles southwest of Florence on Ariz. 287

The Adamsville Ruin covers a 40–acre area and is one of a very few surviving similar sites once common in the Gila and Salt River valleys. These mounds mark a prehistoric village situated near ancient irrigation ditches. A large house mound is visible, and the ballcourt has been excavated. The village was probably inhabited from 1200 to 1450, and its site remains largely unexcavated today. The majority of other such sites have been destroyed by level grading.
State

SANTA CRUZ COUNTY
Nogales vicinity
CALABASAS
North of Nogales on the east bank of the Santa Cruz River
18th and 19th centuries

Calabasas was the site of a Pima Indian village first referred to in writing by a Jesuit priest in 1756. Priests from the Mission of Los Santos Angeles de Guevavi held services occasionally at Calabasas, but the settlement probably had no church building until the 1770's. By 1783 the Spanish and Indians had abandoned the village because of fierce and repeated attacks by Apaches. The Mexican governor of Sonora, Manuel Maria Gandara, acquired the village in 1844 and spent large sums of money repairing and rebuilding it as well as stocking the land as a ranch. Today only the ruins of the Spanish church, which was remodeled by Gandara as a ranch house, remain.
Private
HABS

SANTA CRUZ COUNTY
Nogales vicinity
TUMACACORI NATIONAL MONUMENT
18 miles north of Nogales on Int. 19
Late 17th century

The mission of San Jose de Tumacacori was a northern outpost of the Sonora mission chain founded by Jesuit priests in the 17th century. This frontier mission church illustrates Spanish colonial endeavor and commemorates the introduction of Christianity into southern Arizona. Although the settlement was first visited by Father Kino in 1691, mission activity reached its peak between 1790 and the end of Spanish rule in 1821. The chapel still stands, partly in ruins, and a museum houses exhibits of early Indian and Spanish history.
Federal
NPS; 10.15 acres

SANTA CRUZ COUNTY
Tubac
TUBAC PRESIDIO
Broadway and River Road
c. 1760

The Tubac Presidio is the oldest of three Spanish military outposts built in Arizona and was established as a result of the Pima Indian rebellion of 1751. Today low mounds mark the outline of the presidio's walls which long ago disintegrated or were pulled down. The north wing is roughly 100 feet long, the east wing, 125 feet, and the west wing, 145 feet. Unfired adobe bricks were used for construction, and closely spaced cottonwood or pine poles spanned the interior rooms and carried the roof. Roof construction was ocotillo, willow wands, grass, and packed dirt, in that order.
State and municipal

SANTA CRUZ COUNTY
Village of Tubac
OLD TUBAC SCHOOLHOUSE
1885

The Tubac School was constructed as a one-room, one-story adobe brick structure. In 1907 the roof was replaced and a room added, and in 1914 the interior space was partitioned to form smaller classrooms. The school is roughly cruciform in shape, measuring 104 feet by 63 feet. Citizens of Tubac also used the building for community activities, so it has been, since 1885, a social and educational center.
Municipal; not accessible to the public

YAVAPAI COUNTY
Clarkdale vicinity
TUZIGOOT NATIONAL MONUMENT
2 miles east of Clarkdale
c. 1125–1450

The extensive ruin of Tuzigoot is a significant example of the periodic additions made to late-prehistoric pueblos of the Verde River Valley. The hilltop pueblo of 110 clustered rooms is about 500 feet long and 100 feet across at its greatest width. There are few doors, as the rooms were entered through small openings in the roofs. Abandonment of the area occurred about A.D. 1400. Tuzigoot National Monument includes not only the pueblo ruins but also a museum housing the entire collection recovered during excavations.
Federal
NPS; 42.67 acres

YAVAPAI COUNTY
Flagstaff vicinity
MONTEZUMA CASTLE NATIONAL MONUMENT
40 miles south of Flagstaff on Int. 17
c. 1125–1450

High in a limestone cliff in the Verde Valley is Montezuma Castle, one of the best-preserved cliff dwellings in the United States. The occupants were agrarian Indians who worked the farmland on a nearby river terrace. Overpopulation due to drought in other areas brought more Indians to the site. The pueblo, a five-story building with 20 rooms, is largely intact. The monument also includes Montezuma Well, whose waters were used to irrigate the Indians' farmlands.
Federal/non-federal
NPS; 842.09 acres

YAVAPAI COUNTY
Jerome
JEROME HISTORIC DISTRICT
1883

As a result of the large-scale production of high grade copper ores at the United Verde Mine, Jerome was by 1907 the major mining town in Arizona and one of the greatest copper-producing centers in the world. The demand for copper during World War II led to intensive mining which depleted the known ore deposits, and Jerome is today virtually a ghost town. With its frame buildings propped on stilts and its narrow, steep streets, the town retains much of its original appearance and atmosphere. One of the original buildings, the James H. Douglas Mansion, houses a mining museum.
Multiple public/private
NHL

YUMA COUNTY
Ehrenberg vicinity
OLD LA PAZ (LAGUNA DE LA PAZ)
Northeast of Ehrenberg in the
Colorado River Indian Tribes
Reservation

La Paz, once the county seat of Yuma County and an important contender for territorial capital of Arizona, is now a collection of low mounds where houses and streets were once. Gold was discovered here in 1862, and almost overnight La Paz became a frenetic tent city of miners, entrepreneurs, and charlatans, as well as an active port on the Colorado River. Indian troubles necessitated the shipping of gold south to Mexico, and this drain of a valuable resource influenced lawmakers in Washington to create the territory of Arizona (1863) and dispatch soldiers to La Paz to guard the gold shipments east. In 1870 the Colorado River shifted its course and left La Paz two miles inland. The gold placers were becoming depleted, and by 1875 the town, which once had boasted a population of 5,000, was completely deserted. Today La Paz consists of more than 100 low house mounds and several larger mounds (where public and commercial buildings stood) and depressions indicating where streets ran. All buildings were adobe, and wind and water gradually destroyed their walls.
Indian trust land

YUMA COUNTY
Parker vicinity
OLD PRESBYTERIAN CHURCH (MOJAVE INDIAN PRESBYTERIAN MISSION CHURCH)
Southwest of Parker on 2nd Avenue
1917

In the early years of the 20th century the Presbyterian Church made initial overtures to the Mojave Indians living on the Colorado River agency. A crude mission building of mud and sticks had been erected by 1910, and the present church was completed shortly thereafter using timbers from an earlier school building. The structure measures 43 by 24 feet and has walls of adobe brick. There is a belfry on the east end, and the interior is basically one room. Since its completion the mission church has served as a religious and community center for the Indians.
Indian trust land

YUMA COUNTY (also in Imperial
County, California)
Yuma
YUMA CROSSING AND ASSOCIATED SITES
Banks of the Colorado River
18th and 19th centuries

The prime significance of Yuma Crossing lies in its role as a transportation and communication gateway between New Spain and Alta California during the Spanish colonial period and between the American Southwest and California during the westward expansion movement. Physically and historically associated with the crossing are three groups of historic structures: the surviving buildings of Fort Yuma (1850) on the California shore; the buildings of the Yuma Quartermaster Depot (1864) opposite the fort in Arizona; and the stone cell blocks and guard towers of the Arizona Territorial Prison (1876) north of the Depot. The individual sites are not regarded as nationally important, but together they possess a high degree of historical significance.
Federal
NHL

Canyon De Chelly National Monument,
Chinle, Arizona. *NPS*

Tuzigoot National Monument, Arizona. *NPS*

Arkansas

Old Main, University of Arkansas, Fayetteville, Arkansas. *University of Arkansas*

The Tavern
(Arkansas Territorial Restoration),
Little Rock, Arkansas.
Earl Saunders

Eureka Springs Historic District,
Eureka Springs, Arkansas.
Detail from stone retaining wall.
Environmental Design, Inc.

Hudson-Grace-Borreson House,
Pine Bluff, Arkansas. *W. H. Hubbard*

ARKANSAS COUNTY
Gillett vicinity
**ARKANSAS POST NATIONAL
MEMORIAL**
   8 miles southeast of Gillett on Ark. 1
   and 169
   1682

Established by Henri de Tonty, Arkansas Post was the first settlement by white men in the lower Mississippi Valley and the later Louisiana Territory. While the post changed locations several times and may not have been operated continuously, it became a thriving village after the establishment of the John Law Colony in 1720. Evidences of late 18th-century structures of Spanish origin have been uncovered.
Federal
NPS; 220.60 acres

BENTON COUNTY
Pea Ridge
**PEA RIDGE NATIONAL MILITARY
PARK**
   1862

The culmination of the Pea Ridge campaign was the battle of Pea Ridge, March 7-8, 1862. Also called the battle of Elkhorn Tavern, the Pea Ridge engagement was among the major Civil War battles west of the Mississippi. It was precipitated by the advance of the Union forces of General Samuel R. Curtis in an attempt to destroy Confederate forces in southwest Missouri. The victory for the Union forces thwarted Confederate attempts to take Missouri and ended major hostilities for a considerable period in the area west of the Mississippi River.
Federal/non-federal
NPS; 4278.75 acres

CARROLL COUNTY
Eureka Springs
**EUREKA SPRINGS HISTORIC
DISTRICT**
   1880's

Attracted by the reputed curative powers of springs in this area, county residents began building cabins during the summer of 1879. Dr. Alvah Jackson is credited with discovery of the spring water's medicinal powers. Invalids living in tents and wagons collected around Basin Spring, and by mid-August the population had reached 300 persons. Rail heads at Pierce City (55 miles distant) and Ozark (85 miles away) were major points of embarkation for visitors who traveled the remaining distance by hack. The major building boom occurred in the 1880's, and by 1881 there were 13 hotels in Eureka Springs. Gradually, throughout America, the health spa declined in popularity. Eu-

reka Springs also became less frequented —a condition speeded by the legalization of horse racing in Arkansas early in the 20th century. No new construction was undertaken after 1905, yet, except for the dismantling of some wooden homes, little razing of the commercial and residential sections occurred. Today the buildings in downtown Eureka Springs date almost exclusively from the period 1880 to 1900. Rough-faced stone, sometimes faced with pressed brick, was the principal construction material, and cast and sheet iron were used extensively for ornament.
Multiple public/private

CLEVELAND COUNTY
Fordyce vicinity
MARKS' MILLS BATTLEFIELD PARK
   Junction of Ark. 8 and 97
   1864

Major General Frederick Steele, Union commander in Arkansas, had had his supply line severed on April 18, 1864, by Confederate raiders who struck near Poison Spring. The supply situation was improved somewhat by the arrival of a wagon train from Pine Bluff on April 20. Steele made preparations to return 240 wagons to Pine Bluff for more rations and forage for animals. Confederate soldiers under the command of Major General James B. Fagan attacked the long line of wagons at the road junction near Marks' Mills on the morning of April 25. Union losses were one infantry brigade, the 240 wagons, and four cannon. Ultimately, the failure to obtain additional supplies forced Steele to leave Camden and retreat to Little Rock.
State

CROSS COUNTY
Parkin vicinity
PARKIN INDIAN MOUND
   North edge of Parkin
   Prehistoric

The prehistoric Parkin Site exemplifies the Parkin phase, a Mississippian or temple mound culture component in northeast Arkansas. Many burials, usually accompanied by pottery vessels and other artifacts, have been uncovered there. A large pyramidal temple mound and deep middens that cover much of the site promise to reveal a great deal of scientific information concerning the prehistoric inhabitants of Arkansas.
Multiple public/private
NHL

GRANT COUNTY
Leola vicinity
**JENKINS FERRY BATTLEGROUND
STATE PARK**
   Northeast of Leola on Ark. 46
   1864

Union General Frederick Steele, leading his men and equipment in a retreat towards Little Rock, was constantly harassed by pursuing Confederate troops. At Jenkins Ferry across the Saline River, Steele's men attempted to stall the enemy by erecting a breastwork on the right bank. This delaying action on April 30, 1864, was fought to enable most of the men and artillery to cross the river. Casualties were high, and Union efforts to save their ammunition and supply trains, unsuccessful. The retreat to Little Rock was effected, but the Confederates had prevented General Steele from uniting his forces with those of Major General Nathaniel P. Banks in Louisiana.
State

HEMPSTEAD COUNTY
Washington
ROYSTON, GRANDISON D., HOUSE
   Alexander Street, 200 feet southwest
   of Columbus Street (Ark. 4) and
   approximately 450 feet southeast of
   Old Military Road (Ark. 195)
   c. 1830

The Royston House is a one-story, Greek Revival dwelling with a four-room, central hall plan. Notable is the construction which consists of solid, hand-hewn sills 10 inches square resting on brick and stone piers and supporting sawn stud walls and floor joists. The exterior is finished with horizontal beveled siding and corner boards. A gable-roofed entrance pediment is supported by four, square, tapered columns with molded capitals and square plinths. Grandison D. Royston (1809-1889) was a lawyer active in politics. He served as prosecuting attorney for the Third Judicial District of the Territory of Arkansas, was a delegate to the territorial constitutional convention (1835), a representative to the first state legislature (1836), and was elected speaker of the legislature. He was also appointed U.S. District Attorney for Arkansas and served in the Confederate Congress.
Municipal
HABS

INDEPENDENCE COUNTY
Batesville
GARROTT HOUSE (CASE-MAXFIELD
HOUSE)
561 E. Main Street
c. 1842

The one-and-one-half-story Garrott House is frame and has decorative bargeboard trim at the eave line and inside the single gabled roof dormer. A one-story porch surrounds the main entrance and is topped by a railed deck. The house was built for George Case and a subsequent owner was Will Maxfield.
Private

JACKSON COUNTY
Jacksonport
JACKSONPORT STATE PARK
Between Dillard Street and the White River
19th century

Jacksonport was once a thriving commercial center near both the Black and White rivers. Laid out in 1833, the town grew rapidly as a point of transfer for cargoes going upriver as well as to the Ozark hinterlands. Civic leaders refused, in the 1870's, to allow construction of spur tracks by the railroad. From that point on the town declined. A flood and fire in 1882 hastened its demise, and by 1891 court records and archives were turned over to Newport, the new county seat. Only the 19th-century courthouse remains, reminiscent of a bygone period of prosperity.
State

JEFFERSON COUNTY
Pine Bluff
DuBOCAGE
1115 W. 4th Street
1866

DuBocage was built for Joseph W. Bocage (1819–1898). It represents a phase of Arkansas architecture in transition from late Greek Revival to Victorian. The house has a one-bay, two-story, pedimented entrance portico projecting from its main facade. A balcony extends across the entire front of the house at the second floor, and the gable ends of the roof contain triangular capped and louvered vents. Sidelights and a transom surround the paneled doors on both floor levels. Bocage was a lawyer and planter who turned to lumber manufacture after the Civil War.
Private

JEFFERSON COUNTY
Pine Bluff
HUDSON-GRACE-BORRESON HOUSE
716 W. Barraque
19th century

The Hudson-Grace-Borreson House, which evolved from a one-story, two-room cabin, combines elements of Greek Revival, Victorian, and New Orleans style dwellings. The cabin was built about 1830 and expanded and remodeled in 1860. Elaborate carved wood detailing decorates the exterior, particularly the roof cornice, window pediments, porch posts, and window frames. Scrolled consoles, a continuous row of triangular blocks, and a delicate scrollwork band ornament the roof cornices. The roof itself is a steep mansard with a hip cap. All windows are tall and narrow, and the main doors are double and contain round-arched inset glass panels.
Private

LAWRENCE COUNTY
Powhatan
POWHATAN COURTHOUSE
1888

Overlooking the Black River, the Powhatan Courthouse was built to replace an earlier one which burned in 1885. The two-story structure is built of brick, and two-story brick pilasters emphasize its corners and bays. Other notable details are the segmental arches above the windows and the central tower on the facade. Elaborate Victorian detailing appears on the wooden surfaces of the tower, and Italian influence is evident in the roof brackets, dormers, and modified mansard roof. The original chimneys were altered in the 1930's. The courthouse has not been used since 1966.
County

MISSISSIPPI COUNTY
Wilson
NODENA SITE
South edge of Wilson
1200

Nodena is the type site of the Nodena phase, an important part of the Late Mississippian or temple mound culture in Arkansas. Excavations produced over 1,500 burials and great quantities of pottery vessels and other artifacts characteristic of the period. A small museum near the site preserves much of the recovered material.
Private
NHL

OUACHITA COUNTY
Camden
McCOLLUM-CHIDESTER HOUSE
926 Washington Street, N.W.
1847

The one-and-one-half-story, frame McCollum-Chidester House is rectangular and has low wings on the east and west elevations. It rests on brick piers that have pierced brick underpinning between them. A veranda extends the width of the main house, and the double entrance doors are framed by sidelights and a transom.
Private

OUACHITA COUNTY
Chidester vicinity
POISON SPRING STATE PARK
E 1/2 NE 1/4 sec. 1, T. 13 S., R. 19 W.
1864

Federal General Frederick Steele captured and occupied Camden, Arkansas, on April 15, 1864. Fearful of being outnumbered by the combined Confederate forces of Generals Kirby Smith and Sterling Price, Steele planned to withdraw to Little Rock. Prior to departure he sent a foraging party toward Washington to secure a reported cache of corn hidden by the Confederates. On April 18 when returning to Camden, the Federal wagon train containing the corn was attacked and captured. Principal military action occurred within the park boundaries.
State

POPE COUNTY
Pottsville
POTTS' INN
Main and Center Streets
c. 1830

Potts' Inn was built as a home by Kirkbride Potts and eventually became a coach stop on the Memphis (Tennessee) to Fort Smith (Arkansas) stage route. The frame house is two stories high and has a two-story, pedimented projecting portico above the main entrance. Unusual features of the exterior are four large outside chimneys, three of brick and one of local stone. Inside, there are four rooms on each floor separated by a large hall and stairway.
Private

PULASKI COUNTY
Little Rock
THE LITTLE ROCK
On the south bank of the Arkansas
River at the foot of Rock Street

Arkansas' largest city, which is also the
state capital, is named for this unusual
rock formation. The "Little Rock" also
served as the starting point for most land
surveys south of the Arkansas River. The
first known reference to rocks along the
Arkansas was made by Bernard de La
Harpe in 1722. The "Little Rocks" were
first officially mentioned by name in an
1805 letter to the Secretary of War, and in
1818 the Little Rock was used as a
reference point for a survey of Indian
lands. Now only a portion of the original
formation remains. It rises to a height of
18 feet above the river and extends about
40 feet along the bank. Early maps show
the site jutting out into the river, so the
size of the rock formation has evidently
been much reduced.
Private

PULASKI COUNTY
Little Rock
MOUNT HOLLY CEMETERY
12th Street and Broadway
19th century

Mount Holly Cemetery occupies an area
equal to four city blocks. Land for the
cemetery was donated in 1843, and the
first burial took place the same year. Ten
former governors, three U.S. Senators,
twelve state supreme court justices, twenty mayors of Little Rock, and five Confederate generals are interred here. Maintenance of the cemetery has been assumed
by the Mount Holly Cemetery Association, which was incorporated in 1915.
Within the cemetery are numerous and
varied examples of funerary sculpture
spanning 126 years. Burials still take
place.
Municipal

PULASKI COUNTY
Little Rock
OLD ARKANSAS STATEHOUSE
300 W. Markham Street
1833–1842, Gideon Shryock and
George Weigart

The Old Statehouse served as the Arkansas capitol from 1836 until 1911. A secession convention and four constitutional
conventions were held here, and the building was headquarters for the Confederate
state government during the Civil War and
for a Union state government afterwards.
The exterior walls are brick covered with
stucco, and the temple front portico is
supported by four Greek Doric columns.

Originally there were three parts to the
capitol, a center section and two wings,
but these were connected by frame
passageways between 1840 and 1861.
State
HABS

PULASKI COUNTY
Little Rock
THE TAVERN (ARKANSAS
TERRITORIAL RESTORATION)
214 E. 3rd Street
19th century

The Tavern is one of eleven buildings, occupying a city block in downtown Little
Rock, which have been designated the Arkansas Territorial Restoration. A two-
story, clapboard-covered log structure, the
tavern existed before statehood, when Little Rock was the territorial capital of Arkansas. Some remodeling occurred in
1834, and a general restoration was undertaken in 1939–1941. Exterior clapboarding was replaced, and a new
ridgepole, rafters, and joists were installed. The present structure is assumed
to resemble the tavern as built and it
stands on the original site.
State
HABS

PULASKI COUNTY
Little Rock
U.S. ARSENAL BUILDING
MacArthur Park, 9th and Commerce
Streets
1838–1840

Arkansas became a state in 1836. Settlers
felt that protection was needed because
they were in a frontier area with Indians
passing through frequently enroute to the
West. The arsenal was operative until
1892, when the federal government
turned it over to the city for use as park
land. In 1861 the commanding officer surrendered the arsenal to Governor Henry
M. Rector, and it remained in Confederate hands until Union forces captured Little Rock in September, 1863.
The arsenal building is two stories high
with a central, octagonal, crenelated
tower flanked by two wings. External
dimensions are 122 feet by 42 feet. Rubble walls extend from the foundation to
the first floor. Above this the walls are
brick. The basic brick and masonry building is unaltered, but the wooden verandas
and stairways have been noticeably
changed.
Muncipal
HABS

PULASKI COUNTY
Little Rock
VILLA MARRE (ANGELO MARRE
HOUSE)
1321 Scott Street
c. 1882

The three-story Villa Marre is Second Empire in style. Characteristic of the style are
the high mansard roof with a curb around
the top of all visible slopes, projecting
pavilions, and dormer windows. The
quoins and window lintels are prominent.
Some alterations have been made on the
interior and exterior but basically the
house remains as built.
Private

PULASKI COUNTY
Mabelvale vicinity
TEN MILE HOUSE (STAGECOACH
HOUSE)
North of Mabelvale on Ark. 5
Prior to 1835

Archibald McHenry was the first occupant
of Ten Mile House, located approximately
that distance southwest of Little Rock.
Situated on the Old Southwest Trail, an
early traffic artery to Texas, the house was
frequently visited by travelers who were
friends of the owner. The one-and-one-
half-story brick dwelling has large double
end chimneys with a bridging wall
between each pair. Few alterations have
been made, and the original well, dairy,
smokehouse, and kitchen are extant. The
architectural style is Federal.
Private; not accessible to the public
HABS

SEBASTIAN COUNTY
Fort Smith
CLAYTON, W. H. H., HOME
514 N. 6th Street
Late 19th century

The W. H. H. Clayton Home is typical of
residences built in Fort Smith during the
late 19th century. Detailing above the
windows and carving on the front porch
are Victorian. William Henry Harrison
Clayton came to Fort Smith in 1874, when
he was appointed U.S. District Attorney
for the Western District of Arkansas,
which, at that time, included the Indian
Country. While Clayton was prosecutor he
appeared before Judge Isaac Parker, the
famous "hanging judge."
Private; not accessible to the public

SEBASTIAN COUNTY
Fort Smith
FORT SMITH NATIONAL HISTORIC SITE
1817

One of the first United States military posts in Missouri Territory, Fort Smith was until 1896 a center of law and order for the lawless regions to the west. The first fort built on the site was established to prevent inter-tribal warfare resulting from Cherokee Indian encroachments on Osage lands west of the Mississippi. With the gradual increase of white settlement in the area, a second fort was begun in 1838. Troops were stationed here until 1871 when the United States District Court for the Western District of Arkansas was moved to the town. Judge Isaac C. Parker gained a national reputation here for his efforts to maintain law and order. Important remains include the Old Stone Commissary, now maintained as a museum, the altered building that served as the courtroom, and the jail.
Federal/non-federal
NPS; 18.58 acres
HABS

WASHINGTON COUNTY
Fayetteville
HEADQUARTERS HOUSE (TEBBETTS HOUSE)
118 E. Dickson Street
1850's

The frame one-and-one-half-story Tebbetts House has a central section flanked by wings on each side with an ell at the rear. An entrance portico on the main facade has two fluted columns and fluted pilasters, and within the portico pediment there is a small dentil design which is re-peated on the cornice of the entire house. The interior has been altered. Jonas M. Tebbetts, first owner of the house, was an attorney who served in the general assembly of Arkansas. His home served as a Union headquarters (1862, 1863) and Confederate headquarters (1863).
County/private

WASHINGTON COUNTY
Fayetteville
OLD MAIN, UNIVERSITY OF ARKANSAS
Arkansas Avenue
1873–1879, John Mills Van Osdel

The University of Arkansas, originally Arkansas Industrial University, was chartered in 1871. Patterned after University Hall at Illinois Industrial University (now the University of Illinois), Old Main forms three sides of a hollow square. It measures 214 feet across the front and 120 feet along each side. Red brick walls trimmed with limestone stand on a rusticated sandstone basement which rises 10 feet above grade. Two towers project above the mansard roof, and their tops are pierced by oculi.
State

WASHINGTON COUNTY
Fayetteville
STONE HOUSE
207 Center Street
1845

The Stone House is an impressive 19th-century brick dwelling on one of Fayetteville's main streets. It is rectangular, measuring 52 feet long by 30 feet wide. There is a one-story wing at the west end which is 20 feet by 30 feet. Both the north and south entrances are panelled and have side- and transom lights. A two-story portico on the south is Victorian in detail with elaborately carved scrollwork and a second-floor balustrade. Stephen K. Stone purchased the house from Judge David Walker, the first owner, in 1850.
Private; not accessible to the public

WASHINGTON COUNTY
Prairie Grove
PRAIRIE GROVE BATTLEFIELD PARK
Within a triangle formed by North Road on the northwest and U.S. 62 on the south

In the late summer of 1862 Federal troops west of the Mississippi River launched a two-pronged drive on Confederate Arkansas. One army swept down the White River in eastern Arkansas, while a second, commanded by General James G. Blunt, moved into northwest Arkansas and pushed the Confederates south. Commander of the Southern troops in Arkansas was General T. H. Holmes. By November General Blunt had reached Fayetteville and turned his attention to Holmes' First Corps under General Thomas C. Hindman. A cavalry engagement took place at Cane Hill which alerted the Federals that they were to be attacked, and Blunt requested reinforcements. General F. J. Herron was sent to Blunt's aid, but before their forces could unite, Hindman attacked at Prairie Grove on the morning of December 7. Both Federal armies became involved, and, although the battle seesawed for a while, Hindman was finally forced to withdraw on the following day. As a result the Confederacy lost northwest Arkansas. The 64–acre battlefield park contains monuments and markers describing the engagement.
State

Ten Mile House, Pulaski County, Arkansas.
Arkansas Parks, Recreation and Travel Commission

Pea Ridge National Military Park,
Pea Ridge, Arkansas. *Fred Mang, Jr. for NPS*

California

Interior Court, Bradbury Building, Los Angeles, California. *HABS*

![Bodie Historic District, Bridgeport vicinity, California. NPS](#)

Bodie Historic District, Bridgeport vicinity, California. *NPS*

Santa Barbara Mission Church,
Santa Barbara, California. *NPS*

ALAMEDA COUNTY
Berkeley
ROOM 307, GILMAN HALL, UNIVERSITY OF CALIFORNIA
University of California campus
1941

In this small laboratory on February 23–24, 1941, Joseph W. Kennedy, Glenn T. Seaborg, and Arthur C. Wahl first identified the man-made element plutonium. Other transuranium elements were recognized shortly thereafter, but plutonium remains the most important, as it is used both in nuclear reactors and atomic explosives. The room is still used as a research laboratory.
State; not accessible to the public
NHL

ALAMEDA COUNTY
Fremont
CALIFORNIA NURSERY COMPANY GUEST HOUSE (JOSE DE JESUS VALLEJO ADOBE)
California Nursery Company, Niles Boulevard at Nursery Avenue
Mid–19th century

The Rancho Arroyo de la Alameda was granted to Jose de Jesus Vallejo on August 8, 1842. It consisted of 17,705 acres. Vallejo was *comisionado* and administrator at the Mission San Jose (1836–1840) and military commander at the Pueblo de San Jose (1841–1842). In 1850 he was appointed postmaster at the mission. This adobe was the first of several built by Vallejo in the vicinity. It is a one-story, one-room structure with 28–inch exterior walls of sun-dried, locally made brick. The adobe has recently been restored as a guest house.
Private

ALAMEDA COUNTY
Oakland
THE ABBEY (JOAQUIN MILLER HOUSE)
Joaquin Miller Road and Sanborn Drive
1886

Joaquin (Cincinnatus Hiner) Miller, known as "Poet of the Sierra," was the first major poet of the far western frontier. His *Songs of the Sierras*, *Songs of the Sunlands*, and numerous plays, novels, essays, and autobiographical writings deal for the most part with the exploits of pioneers, outlaws, Indians, and the scenic marvels of the West. The Abbey consists of three one-story, one-room, frame buildings connected to form a unit. Miller's home until his death in 1913, the Abbey is now a museum.
Municipal
NHL

ALAMEDA COUNTY
Oakland
LAKE MERRITT WILD DUCK REFUGE
Lakeside Park, Grand Avenue
1870

Lake Merritt Wild Duck Refuge is the oldest legally established public wildlife sanctuary in the United States. Lake Merritt is a 160–acre saltwater body located in what is now the business district of Oakland, California. Despite its urban environment, the lake attracts thousands of migrating ducks each winter. A Natural Science Center is maintained to interpret the wild life story to visitors.
Municipal
NHL

AMADOR COUNTY
Volcano vicinity
INDIAN GRINDING ROCK (CHAW'SE)
2.25 miles southwest of Volcano on Pine Grove-Volcano Road
Pre-Columbian

The Indian Grinding Rock is the largest known bedrock mortar concentration in California and probably in the United States. It is a limestone outcropping measuring 175 by 85 feet and containing more than 1,100 mortar pits formed by the Indians as they pounded acorns and seeds. There are also several hundred petroglyphs on the rock. Two middens, marking former village areas, are adjacent. The site was used by Northern Miwok Indians.
State

BUTTE COUNTY
Chico vicinity
PATRICK RANCHERIA
3 miles south of Chico
Pre-Columbian

The Patrick Rancheria site consists of a large mound of village midden with 36 surface depressions which are the remains of aboriginal dwellings. One of the few large Historic Valley Maidu Indian sites remaining in the Chico area, the Patrick Rancheria probably contains data on the economy and culture of the Valley Maidu people in the proto-historic period. Also, the site marked the northernmost extension of a "Ghost Dance" cult which reached its peak of popularity in the late 1800's. A large circular depression on the southeast edge of the site indicates the remains of a Ghost Dance ceremonial structure. In 1967 and 1968 the site was extensively tested by the Field School of the University of California at Los Angeles.
Private

COLUSA COUNTY
Grimes vicinity
NOWI RANCHERIA
1 mile southeast of Grimes on Calif. 45
Prehistoric and early 1800's

The Nowi Rancheria consists of a large mound of occupational midden covering approximately three acres and rising about six feet above the ground. It is the site of a Patwin Indian village occupied in prehistoric and historic (into the early 1800's) times. The site may have been one of the cultural centers in the northeastern portion of the Patwin group. Essentially intact, the mound is believed to be stratified and complex internally and could provide invaluable data on the prehistory of the area.
Private

CONTRA COSTA COUNTY
Danville vicinity
O'NEILL, EUGENE, HOUSE (TAO HOUSE)
1.5 miles west of Danville
1937, Frederick L. Confer & Associates

In this house playwright Eugene O'Neill (1888–1953) wrote some of his most significant works: *Long Day's Journey Into Night*, *The Iceman Cometh*, *Hughie*, and *Moon for the Misbegotten*. The two-story dwelling is U-shaped and measures approximately 75 feet by 30 feet. Materials used were concrete, lumber, brick, tile, and teak wood. Foundations are reinforced concrete, and the 12–inch exterior walls are made of reinforced Baselite blocks. O'Neill, who was awarded the Nobel Prize for literature in 1936, moved out of the house because of poor health in 1944.
Private
NHL

CONTRA COSTA COUNTY
Martinez
JOHN MUIR NATIONAL HISTORIC SITE
4440 Alhambra Avenue
1890

This ranch at Martinez was John Muir's home from 1880 until his death in 1914, and it was there that his most important contributions to conservation and literature were made. Through his many published writings Muir established himself as an authority on the glaciers and mountains of the West and made a major contribution to the forest conservation movement in the United States. He was the first to verify the origin of Yosemite

Valley by glacial erosion. His estate consisted of 800 acres on which the Martinez Adobe (Muir's home from 1880 to 1890) and a large Victorian style house were situated. The two buildings stand today on a portion of the original site.
Federal
NPS; 8.9 acres
HABS

CONTRA COSTA COUNTY
Richmond vicinity
EAST BROTHER ISLAND LIGHT STATION
On East Brother Island west of Point San Pablo
1873–1874

The East Brother Island Light is situated on a small, rocky island at the north end of San Francisco Bay. Three wooden buildings comprise the lighthouse group: a turreted light tower with living quarters, a boathouse-engine room, and a combination shop and storage building. Except for the addition of bathrooms and the modernization of the kitchen units in the main building, all three structures are unchanged. Automated in 1969, the light itself is a 1,000-watt bulb magnified into 18,000 candle power visible for 13.5 miles. It serves as a navigational aid to ships entering and leaving San Francisco Bay, at the Oakland docks, and far up San Pablo Bay. The original foghorns were 12-inch, coal-fired steam whistles, replaced by electrically air-powered diaphones, and now activated by a fog detector—a stroboscopic sensor.
Federal
HABS

EL DORADO COUNTY
Placerville vicinity
COLOMA
7 miles northwest of Placerville on Calif. 49
1848

James Wilson Marshall, a foreman for John Sutter, discovered gold at Coloma while inspecting a sawmill race. Two years later, the resulting gold rush of 1849–1850 precipitated the establishment of California as a state. The town of Coloma, which grew up around the gold discovery site at Sutter's Mill, was the first white settlement in the foothills of the Sierra Nevada. A cluster of dilapidated buildings and structures still stands. Archeological investigations in 1947 established the dimensions and structural details of the ruined mill and recovered many artifacts. Sutter's sawmill has been reconstructed near the original mill site.
State
NHL; HABS

HUMBOLDT COUNTY
Eureka vicinity
GUNTHER ISLAND SITE 67 (TOLOWOT)
Northeast end of Gunther Island in Humboldt Bay north of Eureka
Late prehistoric

The Tolowot site is a tremendous shell mound 14 feet deep on which was located a Wiyot Indian village. It contained nine houses in 1850 and six in 1860 at the time of an unprovoked massacre by white men. Excavations have uncovered 11 house pits along with many burials and partial cremations. It is significant as the type site of the late prehistoric period for this coastal region. Tolowot is one of the few professionally excavated sites of its kind for which published data are available.
Multiple public/private
NHL

IMPERIAL COUNTY
YUMA CROSSING AND ASSOCIATED SITES
Reference—see Yuma County, Arizona

INYO COUNTY
China Lake vicinity
BIG AND LITTLE PETROGLYPH CANYONS
China Lake Naval Ordnance Test Station
Date unknown

The Big and Little Petroglyph Canyons comprise probably the most spectacular petroglyph area in the entire western United States. More than 20,000 petroglyphs of a varied and complex nature are located here. There is evidence that the carving of the designs covers a long period of time and represents at least two cultural phases. A large array of geometric and naturalistic forms appear, including mountain sheep, mountain lions, deer, and hunters.
Federal
NHL

KERN COUNTY
Bakersfield vicinity
WALKER PASS
60 miles northeast of Bakersfield on Calif. 178
1834

Joseph Reddeford Walker served as one of the chief guides of Captain B. L. E. Bonneville's fur trapping expedition to the Rocky Mountains in 1833. On July 24, Walker left Bonneville's fort with a trapping party and started west to explore and trap in the country beyond the Great

Salt Lake. They traversed the Sierra Nevada into California and on to the Pacific coast. During the return journey in 1834, Walker discovered the 5,248-foot-high pass that has since borne his name. In 1843 Walker led the first emigrant wagon train into California through this pass.
Multiple public/private
NHL

KERN COUNTY
Lebec vicinity
FORT TEJON
3 miles northwest of Lebec on U.S. 99

The United States Army established Fort Tejon on June 24, 1854. Its purpose was to suppress stock rustling and protect Indians in the San Joaquin Valley. Twenty or more original buildings once surrounded the 400-foot square parade ground. These structures were frame and adobe. One single-story and one two-story barracks building have been restored as have a two-story officers' quarters and a one-story orderlies' quarters.
State

KINGS COUNTY
Kettleman City vicinity
WITT SITE
12 miles west of Kettleman City on Utica Avenue
Pre-Columbian

Chipped stone artifacts found at the Witt Site are closely analogous to specimens of the fluted point tradition (Clovis-Folsom). Discovery of these artifacts has definitely placed California within the distributional sphere of this post-Pleistocene cultural tradition. Other finds have linked the site to the San Dieguito tradition of the Southern California desert region.
Private

LAKE COUNTY
Lakeport
LAKE COUNTY COURTHOUSE
255 N. Main Street
1870–1871

The second Lake County Courthouse served from the date of its construction until September, 1968, when a third courthouse ·replaced it. The structure measures 66 feet by 44 feet and has brick walls covered with concrete on the exterior. Two stories in height, the courthouse has an elaborate cornice and has been remodeled.
County; not accessible to the public

LOS ANGELES COUNTY
Encino
RANCHO EL ENCINO (LOS ENCINOS STATE HISTORIC PARK)
16756 Moorpark Street

The buildings comprising Rancho El Encino are the Osa Adobe, the Garnier Residence, and two outbuildings. Don Vincente de la Osa acquired the ranch in the 1840's and built the one-story dwelling soon thereafter. It measures 20 feet by 150 feet and has a covered porch on three sides. Eugene Garnier bought the ranch in 1869 and completed the two-story, limestone house about 1872. Stylistically it resembles provincial French architecture of the time. Garnier was a Basque, and he made El Encino into a large-scale sheep ranch. The two outbuildings, a food storage structure and a herder's hut, are also limestone.
State

LOS ANGELES COUNTY
Long Beach
LOS CERRITOS RANCH HOUSE
4600 Virginia Road
1844

John Temple, a New Englander who had come to California in 1827, built the house as headquarters for his ranch which pastured 25,000 head of livestock. It was later operated as a sheep ranch, and the main house was a private residence until 1955. The builder combined Monterey Colonial architecture (two-story house with a two-story veranda and two one-story wings) with a traditional Spanish-Mexican hacienda plan enclosing a central courtyard. Foundations are brick and the walls of the building are adobe several feet thick.
Municipal
NHL

LOS ANGELES COUNTY
Los Angeles
BARNSDALL PARK
4800 Hollywood Boulevard

Barnsdall Park was originally laid out by Frank Lloyd Wright as a 36–acre cultural center. The park was commissioned by Mrs. Aline Barnsdall and was to have contained three residences, a theater in the round, and a dance studio. Only the houses were built, and one has since been destroyed. Mrs. Barnsdall's residence, the Hollyhock House, was erected between 1916 and 1922. It is representative of a style that Wright created specifically for the climate of southern California and used in four textile block houses in Los Angeles and Pasadena. Scale and decorative elements were inspired by Mayan

temples. The architect combined these elements with his Prairie Style free floor plan and created a ground-hugging structure which closely followed the contours of the land. The other house, Residence A, is closer in design to Wright's Prairie Style buildings. It was completed about 1919.
Municipal
HABS

LOS ANGELES COUNTY
Los Angeles
LOS ANGELES CENTRAL LIBRARY
630 W. 5th Street
1925, Bertram G. Goodhue

The unadorned angular walls of the Los Angeles Central Library rise perpendicularly for four stories. Located in the center of the complex is a three-story penthouse surmounted by a pyramidal pinnacle. Reinforced concrete and cement plaster were used for the exterior walls. Ornament is minimal—sculptured heroic figures on the entrance pylons and mosaics of colored Spanish tiles on the penthouse and pinnacle. The interior is richly decorated—floors of marble and tile and sculpture and murals on the walls. Lee Lawrie was the sculptor.
Municipal
HABS

LOS ANGELES COUNTY
Los Angeles
LUMMIS HOME
200 E. Avenue 43
1897–1912

Charles Lummis (1859–1928), author and editor, built this unusual two-story, random rubble stone house. The exterior walls are 2 to 4 feet thick and rest on concrete footings. An uneven roofline is broken frequently by towers and chimneys, and the sloping roof is covered with wood shakes. Lummis was greatly interested in the culture and history of the Southwest. He founded both the California History and Landmarks Club and the Southwest Museum.
State

LOS ANGELES COUNTY
Pacific Palisades
ROGERS, WILL, HOUSE (WILL ROGERS STATE HISTORICAL MONUMENT)
14253 Sunset Boulevard
c. 1926

Will Rogers acquired land for his home in 1922 and construction began the following year. The Rogers family moved to the ranch in 1925, although the house was not yet finished. Will Rogers made his home here until his death in 1935, and his

widow lived here until she died in 1944. The house is a one- and two-story frame building with a shingled roof and wide overhanging eaves. There are verandas on the main elevations. Furniture of the period and many personal effects of the famous humorist are displayed inside.
State

LOS ANGELES COUNTY
Pasadena (San Marino)
EL MOLINO VIEJO (OLD MILL)
1120 Old Mill Road
c. 1816

The present Old Mill is a two-story structure of heavy masonry with a clay tile roof. Lower walls are five feet thick and the foundation is quarried volcanic stone. Power was supplied by an innovative horizontal, direct impulse waterwheel. Water was stored in a cistern on the west wall and released into the water chamber through the thick bottom wall by means of a narrow spout. It then poured horizontally against the buckets of the waterwheel, which was connected directly with the millstones by a vertical shaft. The Old Mill was constructed to serve nearby Mission San Gabriel.
Municipal

LOS ANGELES COUNTY
Pomona
PALOMARES, YGNACIO, ADOBE
Corner of Arrow Highway and Orange Grove Avenue
1854

The Palomares Adobe is a good example of a ranchero's residence. The one-story building has thick adobe walls and a shake roof. Don Ygnacio Palomares lived in the ranch house which later functioned as a stage station and tavern. Restored in 1939, the structure presently houses the Historical Society of Pomona Valley.
Private

LOS ANGELES COUNTY
San Fernando
LOPEZ ADOBE
1100 Pico Street
1882–1883

The Lopez Adobe, built by Valentino Lopez, was the first two-story adobe in the San Fernando Valley to be used as a residence. It has walls two feet thick. The original shake roof was replaced in 1928 by tiles. Porches covering the front and ends of both the upper and lower levels have handcut wooden railings with bracket capitals and a jigsaw patterned balustrade. The single-story structure connected on the south was formerly attached to the main building by a breezeway and served as a kitchen. The adobe is typical

of the transitional period after the decline of the missions and before the influx of Americans during and after the gold rush of 1849.
Private
HABS

LOS ANGELES COUNTY
San Fernando vicinity
WELL NO. 4, PICO CANYON OIL FIELD
9.6 miles north of San Fernando and west of U.S. 99
1876

The birthplace of California's petroleum industry, Well No. 4 of Pico Canyon Oil Field was drilled some 15 years after the search for oil in California had begun. It was the first commercially successful well in the state. The site consists of about 850 acres, including the discovery well and a school and frame hotel used by the oilmen in the 1880's.
Private; not accessible to the public
NHL

LOS ANGELES COUNTY
San Gabriel
SAN GABRIEL MISSION
Junipero Street and W. Mission Drive
18th and 19th centuries

The Mission San Gabriel Arcangel was the fourth founded in California. Friars Pedro Cambon and Angel Somera established it on September 8, 1771. Four years later, when threatened by flood, the mission was moved to its present location. This church was begun in 1791, completed in 1805, damaged by earthquake (1812), repaired (1828), secularized (1834), and returned to the Catholic Church in 1859. The adobe mission building is unlike any of its sister churches. The side wall is actually the main facade, and Moorish elements are evident in the capped buttresses and long, narrow windows.
Private

LOS ANGELES COUNTY
Wilmington
BANNING HOME
401 E. M Street
c. 1863–1864

The Banning Home is a two-story frame residence with a full attic, a gable roof, and a two-story veranda across the front. Dimensions of the house are 50 feet by 107 feet. A square, two-stage cupola surmounts the roof. Inside, most rooms have high ceilings and fireplaces. General Phineas Banning, founder of Wilmington, was an entrepreneur in the field of transportation. His business ventures included stagecoaches, railroads, and ocean-going vessels.
Municipal

LOS ANGELES COUNTY
Wilmington
DRUM BARRACKS
1053 Carey Street

Established in 1862 as the U.S. Military Headquarters for Southern California, Arizona, and New Mexico, the Drum Barracks served as a supply base and a military garrison. It was also a terminus for camel pack trains operated by the Army until 1863. Today only the officers' quarters and the powder magazine remain of the nine original structures. The officers' quarters is frame, two stories high, and has a hip roof. Noteworthy architectural details are the porch on the east facade, the bracketed roof cornice, and the sidelights and transoms of the two front doors.
State

MONO COUNTY
Bridgeport vicinity
BODIE HISTORIC DISTRICT
7 miles south of Bridgeport on U.S. 395, then 12 miles east on secondary road
1859

Bodie is one of the most significant mining ghost towns of the West because of its more than 100 surviving buildings. Its history was typical of the strike, boom, and decline cycle of western mining communities. The discovery of an extensive mineral zone in the 1870's precipitated the boom, and the town grew from a few shacks to a population of more than 10,000. Total output of the Bodie mines up to the end of World War II has been estimated at $70,000,000.
State
NHL; HABS

MONTEREY COUNTY
Carmel
CARMEL MISSION
Rio Road
1771

The mission of San Carlos Borromeo, established by Fray Junipero Serra, was the headquarters of the *padre presidente* and, as such, the most important of the California missions. One year after the founding of Monterey, the Spanish-Mexican capital, Father Serra moved his mission away from the presidio. He established nine other mission parishes during his presidency. Fray Fermin Francisco de Lasuen founded an equal number, and both are buried in the San Carlos Church. The present building, built between 1793 and 1797, fell into a state of disrepair following secularization of the mission in 1833. However, the abandoned church was rededicated and restoration

begun in 1884. It contains many original paintings and statues.
Private
NHL; HABS

MONTEREY COUNTY
Monterey
CASA AMESTI
516 Polk Street
1834, 1846

The original adobe dwelling on this site consisted of two small rooms and an attic. It was enlarged in 1846 by Don Jose Amesti, who chose to embody architectural details characteristic of the East in native California materials. The two-story house has a second-floor veranda.
Private

MONTEREY COUNTY
Monterey
LARKIN HOUSE
464 Calle Principal
1834–1835

The Larkin House is both architecturally and historically significant. Its builder, Thomas O. Larkin, was intimately involved with United States efforts to gain possession of California. In 1843 he was appointed the first U.S. consul in Mexican California. California became a state on July 7, 1846, and its first military governor lived in Larkin House. As a result, the building is sometimes called the first American capitol of California. Larkin House, designed in the Monterey building style, marked a distinctive departure from the traditional adobe structures of the period.
State
NHL; HABS

MONTEREY COUNTY
Monterey
MONTEREY OLD TOWN HISTORIC DISTRICT
Two districts, northern and southern; southern district bounded on the west by Dutra Street, on the east by Madison Street, on the south by Polk Street, and on the north by Jefferson Street; northern district bounded by Pacific Street on the west, Scott Street on the south, Alvarado Street on the east, and Decatur Street on the north
19th century.

Monterey served as the Spanish and Mexican capital of California from 1776 to 1849. As the capital and leading city, Monterey was the center of political, economic, and social activity on the Pacific coast for Spanish, Mexican, and American settlers. Forty-three one- and two-story adobe structures dating from the

19th century remain largely concentrated in the two sections described above. Buildings of particular importance or interest are Casa Alvarado (510 Dutra Street), residence of Don Juan Bautista Alvarado, governor of California from 1836 to 1842; Colton Hall (1847–1849), one of the first Greek Revival buildings on the Pacific coast; Sherman's Headquarters (464 Calle Principal), built by master builder Thomas O. Larkin and headquarters for Lieutenant William Tecumseh Sherman (1847–1849); the Old Customhouse (115 Alvarado Street); and the First Brick House (351 Decatur Street), built in 1847–1848.
Multiple public/private
NHL

MONTEREY COUNTY
Monterey
ROYAL PRESIDIO CHAPEL
550 Church Street
1789

For 75 years Monterey was the stronghold of Spanish-Mexican civilization on the Pacific coast. It was the capital of California from 1776 until shortly before the American occupation in 1846. The present Royal Presidio Chapel, then called the Church of San Carlos, was begun by Governor Pedro Fages on the site of a mission established in 1770 by Fray Junipero Serra. It is the only remaining presidio chapel in California, the sole existing structure of the original Monterey Presidio, and the only architectural remains of 18th-century Spanish origin within Monterey. Royal governors under Spanish rule worshiped here, and many state ceremonies were held here. A wing, transept, and altar are 19th-century additions, but the building is essentially unchanged.
Private
NHL; HABS

MONTEREY COUNTY
Monterey
U.S. CUSTOMHOUSE (OLD CUSTOMHOUSE)
Calle Principal at Decatur Street
1827–1846

At Monterey Customhouse on July 7, 1846, the American flag was first raised over California. Accompanied by a proclamation by Commander John D. Sloat, the event officially marked the beginning of United States authority in California. The early history of the Customhouse was related to the California hide and tallow trade, through which the United States first became acquainted with the state's resources. The building is a good example of Spanish Colonial architecture.
State
NHL; HABS

NEVADA COUNTY
French Lake vicinity
MEADOW LAKE PETROGLYPHS
East of French Lake, sec. 22, T. 18 N., R. 13 E.
Pre-Columbian

Petroglyphs near Meadow Lake are the most abstract yet found in the Sierra Nevada and represent an extreme style in contrast to more naturalistic elements at other area sites. A total of 390 pecked design units cover a series of seven major panels, and isolated units are scattered over an area of 500 feet on glacially smooth granite bedrock and large boulders. Design elements consist of abstract curved lines, concentric circles, dots, and only three naturalistic stick figures.
Federal

NEVADA COUNTY
Truckee vicinity
DONNER CAMP
2.6 miles west of Truckee on U.S. 40
1846

At Donner Camp in the high Sierras a California-bound group of emigrants led by Captain George Donner was caught by two early winter storms. Marooned in deep snow, the party of 89 members built rude shelters of wagon tops and brush in their efforts to survive. Seven of the 15 who set out for help reached the California settlements, and on February 19, 1847, the first relief party arrived at the camp. Only 45 survived the winter ordeal. The fate of the Donner party epitomizes the hardships and dangers endured by pioneers of the overland migrations. A monument to the pioneers stands on the site which is now the Donner Memorial State Park.
State
NHL

PLACER COUNTY
Auburn
OLD AUBURN HISTORIC DISTRICT
Bounded approximately by Int. 80, Maple Street, and Hamilton Lane on the north, High Street on the south, and including the westerly frontage on Spring Street, the easterly frontage on Lincoln Way and Sacramento Street, and the Traveler's Rest and Winery property at the southeast part of the historic district
Late 19th century

Auburn was an 1849 mining camp located between the northern and southern mines of the Sierra Nevada. It became the county seat of Placer County in 1851. Today, aside from the paving of streets and the laying of sidewalks, old Auburn remains largely unchanged from its appearance in

the late 1800's. A fire ravaged the town in 1855, and most buildings date from the post-fire rebuilding. Among the extant structures are the American Hotel, the Old Post Office, the Union Bar, the Placer County Courthouse (1897), Lawyers Row (1855), and the Chinese Joss House, a house of worship in the Chinese settlement area.
Multiple public/private

PLUMAS COUNTY
Gold Lake vicinity
LAKES BASIN PETROGLYPHS
Northwest of Gold Lake, sec. 8, T. 21 N., R. 12 E.
Pre-Columbian

The Lakes Basin Petroglyphs include at least six large panels of design elements plus several scattered individual carvings spread over an area of approximately three acres. The various abstract and naturalistic representations of anthropomorphic and circumlinear designs are cut into granite bedrock. There has been little patination of the cut surfaces, although lichens have obscured some designs. The date or dates of the carvings are not known.
Federal

RIVERSIDE COUNTY
Riverside
MISSION INN
3649 7th Street
1890–1901, Arthur Benton

The Mission Inn is the largest Mission Revival style building in California. Hallmarks of this style are arches and low-pitched red tile roofs. Oldest portions of the Inn are the lobby and the two wings along Orange and Main Streets. The Cloister wing, the Spanish wing, and the Rotunda Internationale were added later. High bell towers, arched cloisters with flagstone floors, and low interior ceilings are notable features. The Inn centers around an open patio, and furnishings include antiques and paintings from the Orient, Mexico, and Europe, and Tiffany windows.
Private

SACRAMENTO COUNTY
Locke
LOCKE HISTORIC DISTRICT
Bounded on the west by the Sacramento River, on the north by Locke Road, on the east by Alley Street, and on the south by Levee Street
Early 20th century

During the 1870's, following completion of the transcontinental railroad, the result-

ing surplus of Chinese laborers was employed in constructing a levee system in the delta area of southwestern Sacramento County. The delta is formed by the confluence of the San Joaquin and Sacramento rivers. The Chinese settled at first in Walnut Grove, but a fire in 1915 forced them to relocate and establish the town of Locke. Except for aging and weathering the houses and residences built by the first settlers remain much as they were when constructed. No new buildings have been added in 50 years. A four-block area comprises the historic district and includes commercial structures with second-floor dwellings along Main Street and loading sheds along the levee top near the river. These sheds are believed to have been built in the 1880's. The community is unique as an unaltered ethnic enclave within a rapidly growing and changing state.
Multiple private

SACRAMENTO COUNTY
Sacramento
CALIFORNIA GOVERNOR'S MANSION
Southwest corner of 16th and H Streets
1877–1878, Nathaniel D. Goodell

The California Governor's Mansion was originally built for the president of a Sacramento hardware firm. It was acquired by the state in 1903 and was the residence of the state's chief executive until 1967. The three-story, Second Empire, frame house has a high mansard roof, a central tower, and elaborate hoodmolds above the third-floor and tower windows. The bracketed cornice, roof dormers, and second-floor balcony are all boldly modeled. Author Lincoln Steffens spent his boyhood in this house.
State
HABS

SCRAMENTO COUNTY
Sacramento
CROCKER, E. B., ART GALLERY
216 O Street
c. 1853 (house), Seth Babson;
1871–1873 (gallery), Seth Babson

Edwin Bryant Crocker (1818–1875) was a partner in the legal firm of Crocker, McKune, and Robinson. He acted as counsel to the Central Pacific Railroad and was appointed to the California Supreme Court. His home was built for banker B. F. Hastings and purchased by Crocker in 1868. The gallery was built to house the Crockers' collection of paintings. It is a brick and plaster structure (60 by 120 feet) designed in the style of the 16th-century Italian mannerists.
Municipal
HABS

SACRAMENTO COUNTY
Sacramento
OLD SACRAMENTO HISTORIC DISTRICT
Junctions of U.S. 40, 50, 99 and Calif. 16 and 24
1849–1850

The river port of Sacramento emerged during the California gold rush of 1849 as the interior distribution and transportation center for the gold mines in the Mother Lode country of the Sierra Nevada. In the 1860's, when the mining frontier moved eastward into Nevada, Idaho, and Oregon, Sacramento became the transportation gateway to most of this inland empire. The original business district has a larger number of buildings dating from the gold rush period than any other major city on the Pacific coast. Included among these are banks, express buildings, hotels, offices, restaurants, saloons, and stores.
Multiple public/private
NHL; HABS

SACRAMENTO COUNTY
Sacramento
PONY EXPRESS TERMINAL (B. F. HASTINGS BUILDING)
1006 2nd Street
1853

This two-story brick building was occupied in turn by B. F. Hastings and Company, the State Library, the State Supreme Court, Wells, Fargo and Company, and the California State Telegraph Company. Subsequently it housed the original western terminal of the Pony Express, April, 1860 to March, 1861. It is one of the only two buildings associated with the Pony Express and Overland Mail still standing in California.
Private; not accessible to the public
NHL; HABS

SACRAMENTO COUNTY
Sacramento
SUTTER'S FORT
2701 L Street
1839

John A. Sutter was one of the earliest American settlers in California. He built this fortified post on a large land grant secured from the Mexican governor of California. Most of the central and northern overland immigrant trails converged on this strategically located site

after crossing the Sierras. A welcome resting place, the fort proved an invaluable aid to American settlement of California. After 1850 the fort passed to other hands, and the buildings began to deteriorate. Restored by the state in 1891–1893, it retains its original form with shops, storerooms, and barracks.
State
NHL

SACRAMENTO COUNTY
Sacramento
WOODLAKE SITE
.5 mile southwest of KXOA radio towers
Pre-Columbian

The Woodlake Site is an excellent example of a large river village area in the lower Sacramento Valley. Artifacts and mound debris indicate that occupation occurred in late prehistoric times (c. 1000–1700), and there is slight evidence of an earlier occupation (c. 2000 B.C. to 300 A.D.). The real significance of the site lies in its depth of stratigraphy and its undisturbed quality, both of which should yield information about cultural adaptation to a riverine environment. The debris has built up into a mound two to three feet above the ground level.
Private

SAN BENITO COUNTY
San Juan Bautista
ANZA HOUSE (JUAN DE ANZA HOUSE)
3rd and Franklin Streets
1820–1840

Juan De Anza built the original adobe house sometime during the 20–year period 1820–1840. The one-story, rectangular, two-room adobe was Americanized in the 1850's by the installation of double doors and six-over-six double hung windows and by the construction of a three-room frame section on the rear.
Private; not accessible to the public
NHL; HABS

SAN BENITO COUNTY
San Juan Bautista
CASTRO, JOSE, HOUSE
South side of the Plaza
1840–1841

Jose Castro, commandant general of northern California, built this adobe structure as his administrative office. The building was sold in 1848 to Patrick Breen, a survivor of the hapless Donner party, which was marooned in the Sierra Nevada during the winter of 1846. On the exterior the adobe walls are covered with plaster rusticated to give the appearance of stone. Inside are eight rooms. Restoration work was undertaken in the 1930's.
State
NHL; HABS

SAN BENITO COUNTY
San Juan Bautista
SAN JUAN BAUTISTA PLAZA HISTORIC DISTRICT

Beginning at the intersection of Washington and 2nd Streets, northwest along 2nd to Mariposa Street, northeast on Mariposa to 1st Street, southeast on 1st to Washington Street, southwest on Washington to 2nd Street
19th century

Five buildings, all facing the Plaza and completed between 1813 and 1874, compose the historic district. The mission at San Juan Bautista was founded in 1797, and the present church, built between 1803 and 1813, is the largest in the state. After secularization (1835) it fell into disrepair which was greatly aggravated by the 1906 earthquake. The church has been reconstructed. Also facing the Plaza are the Plaza Hall (1868), a combination residence and hotel; the Plaza Stable (1874); the Castro House (also a National Historic Landmark); and the Plaza Hotel (1813–1814, 1858).
State and private
NHL; HABS

SAN DIEGO COUNTY
Camp Joseph H. Pendleton
LAS FLORES ADOBE

West side of Stuart Mesa Road about 7 miles north of Vandegrift Boulevard junction
1867–1868

Constructed by Marcus A. Forster, the Las Flores or Magee Adobe is a late but little-altered example of a Monterey Colonial ranch house. The Monterey Colonial house was originated by the master builder Thomas O. Larkin of Monterey between 1835 and 1851. In his design Larkin successfully combined the traditional Spanish-Mexican one-story adobe with the New England frame structure, thus evolving a new type of two-story adobe building that adapted well to the warm climate of California. The ease with which Larkin's innovation could be readily applied to the domestic, commercial, and public building architecture of the period made the Monterey Colonial style far more flexible and varied than the traditional Spanish-Mexican Colonial, one-story adobe structures. Utilized over a wide area (from San Diego in the south to Sonoma in the north), the Monterey Colonial style is unique to California. Except for the enclosed rear porches which are later additions, Las Flores Adobe is otherwise unaltered.
Federal; not accessible to the public
NHL

SAN DIEGO COUNTY
Camp Pendleton
SANTA MARGARITA RANCH HOUSE

Off Vandegrift Boulevard
19th century

The oldest part of this adobe ranch house was built during the early 1800's, when the property belonged to the San Luis Rey Mission. The original structure may have had only two rooms. Walls are five to seven feet thick at the base and taper to three feet at the top. Rough-hewn sycamore logs placed across the tops of the thick adobe walls support the heavy roof tiles. The present 23–room, one-story dwelling with central patio is the result of numerous enlargements. In 1882 James L. Flood and Richard O'Neill bought the ranch and used it as the headquarters for their immense cattle raising enterprise. The federal government acquired the property in 1942, and it was converted into a Marine Corps training station.
Federal

SAN DIEGO COUNTY
Oceanside vicinity
SAN LUIS REY MISSION CHURCH

4 miles east of Oceanside on Calif. 76
1811–1815

Father Fermin Francisco de Lasuen founded the Mission San Luis Rey de Francia in June, 1798. A small adobe chapel was constructed at that time but was replaced four years later by a larger, tile-roofed church. The present building was one of two cruciform mission churches erected in California by the Spanish. All architectural trim is of molded brick, and the adobe walls are five feet thick. Three sections compose the facade, and, although only one bell tower was built, the original plan apparently called for two. Secularized in 1834, the mission deteriorated somewhat, but the original buildings were intact enough in 1893 to be rededicated as a Franciscan college.
Private
NHL; HABS

SAN DIEGO COUNTY
San Diego
ESTUDILLO HOUSE

4000 Mason Street
1827–1829

Don Jose Antonio Estudillo, who built the Estudillo House, was a captain in the presidial guard at the time and later became mayor and justice of the peace for the city of San Diego. The U-shaped adobe walls of the house encircle a courtyard on three sides. Hand-hewn beams lashed together with rawhide thongs sup-

port the tile roof, and a one-story veranda extends entirely around the three sides of the inner courtyard. The 12–room home remained in the Estudillo family until 1887. It was restored during the early years of the 20th century.
Private
NHL

SAN DIEGO COUNTY
San Diego
OLD MISSION DAM

North side of Mission Street-Gorge Road
1800–1817

The Old Mission Dam was the first major irrigation-engineering project on the Pacific coast of the United States. Its aqueduct and flume extended about five miles to the Mission of San Diego de Alcala. Water was impounded by the dam and released as needed for the fields around the mission and for milling and domestic use. The dam was a solid masonry wall about 220 feet long, 13 feet thick at the bottom, and approximately 12 feet high at its maximum. It was constructed of native stone and locally produced cement. Enough remains of the dam to impound a small amount of water. Some slight traces of the flume are said to be identifiable, but none remain of the aqueduct.
Municipal
NHL

SAN DIEGO COUNTY
SAN DIEGO MISSION CHURCH

Mission Road, 5 miles east of San Diego
1808–1813

San Diego de Alcala Mission was founded by Father Junipero Serra in July, 1769. It was the first of the 21 missions in the California chain. The mission was moved to its present site in 1774, burned shortly thereafter, and was replaced by an adobe structure in 1777. A third and larger church was constructed in 1780. Secularized in 1834 by the Mexican government, the mission site was owned by the U.S. Army and the Catholic Church and was used as an Indian school and a home for boys. Restoration began in 1931. With the exception of the front wall, front buttress wings, the base of the belfry, the baptistry arch, and some of the sidewalls, the mission is a reconstruction. It measures 150 feet by 35 feet with four-and-one-half-foot thick adobe walls. The most unusual architectural feature is the 46–foot belfry or *campanario*.
Private
NHL

SAN DIEGO COUNTY
San Diego
SAN DIEGO PRESIDIO
Presidio Park
1769

San Diego Presidio is the site of the first permanent European settlement on the Pacific coast of the United States. Here the Portola-Serra land and sea expedition united, and Fray Junipero Serra founded the mission of San Diego de Alcala. The town served as a base of operations for exploring routes into the interior and as the military headquarters for southern California. Remains of the Presidio may still be seen in the city park.
Municipal
NHL

SAN DIEGO COUNTY
San Diego
STAR OF INDIA
San Diego Embarcadero
1863

The *Star of India*, a three-masted, iron-hulled vessel, is the only extant Alaskan salmon bark. Built in Great Britain as the full-rigged, three-masted *Euterpe*, the vessel sailed as a general trader to India, served as a passenger ship, and carried lumber before she was purchased by the Alaska Packers Association in 1901. Modified to a bark and renamed, the ship carried fishermen and cannery employees to the Alaska fisheries until retired in 1923. In 1926 the *Star of India* was purchased by the late James Wood Coffroth as the nucleus of a maritime museum, and in 1959 restoration was begun by the Maritime Museum Association of San Diego. The vessel is the oldest iron-hulled merchantman afloat.
Private
NHL

SAN DIEGO COUNTY
San Diego
VILLA MONTEZUMA (JESSE SHEPARD HOUSE)
1925 K Street
1887, Comstock and Trotsche

The Villa Montezuma defies exact architectural classification as it combines elements, forms, and details of Moorish or Turkish and Gothic influence in the general Queen Anne sytle. Walls from the basement to the first floor are brick faced with cement. On the west and south sides the walls are frame. Various shingle patterns (diamond, round, square, and fish scale) are also scattered over the asymmetrical and alternately projecting and recessed wall surfaces. The roof has ornamental ironwork along its ridge, and there are cast metal gargoyles at the gable ends and atop the roof domes. Interior ceilings, paneling, trim, and doors are mostly polished redwood. Stained glass windows and exotic hardwood fireplace mantels are notable features. The house was built for musician Jesse F. Shepard (1848–1927).
Private
HABS

SAN DIEGO COUNTY
San Diego vicinity
CABRILLO NATIONAL MONUMENT
10 miles from San Diego off U.S. 101, near the southern tip of Point Loma
1542

Cabrillo National Monument commemorates the discovery of the west coast of the United States by Juan Rodriguez Cabrillo on September 28, 1542. His entrance and landing at San Diego mark the first contact of Europeans with this part of the New World. The voyage was but one of many expeditions by means of which Spain extended its dominions in the New World. The principal historic structure in the area is the old Point Loma Lighthouse, which was first lighted in 1855.
Federal
NPS; 80.5 acres

SAN DIEGO COUNTY
Spring Valley
BANCROFT, HUBERT H., RANCH HOUSE
Bancroft Drive off Calif. 94
1856

Historian Hubert Howe Bancroft acquired this one-story adobe house in 1885 and used it until his death in 1918. The monumental historian of the western half of North America, Bancroft wrote much of his major work and experimented with different types of plants and crops while living here. In 39 volumes Bancroft and his associates described the history of a civilization that was then rapidly disappearing. His work is still a pre-eminent authority on the history of Alaska, the western portions of Canada, Central America, Mexico, and the continental United States.
Private; not accessible to the public
NHL; HABS

SAN DIEGO COUNTY
Vista vicinity
GUAJOME RANCH HOUSE
2.5 miles northeast of Vista
1852–1853

Colonel Cave Johnston Couts utilized Indian labor to construct the main house and outbuildings of the Guajome Ranch complex. The ranch house is a one-story adobe with a central, enclosed courtyard. Outbuildings form a second courtyard against the north wall of the house. Around the walls of the outer court are a jail, blacksmith shop, horse stalls, carriage house, and harness room. Outside the court are a family chapel, servants' house, and several barns and sheds. This complex is one of the few extant haciendas with a double courtyard. Couts operated the ranch until his death in 1876, and it remained in the family until 1943.
Private; not accessible to the public
NHL; HABS

SAN DIEGO COUNTY
Warner Springs vicinity
OAK GROVE BUTTERFIELD STAGE STATION
13 miles northwest of Warner Springs on Calif. 79
1858

Oak Grove is apparently the only original stage station still remaining on the entire Butterfield Overland Mail Route. This route was in operation between San Francisco and two eastern terminals from 1858 to 1861. The building was also used as a hospital during the Civil War. This well-preserved one-story adobe building has been enlarged from time to time, but the northern side belongs to the original ranch house.
Private
NHL; HABS

SAN DIEGO COUNTY
Warner Springs vicinity
WARNER'S RANCH
4 miles south of Warner Springs on secondary road
1831

Warner's Ranch was a landmark and stopping place for travelers and emigrants on the southern route into California from the eastern United States. Jonathan T. Warner established his ranch on two land grants secured from the Mexican Governor of California. It was the first place the traveler could find shelter and food after enduring the hardships of the southwestern desert crossing. In 1858 Warner's Ranch became a regular station of the Butterfield Overland Mail Route.
Private; not accessible to the public
NHL; HABS

SAN FRANCISCO COUNTY
San Francisco
C. A. THAYER
San Francisco Maritime State Historic Park
1895

The *C. A. Thayer* is the last surviving example of 122 sailing schooners designed especially for use in the 19th-century Pacific coast lumber trade. The three-

masted schooner stands halfway in design between the small, two-masted schooners first developed in the 1860's and the last, huge four- and five-masters built in 1905. The 453-ton *Thayer* is 156 feet long, with a 36-foot beam and a cargo capacity of 575,000 board feet of lumber. The ship was used as a fishing vessel from 1912 until her retirement in 1950. She was restored as a lumber schooner in 1962–1963.
State
NHL

SAN FRANCISCO COUNTY
San Francisco
FEUSIER OCTAGON HOUSE
1067 Green Street
c. 1857–1858

Octagonal homes became popular in mid-19th century America due to the influence of a book written by Orson Squire Fowler, a phrenologist. Fowler, author of *A Home for All or the Gravel Wall and Octagon Mode of Building* (1848), equated a person's well-being with the shape of his home. The octagon house was designed so every room would receive sunlight at some time of the day. The exterior walls of the house are a mixture of cement or burned lime plus gravel and clay. There is no wood exterior covering. All corners are quoined. The base of the house sits below street level, and the main entrance on the second floor is reached by a stairway. An octagonal cupola surmounts the roof. The Feusier Octagon is one of two that survive in San Francisco.
Private; not accessible to the public
HABS

SAN FRANCISCO COUNTY
San Francisco
FLOOD, JAMES C., MANSION
Northwest corner of California and Mason Streets
1886

James C. Flood was one of the bonanza kings of the Nevada Comstock Lode. In 1873 he and his partners obtained control of the Consolidated Virginia Mine, probably the richest body of gold and silver ore yet found. His brownstone mansion is the only Nob Hill town house to survive the 1906 fire and earthquake.
Private
NHL; HABS

SAN FRANCISCO COUNTY
San Francisco
FORT POINT NATIONAL HISTORIC SITE
Northern tip of the San Francisco Peninsula on U.S. 101 and Int. 480

The San Francisco Presidio was first established by Spanish authority in 1776 to guard the Golden Gate and the harbor beyond. When the area passed to United States control in 1847, a permanent fort was constructed by the Army (1854–1861). That installation, Fort Point, is the most massive (150 feet by 250 feet) brick fortification erected on the west coast of North America. Representative of pre-Civil War technology, it was never attacked and has long been obsolete. The structure was used during World Wars I and II and during construction of the Golden Gate Bridge in the 1930's but was relinquished by lease in 1961 to the Fort Point Museum Association. The Presidio has been headquarters for the United States Army on the west coast since 1849, with the exception of the six years 1850 to 1857, and is presently headquarters for the Sixth Army.
Federal
NPS; 29 acres
HABS

SAN FRANCISCO COUNTY
San Francisco
OLD UNITED STATES MINT
5th and Mission Streets
1869–1874

The Old Mint was associated with the history of the far western mining frontier. It was established as a subsidiary of the Philadelphia Mint as a result of the enormous gold production of the California Mother Lode. The added flood of silver in the 1860's necessitated the construction of a new building in 1869. This building, the present Old Mint, was placed on an independent basis and soon became the principal mint in the United States and the chief Federal deposit for gold and silver produced in the West. This 19th-century Federal style building is one of the few in downtown San Francisco that survived the 1906 earthquake and fire.
Federal
NHL; HABS

SAN FRANCISCO COUNTY
San Francisco
PHELPS, ABNER, HOUSE
329 Divisadero Street
1850–1851

The Gothic Revival style Phelps House is considered to be the oldest unaltered residence in San Francisco. Set upon a high foundation, the house has a steep gable roof and a one-story veranda across the main facade. The frame exterior is covered with shiplap siding. Roof dormers are lighted by French doors, and the central dormer is larger and has more prominently projecting eaves than the others. Balusters on the veranda and on the balcony which form the veranda roof are classic, well-turned wooden spindles. Bargeboards in the gable ends are ornately carved. The house has been moved twice.
Private; not accessible to the public
HABS

SAN FRANCISCO COUNTY
San Francisco
THE PRESIDIO
Northern tip of San Francisco Peninsula on U.S. 101 and Int. 480
1776

The Presidio was first established by Spanish authority to guard the entrance to San Francisco harbor. After the Presidio passed to United States control in 1847, the Federal Government built a fort in 1853 on the site of the second Spanish fort. Though militarily inactive since 1914, the fort is still standing. The Presidio has been the headquarters of the United States Army on the Pacific coast since 1849, except from 1851 to 1857. The present Fort Mason was built on the site of the third Spanish fort. Its officers' club, a one-story, restored adobe building, includes about 75 per cent of the original walls of the Spanish commandant's house. There are no remains of the second or third forts.
Federal
NHL; HABS

SAN FRANCISCO COUNTY
San Francisco
SAN FRANCISCO CABLE CARS
1873

The cable car was contrived by Andrew S. Hallidie, an English builder of aerial cable systems for mines in the western United States. He arranged a system by which heavy underground cables would draw the cars up the steep San Francisco hills. The first cable was laid from Kearny Street over Nob Hill to Leavenworth Street. Once eight companies operated 112 miles of track. There are approximately 10 miles of cable car tracks remaining in the San Francisco Municipal Railway, the only ones still operating in the United States. Despite proposals to remove this last vestige of cable cars transportation, the city has legislated that the Powell Street line will continue to run, at a deficit, because of its historic significance as a landmark of San Francisco.
Municipal
NHL

SAN LUIS OBISPO COUNTY
Nipomo
DANA ADOBE
Southern end of Oak Glen Avenue
c. 1839

Captain William G. Dana began construction of the 13–room Dana Adobe in 1839. The house is one and one-half stories high with a gable roof and a one-story, two-room projection at the rear. Dana provided goods (soap, candles, and cloth) and services such as carpentry and blacksmithing to the surrounding ranchos and the missions of La Purisima and Santa Ynez. The adobe was one of four stopping places on the road between San Luis Obispo and Santa Barbara, and here mail riders from northern and southern California exchanged pouches and spent the night.
Private; not accessible to the public

SAN MATEO COUNTY
Belmont
RALSTON, WILLIAM C., HOME
College of Notre Dame campus
1864–1868, attributed to Henry
Cleaveland

William C. Ralston was an eminent San Francisco financier. From 1864 to 1875 he played a major role in the exploitation of the Comstock Lode mines in Nevada and in developing and financing industry and railroad construction in California. These activities helped make San Francisco the commercial, financial, and industrial center of the far West. The exterior of his mansion is largely unchanged, although the original wooden trim has been simplified and a third story added on the south wing. The first floor of the interior, with its large ballroom, numerous parlors, library, and large dining room, is unaltered.
Private
NHL; HABS

SAN MATEO COUNTY
San Bruno vicinity
**SAN FRANCISCO BAY DISCOVERY
SITE**
4 miles west of San Bruno via Skyline
Drive and Sneath Lane
1769

From the crest of Sweeney Ridge on November 4, 1769, the main body of the Gaspár de Portolá exploring expedition first sighted San Francisco Bay. The discovery of the bay was a major achievement of this expedition and of the entire era of early Spanish exploration in this area. Recognizing the superiority of this great inland bay, the Spanish administrative hierarchy ultimately made the decision to establish a presidio and two missions in the area. In 1776 Juan Bautista de Anza founded the mission and presidio of San Francisco.
Private
NHL

SANTA BARBARA COUNTY
Lompoc vicinity
LA PURISIMA MISSION
4 miles east of Lompoc, near the
intersection of Calif. 1 and 150
Early 19th century; reconstructed,
1935–1942

The first mission to be called La Purisima Concepción was founded in 1787 by Father Fermin de Lasuen. Located in the town of Lompoc, this mission was destroyed by an earthquake and torrential rains (1812). A year later the work of rebuilding (on the present site) commenced and was completed by 1818. In 1834 the mission was secularized and gradually fell into disrepair. One hundred years later the state of California acquired 966 acres at the mission site and began reconstruction of the buildings. Those structures which were rebuilt are the padres' residence, the shops and soldiers' quarters, and the church. A Spanish colonial mission complex consisted of an entire settlement — living quarters, storehouses and workshops — usually constructed around a quadrangle. At La Purisima Mission the buildings stood in a straight line along the valley floor.
State
NHL; HABS

SANTA BARBARA COUNTY
Los Alamos vicinity
LOS ALAMOS RANCH HOUSE
3 miles west of Los Alamos on old
U.S. 101
c. 1840

The land of Rancho Los Alamos was originally a grant of almost 50,000 acres made by Juan Bautista Alvarado, Mexican governor of California, in 1839. The ranch house itself is a good example of a one-story adobe, Spanish-Mexican hacienda. Indians, who also performed all ranching duties, constructed the building, and its location on the main road between Santa Barbara and Monterey made it a popular overnight stop. All rooms within are interconnecting and each opens directly to the outside. Recent alterations, such as the installation of electricity, central heating, and two picture windows, do not greatly change the overall appearance of an early ranch dwelling.
Private; not accessible to the public

SANTA BARBARA COUNTY
Santa Barbara
GONZALES HOUSE
835 Laguna Street
c. 1825

Named for its builder, Raphael Gonzales, the Gonzales House is one story high and has two one-room wings projecting from both ends. Covered verandas extend along both long sides of the house, and the roof is tile. Restoration work was done in the 1920's, at which time several new windows were installed in the facade.
Private; not accessible to the public
NHL; HABS

SANTA BARBARA COUNTY
Santa Barbara
SANTA BARBARA MISSION
2201 Laguna Street
1786

Santa Barbara Mission was one of 21 missions founded by Fray Junipero Serra along the California coast. The present church, the fourth on this site, was completed in 1820. As an architectural landmark it has been influential in the development of the mission style in California. The only California mission not secularized in the Mexican decree of 1833, Santa Barbara became the Franciscan capital and the see of the first Spanish Bishop. The library and museum contain a large collection of original mission treasures, including the original altar and 17th- and 18th-century paintings.
Private
NHL; HABS

SANTA CLARA COUNTY
Gilroy vicinity
NORRIS, FRANK, CABIN
10 miles west of Gilroy via Calif. 152
and secondary roads
c. 1900

Frank Norris, a writer of the early American naturalist school, lived in this cabin prior to his death in 1902. In novels such as *The Octopus* and *The Pit*, he concentrated on portraying the ills of the social systems of his day. The cabin, surrounded by magnificent redwoods, is in its original condition.
Private; not accessible to the public
NHL

SANTA CLARA COUNTY
San Jose vicinity
NEW ALMADEN
14 miles south of San Jose on County
Route G8
1824

New Almaden is the site of the first mercury deposit discovered in North America.

The mines, one of the world's four great sources of mercury, were essential to the mining process during the boom days of the California Mother Lode and the Nevada Comstock Lode. The New Almaden mine, the oldest in the state, has yielded metal of greater total value than any other mine in California. Operated only intermittently since 1927, the mines are at present inactive. Among the remains of the former mining town are several wood and adobe buildings, along with offices, mine structures, and old furnace buildings.
Private
NHL; HABS

SANTA CRUZ COUNTY
Santa Cruz
OCTAGON BUILDING
Corner of Front and Cooper Streets
1882

Octagon buildings were a novelty and a source of fascination for 19th-century architects. This Octagon Building is one story high and built of brick. An addition was made to the Front Street side in the early 1900's which detracts from the building's original octagonal shape (its removal is planned). The Octagon Building, which served 86 years as the county's Hall of Records, will be used as the Santa Cruz County Historical Museum and as a tourist information center.
County

SHASTA COUNTY
Redding vicinity
OLSEN PETROGLYPHS
Bear Mountain Road, northeast of Redding
Pre-Columbian

The Olsen Petroglyphs were etched on horizontal sloping sandstone slabs along the west bank of Stillwater Creek. Carved into the surface of the sandstone are designs such as wheels, rosettes, ladders, rattlesnakes, sunbursts or flowers, bear tracks, and some abstract symbols. Adjacent to the south side of the petroglyph site, across a dry stream bed, is the large midden of a habitation site. Ethnographically the site is in the area occupied by the Wintu Indians of northern California. Examination of the midden area has indicated an absence of European trade goods, reinforcing a belief that this site predates the contact period (c. 1830). Special significance is attached to the petroglyphs because such sites associated with village habitation areas are rare in northern California.
Private

SIERRA COUNTY
Gold Lake vicinity
HAWLEY LAKE PETROGLYPHS
West of Gold Lake, sec. 14, T. 21 N., R. 11 E.
Pre-Columbian to 19th century

The Hawley Lake site is one of the largest petroglyph areas in the northern Sierra Nevada. More than 500 different designs have been carved into a large exposed section of bedrock. The carvings include track forms of deer, bear, elk, and man, abstract forms such as circles, wavy lines, and grids, as well as cupules, vulvaforms, anthropomorphs, and animals (mountain sheep and lizards). Stylistically the petroglyphs appear to be related to a greater tradition of rock art found from this region through the Great Basin and possibly as far south as Texas. The petroglyphs were pecked, rubbed, and scratched into the rock surface. A lack of associated midden sites suggests that this was strictly a ceremonial or religious center.
Federal

SIERRA COUNTY
Truckee vicinity
SARDINE VALLEY ARCHEOLOGICAL DISTRICT
Portions of secs. 7 and 18, T. 19 N., R. 17 E.
Pre-Columbian to historic times

The Sardine Valley Archeological District contains a more or less continuous surface scattering of occupational debris plus two distinct midden concentrations. Surface artifacts and limited data from test excavations of one midden suggest that the area was occupied as much as 7,000 years ago up to historic times by a hunting and gathering people on a seasonal basis. The occupational debris includes a widespread scattering of material typical of the Martis Complex, dates for which have not been established.
Private

SISKIYOU COUNTY (also in Klamath County, Oregon)
Dorris vicinity
LOWER KLAMATH NATIONAL WILDLIFE REFUGE
Lower Klamath Lake, east of Dorris
1908

Set aside by President Theodore Roosevelt, Lower Klamath National Wildlife Refuge was one of the first areas of public land to be reserved as a Federal wildlife sanctuary. The Klamath Basin in northern California and southern Oregon attracts large flocks of ducks and geese migrating within the Pacific Flyway. From 1921 to 1942, diversion of water for irrigation nearly dried Lower Klamath Lake, and the area declined as a nesting and resting place for waterfowl. Restored to a fraction of its original size, the lake now includes an intricate system of dikes, canals, and water control structures separating artificial impoundments of marsh and water from grain fields. The refuge is again noted for the number and diversity of its nesting waterfowl and for its variety of marsh and shore birds. It is additionally significant as an example of conflict and compromise between irrigation interests and wildlife preservationists.
Federal
NHL

SOLANO COUNTY
Benicia
BENICIA CAPITOL-COURTHOUSE
1st and G Streets
1853-1854

The Benicia Capitol is the third such structure to be erected in California and the only one remaining from the first decade of statehood. From February 4, 1853, to February 25, 1854, it was California's seat of government. The two-story brick building has triangular pediments at both gable ends and a modillion cornice at the eave line and within the pediments. There is a distyle-*in-antis* portico on the main facade, and pilasters accentuate all four corners and the main entranceway. The state of California restored the former capitol in 1956–1957.
State

SONOMA COUNTY
Fort Ross vicinity
FORT ROSS
North of Fort Ross on Calif. 1, Fort Ross State Historical Monument
1812

Fort Ross was the largest single Russian trading center south of Alaska. Founded as part of the Russian fur trading operation, it represented a Russian attempt to colonize California. Continuing Russian expansion in western North America was a major factor behind the drafting of the Monroe Doctrine. Financial failure of the Fort Ross operation, along with Spanish demands for withdrawal from their territory, resulted in the sale of the fort to John Sutter in 1841. Fort Ross is now a State Historical Museum. Several restored buildings are located within its reconstructed walls.
State
NHL; HABS

SONOMA COUNTY
Fort Ross vicinity
FORT ROSS COMMANDER'S HOUSE
North of Fort Ross on Calif. 1, Fort
Ross State Historical Monument
1812

Fort Ross was built by the Russian American Fur Company under the supervision of Ivan Kuskoff, who arrived in the spring of 1812 with 95 Russians and about 80 Aleuts. A stockade with blockhouses, barracks, and officers' quarters was constructed. The Commander's House, which is largely original, measures approximately 36 feet by 48 feet and is made of hand-squared redwood timbers that are mortised together at the corners. In 1841 the fort was sold by the Russians to John A. Sutter.
State

SONOMA COUNTY
Glen Ellen vicinity
LONDON, JACK, RANCH
.4 mile west of Glen Ellen, Jack
London Historical State Park
1905

Jack London was a significant American literary figure of the early 20th century. Several of his major novels, including *Valley of the Moon*, were written at this 130–acre hill ranch. "Wolf House," his elaborate home on the site, was destroyed by fire almost immediately after its construction. The Jack London State Historic Park, dedicated in 1960, includes 49 acres of the original ranch, the ruins of "Wolf House," and the "House of Happy Walls" erected by London's widow after his death in 1916 and now used as a museum. London is buried on the property.
State
NHL

SONOMA COUNTY
Petaluma vicinity
PETALUMA ADOBE
4 miles east of Petaluma on Casa
Grande Road
1836–1846

Mariano Vallejo, commandant of the Sonoma Pueblo, built the Petaluma Adobe. Sonoma Pueblo was organized after the secularization of the mission San Francisco Solano in 1834. Today Petaluma Adobe is the largest known existing example of domestic adobe architecture in the United States. Vallejo used the house as headquarters for his extensive ranching operation which employed over 2,000 Indians. In 1857 Vallejo sold the house, and in 1951 it was acquired by the state of California. The house, as restored by the state, is U-shaped (a fourth or enclosing wall was never built) with a two-story veranda on the exterior and interior elevations. Native fieldstone forms the foundation, adobe brick was used for the walls, and hand-hewn redwood timbers cover the interior.
State
NHL; HABS

SONOMA COUNTY
Santa Rosa
BURBANK, LUTHER, HOUSE AND GARDEN
200 Block of Santa Rosa Avenue
1883

Often called the "Plant Wizard," Luther Burbank was an internationally-known horticulturist at the time of his death in 1926. For 50 years his experiments with thousands of plants produced many important cultivated varieties of flowers, vegetables, grains, grasses, and fruits, particularly plums. The site consists of three acres of land, including the experimental garden and his house, the original greenhouse, and a stable.
Multiple public/private
NHL

SONOMA COUNTY
Sonoma
SONOMA PLAZA
Center of Sonoma
1846

The raising of the Bear Flag over Sonoma Plaza on June 14, 1846, represented the beginning of the American revolt against Mexican rule in California. Thirty-three patriots took possession of Sonoma, the political and military center of the province north of Monterey, and elected William B. Ide to represent them. Soon thereafter came official news of the outbreak of the Mexican War, after which the Bear Flag movement was of no further use. Most of the original buildings still surround Sonoma Plaza, which contains a bronze statue of a young pioneer holding the staff of the Bear Flag.
State
NHL; HABS

SONOMA COUNTY
Stewarts Point vicinity
SALT POINT STATE PARK ARCHEOLOGICAL DISTRICT
15 miles south of Stewarts Point on
Calif. 1

Archeological resources at Salt Point State Park are 44 sites of various types including historic sites, shell middens, lithic sites, and a cupule rock. Twenty-five of the sites are shell middens of aboriginal or non-European origin. The location of the middens and lithic sites in protected areas along the coast indicates that the region was visited by Indians (Kashia Pomo in historic times) who exploited the marine resources on a seasonal basis. The cupule rock gives visual evidence of the religious-ceremonial nature of these early peoples. Most of the sites are in good condition and represent a major source for research and interpretation of the aboriginal living patterns of both prehistoric groups and the historic Kashia Pomo.
State

TUOLUMNE COUNTY
Sonora vicinity
COLUMBIA HISTORIC DISTRICT
4 miles northwest of Sonora on Calif.
49
1850

A well-preserved gold-mining camp of the California Mother Lode region, Columbia was phenomenally productive until about 1860. Because the town has been continuously occupied and maintained since its inception, a large number of the original buildings have survived. Today most of Columbia's historic section is included within the boundaries of a state historical monument. Evidence of mining is visible outside the town, and rocks, pits, and hummocks show where the earth was washed away from the gold-bearing rock.
Multiple public/private
NHL; HABS

YOLO COUNTY
Broderick
FIRST PACIFIC COAST SALMON CANNERY SITE
On the Sacramento River, opposite
the foot of K Street
1864–1866

Here William and George Hume and Andrew Hapgood successfully perfected the canning techniques that led to the development of the multi-million dollar Pacific coast salmon cannery industry. The cannery was situated on a large scow anchored in the Sacramento River offshore from the cabin in which they lived. By 1923 the Pacific coast canneries had produced more than eight billion pounds of canned salmon. Today nothing remains of either the cabin or the cannery scow.
Private
NHL

Old Customs House, Monterey, California. *Charles W. Snell for NPS*

C. A. Thayer, San Francisco, California. *Charles W. Snell for NPS*

Colorado

Osgood Castle (Cleveholm), Redstone vicinity, Colorado. *Denver & Rio Grande Railroad*

447-895 O - 73 - 5

Daniels and Fisher Tower,
Denver, Colorado. *Wm. Edmund Barrett*

Emmanuel Shearith Israel Chapel,
Denver, Colorado. *Colorado State Museum*

Governor's Mansion,
Denver, Colorado.
Colorado State Museum

The Great Kiva, Lowry Ruin,
Pleasant View vicinity, Colorado.
Chicago Natural History Museum

ARAPAHOE COUNTY
Strasburg vicinity
COMANCHE CROSSING OF THE KANSAS PACIFIC RAILROAD
On the Union Pacific Railroad tracks east of the Strasburg depot
1870

Comanche Crossing is significant in the history of transcontinental railroad development because it was here that the final spike was driven connecting the east and west coasts entirely by continuous rail track. The golden spike which was driven at Promontory, Utah, in May, 1869, did not complete a continuous rail link between the Atlantic and Pacific oceans. A gap of 111 miles existed from Sacramento to Alameda, California, which was closed in September. At Strasburg, on August 15, 1870, the final spike was driven to link the country by rail via Denver using a Missouri River bridge (at Kansas City) and a Mississippi River bridge (at Quincy, Illinois). Originally part of the Kansas Pacific Railroad, the site is now owned by the Union Pacific Railroad. It derives its name from Comanche Creek, which is spanned by the tracks.
Private

___

ARCHULETA COUNTY
Chimney Rock vicinity
CHIMNEY ROCK ARCHEOLOGICAL SITE
San Juan National Forest, 2 miles east of the Piedra River and 1.5 miles north of Colo. 151

Chimney Rock Archeological Site is located on a high mesa overlooking the Piedra River. Aboriginal remains, ranging from pit houses to pueblo structures, have been found in the vicinity; and on the mesa itself are pueblo ruins, kivas, and pit house dwellings. Other findings were black-on-white pottery, corrugated pottery, and evidence of cremation burials. No dates of occupation have been deduced, but evidence indicates that the population may have been large.
Federal

___

CLEAR CREEK COUNTY
Georgetown
HOTEL DE PARIS
Alpine Street
c. 1889

Louis Dupuy, a Frenchman, enlarged and remodeled the Delmonico Bakery into the present Hotel de Paris. The building is two stories high and constructed of masonry overlaid with stucco. There are ten bedrooms on the second floor with the public rooms downstairs. Dupuy operated a restaurant in the hotel which featured imported wines. The hotel remained open until 1932 and is now a museum and tearoom.
Private

___

CLEAR CREEK COUNTY
Georgetown
TOLL HOUSE (JULIUS G. POHLE HOUSE)
South side of town adjacent to Int. 70 right-of-way

Exact date of construction for the Pohle House is unknown, although it appears on an 1878 map of Georgetown. Julius G. Pohle was superintendent of the Lebanon Mining Company, which owned and operated a local hard rock silver mine productive from 1870 until the 1940's. The house is frame covered by a brick veneer. Architectural detail is Gothic Revival, notably the center front lancet window, the steep central cross gable, and the carved wood porch balustrade. The house was moved from its original location when endangered by a highway, and a 56-foot ell was removed at that time and not rebuilt. Locally, the house was called the Toll House because it stood near the toll gates of a private road linking Silver Plume and Georgetown and the nearby mines.
State; not accessible to the public

___

CLEAR CREEK COUNTY
Georgetown-Silver Plume vicinity
GEORGETOWN-SILVER PLUME HISTORIC DISTRICT
Mid-19th to early 20th century

The Georgetown-Silver Plume area is among the most scenic and historic in Colorado. It flourished first because of gold and silver production and later as a recreational center. Next to Leadville it was the most important silver camp in Colorado, and up to 1939 it produced more than 90 million dollars in gold, silver, lead, copper, and zinc. A branch of the Colorado Central Railroad, the famous Georgetown Loop, was built between the two towns in 1884 for the purpose of hauling silver ore. The railroad eventually became a popular tourist attraction before being dismantled in 1939, and its roadbed is part of the National Historic Landmark. The still-active communities of Georgetown and Silver Plume have retained much of their 19th-century boom-town atmosphere as many buildings have been preserved or restored. Among the surviving buildings in Georgetown are the Maxwell House (c. 1880), the Hamill House (1867), the Protestant Episcopal church (1869), and the Hotel de Paris (1875).
Multiple public/private
NHL

___

CLEAR CREEK COUNTY
Georgetown vicinity
ORE PROCESSING MILL AND DAM
Approximately 1 mile southwest of Georgetown, adjacent to Int. 70 and Clear Creek
19th century

The Ore Processing Mill is a two-story wooden structure. Ore was carried by elevator from the first-floor receiving room to the second floor where it was crushed by a jaw crusher, then sampled and sacked. According to newspaper accounts the mill, patented in 1872, contained an automatic sampling system, considered quite innovative at the time. The horizontal water wheel used to drive the machinery now lies buried beneath an accumulation of earth and water; only the foundation of the dam is still visible. The mill is one of the few remaining structures of its type and size in Colorado.
State; not accessible to the public

___

CLEAR CREEK COUNTY
Silver Plume
SILVER PLUME DEPOT
Int. 70
1884

The Silver Plume Depot was constructed at the terminus of the Colorado Central Railroad, which connected Denver with the Clear Creek mining region. The segment between Georgetown and Silver Plume, the Georgetown Loop Railroad, was built to haul silver ore between the two mining towns, but eventually it became a popular tourist attraction. The depot is a one-story frame structure with a wide roof overhang on all sides. Vertical board and batten siding covers the exterior walls, and various alterations have been made to the original building. It was moved twice due to construction of Interstate 70.
State

___

CONEJOS COUNTY
Sanford vicinity
PIKE'S STOCKADE
4 miles east of Sanford on Colo. 136
1807

Zebulon Pike led the second official United States expedition into the Louisiana Territory. At Pike's Stockade, in February 1807, he raised the American flag over Spanish soil and was taken into custody by Spanish dragoons. The state of Colorado has constructed a replica of the stockade which closely follows the specifications recorded by Pike. Made of cottonwood logs, the fort was 36 feet square and 12 feet high.
State
NHL

COSTILLO COUNTY
Fort Garland
FORT GARLAND
On Colo. 159, one block south of
U.S. 10–160
1858

Fort Garland was constructed to replace another military post, Fort Massachusetts, located six miles north and also within the territory of New Mexico. Named in honor of Brigadier General John Garland, commander of the territory, Fort Garland served as a base for operations against hostile Indians and as protector of settlers in the San Luis Valley. Fort Garland was abandoned in 1883, and only six buildings remain of the original fourteen. Construction materials were adobe plastered with mud and white lime for the walls, sod for the roofs, and laid board flooring. The fort complex formed a rectangle around the parade ground. Today, only the officers' quarters and the barracks still stand.
State

DENVER COUNTY
Denver
BROWN PALACE HOTEL
17th Street and Tremont Place
1889–1892, Frank E. Edbrooke

The Brown Palace Hotel was built after rich silver strikes in the area had made Denver a financial and social center of the West. Some interior changes have been made, but basically the hotel remains as built. Its triangular steel and iron structural frame rests on a granite foundation. The walls of red granite and Arizona sandstone rise ten stories above the street. The original hotel contained 400 rooms.
Private

DENVER COUNTY
Denver
BYERS-EVANS HOME
1310 Bannock Street
1880

The brick Byers-Evans House is two stories high with a projecting central bay. Segmental and Tudor arches above the second-story windows are repeated on the first-floor porch. Wrought iron cresting along the porch roof has Gothic trefoil arches alternating with five-armed starburst finials. More cresting runs along the main roof just above the dentil cornice. William N. Byers, publisher of the *Rocky Mountain News*, was the first owner of the house, which was acquired by William Evans in 1890. Evans was a railroad entrepreneur, organizer of the Denver Electric and Cable Company, and president of the board of trustees of Denver University.
Private; not accessible to the public

DENVER COUNTY
Denver
COLORADO GOVERNOR'S MANSION
400 E. 8th Avenue
1908

Colorado's governors have lived in this house since 1960. Prior to that time it was owned by two prominent Denver families, the Cheesmans and the Boettchers. The house was built of wood and brick, and its architecture may be termed Colonial Revival.
State

DENVER COUNTY
Denver
CONSTITUTION HALL (FIRST NATIONAL BANK BUILDING)
1507 Blake Street
1865

In December, 1875, a delegation of 39 men met within this building to draw up Colorado's constitution. The building has 18-inch thick brick walls and was only two stories high when erected. A mansard roof with dormer windows was added prior to 1870. The dormer windows have classic pediments, and the entire upper story is wood and shingle rather than brick. First floor arcades were bricked up in 1936, and the area now serves as store fronts. The First National Bank, once housed here, is Colorado's oldest continuously operating banking firm.
Private

DENVER COUNTY
Denver
DANIELS AND FISHER TOWER
1101 16th Street
1911, F. G. Sterner

The Daniels and Fisher Tower stands 393 feet above the city of Denver. On the twentieth floor is an observation deck, and above this is a large Seth Thomas clock measuring 16 feet across its face. Architecturally the tower is Italian Renaissance, patterned after the campanile of St. Mark's in Venice. Its exterior is buff terra cotta, and the construction materials are steel and concrete.
Private; not accessible to the public

DENVER COUNTY
Denver
EMMANUEL EPISCOPAL CHAPEL (EMMANUEL SHEARITH ISRAEL CHAPEL)
1201 10th Street
1876

Emmanuel Shearith Israel Chapel is the oldest church building in Denver. It was built as an Episcopal chapel, but by the 1890's the neighborhood had changed and in 1903 the building became a synagogue. Stone was used for the exterior walls, and the architecture is a mixture of Romanesque and Gothic. Services in the synagogue were discontinued in 1958. Since that time the building has been converted to an artist's studio with few alterations.
Private

DENVER COUNTY
Denver
FOUR MILE HOUSE
715 S. Forest Street
c. 1858

Four Mile House served for a time as a stop on the El Paso, Texas, to Denver stage line. The earliest structure is two stories high and was originally made of logs. An addition was built in 1881–1882, and the logs were then covered with clapboard siding.
Private
HABS

DENVER COUNTY
Denver
GRANT-HUMPHREYS MANSION
770 Pennsylvania Street
1902, Boal and Harnois

The first owner of the Grant-Humphreys Mansion was James Benton Grant, governor of Colorado (1882–1886), president of the Omaha and Grant Smelting Company, and a co-founder of Colorado Women's College. After Grant's death in 1911, the house was purchased by Albert Humphreys, a mine and oil field owner. Somewhat eclectic in style, the house is symmetrical in plan and constructed of buff colored masonry with terra cotta ornament. A large garage, servants' quarters, and a sundeck are connected to the main section. On the west front there is a semicircular portico with four fluted Corinthian columns. Matching Corinthian pilasters ornament the corners of the house. Running around the entire roofline is a balustrade of Italian Renaissance design which serves to unite the structure. Ground level windows are crowned by lunettes, and there are two bull's-eye windows on either side of the main entrance.
Private
HABS

DENVER COUNTY
Denver
ST. ELIZABETH'S CHURCH
10620 11th Street
Late 19th-century

St. Elizabeth's parish was organized by German Catholic families of the Denver area in 1878. It was the second Catholic parish in Denver. An earlier church on the site was torn down in 1890. Built of stone, St. Elizabeth's is German Gothic in style. Statues and interior woodwork were carved in Germany.
Private

DENVER COUNTY
Denver
TRINITY UNITED METHODIST CHURCH
E. 18th Avenue and Broadway
1887–1888, Robert S. Roeschlamb

The congregation which built Trinity Methodist Church was organized in 1859 and is believed to be the oldest in Denver. Outside, the church is sandstone, and its ground plan is that of a cross. Soaring more than 181 feet above the ground is a distinctive, turreted spire. Inside there is a second-floor sanctuary with a balcony on three sides. An oak and bronze pulpit in the sanctuary was designed by Henry Augustus Buchtel, later pastor of the church. A Tiffany stained glass window, "Resurrection," and a 4,290–pipe organ made by Hilborne Roosevelt are outstanding interior features.
Private

EL PASO COUNTY
Colorado Springs vicinity
PIKES PEAK
15 miles west of Colorado Springs, Pike National Forest

Pikes Peak was discovered by Zebulon Pike in 1806, although long familiar to the Indians and Spaniards. Set forward from the front range of the Rockies, this prominent landmark appears to rise much higher than its actual 14,110 feet. The ascent by automobile or cog railway affords the visitor a panorama of both mountain scenery and the eastern plains.
Multiple public/private
NHL

GILPIN COUNTY
Central City
CENTRAL CITY HISTORIC DISTRICT
c. 1860

Heart of the first great mining boom in Colorado, Central City is well preserved in both appearance and atmosphere. It was the cradle of most of Colorado's mining laws. Most of the remaining buildings were constructed after the fire of 1874. They include the Teller House (1872), the Old Armory (1875), St. James Methodist Church (1872), and the Opera House (1878). During the 1870's and 1880's the town was a cultural center, and in recent years dramatic and operatic productions have again become popular.
Multiple private
NHL; HABS

JEFFERSON COUNTY
Golden vicinity
MOUNT VERNON HOUSE (ROBERT W. STEELE HOUSE)
About 1 mile south of the Golden city limits at the junction of Int. 70, Colo. 26, and Mount Vernon Canyon Road
Mid–19th century

Robert W. Steele, governor of the extralegal territory of Jefferson, occupied this house from October, 1859, until June, 1861, when President Lincoln's gubernatorial appointee arrived. Steele was elected by local citizens in an effort to bring some sort of government to Colorado. The house itself was also used as a stage station, saloon, and general store. The first floor is stone and the second story, wood; the shape is polygonal. Oldest of the several sections is the northeast wing, and various additions have been made over the years.
Private; not accessible to the public
HABS

LAKE COUNTY
Leadville
DEXTER CABIN
912 Harrison Avenue
1879

James Viola Dexter, banker and mining magnate, built this cabin as a hunting lodge. The exterior of square-hewn logs chinked with plaster belies the luxury and elegance of the interior which exhibits a multiplicity of texture, color, and pattern. Alternate light and dark boards are used for flooring, and the wall covering is Lincrusta-Walton, a hand-stamped paper board. Window blinds are hand painted, and Dexter's furniture included a Persian rug and a zinc-lined bathtub. The contrast between exterior and interior is striking.
State

LAKE COUNTY
Leadville
HEALY HOUSE
912 Harrison Avenue
1878

Leadville, by 1880, was an important Colorado mining camp. The Healy House, named for a later owner, Daniel Healy, was built by August R. Meyer, a mining engineer. A third story was added in 1888. A Victorian porch ornaments the main facade of the frame house, which is furnished to resemble a comfortable residence of the late 19th century.
State

LAKE COUNTY
Leadville
LEADVILLE HISTORIC DISTRICT
1860

Once the world's greatest silver camp, Leadville has yielded a greater number of minerals of total value over a longer period than any other in the United States. It has been estimated that the district produced some $136,000,000 in silver between 1879 and 1889. Its first boom, however, was in gold, and after the collapse of silver prices in 1893, it was again a gold camp until the end of the century. Since that time, lead, zinc, manganese, and molybdenum have been mined in the district. Because of the area's stability, a relatively large number of early structures survive: the Elks Opera House, the Old Pioneer Bar, the Dexter Cabin, the Tabor Opera House, and the Healy House, now a museum.
Multiple public/private
NHL

LA PLATA COUNTY (also in San Juan County)
Durango
DURANGO-SILVERTON NARROW-GAUGE RAILROAD
Right-of-way between Durango and Silverton
1882

This narrow-gauge railroad is the sole surviving passenger operation railroad of its kind in the United States. Now part of the Denver and Rio Grande Western Railroad system, it was built originally to haul ores economically and efficiently from isolated mountain areas to points where smelters could operate. Today, tourists enjoy Rocky Mountain scenery as the train snakes along the gorge of the Las Animas River and through Los Angeles National Forest Wilderness Area. The locomotive and coaches, vintage 1880's, are used to transport passengers to Silverton Historic District at the end of the line.
Private
NHL

Fort Collins Vicinity
LINDENMEIER SITE
28 miles north of Fort Collins, 1.75
miles south of Wyoming state line
9000 B.C.

The Lindenmeier Site is the only extensive
Folsom camp site yet known. The Folsom
Site in New Mexico established the fact
that man appeared in the New World sufficiently early to hunt animals now extinct.
However, it provided knowledge of
weapons only. Because Lindenmeier was a
habitation site, it provided a fuller picture
of the life of the early hunters.
Private; not accessible to the public
NHL

LAS ANIMAS COUNTY
RATON PASS
*Reference—see Colfax County, New
Mexico*

LAS ANIMAS COUNTY
Trinidad
BACA HOUSE AND OUTBUILDING
300 block of Main Street
1869

Baca House was the home of Don Felipe
Baca, a well-to-do Spanish-American
rancher and freighter. Baca provided land
for the townsite of Trinidad, located on
the mountain branch of the Santa Fe
Trail. The two-story house was built of
adobe bricks. Behind it is a one-story
adobe outbuilding which housed the ranch
hands.
State

LAS ANIMAS COUNTY
Trinidad
BLOOM, FRANK G., HOUSE
300 block of Main Street
1882

The three-story Bloom House is an
elaborate Victorian residence with a mansard roof, wooden porticoed porch, and
ornate rooftop iron tracery work. Building
materials are brick and native stone.
Owner and builder Frank G. Bloom of the
Bloom Land and Cattle Company was a
wealthy Trinidad merchant and banker.
State

MONTEZUMA COUNTY (also San Juan
County, Utah)
Cortez vicinity
**HOVENWEEP NATIONAL
MONUMENT**
Northwest of Cortez
c. 400–1300

Six groups of Anasazi ruins make up the
Hovenweep National Monument: the
Square Tower Canyon Cluster and the

Cajon Group in Utah; and the Holly
Group, Hackberry Canyon Group,
Cutthroat Castle, and Goodman Point in
Colorado. The Colorado sites contain numerous towers and large pueblos. Goodman Point includes a large unexcavated
pueblo and several smaller sites. The
prehistoric inhabitants were Pueblo Indians, part of a farming group which occupied the Four Corners area from before
A.D. 400 until almost 1300. Failing crops
and diminishing water supplies forced
them to abandon the area.
Federal
NPS; 345.43 acres

MONTEZUMA COUNTY
Cortez vicinity
MESA VERDE NATIONAL PARK
10 miles east of Cortez on U.S. 160
c. 400–1300

Mesa Verde National Park preserves hundreds of prehistoric dwellings and villages
inhabited by the Basket Makers (c.
400–700) and the Pueblo Indians (c.
700–1300). Two pit houses of the type
inhabited by the Basket Makers are
open for viewing. During the height of the
Pueblo development some of the Indians,
commonly called Cliff Dwellers, left the
open pueblos on the mesas for caves,
possibly for protection. Far View House
typifies the open pueblo, and Cliff Palace
illustrates the cliff dwelling.
Federal/non-federal
NPS; 52,073.62 acres

MONTEZUMA COUNTY
Cortez vicinity
**YUCCA HOUSE NATIONAL
MONUMENT**
12 miles south of Cortez via U.S. 666
and secondary roads
c. 1000–1300

Yucca House National Monument consists
of two large rubble and earth mounds, the
larger probably representing the ruins of a
three- or four-storied building. Also at this
prehistoric Indian site are depressions suggesting kivas associated with the pueblo.
The ruins have not been excavated.
Federal; not accessible to the public
NPS; 9.60 acres

MONTEZUMA COUNTY
Pleasant View vicinity
LOWRY RUIN
30 miles northwest of Cortez via U.S.
160 and secondary road
c. 1100

Lowry Ruin is a pueblo of about 50
rooms. Its early masonry and associated
pottery are closely related to those of the
Chaco Canyon area to the south. Though
originally a small unit similar to others in

the area, it differs in having a great kiva.
The great kiva, a large ceremonial struc-
ture, is more commonly found further
south in New Mexico and Arizona.
Federal
NHL

MONTROSE COUNTY
Montrose vicinity
UTE MEMORIAL SITE
2 miles south of Montrose on U.S.
550
19th century

The Ute Memorial Site occupies approximately 13 acres of what was once ranch
land belonging to Ute Chief Ouray. Before
the coming of the white man the Utes occupied land in Colorado, Utah, and parts
of northern New Mexico. Gradually these
lands were ceded to the federal government, and the Utes now occupy a strip of
land 100 miles long by 20 miles wide
along Colorado's southwestern border.
Chief Ouray (d. 1880) represented his
people in negotiations with the U.S.
government and was a mediator between
white man and red as well as an advocate
for peace. The Indian museum on the
grounds tells the story of the Utes, and buried nearby are Ouray's wife Chipeta and
her brother Chief John McCook.
State

OTERO COUNTY
La Junta vicinity
**BENT'S OLD FORT NATIONAL
HISTORIC SITE**
8 miles west of Las Animas on Colo.
194
1833

From 1833 until the outbreak of the Mexican War in 1846, Bent's Old Fort was a
principal outpost of American civilization
and commercial penetration on the
southwestern plains. The fort was strategically located for trade in relation to
southern plains Indians, on the mountain
branch of the Santa Fe Trail. Built by
Charles and William Bent and Ceran St.
Vrain, the post was the hub of a trading
empire stretching from Texas into Wyoming, and from the Rockies to central Kansas. The success of Bent and St. Vrain depended upon friendly relations with the
Indians and suppression of competition. A
sharp decline in trade with Indians followed the influx of Americans after the
Mexican War. The adobe fort was composed of a series of adjoining compartments forming a hollow square. Round
tower bastions on the northwest and
southeast corners constituted the flanking
protection arrangements. Only the foundations remain today.
Federal
NPS; 178 acres

PITKIN COUNTY
Redstone vicinity
OSGOOD CASTLE (CLEVEHOLM)
Approximately 1 mile south of
Redstone on Colo. 133
1903, Boal and Harnois

John C. Osgood came to Colorado in 1882 to investigate the possible existence of coal fields. Twelve miles from Redstone he discovered the Coal Creek deposits and shortly thereafter formed the Colorado Fuel Company (which eventually became the Colorado Fuel and Iron Company). Osgood's own home is an irregularly shaped stone dwelling of varying heights ornamented by towers, oriel windows, and a turret. Cut stone, shingles, and some half timbering constitute the wall surfaces, corners are quoined, and the pointed-arch windows and doors have radiating voussoirs. Window shapes vary, and the polygonal turret is accented by decorative buttressing. Interior rooms have Tiffany light fixtures, red velvet, green leather, and green brocade wall coverings, marble fireplaces, crystal chandeliers, and molded plaster ceilings. The mines and coke ovens closed in 1909, and Osgood died in 1926.
Private

SAN JUAN COUNTY
DURANGO-SILVERTON NARROW-GAUGE RAILROAD
Reference—see La Plata County

SAN JUAN COUNTY
Silverton
SILVERTON HISTORIC DISTRICT
Late 19th century

Silverton is one of the two principal mining towns in the San Juan basin of southwestern Colorado. Particularly rich in silver, this mining center played an important role in the mining and economic development of the Rocky Mountain area for almost 50 years. A few of the mines still operate in Silverton, which also has some extant early buildings. Among them are the Imperial Hotel (1882), the Congregational church (1881), the city hall (1908), and the courthouse (1907).
Multiple public/private
NHL

SAN MIGUEL COUNTY
Telluride
TELLURIDE HISTORIC DISTRICT
Late 19th century

Claims were first staked in the Telluride area in 1875, and later the Smuggler was struck, uncovering a vein that assayed at $1200 per ton. Telluride grew slowly at first, but became one of the busiest gold camps in Colorado after the narrow-gauge railroad was built to it in 1890. Its prominence lasted only a few years, however, and only a few mines are still in operation. Several buildings dating from the late 19th and early 20th centuries still remain. Among them are the City Hall (1883), the Sheridan Hotel (1890's), the Opera House (c. 1900), and the Miner's Union Building (1902).
Multiple public/private
NHL

TELLER COUNTY
Cripple Creek
CRIPPLE CREEK HISTORIC DISTRICT
1891

One of the world's largest gold fields was discovered here, and unlike so many boom areas, the district prospered for many years. During 1901, its peak year, almost 25 million dollars was taken from the field, a record unequaled in the United States. Most of the original structures were destroyed by fire in 1906. The abandoned railroad depot now serves as a municipal museum. Other extant buildings include Johnny Nolan's Saloon and the Western Federation of Miners Building.
Multiple public/private
NHL

WELD COUNTY
Greeley
MEEKER MEMORIAL MUSEUM
1324 9th Avenue
1870

Nathan C. Meeker, original owner and builder of this house, was a founder of Union Colony, later Greeley, Colorado. Meeker had been agricultural editor of Horace Greeley's *New York Tribune* before moving west. At first Meeker constructed a frame shack on the land given him by the city, but he replaced it with the adobe house in 1870. Alterations were made in 1882, 1890, and 1916. The city of Greeley has restored the structure to its 1870 appearance. Nathan Meeker was appointed Indian agent for the Ute Indians at the White River Agency. His policies were not accepted by the Utes who rose up and massacred Meeker and the other men of the agency in 1879.
Municipal

WELD COUNTY
Platteville vicinity
FORT VASQUEZ
On U.S. 85
c. 1835

Louis Vasquez and Andrew Sublette operated this trading post from 1835 until 1840 or 1841. Indians from the South Platte River area brought their buffalo hides to the fort and exchanged them for knives, food, cooking implements and "Taos lightning"—whiskey. Occasionally gold dust and beaver skins were traded by the Indians. Surrounding the complex was an adobe wall 12 feet high and approximately 100 feet square. Inside were living quarters, a barn, storage areas, and stalls for trading. Guard towers were located at two corners of the wall. Today the foundations remain for archeological investigation.
State

Connecticut

Center Church, New Haven Green, New Haven, Connecticut. *Sydney Bradford for NPS*

New London Public Library,
New London, Connecticut.
Connecticut Historical Commission

Bushnell Park,
Hartford, Connecticut.
Connecticut Historical Commission

Newson House,
Old Wethersfield
Historic District,
Wethersfield, Connecti
H. Darbee

Elisha Payne House,
Canterbury, Connecticut.
Connecticut Historical Commission

FAIRFIELD COUNTY
Bridgeport
**BROOKS, CAPTAIN JOHN, SR.,
HOUSE**
199 Pembroke Street
1788

The plan of the Brooks House is locally known as a "half house." It consists of one room, two stories high with an attic, end chimney, and entryway, all of which were added later, thus forming the better known central chimney house. The frame house has a gambrel-roofed ell, and there is a distinctive curved hood over the main doorway. Inside is an unusual stairway hidden between partitions in back of the front hall instead of being an exposed stairway leading up from the hall. An addition was made at the rear of the house sometime late in the 19th century; at this time an ell on the west side may have been torn down. Both original chimneys have been rebuilt.
Private; not accessible to the public

FAIRFIELD COUNTY
Darien
MATHER, STEPHEN TYNG, HOME
Stephen Mather Road
1778

Stephen T. Mather was largely responsible for the creation of the National Park Service. When he became its first director in 1915, the Service had acquired a scattering of 14 more or less related national parks. When he retired in 1929, these, plus seven new parks, had been organized into a strong National Park system, in which educational and interpretive programs had been instituted to make the parks more meaningful to visitors. Though his house has undergone exterior and interior alterations, it retains its basic 18th-century integrity.
Private; not accessible to the public
NHL; HABS

FAIRFIELD COUNTY
Fairfield
FAIRFIELD HISTORIC DISTRICT
All buildings bordering the Old Post Road from its intersection with Turney Road (including buildings southeast and northeast of the Town Hall on both sides of Beach Road and the Old Burying Ground)
18th and 19th centuries

Fairfield was settled at the end of the Pequot War (1637). Roger Ludlowe and a small band of Englishmen laid out the town along four squares of 25 to 30 acres each. These squares comprise the major part of the historic district. About 75 buildings are located within the district, and these range in style and date from pre-Revolutionary to a Richardsonian

Romanesque library. The Town Hall and green are the focal point of the original squares. The Town Hall was rebuilt in 1794, remodeled a century later, and has recently been restored to its 18th-century appearance. The Rising Sun Tavern (1780) is also on the green; it is five bays wide and has a gambrel roof and several additions at the sides and rear. The Fairfield Academy has been moved, but its exterior is distinguished by a cupola on the roof and small circular windows in the gables. The Burr Mansion (739 Old Post Road) was built in 1740 and remodeled in the Greek Revival mode 100 years later. The house at 349 Beach Road is a saltbox constructed prior to 1750.
Multiple public/private

FAIRFIELD COUNTY
Fairfield
SOUTHPORT HISTORIC DISTRICT
Bounded generally by the New York, New Haven & Hartford Railroad on the north; by Mill River and Southport harbor on the south; on the west by Old South Road (including properties on both sides of the road); and on the east by Rose Hill Road (including properties on Church Street and both sides of Rose Hill Road, but excluding commercial and industrial property along Pequot Avenue)
18th and 19th centuries

The Southport Historic District is a still viable section of Fairfield, which was once linked completely to the sea for its livelihood. Most of the more than 150 buildings postdate 1779, when the town was burned by the British. Fairfield was founded in 1639, and shipyards and wharves sprang up along Mill River until 1831, when Southport was designated a separate borough by the Connecticut General Assembly (it remained so until 1854). Homes within the historic district were built mainly by men of wealth involved in commerce, banking, and shipping. Noteworthy among them are 750 Harbor Road (Greek Revival); 780 Harbor Road (Federal, 1830); 824 Harbor Road (frame, c. 1766, only known Southport house which escaped burning in 1779); 658 Pequot Road, 385 and 418 Harbor Road (all Victorian houses built between 1855 and 1870); and the Pequot Library (Richardsonian Romanesque, 1890's).
Multiple public/private

FAIRFIELD COUNTY
Greenfield Hill
GREENFIELD HILL HISTORIC DISTRICT
The area comprising the village green and adjacent properties on Meeting

House Lane, Hillside Road, and Old Academy Road; extending south on both sides of Bronson and Hillside Roads to a point beyond the Old Cemetery on the former and to a point beyond Verna Hill Road on the latter
18th and 19th centuries

Greenfield Hill is a rural community little touched by industrial development. There are 38 principal buildings and 20 subsidiary structures within the district. Thirteen of the buildings were constructed before 1800 (the majority are pre-Revolutionary), six date from the period 1800–1850, and nine are of late 19th-century vintage. Notable among these buildings are the Greenfield Hill Congregational Church (1855), modeled after its Colonial style predecessors, the saltbox house at 1081 Hillside Road (1751); the gambrel-roofed house at 3171 Bronson Road (c. 1757); and a windmill at 3015 Bronson Road (last quarter of the 19th century).
Multiple public/private

FAIRFIELD COUNTY
New Canaan
ROGERS, JOHN, STUDIO
10 Cherry Street
1877

John Rogers was an American sculptor of the 19th century. Largely self-taught, he was an engineer and a machinist before devoting his full time to sculpture. "Rogers' groups," as they are called, are of three types; the Civil War groups; the literary and dramatic groups; and the genre groups, which depict contemporary everyday life. This frame studio was his residence from 1877 until his death in 1904.
Private
NHL

FAIRFIELD COUNTY
Norwalk
LOCKWOOD-MATHEWS MANSION
295 West Avenue
c. 1864, Detlef Lienau

The sixty-room Lockwood-Mathews Mansion is a good local example of Chateauesque architecture. Alternating recessed and projecting masses enliven the exterior walls, which are hand-cut Italian granite covering inner walls of brick. The mansard roof is topped by finials and ironwork. Internally, rooms are arranged around a central octagonal rotunda lighted by a four-story skylight. The entrance vestibule has frescoed side walls and a groined and frescoed ceiling. Notable among the rooms is the library with mantel doors, door frames, and bookcases of hand-carved walnut, a black walnut coffered and paneled ceiling, wall-

paper simulating Moroccan leather, and five woods in geometric patterns in the parquet floor. Le Grand Lockwood, for whom the house was built, was a banker and treasurer of the New York Stock Exchange. Charles D. Mathews bought the estate in 1876.
Municipal
NHL; HABS

FAIRFIELD COUNTY
Redding
PUTNAM MEMORIAL STATE PARK
Intersection of Routes 58 (Black Rock Turnpike) and 107 (Park Road)

During the winter of 1778–1779 a contingent of Continental troops under Major General Israel Putnam wintered on this site. The location was selected because the soldiers could defend southeastern Connecticut and easily reach the Hudson River or Long Island. Within the 250-acre park are firebacks or chimneys once part of the soldiers' houses, foundations of an oven and a powder magazine, and a reconstructed barracks.
State

FAIRFIELD COUNTY
Ridgefield
REMINGTON, FREDERIC, HOUSE
1909

Through his drawings, paintings, and sculpture, Frederic Remington realistically documented the life and land of the post-Civil War West. Among his best-known works are "Broncho Buster" (sculpture), and "Cavalry Charge on the Southern Plains" and "The Emigrants" (paintings). He designed and supervised the construction of his house, a fieldstone and shingle two-story building.
Private; not accessible to the public
NHL

FAIRFIELD COUNTY
Stamford
HOYT-BARNUM HOUSE
713 Bedford Street
17th century

The present house, although altered in part during the early 1800's, remains basically as it was built in the 17th century. A small, one-and-one-half-story wood frame farmhouse, the Hoyt-Barnum House has a central chimney of native stone which is completely original. Three sides of the exterior are clapboard, and the fourth is shingle. An open porch on the north side, incorporated under the main roof, is of Dutch influence. There are five rooms on the first floor; the second or attic floor is completely open around the chimney, and the stairway is built directly against one of

the walls. The cellar (original) is only under the southwest portion of the house. Much of the interior (the windows, doors, wall and post sheathing, chimney mortar, and some flooring) is also unchanged.
Private

HARTFORD COUNTY
East Granby
OLD NEWGATE PRISON
Newgate Road

The property on which the Old Newgate Prison is situated was chartered as a copper mine in 1707. Mining was carried on here for 40 years, and the area worked consisted of a vertical shaft sunk into the western side of Talcott Mountain. Other shafts were sunk and used for ventilation and as wells. Horizontal tunneling from the base of the shaft created a series of interconnected caverns. The land was used as a prison after 1773, when it was sold to the colony of Connecticut. During the Revolution British prisoners and Tories were kept here, sometimes being confined underground. After the Revolution Newgate became Connecticut's first state prison (1790) and continued as such until 1827. Stone buildings were erected from 1790 to 1802. The copper mines were briefly reactivated in 1830–1837 and 1855–1857. A substantial amount of the original great wall surrounding the prison remains as do the ruins of many stone buildings.
State

HARTFORD COUNTY
Farmington
STANLEY-WHITMAN HOUSE
37 High Street
c. 1660

The Stanley-Whitman House is representative of those few surviving frame houses built in 17th-century New England. The plan is of the central chimney type. Its second story overhang is accentuated by the carved pendants at the base of the second story posts. The lean-to at the rear was added sometime after 1700. The house was restored in 1934.
Private
NHL

HARTFORD COUNTY
Glastonbury
WELLES, GIDEON, HOUSE
37 Hebron Avenue
Late 18th century

Gideon Welles, Abraham Lincoln's Secretary of the Navy, was born here on July 1, 1802. Welles' maternal grandfather built the house at the time his daughter married Samuel Welles. The two-story house has a five-bay facade and a one-and-one-half-

story ell adjoins the north wall. Both the front entrance and the ell porch have Doric columns. In 1936 the house was moved to its present location from the corner of Main Street and Hebron Avenue. A slave house ell has been removed and made into a separate house.
Private; not accessible to the public
HABS

HARTFORD COUNTY
Hartford
ARMSMEAR (SAMUEL COLT HOME)
80 Wethersfield Avenue
1855

Armsmear was built by Samuel Colt, the inventor of the Colt revolver and one of the developers of mass production techniques. The Mexican War popularized the revolver, which at first had not been widely used. By the outbreak of the Civil War, Colt's manufacture of the weapon had been greatly expanded. Colt died before the revolver had reached its zenith of popularity, however. His large Italianate house has recently undergone extensive alterations.
Private; not accessible to the public
NHL

HARTFORD COUNTY
Hartford
BARNARD, HENRY, HOUSE
118 Main Street
1807

Henry Barnard, a pioneer educator, was instrumental in stimulating the growth of the public school system throughout the United States. He served the state of Connecticut as its first secretary of the State Education Commission and its first superintendent of schools. In 1867 he was appointed by President Andrew Johnson as the first U.S. Commissioner of Education. The three-story brick house in which he was born was his residence for most of his life.
Private; not accessible to the public
NHL

HARTFORD COUNTY
Hartford
BULL, AMOS, HOUSE
350 Main Street
18th century

The Amos Bull House is one of a few 18th-century structures remaining in the city of Hartford. It probably stood originally on a narrow lot with adjacent or attached two-story buildings on either side as indicated by the absence of side windows on the first two floors. On the exterior the plain, regularly placed second-floor windows are believed to be original as are the three dormers above them and much

of the brickwork. The paneled wainscoting, cornices, and fireplace trim of the second-floor interior are also thought to be original features. Amos Bull, first owner of the house, operated a drygoods business here in 1791, but he sold the property around 1820. Since then it has had several uses. In the early 1900's the house, which is less than 30 feet wide, was moved back from the sidewalk line to its present location. The roof is a replacement of the original, as are the first-floor arched windows.
Municipal; not accessible to the public

HARTFORD COUNTY
Hartford
BUSHNELL PARK
Bounded by Elm, Jewell, and Trinity Streets
1868

Bushnell Park, originally called Hartford Park, came into being largely through the efforts of Horace Bushnell (1802–1876), prominent 19th-century Protestant theologian. Bushnell attempted to formulate a complete synthesis of Protestant thought during the mid–19th century. In his sermons and books he set forth a philosophic basis for the secular expression of religious activity. As Bushnell envisioned it, the park would be for the enjoyment and rejuvenation of people working downtown. The original 35 acres have been increased to 50, and the park contains a memorial fountain, statues of Israel Putnam (Revolutionary War soldier) and Horace Wells (discoverer of anesthesia), a Soldiers and Sailors Monument, and a Spanish-American War memorial.
Municipal

HARTFORD COUNTY
Hartford
BUTLER-McCOOK HOMESTEAD
396 Main Street
1782

The large, rambling two-and-one-half-story Butler-McCook Homestead was built as a central-hall, two-story frame residence in the late 18th century. An older ell (c. 1740) was added onto the rear and converted into a kitchen; it had been a blacksmith shop. Nineteenth-century additions include chimneys, dormer windows, a second-story gable in the center of the facade, and a small entrance porch. Gardens for the house were designed by a Swiss landscape gardener, Jacob Weidenman. The Butlers and the Mc-Cooks were locally prominent families.
Private; not accessible to the public

HARTFORD COUNTY
Hartford
CHENEY BUILDING (G. FOX BUILDING)
942 Main Street
1875–1876, H. H. Richardson

The Cheney Building is easily recognizable as the work of 19th-century architect Henry Hobson Richardson. Rough-faced blocks of Berea limestone give the exterior a rugged appearance, and the five broad, cavelike arch openings at street level are typical of Richardson. The architect originally intended to use brick, but abandoned this in favor of limestone and Portland brownstone which contrasted strikingly. Bands of ornamentation and fluting divide the seven-story structure into three major areas, all of which contain arches of different sizes and groupings. Pairs of three-story arches surmount each ground arch, and above these are groups of three arches (at the corners) and four arches (forming an arcade). Colonnettes support the arches at this level. Alterations to the original structure include removal of one entrance portal and the southern member of two pointed arches between the portals. An original interior court has been filled in, and the rest of the inside has been reworked.
Private

HARTFORD COUNTY
Hartford
CONNECTICUT STATE CAPITOL
Capitol Avenue
1872–1880, Richard M. Upjohn

The Connecticut Capitol is a three-story marble and granite edifice highlighted by a tall central dome, end pavilions with corner turrets, and a projecting center pavilion with four-story corner towers. Window openings are pointed-arched, as is the arcade in the center section. Crockets ornament roof gables and dormers, finials appear on the roof balustrade, and there is iron cresting atop the roof ridges. Marble statues of famous Connecticut citizens adorn all sides of the capitol, and there are 12 figures crowning the pillared buttresses of the 12–sided dome which itself is crowned by a lantern. Interior columns are marble and granite and woodwork is oak, black walnut, and ash.
State
NHL

HARTFORD COUNTY
Hartford
CONNECTICUT STATEHOUSE (OLD STATEHOUSE)
Main Street at Central Row
1796, Charles Bulfinch

The Connecticut Statehouse was the first of the public buildings designed by Charles Bulfinch. In addition to its architectural distinction, this Federal period building is significant as the scene of the Hartford Convention of December 1814. This convention, with muted threats of secession, voiced New England opposition to the War of 1812 and resulted in great embarrassment and political harm to the Federalist party. From 1879 to 1915 the Statehouse served as the Hartford City Hall. A major restoration of the building was undertaken in 1918.
Municipal
NHL; HABS

HARTFORD COUNTY
Hartford
DAY HOUSE
77 Forest Street
1884, Francis Kimball

This Queen Anne style house was designed for Franklin Chamberlin. The plan is irregular with projecting bays and porches and a two-story wing to the west. The exterior exhibits a variety of complex and interrelated contrastings of style and color. The limestone of the exterior walls is organized in patterns by string courses of brownstone and below the eaves by a checkered pattern of blue and pink limestone. Originally the shingles on the roof and dormers were all deep red but now only the latter have this color shingle. The interior is typical of the period. Fireplaces on the ground floor have elaborately carved mantels, and fireplace openings are framed with tiles in colorful patterns.
Private

HARTFORD COUNTY
Hartford
STOWE, HARRIET BEECHER, HOUSE
73 Forest Street
1871

The Stowe House was the second Hartford home of Harriet and Calvin Stowe. It is a two-and-one-half-story brick structure exhibiting plenteous wooden Gothic trim. Dramatic placement of architectural details and a good sense of proportion were employed by the unknown architect. A variety of porches, graceful barge boards, brackets, and drops, plus a steep hip roof containing jerkinhead gables ornament the exterior. Harriet Beecher Stowe (1811–1896) lived here until her

death. The house has recently been restored.
Private

HARTFORD COUNTY
Hartford
TWAIN, MARK, HOME
351 Farmington Avenue
1874, Edward T. Potter and Alfred H. Thorp

Though Samuel Clemens, or Mark Twain, lived in many parts of the United States, the bulk of his literary production was written during his years in Hartford. Here he wrote such books as *Life on the Mississippi*, *The Adventures of Tom Sawyer*, and *The Adventures of Huckleberry Finn*, all of which reflected the growing popular emphasis on American ideas and customs. The three-story brick house reflects the character of the author, especially in such rooms as the conservatory, the library, billiard room, and the porch, which resembles the deck of a Mississippi River steamboat. Items connected with the life of Mark Twain are on exhibit.
Private
NHL

HARTFORD COUNTY
Hartford
WADSWORTH ATHENEUM
25 Atheneum Square, North
1842, Ithiel Town

The Wadsworth Atheneum is a Gothic Revival building possessing crenelated towers and diamond pane windows with elaborate tracery. Cream colored granite is the basic building material. The main facade measures 100 feet, the central section is 80 feet deep, and the two wings are each 70 feet. Ithiel Town (1784–1844) was an architect and engineer, but he styled buildings as a romantic classicist. He was a partner of Alexander Jackson Davis and did his work primarily in New England and New York. Money for the Atheneum was given to Hartford by Daniel Wadsworth, a wealthy philanthropist, and he also donated land for its construction. An art gallery was to occupy the center section, while the two wings housed the Young Men's Institute and the Connecticut Historical Society. Recent renovations (1969) have left only the 1842 facade and adjacent side walls from the original building, and extensive additions have been built on the rear.
Private

HARTFORD COUNTY
Wethersfield
BUTTOLPH-WILLIAMS HOUSE
249 Broad Street
1692

The Buttolph-Williams House, constructed by David Buttolph in 1692, is an example of a 17th-century frame house of medieval design. The two-story structure is of post and girt construction and is sheathed with riven oak clapboards. The heavy corner posts, rising from the foundation sill to the second floor, end in projecting carved brackets or corbels. The house has two rooms on each floor flanking a central chimney. The first floor contains a small entrance hall with a parlor to the left and the hall or kitchen to the right. There are two bedrooms on the second floor. Although altered during the 18th and 19th centuries, the house has been restored to its original 17th-century appearance and is furnished with period pieces.
Private
NHL

HARTFORD COUNTY
Wethersfield
DEANE, SILAS, HOUSE
203 Main Street
1764

Silas Deane built this house after his marriage. It is frame and two and one-half stories high with a gable roof and a wing on the west wall. There is an unusual hallway in the northeast corner containing an elaborate staircase which has three differently turned balusters on each tread. The imbalanced front and north elevations indicate externally the existence of the hall. A flat pediment and modillion cornice crown the front doorway, and the door itself has raised panels. The interior paneling is notable. Silas Deane, lawyer, merchant, and politician, was a delegate to the First Continental Congress, and in 1776 Congress granted him funds to go abroad and develop Franco-American trade. His activities in France fell under a cloud, political quarrels led to his fall from favor, and Congress refused to pay his back salary. His last days were spent in unsuccessful attempts to clear his name.
Private

HARTFORD COUNTY
Wethersfield
OLD WETHERSFIELD HISTORIC DISTRICT
Bounded on the north and west by the New York, New Haven & Hartford Railroad tracks, on the east

by Int. 91, and also on the north by Wethersfield Cove
17th and 18th centuries

Wethersfield is one of the earliest settled areas in Connecticut. A group of adventurers from the Massachusetts Bay Colony acquired land here in 1634. The town grew rapidly and was, until 1700, the head of navigation on the Connecticut River. Ships built here engaged in extensive trade with Europe, the West Indies, and other Atlantic ports. The historic district contains about 1200 dwellings, nearly 100 of them dating from colonial times. The one-half mile town green is lined with residences and nearby is the brick, 18th-century church. Notable structures are the Buttolph-Williams House (1692), the Silas Deane House (1766), the Joseph Webb House (1752), the Isaac Stevens House (1774), the Henry Deming House (1790), the Old Academy (1801), and the Old Warehouse (c. 1690). The latter was one of seven warehouses built to handle trade goods to be shipped inland after their removal from ships.
Multiple public/private
HABS

HARTFORD COUNTY
Wethersfield
WEBB, JOSEPH, HOUSE
211 Main Street
1752

In the spring of 1781 General George Washington and the Count de Rochambeau met at the Joseph Webb House to lay plans for a joint offensive against the English. The meeting marked the implementation of the Franco-American military alliance in actual field operations. It resulted in uniting the American and French armies for a move southward, timed to coincide with the arrival of a French fleet from the West Indies. The south parlor of the two-story gambrel-roofed frame house has traditionally been identified as the conference room.
Private
NHL

HARTFORD COUNTY
West Hartford
WEBSTER, NOAH, BIRTHPLACE
227 S. Main Street
c. 1676

Noah Webster, famous lexicographer and spelling book author, was born in this house in 1758. His various literary achievements include the publication of textbooks, histories, and dictionaries. Most noted is his two-volume work, *An American Dictionary of English Languages*, which appeared in 1828. The two-story

frame house with its central brick chimney is characteristic of late 17th-century New England colonial architecture.
Private
NHL

HARTFORD COUNTY
Windsor
ELLSWORTH, OLIVER, HOMESTEAD (ELMWOOD)
778 Palisado Avenue
c. 1740

The original section of the Ellsworth Homestead was built about 1740 and consisted of a single rectangular section with a five-bay facade and a central entrance. A portico with plain Doric columns and a shallow sloped pediment shelters the entranceway. Two chimneys define the original end walls, and the entire house is frame covered with clapboards. Ellsworth added the south ell with its two-story colonnade in 1783, and another wing extends eastward from the rear of the house. Oliver Ellsworth was a delegate from Connecticut to the Continental Congress (1777–1784) and to the Constitutional Convention. He was a U.S. Senator (1789–1796) and Chief Justice of the Supreme Court (1796–1799). He lived here from 1782 until his death in 1807.
Private

LITCHFIELD COUNTY
Litchfield
LITCHFIELD HISTORIC DISTRICT
East and west sides of North and South Streets, to the rear property lines, from Prospect Street on the north to Gallows Lane on the south, the Village Green between East and West Streets, and structures fronting on the northeast side of The Green
Late 18th century

Litchfield is one of New England's best surviving examples of a late 18th-century town. It served as an outpost and trading center on Connecticut's northwest frontier until the late 1700's. The present streets remain the same as the original ones shown on early maps. The four main thoroughfares, stretching toward the cardinal points of the compass, became known as North, South, East, and West Streets. At their intersection was the central common, now called The Green, which was the focal point of the town. Litchfield today has a total of 15 frame houses that were erected in the last half of the 18th century. Also situated in this same area are three structures that were built between 1800 and 1828.
Municipal/private
NHL; HABS

LITCHFIELD COUNTY
Litchfield
REEVE, TAPPING, HOUSE AND LAW SCHOOL
South Street
1772, house; 1784, law school

The first law school in the United States stands beside the house belonging to the school's founder, Tapping Reeve. As many of the men who studied here became prominent lawyers, judges, and politicians, the school significantly influenced the development of American law. Among its graduates were Vice Presidents Aaron Burr and John C. Calhoun, three justices of the United States Supreme Court, 90 members of the House of Representatives, and 26 Senators.
Private
NHL

LITCHFIELD COUNTY
Woodbury
BACON, JABEZ, HOUSE
North side of Hollow Road just above the intersection with U.S. 6
1760

This house is an excellent example of mid–18th century domestic architecture built by joiner Roswell Moore. The large, five-bay building is two and one-half stories with a gambrel roof, three pedimented dormer windows on the third floor, and a large central chimney. The front door is a restoration. The floor plan is a typical center chimney, four-square type with an unusually wide center hall. There is much good paneling on all three floors and almost all of the original flooring remains. In addition to the main house there is a gambrel-roofed outbuilding which is probably older.
Private; not accessible to the public

LITCHFIELD COUNTY
Woodbury
GLEBE HOUSE
South side of Hollow Road at the head of Hollow Road No. 2
1746

After the Revolution the Church of England in America had no head. Consequently, a group of its Connecticut clergy met in the Glebe House on March 25, 1783, and elected one of their number, Samuel Seabury, as bishop. Seabury crossed the Atlantic and, although refused consecration by English archbishops, was received and consecrated in Scotland. He thus became the first American bishop of the Episcopal Church. The Glebe House was constructed in stages. Earliest portions are the lower and upper rooms at the left of the chimney and the staircase. Rooms to the right of the chimney, a lean-

to or kitchen behind, and a second stairway were added subsequently; a second lean-to kitchen was an even later addition. The main door has raised panels and a transom above.
Private

LITCHFIELD COUNTY
Woodbury
WOODBURY HISTORIC DISTRICT NO. 1
Both sides of Main Street (U.S. 6) for a distance of two miles; also included are Hollow Road and Sycamore Street to the Pomperaug River, Judson Avenue to the river, School Street, Orenaug and Park Roads up to Orenaug Park, and Pleasant Street
17th–20th centuries

Woodbury was founded in 1673. By 1776 it has a population of 5,325. Within the historic district are Colonial, Federal, Greek Revival, and Victorian buildings. There are 142 houses, 5 public buildings, 3 greens, 2 schools, 9 churches, and 3 privately supported historic structures. Notable among these are the Glebe House; the Hurd House (1680), oldest in Woodbury; the Old Blacksmith Shop (c. 1825); St. Paul's Episcopal Church (1785); the First Congregational Church (1817); and St. Teresa's Roman Catholic Church (1902).
Multiple public/private

MIDDLESEX COUNTY
Middletown
ALSOP HOUSE (DAVISON ART CENTER)
301 High Street
1840

The most unique element in the Alsop House is the painted oil on plaster decorations inside and out. Basically a Greek Revival house, it has a wrought iron porch surmounted by a balcony running across the facade. The outstanding features of the exterior are a painted frieze of swags and ribbons and three sunken panels painted to represent niches containing life-size statues. Oblong windows reach from floor level almost to the ceiling all over the house. Stucco on the exterior has been painted pink, and the eaves and ceiling of the porch are blue. Inside, the staircase has been lined and painted to simulate marble. The walls of the two parlors are painted to look like paneling, and other painted decorations include dancing girls, angels, cherubs, birds, and insects. The design of the house has been tentatively attributed to Ithiel Town, but close parallels may be drawn to the work of two German architects, Ludwig Persius and Karl Friedrick Schinkel. Some alterations

were made when the house was converted to an art gallery.
Private
HABS

MIDDLESEX COUNTY
Middletown
RUSSELL HOUSE
    Corner of Washington and High Streets
    1827–1829, Ithiel Town

The Russell House has the form and appearance of a Greek temple. Rectangular in shape, the two-story dwelling has a front portico with six giant Corinthian columns supporting a heavy entablature. On the front wall are five vertical accents provided by first- and second-story windows with inset panels between them. Pilasters frame the main doorway and support a high entablature. Sidelights and the overdoor light contain frosted glass etched with floral patterns. The garden facade has been altered and extended. Pilasters on the south wall indicate the original length of the house, and the present pilastered facade replaced a porch. A centrally located double stairway leads to the garden entrance. The north wing was added in 1860.
Private
HABS

MIDDLESEX COUNTY
Middletown
WETMORE, SETH, HOUSE (OAK HILL)
    Northwest coner of Route 66 and Camp Road
    1742

The Seth Wetmore House is a large frame dwelling of two and one-half stories. The original gambrel roof has been replaced by the present gable one. Above the main doorway is a broken scroll pediment (a replacement for the original), and the doorway itself is framed by fluted pilasters topped by carved Jacobean rosettes. The interior plan is central hall with two rooms on either side. Seth Wetmore was a judge in Middletown, and his wife was a sister of Jonathan Edwards.
Private; not accessible to the public

NEW HAVEN COUNTY
Ansonia
MANSFIELD, RICHARD, HOUSE
    35 Jewett Street
    1748

The Mansfield House has the central chimney and rear lean-to characteristic of mid–18th-century Connecticut homes. There is an overhang at the eave line, and the front door has two leaves and an iron latch. In 1926 the house was moved to its present location. The Reverend Richard Mansfield was rector of the Episcopal church in Derby for 72 years.
Private

NEW HAVEN COUNTY
Derby
THE STERLING OPERA HOUSE
    Northwest corner, 4th and Elizabeth Streets
    1889

Built as a civic center, the Sterling Opera House served as a theater until 1945. After the theater was closed, the first floor continued to be used as the Derby city hall for another 20 years. The theater itself, located on the second floor, seats 1,250, and the dimensions of the stage are 64 feet wide by 30 feet deep. Period details of the interior include wrought iron work and keystone arches. Gallery rails are decorative iron, and the red velvet seats are supported by iron frames. A row of Palladian windows ornaments the top floor.
Municipal; not accessible to the public

NEW HAVEN COUNTY
New Haven
CONNECTICUT AGRICULTURAL EXPERIMENT STATION
    123 Huntington Street
    1882–1883

In 1874 Connecticut became the first state to create an agricultural experiment station. Its establishment was due largely to W. O. Atwater, who became its first director. This station has consistently contributed to American agricultural development. It was the first institution of its kind to assume responsibility for administering a state food law. Here a study by Thomas B. Osborne established the significance of amino acids in the human diet. The oldest in its complex of buildings is the Osborne Library, a one-story brick building with cross gables.
State
NHL

NEW HAVEN COUNTY
New Haven
CONNECTICUT HALL, YALE UNIVERSITY
    Bounded by High, Chapel, Elm, and College Streets
    1750–1752

Located on the "Old Campus," Connecticut Hall is Yale University's only pre-Revolutionary building. It is the lone survivor of "Brick Row," a group of brick buildings erected in the Georgian style. The three stories are topped by a gambrel roof, beneath which dormer windows and a fourth story were added in 1796–1797.

The interior of the building was completely rebuilt in 1954. Used for many years as a dormitory, it has housed a faculty room, seminars, and freshman reading and refreshments rooms since its rededication.
Private
NHL; HABS

NEW HAVEN COUNTY
New Haven
DANA, JAMES DWIGHT, HOUSE
    24 Hillhouse Avenue
    1849, Henry Austin

James Dwight Dana transformed the science of geology from an investigation of distinct rocks and minerals into a study of the geologic history of the world. For many years he held the Silliman Professorship of Natural History and Geology at Yale University, and throughout his career he was active in geological research. Stylistically the house represents the change from the Greek Revival to the more eclectic Italianate style of the mid–19th century. It now houses Yale's Department of Industrial Administration.
Private
NHL; HABS

NEW HAVEN COUNTY
New Haven
FIRST TELEPHONE EXCHANGE
    741 Chapel Street
    1878

A small switchboard on the ground floor of the Metropolitan Building served as the world's first commercial telephone exchange. Its operations were limited: only two calls could be made at the same time, and six separate connections were required to complete one call. The room in which the exchange was operated is now a restaurant, and nothing associated with the first exchange remains.
Private
NHL

NEW HAVEN COUNTY
New Haven
FORT NATHAN HALE
    At the southern end of Woodward Avenue

This site was fortified four times between 1649 and 1863. The earliest fortification was an earthwork erected to defend the New Haven colony. A second defense work, a log fort constructed in 1775, was successfully attacked by a British force on July 5, 1779, and all defenders taken prisoner. Early in the 19th century the federal government purchased the site and constructed a brownstone and brick fort which was manned during the War of 1812. At this time the fort was named for Nathan Hale. The second Fort Hale was

built between 1863 and 1866. It consisted of five concrete buildings (three still remain) enclosed and covered by earthworks. The site was deeded to the state in 1921.
State

NEW HAVEN COUNTY
New Haven
MARSH, OTHNIEL C., HOUSE
360 Prospect Street
1878

Othniel C. Marsh was America's first professor of paleontology. In addition to his teaching duties at Yale University, he initiated the Yale scientific expeditions to the American West. His classification of dinosaur bones from Wyoming was his major contribution. His three-story brownstone house is now Marsh Hall of the Yale Forestry School.
Private
NHL

NEW HAVEN COUNTY
New Haven
NEW HAVEN GREEN HISTORIC DISTRICT
Bounded by Chapel, College, Elm, and Church Streets
1812–1816

Three impressive churches were erected on the east side of the New Haven Green between 1812 and 1816. Two of them, Center Church (1812–1814) and United Church (1813–1815), are outstanding examples of Federal architecture, while Trinity Church (1814–1816) is one of the earliest sophisticated expressions of the Gothic Revival style in America. Although Asher Benjamin drew the initial plan for Center Church, it was Ithiel Town who completed the design. Town drew the plans for Trinity Church. The third structure, United Church, shows the influence of early New York architect John McComb, although local builder Ebenezer Johnson was responsible for its construction. All three churches retain their original exterior appearance.
Private
NHL

NEW HAVEN COUNTY
Northford
WILLIAMS, WARHAM, HOUSE
Intersection of the Old Post Road with Conn. 17 and 22
c. 1752

The Warham Williams House is a two-story frame dwelling with a steeply pitched gable roof and a central chimney. The front doorway has a decorative broken scroll pediment that terminates in rosettes. These rosettes are repeated in a simpler form above the flanking fluted pilasters. All first-floor windows and those in the gable ends are pedimented. Original beaded clapboards survive on the front and north elevations. An unusual feature is the carrying of the cornice across the gable ends.
Private; not accessible to the public

NEW HAVEN COUNTY
Southbury
SOUTHBURY HISTORIC DISTRICT NO. 1
Main Street from the Woodbury town line to Old Waterbury Road
18th and 19th centuries

The Southbury Historic District consists of properties on both sides of Main Street extending approximately two miles from end to end. Buildings in this area are predominantly 19th-century or earlier, and much open space exists between them. The atmosphere is that of a 19th-century residential community. Dwellings and other structures fall into several categories, the largest of which is the pre-Revolutionary group. These 18 buildings are two stories, of frame construction, and have gable roofs and central chimneys. A second group, of post-Revolutionary structures, was built between 1777 and 1812. These include the Bullet Hill School and a Greek Revival residence. A third group dates from 1813 to 1860, while the last major architectural period is 1861 to 1966 and includes several colonial reproductions.
Multiple private
HABS

NEW LONDON COUNTY
East Lyme
LEE, THOMAS, HOUSE
Southeast corner of Conn. 156 and Grant's Neck Road
c. 1660–1735

The Thomas Lee House is a saltbox, and its development from a one-room dwelling is easy to trace. Originally the single room faced south and contained a stone chimney in its west end. Later another room was added on the other side of the chimney, and the final addition was a lean-to across the rear (south). The cellar stair, which is believed to date from a 1725 remodeling, is formed of solid logs cut in triangular section and nailed on two sloping stringers. An unusual casement in the south wall of the west chamber is one of two such windows discovered in place in Connecticut, and it is evident that the house was built to face south since windows were not put in the rear walls. Restoration work was done in 1914.
Private

NEW LONDON COUNTY
Groton
FORT GRISWOLD
Bounded by Baker Avenue, Smith Street, Park Avenue, Monument Avenue and the Thames River

Fort Griswold was constructed between 1775 and 1778 to defend the shore at Groton and New London. A major Revolutionary engagement took place here in September, 1781, when British forces commanded by Benedict Arnold attacked the American garrison. Arnold directed the burning of New London and the successful storming of Fort Griswold. The American commander, Lieutenant Colonel William Ledyard, was killed and the fort severely damaged when the victorious British blew up the powder magazine. As constructed the fort had stone walls 10 or 12 feet high and was surrounded by a ditch. On its lower side was a barbette battery, and the remaining walls were fraised. Presently within the park grounds are an 1840 stone house for storing powder, rifles, and ammunition and a brick hot shot house (1812) where cannon balls were heated.
State

NEW LONDON COUNTY
Lebanon
TRUMBULL, JOHN, BIRTHPLACE (GOVERNOR JONATHAN TRUMBULL HOUSE)
The Common
c. 1735

John Trumbull is best known for his paintings of leaders and dramatic scenes of the Revolutionary War. His paintings of the Nation's early leaders and his sketches of the battlefields of the Revolutionary War provided material for many of his later paintings. Among his best-known works are "Battle of Bunker Hill," "Declaration of Independence," and "Resignation of Washington." His commission in 1817 to paint four Revolutionary War scenes for the rotunda of the Capitol was the first awarded to an American artist by the federal government. His two-story clapboard birthplace was also the home of his father, Governor Jonathan Trumbull.
Private
NHL; HABS

NEW LONDON COUNTY
Lebanon
WAR OFFICE (CAPTAIN JOSEPH TRUMBLE STORE AND OFFICE)
West Town Street
c. 1732

Joseph Trumble (1678–1755) used this building as a store and an office for his ex-

tensive shipping business. The business was eventually taken over by his son Jonathan, who changed the spelling of the family name. Jonathan Trumbull was governor of Connecticut between 1769 and 1784. During the Revolution a War Council of Connecticut assisted the governor when the General Assembly was not in session, and meetings were held in this building. The office is a small gambrel-roofed structure with a central chimney. Positioning of the front door near the left front corner creates an asymmetrical facade. The Trumbull home is nearby.
Private

NEW LONDON COUNTY
Mystic
CHARLES W. MORGAN
Mystic Seaport
1841

The *Charles W. Morgan* is the last of the 19th-century wooden whaling vessels. Owned principally by a New Bedford whaling merchant of the same name, she sailed in pursuit of whales for almost 80 years. Constructed of live oak and pine, she is a typical, square-rigged whaler of the period. The *Morgan* is more than 105 feet overall and has a 27–foot beam. In recent years the vessel has been restored.
Private
NHL

NEW LONDON COUNTY
New London
DESHON-ALLYN HOUSE
613 Williams Street
1829

Captain Daniel Deshon, a whaling master, built the Deshon-Allyn House, which exhibits both late Federal and early Greek Revival architectural features. The hip-roofed dwelling has a regular five-bay facade, two end chimneys, and a central second-story Palladian window on the main facade. The exterior walls are granite ornamented at the corners with stone quoins, and beneath the carved cornice there is a simple frieze containing triglyphs and metopes. Inside, the house has a central hall plan and four rooms on each floor. A later owner of the house (1851) was Captain Lyman Allyn.
Private

NEW LONDON COUNTY
New London
HEMPSTED, JOSHUA, HOUSE
11 Hempstead Street
c. 1678

The Hempsted House is one of the oldest dwellings in Connecticut. As such it is frequently studied by architectural historians interested in the development of the 17th- and 18th-century house. Entirely frame in construction, the house has two front gables, and the older section (the west end) has casement windows on all three levels. Set on a quarried stone foundation, it has an overhanging cornice and was originally a one-room, end-chimney dwelling.
Private

NEW LONDON COUNTY
New London
HEMPSTED, NATHANIEL, HOUSE (OLD HUGUENOT HOUSE)
    Corner of Jay, Hempstead, Cort, and Truman Streets
    c. 1759

The Hempsted House is unusual because it is built of stone. Local legend attributes its construction to Huguenots, but no record of Huguenot workers in New London has been found. More probably exiled Acadians from Nova Scotia (who arrived in New London in 1756) erected the house; the stone is evenly finished and laid in regular horizontal beds, characteristic of French rather than English craftsmanship. Now covered completely with ivy the house has two end chimneys and a gambrel roof. The dormer windows are later additions.
Private; not accessible to the public
HABS

NEW LONDON COUNTY
New London
NEW LONDON COUNTY COURTHOUSE (STATE COURTHOUSE)
70 Hunting Street
1784, Isaac Fitch

The New London County Courthouse has served as a civic and social center for New London since its construction. Georgian in style, the courthouse has a central octagonal cupola on its roof. The facade is seven bays wide, three on either side of a central pavilion containing the main entrance and a Palladian window above. Blocks of wood cut to resemble angle quoins frame the central doorway which is recessed. Pilasters of similar wooden blocks mark the first-floor corners, and there are fluted pilasters at the second level. A gallery once ran around the entire building, but it has been removed. The courthouse does not stand on its original site, and the interior was extensively altered in 1909.
State
HABS

NEW LONDON COUNTY
New London
NEW LONDON CUSTOMHOUSE
150 Bank Street
1833, Robert Mills

Built to serve New London in its heyday as a port, the Customhouse was designed by one of America's well-known architects. The exterior is rectangular in shape, three stories high, and constructed of light and dark gray granite. A flat-roofed entrance portico with two plain Ionic columns supporting an entablature, architrave, and frieze is the focal point of the three-bay facade. At the corners of the building are massive granite pilasters, and the sills of the upper windows continue in a belt course which girdles the entire building and decreases the apparent size of the second story. A filet molding over the upper windows projects like eyebrows above them.
Federal

NEW LONDON COUNTY
New London
NEW LONDON PUBLIC LIBRARY
63 Huntington Street
1889, Shepley, Rutan, and Coolidge

Although Henry Hobson Richardson had died before plans were drawn for the New London Library, the resulting building was clearly influenced by his ideas. The structure is compact but massive with walls of Milford granite and contrasting brown-stone trim. Composed of two sections which intersect at right angles, the library also has a central round turret with polygonal roof on the main facade. There is an unusual eyelid dormer in the gable roof, and over the gable is a tympanum containing the city's coat of arms—a ship under full sail. The main entrance porch has four Syrian arches and three groined vaults.
Private

NEW LONDON COUNTY
New London
SHAW MANSION
11 Blinman Street
c. 1756

Captain Nathaniel Shaw built this three-story granite dwelling which originally had a three-story wooden annex. The exterior was altered in 1840 by the construction of the present granite annex and the addition of the front portico and the roof balustrades. Inside, the house has a slightly asymmetrical central hall plan. The 18th-century paneling was covered with plaster and wallpaper in 1840. Connecticut's Naval Office was located here during the Revolution.
County
HABS

NEW LONDON COUNTY
New London
WHALE OIL ROW
105–119 Huntington Street
1835–1845

The four Greek Revival structures comprising Whale Oil Row reflect the prosperity of New London during its peak whaling years (1820–1850). All four have similar facades highlighted by two-story porticos with fluted Ionic columns and pediments containing semicircular lights. Pilasters ornament the corners of the rectangular houses. Primary differences in the four facades are evident in the door frames and the mullions of the overdoor and sidelights. All four have been coverted to offices.
Private

NEW LONDON COUNTY
Norwich
BACKUS, NATHANIEL, HOUSE
44 Rockwell Street
1750

Although built in 1750, the Backus House was altered by the introduction of Greek Revival elements in the 19th century. Most noticeable of these is the ornate main doorway with its engaged Ionic columns, full entablature and sidelights, all framed by fluted molding with rosettes. The entablature directly above the door contains a cushion frieze topped by an egg and dart molding. Changes in the positions of the windows and the elimination of a central door occurred in the 19th century. The chimneys postdate the house itself. Nathaniel Backus was a prominent citizen of Norwich.
Private

NEW LONDON COUNTY
Norwich
CONVERSE HOUSE AND BARN
185 Washington Street
c. 1870

High Victorian Gothic was a popular architectural style when the Converse House was built. Its vertical proportions, irregular shape, and polychrome exterior are typical of the period taste. An irregular roofline is broken by many small gables and dormers. A hip-roofed tower covering the center hall and stairway inside is fronted on the exterior by a seven-sided porch. The trim consists of brackets, wooden arches, wooden supports for the porch, and window framing, all of which contrast strikingly with the lighter building walls. A large L-shaped barn and carriage shed on the property is similar in style to the house. It has steep gable roofs and pierced bargeboards carved in a diamond pattern.

Private; not accessible to the public
HABS

NEW LONDON COUNTY
Norwich
EAST DISTRICT SCHOOL
365 Washington Street
Late 18th century

Built sometime during the second half of the 18th century, the East District School was used for its original purpose until 1885. The building is brick with a gambrel roof. It stands two and one-half stories high and is nearly square in plan. In 1798 a local scholar, Consider Sterry, conducted a night school here, offering instruction in writing, bookkeeping, mathematics, and surveying without plotting. Sterry also taught sailors how to obtain longitude at sea by lunar observation and latitude by the sun's altitude. Used for some years as a clubhouse, the building is now vacant.
Municipal; not accessible to the public

NEW LONDON COUNTY
Norwich
LITTLE PLAIN HISTORIC DISTRICT
The east and west sides of Broadway and Union Street; portions of the south side of Otis Street, and including all residences around Little Plain Park and Huntington Place
18th and 19th centuries

The variety and quality of architecture in the Little Plain Historic District is a permanent reminder of the prosperity brought to Norwich by trade and manufacturing. Representatives of all major architectural styles popular between 1775 and 1875 cluster around the park and the narrow green of Huntington Place. Specific examples worthy of mention are the Deacon Jabez Huntington House (181 Broadway), Georgian; the Hezekiah Perkins (185 Broadway) and the DeWitt-Sigourney (189 Broadway) houses, Federal; the Johnson (171 Broadway) and Woodhull (167 Broadway) houses, Greek Revival; and a Victorian home (93 Union Street). The district also contains a few late 19th- and early 20th-century shingle style houses.
Private
HABS

NEW LONDON COUNTY
Norwichtown
BRADFORD-HUNTINGTON HOUSE
16 Huntington Lane
c. 1691–1740

The Bradford-Huntington House is a frame dwelling that was built in several stages. Authorities do not agree as to which part of the house John Bradford erected in 1691. The present house is

roughly L-shaped with one wing facing south and the other, east. Each wing has a large central chimney and a gambrel roof. Window placement on the main facade is irregular, and the roof has a slight overhang on three sides. The later additions were constructed by the Huntingtons, an early Norwich area family.
Private; not accessible to the public
HABS

NEW LONDON COUNTY
Norwichtown
CARPENTER HOUSE (RED HOUSE)
55 E. Town Street
1793

The Carpenter House is a symmetrical, five-bay facade, Georgian house. The walls are brick laid in Flemish bond, and there is a small gabled porch over the main doorway. This doorway is not original. About 1816 the gambrel-roofed third story was added. There have also been several one-story additions at the rear of the house.
Private
HABS

NEW LONDON COUNTY
Norwichtown
CARPENTER, JOSEPH, SILVERSMITH SHOP
71 E. Town Street
1772–1774

Joseph Carpenter was a successful silversmith, clockmaker, and pewterer. His shop is evidence of Norwich's flourishing 18th-century silver and pewter industry. The one-and-one-half-story frame structure is rectangular and has a gambrel roof. There is one brick chimney in the southwest corner which was originally intended for a forge. The exterior, which measures 30 feet by 24 feet, is covered with clapboards. Inside, the single room has been partitioned by recent owners. Owned by the Carpenter family until 1915, the shop was restored the following year.
Private; not accessible to the public
HABS

NEW LONDON COUNTY
Norwichtown
CHARLTON, CAPTAIN RICHARD, HOUSE
12 Mediterranean Lane
Late 18th century

This frame cottage is a restored example of a sea captain's house of the late 18th or early 19th century. Measuring 18 feet by 27 feet, the house is one and one-half stories high, five bays wide, and has a central chimney. Its heavy timber frame has unused mortises, indicating that it

probably came from an earlier building and was reused. There is little decoration on the house aside from the front door with sidelights framed by four flat pilasters.
Private; not accessible to the public
HABS

NEW LONDON COUNTY
Norwichtown
HUNTINGTON, GENERAL JEDIDIAH, HOUSE
23 E. Town Street
1765

The Huntington House is a large, nine-bay, Georgian, frame dwelling. Resting on a stone foundation, the house has a gambrel roof and an interior central hall plan. There is a projecting center section on the facade that contains the paneled main door framed by sidelights and topped by a semielliptical window. A one-story wing on the southeast was added later. Jedidiah Huntington was an officer in the Revolution and later took an active part in local and state politics.
Private; not accessible to the public

NEW LONDON COUNTY
Norwichtown
HUNTINGTON, GOVERNOR SAMUEL, HOUSE
34 E. Town Street
1783

This 18th-century Georgian house has been extensively altered from its original appearance as a rectangular five-bay frame building with a gable roof and corner pilasters. A projecting central portico and two sets of double columns have been added to the main entrance. Central second-story windows have been replaced by double doors, while the main doorway has strong Greek Revival overtones (square panels, rectangular sidelights, and fluted pilasters). A large two-story ell was built on the south side and a bay window added on the west. Samuel Huntington (1732–1796) was a member of the Connecticut General Assembly (1764), a member of the state Council of Safety (1775), a delegate to the Continental Congress, and a signer of the Declaration of Independence. He became president of Congress in 1779, chief justice of Connecticut (1784), and served as governor from 1786 until his death.
Private

NEW LONDON COUNTY
Norwichtown
LATHROP, DR. DANIEL, SCHOOL
69 E. Town Street
1782

Named for the man who was instrumental in its founding, this school is one of the oldest of its kind still standing in the state. Identical in scale, size, and color to the Joseph Carpenter Shop next door, the school is brick with a gambrel roof and one interior room. There is a wooden belfry on the roof, and the front door is paneled. The foundation is stone.
Municipal; not accessible to the public

NEW LONDON COUNTY
Norwichtown
LATHROP, DR. JOSHUA, HOUSE
377 Washington Street
c. 1750

Two sections comprise the Joshua Lathrop House, a saltbox and a five-bay Georgian dwelling. The asymmetrical placement of windows and doors and the location of dormers in the center of the sloping lean-to roof attest to the many changes which have been made since construction. The two-story lean-to is attached to the rear of the Georgian portion, and its double front doors have seven panels. All fireplaces are original.
Private; not accessible to the public
HABS

NEW LONDON COUNTY
Norwichtown
LEFFINGWELL INN
348 Washington Street
1675, 18th century

The Leffingwell Inn, presently an L-shaped structure formed by the joining of two saltboxes, evolved in three stages. The earliest portion, the tavern room, is located in the northeast corner. An addition was made prior to 1724 by fastening a separate building onto the original room (the present entrance hall and south parlor). Most of the original (c. 1720) sash is intact except in the parlor. The third stage of construction (c. 1730–1765) resulted in the kitchen and north parlor. Thomas Leffingwell purchased the property in 1700 and operated it as an inn.
Private
HABS

NEW LONDON COUNTY
Norwichtown
TURNER, DR. PHILIP, HOUSE
29 W. Town Street

The Turner House is believed to have been built prior to 1700, and inside it has a variant of the usual saltbox floor plan.

An interesting feature is the dramatic sweep of the roofline which, at the rear, is only six feet above ground. There is a break in this roofline indicating that a second lean-to has been incorporated into the first. The chimney was originally stone, but bricks have replaced the stones on the outside. Dr. Philip Turner was an army surgeon during the Revolution.
Private; not accessible to the public

TOLLAND COUNTY
Coventry
HALE, NATHAN, HOMESTEAD (DEACON RICHARD HALE HOUSE)
South Street
1776

Richard Hale, father of Nathan Hale, whom the British hanged as a spy on September 22, 1776, built this home for his family and occupied it in October. The frame, two-and-one-half-story dwelling has a five-bay facade and a one-story ell attached at the rear. The ell originally measured 26 feet and was later extended considerably. Architectural ornament is lacking, and the exterior of the house is plain except for paneled doors, overlights, and door surrounds.
Private

TOLLAND COUNTY
Mansfield Center
WILLIAMS, ELEAZER, HOUSE
East side of Storrs Road just south of the intersection with Dobbs Road
1710

The Williams House illustrates the evolution of a single dwelling through 75 years of service as a parsonage. Original construction of the frame house is visible in the south chamber. Between 1750 and 1775 remodeling took place resulting in a two-chimney, center hall plan residence. Paneling from this period survives in the north parlor and north chamber. The clapboards on the main facade date from this period also. About 1800 the roofline was altered from sloping saltbox to simple gable. The 18th-century chimneys were demolished in 1853. Eleazer Williams was minister of the local Congregational church from 1710 to 1745.
Private; not accessible to the public

WINDHAM COUNTY
Brooklyn
TRINITY CHURCH
East side of Church Street
1771

This Georgian church was modeled upon two well-known colonial houses of worship designed by Peter Harrison: King's Chapel in Boston and Trinity Church,

Newport, Rhode Island. The building measures 46 feet by 30 feet and is frame covered with clapboards and fastened together by hand wrought nails. The arched windows are two stories high. Window frames and the wide muntined sash are believed to be original, although the pedimented entry and double front doors are replacements. Inside, the box pews and balconies are paneled.
Private

WINDHAM COUNTY
Canterbury
CLARK, CAPTAIN JOHN, HOUSE (DYER-CLARK HOUSE)
East side of Route 169

Dates for construction of the Clark House range from 1790 to 1802. It is a large Georgian house, somewhat elaborate in detail for its rural setting. A low gable tops the hip roof, and there are twin chimneys at either end of the gable. Beneath the modillion cornice is a Greek fret, and the vertical faces of the cornice are fluted. Large fluted pilasters highlight the corners, and two free standing Roman Doric columns frame the main entrance. There is a pediment over the front door which has sidelights and a transom containing spider web muntins. Above this is a Palladian window framed by miniature fluted pilasters. The south front is also elaborate. It contains a Palladian window with muntins forming Gothic arches; below this is a cornice with mutules and a frieze containing triglyphs and metopes. All these features are characteristic of a local building style referred to as the "Canterbury type."
Private; not accessible to the public

WINDHAM COUNTY
Canterbury
PAYNE, ELISHA, HOUSE (PRUDENCE CRANDALL HOUSE)
Southwest corner of the intersection of Conn. 14 and 169
c. 1805

The Payne House is a Georgian residence standing two stories high with a gable-on-hip roof. The main entrance is within a projecting pedimented central pavilion flanked by fluted pilasters. A Palladian window is set in the second story of the pavilion. The modillion cornice has a Greek fret immediately below, and this combination also appears in the triangular roof pediment and above the front door. In 1831 Prudence Crandall came to Canterbury to head a school for young ladies. When Sarah Harris, a Negro girl, applied for admission, Miss Crandall accepted her, but opposition arose among the townspeople which caused her to convert the school into one for training Negro girls to be teachers. Hostility mounted until Miss Crandall's opponents secured passage by the Connecticut assembly of the so-called "Black Law" (1833). This legislation prohibited the entrance of non-resident Negroes into private schools in the state unless specifically given permission by the local ruling body. Under terms of this law Miss Crandall was arrested and tried, although the case was set aside on technical grounds. Prudence Crandall and her attempts to educate Negro girls became a cause célèbre for 19th-century abolitionists.
State; not accessible to the public
HABS

WINDHAM COUNTY
Chaplin
WITTER HOUSE
Chaplin Street
1820–1821

The Witter House is a large New England Georgian dwelling. It is two stories high and has a five-bay facade, four end chimneys, and a large modillion cornice. A small ell projects from the rear, and the central hall plan is typically Georgian. The front door has a center fanlight and two small fans above the detached sidelights. This fan motif is repeated in wood above every window, and there is a large wooden fan above the side door. An unusual feature is the monitor roof with tiny windows. The roof began as a hipped gambrel, and a vertical board was added to tighten the two pitches and eventually raised a foot or so. Members of the Witter family owned the house until 1960.
Private; not accessible to the public

WINDHAM COUNTY
Windham Center
HUNT, DR. CHESTER, OFFICE
Windham Center Road
c. 1800–1810

This miniature scale, Federal style commercial building was used as an office and dispensary by Dr. Chester Hunt during the middle years of the 19th century. Its original purpose is not known. The two-story frame structure has a gambrel roof and tall, narrow windows with many lights on the ground floor. There is elaborate stencil work on some of the interior plaster, and the only second-story window has Gothic tracery muntins.
Private

Delaware

Old State House, Dover, Delaware. *Delaware State Archives*

Parson Thorne Mansion, Milford, Delaware. *Thomas R. Draper*

Brandywine Village
Historic District,
Wilmington, Delaware.
Ellsworth J. Gentry

KENT COUNTY
Cowgill vicinity
EIGHT-SQUARE SCHOOLHOUSE
East of Cowgill off Del. 9
c. 1836

In 1829 Delaware established a permanent system of free district public schools. The Eight-square Schoolhouse is the last surviving octagonal school building in the state. Its walls are undressed stone which has been stuccoed and whitewashed. The pyramidal roof is shingled, and beneath the eaves is a stepped brick cornice. The vestibule sheltering the main entrance is recent.
State; not accessible to the public

KENT COUNTY
Dover
LOOCKERMAN HALL
Delaware State College Campus
c. 1730

Loockerman Hall was a Georgian plantation house once surrounded by dependencies including a kitchen, smokehouse, wash house, and carriage house with outlying barns, stables, granaries, and quarters for field hands. The brick house has an unusually handsome cornice with modillions and "wall-of-Troy" dentils. Both the front porch and the roof dormers are later additions. Inside, the house has a central hall flanked on each side by two rooms. Each first-floor room has a fully paneled fireplace wall. Cornices, chair rails, stair rails, and balusters are all of good quality. Since 1891 Loockerman Hall has been used by Delaware State College.
State

KENT COUNTY
Dover
OLD STATEHOUSE
The Green
1787–1792

A courthouse built on this site in 1722 served as the predecessor of the Old Statehouse. The five-bay, brick Georgian building was erected using salvageable materials from the courthouse. Marble lintels highlight the window openings, and marble was used to top the water table. Fenestration is regular, and there is a large central Palladian window on the southwest facade. Wings have been added at various times: a brick, two-story addition in 1836 which was extended, 1895–1897; a pillared rotunda and south wing, 1910; and an eastern annex, 1925–1926. The rotunda was removed in 1968–1969.
State

KENT COUNTY
Dover vicinity
DICKINSON, JOHN, HOUSE
5 miles southeast of Dover and 3 miles east of U.S. 113 on Kitts Hummock Road
1740

John Dickinson (1732–1808), statesman and legislator, lived in this house as a youth and briefly during his adult life. Dickinson served in the Delaware and Pennsylvania legislatures, was a member of the Stamp Act Congress (1765), the first and second Continental Congresses (1774, 1775), and the Constitutional Convention (1787). His conservatism caused Dickinson to favor conciliation with Great Britain. Although he opposed the Stamp Act, he refused to sanction the use of force to resist it. He even voted against the Declaration of Independence, but when war came he took up arms on behalf of the colonies. Dickinson's position with regard to Britain was set forth in his anonymously published "Letters from a Farmer in Pennsylvania to the Inhabitants of the British Colonies" (1768).
State
NHL; HABS

KENT COUNTY
Dutch Neck Crossroads vicinity
ALLEE HOUSE
Dutch Neck Road east of Del. 9
Mid–18th century

The Allee House is a three-bay, two-story plus attic country residence. The brick walls are laid in Flemish bond. Ornament is provided by the molded brick water table, a belt course between floors, and a plaster cove cornice. There are flat plaster arches above the first-floor windows. Interior woodwork is original, and much of the early wrought iron hardware has survived. The abutting one-story brick kitchen was added later.
Federal

KENT COUNTY
Kenton vicinity
ASPENDALE
1 mile west of Kenton on Del. 300
1771–1773

Aspendale is a two-story Georgian brick dwelling with a gable roof and two sets of twin end chimneys. The roof was remodeled at the time of the Revolution. Both north and south facades are three bays wide and symmetrical in design. A one-and-one-half-story frame wing at the west end may predate the main brick portion of the house. Some restoration work has been done, primarily removal of interior partitions and a south front cornice and porch.
Private; not accessible to the public
NHL; HABS

KENT COUNTY
Magnolia
LOWBER, MATTHEW, HOUSE
East of Main Street, north of the intersection
1774; frame addition, 1855

This house, built of brick, represents the small but comfortable country homes of the latter part of the 18th century. The original house has two rooms on each floor. There is a belt course and watertable and a flush chimney on each end. The wooden addition also has a flush chimney. The date of construction and the builder's initials set in black headers are near the peak in the southeast gable.
State; not accessible to the public

KENT COUNTY
Milford
PARSON THORNE MANSION
501 Northwest Front Street
1730–1735 (original wing);
1745–1750 (main house)

This 18th-century plantation house is a Georgian five-bay, two-and-one-half-story brick structure with a one-and-one-half-story wing attached to either end by a covered way. Attached to the rear of the main section is a two-story frame wing, the oldest portion of the house. In 1879 the roofs were raised to their present steep pitch and the three roof gables were added. The interior remained unaltered. The house was named for the Reverend Sydenham Thorne, an early owner who was rector of Christ Church, Milford, and a co-founder of the community.
Private

NEW CASTLE COUNTY
Claymont
BLOCKHOUSE AND ROBINSON HOUSE
Naaman's Corner

The Blockhouse and Robinson House are part of a sprawling group of connected structures, some stone and some frame, erected at different times between the 17th and 19th centuries. The Blockhouse may be the oldest surviving building in Delaware. Believed to have been built in 1654, it originally had no windows at ground level other than loopholes under the eaves. A narrow inside stairway leads to the second floor. Erected in two parts, the Robinson House has an eastern end of stone (c. 1723) and a later western end covered by wide, smoothly matched ship lapped siding. The portico (c. 1915) and enclosed side porch are later additions. Since the mid–17th century the area around Naaman's Corner has been an important milling center.
State

76 DELAWARE

NEW CASTLE COUNTY
New Castle
NEW CASTLE HISTORIC DISTRICT
Bordered by Harmony Street, The
Strand, Third and Delaware Streets
17th, 18th, 19th, and 20th centuries

New Castle was founded by Peter
Stuyvesant in 1651 as the seat of New
Netherlands government on the Delaware
River. Its present name dates from the
beginning of British occupation in 1664. It
was the colonial capital of Delaware until
1776 and very briefly, in 1776–77, the
state capital of Delaware. The town's
buildings illustrate a broad range of
architectural styles from the 18th and
early 19th centuries. Along the town's first
street, The Strand, which parallels the
river, the houses face each other rather
than the street. Almost no modern intrusions mar New Castle.
Multiple public/private
NHL; HABS

NEW CASTLE COUNTY
Odessa
CORBIT-SHARP HOUSE
Southwest corner of Main and
Second Streets
1772–1774

Constructed for William Corbit by Robert
May, a master builder, this house marks
the height of the late Georgian style in
Delaware's domestic architecture. The
two-and-a-half-story house has a central
hall floor plan and hipped roof. Its brick
masonry, stone belt course, window lintels, paneled shutters, arched doorways,
and dormer windows are typical of the regional style.
Private
NHL; HABS

NEW CASTLE COUNTY
Odessa
ODESSA HISTORIC DISTRICT
Bounded roughly by Appoquinimink
Creek on the southeast; by High
Street on the northeast; by 4th Street
on the northwest; and by Main Street
on the southwest
18th and 19th centuries

Odessa, also known as Appoquinimink or
Cantwell's Bridge, was once a busy tidewater port. When bypassed by the railroad
in the 1850's, the community turned to
agriculture for its livelihood. Today the
four-block historic district contains 23
buildings from the 18th and early 19th
centuries. The district has suffered from a
minimum of commercial encroachment,
and most structures have been spared any
major architectural changes. Most have
retained their original sections, although
enlarged, and five 18th-century houses altered after 1800 have been restored.

Characteristic are the Collins-Johnson
House (c. 1700), which was moved to
Odessa in 1962; the Corbit-Sharp and Wil-
son-Warner houses (Georgian); the John
Janvier House (1775); the Brick Hotel
(1822, Federal); the Davis Store (1824)
and residence (1830); and the Cyrus Polk
House (1853, Italian Villa). Elements of
Victorian architecture are also present.
Multiple; private

NEW CASTLE COUNTY
St. Georges vicinity
BUENA VISTA
5 miles north of St. Georges on U.S.
13, 1.5 miles south of its junction
with U.S. 40
1845–1847

Buena Vista was built by John M. Clayton,
Secretary of State to Zachary Taylor
(1849–1850). His most notable achievement was the Clayton-Bulwer Treaty,
which provided for a neutralized international canal across Central America. The
original brick house has five bays and is
two stories high. There is a veranda across
the full front with Doric columns and an
iron balustrade on the roof. The two chimneys at each end are also connected by an
iron balustrade. A service wing extends to
the west from the north end of the house.
In the present century a long, two-story
wing was added to the south side. The
original part of the house is furnished with
appropriate period furniture some of
which belonged to Clayton.
State

NEW CASTLE COUNTY
Wilmington
**BRANDYWINE VILLAGE HISTORIC
DISTRICT**
Bounded roughly by Tatnall Street,
22nd Street, Vandever Avenue,
Mabel Street, and Brandywine Creek
18th and 19th centuries

In 1637 Captain Jacob Vandever first
visited the site of present-day Brandywine
Village. The first land patent was granted
to him in 1669, and the burgeoning settlement which developed depended first on
agriculture and then on flour milling.
Flour mills, millers' homes, mill workers'
dwellings, shops, and artisans' residences,
constructed mainly during the last quarter
of the 18th century, formed the core of
Brandywine Village, which soon became a
part of Wilmington proper. Market Street,
the old toll road between Philadelphia and
Wilmington, was lined with sturdy houses
of local granite six of which still remain.
All are two stories high and have molded
cornices and gable roofs. Mill workers'
homes were brick or frame, and they have
been largely obscured by store fronts and
signs. Three significant structures within

the historic district are St. John's
Episcopal Church (1857, original design
by John Notman), the Brandywine
Methodist Episcopal Church (1857), and
the Brandywine Academy (two-story,
stone structure topped by an octagonal
cupola).
Multiple public/private
HABS

NEW CASTLE COUNTY
Wilmington
DINGEE, JACOB, HOUSE
105 E. 7th Street
1771

The Jacob Dingee House and its closely
related neighbor, the Obadiah Dingee
House, date from Wilmington's period of
Quaker settlement (1736 to the early
1800's). The former is the older of the
two houses. A rear wing was constructed
in two stages, the older, of brick, and the
newer, of wood. The cornice is simply
molded, and a projecting belt course divides the stories. Brickwork is Flemish
bond on the first level and common bond
above. A change in the street level
resulted in the cellar door and additions to
the later marble steps. Jacob Dingee was a
joiner, carpenter, and probably a cabinet
maker.
Private; not accessible to the public
HABS

NEW CASTLE COUNTY
Wilmington
DINGEE, OBADIAH, HOUSE
107 E. 7th Street
1771–1773

The Obadiah Dingee House is one of a
very few dwellings that survive from the
first period of Quaker settlement in
Wilmington (c. 1736 to the early 1800's).
Wilmington was laid out by Thomas
Willing in 1736, and it grew rapidly into
an important port and center of commerce. The house is a two-story brick residence. Both the rear wing and the front
of the first floor have been greatly altered,
but the three second-floor windows have
their original molded wood sills and
12-pane sash with heavy muntins.
Obadiah Dingee was a cabinetmaker,
house carpenter, and joiner.
Municipal; not accessible to the public
HABS

NEW CASTLE COUNTY
Wilmington
FERRIS, ZACHARIAH, HOUSE
414 W. 2nd Street
1718

The Zachariah Ferris House may be the
oldest dwelling in Wilmington. It is a simple, two-story brick house with a later

brick extension on the east side. Both the north and south walls are laid in Flemish bond with dark glazed headers. A pent roof was once carried across both facades between the two floors. Between the two second-story windows is a panel of brickwork in which a double row of numerals and letters was built with dark glazed headers. The writing is no longer legible. Zachariah Ferris, a tanner, purchased the house in 1768.
Private; not accessible to the public

NEW CASTLE COUNTY
Wilmington
FORT CHRISTINA
E. 7th Street and the Christina River, Fort Christina State Park
1638

The first Swedish expedition to the present State of Delaware landed at Fort Christina. This initial fortification became the nucleus of the Swedish settlement on the Delaware River. The natural wharf of rocks where the first landing was made is preserved in Fort Christina State Park. Also within the park is a monument designed by Swedish sculptor Carl Milles commemorating Swedish settlement.
State
NHL

NEW CASTLE COUNTY
Wilmington
HOLY TRINITY (OLD SWEDES) CHURCH
7th and Church Streets
1698

Holy Trinity, which is the oldest surviving church of a Delaware Valley Swedish congregation, is built on the site of the Fort Christina settlement's first burial ground. It is rectangular in plan, with a brick floor, shingled roof, and gabled ends; a tower, gallery, and porch are additions. Subsequent alterations were corrected by a restoration in 1899 so that the church might retain its architectural integrity. An adjacent Swedish dwelling serves as a museum and library on Delaware Swedish life.
Private
NHL; HABS

NEW CASTLE COUNTY
Wilmington
MENDENHALL, CAPTAIN THOMAS, HOUSE
205 E. Front Street
c. 1790

The Mendenhall House is one of the few surviving examples in Wilmington of an 18th-century town house. Its brick exterior measures 20 feet wide by 32 feet deep. Belt courses mark all floor divisions in-cluding the attic. Windows are graded in height, the tallest located on the ground floor. The front door has a pediment above containing raised fretwork. Thomas Mendenhall was a Quaker sea captain who prospered in the West Indies trade. He eventually purchased the entire block on which this house is situated, and the property contained a large storehouse, a house for teamsters, a large yard for wagons, and sheds for horses.
Private; not accessible to the public
HABS

NEW CASTLE COUNTY
Wilmington
STARR HOUSE
1310 King Street
1801–1806

The Starr House is one of a very few remaining Wilmington buildings dating from the late 18th and early 19th centuries. It exhibits the craftsmanship of local workmen and of its builder Michael Van Kirk (Van Kuik), a stone cutter. The carved mantel and fireplace in the parlor may be his handiwork. The exterior of the brick house is laid in Flemish bond from the fourteenth course to the cornice; all other brickwork is English bond. A marble belt course separates the first and second floors, there are marble voussoirs above the first-floor front windows, and windows on both floors have marble sills. Inside, new doorways have been cut, but original paneling, woodwork, and hardware survive.
Private
HABS

NEW CASTLE COUNTY
Wilmington vicinity
ELEUTHERIAN MILLS
North of Wilmington on Del. 141 at Brandywine Creek Bridge
1802

Eleutherian Mills is the site of the powder works that revolutionized powder manufacturing in America. Established in 1801 by E. I. du Pont, the factory had become the country's largest by 1810. After 1860 the company began to diversify its interests, and presently it is one of the Nation's major industries. Among the buildings at the site are du Pont's residence, the company's first office building, and many of the 19th-century mills.
Private
NHL

NEW CASTLE COUNTY
Wilmington vicinity
THE WINTERTHUR MUSEUM AND GARDENS
6 miles northwest of Wilmington on Del. 52

The nucleus of the present Winterthur Museum was built in 1839 on land owned by James Antoine Bidermann. This dwelling was enlarged and remodeled in the Georgian style in the 19th century. Additional alterations were made in the first quarter of the 20th century. The present mansion is composed of a three-and-one-half-story main section with flanking wings of five and one-half stories. Sixty acres of gardens and woodlands surround the house, and these contain trees, flowers, and flowering shrubs. Azaleas and daffodils are abundant in the spring. The overall impression is one of naturalness achieved by a harmonious blending of color and tone. The Winterthur Museum contains perhaps the finest collection of American decorative arts and domestic interiors to be found in the country.
Private

SUSSEX COUNTY
Cool Spring vicinity
FISHER HOUSE
Southeast of Cool Spring, Broadkill Hundred
c. 1728

The Fisher House is a one-story plus attic frame dwelling with a gambrel roof and a cockloft. The walls are half-timbered, nogged with brick, and covered by clapboards. Exterior detailing not commonly found in small country houses is visible in the box cornice with its molded frieze and dentils beneath, and in the weatherboarding on the oldest section which is matched, beaded, and molded. At an early date the house was enlarged to its present size. It now contains two rooms and a central hall downstairs and four bedrooms upstairs. The house was probably built for Joshua Fisher, the son of Thomas Fisher, an early Quaker settler.
State; not accessible to the public

SUSSEX COUNTY
Dagsboro vicinity
PRINCE GEORGE'S CHAPEL
East of Dagsboro on Del. 26
1757

Prince George's Chapel was designed like most 18th-century churches but executed in wood rather than masonry. Originally it served as a chapel-of-ease for Worcester parish in Maryland. The exterior shingles were added as a protective measure in 1929, but the interior has been little changed. The vaulted ceiling of heart pine, some of the paneled box pews, and most of the gallery remain. Benches have replaced many of the box pews, and the pointed arch windows are 19th-century alterations.

State; not accessible to the public

SUSSEX COUNTY
Georgetown
OLD SUSSEX COUNTY COURTHOUSE
S. Bedford Street
1793

Rival factions in Sussex County were unable to agree upon a location for the county seat. A centrally located piece of open farmland was purchased under authority of the General Assembly in 1791. This courthouse, originally located on The Circle, became the focal point of the new community's town square. It is a two-story plus attic structure which looks more like a house than a public building. The five-bay exterior is covered with shingles, and the present front porch is a later addition. In 1837 the courthouse was moved to its present location and supplanted by the present one. The exterior is largely unchanged.

State; not accessible to the public

SUSSEX COUNTY
Lewes
MAULL HOUSE
542 Pilottown Road
c. 1730–1740

The Maull House is the oldest building in Lewes in its original location. It has also undergone very little alteration. Covered by a gambrel roof, the one-and-one-half-story frame dwelling is typical of Quaker homes common to this area in the early 18th century. A rear wing was added about 1890 at the same time that a wing at the north was removed. Paneling and molding on the interior are largely intact.
Private
HABS

Corbit-Sharp House, Odessa, Delaware.
The Henry Francis duPont Winterthur Museum

Block House and Robinson House, Claymont, Delaware. *Sophie Consagra*

District of Columbia

Old State, War and Navy Building, Washington, D.C. *Ronald Comedy for HABS*

Pan American Union,
Washington, D.C.
J. Alexander

De La Roche Tenant House,
Washington, D.C.
J. Alexander for HABS

Pension Building, Washington, D.C.
Jack E. Boucher for HABS

Frederick Douglass Home National Memorial,
Washington, D.C. *NPS*

WASHINGTON
ADAS ISRAEL SYNAGOGUE
3rd and G Streets, N.W.
1873–1876

Adas Israel Synagogue was the first synagogue in the District of Columbia. A Hebrew congregation was organized in Washington shortly after the Civil War. After a time liturgical reforms were instituted, and the more conservative members withdrew to form the Adas Israel congregation. Thirty-five families composing the new congregation met and worshiped in members' homes or rented quarters. On August 16, 1870, three trustees of the congregation purchased a lot at 6th and G Streets, NW, engaged a contractor and a draftsman, and construction on the synagogue was begun by 1873. Dedication ceremonies took place on June 9, 1876, with President Ulysses S. Grant present. The Adas Israel congregation continued to use the building until 1907 when the group moved to a larger house of worship at 6th and I Streets, NW. A Greek Orthodox church and an evangelical Church of God have both been located on the premises, and a variety of small businesses have occupied the ground floor. Classrooms, offices, and a weekday chapel were originally on the ground floor and the synagogue proper, on the second floor. The synagogue area has been used for storage, but remains very nearly in its original condition. Subway construction caused the building to be moved again in 1969.
State; not accessible to the public.

WASHINGTON
ADMINISTRATION BUILDING, CARNEGIE INSTITUTION OF WASHINGTON
1530 P Street, N.W.
1910, Carrère and Hastings

The Carnegie Institution, an expression of Andrew Carnegie's generosity, is an early example of American philanthropy. Founded to promote basic scientific research for the enrichment of human existence, its contributions include the Mount Wilson Observatory and research programs in the fields of geophysics, embryology, genetics, and history. Today the organization has limited its activities to research in the physical and biological sciences. Its administration building is a neo-French Renaissance structure of Indiana limestone.
Private
NHL

WASHINGTON
AMERICAN NATIONAL RED CROSS
17th and D Streets, N.W.
1915–1917, Trowbridge and Livingston

This Greek Revival building houses the administration of the Nation's official relief organization. Built with both Federal and private funds, it illustrates the cooperation of government and private efforts in carrying out the organization's duties. Although the international Red Cross movement originated in the Geneva Convention of 1864, nearly 20 years passed before the United States accepted its principles, even then due largely to the efforts of Clara Barton. Its services today far exceed those conceived by Miss Barton or performed by the pre-World War I organization. Services to the armed forces and to veterans, nursing services, volunteer programs, the blood donor program, first aid, and water safety instruction have been added to the basic functions of relief to victims of both natural and man-made disasters.
Private
NHL

WASHINGTON
ANDERSON, LARZ, HOUSE
2118 Massachusetts Avenue, N.W.
1902–1905, Little and Browne

The Anderson House is a large, 50-room mansion with lavish eclectic interiors designed in the Late Renaissance Revival manner for Larz and Isabel Anderson, who planned to present it to the Society of the Cincinnati, which now owns it. Constructed of brick and stone with a partial steel frame, the building is four stories high and basically U-shaped. The central facade is 85 feet long with a 30-foot-wide wing on both sides extending out 40 feet. The wings are connected by a screen wall with two openings forming a forecourt. The interior is most elaborate with a two-story great hall in the center of the block on the first floor. The main dining room and drawing rooms are on the second floor and the bedrooms on the third floor.
Private

WASHINGTON
ARTS CLUB OF WASHINGTON
2017 I Street, N.W.
1802–1808

The Arts Club of Washington, an early 19th-century Federal townhouse, served for a time as the nation's Executive Mansion after the White House was burned by the British in the War of 1812. The first portion of the house, the kitchen wing, was built in 1802. The remainder was begun in 1805 and finished in 1808. James

Monroe lived in the house as Secretary of War under James Madison and during the first 6 months of his own Presidency (March to September 1817). About 1822 the house became the British legation, and residents of subsequent years included Charles Francis Adams and General Silas Casey. The building served as a boardinghouse, a girls' school, and a private residence before it was purchased by the Arts Club of Washington in 1916. Measuring 32 feet in width, the house is red brick laid in a Flemish bond pattern with buff-colored stone trim. The original house was two stories high with a dormered attic and was converted to the present three-and-one-half stories in 1881. The interior contains several fireplaces, decorative plaster moldings and woodwork, and a main stairway with bas-relief garlands and mahogany handrail and balusters.
Private; accessible to the public with permission
HABS

WASHINGTON
BANK OF COLUMBIA
3210 M Street, N.W.
1796

This three-story, late 18th-century, brick, commercial structure has housed many activities and undertakings vital to the development of the Georgetown area. The Bank of Columbia, the second bank established within the District of Columbia, was the first occupant, but moved to new quarters in 1806. From 1807 to 1822 the Bureau of Indian Trade occupied the premises; and between 1823 and 1858 the building served as the Town Hall and Mayor's office for Georgetown. In 1883 extensive remodeling took place so the old bank could be used as an engine house. It ceased to serve this purpose in 1940. The ground story has been altered, and the interior has been almost entirely done over. The building contributes to the streetscape of the historic Georgetown area.
State

WASHINGTON
BATTLEGROUND NATIONAL CEMETERY
6625 Georgia Avenue, N.W.
1864

Battleground National Cemetery was established during the summer of 1864 after the Confederate assault on Washington, D.C. The attack, led by General Jubal Early, culminated in the battle of Fort Stevens on July 11 and 12. Forty Union soldiers who fell on the field, located about a half mile north of the cemetery, are buried here. The graves are arranged in a circle with regulation markers. There is a marble speaker's rostrum for memori-

al services and monuments to New York, Ohio, and Pennsylvania units which participated in the defense of Fort Stevens.
Federal
NPS; 1.03 acres

WASHINGTON
CENTRAL PUBLIC LIBRARY
Mount Vernon Square, 8th and K Streets, N.W.
1899–1902, Ackerman and Ross

This turn-of-the-century Beaux Arts structure was one of many libraries given to American cities by Andrew Carnegie. The three-story building has basement walls of pink granite and upper exterior walls of white marble. While the exterior is heavily ornamented with decorative carvings, the interior represents a more functional design. The library has a collection of almost two million volumes. Of particular interest is the Washingtoniana Collection, which is the most complete assemblage of its kind in existence.
Municipal

WASHINGTON
CHAPEL HALL, GALLAUDET COLLEGE
Florida Avenue and 7th Street, N.E.
1870, Vaux and Withers

Opened in 1864, Gallaudet College is the only institution of higher learning devoted specifically to the education of the deaf. A pre-school, elementary, and secondary school for children; a training center for teachers of the deaf; and the undergraduate college have comprised Gallaudet College since 1954. Chapel Hall, the "Main Central Building," is a large Gothic Revival structure.

WASHINGTON
CHESAPEAKE AND OHIO CANAL NATIONAL HISTORICAL PARK
Reference—see Allegany County, Maryland

WASHINGTON
CHRIST CHURCH
620 G Street, S.E.
1806–1807

Washington parish (Episcopal), which originally included all of Washington and Georgetown, was incorporated on December 24, 1794. Services were held in a tobacco warehouse on New Jersey Avenue near D Street, SE, until 1807, when the present Christ Church building was completed. Gothic in style, the present church is greatly altered from the original building of 1806. This plan probably was for a simple, rectangular, two-story structure about 38 feet wide and 45 feet long with a U-shaped gallery over a two-aisled ground floor. In the first al-

teration of 1824 the building was extended about 20 feet at the north end, which added two bays and increased the number of pews. In 1849 the narthex and square bell tower were added. The battlemented Gothic exterior also dates from this period. In 1877 the east and west galleries were removed, and the old gallery supports replaced. Stained-glass lancet windows were installed, and the present gray-brown pebble-dash stucco was applied to give the exterior the appearance of stone. In 1891 the bell tower was raised to its present height of 73 feet, the single-story projecting entrance porch was added to the narthex, the chancel windows were removed, and the interior was fescoed and decorated in Victorian style. Little changed since 1891, the south facade has a small, flat-roofed entrance porch with a pointed-arch double entrance door, small lancet windows in either side wall, and a crenellated parapet with corner towers. The top of the gabled wall is crenelated, and the bell tower behind the porch is framed by slender, double, two-stage buttresses with gabled caps. The top of the tower has a dogtooth cornice and a crenelated parapet with galvanized iron pinnacles on square piers at each of the four corners.
Private

WASHINGTON
CITY HALL (DISTRICT COURTHOUSE)
4th and E Streets, N.W.
1820–1849, George Hadfield

This Greek Revival building is one of the earliest Federal buildings erected in the city. Designed by one of the architects of the Capitol, the central portion served first as the City Hall. Historically significant are the many trials of national interest held here, including the trial of John Surratt, one of the Lincoln conspirators.
Federal
NHL; HABS

WASHINGTON
CONGRESSIONAL CEMETERY
1801 E Street, S.E.
1807

The original four-and-one-half acre tract which eventually became the Congressional Cemetery was purchased from the Government in 1807 as a private burying ground. Five years later the land was deeded to Christ Church under the name of the Washington Parish Burial Ground. In 1849 the vestry changed the name to the Washington Cemetery, although it has continued to be called the Congressional Cemetery because of its close association with the national legislature. The first Congressman to be buried in the cemetery

was Senator Uriah Tracy of Connecticut. As early as 1817 the vestry assigned 100 burial sites for the use of the Federal Government, and it soon became customary to bury Congressmen, Senators, and executive officials who died in Washington in this cemetery. Between 1824 and 1834 Congress made several appropriations for the construction of a Keeper's house, a receiving vault, and a wall around the grounds. Three Presidents were briefly interred here: William Henry Harrison, Zachary Taylor, and John Quincy Adams. Still buried in the Congressional Cemetery are the remains of 14 Senators and 43 Representatives including Vice President Elbridge Gerry and Speaker of the House Philip P. Barbour. Other notables are Scarlet Crow, a Sioux chief and U.S. scout; Col. Tobias Lear, personal secretary to George Washington; Push-Ma-Ta-Ha, a Choctaw chief; John Philip Sousa, composer and musician; Mathew Brady, photographer; and George Hadfield, William Thornton, and Robert Mills, architects.
Private

WASHINGTON
CORCORAN GALLERY OF ART
17th Street at New York Avenue, N.W.
1894–1897, Ernest Flagg; 1925–1928 (addition), John Platt

The Corcoran Gallery is an excellent example of French Beaux Arts design with Neo-Grec details. The William Wilson Corcoran art collection was moved here from the original gallery at 17th Street and Pennsylvania Avenue when the new quarters were completed. The present structure is L-shaped with the two straight facades joined by a hemicycle. Constructed of brick, it is faced with pink granite on the basement level and white Georgia marble on all upper stories. Dominating the attic story is an elaborate frieze and architrave above which is a projecting cornice capped by a richly carved Greek cheneau. The roof of copper and glass serves as a skylight for a spacious two-story atrium surrounded by 40 fluted Doric limestone columns which support a loggia.
Private

WASHINGTON
DECATUR HOUSE
748 Jackson Place, N.W.
1818–1819, Benjamin H. Latrobe; 1944, Thomas T. Waterman

Built for Commodore Stephen Decatur, suppressor of the Barbary pirates, this early 19th-century residence is among the few that have survived the structural changes around Lafayette Park. Among

the later occupants of the house were Henry Clay, Martin Van Buren, and Judah P. Benjamin. Designed by one of America's first professional architects, the house has changed little in its exterior appearance, but the interior has been restored according to 11 original Latrobe drawings. The house is particularly noted for the proportions of the interior. The first floor contains Decatur memorabilia and furnishings. The second, Victorian in style, represents the occupancy of General Edward F. Beale's widow, who purchased the house in 1877.
Private
NHL; HABS

WASHINGTON
EASTERN MARKET
   7th and C Streets, S.E.
   1873, Adolph Cluss; 1908 (addition)

Eastern Market is one of the few remaining public markets in Washington. Meat, fish, and produce are still sold here as they were in the 1870's. The market is typical of commercial structures of its time. Dimensions of the brick building are 300 feet by 50 feet and the original portion (fronting on Seventh Street) is one-story high. The addition is composed of a two-story connecting section plus a nine-bay rectangular section. Windows and doors alternate in the bays of the older portion. Each bay is defined by brick pilasters and enclosed by decorative corbeled brick trim. Doors are framed by roundheaded brick arches above which are bull's-eye windows. Inside each market building is a single unbroken open space for stalls under a ceiling of exposed iron trusses.
Federal

WASHINGTON
EXECUTIVE OFFICE BUILDING
   Southeast corner, Pennsylvania Avenue and 17th Street, N.W.
   1871-1888, Alfred B. Mullett

The French Renaissance Revival Executive Office Building was constructed for the State, War, and Navy departments. The south wing (State) was begun in June 1871, and completed by December 1875. The east wing (Navy) was begun in 1872 and completed 7 years later; the north wing (War) was started in 1879 and finished in 3 years. The west wing and central portion were begun in 1884 and took 4 years to complete. The present structure is approximately 520 feet long, 285 feet wide, and stands about 134 feet (six stories) above the sidewalk level. Constructed of purple-gray Virginia granite with a purple slate mansard roof, the building rests on a rusticated subbasement and basement. Decoration of the interior is attributed to Richard von Ezdorf,

and among the most notable features are elaborate gaslight chandeliers (since converted to electricity), carved mantels, skylights, and large spiraling staircases, one at each corner and double ones at the centers of the east and west wings. The Executive Office Building also had a central hot-water heating and plumbing system which was modern for its time. After the War Department moved to new quarters, the State Department and the Bureau of the Budget were the principal occupants. The building now houses part of the latter department plus much of the White House staff.
Federal; not accessible to the public

WASHINGTON
FOLGER SHAKESPEARE LIBRARY
   201 E. Capitol Street, S.E.
   1929-1932, Paul P. Cret

Henry Clay Folger (1875-1930) was a Standard Oil executive who devoted much of his life to acquiring and eventually building up the world's largest collection of Shakespeareana. To house his collection, the architect Paul P. Cret designed a building composed of a library housing 75,000 volumes (with space for 150,000 more), an exhibition gallery, a reading room, and administrative offices. The cornerstone was laid in November 1929, and the simple, modern classical building was dedicated 3 years later. Built of white Georgia marble, the Library measures 48 feet high by 226 feet from east to west, and 111 feet from north to south. Low flights of marble steps are at either end of the principal north facade. The two main entrance doors are flanked by block carvings of Pegasus and are surmounted by masks of Comedy and Tragedy. Between the doors nine, high, recessed grilled windows are separated by modified fluted piers. Under the windows are bas-reliefs with scenes from Shakespeare's works. On the Second Street facade two ground-level doors flank five recessed two-story windows which open (on the first level) onto a marble balcony with an iron handrail overlooking a small garden and a fountain. Behind the rather severe facade is a true Elizabethan interior, designed to create a suitable environment for the collection. The reading room represents a typical Tudor great hall, while the lecture hall was patterned after an Elizabethan theater.
Private

WASHINGTON
FORD'S THEATRE NATIONAL HISTORIC SITE
   10th Street, N.W., between E and F Streets
   1863

On April 14, 1865, President Abraham Lincoln was assassinated by John Wilkes Booth while attending a production of *Our American Cousin* at Ford's Theatre. The mortally wounded president was carried across the street to the house of William Petersen, where, at 7:22 the following morning, Lincoln died in a small first-floor bedroom. Secretary of War Edwin M. Stanton reportedly announced the death of the President with the words: "Now he belongs to the ages." Federally owned since 1896, the house appears substantially as it did in 1865. The Theatre itself, considered one of the finest of its day, was closed immediately following the assassination. For many years thereafter the building was occupied by various agencies of the War Department. Following the complete restoration of the interior and a number of changes to the exterior, the theater reopened in 1968.
Federal
NPS; .23 acre

WASHINGTON
FREDERICK DOUGLASS HOME NATIONAL MEMORIAL
   1411 W Street, S.E.
   c. 1855

Frederick Douglass was born into slavery near Easton, Maryland, about February 14, 1817. After escaping from slavery, the self-educated Douglass began a steady rise to prominence. During his lifetime he was an effective orator for the abolitionist cause, and for 17 years he issued the *North Star*, a militant anti-slavery paper. Following the Civil War, he was secretary of the Santo Domingo Commission, marshal and recorder of deeds for the District of Columbia, and United States Minister to Haiti. Douglass's two-story brick home, Cedar Hill, which overlooks the Anacostia River, has been altered since his occupancy, 1879-1895.
Federal
NPS; 8.07 acres
HABS

WASHINGTON
FREER GALLERY OF ART
   12th Street and Jefferson Drive, S.W.
   1923, Charles A. Platt

In 1904 Charles Lang Freer, a wealthy Detroit manufacturer of freight cars, offered his personal collection of American and Oriental art to the Federal Government with provision for a suitable building

to house it. Freer's offer was accepted in 1906, the government approved Charles A. Platt's plans for a building in 1915, and the Freer Gallery of Art, under the trusteeship of the Smithsonian Institution, was officially opened to the public on May 2, 1923. Modeled after a Florentine Renaissance fortress palace, the building is rectangular with an exterior of heavily rusticated, gray Massachusetts granite. A wave motif string course separates the basement story from the high main story, and a classical entablature and balustrade crown the building on all four sides. The principal north Mall entrance facade is composed of a three-arched central pavilion flanked by side wings with Doric pilasters rising to the entablature. In the interior on the main floor 19 exhibition rooms surround an arcaded corridor and central court. The exhibition space in the galleries is kept low, and the vaulted ceilings have skylights equipped with diffusing glass and adjustable curtains to meet the special lighting requirements of the objects on exhibition. Among the American works of art housed in this gallery is the world's largest collection of paintings, prints, and drawings of James Abbott McNeill Whistler. Whistler's Peacock Room, once in the London home of Frederick R. Leyland and decorated by Whistler to harmonize with his painting, *The Princess from the Land of Porcelain*, has been reerected in the southeast corner of the gallery.
Federal

WASHINGTON
GEORGETOWN HISTORIC DISTRICT
18th, 19th, and 20th centuries

For the first quarter of the 19th century, Georgetown was the center of the social and diplomatic life of the District of Columbia. The original town, however, had been laid out in 1751. Houses dotted the area from Bridge (M) Street to the Potomac River, and several mansions crowned the heights beyond. Along the waterfront were warehouses and wharves, sailors' taverns, and flour mills. Although several examples of pre-Revolutionary houses still exist, most of the buildings postdate 1800.
Multiple public/private
NHL; HABS

WASHINGTON
GEORGETOWN MARKET
3276 M Street, N.W.
1865

This one-story brick market is a reminder of Georgetown's long history of commercial activity. A recessed round-arched central door flanked on either side by round-arched windows (formerly doors)

dominates the main facade. The common bond wall rises to an elaborate stamped tin cornice with decorative Italianate brackets. The building was used as a market until 1945. Projects requiring refrigeration were located against the thick interior walls, butter stalls were generally in the center, and produce was sold outside. In 1966 legislature was passed directing the District of Columbia to preserve the landmark and operate it as a public market again, but funds have not yet been appropriated.
Federal

WASHINGTON
GRACE PROTESTANT EPISCOPAL CHURCH
1041 Wisconsin Avenue, N.W.
1866–1867

Grace Church was founded in the mid–19th century as a mission for sailors and canal boatmen who frequented Georgetown. The sum of $25,000 was donated to build the present church. It is a rectangular, two-story, gable-roofed, Gothic Revival structure with exterior walls of coursed rubble and ashlar masonry construction. Projecting from the main facade is a small, one-story, gable-roofed porch with a central entrance door. Above the porch is a leaded glass window set within a pointed sandstone arch. Astride the main gable is a rectangular, gable-roofed, masonry bell-cote capped by a simple wooden cross. Adjoining the church to the north is the 1898 parish hall, and to the west of it, the 1895 rectory.
Private

WASHINGTON
HALCYON HOUSE
3400 Prospect Street, N.W.
1787

The Halcyon House was built by Benjamin Stoddert, first Secretary of the Navy (1796) and Secretary of War (1800). Stoddert was one of the original "proprietors" who signed the agreement establishing the "Ten Mile Square," now the District of Columbia. The house is a two-and-one-half-story brick Georgian mansion with a slate gable roof and two flanking lower wings. Although enlarged and remodeled as apartments (1900 to 1938), the house was partially restored in 1942.
Private; not accessible to the public

WASHINGTON
HEALY BUILDING, GEORGETOWN UNIVERSITY
Georgetown University campus
1877–1879, Smithmeyer and Pelz

Georgetown University was founded in the last years of the 18th century by the

Reverend John Carroll (1735–1815). In 1815 its status was changed from college to university. Completed largely through the efforts of the Reverend Patrick Healy, S.J. (1783–1882), for whom it was named, Healy Hall is a massive rectangular structure in the Northern European Romanesque style. A central section is flanked by pavilions, and a tower above the east front entrance rises 200 feet above grade. The four-story building has walls of masonry and load bearing brick. The east, north, and south sides are laid in Potomac gneiss while the west is brick. Towers, dormers, tall chimneys, and spiky finials enliven the exterior; fenestration is varied, and a number of imaginative copper gargoyles project from the eave line. An interior area of note is Gaston Hall Auditorium on the third floor of the north wing.
Private

WASHINGTON
HEURICH, CHRISTIAN, MANSION
1307 New Hampshire Avenue, N.W.
1892–1894, John Granville Meyers

The entrance facade of the Norman Revival Heurich Mansion is of rough-faced brownstone ashlar and consists of a partially exposed basement with three stories above. The fourth, a dormer floor, rises behind the green, standing seam metal roof. The most distinctive element of the exterior design is the massive corner tower with a pointed metal dome rising one story above the mansard roof. Partially balancing this tower on the left is a rectangular bay with a late Gothic style dormer. The arched central entrance door is concealed behind a rectangular porte-cochere which juts out of the building to the sidewalk. Behind the porte-cochere the two-bay central section of the house is flanked by slender, multi-textured turrets which rise through the second and third stories and the cornice to frame a second, gabled dormer. Christian Heurich, who lived in this house for 53 years, was born in Germany and came to the United States at the end of the Civil War. By 1873 he was sole owner of the Christian Heurich Lager Beer Brewery, later the Christian Heurich Brewing Company, and eventually he became active in civic affairs and philanthropic organizations.
Private

WASHINGTON
JEFFERSON MEMORIAL
South bank of the Tidal Basin
1943, John Russell Pope

As the third President of the United States (1801–1809), Thomas Jefferson continued to implement his belief in the natural and civic rights of the individual.

Through the Louisiana Purchase he expanded the Nation's frontiers and political systems. The Jefferson Memorial, built in the Classical style of his own liking, features inscriptions giving his views of liberty and democracy which he had also voiced in the Declaration of Independence. The domed interior of the memorial is dominated by a statue of Jefferson sculptured by Rudolph Evans. The circular colonnaded structure, on a line with the south axis of the White House, was dedicated on April 13, 1943.
Federal
NPS; 6.44 acres

WASHINGTON
LAFAYETTE SQUARE HISTORIC DISTRICT
Includes those buildings fronting on H Street, Jackson Place, Madison Place, and Pennsylvania Avenue

Washington was chosen as the federal capital in 1791, and the land which is now Lafayette Park was designated as the President's Park. Located directly north of the President's House, the land was set aside to be landscaped. It was known as the President's Park until 1824. A triumphal visit by the Marquis de Lafayette caused the name to be changed in his honor. In the spring of 1851 the noted landscape architect Andrew Jackson Downing was invited to plan gardens and walks for the park. His death, in 1852, and the intervention of the Civil War prevented serious alterations. Major landscaping was not undertaken until 1872. Houses fronting Lafayette Park have been the residences of prominent political and military figures. The location was desirable because of its proximity to the White House. Residences which remain (dating from the 19th and early 20th centuries) have recently been internally and externally refurbished, and the architecture, although ranging from Victorian to Beaux Arts, is predominantly Federal. Notable structures surrounding the park are the Executive Office Building, the Blair-Lee Houses, Decatur House, and St. John's Church.
Federal/private
NHL; HABS

WASHINGTON
LINCOLN MEMORIAL
West Potomac Park
1922, Henry Bacon

In 1912 a Congressional commission authorized the location of a memorial to Abraham Lincoln in Potomac Park on the axis of the Capitol and the Washington Monument. In addition to the architect, Henry Bacon, the commission authorized Daniel Chester French to sculpture a statue of Lincoln, and Jules Guerin to design and execute interior murals and ornamentation. Ernest C. Barnstow carved the frieze and the decorations of the attic wall. Eight classic columns, four to a row, divide the interior into three chambers. The central chamber contains the statue, near the west wall and facing the entrance. On the walls of the north and south chambers are inscribed the Second Inaugural Address and the Gettysburg Address, respectively. The memorial, inspired by the Greek temple form, rests on an elevated terrace. Symbolic of the Union, the colonnade contains 36 Doric columns which represent the states existing at the time of Lincoln's death. The memorial was dedicated on Memorial Day, May 30, 1922.
Federal
NPS; 6 acres

WASHINGTON
THE LINDENS
2401 Kalorama Road, N.W.
1754, 1935

In 1754 Robert Hooper, a merchant of Marblehead, built The Lindens in Danvers, Mass. In the spring of 1774 Gen. Thomas Gage, formerly commander in chief of the British forces in North America, was appointed Governor of Massachusetts. Hooper, a Loyalist, invited Gage to make The Lindens his home from June to September of that year. Several people owned the house before it was moved in 1935 from Danvers to its present location in Washington. The Lindens, a New England Georgian mansion, was carefully restored to its original condition after it was moved. It is a 2 1/2-story frame house painted brown with a wooden shingle gambrel roof and low stone foundation walls. The north, east, and west facades are clapboard while the principal southern facade wall is made of sanded wooden blocks notched to simulate rusticated stonework. The quoins, first-floor window lintels, and trim are of white painted wood. Flanking the main entrance are two engaged, fluted Corinthian columns which rise through two stories and support a steep-pitched, gable-roofed pediment. The interior plan is Georgian with four rooms, each containing a fireplace, opening onto a central hallway on both the first and second floors. Most of the interior walls are paneled with many of the doors and mantels framed by fluted pilasters. Stenciled decorations are still visible on some of the floors.
Private; not accessible to the public
HABS

WASHINGTON
MEDICAL MUSEUM
Armed Forces Institute of Pathology

Surgeon General William A. Hammond established the Medical Museum for the purpose of preserving the medical experience of the Civil War. Its intention was to minimize death and physical impairment from wounds through centralized study of surgical and medical specimens. Its exhibits, which range from anatomy to embryology, comprise the largest medical museum in the United States. Its library, now removed to another site, is among the world's largest.
Federal (temporarily closed)

NHL; HABS

WASHINGTON
THE NATIONAL ARCHIVES
Constitution Avenue between 7th and 9th Streets, N.W.
1931–1935, John Russell Pope;
1935–1937 (interior extension)

Since its creation the federal government has needed a central repository for official documents. Not until the late 1920's did Congress appropriate funds for the plans and the acquisition of a Constitution Avenue site for this purpose. The resulting Neo-Classical building designed by John Russell Pope is the dominant element in the Federal Triangle. Its steel-framed limestone walls measure 330 feet by 206 feet. Stairs on the main facade are flanked by granite pedestals supporting figures of "Heritage" and "Guardianship" by James Earle Fraser; the stairs lead to a projecting portico with five Corinthian columns (each 53 feet high) on either side. The main doorway is ornamented by high relief figures by Robert Aiken, and pedimental figures above are by Adolph Weinman. On the east and west facades are colonnades of ten Corinthian columns supporting entablatures. Above the respective colonnade is a solid mass broken by an ornamental frieze and terminating in a cornice of ornamented cresting and a plain cornice. This outer structure encloses an inner core which rises above the exterior like a monumental attic. Inside, within the enormous half rotunda the Constitution of the United States, the Declaration of Independence, and the Bill of Rights are displayed.
Federal

WASHINGTON
NATIONAL PORTRAIT GALLERY (OLD PATENT OFFICE)
F and G Streets between 7th and 9th Streets, N.W.
1840, William P. Elliot; 1849–1851, Robert Mills; 1851–1867, Edward Clark

Within this Greek Doric building, the United States Patent Office encouraged inventors through the legal protection offered by patent laws and stimulated them through its displays of patent models and its library. It now houses the offices and galleries of the National Collection of Fine Arts and the National Portrait Gallery of the Smithsonian Institution.
Federal
NHL; HABS

WASHINGTON
OCTAGON HOUSE
1799 New York Avenue, N.W.
1800, Dr. William Thornton

Octagon House, an eight-sided building, stands as an unusual example of a Federal town house. It was built for Colonel John Tayloe, a wealthy Virginian of his time, by the architect who designed the Capitol. Occupied temporarily in 1814 by President James Madison after the burning of the White House, it was the scene of the signing of the Treaty of Ghent, which ended the War of 1812. It is currently the national headquarters of the American Institute of Architects.
Private
NHL; HABS

WASHINGTON
OLD NAVAL OBSERVATORY
23rd and E Streets, N.W.
1844

Under the direction of Matthew Fontaine Maury, the "Pathfinder of the Seas," the Naval Observatory won world-wide recognition as a center for advances in oceanography and navigational information. The original brick building, enlarged since Maury's time, now provides offices for the Potomac Annex of the Navy's Bureau of Medicine and Surgery.
Federal
NHL

WASHINGTON
PAN AMERICAN UNION
17th Street between C Street and Constitution Avenue, N.W.
1908–1910, Albert Kelsey and Paul P. Cret

The Pan American Union is the Secretariat of the Organization of American States, a voluntary international association uniting the 21 republics of the western hemisphere in a community for the achievement of peace, security, and prosperity for all Americans. Secretary of State James G. Blaine organized the first meeting of the International Bureau of American Republics (later the Pan American Union) in 1889–1890. In 1903 the member nations approved a plan to construct a building in Washington, and Andrew Carnegie donated $750,000 of the estimated $1 million needed. The architecture, a blending of South American motifs and the classical style then in vogue in the United States, was intended to symbolize the organization's unity of purpose. The 17th Street or principal facade is composed of a three-arched central, recessed portico flanked by pylons and two-story end pavilions. Corinthian pilasters between the entrance arches are crowned by a paneled frieze with the inscription PAN AMERICAN UNION. A sloping, corrugated tile roof above the frieze is surmounted by a balustrade. Inside the arcaded portico a vaulted, two-story, white marble entrance hall leads into an inner patio enclosed by loggias and surrounded with tropical plants. An overhanging wooden cornice with a sloping, red tile roof is surmounted by a gabled, rolling glass roof which permits the tropical vegetation to flourish all year.
International

WASHINGTON
PENNSYLVANIA AVENUE NATIONAL HISTORIC SITE
Pennsylvania Avenue, from Capitol Hill to the White House
18th, 19th and 20th centuries

Since the early 19th century, the segment of Pennsylvania Avenue between the White House and the Capitol has been the Nation's chief ceremonial route and has symbolized its triumphs and tragedies. The evolution of Pennsylvania Avenue as a ceremonial way began in 1791, when Major Pierre L'Enfant, designer of Washington, D.C., laid the street out as the shortest distance between the Capitol and the Executive Mansion. The designated portion includes such historically related environs as the Federal Triangle, Judiciary Square, the Lincoln Museum, and parts of downtown Washington's commercial district. Along this thoroughfare have traveled the Presidents of the United States following their inaugurations. Along it have come the funeral processions of six Presidents and numerous national leaders. This area has been the scene of victory processions signaling the close of four major wars, public ceremonies recognizing national and personal achievements, and the official reception of visiting dignitaries.

Federal/non-federal
NPS; HABS

WASHINGTON
PENSION BUILDING
4th and 5th Streets between F and G Streets, N.W.
1882–1885, Montgomery C. Meigs

The Pension Building was constructed as a memorial to the veterans of the Civil War and to house the then newly established Pension Office. The most notable feature is its open, four-storied, free flowing central interior space, the scene of several inaugural balls (Cleveland's, 1885 and 1893; Harrison's, 1889; McKinley's, 1897 and 1901; Theodore Roosevelt's, 1905; and Taft's, 1909). The Pension Bureau occupied the building from the time of construction until 1926, and the General Accounting Office was the chief tenant until 1950. Since then several Government agencies have had office space here. The building itself is a common-bond, red-brick rectangle measuring 400 feet by 200 feet. It is three stories high with a fourth gallery floor immediately under the roof. The high inner court is lighted by a gabled clerestory rising three stories above the outer roof. On the exterior the first and second floors are delineated around the entire building by a 3-foot terra cotta frieze executed by the Bohemian-American sculptor Casper Buberl. It depicts Union infantry, cavalry, artillery, naval, quartermaster, and medical forces in the Civil War. The central portal of each facade has a plaque which names the doorway beneath: at the north, Gate of the Invalids; west, Quartermaster's Gate; south, Infantry Gate; and east, Naval Gate. In the spandrels over the east and west doorways are figures of Mars and Minerva, symbolizing war; in those over the north and south gates are Justice and Truth, symbolizing peace. Inside, two rows of four mammoth Corinthian columns (89 feet high and 25 feet in circumference), made of brick and now painted, divide the court into three sections. Galleries ring the court at each floor level.
Federal
HABS

WASHINGTON
PHILADELPHIA (GUNDELO)
Smithsonian Institution, Museum of History and Technology, 14th Street and Constitution Avenue, N.W.
1776

The United States gundelo *Philadelphia* is the only surviving gunboat built and manned by American forces during the Revolutionary War. She is one of the 15 small craft with which Benedict Arnold fought 29 British vessels in the battle off Valcour Island, Lake Champlain, October

11, 1776, a battle which paved the way for the American victory at Saratoga the following year. In 1935, well preserved by the cold water, she was salvaged from the bottom of Valcour Bay. In addition to her guns, many other items were found on the vessel: shot, cooking utensils, tools, buttons, buckles, and human bones.
Federal
NHL

WASHINGTON
PIERCE MILL
Rock Creek Park, northwest corner of Tilden Street and Beach Drive, N.W.
1820's

The Pierce Mill is the last surviving grist mill in the District of Columbia. The property was deeded to Isaac Pierce in 1794. The mill was constructed on its present site sometime in the 1820's. The milling apparatus was powered at first by an undershot wheel and two runner wheels, but these were replaced in 1840 by an overshot wheel. After Pierce's death in 1841, his property passed on to his son and then to a grandson, Pierce Shoemaker, under whom the mill flourished (1860–1870). In 1876 the wooden water wheel was replaced by an iron Leffel turbine wheel. By 1880 steel roller-mills were being used in most mills, instead of the old-fashioned millstones, to produce cheap flour, and grist mills, including the Pierce Mill, became obsolete. The federal government purchased the mill property in 1892 as part of Rock Creek Park. Alcibiades and Charles White, from whom the mill was purchased, continued to operate it until 1897. The structure was inoperative until the mid–1930's when it was restored by the Work Projects Administration and used until 1958 to grind corn and flour for Government cafeterias. Presently the mill is a historic site.
Federal
HABS

WASHINGTON
RENWICK GALLERY
Northeast corner, 17th Street and Pennsylvania Avenue, N.W.
1859–1860, James Renwick

In the late 1850's, W. W. Corcoran, a wealthy Washington merchant-banker and one of America's first great art patrons, commissioned architect James Renwick to design a public art gallery in the Nation's Capital to house his extensive collection of paintings and statuary. This building is one of the earliest French Renaissance structures in the United States and exhibits many outstanding features of architectural embellishment and design. It

is red brick with brownstone trim, two stories in height with a mansard roof. Its Pennsylvania Avenue facade is divided into a central pavilion flanked by single bay wings and an end pavilion at each corner. An unusual feature is the curve of the central pavilion mansard roof which contrasts with the straight lines of the smaller end pavilion mansards, yet does not detract from the essential formal and decorative symmetry of the entire facade. The building was used for a short time during the Civil War as the Quartermaster General's headquarters; it housed the Corcoran collection after the war until it was moved to a new building in 1897. In 1899 the gallery was purchased by the Government for the U.S. Court of Claims. It has been restored to its original appearance and was reopened as a museum by the Smithsonian Institution as part of the overall plan to preserve the historical appearance and integrity of buildings on and near Lafayette Square.
Federal
HABS

WASHINGTON
RHODES' TAVERN (HOTEL)
601–603 15th Street and 1431 F Street, N.W.
1800–1801

As well as being the oldest extant commercial structure in downtown Washington and one of the city's few remaining examples of early Federal-style architecture, the Rhodes' Tavern building has significant historical associations. It served as a polling place in the first municipal election of 1802, was one of the first banks in the District, and was the tavern from which the British command directed the burning of the White House and the Treasury in 1814. It was run as a boardinghouse, and the F Street frontage was converted to a store between 1807 and 1814. It was later operated as a bookstore by Roger C. Weightman, the eighth mayor of Washington (1824–1826). The Bank of the Metropolis opened for business on this location in 1814; Gen. John Van Ness was its first president, and Andrew Jackson was one of the original stockholders. On April 15, 1840, the partnership of Corcoran and Riggs was formed and began business as a bank of deposit in the building. While occupying the building, this bank (now the Riggs National Bank) financed the first telegraph line in the United States (from Washington to Baltimore). Through its long history the building has undergone structural changes, but much of the original Federal style details, both interior and exterior, still remain.
Private

WASHINGTON
RICHARDS, ZALMON, HOUSE
1301 Corcoran Street, N.W.
Mid–19th century

Zalmon Richards was the principal founder of the National Teachers Association, now known as the National Education Association. He served as the first president of the association after its organization in Philadelphia in 1857. In addition, he was largely responsible for the passage in 1867 of the bill establishing a Federal Office of Education. After a period of service in this office, he was instrumental in the creation of the Office of Superintendent of Washington, D.C.'s public schools and the first to hold this post. In the three-story brick house where Richards spent the last years of his life, 1882–1899, he taught several classes to support himself.
Private; not accessible to the public
NHL

WASHINGTON
RIGGS NATIONAL BANK, WASHINGTON LOAN AND TRUST COMPANY BRANCH
SW corner of 9th and F Streets, N.W.
1891, James Hill; 1926–1927 (addition), Arthur Heaton

The Washington Loan and Trust Company, the oldest and, for a time, the largest trust company in the city, was established in 1889. The original L-shaped building was transformed into a U-shaped one by the addition of a western wing in 1926. The nine-story bank is constructed of red brick faced with rough hewn gray granite ashlar on the two principal facades. Its architectural distinction lies principally in the round-arched windows, and the vertical emphasis of the main elevations. The facades are divided horizontally into four separate courses of different widths divided by cornices of varied designs. The top story has a full entablature containing plain architrave, a bracketed frieze, and a modillion cornice.
Private

WASHINGTON
ST. JOHN'S CHURCH
16th and H Streets, N.W.
1816, Benjamin H. Latrobe; 1883, James Renwick

Known as the "Church of the Presidents," St. John's Church has traditionally set aside pew 54 for the President and his family since President James Madison's administration. Benjamin H. Latrobe's original design gave the building a Greek cross plan of equal dimension with a low, classic dome topped by a lantern. The portico, steeple, and extended nave are

the work of subsequent architects. James Renwick made additions to the rear and added several stained glass windows. It remains today as a notable example of early 19th-century Federal architecture in America.
Private
NHL; HABS

WASHINGTON
SMITHSONIAN BUILDING
Jefferson Drive at 10th Street, S.W.
1855, James Renwick

The Smithsonian Institution was established in 1846 with funds willed by an Englishman, James Smithson. It houses perhaps the most important group of collections in the United States for education in the sciences. Within the present complex of buildings is one of the world's largest collections of books and objects pertaining to the natural history, ethnology, paleontology, and geology of the United States. In addition, there are objects of technical, historical, and scientific interest from this and other countries. For over a century, the original building which contained a library, a gallery, and a museum, has housed the Institution's administrative offices. The reddish-brown Seneca sandstone building is in the Norman Revival style.
Federal
NHL; HABS

WASHINGTON
TARIFF COMMISSION BUILDING
E and F Streets between 7th and 8th Streets, N.W.
1839, Robert Mills; 1855, Thomas U. Walter

Greek Revival in style, the Tariff Commission Building was built in two parts, the southern portion (the E Street facade and seven bays along both Seventh and Eighth Streets) being the oldest. Work was halted during the Civil War but resumed after the cessation of hostilities. The Post Office Department, for which it was built, occupied the building from 1844 until 1897. The building was then transferred to the U.S. Department of the Interior to house the General Land Office, the Bureau of Education, and a central power and heating plant. In April of 1917 these offices were moved elsewhere, and Gen. Enoch Crowder, Provost Marshal General of the Army, operated the National Selective Service Board from the building. In 1922 the Tariff Commission and Patent Office were moved in, and the former agency now occupies the entire premises, except for the F Street Post Office substation. The building measures 204 feet by 208 feet and encloses an interior court 95 feet by 194 feet. Built of marble, the edifice is distinguished externally by monumental engaged Corinthian columns and pilasters, a rusticated ground floor, square third-story windows, and square, double-hung second-story windows. Second-floor window pediments are both triangular and segmental. Noteworthy interior features are groined and vaulted corridors with friezes and two granite stairways in the older section.
Federal

WASHINGTON
TUDOR PLACE
1644 31st Street, N.W.
c. 1815, Dr. William Thornton

For many years Tudor Place was one of the centers of Georgetown society. Its guests have included such personages as Robert E. Lee and the Marquis de Lafayette. As the residence of Martha Washington's granddaughter, the house contains many mementos of the Washington family. This early Federal house is among the architecturally significant private dwellings in the District of Columbia. It features a central portico in an ellipse, a form similarly used by Thornton in the design of the Capitol and the Octagon House. The dome roof is supported by tall Doric columns. Still in excellent condition, the house is little changed from the original.
Private; not accessible to the public
NHL; HABS

WASHINGTON
UNION STATION
Intersection of Massachusetts and Louisiana Avenues and 1st Street, N.E.
1903–1908, Daniel H. Burnham

In 1901 Senator James McMillan of Michigan, chairman of the Senate's District Committee, effected passage of a resolution providing for the formation of a District development planning committee. The committee members (Daniel Burnham and Charles McKim, architects; Augustus Saint-Gaudens, sculptor; Frederick Law Olmsted, landscape architect; and Charles Moore, secretary) prepared a long-range, comprehensive plan for the development of the Nation's Capital based upon the ideas of Pierre Charles L'Enfant. A primary objective of the committee's plan was removal of unsightly railroad tracks and buildings from the Mall. Relocation of these facilities resulted in construction of a single railroad terminal, the present Union Station. Burnham was chosen to design the edifice which he patterned externally after the Arch of Constantine and internally after the Baths of Diocletian. Augustus Saint-Gaudens' brother, Louis, was commissioned to execute the exterior sculpture. Burnham designed the station to accommodate inaugural crowds of 100,000 and 120,000, but by 1968 the number of daily passengers had dwindled to an estimated 7,000.
Private
HABS

WASHINGTON
VIGILANT FIREHOUSE
1066 Wisconsin Avenue, N.W.
1844

As the oldest standing firehouse in the District of Columbia, this structure is an important link in the development of organized firefighting techniques. The Vigilant was formed as a private company in 1817. Erected and occupied in 1844, the present building is a two-story rectangular brick structure with additions to both sides and the rear. In the gable of the front facade is a stone inscribed "VIGILANT, INSTITUTED, 1817," and below it is a wrought iron "V" which served as a trademark as well as a tension rod. Capping the gable end of the structure is a small square wooden bell tower with a convex-curved roof.
Private

WASHINGTON
WASHINGTON MONUMENT
The Mall, between 14th and 17th Streets
1848–1885

Built between 1848 and 1885 with both Federal and private funds, the Washington Monument commemorates the achievements of George Washington in peace and war. The original design submitted by Robert Mills was selected but later greatly revised. The hollow shaft, free of exterior decoration or embellishment, is the tallest masonry structure in the world at slightly over 555 feet. The interior is embellished by about 190 memorial stones donated by various nations, states, municipalities, societies, and individuals.
Federal
NPS; 106.01 acres
HABS

WASHINGTON
WILSON, WOODROW, HOUSE
2340 S Street, N.W.
1915, Waddy B. Wood

Following his retirement from the Presidency in 1921, Woodrow Wilson occupied this house until his death in 1924. Physically weakened by his exhausting efforts to win support for the League of Nations and the Treaty of Versailles, Wilson spent these last years as a semi-invalid. This red brick neo-Georgian dwelling contains memorabilia and furnishings associated with the lives of President and Mrs. Wilson.

Private

NHL; HABS

WASHINGTON

WINDER BUILDING
604 17th Street, N.W.
1847–1848

One of the few extant pre-Civil War office buildings in the city of Washington, the L-shaped, buff-colored Winder Building is notable for its structural innovations. These include its height of five stories, the use of iron beams, and a central hot-water heating system, all of which were unusual and modern for a mid–19th-century building. Designed exclusively for Government use, the Winder Building housed the Quartermaster General and the Chief of Ordnance during the Civil War. Later the Judge Advocate General, the Office of the Commissioner for Exchange of Prisoners, and the Bureau of Military Justice were moved in, and the search for and prosecution of the conspirators in Lincoln's assassination were directed from here. Since that time several federal offices have occupied the structure, and it now houses the Office of Emergency Planning, formerly the Office of Civil Defense Mobilization.

Federal

Florida

Yulee Sugar Mill Historic Memorial, Homosassa, Florida.
Florida Department of Natural Resources

Fort Jefferson National Monument,
Dry Tortugas Islands, Florida. *NPS*

Kingsley Plantation,
Fort George Island,
near Jacksonville, Florida.
*Florida Bureau of
Historic Preservation*

Viscaya, Miami, Florida. *Miami-Metro News Bureau*

Cape Florida Lighthouse, Cape Florida, Florida.
Florida News Bureau, Department of Commerce

ALACHUA COUNTY
Cross Creek
RAWLINGS, MARJORIE KINNAN, HOUSE
Fla. 325, .25 mile south of the creek

The Marjorie Kinnan Rawlings House is a typical late 19th-century, central Florida "cracker" farmhouse. Mrs. Rawlings purchased the house in 1928 and was living here when she wrote her Pulitizer Prize winning novel *The Yearling*. The cottage is frame with wide porches and roof overhangs. Three separate units (living, dining, and sleeping) compose the house and were probably built at different times. All three are connected by porches or breezeways.
State
HABS

BAKER COUNTY
Olustee vicinity
OLUSTEE BATTLEFIELD
2 miles east of Olustee on U.S. 90

Union troops reoccupied Jacksonville in early February, 1864, as step one in a planned invasion of the interior. As the Federals began their advance, Confederate commander General Joseph Finegan asked for reinforcements. By the 18th a force of 5,000 had gathered near Olustee and were preparing defensive positions. By noon of that day the two sides had encountered each other, and the battle continued all day. The Union forces finally retreated, leaving the scene of Florida's major Civil War conflict. Although not expelled from the state, Federal soldiers were henceforth confined to Jacksonville, Fernandina, and St. Augustine.
State

CITRUS COUNTY
Crystal River vicinity
CRYSTAL RIVER INDIAN MOUNDS
2 miles northwest of Crystal River on U.S. 19–98
Pre-Columbian

Surface features of this prehistoric site consist of two large, truncated mounds, one conical burial mound, a long, irregularly shaped shell midden ridge, and a small oval-shaped shell midden mound. More recently found were two rock stelae or upright slabs, one of which bears some faint carving or incising. Periods of use cover 1,500 years, from the Santa Rosa-Swift Creek cultures through that of Weeden Island to Safety Harbor times. The earliest occupants built the main burial mound, and artifacts associated with them are copper ear spools, shell, stone, and copper plummets, conjoined copper tubes, and mica sheets, all of which resemble ornamental artifacts from the Hopewell people of the Upper Ohio Valley (100 B.C. to 200 A.D.). The cultural and temporal origin of the two flat-topped mounds is unknown. Pottery types representing all the archeological periods have been found.
State/private

CITRUS COUNTY
Homosassa
YULEE SUGAR MILL RUINS
Fla. 490, west of U.S. 19
Mid–19th century

This land was once the site of a thriving sugar plantation owned by David Levy Yulee. Operations commenced in 1851 on the then 5,100–acre plantation, but in May, 1864, the Yulee house was burned by Federal troops and the mill was never again operated. The original platforms which supported the steam engine and associated cane crushing machinery have disappeared. Most of the machinery remains and has been reassembled on reconstructed bases. Three of five original kettles and the old wells all survive. Yulee himself was a member of Florida's first constitutional convention (1839), served as a territorial delegate to Congress (1841), and became Florida's first U.S. Senator (1845).
State

DADE COUNTY
Cape Florida
CAPE FLORIDA LIGHTHOUSE
Southeastern tip of Key Biscayne off U.S. 1
1825

As originally built the Cape Florida Lighthouse has 65-foot-high brick walls surrounding a central shaft. In July, 1836, during the Second Seminole War, Assistant Keeper John W. B. Thompson and his helper barricaded themselves in the light tower, which hostile Indians then set afire. Oil for the light was used to feed the blaze, and the two trapped men were forced out of the lantern onto a platform only two feet wide. Thompson tossed a bag of gun powder down the shaft, hoping to end his ordeal, but the men were not killed by the explosion which apparently destroyed all wood that was feeding the fire. A Navy schooner heard the blast and rescued Thompson, but his helper died from injuries. Rebuilding of the light was delayed until 1846 because of the Indian threat. In 1855 the height of the tower was increased to 95 feet. The light went out of service in 1878.
State

DADE COUNTY
Miami
VIZCAYA (JAMES DEERING ESTATE)
3251 S. Miami Avenue
1914–1916, F. Burrall Hoffman, Jr., and Paul Chalfin

Vizcaya is a 70–room mansion occupying a tract of more than 36 acres which was the home of industrialist James Deering. The house itself resembles an Italian Renaissance palace and is constructed of stuccoed concrete with native coral window and doorway decorations. Open loggias and arcades also have coral ornament. There is an open central courtyard, and the roof is covered with red barrel tile. Inside are period rooms dating from the Renaissance to Neo-Classic times. Entire ceilings, chimney pieces, mural paintings, carved paneling, and doorways were removed from European palaces and reassembled at Vizcaya. Tapestries, rugs, gates, and fountains were also imported for use inside and out. Formal gardens extend south from the main house to the Casino at the water's edge. They contain Australian pines, bougainvillea, roses, water lilies, grottoes, statues, and fountains. There is also a stone barge east of the house which acts as a breakwater.
State

DUVAL COUNTY
Jacksonville vicinity
FORT CAROLINE NATIONAL MEMORIAL
10 miles east of Jacksonville
1564–1565

At Fort Caroline the struggle between France and Spain for supremacy in southeastern North America began and virtually ended. When the fort was founded, there was no other European colony on the North American continent this side of Mexico, and France hoped this colony would help to establish her claim in the New World. Recognizing the move as a threat to Spanish commerce, King Philip sent an armada to Florida in 1565. Spanish forces under Pedro Menendez de Aviles, founder of St. Augustine, captured the fort, as its garrison had already been weakened by famine, internal dissension, and Indian attacks. Renamed San Mateo, the post was maintained by Spain through the colonial period. Recent reconstruction of Fort Caroline was based on a 16th-century sketch.
Federal
NPS; 119.51 acres

DUVAL COUNTY
Jacksonville vicinity
KINGSLEY PLANTATION
Northern tip of Fort George Island at
Fort George Inlet
Early 19th century

Zephaniah Kingsley, a Scotsman, purchased Fort George Island in 1817. He raised cotton, sugar, and rice, experimented successfully with citrus growing on the land, and was actively engaged in the African slave trade. The main plantation house may be the oldest in Florida. It is two stories high with an attic and a basement. The foundation and basement are stuccoed tabby (a mixture of lime, crushed oyster shell, water, and sand poured into frames) while the rest of the dwelling is frame. Connected to this house by a covered walkway is Anna's House, named for Anna Madagegine Jai, Kingsley's wife. It is also two stories with a gable roof and a first story of stuccoed brick made of tabby and reinforced by conventional brick, a rare type of construction. The second story is wood. Other related buildings are a large brick and tabby barn, a tabby-brick house, a tabby-brick house ruin, and the remains of 24 slave cabins.
State

DUVAL COUNTY
Jacksonville vicinity
YELLOW BLUFF FORT
1 mile south of Fla. 105 on New
Berlin Road
19th century

During the summer of 1862 batteries were constructed by Confederate soldiers on the St. Johns River below Jacksonville. Early in September the batteries prevented the advance of a Federal squadron of six gunboats upriver to Jacksonville. Situated on elevated terrain rising steeply from the river bank, Yellow Bluff Fort commanded a wide stretch of the river. Fortifications consisted of triangular earthworks protecting the gun emplacements. Prior to 1864 Yellow Bluff Fort changed hands four times, but it was retained by the Confederacy until the end of the war.
State

ESCAMBIA COUNTY
Pensacola
FORT SAN CARLOS DE BARRANCAS
U.S. Naval Air Station
1787

Fort San Carlos de Barrancas, a semicircular brick fortification, replaces a fort built in 1698 and destroyed by the French in 1719. Important in the control of West

Florida, it became the northern outpost of the Spanish Caribbean empire in 1781. Its capture by Andrew Jackson in 1814 quickened the surrender of the Spanish governor in San Carlos in 1818, marking the end of Spanish occupation of West Florida. The fort was occupied by the Confederates during the Civil War.
Federal
NHL; HABS

ESCAMBIA COUNTY
Pensacola
LAVALLE HOUSE
203 E. Church Street
Early 19th century

Charles Lavalle, builder, land owner, and brick mason, constructed this one-and-one-half-story Gulf Coast cottage sometime between 1803 and 1815. It is one of the few remaining early 19th-century frame houses in Pensacola. All the original mortise and tenon framing still exists as does most of the flooring and woodwork. Elevated on brick piers, the house has the characteristic apron porch, gable roof, large loft, and front veranda. There is brick nogging in all the walls (even the interior partitions), probably Lavalle's own work.
Municipal
HABS

ESCAMBIA COUNTY
Pensacola
PENSACOLA HISTORIC DISTRICT
The historic district is bounded on the north by Chase Street; on the east by 9th Avenue; on the south by Pensacola Bay; and on the west by Palafox Street
18th and 19th centuries

Pensacola was settled in the 18th century and served as the capital of West Florida during the British occupation (1763–1781) and the last Spanish period (1781–1821). The changing of flags to symbolize American possession (1821) took place in Plaza Ferdinand VII. Pensacola became a fishing, shipping, and transportation center in this part of Florida, and structures within the historic district illustrate the city's commercial prosperity. Dwellings are a variety of styles (Victorian, Greek Revival, and Gulf Coast or Creole cottages), and all date from the 19th century. The Gulf Coast cottage is a distinctive, one-and-one-half-story house on a raised basement with a steeply pitched gable roof and a veranda across the main facade. The design was brought by settlers from the West Indies who came to Florida by way of New Orleans.
Multiple public/private
HABS

ESCAMBIA COUNTY
Pensacola
PLAZA FERDINAND VII
Palafox Street between Government and Zaragossa Streets
1821

Plaza Ferdinand VII is the site of the formal transfer of Florida from the rule of Spain to the United States. On the morning of July 17, 1821, Andrew Jackson, newly commissioned governor of the Territory, met the Spanish governor, and after the transfer ceremony was completed Jackson officially proclaimed the establishment of the Florida Territory. The present square is a remnant of the original city square laid out by the British in 1765, a large part of which was subdivided and sold as building lots in 1802.
Municipal
NHL

FLAGLER COUNTY
Bunnell vicinity
BULOW PLANTATION RUINS
9 miles southeast of Bunnell on Fla.
S–5a
1836

In 1821 Charles Bulow purchased a 4,000–acre plantation from the heirs of the original grantee, John Russell. Bulow himself did little to develop the property, which passed to his son John Joachim within a short time. The younger Bulow demonstrated extreme competence in the developing and management of a prosperous agricultural complex that was worked by 300 slaves. One thousand acres were planted in sugar cane and 1,200 in cotton. With the outbreak of the Second Seminole War in December, 1835, area inhabitants and their property were in grave danger. Toward the end of January refugees evacuated the environs and retreated to St. Augustine. Sometime prior to February 5 Bulow Plantation was destroyed. All that remains are the coquina ruins of the sugar mill, several well-preserved wells, the ruins of a springhouse and the crumbling foundations of Bulowville, the once grand manor house.
State

INDIAN RIVER COUNTY
Sebastian vicinity
PELICAN ISLAND NATIONAL
WILDLIFE REFUGE
East of Sebastian in the Indian River
1903

This refuge, the first federal sanctuary for the protection of wildlife, was established by President Theodore Roosevelt to protect brown pelicans. Originally placed under the administration of the Bureau of

Biological Survey, the refuge has been administered by the Fish and Wildlife Service of the Department of the Interior since its inception in 1940. Subject to partial tidal inundation, the mangrove island is essentially one large rookery for brown pelicans, cormorants, egrets, herons, and ibis.
Federal
NHL

LEON COUNTY
Tallahassee
BELLEVUE
   Southwest of Tallahassee, on Big
   Bend Pioneer Farm
   19th century

This one-and-one-half-story frame house has a gable roof and a square-columned porch across the main facade. It was once the main residence of a 500–acre plantation but was moved from its original location in 1967. Catherine Daingerfield Willis Murat, wife of Napoleon Bonaparte's nephew Archille Murat, lived here after her husband's death. The house has been altered, and restoration work is currently in progress.
Private

LEON COUNTY
Tallahassee
CASCADES PARK
   Bounded roughly by Apalachee
   Parkway on the north; E. Bloxham
   and Suwanee Streets on the east; the
   state property line on the south; and
   S. Monroe and Meridian Streets on
   the west

Cascades Park forms the nucleus of an area selected by commissioners John Lee Williams and William H. Simmons to be the capital of the Territory of Florida in 1824. Included within the approximately 35–acre tract is the Prime Meridian Marker. The first such marker was erected in 1824, and the point has since served as a reference for all land surveys in the state.
State

LEON COUNTY
Tallahassee
THE COLUMNS (BENJAMIN CHAIRES HOUSE)
   Corner of Adams Street and Park
   Avenue
   c. 1830

Benjamin Chaires, architect and builder of The Columns, used this three-story brick, Greek Revival style dwelling as his town house. Dominating the main facade is a four-columned portico with porches on the first and second floors. The wood railings on both levels have turned bal-

usters. The gabled roof has a simple wood cornice with boxed eaves, and a triangular fan louver adorns the portico gable. Inside, four rooms flank a central hall.
Private
HABS

LEON COUNTY
Tallahassee
UNION BANK
   106 S. Adams Street

Chartered by the territorial council in 1833, the Union Bank was the first major institution of its kind in Florida. The bank opened its doors in January, 1835, and remained solvent until 1843, when unsound banking practices, the panic of 1837, and the Florida Indian wars caused it to close. The building is one story high with brick bearing walls. There is a semicircular fanlight above the main entrance flanked by recessed semicircles over each window. The wooden porch appears to be a later addition, although the door, transom, and frame seem original. No banking functions were carried on here after 1879.
Private
HABS

LEON COUNTY
Tallahassee vicinity
ESCAMBÉ (SAN COSMOS Y SAN DAMIAS DE ESCAMBÉ)
   3 miles northwest of Tallahassee on
   Int. 10, .5 mile west of Old
   Bainbridge Road
   16th and 17th centuries

Escambé is important as the site of a Spanish mission village dating from the early 1600's. There was also prehistoric aboriginal occupation. Five associated sites composed the mission complex: the church, cemetery, Indian village, water source area, and connecting trails. Excavations were undertaken in 1968 and 1970 which revealed that the church and related buildings were wood rather than wattle and daub. Established by the Franciscan Order of Friars Minor, the Escambé Mission was burned by the British in 1704.
Federal/private

LEON COUNTY
Tallahassee vicinity
LAKE JACKSON MOUNDS
   4.5 miles north of Tallahassee via
   U.S. 27, on south shore of Lake
   Jackson
   1300–1600

This site represents a late prehistoric Fort Walton ceremonial center, the largest known in northeast Florida. Included in the site are truncated temple mounds,

plaza and village areas, and a probable cemetery outside the village. A group of six or seven mounds forms a quadrangle around an open plaza area, probably used for ceremonies and games. The largest mound has an estimated height of 8 meters and base measurements of 65 by 48 meters; the smallest is not more than one meter high and 20 meters in diameter. It is believed that the residents of the site were the prehistoric ancestors of the historic Apalachee Indians, who occupied much of northwest Florida during the Spanish mission period (c. 1625–1750).
State/private

LEON COUNTY
Tallahassee vicinity
SAN LUIS DE APALACHE
   2 miles west of Tallahassee on U.S.
   90
   1633, 1663

This mission, which typifies the mission system in Spanish Florida, became the administrative center for the old Spanish Province of Apalache. San Luis was abandoned when Governor James Moore, supporting the English cause in the territorial rivalry of Spain and Great Britain, began the systematic destruction of the Florida missions in 1702. Little remains of the mission, but archeological investigations have furnished many artifacts and much information about the building.
Private; not accessible to the public
NHL

LEON COUNTY
Woodville vicinity
NATURAL BRIDGE BATTLEFIELD
   6 miles east of Woodville on U.S. 319

In March of 1865 a Federal force numbering between 600 and 700 men landed at St. Marks and began moving inland toward Tallahassee. The St. Marks River presented a natural barrier to the advancing Federals, who determined to undertake a night march to the so-called Natural Bridge and ford the river there. Natural Bridge is a swampy area where the river flows through a series of underground passages between sinks and rises for a distance of about one-half mile. At daybreak on March 6 the Union troops encountered the Confederates, who were able to concentrate their fire on the point of crossing. The Federals were routed, and Tallahassee did not fall until after the close of the Civil War.
State

MANATEE COUNTY
Bradenton vicinity
DE SOTO NATIONAL MEMORIAL
5 miles west of Bradenton
1539–1543

De Soto National Memorial commemorates the landing of Hernando De Soto in Florida and the first extensive organized exploration of the interior of the southeastern part of the present United States. After landing in the vicinity of Tampa Bay, the Spanish began their march through 4000 miles of unknown land. They penetrated as far north as present Tennessee and as far west as Texas. When De Soto died in 1542 he was buried in the Mississippi River. At the confluence of the Arkansas and Mississippi Rivers the remnants of the expedition built ships that were floated off the stocks in the spring floods of 1543. They sailed down the Mississippi River, returning to civilization in Mexico in September of that year.
Federal/non-federal
NPS; 30 acres

MANATEE COUNTY
Ellenton
GAMBLE, ROBERT, HOUSE (JUDAH P. BENJAMIN MEMORIAL)
On U.S. 301
1845–1850

Manatee County was opened for settlement at the end of the Second Seminole War (1842). Among the planters who came here was Major Robert Gamble, who developed a 3,500-acre sugar plantation and built this residence. It is two stories high with walls of stucco-covered brick. Eighteen columns, 25 feet tall, support the roof overhang and a second-floor balcony forming a double veranda. Confederate Secretary of State Judah P. Benjamin is believed to have hidden here while escaping to England after the Civil War.
State
HABS

MANATEE COUNTY
Terra Ceia Island
MADIRA BICKEL MOUND
Off U.S. 19
Pre-Columbian

Evidence indicates that the Madira Bickel Mound site was occupied from pre-Weeden Island times (before A.D. 700–1300) through the Safety Harbor Period (A.D. 1300–post 1600). There are two prehistoric mounds on the site; the larger is oblong and composed of shell, sand, and village debris. It is 20 feet high and has base dimensions of 170 and 100–115 feet. The smaller mound measures 100 feet in diameter but is only 18 inches high. It has been considerably disturbed by unauthorized digging and road construction. This larger configuration is a ceremonial substructure mound of the Safety Harbor Period and represents the central west Florida Coast expression of the temple mound tradition.
State

MONROE COUNTY
Dry Tortugas Islands
FORT JEFFERSON NATIONAL MONUMENT
68 miles west of Key West in the Gulf of Mexico
1846

During the first half of the 19th century the United States began a chain of seacoast defenses from Maine to Texas. Fort Jefferson, the largest of these, was once the key to control of the Gulf of Mexico because of its strategic location. Commerce from the Mississippi Valley to the Atlantic coast passed through this vital area. The fort was active during the Civil War, Spanish-American War, and World War I. The Lincoln conspirators were confined there for several years. The fort's massive ruins offer eloquent proof of its former strength as a guardian of the southernmost coastlines of the United States.
Federal
NPS; 47,125 acres
HABS

MONROE COUNTY
Key West
THE ARMORY
600 White Street
1901, T. F. Russell

Key West was settled in 1822, and its strategic importance to the United States has been recognized since that time. By 1890 the city had become a major seaport and the largest and wealthiest city in Florida. The Armory is one of the few remaining large frame buildings constructed during Key West's period of prosperity. It is a rectangular structure, two stories high on all but the main facade, which has a false front flanked by hexagonal pointed turrets. The double doors of the central entrance are surmounted by a fanlight.
State; not accessible to the public

MONROE COUNTY
Key West
FORT ZACHARY TAYLOR
U.S. Naval Station
1844–1846

Construction of Fort Taylor was completed just at the commencement of the Mexican War (1846–1848). It was originally located 1,000 feet offshore, but continuous land filling has now landlocked it on three sides. Shaped like a trapezoid, the fort has three seaward walls of 225 feet and a barracks area on the landface measuring 495 feet. All walls were five feet thick and built of brick masonry. New England granite was used for foundations, stairways, and trim. Cisterns were placed underneath the fort to collect water, and, when these proved inadequate, a French patented desalting plant was installed. Fort Taylor was impregnable, and for this reason remained a bastion of Union strength in the South throughout the Civil War. At the end of the Spanish-American War, Fort Taylor was reduced from a two-and-one-half-story casemate and three-story barracks to a level single story plus terreplein construction. The first tier of casemates and the south curtain were filled with sand and rubble and, as revealed by recent excavations, various cannon, gun cradles, cannonballs, and the desalting plant. The ordnance thus found has been well-preserved and is being recovered.
Federal

MONROE COUNTY
Key West
HEMINGWAY, ERNEST, HOUSE
907 Whitehead Street
1931–1940

Critics agree that Ernest Hemingway was one of the most influential writers of the 20th century. In 1953 he won the Pulitzer Prize in literature for *The Old Man and the Sea*, and in 1954 he became the fifth American to be awarded the Nobel Prize for literature. Among his best known books and short stories are *The Sun Also Rises* (1926), *A Farewell to Arms* (1929), *For Whom the Bell Tolls* (1940), "The Killers," "The Snows of Kilimanjaro," and "The Short Happy Life of Francis Macomber." In 1931 Hemingway and his wife Pauline bought this large, two-story, Spanish style house made of native stone with a flat roof, yellow shutters, and wrought-iron balconies, and they established permanent residence there. Later they built a pool house in the rear, the upper story of which Hemingway used for a study. The Hemingways lived here until 1940.
Private
NHL

MONROE COUNTY
Key West
KEY WEST HISTORIC DISTRICT
Bounded roughly by White Street on the northeast; on the southeast by Angela, Windsor and Passover Streets; on the southwest by Thomas and Whitehead Streets; and on the northwest by the Gulf of Mexico

Florida became a territory of the United States in 1821. John Simonton, foreseeing its potential as a port and a defense outpost, bought the island of Key West the same year. Two years later the federal government established a naval station at Key West (which already had a custom-house), and the city was incorporated in 1828. Construction had begun on Forts Jefferson and Taylor by 1845. Key West remained in Union hands throughout the Civil War, and it was an embarkation point for men and supplies during the Spanish-American War. The homes and public buildings in Key West were built by settlers from Europe, the eastern United States, Cuba, and the Bahamas. Most common among many types is the wooden Bahama style dwelling which was made by ship's carpenters. It withstands high winds and has a wide porch with slender, square columns. All windows are protected by shutters, and the high-pitched roof was designed to catch rain water which was collected by a cistern. Basically simple in exterior design, the houses were sometimes ornamented by lacy woodwork or delicately carved spindles on the porches. Nearly all the oldest buildings are wood. Brick was not used for construction to any great extent until after the fire of 1886.
Multiple public/private
HABS

OKALOOSA COUNTY
Fort Walton Beach
FORT WALTON MOUND
U.S. 98
Late prehistoric

Fort Walton Mound is a type site for a late prehistoric and early historic manifestation of the Indian culture present along the northwest Florida coast and in adjacent northern states at the time of the exploration of Florida by Hernando De Soto. Many burials have been uncovered at the 12-foot-high temple mound whose summit platform is reached by an earthen ramp located on the south side. Excavations at the site have revealed a large number of burials accompanied by pottery vessels.
Municipal
NHL

OKEECHOBEE COUNTY
Okeechobee vicinity
OKEECHOBEE BATTLEFIELD
4 miles southeast of Okeechobee on U.S. 441
1837

On the northern shore of Lake Okeechobee on Christmas Day, 1837, Zachary Taylor won a decisive victory over a band of Seminole and Mikasuki warriors. This victory, which occurred only a few months after General Thomas S. Jesup had inspired Indian resistance by having Osceola and other chiefs seized under a flag of truce, proved to be the turning point in the Second Seminole War. The battlefield location is well established, and the swamp has been brought within the highwater mark of the lake south of the battlefield.
Multiple private
NHL

PINELLAS COUNTY
Safety Harbor vicinity
SAFETY HARBOR SITE
Philippe Park, 1 mile northeast of Safety Harbor
Late prehistoric

Safety Harbor Site depicts a late prehistoric and early historic period representing the Gulf Coast Timucua Indian culture at the time of European contact and somewhat before. The temple mound, 150 feet in diameter and 25 feet high, stands on a point of land protruding into Old Tampa Bay. From the village, debris extends in both directions along the shore and on the land behind the mound. At the northwest end of the village is a smaller sand burial mound.
County
NHL

ST. JOHNS COUNTY
St. Augustine
ALCAZAR HOTEL
79 King Street
1887–1889

The Alcazar Hotel was constructed by financier Henry Flagler in an attempt to create a resort for the wealthy in Florida. Architecturally the hotel may be termed Spanish Colonial Revival. It stands four stories high and has poured concrete walls covered with coquina. Roofs are tile, and the main entrance is flanked by two tall towers. The hotel closed in 1930.
Municipal

ST. JOHNS COUNTY
St. Augustine
CASTILLO DE SAN MARCOS NATIONAL MONUMENT
1 Castillo Drive
1672–1696

Castillo de San Marcos, the northernmost outpost of the Spanish empire in the New World, was established as a permanent defense against foreign settlement and protection for Spanish shipping along the coast. Between 1680 and 1750 it was the hub of turmoil in the Southeast. Spanish forays against the Carolinas and Georgia began here, and it was the target of at least six major raids by the English as well as marauding pirates and Indians. After Florida was ceded to the United States in 1819, the fort served as a military prison. Included in Castillo de San Marcos National Monument are the coquina fort surrounded by moat and outworks, a city gate, and museum exhibits.
Federal/non-federal
NPS; 21.58 acres
HABS

ST. JOHNS COUNTY
St. Augustine
GONZALEZ-ALVAREZ HOUSE (OLDEST HOUSE)
14 St. Francis Street
c. 1723, 1775–1786, 1790

Although the date of construction is not definitely known, it was sometime between 1703 and 1727, very likely in 1723, when Tomas Gonzalez Hernandez was married. The dwelling is a "St. Augustine" style town house adapted to the peculiar climatic conditions of Florida. Originally one story high, it had coquina walls and floors of tabby (oyster shells mixed with lime). The next owner added a second story, and the third owner built a two-story tier of six rooms at the rear of the house. In 1959–1960 extensive restoration took place, returning the building to its 18th-century appearance.
Private
NHL

ST. JOHNS COUNTY
St. Augustine
LLAMBIAS HOUSE (FERNANDEZ-LLAMBIAS HOUSE)
31 St. Francis Street
Late 18th century

The Llambias House is an example of a dwelling combining Spanish and English architectural details. Basically it is a "St. Augustine"-type residence, rectangular, two to four rooms, with a loggia or porch —in this case a sheltered porch. The walls are coquina (a limestone material composed of broken coral and shells) covered

with plaster and whitewashed. As originally built the house was a one-story dwelling enlarged to its present size between 1777 and 1788. The kitchen is a reconstruction.
Municipal
NHL; HABS

ST. JOHNS COUNTY
St. Augustine
RODRIGUEZ-AVERO-SANCHEZ HOUSE
52 St. George Street
18th and 19th centuries

The Rodriguez-Avero-Sanchez House illustrates the evolution of a Spanish residence from a small one-room dwelling into the extant three-story structure. Its plan is typical of St. Augustine architecture in that the entire street frontage is used for the domicile, while the rear portion of the lot contains a patio and garden. The ground floor is made of coquina masonry. Earliest reference to the house was made in 1761, when the owner extended his frame dwelling to the limit of the property line by the addition of the masonry section. Around the turn of the century a second story was added but removed sometime between 1813 and 1834, when the present frame structure replaced it.
Private
HABS

ST. JOHNS COUNTY
St. Augustine
ROMAN CATHOLIC CATHEDRAL OF ST. AUGUSTINE
Cathedral Street between Charlotte and St. George Streets
1797; restored 1887–1888, James Renwick

The parish of St. Augustine was established in 1594 and is the oldest in the United States. An 18th-century church on the site was largely destroyed by fire in 1887 and restored as the present cathedral (it had been designated a cathedral in 1870). The walls of the earlier church were coquina, while the newer portions are cast-in-place concrete. Twin Doric columns stand at either side of the main entrance which is surmounted by a classical broken pediment. Above the main cornice is a central gable outlined by two ogee curves rising to a belfry containing four bell niches. Less than one-half of the present cathedral dates from the original construction. Only the facade and approximately 75 feet of each side wall are not new. The new section extends 12 feet beyond the old rear wall and includes two 37–foot-long and 35–foot-wide transepts. Stained glass in the windows and the six-story bell tower date from 1888.
Private
NHL; HABS

ST. JOHNS COUNTY
St. Augustine
ST. AUGUSTINE HISTORIC DISTRICT
Roughly bounded on the north by Castillo de San Marcos; on the south by St. Francis Barracks; on the west by Cordova Street, and including the Alcazar Hotel; and on the east by the Matanzas River
16th–19th centuries

Pedro Menendez de Aviles founded St. Augustine as a military base in September, 1565. The site of the original settlement is not definitely known but is believed to have been near the mouth of Hospital Creek, about 1,000 yards north of the present Castillo de San Marcos. At that time St. Augustine was the only permanent European settlement in the present United States. It thus has the distinction of being the oldest continuously occupied European settlement within the continental United States. At first the town was only a collection of palm thatch huts. Stone dwellings date from a rebuilding in the early 18th century following a conflagration set by English troops. Fear of future attack resulted in the construction of two earthen defense works, the Cubo Line on the north and the Rosario Line on the west and south. Spain and England vied for possession of Florida until 1821, when it was ceded to the United States. Spanish towns in the New World were laid out around a central plaza, and St. Augustine's plan dates from 1598. Government buildings and the Roman Catholic cathedral were constructed on the plaza. The present streets, all in the original plan, are narrow to provide shade and to act as funnels for drafts and breezes. St. Augustine's town plan has been designated a National Historic Landmark. The historic district contains original residences (31 of which have aboveground portions predating 1821) and several restorations and reconstructions.
Multiple public/private
NHL; HABS

ST. JOHNS COUNTY
St. Augustine vicinity
FORT MATANZAS NATIONAL MONUMENT
15 miles south of St. Augustine
1565

The final scenes of the Spanish-French struggle for Florida took place within and near the present Fort Matanzas National Monument in 1565, resulting in Spanish domination of the Southeast for nearly 200 years. During most of that period Matanzas was a typical Florida outpost that served as a lookout tower to spot approaching enemy sails and to serve St. Augustine, the capital of Spanish Florida. Previous towers had been built of wood, but in 1737–1742 the coquina Fort Matanzas was built to reinforce the garrison in the face of increasing depredations from James Oglethorpe's English colony of Georgia. Having little military value to the Nation, the old tower and its vicinity were abandoned when Florida was ceded to the United States in 1819. In recent years the fort has been restored.
Federal
NPS; 298.51 acres

VOLUSIA COUNTY
New Smyrna Beach vicinity
NEW SMYRNA SUGAR MILL RUINS
1 mile west of New Smyrna Beach off Fla. 44
1835

In 1830 a steam sugar and sawmill was erected on lands belonging to William DePeyster and Eliza and Henry Cruger. The complex is now known as the New Smyrna Sugar Mill. Five years later Seminole Indians plundered the plantation burning the mills and other buildings. Additional damage was caused by soldiers who occupied the ruins and altered them for defense purposes during the ensuing Seminole War. Remaining are portions of coquina block walls, foundation footings, wells, and the engine house chimney. The ruins are mute testimony to a vigorous agricultural economy that once flourished on a remote territorial frontier.
State

VOLUSIA COUNTY
New Smyrna Beach vicinity
TURTLE MOUND
9 miles south of New Smyrna Beach on Fla. A1A
c. 800–1400

Turtle Mound is one of the largest prehistoric shell middens along this section of the Florida coast. It contains the remains of a prehistoric occupation (perhaps seasonal only) that continued over a period of possibly five or six centuries prior to any European contact. The mound is roughly 30 feet high with two 35–foot peaks at the extremities of the oval configuration. Within the mound archeologists have found Indian pottery, animal and fish bones, and charcoal and ash lenses. Turtle Mound has been left relatively undisturbed.
State

VOLUSIA COUNTY
Ormond Beach
ORMOND GARAGE
79 E. Granada Avenue
1903

The Ormond Garage was built by the East Coast Hotel Company in anticipation of the 1904 auto races on the nearby beach. Ormond Beach, the "birthplace of speed," was first used as a raceway in 1902. The 25–mile stretch of sand south beyond Daytona was smooth and hard-packed —ideal for driving racing cars. In the Ormond Garage cars were prepared, tested, and serviced in preparation for test drives on the natural raceway of the beach. Pioneer auto manufacturers such as Olds, Winton, Ford and Chevrolet tested their fastest cars here driven by such men as William K. Vanderbilt, Jr., Arthur MacDonald, Fred Marriott, Ralph DePalma, Barney Oldfield, and Tommy Milton. The shingle-covered building has undergone little change since its construction.
Private

WAKULLA COUNTY
St. Marks
FORT SAN MARCOS DE APALACHE
18 miles south of Tallahassee on U.S. 319 and Fla. 363
1660

Fort San Marcos de Apalache changed hands several times until England acquired Florida in 1763. During the initial period of Spanish possession, three successively stronger wooden fortifications were built on the site, and a final stone structure was partially completed before the English took possession. During the British occupation of Florida a trading post was established at the site, then known as Fort St. Marks. Spain reclaimed the site in 1783, and Andrew Jackson's capture of the fort in 1818 was instrumental in the United States acquisition of Florida in 1819. During the Civil War the Confederates superimposed entrenchments and fortifications upon the earlier ruins.
State
NHL

Georgia

Forsythe Park, Savannah Historic District, Savannah, Georgia. *Mary C. Means*

William A. Snow, Jr. House, Macon, Georgia.
Macon Chamber of Commerce

Grand Opera House, Macon, Georgia. *Drinnon, Inc.*

Owen-Thomas House, Savannah Historic District,
Savannah, Georgia. *Mary C. Means*

BALDWIN COUNTY
Milledgeville
FORMER GOVERNOR'S MANSION
120 S. Clark Street
1838, Charles B. Cluskey

Georgia's first governor's mansion is a two-story Greek Revival building with a projecting central entrance portico. Walls are brick covered with stucco, and all decorative trim is granite. The pedimented prostyle portico has four giant Ionic columns at the top of a flight of steps. Inside there are a variety of room shapes —octagonal, round, rectangular, and square. The most commanding feature is a coffered dome of plaster with gilded ornamental design. In 1868 the structure ceased to be Georgia's executive mansion, and presently is the home of the president of Georgia Military College.
State
HABS

BALDWIN COUNTY
Milledgeville
OLD STATE CAPITOL (GEORGIA MILITARY COLLEGE)
Green Street

Milledgeville, named for Governor John Milledge, was the capital of Georgia from 1807 until 1868. The architect-builder responsible for the later wings (c. 1833) was Joseph Lane. Gothic Revival in style, the capitol has crenelated brick and stucco walls and is three stories high. All windows have pointed arches. In 1941 the building was totally destroyed by fire, but it has since been reconstructed following measured drawings made by the Historic American Buildings Survey (1936, 1937). Alterations to the interior floor plan were made at this time. The Old State Capitol was converted to the Middle Georgia Military and Agricultural College in 1879 (now Georgia Military College).
State
HABS

BARTOW COUNTY
Cartersville vicinity
ETOWAH MOUNDS
3 miles south of Cartersville on Ga. 61
c. 1350

Etowah Mounds, important as an expression of the eastern expansion of Mississippian culture, is one of three prehistoric southern culture centers in the East. This Indian site consists of three large mounds and an associated village area, including a large centrally located plaza. Nearby are numerous grave sites. Major excavations have been made, and a museum at the site presents the history of the area.
State
NHL

BIBB COUNTY
Macon
ANDERSON, CAPTAIN R. J., HOUSE
1730 W. End Avenue
c. 1840's

Exemplary of pre-Civil War Cottage architecture, the Anderson House has a balloon frame and steep roofs with many gables. Originally a small, five-room structure, in later years it was enlarged and refined through the installation of decorative woodwork, including new gables decorated with verge boards, cornice returns along the gable faces, and jigsaw decoration on the central veranda flatpost supports. The main facade consists of a central gabled veranda and entrance flanked on each side by similar projecting gabled wings. To the rear is the kitchen. All windows are protected by wooden louvered shutters.
Private; not accessible to the public

BIBB COUNTY
Macon
BURKE, THOMAS C., HOUSE
1085 Georgia Avenue
c. 1900

The Burke House is a brick Queen Anne style residence. A tower to the left of the main entrance has a conical slate roof, and there are dormers and projecting bays on all elevations. Windows have bracketed heads of carved stone, and sculptured terra cotta tiles ornament the top of the tower, the cornice, and some of the dormer and bay windows. Chimneys are molded and have insets. The porte cochere has fluted Corinthian columns and is a later addition. Thomas Burke was a successful merchant active in civic affairs.
Private; not accessible to the public

BIBB COUNTY
Macon
CANNONBALL HOUSE (JUDGE ASA HOLT HOUSE)
856 Mulberry Street
1853

This two-story, flat-roofed Greek Revival house is covered with clapboards. Exterior architectural features include a two-story Ionic portico and small center balcony with delicate wrought iron. The entablature above the portico is wide and heavy in appearance. Sidelights and transom surrounding the main doorway have square panes. Noteworthy interior woodwork includes the large two-panel doors with wide moldings, the wide baseboards in all major rooms, and attractive wainscoting in the dining room. The name Cannonball House dates from the battle of Dunlap Hill (July 30, 1864), when the house was accidentally struck by a projectile.
Private
HABS

BIBB COUNTY
Macon
COWLES, JERRY, COTTAGE
4569 Rivoli Drive
1830, Elam Alexander

The Cowles Cottage is an excellent example of a Greek Revival cottage and has been widely copied. Following World War II the house was moved to its present location and restored. Consisting of one story plus attic, it has exterior walls of brick covered with stucco. The roof is not original but its stepped, parapeted gable ends are. An Ionic entrance portico is ornamented with four columns and a fanlighted doorway. Moldings in the entablature are elaborate. A wing was added to the west side in 1885 and to the east side at the time of restoration. Jerry Cowles was a banker and railroad builder and a generous donor to Wesleyan Female College.
Private; not accessible to the public
HABS

BIBB COUNTY
Macon
COWLES HOUSE (STRATFORD ACADEMY)
988 Bond Street
1836, Elam Alexander

The Cowles House is a Greek Revival mansion surrounded on three sides by a monumental portico of 18 Roman Doric columns. Exterior walls are covered with stucco, and the main doorway of heavy, carved black walnut is framed by a fanlight and deeply recessed sidelights. The roof cornice has large modillions, and a balustrade runs around the entire roof. One-story wings were added in the 1850's.
Private
HABS

BIBB COUNTY
Macon
DOMINGOS HOUSE
1261 Jefferson Terrace
1844

The Domingos House is a two-story, porticoed, Greek Revival residence set upon a raised basement. Six two-story, fluted, Greek Doric columns on the main facade support a frieze containing laurel wreaths; dentils are located below and in the architrave. The low, hip roof is concealed by the cornice. Exterior walls are covered with clapboards.
Private; not accessible to the public

106   GEORGIA

BIBB COUNTY
Macon
EMERSON-HOLMES BUILDING
566 Mulberry Street
1859, James B. Ayres

Measuring only 23 feet across its street facade, the Italianate Emerson-Holmes Building was constructed for Dr. George W. Emerson, a dentist. Most of the details and ornament of the brownstone building are attributed to imported Italian workmen. The three-story structure has shops at the ground level, round-arched windows above, and an iron-balustraded second-floor balcony supported by masonry scroll brackets.
Private
HABS

BIBB COUNTY
Macon
GOODALL HOUSE
618 Orange Street
1859

The Goodall House is a two-story Italianate structure with a slightly gabled roof. Ornamental detail is evident in the carved rail and baluster of the one-story porch, the carved brackets of the projecting roof overhang, the corbelled brick chimneys, and the cupola whose four sides form a dome. The central doorway has arched panels and etched glass sidelights. On the right side of the main facade is a triple-arched floor-length window with a heavy wood entablature common to all the windows. At the rear of the house stands the original clapboard servants' house.
Private; not accessible to the public

BIBB COUNTY
Macon
GRAND OPERA HOUSE (ACADEMY OF MUSIC)
651 Mulberry Street
1884, Alexander Blair; 1905 (renovated), W. R. Gunn

The original Macon Academy of Music was a dark red brick building of Gothic design. A studio building, rectangular and covered by a steep gable roof, was attached to the present auditorium wing. A seven-story office building was built to replace the studio structure (1905), and the theater has since been entered through a wide lobby in the addition. In 1970 the auditorium was restored to its 1905 appearance through the installation of new seats, replicas of earlier hangings, and restored gold ornament. New stage rigging and lighting were installed, and the original asbestos curtain at the proscenium, cleaned and rehung. Seating capacity for the Opera House is 2,418.
County

BIBB COUNTY
Macon
HATCHER-GROOVER-SCHWARTZ HOUSE
1144–1146 Georgia Avenue
1880

Marshall James Hatcher built this Second Empire dwelling, the only house of its type in Macon. The Hatcher House is distinguished by a mansard roof, tall narrow windows, and a polychromatic exterior. There is a graceful wrought iron porch on the north and east elevations, and all windows (except in the projecting bay) have segmental arched heads. Brick walls are ornamented by carved stone string bands, stone window sills, and stone quoins. The cornice has heavy brackets, while the patterned slate roof is crowned at its peak by a dentil cornice and stone moldings appear at the vertical intersections of the roof planes.
Private; not accessible to the public

BIBB COUNTY
Macon
HOLT HOUSE
1129 Georgia Avenue
c. 1840, Elam Alexander

As originally designed and built, the Holt House had a prostyle Greek Doric portico with six fluted wood columns, continuous guttae on the architrave, applied wreaths on the frieze, and a sloping wood parapet with acroteria. Later additions were well-matched columns of formed sheet metal on the Orange Street side and a rounded corner entablature which occasioned removal of the parapet. Early metal grille railings between the portico columns were replaced by the present turned balusters and molded wooden handrail. Intact are the original granite horseshoe-shaped entrance steps and wrought iron handrails. The unusual bracket support under the front entrance balcony is a cyma reversa shape in a vertical position and suggests possible alteration of the entrance.
Private; not accessible to the public
HABS

BIBB COUNTY
Macon
JOHNSTON-HAY HOUSE
934 Georgia Avenue
1855–1860

This ornate 24-room Italian Renaissance villa is the most elaborate residence in Macon. The front portico, reached by curved marble steps, extends the width of the house and has Corinthian columns supporting a balustraded balcony. Tall arched French windows on the main floor are embellished with keystones. Similar fenestration on the second floor is further ornamented by segmental and triangular

pediments. At the third floor level there are bull's eye windows between the string course and the modillioned cornice under the low pitched hip roof. The roof is surmounted by a massive octagonal stone cupola with alternating arched and bull's eye windows, scroll brackets, and a balustraded octagonal lantern with a walkway. The interior of the house is as detailed and unusual as the exterior, featuring a carved mahogany staircase, oak paneling, sculptured marble, intricate stucco work, and crystal chandeliers.
Private

BIBB COUNTY
Macon
MUNICIPAL AUDITORIUM
415–435 1st Street
1925, Edgerton Swartwout

The Macon City Auditorium is a large, square, Neo-Classical Revival building. A colonnade at balcony level surrounds the auditorium on the First and Cherry Street sides. Principal construction materials were reinforced concrete, steel, brick, tile, copper, and limestone. A series of arched entrances above a raised basement support the Doric colonnade columns and a fully developed Doric entablature. The copper covered dome has a diameter of 152 feet 6 inches. The general plan of the interior is square with a circular main hall, and surfaces are plaster and Georgia marble.
Municipal

BIBB COUNTY
Macon
NAPIER, LEROY, HOME
2215 Napier Avenue
1842, Elias Carter

This nearly square two-story frame house with its slightly pitched roof is a noteworthy example of Macon's Greek Revival architecture. The portico on the front elevation is composed of first- and second-floor porches extending the width of the house. It has two plain square columns at the corners and four fluted Greek Doric intermediary columns. Other features include a frieze containing carved inverted laurel wreathes (anthemia) over the porch, and an undeveloped cornice. The house was moved to its present location about fifty years ago.
Private; not accessible to the public

BIBB COUNTY
Macon
OCMULGEE NATIONAL MONUMENT
1250–1821

Ocmulgee represents a zone or location where many important historic and prehistoric cultures overlap. The Swift

Creek Indians settled the land about 1250 but were replaced or driven out by the Macon Plateau Indians about 1350. It was the Macon Plateau who built the huge mounds, the fortified village, the ceremonial earth lodge, the two lines of ditches, and cultivated the surrounding fields. The 40–acre tract south of Ocmulgee was occupied by the Lamar Indians (A.D. 1350–1500) who probably represent the first arrival of the Creeks. These inhabitants built mounds and lived inside a stockaded village in the swamps. The Creek Indian occupation proper began about 1690. Burials of the historic Creek Indians on the middle section of the plateau are preserved exactly as they were found.
Federal
NPS; 683.48 acres

BIBB COUNTY
Macon
RAINES-CARMICHAEL HOUSE
1183 Georgia Avenue
Late 1840's, Elam Alexander

The plan of the Raines House is that of a modified Greek cross. Rooms branch off in four directions from an octagonal hall. The dentil cornice continues inside the roof pediments of the arms. There are porches between each arm of the cross, and an octagonal central cupola surmounts the two-story frame house. Minor alterations include the rounding of the originally three-sided front porch. The house was built for Cadwallader Raines.
Private; not accessible to the public
HABS

BIBB COUNTY
Macon
SMALL HOUSE (NAPIER-SMALL HOUSE)
156 Rogers Avenue
1846

This two-story frame house was built by Shelton Napier and illustrates the variety of detail possible within the overall classic Greek Revival style. Common features are the five-bay hexastyle portico, the low-pitched hip roof truncated by a small flat deck, the cornice and the frieze, modified where the portico adjoins the house. Unusual features are the use of antae (square columns) at the corners of the portico and a low pedimented parapet containing anthemia and topped by acroteria. The badly weathered parapet has been removed, but the carvings remain in good condition.
Private; not accessible to the public
HABS

BIBB COUNTY
Macon
SOLOMON-CURD HOUSE
770 Mulberry Street
c. 1830–1840

This two-story, frame, antebellum structure is a provincial adaption of a more sophisticated Greek Revival house. The dominant architectural feature is a large prostyle wood-floored portico with square, two-story wooden piers. It extends across the entire front. The six-pane front door is flanked by sidelights and has a transom overhead. A once separate one-story cottage to the rear of the house is now connected, and porches added across the rear at both levels have been enclosed as rooms. An original door which led to the front balcony has been replaced by two double-hung windows.
Private

BRYAN COUNTY
Richmond Hill vicinity
FORT McALLISTER
10 miles east of Richmond Hill via Ga. 67
1861–1864

Located on the south bank of the Great Ogeechee River, Fort McAllister was a Confederate earthwork fortification constructed to protect Savannah, a vital trestle of the Atlantic & Gulf Railroad, and several rice plantations along the river. The fall of Fort Pulaski had demonstrated the inadequacy of masonry defense works. Prior to its capture in December, 1864, Fort McAllister had successfully withstood bombardment from wooden gunboats and an ironclad, the U.S.S. *Montauk*. A rear assault by General William Tecumseh Sherman's forces overran the defenders and rendered the defense of Savannah useless. Fort McAllister had five irregular sides with its rear protected by a deep dry ditch. Within its walls were several large earthen mounds called bombproofs in which the garrison ate and slept. Restoration of the protective walls and the bombproofs has been effected.
State

CARROLL COUNTY
Carrollton
BONNER-SHARP-GUNN HOUSE
West Georgia College campus
c. 1844

The Bonner House is an example of a fine eastern Georgia house in a one-time frontier setting. It is a two-story frame dwelling with a projecting pedimented and pillared entrance portico. Windows and doors on the street facade have sidelights. An early shed addition is attached at the

rear and minor changes have been made in the chimneys and some of the doors and windows. In 1913 the house was moved to its present location.
State

CATOOSA COUNTY (also in Hamilton County, Tennessee)
Chattanooga, Tennessee, vicinity
CHICKAMAUGA AND CHATTANOOGA NATIONAL MILITARY PARK
9 miles south of Chattanooga on U.S. 27
1863

Chickamauga and Chattanooga National Military Park was established in commemoration of two Civil War battles fought for control of Chattanooga, Tennessee, an important railroad junction and a key to the communications system of the South. In the battle of Chickamauga, September 19–20, 1863, the Confederates routed two Union corps and seized all the roads but one into Chattanooga, thus placing the Army of the Cumberland under siege. The battle of Chattanooga, November 23–25, 1863, resulted in victory by the Federal troops and a retreat of the Confederate Army into northwest Georgia.
Federal
NPS: 6340.63 acres

CHATHAM COUNTY
Savannah
CENTRAL OF GEORGIA RAILWAY COMPANY SHOP PROPERTY
Between W. Jones Street and Louisville Road
1850–1855, William Morrill Wadley

The Central of Georgia Railroad began operating in the 1830's hauling cotton from the interior of Georgia to the port of Savannah. William M. Wadley, a native of New Hampshire and later president of the Central of Georgia, designed the railroad complex. Buildings within it are a machine shop, blacksmith shop, engine house, storage shed, and smokestack. All are brick. The smokestack is encircled by a 40,000-gallon, cast iron tank with ornamental exterior panels. The railroad still operates, but the shop complex has not been used for several years.
Private

CHATHAM COUNTY
Savannah
LOW, JULIETTE GORDON, BIRTHPLACE
10 Oglethorpe Avenue, East
1818–1821, William Jay

Through her acquaintance with Sir Robert Baden-Powell and his sister, who in England founded the Boy Scouts and the Girl Guides respectively, Juliette Low became interested in establishing a Scout movement in the United States. On March 12, 1912, she enrolled 16 Savannah area girls into two patrols. The old carriage house and servants' quarters behind the Low house provided a meeting place. In 1915 the organization was incorporated as the Girl Scouts, and Juliette Low became its first president. The house in which she was born and reared, a three-story stuccoed brick dwelling in the Classical Revival style, contains many original furnishings and mementoes of Juliette Low.
Private
NHL; HABS

CHATHAM COUNTY
Savannah
SAVANNAH HISTORIC DISTRICT
Bounded by E. Broad, Gwinnett, W. Broad Streets and the Savannah River
1732

James Oglethorpe's plan for the city of Savannah created a community pattern with important innovations in urban design. This district is significant not only because it retains much of the original plan, but also because it includes many buildings of architectural merit built by the English architect William Jay between 1816 and 1822. Among them is the Owens-Thomas House, illustrating the English Regency style. Other important buildings in the district include the Pink House, a Georgian town house, and the Green-Meldrim House, an example of the early Gothic Revival style. The district also contains a number of notable churches, public buildings, as well as several parks designed by Oglethorpe.
Multiple public/private
NHL; HABS

CHATHAM COUNTY
Savannah
SCARBROUGH, WILLIAM, HOUSE
41 W. Broad Street
1818–1819, William Jay;
c. 1835–1845 (remodeled); 1969 (restored)

William Jay (c. 1794–1837) was an English-born architect who designed several residences in Savannah. The style of the Scarbrough House is English Regency, and the walls are smooth stucco. On the east or main facade is an *in antis* Greek Doric portico. The entablature of the portico contains a frieze with triglyphs and metopes. Above this central entranceway is a large, semicircular window the same length as the entablature. On either side of the main door a semicircular arched recess surrounds a roundhead window. A piazza with fluted Corinthian columns and a detailed iron balustrade decorates the south facade. Inside, the vestibule or entrance hall is a two-story atrium formed by four monumental Doric columns. William Scarbrough (1776–1838), for whom the house was built, was a prosperous Savannah merchant.
Private
HABS

CHATHAM COUNTY
Savannah vicinity
FORT JACKSON
Islands Expressway, 3 miles east of Savannah on the Savannah River
19th century

In 1808 the U.S. government purchased this site and construction began immediately on a river fortification. It was garrisoned during the War of 1812 and sporadically thereafter until 1861, when state troops took it over. Some rebuilding was done in the 1840's and reconditioning in the 1870's. The federal government sold the property to the city of Savannah in 1923, and it has since become the property of the state. Today the fort appears, in the main, as it did in 1850. A moat surrounds the brick walls.
State

CHATHAM COUNTY
Savannah vicinity
FORT PULASKI NATIONAL MONUMENT
17 miles east of Savannah, Cockspur Island
1829–1847

On April 10–11, 1862, Federal rifle cannon forced the surrender of this supposedly impregnable brick fort, demonstrating for the first time that old-style masonry fortifications were ineffectual against modern weapons. The Confederacy's loss of this fort, strategically located at the mouth of the Savannah River, cut Savannah off from foreign trade. It was an important step in the naval blockade that was eventually to throttle the economic life of the South. Fort Pulaski was abandoned as an active post in 1880.
Federal/non-federal
NPS; 5,516.62 acres
HABS

CHATTAHOOCHEE COUNTY
Fort Benning
RIVERSIDE (QUARTERS NO. 1)
100 Vibbert Avenue
c. 1910

Arthur Bussey, a Columbus businessman, purchased this property in 1909. He moved an old meetinghouse located nearby onto his land and gradually enlarged it. The present house is two stories high with a steep gable roof and has a wide two-story veranda on two sides. The square columns of the veranda are repeated in the one-story porte cochere. Camp Benning was established on October 7, 1918, to help meet the need for training replacements for the American Expeditionary Force in Europe. Since that date this house has been the residence of Fort Benning's commanding officer.
Federal

CLARKE COUNTY
Athens
WILKINS HOUSE
387 S. Milledge Avenue
1860

The Wilkins House is one of a group of residences built on Milledge Avenue by the Dearing family just prior to the Civil War. It is basically Classical Revival in style. A Corinthian colonnade, supported by brick piers, surrounds the house on three sides. Like several other 19th-century residences in the area, the mansion rests upon a full raised basement which originally contained service rooms. Several remodellings have taken place since the house was constructed.
Private

COBB COUNTY
Marietta vicinity
KENNESAW MOUNTAIN NATIONAL BATTLEFIELD PARK
2 miles west of Marietta
1864

During the spring of 1864, the Federal "Army Group" in Chattanooga, Tennessee, under General William T. Sherman, made preparations for a campaign designed to destroy the Confederate Army of Tennessee. By May 7 the Federal armies were on the march. A series of flanking movements pushed the Confederates back to positions on and around Kennesaw Mountain. Sherman was determined to break through the Confederates' 10–mile entrenchment and destroy the separated wings. The ensuing battle, however, repulsed the Federals, permitting Sherman to resume his flanking maneuvers. The Confederate forces retired from

their Kennesaw Mountain position to the vicinity of Atlanta.
Federal/non-federal
NPS; 3,682.62 acres

COLUMBIA COUNTY
Augusta vicinity
STALLINGS ISLAND
8 miles northwest of Augusta in the Savannah River
Prior to 1700 B.C.

The Stallings Island site is among the most important shell mound sites in the Southeast. Excavations have revealed that in the period before pottery was made by Indians of southeastern America, there existed other Indians who hunted and gathered shellfish and plants for food. In the site's later stages of occupation, pottery appeared in the form of vessels tempered with vegetable fiber—the earliest pottery ware known in the Southeast.
Private; not accessible to the public
NHL

EARLY COUNTY
Blakely vicinity
KOLOMOKI MOUNDS
8 miles north of Blakely on U.S. 27, Kolomoki Mounds State Park
c. 1400–1600

Extensive archeological excavations have revealed details of burial practices at this type site for the Kolomoki culture, which seems to be a local variant of the Weeden Island culture. Kolomoki was a major ceremonial center which utilized the Temple Mound tradition but was not a part of the Mississippian culture. Preserved in a state park, the site contains the largest mound group in the Gulf Coast area. A small on-site museum exhibits some of the burials and pottery in their original positions.
State
NHL

FLOYD COUNTY
Rome
CHIEFTAINS
80 Chatillon Road
c. 1792, c. 1837

The original dwelling that became Chieftains was a two-story, hand-hewn log cabin built by Major Ridge, a Cherokee chief. Sometime in the first half of the 19th century Ridge enlarged and embellished his modest cabin by the addition of columns, glass windows and doors, and interior paneling. Further remodeling occurred in 1923 when one-story side wings were added and the house took on its present Georgian Colonial appearance. Present measurements of the central block

are 54 feet deep and 38 feet across with flanking one-story wings measuring 28 by 20 feet. Ridge and his partner George Lavender operated a ferry across the Oostanaula River and the first trading post in the Rome area. He was also active in tribal affairs, serving as speaker of the Cherokee National Council, and was a member of the treaty party who agreed to removal of the Cherokees to Indian territory.
Private

FULTON COUNTY
Atlanta
CYCLORAMA OF THE BATTLE OF ATLANTA
Cherokee Avenue, Grant Park

The Atlanta Cyclorama depicts the battle (July 22, 1864) which was the major conflict of General William Tecumseh Sherman's Atlanta campaign. It is one of the largest paintings in the world (measuring 50 feet in height, 400 feet in circumference, and weighing 18,000 pounds) and one of three extant cycloramas. A group of ten German artists, under the direction of August Lohr and R. M. Heine, produced the cyclorama in the studios of the American Cyclorama Company in Milwaukee, Wisconsin. The artists studied the Atlanta terrain carefully before commencing their work, and the group included landscape painters, figure painters, and animal painters. Begun in 1885, the painting was first displayed in Detroit in 1887 and then toured other American cities. After passing through a series of owners, the painting was given to the city of Atlanta in 1897. Housed at first in a wooden structure, the painting is now within a granite and marble building. Between 1934 and 1936 the cyclorama acquired a three-dimensional appearance through the addition of plaster figures, exploded shells, fragments of rails and crossties, blasted stumps, and simulated grass and bushes in the foreground.
Municipal

FULTON COUNTY
Atlanta
GEORGIA STATE CAPITOL
Capitol Square
1889, Edbrooke and Burnham

Atlanta became the official capital of Georgia in 1887, and this building is the third erected by the state to house the legislature and related government offices. Indiana limestone was used to finish the exterior and Georgia marble appears on interior walls, floors, and steps. The overall appearance of the capitol is that of a monumental, classical, domed and columned structure. A four-story pedi-

mented portico with six Composite columns dominates the main facade. Front and rear facades are essentially the same. The high dome and lantern, both covered with gold leaf, rise directly behind the portico. Inside, the open rotunda extends from the second floor through the upper stories to a height of 237 feet. Oak paneling was used in the house and senate chamber.
State

FULTON COUNTY
Atlanta
HARRIS, JOEL CHANDLER, HOUSE
1050 Gordon Street, S.W.
1881–1908

Joel Chandler Harris, author of the "Uncle Remus" tales and other Negro dialect stories, lived here from 1881 until his death in 1908. During this time he was on the staff of the *Atlanta Constitution*. His rural house, which he called "Wren's Nest," contains many original furnishings and a collection of objects associated with the author. A small amphitheater has been built on the grounds to accommodate those attending an annual Uncle Remus festival held in May.
Private
NHL

FULTON COUNTY
Atlanta
SMITH, TULLIE, HOUSE
3099 Andrews Drive, N.W.
c. 1835–1840

The Tullie Smith House is an early Georgia farmhouse of frame construction with a low pitched gable roof and two brick end chimneys. A shed roof runs the length of the rear elevation and, at one time, a simple pedimented porch sheltered the main entrance. Such homes were frequently built in Georgia when Federal architecture had begun to wane in popularity and before the Greek Revival style had been fully developed. A detached one-story frame kitchen stands behind the house, and both it and the house have been moved from their original locations. Robert H. Smith, a native of North Carolina, built the farmhouse, which takes its name from his great-granddaughter.
Private

FULTON COUNTY
Roswell
BULLOCK HALL
Mimosa Boulevard
c. 1840

Bullock Hall is a temple-form, Greek Revival house in which the gable end forms a large-scale pedimented portico. Completed according to the design of its

owner Major James Stephens Bullock and his craftsman-architect Willis Ball, the frame structure contains a functionally convenient plan within the strict framework of the classical form. The two-story portico has four massive round columns. Above the central entrance is a seven pane transom, and to either side are four sidelights. The house remains basically unaltered since construction.
Private
HABS

GLYNN COUNTY
Brunswick vicinity
FORT FREDERICA NATIONAL MONUMENT
   12 miles north of Brunswick
   1736

Fort Frederica served as headquarters for General James Oglethorpe's military operations against the Spanish in Florida during the Anglo-Spanish struggle for control of the Southeast. The strategic location of the fort on St. Simon's Island also checked Spanish advances toward the English southern colonies. The peace of Aix-la-Chapelle in 1748 was a death warrant for the thriving fortified settlement. British diplomats decided to treat the land between the Altamaha River and Florida, which included Frederica, as neutral ground. A guard was maintained at the fort until Florida was ceded to England in 1763, at which time the fort was abandoned completely. The monument includes the fort site, the walled area of the town, and a burying ground. The moat surrounding the town, the cemetery, and portions of the citadel and barracks are also extant, as are foundations of a number of dwellings.
Federal/non-federal
NPS; 250 acres

GRADY COUNTY
Beachton vicinity
SUSINA PLANTATION (CEDAR GROVE)
   1.5 miles west of Beachton on
   Meridian Road
   c. 1841, John Wind

Susina Plantation or Cedar Grove is a two-story, frame, Greek Revival plantation house. The front portico features four giant Ionic columns, and there is a hand-carved sunflower rosette in the pediment. Under the portico is a balcony with a sheaf and wheat design railing. The main entrance has double doors, sidelights, and a transom. Susina was remodeled in 1891, when the rear wing and side porches may have been added. In 1967 the entire house was restored and all the woodwork was repaired or replaced. The house was built for James Joseph Blackshear.
Private; not accessible to the public

GWINNETT COUNTY
Lawrenceville
OLD SEMINARY BUILDING (LAWRENCEVILLE FEMALE SEMINARY BUILDING)
   Perry Street
   1838

The Greek Revival Old Seminary Building is a two-story brick structure measuring 36 feet by 52 feet. Wide pilasters separate the bays on all sides. There is a heavy box cornice under the eaves of the low pitched gable roof, and the windows are capped by stone lintels. A delicate fanlight and a large keystone ornament the Perry Street entrance, a semicircular arched doorway. In 1860 the local Masonic lodge began using the second floor and continued to do so for a century. The Lawrenceville Female Seminary ceased using the building in 1886.
Private

HANCOCK COUNTY
Jewell vicinity
SHIVERS-SIMPSON HOUSE (ROCK MILL)
   Mayfield Road, on the Ogeechee
   River
   c. 1820

The three-story Shivers-Simpson House is rectangular and covered with clapboards. A raised basement supports the first floor. The original fanlight, sidelights, and wide double doors survive, and the structure is topped by a gable roof. Inside are wide hallways flanked by two 18-foot by 20-foot rooms. Large fitted granite blocks have been used as flooring for the first floor hall. William Shivers, for whom the house was built, operated a grist mill—the first Rock Mill. The second owner of the property was William Simpson.
Private

JENKINS COUNTY
Millen vicinity
BIRDSVILLE PLANTATION
   Plantation
   West of Millen on Route 2
   c. 1789 (rear section), c. 1850 (front section)

Birdsville is the only complete and fundamentally unaltered plantation complex to survive in Georgia. Land was granted to Philip Jones in 1784 as payment for his service in the Revolutionary army, and though enlarged, the property still remains in the same family. The earlier portion of the frame house contained two rooms on each of the two stories with shed rooms behind. A later owner added the imposing front entrance with twin Corinthian columns *in antis* crowned by a heavy cornice and pediment. The twin bays, ironwork, corner pilasters, and Carpenter Gothic scrollwork all date from the 1850's. Woodwork inside is Federal in one part of the house and Greek Revival in the other. The Birdsville complex also contains a two-room kitchen, a well house, a necessary, a smokehouse, a blacksmith shop, and a stage stop-apothecary shop.
Private

LIBERTY COUNTY
Midway vicinity
FORT MORRIS
   About 10 miles east of Midway off
   Ga. 38
   18th century

Fort Morris was manned during the Revolution to protect the now dead town of Sunbury, then Savannah's rival for river trade. Situated on a bluff south of Sunbury, the fort, which was protected on the south by marshlands and was surrounded by a moat, commanded the Midway River. The enclosed earthwork contained a parade ground of about one acre. Its eastern length measured 275 feet, the north and south faces were 192 and 140 feet, and the curtain at the west was 241 feet long. A British attack in late 1778 was repulsed, but the 200–man garrison was finally forced to surrender in January, 1779.
State

LIBERTY COUNTY
South Newport vicinity
ST. CATHERINES ISLAND
   10 miles off the Georgia coast
   between St. Catherines Sound and
   Sapelo Sound
   16th–20th centuries

St. Catherines Island was one of the most important Spanish mission centers in southeastern North America from 1566 to 1684. Jesuit priests founded the Mission Santa Catalina in 1568, but continued attacks by Indians and the British forced the Spanish to abandon it in 1684. Button Gwinnett, delegate to the Continental Congress and signer of the Declaration of Independence, purchased the island in 1765 and made his home here. In more recent years St. Catherines has been a private estate and game preserve. No structures from the mission period exist, but there are archeological remains containing evidence of Indian and Spanish occupation. Button Gwinnett's 1770's plantation home was enlarged and remodeled to its present appearance in 1929. Slave quarters exist in several locations on the island, as do dozens of Indian burial mounds.
Private; not accessible to the public
NHL

LUMPKIN COUNTY
Dahlonega
DAHLONEGA COURTHOUSE GOLD
MUSEUM (OLD LUMPKIN COUNTY
COURTHOUSE)
U.S. 19
1838

Dahlonega is the English equivalent of a Cherokee word meaning "precious yellow." Lumpkin County, specifically the Dahlonega area, was the scene of one of the country's first gold rushes. A branch mint was opened at Dahlonega in 1838. The two-story brick courthouse has a strong Jeffersonian flavor. A one-bay, two-columned Tuscan portico rises the full height of the building on the main facade. The courtroom and county offices were on the second floor and the lower level served as a market place. Doors are set in semicircular arches and topped by fanlights. All facades have five bays, and the roof features a modillion cornice that is continued inside the gable ends and portico pediment. A new courthouse was constructed in 1965, and this building was converted to a gold rush museum.
State
HABS

MCDUFFIE COUNTY
Thomson vicinity
THE OLD ROCK HOUSE
Old Rock House
About 3 miles northwest of Thomson
on Old Rock House Road
c. 1784

Thomas Ansley, the builder of the Old Rock House, migrated to Georgia from New Jersey via North Carolina in 1768. He came with a group of 40 families who were to establish a Quaker colony on Georgia's frontier. The settlement was named Wrightsboro for colonial Governor James Wright, who had granted permission to settle here. Today only the cemetery and the Old Rock House give evidence of the once-thriving town. Walls are fieldstone, 24 inches thick, and covered with cement scored in imitation of sandstone blocks. A pitched roof covers the two-story house, and the original box cornice survives under the rear eave line. Occupied until 1950, the house is presently in a deteriorated condition, but restoration work is planned.
Private

MCINTOSH COUNTY
Darien vicinity
FORT KING GEORGE
East of U.S. 17

The Fort King George area formed a strategic buffer zone between three nations, all attempting to colonize the coast of Georgia. Excavations in 1952 uncovered the outline of a Spanish mission building and the remains of associated Indian structures dating from the mid–17th century. The site was deserted from the beginning of the 18th century until the summer of 1721, when the construction of Fort King George began—an effort by the British to discourage French expansion and to provide protection from the Spanish. The garrison of Fort King George was removed to Port Royal in 1727. Nine years later a group of Scottish Highlanders settled in the vicinity of the fort and established sawmill operations lasting until the early 20th century. Only brick remnants of the sawmill foundations remain on the site.
State

MACON COUNTY (also in Sumter County)
Andersonville vicinity
ANDERSONVILLE NATIONAL
HISTORIC SITE
1 mile east of Andersonville on Ga.
49
1863

During the Civil War Andersonville, formally called Camp Sumter, became the death site of nearly 13,000 Union prisoners. In the peak month of August 1864 almost 33,000 men were crowded into the stockade. For his part in the catastrophe Captain Henry Wirz, the prison commandant, became the only Confederate official to be executed for war crimes. Today the Andersonville National Historic Site includes the site of the stockade, the fortifications surrounding it, and a right-of-way to the Andersonville railroad station.
Federal/non-federal
NPS; 201 acres

MORGAN COUNTY
Madison vicinity
CEDAR LANE FARM
Off Ga. 83 north of Madison
c. 1839

The house at Cedar Lane Farm was built by Henry Hilsabeck, son of a German emigrant to the Moravian section of North Carolina. Hilsabeck's home is typical of a planter or farmer who owned 200 to 500 acres of land and less than 25 slaves.

Weatherboarding covers the exterior of the frame dwelling. A shed roof runs the length of the rear elevation, and there are four chimneys constructed of fieldstone and brick. The main entrance has a seven-light transom and three-pane sidelights. Inside, the house has a four-room, center hall plan.
Private

MURRAY COUNTY
Spring Place
VANN HOUSE
Intersection of U.S. 76 and Ga. 225
1803–1805

James Vann (1768–1809) was the son of a Cherokee mother and a Scots father. In an effort to aid his mother's people, Vann, a wealthy businessman, sponsored and supported a Moravian mission in Spring Place. Moravian craftsmen helped construct the Federal style house which has some Georgian elements. Two single outside brick chimneys rise at the gable ends of a saddleback roof and frame the two-story walls. Bricks for the house were made on the property and are laid in both Flemish and English bond. The present porches are conjectural reconstructions of the originals.
State
HABS

MUSCOGEE COUNTY
Columbus
COLUMBUS HISTORIC DISTRICT
Roughly bounded by 9th Street on
the north, 4th Street on the south,
Broadway on the west, and 2nd
Avenue on the east
19th century

Columbus was one of four early Georgia cities which were planned communities. It was surveyed and laid out in 1828. The historic district is composed of twenty full blocks and nine partial blocks which were included in the original plan of the city of Columbus. Within this area are approximately 612 structures, some of which are as old as the city itself. Architectural styles range from simple Georgian cottages to large Greek Revival and Gothic Revival homes. Of principal interest, however, is the indigenous architecture of those structures particularly well-suited to the local climate and environment. These are small, frame houses of classical design with rectangular floor plans and low, hip roofs resting in part or totally on the columns or piers of a veranda. Wood was plentiful in the area, and it was the most commonly-used building material. There are also examples of stucco on brick and stucco-fronted frame houses.
Multiple public/private

MUSCOGEE COUNTY
Columbus
COLUMBUS IRONWORKS
901 Front Avenue
1853, 1865, 1903

The Columbus Ironworks is noted not only as the site of a major arsenal of the Confederacy, but also as the first commercial ice plant in the United States and as the producer of one of the earliest breechloading cannons. At present the plant is one of the few sources of commercial drop forgings in the Southeast. Although the ironworks was completely destroyed by fire in 1865 and 1902, the building is nevertheless typical of late 19th-century warehouses.
Private

MUSCOGEE COUNTY
Columbus
GOETCHIUS-WELLBORN HOUSE
405 Broadway
1839

This modified Greek Revival, New Orleans style house has recently been moved into the Columbus Historic District. The wide veranda across the entire front of the house has wooden piers and balustrades to replace the original wrought iron lacework. Inside, the decorative detailing is highlighted by carved cornices, and there are medallions in an intricate scroll pattern on the ceilings of the entrance hall and the two parlors.
Private

MUSCOGEE COUNTY
Columbus
GUNBOATS C.S.S. *MUSCOGEE* **AND**
CHATTAHOOCHEE
4th Street west of U.S. 27

The ironclad ram *Muscogee* was designed for coast defense and was modeled upon the Confederate prototype, the C.S.S. *Virginia*. She was constructed of iron covered wood and measured approximately 200 feet. Powered by steam, the gunboat had twin propellers. The *Chattahoochee* was a 130-foot, wooden, three-masted sailing vessel also equipped with steam driven double propellers. Both boats were sunk during a Federal raid on Columbus in April, 1865. Sections of both boats were recovered in the 1960's and are presently on display at the Confederate Naval Museum.
State

MUSCOGEE COUNTY
Columbus
JOSEPH HOUSE
828 Broadway
1842

One of the oldest buildings in the Columbus Historic District, the Joseph House is a one-story, white frame structure typical of the cottage-like homes built in this area in the 1840's and 1850's. On the exterior, Gothic wooden trim has been added to a Greek Revival building. The wide veranda, running the length of the west facade, has slender wooden columns topped with ornamental wooden brackets supporting the veranda roof. A long ell at the left rear of the building houses a kitchen.
Private; not accessible to the public

MUSCOGEE COUNTY
Columbus
OCTAGON HOUSE
527 1st Avenue
1829–1830, 1863

About 1863 a one-story, four room, octagonal addition was constructed in front of and attached to a simple rectangular-shaped frame house built about 1829–1830, shortly after the original survey of Columbus. The older building had four rooms and a kitchen in a rear outbuilding. The octagonal addition was built around a central chimney. A basic Greek cross floor plan was converted into an eight-sided shape by fitting triangular closets and vestibules into each arm of the cross. The exterior of the house is white clapboard, and the area around the front door is covered with flatsiding to differentiate it from the other seven sides. The double front door is flanked and crested by leaded glass windows framed by moldings. The unusual octagonal shape may reflect the original shape of the older rectangular structure as recent archeological investigations have revealed foundations and other structural details suggesting that an older octagon was modified to a rectangle when the larger 1863 octagon was built.
Private

MUSCOGEE COUNTY
Columbus
ST. ELMO
2810 St. Elmo Drive
1828–1833

The twelve graceful 40-foot columns on the front and sides of St. Elmo give the house an air of monumentality. The roof above the columns is balustraded, and a hanging iron balcony with a medallion design highlights the central entrance. First-and-second floor doorways are identical. Walls are handmade brick, 18

inches thick, and are covered with stucco. The first floor opens at ground level and houses the kitchen, dining room, storerooms, wine cellar, and servants' rooms. The second and third floors have central hall plans. Seaborn Jones built St. Elmo, which was originally called Eldorado.
Private
HABS

MUSCOGEE COUNTY
Columbus
SPRINGER OPERA HOUSE
105 10th Street
1871; Daniel Matthew Foley

The Springer Opera House was the center of a surprisingly dynamic cultural life in the Chattahoochee Valley in the late 19th and early 20th centuries when it played host to virtually every great name of the American theater, including Edwin Booth, Lillie Langtry, Oscar Wilde, and Otis Skinner. Housed in a three-story brick building which was formerly a hotel, the opera house has been renovated and restored to its late 19th-century appearance. The building itself measures 145 by 150 feet, and the upper two floors are used for storage. Windows on the upper stories have pressed metal lintels and stone sills. The cornice is pressed metal. Inside, seating capacity is 450. The flocked wallpaper in the foyer is a reproduction, and the original brass chandelier in the auditorium has been restored. During the 1930's the Springer became a movie house and operated until 1959. Restoration was completed in the mid–1960's.
Private

MUSCOGEE COUNTY
Columbus
WALKER-PETERS-LANGDON HOUSE
716 Broadway
1828

The Walker-Peters-Langdon House was built in the regional "cottage" style but patterned after larger, more formal Federal style houses of the period. The facade is perfectly symmetrical with a centrally placed walnut door flanked by two windows and balanced by brick chimneys at each end. The house rests on a brick foundation, and the white clapboard siding is attached with wooden pegs. Many of the window panes contain handblown glass. The original house, to which additional rooms were added about 1836, had a rectangular floor plan consisting of a central hall flanked by one room on either side and a shed room at the left rear. A full kitchen was located in the basement.
Private

MUSCOGEE COUNTY
Columbus
WELLS-BAGLEY HOUSE
22 6th Street
1840

This modified Greek Revival style house is located in the Columbus Historic District. It was built of wood and covered with stucco scored to resemble stone. The low, hip roof is supported on two sides by ten square piers which stand at the edge of a veranda created by the roof overhang on the front and one side of the dwelling. As is typical of many Greek Revival houses, there is a line dentil molding above the veranda piers. Inside are four rooms and a central hallway. The house was moved in 1969 to its present location.
Private

OCONEE COUNTY
Watkinsville
EAGLE TAVERN
U.S. 129
c. 1820

Restoration work in the late 1950's revealed the original building to have been a four-room tavern and store. Later additions were removed, and the present stylistically conservative tavern is characterized as "plantation plain style." Two stories high and of frame construction, the tavern has a single chimney, a simple box cornice front and rear, and two front doors. It has been furnished inside as an early frontier hostelry and store which commonly served as the political, social, and economic center of the community.
State
HABS

RICHMOND COUNTY
Augusta
THE AUGUSTA CANAL
Beginning at the Augusta City Lock and Dam and running southeast 9 miles to the point where it rejoins the Savannah River
1846; 1875 (enlarged, remodeled)

Augusta had prospered from her Savannah River trade, but with the advent of the railroads in the 1830's river traffic began to dwindle. Colonel Henry H. Cumming and several other Augusta citizens urged construction of a canal to provide power for factories and a plentiful city water supply. As dug, the canal was 5 feet deep, 20 feet wide at the bottom, and 40 feet at the surface. A low dam (800 feet long) turned water into the canal, and the water flow was regulated by a stone guard wall containing six gates. Increased traffic and use necessitated enlarging and remodeling the canal in the 1870's. The width was ex-

panded to 106 feet at the bottom and 150 feet at the surface with a depth of 11 feet.
Municipal

RICHMOND COUNTY
Augusta
MACKAY HOUSE
1822 Broad Street
c. 1760

Mackay House was an 18th-century trade center for merchants involved in commerce with the Indians, the West Indies, the Carolinas, and Rhode Island. The three-story frame house has a two-story piazza on the front facade and a gambrel roof, rare in Georgia. The rear galleried piazza shelters a staircase which is the only access to the second and third stories. Other features of the clapboard exterior include a simple modillion cornice, a rear piazza insert between small rooms, a front doorway with fluted pilasters on pedestals, and an entablature ornamented by a pulvinated frieze and modillion cornice.
State
HABS

STEPHENS COUNTY
Toccoa vicinity
TRAVELER'S REST
6 miles east of Toccoa on U.S. 123
1764

Traveler's Rest was erected by Major Jesse Walton, Revolutionary soldier and Indian fighter. It remains as an example of an early tavern and inn in a rural frontier setting. Devereaux Jarrett, its second owner, opened it to the public as a facility combining tavern, trading post, and post office. Soon it was a favorite stopping place between Charleston and Chattanooga. Its significance also lies in its continuity of service, from the late 18th century until well into the 19th century.
State
NHL; HABS

SUMTER COUNTY
ANDERSONVILLE NATIONAL HISTORIC SITE
Reference—see Macon County

TALIAFERRO COUNTY
Crawfordville
LIBERTY HALL
Alexander H. Stephens
Memorial Park
U.S. 278
c. 1830

Alexander H. Stephens (1812–1883), Vice President of the Confederate States of America, lived in this two-story frame house between 1845 and 1883. A shed

porch of one story with square posts runs the full length of the main facade. The roof is hipped and is flanked by two end chimneys. There is a two-room ell at the rear. Outbuildings include servants' quarters, wash house, smokehouse, woodhouse, dry well, and gas plant. Stephens' grave is on the property.
State
HABS

THOMAS COUNTY
Thomasville
BRANDON, DR. DAVID, HOUSE (HAYES HOUSE)
329 N. Broad Street
c. 1851, 1870's (altered)

The Brandon House was built by Thomas Jones as a wedding gift for his daughter, Mrs. David Brandon. Originally a one-story brick dwelling, it was altered in the late 1870's when a mansard roof was added and the exterior was covered with stucco scored to resemble stone. There are dormer windows in the roof, and the one-story front porch has a low center pediment and jigsaw railings. At the front entrance a wood double door forms a semicircle around which are cast rope garlands, stars, and pearl moldings. The door contains etched glass panels.
Private; not accessible to the public

THOMAS COUNTY
Thomasville
BRYAN, HARDY, HOUSE (CATER HOUSE)
312 N. Broad Street
c. 1833

The Hardy Bryan House is a two-and-one-half-story frame dwelling typical of early 19th-century plantation houses. It has a classical portico on the main facade which is supported by four, two-story square columns. All windows have 16 over 16 panes, and those on the first floor have semicircular caps containing three magnolia leaves. A massive triangular pediment containing an unusual geometric medallion overshadows the main facade. Hardy Bryan was an early settler of Thomasville.
Private; not accessible to the public

THOMAS COUNTY
Thomasville
HANSELL, AUGUSTINE, HOUSE (JEFFRIES HOUSE)
429 S. Hansell Street
1852–1853, John Wind

The Jeffries House is a low one-and-one-half-story frame cottage designed by John Wind for Augustine Hansell. A kitchen wing and a bedroom wing were added in 1927, but otherwise the house is largely

unchanged. Six square columns support the pediment of the central portico, and the front entrance is composed of a paneled door, flanking sidelights, and a fixed transom.
Private; not accessible to the public

THOMAS COUNTY
Thomasville
MITCHELL HOUSE (MUNRO HOUSE)
737 Remington Avenue
1856

The Mitchell House is a one-and-one-half-story frame cottage with a large projecting roof pediment which forms the attic story. Six square columns support the overhang, and there are two windows centered in it. The main doorway is Greek Revival, and there is a fine dentil cornice around the entire house.
Private; not accessible to the public

THOMAS COUNTY
Thomasville
PARK FRONT (FRANCES STONE HOUSE)
711 S. Hansell Street
1891

Built as a winter residence for Charles S. Hebard, Park Front was a deliberate attempt on the part of the builder to recapture the beauty and grandeur of antebellum plantation homes. The two-story portico on the main facade has four Doric columns. A freestanding balcony projects from the second story front, and Palladian windows appear on the balcony and in the roof pediments. Two semi-octagonal bays are attached to each side of the house, which is frame covered with clapboards.
Private; not accessible to the public

THOMAS COUNTY
Thomasville
PONDER, EPRAIM, HOUSE
324 N. Dawson Street
c. 1854–1856

This modest antebellum residence exhibits a great deal of architectural detail on windows, doorways, and roof cornice. The house is clapboard with a one-story porch on the north side. Pilasters ornament the corners, and the roof cornice contains both dentils and pendant drop brackets. The main entranceway is flanked by leaded glass sidelights and transom and all are enclosed by an ornately carved door frame. Two double windows on the ground floor have the same detailing (dentils and acorn and lotus leaf rosettes) on their frames. A wing has been added to the east side. At one time the building was a dormitory and later the president's house for Young's Female College.
Private; not accessible to the public

THOMAS COUNTY
Thomasville
SCARBOROUGH HOUSE (C. W. LAPHAM HOUSE)
626 N. Dawson Street
c. 1885

The Scarborough House is a highly ornamented and unusual Victorian dwelling. Its decorative carving might be termed Eastlake style. Two octagonal bays on the main facade enclose an octagonal porch with a second porch above. On the exterior, clapboards and shingle siding are combined in various decorative patterns. Stained glass windows appear on the front and rear of the house. Paneling on the north bay is in a herringbone pattern, and the south bay has horizontal, fluted, beaded, and diagonal siding. Jigsaw carving on the porch railing and the porte cochere is quite detailed.
Private; not accessible to the public

THOMAS COUNTY
Thomasville
THOMAS COUNTY COURTHOUSE
N. Broad Street
1858, John Wind; 1888 (restored)

This building is the third courthouse to stand on the site since Thomas County was organized in 1825. Originally measuring 80 feet long by 48 feet wide, the structure is three stories high. The courtroom is located two floors above ground level, and the grand and petit jury rooms are on the third level. Above the hip roof is an octagonal cupola. During the 1888 restoration the front portico was filled in, the columns removed, and a rear addition built. One-story wings were added front and rear in 1918–1919, 1922, and another rear annex was added in 1937.
Private

THOMAS COUNTY
Thomasville
WRIGHT HOUSE
415 Fletcher Street
1854

Built for Arthur P. Wright, banker, alderman, and mayor of Thomasville, the Wright House is an antebellum cottage with a great deal of Greek Revival decoration. One story high, the cottage is frame with a hip roof. The roof of the veranda, which extends across the front, is supported by six square, paneled piers ornamented with intricately carved wooden insets. The front windows are framed by moldings decorated with dentil cornices, and the main entrance has sidelights and a transom composed of many small rectangular panes of glass set in a geometric pattern.
Private; not accessible to the public

WHITE COUNTY
Cleveland
OLD WHITE COUNTY COURTHOUSE
1859–1860

After 1803 Georgia courthouse towns were usually laid out around a courthouse square. Flanking the square on all sides were stores offices, and residences. Cleveland was laid out in 1857, and the courthouse was built to accommodate the functions of a court and a market. Measuring 54 feet by 39 feet, the structure is brick with a cornice of molded bricks and twin end chimneys connected by a parapet. Although built just before the Civil War, the Old White County Courthouse is Georgian in style and has not been altered appreciably. In recent times the market area was converted to county offices, and the building currently houses the White County Historical Society.
County

WILKES COUNTY
Washington
WASHINGTON-WILKES HISTORICAL MUSEUM (BARNETT-SLATON HOUSE)
308 E. Robert Toombs Avenue
c. 1835, 1857

The earlier portion of this house is the section behind the present stair hall consisting of one large room opening onto a front and back porch. A lean-to was added next. In the 1850's the house was enlarged by the addition of front rooms, hallways, and the present staircase. It is presently a two-story frame residence set on a high basement, a typical antebellum house.
State

Columbus Historic District, Columbus, Georgia. *Brady Bynum*

Mackay House, Augusta, Georgia.
Georgia Historical Commission

Hawaii

Kawaiahao Church, Honolulu, Hawaii.
Jack E. Boucher for HABS

Iolani Palace,
Honolulu, Hawaii (Throne Room).
Jack E. Boucher for HABS

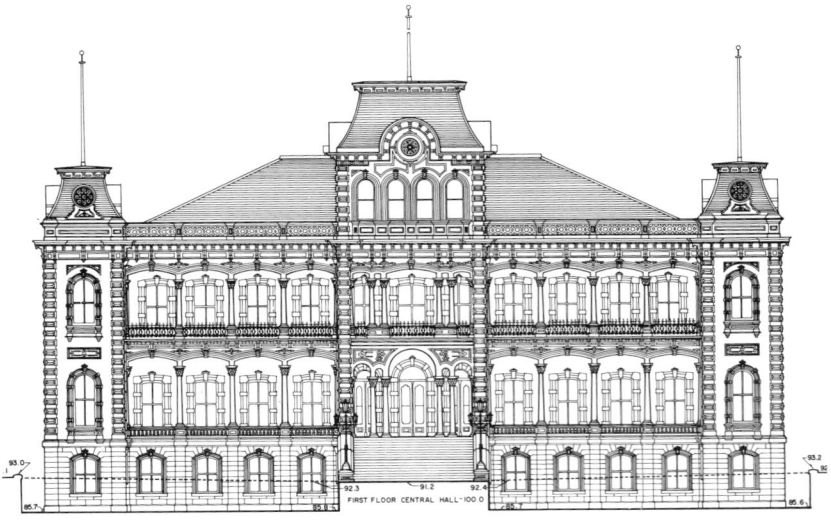

KING STREET ELEVATION
SOUTHWEST (MAKAI)

NOTE: HOTEL STREET ELEVATION SIMILAR.
SEE TEMPORARY ADDITIONS - SHEET

0 5 10   20 FEET

Iolani Palace, Honolulu, Hawaii. *HABS*

Chee Kung Tong Society Headquarters,
Lahaina, Maui, Hawaii.
Jack E. Boucher for HABS

HAWAII COUNTY
Hawi vicinity, Island of Hawaii
MOOKINI HEIAU
Northern tip of Hawaii, 1 mile west of
Upolu Point Airport
1000

Mookini Heiau, one of the largest physical evidences of the ancient Hawaiian religion, is a sacrificial temple with an open stone paved court. This huge temple, which measures about 250 by 130 feet, is enclosed on all sides by 20–foot walls. The sacrificial stone now lies in the field just outside the walls. King Kamehameha I's birthstone at Kokoiki is located about one-half mile from this heiau.
Multiple private
NHL

HAWAII COUNTY
Hilo vicinity, Island of Hawaii
MAUNA KEA ADZ QUARRY
25 miles northwest of Hilo via
mountain trail
Prehistoric

The Mauna Kea Adz Quarry is the largest such primitive quarry in the world. Here prehistoric Hawaiians came to obtain basalt for various stone implements and for adzes, the single most important stone tool in Polynesia. Evidences of the use of this quarry are to be found in the great heaps of chips, some heaps measuring 30 feet wide and 10 feet high. The remains of the quarry are intact.
State
NHL

HAWAII COUNTY
Kailai-Kona vicinity, Island of Hawaii
CITY OF REFUGE NATIONAL
HISTORICAL PARK
20 miles south of Kailua-Kona
c. 1500

One of several such sites in the Hawaiian Islands, the City of Refuge was a sanctuary for all who sought asylum. During a war noncombatants and defeated warriors of both sides were safe until hostilities were over. Anyone who broke the *kapu*, a system of taboos, escaped punishment by entering the sacred ground. When a refugee left the sanctuary, protection went with him. The place of refuge itself, adjacent palace grounds, royal fishponds, nearby stone platforms on which stood the houses of important chiefs, and temples are all within the City of Refuge National Historical Park.
Federal/non-federal
NPS: 181.85 acres

HAWAII COUNTY
Kailua-Kona vicinity, Island of Hawaii
HONOKOHAU SETTLEMENT
Honokohau Bay, just north of Kailua-
Kone
Prehistoric–1920

Included in the Honokohau Settlement are 50 ancient house sites, for heiaus (temples), three fishponds, a holua (toboggan slide), and many tombs. One of the heiaus, Makaopio, is a fisherman's temple noted for two large upright stone slabs which rise above the height of the pavement of its seaward retaining wall. These slabs served as fishermen's gods. Also in the area are scattered petroglyphs and what appear to be ancient bathing pools.
Multiple public/private; parts not accessible to the public
NHL

HAWAII COUNTY
Kailua-Kona, Island of Hawaii
KAMAKAHONU, RESIDENCE OF
KING KAMEHAMEHA I
On the northwest edge of Kailua Bay,
north and west of Kailua Wharf
1812

In 1812 King Kamehameha moved his residence from Honolulu to this site at Kamakahonu Cove, where he instituted some of his most constructive measures, including the promotion of agriculture and trade. Here also his son and successor, Liholiho, abolished the *kapu* (taboo) system and the native Hawaiian religion in 1819. These reforms paved the way for the influential role of American Protestant missionaries, who first came to Hawaii in 1820. Still standing are Kamehameha's personal heiau (temple) and the remains of his stone house.
Multiple public/private
NHL

HAWAII COUNTY
Kawaihae vicinity, Island of Hawaii
PUUKOHOLA HEIAU
North end of Hawaii off Hawaii 26,
about 1 mile southeast of Kawaihae
1791

Puukohola Heiau, built by King Kamehameha the Great, is associated with a principal event in his rise to power. At this temple he sacrificed Keoua, his chief rival, in the summer of 1791. With the death of Keoua, Kamehameha proceeded to unify the Hawaiian Islands and found the Kingdom of Hawaii. The temple, built of piled stones, is enclosed by walls on three sides. The seaward side is open and terraced.
Private
NHL

HAWAII COUNTY
Keauhou, Island of Hawaii
KEAUHOU HOLUA SLIDE
East of Hawaii 18
Date unknown

The Keauhou Holua (toboggan) Slide is Hawaii's largest and best-preserved slide. This extremely long, steep slide served as the "Olympic Games" holua of the Hawaiians. This pastime, restricted to chiefs, was extremely dangerous. The track was rock, layered with earth and made slippery by grass. Contestants slid rapidly down the slide on a specially-made wooden sled from seven to eighteen feet long.
Private
NHL

HAWAII COUNTY
Naalehu vicinity, Island of Hawaii
SOUTH POINT COMPLEX
South Cape, southern tip of Hawaii,
Ka'u District
124–1750

The South Point Complex is a group of sites which provides the longest and most complete record of human occupation in the Hawaiian Islands. The Puu Alii Sand Dune Site, which has given the earliest recorded date for the state of Hawaii, was a fisherman's habitation and workshop later covered by a sand dune and used as a burial ground. Another site still in use is a fisherman's heiau (temple) of the small court type. Other sites include mooring holes in a lava ledge, numerous carved and natural salt pans, and the Pohakuokeau Stone, which allegedly turns over each time a reign changes in Hawaii.
Multiple state/federal; not accessible to the public
NHL

HONOLULU COUNTY
Haleiwa vicinity, Island of Oahu
PUU O MAHUKA HEIAU
4 miles northeast of Haleiwa on
Hawaii 83, overlooking Waimea Bay
Date unknown

Puu o Mahuka Heiau is an important heiau (temple) in the Hawaiian Islands, for Oahu's greatest priests came from this district. The bodies of Captain George Vancouver's men were probably sacrificed at this heiau. They were killed by natives in 1792 while attempting to get water for their ship, the *Dedalus*. This low-walled court platform-type temple is the largest heiau on Oahu. Three adjoining enclosures form what was probably the heiau proper, with two smaller enclosures on the sea side not directly related.
State
NHL

HONOLULU COUNTY
Honolulu, Island of Oahu
IOLANI PALACE
364 S. King Street
1879–1882

Iolani Palace was the royal residence of the last two rulers of the Hawaiian Kingdom, King Kalakaua and Queen Liliuokalani. This important symbol of Hawaiian independence has been the seat of governmental authority for the Provisional Government, the Republic of Hawaii, the Territory of Hawaii, and now the State of Hawaii. The formal transfer of sovereignty to the United States took place on the palace steps on August 21, 1898. The ornate building has double *lanais* or porticos on all four sides. It is being restored.
State
NHL; HABS

HONOLULU COUNTY
Honolulu, Island of Oahu
KAWAIAHAO CHURCH AND MISSION HOUSES
957 Punchbowl Street; 553 S. King Street
1839–1842; 1821, 1822, and 1830–1831

Kawaiahao Church symbolizes the work of the Protestant missionaries in the Hawaiian Islands. Built by the Rev. Hiram Bingham, this Congregational church is of neo-classical design in typical New England style. The three associated mission houses also commemorate the work of the 19th-century missionaries in Christianizing the Hawaiians and revolutionizing Hawaiian culture, education, medical practices, and economics. The church is still an active house of worship.
Private
NHL; HABS

HONOLULU COUNTY
Kaneohe vicinity, Island of Oahu
HUILUA FISHPOND
On Kahana Bay, 13 miles north of Kaneohe on Hawaii 83 adjacent to Kahana Bay State Park
Date unknown

Huilua Fishpond is one of the last surviving ponds on the Island of Oahu. According to tradition, it was built by the Menehunes for hatching and keeping fish. The 200-acre pond is fed by fresh water springs and is affected by the tides. On the land side of the outlet was once a fishing shrine, most of which has been removed, but a line of large stones remains. A low stone wall separates the pond from the sea.
Private; not accessible to the public
NHL

HONOLULU COUNTY
Pearl City vicinity, Island of Oahu
U.S. NAVAL BASE, PEARL HARBOR
3 miles south of Pearl City on Hawaii 73
1911

Because of its strategic location, Pearl Harbor has been a key to the development and maintenance of American naval power in the Pacific. The U.S.S. *California* officially opened the base in 1911. In 1916 Pearl Harbor became headquarters of a Naval District and later the command center for the Pacific Fleet. Here Japan struck with a carrier-borne air force on December 7, 1941, catching most of the American fleet at anchor. This attack precipitated the United States into World War II. The U.S.S. *Arizona*, sunk that day with more than 1100 men entombed within, is now a memorial to all those who gave their lives at Pearl Harbor. The shrine on the ship's superstructure, which alone remains above water, is reached by motor launch.
Federal
NHL; HABS

KAUAI COUNTY
Koloa, Island of Kauai
OLD SUGAR MILL OF KOLOA
1841–1842

The Sugar Mill at Koloa was the successor to an earlier one on the first commercially successful sugar plantation in the Hawaiian Islands. A group of New Englanders with missionary backing leased land from King Kamehameha III in 1835 and organized their enterprise under the name of Ladd and Company. This venture marked the beginning of the sugar industry, destined to become Hawaii's largest. The square stone foundations of the mill chimney and the mill foundations still stand in the middle of the sugar fields.
Private
NHL

KAUAI COUNTY
Wailua vicinity, Island of Kauai
WAILUA COMPLEX OF HEIAUS
East coast of Kauai at the mouth of the Wailua River, Lihue District
Prehistoric

The Wailua Complex of Heiaus consists of a city of refuge, four heiaus (temples), royal birthstones, and a sacrificial rock. Together they form an important archeological complex covering a long period in Hawaiian prehistory and many facets of Hawaiian aboriginal culture. The ruins are in excellent condition, and the Holopoloku Heiau, which was restored in 1933, contains three reproductions of

Polynesian idols and a restored priest's house.
State
NHL

KAUAI COUNTY
Waimea, Island of Hauai
COOK LANDING SITE
2 miles southwest of Hawaii 50
1778

According to available evidence, Captain James Cook, the English explorer, made his first landing in the Hawaiian Islands at Waimea Beach in 1778. He was the first European to discover and land on the islands. At the time of discovery Cook was sailing across the Pacific Ocean from the Society Islands to the northwest coast of North America.
Multiple public
NHL

KAUAI COUNTY
Waimea vicinity, Island of Kauai
RUSSIAN FORT
On Hawaii 50, 200 yards southwest of the bridge over the Waimea River
1816–1817

Dr. Georg Anton Scheffer, an agent of Alexander Baranov, manager of the Russian American Company at Sitka, Alaska, built this stone fort in 1816–1817. Prevented from opening a trading establishment on Oahu by King Kamehameha I, he transferred his activities to Kauai. Sent to Kauai to salvage the cargo of a wrecked ship, Scheffer made an agreement with the king of Kauai to cede the island to Tsar Alexander I of Russia. American ship captains and Kamahameha succeeded in pressuring the king to expel the Russian and Aleutian settlers in 1817. The ruins of the fort commemorate the period of international rivalry for influence in the Hawaiian Islands.
Private
NHL

MAUI COUNTY
Hana vicinity, Island of Maui
PIILANIHALE HEIAU
4 miles north of Hana, at the mouth of Honomaele Gulch near Kalahu Point
16th century

Piilanihale Heiau, the largest temple in the Hawaiian Islands, illustrates a combination platform and court-type heiau. The building, which measures approximately 340 feet by 425 feet, is believed to have been built by Piilani, one of the great ruling chiefs of Maui. Inside the walls enclosing the court are "spirit" holes, many interior walls, and a number of stone images.
Private; accessible to the public (with special permission)
NHL

MAUI COUNTY
Kaupo vicinity, Island of Maui
LOALOA HEIAU
Southeast coast of Maui on Hawaii
31, about .25 mile north of Kaupo
16th century

Loaloa is a large platform heiau site overlooking the ocean. The temple, believed
to have been built by King Piilani, was the
center of a culture complex around Kaupo
which includes Hawaiian village sites and
other heiaus. The heiau is well preserved
and intact.
Private
NHL

MAUI COUNTY
Lahaina, Island of Maui
LAHAINA HISTORIC DISTRICT
West side of Maui on Hawaii 30
Mid–19th century

Lahaina preserves the atmosphere of a
mid–19th-century Hawaiian seaport. It is
prominently associated with the American
whaling industry in the Pacific, an important commercial activity that influenced
the Americanization of Hawaii and its subsequent annexation by the United States.
As the former capital of Maui, it was intermittently the residence of the Hawaiian
kings. American missionaries made
Lahaina a center of activity and left important architectural influences.
Multiple public/private
NHL; HABS

MAUI COUNTY
Lanai City vicinity, Island of Lanai
KAUNOLU VILLAGE SITE
On Kaunolu Bay, on the southwest
cape of the Island of Lanai
Date unknown

Kaunolu was once a vigorous Hawaiian
fishing community. Though the site has
been deserted since about 1880, its extreme isolation and dry climate have
preserved the ruins which represent nearly
all phases of Hawaiian culture. Halulu
Heiau, a temple and place of refuge,
dominates the village; a stone altar to the
fish god, Kunihi, is directly below. Other
features include house platforms, stone
shelters, pens and garden patches, a canoe
shed, petroglyphs, and several graves and
tombs.
Private
NHL

MAUI COUNTY
Ualapue vicinity, Island of Molokai
HOKUKANO-UALAPUE COMPLEX
Along Hawaii 45
Date unknown

The Hokukano-Ualapue Complex includes
six heiaus (temples) and two fishponds
which together form an important
archeological exhibit. Five of the six
heiaus, all of which are set in a vertical
line up the hillside, may have been used as
a place of refuge. The sixth was used for
human sacrifices. Both fishponds are still
being used for their original purposes.
Multiple public/private
NHL

Idaho

City of Rocks,
Cassia County, Idaho. *NPS*

ADA COUNTY
Boise
ASSAY OFFICE
210 Main Street
1870–1871, Alfred B. Mullett

The Assay Office Building, symbol of the importance of mining in the development of the Pacific Northwest, is one of the most important public buildings remaining from Idaho's territorial days. Measuring only 48 by 46 feet, the building is two stories in height and is built of coursed native sandstone. The hipped roof is topped with a raised ventilator. Prior to remodeling, the first floor contained the assayer's office, vaults, and safes for the storage of bullion, the assaying and melting rooms with their furnaces, and the laboratory. The second floor served as the living quarters of the chief assayer. Supplies, fuel rooms, and guard's quarters were in the basement. The primary business of the office was evaluating gold, silver, and other metals so that they could be priced and sold by their producers.
Federal
NHL

ADA COUNTY
Boise
MOORE-DeLAMAR HOUSE
807 Grove Street
1879

Christopher W. Moore, an Idaho miner, merchant, and banker, built this three-story, eclectic Victorian mansion. The high mansard roof originally had a decorative iron railing around its edge with matching balcony railings. The interior woodwork is ornately carved and still in good condition. Outside and inside many alterations have been made which have not changed the basic lines but have obscured or covered over original building materials. It is presently used as a rooming house.
Private

BANNOCK COUNTY
Fort Hall vicinity
FORT HALL
11 miles west of Fort Hall, Fort Hall Indian Reservation
1834

Fort Hall, located on the great bend of the Snake River near its confluence with the Portneuf River, occupied one of the most strategic sites of the American West. Built by Nathaniel Wyeth at the division of the Oregon and California trails, the fort was importantly associated with the fur trade, the overland migration, and the transportation and supply network to the gold mines in both Idaho and Montana. The precise location of the fort was once lost

due to flooding of the Snake River, but in 1916 the site was identified from artifacts taken from the ground at the presently established location. A group of low mounds encloses the site today.
Federal
NHL

BUTTE COUNTY
Arco vicinity
EXPERIMENTAL BREEDER
REACTOR NO. 1
National Reactor Testing Station
1950

The Experimental Breeder Reactor No. 1 demonstrated that nonfissionable uranium could be transmuted into fissionable uranium in a process producing more fissionable material than it consumes. It also produced the first usable amounts of electricity created by nuclear means and achieved a self-sustaining chain reaction using plutonium instead of uranium. The reactor was decommissioned in 1964.
Federal; not accessible to the public
NHL

CASSIA COUNTY
Almo vicinity
CITY OF ROCKS
City of Rocks State Park
1842–1875

The City of Rocks, one of the natural landmarks of the California Trail, was probably first opened in 1842 by the Joseph B. Chiles party, which was exploring for a satisfactory route for the trail. The site received its name from the formations of rock found in the valley of Circle Creek. Here thousands of emigrants camped, some of whom carved their names in the curious rock formations. Visible tracks left by wagon trains still remain. The area is largely in the same condition as when the wagon trains were passing through this section of the country.
State
NHL

CLEARWATER COUNTY (also in Idaho County and in Missoula County, Montana)
Lolo Hot Springs vicinity
LOLO TRAIL
Parallel to U.S. 12 on ridges of Bitterroot Mountains, from Lolo Pass to Weippe
1805

The Lolo Trail is the 150–odd miles of the Nez Perce Indian Buffalo Trail that was followed by Lewis and Clark in their 1805 crossing of the Bitterroot Mountains to navigable waters of the Columbia River

system. In general, the Lolo Trail traveled the high backbone of the mountain mass north of the Lochsa River. Today the trail extends through wilderness country from the mouth of Lolo Creek near Missoula, Montana, to Pierce, Idaho.
Federal
NHL

CLEARWATER COUNTY (also in Idaho, Lewis, and Nez Perce counties)
Spalding (park headquarters)
NEZ PERCE NATIONAL HISTORICAL
PARK
Within an area 90 miles south and 150 miles east of Spalding

The vast stretch of Nez Perce Indian country in northern Idaho is the setting for a new kind of historical park. Scattered over 12,000 square miles are 18 separate historic sites, many privately owned, which preserve and interpret the history and culture of the Nez Perce Indians and of the whites who eventually engulfed them. Some of the sites, such as the Weippe Prairie, are merely scenic views which recall significant events. Others, such as Coyote's Fishnet and Ant and Yellow Jacket, are natural formations which figure in the religion and legends of the Nez Perce. A few consist of historic buildings, as at Fort Lapwai, that are now open to the public.
Federal/non-federal
NPS; 3000 acres

CLEARWATER COUNTY
Weippe vicinity
WEIPPE PRAIRIE
South of Weippe and Idaho 11
1805

On September 20, 1805, members of the Lewis and Clark Expedition emerged from the Bitterroot Mountains onto the Weippe Prairie, where they first encountered the Nez Perce Indians. Here at the western terminus of the Lolo Trail, Meriwether Lewis and William Clark established friendly relations with these Indians which continued unbroken for 70 years. A few farmhouses and some fences are present on this upland plain of about 3000 feet elevation, but enough open area still remains to suggest the unspoiled prairie seen by Lewis and Clark.
Private
NHL

IDAHO COUNTY
LOLO TRAIL
Reference—see Clearwater County

IDAHO COUNTY
NEZ PERCE NATIONAL HISTORICAL
PARK
Reference—see Clearwater County

KOOTENAI COUNTY

Cataldo

CATALDO MISSION

Off U.S. 10

1848–1853

Jesuit missionaries labored at Cataldo Mission, formerly called the Sacred Heart Mission, from 1846 to 1877. During this time they revolutionized the life of the Indians, converting small nomadic hunting bands into farmers. This building, the oldest in Idaho, was built with no tools more complicated than broad axes and augers, pocketknives, and some ropes and pulleys. The outbuildings disappeared, however, and the mission fell into disrepair after 1877. The church is in excellent condition today due to restoration work carried on between 1928 and 1930.

Private

NHL

LEMHI COUNTY

Tendoy vicinity

LEMHI PASS

12 miles east of Tendoy off Idaho 28

1805

Lemhi Pass is associated with many events crucial to the success of the Lewis and Clark Expedition. It is the point where the party crossed the Continental Divide and where it left the United States as represented by the boundary of the Louisiana Purchase and entered Spanish territory. The success or failure of the expedition rested with the Shoshone Indians, who lived on either side of the crest of Lemhi Pass. The cooperation of these Indians in supplying horses, food, and guides made possible the overland journey of the party to the navigable waters of the Columbia River. Lemhi Pass, elevation 8,000 feet, has changed little in the intervening years.

Federal

NHL

LEWIS COUNTY

NEZ PERCE NATIONAL HISTORICAL PARK

Reference—see Clearwater County

NEZ PERCE COUNTY

NEZ PERCE NATIONAL HISTORICAL PARK

Reference—see Clearwater County

Cataldo Mission, Cataldo, Idaho. *NPS*

Illinois

Rookery Building, Chicago, Illinois. *Cervin Robinson for HABS*

Monadnock Building, Chicago, Illinois. *Richard Nickle*

Unity Temple, Oak Park, Illinois. *Richard Nickle*

Carson, Pirie, Scott and Company,
Chicago, Illinois. *HABS*

Bishop Hill Historic District,
Bishop Hill, Illinois.
*Illinois Department
of Conservation*

Holy Family Church,
Cahokia, Illinois.
Paul Piaget for HABS

ADAMS COUNTY
Quincy
WOOD, JOHN, MANSION
425 S. 12th Street
1835

John Wood, who arrived in 1822, was the first white settler in the Quincy area. As Quincy grew and prospered as a shipping center on the Mississippi River (until the Civil War it was the second largest city in Illinois), John Wood took part in local and state politics. His home is a frame dwelling with a pedimented Greek Revival Doric portico added in 1907. The house was moved from its original site in 1864.
Private

ALEXANDER COUNTY
Cairo
MAGNOLIA MANOR
2700 Washington Avenue
1869–1872

Cairo grew up on a delta at the confluence of the Ohio and Mississippi rivers. This location was a strategically important one and was fortified during the Civil War. After the war the city continued to prosper as a port and commercial center. A number of homes were built with the profits from mercantile endeavors. One such house was Magnolia Manor, home of Charles A. Galigher, a milling and lumber merchant. The Italianate Victorian style architecture is embellished by console window heads of fabricated sheet metal, twisted rope pattern wooden window frames, and ornate wooden cornice and eaves brackets. Ornamental cast iron decorates the verandas and balconies. Inside are decorative plaster cornices, Carrara marble fireplaces, ornate chandeliers, and hand carved furniture.
Private
HABS

CHAMPAIGN COUNTY
Urbana
ALTGELD HALL, UNIVERSITY OF ILLINOIS
University of Illinois campus, corner of Wright and John Streets
1896–1897, Nathan C. Ricker and James M. White

During his term as governor of Illinois (1892–1896), John Peter Altgeld did much to increase the size and academic quality of the University of Illinois. The three-story Altgeld Hall, now the library building, is Richardsonian Romanesque in style and built of quarry-faced Minnesota sandstone. Its asymmetrical shape is accentuated by a 132–foot tower on the east facade.
State

CHAMPAIGN COUNTY
Urbana
MORROW PLOTS, UNIVERSITY OF ILLINOIS
Gregory Drive at Matthews Avenue
1876

The Morrow Plots at the University of Illinois were the first soil experiment plots established by a college in the United States. Professor Manly Miles laid out the first three of these in 1876, each one-half acre in size. In 1879 Professor George E. Morrow laid out seven additional plots. The purpose of the experiment was to prove that the continuous growing of corn would deplete prairie soil and, conversely, that crop rotation would increase plant yields. By 1904 the number of plots had been reduced to six, each one-tenth of an acre. They continue to provide data of the effects of crop rotation and the impact of organic and chemical nutriments on plant yields.
State
NHL

COOK COUNTY
Chicago
AUDITORIUM BUILDING, ROOSEVELT UNIVERSITY
Michigan Avenue and Congress Street
1887–1889, Adler and Sullivan

Dankmar Adler made Louis Sullivan his partner in 1881, and the partnership lasted until Adler's death in 1900. When the firm received the commission to construct the combination theater, hotel, and office building, they were accepting the biggest building project theretofore in Chicago's history. Outside, the first three stories are rusticated gray granite, and the upper seven are dressed Indiana buff limestone. A cast iron interior frame was used with wrought iron trusses; concrete reinforced with timber and steel rails was employed to equalize settlement of the building. Inside, the rich ornamentation is Sullivan's, and a variety of materials (onyx, marble, wood, and mosaic) was dramatically employed.
Public
HABS

COOK COUNTY
Chicago
CARSON, PIRIE, SCOTT AND COMPANY
1 S. State Street
1899, 1903–1904, Louis Sullivan

Carson, Pirie, Scott and Company was Louis Sullivan's last large commercial commission. The store was designed in two sections, the earlier one is nine stories

high, and the later, twelve. An iron and steel framework supports the structure which is most notable for its elaborate ironwork ornament on the first and second floor facades. Sullivan's designs, many of which were executed by his assistant George G. Elmslie, combine organic and geometric shapes in intricate and delicate patterns. This type of ornament is the hallmark of his work.
Private
HABS

COOK COUNTY
Chicago
CHARNLEY, JAMES, HOUSE
1365 N. Astor Street
1891–1892, Adler and Sullivan

The plan and construction of the Charnley House are attributed to Adler and Sullivan, but the low, horizontal lines suggest that the design was probably executed by Frank Lloyd Wright, a draftsman in Sullivan's office. A base or dado on the first floor exterior is sheathed with smooth-faced limestone ashlar, and a limestone belt course separates the second and third floors. Yellow Roman brick is the primary wall material. Sullivanesque ornament on stained wood decorates the projecting second-floor balcony, and similar shapes appear on the front door.
Private; not accessible to the public
HABS

COOK COUNTY
Chicago
CLARKE, HENRY B., HOUSE
4526 S. Wabash Avenue
1836

The Clarke House is regarded as the oldest extant building is Chicago. It is a rectangular frame dwelling of rough-hewn oak beams. Greek Revival elements are evident in the low-pitched roof pediment and the simple moldings. There are tall narrow windows on the main floor and small eyebrow windows on the second. The first-floor rooms are large and have high ceilings. They are enhanced by Georgia pine trim and marble fireplaces. The original columned portico on the front facade has been removed and an Italianate Victorian cupola added at the center of the roof.
Private
HABS

COOK COUNTY
Chicago
GLESSNER, JOHN J., HOUSE
1800 S. Prairie Avenue
1886, Henry Hobson Richardson

The U-shaped Glessner House was designed by Richardson in his

Romanesque style characterized by the use of stone, the massive solidity of the building, and the employment of towers, gables, and round-arched door openings. The exterior walls are stone while the courtyard walls are brick. Inside, the house has been extensively paneled in oak.
Private
HABS

COOK COUNTY
Chicago
HULL HOUSE
800 S. Halsted Street
1856

On September 4, 1889, Jane Addams moved into Hull House in the slums of Chicago. Here she worked to improved the lot of the poor and the unfortunate by providing a wide variety of social services ranging from feeding and lodging destitute persons and helping them to find jobs to providing day schools for children of working mothers. Although not the first settlement house in the United States, Hull House gained international notice. The two-story brick building is now included within a new campus of the University of Illinois. The building, the only one remaining of the original complex, has been restored to its original appearance.
State
NHL; HABS

COOK COUNTY
Chicago
McCLURG BUILDING
218 S. Wabash Avenue
1898–1900, Holabird and Roche

The nine-story McClurg Building rests on pile foundations and caissons under the south party wall. Its interior structure is supported by steel beams and two rows of interior iron columns. The facade is terra cotta with a large number of regularly spaced windows which divide the building into three bays. All interior space has been remodeled.
Private
HABS

COOK COUNTY
Chicago
MADLENER, ALBERT F., HOUSE
4 W. Burton
1902, Richard E. Schmidt

The Madlener House embodies many characteristics of Frank Lloyd Wright's Prairie School of architecture. Three stories high and cubical in shape, it resembles a Florentine palazzo, though lacking the traditional classic external ornament. Exterior walls are brick. Buff-colored Indiana limestone is used for belt courses, window and door enframements, roof cornice, and horizontal banding on the first floor. There are patterned brick rectangles alternating with window groupings on the third floor. The main doorway is accentuated by a wide limestone frame incised with Sullivanesque ornament. The overall impression created by the house is one of simple solidity. Interior alterations have been made to the original room arrangement.
Private
HABS

COOK COUNTY
Chicago
MONADNOCK BUILDING
53 W. Jackson Boulevard
1891, Burnham and Root

The 16-story Monadnock Building is a monumental masonry skyscraper, the highest wall-bearing structure in Chicago. Cast iron columns and wrought iron beams support part of the floor weight. The rest of the load is carried by the walls themselves. Dimensions are 70 feet by 420 feet at ground level and the overall height is 215 feet. Designer John Wellborn Root chose unornamented brick for the exterior wall surfaces to convey a sense of strength and solidity which he felt was associated with American business.
Private
HABS

COOK COUNTY
Chicago
PULLMAN HISTORIC DISTRICT
Bounded on the north by 103rd Street, on the east by C.S.S. and S.B. Railroad spur tracks, on the south by 115th Street, and on the West by Cottage Grove Avenue
1880

George M. Pullman (1831–1897), industrialist and inventor of the Pullman sleeping car, commissioned architect Solon S.

Boman and landscape architect Nathan F. Garrett to design a self-contained company town for his employees which was to include parks, shops, recreational and cultural centers, a church, school, bank, health facilities, and a variety of houses. This project developed into a model town, and by the 1890's it had a population of 11,800. The residences were predominantly row houses, and all structures were made of locally produced brick. The town of Pullman was generally acknowledged to the the cleanest, most comfortable, and most complete company-sponsored settlement in America of its time. It was designated the most perfect town in the world at the Prague International Hygienic and Pharmaceutical Exposition of 1896. Today hundreds of the original dwellings remain and are virtually unaltered on the exterior.
Multiple public/private
HABS

COOK COUNTY
Chicago
RELIANCE BUILDING
32 N. State Street
1895, D. H. Burnham and Company

John Root was commissioned in 1890 to design a 16-story office building on this site. Four stories of an extant structure were jacked up while construction began on Root's basement and ground floor. In 1894 Daniel Burnham's firm undertook the designing of 14 additional stories to replace the four already on Root's structure. This new building had a steel framework and was covered with terra cotta sheathing in contrast to the granite first floor. Vertical members on the facade are narrow. Windows form continuous bands and are "Chicago windows"—large single, fixed panes of glass which fill an entire bay except for narrow, movable, double hung sash in the projecting bays. The building stands 200 feet high.
Private

COOK COUNTY
Chicago
ROBIE, FREDERICK C., HOUSE
5757 S. Woodlawn Avenue
1907–1909, Frank Lloyd Wright

The Robie House was designed by Frank Lloyd Wright for Frederick Carleton Robie, a native Chicagoan who had made his fortune in bicycles and sewing

machines. The brick house, with its low horizontal emphasis, was designed by Wright in his Prairie style to fit the confines of a corner city lot. He utilized an open plan focused on a large central chimney mass, formed windows in continuous strips, and projected the roof in wide cantilevers. He continued inside walls out to the exterior to tie the surrounding landscape to the house, incorporated the garage as a part of the house, and integrated the mechanical systems into the total design. The house has won international acclaim as a monumental achievement in modern architecture.
Private
NHL; HABS

COOK COUNTY
Chicago
ROOKERY BUILDING
209 S. LaSalle Street
1886, Burnham and Root

Daniel Burnham and John Root were in partnership from 1873 to 1891. Most of the buildings they undertook in Chicago have been demolished. The Rookery Building, which is one of a few that remain, combines skeletal cast iron columns and spandrel beams supporting masonry with granite and brick and terra cotta. A transitional structure resulted which presaged the modern steel frame office building. Standing eleven stories above a basement, the Rookery surrounds a large interior light court. Frank Lloyd Wright remodeled the ground floor lobby in 1905.
Private
HABS

COOK COUNTY
Chicago
ROOM 405, GEORGE HERBERT JONES LABORATORY, THE UNIVERSITY OF CHICAGO
S. Ellis Avenue between E. 57th and 58th Streets
1942

In Room 405 on August 18, 1942, a group of chemists under the direction of Dr. Glenn T. Seaborg first isolated a pure compound of the man-made element plutonium. This sample was the first synthetically produced isotope of any element seen by man. On September 10, 1942, B. B. Cunningham and L. B. Werner prepared the first weighable sample of a synthetic element. This first isolation and weighing of plutonium, a basic fuel for nuclear reactors, was a milestone in the development of nuclear energy. The room in which these events occurred is essentially unchanged.
Private
NHL

COOK COUNTY
Chicago
SITE OF FIRST SELF-SUSTAINING NUCLEAR REACTION
S. Ellis Avenue between E. 56th and 57th Streets
1942

Here, in a converted squash-racquets court in the West Stands of Stagg Field, man produced the first self-sustaining nuclear chain reaction. Under the direction of the Italian-born physicist Enrico Fermi, the final control rods were pulled out on the afternoon of December 2, 1942, and the world's first nuclear chain reactor continued to operate for 28 minutes. The original pile of alternate layers of uranium and graphite used in the experiment was disassembled and moved to the Argonne National Laboratory in 1943.
Private
NHL

COOK COUNTY
Chicago
TAFT, LORADO, MIDWAY STUDIOS
6016 S. Ingleside Avenue
Early 20th century

A sculptor of realistic works of monumental scale, Lorado Taft executed numerous memorials, fountains, group sculptures, and military monuments. Among them are "Awakening of the Flowers" (1893), "Columbus Memorial Fountain" (1912), and "Lincoln-Douglas Debate" (1936). From 1886 to 1929 he lectured and taught at the Chicago Art Institute and was subsequently associated with the University of Chicago and the University of Illinois. His *History of American Sculpture* (1903) was the first comprehensive work on the subject. He also encouraged art education in the public schools. The Midway Studios, the nucleus of which is an old hip-roofed barn, are used as classrooms and studios by the University of Chicago.
Private
NHL

COOK COUNTY
Evanston
WILLARD, FRANCES, HOUSE
1730 Chicago Avenue
1865

Frances Willard made the temperance movement nationally significant by publicizing the social evils of liquor. After resigning her position at Northwestern University in 1874, she turned her full attention to the movement. Following tenure as president of the Chicago Women's Christian Temperance Union, she became president of the national organization in 1879 and the international organization (which had been organized in 1883 largely through her efforts) in 1891. Her house, essentially unchanged and furnished with many of her belongings, is presently the headquarters of the Women's Christian Temperance Union.
Private
NHL; HABS

COOK COUNTY
Forest View
CHICAGO PORTAGE NATIONAL HISTORIC SITE
Forest Preserve District, northwest corner of S. Harlem Avenue at the Chicago Sanitary and Ship Canal
17th, 18th, and 19th centuries

Preserved here is a portion of the famous portage discovered by Jacques Marquette and Louis Joilet in 1673. It was used by French and American pioneers to link the waters of the Great Lakes with those of the Mississippi River. As a tie between these two key waterways, it was a major economic foundation of Chicago, now one of America's largest cities.
Private
NPS: 91.20 acres

COOK COUNTY
Oak Park
GALE, MRS. THOMAS H., HOUSE
6 Elizabeth Court
1909, Frank Lloyd Wright

The Gale House is a notable example of Frank Lloyd Wright's Prairie School of architecture. It is a compact dwelling composed of interlocking rectilinear forms surrounding a fireplace core. The scale is smaller than many of Wright's residences, but the cantilevered roof, strip windows, and dark horizontal wooden bands, all hallmarks of Wright's work, are evident.
Private; not accessible to the public

COOK COUNTY
Oak Park
UNITY TEMPLE
875 Lake Street
1906, Frank Lloyd Wright

Frank Lloyd Wright designed Unity Temple unlike traditional centers of worship. Rather than a steeple pointing skyward, the architect planned to install a rooftop skylight. Structurally, the temple is a concrete cube connected to a rectangular parish house. Both are constructed of poured concrete and have few exterior openings. Inside, the walls are stark and unornamented except for dark horizontal and vertical bands on the ceiling, walls, and balconies.
Private
NHL; HABS

COOK COUNTY
River Forest
DRUMMOND, WILLIAM E., HOUSE
559 Edgewood Place
1909, William E. Drummond

William E. Drummond was a follower of Frank Lloyd Wright and his Prairie School of architecture. Drummond was employed for a time in Wright's Chicago office. In this house horizontal planes are emphasized on the exterior by the cantilevered roofs and projecting window bays. The light concrete walls are relieved by dark bands of wood outlining windows, roofs, and large central blocks of space on the walls. Strips of windows, rather than single or double glass openings, maximize the amount of natural light that penetrates the interior.
Private; not accessible to the public
HABS

COOK COUNTY
River Forest
WINSLOW, WILLIAM H., HOUSE AND STABLE
515 Auvergne Place
1893, Frank Lloyd Wright

The William Winslow House was Frank Lloyd Wright's first independent commission after leaving the firm of Adler and Sullivan. A low roof above a compact, two-story house mass is characteristic of Wright's later Prairie style. Louis Sullivan's influence on Wright is manifest in the round arched porte cochere and the modeled plaster frieze marking the second floor. Yellow-orange Tiffany bricks constitute the first floor facade, the doorway is surrounded by limestone, and the frieze is painted dark brown. The stable, or garage, which is separate, is built of wood.
Private; not accessible to the public
HABS

COOK COUNTY
Riverside
COONLEY, AVERY, HOUSE
300 Scottswood Road and 281 Bloomingbank Road
1907–1909, Frank Lloyd Wright

The Avery Coonley House is a U-shaped two-story residence which Frank Lloyd Wright called "the most successful of my houses. . . ." In his design Wright utilized a centrifugal plan, a raised basement, low-pitched overhanging roofs, broad central chimneys, flowing interior spaces, windows in unbroken strips, and continuous inside to outside walls to unite house and garden. The stucco-covered frame walls rest on a flat concrete base. In the upper story gold and orange tiles have been pressed into the stucco and arranged in geometric patterns. All wood trim is

stained brown. The house has been divided into two residences.
Private; not accessible to the public
NHL

COOK COUNTY
Riverside
RIVERSIDE LANDSCAPE ARCHITECTURE DISTRICT
Bounded roughly by 26th Street on the north, Harlem Avenue on the east, Ogden Avenue and the Des Plaines River on the south, and Forbes Road on the west
1869, Frederick Law Olmsted and Calvert Vaux

Frederick Law Olmsted was a principal advocate of open space in American communities. His plan was to lead people from crowded tenements into model, planned communities in two steps: first, by bringing nature into the city and setting aside land for parks, and, secondly, by making nature an integral part of the urban community. As a result of his reputation as the foremost landscape architect in America, Olmsted was invited by the Riverside Improvement Company to design a model community. The result was Riverside, where families would dwell together amid a setting of wooded groves and meadows along a curving stream; in this way the enjoyment of open spaces and parks with their undisturbed natural appearance was to become a part of everyday urban living for all economic classes. Riverside is the first planned model community in the nation, and as such it attracted the work of outstanding architects. Homes by William LeBaron Jenney, inventor of the skyscraper, Frank Lloyd Wright, Louis Sullivan, and William Drummond are encompassed in the original Olmsted plan.
Multiple public/private

COOK COUNTY
Winnetka
LLOYD, HENRY DEMAREST, HOME (THE WAYSIDE)
830 Sheridan Road
1878

A paramount critic of America's industrial monopoly during the 1880's and 1890's was Henry Demarest Lloyd. During his years with the *Chicago Tribune* he increasingly criticized the consolidation and centralization of business. One of his most notable accomplishments was his book, *Wealth Against Commonwealth*, which appeared in 1894. This remains a landmark in the history of monopolism. The Wayside, his rambling brick house, contains many original furnishings and has been little changed since Lloyd's death in 1903.
Private; not accessible to the public
NHL

HANCOCK COUNTY
Nauvoo
NAUVOO HISTORIC DISTRICT
c. 1840

Nauvoo was the headquarters and principal town of the Mormons before the exodus that took them first to Omaha, Nebraska, and finally to Salt Lake Valley, Utah. The settlement flourished until 1845, when violence against the Mormons resulted in the death of Joseph Smith, the church's founder and leader. The continued hostility of Illinois authorities made a move necessary, and in 1846 most of the inhabitants abandoned the city. Under the leadership of Brigham Young, they began the trek westward which brought them to Utah in 1847. Among the Mormon buildings of the 1840's which remain are the Joseph Smith Homestead, the Brigham Young House, the "Time and Seasons" building, and the old Mormon arsenal.
Multiple private
NHL; HABS

HENRY COUNTY
Bishop Hill
BISHOP HILL HISTORIC DISTRICT
Roughly bounded on the north by Edwards River; on the east by Erickson Street; on the south by the Bishop Hill corporate line; on the west by Johnson Street, and Kronberg Street from the river to Knox Street
1846–1861

In the mid–19th century a movement to reform the Swedish Lutheran State Church began but met with little success. By 1846 a group of 1,100 emigrated to America, and, under the leadership of Eric Jansson, founded a colony in Illinois. Bishop Hill was named for Jansson's birthplace in Sweden. The settlers owned all their land in common, lived in communal buildings, and shared equally the labor and profits of the agricultural economy. After Jansson's death in 1850, the colony lacked capable leadership, and in 1861 all goods were distributed to the remaining settlers. Twelve pre–1861 buildings and one outbuilding still stand, and these plus 30 post–1861 Greek Revival or Victorian structures compose the historic district. Restoration work is in progress.
Multiple public/private
HABS

JO DAVIESS COUNTY
Galena
GALENA HISTORIC DISTRICT
That part of the city of Galena recorded as the city limits on March 28, 1838, and all subdivisions added

to the city prior to December 31, 1859
19th century

Lead sulphide, or galena, was first mined by the French in the late 17th century. Crude mines began to operate during the next one hundred years. By 1816 traders were buying lead from the Indians, and ten years later a post office was established and town houses began to supplant ruder log dwellings in the growing riverport. Within the historic district architectural styles are mixed, and simple homes of the 1820's and 1830's are scattered among later, more elaborate Greek Revival and Victorian structures. Commercial and public buildings of limestone, brick, wood, and cast iron are vestiges of Galena's period of prosperity (1830–1860). Galena had declined as a port and mining area by the 1860's due to the rise of railroads and falling prices on lead and zinc. Today the town retains a large number of its old homes, commercial, public, and industrial structures in an unaltered condition, thus preserving the atmosphere of a once wealthy and bustling riverport and mining town.
Multiple public/private
HABS

JO DAVIESS COUNTY
Galena
GRANT, ULYSSES S., HOME
511 Bouthillier Street
1857

In August 1865, the town of Galena presented this house to the victorious Union commander, Ulysses S. Grant, when he returned to that city after the Civil War. Grant lived here until he became Secretary of War in 1867 and returned to the house after serving as the eighteenth President of the United States, 1869–1877. On April 27, 1904, Grant's son Frederick Dent Grant presented the house to the city to be kept as a memorial. The house contains a parlor, library, and bedrooms furnished with Grant family possessions.
State
NHL

KNOX COUNTY
Galesburg
OLD MAIN, KNOX COLLEGE
Knox College campus
1856–1857, Charles Ulricson

Old Main, central building of the Knox College campus, is noteworthy because one of the Lincoln-Douglas debates was held here in 1858. These debates between Stephen A. Douglas and Abraham Lincoln, his Republican challenger for the

United States Senate, keynoted the issues of the sectional controversy which was carrying the Nation toward civil war. Although Lincoln lost the election, his logic and oratory brought national attention to him and strength to the new Republican party. Extensive restoration of Old Main was undertaken in the 1930's.
Private
NHL

LA SALLE COUNTY
Ottawa vicinity
OLD KASKASKIA VILLAGE
4 miles west of Ottawa on U.S. 6
17th century

Old Kaskaskia is the best-documented historic Indian site in the Illinois River Valley. It was first recorded in 1673 by Louis Joliet and Père Jacques Marquette, who canoed up the Illinois River returning from their pioneer voyage down the Mississippi River. The village was then inhabited by the Kaskaskia, one of the bands which composed the Illinois tribe. Abandoned in 1680, it was apparently reoccupied after the French completed Fort St. Louis on nearby Starved Rock in 1683. It was permanently abandoned by 1691.
Private; not accessible to the public
NHL

LA SALLE COUNTY
Ottawa vicinity
STARVED ROCK
6 miles from Ottawa on Ill. 71, Starved Rock State Park
1673

Starved Rock was the first major center of French influence in the Illinois country. The first white men to visit the promontory were Louis Joliet and Père Jacques Marquette, who were returning northward after their pioneer journey down the Mississippi River. Here on the lower rapids of the Illinois River, Robert LaSalle built Fort St. Louis in 1683 to control the strategic waterway linking Canada with the Mississippi Valley. Under mounting pressure from the Iroquois Indians, the fort was abandoned in 1691, but some traces of the Indian settlements that clustered around it may still be seen.
State
NHL

MASSAC COUNTY (also in Pope County)
Brookport vicinity
KINCAID SITE
East of Brookport on the Ohio River
c. 1200–1300

The Kincaid Site is one of the major temple mound sites in southern Illinois. Intensive archeological excavations in the 1930's revealed that the site was probably a trade station along the Ohio River. Because of its strategic location between the Cahokia site and other temple mound areas further south, it may have influenced several other centers including the Angel Mounds site in Indiana and Mississippian sites in southeast Missouri.
Private; not accessible to the public
NHL

OGLE COUNTY
Grand Detour
DEERE, JOHN, HOME AND SHOP
1836

In the small village of Grand Detour John Deere invented and manufactured a steel plow that transformed farming in the rich land of the Old Northwest. First manufactured in 1837, the plow made a clean furrow instead of becoming clogged with dirt. The introduction of this tool led to intensive cultivation of vast areas of Ohio, Indiana, and Illinois. In 1920 a front porch, fireplace, and chimney were added to Deere's story-and-a-half clapboard house.
Private
NHL

PIKE COUNTY
Pittsfield
PITTSFIELD EAST SCHOOL
400 E. Jefferson
1862–1866, John M. Van Osdel

Van Osdel, who also designed the Illinois Executive Mansion in Springfield, practiced in Chicago. The Pittsfield School is the only one of his buildings which has not been altered. It is a brick structure highlighted by two-story pilasters, a bracketed wood cornice, and a two-stage clock tower. Each facade has a projecting, pedimented central section extending forward from the central mass. Windows on the ground floor have segmental arches, and those above are round arched. A limestone string course separates the floors.
Municipal

POPE COUNTY
KINCAID SITE
Reference—see Massac County

RANDOLPH COUNTY
Ellis Grove vicinity
MENARD, PIERRE, HOUSE
Fort Kaskaskia State Park
c. 1802

Pierre Menard was born in Canada and came to Kaskaskia in 1790. He was a trader and later became active in state politics, serving as presiding officer of the first territorial legislature and first lieutenant governor of the state in 1818. His home is a two-and-one-half-story French Colonial raised cottage with a wide *galerie* or veranda on two sides and the front. A reconstructed stairway leads from the ground to the *galerie*. Menard used the stone basement to store his trading goods. Almost all of the extant structure is original including interior hardware and much of the window glass. Some reconstruction work on the *galerie* has been done. The upper floor was never finished and the trusswork is visible. Two outbuildings, a stone kitchen, and a brick smokehouse, adjoin the main dwelling.
State
NHL

RANDOLPH COUNTY
Modoc vicinity
MODOC ROCKSHELTER
2 miles north of Modoc
c. 8000 B.C. to A.D. 1500

Modoc Rockshelter is one of the most important archeological sites discovered in the midwest to date. It contains stratified deposits giving evidence of four periods of Archaic Indian occupation as well as one later period of prehistoric Indian life. Excavations at the site indicate that the Archaic cultures of the eastern United States may have been of an antiquity comparable to that of the western hunting cultures.
State; not accessible to the public
NHL

RANDOLPH COUNTY
Prairie du Rocher vicinity
FORT DE CHARTRES
Terminus of Ill. 155 west of Prairie du Rocher, Fort Chartres State Park
1753–1758

Fort de Chartres was the center of French civil and military government in the Illinois country in the 18th century. During the French and Indian War the British never attacked this imposing fortification, and it was not relinquished to the British until 1765, two years after British victory in the war. In 1772 the British destroyed the fort. Built of massive stone walls, the post enclosed four acres of ground with

barracks, officers' quarters, kitchen, powder magazine, and outhouses. Much of the fort has been reconstructed.
State
NHL; HABS

ROCK ISLAND COUNTY
Rock Island
ROCK ISLAND ARSENAL
Rock Island in the Mississippi River

Located on an island midway between Davenport, Iowa, and Moline, Illinois, the Rock Island Arsenal was established by an act of Congress on July 11, 1862, and is still operative. On the arsenal grounds are stone production shops with cast and wrought iron columns on their facades, and Italianate officers' quarters built of limestone with hooded windows and ornate cornice brackets (these quarters date from 1870 to 1874 and two others were added in 1905 and 1907). Later structures were added during both World Wars. Rock Island's second commander, Thomas Jefferson Rodman, developed the Rodman gun. Other structures or sites on the arsenal grounds are Fort Armstrong on the western end of the island, which was garrisoned between 1816 and 1836 and burned in 1855; and the frame home of George Davenport, a trader who built the first permanent dwelling in the area in 1833. In 1835 the famous slave Dred Scott lived at the arsenal for a few months with his master who was an army surgeon, and from 1863 to 1865 a Confederate prison was maintained on the island.
Federal
HABS

ST. CLAIR COUNTY
EADS BRIDGE
Reference—See St. Louis, Missouri

ST. CLAIR COUNTY
Cahokia
CHURCH OF THE HOLY FAMILY
Just off Ill. 3
1786–1799

Catholic priests founded a mission at Cahokia in 1699. The present structure, typical of French Colonial upright log construction, served as parish church until 1891. Rectangular in shape, the building measures 74 feet long by 32 feet wide. *Poteaux sur sole* or posts on sill construction was employed for the walls. Two rectangular wings were added in 1833. In 1949–1951 the church foundations and walls were repaired and reinforced, a belfry was added, and the interior remodeled.
Private
NHL

ST. CLAIR COUNTY
Collinsville vicinity
CAHOKIA MOUNDS
7850 Collinsville Road, Cahokia
Mounds State Park
600–1400

Cahokia, the largest prehistoric Indian site in the United States, was the fountainhead of Mississippian culture. The area is dominated by the great Monks Mound, nearly 100 feet high. At one time the site contained nearly 100 mounds and covered three square miles. The central portion of the area is preserved by a state park, but a great many of the outlying mounds have been destroyed by recent construction.
State
NHL

SANGAMON COUNTY
Springfield
EDWARDS PLACE
700 N. 4th Street
1833, 1850 (enlarged)

Benjamin S. Edwards, son of Illinois' first territorial governor, purchased a home in 1843 which he later enlarged and remodeled to the present two-and-one-half-story Italian Villa style residence. Abraham Lincoln, who was then serving in the state legislature, was a frequent visitor in the Edwards home. In 1913 Benjamin Edwards' daughter deeded the house to the Springfield Art Association for use as a club, museum, and art school. The one-story structure on the east side of the house is an art gallery added in the late 1930's.
Private
HABS

SANGAMON COUNTY
Springfield
LINCOLN HOME NATIONAL HISTORIC SITE
8th and Jackson Streets
1844

In this house Abraham Lincoln spent the crucial years from 1844 to 1860, during which time he rose from a small-town lawyer to the Presidency of the United States. On May 17, 1860, Lincoln received a committee here from the Republican Nominating Convention bearing formal notification of his nomination as the party's presidential candidate. During the campaign he received well-wishers, and here he bade farewell to his friends on the eve of his departure for Washington, D.C. In this house, the only one he ever owned, Lincoln and his wife spent most of their married life, and in it three of their sons were born.
Federal
NPS; 12.28 acres

SANGAMON COUNTY
Springfield
LINCOLN TOMB
Oak Ridge Cemetery
1874

The Lincoln Tomb is the final resting place of Abraham Lincoln, sixteenth President of the United States, his wife, and three of their four sons. Immediately after his death on April 15, 1865, citizens of Springfield spearheaded a drive to erect a tomb and memorial to the martyred President. During the construction his body lay in a temporary vault near the present memorial. In 1901 it was placed in a cement vault ten feet below the floor of the tomb, a short distance from the cenotaph which the visitor sees today.
State
NHL

SANGAMON COUNTY
Springfield
OLD STATE CAPITOL
Bounded by 5th, 6th, Adams, and
Washington Streets
1837, John F. Rague

The Sangamon County Courthouse served as the fifth capitol of Illinois, 1837–1876.

Here Abraham Lincoln sat in the State legislature, 1840–1841, argued cases before the State Supreme Court, and accepted the Republican nomination for United States Senator. On the last occasion, June 16, 1858, he made his noted "House Divided" speech. The original two-story rectangular stone building, set in the middle of a city block, is designed in the Greek Revival style. The north and south elevations have a central projecting portico with four Doric columns supporting a low pediment. Pilasters divide the window bays of the elevations. The central interior rotunda is covered by a raised dome. Changes made in 1899 considerably altered the character of the building, and it is currently undergoing restoration.
State
NHL; HABS

WILL COUNTY
Joliet vicinity
ILLINOIS AND MICHIGAN CANAL
(LOCKS AND TOWPATH)
7 miles southwest of Joliet on U.S. 6,
Channahon State Park
1848

Just as the Erie Canal made New York City the dominant metropolis in the East, so did the Illinois and Michigan Canal propel Chicago into prominence as a leading grain market and meat packing center in the Midwest. Linking Chicago to the Mississippi River, the canal completed a continuous waterway to New York City. Though commercial use of the waterway ended in 1933, many of its locks and other appurtenances had been restored by 1940. The lock at Channahon is still in working condition.
State
NHL

Indiana

James Whitcomb Riley House, Indianapolis, Indiana.
Jack E. Boucher for HABS

Old Vanderburgh County Courthouse,
Evansville, Indiana. *Aubrey A. Larsen*

Rappite Dye House, New Harmony, Indiana.
J. Waring Doane for HABS

KNOX COUNTY
Vincennes
GEORGE ROGERS CLARK
NATIONAL HISTORICAL PARK
18th and 19th centuries

At this site is honored George Rogers Clark, frontier leader of the American Revolution. Nearby is the site of Fort Sackville, the British fortification captured by Clark, then a lieutenant colonel in the Virginia militia, following a surprise attack on February 25, 1779. The George Rogers Clark Memorial commemorates Clark's achievements and the history of the old Northwest Territory. Also within the park are the two-room frame building that served as the first capitol of the Indiana Territory from 1800 to 1813; Grouseland, home of President William Henry Harrison, now a registered National Historic Landmark; and St. Francis Xavier Catholic Church, built in 1823–1824.
Federal
NPS; 17 acres

KNOX COUNTY
Vincennes
HARRISON, WILLIAM HENRY,
HOME (GROUSELAND)
3 W. Scott Street
1803–1804

Grouseland was the residence of William Henry Harrison from about 1804–1812. During this period Harrison was territorial governor of Indiana and a foremost defender of white settlement against Indian tribes attempting to block the tide of westward expansion. It was here that Harrison met the Indian leader Tecumseh, and it was from here also in 1811 that he launched the campaign which ended in the bloody battle of Tippecanoe, at which time Tecumseh's followers were scattered. William Henry Harrison was President of the United States from March 4 to April 4, 1841, when he died in office.
Private
NHL; HABS

MARION COUNTY
Indianapolis
ALLISON MANSION
3200 Cold Spring Road
1911–1914

The lavishness and workmanship of this early 20th-century home made it a showplace of its time. Red brick veneer was applied to poured concrete reinforced with steel on the exterior, and the stone trim was hand carved. Inside, each room is elaborately decorated. Wall coverings are velour or silk, floors are oak parquet, and the woodwork is solid mahogany. The ground floor den has a sloping Gothic ceiling covered with sporting scenes of carved

pressed leather. Each of the five second-floor bedrooms has its own fireplace, and there is a 30- by 60-foot heated indoor swimming pool on the ground level. James A. Allison co-founded the Prest-O-Lite Company which manufactured headlights for early automobiles. He founded the Allison Engineering Company, designer and developer of high-powered motor launch engines later adapted to airplanes.
Private
HABS

MARION COUNTY
Indianapolis
HARRISON, BENJAMIN, HOME
1204 N. Delaware Street
1874–1875

Benjamin Harrison, twenty-third President of the United States, accepted the Republican Party's nomination for the presidency in the back parlor of this house on July 4, 1888. Prior to his term as President (1889–1893), Harrison served as U.S. Senator (1881–1887). Ten of the original 16 rooms of the brick house have been restored. Today the house, which Harrison occupied from 1872–1901, contains much of the original furniture.
Private
NHL

MARION COUNTY
Indianapolis
MILITARY PARK
Bounded on the west by Blackford Street, on the north by New York Street, on the east by West Street, and on the south by the Canal
19th century

Military Park was created in the mid–19th century from a tract of land given to the state of Indiana by the federal government for use as a state capitol complex. The first Indiana State Fair was held here October 19–21, 1852. During the Civil War the park was made into a military camp by order of the governor. Today it serves as a recreational area in downtown Indianapolis.
State

MARION COUNTY
Indianapolis
RILEY, JAMES WHITCOMB, HOUSE
528 Lockerbie Street
c. 1850

James Whitcomb Riley, the "Hoosier poet," is remembered for his poems in the American vernacular and his speeches on the genre subjects with which he was familiar. The homespun quality of his poems, including "When the Frost is on the Punkin" and "The Old Swimmin' Hole," has been enjoyed by many Amer-

icans. His two-and-a-half-story Victorian residence contains memorabilia of the poet and furniture which he used during his lifetime.
Private
NHL

PORTER COUNTY
Porter vicinity
BAILLY, JOSEPH, HOMESTEAD
.5 mile west of Porter on U.S. 20
1822

The independent fur trader, Joseph Bailly, is often referred to as the first white settler in northern Indiana. His home, begun in 1822 and situated on the trails from Fort Dearborn to Fort Wayne and to Detroit, became a meeting place for whites and Indians, an "oasis" for travelers, and a religious and cultural center. The homestead consists of several buildings. A portion of the "big house" was begun by Bailly but completed after his death.
Private
NHL; HABS

POSEY COUNTY
New Harmony
NEW HARMONY HISTORIC
DISTRICT
Main Street between Granary and Church Streets
1825

New Harmony is unique in the history of 19th-century American communal experiments because it was the scene of both religiously and secularly inspired utopian colonies. Founded by the Rappites in 1815, it was purchased in 1825 by Robert Owen, who attempted to alleviate the human misery and degradation spawned by the growth of the factory system. Because of dissension and discouragement in the community, the undertaking failed by the end of 1826. New Harmony now contains about 35 of the original 180 Rappite buildings and sites.
Multiple public/private
NHL; HABS

ST. JOSEPH COUNTY
South Bend
OLD COURTHOUSE (SECOND ST.
JOSEPH COUNTY COURTHOUSE)
112 S. Lafayette Boulevard
1855, John M. Van Osdel

The temple-form, Greek Revival Old Courthouse is believed to be the oldest building in downtown South Bend. Six fluted, two-story columns carry the projecting pediment of the entrance portico. The columns are brick finished with cement, and their capitals display a modified Corinthian order. The brick walls of the

courthouse, measuring 93 feet by 61 feet, are faced with limestone. A three-story octagonal cupola enlivened by a series of volutes surmounts the roof at a distance of 12 feet from the front of the portico. In 1896 the courthouse was turned around and moved to a neighboring lot. Little basic alteration has been made on the building's exterior, but the inside has been greatly changed.
County
HABS

SPENCER COUNTY
Lincoln City
LINCOLN BOYHOOD NATIONAL MEMORIAL
1816–1830

The family of Abraham Lincoln came to southern Indiana in 1816 and remained until they moved westward to Illinois in 1830. During these years the young Lincoln had one of his few experiences with formal schooling, attending the school conducted by Andrew Crawford. In southern Indiana Lincoln was introduced to the theory and application of the law, receiving his early instruction in reading law from Justice David Turnham. Incorporated in this National Memorial are the Nancy Hanks Lincoln State Memorial, which includes the grave of Lincoln's mother and the site of the Lincoln cabin.
Federal/non-federal
NPS; 200 acres

TIPPECANOE COUNTY
Lafayette vicinity
FORT OUIATENON
SE 1/4 SE 1/4 sec. 28, T. 23 N., R. 5 W
18th century

Fort Ouiatenon was the first of three outposts built to protect French fur trading interests and offset growing British influence over the local Indians. The fort was constructed in 1717 and remained active until the end of the French and Indian War (1763). Located on the Wabash River, a main travel and trade route, Fort Ouiatenon was also surrounded by numerous Indian settlements. No more than 150 persons lived on the post at one time, but its influence and importance as a trade center was great. During the summers of 1968 and 1969 archeological investigations were carried out by the Indiana Historical Society and Indiana University. The restored blockhouse nearby is not on the original fort site.
Private

TIPPECANOE COUNTY
Lafayette vicinity
TIPPECANOE BATTLEFIELD
7 miles northeast of Lafayette on Ind. 225
1811

William Henry Harrison's November 7, 1811, victory at Tippecanoe Battlefield destroyed the Shawnee Chief Tecumseh's plans for a confederation of northern and southern Indian tribes to block westward expansion. The battle of Tippecanoe sparked agitation for war against Britain for the settlers believed that British aid had enabled the tribes to harass the settlements beyond the Appalachians. In June of 1812 war was declared against Britain.
State
NHL

VANDERBURGH COUNTY
Evansville
FORMER VANDERBURGH COUNTY SHERIFF'S RESIDENCE
4th Street between Vine and Court Streets
1891

Constructed of rusticated Indiana limestone, the Former Sheriff's Residence resembles a feudal castle and its design was influenced by Schloss Lichtenstein in Baden-Wurttemburg, Germany. The unusual crenelated roof lines, stepped gables, turrets, portcullises, and central tower contribute to the castle-like appearance. A tunnel connected the house with the courthouse across Fourth Street. The sheriff and his family lived here until 1969.
County; not accessible to the public

VANDERBURGH COUNTY
Evansville
OLD VANDERBURGH COUNTY COURTHOUSE
Entire block bounded by Vine, 4th, Court, and 5th Streets
1888–1891, Henry Wolters

The Old Vanderburgh County Courthouse is an unusual example of a Neo-Baroque, Beaux Arts building. Symmetrically balanced by two projecting pavilions on either side, the main section is rectangular and topped by a dome at the crossing point of the pavilions and the main building. Cartouche type windows surrounded by elaborate scrollwork ornament the third level. Along the cornice line of the roof runs a marble balustrade interrupted only by segmental pediments at each end

of the main building. Doorways are accented by four protruding bays topped by hemispherical domes at the four corners. Indiana limestone was used for the exterior walls, and inside the floors are marble and the walls are lined with marble panels. The courthouse served its designated purpose until May, 1969.
County

VANDERBURGH COUNTY
Evansville vicinity
ANGEL MOUNDS
8 miles southeast of Evansville, Angel Mounds State Memorial
1400–1600

Angel Mounds, a 100-acre area, represents the northeasternmost extension of the so-called Mississippian culture which flourished from about A.D. 1000–1600. The living and religious area centered around a town square or plaza, and the whole area was surrounded by a defensive palisade with evenly spaced bastions. A portion of the palisade has been reconstructed, and artifacts from the site are displayed in a small museum.
State
NHL

VIGO COUNTY
Terre Haute
DEBS, EUGENE V., HOME
451 N. 8th Street
1885

Eugene V. Debs, founder of industrial unionism in the United States, organized the American Railroad Union in June 1893. It was this union which struck against James J. Hill's April 1894 announcement of a reduction in wages on the Great Northern Railroad. This same union also was involved in the Pullman strike which began in June 1894. Debs later turned his attention to the Socialist Party. He was the party's presidential candidate in 1900, 1904, 1908, 1912, and 1920. Debs' two-story frame house has changed little since its completion.
Private
NHL

WAYNE COUNTY
Fountain City
COFFIN, LEVI, HOUSE
115 N. Main Street
1827

Levi Coffin, frequently termed "president" of the Underground Railroad for runaway slaves, opened his house as a depot in 1826. After the issuance of the

Emancipation Proclamation in 1863, he began to work for the freedmen. In 1864 he assisted in the formation of an English Freedmen's Aid Society which con- tributed over $100,000 to the newly freed Negroes. In 1867 he attended the International Anti-Slavery Conference in Paris. The Federal style two-story brick house in which he lived has been altered little over the years.

Private; not accessible to the public
NHL

Iowa

Grenville M. Dodge House, Council Bluffs, Iowa. *Nonpareil, Council Bluffs*

Original Church, Amana Villages, Middle Amana, Iowa. *Fred Kent*

Dubuque County Courthouse,
Dubuque, Iowa.

ALLAMAKEE COUNTY (also in Clayton County)
Marquette vicinity
EFFIGY MOUNDS NATIONAL MONUMENT
3 miles north of Marquette on Iowa 13
c. 1000

Effigy Mounds National Monument preserves traces of Indian peoples who thrived here nearly 1,000 years ago. The monument area is divided into two parts by the Yellow River. The Fire Point Mound Group to the north contains Great Bear Mound which is 137 feet long and perhaps 3 feet high. It is the largest bear effigy remaining in Iowa. To the south is the Marching Bear Mound Group containing an alignment of 10 bear effigies, three bird effigies, and two linear mounds. Other mounds are scattered nearby. Though the effigies and other mounds sometimes differ in external shape and internal features, they all provide information on the burial customs of prehistoric peoples who were of the Middle Woodland, Late Woodland, or Late Hopewellian culture.
Federal/non-federal
NPS; 1,467.50 acres

CEDAR COUNTY
West Branch
HERBERT HOOVER NATIONAL HISTORIC SITE
c. 1870

In this two-room frame cottage Herbert Hoover was born on August 10, 1874. Included in the site are the birthplace cabin, restoration of which was begun in the 1930's; the graves of President and Mrs. Hoover; a restored blacksmith shop similar to the one operated by Hoover's father; and the Hoover Presidential Library. The restoration of the original dwelling has eliminated all superfluous later additions, and the house contains some original furniture. Before his term as President, 1929–1933, Hoover had achieved prominence as Food Administrator during World War I and as Secretary of Commerce from 1921 to 1928. Between 1933 and his death in 1964 Hoover served the Nation in several capacities, among which was his chairmanship of the Hoover Commission.
Federal/non-federal
NPS; 148 acres
HABS

CHEROKEE COUNTY
Cherokee vicinity
PHIPPS SITE
3 miles north of Cherokee
c. 1000

The Phipps Site is the type site of the Mill Creek Indian culture. It represents late Woodland-Mississippian peoples who were developing or acquiring plains agricultural patterns late in the first millennium or early in the second millennium A.D. The site is unusual in that the house floors are found on and in a very large midden which was lived on as it accumulated.
Private; not accessible to the public
NHL

CLAYTON COUNTY
EFFIGY MOUNDS NATIONAL MONUMENT
Reference—see Allamakee County

DUBUQUE COUNTY
Dubuque
DUBUQUE COUNTY COURTHOUSE
720 Central Avenue
1891–1893, Fridolin and Son

The scale of the Dubuque County Courthouse is monumental. Its architecture is eclectic with Romanesque and Renaissance influence evident in the detailing. The first story is Bedford limestone and those above are brick and molded terra cotta. Noticeable features are the round-arched windows, the pediment ornamentation, the bracketed roof cornice, and the allegorical figures of laminated pewter at the building corners. The central tower rises to a height of 190 feet and is topped by a statue of Justice. Inside, the tower terminates in a stained glass dome, and the woodwork is oak.
County

IOWA COUNTY
Middle Amana
AMANA VILLAGES
Northeastern Iowa County
1855

Of the utopian societies that flourished in the 19th century, the Amana Society has been the most durable. Historically an outgrowth of a persecuted German religious minority group, "The Community of True Inspiration," the sect emigrated first to New York State and subsequently to Iowa, founding the village of Amana in 1855. During the next seven years five other villages were established, and the town of Homestead was purchased to gain access to a railroad. In 1859 the community was incorporated under the laws of

Iowa as the Amana Society. In all of the villages there are buildings built in the 1850's, 1860's, and 1870's, primarily two-story houses. Many of the mills, shops, and factories also remain, a number of which are still in use.
Multiple private
NHL

LOUISA COUNTY
Toolesboro vicinity
TOOLESBORO MOUND GROUP
North of Toolesboro
Date unknown

The Toolesboro Mound Group is the best preserved Hopewell site in Iowa. It represents an extension, on the west bank of the Mississippi River, of the "classic" Hopewellian mortuary practices of the Illinois River Valley center. As such, it occupies a significant position in American archeology for, on the basis of present knowledge, it probably was a source of Hopewellian cultural influence, the results of which may be seen to the north in Iowa and Minnesota and to the west and south in Iowa and Missouri.
State; not accessible to the public
NHL

LYON COUNTY (also in Lincoln County, S.D.)
Sioux Falls vicinity
BLOOD RUN SITE
South of Sioux Falls at the junction of Blood Run Creek and the Big Sioux River

The Blood Run Site contains remains of an Indian village and numerous conical mounds. The village area is extensive, and at one time more than 158 mounds were visible. Ranging in size from 30 to 60 feet in diameter and 2 to 8 feet in height, the mounds have been reduced in number by cultivation. Traces remain of an effigy earthwork believed to have been constructed after the mounds. Occupation dates are roughly estimated at 1700 to 1750, and artifacts recovered (projectile points, scrapers, pottery) suggest the inhabitants were Oneota people. Historic trade materials of copper and brass and blue glass beads have also been unearthed, and the burial mounds have yielded human skeletons.
Private
NHL

Sutherland vicinity
INDIAN VILLAGE SITE (WITTROCK AREA)
   3 miles east of Sutherland
   1000–1500

The Wittrock Site, a small Mill Creek Indian culture village, is unique among Mill Creek sites and possibly among village sites in Iowa because it has apparently been little disturbed since its occupation. Seventeen circular house depressions and the roughly square fortification ditch that enclosed the village are still visible. Archeological materials recovered from the site indicate a culture which was in transition from eastern forest agriculture to plains horticulture patterns of subsistence. The inhabitants of this and other Mill Creek settlements in northwestern Iowa are believed to have been ancestors of tribes that occupied the Middle Missouri River basin in early historic times.
State
NHL

POTTAWATTAMIE COUNTY
Council Bluffs
DODGE, GRENVILLE M., HOUSE
   605 S. 3rd Street
   1869

Active for half a century as a planner, builder, financier, lobbyist, and director of railroads in the West and Southwest, Grenville Mellen Dodge supervised, as chief engineer, the completion in 1869 of the Union Pacific, the Nation's first transcontinental railroad. This project is considered to be his greatest single achievement. At the time of its completion, Dodge's 14–room Victorian mansion was considered one of the finest residences in Iowa. The external features of the house appear to be unchanged.
Municipal
NHL

STORY COUNTY
Ames
KNAPP-WILSON HOUSE (THE FARM HOUSE)
   Iowa State University campus
   1861

The Farm House on the campus of Iowa State University was the home of Seaman A. Knapp, noted agriculturist and teacher, and James Wilson, Secretary of Agriculture, 1897–1913. It also commemorates Iowa State University as the first land-grant college to be formally authorized. Through a large colonization experiment in Louisiana in 1886, Knapp achieved national recognition for his demonstration of the success of good farming methods. Under Wilson's leadership as Secretary of Agriculture, farm demonstration work was begun in the South, and experts were employed to gather information and conduct research. The two-story brick building, presently serving as the residence of the university's Dean of Agriculture, is in excellent condition, having undergone some interior and exterior alterations.
State; not accessible to the public
NHL

WOODBURY COUNTY
Sioux City
SERGEANT FLOYD MONUMENT
   Glenn Avenue and Lewis Road
   1804

Sergeant Charles Floyd, a kinsman of Captain William Clark, who was co-leader of the Lewis and Clark Expedition, died of an illness in 1804 as the expedition proceeded up the Missouri River. He was the only member of the expedition to lose his life west of the Mississippi River. Though Sergeant Floyd's remains were first buried on the summit of Floyd's Bluff overlooking the Missouri River, they were ceremonially reinterred in 1857. In 1900 his remains were placed in a concrete foundation, and the cornerstone of the memorial was laid. The 100–foot obelisk commemorates a famous site of the Lewis and Clark Expedition.
Municipal
NHL

Herbert Hoover National Historic Site, West Branch, Iowa. *NPS*

Kansas

Amelia Earhart Birthplace, Atchison, Kansas.
Kansas Department of Economic Development

Old Lawrence City Hall, Lawrence, Kansas.
Kansas State Historical Society

Old Castle Hall,
Baldwin, Kansas.
Kansas State Historical Society

Infinity Archeological Site, Independence, Kansas.
Kansas State Historical Society

Old Santa Fe Trail Remains, near Dodge City, Kansas.
Kansas Industrial Development Commission

ALLEN COUNTY
Iola
ALLEN COUNTY JAIL
204 N. Jefferson Street
1869

This jail served Allen County until the late 1950's. It is a two-story limestone block with walls two feet thick. There are two barred windows on the second floor and a double door at ground level. Steel cages were installed on the lower floor, and the jailer lived on the second floor until the later years of operation when prisoners were confined there.
County

ATCHISON COUNTY
Atchison
EARHART, AMELIA, BIRTHPLACE
223 North Terrace
1861

Judge Alfred G. Otis, grandfather of aviatrix Amelia Earhart, built this two-story frame house with horizontal lap siding and a double pitch gable roof. A full width porch runs across the entire front. Amelia Earhart was born here on July 24, 1897. Her accomplishments in the field of aviation were many, but she is best remembered as the first woman to make a solo flight across the Atlantic, May 20–21, 1932. On July 2, 1937, while on a round-the-world flight with her navigator Fred Noonan, she disappeared in the Pacific and was presumed dead.
Private; not accessible to the public

BARBER COUNTY
Medicine Lodge
NATION, CARRY, HOME
211 W. Fowler Avenue
1882

Carry Moore Nation (1846–1911) and her husband David, moved to Medicine Lodge from Texas in 1889. Kansas then had a prohibition law, but it was openly violated. Soon after her arrival Mrs. Nation formed a local chapter of the Women's Christian Temperance Union. In the late 1890's she claimed to have had a mystical religious experience and was thus motivated to undertake her militant crusade against liquor. She forced the closing of seven saloons in Medicine Lodge (1899) and extended her activities to Kiowa, Enterprise, Topeka, and Wichita, where she first used a hatchet to smash a saloon. Divorced from David Nation, Mrs. Nation owned the Medicine Lodge house herself for a short time. It is a one-story brick cottage

with a gable roof. Many original furnishings have been returned to the home, which is now operated as a museum by the W. C. T. U.
Private

BARBER COUNTY
Medicine Lodge vicinity
MEDICINE LODGE PEACE TREATY SITE
Just south and east of Medicine Lodge
1867

The peace conference at Medicine Lodge and the resulting treaties signed with the Kiowa, Apache, Comanche, Arapaho, and Cheyenne Indians marked a definite change in the attitude of the federal government toward the native peoples of North America. Heretofore, the conquered tribes had been uprooted from their homelands and moved west to a government reservation. No provision was made for their education or economic welfare. Under the provisions of the Medicine Lodge treaty, the Plains Indians were to give up their lives as nomadic hunters and adopt a specific vocation—farming. In return for relinquishing their ancestral claims to land in Kansas, Colorado, and Texas, the Indians were to be supplied with farm implements, schools, and teachers so that they might begin to live more like the whites.
Municipal
NHL

BARTON COUNTY
Pawnee Rock vicinity
PAWNEE ROCK
.2 mile north of Pawnee Rock off U.S. 56

Comanche, Kiowa, Arapahoe, Cheyenne, and Pawnee Indians used Pawnee Rock for tribal councils for many years before white men came to Kansas. The prominence rises 50 or 60 feet above the prairie and is reputed to have been twice that size, but homesteaders and railroad men removed considerable portions to build homes and to lay the Santa Fe roadbed. Pawnee Rock was a landmark on the Santa Fe Trail, which passes within 100 yards. Caravans often camped in the shelter of the rock, and traders, soldiers, and emigrants chiseled their names on its sandstone surface.
State

BOURBON COUNTY
Fort Scott
FORT SCOTT
1842

Named for General Winfield Scott, Fort Scott was built primarily to preserve peace among the Osage, Cherokee, and other Indian tribes in the territory. The post had three distinct periods of activity. Its primary period was from 1842 to 1853, when the original fort served as an intermediate post between Fort Leavenworth (Kans.) and Fort Gibson (Okla.). Several buildings dating from the early 1840's are among the oldest extant in Kansas. During the 1850's settlers founded the town of Fort Scott around the post. It was the scene of bloodshed and terror during the period of Bleeding Kansas when pro-slavery and free soil forces struggled for supremacy. From 1861 to 1865 Fort Scott's strategic location made it a Union supply depot for military operations. Reactivated in the period 1869–1873 to maintain order in settler-railroad troubles, Fort Scott was finally abandoned in 1873.
Municipal; not accessible to the public
NHL

CHASE COUNTY
Cottonwood Falls
CHASE COUNTY COURTHOUSE
On the square at the south end of Broadway
1873, John G. Haskell

The Chase County Courthouse is a three-story, tooled limestone building with a high mansard roof surmounted by a clock tower. A belt course separates the first and second floors. The cornice is bracketed and the roof is ornamented by iron cresting. Windows on the first and second levels are paired beneath arched lintels. Inside, a spiral stairway connects all floors. This is the oldest courthouse in Kansas still being used.
County

CHASE COUNTY
Strong City vicinity
SPRING HILL FARM AND STOCK RANCH HOUSE
3 miles north of Strong City on Kans. 177
1881

The Spring Hill Ranch House is a large stone dwelling built against a hillside with three stories on the front and two on the rear. It has a mansard roof and is built of native limestone cut to uniform size and laid in regular horizontal courses. All corners are quoined with projecting stone blocks. A large porch with classic columns extends along the lower floor of the three-story facade. There is a rubble stone barn with smoothed blocks at the corners and a modified gable roof. Other outbuildings are squared stone block construction with hip roofs. The house and outbuildings together form a unified complex in appearance and function.

Private; not accessible to the public

DICKINSON COUNTY
Abilene
EISENHOWER HOME
201 Southeast 4th Street

Dwight David Eisenhower (1890–1969) spent his boyhood years in this house, departing in 1911 to enter the U.S. Military Academy at West Point. Eisenhower was an outstanding soldier and a good tactician. He was appointed Supreme Commander of the Allied Expeditionary Force by President Franklin D. Roosevelt (1943) and directed the Allied invasion of Europe. Eisenhower achieved the rank of permanent General of the Army (1944) and became Army Chief of Staff in 1945. He was the commander of Allied Powers in Europe (1950–1951) and organized the armed forces of NATO. From 1952 to 1960 he served his country as its highest elected official. The Eisenhower Home is a two-story, hip-roofed dwelling with a flat-roofed front porch on the south. Original family articles and furnishings are still in the house.
Federal
HABS

DONIPHAN COUNTY
Highland
IRVIN HALL, HIGHLAND COMMUNITY JUNIOR COLLEGE
Highland Community Junior College campus
1859

Irvin Hall was the first permanent structure of Highland University, chartered by the Kansas territorial legislature in 1858. The building was named for the Reverend Samuel M. Irvin, founder of and missionary at the nearby Iowa, Sac, and Fox Presbyterian Mission and a founder of Highland University. The hall is rectangular and built of brick. The second story was added at a later time. Pilasters divide the bays on the south and east sides. The roof is gabled, and all window and door openings have stone lintels. There is a

wooden bell tower at the east end. Now a junior college, Highland is the oldest continuously operative institution of higher learning in Kansas.
County
HABS

DONIPHAN COUNTY
Highland vicinity
IOWA, SAC, AND FOX PRESBYTERIAN MISSION (HIGHLAND PRESBYTERIAN MISSION)
1.5 miles east of Highland on U.S. 36 and .2 mile north on K-136
1846–1863

In 1837 the Presbyterian Board of Foreign Missions sent Samuel M. Irvin and his wife to establish a mission among the Iowa, Sac, and Fox Indians who had been removed to Kansas. The mission was the first permanent white settlement in present-day Doniphan County. A permanent mission building was completed in 1846. It housed an Indian school which could accommodate 100 students but seldom had more than 40. Lessons were taught in English and the Iowa language. During the 1840's and 1850's cholera and smallpox epidemics hit the area, and the already weak Indian support of and interest in the mission was virtually destroyed. The mission was inactive after 1863. Its original building measured 106 feet long by 37 feet wide. The ground level was native stone and the upper two, brick. Inside were 32 rooms, including a dining room, chapel, teachers' rooms, and dormitory space. The present structure is only 46 feet long, the remainder having been razed sometime after 1868.
State

DOUGLAS COUNTY
Baldwin
OLD CASTLE HALL, BAKER UNIVERSITY
513 5th Street
1858

In February, 1858, the Kansas territorial legislature granted a charter to the Kansas Education Association of the Methodist Episcopal Church for the founding of a college. The resulting Baker University is today the oldest four-year college in the state. A temporary building was erected a block from the campus, and this Old Castle Hall housed the university until 1871. It is a three-story, rubble stone edifice with crude quoins at the corners. All window and door openings have stone lintels

and sills. The third floor was removed and rebuilt in 1908. Other uses for the Old Castle Hall have been as a mill, rooming house, and public school.
Private

DOUGLAS COUNTY
Lawrence
HASKELL INSTITUTE
1884

First known as the Indian Training School, Haskell Institute has been a leader in Indian education since 1884. It is one of the few surviving non-reservation schools established in the late 19th century. Its four-year high school course is designed to prepare the student who returns to his people to improve the social and economic conditions of his tribe and himself. A few 19th-century buildings still stand: Keokuk Hall, a boys' dormitory (1884); the hospital (1886), now serving as employee quarters; Winona Hall, a girls' dormitory (1898); and Hiawatha Hall, now a girls' gymnasium (1898).
Federal
NHL

DOUGLAS COUNTY
Lawrence
LUDINGTON HOUSE
1613 Tennessee Street
1860, John G. Haskell; 1872 (remodeled)

Originally designed in the Italianate style and constructed for Reuben W. Ludington, a Lawrence businessman, the Ludington House was extensively remodeled by the addition, at the rear, of a round tower and porte cochere. It is a brick dwelling with light-colored stone quoining on corners of the older section. The roofline varies in height from one to three stories, and there is a square tower above the main entrance. Two balconies extend from the east facade, and windows and doors have stone lintels and sills. Judge Solon O. Thacher had the house enlarged following his appointment as ambassador to Central and South America and Mexico.
Private; not accessible to the public

DOUGLAS COUNTY
Lawrence
OLD LAWRENCE CITY HALL (WATKINS NATIONAL BANK)
1047 Massachusetts Street
1887

Measuring 75 feet by 117 feet, the Old Lawrence City Hall is a two-and-one-half-

story brick building with a combination hip and gable roof. There are three roof dormers on the side elevations and a single one on the main and rear facades. The off-center entrance at ground level is surrounded by a massive, semicircular, rough stone archway. Jabez B. Watkins established the J. B. Watkins Land Mortgage Company and the Watkins National Bank. His widow donated the building to the city of Lawrence.
Municipal

DOUGLAS COUNTY
Lecompton
CONSTITUTION HALL
Elmore Street between Woodson and 3rd Streets

Lecompton was the official territorial capital of Kansas until 1861, when statehood was achieved. Constitution Hall was the meeting place of the second territorial legislature (January 12 to February 20, 1857). Here the Lecompton Constitution was drawn up, a document which would have made Kansas a slave state. The electorate were given the choice only of this constitution with slavery or with no slavery, the latter meaning that no additional slaves could be brought into Kansas. All who were already slaves and their descendants were to remain so. The constitution was rejected. On December 7, 1857, and January 4, 1858, the third territorial legislature met at Lecompton in Constitution Hall as prescribed by law but immediately adjourned to Lawrence. Constitution Hall is a rectangular, two-story frame building with a gable. Minor remodeling has taken place on the inside, but the exterior is unchanged.
Private

DOUGLAS COUNTY
Lecompton
LANE UNIVERSITY
1882

Lane University was founded by the United Brethren in Christ Church (1865) and named for Kansas Senator James H. Lane. The Kansas legislature donated 13 acres of land in Lecompton, a site containing the foundation and ruins of what was to have been the proslavery capitol of Kansas. Measuring 65 by 50 feet, the university's sole building occupied the south one-third of the old capitol foundations. Four classrooms were located on the ground floor, and the second floor

contained the chapel. A lack of students and financial backing plagued the school from the beginning. In 1902 it merged with Campbell University in Holton and all movable property was taken from Lecompton. The university building is presently unused.
Municipal

ELLIS COUNTY
Hays
FORT HAYS
Frontier Historical Park
1867–1889

Fort Hays, originally called Camp Fletcher, was established on this site in June, 1867. Both cavalry and infantry were stationed here, although the garrison varied from 567 to a low of 12. When the railroad came, Fort Hays was turned into a quartermaster's depot supplying other military posts in the West and Southwest. Thirty-eight buildings were standing when the fort was abandoned on November 8, 1889. Today only three remain. The blockhouse is a hexagonal stone structure with wings on the north and south sides. Used as a post headquarters and adjutant's quarters, it has rifle slits in the walls. Extensive restoration work has been done on the blockhouse. The guardhouse is also stone and measures 100 feet by 24 feet. The frame officers' quarters was moved to the site of a Fort Hays' officers' quarters in 1963. It is two stories high and has two rooms on each floor. Archeological investigation has been carried out on the site.
State

ELLIS COUNTY
Victoria
ST. FIDELIS CATHOLIC CHURCH
Southeast corner of St. Anthony and Delaware Streets
1908–1911, John T. Comes; modified, John Marshall

St. Fidelis Church is a monumental limestone structure with a rusticated rough-hewn appearance. Towering as it does above its surroundings, the church is known locally as the Cathedral of the Plains. Double, 141-foot towers flank the main entrance, and the building itself is 220 feet long, 110 feet wide at the transept, and 73 feet at the nave. The main roof is a double pitch, and there are buttresses on both sides. Windows are nar-

row slits rising from a stone sill and terminating in a circular stone arch. A monastery built by the Capuchin Order (1901–1903) adjoins the church on the south. St. Fidelis' original parish members were Russian-German immigrants.
Private

FORD COUNTY
Dodge City vicinity
SANTA FE TRAIL REMAINS
9 miles west of Dodge City on U.S. 50
1820–1850

The longest continuous stretch of clearly defined rut remains of the Santa Fe Trail in Kansas are preserved in rough, unplowed rangeland. These remains on a hill overlooking the Arkansas River Valley form a two-mile arc intersecting U.S. 50. Except where a long-abandoned irrigation ditch winds across the trail at several points, many clear stretches remain, some 300 to 400 feet wide. This site derives additional significance from the fact that the trail divided 10 to 20 miles upstream at the Cimarron Crossing, at which point some travelers followed the Arkansas River while others took the shorter Cimarron Cutoff route.
Private
NHL

GEARY COUNTY
Junction City vicinity
FIRST TERRITORIAL CAPITOL
On K–18 in Fort Riley Military Reservation
1855

Governor Andrew H. Reeder summoned the first Kansas territorial legislature to meet in the town of Pawnee on July 2, 1855. Their meeting place was a two-story native limestone warehouse measuring 40 feet by 80 feet. The house members used the lower floor and the senate occupied the upper one. Members of the legislature felt Pawnee was too far west and thus too isolated to be the capital and voted to move east to Shawnee Mission. The warehouse fell into disrepair and was unused until 1927, when the Union Pacific Railroad undertook its restoration. Then the building was given to the state of Kansas and is now a museum.
State
HABS

GRANT COUNTY
Ulysses vicinity
WAGON BED SPRINGS
12 miles south of Ulysses on U.S. 270
c. 1820–1850

Sometimes called lower Cimarron Springs, Wagon Bed Springs was an oasis on the dry 60–mile stretch of the Cimarron Cutoff route of the Santa Fe Trail. After travelers crossed the Arkansas River, this spring was their objective, a welcome stopping place. The physical integrity of the spring has been little impaired by the passage of time; the ruts of the Santa Fe Trail are still evident in its vicinity.
Private
NHL

HARVEY COUNTY
Newton
WARKENTIN HOUSE
211 E. 1st Street
1886–1887

The Warkentin House was the residence of Bernhard Warkentin (1847–1908), a Russian immigrant and later a Kansas wheat magnate. Warkentin led a Mennonite migration to Kansas in the 1870's and was responsible for the introduction of Turkey Red wheat seed from southern Russia to Kansas. The Turkey Red variety grew well in the American Southwest and made Warkentin prosperous as well as famous. The house itself is a large, three-story clapboard dwelling with a restrained Victorian exterior.
Private; not accessible to the public

HARVEY COUNTY
Newton
WARKENTIN MILL
3rd and Main Streets
1879; 1886 (enlarged)

The first building of the Monarch Steam Mills was built in 1879. The original structure was stone and brick and stood four floors high above a basement. In 1883 the mill was converted to a full roller mill, and three years later Bernhard Warkentin purchased the mill, renaming it the Newton Milling and Elevator Company. Warkentin made further external alterations and additions after 1886. A one-story office wing was added to the east side, a

two-story warehouse on the north, and another one-story addition on the west side. The building is still used as a commercial property.
Private; not accessible to the public

JOHNSON COUNTY
Fairway
SHAWNEE MISSION
53rd Street at Mission Road
1839–1845

The Shawnee Methodist Mission and Indian Manual Labor School, established by the Reverend Thomas Johnson in 1830, was among the earliest of such institutions in the Louisiana Purchase territory. At its peak the enrollment was almost 200 students who received vocational, academic, and religious training. Located on the Santa Fe and Oregon Trails near their points of origin, the mission was one of the last outposts of civilization on the pre-Civil War frontier. The offices of the first territorial governor of Kansas were located here in 1854, and the first territorial legislature met here in 1855. The mission was one of the largest and most important Indian schools in the trans-Mississippi West until its closing in 1862. Three brick buildings still stand on the site chosen in 1838: the West Building (1839), the East Building (1841), and the North Building (1845).
State
NHL; HABS

JOHNSON COUNTY (also in Jackson County, Mo.)
Leawood
MAJORS, ALEXANDER, HOUSE
8145 State Line Road

The house which Alexander Majors, field coordinator for the freighting firm of Russell, Majors, and Waddell, occupied for two years (1856–1858) is partly in Kansas and partly in Missouri. It is a two-story frame dwelling built in the shape of a "T." Alterations have been made on the outside.
Private; not accessible to the public

LEAVENWORTH COUNTY
Lansing vicinity
LANSING MAN ARCHEOLOGICAL
SITE
1 mile east of Lansing to Kans. 5, .66 mile south and .25 mile east
Pre-Columbian

Human skeletal material found here is the oldest thus far recovered and studied in the area. In 1902 the remains of an adult male and a young child were excavated 20 feet below the surface. Anthropologists and geologists debated the age of the find and could not agree. A recent radiocarbon dating gave an age determination of 3835 B.C. plus or minus 105 years. Additional material may exist near the site of the original discovery.
Private

LEAVENWORTH COUNTY
Leavenworth
FORT LEAVENWORTH
1827

Established to help protect caravans on the Santa Fe Trail, Fort Leavenworth played a major role in the Indian wars, the Mexican War, and the Civil War. During the 1820's and 1830's, it occupied the center of the line of forts that defined the "permanent Indian frontier." Its strategic location near the eastern terminals of the Santa Fe and Oregon trails made it a base for several important expeditions to the plains. When the Territory of Kansas was organized in 1854, Fort Leavenworth became its temporary capitol. Among the early buildings and structures remaining is the Historic Stone Wall (1827), the former home of Governor Andrew H. Reeder (1834), and a brick house (c. 1840) which was the home of the post commander. It remains an active military installation.
Federal
NHL; HABS

LINN COUNTY
Trading Post vicinity
MARAIS des CYGNES MASSACRE
SITE
5 miles northeast of Trading Post

Passage of the Kansas-Nebraska bill in 1854 established the concept of popular

sovereignty. As Free State and proslavery forces vied for control of the Kansas Territory, numerous instances of lawlessness occurred, and in effect, a state of civil war existed in eastern Kansas along the Missouri border. On May 19, 1858, a band of proslavery sympathizers, led by Charles Hamelton, entered Kansas from Missouri. Hamelton was a former resident of Trading Post who had been forced to leave by the Free State men. He and his band of 30 captured 11 Free Staters, lined them up in a ravine northeast of town, and dispatched them with gunshots. Five were killed, five wounded, and one was unhurt. Leaving the victims for dead, Hamelton and his men returned to Missouri. Only one raider was ever caught and punished for this outrage. Marais des Cygnes was the last significant display of mob violence in Kansas as Governor John W. Geary, with the aid of federal troops, was able to restore order.
State

LYON COUNTY
Emporia
WHITE, WILLIAM ALLEN, HOUSE
927 Exchange Street
1880's

William Allen White (1868–1944), editor and journalist, purchased the Emporia *Gazette* in 1895. He published this paper for more than 40 years, and as its editor, was known throughout America for his writings on national and international issues. His first editorial to receive nationwide prominence was "what's the Matter with Kansas?" (1896). Throughout his lifetime White acted as spokesman for middle class, small-town Americans. The home which he bought in 1900 has a first story of Colorado sandstone, a second story of brick, and a third of frame and half-timber construction. In the early 1920's a fire damaged the house, and subsequent restoration work was based on plans drawn by Frank Lloyd Wright.
Private; not accessible to the public

MIAMI COUNTY
Osawatomie
BROWN, JOHN, CABIN (SAMUEL ADAIR CABIN)
John Brown Memorial Park
1854

Samuel Adair, brother-in-law of John Brown, owned this cabin when Brown came to Kansas in 1855. His arrival was in response to a plea for aid sent him by his five sons who had come the previous spring to oppose proslavery sentiment and action. On May 23, 1856, Brown and six others set out for nearby Potawatomi Indian country, and the following night they savagely murdered five designated victims. This incident terrorized the countryside, and "Old Osawatomie Brown" became a feared person among the slavery supporters That August Osawatomie itself was sacked and burned in retaliation for Brown's bloody deeds of May. He left Kansas shortly thereafter. Brown was a frequent visitor at the Adair Cabin, which served occasionally as his headquarters. It contains a living room, kitchen, and loft. In 1912 it was moved to its present location, and a protective stone shelter has been built around it.
State
HABS

MONTGOMERY COUNTY
Independence vicinity
INFINITY ARCHEOLOGICAL SITE
8 miles west of Independence on U.S. 160, 1.5 miles north and 1.5 miles east on a secondary road
Pre-Columbian

The Infinity Site is located in a field adjacent to the Elk River and is periodically flooded when the Elk City reservoir is full. Three intermittent occupation periods have been recognized as a result of archeological investigation. The most recent (c. 1300), was by a cultural group identified as Pomona Focus; the next oldest and most extensive habitation was by a group heretofore unknown in this area and identified as the Cuesta Phase of the Middle Woodland period (c. 800). The oldest occupants of the site have not been accurately identified by culture. Digging has uncovered pits, postholes, lodge sites, hearths, refuse mounds, human burials, tools, and ornaments.
Federal

MORRIS COUNTY
Council Grove
COUNCIL GROVE HISTORIC DISTRICT
1858

Because of its water, abundant grass, and timber, Council Grove was an important way-point on the Santa Fe Trail. The town, which was incorporated in 1858, was named on the occasion of a treaty negotiation with the Osage Indians in 1825. Later, other councils were held here as caravans organized themselves to cross the area inhabited by hostile Indians. Within the town a number of landmarks survive: the Last Chance Store (1857); the Old Kaw Mission (1850–1851); the Post Office Oak; the Hays Tavern; and the Council Oak Site.
Multiple public/private
NHL; HABS

MORRIS COUNTY
Council Grove
FARMERS AND DROVERS BANK
201 W. Main Street
1892

The Farmers and Drovers Bank is a brick structure with hand-hewn stone trim. First-floor windows are topped by semicircular arches containing stained glass, and the rectangular second-floor windows also have stained glass panels. Protruding limestone towers divide the upper windows into pairs. These towers terminate in turrets at the roof. The Farmers and Drovers Bank was organized on January 26, 1882.
Private

MORRIS COUNTY
Council Grove
LAST CHANCE STORE
500 W. Main Street
1857

The Last Chance Store, built by Tom Hill, is one of the two oldest commercial structures in Council Grove. Located on the north side of the Santa Fe Trail, the store presented traders with their final opportunity to purchase supplies between Council Grove and Santa Fe, New Mexico. The rectangular, one-story, one-room building has walls of hand-hewn limestone. Windows and doorways are simple rectangular openings with rough stone sills and flat, smoothed stone lintels. A post office was once housed in the store, which also served as a government trading house.
Private

MORRIS COUNTY
Council Grove
OLD KAW MISSION
500 N. Mission Street
1851

An 1846 treaty with the Kansas or Kaw Indians relegated them to a 20–mile-square reservation including the site of present-day Council Grove. In 1850 the Methodist Episcopal Church, South, signed a government contract thereby agreeing to establish a mission and school for the Kaw Indians at Council Grove. The mission building is a two-story, rectangular, stone structure with a gable roof and end chimneys. It could house 50 students plus teachers and mission workers. High costs of operation and poor attendance resulted in the withdrawal of government money, so the school was forced to close in 1854. The mission is within the Council Grove Historic District, a National Historic Landmark.
State

MORRIS COUNTY
Council Grove vicinity
WILLIAM YOUNG ARCHEOLOGICAL SITE
4.5 miles north of Council Grove off Kans. 177
Pre-Columbian

Artifacts found at this location represent a heretofore unrecognized prehistoric culture. Termed the Munkers Creek Phase, the cultural group falls within the Archaic Period, and radiocarbon tests indicate habitation dates were 3,000 to 5,000 years ago. The site is a buried camp situated four to seven feet below ground. Artifacts found include projectile points, knives, and celts of distinctive types.
Federal

PAWNEE COUNTY
Larned vicinity
FORT LARNED NATIONAL HISTORIC SITE
5 miles west of Larned
1859

In the 1860's and early 1870's Fort Larned was among the more important forts which helped guard the Santa Fe Trail. In addition, it was a base of operations against hostile Indians on the central plains. The fort remains one of the best-preserved mid–19th-century western military posts. Among its extant buildings constructed in 1867 and 1868 are three officers' quarters, the commissary storehouse, quartermaster warehouse, workshops, and two stone barracks. The post was abandoned in 1878.
Federal/non-federal
NPS; 681 acres

REPUBLIC COUNTY
Republic vicinity
PAWNEE INDIAN VILLAGE SITE
On Kans. 266 and the Republican River, 8 miles north of U.S. 36

A Republican (Kitkehahki) Pawnee village was located on this site in the 1820's and 1830's. The village contained an estimated 30 or 40 earth lodges which were round, domelike structures with heavy timber framework covered by sod. These lodges measured 30 to 40 feet in diameter. As many as 1,000 people may have occupied the village site. A museum and interpretive center were built in 1967. This site is the only major Pawnee village location in the central Plains to be preserved, and the only such site in Kansas to have been excavated.
State

RICE COUNTY
Geneseo vicinity
TOBIAS-THOMPSON COMPLEX
4 miles southeast of Geneseo
16th century

The Tobias-Thompson Complex is a Wichita Indian village which shows contact with the Europeans at about the time Coronado reached the village he called Quivira. Archeological excavations have revealed fragments of 16th-century chain mail and sherds of Indian glaze pottery of the Southwest, the area from which the early Spanish explorers came. Within the complex are 29 small mounds, including one termed a "council circle." Although the actual use of "council circles" has not been determined, they are believed to have been ritual centers or sites for temples. Because the site is in grassland, a part of which has never been cultivated, it 's well preserved.
Private; not accessible to the public
NHL

RILEY COUNTY
Manhattan
GOODNOW HOUSE
2301 Claflin Road
1857

When built the Goodnow House was just a stone cabin with a basement and a wine cellar. Isaac T. Goodnow (1814–1894) purchased the house in 1859 and enlarged it. The present two-story portion has walls of rough cut limestone and the corners are quoined with smooth cut stones. All windows and doors have stone lintels and sills. Wooden additions were made periodically, the last in 1876. Goodnow helped

establish Bluemont College (1859), which later became Kansas State University, and served as superintendent of public instruction in 1862 and 1864.
State

SALINE COUNTY
Salina vicinity
WHITEFORD (PRICE) SITE
3 miles east of Salina
Prehistoric

Presently a commercial exhibit, Whiteford (Price) Site is a prehistoric cemetery in which some 146 skeletons of the Smokey Hill Indian culture have been left *in situ*, protected by a building. Nearby is a village site in which one house and part of another have been excavated. The remaining house sites are undisturbed except for cultivation. This site provides a fortunate record of the early Central Plains Village period in Kansas.
Private
NHL

SCOTT COUNTY
Scott City vicinity
EL CUARTELEJO
12 miles north of Scott City, Scott County State Park
1691

This Puebloan ruin is attributed to a group of Picuris Indians who left the Southwest because of friction with the Spanish. Other Puebloans had fled to El Cuartelejo as early as the 1660's. Excavations have produced almost no artifacts of Southwestern origin, suggesting a short stay or adoption of the utensils of the local inhabitants. Although traces of the pueblo ruin are rather obscure, the site is well preserved.
Private
NHL

SEDGWICK COUNTY
Wichita
OLD SEDGWICK COUNTY COURTHOUSE
504 N. Main Street
1888

The Old Sedgwick County Courthouse served as the seat of government until 1959. It is a native stone building generally three stories high, although portions have two additional stories. A decorative stone band divides the stories, and the roof has a projecting bracketed cornice. The four corner towers have steeply pitched hip roofs. Window openings are rectangular, with stone sills and lintels, or narrow with circular arched tops. Interior remodeling has been extensive, and the upper sections of the central tower have been removed for reasons of safety.
County

SEDGWICK COUNTY
Wichita
UNIVERSITY HALL, FRIENDS UNIVERSITY
2000 University Avenue
1886–1888, Proudfoot and Bird

University Hall was the main building of Garfield University, founded under the auspices of the Christian Churches of Kansas. The school was also to be a memorial to assassinated President James A. Garfield. Measurements of the brick building are 232 feet long by 150 feet wide. All four stories exhibit stone quoins, banding, and decorative window spandrels. There are circular towers at the corners of the west wing and at the north and south ends, and the central tower rises 148 feet. Most window and door openings are round arched. Friends University acquired the property and opened its doors in September, 1898.
Private

SEDGWICK COUNTY
Wichita
WICHITA CITY HALL
204 S. Main Street
1889–1892, Proudfoot and Bird

The Wichita City Hall is a large, three-story building with round towers on all four corners and exterior walls of rough-cut limestone. The corner towers have conical roofs, while the central, square clock tower has a pyramidal roof. Window openings are rectangular—with arched or horizontal lintels—or semicircular. Stones are laid in alternating wide and narrow courses. Both the west front entranceway and the northwest corner have false porches at the second-floor level. There is a cylindrical tower with a multilayered conical roof at each corner of the clock tower. In 1938 an annex was built and connected to the east side of the main building. The interior has been remodeled and modernized several times.
Municipal

SHAWNEE COUNTY
Topeka
ST. JOSEPH'S CATHOLIC CHURCH
235 Van Buren Street
1901

Distinguished by its two tall symmetrical spires, St. Joseph's Catholic Church is a Romanesque brick building on a limestone foundation. The steeples, which begin as squares, are topped by octagonal roofs. Corbeling appears beneath the central pediment, which contains a rose window. Other exterior design features include brick dentils and applied pilasters. The parish served by St. Joseph's was a German-speaking one.
Private

SUMNER COUNTY
Caldwell vicinity
BURESH ARCHEOLOGICAL SITE
Northwest of Caldwell on F.A.S. 299

Archeological excavations by the Kansas State Historical Society in the summer of 1969 exposed three house floors and some 30 detritus-filled storage pits and borrow areas. The house types and the recovered pottery sherds and stone and bone artifacts indicate an affiliation with the Washita Focus of central Oklahoma. Radiocarbon dates indicate an age of approximately 1050 A.D.
Private; not accessible to the public

WABAUNSEE COUNTY
Wabaunsee
BEECHER BIBLE AND RIFLE CHURCH
Southeast corner of Chapel and Elm Streets
1862

After passage of the Kansas-Nebraska Act (1854), allowing the residents of a territory to decide whether it was to be slave or free, interest in the settlement of Kansas grew. A group of antislavery men met in New Haven, Connecticut, in the spring of 1856 with the intent of settling in Kansas. The Reverend Henry Ward Beecher addressed their final meeting and suggested that Sharps carbines would be of more use to the colony than Bibles. Beecher's congregation in Brooklyn, New York, supplied money for some of the rifles. About 70 colonists arrived in Kansas in April, 1856, and founded the town of Wabaunsee. Their church, completed in 1862, is built of native limestone with cut stone quoins and window and door sills and jambs. It is surmounted by a wooden belfry; the wooden entry is a later addition. The structure is one of the earliest churches in Kansas.
Private
HABS

WASHINGTON COUNTY
Hanover vicinity
HOLLENBERG (COTTONWOOD) PONY EXPRESS STATION
1.5 miles east of Hanover on a secondary road
1857

Built by George Hollenberg, the Cottonwood Pony Express Station is perhaps the only surviving unmoved and unaltered Pony Express station. An important stop on the Oregon-California Trail, it served as a relay station for both the Overland Mail (1858–1869) and the Pony Express (1860–1861). Built originally as part of a ranch, it later included a store, post office, kitchen, dining room, and sleeping quarters.
State
NHL

WYANDOTTE COUNTY
Kansas City
TROWBRIDGE ARCHEOLOGICAL SITE
Between 61st and 63rd Streets north of May Lane and Leavenworth Street
Pre-Columbian

The Trowbridge Site was once the focus of a small village identified as Kansas City Focus of the Hopewellian Phase. A date of approximately 200 A.D. has been assigned to the period of occupation. The inhabitants were affiliated with the eastern Woodland peoples (Illinois Hopewellians) and represented a westward extension of this culture.
Multiple private

WYANDOTTE COUNTY
Kansas City
ST. AUGUSTINE HALL (MATHER HALL)
3301 Parallel Avenue
1896

Constructed as Mather Hall of Kansas City University, this three-story brick and cut stone building was used for educational purposes until 1932. A tall central tower above the main entrance dominates the entire structure. There is an elongated false window in each side of the tower, and an elaborate cornice underlies the tower platform. Window treatment varies from round-arched to semi-Palladian and is different on every level. Other trim includes pilasters, columns, and belt courses. In 1913 Campbell College, under control of the United Brethren in Christ, merged with Kansas City University. The present owner is the Augustinian Order of the Catholic Church.
Private

WYANDOTTE COUNTY
Muncie
GRINTER PLACE
1420 S. 78th Street
1857

Moses Grinter came to Cantonment Leavenworth, Kansas, in 1828 and began operating the first ferry across the Kansas River three years later. The ferry was part of the Fort Leavenworth-Fort Scott military road and thus vital to communication and the flow of supplies. Grinter operated a trading post at the ferry landing (1855–1860), and his two-story brick home is considered the oldest in the country. Grinter Place has a five-bay main facade and an interior center hall, two-room plan. On the south facade there is a two-story wooden porch with an overhanging pediment, carved wood railings, and thin, elongated columns. It covers a single bay. The rear porch is only one-story high and has a sloping shed roof.
Private

Kentucky

Locust Grove, Louisville, Kentucky. *Lin Caulfield*

Lieutenant Governor's Mansion, Frankfort, Kentucky.
Kentucky Department of Public Information

Jacobs Hall,
Kentucky School for the Deaf,
Danville, Kentucky. *NPS*

BELL COUNTY (also in Claiborne
County, Tennessee, and Lee County,
Virginia)
Middlesboro vicinity
**CUMBERLAND GAP NATIONAL
HISTORICAL PARK**

Through Cumberland Gap passed the Wilderness Road, main artery of the trans-Allegheny migration that won the Northwest Territory and extended the western boundary of the United States to the Mississippi River. Long traveled by Indians, this mountain pass was discovered by Dr. Thomas Walker and five companions in 1750. In 1775 Daniel Boone was engaged to blaze a trail through the gap to open the region to settlement. The trail, known as the Wilderness Road, was also important to the colonists during the Revolutionary War. The mass immigration following the Revolution was accommodated by use of the road until more direct routes across the mountains were found.
Federal/non-federal
NPS; 10,690.38 acres

BOYLE COUNTY
Danville
**JACOBS HALL, KENTUCKY SCHOOL
FOR THE DEAF**
S. 3rd Street
1857

Established in 1823, the Kentucky School for the Deaf was the first publicly supported institution for the education of the deaf in the United States. Jacobs Hall is the oldest surviving building on the campus. Now used as a girls' dormitory, it served until 1882 as the school's main building.
State; not accessible to the public
NHL

BOYLE COUNTY
Danville
McDOWELL, DR. EPHRAIM, HOUSE
125–127 S. 2nd Street
c. 1795

Recognized today as the father of abdominal surgery, Dr. Ephraim McDowell successfully performed a difficult abdominal operation in 1809. His achievement helped to overcome the widespread misconception that opening the abdomen was invariably fatal. His frame house, the site of the operation, has been restored and refurnished with many of his personal belongings. Adjoining the house is the small brick McDowell Apothecary Shop.
Private
NHL; HABS

BOYLE COUNTY
Perryville vicinity
PERRYVILLE BATTLEFIELD
West of Perryville on U.S. 150
1862

On this site in October, 1862, was fought the battle which climaxed the major Confederate invasion of Kentucky. In the geographical sense that Gettysburg was the "high water mark" of Confederate operations in the eastern theater, Perryville had that distinction in the central South. One tract located near the northern end of the battleline comprises the Perryville Battlefield Monument. Still standing are the Crawford House, General Braxton Bragg's headquarters; and the H. P. Bottom House, scene of some of the heaviest fighting.
State
NHL

FAYETTE COUNTY
Lexington
ASHLAND (HENRY CLAY HOME)
2 miles southeast of Lexington on
Richmond Road
1806, Benjamin H. Latrobe; 1857,
Major Thomas Lewinski

Distinguished pre-Civil War political leader and statesman Henry Clay served first in the Senate. Later in the House of Representatives, he led the "War Hawks" and formulated the "American System," a program of internal improvements and the protection of American industry. During his tenure in the House he served as Speaker. He served as Secretary of State under John Quincy Adams. He earned his nickname, "The Great Pacificator," through his role in formulating the Missouri Compromise and the Compromise of 1850. The present brick building, reconstructed by Major Thomas Lewinski in 1857, follows the plan of the original house, but the architectural detail is greatly changed. The exterior is Italianate in style, the interior predominantly Victorian, with original furniture of the Clay family.
Private
NHL

FAYETTE COUNTY
Lexington
CLAY, HENRY, LAW OFFICE
176 N. Mill Street
1803

The Henry Clay Law Office is a one-story, 20- by 22-foot brick building which is the only one of several offices he occupied to remain standing. It is believed to be one of two extant early 19th-century structures in Lexington built as professional offices.

Clay erected the structure and had his office here until 1810. A larger building was put up around the office (1830), but it has been dismantled and the law office restored.
State

FAYETTE COUNTY
Lexington
**OLD MORRISON, TRANSYLVANIA
COLLEGE**
W. 3rd Street between Upper Street
and Broadway
1833, Gideon Shryock

Chartered in 1780, Transylvania College is one of the oldest institutions of higher learning west of the Appalachians. It was at the height of its influence in the early 1800's. Among the first buildings constructed on the present campus was "Morrison College," still in use today. This Greek Revival building, with a massive Doric portico, is the oldest remaining on the Transylvania College campus.
Private
NHL; HABS

FAYETTE COUNTY
Lexington
**WEST HIGH STREET HISTORIC
DISTRICT**
North side of the 100, 200, and 300
blocks of West High Street
18th and 19th centuries

Within these three blocks are architectural styles covering a period of almost 100 years. Notable buildings are the William Bowman House (c. 1816), a three-story Flemish bond structure with later alterations; the Richardson House (c. 1832), a two-and-one-half-story Flemish bond dwelling with Greek Revival features; the John Leiby House (c. 1805), Flemish bond, two-and-one-half-story house; the David Dodge House (c. 1804); the William C. P. Breckinridge House (c. 1784), possibly the oldest house in Lexington still on its original site; the Nicholas Brobston House (c. 1786), a two-story frame house with brick chimneys; the Hill Street Church (c. 1828–1831), the western half of which was an early 19th-century spinning mill now greatly altered; and the Asbury Methodist Episcopal Church (c. 1880), designed by architect John McMurtry.
Municipal; not accessible to the public

FRANKLIN COUNTY
Frankfort
CORNER IN CELEBRITIES HISTORIC DISTRICT
Bounded roughly by the Kentucky River on the west; by Main Street on the north with extensions northward along Wilkinson and Washington Streets; by Madison and St. Clair Streets on the east; and by Wapping Street on the south with extensions southward to the river
18th, 19th, and 20th centuries

The Corner in Celebrities Historic District is so named because an unusually large number of famous and important people have lived within its boundaries. This list includes two Supreme Court justices, two cabinet officers, nine U.S. Senators, four Congressmen, five representatives to foreign nations, five major generals of the Army, and four admirals of the Navy. Frankfort was established in 1786 on land belonging to General James Wilkinson, and the historic district encompasses the oldest residential section of the city. It is an area of bell towers and steeples, walled gardens and overhanging trees. Structures to be noted are Liberty Hall (1796), a Georgian House; the Orlando Brown House (1835), Greek Revival and designed by Gideon Shryock; the John Bibb House (1857), Gothic Revival; the Thomas Todd House (1812), Federal; the Catholic Church of the Good Shepherd (1850); the Old Post Office and Customshouse (1887); and the Franklin County Courthouse (1813), also by Gideon Shryock. All these buildings, in fact all within the district, have remained in good condition and in architectural harmony with their surroundings.
Multiple public/private
HABS

FRANKLIN COUNTY
Frankfort
OLD GOVERNOR'S MANSION
420 High Street
1797–1798

This Georgian style house was the residence of Kentucky governors from 1798 until 1914. Walls are brick and trim is wood. The cornice contains both modillions and dentils. A recessed and paneled entranceway is framed by attached, fluted Doric columns supporting a full entablature. The door itself is set inside a semicircular archway containing a keystone. A veranda across the two-story main facade has been removed. Today Kentucky's Lieutenant Governor occupies the house.
State

JEFFERSON COUNTY
Louisville
TAYLOR, ZACHARY, HOUSE (SPRINGFIELD)
5608 Apache Road
c. 1780

Springfield was the home of Zachary Taylor for more than 20 years prior to his military career. During that period he rose from first lieutenant to major general, his role in the Mexican War bringing him national recognition. His death in 1850 marked the end of little more than a year's service as President of the United States. His three-story brick house apparently has not undergone any large-scale alterations, and extensive restoration has been effected by the present owners.
Private; not accessible to the public
NHL; HABS

JEFFERSON COUNTY
Louisville vicinity
LOCUST GROVE
561 Blankenbaker Lane, northeast of Louisville
c. 1790

Locust Grove is a two-story, brick, vernacular Georgian house distinguished by a steep gable roof containing twin end chimneys, a modillion cornice, and the applied pilasters and rectangular transom of the main entrance. Resting on a stone foundation of random ashlar, the house has walls laid in Flemish bond and windows topped by flat arches. A belt course visually separates the two floors. Major William Croghan built Locust Grove, and it was the home of Croghan's brother-in-law General George Rogers Clark from 1809 to 1815.
State

KENTON COUNTY
Covington
BEARD, DANIEL CARTER, BOYHOOD HOME
322 E. 3rd Street
c. 1850

Daniel Carter Beard was one of the key figures in the movement that led to the founding of the Boy Scouts of America in 1910. He served from that time until his death in 1941 as its National Commissioner. Because of his dedicated service, he came to be regarded as the personification of the spirit of scouting. Beard's boyhood home, a large two-story brick house, is used now as a school for practical nurses.
Private; not accessible to the public
NHL

LARUE COUNTY
Hodgenville vicinity
ABRAHAM LINCOLN BIRTHPLACE NATIONAL HISTORIC SITE
3 miles south of Hodgenville
1809

In 1808 Thomas and Nancy Lincoln bought Sinking Springs Farm and occupied a one-room log cabin near a large limestone spring. Here Abraham Lincoln was born on February 12, 1809. The family lived here only about two and a half years when it lost the land because of a defective land title. The site includes nearly 100 acres of land which were included in the original Thomas Lincoln farm. Here are the memorial buildings housing the traditional log cabin birthplace, the Sinking Spring, and the ancient boundary oak tree which was a landmark at the time of Lincoln's birth.
Federal
NPS; 116.50 acres

LOGAN COUNTY
Adairville vicinity
SAVAGE CAVE ARCHEOLOGICAL SITE
About 1 mile east of Adairville on Ky. 591
Pre-Columbian

Savage Cave has been examined by several archeologists who have determined that it was inhabited by pre-Columbian peoples. Several rooms surround the large entrance chamber, and artifacts have been recovered both inside the cave and around the entrance on the outside. Scientific investigation and excavation by competent archeologists is necessary to determine the exact dates of occupancy and the cultures represented here.
Private

MADISON COUNTY
Richmond vicinity
WHITEHALL
Clay Lane, 7 miles north of
Richmond
1798, 1864–1868

Whitehall, home of Cassius Marcellus Clay (1810–1903), is a complex of three separate buildings as evident in both the foundations and the wall fabric. The first stage of construction took place c. 1798; stages two and three apparently began c. 1864 and were completed in 1868. Earlier architecture could be termed Colonial and Georgian vernacular, while the third stage is Italianate. Stage one door openings are set under flat lintels, major access to stage two is through a classical portico, and stage three's entranceway was a double hung door containing a glazed panel above a wood inset. Eaves of stage three have brackets while stage one eaves are unembellished. An 1860's plumbing system is intact. Rainwater was drained into a tank under the roof from which lead pipes ran to a zinc-lined, wood-encased tub and crude commode. Cassius M. Clay was a soldier, legislator, abolitionist, and diplomat. He published *The True American,* an abolitionist newspaper, supported Abraham Lincoln for President, and served as minister to Russia (1863–1869).
State

MASON COUNTY
Washington
WASHINGTON HISTORIC DISTRICT
Corporate limits of the city of
Washington in 1969
18th and 19th centuries

The houses and civic structures of Washington span three quarters of a century of local architecture. Washington remains today a little-altered, early 19th-century Kentucky town. Historic personages connected with Washington include Albert Sidney Johnston, Confederate general who was born here in 1803; Harriet Beecher Stowe, who visited the town in 1833 and witnessed a slave auction on the courthouse lawn; and Chief Justice John Marshall's brother, Thomas, who lived in a large, two-and-one-half-story brick house called Federal Hill. Washington was once the county seat of Mason County.
Multiple public/private
HABS

OHIO COUNTY
Paradise vicinity
INDIAN KNOLL
c. .5 mile upstream from Paradise
ferry landing on the Green River
c. 3000 B.C.

Indian Knoll is one of the largest and most fully documented of the Archaic shell heap sites in the eastern United States. The thousands of artifacts found here have provided vital information on the life of the Archaic Indian. The discovery of some 800 graves has made it possible to learn much about burial practices. Studies of the skeletons found have provided the basis for the clear definition of one type of prehistoric American Indian.
Private; not accessible to the public
NHL

Louisiana

Vieux Carre Historic District, New Orleans, Louisiana. *HABS*

Courtyard, 701 Bourbon Street, Vieux Carre Historic District,
New Orleans, Louisiana. *Dan Leyrer for HABS*

Parlange Plantation, Mix, Louisiana. *NPS*

Royal Street, Vieux Carre Historic District, New Orleans, Louisiana. *HABS*

AVOYELLES PARISH
Marksville vicinity
MARKSVILLE PREHISTORIC INDIAN SITE
Marksville Prehistoric Indian Park
State Monument
First century A.D.

Marksville Prehistoric Indian Site is the type site for the Marksville culture, a southern variant of the Ohio Hopewell. This Indian culture is characterized by extensive burial mounds, often associated with elaborate earthworks. Most of the mounds have been restored to their original condition. Artifacts also showing Hopewell influences are displayed in an interpretive on-site museum.
State
NHL

ORLEANS PARISH
New Orleans
THE CABILDO
Jackson Square, Chartres and St. Peter Streets
1795, Gilberto Guillemard

The Cabildo originally housed the Administrative and Legislative Council which ruled Spanish Louisiana. Under the French rule of Louisiana from 1800 to 1803, it continued in similar use as the Maison de Ville (Town Hall). Composed of an array of Renaissance architectural forms, the stuccoed brick building exhibits the marked Spanish influence in Louisiana. It presently houses the Louisiana State Museum.
Municipal
NHL; HABS

ORLEANS PARISH
New Orleans
CABLE, GEORGE WASHINGTON, HOUSE
1313 8th Street
1874

As the voice of the Louisiana Creoles, George Washington Cable made major contributions to American regional literature. Through his work the term "Creole" became better known and understood. The author's regional writings include his first book, *Old Creole Days; The Creoles of Louisiana; Bonaventure;* and *Strange True Stories of Louisiana.* While the surroundings of his house have been changed materially, the Cable residence itself is substantially unaltered, aside from interior alterations.
Private; not accessible to the public
NHL

ORLEANS PARISH
New Orleans
THE GARDEN DISTRICT
Bounded by properties fronting on Carondelet Street on the north, Josephine Street on the east, Magazine Street on the south, and Louisiana Avenue on the west
19th and 20th centuries

New Orleans' Garden District has remained a fashionable residential section since the 1830's. Homes along its streets represent all styles of architecture popular from antebellum times to the present. Examples of Greek Revival, Georgian, Southern Colonial, Chateauesque, Gothic Revival, late Victorian, Steamboat Gothic, and even contemporary dwellings which conform to their surroundings are evident. Constructed generally of brick, houses in the district are covered with plaster or stucco on the exterior.
Multiple public/private

ORLEANS PARISH
New Orleans
GIROD, NICHOLAS, HOUSE (MAYOR GIROD HOUSE)
500 Chartres Street
1797, service wing; 1814, main house

The three-story Nicholas Girod House has walls of stuccoed brick and is surmounted by an octagonal cupola. There are ironwork balconies on the second floors of both the main house and the smaller, two-story service wing. Nicholas Girod, who built the house, was mayor of New Orleans from 1812 to 1815.
Private; only first floor accessible to the public
NHL; HABS

ORLEANS PARISH
New Orleans
JACKSON SQUARE (PLACE D'ARMES)
Bounded by Decatur, St. Peter, St. Ann, and Chartres Streets
18th, 19th, and 20th centuries

On December 20, 1803, in Jackson Square, the American flag was raised for the first time over the newly-purchased Louisiana Territory, the greatest single acquisition of territory in United States history. The center of the city since its first plan in 1720 and now a public park, the square offers views of the Cabildo, St. Louis Cathedral, and other historic buildings lining it. In the center is the historic flagpole and a statue of Andrew Jackson (1856).
Municipal
NHL

ORLEANS PARISH
New Orleans
LAFITTE'S BLACKSMITH SHOP
941 Bourbon Street
Late 18th century

This one-story cottage is traditionally associated with Jean and Pierre Lafitte, who supposedly posed as blacksmiths while engaging in less respectable economic ventures. The building is a one-story, nearly square example of a French Colonial town house with a hip roof and two symmetrically placed dormer windows. Construction of the walls is "*briquette-entre-poteaux,*" meaning that the spaces between the upright timbers and the diagonal wall supports were filled with bricks covered over by a coat of lime plaster.
Private
NHL; HABS

ORLEANS PARISH
New Orleans
MADAME JOHN'S LEGACY
632 Dumaine Street
1722–1728, 1788 (rebuilt)

Madame John's Legacy was built as a French Colonial, raised cottage town house, once a popular type of city dwelling. Country homes were raised six or eight feet as a flood precaution, but in town this feature was unnecessary. The two-and-one-half-story cottage has brick walls at the first level and a second story of wood. Front and rear *galeries* extend the full length of the house which has a hip roof with a double pitch. In 1783 the cottage was moved to its present location. A fire five years later did extensive damage, and the existing house was built from salvaged materials—hardware, doors, and some beams.
State
NHL; HABS

ORLEANS PARISH
New Orleans
OLD URSULINE CONVENT
1114 Chartres Street
1748–1752

Ursuline Convent was constructed under the direction of a group of nuns who had come to New Orleans to relieve the poor and the sick and to teach young girls. In subsequent years it was used as the archbishopric, as offices for the archdiocese, and as a seminary. At present it serves as the rectory for the adjacent St. Mary's Church. Despite some alterations, the convent is considered an important historic and religious monument in the United States. It is one of the few remaining links with the French capital of Louisiana.
Private; not accessible to the public
NHL; HABS

ORLEANS PARISH
New Orleans
THE PRESBYTÈRE
713 Chartres Street
c. 1791–1813, Gilberto Guillemard

Gilberto Guillemard designed the Presbytère as a companion building to the Cabildo. Both flank St. Louis Cathedral and the former was intended to be the parish rectory. Two and one-half-stories high, the Presbytère was constructed during the Spanish rule in New Orleans. The exterior is stuccoed brick with classical ornamentation in the form of pilasters, a central pediment, and an arcaded first-floor portico. A rear wing was added in 1840 and the mansard roof in 1847. Upon completion the Presbytère was rented by the city as a courthouse. In 1911 the state acquired the building for a museum.
State
NHL; HABS

ORLEANS PARISH
New Orleans
VIEUX CARRÉ HISTORIC DISTRICT
Bounded by the Mississippi River, Rampart Street, Canal Street, and Esplanade Avenue
18th and 19th centuries

Also called the "French Quarter," this 85–block area coincides approximately with the original area of the city of New Orleans. The city was laid out in 1721 on a gridiron plan and was among the earliest planned cities in America. A focal point of the plan was the town square—the Place d'Armes—now known as Jackson Square. Within the district is to be found a continuum of architectural development. The styles represented include the French and Spanish Colonial (1720–1803); early Federal (1803–1825); antebellum (1825–1860); post-Civil War (1850–1900); and modern. Fires in 1788 and 1794 destroyed over 1,000 18th-century buildings. Other National Historic Landmarks within the district are Jackson Square (1721), the Ursuline Convent (1748–1752), and the Cabildo (1795).
Multiple public/private
NHL; HABS

PLAQUEMINES PARISH
Phoenix vicinity
FORT DE LA BOULAYE SITE
Near Phoenix on the Mississippi River, near La. 50
1700

Fort de la Boulaye was founded by Pierre le Moyne, Sieur d'Iberville, as a formal act proclaiming possession of the mouth of the Mississippi River in the name of France. Here in a wooden blockhouse the French successfully defended themselves against English and Spanish encroachment until in 1707 when hostile Indians forced its abandonment. No physical traces of the fort remain above ground.
Private
NHL

PLAQUEMINES PARISH
Triumph vicinity
FORT JACKSON
2.5 miles southeast of Triumph on La. 23, on the west bank of the Mississippi River
1822

The failure of Fort Jackson, citadel of the lower Mississippi River, to stop the Union Navy, caused the Confederacy to lose New Orleans. Fort St. Philip, on the opposite bank of the Mississippi River, also played a part in the fight against Admiral David G. Farragut's fleet in 1862. An active military post until 1920, Fort Jackson is a bastioned pentagon of brick and, except for a few late 19th-century additions, it appears to be little altered from its original state.
Private; not accessible to the public
NHL

PLAQUEMINES PARISH
Triumph vicinity
FORT ST. PHILIP
2.5 miles southeast of Triumph on La. 23, on the east bank of the Mississippi River
1795

Fort St. Philip was erected by the French in 1795, during the administration of Governor Francisco Carondelet. When Admiral David G. Farragut attacked the fort in 1862, the Confederate-occupied post was garrisoned by 700 men. Fort St. Philip, with Fort Jackson, surrendered to the Union forces ten days after the attack had begun. The fort was not regularly garrisoned after 1871. Today the site is in a primitive state and is difficult to reach.
Private
NHL

POINT COUPEE PARISH
Mix vicinity
PARLANGE PLANTATION HOUSE
Junction of La. 1 and 78
c. 1750

The Marquis Vincent de Ternant built the Parlange Plantation House, and upon his death the property passed to his wife, who later married Charles Parlange, a French naval officer. The house is one of the two best examples in the United States of a French Colonial plantation house of the two-story, raised cottage type. Ground-story walls are brick and the upper story is made of cypress timbers filled in with clay or adobe and Spanish moss. Prior to 1860 the hip roof was extended to the rear of the house and the rear gallery added. The house has never been restored.
Private
NHL; HABS

SABINE PARISH
Many vicinity
FORT JESUP
7 miles northeast of Many on La. 6, Fort Jesup State Monument
1822

From its establishment until the outbreak of the Mexican War, Fort Jesup was the most southwesterly military outpost in the United States. From here, in 1845, Zachary Taylor's Army of Observation marched to launch the opening campaign of the war. The fort was inactivated in 1845 after the annexation of Texas moved the United States boundary 600 miles to the southwest. The only remaining original building, a log kitchen, has been restored. One of the officers' quarters has been reconstructed as a visitor center and park office.
State
NHL

ST. BERNARD PARISH
New Orleans vicinity
CHALMETTE NATIONAL HISTORICAL PARK
6 miles south of New Orleans
1815

Chalmette National Historical Park commemorates the Battle of New Orleans between American and British forces, January 8, 1815, in which Andrew Jackson won the greatest American land victory of the War of 1812. This victory, which proved to be the impetus for the rise of American nationalism, assured continued American jurisdiction over the Louisiana Territory and the ratification by both parties of the peace treaty. The park embraces a portion of the ground over which the battle was fought. The land is crossed by the Rodriguez Canal, the line of decisive action, where a series of historical markers identify the various sites of important battle events. A 100–foot high monument commemorates the action and memorializes the American soldiers who died in the battles here.
Federal/non-federal
NPS; 141.32 acres
HABS

ST. CHARLES PARISH
Hahnville vicinity
HOMEPLACE PLANTATION HOUSE
La. 18, .5 mile south of Hahnville
Post Office
c. 1801

Homeplace Plantation House is a large French Colonial, two-story, raised cottage. A wide veranda or *galerie* surrounds the second floor. The ground floor walls and the piers supporting the *galerie* are brick, while the second-story walls are cypress timbers filled in with a mixture of clay or adobe and Spanish moss. Still in a good state of repair and very little altered since the time of its construction, Homeplace is considered to be one of the two best examples of the raised cottage still extant (the other is Parlange Plantation House).
Private; not accessible to the public
NHL; HABS

ST. MARTIN PARISH
New Iberia vicinity
SHADOWS-ON-THE-TECHE
1831–1834

David Weeks, wealthy planter and land-owner, selected a site on Bayou Teche for construction of his home. Under the direction of master builder James Bedell the house developed into a two-story porticoed mansion with eight giant Tuscan columns across the facade and a veranda at the second-floor level. Walls were brick and the gable roof contained three dormers and two interior chimneys. A classical cornice encircles the house at the eave line, and the rear facade contains a three-bay arcade surmounted by an open porch, both typical of Louisiana cottages. No major changes were made after the Civil War.
Private

WEST CARROLL PARISH
Delhi vicinity
POVERTY POINT
12 miles north of Delhi on Bayou Macon
c. 700 B.C.

The largest and most complex ceremonial earthworks of its kind known in North America, Poverty Point is apparently unique among archeological sites in North America. The central feature is Poverty Point Mound, which has a large area at its base enclosed by concentric octagonal earthworks. Motley Mound, 1.5 miles north, is of the same outline and only slightly smaller.
Private
NHL

Maine

Fort Edgecomb, Edgecomb, Maine. *Maine Department of Economic Development*

Tugboat *Seguin*, Bath, Maine.
Bath Marine Museum

The Cotton Factory, Hallowell, Maine.
Row House, Inc.

Tate House, Portland, Maine.
Maine Department of Economic Development

ANDROSCOGGIN COUNTY
Lewiston
HATHORN HALL, BATES COLLEGE
Bates College campus
1852–1857, G. J. E. Bryant

Bates College was incorporated in 1856 as the Maine State Seminary. The college was founded by Free Baptists, and its charter provided freedom from denominational control, although education and religion were to be inseparably connected. Hathorn Hall was the first building of the Seminary and it contained the library, chapel, lecture rooms, and offices. The name was changed to Bates College in 1864, when the seminary was rechartered. The red brick building has granite quoins and a granite belt course above the raised basement, a cupola and bell at the center of the roof, and the second-story windows all have overhead fanlights.
Private

ANDROSCOGGIN COUNTY
Livermore
THE NORLANDS
The Norlands Road
19th century

The Norlands or the Israel Washburn Homestead is a large Italianate home, two stories high, with an open pillared veranda on three sides. Israel and Martha Washburn, who bought the property in 1809, had seven sons and three daughters. Four of the sons were Congressmen, one a banker, one a naval officer, and one the U.S. commissioner to Paraguay. The present house was built to replace a cottage which burned in 1867. Included in the complex are a one-room schoolhouse, a library, and a church.
Private

ANDROSCOGGIN COUNTY
New Gloucester
SHAKER VILLAGE
On Route 26
18th, 19th, and 20th centuries

The Shakers, or United Believers in Christ's Second Appearing, founded the Shaker Village in 1783. By 1850 the community contained more than 25 buildings, but today only 14 buildings and 3 structures (water tank and tower, the springhouse, and the ash house) remain. Among the extant buildings are the meetinghouse and Central Dwelling House, all of which are simple frame construction covered by wooden siding or shingles (the Dwelling House is brick and granite). A representative collection of Shaker implements and furniture is housed in the buildings, and the Shaker Library contains research materials for the scholar. Only nine Shakers, all women, live today at New Gloucester.
Private
HABS

AROOSTOOK COUNTY
Fort Kent vicinity
FORT KENT
c. .75 mile southwest of Fort Kent off Me. 11
1839–1843

Built as a result of the boundary dispute with Canada, Fort Kent was abandoned after the signing of the Webster-Ashburton Treaty (1842). A local militia company began construction of a blockhouse on the site in the early winter of 1838–1839. By September, 1840, federal troops relieved the militiamen and built barracks and officers' quarters. The fort saw no military action.
State

AROOSTOOK COUNTY
Littleton vicinity
WATSON SETTLEMENT BRIDGE
1 mile west of U.S.-Canadian border
1911

One of the ten remaining covered bridges in Maine, the Watson Settlement Bridge spans the Meduxnekeag Stream. Measuring 150 by 20 feet, it was constructed with the Howe Truss system consisting of a series of crossed beams without king posts between the bottom and top chords. Abutments at each end and a pier in midstream, all of rubble, support the bridge.
Municipal/state

CUMBERLAND COUNTY
SHAKER VILLAGE
Reference—see Androscoggin County

CUMBERLAND COUNTY
Brunswick
FIRST PARISH CHURCH
207 Main Street
1845, Richard Upjohn

The First Parish Church of Brunswick is considered to be one of the outstanding Gothic Revival structures in Maine. Typical of Upjohn's "carpenter Gothic" mode, the building is of board and batten construction with double lancet windows and a tower distinguished by wooden tracery and finials. The tower forms the base of a cruciform plan. Inside, the open trusswork projects well into the nave, giving it a deceptively narrow appearance.
Private

CUMBERLAND COUNTY
Brunswick
STOWE, HARRIET BEECHER, HOUSE
63 Federal Street
1804

In this white frame building in 1851–1852, Harriet Beecher Stowe wrote her indictment of slavery, *Uncle Tom's Cabin*. Its success prompted Abraham Lincoln to remark, upon meeting the author, that she was "the little lady who started this great war." Mrs. Stowe's study is intact and furnished with original items. Although interior alterations have been made elsewhere, the exterior remains unchanged.
Private
NHL

CUMBERLAND COUNTY
Brunswick vicinity
HARPSWELL MEETINGHOUSE
Harpswell Center on Me. 123, 9 miles south of Brunswick
1757–1759

The simple, clapboarded, two-story frame Harpswell Meetinghouse is a little-altered example of a small New England colonial church. It was erected in 1757–1759, probably by Elisha Eaton, a carpenter and son of the first pastor. The church has a rectangular floor plan and measures about 30 by 40 feet on the inside. The interior of the main structure contains one large room with galleries at the second-floor level extending around three sides. The building was used both as a church and town meeting hall from 1757 to 1844. In the latter year the structure was acquired by the town and has been used ever since that date as a town meeting place. The building is virtually unaltered except for the removal of the center pews.
Municipal
NHL; HABS

CUMBERLAND COUNTY
Cape Elizabeth
SPURWINK CONGREGATIONAL CHURCH (SOUTH MEETINGHOUSE)
Spurwink Avenue
1802; rebuilt, 1830

The Spurwink Congregational Church stands on a foundation of rough granite blocks. Clapboards cover the exterior, and a square bell tower and cupola ornament the street facade. Notable features include an entrance pavilion and Gothic windows with stationary louvres flanked by shutters. Inside are the original box pews. Spurwink Church was a branch of the First Congregational Church (301 Cottage Road) until 1935 when it became an independent church.
Municipal

CUMBERLAND COUNTY
Freeport
PETTENGILL HOUSE (CAPTAIN GREENFIELD POTE HOUSE)
Wolf Neck Road
c. 1750

The Pettengill House was built in Falmouth and moved to its present location in 1765 by Captain Greenfield Pote, a Yankee sea captain. It is probably the oldest house on Wolf's Neck. Set on a foundation of fieldstones, the two-story frame house is a saltbox. Its framing, timbers, and chimney are original, but the shingles, window frames, and panes are replacements.
Private

CUMBERLAND COUNTY
Harpswell vicinity
EAGLE ISLAND (HOME OF ADMIRAL ROBERT E. PEARY)
1904

Explorer Robert E. Peary (1856–1920) bought Eagle Island in 1880 and in 1904 built the frame, two-story, single bay, gable-roofed cottage which served as his summer home. The island was named in honor of the whaling ship *Eagle*, which first took Peary to the Arctic. Peary's expedition to Greenland in 1891 proved that Greenland was an island. Other expeditions to the Arctic were undertaken in 1893–1895, 1896, 1897, 1898–1902, and 1905–1906. It was at his Eagle Island home that Admiral Peary made plans for his historic 1909 expedition during which he reached the North Pole.
State

CUMBERLAND COUNTY
Portland
THE GOTHIC HOUSE (JOHN J. BROWN HOUSE)
86 Spring Street
1845, Henry Rowe

The Gothic House is a good example of a mid-19th century Gothic Revival cottage similar to those designed and popularized by the architect Andrew Jackson Downing. It is also the only documented example of architect Henry Rowe's work known to exist. The house is two stories high with a hip roof. The facade is highlighted by a projecting gabled central section with a one-story Gothic portico topped by a roof balustrade. Also noteworthy are the finely carved bargeboards of the gable and the square-headed motifs above the windows. The house is within Portland's Spring Street Historic District.
Private

CUMBERLAND COUNTY
Portland
McLELLAN-SWEAT MANSION
111 High Street
Early 19th century

The McLellan-Sweat Mansion, presently the L.D.M. Sweat Memorial Art Museum, was built according to designs of Massachusetts architect Alexander Parris. No basement was dug for the house; instead stones were placed at grade level and earth was heaped up around them to elevate the entrance. Basically Federal in style, the dwelling is highlighted by a semicircular entrance portico with fluted Doric pillars. The low hip roof is balustraded, and white denticulated cornices accent the window heads. The panelled front door is framed by sidelights and an elliptical fanlighted window transom. Above the doorway on the second floor is a Palladian window, and the windows on the first-floor facade have been lengthened. Inside is an unusual flying staircase. An art gallery has been added to the rear of the residence.
Private
NHL; HABS

CUMBERLAND COUNTY
Portland
MORSE-LIBBY MANSION
109 Danforth Street
1859–1863, Henry Austin

Ruggles Sylvester Morse, a New Orleans businessman who had been born in Maine, built the Morse-Libby Mansion as a summer home. Eventually used as a permanent residence, the house is a two-story, Italianate brownstone. A central square tower rises one story above the main block. Triangular and semicircular pediments and pilasters with scroll brackets ornament the windows. Ionic columns support the front porch, and quoins mark the corners of all walls and wall projections. Inside are Carrara marble fireplaces, mahogany, rosewood and chestnut doors, and some original French carpets.
Private
NHL; HABS

CUMBERLAND COUNTY
Portland
SPRING STREET HISTORIC DISTRICT
Bounded roughly on the northwest by Pine and Congress Streets; on the northeast by an imaginary line from Forrest Street to Danforth Street; on the southwest by Brackett Street; and on the southeast by Danforth Street
19th century

Portland's Spring Street Historic District contains examples of houses spanning a century of architectural styles. The oldest of these is the Daniel How House of 1799. First settled in 1632–1633, Portland received its present name in 1786. Its excellent harbor fostered a booming maritime trade, and soon shops, distilleries, and tanneries sprang up to supplement the sea based economy. Portland served as the capital of Maine from 1820 to 1832. Railroads soon began to link the city with inland lumber and grain producers. The days of prosperity are reflected in the comfortable dwellings which have survived. Styles represented are Greek Revival, Federal, Victorian, Gothic Revival, and Italianate. Building materials are red brick, granite, brownstone, and wood. Of the 25 most noteworthy buildings in the district, the majority date from the first half of the 19th century.
Multiple public/private
HABS

CUMBERLAND COUNTY
Portland
WADSWORTH-LONGFELLOW HOUSE
487 Congress Street
1786

Henry Wadsworth Longfellow lived in this 17-room brick house from his birth in 1807 until his second marriage in 1843. After his graduation from Bowdoin College in 1829 he remained there as professor of modern languages until 1835. He held a similar position at Harvard University from 1835 to 1854. He composed the poem "The Rainy Day" in the Wadsworth-Longfellow House following the death of his first wife in 1835. The house contains many objects associated with Longfellow and his family.
Private
NHL; HABS

CUMBERLAND COUNTY
Scarborough
HOMER, WINSLOW, STUDIO
Winslow Homer Road, Prout's Neck
c. 1870

Winslow Homer is particularly noted for his seascapes, landscapes, and Civil War paintings. After deciding in 1870 to devote his life to painting, Homer converted an empty stable near his brother's cottage into a residence. This studio is a small wooden building with a mansard roof. From the balcony upstairs Homer spent countless hours gazing out to sea.
Private; accessible to the public by appointment only
NHL

CUMBERLAND COUNTY
South Casco
HAWTHORNE, NATHANIEL,
BOYHOOD HOME
Hawthorne and Raymond Cape
Roads
19th century

Richard Manning, uncle of Nathaniel
Hawthorne, built this home in which his
nephew lived from 1813 to 1825. In 1839
the house was remodeled as a
meetinghouse. Presently the two-and-one-
half-story, ten-room frame house contains
only three rooms and is used occasionally
for public functions.
Public/private

CUMBERLAND COUNTY
Stroudwater
TATE HOUSE
1270 Westbrook Street
1755

The three-story Tate House has a symmetrical Georgian facade covered by
feathered clapboarding. A distinguishing
and unusual feature of the exterior is the
indented gambrel roof. Inside are eight
fireplaces connected to a central chimney. The interior is enhanced by carved
paneling, bolection moldings, and a cove
ceiling in the front hall. George Tate, a
local mast agent for the Royal Navy, built
the Tate House and occupied it until
1794.
Private
HABS

FRANKLIN COUNTY
Farmington vicinity
NORDICA HOMESTEAD
19th and 20th centuries

Madame Lillian Nordica, nee Lillian Norton (1857–1914), was born in this house
and lived here for five years. As a young
girl she moved to Boston and began the
vocal training which led to an international career as an operatic soprano.
Madame Nordica lived abroad much of
her life and did not return to Farmington
until the fall of 1911, when she paid a
brief visit. Edwin Norton, father of
Madame Nordica, built the frame house in
1840. Typical of Maine domestic architecture, the house lacks a front porch and is
one and one-half stories with a gable roof
and rear ell. It houses a collection of
jewels, gowns, and mementos reminiscent
of Madame Nordica.
Private

FRANKLIN COUNTY (also in Kennebec,
Sagadahoc, and Somerset counties)
**Popham Beach vicinity to Coburn
Gore**
ARNOLD TRAIL TO QUEBEC
Along the Kennebec River, through
Wyman and Flagstaff lakes, along the
Dead River and Chain of Ponds to
Quebec, Canada
1775

American strategy in the early months of
the Revolutionary War was designed to
cut off British troops in Canada under Sir
Guy Carleton from other forces in the
colonies. George Washington ordered
thirty-four-year-old Colonel Benedict Arnold to lead an expedition northward
through Maine to attack Quebec City.
General Richard Montgomery led a
second group of men simultaneously
against Montreal. The route through
Maine was regarded as the shortest and
most direct to Quebec. Arnold headquartered at Fort Western in Augusta, departing from there on September 25, 1775.
His march from Fort Western to Quebec
took 45 days and covered 180 miles. Ultimately the expedition proved unsuccessful
because Quebec was too heavily garrisoned.
State

HANCOCK COUNTY
Blue Hill
JONATHAN FISHER MEMORIAL
Outer Main Street (Route 15)
18th century (barn), 19th century
(house)

The Reverend Jonathan Fisher (1768–
1847) studied divinity at Harvard University and came to Blue Hill in 1796.
He was to serve as the first settled minister
for the Congregational church and held
this post 41 years. Fisher was a linguist,
printer, inventor, artist, architect, teacher,
poet, and botanist as well as a parson. The
present homestead was built in 1814 and
has been restored. The barn was constructed in the late 18th century.
Private

HANCOCK COUNTY
Castine
CATE HOUSE
Corner of Court and Pleasant Streets
1815

The Cate House is a two-and-one-half-
story frame, Colonial style house built for
Thomas Adams, a Castine businessman.
He left it to his daughter, Mrs. Charles
Cate. The house is marked by its simple
exterior and the absence of a front porch.
Private; not accessible to the public

HANCOCK COUNTY
Castine
FORT GEORGE
Bounded on the northwest and
southwest by a golf course, on the
north and east by Wadsworth Street,
and on the south by Battle Avenue
1779–1815

Fort George was constructed by the
British to protect shipping in the Bay of
Fundy and settlements in lower Canada.
An American force tried unsuccessfully to
capture the fort in August, 1779, and was
later annihilated by the British. After the
Revolution the fort was abandoned and
not garrisoned again until the War of
1812. In 1813 a British force from Halifax
took possession of Maine east of the
Penobscot River and repaired and fortified Fort George. Peace was effected by
the Treaty of Ghent (December 24,
1814), but news did not reach Castine for
several weeks afterwards, and it was April
before the fort was blown up and the
troops evacuated. Two powder magazines
and the southernmost bastion have been
restored and the earthworks are still
evident.
State

HANCOCK COUNTY
Castine
PERKINS, JOHN, HOUSE
Perkins Street
1765, 1783

The John Perkins House is Castine's only
pre-Revolutionary dwelling. Recently
dismantled and moved to its present location, the house had survived a British
bombardment in 1779 and enemy occupation during the War of 1812. The timbers
of the house are hand hewn, and the
cracks between the wall boards are
covered with strips of birch bark. The Perkins House was undoubtedly built by local
craftsmen, and it is a good example of vernacular Georgian architecture.
Private

HANCOCK COUNTY
East Sullivan vicinity
WICKYUP (ADMIRAL RICHARD E.
BYRD ESTATE)
8 miles northeast of East Sullivan at
the south end of Tunk Lake

Admiral Richard Evelyn Byrd
(1888–1957) was a pioneer in the
development of long range, transoceanic,
and high altitude flying and the first man
to fly over both the North (1926) and
South (1929) Poles. He is also credited
with exploring or directing the exploration
of more previously unseen lands than any
other individual of the 20th century. In
1937 he purchased this log residence in

Maine, a lodge built by the Eagle Mountain Lake Club in 1929. Here Byrd planned his three Antarctic expeditions (1937, 1946, and 1955) and wrote his last book, *Alone* (1938).

Private; not accessible to the public

NHL

HANCOCK COUNTY
Ellsworth
BLACK HOUSE
West Main Street on Route 172
1824–1827

Soon after the Revolutionary War William Bingham, a Philadelphia banker, bought a large tract of land in Maine which he planned to sell to settlers. Bingham employed David Cobb as his agent, and Cobb had as his assistant a young Englishman, John Black. Black eventually married Cobb's daughter Mary and built the present Black House as a residence and office on land received from his father-in-law. The three-story house is brick and designed in the Federal style. A two-story ell is attached to the northwest corner.

Private

HANCOCK COUNTY
Northeast Harbor
GILMAN, DANIEL COIT, SUMMER HOME (OVER EDGE)
c. 1880

As the first president of Johns Hopkins University from 1875 to 1901, Daniel Coit Gilman made graduate education a recognized university responsibility. He elevated pure research to a pre-eminent position and stressed the necessity for academic freedom. His house is a three-story shingled building situated on a high bluff overlooking the harbor.

Private; not accessible to the public

NHL

KENNEBEC COUNTY
ARNOLD TRAIL TO QUEBEC
Reference—see Franklin County

KENNEBEC COUNTY
Augusta
BLAINE, JAMES G., HOUSE
Capitol and State Streets
c. 1830

James G. Blaine's long and varied political career began with his election to the House of Representatives in 1863. He served as Speaker from 1869 to 1875. Known popularly as the "Plumed Knight," he was twice Senator and twice Secretary of State, but he failed in his bid for the Presidency in 1884. Perhaps his most enduring public service was the establishment of the Pan-American Union in 1890 while he was Secretary of State. In 1919

his house was given to the State of Maine for use as the governor's mansion. His library has been restored to its late 19th-century appearance.

State

NHL

KENNEBEC COUNTY
Augusta
FORT WESTERN
Bowman Street
1754

Fort Western was built on the site of an early 17th-century trading post established by the Plymouth Colony. The fort was constructed in the mid–18th century at the head of navigation on the Kennebec River as a supply depot for the British army. From here supplies were hauled by oxcart to Fort Halifax, now Winslow. Supplies were assembled at Fort Western for General Benedict Arnold's march on Quebec in 1775. By the second decade of the 20th century all of Fort Western had been torn down or fallen down except for the main building or residence. Descendants of the fort's only commandant, James Howard, restored the main building and presented it to the city of Augusta in 1921. The two blockhouses and the stockade are reconstructions.

Municipal

HABS

KENNEBEC COUNTY
Augusta
KENNEBEC ARSENAL
Arsenal Street
c. 1828

In 1827 legislation was passed enabling the federal government to build an arsenal in Augusta for protection of the state's northeastern frontier. A 40–acre site overlooking the Kennebec River was selected, and 15 buildings were constructed. These included storehouses, officers' quarters, barracks, stables, blacksmith shops, armorer's shop, wheelwright's shop, and two magazines. The arsenal manufactured ammunition for the Mexican, Civil, and Spanish-American wars. In 1901 the arsenal was abandoned, although the facilities were maintained by the federal government as a small military post until 1903. Two years later the buildings and grounds were turned over to the state of Maine to be used for a mental hospital. Ten original granite buildings still stand and are in use. Some alterations have been made to accommodate the hospital patients.

State

KENNEBEC COUNTY
Hallowell
ELM HILL FARM (MERRICK COTTAGE)
Litchfield Road
1799

Elm Hill Farm was built for John Merrick (1766–1862), an educator of varied talents whose interests included mathematics, surveying, navigation, geology, astronomy, and anatomy. His one-story frame cottage with gable roof is presently the center of a farm complex. The house plan is central hall. Dormers on the roof are later additions, and the window frames and sash are probably not original. The front steps are granite sections of a grist mill wheel. A two-story ell has been built on the west side of the cottage.

Private; not accessible to the public

KENNEBEC COUNTY
Hallowell
HALLOWELL HISTORIC DISTRICT
18th and 19th centuries

Hallowell was settled in 1754, and 85 percent of the structures within the historic district were built during the 18th and 19th centuries. Three major traffic arteries are also within the historic area—the Kennebec River, the old County Road (U.S. 201) to Brunswick, and the Coos Trail (now Winthrop Road), which linked Hallowell with New Hampshire and Vermont. At one time the city was noted for its publishing and printing establishments. Notable buildings within the district are the Worster House (originally Hallowell House), an 1830's hotel; the Joseph R. Bodwell House (15 Middle Street), Second Empire; the Dr. Benjamin Page House (c. 1800), Georgian; the Ezekial Goodale House (1815), Federal; the Birdcage (1838), an architectural curiosity exhibiting Federal and Greek Revival details; Hubbard Library (1880), Late Gothic Revival; Kennebec Row, a group of commercial structures on Water Street (1815); and the Cotton Factory (1844), also on Water Street.

Multiple public/private

KENNEBEC COUNTY
Hallowell
ROW HOUSE (THE GAGE BLOCK)
106–114 2nd Street
c. 1840

This building is the only known example in Maine of a wooden row house. Isaac Gage, a Hallowell merchant, had the block built as a rental property, and it is virtually unaltered today, though greatly in need of repair. The building consists of five adjoining vertical units with two rooms in the basement, two on the first

and second floors, and a large storage area in the attic. The basement is made of granite, the roof is gabled, and all interior woodwork is original.
Private; not accessible to the public

KENNEBEC COUNTY
Hallowell
VAUGHAN HOMESTEAD
Middle Street off Litchfield Road
1797

Originally a two-story dwelling with a hip roof and four chimneys, the Vaughan Homestead has had several additions built onto the west or rear facade. The house commands a view of the Kennebec River and has four rooms on each floor of the oldest portion. During the early 19th century a two-story wing was built on the rear and a long veranda was added to the front. Later, a second two-story, octagonal addition was put up abutting on the first; and a final two-story portion was added to the first wing. The house is frame covered with clapboards. Benjamin and Charles Vaughan were early and influential citizens of Hallowell who inherited this land from their mother Sarah Hallowell Vaughan.
Private; not accessible to the public

KENNEBEC COUNTY
Winslow
FORT HALIFAX
On U.S. 201 at Winslow
1754

Fort Halifax, erected in 1754, contains the oldest surviving example in the United States of a log blockhouse, a defensive structure that was used by explorers, fur traders, and settlers along the American frontier during the 18th and 19th centuries. A blockhouse could be constructed out of stone, brick, or adobe, as well as of logs, and was a highly effective means of defense on the frontier. It was generally strong enough to repel any enemy force that was not equipped with artillery. Fort Halifax was originally established as a defensive outpost during the French and Indian War by Governor William Shirley of Massachusetts (Maine was part of Massachusetts until 1820). The blockhouse is the only surviving structure of the fort, which was originally a square enclosed by a log stockade with blockhouses at the southwest and northeast corners.
State
NHL; HABS

KNOX COUNTY
Camden
THE CONWAY HOUSE
Conway Road
18th century

This Cape Cod style house is a significant example of early 18th-century rural construction. The original portion, built in the 1770's, has been enlarged, and the last addition was made in the early 1800's. Laths in the walls and ceilings are of hand split hemlock, roof timbers are fastened with treenails, and rose-head nails were used in some of the fastenings. Other features are wide floor boards, a double brick hearth, and L and H hinges. Near the house are an old heavy-timbered barn and a blacksmith shop, both in good condition.
Private

KNOX COUNTY
Rockport
ROCKPORT HISTORIC KILN AREA
On Rockport Harbor at the mouth of the Goose River
19th and 20th centuries

Lime produced in the state of Maine was shipped all over the United States during the late 19th and early 20th centuries. Maine lime was used to build the Capitol in Washington, D.C. The coastal towns of Thomaston, Rockland, Rockport, and Camden were the chief producers. Kilns were employed to process quarried limestone. Prior to the Civil War most kilns were made of stone and used wood as fuel. Later coal and coal gas replaced wood which led to the development of iron kilns. Competition from other lime producing states eventually forced the Rockport kilns out of business. Seven kilns remain on the site.
Private

KNOX COUNTY
Vinalhaven
THE VINALHAVEN GALAMANDER
Bandstand Park
1880's–1914

Vinalhaven, North Haven, and several smaller islands in Penobscot Bay formed the nucleus of a granite quarrying industry in the latter years of the 19th century. With the advent of World War I, Maine's granite industry collapsed. The Vinalhaven Galamander (the origin of the name is unknown) is a restoration built of oak and the original iron. These wagons, measuring 25 feet by 10 feet, were used to transport huge blocks of quarried granite. A derrick or lever attached to a rope tackle was used to lift the granite from the ground. An eight-horse team pulled the galamander to its destination.
Municipal

KNOX COUNTY (also in Waldo County)
Vicinity of Warren, Union, Appleton, and Searsmont
GEORGES RIVER CANAL
Upper Falls, Georges River in Warren to Union town line, extending to Quantabacook Pond in Searsmont
1846

The Maine legislature, in July, 1846, authorized the Georges Canal Company to build from tidewater to Stevens Pond in the town of Liberty. Construction began, and the canal opened in the spring of 1847. Traffic ran between Quantabacook Pond above Searsmont and Lower Falls in Warren. No horses or mules were used to power the canal boats. Rather, the men poled in shallow water and used sails to cross the two large ponds. The canal never was a prosperous venture, and within a few years a shift in population and trade caused a decline in traffic. In 1850 the last boat traversed the canal. Today most of the 28–mile canal route has fallen into disrepair and ruin, but the Knox and Sennebec locks still remain though altered and somewhat decayed.
Multiple public/private

LINCOLN COUNTY
Alna Center
ALNA MEETINGHOUSE
Me. 218
1789

The Alna Meetinghouse is a rectangular, two-and-one-half-story, gable-roofed structure with shingled ends and clapboards on front and back. On the five-bay front is a projecting stair pavilion. Inside are the original box pews and a balcony which extends around three sides of the sanctuary.
Municipal
HABS

LINCOLN COUNTY
Damariscotta
CHAPMAN-HALL HOUSE
Main and Vine Streets
1754

The Chapman-Hall House is believed to be the oldest building in Damariscotta. It is a frame, rectangular, one-and-one-half-story Cape Cod dwelling with a five-bay front. The sides and rear are shingled. A central chimney pierces the gable roof and connects with four fireplaces on the interior. Nathaniel Chapman, a house builder from Ipswich, Massachusetts, built the house.
Private

LINCOLN COUNTY
Damariscotta vicinity
DAMARISCOTTA OYSTER SHELL
HEAPS
Damariscotta River north of
Damariscotta
Pre-Columbian, 15th to 17th
centuries

Artifacts and shells unearthed by archeologists during the past 100 years indicate that these oyster shell heaps are probably 2000 years old. Due to ecological changes, oysters have not lived in this area for over 300 years, and in recent times commercial interests have disturbed the heaps in the process of converting the shells into lime. Some loss has been caused by tidal erosion. Estimates for the total area of the shell heaps (as great as five million cubic feet) place them among the largest in the world.
State

LINCOLN COUNTY
Dresden
BOWMAN-CARNEY HOUSE
.5 mile north of Me. 197 and west of
Me. 128
18th century

Jonathan Bowman contracted with Gersham Flagg to build his house in the last half of the 18th century. Bowman, a kinsman of John Hancock, allied himself with the Sons of Liberty during the American Revolution. Afterwards he was appointed Judge of Probate and became very influential in the District of Maine. In 1805 the house was purchased by James Carney, a blacksmith. He erected barns, a large blacksmith shop, and eventually shipways. He completed building the brig *Dresden* in 1811 and soon began specializing in ship's hardware. The two-story frame house is clapboarded with a low, hip roof. It is rectangular and has a central hall plan. A one-story side ell attached to the north was an addition of the early 19th century. In recent years the house has been restored.
Private
HABS

LINCOLN COUNTY
Dresden
POWNALBOROUGH COURTHOUSE
Cedar Grove Road
1761

Lincoln County was established in 1760, and the following year the Plymouth Company proprietors voted to construct a courthouse for the new county. The site chosen was within the parade ground of Fort Shirley (built in 1752). Georgian in style, the courthouse is three stories high with living quarters located on the first and third floors, and the courtroom on the second. Court sessions were held in the building, the only existing, pre-Revolutionary courthouse in the state, until 1794. Since then the building has served as a private residence.
Private
HABS

LINCOLN COUNTY
Edgecomb
FORT EDGECOMB
On Davis Island in the Sheepscot
River
1808–1812

Fort Edgecomb was built to protect the harbor and shipping port of Wiscasset between 1808 and 1809. Secretary of War Henry Dearborn (1751–1829) supervised work on the batteries during a personal visit in August, 1808. Extensive earthworks were thrown up, a stone and brick powder magazine was constructed, and a substantial garrison was stationed here during the War of 1812. The war demonstrated that wooden blockhouses such as the one at Fort Edgecomb were inadequate for coastal defenses, and in 1816 the garrison was withdrawn and the guns of the fort removed to Boston.
State

LINCOLN COUNTY
Pemaquid vicinity
HARRINGTON MEETINGHOUSE
Northwest of Pemaquid on Old
Harrington Road
c. 1775

The Harrington Meetinghouse is a two-story, gable-roofed, frame structure. Its main doorway, opening onto the graveyard, is surmounted by a triangular pediment, and corner pilasters ornament the street facade. The architectural style is Georgian. In the late 1840's the building was moved across its original lot to the present location. At that time the interior was remodeled. Balconies and box pews were removed, and the window and door arrangement was altered. Recent restoration has returned the meetinghouse to its 18th-century appearance.
Municipal/private

LINCOLN COUNTY
Pemaquid Beach vicinity
FORT WILLIAM HENRY
Northwest of Pemaquid Beach
1692–1696

Four forts have occupied the site of Fort William Henry. The first, Fort Pemaquid, was a stockade built in 1630 as a defense against pirates and burned two years later. Fort Charles, a second wooden defense work, was constructed in 1677 and leveled by the Penobscot Indians in 1689. Fort William Henry was built in 1692, during King William's War, by Sir William Phipps, first royal governor of Massachusetts (Maine was part of Massachusetts until 1820). French and Indian forces destroyed the fortifications in 1696. The fourth and final fort was erected under royal commission in 1729 and named Fort Frederick after the Prince of Wales. Bristol residents demolished the fort during the early years of the Revolution to prevent British occupancy. The present structure is a replica of the 1692 Fort William Henry.
State

LINCOLN COUNTY
Pemaquid Beach vicinity
PEMAQUID RESTORATION AND
MUSEUM
Pemaquid
16th and 17th centuries

The first documented settlement at Pemaquid dates from 1625 when the Indian chief Samoset sold the peninsula to John Brown for 50 beaver skins. Strategically, Pemaquid was important as the last English outpost in the area between the St. Croix and Kennebec rivers also claimed by France. Four forts were erected at Pemaquid between 1630 and 1729. Archeological excavations begun in 1965 have revealed 14 foundations and many artifacts, the best of which are displayed in a museum. Buildings thus far unearthed include several homes, a tavern, a meetinghouse, a customshouse, and a jail.
Private

LINCOLN COUNTY
Waldoboro vicinity
GERMAN CHURCH AND CEMETERY
Me. 32, 1 mile south of Waldoboro
1772

Samuel Waldo, founder of Waldoboro, was responsible for bringing German settlers to the area in 1752. They built and worshiped in the German Church, which was moved to its present location in 1794. Boxlike pews, galleries, and the hanging pulpit date from the 19th century. The church building is two stories high and measures 30 feet by 45 feet. The structure is frame on stone underpinnings without a basement. No regular services are held in the church.
Private
HABS

LINCOLN COUNTY
Wiscasset
NICKELS-SORTWELL HOUSE
Northeast corner of Main and Federal
Streets
1807–1808

The Nickels-Sortwell House is a three-story, L-shaped Federal town house. Crowned by a low hip roof, the house has a notably elaborate facade. The entrance door is flanked by decoratively mullioned sidelights and topped by a wide, elliptical fanlight. A one-story Corinthian portico (added in 1917–1918) shelters the doorway. Two bays on either side of the entrance contain recessed arches, and from this base rise four Corinthian pilasters. Above the main door there is a Palladian window on the second floor and a semicircular window on the third. All third-floor windows are reduced in height. Inside, the house has a modified central hall plan.
Private
NHL; HABS

LINCOLN COUNTY
Wiscasset
U.S. CUSTOMHOUSE (OLD CUSTOMHOUSE) AND POST OFFICE
Water Street
1870, Alfred B. Mullett

Wiscasset has been the seat of a customhouse since 1791. Two other buildings have served in this capacity before the present structure was erected. It is brick with a hip roof, and all the trim (the cornice, door surrounds, and the window keystones and sills) are Hallowell granite. The post office originally occupied the first floor. On the second floor were offices for the postmaster, the collector of internal revenue, the customs collector, and the custom clearinghouse.
Private

LINCOLN COUNTY
Wiscasset
WISCASSET JAIL AND MUSEUM
Me. 218
1809–1811; jailer's house, 1837

Lincoln County was organized in 1760, and two temporary jails had been built prior to 1809. The present jail is granite and the jailer's house is brick. There are six cells on each of the two lower floors. Debtors, women prisoners, and sick persons were quartered on the third floor. Until the state prison was built in 1824, the Wiscasset jail was the principal place in Maine for the incarceration of criminals.
Private
HABS

OXFORD COUNTY
Fryeburg Center vicinity
HEMLOCK BRIDGE
Over the Old Course Saco River, northeast of Fryeburg Center
1857

Measuring 116 feet long by 19 feet wide, the Hemlock Bridge is Paddleford Truss construction. The main feature is an arch of laminated wooden planks in ten courses. These are bolted together with iron threaded rods, and the ends of the arch rest on granite block abutments on the river bank. The Hemlock Bridge is the only remaining of seven covered bridges spanning the Saco River in the Fryeburg area.
State/municipal

OXFORD COUNTY
Newry vicinity
SUNDAY RIVER BRIDGE
Over the Sunday River, west of Newry
1872

This wooden structure measures 100 feet long, 20 feet wide, and 22 feet high from the floor to the peak of the gable roof. The bridge was constructed by local builders who used Paddleford Truss construction. Although used until 1955, the bridge has subsequently been closed to traffic but is still maintained in good condition as a scenic turnoff.
State

OXFORD COUNTY (also in York County)
Porter vicinity
PORTER-PARSONFIELD BRIDGE
.5 mile south of Porter
1876

The present structure is the third bridge erected to connect the towns of Porter and Parsonfield. Spanning the Ossipee River, it measures 152 feet long and 22 feet wide. Three granite block piers, one in midstream, support the covered bridge which utilizes Paddleford Truss construction. The sides of the bridge are open from the roof line to one-third the height of the king posts.
State

OXFORD COUNTY
South Andover
LOVEJOY BRIDGE
Across the Ellis River
1868

The Lovejoy Bridge is 70 feet long, 20 feet wide, and 22 feet high from the floor to the peak of the gable roof. Constructed by the method known as a Paddleford Truss, Lovejoy Bridge is the shortest such covered structure in Maine.
Municipal/state

OXFORD COUNTY
Wilsons Mills vicinity
BENNETT BRIDGE
Over the Magalloway River, 1.5 miles south of Wilsons Mills, Me. 16
1901

Bennett Bridge is a wooden single-span covered crossing 92 feet long. The roof is gabled. Resting on granite block shore abutments, the bridge is Paddleford Truss construction, a modification of a Long Truss system. A series of crossed braces between king posts is employed, the braces being mortised into the king posts. The king posts are then mortised into the top and bottom chords and secured with iron bolts. Additional support is provided by wire cables attached to the top chords of the bridge and anchored to deadmen sunk in the earth 25 feet from the bridge corners.
State

PENOBSCOT COUNTY
Bangor
MORSE BRIDGE
Across the Kenduskeag Stream, Coe Park
1882

The Morse Bridge is the oldest remaining bridge in Bangor and the longest (212 feet) such structure in Maine. Its truss, designed by William Howe, is unique for the use of iron rods as support. Presently used as a pedestrian crossing, the bridge has been moved from its original site.
Municipal

PENOBSCOT COUNTY
Robyville
ROBYVILLE BRIDGE
Across the Kenduskeag Stream
1876

Spanning the Kenduskeag Stream, the Robyville Covered Bridge is 76 feet long, 19 feet wide, and rests on granite block abutments which are 15 feet high. The basic engineering concept employed is the Howe Truss system designed by William Howe of Massachusetts. Variations in the basic construction include the use of double king posts at the center of the span for support, and an extra timber has been added to double timber one of each of the cross braces.
Municipal/state

PISCATAQUIS COUNTY
Brownville Junction vicinity
KATAHDIN IRONWORKS
5 miles north of Brownville Junction
on Route 11, then 6 miles on a gravel
road
1843–1890

Moses Greenleaf discovered iron ore on
Ore Mountain in 1843. Two years later
the Katahdin Ironworks was incorporated.
The works operated, except for the years
1858–1863, until 1890, smelting surface
limonite into large ingots or pigs. From
1873 to 1890 two hundred workers were
employed, and the complex included two
large boarding houses, a town hall, a
school, post office, company store, and
two farms. Only one of the 14 original
charcoal kilns or beehives and the tower
of the blast furnace remain.
State

PISCATAQUIS COUNTY
Sangerville vicinity
LOW'S BRIDGE
Over the Piscataquis River, northeast
of Sangerville
1857

The Piscataquis River separates Gilford
and Sangerville, and Low's Bridge is the
fourth built to connect the two towns.
Resting on two granite block abutments
which are 20 feet high, the bridge is 125
feet long and 22 feet wide. Construction is
the Long Truss system developed by
Colonel Stephen H. Long in the 1830's. It
consists of a series of crossed braces
between upright king posts. Low's Bridge
was built on this principle but varies
somewhat as an extra timber has been
added to double timber one of each of the
cross braces.
Municipal/state

SAGADAHOC COUNTY
ARNOLD TRAIL TO QUEBEC
Reference—see Franklin County

SAGADAHOC COUNTY
Bath
SEGUIN (TUGBOAT)
Bath Marine Museum
19th and 20th centuries

Launched in 1884, the *Seguin* is now the
oldest steam-operated tugboat in Maine.
She operated out of Bath towing four- and
five-masted vessels as well as barges from
the sea to various parts of the Kennebec
River. From 1950 to 1969 her home port
was Belfast on Penobscot Bay. The tub
measures 88 feet 1 inch overall length and
has a 19 foot 8 inch beam. Her draft is 12
feet.
Private

SAGADAHOC COUNTY
Bath
U.S. CUSTOMHOUSE AND POST OFFICE
25 Front Street
1858, Ammi B. Young

Ammi Burnham Young (1800–1874) was
Supervising Architect of the Treasury
from 1852 to 1861. He designed the Bath
Customhouse as a fireproof structure with
solid masonry exterior walls enclosing
spaces vaulted by a parallel series of shallow brick arches. The arches are supported by iron I-beams resting on masonry
interior partitions or cast iron columns.
The five-bay facade has a slightly projecting central pedimented pavilion. Quoins
were used to emphasize corners, and all
windows have full architraves. The triple
entrance has a console-supported cornice,
and the low, hip roof was once railed by a
balustrade. In 1912 a western addition was
constructed and matched with the original
granite structure. The overall design is
restrained and basically classical.
Federal
HABS

SAGADAHOC COUNTY
Popham Beach vicinity
FORT POPHAM
North of Popham Beach on
Hunnewell Point
19th and 20th centuries

Fort Popham was built during the Civil
War to prevent a Confederate invasion,
along the Kennebec River, of Bath.
Granite walls thirty feet high form a
closed lunette or half moon within which
is a parade ground. Spiral stairs at either
end of the fortifications lead to the upper
tiers, and a moat surrounds the entire fort.
Two barracks once situated within the
walls are no longer extant. Fort Popham
was garrisoned during the Spanish-American and First World wars.
State

SAGADAHOC COUNTY
Popham Beach vicinity
POPHAM COLONY SITE
Northeast of Sabino Head at the end
of Me. 209

On this site on August 19, 1607, Sir
George Popham, Raleigh Gilbert (nephew
of Sir Walter Raleigh), and Captain James
Dorrs landed approximately 120 men with
the expectation of establishing a colony on
Sabino Head. They were thus the founders
of the first English colony on the shores of
New England. The colonists erected 15
houses and a meetinghouse and
storehouse and built a 30-ton pinnace, the
Virginia, but the harsh climate and constant harassment by Indians forced their
return to England in late 1609. There are
no aboveground remains of the colony,
but investigation by archeologists in 1966
produced many artifacts.
State

SOMERSET COUNTY
ARNOLD TRAIL TO QUEBEC
Reference—see Franklin County

SOMERSET COUNTY
New Portland vicinity
NEW PORTLAND WIRE BRIDGE
Wire Bridge Road, over the
Carrabasset River
19th century

The New Portland Wire Bridge measures
188 feet in length by 12 feet in width.
Towers supporting the two cables are 25
feet high. Two large Sheffield steel girders
(4 inches in diameter) support the bridge
between the towers. Colonel F. B. Morse
designed the unusual bridge, which was
extensively repaired in 1960–1961. Only
one lane of traffic can cross the bridge at
a time.
State

WALDO COUNTY
GEORGES RIVER CANAL
Reference—see Knox County

WALDO COUNTY
Prospect vicinity
FORT KNOX STATE PARK
On U.S. 1 near Prospect
1844

Fort Knox was constructed soon after settlement of the dispute between Great
Britain and the United States over Maine's
northeastern boundary. The fort was garrisoned during the Civil and Spanish-
American wars. Surrounded by a twenty-
foot-high granite wall, the fort measures
350 feet by 280 feet. It contains
magazines, barracks, storehouses, shot
ovens, gun emplacements, a dry moat, and
rifle galleries, and at one time housed a
blacksmith shop, an implement house, and
a hospital.
State
NHL

WALDO COUNTY
Searsport
PENOBSCOT MARINE MUSEUM
Church Street
19th century

The Penobscot Marine Museum com-
memorates the age of sail and steam and
Maine's period of seagoing prosperity.
Searsport was a leading port in the
mid–19th century with as many as eight
shipyards in operation at once. The entire
Penobscot Bay area from Wiscasset to
Calais shared in the maritime trade and its

profits, and today Searsport ranks second to Portland as a Maine port city. Included in the museum are four buildings: the Searsport Town Hall (1845), a one-and-one-half-story, Greek Revival, brick building; the Captain Merithew House (mid–19th century) a two-and-one-half-story, gable-roofed brick dwelling; the Nickels-Colcord-Duncan House (1860), a frame, clapboard-sheathed structure; and the Fowler-True-Ross House (1825), also frame, gable-roofed, and two and one-half stories high. All contain objects relating to sea trade and shipbuilding.

Private

WALDO COUNTY
Stockton Springs vicinity
FORT POWNALL MEMORIAL
Southeast of Stockton Springs on Fort Point
1759–1775

Fort Pownall was built to guard the Penobscot River from occupation by the French during the French and Indian War (1759–1763). A British garrison was quartered here from July to September, 1759, when the fall of Quebec made protection of the Penobscot unnecessary. Originally the fort measured 90 feet on each side and the breastworks were 10 feet high. A moat, 15 feet wide by 8 feet deep, surrounded the breastworks. Inside the walls was a two-story, square blockhouse. The fort was burned by the colonists in the early years of the Revolution, and only the foundations and the earthworks remain.

State

WASHINGTON COUNTY
Columbia Falls
RUGGLES HOUSE
Main Street
Early 19th century

The Federal style Ruggles House was built for Thomas Ruggles, landowner and merchant. On the main facade is a Palladian window, and the door is flanked by sidelights and topped by a double fanlight. Ruggles brought a woodcarver from England to decorate the interior. Outstanding examples of his work are the mantels, the fluted window sills, and the carved cornices. The most unusual feature of the house is its flying staircase which divides at the landing into two reverse stairs without lateral supports.

Private
HABS

WASHINGTON COUNTY
Eastport
FORT SULLIVAN
Moose Island; barracks, 74 Washington Street
1808

Fort Sullivan was built when Maine was still part of Massachusetts. Governor James Sullivan of Massachusetts ordered its construction for protection of Eastport and to aid in the enforcement of President Thomas Jefferson's Embargo Act. The Embargo Act forbade trade with Great Britain and made Maine's growing commerce with the maritime provinces of Canada illegal. War was declared on Great Britain by the United States in June, 1812. Two years later a British force captured all of eastern Maine, including Fort Sullivan which was renamed Fort Sherbrooke. The Treaty of Ghent (December 24, 1814) ended the war, but British soldiers did not evacuate Fort Sullivan until 1818. A dispute over the boundary between New Brunswick and Aroostook County, Maine (1838–1839), caused reactivation of the fort. It was abandoned shortly thereafter. Today only the powder magazine remains on the original site. The officers' barracks has been removed to 74 Washington Street.

Private

WASHINGTON COUNTY
Machiasport vicinity
FORT O'BRIEN (FORT MACHIAS)
South of Machiasport on secondary road
1775

Fort O'Brien originally consisted of breastworks thrown up by the townspeople of Machiasport as protection against a force of British who arrived by ship. The attack was prompted by local opposition to a British attempt to procure lumber from the area for barracks. A British ship, the *Margaretta*, was captured by the colonists led by Jeremiah O'Brien, for whom the colonial fortification was later named. General George Washington sent a regiment of militia to garrison Fort O'Brien, but no further military action took place. During the War of 1812 the British captured the fort and burned the barracks. The site was reoccupied and fortified in 1863 as a defense against Confederate privateers. The earthworks and powder magazine still remain.

State

WASHINGTON COUNTY
St. Croix Junction vicinity
ST. CROIX ISLAND NATIONAL MONUMENT
On the international boundary, in the St. Croix River
1604

In 1604 on Saint Croix Island the French attempted to found a permanent settlement in the New World. The expedition had a complement of 120 men, but during the extremely severe winter of 1604–1605 one-third of the party died. After this experience the settlers moved in 1605 to Port Royal, Nova Scotia. From Saint Croix the French explorer Samuel de Champlain set out in 1604 on his explorations of the coast of Maine. The settlement plan included a fort, storehouse, blacksmith shop, meeting hall, kitchen, and bake shop, plus houses and a chapel.

Federal/non-federal
NPS; 56.50 acres
Not accessible to the public

YORK COUNTY
PORTER-PARSONFIELD BRIDGE
Reference — see Oxford County

YORK COUNTY
Kittery Point
LADY PEPPERRELL HOUSE
Maine 103
c. 1760

Built by the widow of Sir William Pepperrell, colonial businessman and commandant, the Lady Pepperrell House is a noted residence in the history of American colonial architecture in New England. The two-story, frame, late Georgian style house has a hip roof which is free of dormers. The five-bay main facade has a central projecting pavilion. Ionic pilasters, two stories high, frame the entrance door which is topped by a cornice carried on curved brackets.

Private
NHL

YORK COUNTY
Kittery Point vicinity
FORT McCLARY
Off Me. 103 near Fort McClary State Park
1809

The first Fort McClary was constructed in 1809 and further strengthened in 1844–1845. Pentagonal in shape, the fort measured nearly 2000 feet in circumference and had granite walls. A front seawall facing the Portsmouth (New Hampshire) harbor measures 500 feet by 30 feet. Portions of the wall were never

completed, and large granite blocks have been left on the site. Remains of a rifleman's house, a barracks, and a powder magazine are visible inside the walls. The most noticeable feature on the site is a six-sided blockhouse with a granite first story topped by an overhanging wooden second story.
State

YORK COUNTY
South Berwick
HAMILTON HOUSE
Vaughn's Lane and Old South Road
1787–1788

Colonel Jonathan Hamilton, a Portsmouth, New Hampshire, merchant, built and occupied this dwelling until his death in 1802. His home is a two-and-one-half-story frame building with clapboard walls and a hip roof containing dormers. Measuring approximately 49 by 46 feet, the house has central doors on three sides, all of which are topped by pediments and flanked by pilasters. Above the doors in the east and north elevations are tall Palladian windows. Roof dormers have alternating triangular and broken arch pediments. Inside, the house has a central-hall, four-room plan, and the kitchen contains a large fireplace with an oven. Restoration work was undertaken in 1950.
Private
NHL

YORK COUNTY
York
HANCOCK, JOHN, WAREHOUSE
Lindsay Road
Mid–18th century

John Hancock (1737–1793), Revolutionary statesman and signer of the Declaration of Independence, fell heir at age 27, to the vast mercantile holdings of his uncle, Thomas Hancock, one of the foremost businessmen of colonial America. One of the properties thus inherited was the Hancock Warehouse in York, which served as a wharf, store, and storehouse. The two-story building is frame with open construction on the interior. Minor alterations and repairs were made in the 1950's. The warehouse is the only colonial commercial structure still standing in York.
Private

YORK COUNTY
York
OLD YORK GAOL
4 Lindsay Road
c. 1720

Although this is not the first jail built in York, it is thought to have been built in the early part of the 18th century. On October 6, 1719, the Massachusetts Court of General Sessions ordered, "that a prison of thirty foot long Eighteen foot wide & eight foot wall be built with Stone or brick in the Town of York. . . ." Also the court requested that, "the Old prison and the Land it Stands on Shall be disposed of & a piece of land purchased near the meeting house in sd [sic] York to build the new prison upon." In final form the Old Gaol is a large one-and-one-half-story rectangular building with frame ends that were added around the original stone section. The exterior of the stone cell portion is built of coursed, dressed rubble, and the walls of the frame additions are covered by clapboards of varying widths with lapped joints. From 1720 until the early 19th century the Gaol served as the York County jail. In 1868 the town of York acquired the building, using it as the village jail for 11 years. The Gaol presently serves as a museum and contains its original colonial prison equipment.
Municipal
NHL; HABS

YORK COUNTY
York vicinity
McINTIRE GARRISON HOUSE
On Me. 91 about 5 miles west of
York
c. 1690 or 1707

The McIntire Garrison House is representative of the vernacular log architecture that was widely used in New England during the 17th century as a defense against Indians. If built as early as 1690 as some authorities maintain, the McIntire Garrison House is also one of the oldest log structures in the United States. Garrison fortified houses with thick protective walls were built in almost all New England towns, and they were particularly common in the frontier towns of Maine and New Hampshire. Much like ordinary houses in plan and appearance, garrison houses were used in time of peace as one-family dwellings. Clapboard and shingle siding and sash windows were added to the McIntire Garrison House in the 18th century, but in 1909 the building was restored to its earlier appearance.
Private; not accessible to the public
NHL; HABS

Hemlock Bridge, East Fryeburg vicinity, Maine.
State Park and Recreation Commission.

Victoria Mansion, Portland, Maine.
State Park and Recreation Commission

Maryland

Fort McHenry National Monument and Historic Shrine,
Baltimore, Maryland. *H. J. Mead for NPS*

Thomas Viaduct, Relay, Maryland. *William Edmund Barrett for HAER*

Slicer-Shiplap House,
Annapolis Historic District,
Annapolis, Maryland. *HABS*

SOUTH ELEVATION
SCALE 1/8"=1'-0"

SCALE 1/8"=1'-0"

ALLEGANY COUNTY (also in Frederick, Montgomery, and Washington counties, Maryland; the District of Columbia; and Morgan County, West Virginia)

CHESAPEAKE AND OHIO CANAL NATIONAL HISTORICAL PARK
1828–1924

Soon after the settled frontier was extended beyond the Allegheny Mountains, plans were developed to provide easy communication between east and west by way of the Potomac River. After efforts by other companies failed, the Chesapeake and Ohio Canal Company was organized in 1828 to build a canal up the Potomac River Valley. Navigation commenced as sections were completed; the final link between Dam No. 6 (Great Cacapon) and Cumberland, Maryland, began operation in 1850. Seventy-four locks raised the water from sea level at Georgetown in the District of Columbia to 609 feet at Cumberland, 184.5 miles away. Canal boats carrying coal, flour, grain, and lumber were used on the canal until 1924, when a serious flood caused so much damage that it was not feasible to repair the "Old Ditch." It is one of the least altered of the older American canals.
Federal
NPS; 4,474.07 acres
HABS

ALLEGANY COUNTY
La Vale
LA VALE TOLLGATE HOUSE
U.S. 40
1835–1836

The Cumberland or National Road (now U.S. 40) was constructed, using federal funds, to link Cumberland, Maryland, with the Ohio River (1811–1818). It became the principal transportation artery to the trans-Appalachian West. Ownership of the road was turned over to the individual states, and shortly after accepting its portion, Maryland's legislature established a rate schedule and began building tollhouses. The seven-sided, brick La Vale Tollgate House was the first such structure to be erected. Its five northern sides of equal length form equal angles with one another, while the two south sides are longer and meet at right angles. A one-story brick addition is appended to each of the longer sides, and there is a decorative, non-functional cupola atop the roof.
State

ANNE ARUNDEL COUNTY
Annapolis
BRICE HOUSE
42 East Street
1766–1773

James Brice was the original owner of the Brice House, a five-part, brick, Georgian style dwelling with interiors attributed to William Buckland. The two-and-one-half-story central block is connected to the one-and-one-half-story wings by hyphens. All roofs have steep gables, and foundation of the central block is fieldstone. Two massive end chimneys on the main house rise to a height of 90 feet above ground. Most of the 18th-century structural material and ornament has not been altered.
Private; not accessible to the public
NHL; HABS

ANNE ARUNDEL COUNTY
Annapolis
CHASE-LLOYD HOUSE
22 Maryland Avenue
1769–1774

The Chase-Lloyd House is one of the earliest extant three-story, brick, Georgian town houses erected in the British colonies. It was also the only three-story brick town house known to have been built in Annapolis before the Revolution. The 54-foot-wide house has a seven-bay facade and is 43 feet deep. A three-bay projecting pavilion highlights the front, and the main entrance is an unusual three-part doorway. Inside, the house has a four-room, central hall plan. Much of the interior work was done by William Buckland—carved cornices, window frames, door casings, chair rails, and molded plaster ceilings.
Private; only first floor accessible to the public
NHL; HABS

ANNE ARUNDEL COUNTY
Annapolis
COLONIAL ANNAPOLIS HISTORIC DISTRICT
District boundaries approximate the city boundaries surveyed in 1695
17th and 18th centuries

Annapolis, capital of the colony and later the state of Maryland, was one of the first planned cities in colonial America. The original town plan was designed in 1695 by Sir Francis Nicholson, the second royal governor of Maryland. Unique for the period, the modified baroque plan represents an attempt to create a European urban environment in a North American setting. With few modifications, Annapolis developed in harmony with the

original plan to emerge in the mid–18th century as the focal point of Maryland government, politics, and commerce and as a center of provincial wealth and culture. Streets within Old Town have been widened and a few street names have been altered, but the original plan is little changed. 120 18th-century buildings, many considerably altered, remain in the district. Other National Historic Landmarks within the district are the Statehouse (1772) and Hammond-Harwood House (c. 1774).
Multiple public/private
NHL; HABS

ANNE ARUNDEL COUNTY
Annapolis
HAMMOND-HARWOOD HOUSE
Maryland Avenue and King George Street
c. 1774, William Buckland

The Hammond-Harwood House is among the most significant Georgian period residences in Annapolis. It is a symmetrical brick building with a five-bay center section flanked by two-story end wings with polygonal bays. One wing served the house's builder, Matthias Hammond, as a law office, and the other housed the kitchen and service rooms. The low-pitched hip roof and pedimental projecting portion are typical of the late Georgian period. The arched fanlight doorway, as well as the first floor dining room and second floor ballroom, are all noted for their wealth of carved decorative woodwork.
Private
NHL; HABS

ANNE ARUNDEL COUNTY
Annapolis
MARYLAND STATEHOUSE
State Circle
c. 1772

Several historically significant events occurred in the Maryland Statehouse, which now houses the offices of the governor, secretary of state, and attorney general of Maryland, as well as the State legislature. For nine months the Statehouse was the seat of the Continental Congress while it acted as Revolutionary government. Here the Continental Congress ratified the Treaty of Paris on January 14, 1784, formally ending the Revolutionary War. Here Washington officially resigned as Commander-in-Chief. In September, 1786, the Annapolis Convention entertained a resolution from which grew the convention that drew up the Constitution. This late Georgian style building is the oldest statehouse in the United States still in use.
State
NHL; HABS

ANNE ARUNDEL COUNTY
Annapolis
UNITED STATES NAVAL ACADEMY
Maryland Avenue and Hanover Street
1845, Ernest Flagg (Waiting Room,
1876; Guard House, 1881)

The Naval Academy has played a significant role in American education and naval affairs, producing career officers for more than a century. Most of the Academy's buildings are in late French Renaissance style, the result of a building program begun in 1899. Only a few of its earliest buildings survive. Flanking the Maryland Avenue gate are the two oldest, the Waiting Room and Guard House. The present hub of activity is Bancroft Hall, a dormitory which houses the entire brigade of midshipmen.
Federal
NHL

ANNE ARUNDEL COUNTY
Annapolis
WHITEHALL
Off St. Margaret's Road
c. 1765

Built by Governor Horatio Sharpe as a retreat and entertainment pavilion. Whitehall was later enlarged and became his residence from his retirement in 1769 until his return to England in 1773. The original pavilion, gardens, parks, and entrance court of this 1,000–acre estate were designed and built under Sharpe's supervision. The house is representative of the high achievement in Georgian architectural design. The giant portico on the central portion of the house, with its Corinthian columns, is one of the earliest in the American colonies. The later additions of the wings and connecting lateral passageways extend the original plan considerably. The interiors of the main rooms are rich in carved decoration. William Buckland and John Rawlins are credited with some of the architectural details.
Private; not accessible to the public
NHL

ANNE ARUNDEL COUNTY
Davidsonville vicinity
ALL HALLOWS' CHURCH
Intersection of Md. 2, All Hallows'
Church Road, and South River Club
Road
c. 1710

All Hallows' Church is a low, rectangular brick structure with a hipped roof. There is a small vestry room on the west side, and the main entrance on the south is sheltered by a porch with arched brick pillars forming a "T" in relation to the rest of the building. Set in pairs, the windows are framed by brick, segmental arches. A fire in 1727 gutted the interior which was repaired soon thereafter. Subsequent alterations were made in 1825 and 1885. After a second fire in 1940, which badly damaged the interior, it was restored to its present, early 18th-century appearance with arched ceiling, brick floor, white wainscoted walls, clear-glass windows, and bench pews with doors. The Rev. Mason Locke Weems, biographer of George Washington, served as rector of All Hallows' Church in 1785.
Private
HABS

ANNE ARUNDEL COUNTY
Galesville vicinity
CEDAR PARK
4.4 miles south of Md. 214 and 468
intersection and 1.5 miles north of
Md. 255 and 468 intersection
Mid–17th century

First surveyed for Charles Calvert, third Lord Baltimore and governor of Maryland, the property was assigned by him to Richard Ewen, Jr., high sheriff of Anne Arundel County. The primitive construction of the house (hand-hewn timbers, riven oak siding, vertical supports consisting of logs sunk into the earth) is indicative of mid-17th-century building techniques. Originally one-and-one-half stories high, one room deep, and measuring 50 feet by 20 feet, Cedar Park was enlarged in 1697. Massive exterior chimneys were constructed at the gable ends, a low shed roof covering two cell rooms was added across the length of the west side, and the entire house was encased in brick. A two-story addition projects from the older section forming the stem of a "T."
Private
HABS

ANNE ARUNDEL COUNTY
Galesville vicinity
TULIP HILL
About 2.5 miles west of Galesville
on Owensville Road
1755–1756; 1787–1790 (wings
added)

Tulip Hill, an early Georgian plantation house, is a distinguished five-part composition. The five-bay-wide north facade of the central block is particularly interesting because of a somewhat experimental approach to late Georgian formality: the central pediment, which is three bays wide, has no projecting pavilion beneath it. Two high arched and vaulted chimneys project from the double hip roof of the main block. The entire house measures 135 feet across and is set on a stone basement.
Private; not accessible to the public
NHL; HABS

ANNE ARUNDEL COUNTY
Harwood vicinity
LARKIN'S HILL FARM
Off Md. 2 on Mill Swamp Road
Mid–17th century

Six hundred and fifty acres of land in the center of lower Anne Arundel County were surveyed in 1661 and patented in 1663 to John Larkin, an early Quaker settler in the area. In 1683 the estate served as a temporary capital of Maryland. Larkin later operated an inn here as a stopping place on the first regular postal route in Maryland. This route ran from St. Mary's to Annapolis. Architecturally, the original one-and-one-half-story central portion of the house is typical of those built in tidewater Maryland prior to 1700. It is brick, all-header bond on the east and north walls and English bond on the west and south sides. It has a gambrel roof and chimneys at both the north and south ends. The first-floor windows and the doors of the east and west facades have arched lintels of alternating single, glazed, and rubbed brick headers. The plan of the house consists of four first-floor rooms and the stair hall with two bedrooms above. A north wing and a southern sunporch were added in the 20th century.
Private

ANNE ARUNDEL COUNTY
Harwood vicinity
LARKIN'S HUNDRED
On Mill Swamp Road, 1 mile east of
Md. 2 and .9 mile west of Md. 468
1704

Larkin's Hundred was built in 1704 by Thomas Larkin. It is an excellent example of a Maryland house designed in a transitional style, retaining some medieval characteristics but exhibiting a definite trend toward later, more formal and symmetrical Georgian detail. It is constructed of brick, the south side being laid in Flemish bond and the north, east, and west walls in English bond. Two massive interior chimneys are inset at the east and west ends of the house. The first-floor window lintels are single-brick jack arches, while those on the second floor are segmental brick arches. A single-brick string course is found between the two stories. The white clapboard kitchen wing at the west end was added in 1870.
Private

ANNE ARUNDEL COUNTY
Harwood vicinity
MARY'S MOUNT
.5 mile east of Md. 2 and south of
Mill Swamp Road
c. 1742

Originally a one-and-one-half-story, gambrel-roofed house. Mary's Mount has retained its gambrel roof and underslopes internally, although a false front has now raised the structure to two full stories on the exterior. The house has been enlarged by the addition of two northern bays, each section of which is lower than its neighbor to the south. The house has brick gable ends of English bond while the facade walls are clapboard. The main house contains four rooms; in the north end is a stair hall with an original staircase and handrail, closed stringers, and balusters of solid walnut. Most of the trim, except for the stair and doors, was replaced early in the 19th century.
Private; not accessible to the public

ANNE ARUNDEL COUNTY
Harwood vicinity
OBLIGATION
West side of Md. 2, .2 mile south of
Md. 2 and Mill Swamp Road
intersection
Early 18th century

Construction details of the house indicate that it was built prior to 1743. This dwelling was later enlarged, most noticeably by increasing it from one-and-one-half stories to two-and-one-half stories. The color and texture of the brick of the older portion of the house are readily distinguished from the later, second-story brickwork. Inside, the house is divided into four rooms, and a boxed staircase rises from the outer corner of the southwest room. The south facade has a center door, sheltered by a canopy of recent construction, and three irregularly placed windows. The four windows on the upper story of this facade are symmetrically spaced and topped with flat lintels. The gable roof has a chimney at each end.
Private

ANNE ARUNDEL COUNTY
Owensville vicinity
EVERGREEN
Sudley Road, 2 miles southeast of
Md. 255
Late 17th century

Erected on land that was surveyed in 1663 for Thomas Parsons, Evergreen was known until 1816 as Parsons' Hills. The large, white clapboard house is the result of several building operations. The original portion is the first floor of the southern end of the house. Early features

of this section are six-panel doors with H-L hinges, a closed string staircase, and extremely wide exterior siding with beaded edges. That this portion was originally covered with a gambrel roof is indicated by a box cornice and overhang between the first story and the later second story. Other additions to the original fabric are the two-and-one-half-story central section, 18th century in date, and the two-and-one-half-story northern end, added during the 19th century. Both of these sections have much original interior woodwork intact. In spite of the several dates associated with the additions, the structure presents a unified appearance.
Private

ANNE ARUNDEL COUNTY
South River vicinity
THE SOUTH RIVER CLUB
South River Club Road, 1 mile east of
Md. 2 and .4 mile west of Md. 468
1742

The South River Club, an early social club established by English settlers, survives today as one of the oldest, continuously active organizations of its type in America. In 1740 a fire destroyed the original club building and records, but there is evidence that the club itself existed in 1732 and perhaps as early as 1700. Built in 1742, the present structure is a frame, white weatherboard one-and-one-half-story one-room clubhouse with a low-pitched, A-shaped roof. Inside, the walls are plastered, and the crane and cooking utensils used in the early days of the club stand in the open fireplace. The South River Club can be traced back to English clubs of the same type which held an important place in the social and intellectual life of the mother country. The early members included prominent landowners, merchants, and the local doctor and clergyman, all of whom lived within a 10-mile radius of the clubhouse. The minutes of the club have been kept since 1740, and the present membership of 25 persons includes many descendants of past club members.
Private
HABS

ANNE ARUNDEL COUNTY
Woodland Beach vicinity
LONDON TOWN PUBLIK HOUSE
Northeast of Woodland Beach at the
end of Londontown Road
c. 1750

London Town Publik House, a large Georgian brick inn, is a full two-story structure, seven bays wide and three bays deep, with walls laid in Flemish bond. Its original simple interiors are basically unaltered. The inn originally served a major

north-south turnpike and the ferry crossing at South River. Between 1828 and 1966 the building was used as an alms house by Anne Arundel County.
County
NHL; HABS

_____

BALTIMORE (independent city)
**BALTIMORE AND OHIO
TRANSPORTATION MUSEUM AND
MOUNT CLARE STATION**
Pratt and Poppleton Streets
Mount Clare Station, 1830; Passenger
Car Roundhouse, 1884; Museum
Annex, 1891, Ephraim F. Baldwin

The three structures comprising the museum have many significant associations. In continuous use since its completion in 1830, the Mount Clare Station inaugurated regular passenger service in the United States on May 22, 1830. Through this station passed the Nation's first telegraph message on May 24, 1844, its destination being a nearby station no longer in existence. The roundhouse, with its many unusual architectural features, now houses the bulk of the historical collection, including locomotives and railroad cars. The annex contains some of the smaller exhibits.
Private
NHL; HABS

BALTIMORE (independent city)
CLIFTON PARK VALVE HOUSE
2801 Harford Road
1887–1888

During the latter years of the 19th century the Baltimore City Water Department underwent a vigorous expansion program. Money was appropriated to dam the Gunpowder River, and water was channeled through a tunnel to the northeastern section of the city. A second reservoir was located at the present Clifton Park. Although the reservoir has been filled in and is not used, the old Valve House still stands. It is a massive octagonal stone structure containing alternating Romanesque arches and Gothic windows in each of its eight sides. The tile roof is supported by a complicated system of iron trusses, and the interior still houses the wheels which opened and closed the water gates.
Municipal

BALTIMORE (independent city)
FEDERAL HILL HISTORIC DISTRICT
Bounded on the east by Covington
Street, on the north by Hughes Street,

on the west by Charles Street, and on the south by Hamburg Street

18th, 19th, and 20th centuries

Affording a sweeping panorama of Baltimore and its harbor, Federal Hill has long been the center of the city's commercial activity. Named for the new national government, Federal Hill was the scene in 1788 of a celebration in honor of Maryland's ratification of the Constitution. An observatory built in 1795 was used to signal local merchants of arriving ships. Brickmaking and pottery were important industries of the area, and both red clay and white sand were mined here. Near the northern boundary of the district is Federal Hill Park, measuring four and one quarter acres. Most of the houses around the park and throughout the district date from the mid- to late 19th century, and the majority of them are attached row houses of two or three stories.

Multiple public/private

BALTIMORE (independent city)
FELLS POINT HISTORIC DISTRICT
Bounded on the north by Aliceanna Street, on the east by Wolfe Street, on the south by the harbor, and on the west by Dallas Street
18th and 19th centuries

Fells Point is a harborside, residential, and light industrial community that encompasses approximately 75 acres in the eastern section of Baltimore. The character of its townscape is set by groupings of small, two-and-one-half-story houses which were the homes of seamen, ship's carpenters, sailmakers, and other artisans involved in the port activities. These smaller houses are interspersed with occasional larger, more elaborate three-and-one-half-story houses which were the homes of the shipyard owners, prosperous merchants, and sea captains. William Fell, a Quaker, settled and built his first storehouse on what later became Fells Point some time prior to 1763, when the section was laid out as a town by Edward Fell, his son. By 1770 a bustling harbor settlement had been established which traded Maryland's agricultural products with Europe and the West Indies. Fells Point was incorporated into Baltimore Town in 1773. The shipbuilding industry here is best remembered for the *Constellation* and the Baltimore clippers used during the War of 1812.

Multiple public/private

BALTIMORE (independent city)
THE FLAG HOUSE
844 E. Pratt Street
c. 1793

In August of 1813, Mrs. Mary Young Pickersgill and her daughter finished sewing a 15–star, 15–stripe American flag commissioned to be flown over Fort McHenry. The flag measured 30 feet by 42 feet. It flew over Fort McHenry during the British attack on Baltimore, and on the night of September 13–14, 1814, served as the inspiration for a poem by Francis Scott Key which eventually became the national anthem, "The Star-Spangled Banner." Mrs. Pickersgill's home, a two-and-one-half-story corner row house, is now a historic house museum operated by the Star-Spangled Banner Flag House Association.
Municipal
NHL

BALTIMORE (independent city)
FORT McHENRY NATIONAL MONUMENT AND HISTORIC SHRINE
Locust Point, at the eastern end of Fort Avenue
1794–1803

The successful defense of Fort McHenry against a British naval attack in 1814 assisted in the defense of Baltimore and inspired Francis Scott Key to write our national anthem, "The Star-Spangled Banner." Threatened by war with either England or France, the federal government, aided by local citizenry, erected this fort between 1794 and 1803 on Whetstone Point, where it could command the entrance to Baltimore harbor. It replaced an 18–gun fort, known as Fort Whetstone, which was erected on the site in 1776. The new fort was one in a series of fortifications constructed for the defense of the eastern coast. After the War of 1812, the strategic importance of the fort decreased, but it continued to serve various military purposes through World War II.
Federal
NPS; 43.26 acres
HABS

BALTIMORE (independent city)
MOUNT CLARE
Carroll Park
c. 1763

Mount Clare, a brick Georgian plantation house, is the oldest extant colonial structure in the city of Baltimore. Although the reconstructed wings and hyphens do not follow the original plan, the main house has been faithfully restored. A particularly interesting feature of the south facade is the use of colossal brick pilasters at the corners of the pavilion and house. These pilasters are polychromatic, with the lighter bricks in the center and the dark bricks giving the impression of narrow quoins at the edges. During the Civil War the house served as quarters for Union soldiers. After 1865 the house was used as a German beer garden until 1890. It is now a tourist attraction.
Municipal
NHL; HABS

BALTIMORE (independent city)
OTTERBEIN CHURCH
112 W. Conway Street
1785–1786

The Otterbein Church is the only continuously used 18th-century church building in the city of Baltimore. The church was built for a group of Germans who had separated from the Lutheran Church and called themselves the Church of the United Brethren in Christ. The building is brick with a peaked roof topped on the west gable by a square tower and an octagonal cupola-on-cupola. A white limestone belt course separates the first and second stories, and a wooden modillion cornice encircles the building. The bells, cast in Germany and installed in 1789, are still in use. A major remodeling occurred in 1839.
Private
HABS

BALTIMORE (independent city)
PEALE'S BALTIMORE MUSEUM (MUNICIPAL MUSEUM OF THE CITY OF BALTIMORE)
225 N. Holliday Street
1814

Peale's Baltimore Museum was the first in the United States to be designed and erected exclusively for museum use. Under the direction of its builder, Rembrandt Peale, and later his brother Rubens, the museum operated for 15 years. Having served a number of purposes in the interim, the building again became a museum in 1831. Presently the museum houses both painting exhibitions and permanent exhibits concerning Rembrandt Peale and the history of Baltimore.
Municipal
NHL; HABS

BALTIMORE (independent city)
ROMAN CATHOLIC CATHEDRAL OF BALTIMORE (NOW MINOR BASILICA OF THE ASSUMPTION OF THE BLESSED VIRGIN MARY)
401 Cathedral Street
1806–1863, Benjamin Henry Latrobe

Many alterations to Latrobe's design were made during construction. The most notable was the addition of the two onion-shaped domes instead of the architect's small stepped domes which were originally to resemble the main one. The cathedral is cruciform in plan and constructed of Porphyritic granite. The front portico, composed of ten fluted columns and an Ionic pediment, was added to the original design in 1863. The portico covers a large

central door flanked by two smaller ones. Along both sides of the cathedral is a series of stained glass windows set in recessed arched panels, and a dome set on an octagonal drum tops the rear portico of the church. Internally, the cathedral is vaulted by several shallow domes, and the entire structure exhibits an exceptionally good mixture of spherical and cube-like shapes.
Private
HABS

BALTIMORE (independent city)
SHOT TOWER
Southeast corner of Fayette and Front Streets
1828

The Baltimore Shot Tower is approximately 14 stories high and measures 40 feet in diameter at its base and 20 feet at the top. Crowned at the top by a concrete parapet, the walls themselves are five-and-one-half feet thick at the base and 20 inches thick at the top. Shot was manufactured by dropping molten lead from a platform on top of the tower through a sieve-like device into a vat of cold water. When dried and polished, the shot was sorted into 25-pound bags. At least one million bags of shot were produced per year. Shot was produced here until 1892.

Municipal; not accessible to the public

BALTIMORE (independent city)
U.S.F. *CONSTELLATION*
Pier 1, Pratt Street
1797

Nicknamed the "Yankee Racehorse" because of her speed, the U.S.F. *Constellation* was in commission longer than any other vessel in the United States Navy. She established many firsts: the first commissioned ship in the United States Navy, the first to put to sea, and the first to engage, defeat, and capture an enemy vessel. Last used as relief flagship of the Atlantic Fleet in World War II, she has now been partially restored.
Private
NHL

BALTIMORE COUNTY (also in Howard County)
Relay
THOMAS VIADUCT, BALTIMORE & OHIO RAILROAD
Over the Patapsco River between Relay and Elkridge
1835

Still in use today, Thomas Viaduct is the world's oldest multiple stone-arch railroad bridge and America's earliest notable example of railroad bridge construction. Designed in 1835 by Benjamin H. Latrobe, son of the architect of the same name, the structure has required no major repairs or changes in its many years of service. It is also one of only a few stone masonry bridges ever built on curves.
Private; not accessible to the public
NHL

BALTIMORE COUNTY
Stevenson vicinity
FORT GARRISON
Garrison Farms Court, south of Stevenson
17th, 18th, and 19th centuries

The Council of Maryland began sending bands of rangers to survey the frontier for possible Indian attacks toward the end of the 17th century. In 1693 Governor Francis Nicholson ordered construction of a fortification near the Susquehanna and Patapsco rivers in Baltimore County. The result of this order was Fort Garrison. Today the one remaining building is the only stone blockhouse in Maryland. Built of fieldstone, the blockhouse is rectangular with a stone fireplace at the east end. During the early 19th century a second-story loft was added. The fort was garrisoned during the French and Indian War.
County; not accessible to the public

BALTIMORE COUNTY
Towson
HAMPTON NATIONAL HISTORIC SITE
Hampton Lane, 1 mile north of Int. 695
1783–1790

Hampton Mansion represents an important phase in the history of late Georgian architecture in America. When completed in 1790 by Charles Ridgely, it was one of the largest houses of its day, measuring 175 feet by 55 feet. Built of local stone and then stuccoed, its two-and-a-half-story main section with porticos was set off by balanced one-story wings. The gable roof features a large cupola, ornate columns, and urn-like decorations. The main portion of the house has rooms flanking either side of a central "great hall." The site also includes the restored formal gardens and outbuildings, slave quarters, overseer's house, and barn-granary. Charles Ridgely, builder of the house, was prominent in Maryland affairs as a member of the Maryland House of Burgesses (1773–1789) and member of the committee which framed the State constitution.
Federal
NPS; 45.42 acres
HABS

CALVERT COUNTY
Owings vicinity
MAIDSTONE
Northwest of Owings on Chesapeake Beach Road
Late 17th century

Maidstone is one of the few extant architectural examples of the 17th-century medieval influence in Maryland. It is a one-and-one-half-story clapboard structure, four bays wide and two deep. The steeply sloping roof extends out over the north and south facades to form a porch in the traditional Maryland colonial style. There are three peaked dormers on the north and south and a T-shaped chimney enclosed within the west end containing a brick dated 1678. The fourth bay and one-and-one-half-story kitchen on the west were added around 1800.
Private; not accessible to the public

CARROLL COUNTY
Union Mills
UNION MILLS HOMESTEAD HISTORIC DISTRICT
Intersection of U.S. 140 and Deep Run Road
1797

Union Mills Homestead Historic District contains the Union Mills Homestead, mill, and Bollman-design bridge. Built in 1797, the mill became the center of a small-scale industrial complex and the focal point of an active crossroads settlement. The homestead was erected the same year by Andrew and David Shriver, Jr., as a small log and clapboard double house. With the passage of time wings were added and the early section greatly enlarged. Other artisans were attracted to the area until the complex included a farm, two mills, a tannery, a cooperage, and a blacksmith shop. A post office was established here in the early 19th century, and the house served as an inn for stagecoach passengers. The mill itself is a brick building, two full stories above a basement. A large section of the north facade has been rebuilt, but most window framing and sash is intact. The mill continued to operate until 1942. The queen post iron truss bridge has a fieldstone base and a plank floor. It is only one lane wide.
Private

CECIL COUNTY
Chesapeake City
OLD LOCK PUMP HOUSE, CHESAPEAKE AND DELAWARE CANAL
U.S. 213
1837

The Old Lock Pump House improved the operation of a key section of the Chesapeake and Delaware Canal (between Chesapeake City, Maryland, and Delaware City, Delaware). The structure presently houses two original steam engines and a large scoop wheel which raised water to replace that lost when the nearby canal lock was opened to let a ship pass through. The heavy machinery has been little changed since its installation at various intervals during the mid-19th century. In 1926 the use of the equipment was discontinued.
Federal
NHL

FREDERICK COUNTY
CHESAPEAKE AND OHIO CANAL NATIONAL HISTORICAL PARK
Reference—see Allegany County

FREDERICK COUNTY
Frederick
HESSIAN BARRACKS
242 S. Market Street

An exact date of construction for the Hessian Barracks is not known. Some authorities believe the building dates from the time of the French and Indian War. Structurally the barracks resembles similar quarters built during the 19th century, and the earliest documentary evidence of a barracks on this site is an 1820 deed. Originally there were two L-shaped stone buildings with gallery porches enclosing a yard. One was demolished circa 1870 to supply materials for the Maryland School for the Deaf and Blind. The remaining building has two wooden stairways inside and two outside, and most of the wooden trim appears to be original.
State
HABS

GARRETT COUNTY
Grantsville vicinity
CASSELMAN'S BRIDGE, NATIONAL ROAD
East of Grantsville on U.S. 40
1813

Casselman's Bridge across the Little Youghiogheny River was part of the earliest federal highway project—construction of the National Road. At its completion it possessed the largest stone arch in the United States. The bridge remains essentially unchanged, although some repair work was done in 1911. Congress authorized construction of the National Road (now U.S. 40) in 1806, and by 1818 it stretched from Cumberland, Maryland, to the Ohio River at Wheeling in what is now West Virginia. Controversy developed regarding the propriety of Federal participation in road construction and the project was halted until 1828. The National Road provided ready access to the trans-Appalachian region and greatly stimulated its settlement and growth.
County
NHL; HABS

GARRETT COUNTY
Grantsville vicinity
FULLER-BAKER LOG HOUSE
.5 mile west of Grantsville on U.S. 40
Early 19th century

The Fuller-Baker Log House is typical of dwellings once common on the Maryland frontier. Located near the old National Road, the house stands on land once owned by Thomas Johnson (1732–1819), Maryland's first state governor. The rectangular house is two stories high plus an attic. Log planks, 8 inches thick and 14 to 16 inches broad, were used for wall construction. Their ends are trimmed flush at the corners, and crevices between the logs are chinked with clay plaster and small stones. The building has been somewhat altered, and the exterior is presently covered with insul-brick although restoration work is in progress.
Private; not accessible to the public

HOWARD COUNTY
Ellicott City
ELLICOTT CITY STATION
Just South of the Patapsco River Bridge
1830–1831

The Baltimore and Ohio Railroad station at Ellicott City, erected in 1830–1831 and still in use, is the oldest railroad station in the United States. It served as the western terminus of the railroad's original 13-mile section of track. The Baltimore and Ohio Railroad was the first in the United States to be chartered as a common carrier of freight and passengers, and its supporters looked beyond local needs. They envisaged a railroad running to the Ohio River that would allow Baltimore to compete with New York City's increased western trade resulting from completion of the Erie Canal. The financial success of this first portion of track spurred further westward development of the Baltimore and Ohio and encouraged the construction of other American railroads. The exterior of the station is virtually unchanged, and the second floor, at track level, is still used as a Railway Express office.
Private
NHL

HOWARD COUNTY
THOMAS VIADUCT, BALTIMORE & OHIO RAILROAD
Reference—see Baltimore County

KENT COUNTY
Chestertown
CHESTERTOWN HISTORIC DISTRICT
Bounded roughly by the Chester River on the southeast, by Cannon Street on the southwest, by Maple Avenue on the northeast, and by Cross Street on the northwest
18th century

Between 1750 and 1790 Chestertown, or New Town (until 1780), flourished as the chief tobacco and wheat shipping port of Maryland's Eastern Shore. It was during this period that wealthy merchants and planters constructed many of the elaborate Georgian brick town houses which comprise most of the historic district. Although most of Chestertown's fifty 18th-century buildings have since been considerably altered, many of them, such as the Ringgold-Pearce House (c. 1735) and Widehall (c. 1770), retain features of architectural interest.
Multiple public/private
NHL; HABS

KENT COUNTY
Chestertown
DENTON HOUSE
107 Water Street
c. 1784–1787

The Denton House is located within the Chestertown Historic District, a National Historic Landmark. It is a three-story Georgian residence with a five-bay street facade and brick walls laid in Flemish bond. Windows on all levels but the third are accentuated by flat, rusticated, painted stone arches with keystones. A plain belt course separates the first and second floors. The main doorway and reveals are paneled and flanked by Doric pilasters, while three-story brick pilasters highlight the corners of the facade. The cornice has modillions and plancers (the soffit of the cornice) carved above the capitals only. Each room inside has paneled, recessed interior shutters, a chair rail, dentil cornice, and plaster walls.
State

MONTGOMERY COUNTY
CHESAPEAKE AND OHIO CANAL NATIONAL HISTORICAL PARK
Reference—see Allegany County

MONTGOMERY COUNTY
Glen Echo
BARTON, CLARA, HOUSE
5801 Oxford Road
c. 1890, Dr. Julian Hubbell

Clara Barton, major figure in the founding of the American Red Cross, spent the final 20 years of her life in this house. From 1897 until 1904, it housed the national headquarters of the American Red Cross, of which Miss Barton was president from 1881 until 1904. Constructed partly of materials salvaged from emergency housing, the building was designed to store relief supplies and to accommodate Red Cross workers. The interior resembles a Mississippi River steamboat with railed galleries and a captain's room.
Private; not accessible to the public
NHL

PRINCE GEORGES COUNTY
Accokeek vicinity
ACCOKEEK CREEK SITE
Opposite Mount Vernon on the
Potomac River, west of Piscataway
Park
c. 4000 B.C.

The earliest occupation of the Accokeek
Creek Site occurred before the use of pottery was known. Occupied intermittently
until early colonial times, the site was
principally used during the 14th and 15th
centuries. Extensive archeological excavations have revealed artifacts of the several
periods of occupation.
Private
NHL

PRINCE GEORGES COUNTY
Accokeek vicinity
PISCATAWAY PARK
Across the Potomac River from
Mount Vernon
c. 3000 B.C. to A.D. 1800

Piscataway Park preserves the scenic view
across the Potomac River from Mount
Vernon. The historical value of the area
precedes by many centuries the era of
George Washington. The nomadic Archaic Indians lived here as early as 3000 B.C.
The name Piscataway is derived from the
Piscataway Indians, who are believed to
have inhabited this region from the 14th
century through the late 18th century. English colonists began settling the area in
the early 17th century. In 1752 George
Washington purchased the land to
complete the view of the riverland across
the Potomac. This is also the site of Fort
Washington and of an Indian burial
ground which has been extensively excavated.
Federal/non-federal
NPS; 1091.57 acres

PRINCE GEORGES COUNTY
Laurel vicinity
MONTPELIER
2.1 miles east of Laurel on Md. 197
c. 1745

Montpelier is a distinguished example of a
late-Georgian five-part plantation house.
When the two end wings were added in
1770–1771, the central block was
redecorated with exceptionally fine late-
Georgian interiors. Several early examples
of architectural features that were later to
become popular during the Federal
period, such as a fanlight door and
polygonal bays, are evident on the house.
A kitchen, servants' quarters, and a garage
are 20th-century additions. Formal
gardens surround the house.
State
NHL; HABS

PRINCE GEORGES COUNTY
Rosaryville vicinity
HIS LORDSHIP'S KINDNESS
3.5 miles west of Rosaryville
c. 1735

The Earl of Shrewsbury had His Lordship's Kindness built as a wedding gift for
his niece. The elegantly decorated central
block of the mansion, constructed about
1735, was possibly designed by a professional English architect sent to America
by the earl. The two end wings and two
connecting hyphens, believed to have
been added sometime in the 18th century,
make His Lordship's Kindness an excellent example of a late Georgian, five-part
plantation house composition. Two large
second-story Palladian windows highlight
the north and south facades.
Private
NHL; HABS

PRINCE GEORGES COUNTY
Washington, D.C., vicinity
FORT WASHINGTON
5.5 miles south of D.C. line on Md.
210, west on Old Fort Road
1809, 1814–1824

Fort Washington occupies the site of the
earliest fortification erected for the
defense of the District of Columbia.
Reconstruction began almost immediately
after the original fort was destroyed by its
garrison when it was invaded by the
British during the War of 1812. Designed
by Major Pierre L'Enfant to withstand attack by vessels armed with smooth-bore
artillery, the fort well illustrates the early
19th-century coastal defense. The enclosed masonry fortification has a drawbridge with part of the mechanism still in
place. Also remaining are the officers'
quarters, soldiers' barracks, magazine, and
guardroom. Aside from repairs, the fort
has been altered little since its completion
in 1824.
Federal
NPS; 341 acres

ST. MARYS COUNTY
Drayden vicinity
WEST ST. MARY'S MANOR
About 1 mile east of Drayden on the
St. Mary's River
Early 18th century

West St. Mary's Manor is a rare example
of a small William and Mary brick-and-
frame country house. The center hall,
separating two main front rooms and two
narrow back rooms, illustrates a point in
the shift from the one- and two-room
plans of 17th-century southern houses to
the larger and more symmetrical room arrangements of 18th-century structures.

West St. Mary's Manor was constructed
on a 2,000-acre tract granted to Captain
Henry Fleet on May 9, 1634, the earliest
grant of land known to have been
recorded in Maryland.
Private; not accessible to the public
NHL; HABS

ST. MARYS COUNTY
Hollywood vicinity
RESURRECTION MANOR
4 miles east of Hollywood
c. 1660

Resurrection Manor, built about 1660 and
subsequently enlarged, is a small, unrestored 17th-century brick farmhouse.
Located on one of the earliest manorial
grants made in Maryland, the house is an
excellent illustration of the evolution of a
Southern one-room brick structure into a
hall-and-parlor plan house through the addition of a one-bay wide, one-and-one-
half-story addition.
Private
NHL; HABS

ST. MARYS COUNTY
St. Mary's City
ST. MARY'S CITY HISTORIC
DISTRICT
Bounded on the west by the St.
Mary's River, on the south by St.
Inigoes Creek and a branch of
Broome Creek, and on the north by
Chancellor's Creek; the eastern
boundary extends about two miles
south and east across the peninsula
from Chancellor's Creek to Broome
Creek
1634–1695

St. Mary's City, founded in 1634 by
Leonard Calvert, brother of the second
Lord Baltimore, was the capital of Maryland until 1695. It was also the third permanent English settlement in America and
the site of the first Catholic chapel in the
English colonies. The rural setting of St.
Mary's City as well as the town itself have
been altered little since the late 17th century. Foundations of approximately 60
buildings remain for archeological study.
State and private
NHL; HABS

TALBOT COUNTY
Easton vicinity
WYE HOUSE
6.9 miles northwest of Easton, on
Miles Neck Road
1781–1784, 1799

Built for Edward Lloyd IV (1744–1796), a
wealthy Maryland slaveowner, Wye House
is a little-altered seven-part Roman
country house composition consisting of a
two-story central block, two flanking

lower two-story pavilions, two connecting one-story hyphens, and two large one-story end units. The west pavilion contained the library and the east pavilion housed the kitchen and servants' quarters. Near the house is the Orangerie, a two-story building once used to grow orange and lemon trees, which still possesses a rare example of an 18th-century hot air duct central heating system.
Private; not accessible to the public
NHL; HABS

WASHINGTON COUNTY
CHESAPEAKE AND OHIO CANAL NATIONAL HISTORICAL PARK
Reference—see Allegany County

WASHINGTON COUNTY
HARPERS FERRY NATIONAL HISTORICAL PARK
Reference—see Jefferson County, West Virginia

WASHINGTON COUNTY
Sharpsburg
ANTIETAM NATIONAL BATTLEFIELD SITE
1862

The battle of Antietam, September 16–17, 1862, greatly affected the course of the Civil War. It was the culmination of the first of two eastern attempts on the part of the Confederacy to carry the war into northern territory. About 41,000 Confederates under General Robert E. Lee faced 87,000 Federals under General George B. McClellan. The ensuing conflict resulted in a combined loss of 24,500 killed or wounded. Neither side gained a decisive victory, but the battle brought to an end Lee's first invasion of the North and offered President Abraham Lincoln the opportunity to issue his Emancipation Proclamation.
Federal/non-federal
NPS; 783.63 acres
HABS

WICOMICO COUNTY
Salisbury
PEMBERTON HALL
Pemberton Road
1741

Pemberton Hall is a three-bay, one-and-one-half-story brick house with a gambrel roof. The brick is laid in Flemish bond. Central doors on the front are paneled and double. Notable features are the flat, gauged brick arches over the windows and door, the plaster cove cornice, and the hip-roofed dormers. Inside, the house has a large, square, hall room and two smaller rooms. The second floor is divided into a hall and four bedrooms.
Private

Wye House, Miles River Neck, Maryland. *Jack E. Boucher for HABS*

Chase-Lloyd House,
Annapolis, Maryland.
Jack E. Boucher for HABS

Massachusetts

Old Ship Meetinghouse, Hingham, Massachusetts.
Dorothy Abbe for HABS

Derby Summerhouse, Danvers, Massachusetts.
Cervin Robinson for HABS

Market Square Historic District,
Newburyport, Massachusetts.
Art and Camera, Newburyport

BERKSHIRE COUNTY
Pittsfield
MELVILLE, HERMAN, HOUSE (ARROWHEAD)
Holmes Road
1794

Herman Melville lived at Arrowhead from 1850 to 1863. Here in 1851 he wrote his now classic novel *Moby Dick*. Others of his well-known works include *Typee* (1846), and *Billy Budd* (1891), which was published posthumously in 1924. Largely ignored until the 1920's, Melville is now recognized as a major American literary figure. His writings, often highly symbolic, were drawn largely from his experiences at sea. His eight-room house in the Colonial style has been altered since the 1930's.
Private; not accessible to the public
NHL; HABS

BERKSHIRE COUNTY
Pittsfield vicinity
HANCOCK SHAKER VILLAGE
U.S. 20, Hancock Turnpike, 5 miles south of Pittsfield
1790–1960

The Shakers, or United Believers in Christ's Second Appearing, were a religious group founded in England by Mother Ann Lee in 1747. Approximately 18 Shaker communities, distinguished by successful communal living and fruitful agricultural and industrial activity, had been founded in the northeastern and midwestern United States by 1825. The Shaker community near Pittsfield, organized in 1790 and finally dissolved in 1960, reached its high point during the three decades preceding the Civil War. Eighteen remarkably preserved buildings remain from the early period and are now the property of Shaker Community, a nonprofit corporation that maintains them as a memorial to the sect. They illustrate the communitarian life and distinctive architecture and furnishings of the Shakers. The most unusual building in the village is the Round Barn, built in 1826 to house 52 cattle and the hay to feed them. The barn measures about 270 feet in circumference, and it is believed to be the first round barn built in the United States. To date, nine of the buildings have been carefully restored and refurnished.
Private
NHL; HABS

BERKSHIRE COUNTY
Stockbridge
MISSION HOUSE
Main Street
1739

The Rev. John Sergeant, a missionary to the Housatonic Indians in western Massachusetts, constructed this frame house in 1739 as a home for his bride, Abigail Williams. The two-and-one-half-story frame house has the usual central hall plan of a Georgian house with inner chimneys, except that certain modifications were made for its use as a mission house. Behind the parlor is a small office or study where Sergeant met with the Indians. A long narrow hall with a separate entrance at the east side extends across the rear of the house and connects with the office. This rear hall was built so that the Indians could reach the study without passing through the main rooms in the front portion of the house. Members of the Sergeant family occupied the house from 1739 until 1870. In 1928 the dwelling was taken down, its components numbered, moved from its original location on Prospect Hill, and reconstructed on its present site.
Private
NHL

BERKSHIRE COUNTY
Stockbridge vicinity
CHESTERWOOD (DANIEL CHESTER FRENCH HOME AND STUDIO)
2 miles west of Stockbridge
1900–1901, Henry Bacon

Daniel Chester French gave America two of its best-known statues; that of the Minute Man in Concord, Massachusetts (1875), and the gigantic seated figure of the Great Emancipator at the Lincoln Memorial in Washington, D.C. (1922). Both are fine examples of the patriotic subjects that characterize French's sculpture. The French estate includes his house, studio, and a barn sculpture gallery.
Private
NHL

BRISTOL COUNTY
Dighton vicinity
DIGHTON ROCK
Across the Taunton River from Dighton in Dighton Rock State Park

Dighton Rock is a gray, feldspathic boulder which weighs approximately 50 tons. The exposed surface has dimensions of 10 by 10 by 5 feet, and one face is marked with a number of cryptic symbols and inscriptions. Their meaning and origin are unknown. The markings were first noted and recorded in 1680, and since then an estimated 600 books and articles about Dighton Rock have been published. In 1964 the state of Massachusetts had the rock moved to its present site from the tidal waters of the Taunton River, which were wearing away the markings.
State

BRISTOL COUNTY
New Bedford
NEW BEDFORD HISTORIC DISTRICT
Bounded by the waterfront on the east, Elm Street on the north, Acushnet Avenue on the west, and Commercial Street on the south
18th and 19th centuries

New Bedford began whaling in the 1760's and by the 1840's was America's major whaling port. Although the industry began to decline in the late 1850's, the town had a whaling fleet until 1925. The wealth and commerce produced by whaling are evident in the historic district, where a number of public and private buildings from its whaling era still stand. Prominent among these are the Old Bank (1831) at the foot of William Street, the Customshouse (c. 1835) at Second and William Streets, and the Mariner's Home (1790) on Johnny Cake Hill.
Multiple public/private
NHL; HABS

BRISTOL COUNTY
New Bedford
U.S. CUSTOMHOUSE
Southwest corner of 2nd and Williams Streets
1834–1836, Robert Mills

The New Bedford Customhouse is an oblong granite building covered by a hip roof. Five bays long and three bays wide, it has a front portico with four Greek Doric columns supporting its pediment. A square cupola has been removed from the roof, and the parapet rail between the chimney stacks is a reconstruction. Stone texture is purposely varied on the exterior. Walls are rock-faced granite blocks while columns, pilasters, cornice, water table, and belt course are tooled granite.
Federal
NHL; HABS

ESSEX COUNTY
Amesbury
WHITTIER, JOHN GREENLEAF, HOME
86 Friend Street
1836

John Greenleaf Whittier lived and wrote in this ten-room frame house from the year it was built until his death in 1892. Essentially self-educated, Whittier became a successful editor and a prominent abolitionist. His poetry reflects not only his antislavery sentiments but also his Quaker background and humble origins. Among his best-known poems are the narrative "Snow-Bound" and several hymns. The greater part of the furnishings in the house, including the poet's desk, remains as Whittier left them.
Private
NHL

ESSEX COUNTY
Danvers
DERBY SUMMERHOUSE
　Glen Magna Estate, Ingersoll Street
　1792–1793

The Derby Summerhouse is a formal 18th-century garden house designed in the Federal style with Adamesque decoration. It was built in 1792–1793 and has been attributed by some authorities to Samuel McIntire, the craftsman-architect of Salem. The two-story frame building is 20 feet square and exhibits Georgian influence in its formality, pilasters, cornice, and decorative detail. The second-story windows are decorated with blinds, and the gable pedimented roof has a wooden urn at each corner and is surmounted at the ridgeline by two life-size figures carved from wood: a milkmaid facing east and a farmer whetting his scythe looking west. These statues were carved by John and Simeon Skillin of Boston in 1793. The summerhouse was moved in 1901 from its original site to its present location.
Private
NHL; HABS

ESSEX COUNTY
Gloucester
LANE, FITZ HUGH, HOUSE
　Harbor side of Rogers Street
　1849–1865

Fitz Hugh Lane (1804–1865) was a marine painter of national reputation, best known for his sea and shoreline scenes and portraits of ships. He studied in Boston as an apprentice to William Pendleton and operated a lithograph business there from 1845 until after 1847. Lane lived in this three-story house until his death. Its walls of handcut stone blocks and the granite jambs and lintels give the exterior a rugged appearance. The roofline is broken by seven steeply pitched and irregularly placed gables.
Municipal; not accessible to the public

ESSEX COUNTY
Ipswich
WHIPPLE, JOHN, HOUSE
　53 S. Main Street
　c. 1640

One of the earliest extant New England houses, the Whipple House illustrates the development of the 17th-century house form over a number of years. In its three distinct sections are reflected the evolution of workmanship and architectural detail as the Whipple descendants grew away from their English origins. The house took on its present appearance sometime after 1700, when the lean-to was added at the back.
Private
NHL; HABS

ESSEX COUNTY
Marblehead
LEE, JEREMIAH, HOUSE
　Washington Street
　1768

The Jeremiah Lee House, an excellent surviving example of New England's Georgian period houses, exemplifies the wealth and position of a New England merchant of the 18th century. This three-story building has facades that are of rusticated wood; the wood quoins and keystone window lintels imitate masonry forms. A pedimental projecting pavilion with a small entrance portico breaks the entrance facade. A cupola and two massive brick chimneys dominate the hip roof. The grand scale of the house is manifested in the interior, particularly by the richly decorated eight-foot wide staircase in the central stair hall, the fully paneled banquet room, and the great drawing room on the second floor.
Private
NHL; HABS

ESSEX COUNTY
Newbury
SPENCER-PIERCE-LITTLE HOUSE
　At the end of Little's Lane, on the
　east side of U.S. 1A
　17th or 18th century

The Spencer-Pierce-Little House is one of a few remaining stone houses built in New England during the 17th and 18th centuries. The exact date of construction is unknown, and the house may have been built by John Spencer, the elder or the younger, or by Daniel Pierce, who acquired the property in 1651. The 17th-century portion of the house is a two-and-one-half-story stone structure built in the form of a cross with a large central chimney. The walls, which are 2 feet thick, are comprised of granite interspersed with field stone and brick covered by a thick coating of plaster. The original stone house was enlarged in 1797 by adding a two-and-one-half-story frame wing to the west end of the main axis. Rooms in this newer section are paneled in the Georgian style. The house has been in the possession of the Little family since 1861.
Private; not accessible to the public
NHL

ESSEX COUNTY
Newburyport
MARKET SQUARE HISTORIC DISTRICT
　Market Square and properties
　fronting on State, Merrimac, Liberty,
　and Water Streets
　19th century

Market Square is one of the last remaining seaport business districts in New England that dates from the times of prosperous shipping, fishing, and other maritime activity. Newburyport's economy was based on shipbuilding, fishing, trading, and distilling. Most buildings now standing in the square were constructed during the 21 years following the fire of 1811. Strict building codes were immediately enacted, and massive fire walls were put up between individual structures. These fire walls terminated in the distinctive stepped end gable common throughout the square. The architectural coherence thus achieved makes the district unique. Most buildings are Federal style, common bond brick row houses with stores on the ground level. They are three stories high and three bays wide. The two most important structures in the historic area are the U.S. Customhouse (1835) and the Market House (1823).
Multiple public/private

ESSEX COUNTY
Newburyport
U.S. CUSTOMHOUSE
　25 Water Street
　1835, Robert Mills

The Newburyport Customhouse is a two-story, rectangular building almost devoid of exterior ornament. The walls are regular ashlar gray granite, and the corner pilasters are dressed granite blocks laid up as quoins. A simple Doric entablature extends around the building, and it is repeated above the one-story entrance porch. The middle bay on the main facade projects slightly from the wall, and the projection continues up through the principal entablature. Operations at the Customhouse ceased in 1910.
Municipal; not accessible to the public

ESSEX COUNTY
Salem
BOWDITCH, NATHANIEL, HOME
　North Street
　Early 19th century

A self-educated man, Nathaniel Bowditch effected great advances in navigation and helped to bring European mathematics to America. Utilizing his observations at sea, he compiled *The New American Practical Navigator*, a textbook on navigation which also contained tables and navigational

aids. His translation of one of Pierre Laplace's works, though never completed, effectively introduced continental mathematics to the United States. Bowditch occupied this frame house from 1811 to 1823. Save for the absence of its rooftop balustrade and shutters, the building essentially retains its original appearance.
Municipal
NHL

ESSEX COUNTY
Salem
GARDNER-WHITE-PINGREE HOUSE
128 Essex Street
1804–1805, Samuel McIntire

The Gardner-White-Pingree House, built for Salem merchant John Gardner, is a three-story brick town house covered by a hip roof ringed with a balustrade. Trim is white marble. The center doorway, framed by reeded pilasters, has fanlights and sidelights and is sheltered by a one-story elliptical porch with slender Corinthian columns. Third-story windows are shorter than those on other levels, and the roof has a modillion cornice. Interiors are decorated in the Adam style.
Private
NHL; HABS

ESSEX COUNTY
Salem
HAMILTON HALL
9 Cambridge Street
1806–1807, Samuel McIntire

The political differences between Federalists and Republicans split the townspeople of Salem. One faction, eventually incorporated as the Proprietors of the South Buildings, erected Hamilton Hall to house their social activities. Hamilton Hall is a three-story brick building with a gable roof and four interior end chimneys. The gable end is treated as a pediment and contains a central semi-circular window. A belt course divides the floors and a one-story portico covers the main doorway. There are four rooms on the first floor divided by a center hall. The back half of the upper two floors is a large ballroom.
Private
NHL; HABS

ESSEX COUNTY
Salem
PEABODY MUSEUM OF SALEM
161 Essex Street
1825

In 1799 a group of Salem ship captains organized the Salem East Indian Marine Society. When the Society's financial state forced the sale of part of its collections, philanthropist George Peabody saved the

museum by arranging for its acquisition by the Peabody Academy of Science. Simultaneously the academy bought the ethnological and natural history collections of Salem's Essex Institution. The Peabody Museum, which assumed its present name in 1915, has notable collections of New England maritime history, Pacific ethnology, and the natural history of Essex County. The granite facade of the building is essentially unchanged; its interior has been restored.
Private
NHL; HABS

ESSEX COUNTY
Salem
PEIRCE-NICHOLS HOUSE
80 Federal Street
1782, Samuel McIntire

The late Georgian style Peirce-Nichols House was the first important example of Samuel McIntire's work. McIntire remodeled some of the rooms in 1801 so the existing interiors illustrate both his early Georgian and later Adam styles of decoration. The large, square, three-story house was built for Jerathmeel Peirce. The exterior of the frame clapboard structure has a central Doric pedimented porch and tall, fluted Doric pilasters at the corners. The hipped roof has a balustraded parapet at the edge and a belvedere above. Third-story windows are foreshortened as was usual in Georgian houses, and all windows have exterior blinds and interior shutters.
Private
NHL

ESSEX COUNTY
Salem
SALEM MARITIME NATIONAL HISTORIC SITE
Derby Street
17th, 18th, and 19th centuries

Founded in 1626, Salem owed its early beginnings to a seaboard location. As early as 1643 fish, lumber, and provisions were being shipped from Salem to the West Indies in exchange for sugar and molasses. During the Revolution and the War of 1812, the port aided the American cause as a privateering center. Derby Wharf is an important survivor from Salem's shipping zenith. Nearby is the customhouse where Nathaniel Hawthorne worked as Surveyor of the Port of Salem from 1846 to 1849. The building, its occupants, and the surroundings are described in the introduction to *The Scarlet Letter* (1850). The Derby House (1761–1762) and the Hawkes House (1780) also recall Salem's former commercial eminence.
Federal/non-federal
NPS; 10.73 acres
HABS

ESSEX COUNTY
Salem
WARD, JOHN, HOUSE
132 Essex Street
1684

This house exemplifies the organic growth of a 17th-century frame house and is similar to the more famous house of Seven Gables, also in Salem. The two-and-one-half-story structure originally included only the western half of the present house, consisting of the parlor and its chamber above, the brick chimney, porch, and stair. An unusual feature of the house was an overhang at both the front and west ends, an arrangement that added space to the bedroom in the second story. A wide cross gable was constructed in the roof on the front side to enlarge and light the garret. At some later date Ward added the eastern half to the existing house. This addition contained a hall and large fireplace, a chamber above, and a second cross gable in front to light the added attic room. The overhang was extended across the front of the house only. The final addition, a lean-to across the back of the structure, was completed prior to 1732.
Private
NHL

ESSEX COUNTY
Saugus
BOARDMAN HOUSE
Howard Street
c. 1680

Typical of the 17th-century frame dwellings constructed by English colonists in America, this house is important because so much of the original framework and interior finishing detail remains. The structure is two and one half stories with a central chimney and two rooms on the upper and lower floors. A rear lean-to was added probably at the end of the 17th century. Alterations since the time of construction have not substantially changed the original plan and appearance of the house, and a minumum of restoration work has been done.
Private
NHL

ESSEX COUNTY
Saugus
SAUGUS IRONWORKS NATIONAL HISTORIC SITE
Off U.S. 1
c. 1648

The Saugus Ironworks is a reconstruction of a 17th-century iron works which operated intermittently between 1648 and 1670. The works consisted of a blast furnace, casting house, forge, and a rolling and slitting mill. About 1670, after years of dwindling operations, the ironworks

was abandoned. Although it was not a financial success, it was an important industrial achievement. The plant, one of the few of its type then existing in the world, produced a fine grade of iron. Perhaps more important, the ironworks provided training for skilled workers and ironmasters who built and operated ironworks all along the east coast.
Private
NPS (authorized but not acquired); 9 acres

ESSEX COUNTY
Topsfield
PARSON CAPEN HOUSE
Howlett Street
1683

The Parson Capen House, one of the finest surviving English colonial dwellings in the United States, has a gable roof and an oak frame rising two stories in height. The clapboarded exterior has a front second floor overhang as well as overhangs on each of the gable ends. A pilastered brick chimney projects from the center of the roof's ridge. There is one room at either side of the massive central brick fireplace. A central winding staircase is built against the chimney. The building was restored early in the 20th century.
Private
NHL

FRANKLIN COUNTY
Deerfield
OLD DEERFIELD VILLAGE HISTORIC DISTRICT
c. 1670

At the beginning of the 18th century Deerfield was the outpost of New England's northwestern frontier. It had been laid out in 1666 and was settled a few years later. French and Indian raids in 1675 and 1704 laid waste to the town, but each time it was rebuilt. Many of the 18th-century buildings remain, and today much of the village has been restored to its colonial appearance. Among the surviving buildings are the Frary House (1689), the Willard House (1768), Old Bloody Brook Tavern (c. 1700), and the John Williams House (1707).
Multiple private
NHL; HABS

HAMPDEN COUNTY (also in Suffolk, Norfolk, Middlesex, and Worcester Counties)
Springfield
1767 MILESTONES
Between Boston and Springfield along the Old Post Road
1767

The 1767 Milestones were placed along the Boston Post Road following action by Parliament which directed Massachusetts and the other colonies to survey their post roads. Ninety-nine stones were marked, some new and some already in place. Each bore the distance from Boston, the distance in miles to Springfield, and the date. Legibility of the inscription varies from stone to stone. The milestones east of Worcester County are granite while those to the west are sandstone. Forty of the original stones (or their replacements) have been located. They range in size from one foot ten inches, to five feet high above ground, and from eighteen inches to three feet wide.
State and private

HAMPDEN COUNTY
Springfield
SPRINGFIELD ARMORY
Armory Square
1794

Until it was formally deactivated in 1968, Springfield Armory was the oldest manufacturing arsenal in the United States. In recent years it was the United States Army's principal research and development center and pilot manufactory for small arms. The armory also was the site of the defeat of insurgent farmers in Shays' Rebellion, 1786–1787. A museum exhibits the history of the Armory and interprets the story of America's military growth and power as reflected in its small arms.
State/municipal
NHL

HAMPSHIRE COUNTY
Amherst
DICKINSON, EMILY, HOME
280 Main Street
1813

Emily Dickinson, one of America's preeminent poets, spent her entire life in this house, 1830–1886. In her later years she lived in partial seclusion and wrote poetry for her own pleasure. The first major publication of her work was in 1890, only two of her poems having been published during her lifetime. The 14–room brick house remains in excellent condition.
Private; not accessible to the public
NHL

HAMPSHIRE COUNTY
Cummington vicinity
BRYANT, WILLIAM CULLEN, HOMESTEAD
2 miles from Cummington on side road
c. 1799

William Cullen Bryant, poet and editor, lived in this house until early manhood, composing here two of his best-known poems, "Thanatopsis" and "To a Waterfowl." A lawyer until the age of 30, Bryant subsequently edited the New York *Evening Post* for 40 years. In addition to his journalistic leadership, he exerted great influence as a critic of literature and American public affairs. His house, to which he returned in his later years, is furnished with Bryant memorabilia.
Private
NHL

MIDDLESEX COUNTY
Cambridge
CHRIST CHURCH
Garden Street
1759–1761, Peter Harrison

Christ Church is among the finest surviving 18th-century religious buildings in the New England colonies. The entrance of this Georgian church is formed by a low wood tower which is topped by a smaller cruciform belfry. The rusticated planking on each of the side elevations is broken by a row of seven arched windows connected by a continuous archivolt. Above the windows is a Roman Doric cornice. A Palladian window lights the semicircular chancel. Built for an Anglican congregation, Christ Church was designed as a typical Anglican church with nave, side aisles, and a focus on the altar. Six free-standing raised classic columns along each side of the nave support the ceiling over the aisles. Two bays were added to the nave in 1857.
Private
NHL; HABS

MIDDLESEX COUNTY
Cambridge
ELMWOOD (JAMES RUSSELL LOWELL HOME)
Elmwood Avenue
1766

James Russell Lowell was a prominent man of letters during the period known as the "Flowering of New England." For many years he was a distinguished linguist and professor at Harvard University. Less conventional than many of his literary contemporaries, Lowell used his pen to influence public opinion. His *Bigelow Papers* (1848) was a poetic attack on the Mexican War. He was the first editor of the *At-*

lantic Monthly and was later associated with the *North American Review*. Elmwood, built by Lieutenant Governor Andrew Oliver in 1766, was occupied from 1787 to 1814 by Elbridge Gerry, governor of Massachusetts and Vice President of the United States. Lowell lived in this three-story frame house from his birth in 1819 until his death in 1891.
Private; not accessible to the public
NHL

MIDDLESEX COUNTY
Cambridge
GRAY, ASA, HOUSE
88 Garden Street
1810

Trained as a physician, Asa Gray became one of America's greatest botanists. During his 45 years as professor of botany at Harvard, he published, among other works, *The Genera of the Plants of the United States* (1849) and *Statistics of the Flora of the Northern United States* (1856), the latter of which helped to launch the study of plant geography. Although moved from its original site, the house retains many of its interior and exterior features.
Private
NHL

MIDDLESEX COUNTY
Cambridge
HASTINGS, OLIVER, HOUSE
101 Brattle Street
1844–1845

Oliver Hastings was a Boston merchant, and his home is a frame Greek Revival, T-shaped building enlivened by curved bays, cast-iron verandas and balustrades, and a hip roof terminating in a monitor. The main facade is highlighted by a wide curved bow with a two-story porch situated in the central bay. There are four fluted Corinthian columns on the first floor of the portico and an elaborate cast-iron, trellised balustrade on the roof. Flush siding covers the exterior walls.
Private; not accessible to the public
NHL

MIDDLESEX COUNTY
Cambridge
MASSACHUSETTS HALL, HARVARD UNIVERSITY
Harvard University Yard
1718–1720, John Leverett, Benjamin Wadsworth

Massachusetts Hall is the oldest surviving building of America's oldest institution of higher learning. As such, it is significant not only in the history of American education, but also in the history of the English colonies in the 18th century. Harvard

University, originally designated Harvard College, was established in 1636 through a grant of the Massachusetts General Court. Built as a dormitory, Massachusetts Hall contained 32 chambers and a small private study for each of the 64 students. The three-story brick building now houses administrative offices.
Private
NHL

MIDDLESEX COUNTY
Cambridge
MEMORIAL HALL, HARVARD UNIVERSITY
Cambridge and Quincy Streets, Harvard University campus
1870–1878, William Robert Ware and Henry Van Brunt

The brick walls of Memorial Hall are trimmed with Nova Scotia stone. Built as a memorial to Harvard's Civil War dead, the Late Gothic Revival structure is cruciform in plan, and a massive, square tower surmounts the crossing of the arms. Both apse and nave sections contain Gothic tracery windows in the second story. North and south transept ends are three bays wide and flanked by wide, three-story towers topped by high pyramidal roofs. Rose windows have been incorporated in the Gothic fenestration of the north, south, and west elevations. Inside, the nave was designed as a dining hall, the transepts as the memorial hall, and the apse as a theater.
Private
NHL

MIDDLESEX COUNTY
Cambridge
SEVER HALL, HARVARD UNIVERSITY
Harvard Yard
1878–1880, Henry Hobson Richardson

Designed in the well-known Richardsonian Romanesque style, Sever Hall is a classroom building, and the architect strove to blend it harmoniously with the Georgian and Federal edifices already in Harvard Yard. The brick structure is three and one-half stories high. Front and rear facades are divided into bays by low, twin cylindrical towers capped by steeply sloping roofs. Prominent belt courses divide all floors. The main entrance is set in a deeply recessed Syrian archway, above which is a slightly projecting bay surmounted by a pediment containing panels ornamented with floral patterns in cut brick; similar ornament appears on the rear elevation.
Private
NHL

MIDDLESEX COUNTY
Cambridge
UNIVERSITY HALL, HARVARD UNIVERSITY
Harvard Yard
1813–1815, Charles Bulfinch

Standing three stories high and covered by a hip roof, University Hall has walls of granite and measures 140 by 50 feet. The similar east and west elevations are divided into three sections. The central, seven-bay portion, adorned by four giant, wooden Ionic pilasters with a wooden balustrade on the roof above, is flanked by three-bay wings on each side. Inside, the original commons or dining rooms occupied the first floor until 1842, and the chapel and recitation rooms were located upstairs. The interior has been greatly altered.
Private
NHL

MIDDLESEX COUNTY
Cambridge
VASSALL, JOHN, HOUSE (CRAIGIE-LONGFELLOW HOUSE)
105 Brattle Street
1759

This Georgian period two-story frame house was built by Major John Vassall in 1759. The house was occupied by George Washington during the siege of Boston, 1775–1776. Henry Wadsworth Longfellow lived here from 1837 to 1882. During this time it was a meeting place for the poet's many distinguished associates, and here he wrote his best-known poetry, including *The Song of Hiawatha, Evangeline,* and *The Courtship of Miles Standish.* The street facade of this 18–room house features a central pedimental projecting pavilion, a prominent cornice, and four giant pilasters. The four lower slopes of the double hip roof are crowned with balustrades. The floor plan is the central hall type with interior chimneys. The present interior furnishings and general decor date from the period of Longfellow's occupancy.
Private
NHL; HABS

MIDDLESEX COUNTY
Concord
EMERSON, RALPH WALDO, HOME
Lexington Road and Cambridge Turnpike
1835

Ralph Waldo Emerson, poet, essayist, and lecturer, occupied this square frame house from 1835 until his death in 1882. Now best known for his essays on transcendental philosophy, he was also well known during his lifetime as a lecturer. His house

is furnished as it was during his day, excepting the study and library which is a replica. The contents of the original library have been transferred across the street to the Concord Antiquarian Society.
Private
NHL

MIDDLESEX COUNTY
Concord (also in Lincoln and Lexington)
MINUTE MAN NATIONAL HISTORICAL PARK
1775

The military phase of the American Revolution began with the battles of Lexington and Concord on April 19, 1775. British troops, marching out from Boston to seize a cache of colonial arms, came face to face with the Americans at Lexington Green. Firing broke out, the Americans dispersed, and the British marched on to Concord. After an unsuccessful search for the hidden arms and an exchange of fire at the North Bridge, the British withdrew from Concord. By this time the aroused colonials had gathered from the surrounding countryside, harassing the retreating British column until (exhausted and bloody) it retreated into the haven of Boston. War had begun.
Federal/non-federal
NPS; 750 acres
HABS

MIDDLESEX COUNTY
Concord
OLD MANSE
Monument Street
c. 1765

The Old Manse was constructed by the grandfather of Ralph Waldo Emerson, the Reverend William Emerson, whose family watched the Revolutionary battle at the North Bridge in 1775 from a second-story window. Emerson lived here for a year, during which time he composed the essay "Nature." Nathaniel Hawthorne, who gave the house its present name, lived here with his wife from 1842 to 1846. A description of the house appears in Hawthorne's *Mosses from an Old Manse.* The two-and-one-half-story clapboard dwelling is furnished with objects associated with its famous residents.
Private
NHL; HABS

MIDDLESEX COUNTY
Concord
ORCHARD HOUSE
Lexington Road
Mid–19th century

This frame house was the home of Bronson Alcott, the American transcen-dentalist and educator who established the unsuccessful cooperative community of Fruitlands in 1843. It was also the home of his daughter, Louisa May Alcott, who wrote a part of *Little Women* (1868) here. Others of her well-known works include *Hospital Sketches* (1863) and *Little Men* (1871). Furnishings, books, and other items associated with the Alcott family are exhibited.
Private
NHL; HABS

MIDDLESEX COUNTY
Concord
WALDEN POND
1.5 miles south of Concord

At Walden Pond, Henry David Thoreau lived in a simple cabin from 1845 to 1847. Seven years later he published his account of those years, *Walden, or Life in the Woods.* The site of the cabin is marked with a cairn of rocks. Walden Pond is a reservation of 144 acres, most of which is a lake with a wooded shore line.
State
NHL

MIDDLESEX COUNTY
Concord
WRIGHT'S TAVERN
Lexington Road, opposite the Burying Ground
1747

On April 19, 1775, Wright's Tavern was the scene of meetings of both Minute Men and British Redcoats within a few hours of one another. Prior to the Revolutionary War it was also associated on October 1, 1774, with the meeting of the Provincial Congress of Massachusetts, which gathered in the adjacent meetinghouse of the First Parish. The measures passed at this session gave formal status to the rebellion by ending payment of taxes to England and providing for a defensive force to resist British authority. The hostelry itself has undergone few changes.
Private
NHL; HABS

MIDDLESEX COUNTY
Lexington
BUCKMAN TAVERN
Hancock Street, on the east side of Lexington Green
c. 1690

Oldest of the Lexington hostelries, Buckman Tavern is intimately associated with the initial exchange of shots in the Revolutionary War. The tavern is named for proprietor John Buckman, who was a member of the Lexington company of Minute Men. His public house was a convenient gathering place for his comrades on the days they trained on Lexington Green. Thus it was natural that they should assemble here during the evening and through the night preceding the arrival of British troops on April 19, 1775. The oldest portion of the present building dates from the late 17th century; the main body of the two-story frame building with its hipped roof dates from the 18th century.
Municipal
NHL; HABS

MIDDLESEX COUNTY
Lexington
LEXINGTON GREEN
Massachusetts and Hancock Streets
1775

On Lexington Green on the morning of April 19, 1775, occurred the short but momentous skirmish between the Minute Men and the British forces that initiated the Revolutionary War. Due to failure to obey orders, a shot was fired—by which side it is not known—and when the firing ceased, eight American militiamen lay dead. This clash, which marked the beginning of the battle, continued intermittently as the British troops marched to Concord, seven miles distant. The Revolutionary Monument near the southwest corner of the Common is significant not only for the battle it commemorates, but also for the simple design typical in the early days of the Republic.
Municipal
NHL

MIDDLESEX COUNTY
Medford
ROYALL, ISAAC, HOUSE
15 George Street
Mid–17th century

The Royall House represents the Georgian period in the history of New England's domestic architecture. The nucleus of the present house is a 17th-century, two-and-one-half-story brick dwelling which is one room in depth. Soon after Royall purchased the house in 1732, he raised the height to a full three stories and completed the present east facade, covering the existing brickwork with wood. Royall's son Isaac, Jr., who inherited the estate in the 1740's, doubled the depth of the house, built the large double-end chimneys with their connecting parapets, and completed the present west facade with its rusticated wood siding and giant corner pilasters. It was during this period that the principal interior rooms were refinished or redecorated.
Private
NHL; HABS

MIDDLESEX COUNTY
Medford
TUFTS, PETER, HOUSE
350 Riverside Avenue
1675

The Peter Tufts House erected in 1675 is an example of a 17th-century New England brick structure, of which only 11 are known to have been built. The walls of the house are 18 inches thick and were made of brick probably manufactured in Medford, a leading brick-making center. Two end chimneys were built into the walls. The house is three stories high, and the roof slopes steeply, but is cut before reaching a peak, thus forming an early style gambrel roof. A brick belt course around the house marks the floor level between the first and second stories. Window spacing front and back is irregular or non-Georgian. The Georgian floor plan consists of a central hallway with two rooms on either side in each story. Principal alterations include the addition of the present front porch and dormer windows and replacement of the original casement windows with sliding sash.
Private
NHL

MIDDLESEX COUNTY
1767 MILESTONES
Reference—see Hampden County

MIDDLESEX COUNTY
Waltham
GORE PLACE
52 Gore Street
1805–1806, Jacques Guillaume
Legrand

Gore Place is a noteworthy example of a five-part Federal country house. It is composed of a main block with an elliptical bow in the south facade, two hyphens, and end pavilions standing at right angles to the main axis. Walls are brick laid in Flemish bond. The central section has a hip roof crowned by a low, wooden, octagonal cupola. Hyphens and end pavilions have gable roofs. A nine-foot-wide sandstone terrace extends across the north elevation. Inside are mantels elaborately carved in the Adamesque manner which contrast noticeably with the simpler woodwork. Gore Place was built for Christopher Gore, lawyer and politician.
Private
NHL; HABS

MIDDLESEX COUNTY
Waltham
LYMAN, THEODORE, HOUSE (THE VALE)
Lyman and Beaver Streets
1793–1798, Samuel McIntire

The Lyman House was designed as a five-part, frame composition. It consisted of a two-story main block with one-story hyphens and lower, two-story end pavilions. In 1882 the house was enlarged and extensively remodeled. The end pavilions were increased to two full stories, the west wing was made larger by the addition of an ell at the rear, the hyphens were raised to two stories, and a third floor was added to the central section. All roof units were balustraded, and projecting bays were built on either side of the front door. The interior has been greatly altered.
Private
NHL; HABS

NANTUCKET COUNTY
Nantucket
COFFIN, JETHRO, HOUSE
Sunset Hill
c. 1686

The Jethro Coffin House is a restored example of a 17th-century New England saltbox house. It is a one-and-one-half-story frame dwelling with a long rear roof slope, very small windows of the medieval type, and a big central chimney with four large fireplaces. The floor plan is typical of 17th-century central chimney structures: a small central entry leads to the two front rooms located on either side of the chimney, and a boxed-in staircase provides access to the large bedrooms in the attic.
Private
NHL

NANTUCKET COUNTY
Nantucket
NANTUCKET HISTORIC DISTRICT
Nantucket Island
c. 1700–1874

The American whaling industry originated on Nantucket Island. By 1748 Nantucketers owned 60 ships, and the island retained supremacy in the industry for another 100 years. On Main Street, between Centre Street and Monument Square, are numerous houses associated with this era. Notable among them are the "Three Bricks," a row of houses built between 1833 and 1837 for the three sons of a wealthy whale oil merchant.
Multiple public/private
NHL; HABS

NORFOLK COUNTY
Brookline
JOHN FITZGERALD KENNEDY NATIONAL HISTORIC SITE
83 Beals Street
c. 1908

John Fitzgerald Kennedy, 35th President of the United States, was born at this site on May 29, 1917. The Kennedy family occupied the nine-room frame house until 1920. Before becoming President in 1961, Kennedy served in Congress both as a Representative and as a Senator from Massachusetts. He was assassinated on November 22, 1963, having served only part of his presidential term.
Federal
NPS; .09 acre
HABS

NORFOLK COUNTY
Brookline
OLMSTED, FREDERICK LAW, HOUSE
99 Warren Street
1810

Pioneer landscape architect Frederick Law Olmsted became interested in park development through his world travels in the 1840's and 1850's. His first major project was the development of New York's Central Park, of which he became chief architect in 1858. During subsequent years he was involved with the preservation of Yosemite, the Niagara Reservation, establishment of Adirondack Forest Preserve, Arnold Arboretum, and the Biltmore Estate in North Carolina. By the time of his death, he and his associates had planned some 80 urban parks. The exterior of his house is little changed, but the interior has been greatly altered.
Private; not accessible to the public
NHL

NORFOLK COUNTY
Dedham
FAIRBANKS HOUSE
Eastern Avenue and East Street
c. 1636

The Fairbanks House is one of the oldest frame dwellings in the United States. This survivor of the English colonial period is typical of the "growing house" which the owner added to as his prosperity and family increased. It was built in 1636 by Jonathan Fayerbanke, and eight generations of the family have occupied the house. The oldest part of the house has a massive central brick chimney and abutting stair hall with one room to either side on each of the two floors. Later additions include an enlargement of the original rooms, the addition of a lean-to across the rear, and wings to either side.
Private
NHL; HABS

NORFOLK COUNTY
Milton
FORBES, CAPT. R. B., HOUSE
215 Adams Street
1833

For several decades Boston was the major American port engaged in the China trade. The wealth resulting from this trade is exemplified by the house of Robert Bennet Forbes, who became the head of the firm of Russell and Company in 1839. During the Opium War (1839–1842) his business prospered because the Chinese halted British trading operations. Ultimately the Chinese opened many ports to western trade. Forbes' three-story Greek Revival house, designed by the noted architect Isaiah Rogers and subsequently remodeled in 1871, contains Chinese furniture, furnishing, and art objects and is open to the public as a museum.
Private

NORFOLK COUNTY
Quincy
ADAMS, JOHN, BIRTHPLACE
133 Franklin Street
1681

John Adams, first Vice President and second President of the United States, lived in this house until his marriage in 1764. At that time he moved into an adjacent house left to him by his father. Before his election to the Vice Presidency, Adams was a delegate to the First Continental Congress, a commissioner to France (1777–1778) a negotiator of the Treaty with Britain (1782–1783), and envoy to Britain (1785–1788). The Adams birthplace originally consisted of two lower rooms and two upper chambers; a later lean-to added two lower rooms. Though this saltbox house has undergone extensive alterations, much of the original fabric remains.
Municipal
NHL; HABS

NORFOLK COUNTY
Quincy
ADAMS, JOHN QUINCY, BIRTHPLACE
141 Franklin Street
1663

John Quincy Adams, sixth President of the United States, was born in this house in 1767. For several years its original kitchen room served as the law office of his father, John Adams. The family lived here until 1783, and John Quincy Adams again occupied the house from 1805 to 1807. Prior to his term as President, he was a United States Senator, a negotiator of the treaty ending the War of 1812 (1814), minister to Britain (1815), and Secretary of State (1817–1825). From 1831 to 1841 he served in the House of Representatives. The birthplace originally consisted of two upper and two lower rooms. Later a two-kitchen lean-to was added. Though the house has undergone considerable alteration, much of the original fabric remains.
Municipal
NHL; HABS

NORFOLK COUNTY
Quincy
ADAMS NATIONAL HISTORIC SITE
135 Adams Street
1731

Adams National Historic Site commemorates four generations of the distinguished Adams family, who occupied this house from 1788 to 1927. Here lived John Adams, first Vice President and second President of the United States, 1797–1801. His son, John Quincy Adams, was Senator, Congressman, Secretary of State, and President of the United States, 1825–1829. His son, Charles Francis Adams, was minister to the Court of St. James, 1861–1868. His son, Henry Adams, historian and man of letters, is best known for his autobiography, *The Education of Henry Adams*. A younger son, Brooks Adams, was the last of the family to occupy the "Old House." A stone library, stable, and extensive gardens are other notable features of the house.
Federal
NPS; 4.77 acres

NORFOLK COUNTY
Quincy
MOSWETUSET HUMMOCK
Squantum Street about 1,000 feet northeast of the intersection of Morrissey Boulevard
17th century

In the early 1600's this hill was the seat of the sachem Chicatabot of the Massachusetts Indians. Shaped like an arrowhead (which in the Indians' tongue is *mos* or *mons*), the hummock (or *wetuset*), as slightly altered in pronunciation by the white man, gave rise to the name Massachusetts. Today the hill is still bounded by the sea where the Indians fished, by the marshes that served as a defense, and the original planting grounds of the tribe.
State

NORFOLK COUNTY
Quincy
THE QUINCY HOMESTEAD
34 Butler Street
1706

The Quincy Homestead is one of the few houses in Massachusetts in which the elements of a 17th-century building incorporated in a later structure are clearly visible. The earliest section was presumably built in the 1600's and a second portion constructed by Edmund Quincy in 1706. It appears that the two were joined together during the mid–18th century, and the dwelling had assumed its present appearance by 1822. It is a two-and-one-half-story clapboard structure with both a gambrel and a hip roof. There are dormers on the south and west elevations, and the ridge of the roof supports a balustrade with finials. A pedimented Doric entrance porch highlights the main facade. The interior has four rooms on the main floors separated by a central hall which terminates in a 17th-century kitchen and chamber above. This portion was included in the 1706 remodeling.
State

NORFOLK COUNTY
Quincy
UNITED FIRST PARISH CHURCH (UNITARIAN) OF QUINCY
1266 Hancock Street
1827–1828, Alexander Parris

This building is considered the finest extant Greek Revival church in New England. The scale of the two-story structure is monumental. Walls are granite, and the main facade is covered by a giant, projecting Doric portico above which rests a two-stage stone tower topped by an open wooden cupola. Windows in the north and south walls are tall and round-headed. The four, tapered, monolithic portico columns are 25 feet high including their capitals. Inside, the pews are separated by two side aisles, and galleries extend around the north, south, and west sides. The dominant interior feature is the decorative plaster dome centered in the ceiling.
Private
NHL; HABS

NORFOLK COUNTY
1767 MILESTONES
Reference—see Hampden County

PLYMOUTH COUNTY
Hingham
OLD SHIP MEETINGHOUSE
Main Street
1681

Old Ship Meetinghouse is considered the only surviving New England church built

during the 17th century and the oldest English colonial house of worship still standing in the United States. Designed and built almost as a square, the meetinghouse was altered in 1731 and 1755 and restored in 1930. The roof is supported by curved timbers resembling an inverted ship's hull, hence the name. Indigenous to New England, the frame meetinghouse, with a pulpit opposite the main door, was developed by the Puritans in rejection of the traditional Anglican church interior, characterized by placement of an alter at the long, narrow end of the building. Town meetings and religious services were held here, and the dual use demonstrates the close connection between politics and religion in the Puritan community.
Private
NHL; HABS

PLYMOUTH COUNTY
Plymouth
COLE'S HILL
Carver Street
1620

Cole's Hill is a significant part of the settlement site of the Plymouth Colony. The hill is traditionally considered the burial place of the colonists who died in the "starving time" of the first winter, 1620–1621. On the top of the bank stands a memorial to the *Mayflower* Pilgrims. Beneath is a crypt containing bones uncovered in 18th- and 19th-century excavations. Also on the hill is a statue of Massasoit, the Wampanoag chief whose friendship shielded the colony from Indian attack in its early years. At the foot of Cole's Hill is Plymouth Rock, legendary landing site of the Pilgrims.
Private
NHL

PLYMOUTH COUNTY
Plymouth
PLYMOUTH ROCK
Water Street

Plymouth Rock is a large granite boulder now incised with the date 1620. It symbolizes the landing of the Pilgrims in that year to found the first permanent English settlement in New England. Although no mention of a specific landing place is made in the official Pilgrim records, the value of Plymouth Rock as a historic symbol supersedes the question of its authenticity. In 1774 an attempt was made to move the rock and it split. The two halves were separated but brought together again in 1880 near their original site. At that time the firm of McKim, Mead, and White designed the gray granite Classical canopy as a shelter. The canopy has 16 monolithic columns to support its full entablature which is surrounded by a parapet.
State

SUFFOLK COUNTY
Boston
ARNOLD ARBORETUM
22 Divinity Avenue
c. 1873, Frederick Law Olmsted

Begun as a tree farm for Harvard University in 1873, the Arnold Arboretum is now a pre-eminent institution for plant research. Charles Sprague Sargent, its first director, campaigned vigorously to make the arboretum an aesthetic as well as a scientific endeavor. Today paths allow visitors to enjoy more than 6,000 species of trees and shrubs. Its library, herbarium, and publications aid in scientific research.
Private
NHL

SUFFOLK COUNTY
Boston
BEACON HILL HISTORIC DISTRICT
Bounded roughly by Beacon Street on the south, the Charles River Embankment on the west, Pinckney and Revere Streets on the north, and Hancock Street on the east
18th and 19th centuries

In the heart of Boston, near the city's commercial center, is the residential section known as Beacon Hill. Its Federal and Greek Revival style buildings, some designed by Charles Bulfinch, make the area architecturally significant. It is chiefly famous, however, as the residence of many distinguished persons of the 19th century. Among the more famous were Charles Francis Adams, Francis Parkman, Edwin Booth, Bronson Alcott, William Dean Howells, and William Prescott.
Multiple public/private
NHL; HABS

SUFFOLK COUNTY
Boston
BOSTON ATHENAEUM
10 1/2 Beacon Street
1847

Established in 1807, the Boston Athenaeum, largest of the Nation's early proprietary libraries, continues to be a leading cultural institution. Intended to serve both the scholar and the general reader, the Athenaeum houses more than 430,000 volumes. Included in its collection are numerous rare items, among them large parts of the libraries of George Washington and John Quincy Adams. There are also many early pamphlets and tracts of historical value and a large newspaper collection. The earliest portion of the present building was begun in 1847 and enlarged in 1913–1914. It contains reading rooms, stack areas, exhibition rooms, and administrative offices.
Private
NHL

SUFFOLK COUNTY
Boston
BOSTON LIGHT
Little Brewster Island, Boston Harbor
1716, 1783 (reconstruction)

Little Brewster Island is the site of the first lighthouse in North America. Destroyed by the British in 1776, Boston Light was reconstructed according to the plan of the old lighthouse, probably incorporating the remaining wall of the old tower. The 89-foot tower is a built-up combination of rubble stone, granite, and brick. Now operated by the United States Coast Guard, it throws out a 100,000 candlepower beam every 30 seconds.
Federal
NHL

SUFFOLK COUNTY
Boston
BOSTON NAVAL SHIPYARD
East of Chelsea Street, Charlestown
c. 1800

The Boston Naval Shipyard, one of the Nation's oldest, has built, repaired, and serviced countless naval vessels. Among the famous ships launched here were the *Merrimac* and the *Monadnock*. The installation introduced the use of shelters for shipways, built one of the Nation's first dry docks, made all of the Navy's rope for more than a century, and pioneered in modern ship construction. Still an active facility, it is administered by the Department of the Navy. Its principal feature is the restored U.S.S. *Constitution*.
Federal
NHL

SUFFOLK COUNTY
Boston
BUNKER HILL MONUMENT
Breed's Hill
1825

The battle of Bunker Hill, actually fought on nearby Breed's Hill, June 17, 1775, was the first full-scale action between American militia and British troops in the Revolutionary War. The battle ended in defeat for the inexperienced Americans, but the costly victory convinced the British that defeating the colonists would not be easy. The present monument marking the approximate center of the American redoubt on Breed's Hill is surrounded by a four-acre park.
State
NHL

SUFFOLK COUNTY
Boston
DORCHESTER HEIGHTS NATIONAL HISTORIC SITE
South Boston
1776

In the spring of 1776 cannon captured from Fort Ticonderoga in New York were brought to Boston on sleds and mounted on Nooks Hill, Dorchester Heights. From this location the colonists commanded the city and continually bombarded the British positions. Finally, on March 17, General Howe evacuated Boston. The entire British Army plus many Loyalist citizens sailed to Nova Scotia. Never again during the Revolution was Massachusetts occupied by British troops.
Municipal
NPS; 5.43 acres

SUFFOLK COUNTY
Boston
ETHER DOME, MASSACHUSETTS GENERAL HOSPITAL
Fruit Street
1818, Charles Bulfinch

The first publicized use of ether as a surgical anesthetic took place in the operating dome of Massachusetts General Hospital on October 16, 1846. This event was due in part to the efforts of William Thomas Green Morton, a dentist, who administered the "preparation" to the patient. Although other physicians and dentists of the time had used ether, their experiments had not been publicized. Bare and utilitarian, the ether dome has remained essentially unchanged and is still being used for lectures.
Private; not accessible to the public
NHL

SUFFOLK COUNTY
Boston
FANEUIL HALL
Dock Square
1761, John Smibert; 1805–1806, Charles Bulfinch

Often called the "cradle of liberty," Faneuil Hall was a focal point in the organization of colonial protest against the acts of the British Parliament immediately prior to the Revolutionary War. Here Samuel Adams, James Otis, and other leaders voiced the desire for American self-government. In the 19th century it was a center for the abolitionist movement. Built as a public market, the building was also used for municipal meetings after its owner, Peter Faneuil, provided a room for town meetings. In 1898–1899 the entire building was restored according to the Bulfinch plans. The present three-

story brick building is covered by a gable roof which has a cupola at the east end.
Municipal
NHL

SUFFOLK COUNTY
Boston
FIRST HARRISON GRAY OTIS HOUSE
141 Cambridge Street
1795–1796, Charles Bulfinch

Built for lawyer and politician Harrison Gray Otis, the Otis House underwent considerable alteration during the 19th century and is presently being restored to its earlier appearance. Standing three stories high it has a low hip roof with chimneys at both ends. Windows have stone lintels and sills, and the floor levels are delineated by prominent stone belt courses. The second-story Palladian window on the main elevation and fanlight above have been reconstructed. The present cornice is a careful copy made from fragments of the original. In 1926 the house was moved back 40 feet from its original site. Inside, the second-floor drawing room is the finest room in the house. It has a low dado, finely detailed cornice, and mantels with Adamesque friezes.
Private
NHL; HABS

SUFFOLK COUNTY
Boston
HARDING, CHESTER, HOUSE
16 Beacon Street
1808

Though self-taught, Chester Harding was one of America's notable portrait painters in the four decades before his death in 1866. Settling in Boston in the late 1820's, he became so popular during his lifetime that the demand for his work was termed "Harding Fever." This four-story brick house was Harding's residence from 1827 to 1829.
Private; not accessible to the public
NHL

SUFFOLK COUNTY
Boston
HEADQUARTERS HOUSE
55 Beacon Street
1806; Asher Benjamin

In this four-story building on Beacon Hill, William H. Prescott lived and did much of his writing. His historical works include *The History of the Reign of Ferdinand and Isabella the Catholic* (1838), *History of the Conquest of Mexico* (1843), and *History of the Conquest of Peru* (1847). His work is notable for accuracy and thoroughness in both research and composition.
Private
NHL

SUFFOLK COUNTY
Boston
KING'S CHAPEL
Tremont and School Streets
1749–1754, Peter Harrison

Known today as King's Chapel Unitarian Church, this building is considered a masterpiece of its architect and an excellent example of Georgian church architecture in the American colonies. The main portion is a rectangle built of cut Quincy granite and covered by a hip roof. The north and south elevations have two tiers of arched windows, the east elevation, a Palladian window. The wood front porch with its classic columns was added in 1785–1787. The square stone base for the tower was intended to carry a spire which was never built. Paired, giant Corinthian columns project in front of the galleries. The interior spatial composition and details make it one of the finest Georgian period church interiors. The present building is on the site of the first Anglican church building in Massachusetts. In 1785 it became the first Unitarian church in the United States.
Private
NHL

SUFFOLK COUNTY
Boston
LONG WHARF AND CUSTOMHOUSE BLOCK
Foot of State Street
Wharf, 1710–1721; Customhouse Block, 1848, Peabody and Stearns

Long Wharf and Customhouse Block commemorate the mercantile history of Boston, one of America's major ports. The original Long Wharf was long the city's busiest pier, flourishing as both a commercial port and an embarkation point for travelers. As Boston's mercantile business increased, the wharf was expanded and rebuilt, and the commercial structures along the waterfront were replaced. The Customhouse Block is one of the noteworthy massive granite structures built during Boston's commercial zenith.
Private
NHL

SUFFOLK COUNTY
Boston
MASSACHUSETTS GENERAL HOSPITAL
Fruit Street
1818–1823, Charles Bulfinch; 1844–1846, George Perkins

Massachusetts General is a rare major example of a large, early 19th-century city hospital. The addition of matching five-bay wings in the 1840's nearly doubled the hospital's size, and the entire interior was redone at that time. Exterior walls are

granite in coursed ashlar, and the building stands two stories high above an elevated, rusticated basement. There is a projecting, central pedimented portico with giant Ionic columns. Prior to designing the hospital, Bulfinch visited comparable institutions in New York, Philadelphia, and Baltimore. He recommended that no ward should accommodate more than 20 patients. When completed the hospital had a capacity of 73 beds. Located today in the midst of a huge hospital complex, Bulfinch's original building is used principally for clinical research.
Private
NHL; HABS

SUFFOLK COUNTY
Boston
MASSACHUSETTS HISTORICAL SOCIETY
1154 Boylston Street
1899

Founded through the efforts of the Reverend Jeremy Belknap in 1791, the Massachusetts Historical Society is the oldest such society in the United States. From its inception it has been pre-eminent in the collection, preservation, and publication of historical material, including Paul Revere's account of his famous ride. Its present building contains three stories, the first floor of stone and the upper two of brick.
Private
NHL

SUFFOLK COUNTY
Boston
MASSACHUSETTS STATEHOUSE
Beacon Hill
1789, Charles Bulfinch

The Massachusetts Statehouse (containing the Executive Department and Senate Chamber) has been the center for Massachusetts government since its completion; it is also significant as a monument of Federal architecture. Memorial paintings, tablets, and statuary are in the Bulfinch wing, battle flags from the Civil War through World War II, in Memorial Hall.
State
NHL; HABS

SUFFOLK COUNTY
Boston
OLD CITY HALL
School and Providence Streets
1862–1865, Gridley J. F. Bryant and Arthur D. Gilman

The Second Empire Old City Hall is a monumentally scaled four-story granite building. The main facade contains a projecting, pedimented, five-story central pavilion three bays wide and flanked by four-story wings. Paired columns set off the central bays of the pavilion and corners are marked by paired pilasters. Pilasters also divide the bays on the second and third floors. Inside and out the Old City Hall bears a strong resemblance to the Louvre in Paris. Woodwork of the first floor is butternut and pine on the other levels. The entrance hall is floored with black and white marble, and the most striking interior features are the staircases.
Municipal; not accessible to the public
NHL; HABS

SUFFOLK COUNTY
Boston
OLD NORTH CHURCH, CHRIST CHURCH
193 Salem Street
1723, William Price

From the belfry of Old North Church on the night of April 18, 1775, lanterns notified patriots across the Charles River that British troops were moving toward Lexington and Concord. The next day they were engaged with the Minute Men in the opening skirmish of the Revolutionary War. Boston's oldest surviving church, Old North Church was built from designs based on Sir Christopher Wren's London churches. Its first steeple, blown down in 1804, was replaced by a similar one designed by Charles Bulfinch. The church is still used as a house of worship.
Private
NHL; HABS

SUFFOLK COUNTY
Boston
OLD SOUTH CHURCH IN BOSTON
645 Boylston Street
1874–1875, Cummings and Sears

The Old South Church in Boston is a two-story masonry building with polychrome walls. Its plan is cruciform, and a square dome rests above the crossing of the arms. The south, north, and east gable ends contain two-story window openings with elaborate Gothic tracery. Pinnacles decorate building corners, and there are arcaded entranceways between the arms on three sides. The main entrance is deeply recessed and arched. Interior woodwork is cherry as are the pulpit and screen. The campanile-like tower was rebuilt in the 1930's and reduced 10 feet to its present 235–foot height.
Private
NHL

SUFFOLK COUNTY
Boston
OLD SOUTH MEETINGHOUSE
Milk and Washington Streets
1729–1730, Robert Twelves

Old South Meetinghouse was the scene of many protest meetings prior to the Revolutionary War. One such meeting led to the Boston Tea Party on the night of December 16, 1773. The building was erected by Joshua Blanchard, the mason who later buit the Thomas Hancock House and the original Faneuil Hall. The two-story brick building with gabled roof is among the few pre-Revolutionary meeting houses still standing. It has a side brick tower and wood steeple. The interior, featuring a three-sided gallery and raised pulpit with a suspended sounding board, was restored after the British had used the interior for a riding school during their occupation of Boston in 1775.
Private
NHL; HABS

SUFFOLK COUNTY
Boston
OLD STATEHOUSE
Washington and State Streets
1712–1713, 1740

The Old Statehouse was the seat of government of the province of Massachusetts and the meeting place for colonial courts as well as for civic and military affairs. Here James Otis argued against the legality of the writs of assistance in 1761. With the outbreak of the Revolution the building served as the Statehouse of the Commonwealth of Massachusetts from 1776 to 1798. This Georgian building, which occupies the site of its predecessor, was once the focal point of Dock Street, a major thoroughfare in 18th-century Boston.
Municipal
NHL; HABS

SUFFOLK COUNTY
Boston
OLD WEST CHURCH
131 Cambridge Street
1806, Asher Benjamin

Old West Church is a square, two-story brick edifice with a stepped gable roof and a three-and-one-half-story projecting porch. Above the porch is a square tower topped by a dome and a cupola. Windows of the main building are arranged in two tiers and have lintels and sills of stone. The porch has three roundheaded windows framed by Doric pilasters in its third story. Inside, the central dome measures 42 feet in diameter and is 6 feet high. In 1896 the church became a branch of the public library and remained so until 1960.

Three years later the interior was restored to its early 19th-century appearance.
Private
NHL; HABS

SUFFOLK COUNTY
Boston
PARKMAN, FRANCIS, HOUSE
50 Chestnut Street
1824

Historian Francis Parkman was one of the many prominent people who lived on Beacon Hill in the 19th century. Observations made on a trip over the Oregon Trail in 1846 he recorded in *The California and Oregon Trail* (1849). Other works concern the French in the New World: *Pioneers of France in the New World* (1865), *The Old Regime in Canada* (1874), and *Montcalm and Wolfe* (1884). Parkman's writing is notable for the use of personal observations and his insistence on the critical use of original manuscript material. His early Federal brick house was his home during many of his productive years.
Private; not accessible to the public
NHL

SUFFOLK COUNTY
Boston
PIERCE-HICHBORN HOUSE
29 North Square
1680–1710

The Pierce-Hichborn House, a 17th-century brick town house, is typical of the many pre-Georgian brick dwellings erected in Boston to replace earlier wooden buildings destroyed in the great fire of 1676. Moses Pierce, an artisan-glazier, built the three-story, hipped-roof dwelling for his family. The oblong-shaped, six-room house is constructed of red brick laid in English bond and has its narrow two-bay end facing east on the square. A two-story brick service wing, containing the present kitchen and a chamber over it, was added to the narrow west end of the house in the 18th century. The dwelling was acquired by Nathaniel Hichborn in 1781 and remained in his family until 1864. It is now a historic house museum.
Private
NHL; HABS

SUFFOLK COUNTY
Boston
QUINCY MARKET
South Market Street
1825–1826, Alexander Parris

Quincy Market is a monument to the efforts and abilities of two men, Josiah Quincy (1772–1864) and architect Alexander Parris (1780–1852). Lawyer, legislator, and later president of Harvard,

Quincy served as mayor of Boston from 1823 to 1828 and initiated the city's first public water and sewage systems. Quincy responded to growing discontent over crowded and unsanitary conditions at the Faneuil Hall market with a proposal for a new market. In the face of strong opposition, he held a public meeting and mustered enough support to effect approval of the new market by the state legislature. The cornerstone was laid on April 27, 1825, and the first business was transacted a year later. The main market building (535 feet 3 inches by 50 feet) is built of granite and consists of a central domed section flanked on the east and west by two-story, gable-roofed wings. Ionic porticos on both wings are surmounted by pediments containing single circular windows. The market was originally paralleled on its north and south sides by four-story warehouses, and the entire complex fronts on a portion of Boston harbor which was later filled in. Parts of the market are still in use today.
Public
NHL

SUFFOLK COUNTY
Boston
REVERE, PAUL, HOUSE
19 North Square
c. 1676

In addition to its significance as the home of the Revolutionary patriot, the Paul Revere House is important as downtown Boston's only extant 17th-century dwelling. It was from this house that Paul Revere left for his ride on the night of April 18, 1775, to warn the Revolutionary patriots in Lexington. In 1908 the house was restored to its 17th-century form. The two-story house is one room deep and has a small kitchen ell. The facade has an overhang; a massive end brick chimney projects above the gable roof.
Private
NHL

SUFFOLK COUNTY
Boston
ST. PAUL'S CHURCH
136 Tremont Street
1819–1820, Alexander Parris and Solomon Willard

St. Paul's Church, now the cathedral of the diocese of Boston, is a two-story, gable-roofed sandstone building highlighted by a temple front portico with six Ionic columns. The portico extends the full width of the main facade. There are three entrance doors to the interior which has a curved ceiling containing recessed panels. A gallery is located above the entrance doors. The present chancel and dome were added in 1926–1927; the altar

and reredos were installed at the same time.
Private
NHL

SUFFOLK COUNTY
Boston
SEARS, DAVID, HOUSE
42 Beacon Street
1816, Alexander Parris

The scale of this Federal style town house is monumental, and its walls are composed of carved granite panels. As built the Sears House was a two-story, L-shaped structure with a hip roof and a single projecting central bay. A saucer dome crowned the bay. First-floor windows were full length and those above, regular size; the space between was filled by an oblong, carved granite swag panel. In 1824 one of the bays west of the central bow was removed and a matching, three-bay bow was constructed on the east side. The facade was thus increased from seven to ten bays. A third story was added in 1875, the hip roof was replaced by a gable, and the saucer domes were removed from the double bows.
Private; not accessible to the public
NHL

SUFFOLK COUNTY
Boston
TREMONT STREET SUBWAY
Beneath Tremont, Boylston, and Washington Streets
1895–1898

Boston's subway was the first in North America and the fifth such system in the world. City authorities had been prompted to consider the undertaking because of the crowded streets jammed with horse-drawn vehicles. Though the original subway has been incorporated into the city's present and much-enlarged system, the original section of tunnel is still used. The stone entrances and exits on Tremont Street at the Boston Common are the most visible landmarks.
Municipal
NHL

SUFFOLK COUNTY
Boston
TRINITY CHURCH
Copley Square
1874–1877, Henry Hobson Richardson

Trinity Church was one of H. H. Richardson's best works. The architectural style is Romanesque, which has become synonymous with the architect's name. In his design Richardson subordinated the cruciform church building to its massive square, central tower with corner turrets

which soars 211 feet above the ground. Principal building materials were Dedham granite and Longmeadow freestone. The parish house is attached to the church by a colonnaded cloister. John La Farge executed murals inside the church (1876–1877) and some of the stained glass.
Private
NHL

SUFFOLK COUNTY
Boston
U.S.S. *CONSTITUTION*
Boston Naval Shipyard
1797

Better known as "Old Ironsides," the frigate *Constitution* has retained her identity as a commissioned ship of the United States Navy. The vessel was involved in the undeclared naval war with France (1798–1800), the sea battles with the Barbary pirates (1801–1805), and the War of 1812. She was condemned as unseaworthy in 1830, but Oliver W. Holmes's poem, "Old Ironsides," aroused such public interest that appropriations for rebuilding her were authorized. The square-rigged wooden vessel is 204 feet long with a 43 1/2-foot beam.
Federal
NHL

SUFFOLK COUNTY
Boston Harbor
FORT WARREN
Georges Island
1834–1863

Military engineer Sylvanus Thayer (1785–1872) was responsible for the plan and construction of Fort Warren. Built mainly of Quincy granite, the defense work was a bastioned star fort with outer walls 8 feet thick and 600 feet long. Casemate guns protected the principal wall, and the bastions were armed with howitzers. The fort was twice modernized after the Civil War, in 1871–1876 and again in 1898–1899. Inside the walls is a brick magazine, and outside are a two-story brick hospital (late 19th century) and a mine storage building (World War I). Fort Warren was the most important Civil War site in New England because it was a prison for Confederate leaders, among whom were James Mason and John Slidell, Confederate emissaries to Great Britain who were seized from the British ship *Trent*, and Alexander Stephens, Vice President of the Confederacy. Georges Island itself is an oval-shaped, 40-acre piece of land situated almost centrally in Boston harbor.
Municipal
NHL

SUFFOLK COUNTY
Roxbury
GARRISON, WILLIAM LLOYD, HOUSE
125 Highland Street
1864

William Lloyd Garrison was an articulate and influential exponent of immediate abolition of slavery. Through the columns of the *Liberator*, which he edited from 1831 to 1866, the New England Anti-Slavery Society (1832), the American Anti-Slavery Society (1833), lectures, and brochures, he stirred the North on the slavery issue. This two-story clapboard house was his residence from 1864 to 1879.
Private; not accessible to the public
NHL

SUFFOLK COUNTY
Roxbury
SHIRLEY-EUSTIS HOUSE
31–37 Shirley Street
1747

Shirley Place was among the most formal and imposing Georgian period houses built in New England. Its builder, William Shirley, was royal governor of Massachusetts from 1741 to 1756 and a colonial leader in the generation preceding the Revolutionary War. The original design featured a first and second floor raised on a high stone basement. An imposing double flight of stairs led to the main entrance. The wood exterior, finished to imitate masonry, featured single and paired giant pilasters. The steep-pitched hip roof was surmounted by a balustrade deck and a cupola. After being used by American forces as a barracks and hospital during the siege of Boston, it was purchased and remodeled by Dr. William Eustis in 1819. Eustis had been a surgeon in the Revolutionary War and was twice elected governor of the Commonwealth of Massachusetts.
Private
NHL; HABS

SUFFOLK COUNTY
1767 MILESTONES
Reference—see Hampden County

SUFFOLK COUNTY
West Roxbury
BROOK FARM
670 Baker Street
1841

The Brook Farm Institute of Agriculture and Education was founded to promote the New England transcendentalist's ideal of "plain living and high thinking." George and Sophia Ripley were the founders and leaders of the experiment. Other prominent persons associated with the farm included Bronson Alcott, Ralph Waldo Emerson, and Nathaniel Hawthorne. Common ownership of property, fair division of labor, and a balance between physical and intellectual pursuits were among the practices of the institute. Various difficulties caused the abandonment of the experiment in 1847. Brook Farm remains largely in a natural state, with fields and woods, though a part of the land is used as a cemetery. Only one building dating from the Brook Farm period is extant.
Private; not accessible to the public
NHL

WORCESTER COUNTY
Auburn vicinity
GODDARD ROCKET LAUNCHING SITE
9th fairway, Pakachoag Golf Course, Pakachoag Road
1926

On March 16, 1926, Dr. Robert H. Goddard launched the world's first liquid propellant rocket on a farm near Auburn, Massachusetts. This event established the use of liquid fuel as a propellant for rockets and set the course for future developments in rocketry. It was not until after the appearance of the German V–2 rockets in 1943 that his contribution was fully recognized and his work given serious study. The launch site, marked today by a small obelisk, is substantially unaltered.
Private
NHL

WORCESTER COUNTY
Lancaster
FIRST CHURCH OF CHRIST, LANCASTER
Facing the Common
1816, Charles Bulfinch

The most noteworthy exterior features of the First Church of Christ are the two-stage front tower, topped by a wood cupola surrounded by Ionic columns, and the giant portico. The three portico arches are an "improvement" on Bulfinch's design made by the builder. Bulfinch had envisioned one tall center arch flanked by two lower arches all reflecting the unequal heights of the vestibule doors behind. The rectangular brick church is two stories high. Inside there is a gallery on all but the north wall, and no electric lights or central heating have been installed. The Thayer Memorial Chapel was added in 1881, and in 1900 the walls and ceiling inside were decorated in a fashion similar to Bulfinch's Massachusetts Statehouse.
Private
NHL; HABS

214   MASSACHUSETTS

WORCESTER COUNTY
1767 MILESTONES
Reference—see Hampden County

WORCESTER COUNTY
Worcester
AMERICAN ANTIQUARIAN SOCIETY
185 Salisbury Street
1910–1930

The American Antiquarian Society, established in 1812, was the third historical society founded in this country. The society, under the leadership of Clarence S. Brigham, who became librarian in 1908, rose to prominence as a depository for early Americana. Especially important are its collections of American newspapers (1670–1820), fiction (1774–1850), and imprints before 1820. The present home of the society was completed in 1910 and is a brick, modified Georgian building whose design was influenced by the original 1820 structure. Rear wings of brick in the same architectural style were added in 1924 and 1950. The American Antiquarian Society functions primarily as a research institution.
Private; accessible to the public with permission
NHL

WORCESTER COUNTY
Worcester
ELM PARK
Bounded by Elm, Russell, Highland, and Pleasant Streets and by private properties on the west and north of Federal and Marmon Places (excludes the property of Worcester High School on Highland Street)
Mid–19th century

Elm Park is believed to be the first public park in America, as land for it was acquired in 1854 (acquisition of land for New York's Central Park was begun in 1853 but not completed until 1856). The land was developed by Edward Winslow Lincoln in 1874. Lincoln served as Commissioner of Shade Trees (1870–1885) and Commissioner of Parks (1885–1895) for the city of Worcester. A second piece of land, Newton Hill, was added to the original purchase in 1888.
Municipal

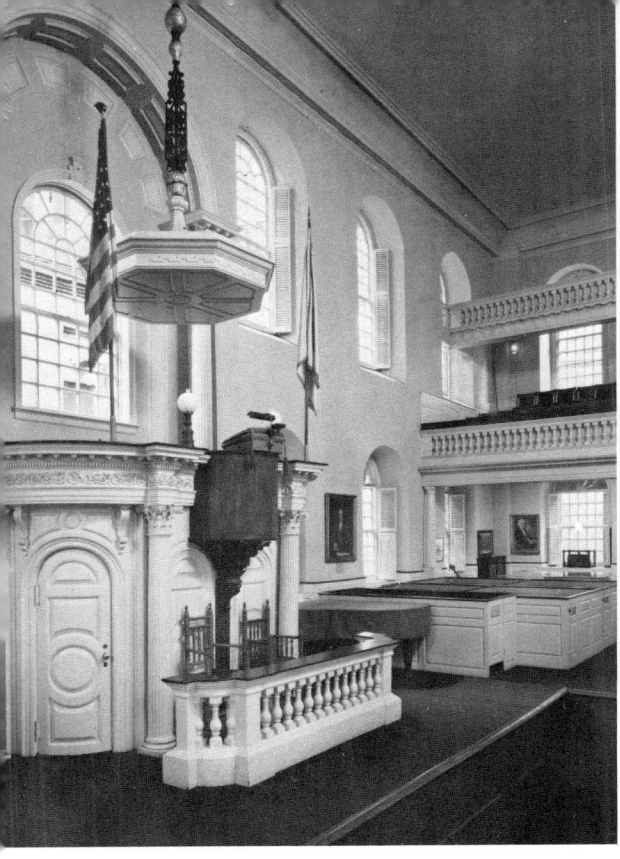

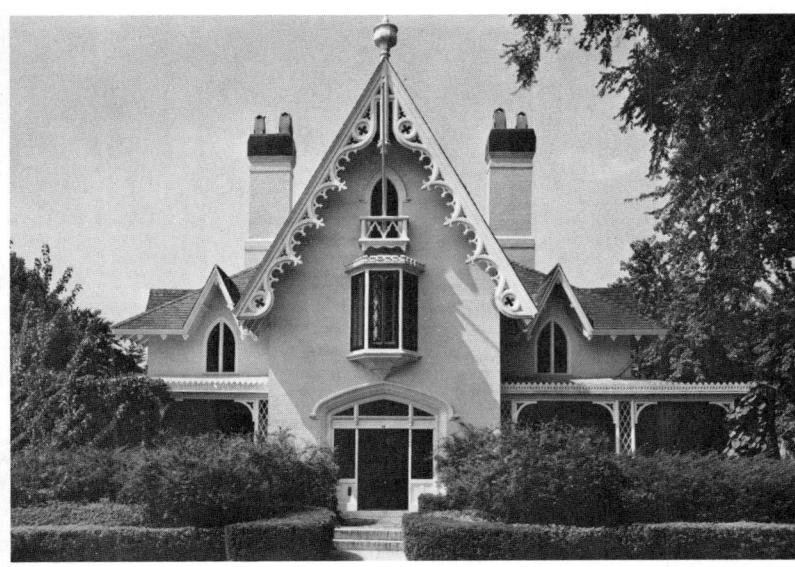

William J. Rotch House, New Bedford, Massachusetts.
Ned Goode for HABS

Old South Meetinghouse, Boston, Massachusetts.
Cortlandt V. D. Hubbard for HABS

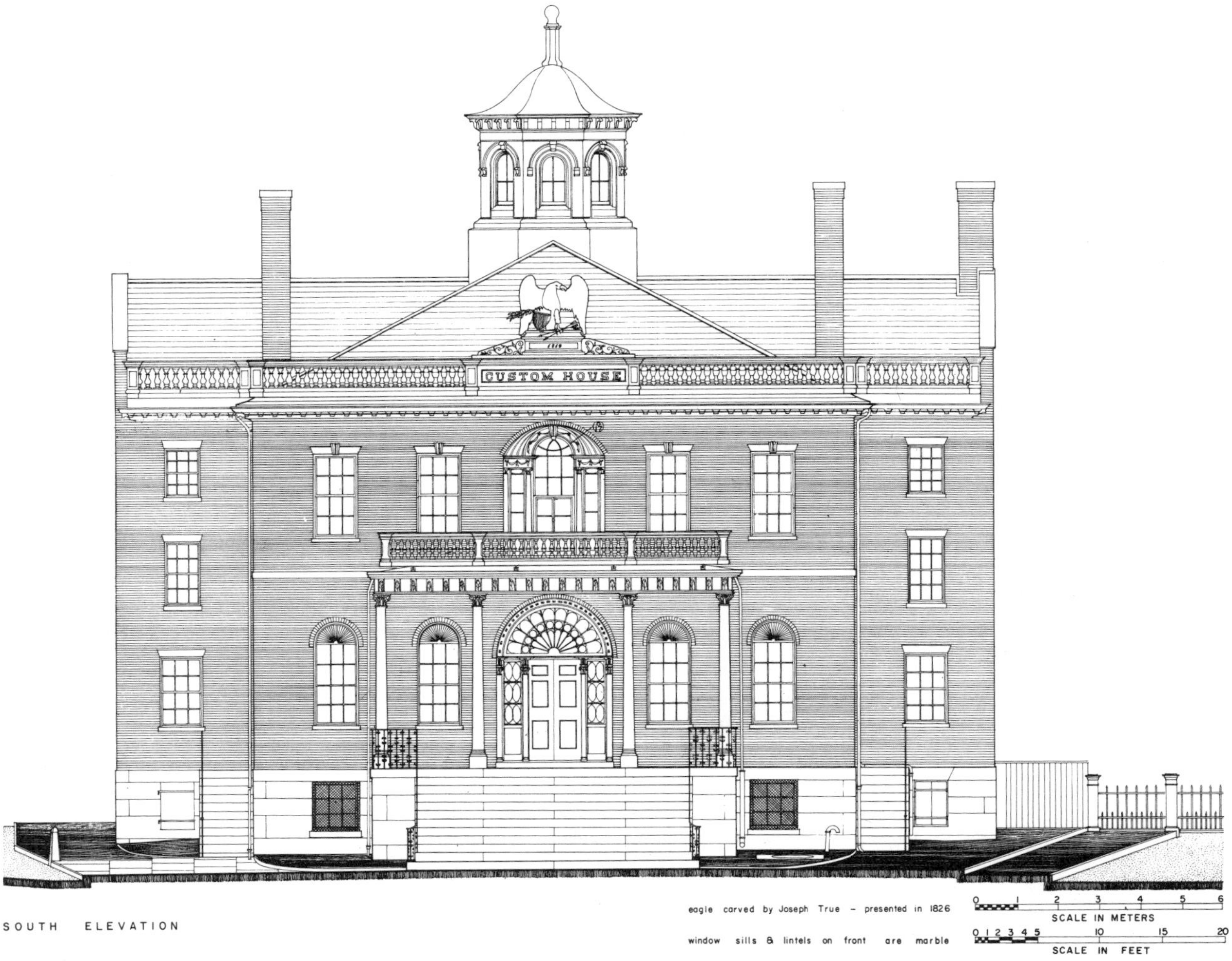
CUSTOM HOUSE
SOUTH ELEVATION
eagle carved by Joseph True – presented in 1826
window sills & lintels on front are marble
0 1 2 3 4 5 6
SCALE IN METERS
0 1 2 3 4 5 10 15 20
SCALE IN FEET

Customs House, Salem Maritime National Historic Site, Salem, Massachusetts. *HABS*

Michigan

Mission Church, Mackinac Island, Michigan. *Mackinac Island State Park Commission*

Ford Motor Company, Mack Avenue Plant,
Greenfield Village Historic District,
Dearborn, Michigan. *The Henry Ford Museum.*

Honolulu House (Abner Pratt House), Marshall, Michigan.
Allen Stross for HABS

Grand Rapids Art Museum (Abram W. Pike House),
Grand Rapids, Michigan. *Allen Stross for HABS*

Gilbert House,
Heritage Hill
Historic District
Grand Rapids, Michigan.
Heritage Hill Association

ALGER COUNTY
Grand Marais
HILL'S STORE
Grand Marais Avenue
1895

Grand Marais developed as a result of the growth of the fishing and logging industries during the mid–19th century. In the last ten years of that century the Alger-Smith Company of Detroit contracted to have its vast timber holdings in the Upper Peninsula cut and transported south. Milling operations were set up in Grand Marais, and people began to flock to town for employment. Two merchants, Wilkes W. Hargrave and Roy C. Hill, came from nearby Seney to open a store which grew into one of the most profitable concerns in the county. Serving as a social center for fishermen, lumbermen, and townspeople, Hill's Store remained in business until 1951. The two-story frame building rests on a cement foundation and has a false front with a bracketed cornice. Windows and doors have been boarded up for protection from vandals.
Private; not accessible to the public

BAY COUNTY
Bay City
FLETCHER SITE
SW 1/4 SW 1/4 sec. 16 and NW 1/4 NW 1/4 sec. 21, T. 14 N., R. 5 E.
Pre-Columbian to 19th century

The Fletcher Site contains material exemplary of the major cultural groups of the eastern United States during the last several thousand years. Among the objects recovered are side-notched projectile points of the Late Archaic Period, thick, crude pottery of the Early Woodland Period, finely worked and elaborately decorated Hopewellian pottery, heavy corded sherds and triangular projectile points of the Late Woodland Period, and a large number of burials of the Middle Historic Period. The site has been almost continuously inhabited from about 3,000 B.C. until 150 years ago. Most archeological work to date has been concerned with the historic burials. However, although the older artifacts are less plentiful, they are expected to add to the archeologists' still scanty knowledge of Michigan Archaic and Woodland periods.
Private

BERRIEN COUNTY
Berrien Springs
BERRIEN SPRINGS COURTHOUSE
North side, corner of Union and Cass Streets
1838–1839

Gilbert B. Avery, a local builder, designed the Berrien Springs Courthouse, adapting classical Greek Revival forms to the skills of local workmen. The courthouse is a frame structure raised on a high brick basement. Four 20–foot fluted Doric columns on masonry piers support the entrance portico, and pilasters ornament the corners of all four walls. A square, two-stage cupola with louvered openings surmounts the gable roof. In 1894 the county seat was moved. Since that time the building has been an armory, a community center, and a Seventh-Day Adventist church.
County; not accessible to the public

CALHOUN COUNTY
Albion
GARDNER HOUSE
509 S. Superior Street
1875

This two-story Victorian brick mansion built for A. P. Gardner was a showplace of its time. Victorian detailing is evident in the box cornices and decorative brackets above the entrance porch and bay window, the gabled round-arched windows in the mansard roof, and in the delicately carved vergeboards over the third-floor windows. All rooms have high ceilings, and the windows are equipped with interior shutters. Gardner was Albion's leading hardware merchant.
Private

CALHOUN COUNTY
Battle Creek
PENN CENTRAL RAILWAY STATION (NEW YORK CENTRAL AND MICHIGAN CENTRAL RAILWAY STATION)
W. Van Buren
1887–1888, Roger & McFarland

The Penn Central Station is a one-and-one-half-story brick building 135 feet long and 35 feet wide with a hip roof, wide bracketed overhangs, and a high clock tower. Windows are arcaded and grouped, the north entrance is an enormous arch, and foundation and trimmings are Lake Superior brownstone. There are rounded bays covered by conical roofs on the east and west elevations. The Michigan Central, the largest railroad in the state, connected Detroit and Chicago. In 1918 the New York Central secured controlling interest in the Michigan, and it in turn became the Penn Central in 1968.
Private
HABS

CALHOUN COUNTY
Marshall
BROOKS, HAROLD C., HOUSE (JABEZ S. FITCH HOUSE)
310 N. Kalamazoo Avenue
c. 1840

The Brooks or Fitch House is an exceptional and impressive example of Greek Revival architecture in the midwest. The five Ionic columns of the temple front portico are an unusual non-classical feature. Windows on the first floor front measure ten feet from bottom to top. Inside the roof pediment is an unusual Palladian motif window with wrought iron grilles on the fanlight and sidelights. Alterations of a minor nature were made about 1910. Jabez S. Fitch, for whom the house was built, was a wealthy Marshall drygoods dealer. Charles T. Gorham, a banker who served as minister to the Hague (1870–1875) and Assistant Secretary of the Interior (1876–1877), purchased the house in 1851.
Private; not accessible to the public
HABS

CALHOUN COUNTY
Marshall
HONOLULU HOUSE (ABNER PRATT HOUSE)
107 N. Kalamazoo Street
1860

The Honolulu House is a unique architectural style reputed to have been modeled upon Hawaiian prototypes. The board and batten structure rests upon a five-foot ashlar sandstone foundation and has a pagoda-roofed central tower. A veranda with an ornamental railing, columns, and wooden Tudor arches runs the length of the building. Large triple convoluted brackets project from the column capitals to the eaves. Two towers at the rear of the house have been removed. Inside the house a wide stairway sweeps upward from the main hall to the observation deck in the tower. Large parlors with 15–foot ceilings open off the hall, and several ornamental wall paintings remain.
Private
HABS

CHARLEVOIX COUNTY
Charlevoix vicinity
O'NEILL SITE
South of Charlevoix off U.S. 31
Pre-Columbian

The O'Neill Site is a multicomponent prehistoric occupation site spanning several centuries. Remains of two distinct occupational units—late Woodland and Archaic—are present. Artifacts recovered include Archaic points and fragments of

Eastport chert from nearby Pewangoing quarry and distinctive Traverse and Mackinac ceramic ware.
Private; not accessible to the public

St. James
MORMON PRINT SHOP
Main and Forest Streets
1850

Following the assassination of Mormon prophet Joseph Smith (1844), several men claimed to be his successor. One of them, James J. Strang, managed to establish authority over a small group of Latter-Day Saints at Voree, Wisconsin. In 1847 while exploring other possible areas of settlement, he wintered with some followers on Beaver Island. Strang was named king of the Beaver Islands colony in July, 1847. St. James became the capital of his kingdom, and Strang eventually represented the Beaver Islands in the lower house of the Michigan legislature (1853–1855). A paper, the *Northern Islander*, was published in this building between 1850 and 1856. Printed first as a weekly and then as a daily, it was one of the earliest newspapers in northern Michigan. During the 1850's tension grew among Strang's followers and between them and the non-Mormons, and Strang was fatally shot by two disaffected followers in 1856. Shortly afterwards a mob invaded the islands. Nearly all Mormons were forced to leave, buildings were sacked, and the uncompleted temple was burned. The print shop is a two-story log building with a one-story rear addition.
Private

Mackinaw City
FORT MICHILIMACKINAC
Near Mackinac Bridge, at the terminus of U.S. 31
1715–1720

Fort Michilimackinac was strategically located on the south shore of the Straits of Mackinac, the crossroads of the upper Great Lakes. Erected by the French, the post was surrendered to the British in 1762 during the French and Indian War. It was the only British garrisoned outpost on the Great Lakes until near the end of the American Revolution. In 1781 the post was moved to Mackinac Island. The site of the original fort has been established by archeological investigation, and the stockade has been reconstructed. Its museum exhibit includes current on-site archeological operations.
State
NHL

Mackinaw City vicinity
MACKINAC POINT LIGHTHOUSE
Michilimackinac State Park
19th century

Mackinac Point Lighthouse is a round tower connected to a service building, both of which are made of light brick and rest on high foundations of stone. The light station was established in 1890 on the Straits of Mackinac, a main crossroads for shipping on the Great Lakes; the lighthouse was not completed until 1892. It was discontinued in the late 1950's.
State; not accessible to the public

Drummond Township
FORT DRUMMOND
Western end of Drummond Island
1815–1828

Fort Drummond or Fort Colyer was occupied by the British Army following their evacuation of Mackinac Island after the War of 1812. The outpost on Drummond Island was established to maintain a British military presence in the upper Great Lakes and to provide some control over the local Indians and the fur trade. The fort consisted of a blockhouse, barracks, commandant's house, storehouse, hospital, bakehouse, forge, officers' quarters, wharf, and several residences. Only ruins and the post cemetery remain.
Multiple public/private

Sault Ste Marie
JOHNSTON, JOHN, HOUSE
415 Park Place
1822

John Johnston, an Irish emigrant to Canada, built his first home in Sault Ste Marie in 1794. This was burned by American forces in 1814 but was rebuilt in 1815. The present structure was an addition to the 1815 house, and all that remains of the latter is the west wall of the later dwelling. Five rooms and a hall are located on the ground floor. The dormer windows on the one-and-one-half-story frame house are late 19th-century additions. The city acquired the house in 1949 and restoration work was undertaken. New windows, floors, and roof were installed. Johnston had married a Chippewa Indian and his home was an important gathering place on the frontier. The Johnston House is believed to be one of the oldest structures on the upper Great Lakes.
Municipal

Sault Ste Marie
OLD FORT BRADY
Bounded by the C.O.E. Service Plaza on the north, by Portage Street on the south, Brady Street on the east, and Bingham Street on the west
19th century

General James Wilkinson and others recommended fortifying the Sault, and the idea was incorporated into Secretary of War (1817–1825) John C. Calhoun's national defense plans. Construction was begun in June, 1822, under the direction of Colonel Hugh Brady. Troops erected winter quarters, built a stockade, and started cutting a road. Two blockhouses stood at the southwest and northeast corners, and sentry boxes were placed on all other corners. Barracks and officers' quarters were situated on three sides within the stockade, while stables and barns were built near the riverbank. Some alterations were made in 1865, and in 1892–1893 the fort was moved to a new location. There are presently no visible evidences of Fort Brady.
Multiple public/private

Sault Ste Marie
ST. MARY'S FALLS CANAL
St. Mary's River
1855

Construction of the St. Mary's Falls Canal enabled the resources of the Lake Superior region to be exploited for the Nation's benefit. The canal, necessitated by the 22-foot difference in elevation between the two lakes, permits passage between Lake Superior and Lake Huron. More modern locks replaced older ones in the 1880's and in 1943, and two additional locks were constructed in 1914 and 1919.
Federal
NHL

Strongs vicinity
NAOMIKONG POINT SITE
NE 1/4 sec. 8, T. 47 N., R. 5 W
Pre-Columbian

Located on the shore of Whitefish Bay, the Naomikong Point Site was occupied no earlier than 400 B.C. and probably not before 200 B.C. Inhabitants in historic times were Chippewa. Cultural material recovered from the site can be ascribed to the Laurel Focus of the Middle Woodland Period. Artifacts include preform blanks, scrapers, drills, celts, pestles, net sinkers and awls, beads, cones, fish hooks, and raw lumps of copper. It is believed that the people who lived at Naomikong fished seasonally (spring and fall) for whitefish using canoes and seines.
Federal

DELTA COUNTY
Fayette
FAYETTE STATE PARK
On a peninsula in Big Bay de Noc, on
Mich. 149
19th century

Fayette was founded in 1867 by the
Jackson Iron Company as a site for the
smelting of iron ore. Two limestone furnaces and a casting house formed the
nucleus of the town. Iron ore was shipped
in by scows, smelted, and the resulting pig
iron was shipped to ports farther south.
Fayette's population was 500 in 1870.
Buildings included 11 charcoal kilns, a
lime kiln, machine shop, blacksmith shop,
dock, sawmill, a store, icehouse, grain
elevators, jail, opera house, hotel, and
many private residences. Furnaces ceased
operation in 1892 due principally to the
depletion of the hardwood forests. The
wood had been used to fire the smelters.
The ruins of the smelting complex have
been stabilized, and one of the charcoal
kilns has been rebuilt. The hotel, opera
house, and 11 private homes are still
standing. All are preserved in the state
park.
State

DELTA COUNTY
Fayette vicinity
SPIDER CAVE
On Big Bay de Noc between Fayette
and Fairport
Pre-Columbian

Artifacts found in Spider Cave include
stone, antler, and bone projectile points,
and stone knives, flakes, and nodules. The
variety of projectile points suggests habitation or use by more than one group or
band. Dating of the artifacts places the
site in the Middle Woodland Period. Many
of the projectile points have shattered tips
indicating that they may have been fired
against some hard object—perhaps into
the cave from canoes—in a magico-reli-
gious rite. Intact projectile points may
represent earlier and later non-ceremonial
uses.
Private

EATON COUNTY
Charlotte
EATON COUNTY COURTHOUSE
W. Lawrence Avenue at Cochran and
Bostwick Streets
1883–1885

The Eaton County Courthouse is a unique
example of Classical architecture tempered by midwestern originality and innovation. The three-story structure has
walls of red brick with finely tooled white

stone tracery; it rests on a raised basement
of rough-tooled fieldstone. Projecting from
the east and south facades of the third
story of the main block are columned
tetrastyle pavilions. An outstanding feature of the courthouse is a three-stage
frame cupola rising from the center of the
hip roof. The cupola has a square base,
columned open belfry, and an octagonal
dome topped by a nine-foot figure of
justice. The building is 111 feet high.
County
HABS

EMMET COUNTY
Cross Village vicinity
WYCAMP CREEK SITE
Northeast of Cross Village on the
north bank of Wycamp Creek
Pre-Columbian

Artifacts found at the Wycamp Creek Site
are similar to findings from other
prehistoric sites in the Great Lakes area.
Pottery sherds resemble an Ontario-
Iroquois type but should probably be attributed to an early historic Ottawa population. Occupation was from Middle
Woodland to early historic times, and a
Late Woodland component has also been
excavated. It is believed that the narrow
northwestern coastal plain of Michigan's
lower peninsula served as a cultural connection between the northern and
southern Great Lakes area. The site will
be likely to yield material left by migrating
peoples who used this corridor. Wycamp
Creek was named for 19th-century
Michigan missionary Father John Bernard
Weikamp.
Private

EMMET COUNTY
Petoskey
**CHESAPEAKE & OHIO RAILWAY
STATION (CHICAGO & WEST
MICHIGAN RAILWAY STATION,
PERE MARQUETTE RAILWAY
STATION)**
Pioneer Park, W. Lake Street
1892

The Chesapeake & Ohio Railway Station
was built just before the turn of the century when northern Michigan promised to
become a tourist center. The original
owners of the station, the Chicago & West
Michigan Railroad, sold out to the Pere
Marquette Railroad Company in 1899.
The latter merged with the Chesapeake &
Ohio Railway Company in 1947. Three
years later the station was abandoned. It
measures 81 feet by 60 feet, and its
second story is a square 39 feet on a side
surmounted by a conical roof. There is a
veranda around the brick station and a
porte cochere on the south side.
*Municipal/private; not accessible to the
public*

EMMET COUNTY
Walloon Lake
**HEMINGWAY, ERNEST, COTTAGE
(WINDEMERE)**
Between the north shore of Walloon
Lake and Lake Grove Road
1904–1921

The Hemingway Cottage, built in 1904
and named Windemere by the Hemingway
family, is a one-story frame structure with
a gabled roof and white clapboard siding.
Ernest Hemingway made his first trip to
Walloon Lake when he was 1 year old and
spent every succeeding summer there, except one, until he reached the age of 21.
Here he learned to hunt and fish, activities
that he continued to enjoy and write about
for the rest of his life. In the summer of
1919 Hemingway first began to write fiction at the cottage. His Michigan experiences later provided him with incidents and settings for 10 short stories
and his first published novel, *The Torrents
of Spring*. Hemingway and his first wife,
Hadley Richardson, honeymooned at the
cottage, and this was his last stay at Walloon Lake except for a brief visit in the
early 1950's. The Hemingway Cottage is
now owned by Madelaine Hemingway
Miller, the younger sister of Ernest.
Private; not accessible to the public
NHL

HILLSDALE COUNTY
Janesville
GRACE EPISCOPAL CHURCH
360 E. Chicago Street
1846–1849

Grace Church is significant as one of the
first churches built in Michigan west of
Detroit. Its design is generally classical
with some Gothic Revival detail. Three
distinct and separate sections constitute
the church building: a one-and-one-half-
story sanctuary, a shallow one-story
vestibule, and a square, central, two-story
belfry tower above the main entrance.
Square pilasters mark the corners, and the
gable roof has a simple cornice with a
plain frieze. Arched windows along the
building's sides have lancet peaks, interlaced lancet-peaked cames, and lancet-
peaked wood surrounds. The church's interior, more distinctly Gothic than the exterior, still contains the original black walnut pews and frescoed panels.
Private

HOUGHTON COUNTY
Hancock vicinity
QUINCY MINE NO. 2 SHAFT HOIST HOUSE
Off U.S. 41
20th century

The Quincy Copper Mining Company was organized in March, 1848, to exploit the then recently discovered Portage Lake copper formations. Mining operations continued through the first decade of the 20th century, when the 8,000-foot level was reached and it became necessary to install a new hoist. The Nordberg Manufacturing Company was commissioned to build the hoist, and it was in operation by 1920. Powered by two high pressure and two low pressure Corliss cylinders using steam at a pressure of 160 pounds per square inch, the Nordberg hoist is the largest cross compound steam hoist in the world. It was used to pull a skip weighing 10,000 pounds loaded with 20,000 pounds of rock. Operating depth was over 9,000 feet on the incline, and hoisting speed was 36.4 miles per hour. Mining operations ceased in 1931. The hoist building and hoist have been restored and are open to the public.
Private

INGHAM COUNTY
East Lansing vicinity
ST. KATHERINE'S CHAPEL
4650 Meridan Road, east of East Lansing
c. 1887

St. Katherine's Chapel is a rural wooden structure of indigenous rustic style. Board and batten siding covers the exterior, and a vestibule and sacristy are attached to the east facade. The belfry is a recent addition. Matched and beaded pine boards have been used to panel the interior. Sheets of red, yellow, and blue glass glaze the windows on the north, south, and west elevations. The reredos was installed in 1945.
Private
HABS

INGHAM COUNTY
Lansing
MICHIGAN STATE CAPITOL
Capitol and Michigan Avenues
1872–1878, Elijah E. Myers

Michigan became a state in 1837 with its capitol located in Detroit. A new site, more centrally situated, was designated for the seat of the state government in 1847. A frame structure served as the capitol for two decades until expanding facilities resulted in enlargements and, eventually, provision for a new capitol. Following an architectural competition, the design of Illinois architect Elijah E. Myers (1832–1909) was approved, and work began with laying of the cornerstone in 1872. Limestone, sandstone, granite, and marble were all utilized in construction. The finished structure is monumental in scale measuring 420 feet long by 274 feet wide by 267 feet high. Topped by an elongated central dome, the capitol has a cruciform floor plan, a rusticated ground story, and Tuscan, Ionic, and Corinthian columns on the exterior. A notable interior feature is the rotunda, open above the ground floor to the top of the dome.
State

IONIA COUNTY
Ionia
HALL-FOWLER MEMORIAL LIBRARY (FREDERICK HALL HOUSE)
126 E. Main Street
1869–1870

A distinctive example of Italianate architecture, the Hall-Fowler Memorial Library is characterized by highly ornate bracketed cornices, elongated windows with hoodmolds, and a central octagonal cupola. Constructed for Frederick Hall, a well-to-do banker, the palatial two-story structure is nearly square and has an extremely low hip roof with extended eaves. Decorative wooden porches shelter the entrances. The house was built of striking, variegated ashlar sandstone which ranges in color from a yellow gray to a reddish brown.
Municipal
HABS

JACKSON COUNTY
Concord
MANN HOUSE
205 Hanover Street
1883–1884

The Mann House is a typical middle-class Victorian home of the late 19th century. Characteristic Victorian features are the tower covered with patterned shingles and the gingerbread under the eaveline of the front gable. The rooms at the rear of the house were altered in 1947–1948, but it is the intention of the Michigan Historical Commission to restore them to their original condition. Many light fixtures, all the furniture, books, wallpaper, and paintings date from the turn of the century. The home, once a social center of the community, is open to the public as a house-museum.
Private

KALAMAZOO COUNTY
Kalamazoo
LADIES LIBRARY ASSOCIATION BUILDING
333 S. Park Street
1879, H. L. Gay

The Ladies Library Association was formed in 1852 and had no permanent meeting place until the present building was constructed. The dual purpose of the Association was to improve the education of its members and to raise the cultural tone of the community. Resting on a foundation of granite blocks, the library building is brick with light colored, cut stone trim. A noticeable feature is the asymmetrically placed tower. In 1913 a two-story wing was added to the rear of the tower.
Private; not accessible to the public

KENT COUNTY
Ada vicinity
ADA COVERED BRIDGE
Across the Thornapple River
Mid–19th century

The Ada Covered Bridge is of wooden truss construction and measures 14 feet wide, by 15 feet high, by 125 feet long. It was built about 1867 and was extensively renovated in 1941. Only pedestrians use the bridge now.
County

KENT COUNTY
Grand Rapids
GRAND RAPIDS ART MUSEUM (ABRAM W. PIKE HOUSE)
230 Fulton Street, East
1844–1845

The Grand Rapids Art Museum is a frame, two-story, Greek Revival house with a gable roof. A two-story pedimented Doric tetrastyle portico with fluted columns fronts the main entrance, and there are two symmetrical, hip-roofed, one-story wings with Doric colonnades on either side. The interior was altered about 1920 and opened in 1924 as an art museum. A few years later the brick addition was constructed at the rear. Abram W. Pike, for whom the house was built, occupied it until 1906.
Private
HABS

KENT COUNTY
Grand Rapids
HERITAGE HILL HISTORIC DISTRICT
Bounded by Michigan Avenue on the north, Pleasant Street on the south, Union Avenue on the east, and by

Clarendon Place and Jefferson and Lafayette Avenues on the west
19th and 20th centuries

Heritage Hill Historic District is a 37-block area within Michigan's second largest city, Grand Rapids. Since the mid-19th century this area has acquired and retained a cohesive residential character unmarred by commercial intrusion. The city of Grand Rapids grew up on the banks of the Grand River, which furnished water power for mills and manufacturing plants, particularly furniture factories. Some buildings within the Heritage Hill District were built as early as the 1840's, and within 30 years it had become the most fashionable residential area of Grand Rapids. Outstanding houses, which run the gamut in style from Greek Revival to Prairie School, include a Greek Revival residence (540 Cherry Street, Southeast), an Italianate dwelling (434 Cherry Street, Southeast), the Gothic Revival Gilbert House (55 Lafayette Avenue, Southeast), and a home by Frank Lloyd Wright (450 Madison Avenue, Southeast).
Multiple public/private

KENT COUNTY
Grand Rapids
TURNER HOUSE (R. C. ALLEN, INC., EMPLOYEES' CLUBHOUSE)
731 Front Street, N.W.
c. 1845

The two-story Turner House is the only remaining residence of a group of mid-19th-century homes along Front Street. Eliphalet H. Turner, for whom the house was built, was an early settler of Grand Rapids. His house was constructed of local limestone from the Grand River. The masonry is ashlar. Ionic columns and sidelights frame the main doorway. Recent alterations (substitution of single lights for the original small pane windows and a frame addition at the rear) have changed the character of the house.
Private; not accessible to the public
HABS

KENT COUNTY
Grand Rapids vicinity
NORTON MOUND GROUP
2 miles south of Grand Rapids on Indian Mound Drive
c. 4 B.C.–A.D. 400

The Norton Mound Group is one of the best preserved of the Hopewell mounds in the western Great Lakes region. Originally consisting of some 40 mounds, 17 of which remain, the site was the center of Hopewellian culture in that area. As such, it represents the northward spread of this culture from the Illinois Valley—its point of origin. Excavations have uncovered numerous grave offerings: copper awls and beads, conch shell containers, deer antlers, worked beaver incisors, and chipped and ground stone artifacts.
Municipal
NHL

KEWEENAW COUNTY
Copper Harbor
FORT WILKINS
Fort Wilkins State Park
1844–1846, 1867–1870

By the Treaty of LaPointe (1842) the Chippewa Indians relinquished all claim to the land west of the Chocolay River near the present city of Marquette. Travelers had long before discovered plentiful mineral deposits (particularly copper) in the area, and one year after the treaty was signed a U.S. Mineral Land Agency was located at Copper Harbor. The miners needed protection, and in 1844 Secretary of War William Wilkins responded by authorizing the construction of a fort at Copper Harbor. The fort was garrisoned until 1846 and again from 1867 to 1870. Today a wooden stockade and thirteen original buildings remain. These are three officers' quarters, two company barracks, two kitchens, a hospital, a powder magazine, and various outbuildings. All are log covered by clapboard except the stone magazine.
State

LENAWEE COUNTY
Cambridge Junction
WALKER TAVERN (CAMBRIDGE STATE HISTORICAL PARK)
On U.S. 12
19th century

In 1825 Congress authorized construction of a road connecting Detroit and Chicago. This was the first major thoroughfare to penetrate Michigan's interior. Ten years later a road from La Plaisance Bay on Lake Erie intersected the Chicago road in Cambridge Township, and the settlement of Cambridge Junction grew up at the crossroads. A tavern was needed to serve travelers, and, by 1837, one was in operation. The original portion of the tavern is that nearest the road. Archeological and architectural evidence indicate that three major additions were made at the rear of the original structure. It is a simple, two-story frame building of hand-hewn white oak timbers. A piazza floored with flagstones surrounds the tavern on two sides. The state of Michigan is undertaking the restoration of the tavern to the period of the 1840's.
State

LIVINGSTON COUNTY
Howell
ANN ARBOR RAILWAY STATION
126 Wetmore Street
1896

The railroad depot in Howell was built for the new Toledo, Ann Arbor & Northern Michigan Railroad as it extended north from Ann Arbor through Livingston County. Howell was already served by the Detroit, Lansing & Northern Railroad, but it was hoped that competition for passengers and freight would increase prosperity. The station is a bracketed brick building with a central bay window on the track side. Interior ceilings are 18 feet high. In the summer of 1970 the structure was painted red with cream-colored trim and restored in preparation for its present use as a museum.
Private

MACKINAC COUNTY
Gros Cap vicinity
GROS CAP CEMETERY
Southeast of Gros Cap on U.S. 2
17th–19th centuries

During the latter years of the 17th century a band of Ottawa Indians engaged in the fur trade settled around West Moran Bay. A tribal cemetery adjoined the village, and burials were often made in an extended position with hands on the chest, possibly indicating conversion to Christianity. European trade goods and Christian or native religious articles were often interred with the bodies. In the 18th century the Indian settlement gradually disappeared, and the early grave sites are now scattered among modern markers of wood and stone. Indians, French Canadians, members of locally prominent families, as well as Alonso Cheeseman, founder of Gros Cap, lie side by side in the five-and-one-half-acre plot.
Municipal

MACKINAC COUNTY
Mackinac Island
FORT MACKINAC
Huron Road
18th and 19th centuries

A French outpost and trading center were established on the Straits of Mackinac in the mid-17th century. At the end of the French and Indian War (1763) the British gained control of the fort by treaty. During the American Revolution the British commander, Captain Patrick Sinclair, requested and received (May, 1780) permission to relocate the garrison in a more defensible position on Mackinac Island. Buildings were erected, defenses con-

structed, and men and supplies transported to the new site. However, the Treaty of Paris (1783) ceded the island to the United States, although American troops did not take possession until 1796. They completed the fortifications begun by Sinclair and built three-story blockhouses. For a brief period during the War of 1812 British forces recaptured Fort Mackinac, but it was returned to American hands by the Treaty of Ghent (1814). All present buildings were put up by the Americans except the Old Stone Quarters (Stone Officers Quarters). In 1875 the federal government designated most of Mackinac Island as a park. Twenty years later it was given to the state of Michigan. Since that time major restoration work has been undertaken to recreate the atmosphere of a frontier outpost c. 1820–1870.
State
HABS

MACKINAC COUNTY
Mackinac Island
GEARY, MATHEW, HOUSE
Market Street
19th century

The land for the Mathew Geary House was purchased by the American Fur Company in the early 1800's. With the decline of the fur trade in the late 1830's, the property was sold to private owners. Mathew Geary, important in local government, acquired the parcel in the mid–1840's and built the present house. The two-story clapboard dwelling rests upon a brick foundation and has a gable roof. Later additions include a central two-story columned porch with a balustraded balcony on the front facade, a one-story sunporch on the west, and a two-story addition to the rear.
State

MACKINAC COUNTY
Mackinac Island
MACKINAC ISLAND
Northeast across the Straits of Mackinac from Mackinaw City
1780

Mackinac Island changed hands three times before American control was secured by the Treaty of Ghent (1814). With the return of American control John Jacob Astor made this island the northern headquarters of his American Fur Company. Business boomed until the 1840's, but thereafter a change in the market and a scarcity of pelts lured hunters to other locales. On the island today there are numerous buildings and museums related to the fort, the fur trade, and community life, including the Biddle House, oldest in the Old Northwest.
Multiple public/private
NHL; HABS

MACKINAC COUNTY
Mackinac Island
MISSION CHURCH
Huron Street
1830

Mackinac Island was, by the 1820's, second in importance to Detroit as a center for trade and military operations in the Michigan territory. In 1823 William Montague Ferry, a missionary, came to Mackinac under the sponsorship of the United Foreign Missionary Society for the purpose of establishing an Indian boarding school. He was responsible for construction of a Mission House (1825) and, later, the Mission Church. The building is frame, patterned after colonial New England churches, with a belfry and a steeple which rises over 18 feet above ground level. The octagonal belfry has louvred openings. Inside, the first floor contains three rows of box pews, many original. Following the withdrawal of the American Fur Company in 1834, the population of the island declined, and the mission was formally closed three years later. It has since been used sporadically.
State

MACKINAC COUNTY
Mackinac Island
MISSION HOUSE
Huron Street
1825

In 1823 the Reverend William Montague Ferry came to Mackinac Island under the auspices of the American Board of Commissioners for Foreign Missions to establish an Indian boarding school. Attendance averaged 150 pupils a year, and within two years new quarters were completed. The Mission House was an all-purpose U-shaped building of wood on a stone foundation. Public rooms were located in the center, and the students and the mission family lived in the two wings. A third story was added later. Eventually the mission became very expensive to maintain, and the Indians retreated inland. Ferry left in 1834, and the mission closed three years later. In 1845 the building was remodeled as a hotel and served as such until the 1960's.
Private; not accessible to the public

MACKINAC COUNTY
Mackinac Island
STUART, ROBERT, HOUSE (AGENCY HOUSE OF THE AMERICAN FUR COMPANY)
Market Street
1817

John Jacob Astor organized the American Fur Company in April, 1808. Less than

ten years later, after failure of his Astoria venture, Astor sent Robert Stuart and Ramsay Crooks west to manage fur trade operations in the Great Lakes area. Eventually Stuart became head of this operation, which totally dominated the economy of Mackinac Island. He remained in his post until 1834, and shortly thereafter the fur trade operations shut down. The Stuart House, originally an agent's residence, has been restored. It was one of four structures forming the nucleus of the fur trade empire (agency warehouse, trading post, and clerks' quarters). It is a two-story frame building with a gable roof containing dormers. Many of the window panes date from construction as do the wooden cross and Bible doors and the fanlight above the main entrance. A kitchen and storage rooms were located in the basement, and agency clerks were housed on the second floor.
Municipal
HABS

MACKINAC COUNTY
St. Ignace
LASENEN SITE
690 S. State Street
17th century

Excavation of the Lasenen Site has yielded human bones and artifacts such as knives, scissors, mission medallions and rings, traded and native beads, and shell gorgets, all roughly dating from the period 1670 to 1700. The 24 burial pits at the site, many unexcavated, were dug into sterile glacial gravels. Most graves are rectangular in shape, measure three to five feet on each side, and are either lined with rocks or unlined, although at least one pit shows evidence of a wooden plank lining. In most cases the burials are multiple and represent delayed interments of partially decomposed skeletal elements. The site should yield information regarding aboriginal contact with Europeans.
Private

MACKINAC COUNTY
St. Ignace
ST. IGNACE MISSION
State and Marquette Streets, Marquette Park
1671

Ten years before the erection of the first Fort Michilimackinac, Père Jacques Marquette helped to establish a mission on Mackinac Island which was moved to the northern shore of the mainland the following year. In 1741 it was moved to the southern shore of the Straits of Mackinac. According to his desires, Marquette's body was brought here in 1677, two years after his death. Though the grave site was lost after a fire in 1706,

it was rediscovered in 1877. His remains were reburied on the site of the mission's chapel.
Private
NHL

MACOMB COUNTY
Romeo
ROMEO HISTORIC DISTRICT
19th and 20th centuries

Settlement of Romeo began about 1822, and the original village was called Hoxie's Settlement. A plat was made of Romeo in 1830, and the earlier log cabins were being replaced by frame structures. Situated in a prosperous farming area, Romeo was reached by the Michigan Air Line Railroad prior to 1873. Today the town retains its 19th-century atmosphere little disturbed by modern intrusions. Architecture representing almost every major style popular between 1830 and 1910 is evident along the streets of Romeo. Examples are the Dr. Watson Loud House (264 N. Main Street), which is Carpenter Gothic; the John Dyar House (168 First Street), Italianate; the David Rowley House (307 Chandler Street), which has unusual and ornately carved bargeboards; and the Charles M. Tackels House (440 N. Main Street), Eastlake style.
Multiple public/private

MACOMB COUNTY
Warren vicinity
HOLCOMBE SITE
Northeast of Warren, SW 1/4 SW 1/4 sec. 23, T. 2 N., R. 12 E.
Pre-Columbian

Habitation dates for the Holcombe Site indicate that men lived here 11,000 years ago. Temporally and culturally the site is affiliated with a number of others located in Wisconsin, Michigan, Massachusetts, Vermont, and Virginia. It has been postulated that they represent some of man's earliest habitation in central and eastern North America.
Private

MUSKEGON COUNTY
Muskegon
HACKLEY, CHARLES H., HOUSE
484 W. Webster Avenue
1887–1889

The three-story frame Hackley House is unusual for its juxtaposition of masses, and the irregularity of shape produced by the use of gables, dormers, and a tower. Three Jacobean chimneys project from the roof. Some windows are ornamented with stained glass, and round and oval windows and arches are plentiful. Profuse ornamentation abounds on the interior —carved, turned, and molded colonnettes, spindles, and panels. A coach house behind the dwelling was shared with the Hume family and is designed half in the Queen Anne style of the Hackley House and the other half like the Hume home. Charles H. Hackley (1837–1905) and his partner Thomas Hume owned large lumber mills. The Hackley House remained in the builder's family until 1943, when it was donated to the American Red Cross.
Private

OAKLAND COUNTY
Franklin
VILLAGE OF FRANKLIN HISTORIC DISTRICT
Bounded approximately by the Franklin River, Bowden Street, Romany Way, Scenic Highway, Franklin Road, and a line extending 300 feet north of, and parallel to, Fourteen Mile Road
19th century

Franklin Village was founded c. 1825 and received its present name in 1828. The historic district is confined within the boundaries of the 1870 community. Approximately 26 properties within this area are considered to be of outstanding historic or architectural significance. A few of these date from the mid–19th century, but the majority were built later in the century. Two structures which housed early businesses, the Broughton Wagon Shop and the Van Every mill, are still standing in essentially their original condition. The uniqueness of the village lies in its high concentration of only slightly modified early buildings, rarely found in the suburban area of Detroit.
Multiple public/private

OAKLAND COUNTY
Ortonville
ORTONVILLE MILL
366 Mill Street
1856

Amos Orton settled in Oakland County about 1848 and began operating a sawmill. In 1852 he constructed a feed mill just above the sawmill and the area began attracting settlers. A small community grew up and was named for its founder, who served as first postmaster, township supervisor, and justice of the peace. The present mill replaced the 1852 structure. It is two-and-one-half-stories high and has a frame of hand-hewn timbers. Present measurements are 36 by 108 feet (the western room is a later addition). In 1889 the mill was converted to the roller process.
Private

OAKLAND COUNTY
Pontiac
MYRICK-PALMER HOUSE
223 W. Huron Street
Mid–19th century

The Myrick-Palmer House is an Italian Villa style frame residence. The front part of the house is cube-shaped, and the rear section is an L-shaped service wing. Double brackets support the hip roof, and ornate wooden balconies decorate many of the second-story windows. Charles Palmer, second owner of the house, was an educator and businessman involved in mining, railroads, and canal building. He bought the house in early 1860's.
Private; not accessible to the public

OAKLAND COUNTY
Pontiac
WISNER HOUSE (PINE GROVE)
405 Oakland Avenue
1845

The Wisner House was built for Moses Wisner, governor of Michigan from 1859 to 1860. He redecorated and enlarged the house before using it as his official residence. The Greek Revival house is composed of a two-story main section with a rear kitchen wing and a single-story hip-roofed wing at the side. A colonnade of fluted Doric columns runs around this wing, and a flat-roofed, similar, Doric portico ornaments the main entrance of the house. The entire house is brick, and the pattern in the kitchen wing suggests that this may be the oldest part. The smokehouse and root cellar to the rear have been restored.
Private

OTTAWA COUNTY
Holland
THIRD REFORMED CHURCH
110 W. 12th Street
1873–1874

The Third Reformed Church was built according to the designs of Holland architect John R. Kleyn. Its Gothic features create a light, symmetrical, and graceful structure, matched by few Michigan churches of the late 19th century. Its balloon frame is covered with board and batten siding and surmounted by a gable roof. The north or main facade contains a large tripartite arched window and a small rose window in the gable above it. A square Gothic tower, the spire of which rises 125 feet, dominates the northeastern corner. Buttresses are spaced along both sides of the building between slender arched windows. Major renovation of the structure took place in 1967–1968.
Private

ST. CLAIR COUNTY
Port Huron
ST. CLAIR RIVER TUNNEL
St. Clair River between Port Huron,
Michigan, and Sarnia, Ontario
1890

The St. Clair River Tunnel provided the first railroad link between the American midwest and the St. Lawrence River valley. Opened on September 19, 1891, it was the last link in the Grand Trunk Railway connecting Port Huron and Sarnia, Ontario. Joseph Hobson directed construction of the tunnel and in so doing employed three new tunneling techniques necessitated by the presence of quicksand and the existence of a shallow overburden above the planned tunnel route. Used in combination for the first time in North America were the Beach tunnel shield (designed in 1868), a cast iron lining, and compressed air. The tunnel is basically an iron tube measuring 21 feet in diameter and containing a single standard gauge railroad track.
Private; not accessible to the public

SANILAC COUNTY
Minden City vicinity
SANILAC PETROGLYPHS
Off Germania Road, 11 miles west of
Minden City

Located near the confluence of the north and south forks of the Cass River, the Sanilac Petroglyphs are carved into the surface of a wide exposure of sandstone bedrock. The drawings represent men, animals, birds, and mythological creatures. Residents of the area were not aware that the petroglyphs existed until late in the previous century. The rate of weathering is impossible to judge so the exact age of the carvings is not known. They are believed to be only a few centuries old. Similar carvings by aborigines have been found in Wisconsin, Minnesota, and Great Lakes Canada.
Private

SHIAWASSEE COUNTY
Durand
GRAND TRUNK RAILWAY STATION
200 Railroad Street
1905

Located at the juncture of several railroads, the town of Durand increased from a population of 250 to 3,000 between 1887 and 1905. At the turn of the century it was described as the busiest railroad town in Michigan, besides Detroit, having 35 passenger, nine local, and 100 freight trains passing through daily. The Grand Trunk Station is a reminder of a time when 50 percent of the town's population was employed by the railway company. Constructed of vitrified brick, the two-and-one-half-story structure measures 244 feet by 49 feet. The northwest side of the station has an extended porch and symmetrical conical roofs atop rounded bays.
Private

WASHTENAW COUNTY
Ann Arbor
PRESIDENT'S HOUSE, UNIVERSITY OF MICHIGAN
815 South University, University of
Michigan campus
1839–1840, Alexander Jackson
Davis; 1860's (altered)

The President's House is the oldest building on the University of Michigan campus. It is the only remaining one of the six original buildings constructed around 1840. Initially, it was a two-and-one-half-story rectangular house. In the 1860's the half story was raised, the roof altered to a truncated hip, double brackets added under the eaves, and the cupola replaced by a balustrade. Between 1864 and 1921 the kitchen wing, library wing, a side porch, sun parlor, and rear study were added. The house was built of brick covered with stucco and with the 1860's alterations assumed an Italianate appearance. It has been the official residence of university presidents since the position was created in 1852, with the exception of one administration (1909 to 1920).
Private; not accessible to the public

WASHTENAW COUNTY
Ann Arbor
WHITE, ORRIN, HOUSE (ROBERT HODGES RESIDENCE)
2940 Fuller Road
1836–1840

The walls of the Orrin White House exhibit the distinct traits of at least two of three principal types of cobblestone architecture used first in upstate New York and later carried to parts of the Middle West. In 1836 White constructed the first story of his L-shaped house (the present rear wing) of small fieldstones crudely matched in size. The second story, added later, is composed of cobblestone uniformly matched in size and contour. Well-matched oval stones laid in a herringbone pattern were used in the front wall of the house. Four years were necessary to complete the entire house. The small stones and crude mortar utilized required long drying periods and the skill of an accomplished mason.
Private; not accessible to the public

WAYNE COUNTY
Dearborn
COMMANDANT'S QUARTERS
21950 Michigan Avenue
1833–1875

The Commandant's Quarters is one of the 11 original buildings of the Detroit Arsenal at Dearborn and the only example of genuine Federal architecture in Michigan. Completed in 1837, the arsenal was intended to serve in the event of an attack from troops in British North America or an Indian uprising. The two-and-one-half-story brick structure has a slate roof with four chimneys, stone window lintels and sills, and a stone water table. Throughout the life of the Detroit Arsenal, the Commandant's Quarters was a center of social and cultural life for Dearborn and Detroit society. In 1875 the Arsenal was abandoned by order of Congress. The Commandant's Quarters was thereafter used as a library, town hall, and newspaper office. The Dearborn Historical Commission acquired it in 1949.
Municipal
HABS

WAYNE COUNTY
Dearborn
FAIR LANE (HENRY FORD ESTATE)
4901 Evergreen Road
1915, W. H. Van Tine

Henry Ford revolutionized transportation in America by mass-producing an inexpensive and reliable automobile. The Model T Ford, which appeared in 1908, introduced the automobile age. By 1914 about 250,000 "Tin Lizzies" were being sold every year. The Ford family lived at Fair Lane from 1915 until Mrs. Ford's death in 1950. Built by Henry Ford, the 56–room house of Indiana limestone is essentially unchanged. It is presently used as a conference center for the University of Michigan's Dearborn campus.
State; not accessible to the public
NHL

WAYNE COUNTY
Dearborn
GREENFIELD VILLAGE AND THE HENRY FORD MUSEUM
Bounded by Michigan Avenue on the
north, Village Road on the south,
Southfield Expressway on the east,
and Oakland Boulevard on the west
17th, 18th, and 19th centuries

Collectively, Greenfield Village and the Henry Ford Museum are known as the Edison Institute. Greenfield Village was intended to be a symbolic representation of what to Henry Ford was the dominant theme of American life: the interaction of

agriculture and industry. Greenfield Village is an open-air museum composed of nearly one hundred buildings, structures, and objects which represent no particular period, architectural style, or mode of living. The Henry Ford Museum is an indoor continuation of Greenfield. Attention is paid to the fine arts, but the bulk of the exhibit space is occupied by machinery with special emphasis upon transportation. Henry Ford's birthplace, Thomas Edison's Menlo Park compound, a tintype studio, and a Sandwich glass plant are examples of buildings in the village.
Private

WAYNE COUNTY
Detroit
CHRIST CHURCH, DETROIT
960 E. Jefferson Avenue
19th century, Gordon W. Lloyd

The congregation of Christ Church was organized in 1845. Christ Church itself is the oldest Protestant church in Detroit still on its original site. A wooden edifice was first built to house the worshipers, but this structure was torn down about 1860 when a stone chapel was begun. The back of the present church is this earlier stone chapel, and the church as it appears now was completed about 1880. Shaped like a Latin cross, Christ Church has walls of limestone ashlar and dressed sandstone trim. There is a 24–foot by 17–foot window in the main facade, and two crocketed pinnacles to the left of the facade are balanced by a four-stage tower to the right. All woodwork inside (except roof timbers and choir pews) is butternut. Hammerbeam trusses support the ceiling. Arches terminate in carved angels holding shields, and drop-light fixtures hang from the shields. There are many stained glass windows, and the main altar is white and brown marble.
Private
HABS

WAYNE COUNTY
Detroit
FORT WAYNE
6053 W. Jefferson Avenue
19th century

Fort Wayne was established by an act of Congress in 1841 at a strategic bend in the Detroit River. It was erected in an effort to insure protection from a British attack from Canada. Present structures include a massive three-and-one-half-story Georgian style barracks (1848), the powder magazine (1848), and the original brick wall. Surrounding the existing structures and the central parade ground are thick masonry walls and earthworks which form a square with bastions at the corners, vaulted casemate galleries, and a triangu-lar masonry demilune south of the earthworks. Lieutenant Montgomery C. Meigs, Union quartermaster-general during the Civil War, designed the fort, which was officially occupied by various commands of the U.S. Army for 88 years. Since 1950 the well-preserved fort has served as a military museum.
Municipal
HABS

WAYNE COUNTY
Detroit
FREER, CHARLES LANG, HOUSE (MERRILL-PALMER INSTITUTE OF HUMAN DEVELOPMENT AND FAMILY LIFE)
71 E. Ferry Avenue
1887, Wilson Eyre, Jr.

Wilson Eyre designed the Charles Lang Freer House as his own interpretation of H. H. Richardson's shingle style. The ground story is stone while the upper story and a half are faced with dark stained shingles. Horizontal lines are emphasized by the first-floor overhang and by projecting eaves at all roof levels. The exterior walls are enlivened by projecting balconies, bay windows, and enclosed porches. The 22 rooms contain 12 fireplaces. Charles Lang Freer amassed a fortune through part ownership of the Peninsular Car Works. He was a connoisseur of oriental art, and his collection is presently housed in the Freer Gallery in Washington, D.C.
Private

WAYNE COUNTY
Detroit
MARINERS' CHURCH
170 E. Jefferson Avenue
1849, Calvin N. Otis

The will of Mrs. Julia Ann Anderson, who died in October, 1842, provided that the residue of her estate was to be used for construction of a mariners' church near the Detroit docks. The Michigan legislature chartered a corporation to carry out these provisions. As financial support was going to be difficult, the church was planned to include commercial enterprises on the ground level. The two-story Gothic Revival building has walls of rough gray rubble limestone. Buttresses and Tudor-arched windows are part of the Gothic design. There is a twelve-foot rose window in the west wall. Interior framing is pine, and all woodwork is walnut. The church was moved about 900 feet to its present site in 1955.
Private

WAYNE COUNTY
Detroit
ORCHESTRA HALL
3711 Woodward Avenue
1919, Charles Howard Crane

Orchestra Hall was designed as a home for the Detroit Symphony Orchestra, organized in 1872. The building is a brick and limestone structure. Above the marquee on Woodward Avenue is an elaborate grouping of five windows framed by pilasters supporting an entablature. The frieze at the roofline contains exaggerated swags, and a large cartouche projects from the center of the cornice. Inside, the auditorium was decorated in ivory with delicate tracings of gold and silver; foyers are paneled, and acoustics are excellent due to the unusual manner in which the ceiling is stepped. Seating is for 2,200. The symphony moved to the Masonic Temple in 1939, and the building has since served as a movie theater and a church.
Private

WAYNE COUNTY
Detroit
SIBLEY HOUSE
976 E. Jefferson Avenue
1848

Sarah Sproat Sibley, widow of Judge Solomon Sibley, built this two-story Greek Revival house for herself and her two daughters. A one-story, pedimented portico shelters the main entrance, and the windows on the first floor front are also pedimented. Inside, the house has a central hall plan, and some alterations have been made. In 1925 the property was sold to Christ Church and now serves as the rectory.
Private
HABS

WAYNE COUNTY
Detroit
WEST CANFIELD HISTORIC DISTRICT
Canfield Avenue Between 2nd and 3rd Streets
Late 19th and early 20th centuries

In the early 1870's West Canfield was one of the newly developed streets at the northern border of Detroit. West Canfield was named for Captain Augustus Canfield, a West Point graduate active in canal construction at Sault Ste Marie. Gradually this section became one of the best residential areas in the city. The present historic district is one block containing more than 30 buildings and structures, principally of brick. Fifteen houses were built in this block between 1871 and 1894, and there has been little recent intrusion by new structures. The predominant architectural style is Queen Anne.
Multiple public/private

Minnesota

Old Federal Courts Building, St. Paul, Minnesota.
Minnesota Historical Society

Alexander Ramsey House,
St. Paul, Minnesota.
Minnesota Historical Society

Mayowood, Rochester, Minnesota.
Olmstead County Historical Society

BROWN COUNTY
New Ulm
FEDERAL POST OFFICE BUILDING
Center Street and Broadway
1909–1910, James Knox Taylor

The New Ulm Post Office is an unusual public building which noticeably reflects the European architectural traditions of the town's early settlers. Leaving homes in Germany, Switzerland, and Luxembourg, they founded New Ulm in 1854. Funds for the present post office were authorized in 1906. Steeply stepped gables topped by blunt finials ornament the roofline, and the building's walls are alternating courses of red brick and gray-white terra cotta. Below the first floor the walls are brick and granite. The roof is steeply pitched, and cartouches and scrolls ornament the gables.
Federal

CASS COUNTY (also in Crow Wing and Morrison counties)
Barrows vicinity
CROW WING STATE PARK
2 miles southwest of Barrows on U.S. 371
18th and 19th centuries

Situated on the Mississippi River, the Crow Wing site was inhabited first by Dakota Indians. Chippewa Indians, coming south from the Great Lakes, drove out the Dakotas in the 18th century and settled on their lands. French fur traders, soon followed by British and Americans, arrived at the mouth of the Crow Wing River in the late 1760's. A town, which became an important trade center on the upper Mississippi, had been established by 1847. A peak of prosperity was reached in the 1850's, and Crow Wing served briefly as the county seat (1857–1860) of Crow Wing County. Railroads bypassed the town during the 1860's and 1870's and people moved away. By 1880 the village was practically deserted. Most buildings were located directly opposite the mouth of the Crow Wing River, but none are standing today.
State

CHISAGO COUNTY
Taylors Falls
MUNCH-ROOS HOUSE
360 Bench Street
1853

The Munch-Roos House is a frame structure composed of a two-story main block plus a one-story kitchen wing at the west side. The main entrance has sidelights and a five-light transom. A full pediment on the street facade contains a semicircular louvred wooden fan. The main entrance is off-center. Emil, Adolph, and Paul Munch emigrated to America from Prussia in 1849 and settled in Taylors Falls in 1852. They operated a carpentry shop north of the house until 1857. Oscar Roos, whose family owned the house for almost 100 years prior to 1965, was a Swede and came to Minnesota in 1850.
Private; not accessible to the public

CHISAGO COUNTY
Taylors Falls
TAYLORS FALLS PUBLIC LIBRARY
417 Bench Street
1854

John Jacob Spengler built this one-story frame building as a residence and tailor shop. Later alterations and the addition of wooden ornament gave the building a late 19th-century appearance. Above the front door is a Gothic style canopy console, and the wall surface of the front gable is covered with hexagonal shingles. There are scalloped vergeboards on the side elevations, and the trim generally could be called Eastlake style. The front room has a notable barrel vault ceiling. The Taylors Falls Library Association purchased and remodeled the building in 1887.
Municipal
HABS

CLEARWATER COUNTY
Lake Itasca vicinity
ITASCA BISON SITE
NW 1/4 NW 1/4 sec. 22, T. 143 N., R. 36 W.
Pre-Columbian

At this site archeologists have found the only evidence in Minnesota linking man with the extinct *bison occidentalis*, which was much larger than the modern buffalo. Indians dried the meat for food, dressed the hides for clothing and shelter, and fashioned piercing and scraping tools from the bones. These nomadic hunters are believed to have wandered about in groups of less than 12 families. Archeologists date the kill site between 5500 and 7500 B.C. Hunters probably drove the animals into a swampy area where they could be killed with primitive weapons.
State

COOK COUNTY
Grand Marais vicinity
GRAND PORTAGE NATIONAL MONUMENT
38 miles north of Grand Marais
Late 18th century

Grand Portage, lying on the western shore of Lake Superior in northeastern Minnesota, was the most important shipping and distributing center of the late 1700's for operations of the North West Company of Montreal, Canada. The "great carrying place" was a nine-mile trail between the log post on the lake shore and a point above the unnavigable falls and rapids of the Pigeon River. This strategic portage, used by Indians before the advent of white men, connected the Great Lakes with the interior network of waterways to western Canada and served as a principal route for explorers, missionaries, fur traders, and military expeditions. A hewn-timber building with stockade, blockhouses, and a "great dining hall" has been reconstructed on the excavated site of the once-great depot and trading post.
Federal/non-federal
NPS; 770 acres

COTTONWOOD COUNTY
Jeffers vicinity
JEFFERS PETROGLYPH SITE
N 1/2 NW 1/4 sec. 9, T. 107 N., R. 35 W.
Pre-Columbian

Southern Minnesota contains many petroglyph sites, but the Jeffers Site has what experts consider to be the finest examples in the state. The figures were probably carved by members of the Dakota nation because many symbols used exhibit Dakota characteristics. Carved on an outcropping of Sioux quartzite, the figures are in excellent condition and represent animals of the area —fish, birds, turtles, bison, and rattlesnakes. There are also representations of human figures. Carvings were made with a round pointed tool, a chisel-like instrument, or a combination of the two.
State

DAKOTA COUNTY
FORT SNELLING
Reference—see Hennepin County

DAKOTA COUNTY
Hastings
LE DUC HOUSE
1629 Vermillion Street
1862–1865

William Gates Le Duc built this home which exhibits the influence of designs by Andrew J. Downing. The house is a three-story limestone structure with a central tower. The scrollwork trim along the eaves, the pointed arch windows, and the pitched roofs are typical of Gothic Revival architecture. There are ten fireplaces in the house.
State

DAKOTA COUNTY
Mendota
MENDOTA HISTORIC DISTRICT
Bounded roughly on the west by government lot 2; on the southwest by Int. 55; on the southeast by Sibley Highway; on the northeast by D Street; and on the north by the Minnesota River
19th century

Henry H. Sibley, fur trader and politician, came to Mendota in 1835 as an agent of the American Fur Company. At that time Mendota was composed of a few log huts. Sibley built the first stone house in 1836, and another was constructed by Jean Baptiste Faribault, also a fur trader, in 1839. Mendota was formally organized ten years later, served as county seat for Dakota County from 1854 to 1857, and was a contender for state capital. Buildings within the historic district which date from the time of Mendota's economic and political prominence are the Sibley and Faribault houses, both built of limestone and three stories high; St. Peter's Roman Catholic Church (1853), also built of limestone; and the two-story brick Depuis House (1854), built by Sibley's secretary. Sibley represented Minnesota Territory in Congress and was elected first governor of the state (1858).
Private
HABS

GOODHUE COUNTY
Red Wing vicinity
BARTRON SITE
NW 1/4 NW 1/4 sec. 9, T. 113 N., R. 15 W., on the southern portion of Prairie Island in the Mississippi River bottomlands
Pre-Columbian

The Bartron Site contains the largest number of undisturbed prehistoric burial mounds in the Red Wing area. It is also one of two major Mississippian village culture sites remaining on the Minnesota side of the upper Mississippi River valley. The site is an open area which has been used as pasture but not cultivated. Such relatively undisturbed sites offer possible evidence of house form, village arrangement, and often yield unbroken artifacts. Archeological investigations were carried on in 1948, 1968, and 1969.
Private

GOODHUE COUNTY
Welch vicinity
FORT SWENEY SITE
SE 1/4 sec. 28, T. 113 N., R. 16 W., across the Cannon River from Welch
Pre-Columbian

Situated on a high hill overlooking the Cannon River valley, the Fort Sweney site contains 41 pits, mounds, and other earthworks. Some excavation has been undertaken leading archeologists to believe that this was a burial ground or ceremonial place. In 1960 portions of one burial mound, two pits, and two cross sections of the surrounding embankment were excavated. The site still remains relatively undisturbed.
Private

HENNEPIN COUNTY
Bloomington
POND, GIDEON H., HOUSE
401 E. 104th Street
1856

Gideon H. Pond, a Presbyterian missionary from Connecticut, came to Minnesota in 1834 to minister to the Dakota Indians. After establishing missions near Lake Harriet and Lac Qui Parle, he finally settled in the area of present-day Bloomington. With his brother, Samuel, Pond developed an alphabet of the Sioux language in order to translate Scripture. At their popular Oak Grove Mission in Bloomington, the Pond brothers preached to the Indians on Sunday mornings and to the whites on Sunday afternoons. In 1856 Pond built the simple, two-story, rectangular, brick house overlooking the Minnesota River which he used as his private residence and as a mission schoolhouse. The house is basically unaltered, although a two-story frame addition containing a kitchen and bathroom was erected in 1910.
Private; not accessible to the public.
HABS

HENNEPIN COUNTY
Edina
CAHILL SCHOOL
Corner of Eden Avenue and Minn. 100
1864

The Cahill School was built to serve grades one through eight of Hennepin County School District No. 16. Named for Father Thomas Cahill, an early Catholic missionary in the Northwest, the one-room schoolhouse also served as Edina's community center. Both Catholic and Lutheran church services were held here at different times. District 16 was annexed by District 17 in 1953, but kindergarten classes continued to be held in this build-

ing until 1963. Soon thereafter the town purchased the school and moved it to the present location. Measuring 26 feet by 40 feet, the Cahill School is frame. An original chimney has been removed.
Municipal

HENNEPIN COUNTY
Edina
GRANGE HALL
Corner of Eden Avenue and Minn. 100
1879

Minnehaha Grange No. 398 is the oldest subordinate grange in Minnesota. Organized on December 12, 1873, it was the center for much of the civic and social life of agricultural Edina. Prior to incorporation of the town (in 1888), organizational meetings were held in the Grange Hall, and after incorporation council meetings and elections took place here until the town hall was built. The one-story frame structure has been moved twice. The front entrance has been altered, but the original dimensions (26 feet by 12 feet) have not. Two woodburning stoves in the main meeting room are still in place. The Grange Hall continues to serve its original purpose.
Private

HENNEPIN COUNTY
Minneapolis
ATWATER, ISAAC, HOUSE
1607 S. 5th Street
Mid–19th century

The Gothic Revival Atwater House is a frame cottage with a steep gable roof and ornate bargeboards at the gable ends. A porch on the north and east elevations features sawn wood ornamentation. Interior alterations have been made, and two additions have been built at the rear of the house. Isaac Atwater moved to Minnesota Territory in 1850 to practice law. He became an associate justice of the Minnesota Supreme Court in 1857.
Private; not accessible to the public

HENNEPIN COUNTY
Minneapolis
BUTLER BROTHERS BUILDING
1st Avenue North at 6th Street
1906–1908, Harry Wild Jones

The Butler Brothers Building is a nine-story warehouse and office building. Its exterior appears austere and simple, an effect produced by the skillful handling of scale and proportion. Mass and the sensitive integration of decorative elements are important aspects of the design. The building is faced with a deep wine-red brick. Window openings are grouped vertically through the use of recessed brick

spandrels and pointed segmental arches on the top floor. A brick frieze above and below the second-story windows provides a horizontal accent.
Private; not accessible to the public

HENNEPIN COUNTY
Minneapolis
MINNEHAHA STATE PARK
South of Minnehaha Parkway between Hiawatha Avenue and the Mississippi River
19th century

Minnehaha Park comprises 170 acres and contains several sites of local interest. A former channel of the Mississippi River now forms the Minnehaha Glen, and Minnehaha Falls, immortalized in Henry Wadsworth Longfellow's poem "The Song of Hiawatha," is within the park. The Minehaha Station of the Minnesota Central Railway was constructed in the 1870's and is now within the park. It is the only such structure of its kind in the city. Also inside the park are the Stevens House, built by John M. Stevens, which was the first dwelling constructed on the Minneapolis townsite; the R. F. Jones House, a replica of the Longfellow House in Cambridge, Massachusetts; and the site of a mill built by Ard Godfrey in 1835 or 1854. The first land for the park was acquired by the city in 1889.
Municipal
HABS

HENNEPIN COUNTY
Minneapolis
PILLSBURY A MILL
Main Street and 3rd Avenue, S.E.
1881

The Pillsbury A Mill symbolizes the role of Minneapolis as the chief flour milling center of the United States from 1880 to 1930. At the time of its completion, it was the largest mill in the world. Beginning with a daily capacity of 5,000 barrels, the mill had increased the output to 14,000 barrels by 1905. The six-story mill, with foundation side walls of limestone and rough coursed ashlar walls, is still in active use.
Private; not accessible to the public
NHL; HABS

HENNEPIN COUNTY
Minneapolis
ST. ANTHONY FALLS HISTORIC DISTRICT
The district lies on both sides of the Mississippi River from the Plymouth Avenue Bridge on the northwest to 10th Avenue South (west bank) and 6th Avenue Southeast (east bank) on the southeast; it extends onto the east river shore as far as University Avenue, and onto the west river shore to 2nd Street South

St. Anthony Falls were discovered and named by Father Louis Hennepin in 1680. The 35-foot falls are the most abrupt drop in the Mississippi River's 2,200-mile course. By 1823 the water power of the falls had been partially harnessed to operate saw- and gristmills. The town of St. Anthony was platted in 1849, and by 1872 it had been absorbed by Minneapolis. Flour mills rapidly replaced the earlier sawmills, and Minneapolis became the nation's largest grain milling center. Engineers then covered the waterfall with a concrete apron to control both water-power and erosion. Presently the tremendous power of the falls is used to generate electricity. The historic district contains primarily warehouses and industrial facilities interspersed with a few dwellings. Sights worthy of mention within the district are cobblestoned Old Main Street; the Pillsbury A Mill (1881, a National Historic Landmark), at 116 Third Avenue Southeast; the North Star Woolen Mills (1864), First and Second Streets South on Sixth Avenue South; the Hall and Dann Barrel Company (1880), Third Avenue South between First and Second Streets South; the Stone Arch Bridge (1882–1883), believed to be the only bridge of its kind spanning the Mississippi; and Eastman Flats (c. 1877), a short row of limestone dwellings with cut stone trim and mansard roofs.
Multiple public/private
HABS

HENNEPIN COUNTY
St. Louis Park
ST. LOUIS PARK STATION
W. 36th Street and Alabama Avenue
c. 1887

The St. Louis Park Station was built by the Chicago, Milwaukee, St. Paul & Pacific Railroad to connect the newly incorporated village of St. Louis Park with Minneapolis. Passenger service on the line continued until 1955, and freight was received and shipped from the station until 1968. The building is of frame construction and is divided into three sections: the passenger section, the office, and the freight section. An asphalt roof was put on in recent years, but no other changes have been made. If the city gains possession of the station, it must be moved to another location more accessible to the public and more suitable as a visitor site.
Private; not accessible to the public

HENNEPIN COUNTY (also in Dakota County)
St. Paul vicinity
FORT SNELLING
Bounded irregularly by Minnehaha Park (north), the Mississippi River (north), Government Lot 2 (east), the east-west quarterline of sec. 28, T. 28 N., R. 23 W. (south), the airport (south), and a line parallel to and 600 feet northwest of Bloomington Road (west)
1820–1824

Zebulon Montgomery Pike arrived at the confluence of the Mississippi and Minnesota rivers in August, 1805. He later recommended the site to Secretary of War John C. Calhoun as a strategic one for the location of a fort. A camp was established here in 1819 by federal troops, who moved one mile upstream the following spring. Colonel Josiah Snelling supervised construction of the fort, which was later to bear his name. Fourteen stone buildings and two log structures within a ten-foot stone wall formed the nucleus of what was to become one of the most important frontier outposts in the area north and west of the Mississippi River. Settlers and trappers heading west outfitted here, Winnebago, Chippewa, and Sioux Indian activities were observed and dealt with here, and trade relations between Indians and whites were supervised by Fort Snelling personnel. Troops trained at the fort during the Civil War and World Wars I and II. Decommissioned in 1946, Fort Snelling is now administered by the Veterans Administration.
Multiple state/federal

HOUSTON COUNTY
Brownsville
EMANUEL EVANGELICAL LUTHERAN CHURCH (METHODIST EPISCOPAL CHURCH)
Main Street
Mid–19th century

The present Emanuel Evangelical Lutheran Church was one of the first frame buildings in Brownsville, which was settled in 1848. Set upon a stone foundation, the church is of board and batten construction. A local craftsman's interpretation of Gothic Revival architecture is evident in the tall pointed windows and doorway. The structure has served as a town hall, a church, and a schoolhouse.
Private; not accessible to the public

LAKE COUNTY
Two Harbors vicinity
SPLIT ROCK LIGHTHOUSE
About 20 miles northeast of Two
Harbors on U.S. 61
1909

Congress authorized the construction of
the Split Rock Lighthouse in 1907, five
years after Minnesota's Mesabi Iron
Range had been in operation. Cargoes of
iron ore as well as the iron deposits in the
lake basin caused the compass needles on
ore-carrying ships to deflect greatly from
true north. Thus thrown off course, ships
frequently ran aground in the shallows of
the rocky coastline. The lighthouse was
built as a navigational aid. The construction itself was a feat of engineering and lo-
gistics since there were no roads in the region, and men and materials had to be
transported by ship and hauled up the face
of the 124–foot cliff. The site is located on
a 7.6–acre tract which includes the octagonal brick light tower, still housing the
original two-paneled lens manufactured in
Paris, an attached service building, fog-
signal building, fuel-storage sheds, and
frame dwellings. There have been no
major changes at the site in the past 60
years even though the lighthouse is no
longer in operation.
Federal

LE SUEUR COUNTY
Le Sueur
MAYO, DR. WILLIAM W., HOUSE
118 N. Main Street
1859–1864

Dr. William Mayo came to Minnesota in
1854 from England and built this home
for his family. In a small office above the
front door, Dr. Mayo carried on his practice for nine years before going to
Rochester, Minnesota, as an army surgeon. His family joined him in 1864 and
the Le Sueur house was sold. Dr. Mayo's
two sons, William J. and Charles H., were
the founders of the Mayo Clinic in
Rochester. The house itself is a simple
two-story frame structure with Gothic gables.
Municipal

MILLE LACS COUNTY
Vineland
KATHIO SITE
U.S. 169, Mille Lacs-Kathio State
Park
c. 1640

Kathio, the ancestral home of a part of the
present-day Dakota Indians, was an important contact site between them and the

French. About 1740 the Dakotas lost the
site to the Chippewa tribe, which still
remains in the area. The Dakotas, more
commonly known as Sioux, moved south
and west, and figured prominently in the
early history of the plains and the Rocky
Mountains states. Archeological findings
at the site substantiate the Dakota claim
that the Mille Lacs region was their homeland.
State
NHL

MILLE LACS COUNTY
Vineland vicinity
COOPER SITE
On the south bank of Ogechie Lake
within Mille Lacs-Kathio State Park

The Cooper Site was inhabited by Mdewakanton Dakota (Santee Sioux) in historic
and prehistoric times. Later, bands of
Chippewa harvested wild rice here. Three
burial mounds of the prehistoric Dakota
people have been excavated.
State

MILLE LACS COUNTY
Vineland vicinity
PETAGA POINT
On the southeast shore of Ogechie
Lake in Mille Lacs-Kathio State Park

Petaga Point is a habitation site containing
remains from two distinct periods of occupation. The earliest peoples were members of the Old Copper or Late Archaic
period culture, and the later ones belonged to the locally known Kathio Focus.
Archeologists from the University of Minnesota excavated portions of the site in
1966.
State

MILLE LACS COUNTY
Vineland vicinity
SAW MILL SITE
On the northeast side of Lake
Ogechie in Mille Lacs-Kathio State
Park

The Sawmill Site, named for a functional
structure of historic times, was once the
location for a prehistoric Indian village. It
is now covered with secondary timber
growth. A test excavation in 1965 indicated the presence of stratified middle
prehistoric village remains. Archeologists
consider the site a distinctive one within
the Mille Lacs sequence.
Indian trust land

MILLE LACS COUNTY
Vineland vicinity
**VINELAND BAY SITE (KATHIO
SCHOOL SITE)**
Southwest shore of Mille Lacs Lake
above the Rum River outlet and
within Mille Lacs-Kathio State Park

The principal period of occupation for this
site was during the late prehistoric times
(c. 800–1100). A 19th-century Chippewa
camp was later located in the same area.
The site is important because the earliest
occupation represents a distinct
archeological unit in what archeologists
call the Mille Lacs sequence.
State

MORRISON COUNTY
Little Falls vicinity
**CHARLES A. LINDBERGH STATE
PARK AND LINDBERGH HOUSE**
Southwest of Little Falls on the
Mississippi River

Charles A. Lindbergh, Sr., purchased land
near Little Falls in 1898. The Lindbergh
family lived here from 1901 to 1920. A
house was built on the site of the present
dwelling in 1901, but it burned four years
later. In 1907 the present two-story frame
house was constructed on the old foundations. Charles A. Lindbergh, Jr., the first
man to fly solo and non-stop between New
York and Paris (1927), spent his boyhood
summers on the Little Falls farm. Lindbergh's father was a lawyer who served in
Congress (1907–1917), so the family lived
in Washington while Congress was in session. Young Lindbergh operated the farm
himself between 1918 and 1920. The
house remains unchanged structurally.
State

NICOLLET COUNTY
Fairfax
FORT RIDGELY
Sec. 6, T. 113 N., R. 32 W.
1853–1955

Frontier defense and supervision of the
Sioux Indians were the two principal
reasons for the construction of Fort
Ridgely. Henry Sibley, Minnesota's territorial governor, proposed establishment of
a fort on the Minnesota River in 1852.
The proposal was approved by Congress.
Two companies of the 6th U.S. Infantry
arrived at the chosen site on April 29,
1853, and construction was completed
within two years. During the Civil War
Minnesota volunteer regiments garrisoned
the outpost and were on duty in August,
1862, when the Sioux attacked the Lower
Agency at Redwood Falls. After the uprising, refugees poured into the fort, which

was also attacked, although unsuccessfully. Fort Ridgely was garrisoned until 1867. Since that time it has fallen into ruin. Excavations in 1935 revealed the foundations of eight original structures, the commissary has been restored to serve as a museum and interpretive center, and an original powder magazine stands on the fort grounds.

State

NICOLLET COUNTY
St. Peter
COX, E. ST. JULIEN, HOUSE
500 N. Washington Avenue
1871

The Cox House is a noteworthy Gothic residence, two stories high and having a central towered cupola. Elaborate pinnacles, finials, and bargeboards with cusped tracery decorate the exterior, and all windows have hoodmolds. The roofs project noticeably beyond the exterior walls which are covered by board and batten siding. The carriage house is the same architectural style. Eugene St. Julien Cox, a lawyer, came to St. Peter in 1857. His subsequent career included election as St. Peter's first mayor and a term in the state legislature. He was appointed a district judge in 1878.

County; not accessible to the public

OLMSTED COUNTY
Rochester
MAYO CLINIC BUILDINGS (1914 AND 1928)
110 and 115 2nd Avenue
1914, 1928

The Mayo Clinic Buildings were constructed to house the growing practice of Dr. William J. Mayo (1861–1939) and his brother Dr. Charles H. Mayo (1865–1939). Both were sons of William W. Mayo (1819–1911), also a physician, who settled in Rochester in 1865 and took up private practice. After completing their education, Dr. William Mayo's two sons joined him in his Rochester practice. The two brothers became skilled surgeons. Their growing reputations brought a flood of patients and necessitated hiring other doctors, resulting in the first private practice of cooperative group medicine. Eventually it became necessary to expand the Mayo facilities, and the 1914 and 1928 Mayo Clinic Buildings were erected. The earlier structure was five stories high and the later one, fifteen stories. These buildings were the first complete clinic facilities independent of a hospital in the United States. Both buildings have been little altered since their construction and the Mayo Clinic continues today as the largest and most successful private practice in the world.

Private

NHL

OLMSTED COUNTY
Stewartville vicinity
MAYOWOOD
On County Road D, northwest of Stewartville

Mayowood was the estate of Dr. Charles H. Mayo, who, with his brother, Dr. William J. Mayo, founded the first successful group practice of medicine in the world. The 10–acre house site includes related outbuildings and large areas of lawn and gardens. The 40–room house is made of poured concrete and is composed of five floor levels. Architecture and interior decoration are varied, although the basic floor plan is rectangular with two attached wings on the east side. All trim is wooden, and iron rails and concrete balustrades ornament exterior porches and stairwells. Other buildings are a groundskeeper's house, an octagonal, two-level tea house, root cellars, and pools, fountains, walkways, statues, and gardens. Dr. Charles H. Mayo lived here until 1935, and his son, from 1939 to 1968.

Private

PIPESTONE COUNTY
Pipestone vicinity
PIPESTONE NATIONAL MONUMENT
1 mile north of Pipestone
Date unknown

Pipestone National Monument was established to preserve the quarries where, for at least three hundred years, Indians of the Middle West quarried the soft red stone from which they made smoking pipes. The pipes and the quarries had great religious and social significance to the tribes who used them. Many Indians in this region believed that the stone was a gift from the gods. A part of all ceremonies surrounding important agreements was the smoking of the pipe. Each local tribal group had its legend explaining the origin of the pipestone and the quarries. Pipestone is called Catlinite after the western artist and pioneer ethnologist George Catlin, whose descriptions of the quarries were the first to be published. A trail at the monument connects the natural, ethnohistorical, and historic points of interest and guides the visitor to several quarry sites, three of which are used today.

Federal/non-federal

NPS; 282.58 acres

RAMSEY COUNTY
St. Paul
BURBANK-LIVINGSTON-GRIGGS HOUSE
432 Summit Avenue
1862–1863

James Crawford Burbank was the first owner and resident of this elaborate and substantial Italianate house on St. Paul's most fashionable street. The walls are rough-hewn limestone blocks topped by a low pitched roof and an unusual wooden balustraded cupola with finial. Under the wide bracketed cornice are regularly spaced eyebrow windows; all other windows are round arched and surrounded by quoins. Some interior alterations were made in 1925 by Mary Livingston Griggs, the married daughter of a subsequent owner, but externally the house retains its original appearance.

State

RAMSEY COUNTY
St. Paul
HILL, JAMES J., HOUSE
240 Summit Avenue
1889

James Jerome Hill was an active leader in American railroad construction from 1878 to 1912. In 1890, the railroads that he controlled were combined as the Great Northern Railroad Company. In an era when most railroads were bankrupted by corrupt management, Hill's enterprises remained prosperous. Often called the "Empire Builder," Hill was also an important financial leader. His house, where he lived until his death in 1912, has an unaltered exterior, but the interior has been remodeled.

Private; not accessible to the public

NHL; HABS

RAMSEY COUNTY
St. Paul
OLD FEDERAL COURTS BUILDING
109 W. 5th Street
1894–1901, James Knox Taylor

The Old Federal Courts Building is an example of Federal building architecture at the turn of the century. It is a mixture of transitional Romanesque and French Renaissance styles. The abundant use of corner turrets, gables, and towers characterized the exterior. There are two clock towers on the structure. The Fifth Street or south tower is 150 feet high, and the Sixth Street or north tower is 296 feet high and more massive with a base 46 feet square. Building materials are brownish-gray granite, iron, concrete, and slate roofing, the last of which has been replaced. The interior of the five-story structure contains courtrooms and chambers on the third and fourth floors which are paneled in cherry wood and decorated with carved, white Georgia marble. The second, third, and fourth floors of the courts section of the building open onto a roofed central court. Original floor surfacing exists throughout except for certain rooms and hallways on the fourth and fifth floors and the post office area on the first floor.

Federal; first floor accessible to the public

RAMSEY COUNTY
St. Paul
RAMSEY, ALEXANDER, HOUSE
265 S. Exchange Street
1868–1872, Monroe Scheire

Alexander Ramsey, a former Congressman, came to Minnesota from Pennsylvania to serve as first territorial governor in 1849. He served for four years, and during his administration the treaties of Traverse des Sioux and Mendota were signed with the Sioux, who thereby ceded 24 million acres to the federal government. In 1863 Ramsey was elected to the U.S. Senate and later (1879–1881) served as Secretary of War under Rutherford B. Hayes. The Ramsey home is Second Empire in style with a mansard roof and dormers, arched doors and windows, and bracketing under the eaves. It is three stories high and built of gray Minnesota limestone. Occupied by members of the Ramsey family until 1964, the house remains much as it was during the original owner's life.

State

REDWOOD COUNTY
Redwood Falls vicinity
LOWER SIOUX AGENCY
9 miles east of Redwood Falls off
County Route N 2

The Lower Sioux Agency was established in 1853 as the administrative center for the Mdewakanton and Wahpekute bands of Sioux. The center was a result of the Treaty of Traverse des Sioux, through which the Indians ceded 24 million acres of land in southern Minnesota and parts of Iowa and South Dakota. Restlessness did not cease, and on August 18, 1862, a band of Sioux warriors surrounded and burned most of the Lower (or Redwood) Agency buildings. Thirteen settlers were massacred. The stone warehouse (built in 1861) is the only original structure remaining on the Agency site. Indian workmen constructed it with walls 18 inches to 3 feet in thickness. The interior has been extensively remodeled. Granite markers on the property indicate the loca-

tion of two trading posts and the agency headquarters.
Public/private

RICE COUNTY
Faribault
FARIBAULT, ALEXANDER, HOUSE
12 N.E. 1st Avenue

Alexander Faribault (1806–1882) was a fur trader and businessman who built the largest of his six trading posts in Faribault. His house is the oldest frame residence in the town and considered one of the oldest in Minnesota. Built in two sections, although at the same time, the house measures 30 feet wide by 74 feet long. The rear section had to be rebuilt in 1945 due to deterioration. Inside, the house is furnished with period pieces.
County

RICE COUNTY
Northfield
NUTTING HOUSE
217 Union Street
1887–1888, J. E. Cook

Now the residence of the president of Carleton College, the Nutting House was built for John C. Nutting, founder of Northfield's First National Bank. Today it is the only remaining house of its size and period in town. Resting on a full limestone basement, the house is frame construction with brick veneer walls two stories high. All openings are trimmed with red sandstone. Changes have been made in the original two-story west entrance porch, and a screen porch was added on the east facade in 1912.
Private

RICE COUNTY
Northfield
ROLVAAG, O. E., HOUSE
311 Manitou Street
1912

Ole Edvart Rolvaag (1876–1931) was born in Norway and emigrated to the United States when he was twenty. His first home was in South Dakota with relatives, and in 1901 he enrolled in St. Olaf College in Northfield, Minnesota. After his marriage in 1908, Rolvaag lived in Northfield and taught Norwegian and religion at St. Olaf College. As time passed he turned more to the study of his native language and the writing of books. Rolvaag is best known for his fiction which dealt with the feelings and reactions of immigrants transplanted to strange surroundings and confronted by overwhelming hardships. His most famous novel, *Giants in the Earth* (1927), provides insight into the psychological cost of readjustment to a totally new environment. Rolvaag lived in

this house until his death and wrote the major part of his literary works here.
Private; not accessible to the public
NHL

ST. LOUIS COUNTY
Hibbing vicinity
HULL-RUST-MAHONING OPEN PIT IRON MINE
3rd Avenue East
1895

The immense iron ore output of this Mesabi Range mine, the largest in the world, enabled the United States to become the world's leading manufacturer of steel. The mine was also among the first to be worked by open-pit or strip-mining techniques. This site contains not one mine, but more than nine open pits operating from what appears to be a single hole in the ground. It is more than 1.5 miles wide, three miles long, and 534 feet deep at one point.
Private
NHL

ST. LOUIS COUNTY
Mountain Iron vicinity
MOUNTAIN IRON MINE
North of the village of Mountain Iron
1890–1956

The opening of the Mountain Iron Mine in 1890 revealed that Minnesota's Mesabi Range possessed the world's largest deposits of iron ore. Production from this mine made Minnesota the Nation's largest supplier of iron ore, thus enabling the United States to become the world's leading steel manufacturer. During its period of operation, the mine yielded more than 48 million gross tons of ore. After operations were discontinued in 1956, the mine quickly filled with water. However, because the water height is relatively low in the crater, the dimensions of the open pit are readily discerned. At the end of Missabe Avenue in the town of Mountain Iron visitors will find an observation platform, telescopes, and a vicinity map offering interpretation.
Private
NHL

ST. LOUIS COUNTY
Tower vicinity
SOUDAN IRON MINE
Tower-Soudan State Park
1884

The opening of Minnesota's oldest and deepest underground mine began the development of one of the richest iron deposits in the United States and spurred the emergence of Minnesota as the leading iron-producing state. Active until 1962, its peak year was 1892, when the

Soudan Mine shipped more than 568,000 long tons of high-grade iron ore. A number of original buildings survive: the engine house, drill shop, crusher house, and dry house.
State
NHL

SHERBURNE COUNTY
Elk River vicinity
KELLEY, OLIVER H., HOMESTEAD
2 miles southeast of Elk River on U.S. 10
c. 1860

The house of Oliver H. Kelley, founder of the National Grange movement, served as headquarters for the Grange during its formative years, 1868–1870. The Patrons of Husbandry, as the Grange was formerly known, was established in 1867. Originally a club intended to bring entertainment and enlightenment into the lives of isolated farm families, the organization soon turned to politics in an effort to solve farm problems. After considerable success in the midwestern states during the 1870's and 1880's, the Grange was supplanted as a leader of agrarian protest by the more radical populist movement. Kelley's house is equipped with typical farm furnishings, mostly of the late 19th century.
State
NHL

STEARNS COUNTY
Sauk Centre
LEWIS, SINCLAIR, BOYHOOD HOME
812 Sinclair Lewis Avenue
Late 19th century

Sinclair Lewis was among the best-known and most widely read American novelists of the 1920's and 1930's. He was a leading figure of the realist movement in the literature of the period. His novel *Main Street* (1920), in which he created an image of the American small town, was based in part on his impressions of his own hometown of Sauk Centre. Refusing the Pulitzer Prize in 1926 for the novel *Arrowsmith*, he became the first American to be awarded the Nobel Prize for literature in 1930. Lewis lived in this house until the age of 18. The two-story, frame, gable roofed building with clapboard siding remains substantially unaltered.
Private; not accessible to the public
NHL

WASHINGTON COUNTY
Marine on St. Croix
MARINE MILL SITE
Mill Reservation, Block 47
19th century

The Marine Mill Site is recognized as the birthplace of Minnesota's white pine lumber milling, the area's first major industry. A sawmill was constructed on the site in 1839 by the Marine Lumber Company. This mill was torn down in 1852, and its replacement burned in 1863. Three years later the last sawmill was erected, improved in 1873, but failed financially in 1888. All that remains of this once-prosperous operation today are the ruins of the stone engine house and a large wheel dating from 1873. All other buildings have been torn down and the machinery transported elsewhere.
Private; not accessible to the public

WASHINGTON COUNTY
Scandia
HAY LAKE SCHOOL
Sec. 27, T. 31 N., R. 19 W.
1895

The Hay Lake School was the first schoolhouse built in Scandia. It is a one-story Victorian brick building with a gable roof surmounted by a wooden belfry. Across the front is a one-story porch decorated with jigsaw work. The building is typical of its era and was operative until 1962, when a modern school was built.
Municipal; not accessible to the public.

WASHINGTON COUNTY
Stillwater vicinity
ST. CROIX BOOM SITE
3 miles north of Stillwater on St. Croix River
1856

The St. Croix Boom Site was the longest-lived of the major log storage and handling areas in Minnesota. From 1856 to 1914 it served as the terminal point for the log drives of the white pine lumber industry. Here millions of logs were sorted, measured, and rafted to sawmills down river. During its existence it handled over 15.5 billion feet of logs. There are no remains of the log boom, but the general setting is unimpaired.
State
NHL

WINONA COUNTY
Winona
WINONA COUNTY COURTHOUSE
Washington Street between 3rd and 4th Streets
1889, C. G. Mayburg & Son

Romanesque in style, the Winona Courthouse is highlighted by round-arched windows and two tall towers. Its exterior walls rise three stories above a basement and are constructed of Dresbach buff sandstone. Trim—water table, window sills, belt courses, lintels, and door and window jambs and arches—is Lake Superior brownstone. The main tower is 24 feet square and rises 136 feet above ground level. Inside, each office has a fireplace and a carved wood mantel; hallways and vestibules on the first and second floors are laid with American or Minton tiles, and both stairways are elaborately carved heavy white oak.
County

WINONA COUNTY
Winona vicinity
PICKWICK MILL
Hamlet of Pickwick

Pickwick Mill is believed to be one of the oldest, still-operative waterpowered grist mills in southeastern Minnesota. Built in 1854 as a combination grist and sawmill, Pickwick Mill was converted two years later to flour production only. In the late 19th century the older stone burr method of grinding was replaced by a more efficient roller system. Shortly after World War I the mill again converted from flour to feed milling. Locally quarried limestone was used to construct the building, which was originally six stories under a peaked roof. In 1907 a cyclone tore off the roof and top storage room, and both were replaced by a flat plank roof. The machinery used for the manufacture of flour is largely intact.
Private

YELLOW MEDICINE COUNTY
Granite Falls vicinity
UPPER SIOUX AGENCY
Secs. 29, 30, and 32, T. 115 N., R. 38 W.

Prehistoric Indians inhabited this site from approximately 2000 B.C. until the coming of the white man in recent times. Artifacts, burial mounds, and village sites provide tangible evidence of pre-Columbian occupation. On the same grounds, between 1854 and 1862, the U.S. government operated the largest Dakota Indian agency in Minnesota. The purpose of the agency was to make the Indians as much

like white men as possible—to civilize them; but the attempt failed and the Dakota Indians were forced to leave Minnesota. Only one building, an employee's duplex, remains, and it has been somewhat altered. Archeological excavations in 1968 and 1969 exposed the foundations of a prison, a warehouse, another duplex, the manual labor school, and a bakehouse. Several cellar depressions, two root cellars, and five cisterns were also examined. The state of Minnesota is acquiring the land and will here interpret federal Indian policy of the mid–1800's.
Multiple public/private

Split Rock Lighthouse, Lake County, Minnesota.
Minnesota Historical Society

Mississippi

Longwood (Nutt's Folly), Natchez vicinity, Mississippi. *NPS*

The Old Capitol,
Jackson, Mississippi.
*Mississippi Department of
Archives and History*

Fort Massachusetts, Gulfport vicinity,
Mississippi. *Chauncey T. Hinman*

Jefferson College, Washington, Mississippi.
David Peabody

ADAMS COUNTY
Natchez
KING'S TAVERN
611 Jefferson Street
c. 1789

King's Tavern is regarded as the oldest building in Natchez. The land itself was granted by the Spanish monarch to Prosper King on May 31, 1789, and there are indications that the building already existed at that time. Shortly thereafter Richard King inherited the land, and he applied for and was granted a license "to keep a public house" in 1799. Located at the end of the Natchez Trace, the tavern served as a mail and stagecoach stop and as a haven for all who traveled along the Trace. Bandits and murderers plagued the unwary enroute from Nashville to Natchez, and the Spanish governor eventually appointed Richard King commander of a mounted police force charged with protecting the citizens and travelers in his district. The primitive two-story tavern structure is constructed of brick with poplar and cypress clapboards. Its handhewn timbers and beams are fitted with wooden pegs. A gallery on the exterior has been enclosed, and a kitchen addition was constructed in the 20th century.
Private; not accessible to the public
HABS

ADAMS COUNTY
Natchez vicinity
FATHERLAND PLANTATION SITE
3 miles southeast of Natchez
c. 1600–1700

The Grand Village of the Natchez (Fatherland Plantation Site), first described in 1700 by Pierre le Moyne, Sieur d'Iberville, is frequently mentioned in early 18th-century sources. In the flat bottom land west of St. Catherine's Creek are three Indian mounds. Mound C, excavated in 1930 and 1962, is a platform mound containing 25 burials in the floor of the temple atop it. The burials were accompanied by large quantities of European artifacts: glass bottles, knives, brass beads, and a flintlock pistol.
Private; not accessible to the public
NHL

ADAMS COUNTY
Natchez vicinity
LONGWOOD (NUTT'S FOLLY)
1.5 miles southeast of Natchez
1860–1862, Samuel Sloan

Designed by the noted Philadelphia architect, Samuel Sloan, Longwood is the largest (296 feet in circumference) and most elaborate octagonal house in the United States. Its eclectic decorative detail includes both Italianate and Moslem, or Oriental, motifs. An enormous onion-shaped dome resting on a 16-sided drum crowns the four-story structure. Although Haller Nutt's slaves manufactured the bricks used in Longwood's construction, most of the material was made in Philadelphia and sent to Natchez by boat. Only the exterior was completed, since most of the master builders engaged by Sloan had abandoned the project by September of 1861, with the outbreak of the Civil War. Nutt then directed his slaves to finish the eight-room basement level, into which he and his family moved. From the first floor to the attic, however, the mansion remains a shell. The extant outbuildings are a kitchen, necessary, servants' quarters, stables and carriage house.
Private
NHL; HABS

ADAMS COUNTY
Washington
JEFFERSON COLLEGE
North Street

Jefferson College, named for then-President Thomas Jefferson, was incorporated by the Mississippi territorial legislature in May, 1802. This was the first act of incorporation passed by that body. Due to insufficient funds the college was unable to accept students until 1811, and the buildings used were not the present ones. The campus itself encompasses 78.5 acres, and the main building was constructed in three stages. The east wing dates from the 1820's, the west wing was erected in 1838–1839, and the center section was built after 1851. All three are brick and three stories high. The wings have hip roofs pierced by three dormer windows, and there is a cupola on the roof of the center building. Two outbuildings behind the main structure are of similar construction, and the wooden president's house was built in the early 19th century. Mississippi's first constitution was drawn up in a church on the Jefferson College grounds in 1817. Jefferson College, which had been a military high school for several years, closed in 1964.
State
HABS

ALCORN COUNTY
Rienzi
JACINTO COURTHOUSE
Route 1
1854–1870

The Jacinto Courthouse is a two-story, Federal style brick building surmounted by an octagonal cupola. Jacinto Courthouse was built to serve old Tishomingo County, created in 1836. In 1870 the original county was divided into the present Alcorn, Prentiss, and Tishomingo counties. The courthouse later housed the Jacinto Male Academy (1870–1908) and served as a Methodist church until 1960. Restoration work in the late 1960's has returned the courthouse to its early appearance.
Public/private

CARROLL COUNTY
Avalon vicinity
TEOC CREEK SITE
SW 1/4 SE 1/4 sec. 9, T. 20 N., R. 2 E.
c. 1392 B.C.

The Teoc Creek Site is a village location of the Poverty Point culture. It is a crescent-shaped area containing large quantities of aboriginal cultural material such as fire-cracked rock, broken clay balls, and flint tools and flakes. Two traverses of bore holes were used to locate the site in 1966, and one of the bore holes revealed a midden about nine feet beneath the water surface at the levee crest. Radiocarbon dating gave an average date of 1392 B.C., thus establishing Teoc Creek as the second oldest recorded Poverty Point site. It is also considered the best preserved.
Private; not accessible to the public

CARROLL COUNTY
Carrollton vicinity
MALMAISON SITE
6 miles northeast of Carrollton

Malmaison, an impressive two-story, porticoed mansion, was designed for Greenwood Leflore by James Clark Harris. The house was completed in 1854 and burned in 1942. All that remains are the foundation, concrete steps, cistern, portions of a brick wall, and a cemetery. Greenwood Leflore (1800–1865), son of a French trader and an Indian mother, was elected chief of the Choctaw Indians in 1830. He effected many reforms in his people's way of life by establishing schools and instituting civil marriages and trial by jury. Leflore played a prominent role in negotiations for the Treaty of Dancing Rabbit Creek (1830), which provided for removal of the Choctaws west of the Mississippi River. He remained in Mississippi, however, and served in both houses of the legislature.
Private; not accessible to the public

CLAIBORNE COUNTY
Port Gibson
VAN DORN HOUSE
Van Dorn Drive
c. 1830

Peter A. Vandorn, builder of the Van Dorn House, was a lawyer and merchant in Port Gibson. He became clerk of the territorial and state house of representatives and helped lay out Mississippi's capital city. His home is a two-story brick dwelling, originally L-shaped, with front and east sides laid in Flemish bond and back and west in running bond. There was a large, covered porch with pillars on the front facade, and both front and rear doors had fan- and sidelights. During the 1880's a one-story brick utility porch and kitchen were added at the south. All porches have now been removed and the house is in a state of disrepair.
Private

HARRISON COUNTY
Gulfport vicinity
FORT MASSACHUSETTS
South of Gulfport on Ship Island
c. 1859–1863

President James K. Polk issued an executive order on August 30, 1847, declaring Ship Island a federal military reservation. Nine years later Secretary of War Jefferson Davis authorized construction of a fort on the island's western end, a site which commanded the only deep water channel from the Gulf into the Mississippi Sound and the port of New Orleans. Construction began only to be interrupted by the Civil War. Held briefly by Confederates, the fort was completed by the U.S. government and used by Major General Benjamin F. Butler and Admiral David Farragut. Having housed Confederate prisoners during the war, Fort Massachusetts continued to be a federal prison until 1870, when it ceased to be a military reservation. The fortification of brick and cut stone is D-shaped and measures 180 by 115 feet. A single entrance to the interior is located on the east wall.
Private

HINDS COUNTY
Bovina vicinity
FLOYD MOUND
NE 1/4 SE 1/4 sec. 34, T. 16 N., R. 5 E.
Pre-Columbian

The Floyd Mound is an undisturbed conical burial mound. It stands approximately 8 feet high and is 50 feet in diameter. All excavated burial mounds in the area are related to the Mississippian period.
Private; not accessible to the public

HINDS COUNTY
Edwards vicinity
DUPREE MOUND AND VILLAGE ARCHEOLOGICAL SITE
SE 1/4 NW 1/4 sec. 21, T. 5 N., R. 3 W.
Pre-Columbian

The Dupree Mound was excavated in 1927 and 1928, and 35 burials were found, all accompanied by early Mississippian burial artifacts, principally pottery. The site was a source for key Plaquemine culture pottery types. A village surrounded the mound. In 1926 the mound measured 60 feet in diameter and 12 feet in height; its present height is six feet and the diameter is variable. Unauthorized digging has destroyed most of the mound.
Private; not accessible to the public

HINDS COUNTY
Jackson
THE CAPITOL GREEN
Bounded on the north by Amite Street, on the south by Pearl Street, on the west by State Street, and on the east by the Gulf, Mobile & Ohio Railroad
1822, Peter A. Vandorn

The Capitol Green was designed in 1822 by Peter A. Vandorn as part of his original city plan for Jackson. It was one of three areas designated for public buildings and is today the only one still serving its original purpose. The second Statehouse, now a museum, was erected on the Green in the 1830's. The War Memorial Building was dedicated in 1940. Several monuments dot the grounds surrounding these two buildings.
State

HINDS COUNTY
Jackson
CITY HALL
203 S. President Street
1847, William Gibbons; 1853, J. Willis; 1963–1964, Frank P. Gates

The City Hall is one of three Greek Revival, antebellum government buildings remaining in Jackson. Originally three-stories high, it was rebuilt or enlarged in 1853 and underwent extensive structural renovation in 1963–1964. Four fluted Doric columns support a narrow portico on the main facade, and in 1928 a similar rear portico was added.
Municipal
HABS

HINDS COUNTY
Jackson
MISSISSIPPI GOVERNOR'S MANSION
316 E. Capitol Street
1839–1841, William Nichols; 1908–1909 (renovated), William S. Hull

Mississippi's Greek Revival Governor's Mansion of masonry construction stands two stories above a full basement. It is square in shape and adorned on the front by a semicircular, two-story, Corinthian portico. The porte cochere and entrance on the east facade were added during the 1908–1909 renovations when a two-story addition at the rear was constructed to provide additional living space.
State
HABS

HINDS COUNTY
Jackson
MISSISSIPPI STATE CAPITOL
Fronting Mississippi Street, between N. President and N. West Streets
1903, Theodore C. Link

Typical of the era in which it was built, Mississippi's State Capitol is an example of Beaux Arts Classicism. Based somewhat on the national capital, the four-story structure is crowned with a massive dome. On either side of the central block are wings leading to pavilions which are capped with low domes. Many different types of marble are used in the interior.
State

HINDS COUNTY
Jackson
MISSISSIPPI STATE CAPITOL (OLD CAPITOL)
100 N. State Street
1839, William Nichols

Much of Mississippi's early history is intimately associated with this building, which served as the state capitol from 1839 to 1903. Virtually abandoned from 1903 until 1916, it was remodeled during the latter year for use as a state office building. The building served this purpose until 1959, when it was restored as the state historical museum. The architectural style is Greek Revival. All three of the Greek orders (Doric, Ionic, and Corinthian) are employed in the structure. The first story of the building is of stone, and the two upper ones are brick. The building is crowned with a dome and lantern.
State
HABS

HINDS COUNTY
Pocahontas
POCAHONTAS MOUND A
SE 1/4 NW 1/4 sec. 10, T. 7 N., R. 1
W.
Pre-Columbian

Pocahontas Mound A has not been substantially altered since prehistoric times except for some minor cultivation. The Mississippi Archeological Survey team recorded the mound in 1926 and 1927 as 350 feet by 250 feet and 25 feet high. Current measurements are 180 feet by 170 feet and 20 feet high, and archeologists are unable to account for this difference. In 1936 the fields around the mound were covered with sherds, flint chips, and animal and human bone fragments.
State

HINDS COUNTY
Terry vicinity
BERRY MOUND AND VILLAGE ARCHEOLOGICAL SITE
Center NE 1/4 sec. 12, T. 3 N., R. 1
W.
Pre-Columbian

Little evidence has been found to indicate the age or cultural affiliation of the Berry Mound and Village Site. The site was first recorded by the Mississippi Archeological Survey team in 1969. Surface material collected consisted of several dozen spalls, seven small sherds, and two projectile points. The mound is conical in shape, measures 60 feet in diameter, and stands 7 feet high.
Private; not accessible to the public

HOLMES COUNTY
Richland
EUREKA MASONIC COLLEGE
On Miss. 17
1847

This two-story brick school was built to house the Richland Literary Institute. One year later its name was changed by an act of the state legislature to Eureka Masonic College. There are two large rooms on the second floor which served as a dormitory, and classes were held in the single room on the ground floor. Dr. Robert Morris, first principal of the college, founded the Order of the Eastern Star in 1850. The Mississippi chapter now owns the school building and has restored it.
Private

LAFAYETTE COUNTY
Oxford
FAULKNER, WILLIAM, HOUSE (ROWAN OAK)
Old Taylor Road
c. 1840

William Faulkner is one of America's major 20th-century novelists. Among his most widely acclaimed books are those set in mythical Yoknapatawpha County, which corresponds in many ways to his own Lafayette County. In 1950 Faulkner received the Nobel Prize for literature for his cumulative work, which included *Sartoris* (1929), *The Sound and the Fury* (1929), and *Light in August* (1932). Two subsequent volumes were awarded Pulitzer Prizes: *A Fable* in 1955 and *The Reivers* in 1963. Faulkner purchased this two-story Greek Revival house in 1929 and occupied it until his death in 1963. It is maintained by the University of Mississippi as it was during the author's lifetime.
Private; accessible to the public by appointment only
NHL

LEE COUNTY
Baldwyn vicinity
BRICES CROSS ROADS NATIONAL BATTLEFIELD SITE
6 miles west of Baldwyn on Miss. 370
1864

Confederate General Nathan Bedford Forrest here won a tactical victory against General S. D. Sturgis's larger Union force on June 10, 1864. This small site is located near the center of the battlefield. Although a spectacular victory, the battle of Brices Cross Roads did not bring relief to the Confederacy. In keeping Forrest occupied in Mississippi, Union General William T. Sherman forestalled a Confederate attack on the Nashville-Chattanooga Railroad, thereby securing the Federal line of communications.
Federal
NPS; 1 acre

LEE COUNTY
Tupelo
TUPELO NATIONAL BATTLEFIELD
On Miss. 6 about a mile west of its intersection with U.S. 45
1864

Tupelo National Battlefield commemorates the Civil War engagement between Union forces under General Andrew J. Smith and Confederate forces under Generals Stephen D. Lee and Nathan Bedford Forrest. The purpose of the battle, fought July 14, 1864, was to protect the railroad which brought food

and ammunition from Louisville through Nashville and Chattanooga to General William T. Sherman's "Army Group." If successful, the Federals would secure the rear of Sherman's forces in his drive upon Georgia. Though neither side could claim complete victory, the railroad was temporarily safe. The battlefield is near the place where the Confederate line was formed to attack the Union position.
Federal/non-federal
NPS; 1.50 acres

LOWNDES COUNTY
Columbus
LEE HOUSE (BLEWETT-HARRISON-LEE HOUSE)
314 N. 7th Street
c. 1847

The Lee House is a two-story brick dwelling which exhibits the architectural influence of both late Georgian and Greek Revival styles. A central, three-bay, pedimented section projects from the main part of the house. Windows have stone lintels and sills, and corners are marked by pilasters. A glassed-in conservatory on the south and a one-story wing on the north side no longer exist. The ironwork porch on the main facade is original. Major Thomas Blewett built the house, which was subsequently owned by his daughter, Mrs. James T. Harrison, and his granddaughter, Mrs. Stephen D. Lee.
Municipal
HABS

MARION COUNTY
Sandy Hook vicinity
FORD HOUSE
South of Sandy Hook on Old Columbia-Covington Road
c. 1810

John Ford, a Methodist minister and builder of the Ford House, came to Mississippi from South Carolina. In 1817 he was named a delegate to the first state constitutional convention and signed the resulting document. His house is a two-and-one-half-story structure with a ground floor of clay brick and the remainder of frame. It is a vernacular expression of the raised cottage popular in the lower Mississippi Valley. Hand-hewn sills and two brick pillars help support the foundation. Both front and back overhanging porches were added after the house was finished.
Private
HABS

WARREN COUNTY
Vicksburg
OLD COURTHOUSE, WARREN COUNTY
Court Square
1861, William Weldon

The Warren County Courthouse was the symbol of Confederate resistance in the Vicksburg Campaign of 1862–1863. Raising the colors over the courthouse, Vicksburg's most prominent landmark, became the goal of the campaign directed by Major General U. S. Grant. After a 47–day siege, the Confederates surrendered, and Colonel William E. Strong ran up the garrison flag from the cupola. The fall of Vicksburg was a crucial blow to the Confederate cause. The South was cut in half, and the Mississippi River was again open for Union trade. The two-story Greek Revival building is substantially unaltered from the Civil War period.
County
NHL; HABS

WARREN COUNTY
Vicksburg
PEMBERTON HOUSE (WILLIS-COWAN HOME)
1020 Crawford Street
c. 1834

During the 47–day siege of Vicksburg in 1863 the Willis-Cowan Home served as the temporary headquarters of Lieutenant General John C. Pemberton, a Northerner who served in the Confederate Army and was responsible for defending Mississippi, Tennessee, and eastern Louisiana. The Willis-Cowan Home, commonly called the Pemberton House, is a large, two-story, brick house which combines features of Federal and Greek Revival architecture. The brick kitchen was attached long after the house was built, and the original fireplaces, mantels, and woodwork remain.
Private; not accessible to the public

WARREN COUNTY
Vicksburg
PLANTERS HALL
822 Main Street
1834

Planters Hall, the second building erected in Vicksburg to house the Planters Bank, is a two-story brick structure with its gable end parallel to the street. Beneath the eaves on the north and east sides are modillions with shaped insets. Doorways at both floor levels on the main facade are highly ornamented. The first-floor entrance is framed by a pair of Corinthian columns flanked by pilasters with Doric capitals. Above these is a segmental arch with a row of dentils beneath the curved cornice. The second-floor doorway features a pair of Tuscan columns supporting an entablature with a broken cornice line. Window sills and lintels are stone. In 1830 the Mississippi legislature chartered the Planters' Bank, to be headquartered in Natchez with branches in Vicksburg, Port Gibson, and Woodville. The bank failed in 1842, and in 1854 the building was converted into a residence.
Private
HABS

WARREN COUNTY
Vicksburg and vicinity
VICKSBURG NATIONAL MILITARY PARK
1863

Vicksburg National Military Park was the site of the decisive campaign in the West during the Civil War. Strategically located on the high bluffs that command a great bend of the Mississippi River, Vicksburg became the storm center of the campaign. The batteries located here formed a link in the chain of Confederate fortifications that stretched along the Mississippi River from Columbus, Kentucky, to New Orleans, Louisiana. After failing to capture the city by assault, the Union forces under General Ulysses S. Grant laid siege to the city. After 47 days the Confederates surrendered on July 4. Remains of nine major Confederate forts, 12 Union approaches, many miles of breastworks, gun emplacements, and rifle-pits are still to be found in the park in varying degrees of preservation. Within the battlefield area is Vicksburg National Cemetery.
Federal/non-federal
NPS; 1,740.78 acres

YAZOO COUNTY
Holly Bluff
HOLLY BLUFF SITE
About 2 miles from Holly Bluff on secondary road
Prehistoric

The Holly Bluff Site has some 20 Indian mounds and the encircling wall and ditch are still intact. It is the type site for the Lake George phase of the Mississippian or temple mound culture. There are indications that a far longer range of culture history is represented by other remains in the general area. Excavations were carried out at the site in 1958–1960.
Private; not accessible to the public
NHL

Holly Bluff Site, Holly Bluff, Mississippi. *NPS*

Missouri

Grand Avenue Water Tower, St. Louis, Missouri, *Philip Cotton*

Louis Bolduc House,
Ste. Genevieve, Missouri. *NPS*

Vaile Park (Harvey M. Vaile House
Independence, Missouri. *M. Patricia Holme*

Bollinger Mill,
Burfordville, Missouri.
H. R. Grant

Old Post Office, St. Louis, Missouri. *Robert F. Arteaga*

ADAIR COUNTY
Kirksville vicinity
THOUSAND HILLS STATE PARK PETROGLYPHS ARCHEOLOGICAL SITE
2.5 miles west of Kirksville
Pre-Columbian

These petroglyphs, carved on sandstone, are surrounded by a chain link fence. The figures represented are birds, snakes, and unidentified four-legged animals.
State

ATCHISON COUNTY
Tarkio
MULE BARN THEATRE (DAVID RANKIN MULE BARN)
10th and Park Streets
c. 1891–1893, Searcy and McCutcheon

David Rankin was a prominent farmer and businessman who came to northwest Missouri in the 1870's, when he was past 50 years of age. He built this three-story octagonal barn to house some of his hired hands and to shelter the 50 to 70 mules used on his extensive land holdings. The barn measures approximately 80 feet in diameter, and each wall is about 33 feet long. There are three bays in each wall, and all windows have stone sills and projecting brick relieving-arch caps with side pendants. Interior illumination and cross ventilation are exceptionally good. The present roof is a truncated peak with sloping sides in eight planes, the result of a 1908 fire which destroyed the original roof, upper walls, and some interior portions. Renovation of the interior in 1966–1968 resulted in the barn's successful adaptation as a theater.
Private

BARTON COUNTY
Lamar
TRUMAN, HARRY S, BIRTHPLACE MEMORIAL
North corner, 11th Street and Truman Avenue
1884–1885

Harry S Truman, thirty-second President of the United States, was born in this house on May 8, 1884. Truman's father, John A. Truman, purchased the house from the builder in 1882. The family continued to live here until Truman was 11 months old when they moved to Independence. In 1927 Truman was elected to the Jackson County Court as presiding judge. In 1935 he was elected to the U.S. Senate and in 1945 became Vice President under Franklin D. Roosevelt. When Roosevelt died that same year, Truman became President and was subsequently elected Chief Executive in 1948. The

house itself is a one-and-one-half-story frame structure covered with clapboard siding.
State

BENTON COUNTY
Cairo vicinity
RODGERS SHELTER ARCHEOLOGICAL SITE
SW SW NE sec. 33, T. 39 N., R. 22 W.
Pre-Columbian to A.D. 1200

Deposits found in the Rodgers Shelter indicate that the site was inhabited from as early as 7000 B.C. to approximately A.D. 1200. These deposits extend to a depth of 30 feet and are divided into four well-defined strata. The first stratum, the earliest, is composed of nearly 17 feet of clay and gravel containing material representing the Paleo-Indian through Early Archaic periods. The second, about 4 feet thick, holds material from Early Archaic through Middle Archaic complexes. The third is a gravelly deposit containing little evidence of human occupation. Thus it separates the two earlier strata from the Late Archaic through Late Woodland period occupations that are indicated by the fourth stratum. The absence of material affiliated with the Mississippian culture makes it possible to assume that the shelter was not occupied after about A.D. 1200.
Federal

BOONE COUNTY
Columbia
SANBORN FIELD AND SOIL EROSION PLOTS
University of Missouri campus
1888

Since its establishment, Sanborn Field has been the site of experiments with soil treatments and cropping systems. It is the oldest completely organized soil and crop experimental field in the United States. One of its major contributions to agriculture is the knowledge that high yields of quality grain may be produced perennially when the land is properly treated with chemical fertilizer or manure.
State
NHL

BUCHANAN COUNTY
St. Joseph
KING'S HILL ARCHEOLOGICAL SITE
Inlots 1–8 and the north 20 feet of Inlot 9, Block 12 in Bowen's Addition (5600 block on S. 1st Street, west side)
Pre-Columbian through 18th century
King's Hill is a Kansa Indian archeological site. The Kansa and the Osage were of the Dhegiha branch of the Siouan tribes.

From the study of plant material of the King's Hill site, knowledge has been gained about the agricultural, eating, and cooking habits of the Indians and about their contact with other Indian groups and Europeans. Seeds of watermelon, peach, and corn have been discovered, indicating contact with whites. Also found were pottery fragments, small, triangular, unnotched arrow points of flint, endscrapers of flint, and other tools made from bone and antler. The site is important for the clues it may provide to an understanding of migration routes, early contact with whites, living habits of the Indians, and seasonal periods of occupation of the site.
Private

BUCHANAN COUNTY
St. Joseph
PATEE, JOHN, HOUSE
12th and Penn Streets
1858

Erected by John Patee at the cost of $200,000, the Patee House was one of the best-known hotels west of the Mississippi and a chief way-point between the East and the West. It served as headquarters in 1860 for the overland freighting firm of Russell, Majors, and Waddell and as the terminus of the Pony Express to Sacramento, California. In front of the hotel a cannon shot started off the first rider on April 3, 1860. The hotel was a financial failure, however, because the principal business section of St. Joseph grew up some distance away.
Private
NHL

BUCHANAN COUNTY
St. Joseph
PONY EXPRESS STABLES
914 Penn Street
1858–1861

On April 3, 1860, the first Pony Express rider left St. Joseph bound for Sacramento, California. The freighting firm of Russell, Majors, and Waddell had organized the Pony Express in an effort to publicize the central route to California (along the Platte River through Nebraska to Bridger Pass, Wyoming) and to obtain the government contract to carry mail to the west coast. Eighteen months later the Pony Express was put out of business by completion of the transcontinental telegraph line. The stables were subsequently sold and passed through several hands before becoming a museum in 1959. The original one-story wooden stable building was redone in 1888 by incorporating brick walls into the extant structure. The facade is highlighted by six applied pilasters. All windows are segment arch headed, and three semi-continuous string courses unify the exterior.
Private

BUTLER COUNTY
Naylor vicinity
**KOEHLER FORTIFIED
ARCHEOLOGICAL SITE**
1 mile northeast of Naylor
Pre-Columbian

The Koehler Fortified Archeological Site is the most important known Mississippian civic-ceremonial center of the Black River drainage in the Western Mississippi Valley north of Arkansas. It is also the largest single component Mississippian site in the area and represents the ceremonial center of the Power's Phase of the Middle Mississippian cultural tradition. Four mounds and evidence of a surrounding fortification are extant. There is a large temple mound and three subsidiaries. Protection was provided by a ditch at least six feet deep. Human occupation is believed to have occurred for more than 9,000 years.
Private; not accessible to the public

CALDWELL COUNTY
Kingston vicinity
FAR WEST
5.5 miles west of Kingston via County Routes D and H

While in Missouri, friction with non-Mormons kept the members of the Church of Jesus Christ of Latter-day Saints constantly on the move. Driven from Jackson County in 1833, the Mormons established a town site at Far West in August, 1836. This was the first time that the Mormons had controlled a local government, and their city prospered. It was one of the largest communities in northwest Missouri, and the population numbered several thousand. On July 4, 1837, the cornerstone was laid for the great Mormon temple, but the only construction completed was excavation of the cellar. As laid out, the town site was one mile square with four main avenues each 132 feet wide and secondary streets measuring 82.25 feet across. Most buildings in Far West were tents or shanties. The Mormons were forced to leave Missouri in 1839 and 1840, and few people remained in Far West, although it continued to be the county seat until 1843. Except for a single church, Far West is rolling farmland today.
Private

CALLAWAY COUNTY
Fulton
**WESTMINSTER COLLEGE
GYMNASIUM**
Westminster College campus
1928–1929

Winston Churchill's speech at Westminster College on March 5, 1946, in which the term "iron curtain" was introduced, marked a turning point in international relations. It was the first step toward recognition of the Cold War and admission that the Soviet Union constituted a threat to the West. Although public opinion was at first unfavorable to this "Sinews of Peace" speech, it prepared the way for the Truman Doctrine or so-called containment policy of March, 1947 and later for the North Atlantic Treaty Organization. The brick gymnasium where Churchill delivered the speech remains basically unchanged.
Private
NHL

CALLAWAY COUNTY
Mokane vicinity
MEALY MOUNDS ARCHEOLOGICAL SITE
2 miles northeast of Mokane
Pre-Columbian

This site represents a large and relatively well-preserved group of Boone Focus Mounds of the Late Woodland period. The mounds have been divided into three groups and comprise a "mound district," since all 14 may not be contemporaneous and all may not be of Boone Focus origin. Group One consists of two mounds, both oval-shaped and joined at their bases. The first is 47 feet long, 44 feet wide, and nearly 8 feet high; the second mound is 50 feet long, 36 feet wide, and 6.5 feet high. In Group Two there are seven mounds (two of which are in very good condition), and their lengths range from 31 to 59 feet. All the mounds in Group Three are roughly circular and their diameters (35 to 45 feet) and heights (3.5 to 5.5 feet) vary.
Private; not accessible to the public

CALLAWAY COUNTY
Portland vicinity
RESEARCH CAVE
c. 6000 B.C.

Research Cave contains significant prehistoric Indian remains deposited intermittently over a span of time exceeding 8000 years. The cave is a sandstone shelter which contains evidence of four major occupations. Because of dry preservative conditions, many vegetal remains from these stages have been found in the cave. Perishable materials found in the cave indicate that agriculture was practiced by the peoples of the two most recent cultures, Woodland and Mississippian. The cave has been partially excavated.
Private; not accessible to the public
NHL

CALLAWAY COUNTY
Tebbetts vicinity
**COTE SANS DESSEIN
ARCHEOLOGICAL SITE**
3 miles southwest of Tebbetts

This site consists of 16 Late Woodland burial mounds located along a ridge of land approximately one mile in length, 660 feet in width, and 100 feet above the flood plain. Formation of Cote Sans Dessein, "hill without design," resulted from a shift in the channel of the Missouri River at the point of its confluence with the Osage River. The sixteen oval mounds range from 30 to 55 feet in length, 24 to 40 feet in width, and from 1 to 7 feet in height. Excavation of one mound revealed a rock chamber containing a burial accompanied by 362 potsherds and a few bone or stone artifacts, the majority of which show the Meramec Springs Focus influence. During the 18th and 19th centuries the site may have been a rendezvous point for Indians, trappers, traders, and explorers.
Private

CAPE GIRARDEAU COUNTY
Burfordville
BURFORDVILLE MILL
Mo. 34
1867–1868

For the past 172 years a mill has occupied this site. The present four-story, water-powered, horizontal gristmill was built by J. R. Burford on the stone foundations of a predecessor. Burford operated the mill for 30 years and equipped it with four-foot French buhrstones which are still in operating position. The company which purchased the mill from Burford installed corrugated steel rolls and a second water wheel in 1912. The "under-house" and first floor of the gambrel-roofed building are of rubble masonry, while its upper floors are of brick laid in common bond. The mill, which is being restored to operable condition, retains its machinery, including inward flow turbines, conveyors and shutes, and various types of sifters, dusters, and storage bins.
State

CAPE GIRARDEAU COUNTY
Burfordville vicinity
BURFORDVILLE COVERED BRIDGE
Eastern edge of Burfordville on
County Route H H
Mid–19th century

The Burfordville Covered Bridge spans the Whitewater River. It measures 140 feet in length by 16 feet 6 inches in width. There are three other covered bridges in Missouri, and this one and two others employ the Howe truss construction. Vertical iron tension rods are secured to the wooden upper and lower chords by nuts and washers. These could be tightened at any time to correct sagging.
State

CAPE GIRARDEAU COUNTY
Oriole vicinity
TRAIL OF TEARS STATE PARK ARCHEOLOGICAL SITE
North of Oriole on the Mississippi River

Within the Trail of Tears State Park is a large, well-protected Woodland village area. The village site is on a hillside at the eastern edge of the park. It was occupied extensively in Woodland times and was also used by Mississippian peoples and historic Indian tribes. In 1838–1839 Cherokee Indians enroute to their new home in Indian Territory (present-day Oklahoma) passed hear here. A treaty signed in 1835 forced the Cherokee to leave their lands in Tennessee, Georgia, and Alabama. In the four years from 1836 to 1839, an estimated 13,000 or more Indians made the westward trek. Many died, and one reported casualty, the daughter of Chief Bushyhead, Princess Otahki, had a grave marker erected in her honor near the village site.
State

CARROLL COUNTY
Miami Station vicinity
WRIGHT II ARCHEOLOGICAL SITE
1 mile south of Miami Station
Prehistoric

This site contains a well-preserved village and mound complex identified with the Hopewell tradition. The larger of the two mounds measures 96 feet long, 64 feet wide, and 10 feet high. Associated with this mound is a smaller conical mound and the extensive remains of what appears to be a village area of the same culture. Hopewellian artifacts—pottery, a platform pipe, and quantities of lithic debris—have been found on the site and indicate Middle Woodland occupation.
Private; not accessible to the public

CASS COUNTY
Harrisonville vicinity
BROWN, ROBERT A., HOUSE
.7 mile north of Harrisonville on U.S. 71 Bypass, .5 mile west and northwest on a gravel road
1850

Robert A. Brown, a Tennessean who moved to Cass County in 1842, built this house and the surrounding outbuildings. The most striking feature of the house is the two-story, central front portico with a carved wood balustrade and well-proportioned columns and arcade. Standing two stories high, the house is red brick on a limestone foundation. It is rectangular in shape with a rear ell joined to the west side of the main block. Bricks for the house were made on the premises. Original outbuildings still standing include a slave house, smokehouse, and an apple house.
Private; not accessible to the public

CHARITON COUNTY
Keytesville
REDDING-HILL HOUSE
100 W. North Street
1832—c. 1876

The Redding-Hill House is an architecturally significant example of a composite residential structure which was enlarged gradually over a period of 44 years. The exterior appearance and interior floor plan reveal a marked predilection for asymmetrical planning in marked contrast to the symmetry characteristic of the period. It is a rambling, two-story, ten-room, white clapboard structure built around what was originally a simple, rectangular, one-story frame house. A two-story eastern section, added in 1866, projects about 25 feet south of the main south facade and is topped with a truncated peaked roof and a square look-out cupola. A one-story west section was added before 1876 and was later enlarged by a second floor and an open tower pavilion. The original structure also gained a second story at this time. The disparate elements of the house are tied together by a large one-story wooden porch (built after 1876) which follows the irregular line of the south facade.
Private

CLARK COUNTY
Canton vicinity
BOULWARE MOUND GROUP ARCHEOLOGICAL SITE
NW 1/4 SE 1/4 sec. 9, T. 63 N., R. 6 W.
Pre-Columbian

Fifty-eight mounds are located here within an area measuring 240 by 350 yards. This group is the largest known concentration of mounds in the entire state. Several mounds have been partially excavated. Burials here were the work of Late and possibly Middle Woodland peoples.
Public/private; some areas not accessible to the public

CLAY COUNTY
Excelsior vicinity
WATKINS MILL
6 miles northwest of Excelsior
1859

Commercially active until 1886, the Watkins Mill is among the best-preserved examples of mid-19th-century woolen mills in the United States. It is unique not only for its original building, but also because its business records and extremely rare textile machinery have been preserved. The owner, Waltus Watkins, had founded a Utopian community in the county in 1838. Now a state park, the site includes the three-story brick mill, a brick manor house constructed in 1851, and an octagonal schoolhouse.
State
NHL

CLAY COUNTY
Liberty vicinity
NEBO HILL ARCHEOLOGICAL SITE
3 miles southeast of Liberty
Pre-Columbian

The Nebo Hill Archeological Site is significant because it is the type site for an extensive Archaic complex found in the Kansas City area of Missouri. Large Archaic sites are uncommon. The possibility exists that considerable information about early inhabitants of northwestern Missouri is obtainable here, particularly about subsistence and settlement patterns, lithic technology, and demography. Artifacts found here include projectile points, three-quarter grooved axes, flat rectangular stone celts, stone mortars, quartzite and chert pestles, manos, and hammerstones. Lithic artifacts suggest an occupation date sometime prior to 1 A.D.
Private; not accessible to the public

COLE COUNTY
Jefferson City
COLE COUNTY HISTORICAL
SOCIETY BUILDING
109 Madison Street
1871

The Cole County Historical Society Building is the north one-third of a two-story, brick row structure with an attic and high basement. The facade is three bays wide with well-proportioned segmental arched windows. Inside, the house is asymmetrical with a long, narrow stair hall and passageway at the southwest side of the building. The parlor fills most of the first floor, and there are two bedrooms on the second floor and a single one under the sloping ceiling of the third floor. This house and the remaining sections of the row building comprise an architectural type relatively uncommon in mid–19th-century Missouri towns. Rows of commercial structures with stores below and living quarters above are prevalent throughout the state, but the urban row house of this period opening directly onto the street is a rarity. Missouri's twentieth governor, B. Gratz Brown, built the house in 1871 on property owned by his wife's family. The Brown family lived in the house during the autumn of 1871 while the old executive mansion was being razed and the present one built.
Private

COLE COUNTY
Jefferson City
LOHMAN'S LANDING BUILDING
West corner, Jefferson and Water
Streets
1834–1836

Jefferson City was designated as the capital of Missouri on January 11, 1822. Four sections of land granted by the federal government as the site for the new city were sold at public auction in early March. Lot 78, later the site of the Lohman's Landing Building, was purchased by Samuel Jamison. In 1834 Jamison sold the lot on the river to Richard Shackleford, who probably built the first section of the landing building. Harvey Colgan, a building contractor, became owner of the land in 1836 and expanded the existing structure to its present size. Originally known as Jefferson Landing, the Lohman's Landing Building was the principal receiving and departure point for passengers and freight until the 1850's when railroads began to vie with riverboats. Charles F. Lohman, a Prussian immigrant, operated the Lohman's Landing Building from 1852 until 1874 as an inn, store, and warehouse. Later used as a steamboat agent's headquarters, wharf master's office, and most recently as a shoe warehouse, the Lohman's Landing Building is considered the last survivor of an era in style and function.
State
HABS

COLE COUNTY
Jefferson City
MISSOURI GOVERNOR'S MANSION
100 Madison Street
1871, George I. Barnett

The Missouri Governor's Mansion is a three-story, mansard-roofed, Victorian residence designed by St. Louis architect George I. Barnett. Situated on a bluff overlooking a wide bend in the Missouri River, the house was built of brick and stone with well-finished moldings, quoins, and cresting. Red granite columns donated by Governor B. Gratz Brown (1871–1873), the first governor to occupy the residence, were quarried on his property in Iron County. The first floor of the house contains a large entrance hall, reception parlors, a library, and a dining room. The second floor is composed of a large hallway, six bedrooms, and four baths. On the third floor are four bedrooms, two baths, a billiard room, and the ballroom which extends the full length of the mansion from north to south. A winding stairway in the central hallway connects all three floors. A carriage porch and entrance on the south side were added in 1900–1901, and the interior was remodeled and modernized in 1938, 1956, and 1960.
State; not accessible to the public

COLE COUNTY
Jefferson City
MISSOURI STATE CAPITOL
BUILDING AND GROUNDS
High Street between Broadway and
Jefferson Street
1917, Tracy and Swartout

A late example of Classic Revival architecture, the Missouri State Capitol was designed by Tracy and Swartout, a New York architectural firm. It was completed in 1917 and dedicated on October 6, 1924. The general form and detail of the structure are presently very close to the original. The four-storied building, covering approximately 3 acres, is symmetrical with two wings for legislative houses flanking a large central rotunda. Carthage, Mo., marble was used for the exterior walls, corridor floors, rotunda, and stairways. The exterior ornament includes pedimental and frieze sculpture executed in an ornate, formal style. The interior of the rotunda is decorated with murals, one of which, done by Missouri artist Thomas Hart Benton, illustrates the social history of the state. The capitol and its grounds are situated on a bluff facing the Missouri River in central Jefferson City. Symmetrical terraces descend from the building on its river side, while driveways and an esplanade encircle it. The area surrounding the capitol is formally landscaped with trees, flowers, shrubbery arrangements, ornate iron lampposts, and monumental sculpture.
State

COLE COUNTY
Osage City vicinity
GAY ARCHEOLOGICAL SITE
.5 mile northeast of Osage City
Pre-Columbian

Located at the confluence of the Missouri and Osage rivers, this site was an important rendezvous and vantage point in prehistoric and early historic times. It is also one of a very few remaining fortified sites in Missouri and the only one in Cole County. Grouped into two divisions, the five mounds possibly reflect two different cultures and time periods, although one or both may be representative of the Boone Focus manifestation of the Late Woodland tradition. The fortification wall and ditch were constructed to augment the steep bluffs, the natural protective feature of the site. Today the fortification ditch is marked only by a shallow depression which is best seen in an aerial photograph. Further controlled excavation is desirable.
Private; not accessible to the public

COOPER COUNTY
Boonville
HARLEY PARK ARCHEOLOGICAL
SITE
SE 1/4 NE 1/4 sec. 34, T. 49 N., R.
16 W.
Pre-Columbian

The Harley Park Archeological Site contains four well-preserved prehistoric mounds which may provide further information concerning the relationship between the Middle and Late Woodland tradition in central Missouri. In actual geographic position the mounds are between the eastern distribution of the Central Missouri Hopewell (Middle Woodland) people and the western distribution of the Boone Focus (Late Woodland) people. The four mounds differ in size and all are in good condition.
Municipal

COOPER COUNTY
Boonville
LYRIC THEATER
Northeast corner, Main (5th) and
Vine Streets
1855–1857

According to the results of a survey taken by the State Historical Society of Missouri, the Lyric Theater is the oldest surviving continuously used theater west of the Allegheny Mountains. Constructed for the Boonville Library, Reading Room and Thespian Association, the Lyric Theater was originally called Thespian Hall. Four years after completion of the hall, the Thespian Association was disbanded because of the Civil War. During the war the building served as a quartering place for troops and later as a hospital and stable. A series of owners used the building after the war, and it is now a movie house. Greek Revival in style, the theater building is two stories high, rectangular in plan, and built of brick. The front or west portico has four unfluted Doric columns. A wooden pediment above and an architrave below complete the gable under a ridge roof. The theater was renovated and enlarged early in the 20th century.
Private

COOPER COUNTY
Lamine vicinity
MELLOR VILLAGE AND MOUNDS
ARCHEOLOGICAL SITE
2 miles north of Lamine
Pre-Columbian

Mellor Village and Mounds consists of 14 visible mounds all situated on a terrace above the Missouri and Lamine river bottoms at their junction. Except for four mounds, the entire site is under cultivation. Three of these four mounds are in a barn lot, and the fourth is in a pasture. They range in size from 4 inches to 6 feet in height by 60 to 63 feet in diameter. Surface artifacts from the site indicate occupation from the early Woodland phase through the terminal Havana phase. No one pottery type has been identified as predominant from among the wide range of decorative motifs, techniques, and styles used. An almost complete Havana wares representation indicates that the occupants had contact with the Havana tradition of the Illinois Valley. Clay figurines which fall into the Havana tradition variation range have also been found on the site.
Private

COOPER COUNTY
Wooldridge vicinity
WOOLDRIDGE ARCHEOLOGICAL
SITE
.5 mile northwest of Wooldridge

Three well-preserved and protected mounds are located here and represent two dissimilar construction styles. The large, round mound and the long mound are probably connected with the Transitional Middle to Late Woodland periods in this section of Missouri. The smaller mound is typical of the Late Woodland period and may represent a western extension of the Boone Focus manifestation of that period. Dimensions of the three mounds are 43 feet by 38 feet by 4 feet high (smaller of the two neighboring mounds), and 105 feet by 48 feet by 8.5 feet high (larger of the two). The third mound, about 400 yards west of the first two, has a diameter of roughly 54 feet and is 6 feet high.
Private; not accessible to the public

CRAWFORD COUNTY
Leasburg vicinity
SCOTIA IRON FURNACE STACK
6.3 miles southeast of Leasburg on
County Route H
1870–1880

The Scotia Iron Furnace was built in 1870 by John G. Scott in association with Thomas Howard, Robert Anderson, and Anvil James. Three hundred people were employed by the Scotia Iron Company at the height of its production. The furnace itself was steam powered. Average capacity of the furnace was 20 tons of pig iron per day. Pig iron produced at the furnace was hauled 6 miles to Leasburg, shipped by rail to St. Louis, and there made into iron products. In 1880 the Scotia Iron Works' machinery was moved to Dent County because of a depleted ore supply and disagreement among the owners. It is thought that at its peak of operation the ironworks consisted of one engine house, a charcoal house, a casting house, and a weighing house. Presently only the furnace stack remains. It was constructed of limestone blocks, measures 35 feet wide at the base, and is about 40 feet high. The property also includes an ore pit, Scotia Mine No. 1, which is 1,000 feet northwest of the stack. The pit is 300 feet long, 200 feet wide, and 20 to 50 feet deep.
State

FRANKLIN COUNTY
Moselle vicinity
MOSELLE IRON FURNACE STACK
1 mile southeast of Moselle
1849–1875

Moselle Iron Furnace Stack serves as physical evidence of advances made in iron smelting during a 25–year period. The Moselle Iron Furnace was built by F. A. Evans and George L. Nuckolls. The furnace was operated by a cold-blast process, and its output at first was small, about 5 or 6 tons per day. Most of the pig iron produced by the furnace was hauled to South Point on the Missouri River and shipped from there. Ore for the smelting operation was obtained from ore banks in the vicinity. Between 1867 and 1874 the furnace was converted to hot blast. The stack was raised in height, a brick and iron hot-blast oven was built, and the machinery was remodeled. Three boilers were added for the production of the hot blast. The stack itself, constructed of cut stone blocks, is the only remaining evidence of the ironworks. The stack is 31 feet high with iron brace supports in the openings at the base. There are three openings, on the east, west, and north sides. The former two were for the introduction of the hot blast, while the north opening allowed for the molten iron run-off.
Private

FRANKLIN COUNTY
St. Albans vicinity
TAVERN CAVE
2 miles northeast of St. Albans off the
Chicago, Rock Island & Pacific
Railroad
18th and 19th centuries

Tavern Cave is located on the Missouri River about 20 miles (once a two-day journey) upriver from St. Charles. Early references by travelers indicate that it may, at one time, have housed a tavern. Lewis and Clark sighted and measured the cave on their 1804 westward trek. Located at the base of a limestone bluff, the cave measures 40 feet deep by 20 feet high by 100 feet wide. An intermittent stream flows from the east wall. Various hand carved names and dates are scattered about the walls, some as early as the 1790–1840 period. Presently set back from the river about 250 feet, the cave entrance was once at the water's edge.
Private

GASCONADE COUNTY
Bem vicinity
PEENIE ARCHEOLOGICAL PETROGLYPH SITE
3 miles east of Bem
Pre-Columbian

The Peenie Archeological Petroglyph Site consists of three distinct groups of associated carvings of single and composite figures. The petroglyphs are exposed on a horizontal sandstone outcropping from the bed of an intermittent stream. The area covered by each of the groups ranges in size from 18 feet by 6 feet to 1 foot by 1 foot. To date, the site is in excellent condition; the carvings are deep and still quite distinct.
Private

GASCONADE COUNTY
Hermann
OLD STONE HILL HISTORIC DISTRICT
Bounded about 343 feet on the north by W. 12th Street, 714 feet on the west by Goethe Street and a line extending approximately 321 feet south and 560 feet east to Iron Road, along Iron Road about 462 feet, then northwest about 214 feet to Stone Hill Highway, and north 214 feet back to W. 12th Street
1869–1920

Old Stone Hill Historic District contains the grounds and extant buildings of the Stone Hill Wine Company, at one time the third largest wine producer in the world and the second largest in the United States. The winery was established on this site in 1847 by Michael Poeschel, who operated it alone until 1861 when he formed a partnership with John Scherer. Both men were German immigrants. Annual production of the winery between 1861 and 1878 was 200,000 gallons. The company was sold in 1878, and in 1883 the business became known as the Stone Hill Wine Company. Eventually wine production became the main industry of Hermann. The winery was closed during Prohibition, but winemaking has recently been resumed on a small scale. All major buildings of the original operation survive: a combination residence and office for the company manager, a processing plant, a warehouse, a barn, and stone-lined aging cellars. The office-residence is a two-story, Federal style brick building which measures 60 by 60 feet. The eight stone cellars for aging wine are cut into the hillside under and just north and east of the office-residence. They are cavernous, vaulted rooms lined with stone masonry, plastered with concrete, and whitewashed.

The cellars are of three sizes: 40 by 60 feet, 60 by 80 feet, and 20 by 120 feet. Light and fresh air enter the cellars through circular wells in the ceiling.
Private

GREENE COUNTY
Ash Grove vicinity
BOONE, NATHAN, HOUSE
1.75 miles north of Ash Grove on Mo. V
1837–1856

The Nathan Boone House is a one-and-one-half-story example of the saddlebag or dog trot pioneer log house common along the east coast from Virginia and North Carolina west to Missouri and Arkansas. The hand-hewn oak log walls rest on a stone foundation, and inside, two large rooms, each 21 feet square, flank a central hallway. Much of the original form and material of the house survives but the structure is deteriorating. Nathan Boone, youngest of Daniel Boone's ten children, built the house. He had come to Missouri in 1799 and settled first in the Femme Osage River Valley. He moved to Greene County in 1837, built this house shortly thereafter, and lived in it until his death in 1856.
Private; not accessible to the public

GREENE COUNTY
Springfield vicinity
WILSON'S CREEK NATIONAL BATTLEFIELD
Southwest of Springfield on Mo. 174
1861

The battle of Wilson's Creek was fought August 10, 1861, between Federal troops under General Nathaniel Lyon and an army of the Missouri State Guard, under General Sterling Price, cooperating with a force of Confederates from Arkansas under General Ben McCulloch. The engagement was the first success for the Confederates in Missouri. The Confederates were soon compelled to withdraw from the state, however, and Missouri came under Union control.
Federal/non-federal
NPS; 1,730 acres

HOWARD COUNTY
Boonsboro vicinity
BOONSLICK STATE PARK
1 mile north of Boonsboro on Mo. 87, 2 miles southwest on Mo. 187, .25 mile on gravel road
1806–1834

Boonslick is a natural spring salt lick. This spring was one of the primary sources of salt for the Indians in the central Missouri area and for settlers along the Missouri

River from 1806 until 1833. It was named for Nathan and Daniel M. Boone, sons of Daniel Boone, who began boiling water for salt using one furnace, forty kettles, and a six- or eight-man working force. Twenty-five or thirty bushels of salt were produced per day and shipped to St. Louis to be sold. Later the salt works was expanded by enlarging the original furnace and building a second one. Production increased to two hundred bushels a day. Within the park area there are two natural salt springs which are called springs Nos. 1 and 2. A third spring was dug to a depth of 1001 feet and has been designated a salt well.
State

HOWARD COUNTY
Fayette vicinity
MORRISON, ALFRED W., HOUSE (LILAC HILL)
1 mile southwest of Fayette on Mo. 5
c. 1830

Lilac Hill was built by Alfred Morrison who came to Missouri from Kentucky in 1822. Morrison surveyed the town site for Fayette and served as one of the trustees when Fayette was reincorporated in May, 1830. He also acted as sheriff, judge of the county court, and State treasurer (1851–1860). The house remained in the possession of the Morrison family until 1952. Originally there were no interior stairways in the structure to give access to the second floor. Slave labor was utilized in construction, and bricks were made on the property. One frame slave cabin still stands and is in good condition.
Private; not accessible to the public
HABS

HOWARD COUNTY
Glasgow
GLASGOW PUBLIC LIBRARY
Northwest corner, Market and 4th Streets
1866

The Glasgow Public Library is the oldest library in Missouri still in continuous use. Benjamin W. Lewis, a prosperous tobacco merchant, left a $10,000 bequest in his will for construction of the library. Lewis had come to Missouri in 1831 and began working in a Glasgow tobacco factory. By the Civil War he and his brother James were partners in their own tobacco business. Employing more than 500 workers, the brothers shipped 4 million pounds of tobacco annually, much of it to Europe. When the Confederate Army captured Glasgow in 1864, Lewis, a Union sympathizer, was taken prisoner and severely beaten. A ransom was paid for his release, but the injuries sustained during his imprisonment resulted in his death two years

later. In 1867 the Lewis College and Library Association was organized to manage the library and newly formed college. For two years the first floor of the library building served as a lecture room, but thereafter the library occupied the entire structure. Italianate in design, the library's exterior is distinguished by round-arched windows and doors, accentuated quoins, a belt course dividing the first and second floors, and a high, bracketed cornice with a broad overhang.
Municipal

IRON COUNTY
Ironton
ST. PAUL'S EPISCOPAL CHURCH
Northwest corner, Knob and
Reynolds Streets
1870–1871

An all-wood, Gothic Revival church, St. Paul's is an outstanding example of a style of architecture which is relatively uncommon in rural Missouri. The church measures 23 feet by 60 feet. Its exterior walls are covered by a vertical wood sheathing with accentuated vertical ribs which terminate at the eaves in a Gothic-type molding. There are wooden buttresses on the exterior side walls of the nave and the end walls of the transept gable. Windows of Gothic proportion and form contain partially restored stained glass framed in wood. The exposed interior roof framing system of the nave is constructed of shaped wooden timbers with Gothic-style ornament including pendants and scroll brackets.
Private

IRON COUNTY
Pilot Knob vicinity
FORT DAVIDSON
On County Route 21 south of the
intersection with County Route V
1864

Fort Davidson was built in 1863 under orders from General J. W. Davidson, commander of the Southeast Missouri District. The hexagonal fort was situated on a level plain encircled by mountains, and it guarded the northern approach to the Arcadia Valley. In the fall of 1864 Confederate General Sterling Price determined to capture Fort Davidson. His force of 9,000 cavalrymen attacked across the open plain and were repulsed by the fort's 1,000 defenders within its nine-foot earthen walls. General Price failed to mount artillery in the surrounding hills on the first day of the battle. The Union commander took advantage of this oversight and with his entire force evacuated the fort during the night. Price's failure to take Fort Davidson was a blow to the

Confederate cause as it enabled the Union forces in St. Louis and Jefferson City to be reinforced.
Federal

JACKSON COUNTY
Independence
JACKSON COUNTY JAIL AND MARSHAL'S HOUSE
217 N. Main Street
1859–1860

The complex contains the Jackson County Jail (1859), the jailer's house (1859–1860), a jail annex (1900–1901), and a one-room, frame schoolhouse moved to the site in 1959. The jailer's or marshal's house is a two-story, Federal style brick structure. The stone jail is made of limestone blocks quarried locally; the jail annex is two stories high and built of brick. In 1933 the county ceased using the complex as a jail, and it presently serves as a museum and as headquarters for the county historical society.
Municipal

JACKSON COUNTY
Independence
TEMPLE SITE
Corner of Lexington Avenue and
River Boulevard

The advent of the Mormons in 1830 was important both socially and politically to the state of Missouri. Independence was revealed to Joseph Smith, prophet of the Latter-day Saints, as the future city of Zion for his people. Consequently the Temple Site was dedicated on August 3, 1831, although construction was never begun, due to conflict between the Mormons and the non-Mormon citizens of Independence. Hostilities grew worse, and in 1833 the Mormons fled from Jackson County across the Missouri River to Clay County. The Mormon wars developed into a bitter political conflict, ended only by a permanent exile of the Latter-day Saints by the governor of Missouri in 1838. A marker indicates where the temple was to have stood.
Private

JACKSON COUNTY
Independence
VAILE PARK (HARVEY M. VAILE MANSION)
1500 N. Liberty Street and 1518 N.
Osage Street
c. 1871–1881, Asa Cross

The Vaile Mansion, home of Colonel Harvey M. Vaile from 1881 until his death in 1895, is an elaborate French Renaissance Revival home. Red brick with white limestone trim, the house has two full stories and a third immediately under the

ornately tiled mansard roof. The most striking aspect of the house is the maximum utilization of each supporting surface resulting from an abundance of wooden carving on the walls and iron filagree work on the roof. The basic four walls do not rise in four planes but have two-story bays terminating in dormers at the third story. A combination horse barn and carriage house is situated to the west of the house.
Private; not accessible to the public

JACKSON COUNTY
Kansas City
KATZ BUILDING (BOLEY BUILDING)
1130 Walnut Street
1909, Louis Curtiss

The Boley Building is noteworthy because of its extraordinary structural daring and design. It was one of the first metal and glass curtain-wall buildings in the world and employed, for the first time anywhere, rolled steel columns rather than columns built up from sections. Louis Curtiss (1865–1924) was assistant superintendent of buildings for Kansas City (1890) and worked on construction of the City Hall. He also experimented with suspended building structures. The Boley Building is six stories high and has a steel frame. Steel columns in the frame are withdrawn from the facades to effect cantilevered floors and curtain walls. The floors are constructed of reinforced concrete, while the walls themselves are brick, white enameled terra cotta, iron, and glass. The south facade of the building is divided horizontally by five iron spandrels into six levels of continuous glass ribbon windows. The lower two stories and the interior of the building have been totally remodeled.
Private

JACKSON COUNTY (also in Johnson
County, Kans.)
Kansas City
MAJORS, ALEXANDER, HOUSE
8145 State Line Road

Alexander Majors, field coordinator for the freighting firm of Russell, Majors, and Waddell, occupied this house for two years (1856–1858). Nearby, wagons were outfitted to haul supplies to army posts scattered along the frontier. Russell, Majors, and Waddell had a virtual monopoly on the army freighting business and Alexander Majors at one time supervised a force of 3,500 wagons, 4,000 men and 40,000 oxen. The firm began encountering financial difficulties in 1857, and in 1861 it was forced to declare bankruptcy. Covered with white clapboard and built in an unusual T-shape, the Majors House is a two-story frame dwelling with Greek Revival woodwork and interior detail.

Some alterations have been made to the exterior, and these are readily discernible. *Private; not accessible to the public*

JACKSON COUNTY
Kansas City
SCARRITT BUILDING AND ARCADE
Corner of 9th and Grand Streets and
819 Walnut Street
1906–1907, Root and Siemens

The architectural dictates of Louis Sullivan strongly influenced construction of the Scarritt Building. There is a curious disorientation of the building's plan in relation to the main entrances, but this was done to allow more natural light to enter. Every exterior element, despite its factual relation to the frame, gives a feeling of verticality and scale, expresses the height and strength inherent within, and does not destroy the unity of composition. The eleven-story steel skeleton supports walls sheathed in brick and terra cotta. At ground level the building is rectangular, but changes to a modified H-plan at the second story. The Arcade is a four-story steel frame structure connected to the main building by a tunnel. The walls are faced with unadorned brick on the north, south, and east and by ranged ashlar on the west.
Private

JACKSON COUNTY
Kansas City
20 W. 9TH STREET BUILDING (NEW YORK LIFE BUILDING)
20 W. 9th Street
1887–1890, McKim, Mead and White

The New York Life Building is a large Renaissance Revival stone and brick office building. The H-plan structure comprises two ten-story arms linked by a twelve-story square tower. The classical facades on the south and west elevations are visually divided into several major horizontal sections, each of which is about two stories high. The first horizontal section on the south facade is cut by five arches; the central arch, which is the widest, serves as the main entrance. Centered over this entrance is a two-ton bronze eagle protecting her young, sculpted by Augustus St. Gaudens. The interior of the building features much pink marble and cherry wood paneling. Once the largest and tallest building in Kansas City, the structure was built during a period of rapid economic development both locally and nationwide.
Private

JACKSON COUNTY
Kansas City
WORNALL HOUSE
146 W. 61st Street
1858

The Wornall House is a two-story, L-shaped brick structure ornamented on the west facade by a central portico with four, giant square pillars. Architecturally the house is significant as one of the earliest Greek Revival buildings in the area. John B. Wornall, a native of Kentucky and a farmer active in community affairs, built the house. He served as president of the National Bank of Kansas City and chairman of the board of trustees of William Jewell College in Liberty, Mo. When conflict developed on the Kansas-Missouri border during the Civil War, the Wornall House became the headquarters for Col. Charles Jennison, Union commander of the 7th Kansas Cavalry. John Wornall had refused to comply with General Order No. 11, issued on August 25, 1863, requiring the evacuation of all Southern sympathizers, and would not give proof of his loyalty to the Union. Thus, his property was seized by the federal government. During the battle of Westport (October 23–24, 1863) the Wornall House was used as a hospital and army headquarters by both Confederate and Union troops.
Private

JACKSON COUNTY
Sibley
FORT OSAGE
North edge of Sibley on the Missouri River
1806

Founded by General William Clark, Fort Osage was the first United States Army post west of the Mississippi River. It was one of the most successful of the 28 trading houses operated by the federal government between 1795 and 1822. The factory system was instituted because of a benevolent desire to guarantee Indians fair prices for their goods and to protect them from the harmful effects of the commercial trader's alcohol. So successful was the operation that for a time most United States furs were secured through the factories. At the insistence of commercial traders, the system was abolished by Congress in 1822.
County
NHL

JEFFERSON COUNTY
Hillsboro vicinity
SANDY CREEK COVERED BRIDGE
5 miles north of Hillsboro on U.S. 21, east on Goldman Road, and southwest on Lemay Ferry Road
1872

Sandy Creek Covered Bridge is one of only four surviving covered bridges in Missouri. It is one of three which employs the Howe truss construction. Spanning Sandy Creek, the bridge was erected as part of a countywide road building program after the Civil War. It measures approximately 75 feet 10 inches long by 18 feet 10 inches wide and is supported by concrete abutments at either end and by concrete piers in the creek bed. High water destroyed the bridge in 1886, but it was rebuilt a few months later. The county chamber of commerce restored the structure in 1952.
State

JOHNSON COUNTY
Warrensburg
JOHNSON COUNTY COURTHOUSE
(OLD JOHNSON COUNTY COURTHOUSE)
Old Public Square
1838–1841

The Old Johnson County Courthouse is a square, two-story, Federal style brick structure which served the county for 40 years. Set upon a limestone foundation, the courthouse is square and has a three-bay facade. Only one original door, on the north side, remains. The hip roof was framed to receive a cupola which was never built, and at each corner of the roof are four rebuilt chimney stacks. Inside on the first floor is the large room used for court proceedings. The second floor is divided into one large and two smaller rooms for a clerk's office and the grand and petty jury rooms.
Private

LAFAYETTE COUNTY
Lexington
ANDERSON HOUSE AND LEXINGTON BATTLEFIELD
Bounded on the west by 10th Street, on the northwest by the Missouri Pacific Railroad, on the south by Utah and Wood Streets, and on the east by the continuation of 15th Street
1853, 1861

The Anderson House, overlooking the Missouri River, was built by Col. Oliver Anderson, a native of Lexington, Ky. Anderson came to Missouri in 1851 and

opened a rope- and bag-making factory to use locally grown hemp. At the outbreak of the Civil War all inhabitants of Missouri were required to take an oath of allegiance to the United States. When Colonel Anderson refused to comply, he was imprisoned and his house and lands confiscated. Confederate troops under the command of Gen. Sterling Price attempted to take the city of Lexington during a 3–day battle (September 18–20, 1861). The Anderson House served as a field hospital for both Union and Confederate armies and changed hands three times during the fighting. Most of the battle was fought on a hilltop about one-quarter of a mile from the house. Confederate forces eventually forced the surrender of the Union defenders. The two-and-one-half-story, late Greek Rivival brick house was repaired in 1933–1934 as a Works Project Administration undertaking and restoration work has been effected since then. Trenches used by the Union soldiers during the battle are visible on the hillside adjoining the house.
State
HABS

LAFAYETTE COUNTY
Lexington
LAFAYETTE COUNTY COURTHOUSE
Public Square
1847, William Daugherty

The classical, temple-form Lafayette County Courthouse is one of the oldest continuously used courthouses in Missouri. It is the third (1825, 1832) such structure built by the county. Rectangular in shape, the two-story courthouse has a tetrastyle portico with Ionic columns across the front and a later wooden cupola on the roof. The main entrance contains double doors framed by pilasters, and pilasters alternate with windows on the other three sides. Inside, the original courtroom has been divided into three rooms (a county court, a county clerk's office, and a storage vault), but it retains its stamped metal ceiling and wood wainscoting. The second-floor courtroom has been refurbished. In 1854 a separate office building was constructed on the east lawn. It was remodeled at the turn of the century and an addition was erected in 1939.
County

LAWRENCE COUNTY
Mount Vernon vicinity
OLD SPANISH FORT
ARCHEOLOGICAL SITE
3 miles south of Mount Vernon
Pre-Columbian

This site is one of only two known fortified areas in Missouri which still retain evidence of the original protective wall. No cultural material of any kind has been found on the site, so it has never been assigned to any definite archeological period. The people who constructed the fort may have been ancestors of the Hopewell builders of Fort Ancient in Ohio. Archeological investigation may link the fort site with other, smaller possible habitation areas in the adjacent valley. The earthwork itself measures roughly 110 yards by 100 yards and is completely surrounded by a ditch.
Private

LINN COUNTY
Laclede
PERSHING, GEN. JOHN J.,
BOYHOOD HOME
State and Worlow Streets
1866–1882

Built about 1857, the house was purchased by the Pershings in 1866, when the future general was six years old. The family lived here through 1882. Pershing received an appointment to West Point, graduated, served with distinction in the Spanish-American War, and was later sent to Mexico to capture Pancho Villa. He is best remembered as commander in chief of the American Expeditionary Forces in Europe during World War I. The house itself is a two-and-one-half-story clapboard, frame structure of modified Gothic Revival design. It contains furniture from the period of the Pershings' occupancy.
State

LINN COUNTY
Laclede vicinity
LOCUST CREEK COVERED BRIDGE
3 miles west of Laclede on U.S. 36, then north one mile and east .63 mile on a gravel road
1868

The Locust Creek Covered Bridge is one of four surviving covered bridges in the state and one of three employing the Howe truss in its construction. William Howe of Massachusetts patented this invention in 1840. He combined wood and metal in his truss, employing wood for the diagonal braces, and lower and upper chords, and the end posts; iron rods were used for the king posts. Traffic still crosses the bridge.
State

MARION COUNTY
Hannibal
TWAIN, MARK, BOYHOOD HOME
206–208 Hill Street
1839

Samuel L. Clemens, universally known as Mark Twain, lived in this house from 1839, when he was four years old, until 1853. Two of his novels, *The Adventures of Tom Sawyer* and *The Adventures of Huckleberry Finn*, reflect Twain's experiences during this period. A frame building adjoining the two-story frame house was built in 1844 by the author's father, Judge John M. Clemens, as a law office.
Municipal
NHL

MARION COUNTY
Palmyra
GARDNER HOUSE
421 S. Main Street
19th century

The Gardner House was a tavern located on the north-south stagecoach route between St. Louis and towns in eastern Iowa. Although the exact date of construction is unknown, it was used as a tavern as early as 1828 and became a local center for public affairs. During the period 1847 to 1870 the building had varied uses (residence, hotel, and elementary school). By 1870 the house was again serving as a tavern. Transitional in style, it exhibits features characteristic of both Federal and Greek Revival architecture. It is built of brick in a two-story, L-shaped plan with a ridge roof and two three-step gables. After restoration the house will function as the town library.
Municipal; not accessible to the public

MISSISSIPPI COUNTY
Crosno vicinity
CROSNO FORTIFIED VILLAGE
ARCHEOLOGICAL SITE
1 mile south of Crosno
Pre-Columbian

Crosno Fortified Village Archeological Site is important because of the span of human occupation and the presence of a temple mound on the site. Cultural artifacts indicate human habitation from Middle Baytown (pre-Mississippian) times through the early part of the Late Mississippian Period. Previously there were four mounds on the site; now only the largest remains. Dimensions of the temple mound (measured in 1954) are 130 feet long, 100 feet wide, and 18 feet high. A barn and trees are on top of the mound which is part of the levee.
Private

MISSISSIPPI COUNTY
Dorena vicinity
BECKWITH'S FORT
ARCHEOLOGICAL SITE
SE 1/4 sec. 29, T. 24 N., R. 17 E.
Pre-Columbian

This site is marked by one large temple mound and six smaller mounds in generally good condition. Two other mounds have been destroyed by flooding and erosion. Excavations have revealed traces of stockades built by many of the groups that occupied the site from Middle Baytown to Middle Mississippian times.
State

MONITEAU COUNTY
California
MONITEAU COUNTY COURTHOUSE
SQUARE
Public Square
Mid- to late 19th century

Moniteau County was organized in 1845, and the town of California was laid out the same year. The present Courthouse Square is representative of many similar complexes of the early 19th century. Brick, stone, cast iron, and wood commercial structures dating from the latter half of the last century surround the courthouse on four sides. They are generally two stories high with structural cast iron elements on the facades. The courthouse is Classical Revival and resembles the former Missouri state capitol which burned in 1911. Built of brick with smooth-faced stone trim, it is three bays wide with recessed panels framing the window and door openings. There is a two-story semicircular portico on the central bay of the main facade which has brick columns with cast iron bases and capitals. An octagonal cupola with a slightly pointed dome is centered on the front half of the roof.
Municipal public/private

MONITEAU COUNTY
Sandy Hook vicinity
GEIGER ARCHEOLOGICAL SITE
NW 1/4, sec. 11, T. 46 N., R. 14 W.
Pre-Columbian

This is one of the noteworthy open sites of the late Archaic period in central Missouri. Although the area is now under cultivation, damage has been limited to the plow zone. The habitation areas are circular and contain buried clay and rubbish. A scraper type known as the Clear Fork gouge and other material found here identify the site with the Sedalia Focus. Further investigation may yield important information concerning late Archaic culture in this locality.
Private

MONROE COUNTY
Florida vicinity
CRIGLER MOUND GROUP
ARCHEOLOGICAL SITE
1 mile north of Florida
Prehistoric

Seven mounds of the Crigler Mound Group Archeological Site are presently visible. Six are in good condition, but the seventh has been almost completely destroyed by road construction. There have been no excavations of the site, consequently the cultural background of the inhabitants and the dates of their occupation are unknown. It is thought, however, that the people were Woodland in affiliation.
Private

MONROE COUNTY
Florida vicinity
TWAIN, MARK, BIRTHPLACE CABIN
Mark Twain State Park, .25 mile
south of Florida on Mo. 107
1835–1839

Samuel Langhorne Clemens was born in this two-room cabin on November 30, 1835. The Clemens family lived in the Florida area until November 1839, when they moved to Hannibal. The cabin is constructed of native red oak clapboard siding with log sills, studs, and joists. The pine floor is original, although some alterations have been made to other portions of the building. Previously located one-quarter of a mile north, the cabin was moved to its present location in 1930.
State

MONROE COUNTY
Paris vicinity
UNION COVERED BRIDGE
c. 6 miles southwest of Paris on the
Elk Fork of the Salt River
1870–1871

Located on the old Paris to Fayette road, the Union Covered Bridge is the only surviving example of the Burr-arch truss construction in Missouri. Theodore Burr, originator of this type of bridge, has altered the more common king post construction by strengthening and extending the truss with an arch composed of segments of hewn timber bolted to the bridge frame. Measuring 125 feet long by 17 feet 6 inches wide, the Union Covered Bridge was restored by the Missouri Park Board in 1968.
State

MONTGOMERY COUNTY
Big Spring vicinity
PINNACLE LAKE ROCKSHELTER
3 miles northeast of Big Spring
Pre-Columbian

Pinnacle Lake Rockshelter is a natural formation in a sandstone outcropping on the right side of Pinnacle Creek. The shelter is 91 feet wide at the entrance, 21 feet high at the highest point of its lip, and 40 feet deep from the entrance to the rear junction of the shelter roof and deposits. To date, the lower levels of the site have not yielded any diagnostic Archaic material since the deposits are only 48 inches deep. Future excavation, however, may associate through seriation the deposits of the Pinnacle Lake site and those of Graham Cave archeological site 10 miles northwest.
Private

MONTGOMERY COUNTY
Mineola vicinity
GRAHAM CAVE
.5 mile north of Mineola
c. 8000 B.C.

Graham Cave was the first site to provide indications of the development of eastern Archaic cultures within the time range previously assigned only to the paleo-Indian. Prior to its excavation there had been little investigation of the Archaic period in the Middle West. Excavations have given evidence of a group of people living in a forest environment and depending on hunting, fishing, and gathering foods from wild plants for subsistence. Especially interesting artifacts were fragments of burnt clay bearing accidental impressions of weaving and basketry, indicating a knowledge of these techniques at an extremely early date in the Mississippi Valley.
State
NHL

NEW MADRID COUNTY
Lilbourn
LILBOURN FORTIFIED VILLAGE
ARCHEOLOGICAL SITE
Within city limits of Lilbourn
Pre-Columbian

This site, commonly known as Mound Cemetery, is marked by four mounds. A portion of the site is currently under cultivation; the presence of non-Indian graves has contributed to the preservation of the mounds over the years. Although house depressions and fortification walls are no longer visible, investigation has shown that the Lilbourn Site represents the New Madrid Focus of the Early Mississippian

Period. The temple mound at the site is one of the three largest remaining in the state.
Private

NEW MADRID COUNTY
Sikeston vicinity
SIKESTON FORTIFIED VILLAGE
ARCHEOLOGICAL SITE
2 miles southeast of Sikeston
Pre-Columbian

Sikeston is one of the largest Mississippian village sites in southeast Missouri. Occupied in both pre-Mississippian (Baytown) and Mississippian times, the area should provide considerable information about changes in burial, architectural, and ceramic traditions over several hundred years. Pottery found here represents both Baytown and Mississippian cultures, and investigations have led one archeologist to suggest that the fortified villages were first built as ceremonial centers with burial mounds and temple mounds and later (during Mississippian times) a residential area grew up and was fortified. All fortified villages had features in common: location on a bluff or river channel, fortification walls and/or ditches, house depressions, a temple mound, and low burial mounds. Five of the original 13 mounds are still visible today.
Private; not accessible to the public

NEWTON COUNTY
Diamond vicinity
GEORGE WASHINGTON CARVER
NATIONAL MONUMENT
3 miles south of Diamond
19th and 20th centuries

Born into slavery in 1860, George Washington Carver overcame great obstacles in his rise to world-wide prominence as a teacher, botanist, agronomist, and pioneer conservationist. His greatest scientific achievements were made during his 47 years on the staff of Tuskegee Institute, Alabama. The George Washington Carver National Monument encompasses a self-guiding trail winding around the woods and fields where Carver walked as a boy. Along the trail can be seen the birthplace cabin site, the Robert Amendola statue of Carver as a boy, the relocated Moses Carver dwelling, and the Carver family cemetery.
Federal
NPS; 210 acres

OREGON COUNTY
Riverton vicinity
PIGMAN MOUND ARCHEOLOGICAL
SITE
3 miles southeast of Riverton
Pre-Columbian

Pigman Mound is in a good state of preservation. It is roughly circular, 7.5 feet high and approximately 170 feet in diameter. Truncated Mississippian temple mounds are quite rare this far west of the Mississippi River Valley in Missouri, so the existence of an isolated mound stimulates inquiry as to its influence and effect upon the older Woodland culture of the area. Limited excavations were carried on in 1959 and 1960. Dr. Carl H. Chapman, of the University of Missouri, feels that the Pigman Mound may be a special ceremonial center similar to the Spiro Mound in Oklahoma. Further excavation of the mound and its environs is desirable.
Private; not accessible to the public

PEMISCOT COUNTY
Caruthersville vicinity
MURPHY MOUND ARCHEOLOGICAL
SITE
Both sides of County Route D, 1.5 miles south of County Routes D and U junction
Pre-Columbian to 16th century

The largest existing Mississippian temple mound in Missouri is located at the Murphy Mound Archeological Site. It measures 300 feet long, 250 feet wide, 15 feet high, and is covered with grass, light brush, and trees. Slight depressions exist in the mound from past looting and vandalism. A few bricks, remnants of a farmhouse that once stood on top of the mound, are visible. A smaller mound, approximately 32 feet high which has been greatly reduced by plowing, lies southeast of the temple mound. Bulldozing and other excavations have exposed burials of extended, bundle, and cremated types. These burials indicate a connection with the Walls Focus in the Memphis area. Present evidence points to an on-site occupation from Middle Mississippian times to the middle of the 16th century. It is assumed that future excavation may help to explain the unusual use of burned clay and cane construction and the ceremonial burial customs of the Mississippian Indians in both prehistoric and early historic times.
Private

PEMISCOT COUNTY
Denton vicinity
DENTON MOUND AND VILLAGE
ARCHEOLOGICAL SITE
1 mile northeast of Denton
Pre-Columbian

This is the best preserved early Nodena Phase (Late Mississippian) site known in Missouri. Several house areas surrounding the mounds are indicated by concentrations of burned clay, ash, bones, and artifact material. In recent times the mounds have been used as burial places by local residents. When the excavated material is further analyzed, the Denton Site may yield important information on the interrelationship of the Indian culture of the Pemiscot Bayou Phase with the Nodena Phase.
Private

PEMISCOT COUNTY
Wardell vicinity
J. M. WALLACE ARCHEOLOGICAL
SITE (WARDELL MOUNDS)
1 mile southwest of Wardell

Two large, well-preserved mounds plus a possible cemetery, village, and fortification are located within the J. M. Wallace Archeological Site. Experts consider this site to be an outstanding example of a civic-ceremonial center representative of the Mississippian theme within the Southeast Riverine region. The larger of the two mounds rises to a height of 11 feet and has a diameter of 90 feet. There is evidence to indicate that a third mound was destroyed by plowing. A 19th-century cemetery was built on the western end of the smaller mound, thus partially destroying it.
Private; not accessible to the public

PERRY COUNTY
Wittenburg vicinity
TOWER ROCK
1 mile south of Wittenburg in the Mississippi River

Standing 80 feet above the normal water level, Tower Rock dominates the Mississippi River at a point 150 feet from the Missouri shore. Formed of eroded limestone, the rock supports a growth of grasses and shrubs on its summit. The rock was known to the Indians before the time of Columbus, and it posed a serious navigational hazard to early river travelers. Before the advent of steam power, river boats could not ascend beyond this point, because of whirlpools and the threat of rocks, unless towed around the cape on the Illinois side.
Federal

PHELPS COUNTY
Newburg vicinity
OZARK IRON FURNACE STACK
SW 1/4 NW 1/4 sec. 21, T. 37 N., R.
9 W. and SE 1/4 NE 1/4 sec. 20, T.
37 N., R. 9 W.
1873–1877

Pig iron production by means of charcoal heated blast furnaces was an important Missouri industry during the late 19th century. William James, son of Thomas James, who founded the Maramec Iron Works, organized the Ozark Iron Company in 1872. The new ironworks was constructed only 50 feet from the Atlantic & Pacific Railroad (now the St. Louis-San Francisco), near a main transportation artery rather than the ore supply. Once in operation, the hot blast furnace produced 30 tons of pig iron per day. Various setbacks plagued James until he was forced to declare bankruptcy in 1877. The furnace operated once more in 1883–1884. Constructed of sandstone blocks, the furnace stack is pyramidal in shape and about 40 feet high. There are three arched openings at the furnace base. The east opening provided egress for the molten metal, while the other two conducted hot blast into the furnace. West of the furnace stack is a similar stone structure which is believed to have supported the boilers and the hot blast heating chamber equipment. Also on the property are the remains of a two-and-one-half-story brick building believed to have been the company store.
Private

PHELPS COUNTY
Newburg vicinity
GOURD CREEK CAVE ARCHEOLOGICAL SITE
8 miles southeast of Newburg
Prehistoric

This site occupies a large cave in a formation of Gasconade dolomite with a small stream flowing in through it. The talus extends to a depth of approximately 20 feet. The significance of the site stems from the possibility that it may contain one of the longest cultural sequences in the Gasconade River drainage area and perhaps in all of southern Missouri. Excavations in 1964 produced materials which may establish connections with the Tick Creek Cave Archeological Site and other cave sites in the region. The lower levels may contain Dalton material; the upper levels have yielded pottery of the Meramac Springs Focus, which dates as late as A.D. 1200.
Private

PHELPS COUNTY
St. James vicinity
MARAMEC IRONWORKS DISTRICT
7 miles south of St. James on Mo. 8
1826–1876

Maramec Ironworks District is Missouri's most complete surviving example of an early, large-scale iron industry. At the height of the operation (1863–1872) the Maramec Ironworks was a densely populated area of 300 people, most of whom were employed at the ironworks. During this period there were 42 industrial, commercial, and residential buildings within the ironworks complex. Structures still extant are the stack of the cold-blast furnace, five refinery forge stacks, and three dwellings (the Maramec House, the McDole Cabin, and the Jolley Cabin). The five refinery forges, located southeast of the blast furnace, converted the pig iron from the furnace into wrought-iron bars or "blooms." Each refinery forge stood about 22 feet high, was constructed of cut sandstone blocks, and had a brick gas chimney. Thomas James and Samuel Massey established the Maramec Ironworks in 1826. By 1847 Thomas James' son William had purchased Massey's share of the business. The works prospered during the Civil War, and in 1874 James erected the Ozark Furnace, a hot-blast furnace located about 50 miles west of Maramec. In the early 1870's the decline in iron prices and the discovery of rich iron deposits in the Lake Superior region initiated the decline of Maramec. In 1876 the Maramec furnace was shut down, and in 1877 the Ozark furnace was also closed.
Private

PIKE COUNTY
Eolia vicinity
ST. JOHN'S EPISCOPAL CHURCH
.25 mile north of Eolia on County
Route D, .25 mile east on County
Route H
c. 1856

St. John's is unusual because it combines elements of both Greek and Gothic Revival architecture in one structure. The basic form of the church is that of a Greek temple, but it lacks the traditional pedimented portico. Gothic elements are visible in the pointed arch windows and the intersecting arc muntins. The exterior bricks were handmade. Inside is one large room with painted plaster walls. There are two vestry rooms at the north end. St. John's closely resembles churches in piedmont Virginia built a few years earlier.
Private

PLATTE COUNTY
Kansas City vicinity
DEISTER ARCHEOLOGICAL SITE
Within Kansas City city limits, Line
Creek Park
Pre-Columbian

The Deister Archeological Site was occupied by Middle Hopewell and Late Woodland peoples. Excavations were made in 1964–1965 and again in 1969. Pottery found then led archeologists to estimate the earlier occupation date as 400 A.D. and the later one as 850 A.D. Located within Line Creek Park, the site is now grassland. Previously, the land was cultivated or used for pasture.
Municipal

PLATTE COUNTY
Kansas City vicinity
RENNER VILLAGE ARCHEOLOGICAL SITE
Within a triangle formed by U.S. 169
and 71 and Mo. 45, and partly on the
west side of U.S. 169
Pre-Columbian

The Renner Village Archeological Site is the type habitation site of the initial pottery-bearing culture of the Prairie-Plains region. Designated Kansas City Hopewell, this aboriginal complex appears to represent a movement of Hopewellian peoples from the Illinois River Valley around the beginning of the Christian era. It apparently coexisted with Plains Woodland complexes until about A.D. 500.
Private

PULASKI COUNTY
Buckhorn vicinity
DECKER CAVE ARCHEOLOGICAL SITE
4.5 miles southwest of Buckhorn
Pre-Columbian

The Decker Site consists of a large cave, an adjacent rockshelter, and a nearby riverside village and campsite. The cave, at the base of a small dolomite bluff, has an entrance measuring 40 feet wide by 8 feet high. Surface material recovered here indicates habitation from Archaic through Late Woodland times. Fragments of lithic artifacts of Woodland variety, an abundance of fresh water mussel shells, bone fragments, numerous potsherds, and a disturbed human burial have been recovered. The pottery type represented by the sherds appears to be of the Meramec Spring Cord Marked variety (Late Woodland). Archeologists believe that the site offers great potential for the study of prehistoric cultures along the

Gasconade River in south central Missouri.
Federal; not accessible to the public

Cairo vicinity
MITCHELL PETROGLYPH ARCHEOLOGICAL SITE
6 miles east of Cairo
Pre-Columbian

The Mitchell Site is a small rock shelter containing numerous pecked and carved pre-Columbian petroglyphs. Of particular interest are some 33 well-executed intaglios which presumably represent elongated human and thunderbird figures.
Private

St. Charles
FIRST MISSOURI STATE CAPITOL BUILDINGS
208–216 S. Main Street
1821–1826

Buildings A, B, and C (lettered from north to south when facing the buildings' facades) are significant as the first official meetingplace of the state legislature after Missouri's admission to the Union. While convened in St. Charles, the territorial legislature passed the second Missouri Compromise. The first constitution submitted by Missouri for congressional approval forbade the immigration of free Negroes into Missouri. Congress objected strongly to this provision so a second compromise was adopted prohibiting Missouri from depriving citizens of other states (i.e., free Negroes) of their rights. On June 4, 1821, the general assembly approved this condition, and on August 10, 1821, President James Monroe signed the enabling act admitting Missouri to statehood. Construction dates for buildings A, B, and C are not known. When St. Charles was selected as the site of the state capital, the owners offered the second floor of these buildings for use as a legislative chamber. The second floor of Building B served as the house of representatives chamber, and the second floor of Building C became the senate chamber. The second floor of buildings B and C were also used by the St. Charles County court, and county circuit court, and the superior court. The second floor of Building A was converted into the governor's office. Building D was not a part of the first state capitol complex, but is of the same period.
State
HABS

St. Charles
ST. CHARLES HISTORIC DISTRICT
Roughly bound on the north by Madison Street; on the east by the Missouri River; on the south by Chauncey Street; and on the west by an alley from Boonslick Road to Madison Street.

St. Charles was founded in 1769 by Louis Blanchette. Located south of the confluence of the Missouri and Mississippi rivers, the village was settled primarily by French traders, hunters, and farmers, and soon became an important outfitting station for water and overland travelers. St. Charles was the starting point of the Boonslick Road, which ran west to Arrow Rock and there joined the Santa Fe Trail. The buildings within this eight-and-one-half-block area date from the late 18th to the early 19th century and are constructed of handmade brick, quarried limestone, and hewn timber. Of the 100 structures in the district, 60 are noteworthy. The earliest buildings are masonry construction on low stone foundations. Typical trim includes simple wooden cornices and monolithic stone lintels or brick relieving arches over window and door openings. Missouri's First State Capitol (208–216 S. Main Street) and Stone Row (314–330 S. Main Street) are already on the National Register. Three other notable buildings in the historic district are the Federal style brick residence at 625 S. Main Street, the Schemmer Brothers Wagon and Blacksmith Shop (late 19th-century), and the Western House (a combination hostelry, stable, and blacksmith shop). Many of the structures on S. Main Street have living quarters above street level businesses.
Multiple public/private

St. Charles
STONE ROW
314–330 S. Main Street
Early 19th century

Stone Row, which dates from the early settlement of St. Charles, is significant architecturally because it has survived almost as built with the original fabric largely intact. The two remaining stone buildings form a row, two and one-half stories in height, which fronts directly onto the sidewalk. At a later date a brick section was constructed to join the two flanking stone structures. Windows and doors have large, cut limestone lintels of uniform size, and the cornice of modillion blocks and the dentil course run across the entire facade including the later brick section. Stone Row housed early St. Charles' business establishments with residences on the upper stories.
Private; not accessible to the public

ANHEUSER-BUSCH BREWERY
721 Pestalozzi Street
1868

In 1861 German immigrant Adolphus Busch married the daughter of Eberhard Anheuser, proprietor of a small brewery. Taking control of the business four years later, he more than trebled its output by 1873. In that year Busch perfected a method of pasteurizing his product prior to bottling it, making distant distribution possible. He also pioneered in the use of refrigerator cars for shipment and icehouses for storage of beer. The oldest buildings are the three-story administration building erected in 1868, a one-story stable built in 1885, and the six-story Brew House erected in 1891–1892. These buildings are of elaborate brick construction ornamented on the exterior with gargoyles and other imaginative figures.
Private
NHL

BISSELL STREET WATER TOWER
Intersection of Bissell Street and Blair Avenue
1885–1886, William S. Eames

The Bissell Street Water Tower is one of St. Louis' three surviving 19th-century towers built to house standpipes. Constant pressure was maintained in the city water mains by pumping water into the standpipes. The Bissell Street Water Tower is 194 feet 8 inches high. Its base is rusticated stonework and is surmounted by a brick shaft with stone string courses. Above the shaft is a brick platform with a terra cotta balustrade which supports a brick lantern and a slate covered iron roof. Inside the tower is the standpipe and a narrow, spiral stairway of wrought iron. The city ceased using the tower in June, 1913, when pumping engines rendered it obsolete.
Municipal; not accessible to the public

EADS BRIDGE
Spanning the Mississippi River at Washington Street
1874, James B. Eads

Named for its designer, Eads Bridge was the first American bridge (as well as the first major one in the world) in which steel was employed in the principal members. The secondary members and the tubes enveloping the steel staves forming the arch ribs are of wrought iron. The arches were erected by the cantilever method rather than being supported during construction upon the traditionally used temporary centering. This innovation was widely copied. The bridge carries a roadway on the upper deck and a railroad on the lower one.

Private

NHL; HABS

ST. LOUIS (independent city)
GOLDENROD SHOWBOAT
400 N. Wharf Street
1909

The *Goldenrod* is the last remaining example of the modern era of showboating that ended in the 1920's. Known as "The World's Greatest Showboat," it was among the largest and most elaborately decorated showboats ever constructed. It was permanently docked on the St. Louis waterfront in 1937. Although somewhat altered, the boat retains much of its original character. The *Goldenrod's* productions feature melodrama typical of the late showboating period.

Private

NHL

ST. LOUIS (independent city)
GRAND AVENUE WATER TOWER
Intersection of E. Grand Avenue and 20th Street
1871, George I. Barnett

The city of St. Louis constructed three water towers between 1871 and 1889 in order to equalize pressure throughout the city. The Grand Avenue Tower was the first built for the purpose of housing an iron standpipe five feet in diameter. A masonry sheathing encases the standpipe, and the entire Corinthian tower is 154 feet high and constructed of brick and stone with cast iron trim. Improved methods of equalizing water pressure were introduced in the early 20th century, so the Grand Avenue Tower was not used after 1912, at which time the central standpipe was removed.

Municipal; not accessible to the public

ST. LOUIS (independent city)
JEFFERSON NATIONAL EXPANSION MEMORIAL NATIONAL HISTORIC SITE
Mississippi River between Washington and Poplar Streets
1803

Jefferson National Expansion Memorial commemorates the growth of the United States that followed President Thomas Jefferson's Louisiana Purchase in 1803. It occupies more than 80 acres on the site of the original village of St. Louis founded by Pierre Laclede in 1764. Two buildings —the Old Courthouse (1839), scene of the first Dred Scott trial, and the Old Cathedral (1834)—have been restored.

The dominant feature of the memorial is a 630-foot stainless steel arch (1967) which stands on the west bank of the Mississippi River. St. Louis was chosen as the focal point for interpreting and memorializing the Nation's westward expansion because of its 19th-century role as "Gateway to the West," the supply base and marketplace of the frontier.

Federal

NPS; 85.46 acres

HABS

ST. LOUIS (independent city)
OLD POST OFFICE
Olive and Locust, 8th and 9th Streets
1874–1882, Alfred B. Mullett

Alfred B. Mullett, Supervising Architect of the U.S. Treasury (1865–1874), designed several post offices and customhouses across the country. The St. Louis Post Office was one of these. Land was acquired by the U.S. government in a then-residential section of St. Louis in 1872, and construction began about two years later. Excavation of the site revealed a shifting, fluid layer of sand between the ground level and the underlying bedrock. Stabilization was effected by driving pine logs into the sand, packing these with cotton bales, and covering the entire area with a 4-foot layer of concrete. Stylistically the post office is French Renaissance Revival composed of three regular stories plus an attic surmounted by a quadrangular mansard dome. Daniel Chester French's sculpture *America at War and America at Peace* adorns the dome's southern facade. Distinctive construction features are a now blocked-in connection with the railroad line crossing Eads Bridge, elevators, and fireproof building materials. The exterior is red and gray granite from Missouri and Maine. Interior decoration consists of cast iron moldings, flooring of ceramic tile, bronze door fixtures emblazoned with the Great Seal of the United States, and Italian marble fireplaces. The building has served as a U.S. courthouse, customhouse, and post office, and as a St. Louis visitor center.

Federal

NHL; HABS

ST. LOUIS (independent city)
ST. LOUIS UNION STATION
18th and Market Streets
1891–1894, Link and Cameron

At the time of its construction the St. Louis Union Station was considered to be the largest in the world to have tracks and passenger service area all on one level. The complex is composed of a train shed and a five-part headhouse. On the exterior the station shows the influence of H. H. Richardson. The east, north, and west

walls are Bedford limestone ashlar masonry heavily rusticated from the foundation through the first floor. The clock tower is 230 feet high. Inside, the most notable area is the Grand Hall waiting room. It has a floor area of 125 feet by 75 feet with a barrel vaulted ceiling 65 feet high. Decorations include ornamental plasterwork, frescoes, ornate light fixtures, and art glass windows. The train shed was designed by George H. Pegram. Built of structural steel, the shed originally covered 31 terminal tracks. Outside, the station has changed little, but numerous interior alterations have been made.

Private

NHL

ST. LOUIS (independent city)
WAINWRIGHT BUILDING
709 Chestnut Street
1890–1891, Louis H. Sullivan

Louis Sullivan's first commission involving the use of complete iron and steel framing was realized in the Wainwright Building, constructed in 1890–1891. Commissioned by Ellis Wainwright, a St. Louis brewer, this building represents a deliberate attempt to create a form expressive of the new mass of the multistory office block. For Sullivan, the potential aesthetic quality of the tall building lay in its unusual height. To emphasize this height to the maximum degree, he devised a system of closely ranked pierlike verticals that give the street elevations their forceful thrust. The building remains a significant prototype of the modern office building and a monument to America's contribution to world architecture—the development of the skyscraper.

Private

NHL; HABS

ST. LOUIS (independent city)
WAINWRIGHT TOMB
Bellefontaine Cemetery, 4947 W. Florissant Avenue
1892, Louis Sullivan

When Ellis Wainwright's young wife, Charlotte Dickson Wainwright, died, he commissioned the Chicago architectural firm of Adler and Sullivan to design a fitting tomb. Louis Sullivan subsequently produced the Wainwright Tomb, a concrete cube surmounted by a large dome and faced on the exterior with limestone slabs. Rich and intricate carving by Sullivan forms a border around the openings and upper half of the tomb. Inside, marble seats line three sides of the mausoleum, and both the floor and ceiling are mosaic. Wainwright and his parents are also buried here.

Private

ST. LOUIS COUNTY
Affton
BENOIST, LOUIS AUGUSTE, HOUSE
7802 Genesta Street
c. 1854, George Ingham Barnett

The Benoist House, Oakland, is one of the few examples of architect George I. Barnett's work which remains in good condition. The house is a two-story Italianate style stone dwelling. It is asymmetrical in plan, roughly L-shaped, with a four-story tower on the east side. The walls are locally quarried white limestone, and the corners are accentuated with large stones. The south and north blocks of the house and tower exhibit a full entablature with a wide overhanging cornice ornamented by elaborate scroll brackets and dentils. Louis Auguste Benoist, builder and owner of the house, was a prominent and successful St. Louis banker. He was born in St. Louis in 1803, studied law there, and eventually opened a broker's office and the city's first bank. Benoist built Oakland just outside the southwest boundary of St. Louis as his country home.
Private
HABS

ST. LOUIS COUNTY
Clayton
HANLEY, MARTIN FRANKLIN, HOUSE
7600 Westmoreland Avenue
c. 1855

The Hanley House is one of the few remaining brick, two-story central hall plan houses which were once prevalent throughout Missouri. Martin Franklin Hanley was the original owner and builder. The main (east) facade of the house is five bays wide with a central entrance and a two-story pedimented wood portico extending across the three central bays. Four square columns of the portico support the second floor balcony. Extending the entire length of the rear elevation is another double-story frame gallery. The house has a low-sloping gable roof with parapet ends and tied chimneys. Related buildings are a summer kitchen, a privy, and a well, plus the foundations of a forge and barn.
Municipal
HABS

ST. LOUIS COUNTY
Crescent vicinity
CRESCENT QUARRY ARCHEOLOGICAL SITE
1 mile east of Crescent
Pre-Columbian

Flint for chipped implements was quarried here during prehistoric times. Crescent Quarry flint artifacts have been discovered in various sections of the midwest, thus illustrating their wide distribution and desirability. Pieces of these artifacts have been identified in Archaic, Early, Middle, and Late Woodland contexts on the east side of the American Bottoms opposite St. Louis. Their dates range from several thousand years B.C. to approximately 1200 A.D. Although the quarry area was as large as one by five miles, only the most intensively worked section has been nominated. It is situated on a hill within a large bend of the Meramec River.
Private; not accessible to the public

ST. LOUIS COUNTY
Webster Groves
HAWKEN HOUSE
9442 Big Bend Boulevard
1857

The Hawken House is a transitional style house with the central hall symmetrical plan of a Federal residence, but also incorporating details and proportions characteristic of mid-19th century Greek Revival and Victorian homes. Built of brick, the house is two stories high. A two-story ell to the rear of the main house is lined by a two-story wooden gallery on its east side. Christopher Hawken, builder of the house, was the son of Jacob Hawken, who manufactured the Hawken rifle in St. Louis from 1822 to 1849.
Private

STE. GENEVIEVE COUNTY
Ste. Genevieve
BOLDUC, LOUIS, HOUSE
123 S. Main Street
1787

The Louis Bolduc House is exemplary of a building style common in the French settlements of the Louisiana country. It was the first house in the Mississippi Valley of that style and period to be restored, and the restoration was undertaken after much detailed research. The house exhibits French Canadian and Caribbean influences. It is rectangular (48 feet by 82 feet), and vertical oak timbers placed on stone sills form the walls. Interstices in the walls are filled with clay and straw; the exterior and interior walls are covered with whitewash. The main entranceway is placed asymmetrically and opens onto a broad hallway leading to a rear entrance opposite. Two rooms are thus formed by the central hallway. The northern or smaller room is the *chambre*. The larger one is a combination living room-dining room, the *salle de milieu*. A steep stairway connects the ground floor with a large attic-storage space under the roof. The restoration includes the surrounding yard —much reduced from its original size —outbuildings (smokehouse and well house), and the replanting of the garden. Louis Bolduc (1734–1815), a prosperous farmer and miner, was an early owner of the house.
Private
NHL; HABS

STE. GENEVIEVE COUNTY
Ste. Genevieve
GUIBOURD, JACQUES DUBREUIL, HOUSE
Northwest corner, 4th and Merchant Streets
c. 1800

The Guibourd House and surrounding grounds survive as part of the first permanent French settlement in Missouri. Although the gables, window sash, and clapboards have been changed, the building remains a good example of French Colonial architecture in the Mississippi Valley. The roof is supported by the original Norman truss, and one casement window on the west wall is original, the others having been converted to double-hung sash. Jacques Dubreuil Guibourd acquired the title to the property in 1799. Prior to this, he had emigrated from Angers, France, to Santo Domingo, where he had served as secretary to a wealthy planter and had been a slaveholder himself. During a slave uprising in the 1790's, Guibourd left Santo Domingo and settled in Ste. Genevieve. Here he married and became active in town affairs, serving as trustee of the Ste. Genevieve Academy and on the territorial district court.
Private; not accessible to the public

STE. GENEVIEVE COUNTY
Ste. Genevieve
SAINTE GENEVIEVE HISTORIC DISTRICT
1735

The old French river town of Sainte Genevieve was founded in the period 1735–1740. The original town, located on the west bank of the Mississippi River three miles below the present town, was abandoned by 1796 because of floods. However, the present town has retained much of the atmosphere of the missionary, fur trading, mining, and military outpost culture. Notable among the remaining buildings are the Green Tree Tavern

(1790), the Jean Baptiste Valle House (1785), and the Louis Bolduc House (1785).
Multiple private
NHL; HABS

STE. GENEVIEVE COUNTY
Ste. Genevieve vicinity
COMMON FIELD ARCHEOLOGICAL SITE
3 miles south of Ste. Genevieve
Pre-Columbian

The Common Field Archeological Site consists of five mounds ranging in height from 2.6 feet to 13 feet, and in diameter from 150 feet to 320 feet. Although the lowest mound has been damaged substantially as a result of plowing, the remaining four mounds have not been disturbed. No evidence of debris from an associated village has been uncovered in the immediate area, but future excavations of this site may yield important cultural remains of Mississippian peoples.
Private

STE. GENEVIEVE COUNTY
Ste. Genevieve vicinity
KREILICH ARCHEOLOGICAL SITE
South of Ste. Genevieve on U.S. 61 to its intersection with County Route J; west on County Route J for .5 mile; the site is on the south side of the road
A.D. 500 to 19th century

The Kreilich Archeological Site is significant because of its long history of human occupation due to the presence of a natural salt spring. The first occupants were probably a Woodland cultural group. The next inhabitants, an early Mississippian group, engaged in the manufacture of a Saline Plain Salt Pan pottery. About A.D. 1000 a Saline Fabric Impressed Salt Pan Ware was produced, possibly stimulated and influenced by activity in the nearby Cahokia region. By 1715 a French and Indian settlement was established as indicated by the presence of aboriginal and European artifacts. The French probably came from Kaskaskia, Ill., with the Kaskaskia tribe of the Illini Confederation. However, the Kaskaskia Indians were alarmed by the increasing number of French in the area, and in 1721 moved 5 miles upstream on the Kaskaskia River where they built another village. They continued to visit the site to procure salt. As late as 1835 a few French settlers were still working the salt spring, but gradually this activity ceased.
Private

SALINE COUNTY
Arrow Rock
ARROW ROCK
Arrow Rock State Park
1817

As the starting point for traders from Old Franklin and Boon's Lick who operated the Santa Fe Trail, Arrow Rock commemorates the beginning of the Santa Fe trade. Even before then, traffic was so great that by 1817 a ferry crossing the Missouri River was in operation. Both of William Becknell's pioneering Santa Fe expeditions of 1821 and 1822 were organized here. The rock cliff of Arrow Rock, remains of the old ferry road, and the Santa Fe Spring used as a rendezvous point are preserved in Arrow Rock State Park.
Multiple public/private
NHL

SALINE COUNTY
Arrow Rock
BINGHAM, GEORGE CALEB, HOUSE
Arrow Rock State Park
1837

George Caleb Bingham was a noted genre, portrait, and landscape painter whose favorite subjects were the river boatmen and politicians of the midwest. Among his famous paintings are "Fur Traders Descending the Missouri" (c. 1845), "Raftsmen Playing Cards" (c. 1847), and "Canvassing for a Vote" (c. 1851). Bingham lived in this two-room brick cottage at Arrow Rock intermittently from 1837 until 1845. During this time he made many of the sketches that formed the bases of his genre paintings.
State
NHL; HABS

SALINE COUNTY
Arrow Rock vicinity
SAPPINGTON, WILLIAM B., HOUSE
3 miles southwest of Arrow Rock on County Route TT
1843–1845

The Greek Revival Sappington House is built of brick and stands upon a limestone foundation. The north facade or main entrance is ornamented by a two-story pedimented portico. A T-shaped wing adjoins the south or rear wall of the square central block, and there is an ell on the south wall of the T-shaped wing. The central block is surmounted by a railed lookout area and by a square, glassed-in cupola. William Sappington, builder of the house, was the son of Dr. John Sappington, who discovered quinine as a treatment for malarial fever.
Private; not accessible to the public
HABS

SALINE COUNTY
Grand Pass vicinity
GUMBO POINT ARCHEOLOGICAL SITE
3 miles northwest of Malta Bend
18th century

Excavations since 1939 at Gumbo Point Archeological Site have produced numerous artifacts which indicate the results of cultural contact between the Little Osage and Missouri Indian tribes. Archeologists believe that the site will continue to produce significant remains.
Multiple public/private

SALINE COUNTY
Malta Bend vicinity
PLATTNER ARCHEOLOGICAL SITE
1 mile north of Malta Bend
18th century

The Plattner Site is significant as an area which witnessed much commerce and some resulting cultural adaptation on the part of the Little Osage Indians. As the Louisiana Territory changed hands among France, England, and Spain, soldiers and traders of all three nations visited this village and left evidence of their presence. Indian occupation of the site has been estimated roughly as 1717 to 1777. House locations, marked by concentrations of household rubbish, ash, and artifacts, are the only visible remains of the settlement. Excavations have uncovered few architectural features but a number of European-made goods.
Private

SALINE COUNTY
Marshall vicinity
UTZ SITE
12 miles north of Marshall, adjoining Van Meter State Park
c. 1673–1728

The Utz Site is believed to have been the principal settlement of the Missouri Indians from before 1673 until 1728. Père Marquette's map of his 1673 journey down the Mississippi River placed the "Messourit" Indians in this approximate location, as do several later maps. Although it is uncertain when the French began to exercise influence over the Missouri, it seems to have begun before 1712, when the Missouri helped to break the Fox and Iroquois siege of Fort Detroit. Before they encountered the French they seemed to have had a large population and far-reaching trade relationships. Their decline after 1778 illustrates the debilitating influence of white contact. After the establishment of Fort Orleans, diseases, liquor, and other factors reduced the Missouri to a remnant which finally merged with nearby related peoples.
State
NHL

SALINE COUNTY
Miami vicinity
GUTHREY ARCHEOLOGICAL SITE
1.75 miles east-northeast of Miami

The Guthrey Site is the earliest known Oneota occupation area in Missouri. Oneota was a general cultural growth which developed in an area bounded by lines drawn from St. Louis to Kansas City, due north to the Minnesota River, east to Aztalan (Wisconsin), and south to Cahokia at East St. Louis. Supported by a subsistence economy, the Oneota peoples hunted, fished, gardened, and gathered wild food plants. Occupation dates are estimated as 1350 to 1400, with the possibility for both earlier and later habitation. Archeological investigation was undertaken in the summer of 1964.
Private; not accessible to the public

SCOTT COUNTY
Diehlstadt vicinity
E. L. BROWN VILLAGE AND MOUND ARCHEOLOGICAL SITE
2.5 miles northeast of Diehlstadt
Pre-Columbian

The mound located on this site is one of the largest and best preserved temple mounds in the state. It measures 175 feet long, by 70 feet wide, by 20 feet high. No systematic archeological investigation of the mound or of the probable village site adjacent to it has been made. Archeologists Carl and Eleanor Chapman have stressed the importance of the vast Cahokia-St. Louis mound and village complex which, about 1000 A.D., served a series of satellite villages located within a 30 to 50 mile radius. A secondary center existed near Kansas City, Missouri, and there was a migrant colony at Aztalan, Wisconsin. Such towns originally contained a temple mound and the chief's mound on top of which was the chief's house. In some villages the large, flat-topped mounds were arranged around a central plaza.
Private; not accessible to the public

SCOTT COUNTY
Diehlstadt vicinity
SANDY WOODS SETTLEMENT ARCHEOLOGICAL SITE
1.75 miles northwest of Diehlstadt
Pre-Columbian

Sandy Woods Archeological Site, a well-preserved mound site with an associated village area, was occupied from the Pre-Mississippian through the Mississippian periods. It has been identified as a type site of the Cairo Lowland Phase of the Mississippian culture. Visible features are eight mounds, ranging in height from 15 inches to 6 feet. The largest mound is

probably a temple mound, while the others may be burial mounds. Two of the mounds, excavated about 1880, contained over 100 skeletons, many accompanied by samples of Mississippian pottery. The site has been cultivated in past years and some house depressions, visible in 1880, no longer exist. Future studies of the site should provide archeologists with a better understanding of the Mississippian culture in Missouri and the southeastern United States.
Private

SHELBY COUNTY
Bethel
BETHEL HISTORIC DISTRICT
Bounded roughly by and including all properties facing Fourth Street on the north; King Street on the east; First Street on the south; and Main and Liberty Streets on the west
19th century

Bethel was founded by Dr. William Keil, a German, as a communal settlement in 1844. It became the most successful communistic society in Missouri. The buildings within the historic district date from 1844 to 1880 and are representative of the plain, functional architecture favored by such groups. In 30 years time the town had expanded to include a church, saw-mill, gristmill, tannery, general store, drugstore, and shops for carpenters, blacksmiths, coopers, tinners, tailors, shoemakers, and hatters. The population in 1874 was only 200 people because Keil had started a second colony in Oregon which drew many people away from Bethel. Keil died in 1877, and the loss of strong leadership led to dissent, eventual division of communal property, and ultimate dissolution of both colonies. Bethel was incorporated as a town in 1883. The 50 remaining buildings stand close to the sidewalks and are of handmade brick construction set upon limestone foundations. The exteriors are generally devoid of ornamentation, and the interiors are characterized by central halls and large open rooms.
Multiple private

SHELBY COUNTY
Bethel vicinity
ELIM (DR. WILLIAM KEIL HOUSE)
1.5 miles east of Bethel
19th century

Elim was the home of Dr. William Keil, founder of the Society of Bethel, the most successful communistic society established in Missouri and one of the most successful in the United States. Influenced by the principles of George Rapp's Economy, Keil founded Bethel in 1844. The sole

bond of union was the personal magnetism of Keil, who served as the group's administrator, preacher and physician. In the late 1840's members of the society erected this two-and-one-half-story brick and stone house for their leader. It also served as his administrative office and as the herbarium where his medicinal herbs were cured and stored. In 1855 Keil moved to the Pacific Northwest to create another communal colony. After his death in 1877, the Bethel Colony dwindled and finally disbanded.
Private; not accessible to the public

STODDARD COUNTY
Bernie vicinity
RICH WOODS ARCHEOLOGICAL SITE
2 miles north of Bernie
Pre-Columbian

At one time there were 35 mounds on this site, making it the largest Mississippian area in southeast Missouri. The entire site, except the easternmost edge, had been disturbed or destroyed by cultivation. As a result, the relative arrangement of houses, mounds, and plazas is not known. The mounds varied in height from 20 to 26 feet, and several burials were discovered during an 1890 excavation. Presently only four mounds are visible above the surrounding terrain. The most important, designated as No. 3, is almost 14 feet high and has a diameter of approximately 125 feet.
Private; not accessible to the public

TEXAS COUNTY
Buckyrus vicinity
WHITE ROCK BLUFFS ARCHEOLOGICAL PICTOGRAPH SITE
2 miles south of Buckyrus
Prehistoric

The pictures on the White Rock Bluffs Archeological Pictograph Site are good examples of American aboriginal art. The rim of the vertical sandstone bluff overhangs the face (on which the pictographs appear) by about 8 feet. At the base of the bluff is a narrow, rocky terrace about 10 feet wide. The section of the bluff containing the pictographs is about 250 feet long. Approximately three-quarters of the 30 or more visible figures are representations of the human form. Birds, animals, and composite figures comprise the remainder. The human figures range in height from 8 to 15 inches. Most of them appear to be using their hands, but weathering has faded out the details of their arms and legs, and many of them are indistinct. The paintings are not situated on any one level above the terrace but are spread out in

small groups. The colors used are various hues of red, yellow, and purple.
Private

VERNON COUNTY
Arthur vicinity
COAL PIT ARCHEOLOGICAL SITE
1 mile northwest of Arthur
18th and 19th centuries

The Coal Pit Archeological Site is primarily significant as a source of information for the study of the relationship between the Big and Little Osage Indians, the Little Osage and the Euro-Americans, and to illustrate the dependency of the Little Osage on Euro-American trade goods. Lieutenant Zebulon M. Pike visited the site in 1806. The Little Osage Indians left their Missouri River location in the late 18th century to settle here; their period of occupation was principally from 1775 to 1815 or 1825. Materials excavated at the site were mostly of European origin. The Osage Indians at this time were almost entirely dependent upon European traders for items such as metal cooking vessels, which they used exclusively.
Private; not accessible to the public

VERNON COUNTY
Fair Haven vicinity
BROWN ARCHEOLOGICAL SITE
2 miles west of Fair Haven
18th and 19th centuries

The Brown Site is one of the three most important known Osage village locations in southwestern Missouri. Artifacts found here illustrate the changes that occurred in Osage culture as a result of early contacts with European traders beginning about 1719. Archeological remains contain more non-European materials than either of the other large occupation areas (the Carrington and Coal Pit sites), indicating that the Brown Site was the earliest. Carl H. Chapman believes the main period of occupation to have been between 1700 and 1777. Excavated houses at the site appear to have been rectangular (roughly 10 feet by 20 feet) and were often superimposed due to successive habitation. Some excavation work has been undertaken.
Private; not accessible to the public

VERNON COUNTY
Nevada vicinity
CARRINGTON OSAGE VILLAGE SITE
North of Nevada, on west edge of
Green Valley Prairie
Late 18th and early 19th centuries

The Great Osage Indian settlement at this site was visited by Captain Zebulon Pike in 1806. Archeological excavation has uncovered large quantities of aboriginal and European materials. Most of the aboriginal artifacts were of stone, with hide scrapers the most numerous. Abundant European artifacts included flintlock rifle parts; iron axes, hoes, and knives; copper kettles, bells, and projectile points; glass beads and bottles; crockery fragments; and small silver ornaments.
Private; not accessible to the public
NHL

WARREN COUNTY
Marthasville vicinity
BORGMANN MILL
5 miles east of Marthasville on
County Route D
c. 1850

The Borgmann Mill is perhaps the only remaining example in the midwest of a barley huller and corn grinder constructed entirely of wood. Frederick W. Borgmann, a German immigrant, built the one-and-one-half-story mill and fashioned the milling machinery from oak and appleroot wood. All pieces are hand carved and connected to each other by wooden pins. Mules or oxen were used to power the mill, and a double door on the east wall provided entry for the animals. The grinding stone and barley huller are located on the second floor. All the milling equipment is in good condition. It is thought that Borgmann operated the mill only a short time.
Private; not accessible to the public

WARREN COUNTY
Marthasville vicinity
CALLAWAY, FLANDERS, HOUSE
One mile south of Marthasville off
Mo. 94
c. 1812

Flanders Callaway and his wife Jemima, one of Daniel Boone's daughters, journeyed to Missouri with Boone in 1799 and settled this land sometime before 1812. The two-story, walnut sheathed, hewn-log frontier house is a rare and early example of Federal style log construction in the Missouri area. The house is symmetrical with a five-bay facade and a central hall with two rooms on each side on both stories. The two end chimneys are contained within the house. Alterations were made to the original structure during the mid- or late 19th century. These include the addition of a one-story frame ell to the north rear, replacement of the original front door, and a one-bay, one-story wooden portico added as a porch in front of the main door.
Private; not accessible to the public

WASHINGTON COUNTY
Caledonia vicinity
LOST CREEK PICTOGRAPH
ARCHEOLOGICAL SITE
2 miles northeast of Caledonia
Pre-Columbian

A series of four overhanging rockshelters extending approximately 100 yards along the east side of Lost Creek constitute the site. It is the only known area in Missouri to contain two excellent examples of Middle Mississippian symbolic art. Other pictographs may be examples of early historic Indian painting, and the rockshelters themselves contain rich cultural deposits. The bilobed arrow and sunburst symbols (believed to be Middle Mississippian in origin) are outlined in red, probably made from ochre or burnt hematite. Paintings dating from historic times may be the work of Indians enroute to Oklahoma; two faces and the horse designs are probably European in origin. In front of each rockshelter are midden deposits of undetermined depths.
Private; not accessible to the public

WASHINGTON COUNTY
Fertile vicinity
CRESSWELL PETROGLYPH
ARCHEOLOGICAL SITE
2 miles east of Fertile
Pre-Columbian

The Cresswell Site contains one of the best preserved and largest known examples of pre-Columbian symbolic art in Missouri. The carvings are considered to be the best group of Mississippian symbols in the Mississippi River Valley. Located on a limestone ledge overlooking Maddin Creek are some 238 individual symbolic carvings. Symbols which appear are crosses, maces, batons, bilobed arrows, hands, weeping eyes, sunbursts, snakes, and birds. In addition there are several groups of symbols which may prove to be crude representations of multiple human births. Influences of both Woodland and Mississippian cultural traditions are evident.
Private; not accessible to the public

WASHINGTON COUNTY
Fertile vicinity
WASHINGTON STATE PARK
PETROGLYPH ARCHEOLOGICAL
SITE
1 mile northeast of Fertile
Pre-Columbian

The petroglyphs in Washington State Park are located in two areas, designated as Group One and Group Two. Located on outcroppings of rock at ground level, the carved pictures probably had magical as

well as religious significance. The exact meaning of the petroglyphs (bird-like and human figures, footprints, and abstract figures) is not known. Possibly the area was a sacred spot where young men were initiated into a secret society and taught the mythology associated with the initiation.
State

Mansfield vicinity
WILDER, LAURA INGALLS, HOUSE
1 mile east of Mansfield on U.S. Business 60
c. 1895–1912

Laura Ingalls was born near Pepin, Wisconsin, in February, 1867. Her family homesteaded in Wisconsin, Kansas, Minnesota, and South Dakota for the next 18 years. In 1885 she married Almanzo Wilder. They lived for nine years in South Dakota and then journeyed south and set-tled in Missouri. At the age of 65 Mrs. Wilder began writing about her girlhood experiences in a series of books—*Little House in the Big Woods*, *Little House on the Prairie*, and others. The books were written in this home, most of which the Wilders built themselves from materials on their 40-acre farm. The plan of the house is irregular. It is a two-story frame dwelling with clapboard siding and a large stone fireplace on the north wall.
Private

Montana

Custer Battlefield National Monument, Hardin vicinity, Montana. *NPS*

Fort Logan Blockhouse,
White Sulphur Springs vicinity, Montana.
Dick Ellis

Grant-Kohrs Ranch,
Deer Lodge, Montana. *NPS*

Chief Plenty Coups Memorial, Pryor vicinity, Montana. *Ron Holliday*

BEAVERHEAD COUNTY
LEMHI PASS
Reference—see Lemhi County, Idaho

BEAVERHEAD COUNTY
Dillon vicinity
BANNACK HISTORIC DISTRICT
22 miles from Dillon on secondary road off Mont. 278
1862

Bannack was the site of Montana's first gold discovery. Abandoned since 1938, Montana's oldest town and first territorial capital is a remarkable example of surviving frontier camps and boom towns. Most of the remaining buildings are of frame and log construction and all are typical of a frontier boom town.
State
NHL; HABS

BEAVERHEAD COUNTY
Wisdom vicinity
BIG HOLE NATIONAL BATTLEFIELD
12 miles west of Wisdom
1877

Big Hole National Battlefield preserves a portion of the battlefield where on August 9–10, 1877, Colonel John Gibbon fought five bands of Nez Perce Indians who were attempting to escape to Canada after fleeing from Idaho. Gibbon's men were outnumbered two to one, but his attack weakened the Nez Perce, who were later forced to surrender within about 30 miles of their destination. Today in the battlefield area, remains of shallow, grass-grown trenches, where Gibbon's men defended themselves, and bullet-scarred trees are found in a natural setting similar to that of 1877.
Federal/non-federal
NPS; 666 acres

BIG HORN COUNTY
Hardin vicinity
CUSTER BATTLEFIELD NATIONAL MONUMENT
15 miles south of Hardin
1876

The clash between northern plains Indians and the United States Army in the valley of the Little Bighorn River on June 25–26, 1876, is commemorated at Custer Battlefield National Monument. The battle was precipitated by shrinkage of Indian land and the government's ultimatum to come into the reservations by January 31, 1876. The Sioux and Cheyenne Indians instead rallied around Sioux leader Sitting Bull, who advocated resistance. In the resulting battle, Lieutenant Colonel George A. Custer and every member of his immediate command of about 225 men were killed. The other seven companies of the regiment managed to defend themselves for about two days, five miles south of where the Custer contingent was annihilated.
Federal
NPS; 756.34 acres

BIG HORN COUNTY
Pryor vicinity
CHIEF PLENTY COUPS MEMORIAL
1 mile west of Pryor off Mont. 416

Plenty Coups was a Crow chief who did much to promote friendly relations between Indian and white. He was born in 1848 near Billings and died in the early 1930's. His career included service with General George Crook as a scout, and, while running a store on the Crow reservation, he took an active part in tribal government and was a strong advocate of education and the vocation of farming for his people. The present memorial was once Chief Plenty Coup's farm. The two-story log house was his home, and the one-story log store still stands. Plenty Coups and two of his wives are buried on the property.
State

BLAINE COUNTY
Chinook vicinity
CHIEF JOSEPH BATTLEGROUND OF THE BEAR'S PAW (BEARPAW MOUNTAIN FIGHT)
About 15 miles south of Chinook

In June of 1877 the federal government attempted to remove the Nez Perce from their home in Oregon's Wallowa River valley. Led by Chief Joseph, the Nez Perce resisted and fled northeast across Idaho and Montana enroute to Canada. On the rolling prairie land at the foot of the Bearpaw Mountains, the Indians were overtaken by soldiers commanded by General Nelson A. Miles. A battle ensued (September 30 to October 5), but the Indians, wearied by their long journey, hungry, and taken by surprise, finally surrendered. "From where the sun now stands, I will fight no more forever," said Chief Joseph. Eight years later, the Nez Perce were settled on the Lapwai Colville Reservation in Idaho.
State

CASCADE COUNTY
Great Falls
RUSSELL, CHARLES M., HOUSE AND STUDIO
1217–1219 4th Avenue, North
1900

Charles M. Russell occupied this house from 1900 until his death in 1926. His log studio was added in 1903. Russell's work in this studio brought him full recognition as a western artist. Among his best-known paintings on Western life are "Waiting for a Chinook" and "Father De Smet Relating the Story of Christ to the Flatheads." During the last decade of his life his canvasses brought the highest sum ever paid to a living American painter. His two-story frame house has undergone almost no changes. The log studio has a recent addition on the west side.
Municipal; only log studio accessible to the public
NHL

CASCADE COUNTY
Great Falls vicinity
GREAT FALLS PORTAGE
Southeast of Great Falls at junction of U.S. 87, 89, and 91
1805

On June 13, 1805, Meriwether Lewis and a small party reached the Great Falls of the Missouri while traveling overland on foot. They were the first white men to view the falls. The 18–mile portage necessitated by the falls, a 31-day trip, was one of the greatest ordeals endured by the Lewis and Clark Expedition on its way to the Pacific coast. The Great Falls have since been harnessed for hydroelectric power, and only a small amount of water flows over them. The great escarpment of jagged rocks and the general landscape remain.
Multiple public/private
NHL

CHOUTEAU COUNTY
Fort Benton
FORT BENTON
1859

Fort Benton commemorates the steamboat era on the upper Missouri River. Although established earlier as a fur trading center, the fort's real prosperity dates from 1859, when the first steamboat arrived. Discovery of gold in 1862 made Fort Benton an overland transportation connection with the river steamers. An invasion of free fur traders in the late 1860's ended monopoly of the Indian trade by the American Fur Company and the Hudson's Bay Company, but the free traders established an empire over the Northwest that centered at Fort Benton. After the advent of the railroads the town of Fort Benton and the river traffic rapidly declined. A block house and a portion of the fort's adobe walls still stand, and the riverfront seems unchanged.
Multiple public/private
NHL

DAWSON COUNTY
Glendive vicinity
HAGEN SITE
5 miles southeast of Glendive on
secondary road
1600

The Hagen Site is a late prehistoric earth
lodge village believed to represent a settlement of the Crow Indians before they
became fully nomadic bison hunters. The
Crow, who split off from the Hidatsa, were
village farmers of the Middle Missouri
River area. Partial excavation of the site in
1938 revealed a midden area covering
more than ten acres. Within it were many
storage pits, a small circular house, and a
low mound which contained fragments of
human skeletons. Bison shoulder-blade
hoes and the general semi-sedentary
character of the site attest to the practice
of farming. Archeologists believe that
shortly after they lived at this site the
Crow forsook agriculture in favor of a
nomadic, buffalo-hunting way of life.
Private
NHL

GALLATIN COUNTY
Logan vicinity
MADISON BUFFALO JUMP STATE
MONUMENT
Sec. 34, T. 1 N., R. 2 E.
Pre-Columbian to 18th century

Before horses were introduced to the
North American continent, Plains Indians
on foot drove large herds of buffalo over
precipices to their death. The practice was
quite successful, and those animals not
killed by the fall were quickly dispatched
by arrows or lances at the bottom of the
cliff. The Madison Buffalo Jump is located
on a 30-foot limestone bluff above the
Madison River valley. A large grassy
prairie covers the land above and behind
the cliff, and the jump area includes an Indian village site, a slaughter site, an
archeological site, an Indian trail, a
gravesite, and a lookout point.
State

GALLATIN COUNTY
Three Forks vicinity
THREE FORKS OF THE MISSOURI
Northwest of Three Forks on the
Missouri River, Missouri Headwaters
State Monument
1805

Captain William Clark discovered the
Three Forks in July, 1805. He and
Meriwether Lewis concluded that the
Missouri River had its beginning at the
point where the Three Forks joined. They
named the three streams the Gallatin, the

Madison, and the Jefferson rivers. The
Three Forks is associated with the history
of the first westward-moving Americans,
for since those early days, numerous paths
of commerce and communications have
passed through this essential point.
State
NHL

GLACIER COUNTY
Browning vicinity
CAMP DISAPPOINTMENT
12 miles northeast of Browning on
the Blackfeet Reservation
1806

Camp Disappointment, the northernmost
point reached by the Lewis and Clark Expedition, was established by Meriwether
Lewis and nine of his men on July 23,
1806, on the return trip from the Pacific.
The purpose of this side trip was to explore an Indian trail, to determine if the
Marias River extended north of the 49th
parallel, and to determine if there was a
short portage between the headwaters of
the Marias and Saskatchewan rivers.
These objectives were stated by President
Thomas Jefferson in his instructions to
Lewis. The site is an undeveloped area
used for livestock grazing, apparently little
changed since 1806.
Private
NHL

LEWIS AND CLARK COUNTY
Helena
FORMER MONTANA EXECUTIVE
MANSION
6th Avenue and Ewing Street
1884, Cass Gilbert

Built as a private residence by William A.
Chessman, this house served as Montana's
executive mansion from 1913 to 1959.
Three stories high, the house was constructed of pressed brick and granite with
terra cotta ornament. Its Queen Anne
style architecture is characterized by roof
turrets and cupolas and the ornamental
trim on windows, porch, and eaveline.
State
HABS

LEWIS AND CLARK COUNTY
Helena
KLUGE HOUSE
540 W. Main Street
1880's

The Kluge House is a rare Montana example of a log and half-timber house commonly built in Prussia in the 17th, 18th,
and 19th centuries. Emil Kluge emigrated
to the United States from Germany and
came to Helena in 1873. The home he
built for his family has a foundation of na-

tive stone. Its first story is hewn, squared
logs, and the second story is half-timber
construction.
Municipal
HABS

MADISON COUNTY
Dillon vicinity
BEAVERHEAD ROCK
NW 1/4 and N 1/2 SW 1/2 sec. 22, T.
5 S., R. 7 W.
1805

Beaverhead Rock was sighted by the
Shoshone Indian woman Sacajawea on
August 8, 1805. She recognized it as a
landmark near the summer camping
ground of her people and was then able to
assure Captains Meriwether Lewis and
William Clark, leaders of the transcontinental exploratory expedition
(1804–1805), that her people were nearby. Shortly thereafter Lewis and Clark encountered the Shoshone and obtained horses from them. Without these horses the
party would have been unable to cross the
Bitterroot Mountains and reach the
Pacific coast.
Public/private

MADISON COUNTY
Virginia City
VIRGINIA CITY HISTORIC DISTRICT
Wallace Street
1863

The gold strike at Alder Gulch in 1863
was one of the greatest in the West. Virginia City grew up on the site. Its period of
greatest importance was from 1865 to
1875, when it was the territorial capital of
Montana. It has close association with one
of the vigilante bands of the mining era,
which was formed to do away with the in-
famous Henry Plummer gang. Among the
older reconstructed buildings of brick and
native stone are the territorial capitol and
the *Montana Post* building. Nearby is the
cemetery where the graves of several of
the Plummer gang may be found.
Private
NHL; HABS

MEAGHER COUNTY
White Sulphur Springs vicinity
FORT LOGAN BLOCKHOUSE
About 17 miles northwest of White
Sulphur Springs

Camp Baker-Fort Logan was established
in 1869 and occupied until 1880. The outpost was the army's main base for protecting the freight route from Fort Benton (at
the head of navigation on the Missouri
River) and Helena and for the defense of
mining settlements and nearby cattle
ranches. Originally named Camp Baker,

Fort Logan was renamed in honor of an officer killed in battle at Big Hole Basin (1877) against the Nez Perce. Structures composing the fort were principally of log construction, and the extant, eight-sided blockhouse is original, though moved to a new location.
Private
HABS

MEAGHER COUNTY
White Sulphur Springs vicinity
FORT LOGAN
17 miles northwest of White Sulphur Springs
1869–1880

Fort Logan, originally called Camp Baker, was established by the army to protect a major trade route, a mining settlement, and scattered cattle ranches. The main road from Fort Benton to Helena, Montana, passed Fort Logan, and troops were stationed here to safeguard miners in nearby Confederate Gulch and ranchers in the Smith and Upper Musselshell River valleys. All structures in the fort complex were built of logs. Today a single blockhouse remains which was moved from its original site in 1862. It is unusual in appearance because the square top story is set upon the square first story at a 45-degree angle, thus allowing the defenders to fire from eight directions.
Private
HABS

MISSOULA COUNTY
LOLO TRAIL
Reference—see Clearwater County, Idaho

MISSOULA COUNTY
Lolo vicinity
TRAVELER'S REST
1 mile south of Lolo near U.S. 93
1805

Traveler's Rest is the campsite where Meriwether Lewis and William Clark stopped to prepare for the westward crossing of the Bitterroot Mountains on their way to the Pacific coast in 1805. On its return from the coast the following year, the expedition stopped here again. It was then that Lewis took a small party to explore the country between Traveler's Rest and the Great Falls of the Missouri. This was deemed essential in order to meet President Thomas Jefferson's instructions to find the shortest and most feasible route between the Missouri and Columbia rivers.
Private
NHL

PONDERA COUNTY
Browning vicinity
TWO MEDICINE FIGHT SITE
About 25 miles southeast of Browning

On his return journey from the Pacific coast, Meriwether Lewis and three companions camped with eight Piegan Indians (one of the Blackfoot tribes) at Two Medicine Creek, July 26–27, 1806. The next morning the white men awoke to discover the red men in the act of stealing their guns and horses. Driving off the Indians, the four explorers rode speedily to the mouth of the Marias River, all the while fearing pursuit by a larger war party. The encounter is significant as the first between the army and the Plains Indians and as the only armed conflict of the Lewis and Clark Expedition. The area is little changed today and contains evidence of Indian occupation—buffalo remains, tipi rings, and a piskun.
Federal trust land

POWELL COUNTY
Deer Lodge
GRANT-KOHRS RANCH
Edge of Deer Lodge
c. 1853

The Grant-Kohrs Ranch is doubly significant in the history of the range cattle industry. John Grant, the original owner, is sometimes credited with being the founder of the industry in Montana. Conrad Kohrs, who purchased the ranch about 1866, was one of the foremost "cattle kings" of the era. He played an influential role in the organization of the Montana Stockgrowers Association. The original frame ranchhouse, erected in 1862, is still standing. Alterations made in the 1890's include a large brick addition on the west side of the house. Other original structures include several log cabins dating from the 1850's and 1860's and some old corrals.
Private; not accessible to the public
NHL

RAVALLI COUNTY
Hamilton vicinity
CANYON CREEK LABORATORY OF THE U.S. PUBLIC HEALTH SERVICE
.75 mile west of the Hamilton city limits

The Canyon Creek Laboratory was built in 1894 as a schoolhouse. During the years 1921 to 1928 Dr. R. R. Parker and his staff from the Montana State Board of Entomology and the U.S. Public Health Service used the building for studies and experiments which led to the eventual control of spotted fever. Although later al-

tered by removal of the top story, Canyon Creek Laboratory is the only substantial building remaining that was used for such studies. The first vaccine was developed here in 1924, and the first human being was vaccinated in the building the same year. Evidence indicates that the vaccine was actually prepared on the building's ground floor. Other tick-borne diseases were studied on the premises.
Private

RAVALLI COUNTY
Stevensville
ST. MARY'S MISSION CHURCH AND PHARMACY
North Avenue
Mid–19th century

The first Catholic mission in the Northwest was located on the Bitterroot River about a mile from this site by Father Pierre de Smet in 1841. Abandoned in 1850, the site was sold to John Owen, who developed a trading post on it. In 1866 the mission was reactivated, and Father Anthony Ravalli built this church at the western edge of Stevensville. Logs from the earlier mission were utilized, and the church's center section was constructed first. The steeple and front portion were added later. Father Ravalli also built the nearby two-story pharmacy-hospital as a place to dispense medicines and care for the sick. It was the first pharmacy in Montana.
Private
HABS

RAVALLI COUNTY
Stevensville vicinity
FORT OWEN
About .5 mile northwest of Stevensville
1857

Fort Owen never served as an official military post. Rather it was a trading post established by John Owen in 1850, after he purchased the property from Jesuit missionaries. Construction of the adobe complex did not begin until 1857. Fort Owen is believed to have contained the first sawmill, flour mill, and school in Montana. Inside the adobe walls were two rectangular sections of buildings used for trade purposes and as living quarters. Only the eastern group remains, and all other above-ground evidence of the trading post has deteriorated. John Owen became ill in 1872, and the property passed to creditors. Several owners worked or lived on the property but gradually only the east buildings were occupied. Archeological investigations have exposed the foundations of the fort's walls and bastions.
State
HABS

ROOSEVELT COUNTY
FORT UNION TRADING POST NATIONAL HISTORIC SITE
Reference—see Williams County, North Dakota

ROOSEVELT COUNTY
Poplar
FORT PECK AGENCY
Parts of T. 27 N., R. 50 E., and T. 27 N., R. 51 E.
1877

An Indian agency was established at Fort Peck (founded in 1867 near the present Fort Peck dam site) in 1871. Six years later the Fort Peck Agency was moved to its present location at Poplar. Government contact with both the recently subdued Sioux and the friendly Assiniboine Indians was maintained here. Also, in late 1880, the 11th Infantry was dispatched from Fort Custer to set up a camp at the Fort Peck Agency to bring in Indians who had scattered after the battle of the Little Big Horn. This post was active until 1893 when the Bureau of Indian Affairs acquired it for use as an Indian boarding school. All earlier buildings were wooden and have been destroyed, but several from the early 20th century are extant. These are the academic building and quarters (1907), the dining hall and kitchen (1915), a hospital (1916, remodeled 1961), and a jail (1920).
Federal

SILVER BOW COUNTY
Butte
BUTTE HISTORIC DISTRICT
1876

Butte is the center of the largest copper mining region in the world. An area less than five miles square beneath Butte has produced more than two billion dollars worth of mineral wealth since 1864. The town site of Butte was laid out in 1876. With the arrival of the first railroad in 1881, the first copper boom began. Surrounded by yellow and gray ore dumps and frames marking mine shafts, Butte is a living mining community whose era of production has not yet ceased.
Multiple public/private
NHL

SILVER BOW COUNTY
Butte
CLARK, W. A., MANSION
219 W. Granite
1884–1888, C. H. Brown

The Clark House is an impressive ressidence built for one of Butte's "copper kings." It is a three-story brick house with an irregular shape produced by projecting bays, gables, and dormers. Belt courses, window lintels, arches, and other trim are white sandstone. The cornice is Montana brownstone, and there are several rectangular bas-relief panels of terra cotta between the first-and second-floor windows. There are iron railings atop the porch roofs, and the main roof is slate. Inside, the house is furnished and decorated according to the taste of the period.
Private

YELLOWSTONE COUNTY
Billings vicinity
PICTOGRAPH CAVE
7 miles southeast of Billings via U.S. 87 and secondary road, Indian Caves Park
c. 2000 B.C.

Pictograph Cave is one of the key archeological sites used in determining the sequence of prehistoric occupation in the northwestern plains. Four cultural levels were recognized, ranging from middle prehistoric to historic times, but no perishable materials from the two lowest levels were preserved. The walls display striking Indian pictographs. The site was partially excavated before World War II, and publication of the scientific finds was begun in 1952.
State
NHL

YELLOWSTONE COUNTY
Pompey's Pillar vicinity
POMPEY'S PILLAR
West of Pompey's Pillar on U.S. 10
1806

Pompey's Pillar, a massive natural block of sandstone, is a well-known landmark of the Lewis and Clark Expedition. It measures 120 feet high and 350 feet across at its widest point. On July 25, 1806, Captain William Clark named the rock and carved his signature on its surface. His inscription remains today.
Private; not accessible to the public
NHL

Bannack Historic District,
Bannack, Montana. *George Grant for NPS*

Nebraska

Palmer-Epard Log Cabin,
Homestead National Monument,
Beatrice, Nebraska. *NPS*

Officer's Quarters,
Fort Robinson and Red Cloud Agency,
Fort Robinson vicinity, Nebraska. *NPS*

Emmanuel Lutheran Church, Dakota City, Nebraska. *Dakota County Star*

ANTELOPE COUNTY
Neligh
NELIGH MILL
111 W. 2nd Street
1873–1874

The present town of Neligh grew up around the Neligh Mill. The mill was built of locally produced brick for John D. Neligh, founder of the town. He suffered financial reverses in the panic of 1873 and was forced to sell the mill. Milling operations began again in October, 1874, and continued to expand until by the early 1900's the mill was shipping flour throughout the United States and to Europe. During the 1930's the mill produced animal feed, wheat flour, whole wheat graham, rye graham, buckwheat flour, and cornmeal. Flour milling ended in 1959, and only a small amount of feed milling and grain storage business has been carried on since then. Power was originally supplied by a sixty-four-inch Leffel turbine wheel and was transmitted to the mill machinery by a Roebling wire cable. Eventually water power and electricity were used to operate the machinery, but after floods destroyed the dam in 1920, water power was no longer used.
Private

BURT COUNTY
Oakland vicinity
LOGAN CREEK SITE
SE 1/4 sec. 11, SW 1/4 sec. 12, T. 12 N., R. 8 E.
c. 6000–4000 B. C.

Archaic peoples inhabited the Logan Creek Site, where four different excavations have been undertaken (in 1957, 1959, 1962, and 1963). Hearths, pits, shallow basins, and a few post molds were found at various occupational levels. Archeologists also discovered an unusual type of projectile that was side notched and often basally ground. The artifacts are similar to those found at sites farther east and suggest the movement of people from eastern North America onto the Great Plains.
Private; not accessible to the public

CASS COUNTY
Murray vicinity
GILMORE, WALKER, SITE (STERNS CREEK SITE)
5 miles southeast of Murray
Date unknown

The deep stratified deposits which occur at the Walker Gilmore Site make it a key archeological site for outlining the prehistoric cultural stages represented in the central plains. It was the site at which the Plains Woodland culture, in the form of the Sterns Creek focus, was first recognized.
Private; not accessible to the public
NHL

CASS COUNTY
Nehawka vicinity
NEHAWKA FLINT QUARRIES
E 1/2 sec. 6, T. 10 N., R. 13 E. and SW 1/4 sec. 32, T. 11 N., R. 13 E.
c. 3000 B.C.–1500 A.D.

Artifacts recovered from the quarry sites during the 1969 excavations by the Nebraska State Historical Society were datable as far back as 5000 years. The flint quarried here was probably most extensively used by the Nebraska Culture Indians between 1200 and 1400 A.D. Flint objects believed to be from the Nehawka quarries have been found on Nebraska sites occupied by other Indian groups.
Private; not accessible to the public

CUMING COUNTY
Bancroft
NEIHARDT, JOHN G., STUDY
Northeast corner, Washington and Grove Streets
c. 1911–1921

John Gneisnau Neihardt (1881–) is today regarded as perhaps the foremost poet of the Great Plains and Rocky Mountain states. He was born in Illinois and moved west with his family, reaching Nebraska in 1891. He worked his way through Nebraska Normal College (Wayne) and held several jobs before *The Lonesome Trail*, a collection of Indian stories, was published (1907) and focused nationwide attention upon the author. Neihardt is one of a few serious American poets who have attempted to write epic poetry. His best known and most ambitious work in this area is *A Cycle of the West*, a series of five epic poems dealing with the exploration and settlement of the trans-Mississippi west. This work was largely written in the Bancroft study. *The Lonesome Trail*, demonstrates his understanding of and sympathy with the Indian mind. The one-room, one-story, frame study has been little altered since Neihardt wrote here. Furnishings duplicate those of his period of occupancy.
Private

CUSTER COUNTY
Broken Bow vicinity
HAUMONT HOUSE
Northeast of Broken Bow
c. 1884–1885

Most of the sod buildings constructed on the Great Plains in the 19th century were dugouts or small, one-story structures. The Haumont House is a large, two-story, rectangular "soddie" with a one-story kitchen annex. The rounded tower-like projections at the wall corners and the steeply pitched hip roof give it an unusual medieval appearance. Lumber was used for the window and door casings and the flooring. Some of the original window panes have been replaced, but few other alterations have been made. The house is believed to have been built for Isadore Haumont (1820–1904) soon after he, his wife, and his son emigrated from Belgium to Nebraska.
Private

DAKOTA COUNTY
Dakota City
EMMANUEL LUTHERAN CHURCH
1500 Hickory Street
1860

Emmanuel Lutheran Church is probably the best and least altered example of Greek Revival ecclesiastical architecture in Nebraska. It is also thought to have been the first Lutheran church in the state. The one-story, cottonwood frame church has a gable roof crowned by a cupola or bell tower. The only major alterations have been replacement of some original siding and the addition of a new roof in 1960. The pilasters of the tower and the heavy cornices and cornice return are Greek Revival. The bell, cast in 1856, is original.
Municipal
HABS

DAWES COUNTY (also in Sioux County)
Crawford vicinity
FORT ROBINSON AND RED CLOUD AGENCY
2 miles west of Crawford on U.S. 20
1871–1874

Events at Red Cloud Agency and nearby Fort Robinson during the 1870's influenced the course of Indian-white relations on the northern plains during the years of Sioux and Cheyenne resistance to the advancing frontier. The Red Cloud Agency, established in 1871, was the storm center for the Sioux. In 1874 troops established Fort Robinson to give the agency military protection. The fort served as a base for several Indian campaigns, including the Custer disaster. A number of Fort Robinson buildings dating from the 1880's and 1890's are still standing, but the Red Cloud Agency buildings have long since disappeared.
Multiple public
NHL

DAWSON COUNTY
Gothenburg vicinity
MIDWAY STAGE STATION
South of Gothenburg
1859–1861

The Midway Stage Station is one of 36 Nebraska buildings which served as Pony Express stations in 1860 and 1861. Three of these stations are supposed to be extant: one at Cozad, one at Gothenburg, and Midway Station. The Midway Station is the least altered of the three and the only one remaining on its original site. In 1859 the Leavenworth & Pikes Peak Express Company built fifteen stage and mail stations across Nebraska to link the Missouri River with Denver and Salt Lake City. The freighting firm of Russell, Majors, and Waddell soon acquired the stations and built 21 more the following year, all to be used by the Pony Express. Originally known as U.S. Mail Station No. 17, Midway acquired its name because it was approximately half way between Atchison, Kansas, and Denver. Eventually Midway was used as a home station to house riders as well as their horses. After the Pony Express was put out of business by the telegraph, Midway became a supply and stage station on the heavily traveled Oregon Trail. Midway is a long, low, one-story cabin built of heavy, squared, hand-hewn cedar logs. Two log sections were added at a later date on the east side of the original structure.
Private

DEUEL COUNTY
Big Springs
PHELPS HOTEL
Northeast corner of 2nd and Pine Streets
1885

The Phelps Hotel is considered to be the most important 19th-century landmark in Deuel County. It is typical of many similar hotels built during western Nebraska's pioneer period. Unlike other early hotels, the Phelps has a well-preserved interior, and it is believed to be the oldest commercial building in Big Springs. In its early days the hotel was a center of community activity and a stopping place for travelers, land seekers, and pioneers. Old hotel registers, which include the names of many early settlers and travelers, may still be examined inside the building.
Private

DOUGLAS COUNTY
Omaha
BANK OF FLORENCE
8502 N. 30th Street
1856

Florence, once an independent town, is now a section of northeastern Omaha. The town was platted in 1854 on the site of the winter quarters established by the Mormons eight years earlier on their trek to the Salt Lake Valley. The Bank of Florence was chartered by the territorial legislature of Nebraska on January 18, 1856, and the building was constructed the following summer. During the latter years of the 1850's the Bank of Florence, along with many other Nebraska banks, issued quantities of wildcat currency and financed much land speculation, and in 1859 the bank failed. Basically Greek Revival in style, the bank has undergone alterations. The original double doors of the east or main facade were replaced by a single door, and the numerous lights and glazing bars of the windows were replaced by large panes of glass. The interior has been extensively remodeled, but the original bank vault remains intact.
Private

DOUGLAS COUNTY
Omaha
CROOK, GEN. GEORGE, HOUSE
Quarters No. 1, Fort Omaha
1879

The Crook House, located at Fort Omaha, is named for General George Crook (1829–1890), a distinguished Civil War officer and Indian fighter. He was stationed at Fort Omaha as head of the U.S. Army's Department of the Platte from 1875 to 1882 and again from 1886 to 1888. In this capacity Crook played a significant role in disarming hostile Indians in the northern Great Plains and opening this area to pioneer settlement. He moved into the house following its completion early in 1879. Although the building has served various purposes in intervening years, it is currently used, as it was originally, as the commanding officer's quarters at Fort Omaha. Although the interior has been modernized to some extent over the years, few alterations appear to have been made to the exterior.
Federal; not accessible to the public

GAGE COUNTY
Beatrice vicinity
HOMESTEAD NATIONAL MONUMENT
4 miles northwest of Beatrice on Neb. 4
1863

Homestead National Monument occupies the site of the claim of Daniel Freeman, one of the first applicants to file under the Homestead Act of 1862. The act permitted every citizen to file claim to one-quarter section (160 acres) of unappropriated Government land. To become full owner, the settler had to live on the land and cultivate it for five years. The monument, which commemorates the influence of the homestead movement on American history, includes the Palmer-Epard homestead cabin, erected in 1867 and later moved here; the site of the Freeman cabin and later Freeman buildings; the graves of Freeman and his wife; and 90 acres of high grass prairie.
Federal
NPS; 162.73 acres

GARDEN COUNTY
Lewellen vicinity
ASH HOLLOW CAVE
2 miles southeast of Lewellen
c. 2000 B.C.–A.D. 1500

Ash Hollow Cave is a rock shelter which was occupied sporadically by prehistoric hunting parties for over 3500 years. The earliest occupation occurred in Plains Archaic times and the most recent in the protohistoric Dismal River cultural period. Because of the long archeological record represented at the site, the careful nature of the excavation done there, and the meticulous reporting of these excavations, Ash Hollow Cave has been instrumental in establishing the sequence of events in central plains prehistory.
Private; not accessible to the public
NHL

HOWARD COUNTY
Cotesfield vicinity
COUFAL SITE
6 miles northwest of Cotesfield on Davis Creek
1138

The Coufal Site is a major village of the central Plains tradition. It represents an Indian culture intermediate between the Upper Republican and Nebraska cultures. Excavations here represent the most comprehensive study of any site of the central Plains tradition. Twenty-two houses were excavated and more than 17,000 specimens collected.
Private; not accessible to the public
NHL

HOWARD COUNTY
Palmer vicinity
PALMER SITE
4 miles north and 1 mile west of
Palmer on Loup River
c. 1800–1840

The Palmer Site is a Skidi Pawnee Indian village first reported by Meriwether Lewis and William Clark in 1804. Zebulon Pike, who visited the Republican Pawnee in 1806, agreed with Lewis and Clark as to the location of the village. It is significant because of its long association with an important division of the Pawnee, believed to be among the longest identifiable residents of Nebraska. The Reverend Jedidiah Morse, who visited the village in 1822, stated that it contained 120 lodges, but according to John B. Dunbar it contained only 70 lodges in 1836. By 1844 the village had been abandoned.
Private; not accessible to the public
NHL

KEITH COUNTY
Brule vicinity
DIAMOND SPRINGS STAGE STATION
1 mile west of Brule exit on Int. 80
1859–1867

At this site are the relatively undisturbed remains of a station used by both the Pony Express and the Overland Stage during the mid–19th century. Diamond Springs Stage Station was built by the freighting firm of Russell, Majors and Waddell. After the telegraph made the Pony Express obsolete, the station continued to be a stopping point for the Overland Stage until 1865, when Indian raids caused its abandonment. Although the aboveground portion of the building has disappeared, an unusual amount of surface detail survives.
Private

LANCASTER COUNTY
Lincoln
CITY HALL
920 O Street
1874–1879, Alfred B. Mullett and
William Appleton Potter

Built of brick and faced with Nebraska limestone, the Lincoln City Hall is a four-story, rectangular structure measuring 60 by 90 feet. Many interior alterations have been made since 1879, but the ornamental cast iron stairways and the original Gothic woodwork are still intact. Few exterior changes have been made; the most important have been the conversion of several doors into windows, the installation of new roofing, and the removal of some iron

cresting and stone cornice brackets. The City Hall incorporates Second Empire elements into its basic style which is Victorian Gothic. Initial plans were prepared by Alfred B. Mullett as Supervising Architect of the U.S. Treasury (1865–1874). In May, 1874, Mullett visited Lincoln to supervise work on the building, but in January of the following year he was succeeded by W. A. Potter. The extent of Potter's involvement in the City Hall is difficult to assess. Possibly the mansard roof, boxlike mass, and symmetrical articulation are Mullett's; but the Gothic ornamentation is most likely part of Potter's revisions, as he favored the latter style over Mullett's Second Empire designs.
Municipal

LANCASTER COUNTY
Lincoln
FAIRVIEW (WILLIAM JENNINGS BRYAN HOUSE)
4900 Sumner Street
1902

Fairview was the home of William Jennings Bryan from 1902 until 1922, when he donated the building to the Lincoln Methodist Hospital. Bryan launched his political career in 1890 by winning a seat in the United States House of Representatives. He was nationally known as a champion of free coinage of silver. Though three times an unsuccessful candidate for the Presidency of the United States, he served as Secretary of State under Woodrow Wilson from 1913 to 1915. Bryan is remembered primarily as an orator and as a champion of popular causes in the economically depressed agrarian and western regions at the turn of the century. Fairview's first floor was restored in 1962, and a number of original furnishings have been placed in the house by the Bryan family.
Private
NHL

LANCASTER COUNTY
Lincoln
KENNARD, THOMAS P., HOUSE (NEBRASKA STATEHOOD MEMORIAL)
1627 H Street
1869, John Keys Winchell

The Nebraska Statehood Memorial, otherwise known as the Kennard House, was built in 1869 as a residence for Thomas Perkins Kennard, one of three men chosen by the state legislature in 1867 to select a capital city for the newly established state of Nebraska. Largely through Kennard's persuasion the Capital Commission selected the present site of Lincoln on July 29, 1867. In 1869 architect John Keys Winchell of Chicago designed three

similar masonry dwellings in Lincoln, one for each of the capital commissioners. Of these three structures, only the Kennard House stands today. It is believed to be the oldest house within the original 1867 plot of Lincoln and is perhaps the best of the few remaining Nebraska examples of Italianate domestic architecture, one of the most popular American styles from the mid–1850's to the mid–1870's, Nebraska's pioneer period. In 1965 the state legislature designated the Kennard House as the Nebraska Statehood Memorial and directed the Nebraska State Historical Society to restore and refurnish it. The house has been refurnished to represent the home of a moderately affluent Nebraska family in the late 1870's.
State

LANCASTER COUNTY
Lincoln
LEWIS-SYFORD HOUSE
700 N. 16th Street
c. 1878

This residence is Lincoln's best example of Second Empire architecture. It is a relatively small, one-and-one-half-story house with a low mansard roof. The roof is pierced by dormer windows and topped by elaborate, cast iron ornamental cresting. A veranda adjoins the main entrance, and there is a porch over the side entrance. Windows at the ground level are high and rectangular. Both the interior and exterior have been very little altered since construction.
Private

LANCASTER COUNTY
Lincoln
NEBRASKA STATE CAPITOL
1445 K Street
1922–1932, Bertram Grosvenor
Goodhue

The Nebraska State Capitol is the fifth to serve both the territory and the state. Bertram Goodhue (1869–1924) drew the plans for an architectural competition sponsored by the Nebraska Capitol Commission. His design won, but Goodhue died before the building was finished. The capitol is square in plan with four interior courtyards separated by the arms of a Greek cross. The crossing of the arms is surmounted by a 400–foot steel frame tower. In his unusual design Goodhue broke away from the slavish imitation of classical styles which characterized most state capitols. He repudiated his earlier penchant for Gothic forms and sought a new means of architectural expression. The result is simple and impressive. Ornament is integrated into the total design rather than applied to it; Goodhue was strongly influenced by avante garde Eu-

ropean architects, notably Eliel Saarinen of Finland. Limestone, granite, marble, and slate are used in the capitol; extension walls are stone and brick faced with limestone. There are bas reliefs and mosaics to depict the history of Nebraska and the evolution of world democracy. Byzantine, Assyrian, Egyptian, Gothic, and American Indian motifs are common. Lee Laurie did much of the sculpture, notably the 19–foot bronze statue, "The Sower," atop the central tower. Augustus Vincent Tack, Kenneth Evett, and James Penney have painted interior murals. The capitol grounds occupy a four-block area.
State

MORRILL COUNTY
Bayard vicinity
CHIMNEY ROCK NATIONAL HISTORIC SITE
3 miles southwest of Bayard
c. 1830–1870

Chimney Rock was a famous natural landmark and campsite on the Oregon Trail migration route to the West. Towering 500 feet above the North Platte River Valley, the rock early became a guidepost for Rocky Mountain traders and trappers on their seasonal migrations between the Rockies and the Missouri River trading marts. It was a welcome campsite because of the excellent spring nearby.
Non-federal
NPS; 83.36 acres

NANCE COUNTY
Genoa vicinity
GENOA SITE
1 mile south of Genoa on Neb. 39
1859–1874

The Genoa Site represents the last cluster of villages occupied by the Pawnee Indians in Nebraska. More than 3,400 people led by Chief Pitalesharo lived in the three villages in 1862. Within ten years more than a thousand members of the tribe died as a result of engagements with enemy war parties or from starvation. In 1874 the Pawnee moved south to a new reservation in Oklahoma. It was from the Genoa villages that Frank and Luther North obtained Pawnee scouts who protected the construction gangs on the Union Pacific Railroad from Sioux raids. All surface features of the villages appear to have been destroyed, but the site can be excavated to identify the original boundaries.
Multiple public/private

NEMAHA COUNTY
Brownville
BROWNVILLE HISTORIC DISTRICT
Bounded on the south by Allen and Richard Streets, bounded on the north by Nemaha and Nebraska Streets, on the west by 7th Street, on the east by the Missouri River, and on the northwest and southwest by 2nd Street
Mid- to late 19th century

Brownville was first settled by Richard Brown in 1854, the same year that Nebraska Territory was created. Nurtured by its location, the community grew rapidly, to become a major steamboat landing, river crossing, overland freighting terminus and milling center. Briefly, in the late 1860's, Brownville was a cowtown, the end of the trail for Texas cattle drives. A land office—one of four in the territory—was opened in 1857. Brownville's hilly and heavily wooded terrain contrasts markedly with the surrounding prairie. Most of the buildings in the historic district were built between 1855 and 1875. Notable among these are the Methodist Church (1859), the Brown-Carson House (1860), the Furnas House (c. 1868), the Muir House (1868–1872), and the Bailey House (1877).
Multiple public/private
HABS

OTOE COUNTY
Nebraska City vicinity
ARBOR LODGE (J. STERLING MORTON HOUSE)
Arbor Lodge State Park, just west of city limits of Nebraska City
1855

Arbor Lodge is the most important structure associated with the career of J. Sterling Morton, a pioneer Nebraska journalist, territorial governor, and leader in the areas of horticulture and conservation. He served as Secretary of Agriculture under President Grover Cleveland and is known today as the founder of Arbor Day, first celebrated in Nebraska in 1872. Morton's house was built about 1855, shortly after Nebraska became a territory and was opened to settlement. Several major enlargements were made, terminating in 1902 when the house assumed its present appearance as a three-story, 52–room Colonial Revival mansion. Morton's house is now preserved along with 65 acres of land as Arbor Lodge State Park and is administered by the Nebraska State Game and Parks Commission. Just south of the house is an Italian terraced garden landscaped by Frederick Law Olmsted about 1903.
State

RED WILLOW COUNTY
McCook
NORRIS, SENATOR GEORGE WILLIAM, HOUSE
706 Norris Avenue
1899

During his long congressional career, Senator George W. Norris promoted social and economic legislation that empowered the federal government to assume major responsibility in furthering national well-being. The Tennessee Valley Authority exemplifies the significance of his legislative accomplishments. Norris purchased this two-story, cross-gabled house in 1899 and remodeled it in 1930–1931. It has been little changed since the Senator's death in 1944.
Private; not accessible to the public
NHL

RICHARDSON COUNTY
Rulo vicinity
LEARY SITE
4 miles southeast of Rulo on Neb. 7
1500–1600

The Leary Site is a large prehistoric village and burial area of the Oneota culture, first mentioned by Meriwether Lewis and William Clark in 1804. The Oneotas were Siouan peoples who migrated up the Missouri River into the plains. The site is unusual in that it is the only Oneota village west of the Missouri that does not contain evidence of contact with whites. It has been partially excavated.
Private; not accessible to the public
NHL

SARPY COUNTY
Bellevue
BURLINGTON DEPOT (OMAHA & SOUTHERN RAILROAD STATION)
Haworth Park
1869–1870

A group of Omaha businessmen began building the Southwestern Railroad in 1869. A year later tracks had almost reached Bellevue, and the name had been changed to the Omaha & Southern. The Burlington Depot is a long, rectangular frame building having a steep gable roof and large eave projections. Decorative brackets support the eaves. Moved from its original site in 1970, the depot has undergone few alterations and is in relatively good condition. It is possibly the oldest railroad depot in the state.
Private

SARPY COUNTY
Bellevue
FONTANELLE BANK
2212 Main Street
1856

Built in 1856, the Fontanelle Bank is a rare Nebraska example of transitional Greek Revival-Italianate styling. It is possibly the oldest commercial building, as well as the oldest public building, in Nebraska. After failing as a wildcat bank in the panic of 1857, the building served as the Sarpy County Courthouse from 1861 until 1875. It then became Bellevue's town hall and remained so until 1959. For the past several years, the building has been used as an antique shop. The future use of the building, now vacant, remains uncertain. An official Nebraska Historical Marker has recently been installed on the lawn in front of the building.
Private; not accessible to the public

SARPY COUNTY
Bellevue
HAMILTON, WILLIAM, HOUSE
2003 Bluff Street
c. 1856

The William Hamilton House is one of the oldest dwellings in Nebraska, and one of the few Greek Revival buildings extant. The first owner of the house was the Reverend William Hamilton (1811–1891), who occupied it from 1856 to 1867. Hamilton was a pioneer missionary in Sarpy and Thurston counties. He first came to Nebraska in 1853 to direct the Presbyterian Indian Mission at Bellevue. The house is a long, rectangular, two-story structure with a gable roof and limestone walls two feet thick. The Greek Revival elements are apparent in the low pitch of the roof, the window design, and the use of cornice boards and cornice returns.
Private; not accessible to the public

SARPY COUNTY
Bellevue
OLD LOG CABIN
1805 Hancock Street

According to local tradition this dwelling was built about 1835. At the time of construction it was probably a one-room, one-story rectangular structure with a central fireplace and an attic. Cottonwood logs were used for the walls and the spaces between were packed with mud (now grout). The cabin was reportedly moved once from its original site before reaching the present location. The first known owner was the local Presbyterian mission. Clapboards once covered the exterior, but they have been partially removed, and a window was added in the south wall.
Private

SARPY COUNTY
Bellevue
PRESBYTERIAN CHURCH
2002 Franklin Street
1856–1858

The Presbyterian Church in Bellevue is believed to be the oldest extant building in Nebraska built to house religious services. The Presbyterian congregation which constructed the church was founded in 1850 and is probably the oldest existing church congregation in the state. The building shows marked Greek Revival stylistic influence with some Italianate elements. Several additions have been made, but much of both the interior and exterior remains intact. The church served the First Presbyterian congregation until 1959, when a larger building was completed. Since 1959 other religious groups have used the property.
Private

SCOTTS BLUFF COUNTY
Gering vicinity
ROBIDOUX PASS
9 miles west of Gering
c. 1840

Robidoux Pass was a natural landmark on the old Oregon Trail. The great migrations of the 1840's passed through it, and from its crest westbound travelers had their first view of Laramie Peak. Joseph and Antoine Robidoux established a trading post here in 1849 and gave the place its name. After the Mitchell Pass route eastward was opened to travel in 1850, the Robidoux Pass route fell into disuse. Extensive remains of the Oregon-California Trail of the pre–1850 period have survived.
Private
NHL

SCOTTS BLUFF COUNTY
Gering vicinity
SCOTTS BLUFF NATIONAL MONUMENT
3 miles west of Gering on Neb. 92
1841–1869

Scotts Bluff, a landmark and campground for thousands of overland emigrants, overlooks the North Platte section of the Oregon Trail to the Far West. It is today a monument to those who moved America westward—on foot, on horseback, and in covered wagons. In 1830, fur traders Jedediah Smith, William Sublette, and David Jackson took the first wagons past Scotts Bluff. In 1843 the first large migration to Oregon passed this spot. Among those who followed were Brigham Young and his band of Mormons. The greatest wave of migration occurred in the years following the discovery of gold in California in

1848. Today the ruts of the trail, worn by iron-rimmed wagon wheels and a quarter million emigrants, can still be seen from the transmonument highway.
Federal/non-federal
NPS; 3,084 acres

SCOTTS BLUFF COUNTY
Gering vicinity
SIGNAL BUTTE
13 miles west of Gering
2500 B.C.

Signal Butte was the first site of the middle prehistoric period to be excavated by archeologists in the central and northern plains. Deposits were found showing three distinct occupations, the most recent a historic Indian group. At the foot of the butte a fossil quarry produced Early Man spear points in association with an extinct species of bison.
Private
NHL

SIOUX COUNTY
FORT ROBINSON AND RED CLOUD AGENCY
Reference—see Dawes County

VALLEY COUNTY
North Loup vicinity
SCHULTZ SITE
3 miles northwest of North Loup
c. 500

The Schultz Site is the only excavated village of the Valley focus, an early Plains Woodland culture. A small, semisedentary village, it was occupied by peoples who apparently lived by hunting animals and gathering wild plant foods. Excavation of this site has made it possible to learn the nature of this way of life on the Great Plains. Some of the sites remain undisturbed except by sheet erosion.
Private; not accessible to the public
NHL

WASHINGTON COUNTY
Blair vicinity
BERTRAND
De Soto National Wildlife Refuge
1865

In the early 19th century an increasing amount of steamboat traffic passed along Nebraska's segment of the Missouri River. This traffic reached its peak in 1859 during the Colorado gold rush and declined in the 1860's due to the Civil War and to competition from the railroads. The 160–by–30–foot stern wheeler *Bertrand*, owned by the Montana and Idaho Steamship Lines, was one of the largest steamboats to ply the Missouri River north of the Platte. It reportedly hit a snag in the

Missouri River north of Omaha and sank in April 1865. A cargo of 35,000 pounds of mercury was believed to have gone down with the ship. The mercury was to have been used in mining operations in Montana or the Dakotas. Large quantities of whiskey and gold may also have been on board at the time of the disaster. The current value of the entire cargo has been estimated at $250,000. The wreck was located near the Iowa border through the use of metal detectors. Thus far only the front section of the deck has been uncovered. The original superstructure above the deck was apparently carried away when the boat sank.
Federal; not accessible to the public

WASHINGTON COUNTY
Fort Calhoun vicinity
FORT ATKINSON
1 mile east of Fort Calhoun
1819

Fort Atkinson lay on the line of forts guarding the western frontier of the 1820's. It was located at Council Bluffs, a center of the fur trade activity. The Upper Missouri Indian Agency was established here in 1825. It operated as a force for peace among the Missouri tribes, insuring their cooperation with the fur traders. Fort Atkinson also played a part in early western explorations into the Rocky Mountains. It was abandoned in 1827 when the Army moved its garrison to the current site of Fort Leavenworth (Kans.). Nothing remains of Fort Atkinson above the surface, but recent archeological excavations have established the exact size of the fort and have uncovered portions of its foundations as well as artifacts relating to the military occupation and the fur trade.
Private; not accessible to the public
NHL

WEBSTER COUNTY
Guide Rock vicinity
PIKE PAWNEE VILLAGE SITE (HILL SITE)
4 miles southwest of Guide Rock
Late 18th and early 19th centuries

The Pike Pawnee Village Site is generally accepted as being Kitkehahki, the village where Lieutenant Zebulon Pike raised the American flag in 1806, ending Spanish authority in Nebraska. Archeological evidence corroborates the identification. Only three of the nearly 100 earth lodges have been excavated. Among the artifacts uncovered were a Spanish peace medal dating from 1797, an American peace medal of the type issued after 1801, and a military button bearing the battalion number of Pike's infantry.
Private; not accessible to the public
NHL

WEBSTER COUNTY
Red Cloud
CATHER HOUSE
Southwest corner, 3rd and Cedar Streets
1884–1890

This house is associated with the author Willa Sibert Cather (1873–1947), who moved from Virginia with her family to the Red Cloud area in 1883. Most of her best known writings deal with life in the Red Cloud vicinity. The Cather House, in which she lived from 1884 to 1890, figures prominently in such works as *The Song of the Lark*, "The Best Years," and "Old Mrs. Harris." Willa Cather's bedroom was located in the attic space above the rear wing. Shortly after the Cather family moved out of the house in 1904, the entire attic was sealed off and not reopened until 1966–1967 when the dwelling was restored and refurnished to represent the 1884–1890 period. This restoration was guided in part by detailed descriptions of the interior contained in Willa Cather's writings. Many early Cather family furnishings have been returned to the house. Still decorated with wallpaper she put up in the 1880's, her bedroom has been refurnished and is open to public inspection. Many of the scenes in Willa Cather's last story, "The Best Years," center around this bedroom and the Cather House attic.
Private

Nebraska State Capitol, Lincoln, Nebraska.
Lincoln Journal-Star Publishing Company

Nevada

Fort Churchill, Weeks vicinity, Nevada. *NPS*

Frame House,
Virginia City Historic District,
Virginia City, Nevada. *HABS*

St. Mary's in the Mountains,
Virginia City Historic District,
Virginia City, Nevada. *HABS*

LYON COUNTY
Weeks vicinity
FORT CHURCHILL
U.S. 95A, 8 miles south of U.S. 50
1860

Fort Churchill was built on the central Overland Mail Route as a result of a Paiute uprising in 1860. It protected the first transcontinental telegraph lines and from 1861 to 1865 served as the headquarters for Nevada military posts. After abandonment in 1870, the quadrangle of adobe structures gradually dissolved until, by 1930, the original walls stood only two or three feet above ground. Some of the adobe buildings were reconstructed on the original foundations in 1935. Ruined walls of some 15 of the reconstructions remain as part of a Nevada state park.
State
NHL

PERSHING COUNTY
Lovelock vicinity
LEONARD ROCKSHELTER
12 miles south of Lovelock off Nev. 59
c. 9000 B.C.

Leonard Rockshelter is formed by the outward tilting of a prominent cliff on the western side of the Humboldt Range. It has provided archeologists with important information regarding early Indian occupations in the Great Basin. Here early hunting and food-gathering peoples lived in prehistoric times, as shown by ancient trash deposits and a series of Indian petroglyphs. The shelter is also important as a climatic indicator.
Private
NHL

STOREY COUNTY
Virginia City
VIRGINIA CITY HISTORIC DISTRICT
1860

Virginia City owes its existence to the discovery in 1859 of the Comstock Lode, which during the next 20 years yielded $300,000,000 in gold and silver. Although richer than most, the town was a prototype for all frontier mining boom towns. Its methods of large-scale industrial and corporate enterprise were a pattern for subsequent mining towns in Colorado, Montana, Idaho, and eastern Nevada. It still possesses an atmosphere and appearance reminiscent of the boom period. The surviving houses, saloons, and public buildings are used for a variety of modern purposes.
Private
NHL; HABS

WASHOE COUNTY
Reno
NEWLANDS, SENATOR FRANCIS G., HOME
7 Elm Court
1889

Senator Francis G. Newlands was involved in Nevada's political and economic affairs for the 30 years of his residence there, 1889–1919. In both the U.S. House of Representatives and the U.S. Senate he supported federal irrigation programs. In 1901 he proposed that the federal government finance irrigation through a Reclamation Fund composed of proceeds from the sale of western public lands. The Newlands bill was signed into law as the Reclamation Act of 1902. The Senator's large, two-story frame house has been little altered since his occupancy.
Private; not accessible to the public
NHL

WHITE PINE COUNTY
Hobson vicinity
FORT RUBY
Near Hobson on a secondary road, west side of Ruby Lake
1862

From 1859 to 1869 Fort Ruby was an important station on the Pony Express and Central Overland Stage Line. It was also a relay station on the first transcontinental telegraph line. An overland stage ranch was placed there in 1865 to supply grain and provisions. The fort was established to protect the stage and telegraph facilities from Indian attacks. It was occupied until transcontinental stage operations ended in 1869. The fort consists today of two original buildings, the post office and a residence, both in excellent condition.
Private; not accessible to the public
NHL

New Hampshire

Little Studio, Saint-Gaudens National Historic Site,
Plainfield vicinity, New Hampshire. *HABS*

Busiel-Seeburg Mill,
Laconia, New Hampshire. *Richard M. Candee*

Franklin Pierce Homestead,
Merrimack County, New Hampshire.
G. Peterick for HABS

Wentworth-Gardner House,
Portsmouth, New Hampshire.
Charles W. Snell for NPS

BELKNAP COUNTY
Laconia
BELKNAP-SULLOWAY MILL
Mill Street
c. 1823

A survey of the architecture of textile mills carried out by Old Sturbridge Village indicates that the Belknap-Sulloway Mill may be the oldest surviving structure of its type in the area. Built on a small scale, the mill is representative of rural manufacturing operations. A wooden mill of the Meredith Cotton and Woolen Manufacturing Company preceded this structure. Situated on the banks of the Winnepesaukee River, the mill is brick and wood. The present cupola appears to be a reproduction of the original. Inside, very little has been changed. Ceilings are open on each floor revealing the joisted flooring of the level above. The mill site formed the nucleus for present-day Laconia.
Municipal

BELKNAP COUNTY
Laconia
BUSIEL-SEEBURG MILL
Mill Street
Mid–19th century

The Busiel Granite Hosiery Mill was begun in 1853 by J. W. Busiel, who had established the firm in 1846. By the turn of the century the company was the largest of its kind in the area. Busiel's mill was one of the first to adopt the new Aiken and Peppers circular knitting machines with latched needles. As originally constructed, the mill included only the present eastern portion. In 1878 the western half was added, and a third section, in 1882. Decorative brickwork on the east end is visible in the plain gable banding and dentil cornice. Fenestration differs only slightly in the east and west sections. Granite sills and lintels appear on all windows. The tall stair tower has an arched window in three sides of the top story which is surrounded by more decorative brickwork. The roof is gabled.
Municipal

HILLSBORO COUNTY
Hillsboro vicinity
PIERCE, FRANKLIN, HOMESTEAD
3 miles west of Hillsboro on N.H. 31
1804

Franklin Pierce, fourteenth President of the United States, lived in this house from infancy until his marriage in 1834. Trained as a lawyer, he was a Representative from New Hampshire (1833–1837) and a United States Senator (1837–1842). He held the Nation's highest office from 1853 to 1857, a most critical period of the antebellum generation. The two-story

hipped roof house is built in the Federal style.
State
NHL

HILLSBOROUGH COUNTY
Nashua
HUNT MEMORIAL LIBRARY
6 Main Street
1903, Cram, Goodhue, and Ferguson

This building, the only early design by Ralph Adams Cram (1863–1942) in New Hampshire, presages the late Gothic Revival style which became his forte. Built of red brick with limestone trim, the library has a high, massive central tower, and north, south, and east wings branch out from this point. Inside, imaginative design techniques utilize space, proportion, and detail in pleasing and unusual ways. Notable are the circulation-delivery room because of skillful lighting effects and the reference-reading room with its carved oak detail.
Municipal

HILLSBORO COUNTY
Peterborough
MacDOWELL COLONY
West of U.S. 202
1907

Edward MacDowell was the first American to win an international reputation as a composer of serious music. In 1896 he purchased a 60–acre farm which has been the site of the MacDowell Colony since 1907. Most of the composer's later music—the "Norse" and "Keltic" sonatas, "Fireside Tales," and "New England Idylls"—was written here in a secluded log cabin. Both the cabin and farmhouse remain intact. The Edward MacDowell Association, Inc., which founded the colony as a retreat and workshop for writers, painters, and composers, was organized in 1907 as a memorial to the composer. The colony covers about 400 acres and has 27 music studios.
Private
NHL

MERRIMACK COUNTY
Concord
PIERCE, FRANKLIN, HOUSE
18 Montgomery Street
Mid–1830's

The Franklin Pierce House, a two-story frame structure with two ells, was the only family home of Franklin Pierce (1804–1869), fourteenth President of the United States. Pierce owned the house from 1842 to 1848 and lived there with his wife, Jane Appleton Pierce, and two children, Benjamin and Franklin. Nathaniel Hawthorne, the novelist and

later Pierce's biographer, and John P. Hale, the Free-Soiler, were among the many distinguished guests entertained here. While changes have been made to accommodate apartments, the original appearance can be ascertained by examination of the twin house next door at 20 Montgomery Street which remains largely as it was first built.
Private; not accessible to the public

ROCKINGHAM COUNTY
Derry vicinity
FROST, ROBERT, HOMESTEAD
2 miles southeast of Derry on N.H. 28
1900–1909

Robert Frost, author of eleven volumes of poetry, is one of the few 20th-century American poets who have commanded both critical respect and wide readership. Between 1900 and 1909 he lived here continuously, farming for a livelihood until 1906. During this time Frost developed his poetic style and composed many of the poems included in his first two volumes, *A Boy's Will* (1913) and *North of Boston* (1914). Two of the poems written or rewritten here are "Death of the Hired Man" and "Trial by Existence." Many of his later poems, such as "Mending Wall," drew on experiences at the Derry Farm. It is anticipated that the house will be restored and the property operated as a "living farm."
State; not accessible to the public
NHL

ROCKINGHAM COUNTY
Exeter
DUDLEY HOUSE (PERRY-DUDLEY HOUSE)
14 Front Street
Early 19th century

The Perry-Dudley House is a square, three-story Federal town house covered with clapboard siding. It was built sometime between 1802 and 1815. Around the time of the Civil War an ell was added at the rear, and a later carriage house was joined to the ell sometime after 1935. A portico with fluted columns and pilasters projects over the main entrance, which still has its original glass sidelights and transom. Both the Perrys and the Dudleys were prominent in the development of Exeter.
Private; not accessible to the public

ROCKINGHAM COUNTY
Portsmouth
JACKSON, RICHARD, HOUSE
Northwest Street
1664

Constructed in 1664 by Richard Jackson, a shipbuilder, the Jackson House is a salt-

box of what may be termed medieval design. Medieval houses were often constructed of timber frames and had walls of wattle and daub or brick masonry. The exterior was covered with various materials; in America clapboards were most common. The central two-story section of the house, erected in the 17th century, has a large chimney and sharply sloping gable roof that nearly reaches to the ground in the rear. There is a lean-to across the rear, and the two, one-story frame wings at each end were added around 1764. Unpainted, weather-stained clapboards cover the exterior, and the windows are replicas of leaded glass casements. The original central portion contains a small center entrance hall with a parlor to the left and the hall or kitchen to the right, a plan common to medieval houses.
Private
NHL

ROCKINGHAM COUNTY
Portsmouth
MacPHEDRIS-WARNER HOUSE
Chapel and Daniel Streets
1718–1723

Built by Captain Archibald MacPhedris, wealthy Scottish fur trader and iron manufacturer, this brick house exemplifies the large, early Georgian style residence once popular in the New England colonies. The two stories are topped by a dormered gambrel roof and balustrade. The present roof form evolved from two parallel gabled roofs with a deep valley between, a form commonly found during the medieval period in England. The five-bay main facade has a central door capped with a broken sequential arch. The plan is of the central hall type with end chimneys. The house is also named for Jonathan Warner, who married Captain MacPhedris' daughter.
Private
NHL

ROCKINGHAM COUNTY
Portsmouth
MOFFATT-LADD HOUSE
154 Market Street
c. 1764

Captain John Moffatt, a wealthy merchant, had ship's carpenters build this house as a wedding gift for his son Samuel. The structure stands on high ground overlooking the Piscataqua River where the owner's merchant vessels docked. It is a late Georgian, square, three-storied clapboard house with corners accentuated by quoins, three end chimneys, and a hip roof surmounted by a balustraded captain's walk. A flight of granite steps leads up to the central doorway which opens into a large hallway occupying more than half the floor space of the front portion of the house.
Private
NHL

ROCKINGHAM COUNTY
Portsmouth
WENTWORTH-GARNER HOUSE
140 Mechanic Street
1760

The Wentworth-Garner House is a New England residence depicting noticeably the changes in Georgian architecture since the early years of the 18th century. The house was built by ship's carpenters for Madam Mark Hunking Wentworth, who presented it to her son Thomas, a younger brother of John Wentworth, the last royal governor of New Hampshire. Maj. William Gardner acquired the house in 1792, and it served as his residence until his death in 1833. The facade of this two-and-one-half-story frame house is comprised of wide, pinewood clapboarding that is rusticated to imitate cut stone, and the corners are emphasized by large quoins. The four first-floor windows are capped by triangular pediments. Five windows on the second floor are topped by lintels. Above the windows is a denticulate cornice, and three dormers and two regular brick chimneys project from the hip roof. The other elevations of the house are finished in clapboard siding set only a few inches to the weather. The plan of the house is of the standard Georgian, four-room, central-hall type. A two-story frame service ell extends to the rear from the kitchen.
Private
NHL

ROCKINGHAM COUNTY
Portsmouth vicinity
WENTWORTH-COOLIDGE MANSION
At the foot of Little Harbor Road, off U.S. 1A, 2 miles south of Portsmouth
1695, 1730, 1750

This rambling, H-shaped frame house was the home and headquarters of Benning Wentworth, appointed first royal governor of the Province of New Hampshire by King George II in 1741. The earliest part of the mansion, which now comprises the west wing, was erected about 1695 as a typical two-story, frame, saltbox farmhouse. In 1730 the small house was enlarged by adding a two-story frame wing to the east or original rear. In 1750 the existing two-story frame east wing was added at right angles to the rear of the 1730 wing, thus giving the house its general H shape. The 1750 wing was constructed to provide additional space for the royal governor to carry out his official duties. On the first floor is a large council chamber, with paneled walls and a carved mantel, where the governor's council met.
State
NHL

SULLIVAN COUNTY
Plainfield vicinity
SAINT-GAUDENS NATIONAL HISTORIC SITE
South of Plainfield off N.H. 12–A
c. 1800

Saint-Gaudens National Historic Site comprises the home, studios, and gardens of Augustus Saint-Gaudens, one of America's eminent sculptors. When the artist and his family moved into the house in 1885, his most productive years were still ahead. Here he completed the standing *Lincoln*, now in Chicago (1887); the *Adams Memorial* (1891); and the equestrian *General William T. Sherman* in New York (1900). Concurrently Saint-Gaudens gathered about him the Cornish Colony of promising young artists and influenced their release from the shackles of academic conservatism.
Federal
NPS; 36 acres
HABS

Dudley House (Perry-Dudley House),
Exeter, New Hampshire. *Ben's Foto Shop*

New Jersey

Barnegat Lighthouse, Barnegat Light, New Jersey.
New Jersey Department of Environmental Protection

Morven, Princeton, New Jersey.
*New Jersey Department
of Environmental Protection*

Vail Factory, Speedwell Village,
Morristown, New Jersey.
Koyce & Koyce, Morristown, New Jersey

Cape May Historic District, Cape May, New Jersey. *Carolyn Pitts.*

ATLANTIC COUNTY
Atlantic City
ABSECON LIGHTHOUSE
Vermont and Pacific Avenues
1856

The Absecon Lighthouse was erected under the direction of Lieutenant George Gordon Meade, later the commander of Federal forces at the battle of Gettysburg (Pennsylvania), July, 1863. Its light, visible for 20 miles, warned ships and mariners of the shoal area off Brigantine Beach and Atlantic City. The 171-foot iron and brick tower measures 27 feet in diameter at the base and 13 feet 7.5 inches at the lens. An iron spiral staircase rises from ground level to the lens where the light was located. It was lit by mineral oil until 1910 when this lamp was replaced by one burning oil vapor. The light was electrified in 1925 and decommissioned eight years later.
State

ATLANTIC COUNTY
Somers Point
SOMERS MANSION
Shore Road and Somers Point Circle
1720's

Unusual because of its Flemish bond exterior and gambrel roof, the Somers Mansion is the oldest house in Atlantic County. The original dwelling was enlarged about 1760, and further changes were made in the late 19th century. Window sash and the present second-story balcony date from the late 1930's. Most of the paneling, brickwork, and flooring is original. The Somers family was prominent in New Jersey's history.
State
HABS

BERGEN COUNTY
Hohokus
THE HERMITAGE (WALDWIC COTTAGE)
335 N. Franklin Turnpike
Mid-18th century; 1845
(remodeled), William H. Ranlett

The earlier 18th-century house was probably a typical North Jersey "Dutch," gambrel-roofed building of red sandstone random ashlar with an overhanging roof which sheltered a western porch. This structure was completely transformed into a Gothic Revival cottage in 1845 and has not changed noticeably since then. The one-and-one-half-story building is irregularly shaped with numerous projections and is covered by three intersecting, steeply pitched gable roofs. The main and dormer gables have pierced barge boards and tall wooden finials. All windows have diamond-shaped panes. West of the kitchen wing is a free-standing, two-story summer kitchen built in the late 19th century. The Hermitage is the only remaining Gothic Revival house definitely attributable to William Ranlett.
Private; not accessible to the public
NHL; HABS

BERGEN COUNTY (also in Orange and
Rockland counties, New York)
PALISADES INTERSTATE PARK
On the west bank of the Hudson
River
1899

The Palisades Interstate Park represents an unusual effort by two states, New Jersey and New York, to preserve the scenic beauty of much of the lower western side of the Hudson River. The integrity of the cliffs in the area was threatened toward the end of the 19th century by the rapid development of stone quarries. The park system created to preserve the area now includes much more land than was at first visualized.
State
NHL

BERGEN COUNTY
River Edge
STEUBEN HOUSE (ACKERMAN-ZABRISKIE-STEUBEN HOUSE)
New Bridge Road
1695

The walls and foundation of this late 17th-century Dutch Colonial farmhouse are sandstone. The present house is twice as long and one-third again deeper than the original. Gables in the roof are brick, and the present gambrel roof was once gabled. George Washington used the house briefly as his headquarters in September, 1780. Confiscated by the New Jersey legislature from its Loyalist owner, the then-Zabriskie House was given to General Friedrich von Steuben in recognition of his service to the patriot cause during the Revolution. Von Steuben never lived here. David Ackerman was the original owner.
State
HABS

BERGEN COUNTY
STATUE OF LIBERTY NATIONAL MONUMENT
Reference—see New York County, New York

CAMDEN COUNTY
Camden
WHITMAN, WALT, HOUSE
330 Mickle Street
c. 1848

Walt Whitman occupied this frame house from 1884 to 1892, the last eight years of his life. It is the surviving building most intimately associated with the "Poet of Democracy." Whitman's *Leaves of Grass*, first published in 1855, was generally rejected by literary critics of the day. Such writers as Ralph Waldo Emerson and John Burroughs recognized his greatness, however, and consistently encouraged him. Among his other well-known poems are "When Lilacs Last in the Dooryard Bloomed," "Crossing Brooklyn Ferry," and "Song of the Open Road." Walt Whitman was not accorded a place in the first rank of American poets until after his death.
State
NHL; HABS

CAMDEN COUNTY
Haddonfield
INDIAN KING TAVERN (CREIGHTON TAVERN)
233 Kings Highway East
1750

Typical of 18th-century wayside taverns, the Indian King Tavern was located on Kings Highway, the main road between Salem and Burlington. The three-story section is three bays wide and contains the tavern. A pent roof separates the first and second floors. The two-and-one-half-story section has a two-room, center hall plan. Both portions are brick covered with stucco. The New Jersey legislature met in the tavern during the spring and fall of 1777.
State
HABS

CAPE MAY COUNTY
Cape May
CAPE MAY HISTORIC DISTRICT
c. 1850–1910

Cape May is one of the oldest seashore resorts in America and at one time ranked in popularity with Newport (Rhode Island), Saratoga Springs (New York), and Long Branch (New Jersey). Henry Hudson sighted Cape May in August, 1609, and the first land was purchased here, by Dutchmen, in 1630. Cornelius Jacobson Mey, a representative of the Dutch West India Company, explored the area which subsequently bore his name. England assumed control of Town Bank (Cape May Town) in the 1660's and developed an economy based on fishing and farming. After the War of 1812, Cape May began to flourish as a resort, continuing to be a noted and much frequented watering place until the early years of the 20th century. Today six hundred 19th-and early 20th-century structures of outstanding architectural quality make Cape May a showcase of late Victorian architecture. Most of these buildings were

conceived and constructed by carpenter-builders who, using textbooks and trade journals, improvised freely upon traditional styles—Greek and Gothic Revival, Queen Anne, Italianate, Eastlake, and others. Notable among these buildings are hotels, churches, private homes, and commercial structures: the Congress Hotel (1879), the Victorian Mansion (1856), the Chalfonte Hotel (1876), the Episcopal Church of the Advent (1867), the Emlen Physick House (1877), the Pink House (1879), and the Windsor Hotel (1878–1879).
Multiple public/private
HABS

ESSEX COUNTY
Newark
SYDENHAM HOUSE
Old Road to Bloomfield
18th and 19th centuries

The Sydenham House is believed to be one of the oldest in Newark. It was probably built early in the 18th century, and the cellar (of roughly squared sandstone laid dry) is older than the aboveground portions. Beams of oak and pine were used to support the upper floors. Constructed as a saltbox with a raised roof in front sloping down over a shed in the rear, the house had its roof raised in 1835. The front wall and entire west end wall have been rebuilt, but otherwise few structural changes have been made. Unique because of its survival in a highly urbanized area, the Sydenham House is representative of an early American homestead.
Private; not accessible to the public
HABS

ESSEX COUNTY
West Orange
EDISON NATIONAL HISTORIC SITE
Main Street, between Alden and
Lakeside Streets
Laboratory, 1887; Glenmont, 1880

On this site are memorialized the illustrious career and scientific achievements of Thomas Alva Edison. The research laboratory where he performed countless experiments also contains his library, notebooks, and models of some of his inventions. In addition to the six original laboratory buildings, there are related buildings erected after 1887. Also included is Glenmont, Edison's 23–room estate in nearby Llewellyn Park, which is furnished as it was during the period the Edison family occupied it.
Federal
NPS; 19.96 acres
HABS

HUDSON COUNTY
Jersey City
HUDSON COUNTY COURTHOUSE
Newark Avenue
1910, Hugh Roberts

The Hudson County Courthouse was the seat of justice in the county for over 50 years. Standing three stories above a high basement, the granite structure is outstanding because of its bronze and marble decoration and the interior murals painted by five well-known artists. The interior is pearl gray marble. A large central rotunda with a dome of stained glass rests upon eight polished, green-veined cippolina marble columns (on the first floor) and on four arches supported by white marble piers (second and third floors). Murals were painted by Frank D. Millet, Charles Y. Turner, Edwin Blashfield, Kenyon Cox, and Howard Pyle.
County; not accessible to the public
HABS

HUNTERDON COUNTY
Lambertville
MARSHALL, JAMES W., HOUSE
60 Bridge Street
1816

Philip Marshall, a wheelwright and wagon maker, purchased the lot for this house in 1815. He constructed a modest brick dwelling for his family, and here James W. Marshall, made famous by his 1848 discovery of gold at Sutter's Fort in California, spent his boyhood. The house is a two-story brick structure with two rooms and a side hall on each floor.
State; not accessible to the public

MERCER COUNTY
Princeton
CLEVELAND, GROVER, HOME, (WESTLAND)
15 Hodge Road
1854

Twice President of the United States, 1885–1889 and 1893–1897, Grover Cleveland was noted for his incorruptibility in an era of corrupt politics. He was much involved in the development of the Civil Service as we know it today. In an effort to restrict the use of government jobs for political patronage, he expanded the number of classified positions covered by the Pendleton Act of 1883. In 1897 Cleveland retired to this large two-and-a-half-story stucco-covered stone house. He maintained this residence until his death in 1908.
Private; not accessible to the public
NHL

MERCER COUNTY
Princeton
HENRY, JOSEPH, HOUSE
Princeton University campus
1837

Joseph Henry began his investigations of electromagnetism in 1826 while a professor of mathematics at Albany Academy. He thus resumed work in a field largely neglected since the era of Benjamin Franklin. Henry's most important discovery was the electromagnet, a core of soft metal wrapped with many coils of insulated wire. In 1830 he produced an induced electrical current by using his magnet. After serving on the faculty of the College of New Jersey, now Princeton University, he was chosen in 1846 to be the first Secretary of the Smithsonian Institution. Joseph Henry's two-story brick house has been moved three times from its original site.
Private; not accessible to the public
NHL

MERCER COUNTY
Princeton
MORVEN
Stockton Street
1754–1755

Morven is a mid–18th-century Georgian residence characterized by its symmetry and emphasis of horizontal planes. The house is brick with wood trim. A two-and-one-half-story central section is flanked by slightly lower wings. The west wing was built first, then the central section (after 1754), last the east wing. In 1848 the wings were raised from one story to two, and the front portico is a later addition. A brick and stucco slave quarters stands behind the main house. Morven was the home of Richard Stockton, a signer of the Declaration of Independence, and has served as the official New Jersey governor's residence since 1954.
State
HABS

MERCER COUNTY
Princeton
NASSAU HALL, PRINCETON UNIVERSITY
Princeton University campus
1754–1756

Named in memory of King William III of the House of Nassau, Nassau Hall was the first important building erected at Princeton University. For almost 50 years it served as the college's only building —providing dormitory, dining room, chapel, and classroom facilities. The hall was a barracks and hospital during the Revolution and was the scene of the last British stand in the battle of Princeton.

The Continental Congress convened here for several months in 1783, during which time it received the news of the signing of the Treaty of Paris ending the Revolutionary War. Designed by Robert Smith of the Carpenters' Company in Philadelphia, the 170–foot long facade is broken by a pedimented central pavilion. The brownstone walls are unadorned except for the quoined and conical entrances and the flat-arch lintels of the windows on the first two stories. The low-pitched hip roof is crowned by a cupola.
Private
NHL

MERCER COUNTY
Princeton
PRINCETON BATTLEFIELD
Princeton Battlefield State Park
1777

General George Washington's victory at Princeton on January 3, 1777, had an effect on the American Revolutionary cause disproportionate to the number of men engaged in the battle. Coupled with a victory at Trenton one week earlier, it heartened the American people with hopes of ultimate success when spirits had been dangerously low. The scene of heaviest fighting is preserved in a 40-acre state park. The Clarke House at the edge of the field was the scene of General John Mercer's death. A memorial arch on the western edge marks the site where unknown American dead were buried.
State
NHL

MERCER COUNTY
Trenton
DOUGLASS HOUSE
John Fitch Way
1766

Typical of dwellings once common in Trenton during the 18th century, the Douglass House is a small frame building covered with beaded siding. A rear ell, one-and-one-half stories high, is attached to the two-story main section. The three-bay facade has a side entrance indicating the interior side hall plan. Alexander Douglass, owner of the house during the Revolution, was a quartermaster in the Continental Army.
State
HABS

MERCER COUNTY
Trenton
OLD BARRACKS
S. Willow Street
c. 1758

The colonial legislature of New Jersey passed an act in 1758 providing for the construction of military barracks. This law ended the practice of quartering soldiers in private homes. Five such barracks were built in New Jersey during the French and Indian War, and only this one has survived. Its middle section is a reproduction. Two-and-one-half stories high, the barracks is U-shaped and has wooden cornices, porches, and porch columns. There are dormer windows in the gable roof, and extensive restoration work has been done on the interior.
State
HABS

MERCER COUNTY
Trenton
TRENT, WILLIAM, HOUSE
539 S. Warren Street
1719

In 1714 William Trent, merchant, shipowner, and judge, began purchasing large tracts of land in the area of present-day Trenton; in 1721 he had the township of "Trent Town" laid out on his property. The William Trent House, erected in 1719, is a carefully restored large brick country house. Although porches and a brick wing were added in the 19th century, few structural changes were made. Approximately 80 per cent of the structure, including the interior paneling and stair, represents original fabric and workmanship.
Municipal
NHL; HABS

MERCER COUNTY
WASHINGTON CROSSING STATE PARK
Reference—see Bucks County, Pennsylvania

MIDDLESEX COUNTY
Cranbury
OLD CRANBURY SCHOOL
23 N. Main Street
1896

The Old Cranbury School is the only public building in the area dating from the late 19th century. It replaced two wooden schools located at either end of town, thus representing an early trend toward centralized educational facilities. As built the Cranbury School had two rooms on each floor. Walls are brick and there is brick corbelling above the windows of the original section. The projecting center bay has a bracketed cornice inside the gable end of the roof. A cupola rises above the roof. Additions were made in 1909 (south wing) and 1922 (north wing).
Municipal

MIDDLESEX COUNTY
Perth Amboy
PROPRIETORY HOUSE (THE WESTMINSTER)
139–151 Kearny Avenue
1764

The proprietors of the province of Eastern Jersey requested, in 1761, that a dwelling be constructed for their governor. Three years later the Proprietory House was completed. Although greatly altered, the house retains much original fabric, and it is the only surviving building erected for a royal governor in the state. Its three-story walls are brick and rest upon a stone foundation. The gambrel roof is topped by a cupola, and the gable ends have brown sandstone copings. A south wing was added c. 1809. Porches, windows, and much of the interior have been changed.
State; not accessible to the public
HABS

MIDDLESEX COUNTY
Piscataway
IVY HALL (CORNELIUS LOWE HOUSE)
1225 River Road
1741

Trader Cornelius Lowe constructed this two-story stone house which measures about 30 feet by 60 feet. It is built of coursed sandstone, cut and fitted blocks on the south elevation, and random pattern on the remaining sides. Over the first-floor front windows are fitted stones. The hip roof has a modillion cornice and four tall chimneys. Most of the eight rooms have their original wide board floors, and several retain the original wood paneling and molding. The three dormers on the front slope of the roof and a small one-story porch were probably later additions; an original stone wing was removed about 1870.
Private
HABS

MONMOUTH COUNTY
Freehold vicinity
MONMOUTH BATTLEFIELD
Northwest of Freehold on N.J. 522
1778

The battle of Monmouth, June 28, 1778, was designed to break up British General Henry Clinton's movement across New Jersey after the evacuation of Philadelphia. Although General George Washington failed to prevent Clinton's escape, he demonstrated his own qualities of leadership and the new prowess of his army created in the misery of Valley Forge. The engagement was the longest sustained action in the Revolutionary War. The major

scene of the battle, an area of about one and one-half by three miles, has retained its historical character. Six farms and several houses of the Revolutionary period still stand on the field
Multiple public/private
NHL

MONMOUTH COUNTY
Highlands
TWIN LIGHTS (NAVESINK LIGHTHOUSE)
South of N.J. 36 on a promontory between the Navesink River and Sandy Hook Bay
1826, 1862

Twin lighthouses are unusual in the United States. Originally the Navesink Lighthouse towers were separate and octagonal. Rebuilt in 1862, they were joined by a fortress-like, brick-lined stone structure, and the south tower is now square. Both towers are 73 feet high (254 feet above sea level) and built of brownstone. The first Fresnel lens used in the United States was installed here in 1841, and the first electric arc lamp, in 1898.
State

MONMOUTH COUNTY
Sandy Hook
SANDY HOOK LIGHT
1764

The tall white lighthouse at Sandy Hook is the oldest standing light tower in the United States. Originally called the "New York Lighthouse," it has served the shipping world with relatively few interruptions since its construction. The original tower of the Sandy Hook Light is octagonal with massive masonry walls. The tower rises 85 feet above the ground and 88 feet above the water.
Federal; not accessible to the public
NHL

MORRIS COUNTY
Morristown
MORRISTOWN NATIONAL HISTORICAL PARK
1777, 1779–1780

During two winters of the Revolutionary War, 1777, and 1779–1780, the hills around Morristown sheltered the main encampments of the Continental Army while the town was headquarters of Commander-in-Chief George Washington. From this strategic location he could watch the British movements in New York and guard the roads connecting New England and Pennsylvania. During the winter of 1779–1780 Washington systematically reorganized his forces almost within sight of British troops in New York. Archeological excavations produced evidence for

the reconstruction of log huts used as quarters for officers and men and the camp hospital hut. Many of the camp grounds still show evidence of army occupation. The Ford Mansion, Washington's headquarters in 1779–1780, has been refurnished as it was at the time.
Federal
NPS; 1,223.68 acres
HABS

MORRIS COUNTY
Morristown
NAST, THOMAS, HOME (VILLA FONTANA)
MacCulloch Avenue and Miller Road
1860–1861

Villa Fontana is a three-story clapboard Victorian period house with a mansard roof. Thomas Nast lived here from 1873 to 1902, during most of his career as a political and reform cartoonist. He joined the staff of *Harper's Weekly* in 1862 and remained there for about 25 years. During this time he made his greatest contribution to the American scene. Such cartoons as "The Tammany Tiger Loose" played an important part in breaking up the Boss Tweed Ring, which controlled New York City politics during the 1860's and 1870's. The exterior of the house has been altered since Nast's period of residence; the interior remains basically unaltered.
Private; not accessible to the public
NHL

MORRIS COUNTY (also in Somerset County)
Morristown
SPEEDWELL VILLAGE
333 Speedwell Avenue
18th and 19th centuries

Speedwell Village was the site of a 19th-century ironworks complex. Iron mining and production was the leading industry in Morris County for nearly two centuries. Located on the premises are the Stephen Vail Homestead, the Vail Factory, several outbuildings, and three dwellings which were recently moved to the site. An iron forge was in operation here before 1776. Sometime prior to 1788 a slitting mill was constructed and powered by the waters of the Whippany River. Stephen Vail purchased the property in 1814. During the family proprietorship (1814–1873), the ironworks was primarily a foundry and machine shop. A triphammer works, blacksmith shop, coal house, sawmill, storehouse, and turning shop were all operative. In 1818 the engine, paddle wheels, and other machinery for the S.S. *Savannah* were manufactured at Speedwell. The *Savannah* was the first ship to cross the Atlantic propelled or aided by steam. Twenty years later, on January 17, 1838, Alfred Vail, Stephen Vail's son, and

Samuel F. B. Morse successfully demonstrated to citizens of Morristown the operation of the electromagnetic telegraph in the Vail Factory. The frame factory still stands and contains millstones, an overshot wheel, and other grist mill machinery. The Vail Homestead is nearby, a two-story dwelling set on a masonry foundation; date of construction is not known, but the exterior corresponds to its 1850 appearance. A small frame cottage (believed to have been built in the early 1800's), the Lhomedieu-Gwinnup House (one of a few pre-Revolutionary houses in Morristown), and the Moses Este House (c. 1787) have all been relocated on this site. Attendant outbuildings in the complex are a carriage house, a granary, and an old farm building. Restoration and interpretive work are underway.
Private

OCEAN COUNTY
Barnegat Light
BARNEGAT LIGHTHOUSE
Northern end of Long Beach Island
1857

Barnegat Lighthouse was one of four such structures erected along New Jersey's coastline from Sandy Hook to Cape May. The 163-foot tower housed a 16,000 candle power light which was operative until replaced by an offshore lightship in 1927. A spiral staircase extends to the top of the brick and iron tower, and the windows below the light level were set at compass points and used as lookouts. George Gordon Meade, who directed the work, later commanded the Union forces at Gettysburg (July, 1863).
State
HABS

OCEAN COUNTY
Lakehurst vicinity
HANGAR NO. 1, LAKEHURST NAVAL AIR STATION
North of Lakehurst on County Route 547
1921

Commissioned in 1921, Lakehurst Naval Air Station became the hub of naval lighter-than-air activities. Known internationally as the American Airship Center, it was the home port for the Navy's rigid airships, or dirigibles: the *Shenandoah*, the *Los Angeles*, the *Akron*, and the *Macon*. The only stopping place in this country for commercial airships, it was the scene of the crash of the German zeppelin *Hindenburg* in 1937, which marked the end of commercial airship travel. During World War II and the Korean War, Lakehurst became the center of activity for non-rigid airships, or blimps. The most significant

building remaining from the rigid airship era is Hangar No. 1, which housed the huge helium-filled dirigibles.
Federal; not accessible to the public
NHL

PASSAIC COUNTY
Hewitt vicinity
RINGWOOD MANOR
3 miles east of Hewitt, Ringwood Manor State Park
Furnace, 1742; manor house, c. 1815

Ringwood Manor was long associated with the American iron industry. Peter Hasenclever, promoter of the American Company (colonial America's largest industrial enterprise), began to direct operations at the Ringwood furnace in 1764. Robert Erskine, a Scot, arrived to assume management of the ironworks in 1771. During the 19th century, two prominent iron manufacturers, Martin Ryerson and Abram S. Hewitt, were associated with Ringwood. Hewitt's descendants sold Ringwood to the state of New Jersey in 1936. Today Ringwood Manor includes the site of the Hasenclever mansion, the tomb of Robert Erskine, and the home of Ryerson and Hewitt.
State
NHL; HABS

PASSAIC COUNTY
Paterson
GREAT FALLS OF PATERSON AND SOCIETY FOR USEFUL MANUFACTURES HISTORIC DISTRICT
Bounded on the north by W. Broadway and Ryle Avenue; on the south by Grand Street; on the east by Morris, Barbour, Spruce, Market, Mill, Van Houten, Curtis, and River Streets; and on the west by the west bank of the Passaic River, crossing at Wayne and McBride Avenues, then south to Grand Street
18th, 19th, and 20th centuries

The area around the Great Falls of Paterson was selected for industrial development in 1793 by the Society for Useful Manufactures (S. U. M.). Thus it may be the first planned industrial site in the United States. The buildings and power works within the district illustrate the growth and changes in industrial planning, engineering, and architecture which took place between 1793 and 1912. Among the remaining mills are the Old Yellow Mill (1803, a paper plant), Hamilton Mill (c. 1812, a cotton factory), John Colt's Gun Mill (1835–1836), the Addy Mill (c. 1851, a metal manufactory), Rogers Locomotive Works, Grant Locomotive Works, and Cooke Locomotive and Machine Works (1860's and 1870's), Barbour Flax Spinning Company (1870's and 1880's), and the S. U. M.'s Electric Generating Plant (1912). All these buildings are masonry walled with wood, metal, and concrete interiors. A three-tiered raceway system in the falls supplied power to the mills. The race walls are masonry, and there is a 22–foot drop between the races which cover a mile in total length. The falls themselves are 70 feet high. A dam in the Passaic River is 8 to 13 feet high and 210 feet long. Built between 1830 and 1840, it is made of masonry and mortar with iron reinforcing.
Multiple public/private

PASSAIC COUNTY
Wayne
DEY MANSION
199 Totowa Road
1740

The Dey Mansion is a Georgian house which exhibits the influence of Dutch architecture. Brownstone quoins accentuate the corners of the house and, in a similar fashion, mark window and door openings. The gambrel roof has a dentil cornice and contains a one-and-one-half-story attic. A tripartite window appears in the second floor above the central entrance. George Washington headquartered here during July, October, and November of 1780, while approximately 4,000 colonial troops camped along the Passaic River and Singac Brook.
County
HABS

SALEM COUNTY
Hancocks Bridge
HANCOCK HOUSE
1728, 1734 (enlarged)

Many similar houses were built in Salem County during the 18th century. These dwellings were distinguished by the blue glazed headers and stretchers used to create patterns in the brick walls. William and Sarah Hancock built this house. Their initials and the date 1734 appear in the western wall, the brick of which is laid in a zigzag pattern. Fireplaces, moldings, floors, and paneling are original. A group of 30 patriots, stationed here to guard the bridge across Alloway Creek, was attacked and killed by a British force in May, 1778.
State
HABS

SOMERSET COUNTY
Kingston vicinity
ROCKINGHAM (BERRIEN HOUSE)
North of Kingston on Old Rocky Hill Road
1734

The oldest portion of Rockingham was a two-story farmhouse containing 20 rooms. Additions were made in 1764, and the house has been moved twice. There is a two-story veranda on the south side, and the addition on the north was built in 1897. George Washington maintained his headquarters here from August to November, 1783, while Congress met at Princeton. The fieldstone kitchen on the grounds is a replica, and the wash house was moved from another site.
State
HABS

SOMERSET COUNTY
MORRISTOWN NATIONAL HISTORICAL PARK
Reference—see Morris County

SOMERSET COUNTY
Raritan
FRELINGHUYSEN, GENERAL JOHN, HOUSE
Somerset Street and Wyckoff Avenue
Early 19th century

This two-story brick residence was probably built around 1810 by General John Frelinghuysen (1775–1833). The main house has its front wall laid in Flemish bond with a chamfered water table, while the remaining three walls are running bond. There are relieving arches above the first-floor windows, and a belt course separates the two stories. The gambrel roof shows Dutch influence, and interior mantels were carved in the Adam style.
Municipal; not accessible to the public
HABS

SOMERSET COUNTY
Somerville
OLD DUTCH PARSONAGE
65 Washington Place
1751

The Parsonage was built for the First Reformed Dutch Church, and the first occupant was the Reverend John Frelinghuysen. A later owner, Jacobus Hardenbergh, was instrumental in founding Queen's College (now Rutgers University) and served as its first president. The two-story brick dwelling has a gable roof and interior chimneys. There are three rooms on the first floor, four on the second, and two rooms and a smokehouse

in the attic. The house was moved about 200 yards in 1913 when threatened by a rail line.
State
HABS

SOMERSET COUNTY
Somerville
WALLACE HOUSE
38 Washington Place
1778

General and Mrs. George Washington were the first occupants of this house, from December 11, 1778, to June 3, 1779, while the Continental army was encamped at Camp Middlebrook (Somerville). A one-and-one-half-story section was built prior to the main house, and it contains a kitchen and three small rooms above. The two-story main house has four rooms on each floor, and retains its original paneling and plaster. Although once a common type in the area, the Wallace House is one of only a few examples surviving today.
State
HABS

SUSSEX COUNTY
Newton
MERRIAM, HENRY W., HOUSE
131 Main Street
c. 1883

Henry W. Merriam, for whom this large Eastlake style house was built, was a well-to-do shoe manufacturer. His two-story frame residence is covered with clapboard siding and has steep, intricately patterned slate roofs. There are many gables and dormers, and a tower protruding from the central mass, and the whole structure is enlivened by ornately carved roof brackets, balustrades, posts, and applied decoration in the gable ends. A one-story porch extends across the main facade, and the windows are decidedly vertical. Inside, the decor is ornate—varnished wood trim, wallpapered walls, and parquet floors. There are seven major fireplaces.
Private

UNION COUNTY
Elizabeth
BOXWOOD HALL (BOUDINOT MANSION)
1073 E. Jersey Street
1750

Elias Boudinot, president of the Continental Congress (1782), purchased Boxwood in 1772. The dwelling itself is frame and originally had wings on either side of the main section. In 1870 these wings were removed. Inside, the house has a central hall and four rooms on each floor. Boudinot was also a signer of the Treaty of Ghent (1814) and superintendent of the U.S. Mint.
State
HABS

UNION COUNTY
Union
FIRST PRESBYTERIAN CONGREGATION OF CONNECTICUT FARMS
Stuyvesant Avenue at Chestnut Street
Late 18th century

The first church on this site was built about 1740 and burned by advancing British troops in 1780. The present stone church was begun in 1782 and completed in 1818. Rectangular in shape, the church is built of stone and red brick. The cornice and hand-hewn timber roof trusses are original. Wooden doors and window frames are reconstructions of the originals. A wooden colonial bell cupola surmounts the front gable, also of wood.
Private
HABS

Dey Mansion, Wayne, New Jersey. *Passaic County Park Commission*

New Mexico

Fort Craig, Socorro vicinity, New Mexico. *Jon Samuelson*

Acoma Pueblo,
Casa Blanca vicinity,
New Mexico. *HABS*

Dorsey Mansion,
Abbott vicinity, New Mexico.
Karl Kernberger

Tyonyi Ruin, Bandelier National Monument,
Los Alamos vicinity, New Mexico. *NPS*

BERNALILLO COUNTY
Albuquerque
SAN FELIPE DE NERI CHURCH
Old Town Plaza, Northwest
1706; 1793 (rebuilt)

Through two centuries the San Felipe de Neri Church has been in continuous use by people who have consistently adapted the building to new conditions and new styles. The great architectural value of the structure comes from its unique amalgamation of work from several periods. Massive adobe walls with wood *vigas* (poles) date from the 18th century. The exterior, including the two bell towers, dates from the mid- or late 19th century. Its single nave and polygonal apse are typical of early New Mexico churches and are common among the 16th-century churches built by the Franciscans in Old Mexico. Also characteristic of New Mexico church architecture are the projecting transepts, the height of the crossing transepts and apse, and the situating of the choir loft over the main entrance.
Private

CATRON COUNTY
Silver City vicinity
GILA CLIFF DWELLINGS NATIONAL MONUMENT
47 miles north of Silver City on N.M. 25 and 527
1300–1400

Gila Cliff Dwellings National Monument contains five well-preserved cliff dwellings in natural cavities in the face of an overhanging cliff. These Indian dwellings were constructed in caverns that permitted closure of the mouths by masonry. Little remained for excavation, but the nearby T J Ruin is planned for excavation.
Federal
NPS: 533.13 acres

COLFAX COUNTY
Abbott vicinity
DORSEY MANSION
About 12 miles northeast of Abbott via U.S. 56 and an unpaved country road 1878–1884

Stephen W. Dorsey, soldier, politician, businessman, and cattle rancher, built and lived in this two-part dwelling from 1879 to 1893. The earlier part (completed, 1879) is a two-story log structure with double entrance doors and a formal stair hall. The newer, turreted sandstone section was finished in 1884. Locally quarried stone was used. Inside there are marble and onyx mantels and hand-fashioned ceiling ornaments around the lighting fixtures. Sculpted portraits of the builder, his wife, and his brother appear on the octagonal tower, and above these are an eagle and two gargoyles representing Senator Dorsey's political adversary, James G. Blaine. Surrounding the house and outbuildings were lavish grounds containing fruit and shade trees, three fountains, and a lake with three islands.
Private

COLFAX COUNTY (also in Las Animas County, Colorado)
Raton vicinity
RATON PASS
U.S. 85–87, Colorado-New Mexico border

This passage through the Raton Mountains was one of the most difficult on the mountain branch of the Santa Fe Trail. It became increasingly important as an invasion route during the Mexican War and during the Civil War, when hostilities with the southern Plains Indians almost halted traffic over the alternate Cimarron Cutoff route. From 1861 to 1865 much of the traffic to Santa Fe crossed Raton Pass.
Multiple public/private
NHL

COLFAX COUNTY
Springer
MILLS HOUSE
509 1st Street

The Mills House combines New Mexican building techniques with a mansard roof, which is characteristic of the more sophisticated Second Empire architecture. Local craftsmen erected the adobe walls of the unusual three-story residence and topped the structure with a metal roof enclosed by a cast iron railing. A two-story wooden porch was constructed on three sides of the house, and many of the first- and second-floor windows are in pairs. Carved walnut trim and paneling decorate the interior. Melvin W. Mills, for whom the house was built, was a Canadian who came to New Mexico in the 1860's and engaged in mining, ranching, and the practice of law. In 1875 he was elected to the state legislature and was instrumental in effecting location of the county seat at Springer.
Private

DOÑA ANA COUNTY
Las Cruces vicinity
FORT SELDEN
18 miles north of Las Cruces via Int. 25 at Radium Springs interchange
1865

Fort Selden was built to protect the main road between Santa Fe (New Mexico) and El Paso (Texas) and the small surrounding settlements from sporadic attacks by Apache Indians who were waging a final struggle for their lands. Built of adobe and stone, Fort Selden consisted of 15 or 20 buildings surrounding a parade ground. These structures included quarters for 200 men, a one-story hospital, a bakery, a school, and a two-story stone guardhouse. In 1884 the fort was renovated by its new commandant, Captain Arthur MacArthur, father of General Douglas MacArthur. Although plans were made to abandon the fort as early as 1875, pressure from neighboring communities kept it active until 1892. Today the fort is in ruins with only the brick walls of many of the buildings remaining.
State

DOÑA ANA COUNTY
Las Cruces vicinity
MESILLA PLAZA
2 miles south of Las Cruces on N.M. 28
1848

The Gadsden Purchase Treaty led to United States acquisition of the southern route to California from the Rio Grande Valley. On July 4, 1854, the United States flag was raised over the Mesilla Plaza, confirming the treaty. Mesilla was also the central point on the Butterfield Overland Mail Route to California, established in 1857. During the Civil War, Mesilla was first a Confederate headquarters and later a Union headquarters. The town was also associated with the range cattle industry and with such frontier figures as Sheriff Pat Garrett and Billy the Kid. Retaining the flavor of a Mexican village, the town is built around Mesilla Plaza, with a church at one end and adobe buildings on the other three sides.
Multiple public/private
NHL

EDDY COUNTY
Carlsbad vicinity
CARLSBAD RECLAMATION PROJECT
North of Carlsbad
1880's

One of the most extensive irrigation projects in the West took place in the Carlsbad area of New Mexico. In the late 1880's inhabitants of the Pecos Valley constructed several stone dams on the Pecos River. From this rudimentary beginning, the system developed and eventually irrigated more than 25,000 acres of farmland. The Carlsbad Reclamation Project differs from any other major project in the country because the original system built by private enterprise is still in operation. The U.S. Bureau of Reclamation now controls only Alamogordo Dam and Reservoir, so that the evolution from private to public operation of reclamation

projects in the arid West can be seen at this one site.
Multiple public/private
NHL

GRANT COUNTY
Cliff vicinity
WOODROW RUIN
About 5 miles northeast of Cliff off N.M. 293
700–1200

Situated on a high bench overlooking the west bank of the Gila River, the Woodrow site is the most intact relic of the Mimbres Branch of the Mogollon culture, one of New Mexico's least-understood prehistoric peoples. Preliminary evidence indicates that the area of the Indian village was more than 900 feet by 500 feet. Evident above ground are 16 separate masonry-walled surface room blocks. Thirty-three depressions, ranging from 15 to 35 feet in diameter, are scattered throughout the site and mark the location of pit houses. Several open areas appear to have been plazas. Professional evaluation of the scenes on the abundant Mimbres black-on-white pottery should reveal much about this extinct cultural group.
Private

LINCOLN COUNTY
Lincoln
LINCOLN HISTORIC DISTRICT
U.S. 380
1870's and 1880's

The Lincoln County War of 1878, one of the famous feuds of the cattle frontier, reached its climax in Lincoln. Fought between the rival Murphy-Dolan and Tunstall-McSween factions, the disturbances involved cattle baron John H. Chisum; General Lew Wallace, territorial governor of New Mexico; and William H. Bonney, "Billy the Kid." Aside from its dramatic history and its importance to the cattle industry, Lincoln is among the best preserved of the frontier cow towns. A considerable part of the town of 1878 remains comparatively unchanged. Still standing are the headquarters of the two rival factions, the adobe brick Murphy-Dolan store and the Tunstall-McSween store.
Multiple public/private
NHL

LINCOLN COUNTY
White Oaks
WHITE OAKS HISTORIC DISTRICT
12 miles northeast of Carrizozo on N.M. 349
Late 19th century

White Oaks was a mining town which sprang up in the 1880's, when gold was discovered in the hillside of nearby Baxter Mountain. The North and South Homestake mines were opened first, followed by the Old Abe, Little Mack, Yellow Jacket, Ferro, Comstock, Rip Van Winkle, Lady Godiva and Boston Bay. White Oaks grew rapidly from a tent city to a substantial town of 4,000. Property prices rose rapidly, but the railroad, which was expected to pass through town, went instead to Carrizozo. Ore production began to fall off and the population declined. By 1967 only seven families remained. At one time White Oaks contained a sawmill, two banks, three churches, an opera house, a schoolhouse, stamp mills, and the necessary mine and processing buildings. Now only the school, the Exchange Bank, the Hoyle House, and several smaller structures remain. Old mine shafts are still visible, and the Cedarvale Cemetery is well maintained.
Multiple private

LOS ALAMOS COUNTY
Los Alamos
LOS ALAMOS SCIENTIFIC LABORATORY
Central Avenue
1943

Los Alamos Scientific Laboratory was founded to develop the nuclear fission bomb. Its second assignment was to create a "super" weapon deriving energy from the thermonuclear fusion of hydrogen. The laboratory has continued to be a foremost development center for nuclear weapons. It has also contributed to fundamental scientific knowledge and the peaceful application of atomic energy. The first enriched-uranium reactor was built here in 1944, the first plutonium-fueled reactor in 1946. Several rocket propulsion reactors have been built and ground-tested at this site.
Federal
NHL

MC KINLEY COUNTY
Manuelito vicinity
MANUELITO COMPLEX
6 miles south of Manuelito on secondary roads
c. 700–1400

Within this valley are sites occupied from about A.D. 700 to 1400, with even earlier

Basketmaker pit house areas. The largest site is a pueblo approximately 280 by 375 feet extending from the valley floor up a steep talus slope onto the mesa top overlooking Manuelito Wash. Portions of masonry walls stand over eight feet high, and in certain mounded areas three to four stories may be represented. This major site, occupied from about 1150 to 1400, contains an estimated 1500 rooms. Pottery indicates trade relationships with surrounding groups and a derivation of local types from earlier occupation in the immediate area.
State; not accessible to the public
NHL

MC KINLEY COUNTY
Thoreau vicinity
CHACO CANYON NATIONAL MONUMENT
64 miles north of Thoreau on N.M. 56
600–1200

The major section of Chaco Canyon National Monument preserves the remains of a Puebloan culture which flourished for more than 200 years. Artifacts and partially fallen walls reveal much of the lives and habits of these prehistoric Indians. The greatest distinction of the Pueblos is the massiveness of the buildings they constructed and the excellence of their masonry—achievements that were realized to the fullest during the 11th and 12th centuries. Among the largest of the pueblos was Pueblo Bonito, built to a height of five stories on a floor plan exceeding three acres and capable of housing up to 1200 persons in about 800 rooms.
Federal/non-federal
NPS; 21,509.40 acres

MORA COUNTY
Wagon Mound vicinity
WAGON MOUND
East of Wagon Mound on U.S. 85

Wagon Mound was the last great landmark of the high plains section of the Cimarron Cutoff of the Santa Fe Trail. First visible from Point of Rocks, it was the guidepost for caravans moving westward from the Rock Crossing of the Canadian River to Santa Fe. Two miles northwest of Wagon Mound is Santa Clara Spring, an important watering point. Beginning in the late 1840's these sites became the scene of frequent Indian ambushes. South and west of Wagon Mound are visible remains of the Santa Fe Trail.
Private; not accessible to the public
NHL

MORA COUNTY
Watrous
WATROUS (LA JUNTA)
U.S. 85
1843, LaJunta; 1879, Watrous

The junction of the Mora and Sapello rivers was the rendezvous point for organizing wagon trains before the venture east into the hostile Indian territory of the open plain. Watrous, or LaJunta, was also the point at which the mountain and Cimarron Cutoff routes of the Santa Fe Trail divided. Extensive cultivation has obliterated much of the trail, but it is possible to trace its approximate route and to locate the main crossing of the two streams. Among the remaining buildings associated with the era are the Watrous Store and Ranch (1849), the Sapello stage station (1850's), and the Fort Union Corral (1850's).
Multiple private; not accessible to the public
NHL

MORA COUNTY
Watrous vicinity
FORT UNION NATIONAL
MONUMENT
9 miles north of Watrous on N.M.
477
1851

Located near the point where the Santa Fe Trail's mountain route and Cimarron Cutoff joined together, Fort Union was the principal quartermaster depot supplying army operations in New Mexico. Soldiers at this post, the largest then guarding the southwestern frontier, saw action against Apache, Ute, Kiowa, Navajo, and Comanche Indians. At the battle of Glorieta Pass, March 28, 1862, Union volunteers based at Fort Union turned back the Confederacy's only serious threat to New Mexico and Colorado. Today only melted adobe walls and a few chimneys rise above ground level.
Federal
NPS; 720.60 acres

RIO ARRIBA COUNTY
Blanco vicinity
FRANCÉS CANYON RUIN
SE 1/4 SE 1/4 sec. 31, T. 30 N., R. 6 W.

Tree ring dates from Francés Canyon Ruin indicate that the structure was built sometime between 1716 and 1742. It is believed that Navajo Indians constructed the fortified village to protect themselves from raiding Utes and Comanches. The Francés Canyon Ruin is one of the largest known villages of these so-called refugee sites. Composed of 40 masonry-walled

surface rooms of varying sizes, the site is arranged in a cluster of four house blocks. Artifacts of pottery, stone, bone, wood, leather, shell, metal, and glass—of Navajo, Pueblo, and Spanish origin—have been found here. Gobernador Polychrome and Dinetah scored were locally made pottery types discovered at the site. Intrusive pottery types include Jemez Black-on-white, Puname Polychrome, Bandelier Black-on-gray, and Hawikuh Polychrome.
Federal

RIO ARRIBA COUNTY
Cañones vicinity
TSIPING
1.3 miles south of Cañones on Pueblo Mesa

Tsiping is a large ruined pueblo situated atop Pueblo Mesa, 800 feet above the valleys of Polvadera and Cañones creeks. There are 200 to 300 rooms in the pueblo, which was constructed entirely of stone blocks cut from the volcanic tuff of Pueblo Mesa. These walls are in a good state of preservation, some standing a full story. Most of the pueblo was on the mesa top, but tiered masonry rooms and adjacent cavate dwellings occupy the east face of the cliff. Between 16 and 18 kivas exist at Tsiping, which takes its name ("Flaking Stone Mountain") from the many chips of colorful chalcedony and chert quarried from nearby Cerro Pedernal. The Tsiping site was probably chosen because it was easily defended, and there were apparently enemies to the northwest. Tree ring analyses of timbers used in constructing the pueblo have yielded dates from 1297 to 1323. Excavation at the site should reveal much about the daily life of 13th-century Indians.
Federal

RIO ARRIBA COUNTY
Española vicinity
PUYÉ RUINS
14 miles west of Española on N.M. 5 and 30, Santa Clara Indian Reservation
c. 1250–1550

Puyé Ruins is among the largest of the prehistoric Indian settlements on the Pajarito Plateau. This site exhibits a variety of architectural forms and building techniques. Cut into the volcanic tuff forming the mesa is a long row of cavates (rooms), in front of which are pueblo rooms. On the mesa top are the remains of a large pueblo with which three kivas (ceremonial structures) are associated. Among the other archeological features are an irrigation canal and a large reservoir dug into the volcanic tuff. Stabilization or restoration of a number of buildings has added to the site's interpretive significance.
Private
NHL

RIO ARRIBA COUNTY
Española vicinity
SAN GABRIEL DE YUNGUE-OUINGE
4 miles north of Española via U.S. 64 and secondary roads
c. 1599

The ruins of San Gabriel de Yungue-ouinge, a Tewa Indian pueblo, mark the site of the first Spanish-built capital of New Mexico, established by Don Juan de Oñate. Excavated remains at the site include the earliest European church and house remains yet found in the continental United States. The colony established here was unsuccessful, however, and the capital was removed to Santa Fe in 1610.
Private; not accessible to the public
NHL

ROOSEVELT COUNTY
Clovis vicinity
ANDERSON BASIN (BLACKWATER DRAW)
12 miles south and 6 miles east of Clovis via U.S. 70 and secondary roads
c. 13000–8000 B.C.

The Anderson Basin and surrounding localities have produced scientific knowledge concerning man's life at the end of the last period of glaciation. Stratified areas of the site have offered evidence of mammoth-hunting peoples who used Clovis type spear points and preceded the Folsom bison hunters. This evidence apparently indicates a change in climate and in animal and plant life during the period following the retreat of the glaciers. The Anderson Basin is both large and undisturbed.
State; not accessible to the public
NHL

SANDOVAL COUNTY
Bernalillo vicinity
SANDIA CAVE
11 miles east of Bernalillo on N.M. 44, Cibola National Forest
c. 9000–8000 B.C.

Sandia Cave apparently represents one of the earliest occupations of the Americas. Excavations in 1936 yielded information on three distinct prehistoric groups, each separated from the other by a well-defined layer. The top level contained objects from the Pueblo occupation of New Mexico. The middle layer revealed artifacts of the Folsom bison hunter period, c. 9000–8000 B.C. The lowest layer contained the still older "Sandia Points," a type of early spearpoint notched on one side only. These points were associated with remains of extinct animals.
Federal; not accessible to the public
NHL

SANDOVAL COUNTY
Casa Salazar vicinity
BIG BEAD MESA
West of Casa Salazar on secondary
roads, Cibola National Forest
c. 1700

The Ute Indians and their Comanche allies drove the Navajos south from their
homeland on the Upper San Juan River
during the first half of the 18th century.
The Navajos subsequently moved into the
Big Bead Mesa region in the middle
1700's and began to plague the pueblos of
Laguna and Acoma. By 1780 they had
formed an alliance with the Gila Apaches.
Their initial southern migration had thus
enabled them to become an aggressive
power in central New Mexico by the early
1800's. Big Bead Mesa commemorates
this series of events which primarily involved inter-tribal conflict and alliance.
Federal
NHL

SANDOVAL COUNTY
Jemez Springs vicinity
SAN JUAN MESA RUIN
SE 1/4 SW 1/4 sec. 28, T. 18 N., R. 3
E.
Pre-Columbian to 17th century

San Juan Mesa Ruin occupies an area
1,200 feet long by 300 feet wide along the
eastern edge of San Juan Mesa. Portions
of the site extend down the adjacent east
slope of the mesa for a distance of several
hundred feet. The site consists of several
contiguous, masonry-walled room blocks.
Walls are made of large, roughly shaped
pieces of volcanic tuff. Two depressions
each in two of the central plazas show locations of subterranean kivas. Indigenous
pottery at the site is Jemez black-on-
white. Intrusive pottery types include Rio
Grande Glaze (group E and F). Pottery
found at the site indicates that the greatest
contact was with prehistoric and historic
period Indians in the vicinity of the
present-day pueblo of Zia, to the south.
Federal

SANDOVAL COUNTY
Los Alamos vicinity
BANDELIER NATIONAL MONUMENT
12 miles south of Los Alamos on
N.M. 4
13th to 16th centuries

The numerous ruins of Bandelier National
Monument are characteristic of prehistoric Indian dwellings of the later Pueblo
period. Following the drought of the late
13th century, several groups settled here
on the canyon-slashed slopes of the
Pajarito Plateau. The present monument is

an area crossed only by trails, the most ac-
cessible features being the ruins of Frijoles
Canyon.
Federal
NPS; 29,661.20 acres
HABS

SAN JUAN COUNTY
Aztec vicinity
**AZTEC RUINS NATIONAL
MONUMENT**
1 mile north of Aztec on secondary
road
12th century

In Aztec Ruins National Monument are
preserved the ruins of one of the largest
pre-Spanish Indian villages in the
Southwest. The largest of these ruins,
which has undergone excavation, was a
three-story building with 500 rooms and a
great kiva. Several unexcavated pueblos
appear today as mounds with parts of
masonry wall protruding from them. The
term Aztec was mistakenly applied to
these prehistoric people, for they were actually ancestors of the present-day Pueblo
Indians.
Federal
NPS; 27.14 acres

SAN JUAN COUNTY
Farmington vicinity
SALMON RUIN
9 miles east of Farmington off N.M.
17

The Salmon Ruin presently appears as a
steep-sided mound measuring 500 feet in
length by 10 to 30 feet high. Recognized
as one of the last undisturbed large
planned centers of Chacoan affiliation,
Salmon Ruin is expected to yield much information on Chacoan culture. The
mound covers a characteristic C-shaped
great house form, believed to have been
three to four stories high, which contained
at least 500 rooms. Tree ring dating of one
of the exposed beams indicates that the
ruin dates back at least to 1089 A.D.,
making it one of the earliest Chacoan settlements in the Aztec-Bloomfield area.
Ceramic fragments found are of the McEl-
mo black-on-white type.
County

SAN JUAN COUNTY
La Plata vicinity
HOLMES SITE
East of La Plata on the east side of
the La Plata River
1050

The Holmes Site is of interest because of
the large number and variety of features
represented. There are small and large
pueblos, some of which are linear and
other square or E-shaped, and towers on

points of the mesa. These and a large kiva
are strung from north to south along the
mesa. Many of the buildings were used
prior to 1050, but the presence of towers
and dressed masonry in some buildings indicates later use. Most of the buildings
have collapsed into mounds, but one
pueblo still stands above the mesa. No excavations have been undertaken.
Private; not accessible to the public
NHL

SAN MIGUEL COUNTY
Bell Ranch vicinity
BELL RANCH HEADQUARTERS
North and east of the Conchas
Reservoir

The original Bell Ranch was made up of
the Pablo Montoya grant (1824), the
overlapping Baca Location No. 2, and
other small properties. An Englishman,
Wilson Waddingham, began consolidating
the land, and in 1875 he recorded the Bell
Grant. The brand and the ranch name
came from a natural landmark in the
country, a small bell-shaped hill called La
Campana. Waddingham encountered
financial difficulties, so his backers, Day
and Stoddard, took over the property,
acquired more land, and formed the Red
River Valley Company (719,000 acres).
Today the Bell Ranch encompasses
130,855 acres. The original ranch building, the center of the main house, consists
of two adobe-walled rooms built about
1860. Adjoining rooms of brick date from
1873. The southwest wing was added in
1914. All these parts form a well-in-
tegrated, shallow, U-shaped structure
measuring 204 feet across by 76 feet deep.
Other buildings in the immediate vicinity
are a post office, the ranch manager's office, the commissary, mess hall, kitchen,
barns, and corrals. Pablo Montoya,
recipient of the earlier grant, was alcalde
of Sante Fe.
Private

SAN MIGUEL COUNTY
Pecos vicinity
PECOS NATIONAL MONUMENT
South of Pecos on N.M. 63
Mission, c. 1620; pueblo, prior to
1540

The pueblo of Pecos, a landmark to many
of the early Spanish explorers, was one of
the largest in New Mexico in the 17th century. It was the point of departure for
Francisco Coronado's expedition in 1540
from New Mexico to search for the wealth
in legendary Quivira. By the 1620's the
mission of Nuestra Señora de los Angeles
de Porciúncula had been completed, only
to be destroyed during the 1680 Pueblo
Rebellion. Pecos began to decline in the

mid-18th century after being besieged by disease and hostile Indians. Today adobe walls of the "new" mission, built in the early 1700's following the Spanish reconquest, rise as high as 50 feet above the foundations of the earlier church. Both the mission complex and the pueblo have been partially excavated.
Federal
NPS; 340.90 acres

SAN MIGUEL COUNTY (also in Santa Fe County)
Santa Fe vicinity
GLORIETA PASS BATTLEFIELD
10 miles southeast of Santa Fe on U.S. 84–85
1862

The battle of Glorieta Pass, March 26–28, 1862, ended a Confederate invasion of New Mexico that attempted to seize a large portion of the Southwest and its resources. Brigadier General Henry H. Sibley's Confederate command achieved success in driving back Brigadier General E. S. Canby's forces, but a Union flanking column succeeded in destroying the Confederate wagon train and supplies from the rear thus forcing Confederate withdrawal from New Mexico. The building of a highway and one railroad line through the pass has impaired the integrity of the scene, but most key positions of the battle are identifiable.
Multiple public/private
NHL

SANTA FE COUNTY
Santa Fe
BARRIO DE ANALCO HISTORIC DISTRICT
Bounded on the south by properties fronting on E. De Vargas Street, on the west by properties fronting on College Street, on the east by property lines on St. Michael's Dormitory and the San Miguel Chapel, and on the north by the San Miguel Chapel, E. De Vargas Street, the State Parks Building property, and the Santa Fe River
1620

The Barrio (or district) de Analco is one of the oldest settled areas of European inception in what is now the United States. It is unique because it represents a still active, working-class neighborhood of Spanish colonial heritage. The term "analco" means "the other side of the water" and contrasted the Barrio with the opposite side of the Santa Fe River, where officials and prominent citizens lived. Settled in 1620, the district contains numerous examples of Spanish Pueblo architecture, characterized by the adobe

construction indigenous to the Southwest. This method of building was first used by Indians of the area in their cliffside dwellings. Though the Spanish moved away from the cliffs to flat land and built one-story structures, they continued to use adobe because of its proven practicality. The flat pueblo roof, with tamped earth and poles (*vigas*), was also retained. As in lower Mexico, the Spanish introduced the technique of adobe bricks—the Indians had puddled or hand-formed their adobe walls—and added an interior patio and a porch. This merging of Indian and Spanish styles produced an architecture which died out under United States jurisdiction but can be seen today in the Barrio de Analco.
Multiple public/private
NHL

SANTA FE COUNTY
Santa Fe
DAVEY, RANDALL, HOUSE
Upper Canyon Road
1847

The central portion of the Randall Davey House, located at the mouth of the Santa Fe Canyon, was originally built by the U.S. Army as a sawmill, the first in the New Mexico territory. The two-story adobe structure is unusual in that the ground floor is made of stone, which was necessary because a ditch surrounding the house carried the water needed to operate the mill. The mill had been sold to its first private owner by 1852, and in 1920 it was purchased by the painter Randall Davey, who converted it into a private residence. Surrounding the main building are other 19th-century adobe structures. The stables have been converted into a gallery to house Davey's paintings and prints.
Private; not accessible to the public

SANTA FE COUNTY
Santa Fe
NATIONAL PARK SERVICE SOUTHWEST REGIONAL OFFICE
Old Santa Fe Trail
1939

The National Park Service's Southwest Region Office is believed to be the largest all-adobe office building in the United States. Stylistically the building is a revival of Spanish Colonial architecture. The two-story eastern section resembles a Spanish mission chapel in plan, while the one-story portion surrounding the patio corresponds to an old *convento*. Local youths of Spanish-American ancestry constructed the building as a Civilian Conservation Corps project. Furniture and tin lighting fixtures were fashioned by local craftsmen. The walls in the two-story section are more than three feet thick and rest on

a foundation of native stone. Hand trimmed pine *vigas* support the roof.
Federal

SANTA FE COUNTY
Santa Fe
PALACE OF THE GOVERNORS
The Plaza
1610–1612

The Palace of the Governors, the oldest public building in the United States, served as the territorial capitol and governor's residence during Spanish, Mexican, and American regimes. Built by Don Pedro de Peralta, it was captured during the Pueblo Rebellion of 1680 and used by the Indians until the Spanish reconquest in 1692. The Mexican period, which began in 1821, was ended by General Stephen Watts Kearny's expedition in 1846. Except for a brief Confederate interlude, the building has been under the American flag since that time. Used as the governor's residence until 1909, it currently houses the Museum of New Mexico.
State
NHL; HABS

SANTA FE COUNTY
Santa Fe
REREDOS OF OUR LADY OF LIGHT
Cristo Rey Church, Canyon Road and Cristo Rey Street
c. 1760

The Spanish governor of New Mexico, Francisco Antonio Marin del Valle, had a military chapel, known as La Castrense, constructed on the Santa Fe Plaza in 1760. The chapel and its central interior decoration—a carved stone reredos—were paid for by the governor. Made of volcanic stone, the reredos was fashioned by artisans from Mexico. Measuring 25 feet 8 inches high by 18 feet 4 inches wide, the reredos was once painted, but the colors are no longer discernible. La Castrense was sold by the Catholic Church in 1859 and the reredos moved to the present cathedral site where it remained until 1940. Then it was placed in the recently constructed Cristo Rey Church. Representations on the reredos are the Lady of Valvanera (a favorite of the Benedictine order), Santiago (patron saint of Spain), St. Joseph with the infant Jesus, St. John Nepomuk (protector of the Jesuit order), St. Francis Solano (a Franciscan missionary), and St. Ignatius Loyola (founder of the Society of Jesus). The portrait niche contains the Lady of Light. This reredos is the only one of its kind dating from the Spanish period still extant in the United States.
Private

SANTA FE COUNTY
Santa Fe
SANTA FE PLAZA
c. 1610

In the heart of the capital of New Mexico is the Santa Fe Plaza, historically the city's commercial and social center. It was also the terminus of the Santa Fe Trail. The Palace of the Governors (1610) and nearby San Miguel Mission (c. 1640) are two other landmarks associated with the site. The palace, which housed the Spanish, Mexican, and American governors of New Mexico, was the site where General Stephen Watts Kearny raised the American flag in 1846 to establish American rule. All caravans entering Santa Fe via the Santa Fe Trail passed the mission, the oldest in Santa Fe and one of the oldest in the United States.
Multiple public/private
NHL; HABS

SANTA FE COUNTY
Santa Fe vicinity
GLORIETA PASS BATTLEFIELD
Reference—see San Miguel County

SANTA FE COUNTY
Santa Fe vicinity
SAN LAZARO
25 miles south of Santa Fe via N.M. 10 and secondary road
Late prehistoric to c. 1690

San Lazaro's two pueblos, one from late prehistoric times and one from early historic times, represent the largest ruin in the Galisteo Basin. The earlier building is made up of irregular blocks of rooms and plazas. The later is a planned unit with four house blocks around a central plaza. Northeast of the pueblo is a reservoir with a dam through the base which supplemented the water supply. A mission church, abandoned about 1690, lies east of the historic site.
Private; not accessible to the public
NHL

SANTA FE COUNTY
Santa Fe vicinity
SETON VILLAGE
6 miles south of Santa Fe off U.S. 84–85 and secondary road
1930

Ernest Thompson Seton informed three generations of Americans concerning the world of nature through his paintings, writings, and lectures. Present-day conservation philosophy was partially shaped by men influenced by his ideas. He was chairman of the committee which brought the Boy Scout movement to the United States. On his ranch he built a 45-room "castle" —a combination home, museum, art gal-

lery, and institute for people in the creative disciplines. The community known as Seton Village grew up around the house, which until recently contained many of his paintings, books, mammal and bird specimens, and Indian artifacts.
Private
NHL

SANTA FE COUNTY
Truchas vicinity
EL SANTUARIO DE CHIMAYÓ
South of Truchas in Chimayó
1816

El Santuario de Chimayó is a well-preserved and unrestored small adobe pueblo church with original religious paintings. The low, flat-roofed church, set in a wall-enclosed garden, has twin tapering front towers with belfries. The interior is notable for its original Spanish-Indian decor: a heavy timber ceiling of closely spaced *vigas* (beams) supported on carved brackets, and the simple plaster walls lined with a low, painted dado and hung with numerous religious paintings. Behind the draped altar is a high reredos decorated with painted religious symbols. The Santuario is still an active church.
Private
NHL

SOCORRO COUNTY
Bingham vicinity
TRINITY SITE
25 miles south of U.S. 380 on White Sands Missile Range
1945

On what is now the White Sands Missile Range, the world's first nuclear device was exploded on July 16, 1945. The code name "Trinity" was chosen for the test by Dr. J. Robert Oppenheimer, director of the project. A "dress rehearsal" was held in May 1945 to provide data for the calibration of instruments for blast and shock measurements. The Ground Zero area, site of the actual test, is surrounded by a fence, and within are structures and objects associated with the historic event.
Federal; not accessible to the public
NHL

SOCORRO COUNTY (also in Torrance County)
Gran Quivira vicinity
GRAN QUIVIRA NATIONAL MONUMENT
1 mile east of Gran Quivira on N.M. 10
c. 800–1675

Mogollon Indians occupied the Gran Quivira area from about A.D. 800 to 1675, when severe drought and Apache raids forced their evacuation. Artifacts un-

covered here demonstrate the influence of the Pueblo Indians and the Spanish on Mogollon culture. The earliest Indian community in the monument, constructed about 1300, was a single-story rectangular masonry unit. Later, larger one-story and multistory buildings were built on the ridge, and by the 1600's this pueblo was the largest in the region. Standing atop one of the ridges is the 17th-century Franciscan church, San Buenaventura. Beside it is the Pueblo de las Humanas, surrounded by yet another Franciscan church, San Isidro.
Federal
NPS; 610.94 acres

SOCORRO COUNTY
Magdalena vicinity
GALLINAS SPRINGS RUIN
SE 1/4 SE 1/4 sec. 27, T. 1 S., R. 6 W.

The significance of the Gallinas Springs site lies in the pottery discovered there. It is a local, much degenerated variant of Mesa Verde black-on-white. The Mesa Verde people abandoned the San Juan Basin area (Mesa Verde, San Juan Valley, and Chaco Canyon) during the 13th century. Studies of the Gallinas Springs pottery indicate that it is closely related to the Mesa Verde ware, and the theory has been advanced that migrating Mesa Verde people settled here. Nestled in the foothills of the Gallinas Mountains, the village site may have had as many as 400 or 500 multi-storied rooms. Blocks of volcanic tuff were employed for building, and construction appears to have been somewhat at random with three to six tiers of rooms around a semi-enclosed plaza.
Federal

SOCORRO COUNTY
Socorro vicinity
FORT CRAIG
37 miles south of Socorro
1854–1885

Fort Craig was established to protect area inhabitants from Navajo and Apache Indian attacks and to provide aid to travelers between Santa Fe and El Paso, Texas. At the outbreak of the Civil War Fort Craig was strengthened against Confederate attack, and troops from the fort saw action against the Texas army at the battle of Valverde, February 21, 1862. The Texans won, and the Federal troops retreated to Fort Craig. When Indian raids ceased, the fort was no longer necessary and it was abandoned in 1885. Walls of several deteriorating stone and adobe buildings are still visible as are the earth mounds and moat constructed at the time of the Civil War.
Private

TAOS COUNTY
Las Trampas
LAS TRAMPAS HISTORIC DISTRICT
1751

The village of Las Trampas, a Spanish-American agricultural community, preserves its 18th-century heritage in both appearance and culture. Tradition still guides its agrarian life, which until World War II was almost untouched by Anglo influence and mechanized techniques. The church of San Jose de Garcia de Las Trampas, completed about 1780, is the center of village communal life. It is an important and well-preserved example of Spanish Colonial church architecture. Around the plaza and along the edges of the valley floor are typical early Spanish Colonial adobe houses.
Multiple public/private
NHL; HABS

TAOS COUNTY
Las Trampas
SAN JOSÉ DE GRACIA CHURCH
North side of the Plaza
1760–1776

The church of San José de Gracia is one of the best preserved Spanish Colonial pueblo churches in New Mexico. The building has a single nave plan 100 feet long by 52 feet wide, with transepts and a projecting apse. A peculiar feature of this and other Spanish Colonial churches in New Mexico is the hidden clerestory window which provides additional light for the sanctuary and the altar. Other features of the church include old paintings on the reredos and along the side walls, and simple designs painted under the balcony at the rear of the sanctuary. The structure is still used by the parish.
Private
NHL

TAOS COUNTY
Ranchos de Taos
SAN FRANCISCO DE ASSISI MISSION CHURCH
The Plaza
c. 1772

San Francisco de Assisi Mission was founded in the early 18th century. The church itself is believed to have been built about 1772, and it is probable that the roof was replaced or rebuilt about 1816. The building, a good example of the New Mexican Spanish Colonial church, is of white-stuccoed adobe and has exceptionally massive walls. With a wide buttress against the apse at the west end and beehive-curved buttresses at the corners of the boldly projecting transepts, the structure almost resembles a piece of ab-

stract sculpture. The church was thoroughly restored in 1967 and still serves the parish.
Private
NHL; HABS

TAOS COUNTY
TAOS
BLUMENSCHEIN, ERNEST L., HOUSE
Ledoux Street
18th century

Ernest L. Blumenschein was a co-founder of the Taos Art Colony in 1898. The modern art movement in the Southwest was inspired by the "Famous Seven" Taos artists, of whom Blumenschein and Bert G. Phillips were the leaders. In 1914 these men formalized their artistic and commercial association in the Taos Society of Artists. Their exhibitions spread the artistic attraction of the region across the United States and into Europe. Soon Taos became the most important art center west of the Mississippi River. Blumenschein's house is an 11–room adobe dating from Spanish times.
Private
NHL

TAOS COUNTY
Taos
CARSON, KIT, HOUSE
Kit Carson Avenue
1825

During the second quarter of the 19th century, Taos was the rendezvous point and winter quarters for many of the western and southwestern fur trappers. Kit Carson was one of the most renowned of these mountain men. His fame as a guide for exploring expeditions and as an army officer in the Southwest Indian wars equaled his earlier reputation as a trapper and mountain man. Carson bought this house in 1843 when he married Josefa Jaramillo. It became their permanent home until their deaths in 1868. The house was restored to its historic appearance after 1910 and stands today as a symbol and museum of the fur trade, the mountain men, and the free trappers of the Southwest.
Private
NHL; HABS

TAOS COUNTY
Taos vicinity
TAOS PUEBLO
3 miles north of Taos
c. 17th century

The Pueblo of Taos, still active today, commemorates Indian resistance to Spanish rule in the 17th century. This terraced pueblo of the Tigua was well known to Spanish explorers as early as 1540. The mission of San Geronimo, one of the earli-

est in New Mexico, was built near Taos Pueblo in the early 17th century. It was twice destroyed and rebuilt prior to the uprising of 1680. Fourteen years passed before Spanish rule was restored and the mission re-established. Though another revolt occurred in 1696, the mission continued until 1847 when it was bombarded by an American force under Colonel Sterling Price during the Taos Rebellion.
Private
NHL; HABS

TORRANCE COUNTY
Abó vicinity
ABÓ
3 miles west of Abó on U.S. 60 and secondary road
c. 1300–1670's

Abó was an Indian village among the Salinas pueblos east of the Manzano Mountains. In the early 17th century, the Spanish established among the Salinas people large missions which were abandoned by 1674. The ruin of Abó represents a relatively little-known period in Southwestern aboriginal culture history. Occupied from late prehistoric through early Spanish times, it typifies the period in which acculturation began in the Southwest. Excavation and archival research have provided vital data on this process. Remains so far uncovered at the pueblo include mounds of debris concealing pueblo walls and mission ruins.
State
NHL

TORRANCE COUNTY
GRAN QUIVIRA NATIONAL MONUMENT
Reference—see Socorro County

TORRANCE COUNTY
Punta de Agua vicinity
QUARAI
1 mile south of Punta de Agua on secondary road
c. 1300–1670's

The pueblo and mission of Quarai commemorate Indian involvement in the controversies between church and state in the middle 1600's. Quarai was in the midst of the Salinas pueblos east of the Manzano Mountains. There appears to have been a resident priest here from about 1630 until the mission was abandoned in 1674. Troubles had begun here in the late 1660's, however. The Tiwas, caught in the middle of a church-state squabble, were discovered in a plot to revolt. The site contains two churches: a small early one whose walls remain, and a large sandstone church and monastery. Limited excavations have indicated that the site is significant in acculturation studies.
State
NHL

UNION COUNTY
Clayton vicinity
RABBIT EARS (CLAYTON COMPLEX)
North and west of Clayton

Rabbit Ears is a double-peaked eminence rising high above the level and featureless plains. This major landmark on the Cimarron Cutoff of the Santa Fe Trail was the guide to travelers westbound from the Upper Spring in Oklahoma to Turkey Creek in New Mexico, a four-day journey. It was also the focal point for a series of camps and other landmarks conveniently grouped as the Clayton Complex. These include McNee's Crossing, Turkey Creek Camp, Rabbit Ears Creek Camp, Mount Dora, and Round Mound. These sites, which dot a well-preserved portion of the trail, include a number of year-round springs which were of paramount importance to early travelers.
Multiple public/private
NHL

UNION COUNTY
Folsom vicinity
FOLSOM SITE
8 miles west of Folsom on the banks of Dead Horse Gulch
c. 13000–8000 B.C.

The Folsom Site has contributed greatly to the knowledge of prehistoric life in the western hemisphere. Here, in 1926, archeologists uncovered flint spear points embedded between the ribs of an extinct species of bison. This find confirmed the theory about man's early advent into the Americas. Early Man finds have now become commonplace in American archeology. As America's original confrontation with the evidence, Folsom stands as a significant landmark in archeological discovery.
State
NHL

VALENCIA COUNTY
Acoma
SAN ESTEVAN DEL REY MISSION CHURCH
On N.M. 23
1629–1642; 1799–1800 (repaired)

The church of San Estevan is an example of Spanish Colonial architecture blending European plan and form with Indian construction and decorative detail. Fray Juan Ramirez founded the mission in 1629 to serve the people of the Ácoma Pueblo. The pueblo itself stood atop a mesa which rose 350 feet above the surrounding desert. All construction materials were transported by the Indians to the mesa top. The walls are adobe brick rising 35 feet from the ground. The church itself measures 150 feet by 40 feet, and the facade is flanked by two square towers.
Private
NHL; HABS

VALENCIA COUNTY
Casa Blanca vicinity
ACOMA
13 miles south of Casa Blanca on N.M. 23
1300

Acoma Pueblo is believed to be the oldest continuously occupied settlement in the United States. It was a familiar landmark in the period of Spanish exploration from 1540 until the 17th century. The Ácoma Indians were generally successful in resisting the Spaniards because of their favorable location on a high mesa, but the San Estevan mission was finally established by the Franciscans in 1629. Though only a few families live at Ácoma today, the tribe reassembles here for periodic festivals. The mission is among the least-altered in New Mexico.
Private
NHL; HABS

VALENCIA COUNTY
El Morro vicinity
EL MORRO NATIONAL MONUMENT
2 miles west of El Morro via N.M. 53
1605

Alongside a prehistoric Indian petroglyph, Juan de Oñate, first governor of New Mexico, carved his name in 1605. For the next three centuries explorers, soldiers, emigrants, and settlers added hundreds of names to "Inscription Rock," or El Morro. The rock is a massive mesapoint of sandstone rising some 200 feet above the valley floor. The Spaniards were not, however, the first to record their presence, for many inscriptions of the ancient Zunis can be found here. Together the inscriptions are a register of the cultural mixtures that make up the Southwest.
Federal/non-federal
NPS; 1,277.72 acres

VALENCIA COUNTY
Zuni vicinity
HAWIKUH
12 miles southwest of Zuni, Zuni Indian Reservation
16th century

The pueblo of Hawikuh was the largest of the "Cities of Cibola" and the first to be visited by Francisco Vasquez de Coronado. Conquered by the conquistador in 1540, it remained a Spanish headquarters for several months. It was visited frequently by subsequent explorers. A few rock and adobe walls may still be seen in the ruin, which was excavated in 1917–1923.
Private
NHL

Reredos of Our Lady of Light, Cristo Rey Church, Santa Fe, New Mexico. *Museum of New Mexico*

Hoyle House,
White Oaks Historic District,
New Mexico. *Jon Samuelson*

Randall Davey House,
Santa Fe, New Mexico
Karl Kernberger

New York

Fifth Avenue-Fulton Street Historic District,
Troy, New York. *John G. Waite*

Central Synagogue,
New York, New York. *Jay Seymour*

Albany Academy (Joseph Henry Memorial),
Albany, New York.
New York State Commerce Department

Schoharie Aqueduct,
Fort Hunter, New York.
Jack E. Boucher for HABS

Gasholder House,
Troy Gas Light Company,
Troy, New York.
Jack E. Boucher for HABS

New York State Capitol, Albany, New York.
New York State Department of Commerce

ALBANY ACADEMY (JOSEPH HENRY MEMORIAL)

Academy Park
1815–1817, Philip Hooker

The Albany Academy is one of two buildings by Philip Hooker remaining in the capital city (the other is the First Reformed Church). Its brownstone exterior is embellished by a belt course, round-arched second-floor windows, and two-story Ionic pilasters which separate the bays. A balustrade runs along the entire roofline, and the domed cupola has arched openings separated by paired Corinthian columns. Joseph Henry, professor of mathematics and natural philosophy at the Academy, experimented in the field of electro-magnetics.
Municipal

ALBANY UNION STATION

East side of Broadway between Columbia and Steuben Streets
1899–1900, Shepley, Rutan and Coolidge

Shepley, Rutan, and Coolidge were the successors to the firm of H. H. Richardson. They also designed Boston's South Station and Union Station in Springfield, Massachusetts. Albany's Union Station was constructed as part of a general rail transportation improvement program taking place throughout the east. The station itself is composed of two three-story sections which flank a large, one-story waiting room. The interior of the waiting room has a polished granite wainscot, an ornate plaster ceiling suspended from iron brackets, and a mosaic floor. Exterior walls are granite. Over the main entrance is a huge clock flanked by a carved replica of the state seal. Each of the four corner piers of the station is topped by a large stone globe surrounded by four stone lions. The three main doorways are iron framed, and a system of underground walkways connected the waiting room with all passenger loading platforms. Four major railroads (the New York Central, the Boston & Albany, the Hudson River, and the Delaware & Hudson) used the Union Station facilities.
State

CHERRY HILL

South Pearl Street between 1st and McCarthy Avenues
1768

This two-and-one-half-story gambrel-roofed dwelling was built by a Dutch master builder. It is rectangular in plan and has a five-bay main facade. At a later date the north wing was completed and the balustrade removed from the roof. Colonel Philip Van Rensselaer built the house. Solomon Van Rensselaer, the later owner, was adjutant general of New York, postmaster of Albany, and a member of Congress. The house contains many family furnishings, portraits, silver, china, and documents.
Private

NEW YORK EXECUTIVE MANSION

138 Eagle Street
c. 1860

Various residences served as the New York governor's home before the present Executive Mansion was purchased by the state in 1883. Architect Isaac G. Perry was commissioned to redesign the house four years later. The resulting Queen Anne style brick dwelling is two and one-half stories high and has a four-story tower adjacent to the main entrance. A one-story wrap-around porch was added on the north side, and the entranceway has a small, carved portico. All four chimneys have corbeled caps. The Executive Mansion is still in use.
State

NEW YORK STATE CAPITOL

Capitol Park
1867–1899, Thomas Fuller, H. H. Richardson, Leopold Eidlitz, Isaac G. Perry

The five-story New York State Capitol is an admixture of styles spanning the 32–year period of its construction. On the first three stories the building is Second Empire with both Doric and Corinthian columns, arched windows, and rusticated stone work. The fourth story is Romanesque with low window arches. The roofline is Chateauesque. A central courtyard is a notable feature. Thomas Fuller was the original architect, but when the building was partially complete, Richardson and Eidlitz replaced him and superimposed their design over the existing one. Isaac Perry was the state architect charged with completion of the capitol. Notable interior work was by Richardson (Senate Chamber) and Eidlitz (Assembly Room). The floors are inlaid marble, the lower walls are covered with ornamental tessera, and even the elevator shafts are elaborately carved. Measurements of the capitol's exterior are 400 by 300 feet. Perry did much of the exterior and interior stone carving, marble and wood paneling and carving.
State

NEW YORK STATE COURT OF APPEALS BUILDING (STATE HALL)

Eagle Street between Pine and Columbia Streets
1839–1842, Henry Rector

The Court of Appeals is a temple-form, marble structure with a five-bay projecting portico on the west side. All three Greek orders appear on the exterior which also exhibits a molded stone cornice. Inside the three-story building are arched ceilings (a fireproofing measure) and marble flag flooring. The roof and dome were sheeted with copper. When the building served as the State Hall, it housed the chancellor, the supreme court judges, the secretary of state, the comptroller, the treasurer, the attorney general, and the Canal Board. It is now occupied by the highest court in New York state.
State
HABS

NEW YORK STATE DEPARTMENT OF EDUCATION BUILDING

Washington Avenue between Hawk and Swan Streets
1908–1912, Henry Hornbostel

The New York State Department of Education Building was the first major building in the United States constructed solely as headquarters for administrators of education. The monumental Neo-Classical structure has as its most prominent exterior features a colonnade on the front elevation containing 36 marble columns with terra-cotta Corinthian capitals and a wide entablature. Inside the T-shaped stone building is a 94–foot high central dome composed of metal tracery with glass infill. The remainder of the room has barrel-vaulted glass ceilings. R. Guastavino, inventor of the process of building masonry domes using specially shaped tiles, is credited with all the tile work in the 50–foot reading room dome.
State

SCHUYLER, PHILIP, MANSION

Clinton and Schuyler Streets
1761–1762

Also known as "The Pastures," the Schuyler Mansion is an example of a late Georgian house in the middle American colonies. The two-and-a-half-story brick house has a hip gambrel roof with six pedimented dormer windows, two large end chimneys, and a unique Chinese Chip-

pendale rail surrounding the roof. A hexagonal brick vestibule leading to the front door was added in 1810. The interior of the house features a highly ornamented center hall stairway and first floor wall paneling. Philip Schuyler was a major general in the Revolutionary War, member of the Second Continental Congress, and a United States Senator.
State
NHL; HABS

ALBANY COUNTY
Albany
WHIPPLE CAST AND WROUGHT-IRON BOWSTRING TRUSS BRIDGE
1000 Delaware Avenue, Normanskill Farm
1867

Squire Whipple (1804–1888) was one of the earliest engineers to evolve a scientific basis for American bridge construction. Whipple Trusses were prefabricated and assembled on site. Sections of the chords fitted together with the aid of locating pins held in place by compression when the vertical rods and the wrought iron bowstring links were tightened. Whipple patented the Iron Bowstring Truss in April of 1841. Bridges built in this manner were inexpensive, relatively lightweight, strong, durable, and available in standard lengths, so hundreds of imitators sprang up. The bridge on the Normanskill Farm was fabricated in 1867 by Simon De Graft. When the Albany and Delaware Turnpike was rerouted in 1899, the farm owners bought the bridge and re-erected it over a deep ravine separating the farm from the new highway. The bridge is one of the earliest iron bridges remaining in the country, a landmark in the history of American civil engineering.
Private; not accessible to the public
HAER

ALBANY COUNTY
Coeymans
COEYMANS SCHOOL (ACTON CIVILL POLYTECHNIC INSTITUTE)
Southwest corner of Westerlo Street and Civill Avenue
1873

The elaborate Second Empire structure built to house the Acton Civill Polytechnic Institute stands three stories above a raised basement. Its roofline is broken by window hoods and towerlike projections at each corner. A central octagonal tower on the north facade rises several levels above the mansard roof. Walls are brick, and there is an unusual amount of cast iron trim—water table, quoins, balustrades, towers, and chimneys. Acton Civill (1804–1889) was a New York businessman who maintained a summer home in Coeymans, where he decided to open an academy. The building was used as a school until 1963.
Private

ALBANY COUNTY
Cohoes
HARMONY MILL NO. 3 (MASTODON MILL)
100 N. Mohawk Street
1866–1868, D. H. Van Auken

The layout of the Harmony Mill is rectangular, although a wing has been added to the east side. Walls are brick, four stories high on a stone foundation, and the roof is a mansard. Trim is cast iron and stone. Each bay contains a hooded dormer, and the central block of the mill is flanked by twin six-story towers, which also have mansard roofs. In 1871 an addition on the south, which was part of the total plan, was begun. The name Mastodon Mill derived from discovery of a mastodon skeleton during the foundation excavations. Originally known as the Harmony Manufacturing Company, the Harmony Mills were incorporated in 1836.
Private
HAER

ALBANY COUNTY
Cohoes
LOCK 18 OF ENLARGED ERIE CANAL (DOUBLE LOCK)
West of 252 N. Mohawk Street, east of Reservoir Street near Manor Avenue
1837–1842

Plans were formulated in the 1830's for enlarging the existing Erie Canal. Canal promoters hoped that by widening the canal and increasing the size of the locks they could compete successfully with the railroads for passengers and freight. The number of locks between Albany and Schenectady, one of the most difficult sections of the canal, was to be reduced. Holmes Hutchinson (1794–1865) was chief engineer for the Erie Canal during the period of improvement, and under his direction Lock 18 was built. It was constructed of cut stone laid up in a random ashlar pattern. The wooden lock gates no longer exist.
State/private
HAER

ALBANY COUNTY
Cohoes
MUSIC HALL
Northwest corner of Remsen and Oneida Streets
1874

James Masten and William Acheson built the Music Hall as a business enterprise.

Post office facilities occupied the north end of the structure, and the upper stories housed a theater (seating capacity 1,000). The city library and the First National Bank have also used the premises. Exterior walls are brick with stone trim, and the mansard roof has a bracketed cornice. It is the theater on the third and fourth levels which is the building's most outstanding feature. The walls and ceiling are covered with the original painted canvas, the gilded loge boxes remain, as do the dressing rooms under the sloping stage.
Municipal

ALBANY COUNTY
Cohoes
VAN SCHAICK HOUSE
Van Schaick Avenue and the Delaware & Hudson Railroad tract
c. 1735

The Van Schaick Mansion was built by Wessel Van Schaick. It was strategically located on the Kings Highway, then the main road north of Albany. The house served as military headquarters for several British generals during the French and Indian War and as headquarters for Generals Richard Montgomery and Horatio Gates during the Revolution. Governor George Clinton used it as the state capitol from August 22 to 25, 1777. The house is a rectangular, one-and-one-half-story Dutch residence. The walls are constructed of brick laid in English bond. Inside, it has a central hall plan. The porch over the main entrance is a 19th-century addition. The house is one of the earliest in the upper Hudson Valley to have a gambrel roof.
Private
HABS

ALBANY COUNTY
Watervliet
WATERVLIET ARSENAL
S. Broadway
1813

Though the War of 1812 stimulated its establishment, Watervliet Arsenal's busiest years occurred during the Mexican and Civil wars. In 1889 it became the government's cannon factory, famous for its production of large caliber seacoast defense guns. Of the post's buildings, the great gun factory is the most significant. Practically unchanged on the outside, the building's interior has been adapted to changing production needs. The Commandant's Quarters (1842) and the prefabricated, cast-iron building erected in 1859 are also noteworthy, as is the Arsenal's collection of historic ordnance.
Federal
NHL

BRONX COUNTY
The Bronx
NEW YORK BOTANICAL GARDENS
Southern and Bedford Park
Boulevards
1896

The early growth of this leading botanical garden was largely due to the leadership of its first director, Nathaniel Lord Britton. The New York Botanical Garden has developed one of the world's largest herbariums; laboratories for research in ecology, plant geography, plant physiology, and systematic botany; an extensive education program; and the world's largest botanical library. Notable features of the 250–acre garden include a 40–acre virgin hemlock forest and the original conservatory and museum building.
Private
NHL

BRONX COUNTY
The Bronx
VAN CORTLANDT, FREDERICK, HOUSE
Van Cortlandt Park at 242nd Street
1748–1749

Built for Frederick Van Cortlandt, the Van Cortlandt House is an L-shaped early Georgian country house. The two-and-a-half-story house is constructed of dressed fieldstone with brick trim around the windows. The mansard roof is pierced by dormer windows. The paneling in the principal rooms is among the best surviving examples of mid–18th century paneling in New York City. The house has recently been restored.
Private
NHL

BROOME COUNTY
Binghamton
BINGHAMTON CITY HALL
Collier Street between Court and
Academy Streets
1897–1898, Francis R. Almirall

The five-story, rectangular Binghamton City Hall was designed in the Second Empire style. Its Collier Street facade is masonry, while the sides and rear are of sandstone and brick with native sandstone trim. There are casement, fan, double-hung, and oculi windows juxtaposed on the four elevations. The mansard roof has dormers with ornately carved stone faces, and an ornamental cupola with metal railings and copper trim crowns the roof. Situated in a downtown urban renewal area, the City Hall provides a visual link between Binghamton's past and present.
Municipal
HABS

CAYUGA COUNTY
Auburn
FLATIRON BUILDING
1–3 Genessee Street
1829

Ezekiel Williams, an early developer of Auburn, built the Flatiron Building. The structure is three stories high and triangular in shape with a rounded apex. Walls are dressed limestone ashlar, and the plain facade is crowned by a wide wooden cornice. All of the first floor, except three bays at the western end of the north wall, has been covered by modern store fronts.
Private; not accessible to the public

CAYUGA COUNTY
Auburn
SEWARD, WILLIAM H., HOUSE
33 South Street
1816

With a background as state senator, governor of New York, and United States Senator, William H. Seward served as Secretary of State from 1861 to 1869. Aside from his record of wartime diplomacy, Seward is most commonly remembered for his part in the purchase of Alaska, ridiculed then as "Seward's Folly." This house was Seward's residence from 1824 until his death in 1872. One of his favorite rooms, the North Library, contains some original furnishings and much of his personal library.
Private
NHL

CAYUGA COUNTY
Poplar Ridge
WOOD, JETHRO, HOUSE
N.Y. 34B
Date unknown

Jethro Wood patented the first successful iron plow in 1819. This plow possessed two outstanding features: an improved moldboard which cut through the soil cleanly and easily, and it was made of three parts rather than one. The interchangeability of the parts was a major contribution to the development of the plow. His two-story clapboard and gabled house is still used as a residence.
Private; not accessible to the public
NHL

CHAUTAUQUA COUNTY
Chautauqua
MILLER, LEWIS, COTTAGE, CHAUTAUQUA INSTITUTION
N.Y. 17J
1875

Inaugurated as the Methodist Sunday School Teachers' Assembly, the Chautauqua Institution soon became a secular, year-round program of adult education. The collaboration of Lewis Miller, an Ohio businessman, and John Heyl Vincent, a Methodist minister, marked the founding of the movement in 1874. Of the several early buildings, the Lewis Miller Cottage is of special significance. Within the two-story frame building resembling a Swiss chalet, Miller entertained many prominent visitors, including President Ulysses S. Grant. Remodeled in 1922, the cottage is still occupied by Miller's descendants. Also of interest in the early history of Chautauqua are the Atheneum Hotel, built in 1873, and Pioneer Hall and the Octagon House, both built in 1885.
Private; not accessible to the public
NHL

CLINTON COUNTY (also in Essex,
Franklin, Fulton, Hamilton,
Herkimer, St. Lawrence and Warren
counties)
ADIRONDACK FOREST PRESERVE
Northeastern New York State
1885

The Adirondack Forest Preserve became the first state forest preserve in the nation when New York established it as a wilderness area in 1885. Today it includes some 2,115,381 acres of state-owned land. In addition to providing for the continued protection of the forests, the preserve also serves as a recreational area. Roads make many areas accessible to the camper and hiker.
State
NHL

CLINTON COUNTY
Plattsburgh
KENT-DELORD HOUSE
17 Cumberland Avenue
1797

The Kent-Delord House is believed to be the oldest in Plattsburgh. The second owner was Elizabeth Bailey Kent, whose husband James Kent was chief justice of New York's state supreme court and wrote *Kent's Commentaries on American Law*. During the battle of Plattsburgh (September 11, 1814) the house was the headquarters for British officers. The frame dwelling is two stories high and has a gable roof. There is a one-story central entrance porch on the south facade.
Private

CLINTON COUNTY
Plattsburgh
OLD STONE BARRACKS
Rhode Island Avenue, Plattsburgh Air Force Base
1838–1840

Six months after the battle of Plattsburgh (September 11, 1814) the federal government purchased 200 acres along the shoreline of Lake Champlain on which to establish a military reservation, Plattsburgh Barracks. The present stone quarters were constructed as one side of a two-sided hollow square. The other barracks was demolished in 1964. The Old Stone Barracks has two-story limestone walls and is the oldest building still standing on the base, now Plattsburgh Air Force Base. Its gable roof has a wooden cornice, and a two-story wooden veranda covers the north facade.
Federal; not accessible to the public

CLINTON COUNTY
Plattsburgh vicinity
PLATTSBURGH BAY
Cumberland Bay, east of Plattsburgh
1814

The naval battle of Plattsburgh, September 11, 1814, halted a major British thrust into the United States along the traditional invasion route of Lake Champlain and the Hudson River. This victory in the War of 1812 resulted in the destruction of the British fleet on Lake Champlain and compelled invading troops to withdraw to Canada, leaving behind a vast store of supplies. Overlooking the scene of the action is the Macdonough Memorial, commemorating Captain Thomas Macdonough, American naval commander at the battle.
State
NHL

CLINTON COUNTY
Plattsburgh vicinity
VALCOUR BAY
7 miles south of Plattsburgh on the west shore of Lake Champlain
1776

Benedict Arnold's fleet action off Valcour Island on October 11, 1776, had a far-reaching effect on the outcome of the Revolutionary War. Although the American force was defeated, its presence and its stubborn fight were strategically advantageous. The delay caused the British command to wait until the following year to carry out its projected movement toward Albany. By that time the Americans were better prepared, and they repulsed the British at Saratoga, the turning point of the Revolution. The only commemorative monument is on the mainland about five miles south of Plattsburgh.
State
NHL

COLUMBIA COUNTY
Church Hill
OLANA (FREDERIC E. CHURCH HOUSE)
Church Hill, east end of Rip Van Winkle Bridge
1874, Frederic Church and Calvert Vaux

Frederic E. Church was one of the leading American landscape artists of the 19th century. First becoming prominent through paintings of the Catskill Mountains, Church is noted for his treatment of light in sunsets, storms, and volcanic explosions. Extensive travel to South America, Labrador, Europe, and the Near East provided material for many of his paintings. Olana, overlooking the Hudson River, is reminiscent of these travels, reflecting Persian, Moorish, Italian, and East Indian styles. Many of his paintings are displayed in the house.
State
NHL

COLUMBIA COUNTY
Germantown
CLERMONT
Clermont State Park
18th and 19th centuries

Clermont was originally a 13,000-acre estate which Robert R. Livingston (1746–1813) inherited from his father. The present house was constructed sometime after 1777 and incorporated an earlier (c. 1730) dwelling into its fabric. In its present form the house is three stories high and has walls of brick covered with stucco scored to resemble stone. Alterations have been made through the early 20th century, most notably the addition of a combination third floor and hip roof. Robert Livingston was a delegate to the Continental Congress, the first Secretary of Foreign Affairs, and a negotiator for the Louisiana Purchase.
State
HABS

COLUMBIA COUNTY
Hudson
FRONT STREET-PARADE HILL-LOWER WARREN STREET HISTORIC DISTRICT
Warren Street between 2nd Street and Parade Hill, both sides of N. Front and S. Front Streets between Diamond and Allen (Ferry) Streets, both sides of Prison Alley between N. Front Street and the bluff, Parade Hill, Franklin Square, and the north side of Fleet Street
18th–20th centuries

Hudson, originally called Claverack Landing, was established in the late 18th century as a commercial venture by a group of New England Proprietors. For this reason the architecture contrasts markedly with that of other Hudson River towns which were founded and settled by the Dutch. Hudson prospered as a whaling and shipbuilding port, until, by the 1840's, its economy was no longer tied to the sea but to industry. Within the district are many frame and brick buildings dating from the late 18th through the early 20th centuries that vary in architectural style as well as use. A common building type contains living quarters above a first floor business. On top of the bluff above the river are a number of late 18th-century commercial structures. Today the entire historic area retains much of its original character, scale, and land use. The environment, relatively unaltered by modern intrusion, relates strongly to the river which first engendered Hudson's prosperity.
Multiple public/private

COLUMBIA COUNTY
Kinderhook vicinity
LINDENWALD (MARTIN VAN BUREN HOUSE)
East of Kinderhook on N.Y. 9H
1797

Martin Van Buren, eighth President of the United States, occupied Lindenwald from his retirement from the Presidency in 1841 until his death in 1862. Van Buren played a leading role in the emergence of Jacksonian democracy in the 1830's and remained a prominent political figure until the outbreak of the Civil War. His brick house, originally Georgian in style, was enlarged and renovated for Van Buren after 1840 by Richard Upjohn.
Private
NHL; HABS

COLUMBIA COUNTY
Kinderhook vicinity
VAN ALEN, LUYCAS, HOUSE
N.Y. 9H, 2.1 miles south of U.S. 9
1737–1750

The Van Alen House illustrates the type of Dutch Colonial brick house built in New York's northern counties during the 18th century. It is one of the few remaining examples that has not been severely altered by later additions and remodeling. Constructed by Luycas Van Alen, the farmhouse is a rectangular brick building with a sharply pitched roof. It has been restored by the Columbia County Historical Society.
Private
NHL; HABS

COLUMBIA COUNTY
Livingston
LIVINGSTON, HENRY W., HOUSE, THE HILL
At the intersection of U.S. 9 and N.Y. 82
c. 1803

The Classical architectural details of The Hill set the house apart from the Colonial dwellings of the previous century. A giant portico with two-story Ionic columns highlights the three bays of the west facade, and a modified dome roof covers the central block. Curved bays were built on the westernmost portions of the side elevations, and wings extend from the eastern portion of the sides and terminate in octagons. Walls are brick covered with stucco. Henry W. Livingston (1768–1810) was minister to France, county judge, and a member of the state assembly and of Congress.
Private; not accessible to the public

COLUMBIA COUNTY
New Lebanon
MOUNT LEBANON SHAKER SOCIETY
U.S. 20
1787

The Mount Lebanon Shaker Society was the first and most economically successful of the 19 Shaker communities in the United States. It was the central ministry which directed the affairs of the other communities. The Shakers lived in communal fashion, granted equality of the sexes, and practiced celibacy. Though the community had died out by the 1920's, a large number of the original buildings remain, most of which are owned by the Darrow School. Among the most important are the original meetinghouse, a five-story dormitory, the tannery, a chair factory, and a smithy.
Private
NHL; HABS

DELAWARE COUNTY
Roxbury vicinity
BURROUGHS, JOHN, HOME (WOODCHUCK LODGE)
2 miles from Roxbury
1908

John Burroughs was both a scientist and a literary critic, and the combination of these talents produced one of America's important nature writers. Some of his best-known nature essays include *Wake-Robin* (1871) and *Locusts and Wild Honey* (1879). In addition, he was an authority on his personal friend, the poet Walt Whitman. His summer retreat in the Catskills, a frame house with rustic trimmings,

was used both for writing and for entertaining friends, among whom were Thomas A. Edison and Henry Ford.
Private; not accessible to the public
NHL

DUTCHESS COUNTY
Hyde Park
HOME OF FRANKLIN D. ROOSEVELT NATIONAL HISTORIC SITE
2 miles south of Hyde Park on U.S. 9
1826

In this house at Hyde Park, Franklin D. Roosevelt was born on January 30, 1882. Here he grew up, and here he made his home for much of his adult life. During his years as President of the United States, 1933–1945, it served as the "Summer White House." It was from this district that he first campaigned successfully for office, representing the district as New York state senator from 1911 to 1913. In subsequent years he served as Assistant Secretary of the Navy (1913–1920) and governor of New York (1929–1933). To this home he came often while recuperating from infantile paralysis contracted in 1921. The site also includes Roosevelt's grave and the Franklin D. Roosevelt Library.
Federal
NPS, 187.69 acres
HABS

DUTCHESS COUNTY
Hyde Park
VANDERBILT MANSION NATIONAL HISTORIC SITE
North edge of Hyde Park, U.S. 9
1896–1898, McKim, Mead, and White

Vanderbilt Mansion National Historic Site is a significant example of the great estates developed by financial and industrial leaders in the era following the Civil War. The grounds have been maintained since colonial days as a country seat by prominent individuals including Dr. Samuel Bard, attending physician to George Washington, and heirs of John Jacob Astor. In 1895 the estate was purchased by Frederick W. Vanderbilt, grandson of Commodore Cornelius Vanderbilt. The three-story Italian Renaissance mansion he built on the property is furnished predominantly in Continental motifs. Vanderbilt also improved the grounds and built new farm buildings, carriage houses, and entrance ways.
Federal
NPS; 211.65 acres
HABS

DUTCHESS COUNTY
Poughkeepsie
MORSE, SAMUEL F. B., HOUSE (LOCUST GROVE)
370 South Street
1830

Samuel F. B. Morse purchased Locust Grove in 1847, three years after the famous telegraph message had flashed over the wire from Washington to Baltimore. Although he was a painter and professor, he is chiefly noted for his pioneer work in telegraphy and development of the Morse code. He enlarged this summer residence by adding rooms on the north and south sides so that the house is octagon-shaped; another four-story addition forms a tower.
Private; not accessible to the public
NHL

DUTCHESS COUNTY
Poughkeepsie
SPRINGSIDE (MATTHEW VASSAR HOUSE)
Academy and Livingston Streets
1850–1852, Andrew Jackson Downing

When Matthew Vassar purchased a 43-acre tract in Poughkeepsie in 1850, he engaged the well-known landscape architect Andrew Jackson Downing (1815–1852) to design what was to be Vassar's country estate. A large villa planned by Vassar was never built but the gatehouse and a cottage designed by Downing remain. About half of the original estate, or 26.5 acres, exists today as the sole evidence of Downing's work to have survived intact to the present. Downing is considered to be the first American landscape architect, and his ideas strongly influenced national tastes. The grounds of Springside encompass meandering drives and paths, and natural features are subtly blended with man-made ones to enhance the natural setting. The cottage is Gothic Revival, one and one-half stories with a projecting central gable and jerkinhead end gable.
Private; not accessible to the public
NHL; NABS

ERIE COUNTY
Buffalo
ALBRIGHT-KNOX ART GALLERY
1285 Elmwood Avenue
1900–1905, Edward B. Green

The Buffalo Fine Arts Academy was founded in 1862 and a half century later commissioned Edward B. Green to design an art gallery. His building is two stories high and roughly L-shaped. Walls are faced with marble, and the roof is com-

posed of gabled and modified gambrel sections covered with tile and pierced by skylights. The east elevation has a central Ionic portico flanked on both sides by wings composed of colonnaded sections connecting projecting pedimented portions with four caryatid figures by Augustus Saint-Gaudens. On the west side is a hemicycle with Ionic columns also flanked by Ionic colonnaded wings.
Private

ERIE COUNTY
Buffalo
THEODORE ROOSEVELT INAUGURAL NATIONAL HISTORIC SITE
Delaware Avenue
c. 1838, c. 1901, Georgy Carey

The Ansley Wilcox House was originally part of an army post, Poinsett Barracks, established in 1838. In the late 1840's the house became a private residence. After a number of ownerships, it was purchased in 1883 by Dexter P. Rumsey. It was remodeled on the inside and an earlier frame addition rebuilt. In this Victorian period house Vice President Theodore Roosevelt took the oath of office as President of the United States on September 14, 1901, following the assassination of President William McKinley.
Federal; not accessible to the public
NPS 1.03 acres
HABS

ESSEX COUNTY
ADIRONDACK FOREST PRESERVE
Reference—see Clinton County

ESSEX COUNTY
Crown Point
FORT ST. FREDERIC
Junction of N.Y. 8 and 9N
1731

For almost a quarter of a century Fort St. Frederic was a keystone of France's defense of Canada. During the French and Indian War, however, the fort was abandoned and destroyed after the fall of Fort Ticonderoga to the British in 1759. Though fragmentary, the ruins give an impression of the life in a frontier outpost on the shores of Lake Champlain. A museum contains artifacts found in and near Fort St. Frederic and nearby Fort Amherst.
State
NHL

ESSEX COUNTY
Crown Point vicinity
FORT CROWN POINT
Crown Point Reservation, west of the south end of the Lake Champlain Bridge and N.Y. 8
1760

Fort Crown Point, in its ruined, but unaltered state, is considered one of the best existing architectural and archeological examples of 18th-century military engineering in the United States. Included in the Crown Point Reservation are the ruins of Fort Crown Point, Fort St. Frederic (a post built and occupied by the French from 1731 to 1759), and the sites of 18th-century French and English villages. Construction was started on the British fort in 1760 after the capture of the site from the French during the French and Indian War. The fort was called Crown Point or Fort Amherst, after Gen. Lord Jeffrey Amherst, commander of the British forces that drove the French Army from the shores of Lake Champlain. Disaster struck the new fort in 1773. The powder magazine blew up, and the entire fortress was damaged by fire. Reconstruction began, but before the work was completed the Revolution broke out, and the fort was never rebuilt. The post played a minor role in the Revolution as an outpost of Fort Ticonderoga. Eventually the entire area of the fort reverted to pasture and orchard. The moat, wall, most of the stonework, and the five great bastions which extended from the corners are still largely intact, although overgrown with vegetation. Inside are the well-preserved remains of two of the three original stone two-story barracks.
State
NHL

ESSEX COUNTY
Port Kent
WATSON, ELKANAH, HOUSE
3 miles east of U.S. 9
1828

Remembered primarily as an originator of the agricultural fair, Elkanah Watson was also a diplomat, businessman, banker, canal promoter, and educator. With ideas far in advance of his time, he persistently supported the creation of a National Board of Agriculture. Watson's two-story stone house sits high above Lake Champlain, affording a view across the lake to Vermont. The house remains essentially unchanged.
Private; not accessible to the public
NHL

ESSEX COUNTY
Ticonderoga vicinity
FORT TICONDEROGA
2.5 miles south of Ticonderoga on N.Y. 22
1755–1757

Located at the junction of Lake Champlain and Lake George, Fort Ticonderoga was the key to both Canada and the Hudson River Valley in the 18th century. Built by the French and originally named Fort Vaudreuil, it was captured by the British in 1759 and renamed Ticonderoga. During the American Revolution it changed hands many times, first coming into American possession on May 10, 1775, when a small force of Green Mountain Boys under Ethan Allen defeated its British defenders. The fort has been largely restored.
Private
NHL

FRANKLIN COUNTY
ADIRONDACK FOREST PRESERVE
Reference—see Clinton County

FULTON COUNTY
ADIRONDACK FOREST PRESERVE
Reference—see Clinton County

FULTON COUNTY
Johnstown
JOHNSON HALL
Hall Street
1763

Johnson Hall was for the last 11 years of his life the home of Sir William Johnson, Superintendent of Indian Affairs for the northern colonies and a foremost frontier leader of pre-Revolutionary New York. Johnson's influence on the Indians of the Six Nations was significant in the defeat of French power in North America and in the westward advance of the English colonies. The rectangular frame building in Georgian style has been restored and contains some furnishings which belonged to the Johnson family. The adjacent blockhouse is one of the two which guarded Johnson's house.
State
NHL; HABS

GENESEE COUNTY
Batavia
HOLLAND LAND OFFICE
W. Main Street
1815

The Holland Land Company played a vital role in developing western New York and northern Pennsylvania in the late 18th and early 19th centuries. Created by a group of Dutch investors in the 1790's, its land

office in Batavia was run for many years by a local agent, Joseph Ellicott. A responsible land company, the Holland Land Office provided orderly assignment of land to settlers, helped newcomers adjust to life on the frontier, and stimulated the federal government to provide good roads and protection for settlers.
County
NHL

GREENE COUNTY
Catskill
COLE, THOMAS, HOUSE
218 Spring Street
1812–1814

The Hudson River School of painting developed largely because of the work of Thomas Cole, an American landscape and allegorical painter of the 19th century. His European travels led to an increasing concentration on allegorical scenes, but his love for natural scenes never dwindled. The brick house in which he lived has been little altered since its construction. From his bedroom Cole could view the Catskill Mountains which he so often painted. To the east of the house is the two-story clapboard studio in which Cole worked until two years before his death.
Private; not accessible to the public
NHL

GREENE COUNTY
Coxsackie vicinity
BRONCK, PIETER, HOUSE
2 miles west of Coxsackie on the west side of U.S. 9W
1663, 1682, 1738

The Bronck House illustrates the architectural development of Dutch Colonial dwellings. Constructed by Pieter Bronck, the first house had fieldstone walls, a high gable roof, and tall casement windows. The dwelling contained one large room on each of the two floors and an attic. The first expansion in 1682 saw the addition of a one-and-a-half-story wing to the rear of the original house. In 1738 Leendent Bronck built a larger brick house to the north, connecting it to the original dwelling by a brick passageway. Still in excellent condition, the house is furnished with much of the original Bronck furniture.
Private
NHL

HAMILTON COUNTY
ADIRONDACK FOREST PRESERVE
Reference—see Clinton County

HERKIMER COUNTY
ADIRONDACK FOREST PRESERVE
Reference—see Clinton County

HERKIMER COUNTY
Danube
HERKIMER HOUSE
Near N.Y. 5S
1750's

Situated on the bank of the Mohawk River, Herkimer House was built by Nicholas Herkĭmer (1728–1777), brigadier general of the Tryon County militia. His command was ambushed at Oriskany while enroute to Fort Stanwix (August 6, 1977), and Herkimer was fatally wounded. His home is a two-story brick dwelling with a central hall plan. In the 1820's the house was remodeled inside and out for use as a canal tavern. A portion was destroyed by fire in 1908, and the state of New York bought the house five years later. Drastic alterations were undertaken in the 1960's to restore the structure to its 18th-century appearance. Steel framing was introduced, two wooden porches were added, and the two interior chimneys date from the 20th century. The wood Greek Revival cornice is early 19th century.
State

HERKIMER COUNTY
Indian Castle vicinity
INDIAN CASTLE CHURCH
East of Indian Castle on N.Y. 5S
c. 1769–1770

The Indian Castle Church was erected under the direction of Sir William Johnson, Superintendent of Indian Affairs for the northern colonies. It is a rectangular, one-story frame structure covered with clapboards. The present steeple and much of the other fabric have been extensively altered.
State

HERKIMER COUNTY
Little Falls
HERKIMER COUNTY TRUST COMPANY BUILDING
Corner of Ann and Albany Streets
1833, 1874

Originally called the Herkimer County Bank, the Herkimer County Trust Company is the oldest bank in the county. This Greek Revival building housed the bank until 1917. Only one story high and rectangular in shape, the structure's small scale makes it unusual. The facade is constructed of cut stone while the south wall and basement are broken range masonry. Four hand-carved stone columns support the pediment of the front portico, and a small addition on the north side was built in 1874 to provide living accommodations for a junior clerk who guarded the bank funds.
Private; not accessible to the public

KINGS COUNTY
Brooklyn
BROOKLYN BRIDGE
Connecting the boroughs of Manhattan and Brooklyn across the East River
1883, John A. and Washington A. Roebling

Brooklyn Bridge was one of the world's first wire cable suspension bridges. During its construction numerous technical problems were faced, and their solutions established precedents in bridge building. For example, steel rather than wrought iron wire was used for the main cables and the individual wires were galvanized to protect them from the salt spray. The cables themselves are supported by two massive Gothic pylons, each with two pointed arches. The main span of the bridge is 1,595 feet long, but the overall length is 3,455 feet.
Municipal
NHL

KINGS COUNTY
Brooklyn
BROOKLYN HEIGHTS HISTORIC DISTRICT
Borough of Brooklyn, bounded by Atlantic Avenue, Court Street, Fulton Street, and the East River
19th century

During the 19th century, Brooklyn Heights, situated on a bluff opposite the southeastern tip of Manhattan, was the leading residential district of New York City. The extant buildings reflect the architectural styles of the Victorian era as well as the opulence of the times. Within recent years Brooklyn Heights has been revived as a residential area. The influx of new residents has helped to preserve the architectural interest and residential character of the area.
Multiple public/private
NHL; HABS

KINGS COUNTY
Brooklyn
PLYMOUTH CHURCH OF THE PILGRIMS
75 Hicks Street
1849

Established in 1847, Brooklyn's Plymouth Church of the Pilgrims was a foremost center of antislavery sentiment. From its pulpit spoke not only its well-known minister, Henry Ward Beecher, but also such other noted abolitionists as William Lloyd Garrison, Charles Sumner, and John Greenleaf Whittier. During the latter half of the 19th century, the church con-

tinued its prominence through support of social and cultural movements. The original building has changed little since its opening, the major alteration being the addition of stained glass windows.
Private
NHL; HABS

KINGS COUNTY
Brooklyn
WYCKOFF, PIETER, HOUSE
5902 Canarsie Lane
1639

Pieter Wyckoff, builder of the Wyckoff House, was the superintendent of Peter Stuyvesant's estate. His Flemish Colonial residence illustrates the regional type of frame dwelling utilized by Dutch settlers on western Long Island. Expanded near the end of the 17th century and enlarged in 1730, this farmhouse is New York City's oldest house. The one-story building has a pair of end chimneys and a small one-story wing on the same axis at the west end.
Private; not accessible to the public
NHL; HABS

LEWIS COUNTY
Lowville
HOUGH, FRANKLIN B., HOUSE
Collins Street
c. 1861

Dr. Franklin B. Hough, the father of American forestry, so impressed upon the public and the federal government the danger of depletion of the nation's forests that in 1876 he was appointed Forestry Agent in the Department of Agriculture. In addition to being the first federal forestry official, Hough is credited with the first book on forestry prepared in the United States, the first American forestry journal, and with helping to write the bill that made the Adirondack Forest Preserve the nation's first state forest preserve. His brick residence is essentially the same as it was during his occupancy.
Private; not accessible to the public
NHL

MADISON COUNTY
Cazenovia
LORENZO
Ledyard Street (U.S. 20)
1807–1809

Colonel John Linklaen, founder of Cazenovia, built Lorenzo. It is a two-story Georgian dwelling which exhibits, both inside and out, the influence of the Adam style. Exterior walls are brick. On the north or main facade the bays are separated by pilasters topped with elliptical arches forming a blind arcade. A pediment containing an elliptical window tops

the three center bays of the main facade, and a balustrade runs along the roof of the central block. The rear ell lacks the balustrade. Inside, the wide hallway contains a spiral staircase. Woodwork and ceiling cornices are finely executed.
State
HABS

MADISON COUNTY
Oneida
ONEIDA COMMUNITY MANSION HOUSE
Sherrill Road
1860

The Oneida Community, founded in 1848 by John Humphrey Noyes, illustrates one of 19th-century America's communitarian experiments. Progressive in many ways, the community flourished until 1879. External social pressures and internal dissension led to the cessation of multiple marriage, and in 1881 the experiment ceased. The large brick mansion house of about 400 rooms remains essentially unchanged.
Private; not accessible to the public
NHL

MONROE COUNTY
Rochester
ANTHONY, SUSAN B., HOUSE
17 Madison Street
c. 1866–1906

Susan B. Anthony, who was associated with many reform movements, was a leading figure in the women's rights movement during the second half of the 19th century. A teacher in her younger years, she was drawn away from the classroom by her interest in current issues. During her lifetime she supported the temperance movement, the abolitionist cause, and the move for Negro suffrage, as well as women's suffrage movements on state, national, and international levels. The two-story brick building in which Miss Anthony lived the last 40 years of her life is now a museum containing many original furnishings.
Private
NHL

MONROE COUNTY
Rochester
CAMPBELL-WHITTLESEY HOUSE
123 S. Fitzhugh Street
1835–1836, Minard Lafever

The Campbell-Whittlesey House is exemplary of the Greek Revival architecture popular in western New York state during the second quarter of the 19th century. A two-story pedimented portico with four, fluted Ionic columns graces the north elevation. All walls are brick and the windows and doors have stone lintels and sills. The cornice is wood and there are grilles

in the frieze. Benjamin Campbell, a merchant and miller, built the house.
Private
HABS

MONROE COUNTY
Rochester
CHILD, JONATHAN, HOUSE AND BREWSTER-BURKE HOUSE HISTORIC DISTRICT
37 S. Washington Street and 130 Spring Street
19th century

These two houses comprise a historic district because their styles are contemporary, and both are examples of Rochester residences fashionable when the city was expanding. The Jonathan Child House is a two-story Greek Revival dwelling with a full two-story portico across the front. There are five fluted columns on the main facade, and the wooden cornice has a carved egg and dart motif. It was built in 1837–1838. The companion Brewster-Burke House has a central block and west wing of two stories and a one-story wing on the extreme west elevation. Walls are brick, and the bracketed cornice, iron balconets, and low cupola are typical of Italian Villa architecture. An entrance porch on the south side features elaborately carved, Moorish style ornament. The house was built about the middle of the 19th century.
Private
HABS

MONROE COUNTY
Rochester
EASTMAN, GEORGE, HOUSE
900 East Avenue
1905, J. Foster Warner

George Eastman made photography a popular pastime by introducing film and a camera, the Kodak, which could be easily mastered by the general public. After marketing the first roll film in 1885, Eastman turned to the development of a simple camera which first appeared in 1888. The success of his products gave him the title "Kodak King," and the Eastman-Kodak Company has continued to be a leader in the industry. This two-story concrete residence presently houses a photographic museum.
Private
NHL

MONROE COUNTY
Rochester
FIRST UNIVERSALIST CHURCH
Southeast corner of S. Clinton Avenue and Court Street
1907–1908, Claude F. Bragdon

The First Universalist Church is a large, solid brick building of harmonizing pro-

portions and colors. Architectural detail is unusual, and this church is considered one of Claude Bragdon's outstanding works. A tower-like section rises from the center of the building above four gabled wings. The tower is surmounted by a low octagonal lantern and cupola. Exterior trim is stone and ceramic tile. The central tower has two corbeled cornices of brick with tile insets, and the four main gables have semicircular arched brick corbel cornices coped with tile. At each end of the west facade is a one-story, arcaded, gabled entrance porch.
Private
HABS

MONTGOMERY COUNTY
Amsterdam vicinity
ERIE CANAL
6 miles west of Amsterdam on N.Y. 5S
1825

The completion of the Erie Canal in 1825 by the state of New York opened the Old Northwest to rapid settlement and gave western agriculture direct access to eastern markets. Aside from its role in the commercial development of the nation, the canal was one of the remarkable engineering feats of its time. Preserved in and near Fort Hunter are the ditch and a lock of the original canal (1820–1840); two locks, the Schoharie Aqueduct and Lock Grocery of the improved canal of 1841; and Lock 12 of the modern New York State Barge Canal.
Multiple public/private
NHL

NASSAU COUNTY
Oyster Bay, Long Island
SAGAMORE HILL NATIONAL HISTORIC SITE
End of Cove Neck Road
1884–1885

This home built by Theodore Roosevelt in 1884–1885 was his permanent home for the rest of his life. Used as a "Summer White House," it was visited by many national and international figures. Before succeeding to the Presidency in 1901 on the assassination of William McKinley, Roosevelt had gained prominence as a state legislator, New York City Police Commissioner, United States Civil Service Commissioner, governor of New York, and a colonel of the Rough Riders in the Spanish-American War. After his tenure as President, 1901–1909, Roosevelt was an unsuccessful candidate for President on the Progressive Party ticket in 1912. He died in this house on January 6, 1919.
Federal
NPS; 85 acres
HABS

NASSAU COUNTY
Port Washington
SOUSA, JOHN PHILIP, HOUSE (WILDBANK)
14 Hicks Lane, Sands Point
c. 1907

John Philip Sousa made great contributions in the field of music as a band director and composer. Under his direction the Marine Band became one of the nation's foremost bands. During the Spanish-American and First World wars he served as director of military bands. As a composer he is best known for marches, including "Semper Fidelis," "Washington Post March," and "Stars and Stripes Forever." Sousa's three-story stucco house was his residence from 1910 until his death in 1932, and the house remains much as it was during his lifetime.
Private; not accessible to the public
NHL

NEW YORK COUNTY
New York
ARTHUR, CHESTER A., HOUSE
123 Lexington Avenue
1885–1886

Although President Chester A. Arthur had risen to political prominence through a powerful Republican machine which depended on the spoils system, he supported civil service reform. In his first annual message he recommended the passage of a civil service law. In 1883 Congress passed a bill which removed many federal positions from the spoils list, forbade compulsory political contributions, and authorized the creation of a commission to enforce the law. Arthur returned to his five-story brownstone town house after his term as President, 1881–1885.
Private; not accessible to the public
NHL

NEW YORK COUNTY
New York
CARNEGIE, ANDREW, MANSION
2 E. 91st Street
1901, Babb, Cook, and Willard

When he retired in 1901, Andrew Carnegie, the "King of the Vulcans," sold his iron and steel properties for almost $500 million. He spent his remaining years giving away a major part of his fortune. His gifts to establish public libraries, to further education, and to promote scientific research and international peace reflect his love of books, the arts, and nature, and his desire for human progress. His 64–room brick mansion is presently occupied by the Columbia University School of Social Work.
Private
NHL

NEW YORK COUNTY
New York
CARNEGIE HALL
7th Avenue, 56th to 57th Streets
1891, William B. Tuthill

Originally called the Music Hall, the name was changed in 1898 to honor Andrew Carnegie, a principal benefactor. This important center for American musical activities has contributed greatly to New York City's musical eminence. Major artists such as Tchaikovsky and Paderewski have performed at Carnegie Hall through the years. Here also Arturo Toscanini conducted the New York Philharmonic Symphony Orchestra for a decade beginning in 1926. This six-story Italian Renaissance building is topped by a 16–story tower containing studio apartments.
Municipal
NHL

NEW YORK COUNTY
New York
CASTLE CLINTON NATIONAL MONUMENT
South Ferry
1811

The harbor fortification of Castle Clinton at the southern end of Manhattan Island symbolizes a century and a half of American growth and change. It was built to protect New York in the tense years prior to the War of 1812, but was never tested during the war. In 1824 Castle Clinton was leased by New York as a place of public entertainment. Among those who performed here was Jenny Lind, the "Swedish Nightingale," presented by P. T. Barnum in 1850. From 1855 to 1890 it was the greatest of 19th-century immigration depots. It served as the New York City Aquarium from 1896 to 1941. The original fort is being restored.
Federal
NPS; 1 acre

NEW YORK COUNTY
New York
CENTRAL PARK
Bounded by Central Park South, 5th Avenue, Central Park West, 110th Street
1859–1876, Frederick Law Olmsted and Calvert Vaux

Central Park occupies a pre-eminent position in the history of the park movement in the United States. It was the first to dramatize the need for and give impetus to

the nation's urban park movement. A design competition was held and won by Olmsted and Vaux. Their plan called for a forest atmosphere with all architectural features subordinated. Included in the park are woods, fields, gardens, ponds, bridle paths, and a network of paths for pedestrians and roads for vehicles. The park has been recognized as an outstanding example of the art of landscape architecture.
Municipal
NHL

NEW YORK COUNTY
New York
CENTRAL SYNAGOGUE (CONGREGATION AHAWATH CHESED-SHAAR HASHOMAYIM)
646–652 Lexington Avenue
1870–1872, Henry Fernback

The Ahawath Chesed congregation was organized in 1846. In 1864 land was acquired for a temple at the southwest corner of Lexington Avenue and East 55th Street. As completed, the synagogue is rectangular in shape and built of stone with contrasting stone trim. On the east facade are two minaret-like octagonal towers surmounted by multi-sided globes. Inside, cast iron columns support an arcade on either side of the main aisles, and there are stencil designs on the walls.
Private

NEW YORK COUNTY
New York
CITY HALL
Broadway and Chambers Street
1803–1811, Joseph Mangin and John McComb, Jr.

Since its completion, New York's City Hall has been the center for the administration of the nation's largest city. Apart from its historic role as a public building, it has equal significance in the history of American architecture. It is to Joseph Mangin, a Frenchman, that the strong Louis XVI French character of the building can be attributed. The two-story stone building has two symmetrical wings balanced against a raised central pavilion, which is further emphasized by a cupola and an open entry porch surmounting a grand flight of stairs. A focal point within is the central domed rotunda. The building houses the offices of the mayor and the president of the City Council, the chambers of the City Council and Board of Estimate, and the Governor's Room.
Municipal
NHL

NEW YORK COUNTY
New York
COOPER UNION
Cooper Square, 7th Street and 4th Avenue
1850

Speaking at Cooper Union on February 27, 1860, about the crisis which threatened to destroy the Union, Abraham Lincoln established himself as a serious candidate for the Republican presidential nomination. At that time Cooper Union was a pioneer effort in private support of free public education. In addition to its role as an educational center for more than a century, Cooper Union has served as a forum for important issues throughout the last hundred years. Morever the structure incorporates innovative building technology into its plumbing, ventilation, and heating systems.
Private
NHL

NEW YORK COUNTY
New York
DYCKMAN, WILLIAM, HOUSE
4881 Broadway
1783

The Dyckman House is an example of the final refinements of the Flemish Colonial style during the late 18th century. It displays the use which the Dutch made of varied building materials. William Dyckman built his farmhouse with end walls of uncoursed fieldstones in mortar, a front wall of brick, and gables covered with clapboards. Largely reconstructed, the house is the only 18th-century farmhouse extant on Manhattan Island.
Municipal
NHL; HABS

NEW YORK COUNTY
New York
FEDERAL HALL NATIONAL MEMORIAL
Wall and Nassau Streets
1699–1703

On the site of this memorial stood Federal Hall, which served as the first seat of the new federal government from 1788 to 1790. Previously it had been the scene of other significant events. Here the printer John Peter Zenger was tried and acquitted in 1735. The Stamp Act Congress, which protested British "taxation without representation," met here in 1765. At this site the Continental Congress convened from 1785 to 1788. On the balcony of Federal Hall, George Washington was inaugurated first President of the United States on April 30, 1789.
Federal
NPS; 0.45 acre
HABS

NEW YORK COUNTY
New York
GENERAL GRANT NATIONAL MEMORIAL
Riverside Drive and W. 122nd Street
1897, John H. Duncan

The General Grant National Memorial commemorates the life of Ulysses S. Grant. Within the classical-styled monument are the sarcophagi of Grant and his wife. Two trophy rooms display Union army battle flags and mural maps of Civil War campaigns. These illustrate Grant's career as a supreme commander of the Union army, 1863–1865. Between the arches of the rotunda are allegorical figures representing various phases of his life. In addition to his military honors, Grant was President of the United States for two terms, 1869–1877.
Federal
NPS; 0.76 acre
HABS

NEW YORK COUNTY
New York
HAMILTON GRANGE NATIONAL MEMORIAL
287 Convent Avenue
1801

Hamilton Grange, the only home ever owned by Alexander Hamilton, is a two-story frame house which has been moved from its original site. Hamilton, who occupied the house for only three years before his death, was a major draftsman and proponent of the Constitution and a foremost architect of American fiscal policy in the critical first years of the federal union. Despite minor modifications, the basic structure of this Federal period building is intact. Present plans call for enlarging its site and restoration of the house.
Federal
NPS; 0.71 acre

NEW YORK COUNTY
New York
MORGAN, PIERPONT, LIBRARY
33 E. 36th Street
1906, McKim, Mead, and White

John Pierpont Morgan exemplifies the emergence of the financier as a major force in modern American industry. He acquired a powerful influence in the railroad industry after 1879, organized the

U.S. Steel Company in 1901, and helped to avert a financial panic in November 1907. The Renaissance style library and the annex, erected in 1927, contain literary and artistic collections acquired during and after Morgan's lifetime.
Private
NHL

NEW YORK COUNTY
New York
MORRIS-JUMEL MANSION
160th Street and Edgecombe Avenue
1765

In addition to its importance as a pre-Revolutionary residence, the Morris-Jumel Mansion is the major surviving landmark of the battle of Harlem Heights. This battle on September 16, 1776, restored the offensive spirit of the American army, the patriots forcing the British to retreat. The house served as General George Washington's headquarters from September 14 to October 18, 1776. It was originally owned by Lt. Colonel Roger Morris, a Loyalist, whose property was confiscated and sold after the war. In 1810 Stephen Jumel purchased the house and restored it in the Federal style. The house has been recently renovated and refurnished.
Municipal
NHL; HABS

NEW YORK COUNTY
New York
NEW YORK PUBLIC LIBRARY
5th Avenue and 42nd Street
1911, Carrère and Hastings

Its extensive manuscript and rare book collections, plus some seven million volumes for general use, make the New York Public Library a major center of study and research in the United States. The library's reference department was formed in 1895 by the consolidation of the Astor, Lenox, and Tilden libraries. In 1901, as the result of a gift of Andrew Carnegie, the New York Public Library consolidated with 10 independent circulation libraries to form the circulation department. The building sits well back from 5th Avenue, and two flights of steps lead from the sidewalk to the triple-arched and Corinthian-columned main entrance.
Municipal
NHL

NEW YORK COUNTY
New York
NEW YORK SHAKESPEARE FESTIVAL PUBLIC THEATER (ASTOR LIBRARY)
425 Lafayette Street
1849–1853, (south wing), Alexander Saeltzer; 1856–1859 (central section), Griffith Thomas; 1879–1881 (north wing), Thomas Stent

Constructed in three sections, the Astor Library demonstrates the evolution of 19th-century building technique from solid stone to light iron. The central block is four stories high and each of the wings, three. Walls are brick with stone trim, and the older sections have masonry columns while the columns on the more recent portion are iron. Windows are round arched, and the architectural style of the building is Italianate. Important interior features are elaborate cornice panels and moldings, decorative cast iron columns, and ornamented skylights.
Private

NEW YORK COUNTY
New York
OLD MERCHANT'S HOUSE (SEABURY TREDWELL HOUSE)
29 E. 4th Street
1832

Purchased in 1835 by Seabury Tredwell, a successful hardware merchant, the Old Merchant's House illustrates the life of the prosperous urban mercantile class of the mid–19th century. The three-story, three-bay brick town house, with its gable roof, is representative of the transition in architectural styles from the Federal to the Greek Revival period. The house, including its furnishings, has been preserved intact.
Private
NHL; HABS

NEW YORK COUNTY
New York
170–176 JOHN STREET BUILDING
170–176 John Street
1840

This building was erected as a commercial facility and serves the same purpose today. It may be the only notable surviving structure from an era of flourishing international commerce in this area of lower Manhattan. Five stories high, the building is rectangular and has 13 granite columns at street level. The roof is flat and has a simple cornice.
Private

NEW YORK COUNTY
New York
THE PLAYERS
16 Gramercy Park
1888, Stanford White

This landmark in American theatrical history was originally the home of Edwin Booth, founder and first president of the Players Club. The three-story building, redesigned for use of the club by architect Stanford White, houses a large collection of material pertaining to the theater. Memorabilia of the Booth family and other actors and actresses are on display, and the library includes bound volumes, letters, playbills, and photographs.
Private
NHL

NEW YORK COUNTY
New York
PUPIN PHYSICS LABORATORIES, COLUMBIA UNIVERSITY
Broadway and 120th Street
1939

In this laboratory Enrico Fermi conducted his initial experiments on the nuclear fission of uranium. In addition, the uranium atom was split here for the first time in the Western Hemisphere on January 25, 1939, ten days after the world's first atom splitting in Copenhagen, Denmark. The experiment was carried out by Dr. John B. Dunning and several colleagues. The cyclotron control room contains the table which held the instruments used on that night.
Private; not accessible to the public
NHL

NEW YORK COUNTY
New York
ST. PAUL'S CHAPEL
Broadway, between Fulton and Vesey Streets
1764–1766, Thomas McBean; 1794, James C. Lawrence

The inspiration for this Georgian-style church was taken from London's St. Martin's-in-the-Fields. The sole surviving church of New York's colonial era, St. Paul's has many important historical associations. Here Sir William Howe and other officers of the British army worshiped when New York was occupied by the British during the Revolutionary War. Following George Washington's inauguration, April 30, 1789, the President and members of the Congress assembled here for a special service.
Private
NHL; HABS

NEW YORK COUNTY
New York
**SCHERMERHORN ROW BLOCK
(NEW YORK STATE MARITIME
MUSEUM BLOCK)**
Bounded by Front, Fulton, and South
Streets and Burling Slip
19th century

The group of buildings on Fulton Street
originally known as Schermerhorn Row
was financed and constructed by Peter
Schermerhorn in 1811–1812. Schermerhorn, a ship's chandler, envisioned his
block as one of the most important mercantile centers in New York City. These
early structures were brick and of a
uniform design, but, as the owners or te-
nants prospered, alterations were made to
"update" the structures according to the
popular architectural styles. A mansard
roof was added to Nos. 92 and 93 South
Street and 2 Fulton Street (1868). Other
buildings in the block were erected at
various times, mostly during the first half
of the 19th century. These structures are
the last on the waterfront dating from
New York's sailing age.
State

NEW YORK COUNTY (also in Hudson
County, New Jersey)
New York
**STATUE OF LIBERTY NATIONAL
MONUMENT**
Liberty Island, New York harbor
1886

The Statue of Liberty was a gift from the
people of France to the people of the
United States. Dedicated by President
Grover Cleveland in 1886, it commemorates the alliance of France and the
United States during the American
Revolution. The colossal copper statue
designed by Frederic Auguste Bartholdi is
152 feet high. The pedestal on which it
rests is almost 150 feet in height. The
base, originally a masonry fort, is in the
form of an 11–pointed star. The tablet in
the statue's left hand symbolizes freedom
and liberty, to which the torch lights the
way.
Federal
NPS; 58.38 acres

NEW YORK COUNTY
New York
**THEODORE ROOSEVELT
BIRTHPLACE NATIONAL HISTORIC
SITE**
28 E. 20th Street
mid–19th century

In this four-story brownstone house
Theodore Roosevelt spent the first 15
years of his life, 1858–1873. Here to improve his health he embarked on a program of physical fitness with the vigor and
enthusiasm which so characterized his
adult life. Roosevelt gained acclaim as
United States Civil Service Commissioner,
New York Police Commissioner, and
colonel of the "Rough Riders" in the
Spanish-American War. Becoming President upon the assassination of William
McKinley in 1901, he was elected to the
Presidency in 1904. His tenure was
marked by internal reforms to harness the
industrial revolution, to conserve natural
resources, and to control trusts, and by
significant advances in foreign relations.
The living rooms and two bedrooms in the
reconstructed house have been restored to
the period of Roosevelt's boyhood.
Federal
NPS; 0.11 acre

NEW YORK COUNTY
New York
WOOLWORTH BUILDING
233 Broadway
1913, Cass Gilbert

Unperturbed by early business failures,
Frank W. Woolworth eventually made his
variety chain store, which featured innovations in merchandising techniques,
into a multi-million dollar enterprise. Built
as his corporate headquarters, the Woolworth Building was, at the time of its
completion, the world's tallest edifice, 792
feet high. Architecturally, the building
reflects the application of the verticality
of the Gothic style to the skyscraper. Known
as the "Cathedral of Commerce," the
building is still used for commercial purposes.
Private
NHL

NIAGARA COUNTY
Niagara Falls
NIAGARA RESERVATION
1885

Creation of the Niagara Reservation and
subsequent elimination of environmental
eyesores near the falls was the first use of
a State's power of eminent domain to
acquire land for aesthetic purposes.
Although the town of Niagara surrounds
the reservation, the visitor may view
Niagara Falls from an area free of commercial distractions. The reservation,
which covers 430 acres, includes an observation tower and numerous paths from
which the falls are visible.
State
NHL

NIAGARA COUNTY
Youngstown vicinity
OLD FORT NIAGARA
North of Youngstown on N.Y. 18
1678, 1725–1726

Throughout the colonial period and the
early years of the United States, the
strategic site of Fort Niagara made its control the goal of major military operations
by France, England, the United States,
and the great Iroquois federation. First
built by order of Robert Cavelier, Sieur de
la Salle, it was twice rebuilt. Restored features include the Stone House, a fortified
building resembling a French provincial
chateau; the moat, drawbridge, and
blockhouse; earthen ramparts and masonry casemates; and parade ground.
Private
NHL

ONEIDA COUNTY
Rome
**FORT STANWIX NATIONAL
MONUMENT**
Bounded by Dominick, Spring,
Liberty, and James Streets
1758

The stand by an American garrison at Fort
Stanwix in August 1777 during the
Revolutionary War disrupted British
strategy and contributed to the defeat of
General John Burgoyne at Saratoga a few
months later. It was also the site of a
treaty with the Iroquois in 1768 which
cleared the way for a new surge of westward expansion. The fort was razed early
in the 19th century, but recent archeological excavation has uncovered many artifacts.
Non-federal; not accessible to the public
NPS (authorized but not acquired); 18
acres

ONEIDA COUNTY
Rome vicinity
ORISKANY BATTLEFIELD
5 miles east of Rome on N.Y. 69
1777

At Oriskany on August 6, 1777, was
fought a significant Revolutionary War action between American militiamen attempting to relieve Fort Stanwix and a
combined force of Loyalists and Indians.
Although the Americans failed, they held
their ground, and the British were forced
to retreat. The three-fold strategic plan of
the British suffered its initial setback here,
followed by General John Burgoyne's surrender at Saratoga. A monument commemorates the action, and the area has a
minimum of modern encroachments.
State
NHL

ONONDAGA COUNTY
Syracuse
ONONDAGA COUNTY SAVINGS BANK BUILDING (GRIDLEY BUILDING)
101 S. Salina Street
1869, Horatio N. White

The Onondaga County Savings Bank has a mansard roof and walls of Onondaga limestone. Windows in the roof have hooded or pedimented dormers. The main entrance was originally on the west side but has been changed. Ornately carved stone quoins mark the first-floor corners of the exterior. Above them are inversely tapered two-story pilasters that are repeated for one story at either side of the third floor balconies. In 1875–1876 a 50–foot addition was made on the east elevation but carefully matched to the existing structure. Iron beams resting on masonry-bearing partitions constitute the frame of the bank building.
Municipal
HABS

ONONDAGA COUNTY
Syracuse
SYRACUSE SAVINGS BANK
102 N. Salina Street
1876, Joseph Lyman Silsbee

The five-and-one-half-story Syracuse Savings Bank building is among the best-known landmarks of the city. Architect Joseph Lyman Silsbee incorporated Gothic details into his design of the rectangular building, among which are several intersecting gable, hip, and pyramidal roofs, windows with pointed arches, and a central tower rising to a height of 170 feet. The buff colored Ohio sandstone walls are decorated with red sandstone. The Syracuse Savings Bank was the first office building in the city built with a passenger elevator. The exterior remains as designed, except for a few entrance alterations. In 1930 the interior was rebuilt with steel framing.
Private

ONONDAGA COUNTY
Syracuse
WEIGHLOCK BUILDING
Southeast corner of Erie Boulevard and Montgomery Street
1849–1850

Weighlocks were constructed as part of the Erie Canal for inspection purposes and the collection of tolls. After a boat entered the lock, both gates were closed and the water drained out. The boat then set-

tled onto a large cradle suspended from the balance beam overhead. Gross weight of boat and load were recorded, and tolls were calculated on the basis of cargo weight. On January 1, 1883, tolls on all New York state canals were abolished. This weighlock was retained to weigh cargoes when desired and to provide an emergency drydock. In 1906 the scales were removed, and the second floor was extended over the lock. Thirty years later the portico which housed the lock was enclosed on the first floor. The Weighlock Building is two stories high; its brick walls measure 80 feet long by 59 feet wide.
County

ONTARIO COUNTY
Victor vicinity
BOUGHTON HILL
1.25 miles south of Victor
c. 1675–1687

Boughton Hill is the site of Gannagaro, the "great town" of the Seneca. These Indians were the westernmost of the five-nation League of the Iroquois during the period of European contact. Although the Seneca returned to this area after their defeat in 1687 by the French and their Indian allies, they were greatly weakened and never rebuilt their large villages.
Multiple private; not accessible to the public
NHL

ORANGE COUNTY (also in Sullivan and Ulster counties)
DELAWARE AND HUDSON CANAL
1828

Completed in 1828, the Delaware and Hudson Canal was the main waterway connecting the anthracite coalfields of northeastern Pennsylvania with the industrial and domestic furnaces of New York. Stretching 108 miles from Honesdale, Pa., to Kingston, N.Y., the canal proved to be enormously profitable during the mid–19th century. In the 1860's when anthracite was the main source of power for industrial America, northeastern Pennsylvania produced from 40 to 50 percent of the entire supply, and the Delaware and Hudson Canal carried the greater share of it to other sources of transport such as the Hudson River. The growth of railroads led to the demise of the canal in 1899. Especially noteworthy elements of the canal still extant are the company offices at Honesdale; the Roebling aqueduct (now a vehicular bridge) between Minisink Ford, N.Y., and Lackawaxen, Pa., the basin and canal bed

at Cuddebackville, N.Y., a 5,000–foot section of canal at Alligerville, N.Y., and locks 15 through 20 at High Falls, N.Y.
State/private
NHL

ORANGE COUNTY
Goshen
HISTORIC TRACK
Main Street
1854

Harness racing originated in the United States at the beginning of the 19th century and by 1875 was popular throughout most of the nation. Although not the first trotting track, Historic Track is one of the older active courses in the United States. Races were first held on what is now Goshen's main street, and the present track site has been rebuilt and altered several times.
Private
NHL

ORANGE COUNTY
Harriman
ARDEN (E. H. HARRIMAN ESTATE)
N.Y. 17
1909

E. H. Harriman was a pre-eminent organizer and builder of railroads in the late 19th and early 20th centuries. His financial acumen and practical knowledge are illustrated in his reorganization and development of the financially troubled Union Pacific Railroad in the early 20th century. Harriman's house crowning the ridge that rises from the Ramapo River was his residence for only a few months prior to his death.
Private
NHL

ORANGE COUNTY
Newburgh
DUTCH REFORMED CHURCH
Northeast corner of Grand and 3rd Streets
1835–1837, Alexander Jackson Davis

A. J. Davis patterned the Dutch Reformed Church upon the Eglise du Saint Esprit in New York City, designed by Ithiel Town and Davis in 1831. There are four giant Ionic columns, each 37 feet high, which carry a deep entablature across the front of the building. The entablature continues along the two sides. Tall untrimmed windows are set in the front and side elevations, and the main entrance is 30 feet high. Walls are stone covered with stucco, and the interior ceiling is formed by a segmental arched barrel vault with deeply recessed coffers. A high dome and lantern were removed before 1859, and the building was extended 20 feet at the rear and low transepts added in 1867–1868.
Municipal
HABS

ORANGE COUNTY
Newburgh
WASHINGTON'S HEADQUARTERS
Liberty and Washington Streets
1750

Hasbrouck House was George Washington's headquarters from April 1, 1782, to August 19, 1783. Washington drafted three memorable documents here. In these he reaffirmed the fundamental principle of subordination of the military establishment to civilian control and helped lay the foundation for orderly transition to peacetime. Here, too, Washington proposed the "Order of the Purple Heart" in 1782. The Hasbrouck House, a Dutch Colonial fieldstone residence, became (in 1850) the first historic site to be preserved by a state.
State
NHL; HABS

ORANGE COUNTY
PALISADES INTERSTATE PARK
Reference—see Bergen County, New Jersey

ORANGE COUNTY
West Point
UNITED STATES MILITARY ACADEMY
N.Y. 218
1778

The United States Military Academy, established at West Point in 1802 and operated continuously ever since, has trained the officers who have developed and commanded the Regular Army. Recognizing its strategic location on the Hudson River, George Washington urged that a regular garrison be posted here. During Benedict Arnold's command of the post during the Revolutionary War, he attempted to betray West Point to the British but fled to the enemy when his plot was discovered.
Federal
NHL

QUEENS COUNTY
Flushing
OLD QUAKER MEETINGHOUSE
South side of Northern Boulevard
1695

The Old Quaker Meetinghouse, the oldest portion of which dates from 1695, is the only surviving example in the state of New York of a typical 17th-century ecclesiastical frame building. It has served continuously since 1696 as a meetinghouse, except from 1776 to 1783 when the British army used it as a prison, hospital, and stable. The austere, gray-shingled frame building has a hip roof and is almost entirely devoid of ornamentation. The oblong, two-story building has a one-story porch and separate front entrances for men and women.
Private
NHL; HABS

QUEENS COUNTY
Richmond Hill
RIIS, JACOB, HOUSE
84–41 120th Street
1888

During the last decade of the 19th century and the first decade of the 20th century, Jacob Riis waged a single-handed but eventually successful campaign to ameliorate slum conditions in New York City and secure reform legislation to protect the downtrodden and exploited. A journalist by profession, Riis enunciated his philosophy in books, *How the Other Half Lives* (1890), *The Battle with the Slum* (1902), and *Children of the Tenements* (1903), which reached a national audience and helped prepare the way for urban reform in other cities. Somewhat modernized, the house he built in 1888 and the cottage study he erected some years later survive in good condition.
Private; not accessible to the public
NHL

RENSSELAER COUNTY
Rensselaer
FORT CRAILO
South of Columbia Street on
Riverside Street
c. 1700

Fort Crailo stands near the center of what was once the estate of Kiliaen Van Rensselaer. His was the first and only successful patroonship (proprietorship) established by the Dutch West India Company. The estate was founded in 1630 under terms of the Charter of Freedoms and Exemptions, and the Van Rensselaer family occupied the house from as early as 1704 until 1871. Restoration of the brick manor house has eliminated most of the 19th-century alterations.
State
NHL; HABS

RENSSELAER COUNTY
Troy
CANNON BUILDING
1 Broadway
1835, Alexander Jackson Davis

Although it has been heavily remodeled, Alexander Jackson Davis' Cannon Building still exhibits Greek Revival features. The window lintels and sills are original as are the piers on the eastern portion of the Broadway facade. Brackets under the roof and the mansard roof itself are later additions (1870's). Building material is brick.
Private

RENSSELAER COUNTY
Troy
FIFTH AVENUE-FULTON STREET HISTORIC DISTRICT
Two blocks of 5th Avenue, on the eastern edge of the downtown Troy business district, bounded on the north by Grand Street, on the south by Broadway, on the east (between Grand and Fulton Streets) by 6th Avenue and (between Fulton Street and Broadway) by Union Street, and on the west by Williams Street
19th century

The Fifth Avenue-Fulton Street Historic District contains 37 residential, religious, industrial, and commercial buildings, constructed between 1862 and 1894, which are relatively consistent in scale and compatible in style. Brownstone row houses are the most common dwellings in the district. Many of them are patterned after designs by M. F. Cummings, a Troy architect who was commissioned to do the Second Presbyterian Church. The area was rebuilt following a fire in 1862, and it has not been significantly altered since that time.
Private

RENSSELAER COUNTY
Troy
GASHOLDER HOUSE, TROY GAS LIGHT COMPANY
Northwest corner of Jefferson Street and Fifth Avenue
1873, Frederick A. Sabbaton

A gasholder house sheltered an iron holder containing coal gas until the gas was needed. Iron gasholders were double or single lift; the Troy house was a telescoping two-lift type. The weight of the holders provided the gas pressure in the mains. Although the gasholder has been removed, the gasholder house still stands. It is circular and approximately 46 feet high. The walls are brick ornamented by window arches, pilasters, and attached piers. Galvanized metal was used for the cornice, the roof dome, and the cupola.
Private
HAER

RENSSELAER COUNTY
Troy
ILIUM BUILDING
Northeast corner of Fulton and 4th Streets
1904, M. F. Cummings & Son

This five-story landmark of downtown Troy was erected for the Ilium Realty Company. The walls are buff-colored brick, and the trim is stone and terra cotta. Romanesque double and single arched windows appear at the fourth and fifth floors, and the cornice is arcaded.
Private

RENSSELAER COUNTY
Troy
McCARTHY BUILDING
255–257 River Street
1904

The McCarthy Building is a highly ornamented commercial structure in downtown Troy. Its five-story facade, of terra cotta, glass, and iron, is decorated by a massive window arch extending across the entire front of the first two stories. The elaborate cornice is topped by a classical scroll design pediment.
Private

RENSSELAER COUNTY
Troy
NATIONAL STATE BANK BUILDING
297 River Street
1904, M. F. Cummings & Son

Several structures in downtown Troy—including the National State Bank—were erected during an early 20th-century building boom. This five-story building has a metal frame and an elevator, thus making it a precursor of the skyscraper. Various materials were employed on the five-story facade: rusticated stone on the first floor and brick with stone and terra cotta trim on the second through the fifth floors. There are carved stone panels under the third- and fourth-floor windows. Fenestration is similar to that of the Ilium Building.
Private

RENSSELAER COUNTY
Troy
W. & L. E. GURLEY BUILDING
514 Fulton Street
1862

William and Lewis E. Gurley formed their partnership in 1852 for the manufacture of mathematical and later surveying instruments. The four-story structure is U-shape and is built around an open courtyard. The stylization of the window openings characterizes the building as High Victorian Italianate. It was originally designed to house Gurley manufacturing operations on the second floor and office space below. Floors three and four were rented to other manufacturing concerns.
Private

RENSSELAER COUNTY
Walloomsac vicinity
BENNINGTON BATTLEFIELD
N.Y. 67, on Vermont line
1777

The American milita's victory at the battle of Bennington was a significant contribution to the defeat of Burgoyne's British Army at Saratoga. This Revolutionary War battle cost the British about 10 per-cent of their entire strength, denied them supplies needed for the offensive down the Hudson River, discouraged Burgoyne's Indian allies, and encouraged enlistment in the American militia.
State
NHL

RICHMOND COUNTY
Rosebank
AUSTEN, ELIZABETH ALICE, HOUSE
2 Hylan Boulevard
18th and 19th centuries

The oldest portion of the Austen House, which has been incorporated into the central section of the present house, was constructed in the late 17th or early 18th century. Sometime prior to 1730 a second room, a hallway, and a large fireplace were added on the south end. The stone addition at the rear is pre-Revolutionary. A few years after 1844 another room with a fireplace was built onto the north end of the house to give the entire structure a T-shape. External carving on the front porch columns and the dormer bargeboards gives the house a Gothic Revival appearance. The one-and-one-half-story cottage is frame on a field stone foundation.
Private
HABS

RICHMOND COUNTY
Staten Island
THE VOORLEZER'S HOUSE
Arthur Kill Road, opposite Center Street
1690

The Voorlezer's House, an important surviving relic of 17th-century Dutch settlement in New York, is the oldest known elementary school building in the United States. The two-story clapboard building is two feet higher in front than in the rear, giving the roof an unequal pitch.
Private; accessible to the public by appointment only
NHL

RICHMOND COUNTY
Tottenville, Staten Island
CONFERENCE HOUSE
Hylan Boulevard
1680

On September 11, 1776, the Conference House, a large stone house with a steep gabled roof, was the scene of a meeting between British and American representatives. Admiral Lord Richard Howe, commander in chief of the British fleet in America, met with a committee of the Continental Congress composed of John Adams, Benjamin Franklin, and Edward Rutledge. Howe offered peace and amnesty if the Americans dissolved their ar-mies and congresses and withdrew the Declaration of Independence. The committee refused his offer.
Municipal
NHL; HABS

ROCKLAND COUNTY
PALISADES INTERSTATE PARK
Reference—see Bergen County, New Jersey

ROCKLAND COUNTY
Stony Point vicinity
STONY POINT BATTLEFIELD
North of Stony Point on U.S. 9W and 202
1779

The battle of Stony Point, July 16, 1779, was fought under the leadership of "Mad Anthony" Wayne. It was one of the last important military actions in the northern theater of war during the American Revolution. By the American victory of Stony Point, General George Washington retained control of the Hudson River and West Point. Extensive earthworks remain, and historical markers trace the course of the American assault. A museum displaying artifacts of the period tells the story of the action.
State
NHL

ROCKLAND COUNTY
Tappan
DE WINT HOUSE
Livingston Avenue and Oak Tree Road
1700

Four times during the closing years of the American Revolution, General George Washington stayed at the DeWint House. During his second visit, September 28 to October 7, 1780, he ordered the trial of the British spy, Major John Andre, who was executed on October 2. Built by Daniel DeClark, the house is an interesting example of Dutch Colonial architecture. Restored and furnished with furniture of the period, it is now maintained as a memorial to George Washington.
Private
NHL

ST. LAWRENCE COUNTY
ADIRONDACK FOREST PRESERVE
Reference—see Clinton County

SARATOGA COUNTY
Albany vicinity
SARATOGA NATIONAL HISTORICAL PARK
30 miles north of Albany via U.S. 4 and N.Y. 32
1777

Between September 19 and October 17, 1777, American Continentals and militiamen led by General Horatio Gates defeated and captured General John Burgoyne's army of British regulars and German mercenaries in the battle of Saratoga. The American success was followed by an alliance with France and the internationalization of the war. The victory thwarted the British invasion of the North and removed from the war an army that was necessary for British success. Called the "turning point of the Revolutionary War," the battle furnished the physical and psychological impetus that brightened a waning cause at a moment when failure would have been disastrous.
Federal/non-federal
NPS; 5,500 acres

SARATOGA COUNTY
Ballston Spa
OLD SARATOGA COUNTY COURTHOUSE COMPLEX
46 W. High Street
1866 (county clerk's office) and 1889 (courthouse and jail), M. F. Cummings; 1902–1903 (enlargements), R. Newton Brezee

The Saratoga County Courthouse Complex consists of three buildings which are now joined by connecting structures on the north side. These buildings are the county clerk's office, the Saratoga County courthouse and jail, and the jailer's residence. M. F. Cummings, a Troy architect, designed the masonry structures in the Romanesque Revival style. Other similarities among the buildings are their rectangular shape, their cut stone foundations, the brick walls all laid in common bond, and the hip roofs. The county clerk's office and courthouse both have square towers with pyramidal roofs.
County

SARATOGA COUNTY
Mount McGregor
GRANT COTTAGE
County Route 101 north of U.S. 9
1872

In June of 1885 the physicians attending Ulysses S. Grant recommended fresh mountain air for the general, who had cancer of the throat. Joseph W. Drexel, owner of this cottage, offered it as a retreat for Grant. Penniless and struggling to complete his memoirs so his widow might be left a source of revenue upon his death, Grant accepted the offer. He died at the cottage on July 23, 1885, after completing his valiant race against time. The memoirs were finished here. The cottage is maintained as it was during Grant's occupancy.
State

SCHENECTADY COUNTY
Delanson vicinity
CHRISTMAN BIRD AND WILDLIFE SANCTUARY
Southeast of Delanson on Schoharie Turnpike

W. W. Christman (1865–1937) undertook a bird feeding program on his family's farm in 1888. The winter had been extremely severe, and Christman scattered feed in sheltered areas of his barn dooryard. The feeding continued, and in the 1920's Christman reforested portions of his 105-acre farm by planting pine, spruce, and larch trees. In June, 1931, under joint sponsorship of the New York State Conservation Department and the Mohawk Valley Hiking Club, the Christman farm was officially designated a bird and wildlife sanctuary. Still owned and operated by a Christman, the wooded tract in the Bozenkill Valley provides a refuge and feeding place for animal life and contains hiking trails for those desirous of observing nature. The Christman Sanctuary came into being at a time of revived interest in outdoor activity, and the Mohawk Hiking Club generated much public support. The sanctuary is also a tangible reminder of W. W. Christman's role in the conservation movement.
Private

SCHOHARIE COUNTY
North Blenheim
OLD BLENHEIM BRIDGE
N.Y. 30 over Schoharie Creek
1855

Constructed by Vermont's well-known bridge builder Nicholas Montgomery Powers, Old Blenheim Bridge is one of the longest single span wooden covered bridges in the world (232 feet). It remained in active service until 1932, when traffic was routed onto a new steel structure. The most unusual feature of the bridge is a single timber arch framed into the center truss and rising from below road level at the abutments to the ridgepole at the center of the span. It is formed of three separate ribs, one above the other.
County
NHL

SCHUYLER COUNTY
Tyrone vicinity
LAMOKA
2 miles west of Tyrone at northern edge of Lamoka Lake
c. 3500 B.C.

This archeological site provided the first clear evidence of an Archaic hunting and gathering culture in the northeastern United States. It also furnished part of the basis for defining the Archaic cultural stage in the eastern United States as a whole. The Lamoka Site consists of about five acres of cultivated land near the head of Lamoka Lake and along a stream connecting Waneta and Lamoka Lakes.
Private; not accessible to the public
NHL

SENECA COUNTY
Seneca Falls
STANTON, ELIZABETH CADY, HOUSE
32 Washington Street
1846

Elizabeth Cady Stanton was an important leader of the women's rights movement in the United States. In Seneca Falls in 1848 she made the opening speech and read a Declaration of Sentiments at the Women's Rights Convention, which formally launched the movement. For over 40 years, she continued to work for temperance and abolition, but eventually devoted most of her time to women's rights. She served as president of two of the movement's national organizations. This two-story, gabled frame house was her residence at the time of the Seneca Falls convention.
Private; not accessible to the public
NHL

SUFFOLK COUNTY
Cutchogue
THE OLD HOUSE
N.Y. 25
1649

The Old House is a surviving example of English colonial domestic architecture in America. After passing through various ownerships, it was finally donated to the Congregational Society of Cutchogue. Construction details throughout the house reflect the work of a master builder. The three part casement windows on the second floor are among the finest examples of their type in the country. Furnishings are of the 17th and 18th centuries.
Private
NHL; HABS

SUFFOLK COUNTY
East Hampton, Long Island
MORAN, THOMAS, HOUSE
Main Street
1884

Thomas Moran was one of the first painters to bring Americans to an awareness of the natural splendors of the West. Following an expedition to the West in 1871, Moran painted "The Grand Canyon of the Yellowstone." His exploration of the Grand Canyon two years later resulted in "The Chasm of the Colorado." The federal government bought the paintings to hang in the Capitol. Moran subsequently produced other notable paintings of the West. His house is a two-story shingled building with a windowed tower. His studio, which occupies the entire front of the first floor, contains paintings by artists who visited Moran.
Private; not accessible to the public
NHL

SUFFOLK COUNTY
East Hampton vicinity
MONTAUK POINT LIGHTHOUSE
Montauk Point
1797, 1860

The Montauk Point Lighthouse was one of the earliest lighthouses built by the federal government. The tower is 108 feet high and the light itself is situated 168 feet above the water. The massive octagonal tower is built of cut stone with walls three feet thick enlarging to 12 feet at the base. The Montauk Light beams 200,000 candlepower illumination. The stationary electric beacon was made a flashing one in 1958, giving off a light every ten seconds. Designed by John McComb, the lighthouse was authorized by President George Washington in January, 1796, on a site selected in 1792. Its location on a major sea approach to New York harbor has made it a landmark for ocean navigation for more than 170 years.
Federal

SUFFOLK COUNTY
Stony Brook
MOUNT, WILLIAM SYDNEY, HOUSE
Gould Road and N.Y. 25
1725

The genre paintings of William Sydney Mount reflect the artist's attachment to the people and land of his local environment. Favorable public reaction to his first painting, "The Rustic Dance" (1830), led him to concentrate on genre scenes. Among his best-known works is "Eel Spearing at Setauket," painted in 1845. Mount produced most of his outstanding works in this large frame house on Long Island.
Private; accessible to the public by appointment only
NHL

SULLIVAN COUNTY
DELAWARE AND HUDSON CANAL
Reference—see Orange County

TOMPKINS COUNTY
Ithaca
BOARDMAN HOUSE
120 E. Buffalo Street
1867

The Boardman House was built by George McChain. The three-story structure constructed of dark red brick laid in Flemish bond is a good example of an Italianate mansion of the period. Notable architectural features are the bracketed roof overhang with a wood cornice and wide frieze below and the tall first- and second-story windows topped by console-bracketed lintels. The house has been slightly altered by the removal of three of the original five chimneys. Douglas Boardman, an attorney, bought the house in 1887 and lived there for many years. The Ithaca College Museum of Art now occupies the mansion.
County

TOMPKINS COUNTY
Ithaca
MORRILL HALL, CORNELL UNIVERSITY
Cornell University campus
1866–1868, Henry W. Wilcox

The opening of Cornell University in 1868 marked a revolution in American higher education. The "Cornell Idea," aimed at preparing students for useful careers in post-Civil War society, offered training in various fields of knowledge on the basis of equality among disciplines. Morrill Hall is named for Justin S. Morrill, author of the Morrill Land Grant Act of 1862. The four-story mansard-roofed stone building originally served as a combination dormitory, classrooms, and administration building. It now houses the departments of modern languages and sociology.
Private
NHL

TOMPKINS COUNTY
Ithaca
SECOND TOMPKINS COUNTY COURTHOUSE
121 E. Court Street
1854, John F. Maurice

The Second Tompkins County Courthouse is considered the oldest surviving Gothic Revival courthouse in New York state; it is also the oldest public

building in Tompkins County. Architect John Maurice designed a rectangular, two-story building measuring 75 by 57 feet. Its red brick walls are divided into bays by buttresses and were covered with gray stucco sometime in the 1920's. The belfry tower, an architectural feature characteristic of English medieval castles, is three stories high. Pointed arch openings on all four of its sides are trimmed by hoodmolds. Similar arched entrances are centered on the north and south facades. Replaced in 1932 by a new courthouse, this building now houses court offices.
County
HABS

ULSTER COUNTY
DELAWARE AND HUDSON CANAL
Reference—see Orange County

ULSTER COUNTY
Hurley
HURLEY HISTORIC DISTRICT
Hurley Street, Hurley Mountain Road, and Schoonmaker Lane
17th and 18th centuries

Preserved in this town between the Hudson River and the Catskills is a collection of stone houses which illustrate the Dutch heritage of the region. Ten of these dwellings, many still occupied by descendants of early Dutch settlers, extend along Hurley Street and others are scattered nearby. Originally named Nieuw Dorp, the town was renamed after English domination began in the 1660's. For more than a century, however, Hurley remained a Dutch provincial town in language, customs, and architecture.
Private
NHL; HABS

ULSTER COUNTY
Kingston
CLINTON AVENUE HISTORIC DISTRICT
Includes all of Clinton Avenue between Westbrook Lane and N. Front Street, N. Front Street between Clinton Avenue and Fair Street, and the east side of Fair Street between N. Front and John Streets
17th–20th centuries

The Clinton Avenue Historic District is within an area laid out as a Dutch village in the mid–17th century. Peter Stuyvesant had a stockade built around the village in 1654, and all streets in the historic district follow the same general pattern as that laid out by the Dutch. The buildings in the district are representative of architecture from the late 17th through the early 20th centuries. Located in the district is the Senate House, a one-and-one-half-story

building dating from 1676. New York's first constitution was adopted here in 1777, and the state senate met in the house until driven out by British troops.
Multiple public/private

ULSTER COUNTY
New Paltz
HASBROUCK, JEAN, HOUSE
Huguenot Street, opposite its junction with North Street
1694

The Jean Hasbrouck House is an example of a Flemish Colonial stone residence. Constructed as a small, one-room house, the building was enlarged to its present size in 1712 by Jean Hasbrouck. Used as a store and residence, the one-story house is nearly square, with a full cellar, large attic, and a steeply pitched gable roof. The interior has a central hall plan with two rooms on each side.
Private
NHL; HABS

ULSTER COUNTY
New Paltz
HUGUENOT STREET HISTORIC DISTRICT
Huguenot Street
17th and 18th centuries

Five stone houses clustered along Huguenot Street reflect the 17th- and 18th-century Walloon and French Huguenot cultures of the settlers. The Jean Hasbrouck House (1712) and Abraham Hasbrouck House (1717) are little altered. The Daniel de Bois House (1775) and the Bevier House (late 17th century) have undergone more extensive changes. The Freer House (early 18th century) is still another example of the Dutch Colonial architecture characteristic of this area.
Multiple public/private
NHL; HABS

ULSTER COUNTY
West Park
BURROUGHS, JOHN, RIVERBY STUDY
Between N.Y. 9W and the Hudson River
1881

John Burroughs published his first significant nature essay in the *Atlantic Monthly* in 1865 and, until his death in 1921, continued to produce articles and books in which he presented facts about the natural world in a realistic and interesting style. Burroughs did more than any other popular writer of this time to create a receptive climate for conservation legislation, and he is credited with establishing the nature essay as a literary form. In 1881 Burroughs built a small one-room study on his

Riverby estate in West Park, N.Y. Until 1895 the study was his only writing studio, and he continued to use it sporadically thereafter until his death. The book-lined study, which contains many of the writer's mementos, is preserved exactly the way it was the day Burroughs died.
Private; not accessible to the public
NHL

ULSTER COUNTY
West Park vicinity
BURROUGHS, JOHN, CABIN (SLABSIDES)
Just west of West Park
1895

In 1895 John Burroughs built a cabin about 2 miles west of his home, Riverby, in Ulster County, N.Y. Called "Slabsides" because of its bark-covered siding, the cabin became the writer's summer residence and retreat. Here he observed nature and wrote many of the essays collected in *Ways of Nature* (1905), *Bird and Bough* (1906), and other books. Burroughs entertained many of the great men of his day at Slabsides, and the cabin soon became as well known as its builder. Although Burroughs began to spend the greater part of his summers at Woodchuck Lodge in Delaware County after 1908, he continued to stay at Slabsides intermittently until his death. Preserved exactly as it was during Burroughs' lifetime, the cabin contains furniture he made by hand.
Private; accessible to the public by appointment only
NHL

WARREN COUNTY
ADIRONDACK FOREST PRESERVE
Reference—see Clinton County

WESTCHESTER COUNTY
Croton-on-Hudson
VAN CORTLANDT MANOR
U.S. 9, north of intersection with U.S. 9A
c. 1650

The Van Cortlandt Manor is one of the most authentic survivals of the 18th-century Dutch-English manorial system in the Hudson River Valley. Its simplicity of line and detail sets it apart from more elaborate later houses. The house reflects the mid–18th century period, during which Pierre Van Cortlandt occupied and modified the building. Other extant buildings on the estate include an office building, the ferry house, and a tavern.
Private
NHL

WESTCHESTER COUNTY
Mount Vernon
ST. PAUL'S CHURCH NATIONAL HISTORIC SITE
Eastchester, Mount Vernon
1790

St. Paul's Church was founded in the new settlement of Eastchester in 1665. The present building, begun in 1763, served for a time as headquarters for Hessian troops during the Revolutionary War. Completed about 1790, it has been restored to its appearance at that date. The church is an example of the Renaissance Revival architectural style in the United States. On the town green was held the election of October 29, 1733, famous for its connection with the patriot printer, John Peter Zenger, and the establishment of an American free press.
Private
NPS; 6.09 acres
HABS

WESTCHESTER COUNTY
North Tarrytown
DUTCH REFORMED (SLEEPY HOLLOW) CHURCH
North edge of Tarrytown on U.S. 9
c. 1700

This Dutch Reformed Church is a significant reminder of the Dutch in colonial America. Built of rubblestone, it has a rectangular plan and is covered by a flared Flemish gambrel roof. The open octagonal belfry and weathervane are prominent features on the roof. The pointed arch windows framed in brick are a result of an 1837 remodeling. Shortly after the Civil War another church replaced the original building as a regular place of worship. The adjacent burial ground includes the grave of Washington Irving, creator of "The Legend of Sleepy Hollow," from which the church takes its popular name.
Private
NHL; HABS

WESTCHESTER COUNTY
Tarrytown
LYNDHURST (JAY GOULD ESTATE)
635 S. Broadway
1838, Alexander Jackson Davis, Ithiel Town

Jay Gould was a post-Civil War financier whose shrewdness epitomizes the era of unrestrained capitalism known as the "Gilded Age." Notable among his activities was his battle with Cornelius Vanderbilt for the control of the Erie Railroad in 1867–1868, an attempt to corner the nation's gold supply in 1869, and his acquisition of the Western Union Company in 1881. In 1880 Gould acquired the mansion which had been built for William Paulding, a former Congressman and mayor of New York City. Lyndhurst derives its architectural significance from its Gothic Revival style. Built of marble and wood sanded to imitate stone, the mansion contains 16 rooms, baths, kitchens, and servants' quarters. Additions were made to the house in 1864 after its purchase by George Merritt.

Private

NHL

WESTCHESTER COUNTY

Tarrytown vicinity

SUNNYSIDE (WASHINGTON IRVING HOUSE)

Sunnyside Lane

c. 1780; 1836–1847 (remodeled)

This stone house, built partially by the Van Tassel family, was purchased in 1835 by Washington Irving, who added to it and reworked it to reflect the romantic taste of the day. Though much of Irving's literary production resulted directly from extensive European travels, he first achieved widespread recognition for his humorous history of New York, supposedly written by Diedrich Knickerbocker. He is best remembered for his tales of the Hudson River Dutch settlements, chiefly "Rip Van Winkle" and "The Legend of Sleepy Hollow." Sunnyside was his residence for almost 25 years, during which time he served as Ambassador to Spain.

Private

NHL

WESTCHESTER COUNTY

Upper Mills

PHILIPSBURG MANOR

381 Bellwood Avenue

c. 1683

Built by Frederick Philipse, this stone manor house was used as a permanent residence only by his son Adolphus. The house fell into disuse after Adolphus Philipse's death, although a frame wing was added in 1785. Recent restoration has preserved the building as an example of country life in the Dutch settlement of the lower Hudson River Valley.

Private

NHL

WESTCHESTER COUNTY

Yonkers

PHILIPSE MANOR

Warburton Avenue and Dock Street

c. 1700

Philipse Manor is a survivor of the 18th-century Dutch manorial system in the lower Hudson River Valley. The mansion served as the social and administrative center of the great manor of Philipsburg, created under English rule in 1693. The manor estate extended more than 20 miles along the east side of the Hudson River and included some 156,000 acres. Frederick Philipse was its first lord. Erected in stages between 1682 and 1758, the building in its present form is a notable example of early Georgian architecture in the American colonies. This large, two-and-a-half-story brick and stone building has an L-shaped plan.

State

NHL

North Carolina

Charles B. Aycock Birthplace, Fremont, North Carolina. *Tony Vaughn*

Hope Plantation,
Windsor vicinity, North Carolina.
Stewart C. Schwartz

St. Mary's Chapel,
Raleigh, North Carolina. *Tony Vaughn*

Coolmore Plantation, Tarboro, North Carolina. *Tony Vaughn*

Cotton Press, Tarboro, North Carolina.
State Department of Archives and History

ALAMANCE COUNTY
Burlington vicinity
ALAMANCE BATTLEGROUND
Southwest of Burlington on N.C. 62
1771

Alamance Battleground was the site of the defeat of a force of Regulators by colonial militia commanded by royal Governor William Tryon. The Regulators sought to challenge the misuse of power by judges, sheriffs, and tax collectors while objecting simultaneously to the eastern or tidewater planters' domination of the provincial government. Their first efforts through legal and peaceful channels were unsuccessful. Alarmed by incidents of mob violence the assembly passed a riot act aimed at the Regulators, who thereupon threatened greater outbreaks. The militia was called out, and 1,000 of them attacked a force of poorly armed Regulators numbering 2,000 on May 16, 1771. Their defeat marked the collapse of the Regulators' resistance, and shortly thereafter Governor Tryon offered clemency to all who would take an oath of allegiance. Social and economic differences between tidewater and piedmont were reflected in the uprising, and this mounting tension was evidence of the growing pains of the young colony.
State

ALAMANCE COUNTY
Burlington vicinity
ALLEN HOUSE
Southwest of Burlington on Route 1, off S.C. 62 near the intersection with Route 1129
Late 18th century

The Allen House is a two-story hewn log dwelling with a gable roof covered by wooden shingles. It rests on a stone foundation. The front facade is sheltered by a shed porch supported by crudely hewn wooden posts. Gable ends on the east and west sides are covered by lapped weatherboards. Interior walls are exposed logs. John Allen, builder of the house, was a supporter of the Regulator cause. The house was moved to the Alamance battleground in 1966.
State

BEAUFORT COUNTY
Bath
BATH HISTORIC DISTRICT
Bounded on the west by Bath Creek, on the north by N.C. 92, on the east by King Street, and on the south by Bath Creek
18th and 19th centuries

The town of Bath was incorporated in 1705 and ten years later was designated by the Lords Proprietors as a port of entry for the colony of North Carolina. Main or Water Street ran the length of town and was planned as the community's business center. Political and economic decline took place during the latter part of the 18th century. Vessels began unloading their cargoes 20 miles inland at Washington, and the county courthouse was moved there in 1785. Few modern intrusions have been introduced to mar the rural, 19th-century charm of present-day Bath. Three 18th-century structures (St. Thomas Episcopal Church, the Palmer-Marsh House, and the Van Der Veer House) still stand, and Main Street lacks both curbing and sidewalks. The church (c. 1734) is brick and measures 30 by 52 feet; the Palmer-Marsh House (c. 1750) is a two-story town house; the Van Der Veer House (c. 1790) is frame with a gambrel roof. Noteworthy 19th-century structures are the Williams (Glebe) House (c. 1830), frame; the Bonner House (c. 1835), a two-story frame structure with a gable roof; and Swindell's Store, a two-story brick commercial building.
Multiple public/private
HABS

BEAUFORT COUNTY
Bath
BONNER HOUSE
Front Street
c. 1830–1840

The Bonner House is a two-story residence covered with molded weatherboarding and set on a brick foundation. A one-story wing with a shed addition at the rear adjoins the east side, and both front and rear elevations have shed porches. Paneled corner posts and molded cornices with returns occur regularly on the exterior. There is a double-shoulder Flemish bond chimney at the west end. Inside, the house has a side hall plan. The second floor is divided into two small rooms and a larger bedroom. Baseboards, doors, and the upstairs newel post are decorated with wood graining, and Adam mantels are found in the parlor and wing room.
State

BEAUFORT COUNTY
Bath
PALMER-MARSH HOUSE
Main Street, south of N.C. 92
c. 1774

The Palmer-Marsh House is a large, two-story, frame town house designed for use as a place of business as well as a private residence. The house, which is about 54 feet long and 30 feet wide, rests on a full stone basement. A large room, located in the narrow west end and having its own street entrance, has served at various times as a store, a council room, a

courthouse, and a parlor. On the east end are two great chimneys with a fine two-story brick pent between them. Although portions were considerably altered in the 19th century, the house has since been restored to its original condition.
State
NHL; HABS

BEAUFORT COUNTY
Bath
ST. THOMAS EPISCOPAL CHURCH
Craven Street
Mid–18th century

This simple brick building with walls laid in Flemish bond is believed to be the earliest extant church in North Carolina. Dimensions of the church are 30 by 52 feet. Both east and west gable ends have been rebuilt, and the north and south sides are each four bays long and contain rectangular windows. Inside, the arrangement of the furniture and altar is probably original, although most of the fabric is not.
Private
HABS

BEAUFORT COUNTY
Washington
BANK OF WASHINGTON, WEST END BRANCH
216 W. Main Street
Mid–19th century

The Bank of Washington was incorporated by act of the North Carolina General Assembly on January 22, 1851. The bank building, a temple-form structure, was constructed shortly thereafter. There is a prostyle tetrastyle Ionic portico on the south facade which is rusticated stucco over brick. The central entrance and flanking windows are each surmounted by a small, unacademic pediment above a row of large dentils. The portico has a full entablature carried around three sides of the building. Both the east and west sides have four bays separated by pilasters. The single large interior room has been completely remodeled.
Private

BEAUFORT COUNTY
Washington
BEAUFORT COUNTY COURTHOUSE
Corner of W. 2nd and Market Streets
1786

The Beaufort County Courthouse was built as a two-story square with brick walls laid in Flemish bond. Later, a two-bay brick extension was added at the rear and a clock tower constructed on the gable roof. The central entrance contains a flat-panel double door which is framed by a

heavy molded architrave and surmounted by a six-pane transom. Over the east gable is the square clock tower, the top of which is adorned by a four-faced clock. The courthouse is one of the earliest permanent public buildings in North Carolina and has served continually as the seat of Beaufort County government.
County

BERTIE COUNTY
Windsor vicinity
HOPE PLANTATION
4 miles northwest of Windsor off N.C. 308
1803

The main house of Hope Plantation was built by David Stone (1770–1810), lawyer, judge, Congressman, U.S. Senator, and governor of North Carolina. Standing two stories above a raised basement, the plantation house is frame construction with beaded weatherboarding. The five-bay facade is highlighted by a pedimented, two-story portico, and a modillion cornice follows the entire roofline. A Chinese Chippendale railing stands atop the deck-on-hip roof.
Private

BRUNSWICK COUNTY
Orton vicinity
ST. PHILIP'S CHURCH RUINS
South of Orton off N.C. 1533
Mid–18th century

The town of Brunswick on the Cape Fear River was laid out about 1727. When Brunswick County was formed in 1764, this town became the county seat. St. Philip's Church was dedicated in 1768. At the outbreak of the Revolution the inhabitants moved to more protected locations, and most of the buildings, including St. Philip's, were burned by the British. The site gradually became overgrown and the church itself, which was never rebuilt, now consists of the only four aboveground brick walls. The most striking feature of the church is the large Palladian window, once situated above the altar, which still dominates the east wall. St. Philip's is a reminder of a town, destroyed long ago, that played a vital role in North Carolina's history.
State
HABS

BUNCOMBE COUNTY
Asheville
BILTMORE ESTATE
Biltmore Plaza
1888, Frederick Law Olmsted

George W. Vanderbilt, owner of the Biltmore Estate, appointed Gifford Pinchot as superintendent of his forests in 1892. Here Pinchot demonstrated for the first time that scientific forest management could be good business practice. In 1898 Vanderbilt set up the Biltmore Forest School, the first of its kind in the United States. Nearly 87,000 acres of the estate's forest land is now included in the Pisgah National Forest, the first national forest created in the East. The large story-and-a-half building in which the Biltmore Forest School was conducted is substantially unchanged.
Municipal
NHL

BURKE COUNTY
Morganton
BURKE COUNTY COURTHOUSE
Courthouse Square, bounded on the northwest by Union Street, on the northeast by Sterling Street, on the southeast by Meeting Street, and on the southwest by Green Street
1835

Burke County was formed in 1777, and the present courthouse is the second on the site. Extensively remodeled in 1901, the courthouse has been used continuously since 1835. It stands one story high over a full basement. The exterior was originally native stone which was covered with stucco during the remodeling. Both pedimented porticos were raised four feet at that time to correspond to the roofline, and an elaborate Baroque style cupola constructed to replace its simpler predecessor. The carved cornice was added in 1901, and all interior courtroom furnishings were replaced then.
County

CABARRUS COUNTY
Concord vicinity
REED GOLD MINE
11 miles southeast of Concord on U.S. 601 and N.C. 200
1799

Several nuggets found at the site of Reed Gold Mine set off the first gold rush in the United States. The gold industry became second only to agriculture in North Carolina, which furnished all the gold minted at the Philadelphia Mint before 1829. Unspoiled by modern development, many of the diggings and structures still remain.
Private; not accessible to the public
NHL

CALDWELL COUNTY
Lenoir vicinity
FORT DEFIANCE
North of Lenoir on N.C. 268

Fort Defiance, named for an early frontier fort on the site, was the home of Revolutionary Captain William Lenoir. Lenoir was active in North Carolina politics, serving in both houses of the state legislature, and was president of the University of North Carolina's first board of trustees. The main portion of Fort Defiance is a two-story frame structure which was originally a five-bay house with a one-story shed porch across both the front and rear elevations. A wing was added on the west end in 1823. Inside, the house has a central hall plan with four rooms on each floor, and these contain some well-executed mantels.
Private

CARTERET COUNTY
Atlantic Beach vicinity
FORT MACON
Bogue Point on Fort Macon Road, 4 miles east of Atlantic Beach
19th century

Surveys for a federal fort on Bogue Point were completed in 1821, but construction did not begin until 1826. Troops occupied Fort Macon, which was named for North Carolina Congressman Nathaniel Macon (1758–1837), from 1834 to 1836. Following an inspection in the 1840's, Captain Robert E. Lee recommended the construction of jetties to stabilize the fort site. The jetties were built, the fortifications were reinforced, and troops were again stationed here in 1842–1844 and 1848–1849. Confederate soldiers held the fort from April, 1861, to April, 1862, when it was retaken by Union forces. Fort Macon was active until 1876, serving also as a military prison. Given in 1924 to the state of North Carolina, it was reactivated during World War II, before being returned to the state. The pentagonal fort is primarily brick with Connecticut freestone used in ramps, lintels, sills, stairs, and string courses. The interior woodwork is Greek Revival.
State
HABS

CATAWBA COUNTY
Claremont vicinity
BUNKER HILL COVERED BRIDGE
2 miles east of Claremont on U.S. 70
1895

Originally constructed as an open span, the Bunker Hill Bridge is 80 feet long and built on dry wall stone ramps. The bridge

employs a combination of the multiple king post truss and the Haupt truss systems joined with trunnels. In 1900 the open span was covered. This bridge and three others of similar construction are the only ones to survive in the state.
County

CHOWAN COUNTY
Edenton
CHOWAN COUNTY COURTHOUSE
E. King Street
1767

Edenton, known as Queen Anne's Town until it was incorporated in 1727, was founded in 1658 and was the site of the first permanent colonial settlement in North Carolina. The present courthouse replaced an earlier one completed in 1719. The two-story, late Georgian structure has a T-shaped plan with a one-story, semi-circular apse at the center rear. A two-story cupola topped by an ogival roof is a noteworthy feature of the south facade. Above the courtroom are offices and a large room once used as an assembly hall and ballroom. Although several features on the first floor were altered during the 19th century, the dado of the apse, the courtroom balustrade, and the judge's chair are original.
County
NHL; HABS

CHOWAN COUNTY
Edenton
CUPOLA HOUSE
408 S. Broad Street
c. 1725, 1750's (remodeled)

The two-story frame Cupola House illustrates the combining of 17th-century architectural forms with 18th-century Georgian motifs. It is a rare example of a colonial house in the South having a Jacobean second-story "jetty" or overhang. In combination with beaded clapboards and a steeply pitched gable roof, this feature is usually associated with 17th-century New England architecture. When the house was remodeled in the 1750's, Georgian features were added: fine interior Queen Anne paneling, sliding sash windows, a carved stairway, and a front portico. The roof is crowned by an octagonal wood cupola with carved cornice brackets and a tall terminal finial. Although the original paneling of two major first floor rooms was sold in 1918, this woodwork has been carefully restored and the house is in excellent condition.
Private
NHL; HABS

CHOWAN COUNTY
Edenton
IREDELL, JAMES, HOUSE
107 E. Church Street
18th and 19th centuries

The earliest extant portion of the James Iredell House was built about 1776 as a rectangular, two-story frame structure with its south gable end facing Church Street. About 1816 a two-story addition was constructed perpendicular to the west facade, thus forming the present configuration. Inside, the house has two separate floor plans. The east section contains a side hall across the south end; the west section has a central hall. Outbuildings are a kitchen, necessary house, carriage house, and a school. James Iredell (1751–1799) was a member of the North Carolina Provincial Congress, attorney general for the state, and associate justice of the U.S. Supreme Court.
State

CRAVEN COUNTY
New Bern
STANLY, JOHN WRIGHT, HOUSE
307 George Street
Late 18th century

Although no longer on its original site, the Stanly House is an outstanding example of Georgian architecture in North Carolina. The hip roof, symmetrical facade, pedimented windows, and doorway articulation are characteristic of this style. Inside, the house has a central hall plan with four rooms on each of the two floors. Wood is the basic building material.
State
HABS

CUMBERLAND COUNTY
Fayetteville
MARKET HOUSE
Market Square
1838

The Fayetteville Market House is patterned after 18th-century English town halls having an open, arcaded ground floor and a second floor containing one or more public rooms. The hip roof of the two-story center section is surmounted by a two-story cupola. Meat and produce were originally sold by local farmers under the first-floor arcade, while the second floor served as the town hall. Two single-story wings flank the three-bay center block, and they are topped by a classical balustrade. Above the belt course of the main block are Ionic pilasters dividing the bays. The two-section cupola is square below and octagonal above, and an obelisk ornaments each corner of the splayed roof. The Market House is the focal point of downtown Fayetteville.
Municipal
HABS

DARE COUNTY
Kitty Hawk
WRIGHT BROTHERS NATIONAL MEMORIAL
1903

At Kitty Hawk, North Carolina, on December 17, 1903, Orville and Wilbur Wright changed the technical complexion of the 20th century. Orville Wright's 12–second flight was the first in which a machine carrying a man had raised itself by its own power and had sailed forward without reduction of speed. The Wright Memorial Shaft on Kill Devil Hill commemorates the flight, and markers nearby indicate the take-off and landing spots. Two wooden structures nearby are reconstructions of the Wrights' 1903 camp based on research and photographs. On display in the visitor center is a reproduction of the Wrights' 1903 airplane.
Federal/non-federal
NPS; 425.40 acres

DARE COUNTY
Manteo vicinity, Roanoke Island
FORT RALEIGH NATIONAL HISTORIC SITE
4 miles north of Manteo on U.S. 158
1585–1591

Fort Raleigh National Historic Site is the scene of Sir Walter Raleigh's ill-fated attempts to establish an English colony in America. The first settlement, 1585–1586, failed because of hardships and trouble with Indians. The "Lost Colony" settlement of 1587 was the birthplace of Virginia Dare, first child born of English parents in the New World. War with Spain isolated the colony until 1591, by which time the colonists had disappeared. Their fate was never determined. Among the men who figured in the history of the settlements were "sea dogs" Sir Richard Grenville and Sir Francis Drake. Based on historical and archeological evidence, Fort Raleigh was reconstructed in the early 1950's.
Federal/non-federal
NPS; 159.66 acres

DAVIDSON COUNTY
Lexington
OLD DAVIDSON COUNTY COURTHOUSE
Main and Center Streets
Mid–19th century

The Old Davidson County Courthouse is a grand scale temple building with stucco-covered walls of stone. Its full facade prostyle hexastyle portico has slightly attenuated, fluted, Roman Corinthian

columns which support a well executed entablature. The notable cartouche in the tympanum above is molded in high relief. There are only two openings in the front wall—the central pedimented portal and a triple window with round-arched heads above it. The rear elevation features a fully developed pediment and an entranceway flanked by rectangular windows.
County

DURHAM COUNTY
Durham
BENNETT PLACE STATE HISTORIC SITE
At the intersection of State Routes 1313 and 1314

Following Lee's surrender to Grant at Appomattox Court House (April 9, 1865), another force of Confederate soldiers, commanded by General Joseph E. Johnston, remained in the Carolinas, Georgia, and Florida. Johnston decided to surrender his command and met with Union General William Tecumseh Sherman in April to negotiate terms. The site selected was the Bennett farmhouse. Talks took place on April 17–18 and the final document was signed on April 26. In 1921 the Bennett house burned, but it has since been reconstructed by the state of North Carolina as the site of the event which virtually ended the Civil War in the southeast. The house is a one-story log structure covered by weatherboards. It has a gable roof and a rear shed addition and incorporates the original chimney. Other structures of the farm complex include a log kitchen and smokehouse.
State

DURHAM COUNTY
Durham vicinity
DUKE HOMESTEAD AND TOBACCO FACTORY
.5 mile north of Durham on Guess Road and east on N.C. 1025
1851

Following the Civil War Washington Duke and his sons entered the tobacco industry, organizing the American Tobacco Company in 1890. Preeminent in its time, the company was dissolved by the Supreme Court in 1911. The frame house of the Dukes has been restored and refurnished. Also standing is the first tobacco "factory," a small log building near the house.
Private
NHL

EDGECOMBE COUNTY
Battleboro
ST. JOHN'S EPISCOPAL CHURCH
E. Main Street
1891

St. John's is a simple vernacular type of building found, at one time, throughout the rural South. The nave is a board-and-batten rectangle with a steep gable roof. At the east end is a three-part extension consisting of a central rectangular sanctuary flanked by two smaller projections, a baptistry, and a sacristy. The nave is four bays long, and all but the west bay contain lancet windows with diamond panes. In the fourth bay is a tower which rises in two distinct stages divided by a simple horizontal wooden stringer. The top of the tower is crenellated with primitive pinnacles at each corner. On the interior St. John's has a center aisle plan. The most interesting feature is the roof construction. It is essentially a tie-beam truss system consisting of a pair of rafters pitched against one another with a tie beam connecting their bases.
Private

EDGECOMBE COUNTY
Tarboro
THE BARRACKS
1100 Albemarle Street
Mid–19th century, William Percival

William Percival was a retired British army officer who practiced architecture in Virginia and North Carolina. His very personalized style is evident in The Barracks, which exhibits a formalized version of the proportion and massing common to the Italian Villa style combined with an overlay of Greek Revival and Italianate detail. The main facade of The Barracks is dominated by a central projecting bay with a distyle pedimented portico. Two tall fluted columns of the portico support a heavy entablature which is carried around the entire house. The frieze is punctuated by elaborate brackets grouped in pairs. Centered in the spaces between these brackets are circular vents with decorative grates. Windows are set in frames of projecting unmolded brick, and projecting brick pilasters mark all corners. The single flanking bays feature one-story loggias with coupled columns of the same order as the main portico. Most of the original interiors are intact.
Private

EDGECOMBE COUNTY
Tarboro
BLOUNT HOUSE (THE GROVE)
130 Bridgers Street
c. 1808

Thomas Blount, an Edgecombe County resident active in politics, built The Grove, which remained in the Blount family until 1831. The dwelling is a two-story, Federal style frame house on a raised basement. Both north and south facades are five bays wide, and the roof is gabled. In each gable there is a fanlight centered between a pair of brick, double-shouldered chimneys. The shed porch surrounding the house is a later addition. Now used as administrative offices for the city school system, the Blount House is a good example of an ambitious vernacular design in the Federal style.
Municipal

EDGECOMBE COUNTY
Tarboro
CALVARY EPISCOPAL CHURCH AND CHURCHYARD
411 E. Church Street
1867, William Percival

Calvary Episcopal Church may be characterized as "Early English" Gothic due to the minimal use of surface decoration on its exterior. Its brick walls are laid in common bond, and the roof is gabled. Buttresses with sloping shoulders divide the nave into six bays. Pointed-arch window and door openings are common. Steeples are located at the north and south corners of the west front. Inside there is a center aisle and a gallery above the west end of the nave. The sanctuary is framed by a broad chancel arch and has a simple timber roof. An outstanding interior feature is the hammerbeam roof. Hobart Upjohn designed a parish house (1922) which is similar in scale and material to the church.
Private

EDGECOMBE COUNTY
Tarboro
COTTON PRESS
Town Common
c. 1840

Isaac Norfleet, a local planter, had the Cotton Press constructed on his property about two and one-half miles from Tarboro. It was used originally for pressing cider and wine and was converted to cotton baling about 1860. Standing 22 feet high, the Cotton Press was constructed of heart pine mortised and tenoned together. The sweeps were rotated by mules, thus driving the central shaft down onto a wooden packing block. Three hundred

pounds of cotton were placed under the packing block and compressed into single bales. The Cotton Press was moved into Tarboro in 1938 and is one of the few remaining pieces of 19th-century cotton processing machinery.
Municipal
HABS

EDGECOMBE COUNTY
Tarboro
TARBORO TOWN COMMON
Bounded by Wilson Street, Albemarle Avenue, Park Avenue, and St. Patrick Street

In 1760 five proprietors purchased the present site of Tarboro for the purpose of laying out a town. Fifty acres were set aside as the town commons which surrounded the settled portions on three sides (north, south, and west). All but the northern common were whittled away as Tarboro grew. Two of the remaining nine acres were eventually sold and schools erected thereon. Today this unique example of early urban planning in the South survives as a park for Tarboro residents. The triangular-shaped park contains several memorials and a fountain.
Municipal

EDGECOMBE COUNTY
Tarboro
WALSTON-BULLUCK HOUSE (PENDER MUSEUM)
1018 St. Andrews Street
19th century

This house is typical of eastern North Carolina farmhouses during the 18th and early 19th centuries. It is a one-story, three-bay frame structure covered with beaded weatherboards. The double-shouldered exterior end chimneys have been reconstructed. There are two shed rooms with a small porch between at the rear of the house and a shed porch supported by tapered columns with molded caps across the front. The interior consists of a hall and parlor with an enclosed stairway leading to the finished attic. These two principal rooms have two ranges of flat horizontal panels in the dado with horizontal sheathing above the chair rail.
County

EDGECOMBE COUNTY
Tarboro vicinity
BRACEBRIDGE HALL
Near small crossroads of Macklesfield
c. 1826

Bracebridge Hall was originally a one-and-one-half-story frame house. During subsequent years a five-bay, two-story, Greek Revival style dwelling was built perpendicular to the eastern end of the older

house. Its central entrance has an eight-panel door with sidelights which is framed by pilasters. The doorway is sheltered by a one-story pedimented porch featuring fluted Doric columns and a full entablature. In 1884 the earliest section was raised to two stories and a one-and-one-half-story brick section was added to the south of and parallel to the 1826 house. The plan is now essentially U-shaped. Elias Carr, grandson of the builder, was elected governor of North Carolina in 1893.
Private

EDGECOMBE COUNTY
Tarboro vicinity
COOLMORE PLANTATION
West of Tarboro on U.S. 64
1861, E. G. Lind

Coolmore Plantation is an Italian Villa style two-story frame house with one-story wings. The main block has a hip roof intersected by decorative gables, and the wide roof overhang is supported by elaborate brackets. At the apex of the roof is a fanciful belvedere containing stained glass windows. On both floor levels there are coupled pairs of windows. Interior rooms are unusualy ornate. The entrance hall is apsidal with a profusion of wooden and plaster ornament including a false half dome. An elliptical stairway ascends to and is lighted by the belvedere. The parlor contains its original furnishings, marble mantel, wallpaper, and a painted *trompe l'oeil* ceiling. Dr. Joseph J. Powell, a prominent county physician, undertook construction of the house in 1859.
Private
HABS

EDGECOMBE COUNTY
Tarboro vicinity
PINEY PROSPECT (SUGG HOUSE)
5.7 miles south of Tarboro off Route 1601
18th and 19th centuries

Piney Prospect was built first (prior to 1800) as a rectangular one-and-one-half-story frame house with a lean-to addition at the rear. About 1820 this portion was raised to two stories, and a two-story addition was joined perpendicular to the west or front elevation. The main facade features a four-bay, two-tiered, recessed porch which is enclosed on the west end in the Charleston style. The porch is supported by three free-standing and two engaged columns on each level. Windows on the first floor of the west end are set beneath panels with volute-shaped ends decorated by central oval sunbursts. The main cornice has pierced mutules above a diminutive frieze and an architrave adorned by a row of small reeded panels

resembling triglyphs. External detail makes Piney Prospect one of the best exercises of the late Adam style in eastern North Carolina.
Private; not accessible to the public

FORSYTH COUNTY
Winston-Salem
OLD SALEM HISTORIC DISTRICT
Salem College campus and area near Salem Square
c. 1770

Old Salem is a well-preserved example of an 18th-century German community. Established by a Moravian congregation, the town became the chief commercial center of the surrounding piedmont region. The main street was paralleled by several secondary streets; cross streets at regular intervals created a gridiron effect. Several of the extant buildings still serve their original purpose. Others, such as the Salem Tavern and the home and shop of John Vogler, the clockmaker and silversmith, have been restored for public exhibition.
Private
NHL; HABS

FORSYTH COUNTY
Winston-Salem
SALEM TAVERN
800 S. Main Street
1784

Salem Tavern was the first brick building in the Moravian settlement of Salem; its architectural character is that of the Moravian's Germanic building heritage. The main facade of this two-story building is graced by a plain open porch across its entire length. The gabled roof has twin-end chimneys at the ridge. A central hall divides the building with rooms to either side, and a rear wing on the lower level houses the kitchen. The tavern once enjoyed a widespread reputation for hospitality. Among its many distinguished guests was President George Washington, who stayed here during a southern tour in 1791.
Private
NHL

FORSYTH COUNTY
Winston-Salem
SINGLE BROTHERS' HOUSE
S. Main and Academy Streets
1768–1769, 1786

In 1766 Moravian settlers, originally from Bethlehem, Pennsylvania, began constructing a new community which they called Salem, meaning "peace." The Single Brothers' House, a restored example of German half-timbered construction, is the oldest major building still standing in the

Moravian community of Old Salem. The two-story structure, erected in two stages, has a full basement and two attics. The basement and first floor contain nine craft shops where boys in their early teens learned trades and earned a living as journeymen. The building served as a dormitory for unmarried master craftsmen, journeymen, and apprentices.
Private
NHL; HABS

GUILFORD COUNTY
Greensboro
BLANDWOOD
411 W. Washington Street
Mid–19th century, Alexander Jackson Davis

The present Blandwood was originally a two-room house which Alexander Jackson Davis extensively altered and remodeled as an Italianate Tuscan villa. Noteworthy aspects of the house are the central, square entrance tower, the low pitched, projecting roof, casement windows, and unusual chimneys. The walls of the house are brick covered with stucco, and two dependencies (an office and a kitchen) were originally connected to the main block by arcades. John Motley Morehead (1796–1866), for whom the house was built, was a lawyer and businessman who served two terms as governor of North Carolina (1841–1845) and helped to establish the North Carolina Railroad, which ran westward from the coast to Morganton.
Public

GUILFORD COUNTY
Greensboro vicinity
GUILFORD COURTHOUSE NATIONAL MILITARY PARK
6 miles northwest of Greensboro near U.S. 220
1781

The campaign which ended in the battle of Guilford Courthouse was itself part of a larger British campaign in the South which began at Savannah, Georgia, in 1778 and ended at Yorktown, Virginia, in 1781. Here on March 15, 1781, Lord Charles Cornwallis defeated General Nathanael Greene's American forces. Guilford was an instance of a battle lost but a campaign won. It proved to be Cornwallis' last major battle before he was surrounded and besieged at Yorktown. His surrender there on October 19, 1781, ended the major military operations of the Revolutionary War.
Federal/non-federal
NPS; 233 acres

HALIFAX COUNTY
Halifax
HALIFAX HISTORIC DISTRICT
Bounded on the southwest by St. David Street, on the northwest by the Owens House drainage ditch, on the northeast by the Roanoke River, and on the southeast by the Magazine Spring Gut
18th and 19th centuries

Establishment of the town of Halifax dates from 1757, and it continued as a thriving commercial and political center until the end of the 18th century. Halifax was located at the junction of the Roanoke River and a main overland route from Virginia. In 1759 the town became the county seat for Halifax County. In 1776 the Fourth Provincial Congress of North Carolina met here and passed the Halifax Resolves, advocating separation from Great Britain. Following adoption of the Declaration of Independence by the Continental Congress (July 4, 1776), the Fifth Provincial Congress met in Halifax and drew up a state bill of rights and a constitution. The end of the Revolution brought a westward shift of population, and Halifax dwindled in size. Four structures remain as reminders of the past: the Constitution House, where North Carolina's first Constitution is reputed to have been drafted (restored); the Owens House (restored); the clerk's office (c. 1832); and the jail (c. 1838).
State/private
HABS

HENDERSON COUNTY
Flat Rock vicinity
CARL SANDBURG HOME NATIONAL HISTORIC SITE
.25 mile west of Flat Rock
1838

Carl Sandburg, one of America's most versatile writers, is the only American to have received Pulitzer prizes in two fields: one in history for *Abraham Lincoln: The War Years* (1939); and one in poetry for *Complete Poems* (1950). His publications include poetry, history, biography, children's stories, fiction, autobiography, and a collection of folk songs. Sandburg lived at Connemara Farm from 1945 until his death in 1967. Here he wrote his autobiography, *Always the Young Strangers;* a novel, *Remembrance Rock;* and several books of verse. The Sandburg house, built by Christopher G. Memminger, Secretary of the Treasury for the Confederacy (1861–1864), contains all of the author's personal and literary effects.
NPS; 246.58 acres

HERTFORD COUNTY
Como vicinity
HARE PLANTATION HOUSE
1.6 miles west of the junction of Route 1317 and U.S. 258
c. 1815

Jacob Hare constructed this house in an area where his family had owned land since the mid-18th century. It is a two-story, gable-roofed house with a pedimented east end. A modillion cornice on the east end carries around the adjacent sides of the house. Both north and south facades have doors in the end bays suggesting that the house may have faced north originally. On the west end there are two common bond, single-shouldered chimneys. Inside, the house has essentially a side hall plan with two unequal rooms. All rooms have original molded chair rails above plastered dadoes and simple baseboards. The mantels and overmantels are elaborate.
Private

HERTFORD COUNTY
Como vicinity
RIDDICK HOUSE
1 mile south of the intersection of Routes 1319 and 1322
19th century

The present house was erected sometime after 1825 by Abram Riddick. It was originally a two-story, gable-roofed dwelling covered by beaded weatherboards. By the addition of curious full length pents, the house was raised to three stories. The south facade is five bays wide and has a central door with a three-light transom framed by a molded architrave. Along the front is a one-story shed porch (a later addition) supported by four massive reeded columns. Each of the gable ends has two double-shouldered chimneys. The original modillions of the cornice were altered in the late 19th century by the addition of molded bases to form simulated brackets. The house is noteworthy because it incorporates several unusual techniques and stylistic alterations.
Private

HERTFORD COUNTY
Murfreesboro
THE COLUMNS
Jones Drive
1852

Chowan Baptist Female Institute was established in 1848. The Columns originally contained all institute facilities, a chapel, classrooms, offices, and dormitory rooms. In 1910 the name of the school was changed to Chowan College. Built of brick, the Greek Revival structure is three stories high and has a low, hip roof sur-

mounted by an octagonal belvedere. The most distinctive feature is the large portico on the north facade. The eight fluted Doric columns originally supported two galleries but the upper one has been removed. All five bays on the main facade are separated by pilasters, and the main entrance features a double door with transom and sidelights. This arrangement is repeated on the second and third elevations, although the windows on each floor diminish in size. Some alterations have been made on the exterior and more extensive ones inside.
Private
HABS

HERTFORD COUNTY
Murfreesboro
FREEMAN HOUSE (HERTFORD ACADEMY)
200 E. Broad Street
1810

The first classes of Hertford Academy were held here in the spring of 1811. The rectangular, hip-roofed, two-story structure was built of brick laid in Flemish bond. A six-panel door with transom and sidelights and surmounted by a broken pediment has replaced the original doorway on the main facade. Brackets on the roof cornice have a scroll modillion profile, and the cornice also features a row of pierced dentils and an intricate band of fretwork. Windows are topped by jack arches, and those on the ground floor have decorative keys. From 1848 to 1852 the newly formed Baptist Female Institute, which later became Chowan College, occupied this building before moving to The Columns.
Private
HABS

HERTFORD COUNTY
Murfreesboro
MELROSE
100 E. Broad Street
Early 19th century

Melrose is a two-story, gable-roofed mansion probably built during the first decade of the 19th century. The main entrance was originally on the east facade until the addition of a pair of two-bay wings on the east and west facades transformed the house into a T-shaped structure. Dominating the front is a tetrastyle two-story Ionic portico. Melrose was built and owned until 1813 by the Murfrees, one of the South's most important early pioneer families.
Private

HERTFORD COUNTY
Murfreesboro
MYRICK HOUSE
402 Broad Street
Early 19th century

The Myrick House is an interesting example of a Federal town house in northeastern North Carolina. The two-story dwelling is constructed of brick laid in one-to-three American bond. The low hip roof has a corbeled brick cornice featuring a row of brick dentils. The three central bays of the five-bay front facade are covered by a one-story porch with a hip roof supported by four fluted columns and a pair of fluted pilasters. This was a later addition. The most unusual feature of the house is an enclosed barrel stairway which leads from the second floor hall to the attic. The front and rear entrances both have delicate decorative leaded lights.
Private

HERTFORD COUNTY
Murfreesboro
REA, WILLIAM, STORE
E. Williams Street
c. 1790

William Rea was a Boston merchant who traded extensively between Murfreesboro and New England. He and his four brothers outfitted ships at Murfreesboro and helped establish the town as an important export center of the Roanoke Valley. His two-story brick store is believed to be one of the oldest extant commercial buildings in North Carolina. The store measures 40 feet by 28 feet and has one room on each floor; the second floor was used for storage. An office wing was added to the store about 1803.
Private

HERTFORD COUNTY
Murfreesboro
ROBERTS-VAUGHAN HOUSE
130 E. Main Street
19th century

Built as a two-story frame residence, the Roberts-Vaughan House was enlarged in later years and a central Greek Revival portico was added on the main facade. It is a tetrastyle, pedimented portico and covers the three central bays. Reeded Doric columns support a reduced entablature which is carried around the house on all sides. It features brackets which resemble scroll modillions in profile, a row of pierced dentils, and a band of intricate fretwork. On the older (east) end of the dwelling the chimneys are laid in Flemish bond, while those on the west are American bond. A single-story frame kitchen with a gable roof and porches on its east and west sides has been added to the right side of the south wall.
Private

HERTFORD COUNTY
Murfreesboro
WHEELER, JOHN, HOUSE
403 E. Broad Street
Early 19th century

The Wheeler House is a good example of Federal vernacular architecture in North Carolina. The two-story gable-roofed structure has walls of brick laid in Flemish bond. The main feature of the facade is a two-story pedimented portico with four simple square columns. Inside it has a two-room, central hall plan. John Wheeler, town postmaster and a trustee of the Murfreesboro and Hertford academies, bought the house soon after its completion. His son John served as the first United States minister to Nicaragua while Samuel founded the *Murfreesboro Citizen*, and both occupied the house. In 1969 the house was donated to the Murfreesboro Historical Association.
Private

IREDELL COUNTY
Statesville vicinity
FORT DOBBS
Fort Dobbs Road
1756

Fort Dobbs was the only frontier post in North Carolina during the French and Indian War. The fortification was planned by and named for Governor Arthur Dobbs, who had arrived in the colony in the fall of 1754. Inspiration for the design of Fort Dobbs may well have come from 17th-century Irish bawns or fortified residences. The dominant feature was the loopholed and bastioned barracks which was a large log structure. It measured 40 by 53 feet and was three stories high. There may have been palisade flankers or bastions at the southeast and northwest corners of the blockhouse-barracks, and a star-shaped perimeter of ditch and parapet surrounded the entire fort. The perimeter defense is considered a later addition. Closest in appearance to Fort Dobbs were the New England garrison houses and palisaded blockhouses. A Cherokee uprising on the frontier in 1760 put the Fort Dobbs garrison on the alert, but the Indians were defeated the following summer, and the fort was gradually deactivated and completely abandoned in 1764. Archeological excavations have uncovered 85 per cent of the 18th-century remains.
Private

JOHNSTON COUNTY
Clayton vicinity
SANDERS-HAIRR HOUSE
Route 1525 south of Clayton
18th century

The Sanders-Hairr House is noteworthy because of the sophistication of its design and the excellent execution of its architectural detail. The two-story house is covered by molded weatherboards and has a fine cornice consisting of a row of pierced dentils above modillions. At either end of the house is a massive, double-shouldered exterior chimney. The five-bay front facade has a one-story shed porch across its full length. The porch has a concave ceiling and delicate supports composed of tapered fluted posts on pedestals. Both gable ends of the house are pedimented, and the complete cornice carries around the eaves. Each tympanum features a circular oculus, accented by a molded architrave and keystone, on either side of the chimney. The chimney is flanked by elaborately framed windows in each story. Each first-floor window is pedimented, has a molded architrave, a keystone, and is surmounted by a full entablature ornamented with pierced dentils. Reubin Sanders, who built the house, operated a sawmill and a gristmill and served as clerk of the superior court and as a state senator.
Private; not accessible to the public

JOHNSTON COUNTY
Princeton vicinity
BENTONVILLE BATTLEGROUND
South of Princeton, 3 miles off U.S. 701 and Route 1008

The battle of Bentonville (March 19–21, 1865) involved more men (about 80,000) than any other engagement fought in North Carolina. It was also the last full-scale action of the Civil War in which the Confederate command chose the ground and made the initial attack. General Joseph E. Johnston and his 20,000 troops attempted to stop General William Tecumseh Sherman enroute to join General Grant in Virginia. Johnston's army attacked Sherman's left wing of 30,000 men, but, as the battle continued, Sherman brought his right wing of equal strength into the fray. The Confederate forces withdrew and were not pursued. Within three weeks Lee had surrendered the Army of Northern Virginia to Grant, and Johnston himself surrendered on April 26 to Sherman.
State

LENOIR COUNTY
Kinston vicinity
JACKSON, JESSE, HOUSE
On U.S. 11, south of Kinston
c. 1840

This two-story frame house has a gable roof and a brick foundation. The east and west facades are five bays wide, and the latter has a central entrance in each story. Protecting the ground floor doorway is a flat-roofed, one-story porch. The rear facade is covered by a one-story shed porch. A concave-shouldered chimney separates each of the bays on the north and south elevations. Jesse Jackson was a planter.
Private; not accessible to the public

MCDOWELL COUNTY
Pleasant Gardens vicinity
CARSON HOUSE
East of Pleasant Gardens on U.S. 70

The Carson House reached its present form as the result of several expansions. The earliest section was a single-room, log dwelling built about 1810 by Colonel John Carson. Later, another one-room unit was added with a passage or "dog run" between the two. Probably two rear rooms were added and the dogtrot extended sometime later, and the house had completely evolved by the mid–19th century. There is a full length, two-story veranda with tapered wooden pillars along the main facade. The roof pediments extend over the veranda. In 1843 McDowell County was organized, and the Carson home served as the seat of county government until a courthouse was erected.
Private
HABS

MECKLENBURG COUNTY
Charlotte
ALEXANDER, HEZEKIAH, HOUSE
3420 Shamrock Drive
1774

Hezekiah Alexander (1722–1801) built this home for his bride out of native Piedmont stone and oystershell mortar. The walls are two feet thick and plastered on the interior. Two interior end chimneys were connected to fireplaces on the first floor only. German houses in Pennsylvania and the Hudson River valley are similar in construction and appearance. Alexander emigrated from Maryland in the mid–18th century. Trained as a blacksmith, he became prosperous as a farmer and was a framer of North Carolina's first constitution.
Private

MONTGOMERY COUNTY
Mount Gilead vicinity
TOWN CREEK INDIAN MOUND
4.5 miles southeast of Mount Gilead on N.C. 73
Late prehistoric

The Town Creek Indian Mound site was the ceremonial center for a group of people with a Mississippian-influenced culture who had moved northward into the area. On the site is a temple mound, the northernmost on the East coast. Parts of the aboriginal site have been reconstructed, and an on-site museum interprets the culture of the Indians who lived there.
State
NHL

MOORE COUNTY
Glendon vicinity
ALSTON HOUSE (HOUSE IN THE HORSESHOE)
Southeast of Glendon on N.C. 1624
18th century

The House in the Horseshoe is so named because of its location in a horseshoe bend of the Deep River. It is a typical 18th-century plantation house particularly distinguished by the strikingly elaborate and well-executed detail of the doorways and some of the interior woodwork. The exterior of the two-story frame dwelling is covered with replacement lapped weatherboards except under the porches where the original flush siding remains. On the west side the central entrance has a six-panel door flanked by fluted pilasters and is surmounted by a fanlight. The rear entrance is also flanked by fluted pilasters and topped by a pediment. Chimneys are double-shouldered and have T-stacks. Inside, the north parlor is notable for its wainscot and mantel. Phil Alston is believed to have built the house in 1772 or 1773.
State

NASH COUNTY
Rocky Mount vicinity
STONEWALL
Falls Road Extension
c. 1830

Stonewall is the main house of what once was a typical antebellum plantation. It is a late Federal style brick house which stands two stories above a raised basement. The two-story Ionic portico on the five-bay north front was built in 1915. The central entranceway is a six-paneled Federal door framed by Ionic pilasters and crowned by a fanlight. Evidence indicates that the river front was originally the main facade, and it, too, had a portico. Bennett

Bunn, one of Nash County's wealthiest planters, built Stonewall, which derives its name from a heavy granite wall bordering the front lawn on the landward side.
Private; not accessible to the public
HABS

NEW HANOVER COUNTY
Wilmington
CITY HALL-THALIAN HALL
100 N. 3rd Street
1858

Wilmington's Thalian Hall was built by the town as a combination theater and city hall. The theater ceased to be used by professional companies in 1928. The two-story structure rests on a high basement and is made of brick covered with stucco. The stucco may not be original, and the walls may have been rusticated to resemble stone. A projecting pedimented, tetrastyle Corinthian portico with fluted columns covers the main entrance. Above the doorway is a pair of elongated, arched windows framed by an arched hood. The tympanum of the arch contains a blind roundel. All second floor bays are divided by pilasters, and coupled pilasters mark the building's corners. The interior decoration was executed in plaster, and the seating capacity of the theater, including two balconies is 950.
Municipal

NEW HANOVER COUNTY
Wilmington vicinity
FORT FISHER
18 miles south of Wilmington on U.S. 421
1861

Built at the southern tip of the peninsula between the Cape Fear River and the Atlantic Ocean, the Confederate stronghold Fort Fisher formed an impassable barrier for the blockading Union fleet. When this last major Confederate coastal fortification fell on January 15, 1865, the Confederacy was virtually isolated from the outside world. The parapet is still well preserved, and the traverses and gun emplacements are clearly defined.
Multiple public/private
NHL

ORANGE COUNTY
Chapel Hill
OLD EAST, UNIVERSITY OF NORTH CAROLINA
University of North Carolina campus
1795

Chartered in 1789, the University of North Carolina was the first state university in the United States. Old East, the first building constructed on the campus, has been remodeled but still retains its original lines. Several of the other original buildings are still in use on the 600-acre campus, which has grown to a complex of some 70 major buildings.
State
NHL

ORANGE COUNTY
Chapel Hill
PLAYMAKERS THEATRE (SMITH HALL)
Cameron Avenue, University of North Carolina
1850

Thought to have been designed by Alexander Jackson Davis of the firm of Town and Davis, Smith Hall is one of the oldest structures on the university campus. It was named for Governor Benjamin Smith. The temple-form building has rusticated stucco-covered brick walls and a prostyle tetrastyle Corinthian portico on the main facade. Its fluted columns have elaborate capitals of sculptured corn, wheat, and tobacco. The entablature above is simplified and embellished only by widely spaced stylized modillions. Pilasters separate the side bays. Little evidence exists of the original interior arrangement.
State

ORANGE COUNTY
Hillsborough
BURWELL SCHOOL
N. Churton Street

The Burwell School was a Presbyterian female boarding academy for young ladies from the ages of 8 to 18. It was operated for 20 years (1837–1857) by the Reverend Robert Burwell and his wife Anna. The school was originally the Presbyterian manse, which the Reverend Mr. Burwell had enlarged in 1848, and a smaller building. The man who did the work, Captain John Berry, was greatly influenced by designs found in 19th-century architectural books. His alterations resulted in the present central hall plan of the house and a five-bay main facade with a one-story shed porch. In the 1890's Victorian detailing was added, but this has been removed during recent restoration work.
Municipal

ORANGE COUNTY
Hillsborough
EAGLE LODGE
142 W. King Street
1823

Eagle Lodge was originally chartered as Masonic Lodge Number 19 in December 1791. Construction was begun on the hall in 1823. William Nichols is believed to have been the architect and John Berry the builder. It is a two-story square brick structure measuring 40 feet on each side. The walls are brick laid in Flemish bond, and the house has a low hip roof with a heavy box cornice. The central entrance on the south facade is covered by a one-story pedimented porch featuring Ionic columns. During the 19th century the structure served not only as a Masonic lodge, but also as the town's lecture hall, concert theater, and Civil War hospital.
Private; not accessible to the public
HABS

ORANGE COUNTY
Hillsborough
HAZEL-NASH HOUSE
116 W. Queen Street
c. 1820

The Hazel-Nash House is a three-part composition: a two-story pedimented central block with a pedimented single-story wing at each side. The influence of architect Robert Morris, author of *Rural Architecture* (London, 1750), is evident, and the house closely resembles Plate 37 of his book (with the exception of the wings which have been enlarged). In the attic are some of the earliest interiors in the house, including a board-and-batten door with HL hinges and rose-headed nails. The only later addition is a single-story porch on the main facade.
Private; not accessible to the public
HABS

ORANGE COUNTY
Hillsborough
OLD ORANGE COUNTY COURTHOUSE
106 E. King Street
1845

John Berry, a native of Hillsborough and a builder, constructed the courthouse. The two-story, temple-form building has walls laid in Flemish bond with flat pilaster strips separating the individual bays. A well-proportioned Doric tetrastyle pedimented portico covers the north facade, and its four large columns support a full entablature which carries around the building. The two-stage clock tower on the roof has a square base and an octagonal upper section topped by a semispherical dome. The courthouse served as the seat of Orange County government until 1954.
County
HABS

ORANGE COUNTY
Hillsborough
ST. MATTHEW'S EPISCOPAL
CHURCH AND CHURCHYARD
St. Mary's Road
19th century

St. Matthew's is an early example of Gothic Revival architecture. Its chief stylistic elements are narrow pointed arches and a sharp spire. Over a period of 45 years the church evolved to its present form. The first three bays were built in 1825–1826. In 1830 a tower was added, in 1835 a gallery was built, the tower was rebuilt in 1850, in 1868 an exposed beam ceiling replaced the original flat one, and a spire was added in 1875. Windows contain stained galss. Inside, the church has a center aisle plan and dark stained woodwork.
Private
HABS

PENDER COUNTY
Wilmington vicinity
MOORES CREEK NATIONAL
MILITARY PARK
25 miles northwest of Wilmington on
N.C. 210
1776

The battle of Moores Creek Bridge was fought on February 27, 1776, between North Carolina patriots and Loyalists. The American victory was a major factor in preventing a full-scale British invasion in the South in the opening phases of the American Revolution. The victory influenced North Carolina to instruct her delegates to the Continental Congress to vote for independence, thus becoming the first colony to take such action.
Federal/non-federal
NPS; 49.68 acres

PERQUIMANS COUNTY
Hertford vicinity
NEWBOLD-WHITE HOUSE
Southeast of Hertford off Route 1336
north of junction with Route 1337
17th century

Architectural evidence indicates that the Newbold-White House is one of the oldest buildings in North Carolina. It is also notable for its fine exterior brickwork: the water table is English bond, and the rest of the walls are laid in Flemish bond with glazed headers. The house has a steep gable roof and interior end chimneys. A floor division is marked on the gable ends by a two-course brick stringer. Present dormers are modern but believed to be replacements of the originals. A new shed addition encloses the rear facade.
Private; not accessible to the public
HABS

PITT COUNTY
Grimesland vicinity
GRIMESLAND PLANTATION
East of Grimesland on Route 2
Late 18th century

Grimesland Plantation is a two-story house covered by beaded weatherboards. Additions made during the period when Greek Revival architecture was popular include a single-story wing on each end, a two-story addition to the rear, and a one-story veranda across the front. The house was built by William Grimes, a prominent local politican who served several terms in the General Assembly. The plantation house and its accompanying outbuildings, which include a row of frame slave quarters and a stone smokehouse, are a well-preserved reminder of the antebellum era.
Private; not accessible to the public

POLK COUNTY
Tryon vicinity
BLOCK HOUSE SITE
.5 mile east of U.S. 176 on the
boundary between North and South
Carolina
c. 1756

The Block House was built as a "dogtrot" log cabin and had two rooms divided by an open-roofed passage. It first served as a trading post but was remodeled as a fortress during the French and Indian War. In 1772 the boundary between North and South Carolina was established, and the Block House served as its western terminus. A new line was drawn and accepted between 1813 and 1815. The 1813 stone still remains in its original position, but the Block House was moved 300 yards into North Carolina in 1942. The house has been remodeled and enlarged.
Private

ROCKINGHAM COUNTY
Wentworth
WRIGHT TAVERN (REID HOUSE)
N.C. 65

Sometime prior to 1814 William Wright constructed the original section of the Wright Tavern. This section was later replaced by the present three-bay eastern half, so the oldest extant portion of the tavern is the four-bay, two-story western end. The east and west portions together form a dogtrot or "dog-run" structure more typical of log dwellings and rarely seen in frame ones. The open stair hall, the dog-run, is framed by an elliptical arch resting on pilasters and featuring a keystone. The stairway itself is Federal. Several additions have been made to the rear of the tavern: an early, unheated shed

was replaced by a larger one and eventually raised to two stories; the original dining room was enlarged; a porch was attached to the rear elevation and later extended across the east end of the dining room; and a board and batten kitchen was built onto the rear of the dining room (no longer extant).
Private
HABS

ROWAN COUNTY
Salisbury
COMMUNITY BUILDING (ROWAN
COUNTY COURTHOUSE)
200 N. Main Street
Mid–19th century

This building is the third to serve Rowan County as a courthouse. It was dedicated in early 1857 and served its intended judicial purpose until 1914. Simplicity and symmetry characterize the courthouse. Notable classical elements are the hexastyle Doric portico, the carefully proportioned and elongated window openings, and the entablature ornamented by triglyphs. Building material is brick covered stucco.
County
HABS

UNION COUNTY
Monroe
UNION COUNTY COURTHOUSE
Courthouse Square
1886

Union County was formed in December, 1842, and this is the second courthouse to be constructed. It is a two-story brick building with low, hip roof surmounted by a large cupola, the structure's most arresting feature. The original section consisted of a five-bay main block and flanking two-bay wings. In 1922 the addition of two three-bay wings greatly enlarged the courthouse. Front and rear facades are identical and have projecting three-bay pedimented central pavilions. Each pavilion features a one-story arcaded wooden porch with a mansard roof.
County

VANCE COUNTY
Williamsboro
ST. JOHN'S EPISCOPAL CHURCH
Route 1329
1773

St. John's Church remains as the only colonial Anglican church building in the diocese of North Carolina, one of three dioceses in the state. Its construction predated the establishment of Williamsboro. By 1781 the community had developed around the church. The church

itself is a simple rectangle with molded weatherboards on a foundation of brick laid in Flemish bond. Contained in the west gable end is the original double door surmounted by a small pediment. Above the entrance is a row of four windows with molded sills and nine-over-nine sash. The interior of the church has remained basically unaltered and contains some of the best colonial church woodwork in North Carolina.
Private
HABS

VANCE COUNTY
Williamsboro vicinity
BURNSIDE PLANTATION HOUSE
On Route 1335 approximately 1.8 miles east of Williamsboro Crossroads
Early 19th century

Burnside Plantation is one of the best examples of Federal plantation architecture in central North Carolina. The house is a five-bay, two-story structure covered with beaded weatherboards and set on a stone foundation. The principal south facade features a slightly recessed central entrance containing a door with eight octagonal flat-panels. The entrance is covered by a one-story porch with a flat roof, supported by flanking pairs of reeded Doric pilasters on pedestals. The intricate plasterwork and Adam mantels in the interior reflect the influence of styles popular in Virginia at that time. Interesting outbuildings include a board and batten kitchen with Greek Revival interior trim and a large fireplace, plus a smokehouse with a gable roof.
Private
HABS

WAKE COUNTY
Raleigh
CHRIST EPISCOPAL CHURCH
120 E. Edenton Street
1852, Richard Upjohn

Christ Church is a Gothic Revival granite building ornamented with lancet windows and angled corner buttresses. The plan of the church is a Latin cross with two side aisles. There are galleries over the west end of the nave and over each transept. Outstanding interior work includes the hammer-beam roof and truss-work, and the altar and reredos of Caen limestone installed in 1915. A bell tower was built in 1861, and a new chapel and parish house —of similar style—designed by Hobart Upjohn, grandson of the architect, were completed in 1921.
Private
HABS

WAKE COUNTY
Raleigh
FEDERAL BUILDING (RALEIGH POST OFFICE AND COURTROOM)
300 Fayetteville Street
Late 19th century, Alfred B. Mullett

Alfred B. Mullett, as Supervising Architect of the Treasury, drew the original plans for the U.S. Courtroom and Post Office in Raleigh. It was conceived as a second Empire style structure of granite-faced brick topped by a mansard roof. The three central bays of the east facade form a projecting pavilion accentuated by quoins which are repeated on the ends of the flanking three-bay wings. At the base of the roof is a curiously fashioned entablature featuring a band of dentils punctuated by stylized consoles beneath the cornice. Changes were made in 1908, 1912–1913, and 1937–1938. The pavilion entrance on the east side was replaced by double doors behind four massive Tuscan columns set *in antis* forming a loggia. Later the sides were extended from five to nine bays and another triple dormer was added. During the 1937–1938 construction phase a third section of four bays was added to the west. The present structure is almost twice the size of the original.
Federal

WAKE COUNTY
Raleigh
HAYWOOD HALL
211 New Bern Avenue
1790's

John Haywood (1755–1827), for whom Haywood Hall was constructed, was treasurer of the state (1787–1827), a founder and trustee of the University of North Carolina, and a founder, warden, and vestryman of Christ Church in Raleigh. His home is a two-story, Federal dwelling with a center passage plan. A central, two-story portico over the main entrance has attenuated, fluted Doric columns. Beneath the eavesline is a modillion cornice. Three dependencies behind the house include the former kitchen and two stables.
Private; not accessible to the public

WAKE COUNTY
Raleigh
HAYWOOD, RICHARD B., HOUSE
127 E. Edenton Street
c. 1850

Richard Benneham Haywood was a prominent Raleigh physician who, in 1849, helped to establish the North Carolina Medical Society. Haywood also served as a surgeon in the Confederate Army. The Haywood House is a simple, two-story, brick, Greek Revival structure. On both sides of the house are beautifully executed bay windows, and a one-story portico with fluted Doric columns and a full entablature graces the main facade. Although a one-story wing containing a kitchen and a bathroom has been added, the house is otherwise little altered and contains many of its original furnishings.
Private

WAKE COUNTY
Raleigh
LANE, JOEL, HOUSE
728 W. Hargett Street
18th century

The Joel Lane House is a small frame dwelling with a gambrel roof pierced by shed dormers. Inside is a center passage with rooms opening off both sides. A wing was added in the 19th century, and the house was moved to its present location in 1927. At that time the original chimneys were damaged and incorrectly rebuilt. The present porch is a copy of a 19th-century design. Joel Lane was active in state and local politics until his death in 1795. He was one of the commissioners who laid out Wake County, he served on the local committee of safety during the Revolution, and he represented Wake County in the state senate and the state constitutional convention. Lane's own tract of 1,000 acres became the city of Raleigh.
Private
HABS

WAKE COUNTY
Raleigh
MORDECAI HOUSE
Mimosa Street
c. 1785

The older portion was built for Henry Lane, probably as a one-and-one-half-story hall and parlor frame dwelling. This section was eventually raised to two stories. Moses Mordecai, for whom the house was named, married two of Henry Lane's daughters. While owner, Mordecai hired architect William Nichols to enlarge the house. Nichols did so by constructing a Greek Revival, two-story addition on the south side of the existing house to make an L-shaped structure. A two-story pedimented portico projects from the center bay of the main facade. The second story columns are Ionic, and those on the first floor level are Doric.
Public

WAKE COUNTY
Raleigh
NORTH CAROLINA EXECUTIVE MANSION
210 N. Blount Street
1891, Samuel Sloan and Gustavus Adolphus Bauer

The North Carolina Executive Mansion has an irregularity of plan and massing typical of the Queen Anne style, although the verandas and covered balconies feature ornate posts, brackets, and openwork fascias characteristic of designs by the English architect Charles Eastlake. Shaped like an irregular cross, the house has many projecting bays with steep gable roofs. Chimneys of molded brick with corbelled courses and decorative bands project from the hip roof. The exterior is brick with sandstone trim. Two parlors, a dining room, library, and ballroom are located on the first floor, and the private family quarters are on the second floor.
State

WAKE COUNTY
Raleigh
NORTH CAROLINA STATE CAPITOL
Capitol Square
1833–1840, Ithiel Town, A. J. Davis, and David Paton

Architecturally the North Carolina Capitol is an important example of the work of three outstanding 19th-century architects. The building is considered by critics to be an exceptionally fine version of the Greek Revival style. It is roughly cruciform in plan with Doric-columned pedimented porticos on the east and west facades. From the center of the low, hip roof rises the octagonal drum of the hemispherical dome. The ground floor features a central circular lobby directly above which, on the main floor, is a circular rotunda. The interior of the dome is coffered. The chambers of the Senate and the House of Representatives are two full stories in height.
State

WAKE COUNTY
Raleigh
ST. MARY'S CHAPEL
900 Hillsborough Street
1855, Richard Upjohn

St. Mary's Chapel is a simple board and batten, rectangular structure covered by a steep gable roof. The main or south gable contains a pointed segmental-arch portal flanked by narrow lancet windows. Above the entrance is a hood supported by curved brackets with geometric openwork featuring a trefoil in the gable. A cartwheel "rose" window is located in the center of the gable above the hood.

Transepts were added to the church in 1905, so the plan is that of a Latin cross. Inside are stained glass windows set in deep splayed reveals, and the bays of the roof are divided by simple rafters resting on molded brackets. The chapel was originally built for St. Mary's School and has been altered.
Private

WAKE COUNTY
Raleigh
SEABOARD COAST LINE RAILROAD COMPANY OFFICE BUILDING
325 Halifax Street
19th century

The first railroad train reached Raleigh on March 21, 1840, as part of the Raleigh & Gaston Railroad. In November, 1893, the Raleigh & Gaston entered into an agreement with several associated railroads to form the Seaboard Air Line. This company, in turn, merged with the Atlantic Coast Line in 1967 and became the Seaboard Coast Line. The building itself was constructed in at least three stages which conform stylistically to one another. The three-story north section was begun in 1861, and the third floor was added in 1891. In 1886 a single-story, two-bay wing was added on the south side. It was raised a story and lengthened in the early 1940's. The entire structure is brick. It has been used for railroad administration for over a century and is one of the oldest commercial buildings in the state to continue to serve its intended purpose.
Private

WAKE COUNTY
Raleigh
STATE BANK OF NORTH CAROLINA (CHRIST CHURCH RECTORY)
11 New Bern Avenue
1813

The State Bank of North Carolina was incorporated in 1810, and three years later the present bank was built. The building continued to serve its original purpose until bankrupted by the Civil War. From 1873 to 1951 the structure was the rectory for Christ Church and was owned by the church until 1968. The North Carolina National Bank then purchased the building and moved it 100 feet southeast of its original site. The Federal style bank is two stories high and has lunettes in the roof gables. Window lintels and sills are granite. On the east and west elevations are superimposed, two-story pedimented porticos with modified Tuscan capitals. Overall, the bank exhibits the provincial adaptation of classical architectural forms. Inside, some original mantels and doors remain, although the vault is a replacement.
Private
HABS

WAKE COUNTY
Raleigh
WHITE-HOLMAN HOUSE
209 E. Morgan Street
18th century

The White-Holman House is one of the finest and oldest residences in Raleigh and is essential to the study of architectural development in North Carolina. William White, secretary of state for North Carolina (1798–1810), began construction of the house in late 1798. The original two-story structure was covered by beaded weatherboards and had a single-story wing on each gable end. Late in the 19th century the east wing was destroyed and the west wing was enclosed in a two-story addition. The main entrance contains raised-panel double doors framed by a molded architrave surmounted by a transom. Along the rear of the house is a single-story weatherboard addition. The White-Holman House is one of a group of houses in Raleigh that has similar, elaborate interior woodwork.
Municipal

WAKE COUNTY
Raleigh vicinity
MIDWAY PLANTATION
8 miles east of Raleigh on U.S. 64
1848

Charles Lewis Hinton built Midway Plantation and presented it as a wedding gift to his son Charles L. Hinton. The main house at Midway is a three-bay, frame structure with a low, hip roof. A one-story entrance porch on the south facade has four heavy, fluted Doric columns supporting a plain entablature. Three subsidiary rooms at the rear are later additions, although the wings at the east and north sides are believed to be original. All interior and exterior architectural detail on the house is vernacular Greek Revival. The mantels are particularly fine. Surviving dependencies are the carriage house, kitchen, schoolhouse, and east office.
Private
HABS

WAKE COUNTY
Raleigh vicinity
YATES MILL
Lake Wheeler Road

The oldest portion of the mill was probably built in the mid–18th century. Sometime after 1820 this structure was rebuilt and modernized; it is presently a two-story, rectangular, weatherboard building. Attached to the east side is a one-story shed addition, and the building rests upon random coursed rubble piers and secondary wooden supports. Operative until 1953, the Yates Mill is one of the few examples of the early American milling industry in eastern North Carolina. Since construction it has been used for lumber manufacture, corn and wheat milling, and wool carding.

State; not accessible to the public

Vaughan vicinity
BUCK SPRING PLANTATION (NATHANIEL MACON HOUSE)
    North of Vaughan on County Route 1348
    Late 18th century

Nathaniel Macon (1758–1837), later a U. S. Representative and Senator, inherited the several hundred-acre nucleus of the Buck Spring Plantation in 1763. He had the small dwelling built in 1781 and lived in it the remainder of his life. Today 70 acres of Macon's enlarged 1,724–acre tract remain intact. On the site are the graves of Macon, his wife and son, an original corncrib, the reconstructed house, a more modern caretaker's house, and an externally reconstructed smokehouse. The log stable is believed to be late 19th- or early 20th-century.

County
HABS

Creswell vicinity
SOMERSET PLACE STATE HISTORIC SITE
    19th century

Somerset Place was one of the most important antebellum plantations in North Carolina. Situated on Phelps Lake near the Scuppernong River, the plantation contained at the peak of its operation, several thousand acres of arable land, grist and sawmills, and a large labor supply to raise corn, the principal crop. In the 1780's the land, which was then mostly swamp, was drained and planted with rice. Eventually the lands were acquired by one owner. The present mansion house is a two-and-one-half-story frame dwelling almost entirely surrounded by full length porches raised to two stories on the front and two sides of the rear wing. The architecture is vernacular exhibiting Greek Revival details around the doorways. West Indian influence is evident in the open galleries on both floors and the extension of the roof to cover them. Nearby is the two-story Colony House, originally the main house. Extant dependencies surround the house, and foundations for others are visible.

State
HABS

Fremont
AYCOCK, CHARLES B., BIRTHPLACE
    6 miles from the junction of Route 1542 and U.S. 117
    19th century

The farm complex where Charles B. Aycock, forty-ninth governor of North Carolina, was born, consists of a house, kitchen, stable, several small outbuildings, and a late 19th-century weatherboard schoolhouse moved to the site in 1912. Constructed about 1840, the house is a single-story frame dwelling with a gable roof and exterior common bond end chimneys. Across the rear facade is a shed porch supported by simple wooden posts. The kitchen, to the east of the house, has a gable roof and a large common bond chimney on the east gable. Charles Aycock was a strong supporter of free public education.

State

Wilkesboro
OLD WILKES COUNTY JAIL
    N. Bridge Street
    1858–1859

The Old Wilkes County Jail is a rectangular, two-story brick building with interior end chimneys. Its hip roof is low with a wide overhang. The east or principal facade is three bays wide and has entrances through the center and left bays. Inside, the jail has a center passage plan. South of the hall is a flight of stairs, and on the north side there is one large cell. Upstairs the plan is similar. Much original hardware (including strap hinges and several early locks) is intact. Primitive security and sanitary devices remain. Rooms for the jailer were provided. Tom Dula (commemorated in the ballad "Tom Dooley") was incarcerated here briefly after the Civil War. The jail is presently unused.

Municipal

Richmond Hill vicinity
RICHMOND HILL LAW SCHOOL
    North of Richmond Hill on County Route 1530
    Mid–19th century

Richmond Hill was the home and law school of Richmond M. Pearson (1805–1878). Pearson was admitted to the North Carolina bar in 1826, served in the state legislature from 1829 to 1833, and was chief justice of the North Carolina Supreme Court from 1850 to 1878. His home is a two-story brick building with a low, hip roof. The central doorway is framed by sidelights, and the solid areas between the bays are emphasized by vertical, projecting brick panels extending from ground level to the roof. The interior plan is an unusual T-shape.

Private

North Dakota

Theodore Roosevelt National Memorial Park,
Medora, North Dakota. *NPS*

Bison Herd,
Theodore Roosevelt National Memorial Park,
Medora, North Dakota. *NPS*

Big Hidatsa Village Site, Stanton vicinity, North Dakota.
State Game and Fish Commission

BILLINGS COUNTY (also in McKenzie County)
Medora

THEODORE ROOSEVELT NATIONAL MEMORIAL PARK

Theodore Roosevelt's contributions to the conservation of our country's natural resources for public benefit are commemorated in this park. Within the park are the Badlands along the Little Missouri River and the site of Roosevelt's Elkhorn Ranch headquarters. His ranching operations here, 1883–1887, were consistent with his philosophy of the rugged life, and experiences in this area made him aware of the necessity for conservation of natural resources. Here, too, his experiences and observations aided him in the writing of *The Winning of the West,* his major literary contribution to American history.
Federal/non-federal
NPS; 70,436 acres

BURLEIGH COUNTY
Menoken vicinity
MENOKEN INDIAN VILLAGE SITE
1.25 miles north of Menoken, Verendrye State Park
1738

The Menoken Indian Village Site is generally considered the site of the first Menoken Indian village reached by Pierre de la Verendrye's expedition of 1738. The ditch surrounding the site is still clearly visible, and archeological excavation has uncovered evidence of a palisade with four bastions.
State; not accessible to the public
NHL

MC KENZIE COUNTY
THEODORE ROOSEVELT NATIONAL MEMORIAL PARK
Reference—see Billings County

MERCER COUNTY
Stanton vicinity
BIG HIDATSA VILLAGE SITE
North bank of Knife River, 1 mile north of Stanton
1740–1845

The Big Hidatsa Village Site, the largest of five Indian villages in the area, shows the effects of 100 years of contact with fur traders and the resulting acculturation. These five villages formed an extremely important center for the northern Plains fur trade. Several fortification trenches and depressions of more than 108 circular earth lodges are clearly visible.
Private; not accessible to the public
NHL

WILLIAMS COUNTY (also in Roosevelt County, Montana)
Buford vicinity
FORT UNION TRADING POST NATIONAL HISTORIC SITE
West of Buford
1828

As the principal Upper Missouri fur trade depot, Fort Union Trading Post afforded northern plains tribes their first long contact with the alien white culture. Built in 1828, it marked the opening of John Jacob Astor's campaign to secure the Upper Missouri and Rocky Mountain fur trade for the American Fur Company. The extensive, well-built post lasted until 1866, when the Army purchased it and used its materials to build its nearby post, Fort Buford. Little surface evidence of the site remains today.
Federal/non-federal; not accessible to the public
NPS; 380 acres

Ohio

S. S. *Delta Queen*, Cincinnati, Ohio. *Ohio Historical Society*

Seip Earthworks,
Paxton Township, Ohio.
Don E. Weaver

Old Courthouse, Dayton, Ohio.
Cox Heart Institute

First Congregational Church,
Tallmadge Town Square Historic District,
Tallmadge, Ohio. *Perry Borchers*

ADAMS COUNTY
Locust Grove vicinity
SERPENT MOUND
5 miles northwest of Locust Grove on Ohio 73
First century

The Great Serpent Mound, built by either the Adena or Hopewell peoples, is situated on a high, crescent-shaped hill. Conforming to the curve of the hill and occupying its summit is the serpent, its head resting near the top and its body winding back down a slight slope for 1300 feet. This earthen snake effigy site was one of the first areas in the United States to be set aside because of its prehistoric interest and scientific value. Following excavations in 1886, the site was purchased by Harvard's Peabody Museum, and in 1900 it was deeded to the Ohio Historical Society.
State
NHL

ALLEN COUNTY
Spencerville vicinity
MIAMI AND ERIE CANAL, DEEP CUT
2 miles south of Spencerville on Ohio 66
1825

The Deep Cut is a vestige of the Miami and Erie Canal, one of early Ohio's two major artificial waterways. By providing cheap, easy transportation, the canal helped to settle western Ohio and raised land values. It also gave agriculture and the infant industries of interior Ohio many markets, connecting them with Atlantic and southern seaports and, ultimately, with foreign trading centers. The canal thus contributed notably to Ohio's swift rise to a prominent position in the Nation by 1860.
State
NHL

ATHENS COUNTY
Athens
MANASSEH CUTLER HALL, OHIO UNIVERSITY
Ohio University campus
1819

Manasseh Cutler Hall, now the main administration building for Ohio University, is the oldest college building in the Old Northwest. It was named for the New England botanist, physician, and minister, Manasseh Cutler, who wrote the charter for the university in 1804. Among the occupants of the building was William Holmes McGuffey, author of the six *Eclectic Readers*, who was president of the university from 1839 to 1843. The three-story brick building with gable roof has been remodeled and restored.
State
NHL

AUGLAIZE COUNTY
Wapakoneta vicinity
FORT AMANDA SITE
9 miles northwest of Wapakoneta on Ohio 198
1813

Fort Amanda was constructed at the order of William Henry Harrison, commander of troops in the Northwest Territory. He had been charged with the recapture of Detroit from the British and needed a chain of supply depots on the Ohio to accomplish his purpose. Located near the head of navigation on the Auglaize River, Fort Amanda consisted of four two-story log blockhouses connected by an 11-foot palisade. Inside this enclosure was a large warehouse. At the conclusion of the War of 1812 Fort Amanda was abandoned.
State

BROWN COUNTY
Ripley vicinity
RANKIN, JOHN, HOUSE
East of Ripley, Liberty Hill
1828

The Reverend John Rankin was a leader of the abolitionist movement in Ohio. In 1826 he published *Letters on American Slavery*, a collection of 13 epistles written earlier for a local newspaper. Rankin was an active organizer of antislavery groups. During the 1820's he and others who opposed slavery began aiding fugitive slaves trying to escape to Canada. His home is a brick building 35 feet square and practically devoid of ornament. There are double chimneys at each gable end, and most interior woodwork is original.
State
HABS

BUTLER COUNTY
Oxford
FISHER HALL (OXFORD FEMALE COLLEGE)
Miami University campus
1854-1856, James K. Wilson

The Reverend John Witherspoon Scott founded Oxford Female College. Scott had been a professor at Miami University but was forced to leave in 1845 because of his abolitionist views. Operated under the auspices of the Presbyterian synod of Cincinnati, Oxford Female College was chartered by the state of Ohio in 1852. The three-story building is brick trimmed in stone and is surmounted by a five-story central tower. Its central section is flanked by two wings, and the building as a whole may have been conceived in two stages, front and rear. Interior remodeling has been extensive. Oxford Female College

had a student body of over 200. It was forced to close its doors in 1882 because of financial difficulties, and in 1926 the building was purchased by Miami University.
State; not accessible to the public

BUTLER COUNTY
Oxford
McGUFFEY, WILLIAM H., HOUSE
401 E. Spring Street
1833

While living here between 1833 and 1836, William Holmes McGuffey wrote the first three of his six *Eclectic Readers*, which sold 122 million copies over a 70-year period. During this period and in the seven years preceding, McGuffey was professor of modern languages at Miami University. Among the memorabilia preserved in the restored house are the octagonal table upon which he compiled the readers and the lectern he used at the university.
Private
NHL

CARROLL COUNTY
Carrollton
McCOOK, DANIEL, HOUSE
Public Square
1837

Daniel McCook erected this large ell-shaped two-story brick house, and his family occupied it until 1853. They were known as the "Fighting McCooks" during the Civil War, when 14 of them fought for the Union, 13 as officers. The main section of the house has a gable roof with a classical cornice. There is a single chimney at either end, and recessed in the center of the main facade is a stone-arched doorway with sidelights and fanlight. Window trim is also stone. Daniel McCook's sons served as an attorney general of Ohio and as an acting governor of Dakota territory. Among his nephews were a governor of Colorado territory, a congressman from New York, a theologian and natural historian, and a professor of modern languages.
State

CARROLL COUNTY
Carrollton vicinity
PETERSBURG MILL
4.3 miles south of Carrollton on Ohio 332
Mid-19th century

Once the hub of commercial milling activity in Carroll County, the Petersburg Mill was last operated in 1938. Originally powered by water from Little McGuire Creek, the gristmill was converted to a modern roller mill in the 1880's and

powered by steam. The main structure stands two-and-one-half stories above a full basement. A small community with its own post office grew up around the mill in its heyday of operation.
Private

COLUMBIANA COUNTY (also in Beaver County, Pennsylvania)
East Liverpool
THE BEGINNING POINT OF THE U.S. PUBLIC LAND SURVEY
On the Ohio-Pennsylvania boundary
1785

On September 30, 1785, Thomas Hutchins, the first Geographer to the United States, inaugurated the use of the rectangular land survey system which resulted from the Ordinance of 1785 "for ascertaining the mode of disposing of lands in the western territory." Accurate and convenient, the system has been utilized since that time in surveying the millions of acres of land making up the 31 states created out of the public domain.
Private
NHL

CUYAHOGA COUNTY
Valley View Village
OHIO AND ERIE CANAL
Ohio 631
1832

The Ohio and Erie Canal was part of a thousand-mile canal network that connected Lake Erie to the Ohio River and gave access to New York, Pennsylvania, and Indiana canals. For 20 years the system accelerated the growth of population, industry, and commerce, but eventually it could not compete with the greater speed, flexibility, and lower costs of the railroads. The one-and-a-half-mile section which includes locks 37 and 38 also includes the aqueduct over Tinkers Creek, a mill, and a house, all dating from the period of canal use.
State
NHL

ERIE COUNTY
Milan
EDISON, THOMAS ALVA, BIRTHPLACE
1841

Thomas A. Edison, one of America's most illustrious inventors, was born here on February 11, 1847. Uninterested in formal schooling, Edison worked hard to educate himself. Among his many inventions in electricity, sound, and other fields are the microphone, the phonograph, and the incandescent electric lamp. In 1928 Congress awarded him a gold medal for his contributions to mankind. This small brick cottage was his home for only seven years, and was purchased by Edison in 1906. Within are mementos of the Edison family and a few original furnishings.
Private
NHL; HABS

FAIRFIELD COUNTY
Lancaster
SHERMAN, JOHN, BIRTHPLACE
137 E. Main Street
1825

Between 1855 and 1898 John Sherman served as Congressman, United States Senator, Secretary of the Treasury, and Secretary of State. He was the author of the Silver Purchase Act (1890) and the Sherman Anti-Trust Act (1890), which remains the Government's basic law against the undue centralization of business and industry. Sherman's older brother, William Tecumseh Sherman, was also born in this house. It was John Sherman's home until he was nine and then only intermittently between 1835 and 1840. The house consists of two sections, a two-story brick section in front and a two-story frame section behind it. The brick section may postdate Sherman's birth.
State
NHL

FAIRFIELD COUNTY
Tarlton vicinity
TARLTON CROSS MOUND
.5 mile north of Tarlton on County Route 131
c. 300 B.C. to 500 A.D.

Tarlton Cross Mound and the four smaller mounds associated with it are a group erected by the Hopewell Indians. It is an effigy mound shaped like a Greek cross and is the only such prehistoric configuration in the state. Measuring 90 feet across its arms, the mound stands three feet high.
State

FRANKLIN COUNTY
Columbus
CAMPBELL MOUND
McKinley Avenue, .5 mile south of Trabue Road
c. 500 B.C. to 400 A.D.

Campbell Mound is a relatively large conical Indian burial mound measuring 20 feet in height and 100 feet in diameter. It was probably constructed during the Late Adena times, towards the end of the period 500 B.C.–400 A.D. Although the mound may have been erected within a short period, it may also have had additions over a period of several hundred years. If such is the case, future excavations may reveal changes in burial styles, artifact forms, and types of artifacts buried with the dead.
State

FRANKLIN COUNTY
Columbus
FORT HAYES
Cleveland Avenue and Int. 71
19th and 20th centuries

Fort Hayes was established by the U.S. War Department in 1863 for the manufacture and storage of war materials. Buildings of importance on the post are the gate house (late 1890's); the administration building (1910); post exchange and gymnasium (1907); general mess (1894); guardhouse; hospital (1908); living quarters for army dependents (begun in 1894); commandant's residence (1890–1895); and the arsenal itself. The arsenal is Tuscan Revival, three stories high, and built of brick. Its focal point is a five-story tower which originally contained a stairway and hoisting apparatus for elevators. The arsenal was built in 1864.
Federal

FRANKLIN COUNTY
Columbus
HAYES AND ORTON HALLS, THE OHIO STATE UNIVERSITY
The Oval
1893, Hayes and Orton Halls, Yost and Packard

These university buildings were constructed as a result of Justin S. Morrill's land grant college acts of 1862 and 1890. Morrill, a native of Vermont, sponsored congressional legislation which provided federal land and money for the establishment and support of agricultural and technical colleges in several states. Hayes Hall, named for Rutherford B. Hayes, a university trustee, is Richardsonian Romanesque. It was the first Ohio college building to be designed and used exclusively for manual, technical, and domestic instruction, which subjects represented a clear break with the heretofore classics-dominated system of American higher education. Orton Hall, named for Edward Orton, Sr., first president of the university (founded in 1870), was designed and built for laboratory work and as a museum. It was the earliest fire resistant structure on campus.
State

FRANKLIN COUNTY
Westerville
HANBY, BENJAMIN, HOUSE
160 W. Main Street
c. 1850

Benjamin Hanby (1833–1867), a native Ohioan, was a composer of popular songs and ballads. His best-known piece, "Darling Nelly Gray," was written while Hanby was a student at Otterbein College in Westerville, from which he graduated in 1858. The Hanby family moved to Westerville in 1853, and Benjamin's father was a founder of Otterbein. Although moved from its original site, the Hanby House remains unaltered and contains furniture and personal family items. It is a two-story frame building with a gable roof and a low kitchen wing at the rear.
State

FRANKLIN COUNTY
Westerville
TOWERS HALL, OTTERBEIN COLLEGE
West Main and Grove Streets, Otterbein College campus
1872, Robert T. Brookes

Towers Hall has served since 1872 as the main classroom building of Otterbein College. The three-story Gothic structure has pointed windows, doorways, and towers. The masonry bearing walls have stone or brick footings. Architect Robert T. Brookes designed the building as a central block with dependent wings. Timber framed towers rise above the two main entrances located on the east side of the central block. The northern tower houses a bell apparatus. Addition of a library to the rear of the building in 1954 is the only alteration to the original structure. Renovation of the interior is planned.
Private

GALLIA COUNTY
Gallipolis
OUR HOUSE
434 1st Avenue
1819

Village life in early Gallipolis centered around the brick tavern built by Henry Cushing. The Federal style building has bridged chimneys at either end, each separated by a high, semicircular window. Unaltered since construction, the two-story tavern measures 46 by 35 feet. A separate kitchen structure is located at the rear of the tavern.
State

GREENE COUNTY
Fairborn vicinity
HUFFMAN FIELD
Wright-Patterson Air Force Base, 1 mile southwest of Fairborn

Wilbur and Orville Wright, pioneers in the development of American aviation, built a hangar here in 1904–1905. Tests and experiments they carried out led gradually to the perfection of their original flying machine. The warping of the plane's wings and the operation of the tail rudder were first made independent of one another, while the major breakthrough was the invention of the aileron control system. Two "blinkers" were added between the surfaces of the front elevator to assist the rudder in making a turn. A 38–minute flight at an average speed of 38 miles per hour was made here by the Wrights in October, 1905. World War I Army pilots were trained at Huffman Field. Today the Wright hangar no longer exists, although its location is marked by a cement pylon. The rest of the area is covered with grass.
Regional

GUERNSEY COUNTY
Old Washington vicinity
S BRIDGE, NATIONAL ROAD
4 miles east of Old Washington on U.S. 40
1828

The S Bridge, which spans a small stream on U.S. 40, is a tangible reminder of the National Road, built across Ohio between 1825 and 1838. The stone bridge is one of four of its kind extant in Ohio. Bridges of this plan are found where the direction of the road lies at an angle to that of the stream. The bridge proper is straight, crossing the water at right angles, and the approaches are curved. The arch thus is of minimum span and simple form.
State
NHL

HAMILTON COUNTY
Cincinnati
CINCINNATI MUSIC HALL
1243 Elm Street
1878

The Music Hall was built when Cincinnati was a bustling port and still one of the largest cities in the country. It is made of red brick, and the center section, under a tall, peaked roof, features a large rose window. Flanking the center section are two spires. Inside is a large auditorium foyer and various public rooms. The architectural style is best described as Victorian Gothic.
Municipal

HAMILTON COUNTY
Cincinnati
DELTA QUEEN
Public Landing
1926

The sternwheeler *Delta Queen* still carries passengers on tourist excursions from Pittsburgh, Pennsylvania, to New Orleans, Louisiana. She is the last such vessel engaged in the overnight passenger trade on an American river. Built on the River Clyde (Scotland) in 1924 and transhipped to Sacramento, California, for assembly, the *Delta Queen* measures 285 feet length overall, 58 feet at the beam, rises 62 feet above the waterline, and draws 7.6 feet. The steamboat contains stateroom accommodations for 190 passengers and is driven by a paddlewheel connected to a cross-compound steam engine.
Private

HAMILTON COUNTY
Cincinnati
LANGDON HOUSE
3626 Eastern Avenue
1855

The Langdon House is a mid–19th-century Gothic Revival residence, built by Henry Archer Langdon, a Civil War veteran. Langdon served as assistant surgeon to the 79th Regiment, Ohio Volunteer Infantry. After the war Langdon returned to Ohio and practiced medicine at his home until his death in 1876.
Private; not accessible to the public

HAMILTON COUNTY
Cincinnati
PENDLETON, GEORGE HUNT, HOUSE
559 E. Liberty Street
1870

George Hunt Pendleton's most enduring contribution was his chairmanship of the Senate Civil Service Committee. In addition to his career in the Senate, Pendleton served as an Ohio legislator, a United States Congressman, and as United States Minister to Germany. Pendleton's house had direct associations with the final drafting of the Pendleton Act (1883), which created the Civil Service merit system. Here a Senate subcommittee completed revisions of the bill in 1882. In order to emphasize the separation of the new Commission from politics, the Commission met in the Pendleton House for the first two years of its existence.
Private; not accessible to the public
NHL

HAMILTON COUNTY
Cincinnati
PITMAN, BENN, HOUSE
1852 Columbia Parkway
19th century

The Benn Pitman House is a Victorian residence elaborately ornamented with hand-carved woodwork. Benjamin Pitman, a wood carving instructor at the Art Academy of Cincinnati, was known for his efforts in perfecting the system of phonography; for many years the Pitman method was the only one used by stenographers. The intricate interior woodwork design of the house represents twenty years of patient labor, and can be seen throughout —on the doors, panels, wainscoting, and exposed ceiling beams.
Private

HAMILTON COUNTY
Cincinnati
STOWE, HARRIET BEECHER, HOUSE
2950 Gilbert Avenue

Dr. Lyman Beecher, a Presbyterian minister, came to Cincinnati in 1832 to become head of the Lane Seminary. He was accompanied by his daughters Catherine and Harriet. While living here the latter (who later married Calvin Stowe) had her first insight and exposure to slavery and plantation life. Her experiences and impressions were later given in her well-known novel *Uncle Tom's Cabin* (1852). The Stowe House, although never occupied by Harriet Beecher after her marriage, is closely associated with her writing. It is a two-story brick dwelling with a gable roof and has been altered considerably since the 1830's.
State

HAMILTON COUNTY
Cincinnati
WESLEY CHAPEL METHODIST CHURCH
320 E. 5th Street
1831

The simple Classical Revival facade of the Wesley Chapel is broken only by three entrance doors above each of which is a stained glass window. Six pilasters and a large roof pediment give the brick structure a temple-like appearance. The funeral service for President William Henry Harrison was held here in 1841.
Private
HABS

HAMILTON COUNTY
Cincinnati
WILLIAM HOWARD TAFT NATIONAL HISTORIC SITE
2038 Auburn Avenue
c. 1850

Educated as a lawyer, William Howard Taft became a superior court judge in 1884 and Secretary of War in 1903. He served one term as President of the United States, 1909–1913. After eight years as professor of constitutional law at Yale University, he returned to public life as Chief Justice of the United States Supreme Court, a position he held until his death in 1930. Taft spent his first 25 years in this brick house. It had been restored and furnished to interpret the early years of the 27th President.
Federal
NPS; .78 acre

HAMILTON COUNTY
Montgomery
UNIVERSALIST CHURCH HISTORIC DISTRICT
Montgomery Road from 9433 north to Remington Avenue

Four buildings constitute the historic district: the Universalist Church, a brick residence (9463–9465 Montgomery Road), the Old Manse (9449 Montgomery Road), and the Pioneer Building (9433 Montgomery Road). The church (1837) is Greek Revival in style with four brick columns across the main facade. An octagonal cupola surmounts the portico. Inside are the original box pews. The Federal style brick residence (1820's) has a hip roof and contrasting window lintels and sills. The Old Manse (1827) remains largely original inside and out. The Pioneer Building (early 1820's) is also brick and has been remodeled inside.
Private

HIGHLAND COUNTY
Sinking Spring vicinity
FORT HILL STATE PARK
North of Sinking Spring via Ohio 41
300 B.C. to 600 A.D.

Fort Hill is a large prehistoric Indian hilltop enclosure. The stone and earthen wall enclosing the top of Fort Hill measures more than one-and-one-half miles in length and is broken by 33 irregularly spaced openings or gateways. Varying in height from 6 to 15 feet, the wall was built slightly below the crest of the hill. Extensive excavations at two circular enclosures in the valley near the fort have produced pottery fragments, flint spear points, and other items characteristic of the prehistoric Hopewell culture. Also located here

were an "arbor" (a circular structure around a central court in which the Indians lived) and a large rectangular edifice which may have been a workshop.
State

JEFFERSON COUNTY
Mount Pleasant
FRIENDS MEETINGHOUSE
Near Ohio 150
1814

There were Quakers in America as early as 1650, and many migrated to the southern colonies in the 18th century. Uncomfortable in an economic and social system that condoned slavery, the Quakers began moving west in large numbers during the 1790's and early 1800's. Mount Pleasant, founded in 1803, had become the center of Ohio Quaker business, flour milling, and farming by 1814. The Friends Meetinghouse was erected for the Ohio Yearly Meeting, which encompassed five quarterly meetings of the Society of Friends in Pennsylvania, Ohio, and the Indiana Territory. It was the first yearly meeting west of the Alleghenies. The rectangular brick building has a steep gable roof and heavy, prominent window and door lintels. Inside is an auditorium with galleries above, and there is a hand-operated sliding partition to divide the room into two sections.
State

LAKE COUNTY
Kirtland
KIRTLAND TEMPLE
9020 Chillicothe Road
1833–1838

Rectangular in plan and measuring 59 feet by 79 feet, the full two-story (plus attic) Kirtland Temple is a blend of diverse architectural elements exhibiting Venetian, Georgian, Gothic, Egyptian, and Grecian structural motifs and decoration. The frame was constructed of oak beams, and the two-foot thick sandstone walls are covered with a white stucco plaster. The gables, dormers, and balustraded tower topped with an octagonal lantern are all frame. The corners of the building are strongly articulated with contrasting stone quoins, and stone trim of the same color frames the doors and windows. In the interior, the original hand-molded, carved, and painted pews, pulpits, doors, and stairs are made of white oak, walnut, and cherry wood. The first floor was the church area, the second served as an auditorium, and the third floor, or attic, contained schoolrooms. Built between 1833 and 1838 by Mormon residents of Kirtland, the Temple now belongs to the Reorganized Church of Jesus Christ of

Latter-Day Saints and has an active congregation.
Private
HABS

LAKE COUNTY
Mentor
GARFIELD, JAMES A., HOME
(LAWNFIELD)
1059 Mentor Avenue
1832

James A. Garfield became President of the United States in 1881 after serving as a major general in the Union Army and as a Republican Congressman from Ohio from 1863 to 1880. He ran his presidential campaign from Lawnfield. Near the main house is a small frame building that served as a telegraph center. Garfield was assassinated in 1881 after serving only a few months of his term. The first two floors of the house have been restored, and many personal belongings and furnishings associated with the President may be seen in his bedroom and study.
Private
NHL

LICKING COUNTY
Brownsville vicinity
FLINT RIDGE
1.5 miles north of Brownsville on
County Route 668
10,000 B.C.

Outcroppings of the colorful flint found in a five- or six-square-mile area surrounding Flint Ridge caught the eye of roving Paleo-Indians about 8,000 to 10,000 years ago. The Indians laboriously quarried the flint and reduced it to easily transportable form before carrying any to their villages where it was fashioned into tools and weapons. The flint is found in a single stratum ranging from a few inches to one and one-half feet in depth. Pits in the prehistoric quarries vary from 2 to 20 feet in depth and from 10 to 60 feet in diameter.
State

LICKING COUNTY
Newark
NEWARK EARTHWORKS
Mound Builders State Memorial
c. 650 B.C.

The Newark Earthworks is notable for the precision of its layout and the magnitude of its plan. These prehistoric Hopewellian earthworks once covered an area of about two square miles. The site now consists of three main groups of circular and rectangular or octagonal works connected by a series of parallel earthen works.
Multiple public
NHL

LORAIN COUNTY
Oberlin
OBERLIN COLLEGE
Tappan Square
1837

The matriculation of four young women at Oberlin College in September 1837 marked the beginning of co-education on the collegiate level in the United States. With the graduation of three of them in 1841, the precedent of higher education for women began to spread throughout the country. The college was also a center of the abolition movement in the midwest and was one of the first colleges in the nation to admit Negro students. Although none of Oberlin's early buildings survive, Tappan Square, heart of the campus, has retained its original size.
Private
NHL

LUCAS COUNTY
Maumee
HULL-WOLCOTT HOUSE
1031 River Road
1827

The Hull-Wolcott House is an early Ohio interpretation of more sophisticated post-Revolutionary homes built in the seaboard colonies. Additions at the rear were constructed after the main house. A two-story porch on the south facade is crowned by a gable containing an elliptical arch, and both stories of the porch are surrounded by balustrades and supported by Doric columns. James A. Wolcott, merchant and civic leader, and his wife Mary built and occupied the house.
Municipal

LUCAS COUNTY
Maumee vicinity
FALLEN TIMBERS BATTLEFIELD
2 miles west of Maumee on U.S. 24
1794

General "Mad Anthony" Wayne's victory over the Indians in Ohio and their Canadian militia allies here on August 20, 1794, established United States sovereignty in the Old Northwest and opened the Ohio country to settlement. The resulting Treaty of Greenville in 1795 cleared the way for settlers who occupied the area during the next decade.
State
NHL

LUCAS COUNTY
Toledo
NEUKOM, ALBERT, HOUSE
301 Broadway
1888

The Neukom House is one of the few, early, cut stone homes in Toledo. It was constructed for Albert Neukom, who operated a cut stone company. He himself did the stonework for the State Library Building and the Post Office in Ann Arbor, Michigan, courthouses in Coldwater, Michigan, and Rushville, Illinois, and the Toledo Public Library. Neukom's residence is constructed of sandstone and has marble Ionic columns on the front porch, small windows in the frieze, a roof gable with three small arched windows, and a balustraded balcony over the porch. Neukom's own work is visible in two carved ornamental panels between the first- and second-story windows on the main facade.
Private; not accessible to the public

LUCAS COUNTY
Toledo
SUCCESSFUL SALES COMPANY
(OLIVER HOUSE)
27 Broadway
1859, Isaiah Rogers

The Oliver House, now the Successful Sales Company, is probably the only extant hotel designed by Isaiah Rogers. He is well known for his luxurious Tremont House in Boston and the Astor House in New York. This exterior is asymmetric due to the angular intersection of Broadway and Ottawa Street. A cylindrical bay and lobby entrance are situated at the junction of the two wings that parallel these streets. The building itself is brick with sandstone trim. Some major wooden beams have been replaced with steel I-beams, and the interior has been altered. Little original plaster or paneling remains. A sizable factory addition has been made on the side opposite the Broadway and Ottawa Street intersection.
Private

LUCAS COUNTY
Waterville
COLUMBIAN HOUSE
River and Farnsworth Roads
1825–1828

John Pray, owner and builder of the Columbian House, came to Ohio from Rhode Island in 1817. Three years after completing this house, Pray helped to plot the town of Waterville. He designed his trading post-tavern in the Federal mode with a modillion cornice, pediments at each gable end, and sash windows with eight over twelve lights. A three-story frame structure covered with clapboards was a novelty on the Ohio frontier in the 1820's, when most buildings were of crude log construction. Orginally the bar and trading post were on the first floor, the sleeping rooms on the second, and a large ballroom with fireplaces at either end on the top floor. No alterations have been made in the Columbian House which is presently operated as a restaurant.

Private

HABS

MAHONING COUNTY
Coitsville Township
McGUFFEY, WILLIAM H., BOYHOOD HOME SITE
McGuffey Road, near Ohio 616
1802

William Holmes McGuffey, college professor and educator, is best known for his elementary school texts, the *Eclectic Readers*. These six readers were in common use in 37 states for over 70 years, some 122 million copies being sold. Born in Pennsylvania, McGuffey grew up on this Ohio farm. No buildings dating from McGuffey's youth remain.

Private; not accessible to the public

NHL

MARION COUNTY
Marion
HARDING, WARREN G., HOME
380 Mount Vernon Avenue
1890

Warren G. Harding spent most of his adult life in this two-story clapboard house. It was his residence while he edited the Marion *Star* and progressed from state senator to lieutenant governor and eventually to United States Senator. From the front porch Harding conducted his presidential campaign in 1920, greeting visitors who gathered on the lawn. The Hardings left for Washington, D.C., in 1921, and three years later death struck the twenty-ninth President before his term had ended. His house has been restored and refurnished.

Private

NHL

MEDINA COUNTY
Medina
MEDINA COUNTY COURTHOUSE
Liberty Street and Broadway, Public Square
1841; 1873 (enlarged), T. Dudley Allen

The earlier Medina County Courthouse was a two-story, rectangular, Greek Revival building surmounted by a cupola and a 16-inch gilt ball. In 1873 the county

commissioners contracted to build a four-room addition on the front. The rooms were added, one above the other, at the ends of the courthouse with the intervening space now serving as an entrance portico. A mansard roof and an ornamental clock belfry were also put on at that time. The building is constructed of limestone and brick with cast iron detailing. Original masonry chimneys have been removed, and rear additions were made in 1906, 1933, and 1952.

Public

MEIGS COUNTY
Pomeroy vicinity
BUFFINGTON ISLAND
20 miles southeast of Pomeroy on Ohio 124

John Hunt Morgan, Confederate cavalry leader, audaciously carried the Civil War northwest into Ohio in July, 1863. Leading a force of 2,400 men, Morgan raided towns across southern Ohio in a rapid sweep towards Buffington Ford, opposite Buffington Island, from which to escape into West Virginia. On July 19, after reaching the river, Morgan found Federal gunboats awaiting him. A battle ensued and only a handful of Confederates crossed the Ohio River successfully. Morgan escaped into eastern Ohio and was finally forced to surrender on July 26. Buffington Island was the site of the only significant Civil War engagement in Ohio.

State

MERCER COUNTY
Fort Recovery
FORT RECOVERY SITE
Ohio 49

On November 4, 1791, the U.S. Army in the Northwest Territory was soundly defeated by Chiefs Little Turtle and Blue Jacket near the origin of the Wabash River. The American commander was General Arthur St. Clair. Two years after this rout Major General "Mad Anthony" Wayne decided to reoccupy the site of the defeat and construct a fortification impossible to capture. Completed in 1794, Fort Recovery withstood one fierce attack, but two months thereafter General Wayne won the battle of Fallen Timbers, the Treaty of Greenville (1795) was signed, and the Indian wars in the Northwest Territory were over. Fort Recovery had four 20-foot blockhouses connected by pickets. No original structures remain, but two blockhouse reproductions have been erected on the site.

State

MIAMI COUNTY (also in Shelby County)
Lockington and vicinity
LOCKINGTON LOCKS HISTORICAL AREA
T. 7 N., R. 6 E. of Washington Township (Shelby County); T. 6 N., R. 6 E. of Washington Township (Miami County)
1833–1845

The Lockington Locks Historical Area contains seven stone locks and several turning basins. Until 1877, when the canal was officially abandoned, the Lockington area was a part of the 249-mile Miami and Erie Canal between Dayton and Junction. The canal itself was built to connect Toledo and Lake Erie with Cincinnati on the Ohio River. Six locks were needed to raise river traffic to the height of the Lockington plateau. These six locks are located within a three-quarter-mile section of the canal. The remaining three miles contain the seventh lock. Lack of adequate water has prevented complete restoration of the locks to working condition.

State

MIAMI COUNTY
Piqua vicinity
PIQUA HISTORICAL AREA STATE MEMORIAL (JOHN JOHNSTON FARM AND INDIAN AGENCY)
1 mile north of Piqua
19th century

John Johnston acted as Indian agent at Fort Wayne before moving to this farm at Piqua. The original section of his house was completed in 1811, and the second section, in 1815. Johnston was Indian agent to the Shawnee during the war of 1812, charged with the supervision of all Indians who remained at peace with the United States. As many as 6,000 were on his farm at one time. When he was appointed agent of the combined agencies of Piqua and Fort Wayne in 1818, his house served as both a residence and agency headquarters. The Johnston House, now restored, is one of the few remaining Indian agency houses in the United States and the only one in Ohio. The entire farm complex, including brick house, log barn, fruit kiln, cider house, and smokehouse, is being restored.

State

MONTGOMERY COUNTY
Dayton
DUNBAR, PAUL LAURENCE, HOUSE
219 N. Summit Street
c. 1890

Paul Laurence Dunbar was the first American Negro to attain eminence in the field of literature. *Majors and Minors*, a volume of poems published in 1895, was well received. Subsequently, he wrote several other volumes of verse, four novels, and many short stories. He lived in this house during the last three years of his life, 1903–1906. The two-story brick house contains many of the poet's personal belongings.
State
NHL

MONTGOMERY COUNTY
Dayton
MONTGOMERY COUNTY
COURTHOUSE (OLD COURTHOUSE)
Northwest corner, 3rd and Main
Streets
1847–1850

Montgomery County's Old Courthouse is built of native limestone. The architecture is Greek Revival characterized by a single pediment on front and rear facades and a hexastyle portico on the entrance. Architectural treatment of the rear walls is unusual because the full colonnade has been omitted. In its stead, a single column was placed at each corner to serve as a center point for the hollow arc of the two corner walls. Four engaged pilasters ornament the central portion of the rear wall. No court sessions are held here now, and the few remaining county offices are gradually being located elsewhere.
County

MONTGOMERY COUNTY
Miamisburg vicinity
MIAMISBURG MOUND
South of Miamisburg on Mound Road
500 B.C.–400 A.D.

This prehistoric burial mound, measuring 877 feet in circumference at its base and 70 feet high, was constructed by the Adena Indians. Although no scientific exploration has been conducted, in 1869 a shaft was sunk in the mound to a depth two feet below ground level. At eight feet a single skeleton was found, and at 24 feet flat over-lapped stones were encountered which appeared to be an altar. The mound and surounding area became a park in 1920, and the park was donated to the Ohio Historical Society in 1929 by Charles Kettering. Steps to the summit have been built and fences erected at the base and top of the mound.
State

MORGAN COUNTY
Morgan vicinity
BIG BOTTOM MASSACRE SITE
1 mile southeast of Stockport on Ohio
266

In the late 1780's the Ohio Company of Associates began granting land in the Old Northwest Territory for settlement. One such grant was made to a small group in 1790, and they undertook the erection of a blockhouse at Big Bottom, 35 miles below Marietta on the Muskingum River. Little acquainted with Indian warfare, these young men failed to encircle the blockhouse with a palisade and had no defense plan in the event of an attack. Indians, coming upon the settlement and realizing it could not be defended, fell upon the white men, killing 12. Survivors spread word of the disaster, and downriver outposts were quickly fortified. The attack at Big Bottom awakened frontiersmen to the danger from hostiles and signaled the beginning of Indian wars in the Old Northwest. No aboveground evidence remains of the blockhouse or cabin.
State

OTTAWA COUNTY
Gibraltar Island
COOKE, JAY, HOME
Put-in-Bay, Lake Erie
1864–1865

Jay Cooke achieved eminence as a financier during the Civil War by selling millions of dollars worth of bonds for the Union. His success contributed to the stability and eventual victory of the federal government. Following the war, Cooke expanded his banking house and continued to prosper until his firm's failure caused the Panic of 1873. Cooke built his Gibraltar Island house in 1864–1865, using it as a summer residence until his death in 1905. It presently serves as a dormitory for the nearby Franz Theodore Stone Laboratory, which conducts research relating to Ohio's fisheries.
State; not accessible to the public
NHL

OTTAWA COUNTY
Marblehead
MARBLEHEAD LIGHTHOUSE
Ohio 163
1821

The Marblehead Lighthouse is now the oldest continuously operated light on the Great Lakes. Authorized by Congress in 1820, the 55-foot stone tower overlooks the entrance to Sandusky Bay. No alterations have been made in the tower except an addition at the top to contain an improved lighting system.
Federal

OTTAWA COUNTY
Put-in-Bay, South Bass Island
PERRY'S VICTORY AND
INTERNATIONAL PEACE MEMORIAL
NATIONAL MONUMENT
1813, battle; 1915, peace memorial

At the battle of Lake Erie, September 10, 1813, Commodore Oliver Hazard Perry won a decisive victory over a British naval squadron. It had far-reaching effects on both the War of 1812 and the future of the United States. Control of Lake Erie and the subsequent invasion of Canada strengthened the United States claim to the Old Northwest. In 1817 the Rush-Bagot Agreement inaugurated the move which resulted in the permanent disarmament of the 3000–mile land and water boundary between the United States and Canada. A memorial shaft commemorates Perry's victory.
Federal
NPS; 21.44 acres

PIKE COUNTY
Piketon
FRIENDLY GROVE
Ohio 220 east of Piketon
1824

Friendly Grove was built by Robert Lucas, a Virginian, and named for his wife Friendly Ashley Sumner. Similar farm houses were common in Ohio after the first wave of Virginians settled there. The Federal style brick house is two stories high and may have been built in stages. Various outbuildings no longer in existence once stood on the property, and the seamed metal roof is a recent addition. Inside, the house is largely original. Robert Lucas served two terms (1832–1836) as governor of Ohio and was appointed governor and superintendent of Indian affairs for the Iowa Territory in 1838.
Private

PREBLE COUNTY
Eaton vicinity
FORT ST. CLAIR SITE
1 mile west of Eaton
1792

Fort St. Clair, constructed at the order of General James Wilkinson, was named in honor of General Arthur St. Clair, governor of the Northwest Territory. Kekionga, an Indian village located near the present site of Fort Wayne, was designated as the objective of three major military expeditions. Fort St. Clair was built primarily as protection for the supply line, and convoys going to or returning from the expeditions camped beneath its walls. The only major action near the fort involved a battle in 1792 between Major John

Adair's convoy and a band of warriors led by Chief Little Turtle.
State

RICHLAND COUNTY
Mansfield
OAK HILL COTTAGE
310 Springmill Street
1847

The Gothic Revival Oak Hill Cottage is distinguished by its pointed arch windows (the center one containing quarries), the steep, pointed gables of its roof, the carved barge boards under the gables, the veranda and decorative carving of the spandrels of the veranda, and by its unusual window muntins. Only isolated examples of Gothic Revival cottages and villas appeared in the midwest during the first part of the 19th century. Extensive grounds which were once part of the estate have been reduced by subdivision, but the house itself remains in relatively good structural condition and has been altered only slightly.
Private

ROSS COUNTY
Bainbridge vicinity
SEIP EARTHWORKS
U.S. 50, about 3 miles east of Bainbridge
300 B.C. to 600 A.D.

When first described in 1820, the Seip Earthworks consisted of earthen walls enclosing a complex of 20 mounds. The works were constructed by prehistoric Hopewell Indians. Today the only preserved features of the site are the largest mound, Seip 1 (150 feet long, 150 feet wide, and 32 feet high), and one segment of the original embankment. Scientific exploration of the mounds from 1925 to 1927 yielded numerous artifacts—art objects, tools, and implements. More recent excavation has uncovered a Hopewell house post hole pattern revealing a floor littered with midden.
State/private

ROSS COUNTY
Chillicothe vicinity
ADENA
W. Allen Avenue extended
1807, Benjamin Henry Latrobe

Adena, originally called Mount Prospect Hill, was built for Thomas Worthington, sixth governor of Ohio. His home is a three-part, two-story quarried stone residence. The wings project forward from the center section to form a "U." The roofs are hip, and a one-story veranda runs across the main block inside the "U." Adena was once the center of a plantation complex.
State
HABS

ROSS COUNTY
Chillicothe vicinity
MOUND CITY GROUP NATIONAL MONUMENT
4 miles north of Chillicothe on Ohio 104
c. 1000

Mound City was primarily a ceremonial center for the disposal of the remains of prehistoric Hopewell Indians. The Hopewell peoples are best known for their artistic achievements and their practice of erecting mounds of earth over the remains of their dead. Excavations of these mounds have yielded much information about the Hopewellian burial customs. Many artifacts typical of the Indians' culture have been found in association with the graves. This site consists of a rectangular earth enclosure within which are located 24 burial mounds.
Federal
NPS; 67.50 acres

ROSS COUNTY
Hopetown vicinity
HOPETON EARTHWORKS
Near Mound City Group National Monument on U.S. 23
c. first century A.D.

The Hopeton Earthworks is the site of a large Hopewellian ceremonial center. It is composed of large conjoined circular and square earthen enclosures with attached small circular enclosures, four small mounds, and parallel earthen walls. Across the Scioto River is the Mound City Group National Monument, which was possibly the burial area for the same group.
Multiple private
NHL

SANDUSKY COUNTY
Fremont
HAYES, RUTHERFORD B., HOME, (SPIEGEL GROVE)
Hayes and Buckland Avenues
1859–1863

Rutherford B. Hayes, a native of Ohio, was a practicing lawyer before entering politics. He served as a Congressman from Ohio, governor of Ohio, and President of the United States, 1877–1881. Although Spiegel Grove is still the residence of the Hayes family, the estate is maintained as a memorial to the President and his wife, Lucy Webb Hayes, who are buried on the grounds, A library and museum preserve personal collections, diaries, letters, and mementos of the Hayes family.
State
NHL

SHELBY COUNTY
LOCKINGTON LOCKS HISTORICAL AREA
Reference—see Miami County

STARK COUNTY
Canton
McKINLEY, WILLIAM, TOMB
7th Street, N.W.
1907, Harold Van Buren Magonigle

William McKinley (1843–1901) was elected President of the United States in 1896 but was assassinated by Leon Czolgosz, an anarchist, early in his second term. McKinley is interred in this massive, domed, ashlar mausoleum. Heavy bronze doors lead into the interior containing the sarcophagi. The tomb itself was designed as the handle of a sheathed sword. The lawn, reflecting pool (now seeded), and walks form the blade.
State

SUMMIT COUNTY
Akron
FORT ISLAND WORKS
Approximately 600 feet west of the end of Fort Island Drive
1000–1500

Late Woodland Indians are believed to have constructed and inhabited the Fort Island Works. The oval or elliptical earthen enclosure is the only remaining one of its type in northern Ohio. No excavation of the site has been undertaken.
Private

SUMMIT COUNTY
Tallmadge
TALLMADGE TOWN SQUARE HISTORIC DISTRICT
Public Square
1809–1859

The Tallmadge Town Square Historic District consists of the oval town green and two structures fronting on it, the First Congregational Church and the town hall. These two buildings are the best examples in the Western Reserve of the transplanting of New England architectural styles to that area of Ohio. The square and its eight radial roads was the idea of the Reverend David Bacon, a Congregational minister who came to Ohio in 1809. He envisioned a commonwealth governed by clergy and laymen. His town and road plan are unique to Ohio and rare in the nation. The church, designed by Lemuel Porter, has a high classic portico with four giant Ionic columns across the facade, and the entire structure is dominated by a 100–foot steeple. Many interior alterations have been made. The town hall and academy is an

1859 Greek Revival edifice ornamented by two-story pilasters. Neither building now serves its original purpose.
Municipal/private
HABS

TUSCARAWAS COUNTY
Bolivar vicinity
FORT LAURENS SITE
Near Ohio Route 212, .5 mile south of Bolivar

Fort Laurens, named for Henry Laurens, president of the Continental Congress, was erected in 1778 as a part of General Washington's "Great Trail" of blockhouses from Fort Pitt to the British stronghold at Detroit. Garrisoned by 176 men and 5 women, the fort withstood a month-long siege by a force of British-paid Indians led by renegade Simon Girty. In August, 1779, Fort Laurens was evacuated when it was decided that the resources of the new nation could not support an outpost so deep in enemy territory. Fort Laurens, roughly 130 feet square, was contained within a curtain formed by continuous rows of log cabins. A two-story blockhouse was the main defensive point. After its evacuation in 1779, the fort was left to deteriorate and no visible traces remain above ground. Archeological surveys have given promising results.
State

TUSCARAWAS COUNTY
Gnadenhutten vicinity
GNADENHUTTEN MASSACRE SITE
South of Gnadenhutten on County Route

The Delaware Indians moved to eastern Ohio in the mid–18th century and were relatively receptive, as a group, to the tenets of Christianity. Moravian David Zeisberger, founder of the Schoenbrunn Mission, also helped establish a religious outpost at Gnadenhutten in 1772. The Moravians and their Indian converts maintained strict neutrality during the Revolution, but frontiersmen began to believe rumors that the latter had sided with the British. Following a series of Shawnee raids in Pennsylvania, a company of 150 militiamen set out for the towns on the Tuscarawas River determined to seek revenge. At Gnadenhutten they found a dress belonging to a slain woman (which the Shawnee had sold to the Christian Indians) and thereupon held a council and voted to put the Indians to death. Through guile the white men disarmed the Indians and two by two killed and scalped them. According to mission records 90 Indians died. Nothing remains of the Gnadenhutten mission. The massacre site, marked by an obelisk, contains the graves of the Indians.
State

TUSCARAWAS COUNTY
Zoar
ZOAR HISTORIC DISTRICT
Bounded on the north by 5th Street, on the east by Foltz Street, on the south by 1st Street, and on the west by the rear property lines of properties fronting on West Street
19th century

The village of Zoar was settled in 1817 by a group of Separatists from Germany. Although founded primarily as a religious community, Zoar soon began operating on a communal basis so the settlers could pay their debts and insure some measure of economic security. The village contained a church, a bakery, a tin shop, a blacksmith shop, a store, a furniture shop, weaving and sewing houses, a pottery, several mills, a brewery, a large decorative garden with greenhouses, and residences. Under the leadership of Joseph Baumeler (Bimeler) the community prospered in agriculture and industry, and Baumeler reinvested all profits in society enterprises. At his death an economic decline began, and this, coupled with waning idealism and internal dissension, finally caused the dissolution of the colony in 1898. Several structures have been torn down, but the nucleus of the village remains intact. A number of the early log houses still stand as do the bakery, the tin shop, the garden and greenhouse, the sewing house, and Baumeler's residence.
Multiple public/private
HABS

WARREN COUNTY
Lebanon
GLENDOWER
U.S. 42 (Cincinnati Avenue)
1836

Glendower, a large, three-part Greek Revival house, was built in two sections. The three-bay center block preceded the flanking wings which just predate the Civil War. An elaborate entrance portico on the north facade has a dentil cornice and a roof balustrade at the second floor level. There are corner pilasters on the central block and a balustraded deck atop the low hip roof. Notable interior features are the central stairway and the finely carved mantels.
State

WARREN COUNTY
Lebanon vicinity
FORT ANCIENT
7 miles southeast of Lebanon on Ohio 350, Fort Ancient State Memorial
c. 4

Fort Ancient is a hilltop area with large surrounding earthworks which give the impression of a fortification. The site was first built and inhabited by people of the Hopewell culture. The name of Fort Ancient, however, applies to the culture of a people who reoccupied the site in late prehistoric times.
State
NHL

WASHINGTON COUNTY
Marietta
OHIO COMPANY LAND OFFICE
Washington and 2nd Streets, Campus Martius Museum
1788

On April 7, 1788, 47 men from New England, members and employees of the Ohio Company of Associates, landed at the mouth of the Muskingum River. Congress had granted this group 1.8 million acres in the Northwest Territory. They proceeded to lay out the town of Marietta, first permanent settlement and seat of government established in the territory after passage of the Ordinance of 1787. Rufus Putnam, a superintendent of the company, was appointed to handle the task of surveying and dividing this huge tract. He worked in the Land Office, which is believed to be among the first buildings constructed. It is a hewn log structure covered with siding and measuring 27 by 19 feet.
State

WASHINGTON COUNTY
Marietta
PUTNAM, RUFUS, HOUSE
Campus Martius Museum, corner of 2nd and Washington Streets
Late 18th century

After founding Marietta, the settlers, fearful of Indian attack, built a fortified village on a bluff above the river mouth which they named Campus Martius. Rufus Putnam, a superintendent of the Ohio Company, constructed a home within the fort which, though greatly altered, has survived on its original site. Built as a two-story, four-room residence with a three-bay facade, the house has been enlarged and its interior changed. It is believed to be the oldest house in Ohio.
State

WASHINGTON COUNTY
Marietta
W. P. SNYDER, JR.
On the Muskingum River at Sacra
Via
1918

The *W. P. Snyder,* christened in 1918, is a sternwheeler "poolboat," so called because its pilothouse is set forward on the second deck, rather than on the roof. This innovation enabled her to tow coal barges under the low bridges over the Monongahela River. The steel boat, 175 feet by 32.3 feet, has a paddle wheel 21 feet in diameter. An elaborate "hog chain" support, composed of steel cables mounted on posts at each side of the boat, prevents her from buckling in the center. Other features include a pilotwheel, a bell signal system, and stateroom and cabin construction which remains just as it was a century ago. The *W. P. Snyder* is now open to the public as a museum.
State

WOOD COUNTY
Perrysburg
OLD WOOD COUNTY JAIL
240 W. Indiana Avenue
1847

This Greek Revival and Federal style brick building served Wood County and Perrysburg as a jail until 1899. The interior and exterior walls were securely con-
structed of four layers of brick. The cell area was made "breakout" proof by cut stone walls and floors two feet thick. Escape through the ceiling was made difficult by the use of 16 inch by 18 inch black walnut beams laid solid side by side to form the floor of the second story. Despite alterations made when the building was converted to apartments, the Wood County Jail is a significant illustration of the provincial blending of styles.
Private
HABS

WOOD COUNTY
Perrysburg vicinity
FORT MEIGS
1.3 miles southwest of Perrysburg
1813–1815

War with Great Britain was declared by the United States on June 18, 1812. A principal American military objective was the occupation of Canada, which was believed to be extremely vulnerable to invasion. Contrary to expectations, Canada did not fall. Instead the British succeeded in capturing Fort Dearborn (Chicago) and Detroit. Attempts to recapture Detroit failed, and in the winter of 1813 the American commander, General William Henry Harrison, began constructing a fort on the Maumee River near Perrysburg,
Ohio. The fort was situated on the route to Detroit and was named for the governor of Ohio. It covered approximately eight acres and was an irregular ellipse with walls of packed earth and sharpened pickets. Seven blockhouses and five batteries were located in the angles of the walls. In April of 1814 the garrison withstood a siege by British and Indians. Several subsequent American victories (including Oliver Hazard Perry's naval battle on Lake Erie) served to wrest control of the Old Northwest from the British. Fort Meigs was abandoned in May, 1815, a few months after the peace had been signed. Present structures on the site are reconstructions, but original earthworks remain.
State
NHL

WYANDOT COUNTY
Upper Sandusky vicinity
INDIAN MILL
3.5 miles northeast of Upper
Sandusky on Crane Township Road
1861

The present mill, a three-story, oak-framed building, is unique in Ohio because of its construction. Covered bridge cross trusses secured by steel rods and bolts were employed. The name Indian Mill is derived from an earlier mill, located 300 feet upstream, built by the federal government for the Wyandot Indians. Restoration was undertaken in 1968, but a lack of water prohibits operation.
State

Cincinnati Music Hall, Cincinnati, Ohio.
Barbara Hunt Associates

Zoar Historic District, Zoar, Ohio. *Ohio Historical Society*

Marblehead Lighthouse, Marblehead, Ohio
Ohio Historical Society

Oklahoma

Old North Tower, Central State College, Edmond, Oklahoma. *Central State Library*

Erin Springs Mansion, Erin Springs, Oklahoma. *Lacy*

Wheelock Mission Church, Wheelock Academy,
Millerstown vicinity, Oklahoma. *NPS*

Murrell House (Hunter's Home),
Park Hill, Oklahoma. *Mike Shelton*

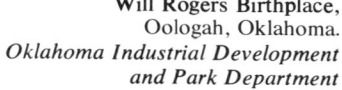

Will Rogers Birthplace,
Oologah, Oklahoma.
*Oklahoma Industrial Development
and Park Department*

ALFALFA COUNTY
Cleo Springs vicinity
SOD HOUSE
About 4 miles north of Cleo Springs
1894

Marshall McCully staked a claim to the quarter section on which the Sod House now stands in September, 1893, shortly after the Cherokee Outlet was opened. He built his two-room sod dwelling the following August and lived in it until 1909. At that time the McCully family moved into a larger frame house nearby. The Oklahoma Historical Society acquired the house in 1963, and it is now believed to be the only extant original example of this type of construction in the state. The walls were smoothed on the inside with plaster, and the original dirt floor was covered with wood in 1895. A sheet iron cover has been put over the house for protection, and the sod roof has been replaced. The furnishings inside are representative of the homesteading period.
State

BLAINE COUNTY
Canton vicinity
CANTONMENT
NW 1/4 sec. 29, T. 19 N., R. 13 W.
19th century

The Cantonment on the Canadian River was established by Colonel Richard I. Dodge in March, 1879. Northern Cheyennes under Dull Knife had moved south from Nebraska and the Dakotas the previous summer leaving death and destruction in their wake. Settlers appealed to the Army for help resulting in the new post. Troops remained here until 1882. Then the installation was turned over to Mennonite missionaries for the operation of an Indian school. It also served as a subagency for the Cheyenne and Arapaho Indian Agency at Darlington. Government use ceased in the 1920's. Presently only one structure remains, a large stone building reduced to a roofless ruin by fire.
Federal trust land

BRYAN COUNTY
Kenefic vicinity
FORT McCULLOCH
Approximately 2 miles southwest of Kenefic
1861–1865

In 1862 General Albert Pike, commander of all Confederate troops in the Department of the Indian Territory, abandoned a strong military post on the Arkansas River and moved the major part of his force 250 miles south to set up a new defense post. Despite the fort's strategic location and its importance as the principal Confederate

stronghold in southern Indian Territory, Federal troops never advanced within 100 miles of it, and the stronghold was completely abandoned after the surrender at Appomattox. The post consisted of clustered log buildings, walled-in tents, and other crude structures. Visible remains include an extensive system of earthen trenches and high breastworks.
Private

BRYAN COUNTY
Nida vicinity
FORT WASHITA
Southwest of Nida on Okla. 199
1842

General Zachary Taylor established Fort Washita, near the junction of the Washita and Red rivers, to protect the Chickasaw Indians and to serve as a way-station for emigrant, stage, and freighter travel over the Southern Overland Trail. It was also a base for exploration of the Southwest and a Confederate supply base and headquarters during the Civil War. Among the extant buildings are two barracks, the commissary warehouse, the quartermaster storehouse, and the officers' quarters.
State
NHL

CADDO COUNTY
Hinton vicinity
ROCK MARY
About 4 miles west of Hinton

Rock Mary was first described by Lieutenant James H. Simpson of the U.S. Corps of Topographical Engineers, who was accompanying Captain R. B. Marcy and an emigrant party in 1849. The landmark was subsequently named for a young lady in the party. Simpson recorded the height of the rock formation as 60 feet and the diameter of its base as 200 feet. Two turret-like projections were noted at the top of Rock Mary. A sketch of the landmark was made by Baldwin Möllhausen, a botanist and artist, in 1853. Travelers and residents of the area have noticed Rock Mary because of its prominence on the landscape.
Private

CANADIAN COUNTY
El Reno vicinity
FORT RENO
3 miles west and 2 miles north of El Reno
19th century

Indian unrest, principally among the Cheyennes, prompted construction of Fort Reno in 1875. Northern Cheyenne, numbering over 900, were resettled here following the massacre of Lieutenant

Colonel G. A. Custer and his immediate command at the Little Big Horn (June, 1876). The 40-acre site contains a military cemetery, an 1876 officers' quarters, barracks, a guardhouse, an 1878 school and chapel, a bakery, an ordnance magazine, and a storehouse. Most of the structures are brick, and those named date from the 1890's. The post was active militarily until 1949, when it became a U.S. Department of Agriculture experiment station.
Federal

CHEROKEE COUNTY
Park Hill
MURRELL HOME (HUNTER'S HOME)
N 1/2 sec. 22, T. 16 N., R. 22 E.
Mid–19th century

George M. Murrell, son-in-law to the brother of Cherokee chief John Ross, built this home in Indian Territory near the Cherokee capitol at Tahlequah. The Indians had been removed to present-day Oklahoma from the southeastern United States and here tried to reestablish their own culture. A mission was opened at Park Hill in 1836, and a quarter century later the Cherokee Female Seminary, also in Park Hill, admitted its first students. The Murrell Home is a two-story frame dwelling with two end chimneys and is distinguished by a projecting, two-story pedimented portico on the entrance facade. The main doorway has an arched fanlight and sidelights. In 1887 the Female Seminary burned, and Park Hill no longer rivaled the growing Tahlequah in importance. The Murrell Home is representative of the town's era of elegance and is unusual for its time and place.
State

CHEROKEE COUNTY
Tahlequah
CHEROKEE NATIONAL CAPITOL
1869

The Cherokee National Capitol symbolize the culmination of a successful period of adjustment beginning in colonial times. The Cherokee Indians apparently realized that their survival lay in peacefully adjusting their culture to a changing environment. As early as 1765 they established schools to educate their youth. In 1820 they adopted a republican form of government, and the following year they issued the first volume of laws ever published by an American aboriginal group. The brick capitol of Victorian style, presently serves as the courthouse of Cherokee County.
County
NHL

CHOCTAW COUNTY
Fort Towson vicinity
FORT TOWSON
1 mile northeast of Fort Towson
1830

The first Fort Towson was a temporary camp of tents and wooden shacks located about six miles south of the present site. It was established in 1824, abandoned in 1829, and reactivated in November, 1830, on the present location. It is Oklahoma's second oldest military post (Fort Gibson is older). The fort buildings were log on stone foundations, and the complex was not palisaded. There were officers' quarters, barracks, a quartermaster's office, a hospital, stables, a sutler's store, and a school. The fort was active during the Mexican War, abandoned in 1854, and occupied by Confederate soldiers from 1861 to 1865. On June 8, 1865, Cherokee General Stand Watie surrendered his Indian troops to Union soldiers here. Only a few sections of wall and the foundations of buildings remain to mark the site of this once-active outpost.
State

CHOCTAW COUNTY
Swink vicinity
CHIEF'S HOUSE
1.5 miles northeast of Swink
1830's

The Treaty of Dancing Rabbit Creek (1830) effected removal of the Choctaw Nation from Mississippi to what is now southeastern Oklahoma. Government funds were provided to construct a council house and residences for three district chiefs. Thomas LeFlore, cousin of Apukshenubbee District Chief Greenwood LeFlore, was chosen to serve in the latter's stead and occupied the Chief's House for many years. Specifications for the dwelling called for a 52-by-20-foot rectangle containing two 20-foot rooms connected by a dogtrot. Following disuse and neglect the northern half of the house was torn down, but the remaining section has been incorporated into the present restoration. One original mantel has survived. Thomas LeFlore supervised a 1,000-acre farm cared for by black slaves.
Private

CIMARRON COUNTY
Wheeless vicinity
CAMP NICHOLS
3 miles northeast of Wheeless on Ranch Road
1865

Camp Nichols was established by Colonel Kit Carson to protect wagon trains using the dangerous Cimarron Cutoff of the Santa Fe Trail. Situated in the heart of the Comanche and Kiowa Indian country, the camp provided a rallying point and furnished escorts for the caravans. It was abandoned in late September, 1865. Today the ruins consist of low stone walls outlining the breastworks and the foundations and walls of the officers' quarters and other buildings. About one-half mile south are clearly visible Sante Fe Trail remains.
Private; not accessible to the public
NHL

COMANCHE COUNTY
Cache vicinity
QUANAH PARKER'S STAR HOUSE
Eagle Park

Quanah Parker was the son of a white woman, Cynthia Ann Parker, who had been captured by Indians as a child, and Peta Nokoni, a Quahada Comanche chief. Eventually Parker himself became a chief and led his people in their resistance of the whites. The attempt was unsuccessful, and on June 24, 1892, the Comanches were given land allotments. Parker selected 160 acres south of Eagle Mountain where he built his home. The Star House consists of a two-story main section measuring approximately 50 feet square. There is an attic above and a two-room addition containing a kitchen and dining room. There are galleries on two sides of the house, which was moved from its original site in 1958. Some work has been done to restore the house as it was when Quanah Parker occupied it.
Private

COMANCHE COUNTY
Lawton vicinity
FORT SILL
North of Lawton
1870

Fort Sill was active in the pacification and control of the hostile southern Plains tribes during the 1870's, 1880's, and 1890's. From 1870 to 1878 it served as the Kiowa-Comanche Agency. Virtually all of the original fort survives. Still standing are the Old Corral (1870), the Old Chapel (1870), the Old Post, and the Post Commandant's Quarters. Still an active military installation, Fort Sill is the Army's artillery school center.
Federal
NHL

GARVIN COUNTY (also in Murray County)
Davis vicinity
INITIAL POINT
About 7.5 miles west of Davis on Garvin-Murray county line
1871

In 1864 Congress initiated the division of Chickasaw Indian lands in present-day Oklahoma. To do so necessitated the establishing of a permanent survey reference point. The surveyors chose the present Initial Point in the center of Chickasaw land and from it divided the area into townships. The point was marked by a stone post that still stands.
Private

GARVIN COUNTY
Erin Springs
ERIN SPRINGS MANSION (FRANK MURRAY HOME)
South of the Washita River
1880

Frank Murray, the builder of Erin Springs and an early settler in the area, was born in Ireland. He married a woman of Chickasaw background and thus migrated to Indian Territory in the 1860's. He purchased property in present-day Erin Springs in 1871 and eventually became a wealthy landowner and cattleman. As first built the Erin Springs Mansion was two stories high. A 1902 remodeling added the dormered third story, the two-story columned portico, and stucco over the native stone walls.
State

HASKELL COUNTY
Kinta vicinity
McCURTAIN, GREEN, HOUSE
NE 1/4 NE 1/4 sec. 35, T. 8 N., R. 20 E.

The McCurtain family played an important role in Choctaw affairs beginning in the early 1800's. Green McCurtain, as the last elected chief of the Choctaw Nation, served from 1896 until his death in 1910. A widely respected leader, he was able to break Choctaw resistance to the Dawes Commission. The Commission was established by Congress in 1893 to negotiate with the Five Civilized Tribes over title to their tribal lands in preparation for statehood. Green McCurtain built a comfortable two-story, L-shaped frame house on his farm in the 1880's. The house, which became an unofficial capitol of the Choctaw Nation when McCurtain was chief, stands as a memorial to one of the Choctaws' most influential leaders.
State; not accessible to the public

KAY COUNTY
Newkirk vicinity
DEER CREEK SITE
6 miles northeast of Newkirk
1700–1750

The Deer Creek Site is believed to have been occupied by the Wichita or related Indian groups during the first half of the 18th century. Archeological remains identify it also as the site of a French trading post known as Ferdinandino about 1725–1750. Surface indications at this well-preserved site have yielded information concerning the chronological development of Plains tribes.
Private; not accessible to the public
NHL

KINGFISHER COUNTY
Kingfisher
SEAY MANSION
Corner of 11th Street and Zellers Avenue
1892

Abraham J. Seay was appointed associate justice of Oklahoma's third district court in 1890. Two years later he was sworn in as second governor of the state. His three-story red brick mansion was an impressive structure on what, until three years earlier, had been the raw frontier. The house contains a reception hall, formal parlor, library, a third-floor ballroom, and an unusual dome-roofed tower. Judge Seay retired from politics in 1893. His home has been restored by the state of Oklahoma as a memorial and as a symbol of the transformation of the sparsely settled Indian Territory into a new state.
State

LE FLORE COUNTY
Hodgens vicinity
CONSER, PETER, HOUSE
3.5. miles west of Hodgens
1894

Peter Conser (1850–1934) built this home and occupied it until his death. Restored by the Oklahoma Historical Society, the house serves as a memorial to the Lighthorsemen of the Five Civilized Tribes (Choctaw, Creek, Cherokee, Seminole and Chickasaw). The Lighthorsemen of the Choctaw were the most famous of these Indian lawmen, organized to maintain order on the frontier. Conser was Chief Lighthorseman, roughly equivalent to county sheriff. His home, a two-story, ell-shaped, frame dwelling with two tall cut-stone chimneys, is typical of farmhouses of the 1890's.
State

LE FLORE COUNTY
Spiro vicinity
SPIRO MOUND GROUP
NE 1/4 sec. 29, W 1/2 NW 1/4 sec. 28, T. 10 N., R. 26 E.
1150–1450

The Spiro Mound Group was originally composed of two large and seven smaller mounds. Archeological excavations between 1936 and 1941 permanently disturbed all but two of these mounds. The mounds themselves and the surrounding village site covered an area of approximately 80 acres. The inhabitants appear to have had contact with other prehistoric peoples in Georgia and the Gulf of Mexico and Lake Superior regions.
Federal

LOGAN COUNTY
Guthrie
CARNEGIE LIBRARY
Oklahoma Avenue and Ash Street
1901

The Carnegie Library in Guthrie was Oklahoma's first Carnegie library. The library played a notable role in both territorial and state politics when Guthrie served as the state's first capital. In 1905 Frank Frantz, the last territorial governor, took his oath of office on the library's front steps. Two years later when Oklahoma was admitted to the Union, Charles N. Haskell was sworn into office and delivered his inaugural address from the steps. The two-and-one-half-story brick and stone building has a massive dome and a three-bay columned portico over the front steps.
Municipal

MC CURTAIN COUNTY
Millerton vicinity
WHEELOCK ACADEMY
East of Millerton off U.S. 70
1832

Wheelock Academy was the archetype for the tribal school systems established by the Five Civilized Tribes in the Indian Territory. As the first national academy founded under the Choctaw Nation's Education Act of 1842, Wheelock set the precedent for some 35 academies and seminaries. The school was closed in 1955, but the oldest building, Old Seminary (1839), and several other historically interesting buildings remain.
Federal; not accessible to the public
NHL

MC INTOSH COUNTY (also in Muskogee County)
Rentiesville vicinity
HONEY SPRINGS BATTLEFIELD
North of Rentiesville

Federal troops permanently occupied Fort Gibson (near present-day Muskogee, Oklahoma), Indian Territory, in 1863. A Confederate force was encamped at nearby Honey Springs Depot on the Texas Road. The Texas Road was the major artery of commerce and travel linking Missouri, Kansas, and Texas. Union commander Major General James G. Blunt decided to attack the enemy at Honey Springs before they attacked him or before their reinforcements could arrive. Six thousand poorly equipped Confederates faced a Federal force half as large but equipped with new uniforms and the most modern rifles and artillery. The battle occurred on July 17, 1863, and resulted in the defeat of the Southern soldiers and the burning of Honey Springs Depot. Black troops, the First Kansas Colored Volunteer Infantry Regiment, were engaged for one of the first times during the Civil War. Honey Springs was the most significant Civil War engagement in Indian Territory. The battlefield today is little changed since 1863, and the foundation of the powder magazine remains.
Multiple public/private

MURRAY COUNTY
INITIAL POINT
Reference—see Garvin County

MUSKOGEE COUNTY
Fort Gibson
FORT GIBSON
1824

Between 1824 and 1840 Fort Gibson played a dominant role in receiving and caring for the Cherokee, Creek, and Seminole Indians removed from the Southeast to the Indian Territory, and in attempting to keep peace between them and the wild Plains Indians. Abandoned just before the Civil War, it was shortly reoccupied by Union troops and remained an active military post until 1889. Although the original fort has disappeared, reconstructions of several buildings have been built.
Multiple public/private
NHL; HABS

MUSKOGEE COUNTY
HONEY SPRINGS BATTLEFIELD
Reference—see McIntosh County

OKLAHOMA COUNTY
Edmond
OLD NORTH TOWER, CENTRAL STATE COLLEGE
400 E. Hurd Street, Central State College campus
1893

Old North was the first structure in Oklahoma to be built expressly for normal school training and the first edifice erected for a state-supported institution of higher learning. Territorial Normal, established by law on December 24, 1890, now Central State College, is the oldest state-supported school in Oklahoma. Old North was first constructed as a three-story brick square. In 1894 the tower and wings of native red sandstone were added, and the center section has since been veneered with sandstone.
State

OKLAHOMA COUNTY
Jones vicinity
"RINGING THE WILD HORSE" SITE
W 1/2 sec. 17 and E 1/2 sec. 18, T. 13 N., R. 1 W.

From a vantage point on a section of Nine Mile Flat beside the North Canadian River, Washington Irving observed and later recorded an attempted roundup of wild horses. This account became a chapter in his book *A Tour on the Prairies*. Irving, in company with Charles J. Latrobe (an Englishman), Count Albert de Pourtales (a Swiss), and Henry L. Ellsworth (a government emissary) left Fort Gibson, Oklahoma, in early October, 1832. They joined a detachment of Rangers on a scouting expedition into the center of present-day Oklahoma. Irving described in his book the deployment of men to encircle a grazing band of wild horses, how one man broke the ring before it was completed, and the resulting stampede of men and animals. Today the site is meadow land.
Private

OKLAHOMA COUNTY
Oklahoma City
OVERHOLSER HOUSE
405 N.W. 15th Street
1903, W. S. Matthews

Henry Overholser (1846–1915), an early settler and entrepreneur in Oklahoma City, was the first owner of this Chateauesque style dwelling. The house is three stories high and built of brick. A large and rather elaborate porte-cochere is attached to the south side and there are porches on practically every exposure. The roof is tile and gable windows and an octagonal tower project from it. Over-holser was responsible for much building and development in Oklahoma City—an opera house, the Overholser Theatre, the first hotel, and the First Presbyterian Church.
Private; not accessible to the public

OKMULGEE COUNTY
Okmulgee
CREEK NATIONAL CAPITOL
1878

The Creek National Capitol symbolizes the successful adjustment of a tribe whose culture and very existence were threatened by white pressure. Through their earlier confederacy, the Creeks had had a form of representative government which, after removal to Oklahoma, they developed into a government similar to the federal government. The capitol, of Victorian style, presently houses a museum of Creek history.
Private
NHL

PAYNE COUNTY
Yale
THORPE, JIM, HOUSE
704 E. Boston Street
1916–1917

Jim Thorpe (1888–1953) first achieved fame as an athlete while playing halfback at Pennsylvania's Carlisle Institute and won all-American honors in 1911 and 1912. He then gained world-wide recognition at the 1912 Olympics in Stockholm as the first competitor ever to win both the pentathlon and decathlon. It was later disclosed that Thorpe had played semi-professional baseball in unknowing violation of the Olympic code of strict amateurism, and he was therefore stripped of his medals. The house which Thorpe occupied from 1917 to 1923 is a modest one-story clapboard building and is the only house he ever owned in Oklahoma. Yale has been officially designated as Thorpe's hometown, and the house has been purchased by the Oklahoma Historical Society and serves as a museum and memorial to one of the world's greatest athletes.
State

PUSHMATAHA COUNTY
Tuskahoma vicinity
TUSKAHOMA (CHOCTAW COUNCIL HOUSE)
2 miles north of Tuskahoma
1883

The Choctaw Council House served as the seat of government for the Choctaw Nation from 1884 to 1907. An earlier log structure at Nanih Waya served as capitol from 1838 to 1849, and from 1850 to 1883 the Choctaws had no established capitol. Measuring 70 feet by 70 feet, the three-story brick building has a mansard roof and rests on a stone foundation. Inside are rooms to accommodate the two branches of the council, executive offices, and the supreme court. The Choctaw people still own the building and use it for tribal purposes.
Public

ROGER MILLS COUNTY
Cheyenne vicinity
WASHITA BATTLEFIELD
Northwest of Cheyenne on U.S. 283
1868

General Philip H. Sheridan's six-month winter campaign was spearheaded by Colonel George A. Custer's Seventh Cavalry. At dawn, on November 27, 1868, Custer's troops attacked a Cheyenne Indian camp beside the Washita River. His victory demonstrated the effectiveness of the new strategy of winter-long campaigns against hostile Plains Indians—the key to the termination of the Indian wars. By spring all of the southern tribes had been forced onto the reservations set aside for them. The battlefield site, now under cultivation, has been marked.
Multiple public/private
NHL

ROGERS COUNTY
Oologah vicinity
ROGERS, WILL, BIRTHPLACE
About 4 miles northeast of Oologah

The original log dwelling which Clem V. Rogers, Will's father, began in 1873 evolved into the present two-story, seven-room frame structure. There is a lean-to at the rear and a two-story projecting portico on the front. Will Rogers was born here on November 4, 1879, and lived in the house until 1902. Construction of Oologah Dam caused flooding of the original home site, so the house was moved to this location in 1960. Now part of the Oklahoma state parks system, the Will Rogers Birthplace is being developed as a late 19th-century frontier ranch.
State

SEQUOYAH COUNTY
Akins vicinity
SEQUOYAH'S CABIN
Okla. 101, Sequoyah's Cabin State Park
1829

By his invention of the Cherokee syllabary, Sequoyah (George Gist), an American Indian teacher and scholar, gave to the Cherokee Indians the gift of literacy. The

syllabary, completed in 1821, has 86 characters, each of which represents a syllable. The giant sequoia trees of California were named for Sequoyah, and he is honored on the doors of the Library of Congress as one of the world's alphabet inventors. His frontier house of hewn logs has undergone minor restorations.
State
NHL

TEXAS COUNTY
Optima vicinity
STAMPER SITE
2.5 miles south of Optima on the south bank of the North Canadian River
1300–1450

The Stamper Site is one of the few excavated sites of the North Canadian River branch of the Panhandle culture. The surface shows numerous low ridges and knolls which are the remains of single-room buildings, of which the lower walls were of upright caliche and adobe. It represents a time when village culture extended across the southern plains from the Caddoan area in the eastern forests to the Pueblo area of New Mexico.
Private; not accessible to the public
NHL

WASHITA COUNTY
Colony vicinity
McLEMORE SITE
4 miles southeast of Colony on Okla. 69
1300

The McLemore Site is among the best known and most carefully excavated sites of the Washita River Focus, a Plains village agricultural complex of central Oklahoma. Archeological excavations have revealed relationships with the Caddoan area to the east and with plains village cultures to the north, south, and west. Of the Washita River sites now known, this one has provided the most information on the activities of the prehistoric Wichita-speaking peoples.
Private; not accessible to the public
NHL

WOODWARD COUNTY
Fort Supply
FORT SUPPLY HISTORIC DISTRICT
Western State Hospital
19th century

This fort was established as Camp Supply in November, 1868, by General Alfred Sully. It was constructed as an advanced base of operations for General Phil Sheridan's campaign against the Cheyenne and Arapaho. The installation had nearly 100 buildings, all of wood except for the guardhouse which was brick. There were 9 double houses of 16 rooms each, 7 barracks, 25 6-room cottages, a hospital, an entertainment hall, and 50 additional houses, including the commandant's residence. Several of the buildings remain including one of the double houses (1879), the guardhouse, and a cabin (early 1870's) believed to be the oldest extant structure. After the military abandoned the installation in 1893 it was turned over to Oklahoma Territory. In 1903 it became the Western State Hospital.
State

Oregon

Pacific Coastline, Fort Clatsop National Memorial, Astoria vicinity, Oregon. *NPS*

Jacksonville Historic District,
Jacksonville, Oregon.
Jack E. Boucher for HABS

The Dining Room,
Dr. John McLoughlin House National Historic Site,
Oregon City, Oregon.
Jack E. Boucher for NPS

Jacksonville Historic District,
Jacksonville, Oregon.
Jack E. Boucher for HABS

CLACKAMAS COUNTY
Oregon City
McLOUGHLIN HOUSE NATIONAL
HISTORIC SITE
McLoughlin Park, between 7th and
8th Streets
1845–1846

Here lived Dr. John McLoughlin, chief
factor of the Hudson's Bay Company,
whose aid to American settlers in the
Oregon country won him enduring acclaim. His house is one of the few remaining pioneer dwellings in the region which
once encompassed Oregon, Washington,
Idaho, and part of Montana. Illustrative of
Dr. McLoughlin's control over the area is
the fact that during his administration,
1824–1846, there were few Indian outbreaks. He not only carried out his
responsibilities associated with the fur
trading industry, but he also developed
agriculture, husbandry, and export markets. The house has been restored to its
original condition.
Multiple public/private
NPS; .63 acre
HABS

CLATSOP COUNTY
Astoria
ELMORE, SAMUEL, CANNERY
On the waterfront at the foot of
Flavel Street
1881

The Samuel Elmore Cannery is the oldest
continuously operated salmon cannery in
the United States. This example of a 19th-
century cannery was established while
Astoria was the salmon capital of the
world, 1876–1887. The firm's equipment
has been modernized, but the main
canning and storage building is little altered and is used for its original purposes.
Also standing and now used as an office is
a two-story frame bunkhouse that formerly housed Chinese laborers.
Private
NHL

CLATSOP COUNTY
Astoria
FORT ASTORIA
15th and Exchange Streets
1812

Launched by John Jacob Astor, an influential figure of the American fur trade,
Astoria represented, both initially and
later, an important American claim to the
Oregon country. Astor's bid to break the
British fur trade monopoly in the
Northwest was initially successful. However, the War of 1812 and the failure of
supply ships to arrive forced Astor to sell
the post in 1813. Although most of the
site has been obscured by the modern city,
one small plot of ground remains, featuring a reconstructed block house.
Municipal
NHL

CLATSOP COUNTY
Astoria vicinity
FORT CLATSOP NATIONAL
MEMORIAL
4.5 miles south of Astoria
1805–1806

Captains Meriwether Lewis and William
Clark wintered here and built Fort Clatsop
in 1805–1806, following their epoch-mak-
ing journey from the Mississippi River to
the Pacific Ocean. Their expedition supplied the most detailed published
knowledge of the American Northwest
available at the time and generated interest in Oregon which led to occupation
of the vast territory. Named Fort Clatsop
after a local Indian tribe, the site was near
the ocean, hunting grounds, timber, and
friendly natives. Nothing of the original

fort has survived, but a replica following
Clark's floor plan dimensions was con-
structed in 1955.
Federal
NPS; 124.97 acres

JACKSON COUNTY
Jacksonville
JACKSONVILLE HISTORIC DISTRICT
1852–1884

Founded because of a nearby gold strike,
Jacksonville was the principal distribution,
financial, and trading center of southern
Oregon until the California and Oregon
Railroad bypassed it. The numerous surviving and basically unaltered commercial
and residential buildings make Jacksonville an important example of a mid-19th-
century inland commercial town in the
Pacific Northwest. Predominant architectural styles are Greek Revival, Gothic
Revival, and Italian Villa, which were
popular during the later half of the 19th
century.
Multiple public/private
NHL; HABS

KLAMATH COUNTY
LOWER KLAMATH NATIONAL
WILDLIFE REFUGE
Reference—see Siskiyou County, California

LAKE COUNTY
Fort Rock vicinity
FORT ROCK CAVE
SW 1/4 NW 1/4 sec. 25, T. 25 S., R.
13 E.
7098 B.C.

In Fort Rock Cave archeologists
discovered the famous "Fort Rock sandals," the oldest articles, dated by a direct
method, so far found in the western hemisphere. The sandals, along with fragments
of basketry, indicate a knowledge of weaving by the prehistoric people of the New
World at an earlier date than is so far indicated in Europe or Asia. No archeological deposits remain in the cave.
Private; not accessible to the public
NHL

Pennsylvania

St. Peter's Walkway, Society Hill Historic District,
Philadelphia, Pennsylvania. *A. K. Strobl*

Ephrata Cloister,
Ephrata, Pennsylvania.
*Pennsylvania Historical and
Museum Commission*

Andalusia, Philadelphia vicinity, Pennsylvania.
Cortlandt V. D. Hubbard for HABS

Brinton's Mill,
Chadds Ford, Pennsylvania.
George Eisenman

Skippack Bridge, Lower Providence Township, Pennsylvania.
Hefelfinger Studio

Old West, Dickinson College,
Carlisle, Pennsylvania. *NPS*

ADAMS COUNTY
Gettysburg
GETTYSBURG NATIONAL MILITARY
PARK
1863

At the battle of Gettysburg, July 1–3, 1863, 75,000 Confederate soldiers of General Robert E. Lee's Army of Northern Virginia were pitted against the 88,000 men in General George G. Meade's Army of the Potomac. The combined losses of both armies were 51,000 killed, wounded, and captured in the bloodiest battle ever fought on the North American continent. The defeat for the South marked the turning of the tide in the eastern theater of the war. Also commemorated in the park is the site of President Abraham Lincoln's Gettysburg Address, delivered on November 19, 1863. On the battlefield site is Gettysburg National Cemetery.
Federal/non-federal
NPS; 3,671.77 acres
HABS

ADAMS COUNTY
Gettysburg vicinity
EISENHOWER NATIONAL HISTORIC
SITE
Southwest edge of Gettysburg
National Military Park
1950's, redesigned by George S. Brock

General Dwight D. Eisenhower, a 1915 graduate of the United States Military Academy, served in World War I and became supreme commander of Allied Forces in Western Europe in 1943. After the Second World War, he served as Chief of Staff of the United States Army from 1945 to 1948. He then served as president of Columbia University for five years before his two terms as President of the United States, 1953–1961. The farm buildings consist of a brick and stone house, a large stock barn, and several small utility buildings.
Federal; not accessible to the public
NPS; 230 acres

ALLEGHENY COUNTY
Pittsburgh
FORKS OF THE OHIO
Point Park
18th and 19th centuries

From the middle of the 18th century through the early 19th century, the Forks of the Ohio at the junction of the Allegheny and Monongahela rivers, was the strategic key to the Ohio Valley and the territory drained by the Mississippi River. The French built Fort Duquesne here in 1754, and an attempt by American colonials to capture it led to the opening battle

of the French and Indian War. In 1758 Fort Duquesne was captured by the British, who erected Fort Pitt nearby. The sites of both forts are now part of Point Park in the Golden Triangle of Pittsburgh, the first permanent English settlement west of the Appalachian Mountains in the present United States.
State
NHL

BEAVER COUNTY
Ambridge
OLD ECONOMY
Pa. 65
1825

Of the many religiously inspired utopian experiments in the United States during the 19th century, the Harmony Society's settlement at Economy was one of the most successful. The society was a communitarian theocracy led by George Rapp, a German immigrant. Primarily an industrial community, Economy became wealthy through its manufactures and the use of labor-saving devices. Its membership began to decline in the 1860's, and in 1905 the society was dissolved. Seventeen of the original buildings survive, among them the Great House (1825) and the Music Hall or Feast Hall.
State
NHL; HABS

BEAVER COUNTY
THE BEGINNING POINT OF THE
UNITED STATES PUBLIC LAND
SURVEY
Reference—see Columbiana County, Ohio

BERKS COUNTY
Morgantown vicinity
HOPEWELL VILLAGE NATIONAL
HISTORIC SITE
10 miles northeast of Morgantown
Interchange, Pa. Turnpike
1770–1883

Hopewell Village is representative of the industrial enterprise of colonial, Revolutionary, and 19th-century America. This iron-making village site includes the old furnace and numerous related buildings: an office-store, a barn, the blacksmith shop, and the ironmaster's house. The charcoal furnace iron industry was gradually supplanted during the 19th century by improved production methods.
Federal
NPS; 848.06 acres
HABS

BERKS COUNTY
Womelsdorf vicinity
WEISER, CONRAD, HOUSE
2 miles east of Womelsdorf on U.S.
422
1751

Conrad Weiser's understanding of Indian affairs and his knowledge of Indian languages promoted friendly relations between Iroquois and British. Weiser considered the Indian problem common to all the colonies and saw its solution on a colony-wide rather than a local basis. The Indian alliances he helped to form were a decisive factor in England's victory in the French and Indian War. Conrad Weiser Memorial Park preserves his restored house, now a museum; several outbuildings; and the graves of Weiser, his wife, and several Indian associates.
State
NHL

BLAIR COUNTY
Altoona vicinity
HORSESHOE CURVE
5 miles west of Altoona on Pa. 193
1854

Horseshoe Curve is a notable example of unusual railroad engineering construction. John Edgar Thomson surveyed the proposed route over the Allegheny Mountains, which had long hindered Pennsylvania's westward movement. The curve, with a central angle of 220 degrees, is 2,375 feet long and is graded 91 feet to the mile. Its completion joined the eastern and western divisions of the Pennsylvania Railroad.
Private
NHL

BLAIR COUNTY (also in Cambria
County)
Johnstown vicinity
ALLEGHENY PORTAGE RAILROAD
NATIONAL HISTORIC SITE
U.S. 22
1831–1834

The Allegheny Portage Railroad was built to carry canal boats across a forested mountain divide and link the eastern and western divisions of the Pennsylvania Canal, a 395-mile waterway between Philadelphia and Pittsburgh. The canal, built between 1826 and 1834 to connect the Ohio Valley and Pennsylvania's eastern seaboard, was the main Pennsylvania transportation line west for over two decades until the railroad made it obsolete. Ten inclined planes, a 901-foot tunnel, and long level stretches carried the double-tracked railroad 36 miles across the Alleghenies from Hollidaysburg to Johnstown.
Federal/non-federal
NPS; 950 acres

BUCKS COUNTY
Morrisville vicinity
PENNSBURY MANOR
    On the Delaware River south of the
    Bordentown Road
    1683–1699; rebuilt, 1932–1938

William Penn, the proprietor of Pennsylvania, instructed Deputy Governor William Markham, who came to America ahead of Penn, to select a site for the proprietor's country estate. Markham chose a location on the Delaware River that was then an Indian encampment. Penn arrived in the New World in 1682, whereupon he approved the site and ordered construction begun. Penn envisioned a self-supporting plantation complex containing a manor house and several dependencies: a bake and brew house, boathouse, sheep shelter, plantation manager's office, icehouse, toolhouse, stable, horse shelter, blacksmith shop, woodshed, family privy, and servants' privy. The house and plantation were recreated by the Commonwealth of Pennsylvania, and the manor house rebuilt on the original foundation.
State

BUCKS COUNTY
New Hope vicinity
HONEY HOLLOW WATERSHED
    2.5 miles south of the Delaware River
    on Pa. 263
    1939

Honey Hollow Watershed was the first small watershed development in the country undertaken on privately owned farmland. In the spring of 1939 five farmers on adjoining farms banded together voluntarily and through the U.S. Soil Conservation Service requested help from the federal government in solving land-use problems caused by erosion. A general plan was formulated through the Service with each farmer working independently of the other. The objectives of the experimental program were soil, water, and wildlife conservation. Methods employed to combat erosion included terracing, contour plowing, diversion ditches, the introduction of wildlife hedges, and the creation of ponds and tree clumps. All lands involved in the watershed conservation area were part of original grants made by William Penn in 1682, and three 18th-century houses still stand on them.
Private
NHL

BUCKS COUNTY
Philadelphia vicinity
ANDALUSIA (NICHOLAS BIDDLE ESTATE)
    1.4 miles north of Philadelphia on
    State Road
    1794; 1834, Thomas U. Walter

Nicholas Biddle, the chief officer of the Second Bank of the United States, made the renewal of the bank's charter an issue in the 1832 presidential campaign. Andrew Jackson's victory doomed the bank and confirmed the triumph of "Jacksonian Democracy." Biddle's association with Andalusia began in 1811 with his marriage to Jane Craig, the daughter of the then owner of the estate. It became his permanent residence in 1821, and in the early 1830's he made a number of additions, employing Thomas U. Walter to add a wing designed in the Greek Revival style. The estate includes a number of outbuildings.
Private; not accessible to the public
NHL

BUCKS COUNTY (also in Mercer County, New Jersey)
Yardley vicinity
WASHINGTON CROSSING STATE PARK
    Between Yardley and New Hope, on
    the Delaware River
    1776

General George Washington's crossing of the Delaware River on Christmas night, 1776, for the raid on Trenton, New Jersey, was a crucial episode in the struggle for American independence. Despite its almost legendary associations, it was a realistic and carefully planned effort to revive a waning cause. By taking the offensive, Washington gave the nation and the army a taste of victory at the Revolutionary War's lowest ebb. Washington Crossing State Park preserves the site of the embarkation of Washington's main force. It contains a number of stone farmhouses and the Ferry Inn, which occupies the site of the original ferry house.
State
NHL

CAMBRIA COUNTY
ALLEGHENY PORTAGE RAILROAD NATIONAL HISTORIC SITE
Reference—see Blair County

CAMBRIA COUNTY
Johnstown vicinity
JOHNSTOWN FLOOD NATIONAL MEMORIAL
    Intersection of U.S. 219 and Pa. 869
    1889

An immense earthen dam, weakened by days of steady rain, gave way on May 31, 1889, and poured millions of tons of water down the narrow valley of the Little Conemaugh River. The flood devastated the steel center of Johnstown and its nearby communities, and the nation rallied to aid the victims. The Johnstown Flood National Memorial was established to commemorate one of the nation's worst disasters and the first instance of the national organization of relief to aid disaster victims.
Federal/non-federal
NPS; 55 acres

CENTRE COUNTY
Curtin
CURTIN VILLAGE (EAGLE IRONWORKS)
    Route 14010
    19th and 20th centuries

Curtin Village is a former ironmaster's plantation which functioned for over 100 years under the auspices of the Curtin family. In 1810 Roland Curtin and Miles Boggs formed a partnership for the purpose of constructing a forge on Bald Eagle Creek. Five years later Curtin bought out his partner. The site chosen was near relatively high quality iron deposits, and there were dense forests to provide fuel, a supply of limestone for a flux, and water for power. Charcoal, bloom, bar, and rod iron were produced here. Two thousand tons of pig iron were produced yearly. Curtin became a self-sustaining community with little or no dependence on the outside world except as a market for iron. The village had its own sawmill, gristmill, store, railroad station, church, and school. Workers' houses, many of which still stand, are one-and-one-half- or two-story frame dwellings. Curtin's mansion house (c. 1830) is a two-and-one-half-story Federal style building with stuccoed exterior stone walls. The ironworks closed in 1921, and the village has been abandoned as it was. The furnace stack (1847), four partial walls of the gristmill, and a late 19th-century Victorian house remain in addition to the mansion and workers' homes.
State/federal

CHESTER COUNTY
Chadds Ford vicinity
BRINTON'S MILL
1.5 miles north of Chadds Ford on
U.S. 100
18th and 19th centuries

The most important buildings at Brinton's Mill are the mill, built prior to 1719 and remodeled and enlarged in the 1760's, and an early 19th-century granary. Both buildings are of random laid stone and have gable roofs. The mill, which is still operational, has played an important role in the commercial life of the area for over two centuries. The granary has been remodeled as an apartment.
Private; not accessible to the public

CHESTER COUNTY
Chadds Ford vicinity
HARVEY, WILLIAM, HOUSE
Northwest of Chadds Ford on
Brinton's Bridge Road just north of
U.S. 1
18th century

William Harvey built this fieldstone house sometime between 1715 and his death in 1754. It is the type of dwelling known as a bank house, being two and one-half stories on the north side and three and one-half on the south. Walls are laid in random ashlar. A frame wing on the east is a 20th-century addition, and the two-story porch on the south replaced an original pent eave.
Private; not accessible to the public
HABS

CHESTER COUNTY
Chester Springs vicinity
GOOD NEWS BUILDINGS (YELLOW SPRINGS SPA)
North of Chester Springs on Art
School Road
18th, 19th, and 20th centuries

Yellow Springs was selected as the site for construction of a three-story Revolutionary War soldiers' hospital in 1777. Used until 1781, it burned in 1902, but extensive stone foundations believed to be those of the original hospital still remain. Early in the next century Yellow Springs began to attract summer visitors and prospered as a health resort. The Good News Buildings (the old hotel, two large residences, a bath house, and a studio) are situated on 145 acres of ground. The hotel began operating in the 1820's and was improved in the 1830's. It is a three-story stone structure covered with stucco. A two-story residence across the road is roughly contemporary. The second residence (now known as the Jenny Lind House) was built in the 1830's or 1840's.

There is a stone and stucco structure over one of the sulphur springs and a wooden summer house over the Iron Spring, both thought to date from 1839. The studio has been greatly altered.
Private; not accessible to the public
HABS

CHESTER COUNTY
Hamorton vicinity
BARNS-BRINTON HOUSE
East of Hamorton on U.S. 1
c. 1726

As early as 1722 William Barns operated a tavern along the road leading to Conestoga and Maryland. Architectural evidence indicates that this building was a tavern, although the exterior has been greatly altered. It is a two-and-one-half-story structure of brick laid in Flemish bond with black headers. Original window frames and cornice have been replaced and the pent roof removed. Much of the interior woodwork is original.
Private
HABS

CHESTER COUNTY
Marshallton
MARSHALL, HUMPHRY, HOUSE
Strasburg Road (Pa. 162) at the
intersection of Northbrook Road
1773

Humphry Marshall (1722–1801), botanist and stone mason by trade, constructed this house himself. Marshall was a practical man of many interests and designed his home according to his needs, thereby ignoring symmetry in the placement of windows and doorways. The two-and-one-half-story stone dwelling has a gabled main roof and pent roofs at the second floor. A wing on the west side is a later addition, and the house itself has undergone several alterations and modifications. A greenhouse and an observatory were incorporated into the original dwelling because Marshall was also an amateur astronomer. A bull's eye on the second floor contains a date stone.
Private
HABS

CHESTER COUNTY
Mendenhall
PETERS, WILLIAM, HOUSE
Hillendale Road
1749–1750

Significant as an extant example of Georgian architecture in the middle colonies, this two-story pent-roofed house was moved to its present site in 1965. Although altered when moved, the house retains its architectural detail. It is five bays wide and has a central hall flanked

by two rooms. The exterior bricks are laid in Flemish bond on the front and western facades and common bond on the rear and eastern facades. Additions made at the time of the move include a rear wing, and dormers in the attic.
Private

CHESTER COUNTY (also in Montgomery County)
Norristown vicinity
VALLEY FORGE
Valley Forge State Park
1777–1778

The bitter winter of 1777–1778 endured at Valley Forge by General George Washington's troops saw the emergence of a stronger, better-trained American Army from the defeated force which had set up camp on December 19, 1777. By spring, the Revolutionary Army was ready for the field as never before. At Monmouth, New Jersey, on June 28, 1778, it proved that it was able to defeat British regulars in open combat. In addition to the stone house in which Washington had his headquarters, Valley Forge State Park includes extensive remains of trenches, earthworks, and the Grand Parade Ground.
State
NHL; HABS

CHESTER COUNTY
West Chester
STRODE'S MILL (ETTER'S MILL)
Intersection of Pa. 100–52 and
County Route 15087
1721

Strode's Mill ground grain for Chester County residents until the middle of the 20th century. Minimal structural changes have been made, and the present appearance is little changed from the original. Constructed of fieldstone, the mill is three and one-half stories on the south side and one and one-half stories on the north. A pent eave on the east side has been removed, and the dormer windows on the west were added in the 1960's. Interior woodwork is largely original but the old floor plan has been changed.
Private
HABS

CUMBERLAND COUNTY
Carlisle
CARLISLE INDIAN SCHOOL
East edge of Carlisle on U.S. 11
1879–1918

The founder of the Carlisle Indian School was Captain Richard Pratt, Civil War officer and later cavalry commander in Texas and the Indian Territory. The school gave thousands of young Indians an

elementary education and practical instruction in mechanical arts, agriculture, and home economics. Its efforts to educate Indians prompted the founding of similar schools elsewhere. Among the surviving school buildings now incorporated into the Army War College are the Commandant's Quarters (c. 1821), Thorpe Hall (named for alumnus Jim Thorpe, one of America's outstanding athletes), the Coven Apartments (1863, a girls' dormitory), Armstrong Hall, and Washington Hall.
Federal
NHL

CUMBERLAND COUNTY
Carlisle
OLD WEST, DICKINSON COLLEGE
Dickinson College campus
1804–1822, Benjamin H. Latrobe

Chartered in 1783, Dickinson College was founded by Dr. Benjamin Rush and supported by such leaders as Thomas Jefferson. The institution took its name from John Dickinson, president of the Supreme Executive Council of Pennsylvania. Old West, which now houses classrooms and administrative offices, retains its position as the physical and traditional heart of the campus. The U-shaped building has undergone only minor alterations.
Private
NHL

DELAWARE COUNTY
Broomall
MASSEY, THOMAS, HOUSE
Lawrence Road, opposite
Springhouse Road
17th, 18th, and 19th centuries

Three centuries of Pennsylvania architecture are represented by the Thomas Massey House. A log house, the earliest on the site, was built between 1683 and 1696. No portions of it still stand, but evidence indicates that it was probably one and one-half stories high and had one room with a large fireplace and a loft room above. In 1696 a brick structure was added at the east end of the log house, and the log section was torn down sometime prior to 1730, when a stone addition was put up at the west end. A second stone addition was constructed in the mid–19th century (first floor, c. 1840; second story, c. 1860). Restoration work has been done inside revealing the original plaster and woodwork.
Municipal

DELAWARE COUNTY
Chadds Ford
BRANDYWINE BATTLEFIELD
Brandywine Battlefield Park
1777

The battle of Brandywine on September 11, 1777, was the only major clash of the two main armies during the Revolutionary War campaign that resulted in the British capture of Philadelphia. Although the Americans were defeated, George Washington extricated his forces in good order, the colonists having demonstrated their ability to withstand the British regulars. Washington's headquarters has been reconstructed, and the house occupied by the Marquis de Lafayette has been restored. Several outbuildings have also been restored and appropriately furnished.
State
NHL

DELAWARE COUNTY
Chadds Ford
CHAD HOUSE
Pa. 100
Pre–1725

The Chad House stands today largely as it looked when built. It is a two-and-one-half-story stone house of irregular ashlar construction. The roof has a steep gable and a pent roof across the gable ends. John Wyeth, Jr., built the house before 1725, and his initials are visible carved in a stone by an upper window on the south facade. He may have been hired by John Chad (or Chads) to do the work.
Private
HABS

DELAWARE COUNTY
Chadds Ford
GILPIN HOMESTEAD
Harvey Road
18th century

The Gilpin Homestead is significant because it reflects the process and methods employed to adapt an 18th-century house to the needs of later generations. The original portion of the house is brick and contains a 1754 datestone. There are two basement rooms, two first-floor rooms, two bedrooms, and an attic. An addition forms the middle of the house, and a second addition forms the east end and is only half the width of the rest of the dwelling. Both additions are stone. The Gilpins were a Quaker family who first settled in the area in the late 17th century. Sir William Howe used the house as his headquarters following the battle of the Brandywine in September, 1777.
Private

DELAWARE COUNTY
Chester
PENN, WILLIAM, LANDING SITE
Penn and Front Streets
17th century

William Penn landed on this spot from the ship *Welcome* in late November, 1682. A memorial stone was placed on the site two hundred years later. The stone also marks the location of Robert Wade's log house, which was standing as early as 1676.
Municipal

DELAWARE COUNTY
Chester
1724 CHESTER COURTHOUSE
Market Street below 5th Street
1724, 1744

The Chester Courthouse was built as a two-and-one-half-story structure with no basement. Street facades are dressed stone, while rubble stone was used on the north and west sides. There are pent roofs above the first and second floors and a square cupola with louvered openings and a convex curved roof in the center of the main roof. A three-sided bay with large, multi-paned windows was built on in 1744. Inside, the first-floor courtroom has a stone paved floor; the grand and petit jury rooms upstairs both have fireplaces. Some restoration work has been done.
Municipal

DELAWARE COUNTY
Dilworthtown vicinity
1704 HOUSE
Oakland Road, near junction of U.S. 202 and County Route 15199
1704

This early stone house, although restored, retains much of its original architectural design and is representative of the larger type of dwelling house of a Chester County English Quaker. The two-and-one-half-story house has a basement kitchen, and a large unfinished attic. There are chimneys at each end of the steep gable roof. The quarried stone walls are laid in courses of various widths. Walnut was used for door and window frames as well as for interior partitions. The small one-and-one-half-story service wing was added in the early 19th century.
Private
NHL; HABS

DELAWARE COUNTY
Essington
THE PRINTZHOF
Taylor Avenue and 2nd Street
c. 1643

The colony of New Sweden was the first permanent white settlement in what later became the colony of Pennsylvania. In

1643 Governor Johan Printz selected Tinicum Island on the Delaware River as his home and built a fort, New Gothenberg. Here for 10 years he ruled New Sweden. Archeological excavations have uncovered the foundations of his house, as well as thousands of Swedish artifacts.
State
NHL

DELAWARE COUNTY
Haverford
NITRE HALL
Karakung Drive
c. 1805–1810

The Nitre Hall Gunpowder Mill complex was constructed shortly after 1800 by Israel Whelen. The plant included a refinery, a willow house for producing charcoal, a stamping mill, a dry house, a press house, a cylinder mill, a barrel mill, testing house, and powder magazine. All that remains today is the mansion house and portions of the powder magazine's exterior walls. The three-story residence is stone covered with stucco. A second-story porch has been removed from the main facade, but the interior is unaltered. Whelen's mill was one of the leading gunpowder producers until the owner's death (1839 or 1840), when operations ceased.
Municipal

DELAWARE COUNTY
Media vicinity
OLD ROSE TREE TAVERN
Junction of Rose Tree and Providence Roads north of Media
1809, 1836

The first Rose Tree Tavern was operated as an inn in 1739 by Daniel Calvert. This later building is typical of taverns of the late 18th and early 19th centuries in eastern Pennsylvania. The two-and-one-half-story structure of local fieldstone was constructed in two stages: the first in 1809, the second in 1836. A shingled overhang, the length of the six-bay front facade, separates the first and second floors. The four dormer windows in the front of the gable roof have arched fanlights and the entrance door in the 1809 section has Georgian dog-eared molded framing and a four-light transom overhead.
County/private; not accessible to the public

DELAWARE COUNTY
Prospect Park
MORTON HOMESTEAD
100 Lincoln Avenue
Mid–17th to mid–19th centuries

The oldest part of the Morton Homestead is a one-story log cabin constructed in 1654. An adjacent structure of similar design was built in 1698. In the late 1790's the two buildings were connected by stone walls and a higher roof added to create a half story above the cabins. Interior alterations were made to the upstairs room in 1835. The homestead presently contains late 17th-century furniture.
State

DELAWARE COUNTY
Swarthmore
WEST, BENJAMIN, BIRTHPLACE
Swarthmore College campus
1724

Benjamin West, who lived and worked in England from 1763 until his death in 1820, made a major contribution to American art by his support of young American artists studying abroad. Among his protégés were Gilbert Stuart and Charles Willson Peale. An innovation he introduced in his painting "Death of Wolfe" (1771) was the use of contemporary costumes, rather than classical robes, in historical scenes. Other notable works include "Penn's Treaty with the Indians" (1772) and "Christ Healing the Sick" (1801). The interior of West's two-story stone house was restored following a fire in 1874.
Private; not accessible to the public
NHL

DELAWARE COUNTY
Upland
PUSEY, CALEB, HOUSE
15 Race Street
c. 1683

The Caleb Pusey House is the oldest surviving English-built house in Pennsylvania. Caleb Pusey (1651–1727) was born in England and came to America soon after 1680 to manage a mill for the Quakers. His home was standing by 1683. It was built in two sections; the eastern one is the earlier. Within its native stone walls was a single large room and a loft. The western portion may have been a roofless, enclosed area for animals or a garden, which was eventually roofed over. The gambrel roof over the eastern part replaced the original which was destroyed by fire. Inside, the walls are rough, unfinished stone, and furnishings date from the early 18th century.
Private
HABS

DELAWARE COUNTY
Wallingford
LEIPER, THOMAS, ESTATE
Avondale Road
18th century

Thomas Leiper (1745–1825), was an inventor, manufacturer and merchant who made his fortune in tobacco and snuff. In 1776 he bought land in Nether Providence Township and constructed two snuff mills. Four years later he purchased the adjoining stone quarries and in 1809 completed a railroad to convey the stone to Ridley Creek. Leiper's home (built in 1785) is a two-story, gable-roofed, stucco-covered stone dwelling typical of late 18th-century Pennsylvania country houses. Other buildings on the property are a barn, carriage house, smokehouse, warehouse, and a tenant's house.
Private
HABS

FAYETTE COUNTY
Mount Braddock vicinity
MEASON, ISAAC, HOUSE (DR. CHRISTOPHER GIST PLANTATION)
U.S. 119 North
1802

The Meason House is a two-and-one-half-story Georgian residence constructed of local stone. Its symmetrical central section is flanked by two wings, and a detached stone outbuilding is situated some distance from each wing. There is a pediment containing a fan transom above the main entrance. Pilasters with Ionic capitals support the pediment. Both the main section and the two wings have end chimneys, and the roof cornice has a dentil molding. Isaac Meason purchased the property from Christopher Gist prior to 1802. Meason, who helped develop the iron industry in western Pennsylvania, was elected to the Pennsylvania assembly and served on the state's Supreme Executive Council and as an associate judge of Fayette County.
Private; not accessible to the public

FAYETTE COUNTY
Point Marion vicinity
GALLATIN, ALBERT, HOUSE (FRIENDSHIP HILL)
3 miles north of Point Marion on Pa. 166
1789

Albert Gallatin lived at Friendship Hill during his years as a public servant. Elected to the House of Representatives in 1795, he had become the leader of the Democratic-Republican minority by 1797. He directed the fight for the election of Thomas Jefferson over Aaron Burr in the disputed election of 1800. From 1801 until 1813 Gallatin served as Secretary of the Treasury. In 1832 he sold Friendship Hill and moved to New York City, where he studied Indian tribes and founded the American Ethnological Society. His house still stands, with the original brick portion somewhat enlarged.
Private; not accessible to the public
NHL

FAYETTE COUNTY
Uniontown vicinity
FORT NECESSITY NATIONAL BATTLEFIELD
11 miles east of Uniontown on U.S. 40
1754

At Fort Necessity on July 3, 1754, occurred the opening battle of the French and Indian War, fought by England and France for control of North America. Colonial troops led by George Washington were forced to surrender after an eight-hour resistance to a numerically superior French force. The fort's stockade, storehouse, and entrenchments have been reconstructed. Overlooking the site of Fort Necessity is Mount Washington Tavern, built about 1818 to serve travelers on the National Road.
Federal/non-federal
NPS; 500 acres

FAYETTE COUNTY
Uniontown vicinity
SEARIGHTS TOLLHOUSE, NATIONAL ROAD
West of Uniontown near U.S. 40
1835

In 1831 the federal government transferred to Pennsylvania the control of its portion of the National Road, which ran from Cumberland, Maryland, to the Ohio River. Four years later six tollhouses were erected, two of which are extant. This tollhouse is a hexagonal two-story brick tower encircled by a portico.
State
NHL

FRANKLIN COUNTY
Chambersburg
BROWN, JOHN, HOUSE
225 E. King Street

In an upstairs bedroom of this frame cottage, John Brown, the radical abolitionist, lived from June to October of 1859. While in Chambersburg Brown amassed weapons and tools for his abortive raid on Harpers Ferry, West Virginia (October 16, 1859). Having assumed the name of Dr. Isaac Smith, Brown said he was engaged in the development of iron mines. The oldest section of the house is two-and-one-half stories high and stands parallel to King Street.
County

FRANKLIN COUNTY
Chambersburg
FRANKLIN COUNTY JAIL
Northwest corner of King and 2nd Streets
1818

Stylistic details of the Franklin County Jail are Georgian. All windows on the facade are ornamented by marble, wedge-shaped lintels and keystones. A jailer's residence originally occupied one wing of the main building, and solitary confinement cells were located in the basement. In the 1880's a cell block was added behind the main jail. The cupola and two brick chimneys appear to be original, and the building continues to serve its original purpose.
County

HUNTINGDON COUNTY
Rockhill Furnace
EAST BROAD TOP RAILROAD
U.S. 522
1872

The East Broad Top Railroad is one of the few narrow-gauge railroads still in operation. Until 1953 its engines transported coal from the mines to the Pennsylvania Railroad. With the decline in the use of coal after World War II, the line was forced to cease operations. The engines are now used for visitors who may also see the original station and roundhouse.
Private
NHL

LACKAWANNA COUNTY
Scranton
POWDERLY, TERENCE V., HOUSE
614 N. Main Street
c. 1870's –1890's

From 1879 to 1893 Terence V. Powderly was the General Master of Work of the Knights of Labor, the largest labor union then existing in the United States. His idealism prompted his support of arbitration, rather than strikes, as labor's principal bargaining tool. Employers refused to accept arbitration, however, and workers turned to the more militant leadership of Samuel Gompers. Internal opposition forced Powderly's resignation. In later years he became chief of the Bureau of Information of the Federal Bureau of Immigration. His two-story frame house has changed little since his death.
Private; not accessible to the public
NHL

LANCASTER COUNTY
Brickerville
STIEGEL-COLEMAN HOUSE
Pa. 501 and U.S. 322
1756–1758, c. 1780

William Henry Stiegel and several associates purchased an iron furnace about 1756, but by 1763 he had become more interested in glass manufacturing. He erected a glass factory at his Elizabeth Furnace and then established a glass-producing center in Manheim, Pennsylvania, in 1765. Robert Coleman first rented and then became sole owner of Stiegel's furnace. Under his direction it concentrated on the production of war material during the Revolutionary War. Following the war the business continued to prosper. Stiegel built the original section of the stone house, and Coleman made an addition which projects forward from the west side.
Private; not accessible to the public
NHL

LANCASTER COUNTY
Ephrata
EPHRATA CLOISTER
1740–1746

The group of buildings known as the Ephrata Cloister is among the most markedly German and medieval Dutch Colonial architecture in Pennsylvania. Ephrata was founded in 1732 by Conrad Beissel, a German Pietist mystic. At its peak around 1750, the self-sufficient community had its own gristmill, bakery, pottery, barns, and stables. By 1800, however, the celibate orders were practically extinct. Extant buildings include the *Saal* (a great hall or community house built in 1740), *Saron* (Sisters' House built in 1742–1743), Almonry (alms and bake house), Beissel's log house, a householder's cabin, three cottages, and the 1837 Academy. The Society continued to occupy the Cloisters until about 1925.
State
NHL; HABS

LANCASTER COUNTY
Lancaster
FULTON OPERA HOUSE
12–14 N. Prince Street
1852, Samuel Sloane

The Fulton Opera House is a four-story structure built in the mid–19th century to serve several civic purposes: county convention center, theater, and meeting hall. Christopher Hager, first owner of the opera house, named it in honor of Robert Fulton, co-inventor of the steamboat and a native of Lancaster County. The

architectural style is early Victorian. Major alterations were undertaken in 1873. Interior and exterior restoration in recent years has returned the opera house to its late 19th-century appearance, and it is now used as a movie house for legitimate theater.
Private
NHL

LANCASTER COUNTY
Lancaster
HERR, HANS, HOUSE
1851 Hans Herr Drive
1719

The Hans Herr House is the oldest dwelling in Lancaster County and the oldest Mennonite meeting place in America. The rectangular sandstone building measures 37 feet 9 inches by 30 feet 10 inches and is one-and-one-half stories high. A stone vaulted root cellar underlies half of the ground floor, while the remaining half was constructed at grade level. Some alterations have been made inside and out: ground-floor window openings have been enlarged, the main entrance has been reduced in size, and first-floor interior partitions removed. The Herrs were Mennonites who emigrated to America seeking religious toleration.
Private; not accessible to the public
HABS

LANCASTER COUNTY
Lancaster
WHEATLAND (JAMES BUCHANAN HOUSE)
1120 Marietta Avenue
1828

Wheatland, a two-and-one-half-story brick house, was from 1849 to 1868 the residence of James Buchanan, who served as President of the United States from 1857 to 1861. During the years when the country was moving toward disunion and civil war, his efforts to placate both sides in the sectional controversy failed. By the time Abraham Lincoln succeeded him in office, several states had already announced their secession from the Union. The 17-room house is unaltered and contains an exhibit room of Buchanan memorabilia.
Private
NHL

LANCASTER COUNTY
Quarryville vicinity
FULTON, ROBERT, BIRTHPLACE
8 miles south of Quarryville on U.S. 222
c. 1765

In his early years Robert Fulton was a painter, but he gradually turned his ener-

gies to the development of canal systems and to transportation problems. He patented several inventions of canal equipment and prepared treatises on the advantages of canal systems. Fulton is best remembered for his design of the steamboat *Clermont*, the first completely successful American steamboat, launched in 1807. The large stone farmhouse with gabled roof little resembles the original.
State
NHL

LEBANON COUNTY
Cornwall
CORNWALL IRON FURNACE
1742

Cornwall Iron Furnace is an example of the charcoal furnaces which produced most of America's iron until 1865. This ironworks made pig iron from 1742 to 1883. The nearby Cornwall mine, still in operation, is the oldest continuously used iron mine in the United States. It is also the nation's deepest open-cut mine. Just east of the furnace is "Miners' Village," a group of two-family houses constructed in the 1860's.
State
NHL

LEHIGH COUNTY
Allentown
NONNEMAKER HOUSE (THOMAS MEWHORTER HOUSE)
301 S. Lehigh Street
c. 1797

The Nonnemaker House is a well-developed, two-story Allentown residence of the late 18th century. A large addition on the east side dates from the 1890's. Wall fabric is rubble limestone stuccoed and scored to imitate masonry blocks. There is a brick chimney at the center of each gable end. The front door and transom are mid-19th century replacements, but the frame, paneled reveal, pilasters, pediment, and carved consoles are original. The roof cornice is rather sophisticated and has a dentil molding and ornamented brackets. Inside, the house has a side hall plan. Thomas Mewhorter, who built the house, served in the state assembly and senate.
Municipal
HABS

LUZERNE COUNTY
Forty Fort
DENISON HOUSE
35 Denison Street
1790

There is a strong resemblance between the Denison House and 18th-century New En-

gland frame houses with central chimneys. The exterior openings appear to be original, and the main entrance is flanked by sidelights and has a four-pane transom. A rear addition was built in the mid-19th century.
State
HABS

MONTGOMERY COUNTY
Collegeville vicinity
KUSTER MILL
On Skippack Creek at Mill Road and Water Street Road
18th century

Hermanus Custer (original spelling Kuster) purchased the mill property in 1717. The property already had several buildings and other improvements by 1706 when the deed was recorded in Philadelphia. By 1767 the house had been expanded to its present size. The Kusters were masons in Germantown, and the house is evidence of their skill. It is two and one-half stories high with a central chimney and corner fireplaces characteristic of Germantown homes. Custer operated the first fulling mill in the county, although the present structure replaced the original mill which burned in 1936.
Private

MONTGOMERY COUNTY
Conshohocken
MOUNT JOY (PETER LEGAUX MANSION)
North Lane and Hector Street
18th century

Pierre Legaux (1748-1827) was born in France, and, having held several diplomatic posts in the Caribbean, he came to Philadelphia in 1785. One year later he purchased Mount Joy, built in 1738 on the west bank of the Schuylkill River. Legaux began at once to improve the value of his lands. He laid out gardens and terraces, established a lime furnace, and eventually began raising grapes. Legaux, a meteorologist, was elected to membership in the American Philosophical Society of Philadelphia in 1787. The house in which he lived is a two-and-one-half-story structure built of stone with a gable roof and two interior chimneys. It is five bays wide on the main facade, and the cove cornice extends across the gable ends of the roof. The porches are not original.
Private

MONTGOMERY COUNTY
Evansburg vicinity
SKIPPACK BRIDGE
East of Evansburg on Pa. 422
1792

Eight arches of locally cut stone comprise the 267–foot Skippack Bridge spanning the creek of the same name. The bridge measures 33 feet wide and is the oldest bridge in Montgomery County. Repairs were made in 1874, but the original proportions and design are intact.
County

MONTGOMERY COUNTY
Horsham vicinity
GRAEME PARK
Keith Valley Road
1721–1722

Built originally as a malt house and converted into a residence in 1739–1740, Graeme Park is an example of a one-room deep, two-and-one-half-story colonial period building with rich Georgian interiors. The exterior fieldstone walls are virtually devoid of decorative elements; the high gambrel roof is broken by window dormers and two brick chimneys. The first and second floors consist of a stair hall, a square center room, and two flanking rooms.
State; not accessible to the public
NHL; HABS

MONTGOMERY COUNTY
Plymouth Meeting
HOVENDEN HOUSE, BARN, AND ABOLITION HALL
1 E. Germantown Pike
18th century

The Hovenden House was built sometime prior to 1784. Through the years it has been expanded from a small two-story stone house to a three-floor structure with fourteen rooms. Many of the original glass windows, door locks and hinges, and random width floor planking are intact. George Carson, an active abolitionist, bought the house in 1839 and converted the original carriage house into a hall for antislavery gatherings. From 1881 to 1895 the property was the home and studio of artist Thomas Hovenden. He converted Abolition Hall into a studio by cutting an eight-foot square window into the northeast wall and lining the entire front of the ground floor with five-foot windows.
Private; not accessible to the public

MONTGOMERY COUNTY
Plymouth Meeting
PLYMOUTH FRIENDS MEETINGHOUSE
Corner of Germantown and Butler Pikes
18th century

The first deed for the Plymouth Friends Meetinghouse property was dated 1704. Although the exact date of construction for the Meetinghouse is not recorded, it is believed to have been standing by 1708. The rectangular Colonial style house was built of native limestone, and in 1780 an eastern wing was added for use as a school. During the Revolutionary War the building served as a hospital. Additions to the house include a porch across the entire front of the structure (1867) and a wing which was added to the rear of the building in 1945.
Private

MONTGOMERY COUNTY
Plymouth Meeting
PLYMOUTH MEETING HISTORIC DISTRICT
18th and 19th centuries

Plymouth Meeting was a Quaker settlement located at the crossroads of Germantown Pike and Old Butler Pike. A 1698 map shows dwellings in this area, thus supporting the belief that it was the first English settlement in Montgomery County. Plymouth was also a stop on the early Postal Service established by 1757. Architecturally, the district contains houses exhibiting English and Welsh Quaker influence, and several good examples of common 18th- and 19th-century housing. One of the more significant structures is Abolition Hall, which was built in the 1790's. The Hovenden House (c. 1794), Plymouth Friends Meetinghouse (c. 1708), the Livezey House (c. 1740), the store and post office (1827), and the Hinterleiter House (18th century) are also within the district. Plymouth Meeting has retained much of its original appearance.
Multiple public/private

MONTGOMERY COUNTY
Trappe
AUGUSTUS LUTHERAN CHURCH
7th Avenue East and Main Street
1743

Augustus Lutheran Church exemplifies the regional type of rural church built by the German settlers in Pennsylvania. Dr. Heinrich Melchior Muhlenberg, a patriarch of the Lutheran Church in America, built this two-story gambrel-roofed building of fieldstone covered with stucco. The east end of the rectangular building features a three-sided apse. The

1795 altar and pews—some with carved wooden doors and elaborately forged hinges—are still in place. Another interior feature is the cut-out gallery railing with heart-shaped figures. Recently restored, the church is now used only for special occasions.
Private
NHL

MONTGOMERY COUNTY
VALLEY FORGE
Reference—see Chester County

NORTHUMBERLAND COUNTY
Northumberland
PRIESTLEY, JOSEPH, HOUSE
Priestley Avenue
c. 1794

Persecuted in England for his religious and political views, the chemist Joseph Priestley sought refuge in the United States in 1794. In 1773 he had begun investigations which culminated in his discovery of oxygen in 1776. By 1786 he had published six volumes of scientific writings. His most important discovery between 1794 and 1804, the year of his death, was carbon monoxide. Priestley's two-and-one-half-story frame house with flanking wings for his kitchen and laboratory has been restored and partially refurnished.
State
NHL

PHILADELPHIA COUNTY
Philadelphia
ACADEMY OF MUSIC
Broad and Locust Streets
1857, Napoleon LeBrun and Gustav Runge

Owned and administered by the Philadelphia Orchestra Association, the Academy of Music is the country's oldest musical auditorium still retaining its original form and serving its original purpose. Pëtr Tchaikovsky, Camille Saint-Saens, Anton Rubinstein, Enrico Caruso, and Sergei Rachmaninoff are among the musicians who have performed here. Since the turn of the century it has been the home of the Philadelphia Orchestra. Restoration of the brick building was begun in connection with its centennial.
Private
NHL; HABS

PHILADELPHIA COUNTY
Philadelphia
AMERICAN PHILOSOPHICAL
SOCIETY HALL
Independence Square
1789, Samuel Vaughan

The American Philosophical Society, the oldest learned society in the United States, traces its origins to the initiative of Benjamin Franklin. On December 20, 1768, two groups merged to form the organization which flourishes today. Benjamin Franklin became the society's first president. Its endeavors in pure and applied science included the erection of an observatory, surveys of canal routes, and agricultural experiments. The society's *Transactions*, first published in 1771, is the oldest scholarly journal in America. The two-story brick building has been restored to its original appearance.
Private
NHL

PHILADELPHIA COUNTY
Philadelphia
ARCH STREET MEETINGHOUSE
302–338 Arch Street
1804, 1811 (addition)

The Arch Street Meetinghouse has served as a religious and social center in the Quaker community since the early 19th century. The late Georgian style of the two-story building is evident in the Flemish bond brickwork, hip roof, projecting center pavilion, and three hip-roofed porticos supported by plain wooden Doric columns. Two cupolas were added for ventilation in 1854. Overall, despite remodelings and alterations, the meetinghouse reflects 19th-century Quaker simplicity of architectural style. It is presently used for the Society of Friends Yearly Meeting.
Private

PHILADELPHIA COUNTY
Philadelphia
ARCH STREET PRESBYTERIAN
CHURCH
1726–1732 Arch Street
1855, Joseph C. Hoxie

The Arch Street Presbyterian Church is a one-story Classical Revival building with a projecting pedimented portico and coffered dome. Four giant Corinthian columns support the portico entablature, and Corinthian pilasters embellish the walls. The interior sanctuary mingles Greek and Roman elements and is an outstanding example of Classical architecture. Features of the sanctuary are 16 Corinthian columns, 22 antae (square columns), and a pulpit modeled upon a Greek votive altar.
Private

PHILADELPHIA COUNTY
Philadelphia
BARTRAM, JOHN, HOUSE
54th Street and Eastwick Avenue
1731

John Bartram was one of America's first native botanists. A self-educated man, Bartram made a number of journeys throughout the colonies to observe and collect plants and to note many facets of the colonial scene; wildlife, people, and the earth itself. Bartram's gardens, filled with rare and exotic plants, were enlarged by his son and after a period of neglect were restored as a memorial to the pioneer American botanist.
Municipal
NHL; HABS

PHILADELPHIA COUNTY
Philadelphia
CARPENTERS' HALL
320 Chestnut Street
1770–1771, Robert Smith

Robert Smith, a master carpenter, designed and constructed Carpenters' Hall for a guild, the Carpenters' Company of Philadelphia. The First Continental Congress met here in 1774. The two-story, late Georgian, brick structure is in excellent condition. Its ground plan is in the shape of a Greek cross, and the gable roof is surmounted by an octagonal cupola. All windows on the first floor have paneled shutters, and on the second floor there are three roundhead windows set above a false balustrade. The main entrance has a fanlight above it and is topped by a pediment. Carpenters' Hall has been used as a historical museum since 1857.
Private
NHL; HABS

PHILADELPHIA COUNTY
Philadelphia
CATHEDRAL OF SAINTS PETER AND
PAUL
18th Street and the Benjamin Franklin Parkway
1846–1866, Napoleon LeBrun and John Notman

The cruciform Cathedral of Saints Peter and Paul is an Italianate Renaissance Revival brownstone structure with a massive dome above the crossing. Four giant Corinthian columns support the roof pediment of the entrance portico. The high altar and the painting of the crucifixion on the interior were executed by Constantino Brumidi.
Private

PHILADELPHIA COUNTY
Philadelphia
CENTENNIAL NATIONAL BANK
3200 Market Street
1876, Frank Furness

The Centennial National Bank is a one-story corner building of red brick and stone. The exterior is enriched by heavy brick cornices, string courses, and massive brick pointed arches above the window openings. Over the angled corner bay is a pediment highlighted by a centered trefoil design containing a clock. The upper chords of the pediment are ornamented by ten spiky projections of graduated length. Thick, squat colonnettes with Gothic capitals frame the main doorway, and there is a projecting pent-like hood of stone above the door. Architect Frank Heyling Furness (1839–1912) also designed the Pennsylvania Academy of Fine Arts (1872–1876), the Provident Life and Trust Company, the Baltimore & Ohio and Pennsylvania railroad stations, the First Unitarian Church, and the University of Pennsylvania Library, all in Philadelphia. His work was massive, bold, and intensely personal, while his ornamentation was based on a free and creative interpretation of floral and faunal motifs.
Municipal; not accessible to the public
HABS

PHILADELPHIA COUNTY
Philadelphia
CHEW HOUSE
Germantown Avenue, between Johnson and Cliveden Streets
1763

The Chew House, Cliveden, is an important surviving landmark of the Revolutionary battle of Germantown, October 4, 1777. George Washington's army narrowly missed defeating a large British contingent guarding the northwestern approaches to Philadelphia. Together with the victory at Saratoga later that month, it was a major influence in bringing about the alliance with France. Designed in the Palladian manner with handsome pediments and cornices and a fine doorway, this two-story stone Georgian style house was built by Benjamin Chew.
Private; not accessible to the public
NHL; HABS

PHILADELPHIA COUNTY
Philadelphia
CHRIST CHURCH
2nd Street, between Market and Filbert Streets
1727–1754

The Christ Church congregation was organized in 1695. The present Christ

Church, a large and ornate Georgian structure, is the third church building to be located at this site. Begun as an extension of the second church, the present house of worship exhibits several features patterned after English models. Perhaps the most striking feature of the elaborate exterior is the great Palladian window and the rich Doric entablature. Although the galleries were remodeled in 1837 by Thomas U. Walter, the church has undergone little structural alteration.
Private
NHL; HABS

PHILADELPHIA COUNTY
Philadelphia
DRINKER'S COURT
236–238 Delancey Street
1765–1766

The two buildings comprising Drinker's Court are the only remaining 18th-century "bandbox" (one room per story) courthouses in the Society Hill area. Each consists of a two-and-one-half-story gambrel-roofed, pent-eaved main house fronting Delancey Street. Attached to the rear of each are the bandbox houses which are stucco-covered brick with lean-to roofs. Doorways from these rear houses open onto a court, access to which is through a passageway to Delancey Street. Built by John Drinker, a bricklayer, this court is typical of many that developed during the city's rapid growth in the 18th century.
Private; not accessible to the public

PHILADELPHIA COUNTY
Philadelphia
EAKINS, THOMAS, HOUSE
1729 Mount Vernon Place
c. 1854

Thomas Eakins specialized in realistic portraits which revealed the basic character of his subjects. Because of this approach and other practices, Eakins was not popular with Philadelphia society. Still he continued to paint portraits, among which is his noted "Walt Whitman." Eakins lived in this house from the age of two until his death in 1916.
Private; not accessible to the public
NHL; HABS

PHILADELPHIA COUNTY
Philadelphia
EASTERN STATE PENITENTIARY
21st Street and Fairmount Avenue
1823–1829, John Haviland

"The Pennsylvania System," whose development led to the construction of the Eastern State Penitentiary, resulted from a movement following the American Revolution to improve prison conditions and reform the inmates. The design of the

building provided for a central rotunda from which radiated seven cell blocks, each containing solitary confinement cells. Far in advance of its time, the penitentiary featured notable improvements in light, heat, ventilation, and space in the cells. The design, which exemplifies the architectural application of a philosophical point of view, gained widespread acceptance throughout the world, although the philosophy itself was eventually discredited.
State; not accessible to the public
NHL; HABS

PHILADELPHIA COUNTY
Philadelphia
ELFRETH'S ALLEY HISTORIC
DISTRICT
Between 2nd and Front Streets
17th and 18th centuries

Elfreth's Alley, the oldest unchanged and continuously inhabited street in Philadelphia, is a remarkable example of the survival of a part of colonial America's largest city. Though located in the heart of Philadelphia, the street is only six feet wide. The two- and three-story houses lining the street are typical urban dwellings of the period. Their facades are flush with the sidewalk; the principal rooms fill the entire front portion of the property. A variety of smaller rooms are strung out along one side of the lot to the rear and lighted by windows facing the narrow open court.
Private
NHL; HABS

PHILADELPHIA COUNTY
Philadelphia
FIRST UNITARIAN CHURCH
2121 Chestnut Street
1882, Frank Furness

The distinctive hand of Frank Furness is evident in this strikingly massive eclectic Victorian church. Originally of rustic stone construction, its appearance was changed somewhat by recent alterations which removed the rustication. A substantial tower and porte cochere highlighted one corner, but was removed in the early 20th century. The main roof is hipped and broken by four elaborate shed dormers. The south elevation features a rose window in an arched recess of the roof gable above a five-bay enclosed stone porch. A small stone bell-cupola surmounts the gable.
Private
HABS

PHILADELPHIA COUNTY
Philadelphia
FORT MIFFLIN HOSPITAL
(MESS HALL)
Marina and Penrose Ferry Roads
18th, 19th, and 20th centuries

The hospital or mess building was built before 1802. It measures 40 feet by 110 feet and is two stories high with a gable roof. There is a two-story gallery on the east front of the brick structure, and the original window glass and double hung sash remain on four of the windows. The hospital is outside the Fort Mifflin complex and is owned by the U.S. Army Corps of Engineers.
Federal
HABS

PHILADELPHIA COUNTY
Philadelphia
FOUNDER'S HALL, GIRARD
COLLEGE
Corinthian and Girard Avenues
1833–1847, Thomas U. Walter

Stephen S. Girard, a wealthy Philadelphia merchant, left a bequest of six million dollars to the city of Philadelphia upon his death in 1831. His will stipulated that the money be used to found an educational institution operated by the city. Ground breaking ceremonies were held in 1833, but the five original Greek Revival buildings, all designed by Thomas U. Walter, were not finished until 1847. Classes were first held in the new school on January 1, 1849.
Municipal
NHL

PHILADELPHIA COUNTY
Philadelphia
GERMANTOWN HISTORIC DISTRICT
Germantown Avenue, between
Windrim Avenue and Upsal Street
18th and early 19th centuries

Germantown exemplifies the successful settlement and development of a non-British group in one of the 13 original colonies. Germantown was founded in 1683 by a group of Netherlanders, who, fleeing religious persecution on the European continent, migrated to Pennsylvania at the invitation of William Penn. Beginning in 1709 large numbers of Germans began to settle here. By the 1750's the area had acquired the decidedly German character that it retained for the remainder of the 19th century, despite the movement of English, Swedish, and French Huguenot settlers into the area

late in the century. Approximately fifty 18th- and early 19th-century buildings are situated in the district. While varying in present integrity, they represent a range of social, economic, and cultural interests. Included among the buildings are residences, churches, a school, and several taverns.
Private
NHL; HABS

PHILADELPHIA COUNTY
Philadelphia
GLORIA DEI (OLD SWEDES')
CHURCH NATIONAL HISTORIC SITE
    Swanson Street, between Christian
    and Water Streets
    1698–1700

Though largely English in architectural form, Gloria Dei was built by Swedish colonists who settled in Pennsylvania. It is the oldest extant church building in Philadelphia. The exterior of this steep-roofed building features a peaked gable, square belfry, and small spire. An entrance porch on the south side and a small vestry on the north were added early in the 18th century. The small entrance vestibule in the tower provides access to the gallery, and to the simple central aisle. The unpaneled galleries are supported by slender posts, and on the gallery at the west tower end are two winged cherubim brought from Sweden in 1643. Polygonal in plan at the east end, the hung ceiling of the nave is vaulted in plaster to an irregular curve. The church is still the center of an active parish of the Protestant Episcopal Church.
Federal/non-federal
NPS; 3.43 acres
HABS

PHILADELPHIA COUNTY
Philadelphia
HILL-PHYSICK HOUSE
    321 S. 4th Street
    c. 1786

The Hill-Physick House is a three-story Georgian dwelling embellished by stone belt courses between floors. Windows diminish in size from the ground floor upwards, and the main entrance is highlighted by a leaded glass fanlight. Henry Hill, a wine importer, built the house, which was later owned by Dr. Philip Syng Physick. It has been restored to its circa 1810 appearance, and is one of the few remaining double pile mansions extant in Philadelphia.
Private
HABS

PHILADELPHIA COUNTY
Philadelphia
INDEPENDENCE NATIONAL
HISTORICAL PARK
    Bounded by Walnut, 6th, Chestnut,
    and 2nd Streets
    18th century

The central feature of Independence National Historical Park is Independence Hall, or the Pennsylvania Statehouse, begun in 1732 and completed in the 1750's. This outstanding example of colonial Georgian architecture now houses the Liberty Bell, which historically is the official bell of the Pennsylvania Statehouse. It was the scene of the adoption of the Declaration of Independence, July 4, 1776. Here the Second Continental Congress convened in May, 1775, and here in June of that year George Washington accepted the post of Commander-in-Chief of the American Army. In 1787 the Constitutional Convention, presided over by George Washington, created the Constitution of the United States. While Philadelphia was the seat of the federal government, 1790–1800, Congress sat in the county courthouse (Congress Hall) and the U.S. Supreme Court in the City Hall. Among other buildings included in the park are Philosophical Hall, Library Hall, the Second Bank of the United States, New Hall, Carpenter's Hall, the First Bank of the United States, and the Philadelphia Exchange.
Federal/non-federal
NPS; 21.84 acres
HABS

PHILADELPHIA COUNTY
Philadelphia
INSTITUTE OF THE PENNSYLVANIA
HOSPITAL
    111 N. 49th Street
    1859

Dr. Thomas Kirkbride built a hospital for the mentally ill that influenced the philosophy of similar institutions throughout America. His concept that the insane should be treated as any sick person was exemplified in his encouragement of patients' work in the hospital gardens and shops, and in the organization of a museum and library. Despite modern additions, the hospital retains its salient features: spaciousness, airiness, and light.
Private; not accessible to the public
NHL

PHILADELPHIA COUNTY
Philadelphia
KOSCIUSZKO HOUSE
    301 Pine Street
    1775

The Kosciuszko House was occupied by Polish General Thaddeus Kosciuszko and his traveling companion Julian Niemcewic, an important Polish literary figure, from November, 1797, to May, 1798. Kosciuszko served as a military engineer during the American Revolution. The three-and-one-half-story house has walls of brick laid in Flemish bond with black glazed headers. Still intact is the original cornice with its fret moulding. A two-story frame bathhouse added to the rear prior to 1853 was replaced by a one-story stucco addition in 1942. The house is presently in good condition but is unused.
Private; not accessible to the public

PHILADELPHIA COUNTY
Philadelphia
MASONIC TEMPLE
    1 N. Broad Street
    1873, James H. Windrim

The Romanesque Revival Masonic Temple is one of the outstanding buildings in Philadelphia. It is three and one-half stories high, and the main facade is dominated by two towers (the taller rises 250 feet). Exterior walls are granite and round arches mark all openings. Interior meeting rooms are unique examples of many architectural types—Moorish, Byzantine, Greek, Norman, Renaissance, Corinthian, and Egyptian. The building serves as the Grand Lodge for Pennsylvania Masonry.
Private
HABS

PHILADELPHIA COUNTY
Philadelphia
MAXWELL, EBENEEZER, HOUSE
    200 W. Tulpehocken Street
    1859

Ebeneezer Maxwell, a merchant, built this Victorian stone house with its unusual cornice, slate mansard roof, and four-story tower. There are two attached wings on the west end and four miniature dormers in the tower roof. Walls of the dwelling are faced with serpentine stone. The cornice is of Tudor Gothic design and runs up the gables, all of which contain round windows. A wooden, crenellated piazza is attached to the west elevation. The metal cresting on the tower may have been repeated on the roof at one time.
Private
HABS

PHILADELPHIA COUNTY
Philadelphia
MIKVEH ISRAEL CEMETERY
Northwest corner of Spruce and
Darien Streets
18th and 19th centuries

In 1740 Nathan Levy, a founder of Philadelphia's Jewish community, obtained this land for use as a burial plot. Interred here are several Revolutionary soldiers and notables such as Haym Salomon, the Gratz family, Aaron Levy, and Nathan Levy himself. Salomon, a financier, did much to stabilize American currency and credit (1781–1784); the Gratz brothers, shipowners and merchants, were active in civic and community affairs; Rebecca Gratz (1781–1869) was a teacher and philanthropist. Aaron Levy founded Aaronsburg, Pennsylvania. This oldest Jewish cemetery in Philadelphia contains some colonial gravestones, but most markers are 19th century.
Private

PHILADELPHIA COUNTY
Philadelphia
MOUNT PLEASANT
Fairmount Park
1761–1762

Mount Pleasant is among the finest surviving examples of late Georgian domestic architecture in Pennsylvania. Constructed by John MacPherson, a Scottish sea captain and privateer, the two-and-one-half-story stone house is raised over a high basement. The exterior architectural emphasis is centered on the east and west facades where projecting pedimented central pavilions break the five-bay facades. The hip roof is topped by a balustraded deck and two arched quadruple chimneys. The house has a central hallway with flanking rooms rich in interior decorations. Two symmetrically placed flanking outbuildings complete the composition.
Municipal
NHL; HABS

PHILADELPHIA COUNTY
Philadelphia
MUSICAL FUND HALL
808 Locust Street
1824, William Strickland; 1847,
Nicholas LeBrun; 1891, Addison
Hutton

The Musical Fund Society was founded in 1820 for the "relief of decayed musicians and for the improvement of taste in music." Four years later a building was erected to house their activities, and it is today the oldest music hall in the country. The first Republican National Convention took place here in 1856. Strickland's

original design was modified in 1847 by LeBrun, who moved the street facade forward 16 feet and changed the stage from the front to the rear of the interior. The present facade dates from the 1891 remodeling. It is buff brick with terra cotta facing and copper cornices. For many years Musical Fund Hall was used as a warehouse and an office.
Municipal; not accessible to the public

PHILADELPHIA COUNTY
Philadelphia
NEW MARKET
S. 2nd Street, between Pine and
Lombard Streets
1745

Philadelphia's New Market illustrates a once-important aspect of distributing food. A street market, open on Tuesdays and Fridays, it served residents of South Philadelphia until well into the 19th century. Two parallel rows of brick pillars support a gable roof and arched plastered ceiling over an open market area. The Head House, a two-story firehouse built in 1804, stands at the market's north end. The first floor housed fire equipment; the second floor provided a meeting room.
Municipal
NHL; HABS

PHILADELPHIA COUNTY
Philadelphia
OLD FORT MIFFLIN
Marina and Penrose Ferry Roads
1772–1775, 1779–1781, 1794–1798,
1814–, 1835–1839, 1870's

Fort Mifflin was laid out in 1771 by British engineer John Montressor. When the Revolutionary War broke out the fortifications were unfinished. A colonial force of 300 men and 20 cannon occupied the site when British troops held Philadelphia, and a six-day attack was required to drive the defenders back across the Delaware River to New Jersey, thus enabling supplies to be brought upriver to General Howe's troops in the city. In 1798 the fort was reconstructed in stone according to the designs and plans of Pierre Charles L'Enfant, who later laid out Washington, D.C. Fort Mifflin was named for Thomas Mifflin, first governor of the Commonwealth of Pennsylvania. Buildings included in the fort complex are a blacksmith shop, soldiers' barracks, officers' quarters, commandant's house, artillery shed, commissary, arsenal, hospital, and main magazines.
Municipal
HABS

PHILADELPHIA COUNTY
Philadelphia
**PEALE, CHARLES WILLSON, HOUSE
(BELFIELD)**
2100 Clarkson Avenue
c. 1750

Charles Willson Peale is noted for his miniatures and portraits of George Washington and other prominent individuals of the Revolutionary War period. During the war he painted many portraits, including 40 miniatures during the bitter winter of 1777–1778 at Valley Forge. Of value to historians is the artist's meticulous attention to detail in portraying military uniforms. Belfield, Peale's residence from 1810 to 1820, has been greatly altered over the years.
Private; not accessible to the public
NHL

PHILADELPHIA COUNTY
Philadelphia
**PENNSYLVANIA ACADEMY OF THE
FINE ARTS**
Southwest Corner of Broad and
Cherry Streets
1872–1876, Frank Furness

The Pennsylvania Academy of the Fine Arts, founded in 1805, has occupied this building since 1876. Designed by Philadelphia architect Frank Furness, the three-and-one-half-story brick and stone building exhibits the originality and creativity of detail characteristic of its designer. Designed in the Venetian Gothic mode, the Academy is the most important of Furness's surviving buildings. Notable is the vigorous polychromy of the exterior and the striking combination of stone, brick, and tile. Floral decoration above the windows and beside the central arched opening incorporates natural forms, a characteristic of Furness's style. The Academy is a powerful and original interpretation of 19th-century architectural forms, an intensely personal statement by a leading architect of the day.
Private

PHILADELPHIA COUNTY
Philadelphia
THE PENNSYLVANIA HOSPITAL
8th and Spruce Streets
1756, Samuel Rhoads

The Pennsylvania Hospital is the oldest established hospital in the United States. Dr. Thomas Bond conceived the idea of founding this hospital to care for the sick, injured, and insane. With Benjamin Franklin's support the hospital was authorized in 1751 and began operations the following year. The hospital has continued to grow as the city has grown. While the exterior of the original building

has been little altered, the interior has changed greatly, but even so the building retains a large measure of its original appearance.
Private
NHL; HABS

PHILADELPHIA COUNTY
Philadelphia
PHILADELPHIA COLLEGE OF ART (ASYLUM FOR THE DEAF AND DUMB)
Northwest corner of Broad and Pine Streets
1824, John Haviland

The Asylum for the Deaf and Dumb was constructed as a U-shaped building three stories high and measuring 96 by 92 feet. A classic pediment and four Doric columns adorn the main facade giving the structure a temple-like appearance. Flanking wings contain shallow arches. In 1852 north and south two-story wings were built, and in 1863 a third story was added to the original long wings (east and west). The basement of the old asylum contained a kitchen, bakehouse, dining room, workshop, and ironing room. Sitting rooms, offices, parlors, and a chapel occupied the first floor, and the second floor had only bedrooms. Interior alterations have been made to accommodate the College of Art.
Private

PHILADELPHIA COUNTY
Philadelphia
PHILADELPHIA CONTRIBUTIONSHIP
212 S. 4th Street
1836, Thomas U. Walter

The Philadelphia Contributionship for the Insurance of Houses from Loss by Fire is the oldest continuing fire insurance company in America. It was founded by Benjamin Franklin and others in 1752. Since 1836 the Contributionship has occupied this three-story brick building. Window sills and frames are marble, and there are heavy molded lintels above the twin windows of the first and second stories. The entrance portico has four fluted Corinthian columns with marble bases and a heavy architrave and a dentil molding. In 1866 extensive alterations were made: the roof was changed to a mansard; the present marble molded dentil cornice was added; and the portico columns and steps were replaced.
Private
HABS

PHILADELPHIA COUNTY
Philadelphia
POE, EDGAR ALLAN, HOUSE
530 N. 7th Street
c. 1830

Edgar Allan Poe lived in this small brick cottage from 1842 to 1844. Here he wrote many of his best-known short stories: "The Gold Bug," "The Fall of the House of Usher," and "The Murders in the Rue Morgue." In the next few years he was also recognized for his poetry, including "Annabel Lee," "The Raven," and "The Bells." The house is furnished with contemporary items and contains manuscripts and first editions of "The Bells," "The Raven," "The Gold Bug," and other tales and poems.
Private
NHL; HABS

PHILADELPHIA COUNTY
Philadelphia
REYNOLDS-MORRIS HOUSE
225 S. 8th Street
1786–1787

The Reynolds-Morris House is one of the finest surviving original examples of a Georgian Philadelphia row town house. The L-shaped three-and-one-half-story brick building has a gable roof and a high chimney set in each of former end party walls. Its double front has two windows on each side of the central doorway, a range of five windows on the second and third floors, and three simple dormers in the gable roof above. Two slightly projecting courses of bricks form decorative horizontal belts at the second- and third-floor levels. A heavy molded cornice and handsome gutter spouts complete the decorative features. The adjoining 18th-century row houses have been removed so that the house now stands alone with a garden space on either side.
Private
NHL; HABS

PHILADELPHIA COUNTY
Philadelphia
ST. CLEMENT'S PROTESTANT EPISCOPAL CHURCH
Southwest corner of 20th and Cherry Streets
1856, John Notman

The architecture of St. Clement's Church is Romanesque. The sanctuary is rectangular with a semicircular chancel. A three-story square tower stands at the northeast corner and was once topped by a spire demolished in 1869. Exterior walls are brownstone. Interior alterations were made at a later date under the direction of Horace Wells Sellers. Highlights of the in-

terior are polychrome statuary, stained glass windows by Charles J. Connick, and the Crypt Chapel containing stones from the ruins of ancient St. Clement's in the Crimea.
Private

PHILADELPHIA COUNTY
Philadelphia
ST. GEORGE'S METHODIST CHURCH
324 New Street
1760's

Old St. George's, the oldest Methodist church in continuous use in the United States, has played a prominent role in the development and history of American Methodism. The Philadelphia congregation which later met at St. George's first gathered in a sail loft on Dock Street in 1767. Two years later they purchased this church building in an unfinished condition from a group of Dutch Presbyterians. Francis Asbury, the first Methodist bishop in America, served as St. George's third pastor. The church itself is a three-story brick building with gable roof and box cornice. Its Fourth Street side has been altered by the addition of a stone wall and a paved entrance terrace necessitated by the lowering of the street level. The adjoining historical center dates from 1812 and consists of two joined brick town houses.
Private

PHILADELPHIA COUNTY
Philadelphia
SOCIETY HILL HISTORIC DISTRICT
Bounded on the north by Walnut Street, on the south by Lombard Street, on the east by the pier line of the Delaware River, and on the west by 8th Street
18th and 19th centuries

The area known as Society Hill comprises the original and oldest portion of Philadelphia as laid out in 1682 by Thomas Holme, surveyor for William Penn. The name Society Hill is taken from the Free Society of Traders, who purchased 20,000 acres from Penn. Within the historic district are more than 575 18th- and 19th-century commercial, residential, and religious structures. The early houses are brick construction with wood trim and water tables and belt courses of either marble or molded brick. Pent eaves are not uncommon. Among the most important structures are the following: the Head House (1804, Second Street), a firehouse; New Market (begun 1745), also on Second Street; St. Peter's Episcopal Church (1763, Robert Smith), Third and Pine; Old St. Joseph's Roman Catholic Church (1838–1839) serving the oldest Catholic parish in the city; St. George's Greek Orthodox Cathedral (1822, John

Haviland), 250 S. Eighth Street; the Powel House (1765), 244 S. Third Street; the Luke Morris House (1787), 255 S. Eighth Street; and the Todd House (1775), 343 Walnut.
Multiple public/private
HABS

PHILADELPHIA COUNTY
Philadelphia
STENTON (JAMES LOGAN HOME)
18th and Courtland Streets
1730

Immigrating to America in 1699, James Logan became a prominent figure in the government of Pennsylvania. He became mayor of Philadelphia in 1722 and Chief Justice of the Pennsylvania Supreme Court in 1731. From his youthful interest in mathematics and botany grew his primary contributions to scientific knowledge. He amassed a scientific and mathematical library of nearly 400 volumes and performed significant botanical experiments. Logan built this three-story brick house and occupied it until his death in 1751.
Municipal
NHL; HABS

PHILADELPHIA COUNTY
Philadelphia
SULLY, THOMAS, RESIDENCE
530 Spruce Street
1796

During his lifetime Thomas Sully was one of America's most prolific portrait painters. He is credited with some 2600 paintings, including some historical scenes. Among his best-known works are "Washington Crossing the Delaware" and "Marquis de Lafayette." This brick row house was his residence for only a brief period, although he lived in Philadelphia from 1808 until his death in 1872.
Private; not accessible to the public
NHL; HABS

PHILADELPHIA COUNTY
Philadelphia
TWELFTH STREET MEETINGHOUSE
20 S. 12th Street
1810–1814

Used continually since its completion, the Twelfth Street Meetinghouse was originally known as the Monthly Meeting of the Friends of Philadelphia for the Western District. The building incorporates many 18th-century building techniques. All reusable timbers and paneling from the 1755 Great Meetinghouse (demolished in 1810) were employed in constructing the present meetinghouse. There are the traditional two entrances, one for men and one for women, and the inside is divided into two rooms by a movable wooden parti-

tion. All shutters, millwork, and window sash are original.
Private

PHILADELPHIA COUNTY
Philadelphia
U.S.S. *OLYMPIA*
Pier 40, at the foot of Chestnut Street
1888

The cruiser *Olympia* is the oldest steel-hulled American warship afloat. The ship measures 340 feet long at the water line and has a beam of 53 feet. During the Spanish-American War she served as Commodore George Dewey's flagship in the battle of Manila Bay. After naval duty in World War I, she was used to return the body of the Unknown Soldier to the United States in 1921. After several more cruises the ship was tied up at the Philadelphia Navy Yard in 1922. The restored ship retains its original engines, and on the berth deck are Dewey's cabin and the crew's sleeping quarters.
Private
NHL

PHILADELPHIA COUNTY
Philadelphia
WALNUT STREET THEATRE
9th and Walnut Streets
1809, John Haviland

The Walnut Street Theatre is one of the oldest surviving theaters in the United States. Originally used for circuses, the theater began presenting legitimate drama in 1811. Among its many performers have been Sarah Bernhardt, Ellen Terry, Richard Mansfield, and John Drew. Despite its several remodelings, both inside and out, the building still illustrates the history of the American theater. The stage is one of the earliest examples of a "raked" or slanted stage still in use.
Private
NHL; HABS

PHILADELPHIA COUNTY
Philadelphia
WOODFORD
East Fairmount Park
1734, 1756

The first of the late Georgian mansions to be erected in the Philadelphia area was Woodford. William Coleman, wealthy merchant and judge, built the house as an L-shaped, two-story brick mansion with a hip roof. The three-bay east facade has a pedimented center pavilion. A projecting cornice between the first and second floors extends around three sides of the house. The main entrance is flanked by two Roman Doric engaged columns that support the comforming entablature with pediment. Above this is a Palladian window set in the narrow central pavilion.
Municipal
NHL; HABS

PHILADELPHIA COUNTY
Philadelphia
THE WOODLANDS
40th Street and Woodland Avenue, West
c. 1770

Built by William Hamilton and greatly enlarged and remodeled in the Adam style in 1788–1789, The Woodlands is a notable example of late Georgian domestic residential architecture. The two-story rectangular-shaped house is of gray stone. Two large brick chimneys rise above the low-pitched hip roof. Two semi-circular bays project from the side elevation of the house, and at the north entrance front six Ionic pilasters support a 34-foot-wide projecting pediment. On the south entrance a flight of stone steps ascends to a central pedimented roof portico supported by six Doric pillars.
Private
NHL; HABS

PIKE COUNTY
DELAWARE AND HUDSON CANAL
Reference—see Orange County, New York

PIKE COUNTY
Milford
PINCHOT, GIFFORD, HOUSE (GREY TOWERS)
West edge of Milford
c. 1886

Grey Towers, a large, stone, chateau-like house, was Gifford Pinchot's home until his death in 1946. Pinchot, America's first professionally trained forester, was a pre-eminent crusader in the cause of federal forestry and conservation from 1901 to 1909. Under his leadership the Forestry Division of the Department of Agriculture was expanded, first into the Bureau of Forestry and then into the present-day Forest Service. In 1901, under Pinchot's chairmanship, the newly created National Conservation Commission produced the world's first national inventory of natural resources.
Federal; not accessible to the public
NHL

VENANGO COUNTY
Titusville vicinity
DRAKE OIL WELL
3 miles southeast of Titusville on Pa. 36, Drake Well Memorial Park
1859

Edwin L. Drake drilled the world's first oil well in the summer of 1859. An oil boom followed, and for the next quarter century the Titusville region remained the oil

center of the United States. A museum and a replica of Drake's first derrick commemorate the event.
State
NHL

WAYNE COUNTY
DELAWARE AND HUDSON CANAL
Reference—see Orange County, New York

WESTMORELAND COUNTY
Harrison City vicinity
BUSHY RUN BATTLEFIELD
2 miles east of Harrison City on Pa. 993
1763

The battle of Bushy Run, August 5–6, 1763, was a decisive British victory over the best organized and most dangerous Indian forces on the colonial frontier in the 18th century. Often called "Pontiac's Rebellion," the uprising was crushed by British General Henry Bouquet's victory at Fort Pitt. The western frontier then became relatively safe for the colonists who shortly began settling in the Ohio Country.
State
NHL

YORK COUNTY
York
BILLMEYER HOUSE
E. Market Street
1860

This Italian Villa style house was built for industrialist Charles Billmeyer. The exterior brick walls are ornamented by quoins while window and door openings are trimmed with cast stone. Atop the hip roof there is a square cupola with a wide bracketed cornice. Both side elevations have double stacked bay windows. The rear wing was probably added after completion of the main structure.
Private; not accessible to the public

Puerto Rico

Chapel, Plaza De Armas, Castillo De San Felipe Del Morro
San Juan, Puerto Rico. *Jack E. Boucher for HABS*

El Morro, San Juan National Historic Site,
San Juan, Puerto Rico. *Jack E. Boucher for NPS*

LA FORTALEZA

San Juan Island, between San Juan
Bay and Calle Recinto Oeste
1533–1540; 1845–1846 (remodeled
and enlarged)

La Fortaleza, the first fortification of San
Juan, Puerto Rico, was built by the
Spanish as a defense against raids by
French and English pirates and Carib Indians. It was captured by the English Earl of
Cumberland in 1598. Falling to the Dutch
in 1625, La Fortaleza was burned by the
retreating army when it failed to capture
the nearby fort at El Morro. Reconstructed after the Dutch campaign, it has
since been the residence of the island
governors.
Territorial
NHL; HABS

SAN JUAN NATIONAL HISTORIC SITE

16th century

San Juan National Historic Site, comprising major defenses of the Spanish Main,
once protected a strategic harbor that
guarded the sea lane to the Caribbean.
Here Spaniards planted the first permanent colony in the present territory of
the United States, and its fortifications are
the oldest within our territorial limits.
Various fortifications, including Casa
Blanca, outside the park, were made in
the early 16th century, but the massive
masonry citadel of El Morro was not
begun until 1591. By the last years of the
18th century the major defenses of San
Juan included El Cañuelo, El Morro, San
Cristobal, and the city walls. These fortifications stand today as a reminder of the
once-great Spanish empire.
Federal/non-federal
NPS; 37.77 acres
HABS

Rhode Island

Bristol County Courthouse, Bristol, Rhode Island.
Clifford M. Renshaw, III

Charles H. Baldwin House,
Newport, Rhode Island.
Cervin Robinson for HABS

The Arcade, Providence, Rhode Island.
Providence Journal-Bulletin

General Ambrose Burnside House,
College Hill Historic District,
Providence, Rhode Island.
Providence Preservation Society

Levi H. Gale House, Newport, Rhode Island.
Cervin Robinson for HABS

BRISTOL COUNTY
Bristol
BRISTOL COUNTY COURTHOUSE
High Street
1816

The Bristol County Courthouse was constructed of stone laid in mortar and faced with brick. At this time the walls are covered with stucco. Its central section is three stories high, three bays wide, and covered by a gable roof. Two-story portions project from the north and south elevations, appearing like wings although they are not. Above the center block is a square wooden two-stage tower, each stage railed, supporting an octagonal belfry with a concave conical roof. Russell Warren, who did much work in Bristol, may have designed the courthouse. Its most distinctive feature is a large, modestly rusticated arched window opening subdivided by wooden colonettes and interlaced Gothic mullions. The state legislature met in the Bristol Courthouse and in four other county seats on an alternating basis.
State

KENT COUNTY
East Greenwich
ARMORY OF THE KENTISH GUARDS
Armory and Peirce Streets
1842

The Kentish Guards, organized in 1774, is a volunteer militia unit or "chartered company." The Armory has been their headquarters since its construction. It is a rectangular (61 by 30 feet), frame, Greek Revival structure with a temple front portico on the west elevation. The portico is shallow and has two Doric columns set between paneled corner piers. Above is an architrave containing small dentils and a well-proportioned pediment. In the 1890's the rear of the building was extended.
State

KENT COUNTY
East Greenwich
KENT COUNTY COURTHOUSE
127 Main Street
c. 1803–1806

The Kent County Courthouse is a two-story frame building with clapboarded exterior and a deck-on-hip roof. Its stone basement is enough above ground to constitute another story. The seven-bay facade has a pediment above and quoins at the sides delineating the three central bays. Quoins also mark the building's corners, and a belt course separates the first and second floors. An oblong clock tower is set atop the balustraded deck of the roof and is, in turn, surmounted by a cupola. Several periods of decor are ap-

parent inside in later moldings and paneling in the various rooms. Until 1854 the Rhode Island legislature met at five county seats on an alternating basis, and for a brief period, each of these towns was the state capital. East Greenwich was one, and the convention convened in the Kent County Courthouse in 1842 for the purpose of framing a new constitution.
State

KENT COUNTY
East Greenwich
WHITMARSH, COLONEL MICAH, HOUSE (JOHN REYNOLDS HOUSE)
294 Main Street
1761–1771

John Reynolds built this two-and-one-half-story brick dwelling which was owned by the Whitmarsh family from 1773 to 1845. The roof is a high gambrel type lacking dormers. Inside, the house has a central hall, four-room plan. Externally the structure is almost devoid of any architectural embellishment except a brick belt course. The main entrance is not original but was added in the 1830's or 1840's. Brickwork around the window openings has undergone sporadic and patchy repair when the windows themselves were apparently shortened and widened. The second-floor chambers retain, to a large degree, their original floors, two-paneled doors, mantels, overmantels, paneling, woodwork, and hardware.
Private

KENT COUNTY
Warwick
RHODES, CHRISTOPHER, HOUSE
25 Post Road
c. 1800

Christopher Rhodes and his two brothers founded a cotton manufacturing business and became the leading entrepreneurs of Warwick in the first half of the 19th century. Also active in politics, Rhodes served in the state legislature. His house is a two-and-one-half-story frame dwelling sheathed with clapboards. The basement is stone and the roof is gabled. The Federal style front entrance is surmounted by a semicircular fanlight, a molded architrave, and a triangular pediment.
Private

NEWPORT COUNTY
Middletown
WHITEHALL
Berkeley Avenue
1729

George Berkeley (1685–1753) came to Newport in 1710 enroute to Bermuda, where he proposed founding a college. Twenty years later, in the early 1730's, he

left Rhode Island and returned to England to become bishop of Cloyne. His two-story timber and clapboard construction house is topped by a hip roof. Alterations have been made on the house, but most of the interior trim is original.
Private
HABS

NEWPORT COUNTY
Newport
BALDWIN, CHARLES H., HOUSE
Bellevue Avenue opposite Perry Street
1877–1878, Potter and Robinson

Built as a summer home for Commodore Charles H. Baldwin, USN, this Shingle Style house was an important element in the residential development of Bellevue Avenue. It is characterized by richly textured decorative surfaces and the dramatic use of open space on the interior. The house is an irregular rectangle measuring about 80 by 60 feet with a steep, many-gabled roof. Timber framed, it is faced with brick, clapboards, and shingles in that order from the ground upwards. Vertical accents are provided by the towering, pilastered chimneys, while strong interlocking patterns are created by the roof slopes and gable forms, the half-timbered and paneled wall surfaces, and the window mullions.
Private; not accessible to the public
HABS

NEWPORT COUNTY
Newport
BRICK MARKET
Thames Street and Washington Square
1762–1772, Peter Harrison

Among the remaining colonial commercial buildings in Newport, the Brick Market is a notable illustration of colonial civic architecture. It was originally built with open arcades on the ground floor; the two upper stories were devoted to retail dry-goods shops and offices. Harrison's model for the design was Inigo Jones's and John Webb's design for the great gallery at Somerset House, London, England. The building was later used for a variety of purposes; theater (1793–1799), town and city hall (1842–1900). Restored in 1928–1930, it currently houses the offices of the Newport Chamber of Commerce.
Municipal
NHL

NEWPORT COUNTY
Newport
CHATEAU-SUR-MER
Bounded by Bellevue, Leroy,
Lawrence, and Shepard Avenues
1851–1852; 1872–1873, Richard
Morris Hunt

Chateau-sur-Mer was built for William S.
Wetmore and remained in the possession
of the Wetmore family until the 1960's.
The present, three-story, Victorian "cottage" reflects Hunt's romanticism and is
an elaborately altered version of the earlier structure. Hunt added a mansard roof,
altered a side entrance, and increased the
number of windows, rooms, and towers.
Fall River granite was used for the exteri-
or walls to emphasize mass; carved woodwork and ceiling beams ornament the
library and dining room; and the floors are
inlaid wood. John LaFarge executed a
large stained-glass window for the main
staircase landing between the first and
second floors. The interior rooms are
grouped around a central hall.
Private; not accessible to the public

NEWPORT COUNTY
Newport
**CLARKE STREET MEETINGHOUSE
(SECOND CONGREGATIONAL
CHURCH)**
Clarke Street
c. 1735

The Second Congregational Society of
Newport engaged Cotton Palmer, a
Providence-Taunton builder, to construct
a meetinghouse for them in 1735. According to specifications the building was to be
62 feet long and 42 feet wide. The original
tower and spire (taken down in 1946) on
the east gable end were built in stages.
The tower rose one square story above the
gable and was surrounded at its top by a
rail or parapet containing short pinnacles
at each corner. This section was surmounted by an octagonal section above
which was the octagonal shingled spire.
The main entrance was originally in the
center of the north side. Following
damage by occupying British troops, the
church interior had been rebuilt by 1785;
more changes occurred in 1847 through
the addition of Greek Revival detailing;
wings and Victorian ornament were added
in 1874–1875. The church is presently
used for storage.
Private; not accessible to the public

NEWPORT COUNTY
Newport
FORT ADAMS
Harrison Avenue
1824

Earliest fortifications on this site were
completed in 1799 and formed a vital
defense of Narragansett Bay and an important link in the coastal defenses of the
eastern seaboard. By the outbreak of the
War of 1812 the 18th-century works were
ruinous and new ones were erected. What
remains is mainly a product of the 1820's
plus some inner and outer additions. Basically a hollow granite pentagon measuring
1,200 by 1,000 feet overall, Fort Adams
has projecting bastions on the northwest,
northeast, and southeast angles that
dominate the channel passage. The walls
have two casemate levels beneath a
parapeted unroofed gallery for artillery
use. A maze of underground tunnels was
dug through rock to provide exits in case
of abandonment. The south wall of the
fort is surmounted by brick additions used
as barracks. These are fronted by galleries
supported on cast iron columns and, with
their chimneys, survive although hollow.
There are no other structures within the
walls. Buildings outside the walls are an
austere, granite, Greek Revival guardhouse and late 19th- and early 20th-centu-
ry brick auxiliary buildings which illustrate
the continuous use and development of
Fort Adams.
State; not accessible to the public
HABS

NEWPORT COUNTY
Newport
GALE, LEVI H., HOUSE
89 Touro Street
1833–1835, Russell Warren

The Levi Gale House is one of only three
surviving monumentally scaled and classically detailed dwellings of the Greek
Revival period in the city of Newport. The
frame structure measures 50 feet square
and is two and one-half stories high with a
hip monitor roof. Its square mass is
strongly articulated by rusticated pilasters
at the corners, and the five bays on the
north and east sides are marked by four
Corinthian pilasters. At the eaves is a deep
entablature scaled to the proportions of
the pilasters. Each pilastered facade has a
central one-story entrance porch with
Corinthian columns. The house was
moved to its present location in 1925.
Private
HABS

NEWPORT COUNTY
Newport
HUNTER HOUSE
54 Washington Street
c. 1748

The Hunter House was constructed for
Deputy Gov. Jonathan Nichols, Jr. It is an
early, New England Georgian, two-story
residence with a balustraded gambrel roof.
Though the house appears to be of frame
construction, the walls are brick-lined.
The early Georgian exterior, with its
heavily molded window caps and projecting cornice, is severe in appearance except for the broken segmental pediment
over the central doorway on the street
facade. The structure has two interior
chimneys and the typical Georgian floor
plan: two rooms on either side of the central hall on both floors.
Private
NHL; HABS

NEWPORT COUNTY
Newport
KING, EDWARD, HOUSE
Aquidneck Park, Spring Street
1845–1847, Richard Upjohn

Richard Upjohn's King House is a good
example of the Italian Villa home popular
during the mid–19th century. This style of
architecture represented a noticeable
break with the traditional symmetry of
design and regularity of plan heretofore
popular. Ornament was characterized by
size and simplicity. The King House is
brick with sandstone cornices, brackets,
string courses, and window dressings.
Porches, balconies, and hoods are wood.
Variations in roof heights produce an extremely irregular mass; both gable and hip
roofs are employed, and there is a large
three-story tower on the southwest corner.
Porches formerly at the southwest,
southeast, and eastern sides have been
removed. Interior decoration is also plain
and heavy, and some of the floors are inlaid wood.
Municipal
NHL

NEWPORT COUNTY
Newport
LUCAS-JOHNSTON HOUSE
40 Division Street
18th century

The original section of the Lucas-Johnston
House, mentioned as existing in 1721,
faced the east and was composed of two
rooms flanking a center chimney. Some
time before 1750 the original house was
enlarged by the addition of rooms on the
west, and the entrance was altered to face
west. The Colonial frame house is now

square in appearance and has a gable-on-hip roof. Fine architectural detail is evident in the main pedimented doorway and in the modillion cornice.
Private; not accessible to the public
HABS

NEWPORT COUNTY
Newport
MIANTONOMI MEMORIAL PARK
Bounded on the south by Admiral Kalbfuss Road, on the west by Girard Avenue, on the north by property of the Newport Housing Authority, and on the east by Hillside Avenue
17th to 20th centuries

This 32-acre park was originally part of a land tract purchased from the Narragansett Indians in 1637 or 1638. The colonists used the hill for a lookout, for public executions, and for beacons. In 1776 Col. Israel Putnam constructed fortifications here. When Newport fell to the British, they held the city for 3 years, strengthening its defenses on the hill. Remains of the British powder magazine and other works are still visible. After the Revolution the entire area around Miantonomi Hill reverted to farm land and remained so until 1921 when the city of Newport purchased it for a park. A memorial tower was erected in the park in 1929 to commemorate the Newport dead of World War I.
Municipal

NEWPORT COUNTY
Newport
THE NEWPORT CASINO
194 Bellevue Avenue
1879-1881, McKim, Mead, and White

The architectural firm of McKim, Mead, and White designed the Newport Casino in their now-famous Shingle Style during Newport's heyday as a summer resort. Stores and restaurants, separated by brick piers, were located on the ground floor. Above them were clubrooms. The exterior of the second floor is shingled and supported by corbels. Decorative carving ornaments the roof pediments, and the center section has a projecting second-story balcony. Alterations and additions have been made over the years, and parts of the Casino have burned. There are sports facilities behind the Casino, and the first official U.S. Lawn Tennis Association championships were played here in 1881. Also situated within the Casino complex is the Casino Theatre designed by Stanford White. It, too, is Shingle Style with a wood and plaster interior.
Private

NEWPORT COUNTY
Newport
NEWPORT HISTORIC DISTRICT
Within an area bounded approximately by Van Zandt Avenue, Farewell, Sherman, High, Thomas, Golden Hill, Thames, Marsh, and Washington Streets
18th century

Newport's numerous Georgian structures illustrate the mid-18th century architectural history of one of the colonies' major ports. Because of the work of Richard Munday, master carpenter, and of Peter Harrison, a distinguished colonial architect, Newport's Georgian public buildings rank among the most advanced and academic in style of those erected in the colonies during the 18th century. Newport's unique architectural character as a colonial city, however, lies not only in its fine public buildings and the mansions of wealthy merchants, but also in the rows of small, 18th-century dwellings and shops that still occupy the old part of the city. The historic structures are largely concentrated near the waterfront and situated within the 18th-century limits of the town. The waterfront is not within the boundaries of the historic district.
Public/private
NHL

NEWPORT COUNTY
Newport
OLD COLONY HOUSE (OLD STATEHOUSE)
Washington Square
1739-1741, Richard Munday

The Old Statehouse is a colonial period building of both historical and architectural distinction. It first housed the General Assembly of the Colony of Rhode Island, and from 1790 to 1900, the Rhode Island legislature. When General George Washington came to Newport to visit the newly arrived French army during the Revolutionary War, a banquet was held in the great hall. The red brick building has a gable roof surmounted by a two-story octagonal cupola. The dominant feature of the main facade is the center doorway and balcony.
State
NHL

NEWPORT COUNTY
Newport
REDWOOD LIBRARY
50 Bellevue Avenue
1750, Peter Harrison

The Redwood Library was the outgrowth of a philosophical society, founded in Newport in 1730, to which Abraham Redwood donated funds for the purchase

of books in 1747. It is one of the oldest library buildings in continuous use in the United States.
Private
NHL

NEWPORT COUNTY
Newport
SHERMAN, WILLIAM WATTS, HOUSE
2 Shepard Avenue
1875-1876, Henry Hobson Richardson

H. H. Richardson successfully imported mid-19th-century English Queen Anne architecture to the United States with his design for the Sherman House. Bold and symmetrical massing of form characterizes this L-shaped, two-and-one-half-story stone and frame residence. The tall, main, gable roof is intersected by a massive subsidiary front gable. First-floor walls are pink granite laid in random ashlar and have sandstone trim. Upper walls are shingled (a Richardson innovation) and are inset with half timber and stucco panels. Casement windows appear on all floors. Interior rooms have beamed ceilings and paneled walls. Architect Stanford White redecorated three principal rooms in 1879-1881, and in 1920 the house was enlarged by the addition of a service wing.
Private
NHL; HABS

NEWPORT COUNTY
Newport
TOURO SYNAGOGUE NATIONAL HISTORIC SITE
85 Touro Street
1763, Peter Harrison

Roger Williams' proclamation of religious liberty in 1647 led to the establishment of a Jewish colony in Newport as early as 1658. In 1763 the dedication of the congregation's synagogue was conducted by Rabbi Isaac Touro. Peter Harrison designed Touro Synagogue in the Georgian style, but modified it to accommodate the Sephardic ritual of the congregation. Congregation Jeshuet Israel—Salvation of Israel—still worships here.
Private
HABS

NEWPORT COUNTY
Newport
TRINITY CHURCH
141 Spring Street
1725-1726

Built under the direction of the master carpenter Richard Munday, Trinity Church is an early, New England Georgian frame church. Its interior and exterior are closely modeled after Boston's Old

North (Christ) Church, which was built of brick a few years earlier. Like Old North Church, Trinity Church is rectangular in shape with arched windows in two levels and a projecting front tower and spire. The wooden steeple, composed of a square tower, arcaded belfry, a lantern, and slender spire, is also modeled after Old North Church. Trinity's spire, designed in 1726, was not actually erected until 1741, and, after damage by wind in 1768, was taken down and rebuilt along the original lines. The interior of the church is marked by superimposed orders of square pillars above and below the galleries, arched vaults above the gallery bays, box pews, and a high pulpit. In 1762 additional length was obtained by sawing directly through the body of the building, shifting the rear portion back about 30 feet, and filling in the central space. The church presently serves an active Episcopal congregation.
Private
NHL; HABS

NEWPORT COUNTY
Newport
UNITED STATES NAVAL WAR COLLEGE
    Coaster's Harbor Island
    1819

In 1884 the Navy established a college offering advanced professional courses for naval officers. The original building is the most important surviving site associated with Alfred Thayer Mahan, president of the college from 1886 to 1889 and 1892–1893. His contributions to United States' naval policies and doctrines influenced almost every major nation during his time. His lectures and further studies were included in the publication of *The Influence of Sea Power upon History* (1890). The stone building in which Mahan lectured and administered the college now serves as the commandant's headquarters.
Federal
NHL

NEWPORT COUNTY
Newport
VERNON HOUSE
    46 Clarke Street
    Late 1750's

The Vernon House is an academically correct late Georgian frame residence noted for its fine interior trim and stairway. The two-and-one-half-story structure has 10 dormer windows protruding from its hip roof. Detailing on the front entrance and the roof cornice is Georgian. It is not known how much of the interior is original. The north parlor, to the left of the hall, is paneled from floor to ceiling, and the windows have interior paneled shutters and deep window seats. Other rooms in the house also have excellent paneling. The hall stairs have twisted balusters, ramped wall paneling and rail, and a Palladian window at the landing. The house was built by Metcalf Bowler, who was to become chief justice of the Rhode Island Supreme Court. It was later acquired by William Vernon, a shipowner and merchant who had served as president of the Eastern Navy Board during the Revolution. It remained in the possession of the Vernon family from 1773 until 1812.
Private
NHL; HABS

NEWPORT COUNTY
Newport
WANTON-LYMAN-HAZARD HOUSE
    17 Broadway
    1695

The Wanton-Lyman-Hazard House illustrates the architectural transition from 17th- to 18th-century style. Its frame construction recalls houses of early New England, while elaboration of structural detail and ornamentation reflects changes of the early 18th century which developed into the Georgian style of middle colonial times. The house was once owned by Richard Ward, who became governor of the Rhode Island colony in 1740. It was damaged by the 1765 Stamp Act riots when it was occupied by the Tory Stamp Master, Martin Howard.
Private
NHL

NEWPORT COUNTY
Newport
WHITEHORNE, SAMUEL, HOUSE
    414 Thames Street
    c. 1800–1810

The Whitehorne House was built for Samuel Whitehorne, a prosperous Newport merchant. Its location, facing the harbor and the waterfront businesses, is typical of other merchants' residences of the time. The three-story Federal style house is 46 feet square and has a low-pitched hip roof surmounted by a square cupola. Its brick walls have no projecting beltcourses or pilasters, and the window and door openings are capped by simple arches. Slight variation is provided by the fanlight and sidelights of the main entrance, roundheaded windows on the second floor, and a bull's-eye window in the center of the third-floor front. Adorning the roof is a richly ornamented modillion cornice. The house is now under restoration for use as a house museum.
Private
HABS

PROVIDENCE COUNTY
Central Falls, Lincoln, Pawtucket, Providence vicinity
BLACKSTONE CANAL
    Extends from Front Street Bridge, Lincoln, to Steeple and Promenade Streets, Providence
    1824–1828

A frenzy of canal building occurred during the first 30 years of the 19th century. Construction was induced by increased industrial and commercial development and the consequent need for a transportation network. It was hoped that the Blackstone Canal, linking Providence, Rhode Island, and Worcester, Massachusetts, would stimulate industry in towns and villages along the way. Its useful life of nearly 20 years was ended by the introduction of a Providence-Worcester railroad. Twenty or more feet wide throughout, the canal was stone-walled in places to contain the canal stream and to support the towpath. As many as 49 granite-walled locks were constructed at numerous points, but there are few visible remains. Masonry retaining walls, some towpaths and wharfage areas, and the path of the canal into downtown Providence still exist.
Public/Private; portions inaccessible to the public

PROVIDENCE COUNTY
Chepachet
CHEPACHET VILLAGE HISTORIC DISTRICT
    Along both sides of R.I. 102–U.S. 44, north from the intersection of U.S. 44 and R.I. 102 to the intersection of R.I. 100 and 102; included are properties on both sides of Dorr Drive, Douglas Hook Road, Point Lane, and Oil Mill Lane
    18th and 19th centuries

Chepachet Village played an important role in Rhode Island's post-Revolutionary industrial development. Located on the Chepachet River, the village grew quickly as a mill town and stage stop. The stagecoach tavern, built about 1800, served as the headquarters of politician Thomas Dorr during the Dorr Rebellion in 1842. Thomas Dorr was the gubernatorial candidate of a splinter party which was promising a new state constitution. The incumbent governor won the election and declared Dorr a traitorous criminal. State militia advanced on Dorr's stronghold in Chepachet only to find him gone. He later surrendered and was sentenced to life imprisonment but was released in 1845. Many of his reforms were later incorporated into the workings of the state

government. Approximately 75 buildings in the district possess architectural and/or historical value. All are of frame construction with the exception of a stone mill built in 1814.
Multiple public/private

JOY HOMESTEAD
156 Scituate Avenue
c. 1764–1778

Job Joy, who built this house, was a shoemaker. The original portion of the house, a gambrel-roofed, one-and-one-half-story section, was built around a central chimney and had a five-room plan. It was standing by 1778, and may have been built as early as 1764. A later, one-story ell with a gable roof was eventually added at the southern end of the main house. Members of the Joy family owned the house until 1884.
Private

SPRAGUE, GOVERNOR WILLIAM, MANSION
1351 Cranston Street
c. 1790, 1864

The Sprague Mansion was constructed in two parts. Both are timber framed and covered by clapboards. Although each is two and one-half stories high, their rooflines are not uniform. The earlier section is a long, gabled rectangle of eight bays, built originally with five bays and extended to the east in the early 19th century. At the same time the present doorway with segmental transom and sidelights was installed. The large western addition is three bays wide on its south front and higher than its adjoined neighbor. Its roof is a high, truncated or decked gable supporting an octagonal cupola. The main entrance is covered by a porch which has both paired and single Tuscan columns.
Private

GLOCESTER TOWN POUND
Pound Road and Chopmist Hill Road
1748

The Glocester Town Pound was built to incarcerate stray animals, although it has not been used for this purpose in 50 years. Dry wall construction was employed on the four-sided, irregular enclosure, and the walls themselves are six feet high. This pound is believed to be one of the oldest in existence.
Municipal

ARNOLD, ELEAZER, HOUSE
Great Road (R.I. 123) near its junction with R.I. 126
1687

Arnold House, erected in 1687, is an example of a "stone-ender" house indigenous to Rhode Island. Rhode Island, unlike Massachusetts and Connecticut, had a plentiful supply of building stone and lime for mortar. Consequently, a common Rhode Island form of colonial dwelling was the stone-ender house. In the 17th century a one-room house with a fireplace at one end was enlarged by the addition of a rear lean-to instead of another room at the opposite side of the chimney as was usually the case in other New England colonies. The lean-to room served as a kitchen, and its fireplace was built beside the original one of the hall. The combined chimneys of these two rooms were so wide that they covered virtually the whole end of the enlarged house, thus giving rise to the name "stone-ender." In the 18th century the original Arnold House was enlarged by raising the roof over the rear to two full stories and by the addition of a two-room-deep, two-story frame section with a separate chimney at the east end and another one-story lean-to across the rear. The original high-peaked front gable was removed during this enlargement.
Private
NHL; HABS

ARNOLD, ISRAEL, HOUSE
Great Road
c. 1720, 1760

Built in two parts of framed timber and clapboard construction, the Israel Arnold House is an interesting example of an 18th-century New England farmhouse. The earlier portion, a "single room" house, is the present one-and-one-half-story gambrel-roofed ell at the west end. It had a single large keeping room, an attic, and a large brick chimney at the gable end. The later two-and-one-half-story section had a front stairhall, two flanking rooms, one rear room, and two small rooms and a secondary stair in the rear corners. All trim, hardware, and woodwork is original, but the house is in need of repair.
Private

BLACKSTONE CANAL (PAUL RONCI MEMORIAL PARK)
From Front Street north to Ashton Dam
1824–1828

The Blackstone Canal was constructed to link Worcester, Massachusetts, and Providence, Rhode Island. Within this 45-mile distance a 451-foot drop in altitude occurred, so granite locks were employed to enable boats to navigate the waterway. At many places canal traffic used the parallel Blackstone River. Great profits were never realized from the canal, principally because it was soon replaced by a railroad. Also, a proper system of reservoirs had not been provided and drought or water diversion by mill owners caused frequent interruption of service. This is the longest section of the canal that is still intact. It contains no locks, but the canal and towpath are in good condition.
Private

OLD SLATER MILL
Roosevelt Avenue
1793

Here in 1793 Samuel Slater founded the cotton textile manufacturing industry in the United States. While serving as an apprentice in a mill in England, Slater committed to memory the plan of such an establishment. After coming to America, he built the Old Slater Mill, thus introducing not only the textile industry, but also the factory system of manufacturing, which soon became common in American industry. The mill, which includes the original building and later additions, is operated as a museum.
Private
NHL

THE ARCADE
130 Westminster Street and 65 Weybosset Street
1828

The Arcade is not only architecturally significant as the principal surviving example of an early 19th-century business arcade erected in America in the 1820's, but also as a good model of monolithic granite construction. Built by Cyrus C. Butler and the Arcade Realty Company, it is a monumental (126 feet long) gable-roofed structure with short, lateral wings near the center. The north facade, which is an Ionic pedimented portico, was designed by James Bucklin; while the south facade, an

unpedimented portico with a paneled attic parapet, was designed by Russell Warren. The three levels of the interior are connected by stairs that have their original cast iron railings. Banks of shops enclosed by galleries face each other and run lengthwise on each floor. The low gable roof, set above a wide coved cornice area, has a long range of glazed skylights set in iron sashes and separated by wooden rafters.
Private
HABS

PROVIDENCE COUNTY
Providence
BRACKETT, CHARLES, HOUSE (GEORGE CORLISS HOUSE)
45 Prospect Street
1875–c. 1882, George Corliss

George Corliss designed and built this three-story Italian Villa style home for himself and incorporated into it engineering innovations reflective of his own inventive character. In the stable complex adjoining the house he installed a small steam engine. The engine drove a fan which sent air, steam heated in ducts, through a tunnel into the house. Other ducts built into the walls heated the interior, and the temperature was controlled by an early version of a thermostat. Two other devices Corliss installed were a hydraulic elevator and sliding screens for the windows. The exterior is brick with brown sandstone trim, and a four-story tower breaks the skyline at one corner.
Private

PROVIDENCE COUNTY
Providence
BROWN, JOHN, HOUSE
52 Power Street
1786–1788

Designed by the noted colonial amateur architect Joseph Brown, the John Brown House is a large, late Georgian mansion. Erected by John Brown, a wealthy merchant and brother of the architect, the three-story house has four exterior chimneys, massive brick walls, and interior brick partitions. The facade is characterized by a central, pedimented pavilion and a balustraded Doric portico. The interior adheres to the usual Georgian plan. The four rooms on each floor are divided into pairs by a wide central hall that extends through the house. The large three-story brick service wing at the rear of the main house is a later addition.
Private
NHL; HABS

PROVIDENCE COUNTY
Providence
COLLEGE HILL HISTORIC DISTRICT
Bounded on the north by Olney Street, on the south by Cohan Boulevard, on the east by Hope Street, and on the west by the Providence and Moshassuck rivers
c. 1730–1880

The College Hill Historic District has been carefully surveyed and evaluated with respect to its architecture and its historic significance. Within these boundaries preservation, restoration, and urban renewal projects have been undertaken harmoniously and in close proximity. Standing in complementary relationship to each other, the structures in the district preserve the integrity of an entire locale. College Hill is steep and few businesses have chosen this location, so the appearance is predominantly residential. It contains most of the original area of 17th-century settlement plus three hundred 18th- and early 19th-century buildings. The district is so named because Brown University is within its boundaries. Noteworthy structures include the Sixth District Courthouse (1860–1862), 150 Benefit Street, brick, designed by Thomas A. Tefft; the Nightingale-Brown House (1791), 357 Benefit Street, an elaborate Federal dwelling; 66 Williams Street (1810), a brick, Federal style house with a two-story front porch; the Tully Bowen House (1853), 389 Benefit Street, Italianate and also by Thomas Tefft; the Providence Athenaeum (1836), 251 Benefit Street, Greek Revival; and the General Ambrose Burnside House (1866), 314 Benefit Street, which has an unusual semicircular entrance porch.
Multiple public/private
NHL

PROVIDENCE COUNTY
Providence
CONGDON STREET BAPTIST CHURCH
17 Congdon Street
1874–1875

This simple Victorian ecclesiastical structure has exterior wooden detailing in the Italian Romanesque Revival manner. The one-story, rectangular, frame church sits on a high brick foundation. The roof is gabled and there is a three-story, square, hip-roofed bell tower on the southwest corner. Tall segmentally arched windows pierce the sides and tower, while a large, tripartite, round-arched window is situated in the south gable. Most of the windows have flat, wooden label moldings and very flat, sawn label stops. The sills project slightly and rest on simple wooden corbels. A sawn wooden cornice resem-

bling a brick corbel table decorates the eaves and gables of the main structure.
Private

PROVIDENCE COUNTY
Providence
CORLISS-CARRINGTON HOUSE
66 Williams Street
1810–1811

The three-story Corliss-Carrington House is brick with brownstone trim. The five-bay main facade is dominated by a two-story porch with superimposed Corinthian and Ionic iron columns. Large brownstone quoins mark the building's corners, and the windows have brownstone trim. The third floor level is marked by a brownstone belt course, while a wooden balustrade extends around the roof above the modillion cornice.
Private; not accessible to the public
NHL; HABS

PROVIDENCE COUNTY
Providence
DEXTER, EDWARD, HOUSE
72 Waterman Street
1795–1797

The Dexter House is one of only a few 18th-century residences to survive in Providence's College Hill area. Basically a frame house, it has two exterior walls (east and west) faced with brick. The low, hip roof is topped by a monitor embellished by an open balustrade with ornamental urns. In 1860 the house was sawn in half, relocated on its present site, and subsequently enlarged. The central bay of the main facade has a pediment supported by giant fluted Tuscan pilasters. Within the bay is a first-floor entrance porch and a second-floor Palladian window. The cornice has both frets and modillions, and the urn-topped parapet at the eaves has panels above solid wall areas and balusters above the window openings.
Private; not accessible to the public
HABS

PROVIDENCE COUNTY
Providence
FIRST BAPTIST MEETINGHOUSE
N. Main Street, between Thomas and Waterman Streets
1774–1775, Joseph Brown, James Sumner

Both architecturally and historically the First Baptist Meetinghouse is one of New England's most notable public buildings of the colonial period. Its origins date from the establishment of the first Baptist organization in America by Roger Williams in 1639. The church is based on an unexecuted design for St. Martin's-in-the-Fields, London, England. An unusual feature is the two tiers of roundheaded windows.

Private

NHL; HABS

PROVIDENCE COUNTY
Providence
HOPKINS, GOVERNOR STEPHEN,
HOUSE
15 Hopkins Street
1707, c. 1742–1743

The oldest portion of the Hopkins House is thought to date from the early 18th century. This was a small dwelling of two ground floor rooms and an attic. When Stephen Hopkins acquired the property in 1742 or 1743, he incorporated the older structure into his new house of two stories as an ell. The newer house is timber and clapboard construction and only one room deep. Interior woodwork, fireplaces, and trim remain relatively intact, and original paint colors have been copied. The house does not stand on its original site. Stephen Hopkins (1707–1785) was chief justice of the Rhode Island Superior Court, ten times governor of the state, a member of the first and second Continental Congresses, and a signer of the Declaration of Independence.

State

HABS

PROVIDENCE COUNTY
Providence
IVES, THOMAS P., HOUSE
66 Power Street
1803–1806

The Ives House is a three-and-one-half-story brick residence with a balustraded roof. Foundations are marble as are the window lintels and sills. The front door has sidelights and a wide elliptical fanlight. All windows are symmetrically spaced, and those on the third floor are reduced in height. Since construction the house has undergone a series of exterior and interior additions. In 1884 a one-story portico was added at the south as was the rear service wing, porch, and vestibule.

Private; not accessible to the public

NHL; HABS

PROVIDENCE COUNTY
Providence
MOSHASSUCK SQUARE (AMERICAN
SCREW COMPANY FACTORIES)
Stevens Street
1840–1873

Although extensively damaged by fire in 1971, the American Screw Company Factories once formed an interesting complex of 19th-century industrial buildings constructed in two stages. Most of the factories were three or four stories high and had gable roofs with protruding stair towers. First to be built was the oblong, three-story Eagle Screw Company factory. A square entrance and stair tower projected from the Stevens Street facade, and the tower originally had a wooden cupola. A smaller stair tower stood at the west end. In 1860 the Eagle Company merged with a smaller producer to form the American Screw Company, and the merger necessitated a second phase of construction. A large triangular mill was erected higher on the slope above the Moshassuck River. Additions to the mills consisted of two- and three-story runs and corner blocks topped by decked mansard roofs. Presently only the shells of the factory buildings remain.

Municipal

PROVIDENCE COUNTY
Providence
RHODE ISLAND STATEHOUSE
90 Smith Street
1895–1900, McKim, Mead, and
White

The imposing central dome of the Rhode Island Statehouse is flanked by four smaller domes supported on columns. Two long wings extend east and west from the center mass and are topped by glass saucer domes. Architecturally the building may be termed Second Renaissance Revival, characterized by the use of classical columns and pilasters. Measuring 333 feet in length by 180 feet in depth, the Statehouse is built of brick supported by iron beams. The exterior is faced and decorated with white Georgia marble. On the south facade there is a central arcade below a two-story loggia. A statue by George T. Brewster, "Independent Man," stands atop the central dome. Inside are the governor's offices, the legislative chambers, the State Library, and Rhode Island's original charter granted in 1663 by King Charles II of England.

State

PROVIDENCE COUNTY
Providence
ROGER WILLIAMS NATIONAL
MEMORIAL
Old Town
1636

Roger Williams National Memorial, which will be located at the site of the old town spring, will commemorate the contributions of Roger Williams to the development of religious freedom in the United States. After being banished from the Massachusetts Bay Colony, he founded the settlement of Providence near a spring in 1636. This settlement, along with three others, was chartered as the Colony of Rhode Island in 1644. It was among the first civil governments in the world to achieve complete religious liberty and separation of church and state. Williams, who had previously been the pastor of a church in Salem, Massachusetts, served as the colony's president from 1654 to 1657. There are no extant buildings which are associated with Williams at this site.

Federal

NPS; 5 acres

PROVIDENCE COUNTY
Providence
SIXTH DISTRICT COURTHOUSE
150 Benefit Street
1760–1762; 1850–1851, Thomas A.
Tefft

This solid brick structure with a deck-on-hip roof and rusticated stone trim served as Rhode Island's capitol from 1776 until 1900. The sandstone ornament is pronounced around window and door openings and in the corner quoining. Originally a rectangle measuring 40 by 70 feet, the capitol had a central pediment (possibly on both the main elevations) containing a circular window, and the roof was topped by a balustraded deck supporting a cupola or clock belfry. Thomas Tefft altered and enlarged the building in the mid–19th century by constructing a new entrance pavilion on the west front and surmounting it with an adaptation of the old wooden cupola. Other changes were made on the east front by architect Alfred Stone in the late 19th century. Inside, only the second-floor northeast room retains its original appearance.

State

PROVIDENCE COUNTY
Providence
STATE ARSENAL
176 Benefit Street
1839, Russell Warren

The Rhode Island Arsenal is a battlemented Gothic Revival building, a pseudo-fortress appropriate to its military purpose. Measuring 80 by 40 feet, the Arsenal is constructed of chipped stone or rubble covered by cement. The two-story main section has a gabled entrance flanked by two, three-story, square, battlemented towers. The windows on the main section have diamond panes. Woodwork on the interior is dark stained. The ceiling of the drill hall has exposed beams and turned wooden pendants where major beams intersect. Since the mid–19th century the building has been leased by the Marine Corps of Artillery.

State

PROVIDENCE COUNTY
Providence
UNIVERSITY HALL, BROWN UNIVERSITY
Brown University campus
1770–1771

University Hall, Brown University's oldest building, is the only extant building closely associated with Horace Mann, prominent American educator. Now housing administrative offices, the late Georgian edifice was Brown's only building when Mann graduated in 1819. As secretary of the state board of education in Massachusetts, 1837–1848, Mann succeeded in improving buildings, professional standards, training, and teaching conditions. He was instrumental in establishing the first normal school in the United States in 1839. His efforts in the field of American education stimulated the movement known as the "common school revival" in the United States.
Private
NHL

PROVIDENCE COUNTY
Providence
WOODS-GERRY HOUSE
62 Prospect Street
1860–1863, Richard Upjohn

Measuring 75 feet by 65 feet, the Woods-Gerry House is the largest town house in Providence. Its walls are brick with wood and sandstone trim. Detailing is simple and restrained; horizontal belt courses and the swell of the curving bay on the east facade both emphasize the wall mass. There is a one-story, triple arcaded loggia on the west side which extends almost the full width of the house. The low hip roof has a wide overhang supported by minimal brackets, and the segmentally arched windows originally had projecting balconies of wooden fretwork carried on angular brackets. The main entrance has been changed.
Private
HABS

WASHINGTON COUNTY
Charlestown
FORT NINIGRET
Fort Neck Road
17th century

At the head of Fort Neck Pond stand the remains of a small earthwork fort, probably built by Dutch traders in the first half of the 17th century. Legend suggests that the fort was later held by the Niantic Indians, who had been driven from Connecticut by the Pequot tribe. Under their chief, Ninigret, the Niantics took refuge among the Narragansett Indians. In 1737 the General Court of Connecticut declared war on the belligerent Pequot people, and late in May Captain John Mason, reinforced by a force of 100 Narragansett Indians, began marching toward a Pequot fort at Mystic, Connecticut. Upon reaching Fort Ninigret they encountered open hostility, but after two days of talk Mason left without bloodshed. On June 7 he reached and destroyed his objective, the Pequot fort.
State

WASHINGTON COUNTY
Narragansett
THE TOWERS
Ocean Road
1883–1885, McKim, Mead, and White

These rock-faced granite towers are the only remaining portions of the Narragansett Casino built by the same architectural firm. The Casino, which burned in 1900, was largely wood, and the towers provided an entranceway to the dining, card, and guest rooms. The twin tower blocks are three stories high and support between them a parallel pair of segmental arches. A single, large, third-story room opening onto the towers is supported by the arches. Two fires have necessitated rebuilding the second and third stories inside the towers, replacing the roof, and closing in sections of the structure once open to weather.
Municipal

WASHINGTON COUNTY
Saunderstown
STUART, GILBERT, BIRTHPLACE
Gilbert Stuart Road
1755

Best known for his portraits of George Washington, Gilbert Stuart was among the best-known American painters of his time. After studying for four years in England under Benjamin West, he continued painting portraits, some of his subjects being John Adams, John Quincy Adams, Thomas Jefferson, and James Madison. Stuart lived in this two-story frame house between 1755 and 1761.
Private
NHL

The Newport Casino,
Newport, Rhode Island.

McKIM, MEAD & WHITE

VIEW OF INTERIOR COURT

CASINO·AT·NEWPORT·RHODE·ISLAND

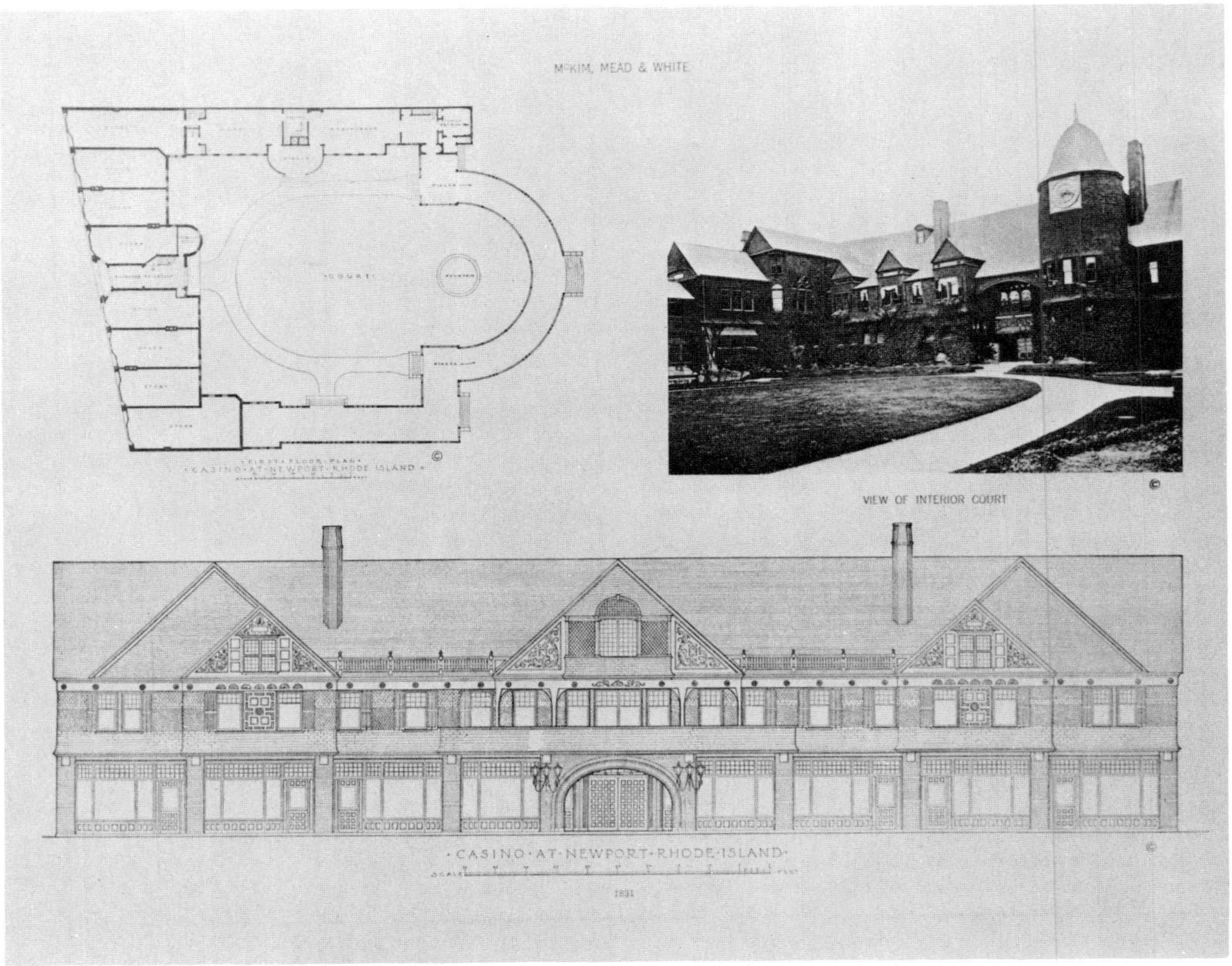

The Newport Casino, Newport, Rhode Island.
Original Drawing By McKim, Mead and White, 1881.
Rhode Island Historical Preservation Commission

South Carolina

The Lace House, Columbia, South Carolina.
James Denning

South Carolina State Arsenal
(The Old Citadel)
Charleston, South Carolina.
William Jordan.

Sheldon Church Ruins,
Gardens Corner, South Carolina.
Ned Brown

Drayton Hall, Charleston vicinity, South Carolina.
Mary C. Means

First Presbyterian Church, Columbia, South Carolina.
E. M. Moore

ABBEVILLE COUNTY
Abbeville
ABBEVILLE OPERA HOUSE
Court Square
1904

The Abbeville Opera House forms part of a complex of government buildings completed in 1904. This was the year the Opera House opened its doors as a circuit theater. Traveling road companies, enroute from Richmond to Atlanta, stopped for one night and gave performances in Abbeville. The three-story brick opera house is enlivened by brick quoins and masonry sunbursts above the windows. Seating inside is in three tiers (capacity 420), and a new lighting system has been installed.
Municipal

ABBEVILLE COUNTY
Abbeville
BURT, ARMISTEAD, HOUSE
306 N. Main Street
Mid–19th century

Jefferson Davis and his official company spent the night of May 2, 1865, at the Armistead Burt House on their flight from the fallen Confederate capital of Richmond. The final Confederate cabinet meeting was held in the house and the decision made to abandon all other goals except that of effecting President Davis' escape. Armistead Burt was an Abbeville lawyer, a personal friend of Jefferson Davis and had served in both the U.S. and Confederate Congresses. His home, designed by David Lesley and built in the mid–19th century, is a two-story white frame structure with a pedimented front portico. The main entrance is ornamented by an Adam fanlight, and all the rooms feature high ceilings and original floors.
Private

ABBEVILLE COUNTY
Abbeville
TRINITY EPISCOPAL CHURCH AND CEMETERY
Church Street
1860, George E. Walker

Trinity Episcopal Church is a Gothic Revival edifice unaltered since its construction. The church was organized in 1842. Exterior walls are brick covered with stucco and measure 81 feet by 43 feet excluding the tower and the chancel. The tower has corner pinnacles and a recessed front entrance with double doors at its base. Other architectural details include ornamental buttresses, battlemented parapets, and lancet windows without tracery. The organ inside is one of two in South Carolina known to have been made by John Baker of Charleston.
Private

ANDERSON COUNTY
Pendleton
PENDLETON HISTORIC DISTRICT

Pendleton, located in northwestern South Carolina, was once the county seat of Old Pendleton District (now Anderson, Oconee, and Pickens counties). Situated at the crossroads of the Cherokee Trading Path into the low country and the Catawba Path to Virginia, the town was laid out in 1790 and grew to become the commercial, political, and social center of the up-country. Skilled workmen settled in Pendleton and gradually gained renown for their cabinet and carriage making. The town was also famous for ironworking and livestock raising. Architecture in Pendleton reflects two waves of settlement: first, men and women from Pennsylvania, Maryland, Virginia, and North Carolina; and a later influx of Charleston families who built summer homes. Buildings of note in town are the Old Stone Church (1802), Farmers Society Hall (1828), the Elam Sharpe House (1802), the Marshalsea (built early in the 1800's as Pendleton jail), and Mi Casa (c. 1840, home of Mrs. John C. Calhoun after her husband's death). The historic district is not confined within a town boundary, but includes many outlying buildings and structures visually tied to the town or closely linked by past events. Among these are Woodburn, summer home of Charles Cotesworth Pinckney; Montpelier (1845), home of Samuel Maverick, wealthy merchant-planter; and Ashtabula (c. 1828), built by the Gibbes family of Charleston.
Multiple public/private

ANDERSON COUNTY
Pendleton vicinity
WOODBURN
End of Woodburn Road, 1.5 miles west of Pendleton
Early 19th century

Charles Cotesworth Pinchney (1789–1865) built Woodburn. It reflects the desire of the many up-country planters who built summer homes in the area for open space and free air circulation. The house itself is two and one-half stories on a raised basement. There is a two-story veranda across the main facade. Outside window and door moldings are wide and deeply fluted with Greek key designs. An original widow's walk has been removed from the roof. Pinckney became lieutenant governor of South Carolina in 1833 and was a trustee of South Carolina College and the College of Charleston.
Private
HABS

BEAUFORT COUNTY
Beaufort
BARNWELL, WILLIAM, HOUSE
800 Prince Street
1816

The William Barnwell House is a square, three-story dwelling with a two-story veranda across its entire main facade. Elongated Tuscan columns, one set atop the other, support the second floor of the veranda and second-floor roof. The double portico is a characteristic of Charleston houses.
Private

BEAUFORT COUNTY
Beaufort
BEAUFORT HISTORIC DISTRICT
Bounded on the north by Boundary Street, on the west by Hamar and Bladen Streets, and on the south and east by the Beaufort River
18th, 19th, and 20th centuries

Beaufort was laid out in 1710, but the buildings which survive today in the historic district date from the early 19th century or later. Unlike town houses in Charleston and Savannah, Beaufort's houses stand on their own lots like small plantations. Most of the old homes front on the river and have two-story verandas or porticos, usually supported by classical columns. Low pitched roofs cover the cube-shaped houses; inside, the rooms are designed to provide good ventilation and a maximum of daylight. Workmanship on the interior woodwork, fireplace mantels, and wainscoting in both plaster and wood is light in design and adds to the feeling of openness. Notable examples of Beaufort's architecture are the Edmund Rhett House, the Means House, the 1844 Baptist Church, the Danner House, and St. Helena's Episcopal Church.
Multiple public/private
HABS

BEAUFORT COUNTY
Beaufort
TABBY MANSE (THOMAS FULLER HOUSE)
1211 Bay Street
1786–1788

The Tabby Manse is one of the few remaining buildings on the South Carolina coast that has exterior walls made entirely of tabby (oyster shells and limestone). Unchanged except for a frame kitchen addition at the rear (c. 1895), the house has two-foot-thick exterior walls covered with scored stucco. The south center front has a projecting, one-bay, double tiered portico with Tuscan and engaged columns on the first level and Doric columns and pilasters below. The roof is hipped.
Private; not accessible to the public
HABS

BEAUFORT COUNTY
Gardens Corner vicinity
SHELDON CHURCH RUINS
Northwest of Gardens Corner on U.S.
21
1745–1753

Sheldon Church was named for Sheldon Hall, the nearby plantation of the locally prominent Bull family. It was built along a row of seven Tuscan columns (six engaged and one outstanding). At the eastern end there was a Palladian window with a roundheaded window to each side. The western facade has a portico crowned by a triangular pediment with a dentil cornice and containing a bulls-eye window. Above the main entrance was a fanlight and two roundheaded windows on either side. British troops burned Sheldon Church in May, 1779. Although rebuilt, it was burned again by Union troops during the Civil War and remains a ruin.
Private

BEAUFORT COUNTY
Hiltonhead vicinity
SKULL CREEK (HILTON HEAD)
North of Hiltonhead off Hickory Bluff-Mount Calvary Church Road
Pre-Columbian

The Skull Creek shell rings Nos. 1 and 2 are believed to date from the second millenium B.C. It is believed that they contain some of the earliest records of sedentary life among people who lived entirely by foraging. The Skull Creek rings are the only known example of a later ring superimposed upon an earlier one. The northernmost ring (No. 2) measures about 133 feet in diameter and has been plowed nearly level; the more southerly ring (No. 1) measures nearly 128 feet in diameter and stands about seven and one-half feet above a flat central area. Probably only 20 percent of the original volume of this ring remains.
Private

BEAUFORT COUNTY
Laurel Bay vicinity
CHESTER FIELD
South of Laurel Bay on Port Royal Island
Pre-Columbian

Chester Field is a prehistoric Indian shell ring. It is one of about 20 stretching from the central coast of South Carolina to the central coast of Georgia. All are believed to date from early in the second millenium B.C., and they contain fragments of some of the earliest pottery found in North America. Although the function of the ring shape is unkown, the deposits appear

to be carefully planned and are expected to yield information about early people who probably lived entirely by foraging. The Chester Field site was partially excavated in 1932 and 1933. About 45 per cent of the ring is still intact.
Private

BERKELEY COUNTY
Goose Creek vicinity
ST. JAMES' CHURCH, GOOSE CREEK
South of Goose Creek
1713–1719

In 1706 the South Carolina General Assembly passed a law making the Church of England the established church in the colony. Disestablishment followed the Revolution, but a revival of Anglican or Episcopal worship took place from 1795 to 1817. St. James' is a rectangular one-story brick building covered with stucco. Quoins mark the corners of the four walls, and all windows are round arched and protected by shutters. The side doorways have segmental pediments above and are flanked by modified Roman Doric pilasters. Most elaborate is the west door. A frieze above it is carried by the flanking pilasters and is adorned by triglyphs and metope reliefs in the form of flaming hearts. The interior is divided into three longitudinal sections by colonnades. The box pews are paneled, and there is a raised pulpit and reading desk with suspended sounding board all dating from the late 18th or early 19th centuries. In 1955 major restoration work was undertaken.
Private
NHL; HABS

BERKELEY COUNTY
Huger
POMPION HILL CHAPEL
.5 mile southwest of the intersection of S.C. 41 and 402
1763–1765

Pompion Hill Chapel is a virtually unaltered example of a South Carolina brick parish church built on a rectangular plan. It is one story high with a jerkinhead roof. The overall length is 48 feet, and the width, 35 feet. Both front and rear doors and all windows have fanlights, and a large Palladian window is set in the chancel. Remarkably, all interior woodwork and nearly all the furnishings are original; only the vestry room, which was in poor condition, has been rebuilt.
Private
NHL; HABS

BERKELEY COUNTY
Huger vicinity
MIDDLEBURG PLANTATION
About 2 miles southwest of Huger, on the East Branch of the Cooper River
c. 1699

Middleburg, a transitional two-story plantation house, is one of the oldest frame structures in South Carolina. Built by Benjamin Simons, a French Huguenot planter, Middleburg combines a one-room-deep medieval plan with the exposed post and girt construction of the 17th century. The single line of rooms, which permitted cross-ventilation, is similar to the basic plan of the Georgian "single house" popular in 18th-century Charleston. Structural evidence indicates that the western portion of the house, the porches, and the adjacent slave house were 18th-century additions.
Private; not accessible to the public
NHL; HABS

BERKELEY COUNTY
Moncks Corner
MULBERRY
Off U.S. 52 on the Cooper River
1714

Mulberry, a plantation house, was constructed by Thomas Broughton, later a royal governor of South Carolina. It illustrates the transition from the ethnic colonial architectural styles to the unified formality of the 18th-century Georgian style. Among the architectural forms incorporated in this residence are the rectangular central block laid up in English-bond brickwork, the flared eaves and iron beam anchors which appear Flemish and Dutch in character, and the four corner pavilions with hip roofs and bell-shaped turrets similar to those found in 17th-century French architecture. The nearly symmetrical floor plan has a central stair hall. The main interior rooms were redecorated in the Adam style about 1800.
Private; not accessible to the public
NHL

BERKELEY COUNTY
Mount Holly vicinity
MEDWAY
2.1 miles east of Mount Holly
1686

Medway was built only 16 years after the founding of the South Carolina colony, by Jan Van Arrsens, who had led a group of Hollanders to Carolina. It is today the oldest recorded house in the state. The architecture is strongly reminiscent of homes in Holland, particularly the stepped gables on the north, south, and west elevations. Later additions (the second story,

the low, spreading wings on the riverfront, and the non-symmetrical wing built towards the landward side) echo the original Dutch motif. The front door originally opened into a large hall which was the main room of the manor house. Medway was one of the first dwellings to have both a land and a river facade.
Private

BERKELEY COUNTY
St. Stephens
ST. STEPHEN'S EPISCOPAL CHURCH
On S.C. 45
1767–1769

St. Stephen's is a rectangular, Georgian style brick church distinguished by its high gambrel roof with Jacobean curvilinear gables. All doors and windows are topped by fanlights and segmental brick arches. Doric pilasters appear on the exterior, and inside is an unusual ornamented tray ceiling. Both inside and out the church appears still to retain its original material.
Private
NHL

CHARLESTON COUNTY
Awendow vicinity
SEWEE MOUND (THE OLD FORT)
2.8 miles south of Awendon
Prehistoric

Sewee Mound is the northernmost known prehistoric Indian shell ring on the South Carolina coast. It also contains possibly the deepest shell deposit. The average diameter of the ring is about 149 feet. The mound is composed of loosely packed oyster shell and lesser amounts of pottery sherds, bone, and other mollusks. About one half of the ring is intact. Nothing is known of the function of the ring shape, but excavations are expected to yield information about habitats and sedentary life on the coast early in the second millenium B.C.
Federal

CHARLESTON COUNTY
Charleston
AIKEN, WILLIAM, HOUSE AND ASSOCIATED RAILROAD STRUCTURES
456 King Street
1807–1811

William Aiken was the first president of the South Carolina Canal and Railroad Company (1828–1831) and builder of the Charleston and Hamburg Railroad. This company inaugurated the steam railroad era by using, for the first time on this continent, a steam locomotive in regular service to pull a train of cars. It was subsequently the first in the country to carry mail. The Aiken House, a brick building

with white stucco, is now used as Division Headquarters of the Southern Railway System. The group of buildings near the house includes the Camden depot and South Carolina Railroad warehouse.
Private; not accessible to the public
NHL

CHARLESTON COUNTY
Charleston
BLAKE TENEMENTS
2–4 Courthouse Square
1760–1772

A tenement in 18th-century parlance simply meant a double house or duplex dwelling. The brick Blake Tenements are three stories above a high basement. A barrel vaulted passage at ground level divides the two and contains service entrances. Brickwork on the front is laid in Flemish bond, and that on the sides and rear is English bond. Segmental relieving arches top the windows. Inside, the floor plan is the same on each floor: a large south room, a stair hall the width of the building, and a small north room. The original flooring is intact, and the woodwork is notable.
County

CHARLESTON COUNTY
Charleston
BRANFORD-HORRY HOUSE
59 Meeting Street
1765–1767

The Branford-Horry House is a good example of a three-story brick Georgian town house or "double house." It has a bisecting center hall flanked by a pair of rooms on either side. The plan is repeated on the second floor, except the center hall extends only half way, and the front portion of the house is divided into a three-bay-wide card room. The street facade was greatly altered in 1831–1834 by the addition of two Regency style porches. The house was built for William Branford, a well-to-do planter. In 1801 it was purchased by Thomas Horry, who had married Branford's daughter.
Private

CHARLESTON COUNTY
Charleston
BREWTON, MILES, HOUSE
27 King Street
1765–1769, Ezra Waite

The Miles Brewton House is architecturally notable as a "Charleston double house," a design which features a symmetrical center hall. This two-story house of almost square proportions has a sharply ridged hip roof, and the Georgian facade is dominated by a two-story portico. Both the exterior and interior are high-

ly ornamented. The house was occupied during the Revolutionary War by British General Sir Henry Clinton and during the Civil War by Union forces.
Private; not accessible to the public
NHL

CHARLESTON COUNTY
Charleston
BREWTON, ROBERT, HOUSE
71 Church Street
1730

Built by Miles Brewton for his son, the Robert Brewton House has a double distinction. It is one of the oldest surviving Charleston houses and the earliest accurately dated "single house," an architectural type peculiar to Charleston. The construction of piazzas facing south made the houses more comfortable during the hot South Carolina summers. With favorable sea breezes as an additional attraction, Charleston, one of the antebellum South's major cities, became a mecca for plantation families. The house has undergone few changes.
Private; not accessible to the public
NHL

CHARLESTON COUNTY
Charleston
CHARLESTON HISTORIC DISTRICT
The total area corresponds to the Old and Historic District delineated in the zoning ordinance of the City of Charleston, ratified on August 16, 1966
18th and early 19th centuries

Englishmen first settled on a site westward across the Ashley River from the present city in 1670. Ten years later the town was relocated. Based on an economy of rice and indigo, trade and commerce grew rapidly, until Charleston was the largest and most prosperous 18th-century metropolis south of Philadelphia. Wealthy merchants and planters began building homes, most of which were characterized by galleries and high basements—both dictated by climate. Single houses were constructed with their gable ends to the street, thus providing greater privacy; in contrast, double houses presented their facades to the street. The majority of the residences and public buildings retain their period character. Portions of the historic district have been designated a National Historic Landmark.
Multiple public/private
NHL; HABS

CHARLESTON COUNTY
Charleston
**CITIZENS AND SOUTHERN
NATIONAL BANK OF SOUTH
CAROLINA**
50 Broad Street
1798

The Citizens and Southern National Bank of South Carolina is a significant example of the commercial architecture of the 18th century. The two-story red brick building with limestone trim has a hip roof and a T-shaped floor plan. The first-floor facade of the extending center wing features a pair of windows with keystone lintels on either side of the central door. Windows on the second floor also have keystone lintels and are surmounted by triangular pediments containing semicircular fanlights. The stairs leading to the main entrance have an iron grillwork railing. Of special interest is the reception room, ornamented by carved woodwork, a black and white tile floor, and cluster columns.
Private
HABS

CHARLESTON COUNTY
Charleston
THE EXCHANGE AND PROVOST
E. Bay and Broad Streets
1767–1771

The Exchange and Provost has figured prominently in the economic and political affairs of both the city of Charleston and the state of South Carolina. Built as a customhouse and mercantile exchange, the Exchange provided meeting rooms for the South Carolina Committee of Correspondence, the state legislature following destruction of the statehouse, and for the committee which ratified the Constitution. Customs business was carried on in the basement level, and colonial offices were located above. Alterations of the Palladian style building include removal of an original cupola, the parapet, and two stair towers; the interior has also been greatly changed.
Private

CHARLESTON COUNTY
Charleston
FIREPROOF BUILDING
100 Meeting Street
1822–1826, Robert Mills

This simple, Greek Doric style building is believed to be the first structure of fireproof construction erected in the United States. The raised basement is made of stone, and the walls are brick stuccoed in imitation of stone. The original roof was copper, and the offices were vaulted in brick. Window sashes and frames are all of iron as are the interior

shutters. Interior stair steps connecting all three floors with the basement are stone and are illuminated by a skylight. Robert Mills, noted American architect, designed the building for the purpose of housing state records with a maximum of security and protection from destruction by fire.
County
HABS

CHARLESTON COUNTY
Charleston
**FORT SUMTER NATIONAL
MONUMENT**
Charleston Harbor
1829–1861

On April 12, 1861, South Carolina artillery opened fire on federally occupied Fort Sumter. With this attack the Civil War began, exploding any hopes that secession could be accomplished peacefully. Two years later the fort became the scene of a siege that lasted 20 months, as the Confederate garrison withstood overwhelming Federal attacks. The fort became a symbol of courage and resistance for the entire South. Fort Sumter National Monument commemorates both events.
Federal
NPS; 36.27 acres
HABS

CHARLESTON COUNTY
Charleston
GIBBES, WILLIAM, HOUSE
64 South Battery
c. 1779

The William Gibbes House, a two-story, late Georgian town house resting on an English basement, is one of Charleston's most elegant wooden "double houses." Its shallow hip roof is broken by a broad central pediment, and this form is repeated in the pedimented entrance and flanking first-floor windows. The twin flight of iron-railed stairs which ascend to the main doorway was added in 1794. At this time the interiors were also redecorated in the Adam style. In 1928 the rear rooms were lengthened and a front room was redecorated in the Chinese Chippendale style.
Private
NHL

CHARLESTON COUNTY
Charleston
HEYWARD, DANIEL, HOUSE
87 Church Street
c. 1770

Daniel Heyward, a rice planter, is believed to have been the builder of this square, three-story brick house. The facade is five bays wide, and beneath the eavesline of

the hip roof there is a narrow denticulated cornice. A fanlighted door, surmounted by a pediment and flanked by a pair of classical columns, is a reconstruction of the original. Inside, rooms are arranged according to the typical Georgian four-room, central hall plan. The house is called a Charleston "double house" because the first floor rooms were service rooms and all entertaining was done on the second floor.
Private

CHARLESTON COUNTY
Charleston
MILLS, CLARK, STUDIO
51 Broad Street
Early 19th century

Clark Mills pioneered in the casting of bronze statues in America. In 1848 he accepted a commission to do an equestrian statue of General Andrew Jackson to be placed in Lafayette Park in Washington, D.C. The statue established his reputation as a sculptor and his skill as a bronze founder. In his Charleston studio, which still stands, he carved a marble bust of John C. Calhoun for which he was awarded a gold medal by the city of Charleston in 1846. He also did the equestrian statue of George Washington in Washington Circle, Washington, D.C.
Multiple private; not accessible to the public
NHL

CHARLESTON COUNTY
Charleston
ROSE, THOMAS, HOUSE
57–59 Church Street
1735–1740

The Thomas Rose House is one of Charleston's best examples of colonial architecture. It is a square, two-and-one-half-story, Georgian brick town house constructed in a typical Charleston "double house" plan. Although it has been restored and modernized a few times since construction, much of the original early Georgian paneling still remains. The exterior is brick covered with stucco. It is five bays wide and four bays deep topped by a hip roof. The main entrance and the two-story porch at the south side were added about 1830.
Private

CHARLESTON COUNTY
Charleston
ST. MICHAEL'S EPISCOPAL CHURCH
80 Meeting Street
1761

St. Michael's Church is among the great ecclesiastical architectural monuments of the colonial period. The South Carolina

Assembly authorized its erection in 1751. The cornerstone was laid in 1752, and the church was dedicated in 1761. The brick walls were covered with stucco. Dominating the facade is a two-story Roman Doric open portico; it was the first giant portico built on a Georgian church in the colonies. The exterior mass of the building is dominated by a 185–foot spire; its square base supports three diminishing octagons which are embellished with openings, pilasters, and cornices. The uppermost octagon supports the terminating spire. The rectangular interior with its coved ceiling is broken in plan only by the projection of the end which houses the apse. St. Michael's is still in active use as a church.
Private
NHL; HABS

CHARLESTON COUNTY
Charleston
SIMMONS-EDWARDS HOUSE
12–14 Legare Street
c. 1800

Considered one of Charleston's finest examples of a "single" house, the Simmons-Edwards House has a noteworthy complex of outbuildings and a large landscaped garden designed by Umberto Innocenti. The three-and-one-half-story dwelling has a hip roof, dormers, a double tiered piazza over an arcaded basement, and, inside, Adam mantels and trim. Outbuildings are a brick kitchen and a stable. The wood and iron gates with brick piers and the wrought iron fence were added after 1816.
Private
HABS

CHARLESTON COUNTY
Charleston
SITE OF OLD CHARLES TOWNE
Albemarle Point
Pre-Columbian, 17th, 18th, 19th, and 20th centuries

Following a stormy voyage which sank her two sister ships, the *Carolina* anchored off Albemarle Point, and the settlers on board went ashore to construct new homes. The landing occurred in April, 1670. Seven months later the name of Charles Towne was bestowed on the settlement, composed of eighty or more houses and a wooden fort. As the population grew, people began to move away from the original townsite to a new location between the Ashley and Cooper rivers. Pottery fragments found here indicate occupation by Indians of the Early Woodland Period (c. 500 B.C.). A plantation was continuously operated on the land beginning shortly after the settlers removed to the new townsite.
State

CHARLESTON COUNTY
Charleston
SOUTH CAROLINA STATE ARSENAL (OLD CITADEL)
2 Tobacco Street (Marion Square)
1830, Frederick Wesner

Built as the South Carolina State Arsenal, this building served as the South Carolina Military Academy from 1843 until 1922. From 1865 to 1881 it was occupied by federal troops. Originally constructed as a two-story brick arsenal with a wooden parapet, it is now four stories high and covered with stucco. Twice made higher when wings were added, the arsenal has a central courtyard enclosed by interior arches. Two tiers of smaller arches were superimposed above the original large spans.
County

CHARLESTON COUNTY
Charleston
STUART, COLONEL JOHN, HOUSE
104–106 Tradd Street
c. 1772

The Colonel John Stuart House is considered to be the finest example in the southern colonies of a three-story, Georgian, frame town house. It has a hip roof with a captain's walk and one interior chimney. First- and second-floor windows on the street facade are flanked with dog-ear trim and crowned with bracketed pediments. The fanlighted entrance is flanked by a pair of Corinthian columns and topped by a pediment. About 1800 the octagonal frame wing was added at the northwest corner, and later in the 19th century the double deck porch was built along the west side. Colonel John Stuart was the royal commissioner for Indian affairs for the southern colonies in the second half of the 18th century.
Private; not accessible to the public
HABS

CHARLESTON COUNTY
Charleston
SWORD GATES HOUSE
32 Legare Street, 111 Tradd Street
c. 1803, 1818

Constructed in two parts, the Sword Gates House consists of an early (1803) frame section which has been heavily remodeled, and a later (1818) brick section, largely intact. The frame section retains the original Legare Street address. Measuring 28 feet by 64 feet, the brick dwelling is two-and-one-half stories with a hip roof. The brick is covered with stucco. When the house was redecorated in 1849, the distinctive Sword Gates were installed.
Private; not accessible to the public
HABS

CHARLESTON COUNTY
Charleston Harbor
CASTLE PINCKNEY
On Shute's Folly Island
1808–1811

Castle Pinckney is a horseshoe-shaped defense work situated on an island in Charleston harbor. The earliest fort on the site was constructed of timber and earth during colonial times. The 19th-century fort was built of brick as an inner harbor or secondary line of defense. Two tiers of guns were mounted on the continuous brick wall. Named for South Carolinian Charles Cotesworth Pinckney, Castle Pinckney was garrisoned by federal troops until its seizure by a Confederate force in December, 1860. It was retaken in February, 1865, but by the 1880's Castle Pinckney had become a ruin. Plans are now underway to restore the fort as a tourist attraction.
Private
HABS

CHARLESTON COUNTY
Charleston vicinity
DRAYTON HALL (JOHN DRAYTON HOUSE)
12 miles west of Charleston on S.C. 61
1738–1742

Drayton Hall, a two-story brick mansion built in the Georgian style by John Drayton, is an outstanding surviving example of South Carolina's plantation houses. Architecturally, it was far in advance of other houses of the same period in its exterior design and plan. Projecting from a recessed central bay, a two-story portico with superimposed Doric and Ionic orders dominates the west facade. The east facade has a classic pediment in the double hip roof to emphasize the main axis; a double flight of steps leads to the first floor entrance. The entrance hall with its elaborate double stairs, the full wood paneling, and the ornamental ceiling were among the finest in the colonies.
Private; not accessible to the public
NHL

CHARLESTON COUNTY
Edisto Island vicinity
BRICK HOUSE RUIN
South of Edisto Island
c. 1725

Destroyed by fire in 1929, the Brick House was a two-story plantation house with false stucco pavilions on the east and west elevations. Of the original hip-roofed, 36- by 40–foot structure, only the shell remains. Stucco quoins, rusticated to simulate stone, still adorn the corners and window jambs, and illustrate the influence of French Huguenots on the colonial architecture of South Carolina.

Private

NHL; HABS

CHARLESTON COUNTY
Edisto Island vicinity
EDISTO ISLAND PRESBYTERIAN CHURCH
1.9 miles north of Edisto Island on S.C. 174
1831

This church serves one of the oldest Presbyterian congregations in South Carolina which was formed about 1695. Originally built as a two-story rectangle, the church had its portico replaced in 1836. Columns on the main facade are Doric and support a triangular pediment. First-floor windows on the side elevations have fanlights and arched shutters above which are six small, square nine-pane lights.

Private

HABS

CHARLESTON COUNTY
Edisto Island vicinity
MIDDLETON'S PLANTATION
3.5 miles north of Edisto Island, then south 2 miles via unnumbered road
c. 1830

Unaltered since its construction, Middleton's Plantation has one-room wings at either side of the main block, and all rest upon a raised arcaded basement. The plan of the house is similar to that of a Charleston single house because it is only one room deep. On the front or land entrance there is a small, Tuscan colonnaded porch; the back porch, recessed into the house, extends the entire length of the rear facade and is also colonnaded. Above the tripartite windows there is a wide board and a wooden keystone.

Private

CHARLESTON COUNTY
Edisto Island vicinity
OLD HOUSE PLANTATION
Northeast of Edisto Island via S.C. 174, County Route 768, and unnumbered road

This dwelling, although extensively altered, is believed to be the oldest house on the island. Originally constructed as a small, one-and-one-half-story building with a gable roof, it was redone early in the 19th century. A pedimented porch with Tuscan columns was added on the main facade, two dormers were put in the roof, and the front doorway acquired a keystone and fanlight. Twentieth-century changes were a rear dormer for the bathroom, a modern kitchen, a rear

porch, and another small room. The 18th-century floor plan appears to be intact.

Private

CHARLESTON COUNTY
Edisto Island vicinity
THE PRESBYTERIAN MANSE
Northwest of Edisto Island via S.C. 174 and unnumbered road
c. 1790

The Presbyterian congregation on Edisto Island is one of the oldest in South Carolina, dating from approximately 1710. The manse is a two-and-one-half-story wooden building with a wide shed-roofed porch across the entire front and along the east side (the screened porch is a 20th-century addition). Two overhanging dormers are set in the medium gable roof. The interior plan is four-room, central hall.

Private

CHARLESTON COUNTY
Edisto Island vicinity
SEABROOK, WILLIAM, HOUSE
North of Edisto Island via S.C. 174 and County Routes 968 and 768
1810

Unaltered since its construction, the William Seabrook House is a two-and-one-half-story frame dwelling with a central, projecting, two-story pedimented portico and is set atop a raised basement. A double flight of steps leads to the first-floor portico. Significant architectural features are an arched entablature on the upper level, a decorative ironwork stair railing, and ornamental facia and frieze boards in dentil design. The interior plan is central hall with four rooms on a floor. William Seabrook was part owner of the Edisto Island ferry.

Private

CHARLESTON COUNTY
Edisto Island vicinity
TRINITY EPISCOPAL CHURCH
About 1.2 miles north of Edisto Island on S.C. 174
1876

The present church was built as a replacement for an older structure that burned. It is the only example of Victorian architecture on Edisto Island. Trinity Church is a one-story wooden building with a porch across the principal facade. Slender square posts support the triangular pediment above the porch. The steeple is covered with shingles and contains decorative louvers. Windows and the main entrance are topped by semicircular fanlights.

Private

CHARLESTON COUNTY
Georgetown vicinity
ST. JAMES, SANTEE
17 miles south of Georgetown on the Santee River
1768

St. James Church, Santee, is five bays long and three bays wide. A classic, pedimented portico originally adorned both front and rear facades, but the rear one was walled in sometime in the 18th century. Four brick columns support each pedimented portico; the columns have molded bases and capitals and the shafts display both diminution and entasis (swelling). The original seating plan was changed, probably in the 18th century, when the chancel was relocated in the north wall. A Palladian window is situated in the east wall.

Private

NHL; HABS

CHARLESTON COUNTY
McClellanville vicinity
HAMPTON PLANTATION HOUSE
8 miles north of McClellanville
1735

The Hampton Plantation house, situated on a 1,285-acre tract of land, was built by a Huguenot settler. With careful symmetrical extensions made around 1757 and 1790, the large two-and-one-half story house is an example of the evolution of a modest frame structure into a large unified Georgian country house. The giant Roman Doric portico, one of the earliest of its kind in America, is of particular interest because it exhibits the slender columns, the paterae, and the delicate flutings characteristic of the Adam style of decoration.

Private

NHL; HABS

CHARLESTON COUNTY
Mount Pleasant
OLD COURTHOUSE
311 King Street
1884

The Old Courthouse is locally significant as one of the few remaining examples of Victorian architecture. It is a two-story, rectangular, stucco over brick building with a large double stairway leading to the main entrance on the second floor. Beneath and between the stairs is a barrel vaulted entrance into the basement. The front facade of the second level contains a double door flanked by pairs of rectangular windows. The side elevations of the upper floor are divided into five equal parts by pilasters rising from piers on the lower level. Between the pilasters are matched pairs of rectangular windows.

The courthouse was the judicial center of Berkeley County from 1884 to 1898.
Private

CHARLESTON COUNTY
Mount Pleasant vicinity
AULD MOUND
Northeast of Mount Pleasant, 1.2 miles southeast of U.S. 17
Prehistoric

Auld Mound is a prehistoric ring-shaped Indian shell midden. It measures about 174 feet in diameter and is composed largely of oyster shells mixed with other shells. Animal bones and pottery sherds are scattered in the earth between the shells. The ring is virtually intact and is closely associated with other similar rings located along the coast of South Carolina and Georgia.
Private

CHARLESTON COUNTY
Mount Pleasant vicinity
BUZZARD'S ISLAND SITE
Northeast of Mount Pleasant, 1.3 miles southeast of U.S. 17
Prehistoric

The Buzzard's Island Site is one of the largest of about 20 prehistoric shell rings located from the central coast of South Carolina to the central coast of Georgia. It is 178 feet in diameter and dates from early in the second millenium B.C. The midden is predominantly oyster shell with lesser amounts of other mollusks. Pottery sherds are common on the outside edges of the ring which is only partially excavated and appears to be largely intact. It contains some of the earliest pottery known in North America and is expected to yield information about the life of coastal people who lived almost entirely by foraging.
Private

CHARLESTON COUNTY
Rockville vicinity
FIG ISLAND SITE
2 miles southwest of Rockville, Edisto Island on the north bank of Ocella Creek
Prehistoric

The Fig Island Site consists of three prehistoric Indian shell middens grouped in a marsh just north of a larger island (Fig Island itself). Fig Island I is about 600 feet long and still contains a great quantity of oyster and other mollusk shells and pottery sherds. Fig Island II is in a ring shape and measures about 215 feet in diameter. It is virtually intact. Fig Island III is quite eroded with slightly less than half of the ring remaining. Though the purpose of such ring deposits is not known, they ap-

pear to be systematically planned. Excavations are now underway.
Private

CHARLESTON COUNTY
Rockville vicinity
HANCKEL MOUND
Northwest of Rockville on Wadmalaw Island
Prehistoric

Hanckel Mound is one of the largest of about 20 prehistoric shell rings ranging from the central coast of South Carolina to the central coast of Georgia. Originally it measured 158 feet in diameter from crest to crest. It is composed almost entirely of oyster shells with periwinkles, animal bone, and pottery sherds along the truncated perimeter. The deposits are expected to yield valuable information about past habitants on the coast.
Private

CHARLESTON COUNTY
Rockville vicinity
HORSE ISLAND
1 mile south of Rockville on Seabrook Island
Pre-Columbian

Horse Island is one of 20 or more similar prehistoric shell rings located along the coasts of South Carolina and Georgia. Together they contain some of the earliest known pottery in North America. Limited excavation has been undertaken and has revealed that the rings were planned and systematically deposited. Most of the rings are now about 5 feet above present mean sea level. Marine erosion has removed about 15 percent of the original ring. The present average diameter is 156 feet, and dense trees and undergrowth now cover the ring.
Private

CHEROKEE COUNTY
Chesnee vicinity
COWPENS NATIONAL BATTLEFIELD SITE
2 miles east of Chesnee at junction of S.C. 11 and 110
1781

At Cowpens General Daniel Morgan's forces defeated a British force under Lieutenant Colonel Banastre Tarleton. The American victory at Cowpens on January 17, 1781, the second enjoyed by the patriots within three months, combined with the earlier victory at Kings Mountain to renew ebbing patriot spirits. The battle was another link in a chain of British defeats that led to their final surrender at Yorktown, Virginia, on October 19, 1781.
Federal
NPS; 1.24 acres

CHESTER COUNTY
Chester vicinity
CATHOLIC PRESBYTERIAN CHURCH
14 miles southeast of Chester on S.C. 97 and County Route 355
1842

Catholic Presbyterian was one of the first churches in up-country South Carolina. The present building is the third on the site. It is rectangular, has walls of handmade brick, and is set on a fieldstone foundation. Inside, side aisles lead to a raised pulpit platform, and the original pews remain. Notable features of the exterior are molded brick cornices and pegged front doors.
Private

CHESTER COUNTY
Chester vicinity
LEWIS INN
6.5 miles northeast of Chester on S.C. 72, then .5 mile west of S.C. 909
18th century

Lewis Inn, constructed about 1750, served as a tavern and stagecoach stop during colonial times. It is a two-story structure built of dovetailed logs pegged together and chinked with clay. Exterior walls were covered with clapboards and re-covered with shingles in 1923. The inn has a gable roof, outside end chimneys, and a single story wing. Tongue and groove paneling throughout the house is 12 to 14 inches wide. All interior doors are of wide boards with wrought iron hinges (except one upstairs bedroom door which has tomahawk hinges).
Private

CHESTER COUNTY
Richburg vicinity
ELLIOTT HOUSE
.3 mile north of Richburg on S.C. 901, then 1 mile on County Road 136
1769–1770

The Elliott House is one of the earliest dwellings in the South Carolina up-country. It was constructed of logs 12 to 14 inches in diameter and has six-inch thick walls. The skilled craftsmanship of Daniel Elliott, builder of the house, is evident in the dovetailing of the logs in the three-by-eight-inch smoothly hewn and planed ceiling beams. Additions to the original 20–foot by 28–foot cabin include a frame section at the rear, a 1930 addition to the east, and a shed-roof front porch supported by round posts. Clapboard siding was recently put over the original log walls, but restoration work is now in progress.
Private

CHESTER COUNTY
Rowell
LANDSFORD CANAL
Off U.S. 21, a two-mile section
parallel to the Catawba River
1830–1850

The Landsford Canal is the only such waterway in an unaltered condition still extant in the state. Within this section the Catawba River drops 34 feet, and three sets of locks lowered boats over the two-mile distance. Ruins of a mill site, a miller's house, and a lockkeeper's house are evident along the canal. Thomas Land was first patentee of the property on which a ford was originally located, and the canal, when constructed, became part of an inland waterway linking Charleston to the up-country.
Private

CLARENDON COUNTY
Summerton
SANTEE INDIAN MOUND
South of Summerton, off U.S. 301
Pre-Columbian

Santee Indian Mound is a large prehistoric burial and/or temple mound probably constructed in the period between 1200 and 1500. Although no archaeological investigation has been undertaken, the mound is believed to have been part of a mound village complex. The mound remains intact except for the construction of some 18th-century fortifications on its summit. At one time Fort Watson, the first fortified British military post in South Carolina, occupied the site. No remains of the fort are visible today.
State

COLLETON COUNTY
Walterboro
COLLETON COUNTY COURTHOUSE
Corner of Hampton and Jeffries
Streets
c. 1820

The exterior of the Colleton County Courthouse is stuccoed brick. Two curving iron stairways lead to the main floor above a raised, arcaded basement. The three-bay center section of the courthouse has a one-bay projecting portico. Four Tuscan columns and two square columns support a massive, undecorated entablature.
County

COLLETON COUNTY
Walterboro
OLD COLLETON COUNTY JAIL
Jeffries Boulevard
1855–1856, Edward C. Jones and
Francis D. Lee

The Old Colleton County Jail is a two-story, stuccoed brick building that resembles a miniature castle. The crenelated roofline, the turret-like structures at the front corners, and the massive tower above the main entrance all contribute to this illusion. An extended enclosed porch with a pointed arch doorway and slit windows shields the entrance, and there is a large lancet window in the tower above. Since 1937 the building has been used for county offices.
County

DARLINGTON COUNTY
Hartsville vicinity
COKER EXPERIMENTAL FARMS
West of Hartsville on S.C. 151
Late 19th and early 20th centuries

James L. Coker and his son David were among the pioneers who transformed the cotton seed business into a modern scientific industry. Planting improvement and seed-breeding techniques grew steadily in scope. In 1904 a new method of corn cultivation was tested, and in 1907 the breeding of an improved corn variety was begun. In 1915 attention was given to breeding short staple cotton. Research in hybridization and cultivation is still actively pursued on this 7000–acre farm.
Private; not accessible to the public
NHL

DARLINGTON COUNTY
Hartsville vicinity
KELLEY, JACOB, HOUSE
3 miles west of Hartsville, Route 2,
S.C. S–16–12
Early 19th century

This residence is an example of architectural evolution from a one-story log house into a simple but functional plantation house later typical of the Pee Dee farm area. The log section predates 1830. It was enlarged, weatherboarded, and a second story added between 1830 and 1840. Later, the size was almost doubled by the addition of a two-story annex on the west. No plaster was used in the house. Walls and ceilings are made of planed boards, and the original mantel is carved heart pine. Jacob Kelley (1780–1874) was the founder of the small agricultural settlement, Kelley Town.
County

DILLON COUNTY
Dillon
DILLON, JAMES W., HOUSE
1302 W. Main Street
1890

The Dillon House, home of James W. Dillon, founder of the town, is a prime example of late Victorian design. It is a two-story frame house with a medium gable roof both front and rear and inset cross gables on the sides. Adding variety to the clapboard exterior are scalloped shingles in the gable ends and between the first and second floors. A one-story veranda, extending across the facade and three-fourths of the southeast wall, has latticework beneath the eaves and is supported by carved posts with gingerbread cornice braces. An ornate front gable over the second story is decorated with gingerbread trim, rectangular louvers, and an oval window with a sunburst design.
Private

DORCHESTER COUNTY
Summerville vicinity
MIDDLETON PLACE
10 miles southeast of Summerville on
S.C. 61
18th, 19th, and 20th centuries

Henry Middleton (1717–1784) built the main section of his plantation home about 1741 and added the north and south flankers in 1755. The house and gardens were situated on a bluff above the Ashley River, and these spacious grounds constitute the first landscaped gardens in America. In 1865 Union troops burned the Middleton house, and the remaining gutted walls were toppled by the earthquake of 1886, leaving only the south wing. It has been rebuilt as an adapted English Tudor country house with Dutch influence. In 1916 restoration and further development of the gardens was undertaken. Today the house faces molded terraces descending to two butterfly lakes. Gardens containing marble statuary, an old rice mill, many native and imported trees, shrubs, and flowers surround the house site. A reconstructed stableyard containing a horse barn, blacksmith shop, implement sheds, and servants quarters was recently (1970) opened to the public.
Private

DORCHESTER COUNTY
Summerville vicinity
OLD DORCHESTER
Dorchester State Park, including the ruins of the village and fort of Dorchester and St. George's Church, on the Ashley River near the mouth of Dorchester Creek
17th and 18th centuries

Dorchester was established in 1695 by a Congregational colony from Dorchester, Massachusetts. At one time the third largest city in South Carolina, the town grew as a major trading area for the frontier. After the Revolution, however, the site was virtually abandoned. Today, visible remains are the tower of St. George's Church, erected before 1753, and the ruins of the fort constructed in 1775. These two edifices are included in Dorchester State Park.
State

EDGEFIELD COUNTY
Edgefield vicinity
BLOCKER HOUSE
About 6 miles northwest of Edgefield on U.S. 25
1775

Originally built as an overseer's house by Michael Blocker, an immigrant from Prussia, this dwelling is the oldest in the area still occupied. The two-story clapboard structure has a one-story, shed-roofed porch with four square columns. End chimneys and the double front doors are original. Floors and walls are made of wide boards.
Private

EDGEFIELD COUNTY
Edgefield vicinity
HORN CREEK BAPTIST CHURCH
South of Edgefield via Routes 34, 133, and a dirt road
1790

The Horn Creek Baptist Church is one of the oldest Baptist churches in the South Carolina up-country. Essentially unchanged since constructed, the simple, one-room structure has no electricity and is supported by fieldstone foundation piers. Notable features are the wide board floors and the louvered shutters.
Private

EDGEFIELD COUNTY
North Augusta vicinity
BIG STEVENS CREEK BAPTIST CHURCH
About 8 miles northwest of North Augusta on S.C. 230
1776

This two-story, rectangular frame building has a gable roof and is covered by clapboard siding. There are hand-hewn pews fastened together with pegs inside the church, and two side aisles lead to a raised pulpit platform. The Reverend Daniel Marshall, a New England minister, founded the Big Stevens Creek Baptist Church. He was a member of a branch of his own denomination called "Separate Baptists," a group characterized as highly emotional and disposed to let women play a prominent role in worship. The "Regular Baptists" were intolerant of the Separatists, and the latter group transferred its missionary efforts to the back country of Virginia, Georgia, and North and South Carolina. Marshall was the first of this group to work in the Edgefield County area, and Big Stevens Creek was the mother church for many others in South Carolina.
Private

FAIRFIELD COUNTY
Monticello vicinity
DAVIS PLANTATION
.25 mile south of Monticello on S.C. 215
Mid–19th century

The Davis Plantation, built by James B. Davis sometime between 1840 and 1850, has been maintained as a plantation from its original cotton-producing days to the present time. The two-story white frame structure with a hip roof and two mammoth chimneys is a good example of the architecture that developed during the period of cotton-based economic prosperity. Dominating the front facade is a two-story classic gabled portico with four Doric columns. There is a fanlight window in the pediment and semi-elliptical fanlights and sidelights around the doors of both floors.
Private

FAIRFIELD COUNTY
Ridgeway vicinity
ST. STEPHEN'S EPISCOPAL CHURCH
About 1 mile northeast of Ridgeway on County Route 106
1854, John Dewitt McCollough

St. Stephen's is the oldest church in Ridgeway. Its modified Gothic Revival architecture is highlighted by pointed-arch windows, doorways, and ceilings, and the

entire nave is groin vaulted. The roof is a steep flared gable with a rose window in one end. About 1920 the original pine exterior was covered with brick veneer. The parish house and church school wing was added in the 1940's, and the stained glass windows were installed in 1949. All interior woodwork is heart pine. St. Stephen's reflects the migration of low country planters to up-country South Carolina and the subsequent construction of Episcopal churches.
Private

FAIRFIELD COUNTY
Ridgeway vicinity
VALENCIA
About 2 miles northwest of Ridgeway on County Route 106
1834

This large, two-story frame dwelling was built by Edward Gendron Palmer, a leader in civic, political, and religious affairs in Ridgeway and Fairfield County. The house remains today as a distinctive example of the home and surroundings of an affluent cotton planter in antebellum South Carolina. A hip roof covers the house, and there is a broad, one-story piazza with unique elliptical arches across the main facade. The house is set on a raised basement, and broad stairs on three sides lead to the veranda.
Private; not accessible to the public

FAIRFIELD COUNTY
Winnsboro
KETCHIN BUILDING
231 S. Congress Street
c. 1830

The Ketchin Building is an unusual example of Federal architecture in central South Carolina. It is three stories high with five front bays and a hip roof. Walls are 18 inches thick to the third floor and 14 inches from there to the roof. The roof and cornice were replaced when the originals burned. Each floor has a central hall with two rooms on either side.
County

GEORGETOWN COUNTY
Georgetown
GEORGETOWN COUNTY RICE MUSEUM
Front and Screven Streets
Mid–19th century

Georgetown is one of South Carolina's oldest ports. Situated in the heart of a rice-producing area, the city was a leading national exporter of this product during the 1850's. The Old Market Building, now the Georgetown County Rice Museum, was

completed in 1842. It is a two-story brick building with a high tower topped by an open cupola. When finished, the upper floor contained town offices, and the ground floor housed an open-air market.
Municipal

GEORGETOWN COUNTY
Georgetown
PRINCE GEORGE WINYAH CHURCH (EPISCOPAL) AND CEMETERY
Corner of Broad and Highmarket Streets
1750

Prince George, Winyah Parish, was formed in 1721. The church is a rectangular brick building with a semicircular apse at the east end and a vestibule at the west. A square tower terminating in two octagonal sections highlights the main (west) elevation. This side has battlements, double front doors, and corner quoins. Windows are roundheaded, and there are semicircular fanlights above the doors. Brick pilasters flank the central side doors and ornament the building's corners, and there are Jacobean gables on the west and east ends of the main rectangle. During the Revolution the interior of the church was burned.
Private

GEORGETOWN COUNTY
Georgetown vicinity
HOPSEWEE (THOMAS LYNCH HOUSE)
12 miles south of Georgetown on U.S. 17
c. 1740

Set upon a brick foundation covered by scored tabby, Hopsewee is a two-and-one-half-story dwelling of mortise and tenon construction. West Indian influence is evident in the double tiered piazza and hip roof. There are four rooms on each floor opening onto a central hall. Thomas Lynch, Jr., a signer of the Declaration of Independence, was born here in 1749.
Private

GREENVILLE COUNTY
Greenville
CHRIST CHURCH (EPISCOPAL) AND CHURCHYARD
10 N. Church Street
1852–1854

Christ Church is Greenville's oldest church edifice. The brick structure has Gothic Revival detailing such as pointed-arch window and door openings and wall buttresses. Measuring 112 feet in length, the church has a 130-foot spire on its southwest corner, and there are five lancet windows on the west facade. A gallery was added to the west end (1875), a south transept put on and the chancel enlarged

(1880), and the east sanctuary wall extended, a north transept added, the balcony enlarged, and a Galilee porch constructed at the northwest corner (1968). All additions have been in keeping with the original style and cruciform plan.
Private

GREENVILLE COUNTY
Greenville
EARLE TOWN HOUSE
107 James Street
19th century

The Earle Town House, a two-story white frame structure on a raised brick basement, is one of the few late Georgian dwellings remaining in South Carolina's upper piedmont region. Elias T. Earle, a United States Congressman and South Carolina merchant, had the house built around 1810. The building retains many of its original features which include fine interior woodwork detail, hand carved mantels, and china doorknobs.
Private

GREENVILLE COUNTY
Greenville
WHITEHALL
310 W. Earle Street
1813

Whitehall is a rare example of the type of country house favored by wealthy Charlestonians of the 18th and 19th centuries as a refuge from the heat of the Carolina coast. Its most distinctive features are the wide first- and second-story West Indian piazzas which served as summer living rooms. Whitehall was owned until 1820 by Henry Middleton, a former president of the Continental Congress and a governor of South Carolina.
Private

GREENVILLE COUNTY
Tigerville vicinity
POINSETT BRIDGE
About 4 miles north of Tigerville on County Route 42
1820

The Poinsett Bridge carried the old State Road, connecting Charleston, South Carolina, with North Carolina, across Gap Creek. Joel Poinsett, for whom the bridge was named, designed the State Road in his official capacity as director of the South Carolina Board of Public Works. The bridge is made of stone put together without cement and has unusual pointed Gothic arches of rough, wedge-shaped stones. It is one of the oldest bridges in the state.
Private

GREENWOOD COUNTY
Cokesbury and vicinity
OLD COKESBURY HISTORIC DISTRICT AND MASONIC FEMALE COLLEGE AND CONFERENCE SCHOOL

The village of Cokesbury was founded in 1824 by Methodists from nearby Tabernacle. They were desirous of relocating their already flourishing boys' school which became the Dougherty Manual Labor School under jurisdiction of the South Carolina Methodist Church. In 1834 the name Cokesbury was chosen for the community to honor the first Methodist bishops in America, Thomas Coke and Francis Asbury. The Masonic Female College of South Carolina was built in 1854. It is a Greek Revival, temple-form structure on a raised basement. A square cupola surmounts the gable roof. Later the building housed the Cokesbury Conference School. Cokesbury was a strong center of developing Methodism in the South. The town itself contains the largest remaining group of antebellum structures in Greenwood County. These include an 1850 store; the 1850 Greek Revival home of Francis A. Connor, first president of Masonic College; an 1850 cottage; an 1840 Methodist rectory; the 1840 Glass-Palmer House; and the 1845 Dr. Thomas Gary Home.
Multiple private

GREENWOOD COUNTY
Ninety Six vicinity
OLD NINETY SIX AND STAR FORT
2 miles south of Ninety Six between S.C. 248 and 27
18th century

From its beginnings as a trading post on the Cherokee Path, Ninety Six grew into a flourishing village on South Carolina's northwest frontier. In 1768 it became a seat of government and subsequently a thriving courthouse town. Ninety Six was a Revolutionary War stronghold and was held by the British in 1780–1781. By 1787, when the town's name was changed to Cambridge, decline had already begun, and 45 years later the settlement had almost ceased to exist. Earthwork embankments, scattered piles of brick, the Charleston Road, and portions of a 1759 fortification now mark the site.
Private

HORRY COUNTY
Conway
OLD HORRY COUNTY COURTHOUSE AND JAIL
Main Street
1824–1825 (courthouse), 1825–1827 (jail)

Together these are the two most important government buildings in Horry County. The brick courthouse is two stories high and has an extended pediment supported by Doric columns which shelters the central second-story portico. There are segmental arches over the windows, and the arched main entrance has sidelights and a fanlight. The ceilings inside are vaulted, the doorways arched, and the mantels plain. In 1914 a hotel was built over the jail and has recently (1968) been removed. From photographs the jail appears to have had small, rectangular windows on the second floor and large arched ones at ground level.
Municipal

JASPER COUNTY
Gillisonville
GILLISONVILLE BAPTIST CHURCH
U.S. 278
c. 1838

The Gillisonville Baptist Church was constructed by local craftsmen and still possesses many original features such as the box pews, the flooring, and the slave gallery supported by chamfered columns. Exterior walls are covered with white clapboard siding. The main portico has Doric columns, and the large central door is flanked by smaller ones. A square tower rises in two sections from the gable roof above the pedimented front portico.
Private

KERSHAW COUNTY
Camden
CITY OF CAMDEN HISTORIC DISTRICT
Bounded on the south by the city limits, on the east and west by the Southern Railroad right-of-way, and on the north by Dicey Creek Road
18th, 19th, and 20th centuries

Camden, first called Fredericksburg (1733) and then Pine Tree (1758), was originally located south of the present town. The city prospered as a natural trading link between Charleston and the hinterlands. Wide streets were laid out in 1774 running north, south, east, and west, and land was set aside for six parks. British troops captured and occupied Camden during the Revolution, and for a short time (1780–1781) the city served as a central British supply post. Most of the original town was destroyed by fire in 1813. During the Civil War Camden was a Confederate storehouse and hospital center, and Sherman's troops occupied it briefly in February, 1865. Camden's architecture ranges from cottage homes and Georgian and Charleston type dwellings to mansions of all periods up through the 20th century. Several buildings were designed by architect Robert Mills. Bethesda Presbyterian Church (1820) is an unaltered Mills building. The courthouse was an 1826 Mills design remodeled in 1847; it has an Ionic four-column portico, a second-floor entrance, and a central stair. The Price House (1835) is a Georgian residence influenced by Charleston styles and the sole remaining example of a combination store-residence. Tanglewood (612 Laurens Street) is a typical up-country home with a raised basement and a wide first-floor porch and central interior hall.
Multiple public/private

KERSHAW COUNTY
Camden
FORT CAMDEN
Southern area of city, DeKalb Township
18th century

During the year preceding the surrender of the British at Yorktown (1780–1781), Camden served as the chief garrison and supply center for all British activities in the South. Such personages as Lord Charles Cornwallis and Lord Francis Rawdon led forces based in Camden in two major Revolutionary War engagements nearby, the battles of Camden and Hobkirk Hill. After the second unsuccessful battle, fought against the forces of General Nathanael Greene in April, 1781, the British destroyed nearly all of the battlements and evacuated the town. Fort Camden, as the site of the war fortifications is commonly called, once consisted of two city blocks of houses and military barracks surrounded by a palisade log fence and five redoubts. A house, a jail, and a powder magazine, all fortified, were located strategically from 100 to 1000 feet outside the town itself. Although war and fire have destroyed all original buildings in the district, several of the features have been restored to their 18th-century appearance.
Multiple public/private

KERSHAW COUNTY
Camden vicinity
ADAMSON MOUNDS SITE
About 2 miles west of Camden, along the left bank of Mound Creek
Pre-Columbian

Adamson Mounds is one of a series of sites that extend through Georgia, South Carolina, and North Carolina. All the sites were inhabited by Indians of a late prehistoric culture called Pee Dee (c. 1400–1700). The importance of the Adamson Mounds stems from its central location within the geographic distribution of the culture and its good state of preservation. One large temple mound, a smaller mound, and a burial mound are located on the site.
Private; not accessible to the public

KERSHAW COUNTY
Camden vicinity
CAMDEN BATTLEFIELD
5 miles north of Camden on U.S. 521 and 601
1780

The battle of Camden, August 16, 1780, was the climax of a series of disasters which had begun with the fall of Charleston to Sir Henry Clinton's British forces. Though a tactical defeat for the Revolutionary forces, it brought Nathanael Greene to the American command. He began a campaign which, though barren of decisive tactical victories, cleared the southern interior of British troops in less than a year. The battlefield site, little changed from its original appearance, is commemorated by a stone monument.
Multiple public/private
NHL

KERSHAW COUNTY
Camden vicinity
McDOWELL SITE (CHESTNUT MOUNDS)
2.5 miles south of Camden, surrounding the mouth of Big Pine Tree Creek on the Wateree River
Pre-Columbian

The McDowell Site contains the remains of a prehistoric Indian village and a single large temple mound. The culture represented is Pee Dee (sometimes called Lamar or Irene) and probably dates from the period between 1400 and 1700. Excavations were undertaken in the 1820's, the 1890's (the Smithsonian), and in the 1940's (the University of Georgia). The Wateree River has cut away part of the village site and about one third of the temple mound. Mound A, as it is called, now measures 9 feet high by 110 feet in diameter. Further investigation of the site should reveal facts about prehistoric coastal and

piedmont Georgia. Several small mounds have been destroyed by plowing.
Private; not accessible to the public

Lancaster
LANCASTER COUNTY COURTHOUSE
104 N. Main Street
1828

This two-story brick building has served as a county courthouse since its completion. Walls are English bond with Flemish bond framing the window openings. The front portico is reached by a double flight of stairs, and window openings are arcaded on the main facade only. The cornice contains both modillions and dentils, and the building rests on an English basement. Robert Mills may have designed the courthouse.

County

Lexington
FOX HOUSE (CLASSICAL AND THEOLOGICAL SEMINARY OF THE EVANGELICAL LUTHERAN SYNOD OF SOUTH CAROLINA AND ADJACENT STATES)
232 Fox Street
1832–1833

The Fox House housed the Southern Lutheran Seminary from 1833 until 1855, when the school was moved to Newberry. It served as a faculty dormitory and some classes were held inside. The two-story frame building has an 11-foot porch across the front and shed rooms at the back. A kitchen and housekeeper's quarters are attached at the rear by open breezeways. Eight fireplaces inside all have original mantels but one, and all doors and windows are original. Restoration work is being done (removal of two bathroom additions and later partitions to reestablish the original floor plan, reconstruction of the old kitchen building, and acquisition of antique hardware) to return the house as much as possible to its mid–19th century appearance.
County

Wallace vicinity
PEGUES PLACE
6 miles north of Wallace, just off U.S. 1 on County Route 266
c. 1770

Claudius Pegues, born in London of French Huguenot parents, received several royal land grants along the Pee Dee River. His home, the only pre-Revolutionary and the oldest house in Marlboro County, is a two-story frame building. Four square columns support a one-story front porch extending the width of the house. Large end chimneys provide fireplaces for two rooms on each floor. The interior paneling and wainscot is hand carved. The Pegues family has owned the property since 1770.
Private

Newberry
NEWBERRY OPERA HOUSE
Boyce and Nance Streets
1881

The Newberry Opera House is a massive brick building, eclectic in style, with a tall central tower. Live dramas took place on its stage, and eventually it became a movie theater. Today municipal offices are located inside.
Municipal

Walhalla vicinity
OCONEE STATION AND RICHARDS HOUSE
11 miles north of Walhalla via S.C. 11 and County Route 95
1760 (Oconee Station), 1805 (Richards House)

Oconee Station is a rectilinear fieldstone building with a gable roof and a wooden lean-to porch having four supporting posts at the front entrance. Shutters have long iron strap hinges, and the walls are two feet thick. The building, oldest in the county, was built as a stronghold for settlers in time of Indian attacks. It later served as a trading post and a residence. The nearby Richards House is two stories high with walls of handmade brick. There are two-piece batten shutters with iron strap hinges on the windows and end chimneys on the north and south facades. Built by William Richards, the house was used as a stagecoach stop.
Private

Walhalla vicinity
STUMPHOUSE TUNNEL COMPLEX
5 miles north of Walhalla via S.C. 28
1852–1859

Stumphouse Mountain and Middle tunnels were part of the Blue Ridge Railroad project, planned as the final link in a shipping route from the Mississippi to the Atlantic. Construction of tunnels, cuts, and embankments in four states was visualized. Had it been completed, the Stumphouse Mountain Tunnel would have been the longest in the country. Only the 365-foot Middle Tunnel was finished, although it has now been closed and is flooded. Seven years after the project began and when it was two-thirds over, the South Carolina legislature refused to appropriate additional funds and work ceased. The Stumphouse Tunnel Complex also contains the 385-foot railroad bed connecting the two tunnels (Stumphouse Tunnel itself is about 4,365 feet long, not in continuous section). A workers' town sprang up near one of the work shafts, and some graves, building foundations, and a path to the tunnel mark its locations.
State, municipal, federal

Westminster vicinity
PRATHER'S BRIDGE
10 miles southwest of Westminster on U.S. 123, 1 mile northwest on County Route 68, .25 mile west on County Route 160
Mid–19th century

Built prior to the Civil War, Prather's Bridge employs cross-timbers and wooden pegs. The bridge spans the Tugaloo River and connects South Carolina with Georgia. Two spans comprise the 158-foot bridge with a Town lattice truss, and there are uncovered approach ramps at each end. A 15-foot center section of the bridge burned in 1950 and was reconstructed.
State

Eutawville vicinity
EUTAW SPRINGS BATTLEGROUND PARK
2 miles east of Eutawville on S.C. 6 and 45

On September 8, 1781, General Nathanael Greene and a force of 2,098 men attacked a British camp of 2,300 at Eutaw Springs. Greene's goal was to prevent reinforcements from being sent to British General Cornwallis in Virginia. The American attack broke the British line, and the defenders retreated. Pursuing Americans yielded to the temptation to loot, and their advance became disorganized. Eventually the British took refuge in the Eutaw House and maintained a cover fire for a two-pronged counter attack which forced the Americans from the field. Although victorious, the British were henceforth confined to Charleston.
State

PICKENS COUNTY
Clemson
FORT HILL (JOHN C. CALHOUN HOUSE)
Clemson University campus
1803

Fort Hill was John C. Calhoun's residence from 1825 to 1850. Calhoun greatly enlarged the house, which contains many of the original furnishings. Calhoun gained recognition as a "War Hawk" in the 12th Congress, as Secretary of War under President James Monroe, and as Vice President under Presidents John Quincy Adams and Andrew Jackson. After becoming a champion of states' rights, he returned to Fort Hill in 1828 to write his "South Carolina Exposition and Protest" embodying the doctrine of nullification. From that time until his death in 1850, Calhoun dedicated himself to promoting the Southern side of an argument that would end in civil war. He served in the United States Senate from 1832 to 1843 and from 1845 until 1850. His son-in-law, Thomas G. Clemson, willed the Calhoun estate to the state of South Carolina for the establishment of the school which became Clemson University.
Multiple public/private
NHL

PICKENS COUNTY
Clemson
ST. JULIEN-RAVENEL HOUSE (HANOVER HOUSE)
1714–1716

This one-and-one-half-story French Huguenot house was built for Paul St. Julien. Pedimented dormers project from the gambrel roof, and there is a pilastered chimney at each end of the house. Interior paneling is walnut. The house was moved to the Clemson campus in the 1940's and has been restored.
State

RICHLAND COUNTY
Columbia
CALDWELL-HAMPTON-BOYLSTON HOUSE
829 Richland Street
c. 1820–1830

This three-story Greek Revival residence is frame covered with clapboards. Each story has a porch with four columns and a balustrade. The upper story on the rear facade possesses three small covered balconies. Interior plan is central hall flanked by two rooms on each side. Gardens to the west of the house are formally arranged, and some planting was probably done when the house was completed.
Private

RICHLAND COUNTY
Columbia
CHESNUT COTTAGE
1718 Hampton Street
c. 1855–1860

The Chesnut Cottage is an example of a "Columbia cottage," the standard, small, Neo-Classical residence adapted to local conditions and taste. It is a one-and-one-half-story building with a central dormer. The slant-roofed portico has four octagonal columns and an unusual balustrade of wood and ironwork. All windows are large. Confederate General James Chesnut and his wife Mary Boykin Chesnut lived here during the Civil War.
Private

RICHLAND COUNTY
Columbia
COLUMBIA HISTORIC DISTRICT I
Bounded on the south by Laurel Street; on the west by a line midway between Gadsden and Wayne Streets and a line midway between Gadsden and Lincoln Streets; on the north by a line two-thirds of the distance north of Calhoun Street between Calhoun and Elmwood Avenue; and on the east by a line midway between Assembly and Park Streets and by Park Street
19th century

Columbia was designated the capitol of South Carolina by the state legislature on March 22, 1786. The site was chosen because of its approximate central geographic location. With the convening of the legislature here on January 4, 1790, Columbia became the official seat of government. The Columbia Historic District I (also called Arsenal Hill) contains residences built before the Civil War. Focal point for the district is the Governor's Mansion (800 Richland Street), built in 1855. Other homes represent a wide variety of architectural styles, both indigenous and unique to the area, which are rapidly disappearing elsewhere in the city. Other buildings of note are the Lace House (803 Richland Street); the Caldwell-Hampton-Boylston House (829 Richland Street), Greek Revival; and the Palmetto Ironworks and Armory (1802 Lincoln Street), c. 1850.
Multiple public/private

RICHLAND COUNTY
Columbia
COLUMBIA HISTORIC DISTRICT II
Bounded on the south by Taylor Street and a line midway between Taylor and Blanding Streets; on the west by a line between Marion and Sumter Streets; on the north by Richland Street and a line between Richland and Calhoun Streets; and on the east by Bull Street, then through the block between Barnwell and Henderson Streets, and by Pickens and Henderson Streets
18th and 19th centuries

Columbia was incorporated for city government in 1805 and during the Civil War was a center of munition and cotton goods production. The Historic District II is one of the oldest residential sections of Columbia and is further distinguished by the presence of houses designed by Robert Mills. The two-story, brick, Greek Revival DeBruhl-Marshall House (1401 Laurel Street) was built in 1820 and is attributed to Mills. Other structures of note are the Greek Revival McMaster-Foard House (1429 Laurel Street), 1853, home of F. W. McMaster, the "father of Columbia city schools"; the Swearingen House (1413) Blanding), an example of the "Columbia cottage" as it appeared in 1882; the Clarke-Shealy House (1419 Blanding), 1857, a baroque form of the Columbia cottage; and the Hale-Elmore-Seibles House (1601 Richland Street), c. 1790, one of the oldest houses in the city.
Multiple private

RICHLAND COUNTY
Columbia
FIRST BAPTIST CHURCH
1306 Hampton Street
1856

The First Baptist Church is Greek Revival in style. A triangular roof pediment overhangs the main entrance and is supported by huge Tuscan columns of molded brick. The central doorway has consoles and is flanked by smaller paneled doors. Inside the church there is a balcony on three sides with a balustrade supported by fluted columns. The coved ceiling has cornice moldings. On December 17, 1860, the South Carolina Secession Convention met here because there was no room available in the statehouse. They adjourned the next day to Charleston but not before adopting a unanimous resolution favoring secession from the Union.
Private

RICHLAND COUNTY
Columbia
FIRST PRESBYTERIAN CHURCH
1324 Marion Street
1854

Columbia's First Presbyterian Church is the second erected on its site. An early English Gothic structure of stucco covered brick, the church has a 188-foot spire and a vaulted ribbed ceiling on the interior. On the exterior the main entrance is flanked by engaged columns and shouldered buttresses and there are pinnacles on the spire, the corners of the walls, and alongside the battlemented roof. Some alterations have been made: the structure was lengthened 40 feet, a gallery was constructed on three sides of the interior, and the front entrances have been changed. The congregation served by this church was organized in 1795.
Private

RICHLAND COUNTY
Columbia
HALL, AINSLEY, HOUSE
1616 Blanding Street
1823, Robert Mills

Ainsley Hall, the merchant for whom Robert Mills designed the house, died before its completion. Thus, the dwelling is more closely associated with the architect than the first owner. Mills (1781-1855) was a native of South Carolina and designed other homes, churches, government buildings, and bridges in the state. The Hall House has an Ionic temple portico with four massive columns on the main facade. The rear entrance has a seven-bay, arched porch or colonnade that emphasizes an unusual entryway—a concave, niched recess separating a pair of doors. A concave, ribbed arch head creates a partial dome effect over the recess. The front windows, typical of Mills, are set in recessed brick arches and have no pilaster trim. Each floor of the house has four large rooms. On the first level are two matching drawing rooms and an entrance hall all with curved ends, a reflection of Mills' ability to create the illusion of space in a small area. The three outbuildings have been reconstructed.
Private

RICHLAND COUNTY
Columbia
HAMPTON-PRESTON HOUSE
1615 Blanding Street
1818, Zachariah Philips

The Hampton-Preston House is a spacious post-colonial city mansion with a front veranda supported by Doric columns and topped by a fanlight. A marble mantel executed by the sculptor Hiram Powers is included among its original furnishings. The house serves as a memorial to its former occupants who include two governors of South Carolina, Wade Hampton III and Franklin J. Moses, and state senator John S. Preston. The house will be used as a museum pending complete restoration of the building and grounds.
State; not accessible to the public

RICHLAND COUNTY
Columbia
HORRY-GUIGNARD HOUSE
1527 Senate Street
19th century

The Horry-Guignard House, probably built before 1813 by Peter Horry, is exemplary of the early architecture of Columbia. It is a two-story dwelling of rabbit edged siding with a hip roof. The facade is five bays wide and the side elevations are three bays deep. A slightly sunken basement with latticed panels between brick supports is covered by a single-story balustraded porch running the width of the house. The slant roof over the porch has tongue and groove siding and is supported by square columns. Stairways from each side of the porch lead to the ground level. The louvered and paneled shutters on the front windows are unusual in design.
Private

RICHLAND COUNTY
Columbia
THE LACE HOUSE
803 Richland Street
1854

The Lace House is a symmetrical antebellum residence, deriving its name from the two-story ornamental cast iron veranda which is its most notable exterior feature. Adjacent to the Boylston House and across the street from the Governor's Mansion, the Lace House was once part of Columbia's fashionable Arsenal Hill section. Elaborate iron fencing fronts the Lace House and the adjoining property.
State

RICHLAND COUNTY
Columbia
OLD CAMPUS DISTRICT,
UNIVERSITY OF SOUTH CAROLINA
Bounded on the west by Sumter Street, on the north by Pendleton Street, on the east by Pickens Street, and on the south by Green Street
Early to mid–19th century

South Carolina's state university was chartered in 1801 as South Carolina College, and the first students matriculated in 1805. It was re-chartered in 1865 under the present name. Notable buildings in the Old Campus District are Rutledge College (1805, Robert Mills), the first structure on the campus; DeSaussure College (1809, Edward Clark); South Caroliniana Library (c. 1840), Greek Revival and perhaps the oldest separate college library building in the country; Harper College (c. 1848); Legare College (1848); the gymnasium (1855, Jacob Graves), Greek Revival, originally designed as a chapel; Lieber House (1810); President's Home (1811, 1853); and the McCutchen House (1813).
State

RICHLAND COUNTY
Columbia
PICRICCORN HOUSE (HALE-ELMORE-SEIBELS HOUSE)
1601 Richland Street
c. 1796

The Picriccorn House may be the oldest in Columbia. It is a two-and-one-half-story house with a first story of brick and the second of clapboard. There are three dormers in the gable roof which is also pierced by two inside chimneys. Piazzas on the front and west have slender Doric columns. The east piazza was replaced about 1900 by a sun porch and a second-floor room.
Private

RICHLAND COUNTY
Columbia
SOUTH CAROLINA GOVERNOR'S MANSION
800 Richland Street
1855

The South Carolina Governor's Mansion was originally constructed as an officers' quarters for Arsenal Academy. In 1865 when Union troops burned Columbia, the barracks was the only principal Academy structure to survive the flames. Three years later it was designated as the gubernatorial residence. The somewhat altered house has stucco walls, a flat roofline, and quoined corners. Its projecting three-bay central pavilion has three

arched entryways, only two of which are open. Ornate, first-floor grillwork porches embellish the flanking pavilions. Inside, the house has a center hall plan. Living quarters are on the second floor. Extensive work was done in the 1960's to strengthen the building and the interior was entirely renovated.
State

RICHLAND COUNTY
Columbia
SOUTH CAROLINA STATE HOSPITAL, MILLS BUILDING
2100 Bull Street
1821–1828, Robert Mills

The Mills Building of the South Carolina State Hospital is the oldest building in the country to be used continuously as a mental institution. The facade of the brick structure is dominated by a monumental two-story, Doric, hexastyle portico. Set upon an arcade, the portico is reached by curved stairs on either side. Walls of the three-story edifice are brick, and window sashes and frames are iron. Long symmetrical wings stretch out at oblique angles from the central pavilion, and the roof is crowned by a cupola. When Mills executed this commission he was serving as Civil and Military Engineer of South Carolina.
State

RICHLAND COUNTY
Columbia
SOUTH CAROLINA STATEHOUSE
Main Street
1855, John R. Niernsee; 1900, Frank Milburn; 1907, Charles C. Wilson

The South Carolina Statehouse is a Classic Revival edifice set on a rusticated, aboveground basement. It was constructed of Carolina granite, brick, and iron. The north and south porticos were added early in the 20th century. A balustrade runs around the entire roof, which is gabled over the entrance portico and hip over the main building. The present dome was substituted for the originally planned tower by architect Milburn. There are two-story Corinthian columns encircling the entrance portico, which is reached by a wide double flight of stairs. The interior was renovated in 1962–1963.
State

RICHLAND COUNTY
Columbia
TRINITY EPISCOPAL CHURCH
1100 Sumter Street
Mid–19th century, Edward Brickell White

Edward Brickell White designed Trinity Church in 1840, but it was not completed in its present form until 1894. The Gothic Revival style church has two tall, ornate towers which flank the main entrance. The towers rise above the roofline and support eight pinnacles with fleur-de-lis ornament. Buttresses on the side walls are four-shouldered. Transepts were added and the chancel extended in 1861–1862. White modeled the church upon Yorkminster Cathedral in England. Inside, the wooden roof rests on hammer beam trusses. There are box pews, a marble chancel rail, and hand-carved walnut choir stalls. Hiram Powers designed the marble baptismal font.
Private

RICHLAND COUNTY
Columbia
WASHINGTON STREET UNITED METHODIST CHURCH
1401 Washington Street
1872

The architecture of this Late Gothic Revival church is highlighted by eight tall pinnacles topped by unusual crown-shaped ornaments. There are four pinnacles on the tower above the left entrance. Window and door openings have pointed arches, and the exterior brickwork is quite ornate. Double shouldered buttresses brace the walls, and the roof cornice features closely spaced modillions. Inside, the ceiling of the church has exposed beams.
Private

RICHLAND COUNTY
Columbia vicinity
MILLWOOD
East of Columbia on Garner's Ferry Road
19th century

Millwood was built in the 1830's by Colonel Wade Hampton II, heir to one of America's largest fortunes. It was a large, frame, Greek Revival mansion. In 1858, upon the death of his father, Wade Hampton III became head of the family. He served as a general in the Confederate Army and after 1876 was elected governor of South Carolina and United States Senator. In February, 1865, under orders from General William T. Sherman, Millwood was burned to the ground leaving only chimneys, foundation piers, and twelve brick pillars. Today the Millwood ruins, two large square pillars and three round ones, remain as the only surface evidence of a once-extensive and prosperous South Carolina plantation and are symbolic of the old order in the South.
Private

RICHLAND COUNTY
Eastover vicinity
KENSINGTON PLANTATION HOUSE
8 miles east of Eastover near Route 764
1851–1853

Kensington is a plain South Carolina farmhouse wrapped around an ambitious central section. This central portion is domed, and there is an iron balustrade atop the roof. Two lower wings flank the center section, and both have arched colonnades across the front. There is a porte cochere on the landward side with Corinthian pilasters and arches. Colonel Richard Singleton, for whom Kensington was built, was the brother of Angelica Singleton Van Buren, President Martin Van Buren's White House hostess.
Private; not accessible to the public

SPARTANBURG COUNTY
Glenn Springs vicinity
CAMP HILL (SMITH HOUSE)
2 miles south of Glenn Springs on S.C. 215
c. 1835

Camp Hill is a well-preserved example of an antebellum plantation house in the South Carolina piedmont. The two-story frame dwelling has a two-story piazza across the front and symmetrical, one-story wings. Pedimented porticos shelter the entrances to these wings, and the architectural detail is a local adaptation of Greek Revival. Woodwork inside is hand carved. In 1940 the exterior was renovated, and the gable on the main roof was added after the house was built. A slave cabin still stands on the property.
Private

SPARTANBURG COUNTY
Moore vicinity
PRICE'S POST OFFICE
Junction of County Routes 86, 199, and 200
18th and 19th centuries

Price's Post Office was built by Thomas Price, landowner and entrepreneur, who moved to Spartanburg County in 1793 and operated a post office near his home. The main house has a Dutch gambrel roof, and the exterior is laid in Flemish bond brick with glazed headers. A central hallway runs through each story, and rooms open onto it from both sides. Connected to the back of the house is a two-room kitchen with an open ceiling and beaded beams. An 1822 estate inventory indicates that the dwelling was the center of a large plantation complex, uncommon in the South Carolina piedmont.
County

SPARTANBURG COUNTY
Spartanburg
EVINS-BIVINGS HOUSE (DR. JAMES BIVINGS HOUSE)
563 N. Church Street
c. 1854

The two-story Doric portico of the Evins-Bivings House features Greek Revival columns. The house itself is covered with clapboards, and the inside has a square, four-room plan on both floors. Notable features are the second-story piazza balustrade, the hand-blown glass of the windows and doors, and the upper and lower entrances with transom and sidelights flanked by fluted Doric pilasters supporting architraves with triglyphs. Dr. James Bivings, for whom the house was built, was a textile manufacturer who was chiefly responsible for promoting manufacturing in the Spartanburg area. A smokehouse and slave quarters are still on the property.
Private

SPARTANBURG COUNTY
Spartanburg
FOSTER'S TAVERN
191 Cedar Spring Road
1801-1807

Anthony Foster built his tavern at the intersection of the old Pinckneyville and Georgia roads, both well traveled stagecoach routes. Constructed of handmade bricks, the structure has walls 18 to 36 inches thick. All interior woodwork is hand carved. The pedimented entrance portico was added in 1845 and the porches, about 1915. Unusual tied chimneys are built into both gable ends. Although occupied continuously, the house is still largely original both inside and out.
Private

SPARTANBURG COUNTY
Spartanburg vicinity
WALNUT GROVE PLANTATION
8 miles southeast of Spartanburg, about 1 mile east of the intersection of U.S. 221 and Int. 26
c. 1765

Charles Moore, a Scotch-Irish immigrant who moved south from Pennsylvania to the South Carolina piedmont, built Walnut Grove on a land grant made in 1763. The main house is a composite of architectural styles partly indigenous to the piedmont and partly influenced by rural Pennsylvania Dutch architecture. All the buildings were originally built of unchinked logs and covered with clapboards. In addition to the main house, there are several outbuildings (a kitchen and schoolroom, a reconstructed smokehouse, and a blacksmith shop). The house and lands remained in the Moore family until 1961.
Private

SUMTER COUNTY
Sumter vicinity
STATEBURG HISTORIC DISTRICT
1 mile north of U.S. 76-378 on S.C. 261, 12 miles west of Sumter
18th, 19th, 20th centuries

Stateburg, which once had its own courthouse, tavern, post office, academy, and race track, is now more an area than a town, and within the perimeters of the district are two churches and many old homes. General Thomas Sumter (1734-1832) founded Stateburg with the expectation that it would become the state capital. Notable buildings within the district are the Borough House (1758), built of buff pise-de-terre (rammed earth); the Greek Revival Church of the Holy Cross (1850, E. C. Jones); High Hills Baptist Church (1803); The Ruins, once owned by General Sumter; Brookland Plantation, (late 1700's); Moorhill (1880); and Millwood Plantation (1840).
Multiple public/private

UNION COUNTY
Cross Keys vicinity
PADGETT'S CREEK BAPTIST CHURCH
2 miles east of Cross Keys on S.C. 18
1844

This rectangular, two-story building is six bays deep, three bays wide, and has a gable roof. A principal alteration has been the addition of a porticoed front on the south elevation. The portico has Doric columns and a low steeple. Few changes have been made on the interior. The congregation that built the church was organized in 1784 as the Church of Christ on the Tyger River. Since 1844 Padgett's Creek Baptist Church has been a center for religious, political, and social gatherings.
Private

UNION COUNTY
Union
HERNDON TERRACE
N. Pickney Street at the corner of Catherine Street
1845-1848

Herndon Terrace is a large, Greek Revival mansion typical of well-to-do Southern homes before the Civil War. There are large porticos on three sides of the house, and their Doric columns are brick covered with stucco. A full entablature rests on the columns. Inside there are high frescoed ceilings and carved woodwork. A slave cabin and cistern stand in the rear yard.
Private

UNION COUNTY
Union vicinity
CROSS KEYS HOUSE
12 miles southwest of Union on S.C. 49
1812-1814

Cross Keys House was once the center of a large and prosperous plantation. It is a Georgian brick house of two stories with a gable roof and identical pairs of end chimneys. A one-story portico shelters the main entrance. Between each pair of chimneys there is a date stone containing the date of construction and initials of the original owner. Interior carving is exceptional.
Private

UNION COUNTY
Union vicinity
PINCKNEYVILLE
13 miles northeast of Union on S.C. 13
1791-1792

Pinckneyville was one of eight circuit court districts established between 1769 and 1791 in an effort to bring law and order to the South Carolina backcountry. Four streets (Meeting, Broad, Tradd, and Watershed) were laid out and several public buildings erected, but Pinckneyville never became the metropolis which its founders had envisioned. The court districts were abolished in 1800, the population dwindled, and only the ruins of the jail, a store building, and a marker where the courthouse stood remain today.
County

UNION COUNTY
Union vicinity
ROSE HILL STATE PARK
9 miles southwest of Union off U.S. 176
1828-1832

Rose Hill, a three-story, stuccoed brick house, has door fanlights, a gable roof and twin end chimneys. The stucco was added after 1860 as were the two-story piazzas on the front and rear facades. A notable interior feature is the spiral staircase. William H. Gist, owner and builder of Rose Hill, served in the South Carolina state legislature (1840-1844), the state senate (1844-1856), as lieutenant governor (1848-1850), and as governor (1858-1860).
State

WILLIAMSBURG COUNTY
Kingstree
THORNTREE (WITHERSPOON HOUSE)
Fluitt-Nelson Memorial Park
1749

Built by Irish immigrant James Witherspoon, Thorntree House is the oldest known residence in the Pee Dee area and was constructed entirely of native materials. The house is frame with end chimneys and piazzas on both front and rear facades. Under the eaves there is a memory work dentil cornice. Inside, everything is pine walls, ceilings, cornices, and mantels. The hardware includes hand-forged locks and HL hinges, and the furniture is of the 1759–1826 period, when James Witherspoon lived here. The house has been moved from its original site.
Private

YORK COUNTY
Bethany vicinity
KINGS MOUNTAIN NATIONAL MILITARY PARK
Northwest of Bethany on S.C. 161
1780

The battle at Kings Mountain between Lord Cornwallis' scouting force under Major Patrick Ferguson and the over-mountain men on October 7, 1780, delayed but did not materially alter Britain's southern campaign. The battle was the first defeat in the final major British campaign of the Revolution and resulted in British surrender at Yorktown, Virginia, on October 19, 1781.
Federal
NPS; 3,950 acres

YORK COUNTY
Rock Hill
THE WHITE HOUSE
258 E. White Street
19th century

This large frame structure is a typical South Carolina up-country plantation home. Built between 1832 and 1842, the house has a two-story piazza and large end chimneys. The White House is the oldest house in Rock Hill and predates the founding of the town, which has grown up around it. Although in need of minor repairs, the building is basically in a good state of preservation.
Private; not accessible to the public

South Dakota

Mount Rushmore National Memorial,
Keystone vicinity, South Dakota. *NPS*

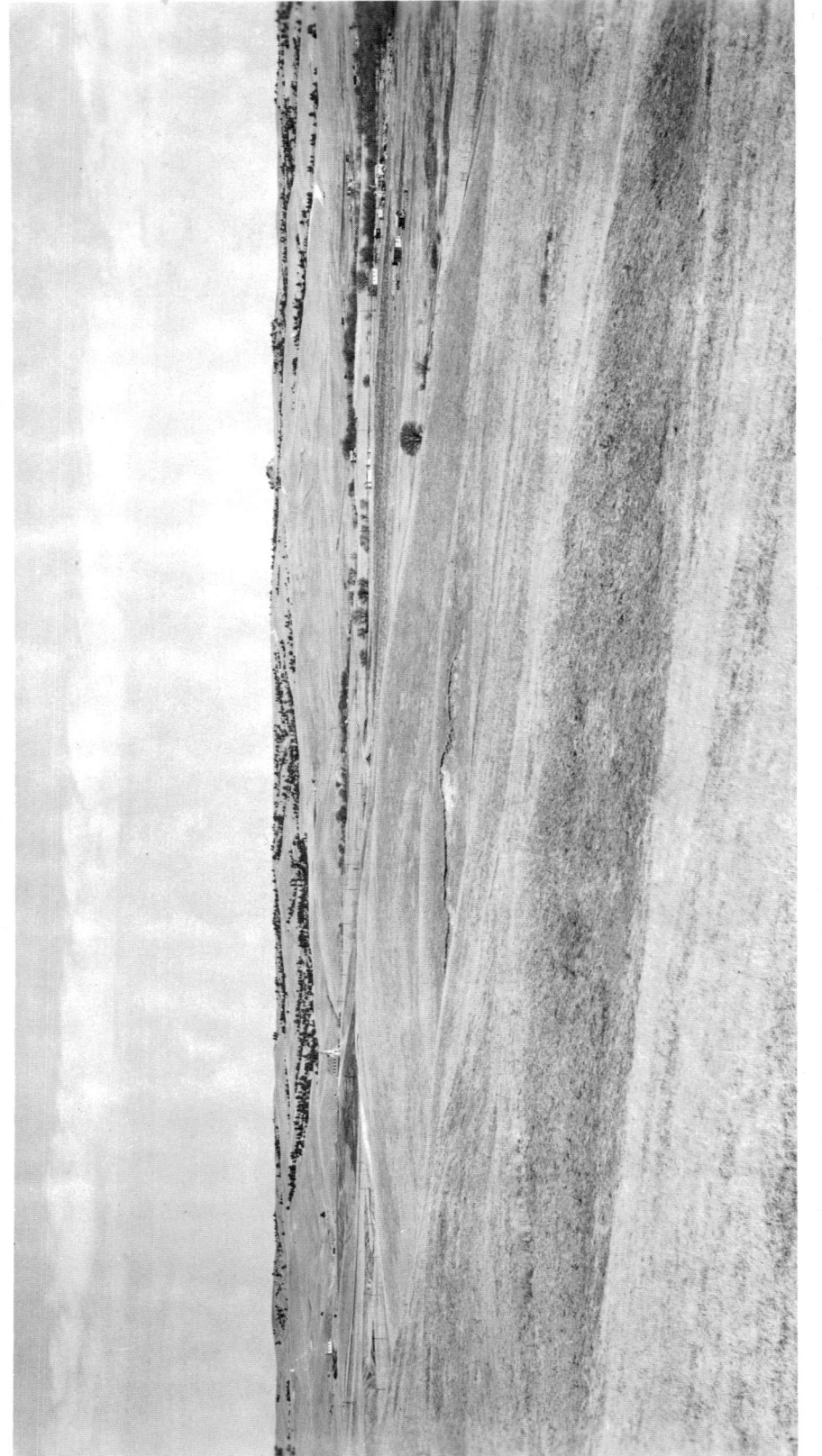

Wounded Knee Battlefield, Batesland vicinity, South Dakota. *NPS*

BUFFALO COUNTY
Chamberlain vicinity
CROW CREEK SITE
15 miles north of Chamberlain on the east side of the Missouri River near S.D. 47
Prehistoric

Crow Creek, a large fortified Indian village site, has been partially excavated. Two occupations are represented: one related to the Over Focus, of the Middle Missouri tradition; the other, to the Campbell Focus, affiliated with the central plains. The site is important in understanding the relation between events on the Middle Missouri and the central plains during the time of Plains village life.
Federal; not accessible to the public
NHL

BUFFALO COUNTY
Fort Thompson vicinity
FORT THOMPSON MOUNDS
Near Fort Thompson on S.D. 50, Crow Creek Indian Reservation
c. 800

The Fort Thompson Mounds are a large group of low burial mounds dating from Plains Woodland times. They contain the only evidence so far found for the first pottery-making peoples in the area. Archeological excavations in the deeper strata show evidences of occupation by pre-pottery Indians dating from much more remote times.
Private; not accessible to the public
NHL

DAVISON COUNTY
Mitchell
MITCHELL SITE
Municipal golf course
c. 1000

Archeological materials excavated at Mitchell Site show the movement of a late Woodland-Mississippian culture from the east to the Missouri Valley. Probably ancestors of the Mandan Indians, these people combined with cultures already present to form the Over Focus complex. On the south and west sides of the site were originally two fortification trenches. Within are more than 40 house depressions, and about 500 feet southwest is a row of five possibly associated burial mounds.
Municipal
NHL

DEWEY COUNTY
Mobridge vicinity
MOLSTAD VILLAGE
18 miles south of Mobridge, overlooking the Oahe Reservoir
Prehistoric

Molstad Village is a tiny fortified village site containing five circular house rings enclosed by a ditch with a bastion. It apparently represents the period of transition when central plains elements were combining with Middle Missouri traits to form the basis for the way of life practiced by the Mandan, Arikara, and Hidatsa Indians at the time of the white man's arrival. This pocket version of a prehistoric village has been excavated by the Smithsonian Institution.
Federal; not accessible to the public
NHL

HANSON COUNTY
Bloom vicinity
BLOOM SITE
East of Bloom on the James River
1000

Bloom Site, a well-preserved example of a prehistoric fortified Over Focus Indian site, lies on a terrace projecting into the James River Valley. A fortification ditch across the projection protects the site, in which some 25 lodge depressions are visible. It may have been the home of a group of ancestral Mandan Indians as they moved from the eastern prairies toward the Missouri River Valley. In the fields to the north and west are some 50 burial mounds, possibly representing the same occupation as the village.
Private; not accessible to the public
NHL

HUGHES COUNTY
Pierre vicinity
ARZBERGER SITE
7.5 miles east of Pierre on the Missouri River
1500

The Arzberger Site is a fortified village atop a low mesa. Forty-four circular house rings occupy more than 40 acres surrounded by a ditched fortification with 24 bastions. This archeological site was the northernmost outpost of the Central Plains tradition, possibly representing the ancestral Arikara Indians at the time when they were in transition from the Pawnee culture. The site is thus significant in interpreting a time of great change in Plains village prehistory.
Multiple state/private; not accessible to the public
NHL

LAWRENCE COUNTY
Deadwood
DEADWOOD HISTORIC DISTRICT
1876

The Deadwood Gulch area of the Black Hills was the site of a rich gold strike in the fall of 1875. Soon after the discovery of gold, people poured into the mining camp, and by summer 25,000 had settled in what became Deadwood. The town itself has one main street, and houses are built above it on both sides of the steep gulch. Today Deadwood still retains its mining town atmosphere, and many original buildings have survived, including the No. 10 Saloon where Jack McCall shot Wild Bill Hickok. Three miles from Deadwood is Lead, site of the Homestake, the largest gold mine in the United States.
Multiple public/private
NHL

LINCOLN COUNTY
BLOOD RUN SITE
Reference—see Lyon County, Iowa

LYMAN COUNTY
Lower Brule vicinity
LANGDEAU SITE
North of Lower Brule on S.D. 47W
Prehistoric

The Langdeau Site is the type site for an as-yet-unnamed archeological complex within the Middle Missouri tradition. Out of a probable 12 houses in the villages, four have been excavated. The houses are unusual in that they are long and rectangular with distinctive benches at each front. There is also evidence for what was probably a roof overhang forming a porch.
Private; not accessible to the public
NHL

PENNINGTON COUNTY
Keystone vicinity
MOUNT RUSHMORE NATIONAL MEMORIAL
3 miles west of Keystone off U.S. 16A
1941

Mount Rushmore National Memorial commemorates four of America's great Presidents: George Washington, Thomas Jefferson, Abraham Lincoln, and Theodore Roosevelt. Carved by sculptor Gutzon Borglum, this gigantic project was also a masterpiece of engineering for the heads are approximately 60 feet high. Washington, our first President, was chosen because of his qualities of leadership and prudence. Jefferson, the author of the Declaration of Independence, labored for a broadly based democracy in the interests of the common man. Lincoln

is memorialized because of his efforts to preserve the Union and free the slaves. Roosevelt, the rugged individualist, represents the vigor and dynamism of 20th-century America.
Federal/non-federal
NPS; 1,278.45 acres

SHANNON COUNTY
Batesland vicinity
WOUNDED KNEE BATTLEFIELD
11 miles west of Batesland, Pine Ridge Indian Reservation
1890

The engagement at Wounded Knee on December 29, 1890, was the last significant clash between Indians and soldiers in North America. Their grievances encouraged the Sioux to adopt the religious beliefs of the Ghost Dance, or Messiah Craze, during the winter of 1889–1890. Army troops attempted to put down the movement by arresting its leaders. The Ghost Dance campaign forced the Sioux to abandon the Ghost Dance religion and to accept the teachings of the white man.
Private
NHL

Deadwood Historic District, Deadwood, South Dakota. *NPS*

Tennessee

Ryman Auditorium, Nashville, Tennessee. *Les Leverett*

The Lee House of the James Lee Memorial,
Memphis, Tennessee. *Les Cooper*

Brown's Ferry Tavern,
Chattanooga, Tennessee. *Herbert Harper*

ANDERSON COUNTY
Oak Ridge
X-10 REACTOR, OAK RIDGE
NATIONAL LABORATORY
1943

First operated on November 4, 1943, the X-10 facility was the world's first full-scale nuclear reactor and the first to produce significant amounts of heat energy and measurable amounts of plutonium 239. The reactor served for many years as the principal atomic research facility in the United States. In 1946 it was the first reactor to produce radioactive isotopes for medical therapy. It was retired after 20 years of service.
Federal
NHL

CARTER COUNTY
Elizabethton vicinity
SYCAMORE SHOALS
2 miles west of Elizabethton on the Watauga River
1770-1780

Here in the early 1770's colonists established settlements. In March 1775, the Cherokees gathered at Sycamore Shoals to sign a treaty by which the United States purchased Watauga lands and 20 million acres of Kentucky land. Here in 1780 Kentucky and Tennessee frontiersmen gathered en route to the successful Revolutionary battle at Kings Mountain, South Carolina. The setting is slightly altered by modern intrusion.
Private; not accessible to the public
NHL

CHEATHAM COUNTY
Kingston Springs vicinity
NARROWS OF THE HARPETH
North of Kingston Springs on Route 2
1818

Montgomery Bell was a leading ironmaster of middle Tennessee. His most famous endeavor was at the Narrows of the Harpeth in 1818. Bell realized the great need for pounding pig iron into bars for use by blacksmiths. In order to build a forge for that purpose he decided to harness the river's potential power by cutting through a limestone cliff separating the two channels of the Harpeth. By cutting a tunnel 8 feet high and 15 feet wide he created a waterfall of 15 to 20 feet, enough to turn a large water wheel and secure power to operate the hammers of his forge. Products from the forge were used locally, hauled to Nashville and Franklin, and floated down the Harpeth and Cumberland rivers to Clarksville and shipped thence to Natchez and New Orleans. All that remains of the forge complex are parts of the foundations and the tunnel.
Private

CLAIBORNE COUNTY
CUMBERLAND GAP NATIONAL
HISTORICAL PARK
Reference—see Bell County, Kentucky

DAVIDSON COUNTY
Hermitage
TULIP GROVE
Lebanon Road
19th century

Tulip Grove was the home of Andrew Jackson Donelson, nephew of Andrew Jackson. The house is a massive example of Greek Revival architecture adapted to conditions in Tennessee. Two stories high and built of brick, Tulip Grove has a Doric entrance portico, flat window and door lintels, and a wide Doric entablature. Donelson sold the house c. 1858, and some slight alterations were subsequently made. The interior has been restored to its conjectural mid-19th-century appearance.
Private

DAVIDSON COUNTY
Nashville
BELAIR
2250 Lebanon Road
1832-1839

Belair is an impressive, 30-room antebellum mansion that John Harding built for his daughter. The exterior walls are of brick laid in Flemish bond. The house was built in an L-shape but has since had many additions. Major alterations were made by William Nichol when he purchased the house in 1838 and added wings on both ends. The architectural style is Federal with some Classic Revival influence visible in the central two-story portico with fluted Doric columns and a one-story deck roof. The kitchen at the rear of the ell was originally separated from the house but has since been connected and remodeled.
Private; not accessible to the public

DAVIDSON COUNTY
Nashville
BELMONT
Belmont Boulevard
1850

Belmont, a center of mid-19th-century Nashville social life, was constructed of brick and stone and has since been plastered on the outside and painted white. The Italianate structure consists of a two-story central block with two-story wings on either side. At the front is a recessed portico with two Corinthian columns supporting a massive cornice; above the doorway is a cast iron balcony. On either side of the portico are project-

ing porches with balustrades and four Corinthian columns. Rising above the roof is an observatory. Elaborate interior features include a long hall with a double colonnade of Corinthian columns and two free-standing staircases on the south side. Still remaining on the grounds are a marble fountain, five summer houses, and a 105-foot brick water tower which was part of an extensive irrigation system.
Private

DAVIDSON COUNTY
Nashville
FIRST PRESBYTERIAN CHURCH
(DOWNTOWN PRESBYTERIAN
CHURCH)
154 5th Avenue North
1849-1851, William Strickland

The Egyptian Revival First Presbyterian Church is an unusual landmark in downtown Nashville. Two 104-foot towers flank the main entrance, there are two lotus-topped columns on the entrance portico, and the characteristic vulture-and-sun-disk symbol is emblazoned upon the gorge and roll cornice of the main portico. The exterior window enframements narrow upward noticeably. Inside, Egyptian motifs (triangles, pyramids, lotus-topped columns, winged orbs, and twin serpents) appear everywhere. A remodeling was undertaken in 1881-1882, at which time the ceiling was painted to resemble sky and clouds and was sectioned by divider moldings. Stained glass replaced the clear glass windows in 1887.
Private

DAVIDSON COUNTY
Nashville
NASHVILLE CHILDREN'S MUSEUM
(LINDSLEY HALL, UNIVERSITY OF
NASHVILLE)
724 2nd Avenue, South
1853, Adolphus Heiman

Adolphus Heiman was one of Nashville's leading architects. Erected to serve as Central Hall for the University of Nashville, this building has been locally important in the field of education. Gothic elements are dominant in the symmetrical plan, in the large lancet window with wood tracery in the central block, and in the slightly projecting buttresses located at regular intervals around the building. The roof of the central block is pitched, but the two large wings have flat roofs. A parapet outlines the entire roof area. An addition constructed in the early 1960's as a children's theatre has been the only exterior alteration.
Municipal

DAVIDSON COUNTY
Nashville
NASHVILLE UNION STATION
Broadway and 10th Avenue South
Late 19th century, Richard Montfort

Nashville's Union Station is a notable example of a public building in the Romanesque Revival style. It is a square structure of Bowling Green gray stone and Tennessee marble. The front tower rises 239 feet, and the shorter rear tower is actually a smokestack composed of flying buttresses supporting a large enclosed chimney. The chimney and smokestack vented smoke from steam engines entering and leaving the station on four sets of tracks. Typical Romanesque Revival features are the rounded arches above all openings, the roughed stone exterior, the cavelike openings of the first floor arcade, and the tall front tower.
Private

DAVIDSON COUNTY
Nashville
PEABODY COLLEGE FOR TEACHERS
21st Avenue South and Edgehill Avenue
1914, Ludlow and Peabody

The Peabody Fund, created by philanthropist George Peabody in 1867 to help rebuild the South's educational system, had a dual objective; to promote elementary education and to further normal school work for the professional preparation of teachers. The first college aided was the University of Nashville, founded in 1815. The present name was adopted in 1909, and the campus was relocated next to Vanderbilt University in 1914. Its buildings are of Classical Revival design and face a landscaped quadrangle.
Private
NHL

DAVIDSON COUNTY
Nashville
RYMAN AUDITORIUM (GRAND OLD OPRY HOUSE)
116 Opry Place
1889–1891

Construction of the Ryman Auditorium was the result of an ardent campaign undertaken by Tom Ryman to build an assembly hall for Sam Jones, a Georgia revivalist popular in the Nashville area. Gothic influence is visible in its gabled roof, arched lancet windows, and the simulated buttresses at the corners and sides. The original wood pews and floors remain. In the early 1900's a stage replaced the pulpit, and the structure which had served as the Union Gospel Tabernacle became a hall for lecturers

and entertainers. Such notables as Victor Herbert, William Jennings Bryan, Enrico Caruso, Ignace Jan Paderewski, Helen Hayes, Katherine Cornell, and Arthur Rubenstein have performed here. Since 1941 the auditorium has been the home of the Grand Ole Opry.
Private

DAVIDSON COUNTY
Nashville
ST. MARY'S CATHOLIC CHURCH
330 5th Avenue North
1845–1847, William Strickland

St. Mary's is a Greek Revival church measuring 110 feet long by 60 feet wide. The ceiling inside is 32 feet above the floor. There is a distyle-*in-antis* portico with two Ionic columns on the main facade, and pilasters ornament the structure both inside and out. Above the main entrance is a triangular pediment, and the roof is crowned by a cupola. In the early 1890's the church underwent extensive remodeling and renovation when new stained glass and electric lights were installed. In 1925 the north and south sides were veneered with brick, and the entire front was finished with stone. Extensive redecorating was done in 1947. Despite the changes, Strickland's original lines are still evident.
Private

DAVIDSON COUNTY
Nashville
TENNESSEE STATE CAPITOL
Capitol Hill
1845, 1854, William Strickland

William Strickland designed the Tennessee State Capitol as a Greek temple with an Ionic portico on each of its four sides. Huge blocks of limestone were quarried nearby to construct the 238–foot by 109–foot building which rests atop a rusticated basement. A central tower (42 feet high) rises above the roof and supports a lantern (37 feet high) graced by Corinthian columns. The interior is simple in design with well-proportioned interior spaces. In 1956 some repair and restoration work was needed. This included the replacement of all the exterior columns, the pediments, parapets, all projecting cornices, the upper and lower terraces, and the engaged columns and the entablature on the tower. Inside, many alterations have been made.
State
HABS

DAVIDSON COUNTY
Nashville
TRAVELLER'S REST
Franklin Road
18th and 19th centuries

Traveller's Rest was built in several stages by John Overton, an early Tennessee judge, and his son. The original section of the house was begun in the last years of the 18th century. Subsequent additions were made in 1812, the early 1820's, and 1887. The house itself is of simple frame construction with a symmetrical facade and a projecting temple front porch. At the rear of the house is a two-story open gallery which was part of the 1820's addition.
Private

DAVIDSON COUNTY
Nashville vicinity
BELLE MEADE
Harding Road at Leake Avenue
19th century

Belle Meade, a three-story Greek Revival plantation house, was built by William Giles Harding. Harding and his son-in-law raised thoroughbred horses and sold breeding stock of ponies, Alderney cattle, Cotswold sheep, and Cashmere goats. Both men were pioneers in the field of animal husbandry. Four brick structures remain of the original complex. It is conjectured that at one time the central house was flanked by two-story wings. Each wing had a smaller dependency behind, the present garden house and the smokehouse.
State

DAVIDSON COUNTY
Nashville vicinity
THE HERMITAGE
12 miles east of Nashville on U.S. 70N
1818–1819

For over 40 years Andrew Jackson lived at The Hermitage, during which time he rose from a frontier militia commander to the Presidency. His service in the Creek War brought him a major general's commission in 1814. After the battle of New Orleans in 1815, the final battle of the War of 1812, he returned a nationally known figure. After serving two terms as President of the United States, 1829–1837, Jackson lived out the rest of his life at The Hermitage. He bought the property in 1804 and gradually converted it into the brick, porticoed mansion that stands today. The house is furnished largely with Jackson's possessions, and most of the original outbuildings still remain.
Private
NHL

DAVIDSON COUNTY
Old Hickory
CLEVELAND HALL
4041 Old Hickory Boulevard
1839

Cleveland Hall was built by Stockley Donelson, an influential lawyer and planter and a close friend of Andrew Jackson's. The two-story Federal house has a one-story Greek portico with four fluted Doric columns, a pediment, and triglyphs on the frieze. The structure is rectangular with a kitchen ell and rear frame porch. The bricks used for construction were made on the site, and the stone for the foundation was quarried locally. A brick smokehouse built in 1910 and a cedar log slave cabin are the last surviving outbuildings on the site.
Private; not accessible to the public
HABS

GREENE COUNTY
Greeneville
ANDREW JOHNSON NATIONAL HISTORIC SITE
Depot and College Streets
c. 1830, tailor shop; c. 1850, house

Andrew Johnson National Historic Site preserves important sites associated with the 17th President of the United States: the tailor shop he owned, his home, and his grave. Before succeeding to the presidency upon the assassination of Abraham Lincoln in 1865, Johnson had had a varied political career. Beginning as a tailor, he became in succession an alderman, mayor, state legislator, state senator, U.S. Senator, and Vice President His term as President was marked by problems of reconstruction, the purchase of Alaska in 1867, and an unsuccessful impeachment trial in 1868.
Federal
NPS; 16.68 acres
HABS

HAMILTON COUNTY
CHICKAMAUGA AND CHATTANOOGA NATIONAL MILITARY PARK
Reference—see Catoosa County, Georgia

HAMILTON COUNTY
Chattanooga
BROWN'S FERRY TAVERN
Brown's Ferry Road
1803

John Brown, a ferry operator, tavern owner, and river pilot who was half Cherokee, had this two-story log structure built and used it as a tavern until 1819. The tavern stood facing a major Indian trail connecting the Creek Nation with northern tribes. It was officially designated a Post Road (between Kingston, Tennessee, and Alabama) in 1820. The house was built with two rooms downstairs connected by a dogtrot and three above. There are stone chimneys at both gable ends, and a porch extends across the main facade. The rear addition post-dates the Civil War, and the open dogtrot was enclosed in recent years. During the Civil War Federal troops captured Brown's Ferry and used the tavern as a commissary. The Post Road was a principal supply line for Union forces in Chattanooga.
Private; not accessible to the public

HAMILTON COUNTY
Chattanooga
CHATTANOOGA UNION STATION
W. 9th and Broad Streets
1858, 1881

The Chattanooga Union Station was the terminal for the first railroad, the Western & Atlantic, to enter the state. The original station was a train shed built in 1858. Approximately one-third of that structure is still standing. In 1881 a two-story Victorian brick addition was constructed. During the Civil War troops of both the Confederate and Union armies, as well as important military and political leaders, used the station. For 70 years Union Station housed the *General*, the Confederate locomotive involved in the celebrated rail chase during the Civil War. The station, now the oldest extant structure in Chattanooga, is a reminder of the great era of railroading.
Private

HARDIN COUNTY
Shiloh
SHILOH NATIONAL MILITARY PARK
1862

Shiloh was the scene of a major engagement in the western campaign in the Civil War, April 6–7, 1862. The Union victory here retained for the Union the initiative gained at Fort Donelson and led to the early capture of Corinth, Mississippi, and Memphis. Shiloh was an important milestone in the Union campaign aimed at securing control of the Mississippi River from Cairo, Illinois, to the Gulf of Mexico. The culmination of the campaign was General Ulysses S. Grant's successful siege of Vicksburg, Mississippi, which split the Confederacy in half. Adjoining the battlefield site is Shiloh National Cemetery.
Federal/non-federal
NPS; 3,515.46 acres

HICKMAN COUNTY
Nunnelly vicinity
PINEWOOD
Approximately 3 miles north of Nunnelly on Pinewood Road (Route 3)
1866–1868, Carter Thurman

Pinewood is significant not only for its architectural grandeur, but also as the center of a vast agricultural and industrial complex. The house is a two-story brick, Italianate mansion. It was built by Samuel Graham, one of the wealthiest men in the state, as the resident center of his industrial-agricultural domain which included a milldam and a factory for spinning cotton and grinding corn. Dominating the front facade of the house is a two-story brick projection and on either side of this is a colonnaded one-story portico. Outbuildings still standing are a brick smokehouse and creamery and a large frame barn built in the 1850's.
Private; not accessible to the public

KNOX COUNTY
Knoxville
BLOUNT, WILLIAM, MANSION
200 W. Hill Avenue
1792

William Blount was influential in the trans-Appalachian frontier movement of the late 18th century and in territorial policies of the Old Southwest Territory. His house served for a time as the capitol of the territory south of the Ohio River. Blount was not only governor of the Southwest Territory, but also Superintendent of Indian Affairs for the Southern Department. He was a leading figure in gaining statehood for Tennessee and one of the founders of Blount College, now the University of Tennessee. The house and the governor's office behind it have been restored and refurnished.
Private
NHL; HABS

KNOX COUNTY
Knoxville
MARBLE SPRINGS
Neubert Springs Road
18th century

Marble Springs is the only remaining home of Tennessee's first governor, John Sevier (1796–1801, 1803–1809). Sevier also served in the state senate and for two terms in Congress. Marble Springs was his home from 1790 to 1815, with the exception of the time he spent in Knoxville as governor. Of the original buildings in the complex, only the main, two-story pine cabin exists. Restoration of the cabin was

undertaken in 1961–1962, and in 1963 a reproduction of the original kitchen was built. Constructed of oak logs, it is separated from the main cabin by a dogtrot and has a lean-to at the rear. Other reconstructed outbuildings include a springhouse, smokehouse, and loom house.
State

KNOX COUNTY
Knoxville vicinity
RAMSEY HOUSE
Thorngrove Pike
1797, Thomas Hope

The two-story Ramsey House is built of red marble and has blue limestone trim. A flight of three steps leads down to the kitchen from the dining room. Attached kitchens were unusual in Tennessee at this time. The house represents a transitional style of architecture which succeeded the log cabin in this area. Francis Alexander Ramsey, builder of Ramsey House, was active in county and state government and served on the board of trustees for both Blount College and the University of Tennessee.
Private

LOUDON COUNTY
Loudon vicinity
BOWMAN HOUSE
East of Loudon on Little River Road
1828

George Bowman, an immigrant from Germany, built this home on the Little Tennessee River for his second wife. The brown brick used in constructing it is peculiar to this area of east Tennessee. Architecturally the house is basically Federal as expressed by local workmen using local materials. It is typical of Tennessee country homes of the period. The first floor windows are not original, although those on the second floor probably are. Later additions were the front porch and the rear wing.
Federal

LOUDON COUNTY
Loudon vicinity
CANNON-CALLOWAY HOUSE
West of Loudon off U.S. 11
1860's–1872

The Cannon-Calloway House, one of the most elaborate houses in Loudon County, was begun during the Civil War and completed in 1872. The two-story dwelling is basically an Italian villa with a mansard-roofed tower. All the second-floor windows are round-arched with hoodmoldings above. Other exterior features are roof brackets, a front bay window, and a frame veranda with delicately carved wooden arches and a decorative railing. Immediately behind the house are the brick smokehouse, springhouse, and washhouse.
Private; not accessible to the public

LOUDON COUNTY
Loudon vicinity
CARMICHAEL INN
Off U.S. 11 across Watts Bar Lake from Loudon
Early 19th century

Built by John Hudson Carmichael (1780–1840) before 1832, the Carmichael Inn is a one-and-one-half-story log structure. The inn once accommodated railroad passengers. The passengers were ferried across the Tennessee River to the inn where they waited for a stagecoach to Knoxville or summer resorts in east Tennessee. Carmichael's sons ran the inn, the ferry, and the stage. The little-altered inn is one of the few remaining log structures in the county.
Private

MADISON COUNTY
Pinson vicinity
PINSON MOUNDS
3 miles east of Pinson on secondary road
Mounds c. A.D. 1000; occupation as early as 5000 B.C.

The Pinson Mounds Site includes two large temple mounds, an effigy mound, and extensive earthworks. Excavations revealed that this Indian site was occupied during several archeological periods, including an Archaic pre-pottery occupation. Most of the artifacts suggest that the major occupation occurred in a period dominated by clay-tempered pottery, a Woodland ceramic tradition. Some features are considered to be characteristic of Mississippian culture. The coincidence of the two cultures suggests that the Pinson Mounds perhaps played a leading role in the development of Mississippian culture.
Multiple public/private; not accessible to the public
NHL

MAURY COUNTY
Columbia
MAYES-HUTTON HOUSE
306 W. 6th Street
1850's

The Mayes-Hutton House was built for Samuel Mayes, a Columbia businessman. Four giant Corinthian columns and two Corinthian pilasters highlight the main facade. Twin chimneys at either end of the brick house are joined by a parapet. The original facade was altered in the 1870's by the addition of rounded windows and door openings and double brackets under the roof cornice.
Private; not accessible to the public.

MAURY COUNTY
Columbia
POLK, JAMES K., HOUSE
West 7th and S. High Streets
1816

James K. Polk lived in this house for several years during his youth. After serving two years in the Tennessee legislature, he was elected to the United States House of Representatives in 1825, becoming Speaker in 1835. He was governor of Tennessee from 1839 to 1841 and President of the United States from 1845 to 1849. The dining room and kitchen have been reconstructed on their original foundations, and the house is furnished with Polk period furniture and Polk family memorabilia.
State
NHL

MAURY COUNTY
Columbia vicinity
BEECHLAWN
South of Columbia on U.S. 31
1850's

Beechlawn is a Greek Revival dwelling composed of a two-story central block flanked by one-story wings. The front portico has four Ionic columns above which are a roof pediment and a bracketed cornice. The main entrance is off center. Beechlawn was built for Major A. W. Warfield and served as headquarters for generals on both sides during the Civil War. Confederate General John Bell Hood established his command post here in November, 1864, and one month later Union General John M. Schofield occupied Beechlawn while in pursuit of Hood. Behind the main house is a cedar log cabin that originally contained two rooms connected by a dogtrot. The dogtrot has been enclosed. Outbuildings are an icehouse and a smokehouse.
Private; not accessible to the public

MAURY COUNTY
Columbia vicinity
CLIFTON PLACE
Southwest of Columbia on Mount Pleasant Highway
1838–1839

Clifton Place is a two-story Greek Revival structure with one-story wings on either side. The impressive facade includes a projecting two-story portico with four giant Ionic columns. Much of the construction material came from the im-

mediate area; the stone for the foundations was quarried on the site, and the wood was taken from nearby forests. The elegant "great house," the several outbuildings, and traces of the extensive formal gardens suggest one aspect of life in the antebellum South. Clifton Place was built for Gideon J. Pillow, a controversial brigadier general who fought in the Mexican War and the Civil War.
Private; not accessible to the public
HABS

MAURY COUNTY
Columbia vicinity
ST. JOHN'S EPISCOPAL CHURCH
6 miles west of Columbia on U.S. 43
1839–1842

St. John's Church was built almost entirely through the efforts of the Polk family. It was built for the family and their slaves, and slave labor was used for the construction. The Gothic Revival structure measures 65 feet by 41 feet, and the central front tower is 50 feet high. Four buttresses on each side support the 16–inch brick walls, and all the windows have pointed arches and numerous diagonal muntins. Inside, the balcony, altar, communion rail, and reredos were all carved from a large cherry tree which stood on the site of the church. In 1889 St. John's ceased to function as an active parish.
Private

MONROE COUNTY
Vonore vicinity
FORT LOUDOUN
U.S. 411
1756–1757

Fort Loudoun was built by the English at the request of the Cherokee Indians. Occupied until 1760, it was instrumental in allying the Cherokees with the British during critical years of the French and Indian War. This alliance held the trans-Appalachian frontier until the British armies in the north had almost completed the defeat of the French and their Indian allies. Archeological evidence has been used to restore the fort, and a large variety of artifacts is on display.
State
NHL

MONTGOMERY COUNTY
Clarksville
SEVIER STATION
West side of Walker Street, 216 feet south of B Street
1792–1794

A one-story limestone block structure with two interior rooms is all that remains of Sevier Station, one of two forts in Tennessee still on its original site and in a virtually unaltered condition. Although Valentine Sevier erected the station in 1792 as protection from hostile Indians, six members of his family were slain nearby in a surprise attack two years later. Sevier sold the property the following year, and it has since had a succession of owners. The blockhouse measures 32 feet by 18 feet and both rooms have dirt floors. Some timbers in the roof and a crude door with strap hinges are thought to be original. In the 1820's a two-story frame house was built onto the front of the blockhouse with a dogtrot between. The house has since been shingled.
County; not accessible to the public

ROANE COUNTY
Harriman
HARRIMAN CITY HALL
Roane Street and Walden
Late 19th century

The building was erected about 1890 to house the East Tennessee Land Company, which founded the town of Harriman. General Clinton B. Fisk, Prohibition party candidate for President in 1888, organized the company. After serving several years as office space, the building housed the American Temperance University, which was established in 1893 and closed in 1909. From 1912 to 1950 it functioned as the city hall. The exterior of the three-story building is of red brick and Indiana limestone. Its Romanesque arches and four Norman towers make it an imposing site on the city's streetscape.
City

ROBERTSON COUNTY
Cedar Hill vicinity
WESSYNGTON
About 3 miles south of Cedar Hill, near Calebs Creek
1815–1819

The Wessyngton land was acquired by Joseph Washington during the years 1796 to 1802. His two-story, Federal style residence was constructed after his marriage in 1808. Originally the dwelling probably had end chimneys and a small, square porch across the front. Additions have been made on the front and a wing has been added at the rear. Like most farmers of his time Washington made whiskey from surplus corn and turned his apples and peaches into brandy. During the 1850's and 1860's tobacco was an important crop. Remaining outbuildings are a smokehouse, a kitchen, a dairy house, and an office.
Private

RUTHERFORD COUNTY
Murfreesboro
OAKLANDS
N. Maney Avenue
19th century

The growth of Oaklands spanned an entire century. The original two-room brick house and kitchen were built in the early 1800's. In 1820 the owner put a two-story, eight-room addition on the south side. A second major addition with Gothic Revival detailing on doorway, windows, and roof cornice was made in the late 1850's. In 1890 a white colonnaded wooden portico was built onto the south front.
Municipal

RUTHERFORD COUNTY
Murfreesboro vicinity
STONES RIVER NATIONAL BATTLEFIELD
3 miles northwest of Murfreesboro on U.S. 41
1862–1863

Stones River was the scene of a battle between the Union Army of the Cumberland under Major General William S. Rosecrans and the Confederate Army of Tennessee under General Braxton Bragg, December 31, 1862, to January 2, 1863. It was the first major battle in the two-year western campaign that cut the Confederacy in two and reached its climax in General William T. Sherman's march to the sea through Georgia. Included at the site are parts of the battlefield and a national cemetery.
Federal
NPS; 330.86 acres

RUTHERFORD COUNTY
Smyrna
DAVIS, SAM, HOME
Tenn. 102
19th century

The Sam Davis Home is a typical farm of an antebellum middle class family. Two stories high, the house has a portico with four square columns and is covered with white clapboards. Architectural detail is Greek Revival. Young Sam Davis was captured by Union troops in November, 1863. Papers containing information about Federal troops and fortifications were found on his person, so he was tried and hanged as a spy. Davis was buried on the property in the family cemetery.
State

SEVIER COUNTY
Sevierville
BUCKINGHAM HOUSE
Sevierville Pike
1795

The Buckingham House is the oldest house in Sevier County. Although it is now L-shaped due to a frame section added about 1900, the original house was rectangular, measuring 33 feet by 20 feet. The Federal style dwelling is constructed of brick laid in Flemish bond on the front elevation and English bond on either end. Two bricks to the right of the front door bear the date of construction and the letters "T & E B," which are the initials of Thomas and Ephriam Buckingham, the builders. Thomas Buckingham was active in politics. He was elected first sheriff of the county and served as a member of Tennessee's 1796 constitutional convention.
Private
HABS

SEVIER COUNTY
Sevierville
SEVIER COUNTY COURTHOUSE
Court Avenue
1895–1896

The Sevier County Courthouse is a rare example of Beaux-Arts Classicism in a rural county. McDonald Brothers of Louisville, Kentucky, were selected as architects. Rectangular in shape, the courthouse has brick walls and a slate roof. The architects employed arches over most of the windows and entrances, and there is an open arched arcade across the central second-story section. This center section is flanked by two end blocks (three stories high), each topped by a cupola surrounded by three smaller, minaret-like towers. The dominant feature of the entire building is a 130-foot central tower. It is crowned by a metal-clad dome.
County

SHELBY COUNTY
Memphis
BEALE STREET HISTORIC DISTRICT
Beale Street, from Main to 4th Streets
Early 1900's

The Beale Street area provided the environment that gave birth to the blues, a unique contribution of the Negro to American music. When W. C. Handy frequented Beale Street, it was lined with saloons, nighclubs, gambling halls, theaters, and pawnshops. In this environment he found inspiration for his music. In Peewee's Saloon, his headquarters, Handy wrote such songs as "Memphis Blues," "St. Louis Blues," and "Beale Street Blues." A number of the pawnshops still operate in the area.
Multiple public/private
NHL

SHELBY COUNTY
Memphis
FIRST BAPTIST CHURCH
379 Beale Avenue
1869

The First Baptist Church is a large brick edifice, many portions of which are covered with stucco. Its street facade has a central pediment or gable end section flanked by two square towers of equal height. A large circular area within the pediment contains eight small, round, stained glass windows. Inside, the church has been little altered. There are balconies on three sides, and the ceiling has delicate wooden vaulting. Since its construction, the church has been a center of cultural activity for the black people of Memphis.
Private

SHELBY COUNTY
Memphis
HUNT-PHELAN HOME
533 Beale Avenue
c. 1830, 1855

Construction of the Hunt-Phelan Home occurred in two stages. The earlier portion was a two-story, brick house consisting of four rooms and a central hall on each floor. A small portico was built on the north or main side, and all windows had stone lintels. During the second phase of construction (1855) a two-story kitchen and service wing was added at the rear and connected by a two-story porch. The small portico was moved to a side entrance and replaced by a large Greek Revival portico with four fluted Ionic columns having cast iron bases and caps. The columns, the dentil cornice, and the architrave are wood. General Ulysses S. Grant used the house as his headquarters when Federal troops occupied the city.
Private; not accessible to the public
HABS

SHELBY COUNTY
Memphis
THE LEE AND FONTAINE HOUSES OF THE JAMES LEE MEMORIAL
680–690 Adams Avenue
19th century

Both the Lee and the Fontaine Houses are Second Empire, a style characterized by a high mansard roof (usually with a curb around the visible slopes), dormer windows, classically detailed chimneys (which are important composition elements), and projecting pavilions. The overall appearance of such a building is strongly three dimensional. The Fontaine House (1870–1873), most notable of the two, is brick and has terra cotta window lintels and elaborate cornices. Filigree ironwork decorates the roof, and there are stonecoat quoins at the corners. Similar in appearance is the Lee House, built in three stages. In 1843 the square rear section was erected. Ten years later the present center section was added, and the present front and tower were put on in 1873. Amos Woodruff, a Memphis businessman and a founder of the Memphis & Charleston Railroad, built the Fontaine House. Its interior has been extensively restored. A later owner, Miss Rosa Lee, left both houses to the city as a memorial to her father.
Private

SHELBY COUNTY
Memphis
RANDOLPH HOUSE
546 Beale Street
Mid–1870's

The large, three-story Randolph House is unique as the last remaining Italianate dwelling in a once-fashionable residential section. Although the rear facade has been remodeled and the brick walls covered with stucco, the house retains its distinctive character. Notable features are the off-center square tower, the round-arched windows, the asymmetrical placement of masses, the ornate roof brackets, and the roof gables of different heights which intersect at right angles. Woodwork inside is ornate. W. M. Randolph, a Memphis lawyer who was city attorney (1869–1874), built the house.
Private

SHELBY COUNTY
Memphis
TRI-STATE BANK
390 Beale Street

Here, in what was then the business district of Beale Street, W. C. Handy (1873–1958), song writer and bandleader, opened a publishing house which was the first distributor of his musical compositions ("Memphis Blues," 1912, "St. Louis Blues," 1914, and "Beale Street Blues," 1917). Handy formed a partnership with Harry Pace, who contributed financial support. In 1918 Handy moved his publishing house to New York.
Private

STEWART COUNTY
Dover vicinity
FORT DONELSON NATIONAL MILITARY PARK
1 mile west of Dover on U.S. 79
1862

Fort Donelson National Military Park commemorates an early decisive battle of the Civil War. This stronghold on the Cumberland River fell to Union forces commanded by General Ulysses S. Grant on February 16, 1862. The capture of this post, Grant's first major Civil War victory, greatly enhanced his prestige as a military leader. Strategically the victory opened an avenue into the heart of the Confederacy by way of the Tennessee and Cumberland rivers and marked the beginning of the campaign that resulted in Union control of the Mississippi Valley. Adjacent to the battlefield site is Fort Donelson National Cemetery.
Federal/non-federal
NPS; 600 acres

SULLIVAN COUNTY
Kingsport
THE NETHERLAND INN AND COMPLEX
2144 Netherland Inn Road
1802–1818

The Netherland Complex was first operated as a warehouse and wharf for shipping salt. Later it was operated as an inn and stage station. Stone comprises the first floor of the three-story inn and the second and third levels are constructed of wood studs and exterior wood siding. Few alterations have been made to the original inn. The Bank Barn, smokehouse, wharf and warehouse have been reconstructed.
Private

SULLIVAN COUNTY
Kingsport vicinity
LONG ISLAND OF THE HOLSTON
South fork of the Holston River

Long Island of the Holston was the scene of several momentous events during the early years of exploration and settlement in the Old Southwest. Daniel Boone made the island the starting point of his Wilderness Road through the Cumberland Gap, a road which was used by more than 200,000 settlers during the two decades following 1775. The battle of Long Island Flats, fought a short distance north of the island in 1776, crushed the Cherokee fighting strength during the early years of the American Revolution.
Private
NHL

SULLIVAN COUNTY
Piney Flats vicinity
ROCKY MOUNT
Southwest of Piney Flats off County Route 11 E.
1770–1772

Rocky Mount, at the time of its construction, was an elaborate frontier residence. The two-story house was built of white oak logs and contained nine rooms. A one-and-one-half-story ell and connecting dogtrot adjoin the east side, and the kitchen, a separate building, has been reconstructed on its original foundations. Rocky Mount served as first capitol of Tennessee from 1790 to 1792.
State

SUMNER COUNTY
Gallatin vicinity
CRAGFONT
About 5 miles west of Gallatin off Tenn. 25
Early 19th century

Gray stone was employed to build this northern Tennessee Georgian residence. Fenestration is even on the facade, but there are no windows on the gable ends. From the rear of the house a two-story, T-shaped wing extends the length of seven bays, and there is a two-story porch or gallery on each side of the wing. The wing houses the dining room and kitchen. General James Winchester, the builder, was a Revolutionary War soldier, speaker of the Tennessee senate, and a founder of Memphis.
State

SUMNER COUNTY
Hendersonville vicinity
ROCK CASTLE
Southeast of Hendersonville on Indian Lake Road
1784–1791

Daniel Smith, a native of Virginia who migrated westward to Tennessee in 1783, built Rock Castle. The house is a vernacular interpretation of styles popular concurrently on the Eastern seaboard. Limestone is the basic building material, and the exterior stonework is excellent. Some of the original mortar has been improperly repointed with concrete. There are no windows in the ends of the main house except small attic lights. In the 1850's the Greek Revival, two-story portico was added to the main facade, but the dentil cornice is original. Wood paneling and wood graining on the inside are well executed. The only remaining outbuilding is the stone smokehouse which has been moved.
State
HABS

WASHINGTON COUNTY
Johnson City vicinity
TIPTON-HAYNES HOUSE
Southeast of Johnson City on U.S. 19 W.
18th and 19th centuries

John Tipton, a native of Maryland, came to Tennessee in 1783–1784 and built a two-story log house which became the nucleus of a large farm complex. The house was expanded in the 19th century by David Haynes, the second owner, and his son Landon Carter Haynes. A long, one-story ell covered with weatherboards was added to the main house. Its interior walls are made of wood studs with wood finish, and the floors are of hand hewn joists covered with pine boards. Landon Haynes built the nearby law office. Plans for the development of a living farm have effected the restoration and/or reconstruction of a double-crib barn, still, springhouse, smokehouse, and pigsty.
State

WASHINGTON COUNTY
Jonesboro
JONESBORO HISTORIC DISTRICT
Bounded roughly by College Street, Sabin Avenue, and properties fronting on Main Street on the north; by Franklin Avenue and Depot Street on the south; by Second Avenue, Oak Grove Avenue, and private property on the west; and by private property on the east
18th and 19th centuries

Jonesboro, county seat of Washington County, is the oldest town in Tennessee (established, 1779). The constitutional convention and early legislative sessions for the state of Franklin (now east Tennessee) were held here until 1785. Of the 152 structures located within the historic district, 72 were judged worthy of preservation. Four distinct architectural styles survive in Jonesboro's historic district, although one, Italianate, tends to predominate. The other three styles are Federal (Chester Inn, Robert May House, Three Sisters House), Greek Revival (Baptist church, Methodist church, and Presbyterian church), and Gothic Revival (Irwin House). An example of Italianate architecture is the Epps House. Italianate porches have been added to buildings of other styles. Overall the residences in the historic district exhibit a unity of type, color, height, texture, and setting.
Multiple public/private

WILLIAMSON COUNTY
Franklin
RAINEY-LAWRENCE HOUSE
244 1st Avenue South
1839

The Rainey-Lawrence House is a one-and-one-half-story brick cottage with Greek Revival features. The windows have side panels of framed glass separated from the main sashes by fluted pilasters. Sidelights and a transom surround the front door which is sheltered by a modified Greek portico. The interior architrave has fluted door and window jambs with ball discs at the corners. The floors, wood trim, doors, and mantels are original. The house was built by Robert Rainey, a Franklin mechanic who later became one of the town's leading merchants, and it is one of the least altered of its period in Franklin.
Private

WILLIAMSON COUNTY
Franklin vicinity
FRANKLIN BATTLEFIELD
South of Franklin on U.S. 31
1864

At Franklin on November 30, 1864, Confederate General John B. Hood shattered the Confederate Army of Tennessee by his uncoordinated attacks on a strongly-posted Union force. The battle marked the failure of Hood's Tennessee campaign, the final defeat coming two and a half weeks later at Nashville. The area south of town, where Hood's troops assembled, is still largely unchanged. The Carter House, which bears the marks of bullets and shells, has been restored.
Private
NHL

Tennessee State Capitol, Nashville, Tennessee. *John Stroud*

Texas

Mission Concepcion, San Antonio, Texas.
Texas State Historical Survey Committee

John Bremond House,
Bremond Block
Historic District,
Austin, Texas
*Texas State Historical
Survey Committee*

McFaddin House Complex,
Beaumont, Texas.
*Texas State Historical
Survey Committee*

Earle-Napier-Kinnard House, Waco, Texas.
Texas State Historical Survey Committee

Officer's Quarters,
Fort Davis National Historic Site,
Fort Davis, Texas. *NPS*

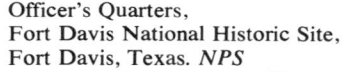

ARANSAS COUNTY
Rockport
MATHIS, THOMAS H., HOUSE
612 Church Street
1867

The Mathis House, late Greek Revival in style, is a one-story frame cottage set on a raised brick basement. Its foundation is arcaded, and the house is reached by a flared staircase. There are square fluted wooden columns on the entrance portico repeated by the corner pilasters on the main facade. The cornice has a bracketed entablature with panels between the brackets. A low, hip roof covers the house. Thomas H. Mathis had large scale ranching and agricultural holdings in three counties as well as shipping and real estate interests. He engaged in road and bridge construction and served as president and principal stockholder of the National Bank of Rockport.
Private; not accessible to the public
HABS

ARMSTRONG COUNTY
Palo Duro vicinity
J A RANCH
Palo Duro Canyon
1879–1889

Charles Goodnight, soldier, plainsman, and pioneer cattleman of the Staked Plains, influenced the pattern by which, in the years after the Civil War, the open range cattle industry developed. The first rancher in the Texas Panhandle, he blazed several of the important cattle trails of the West. By 1900, he was recognized for his scientific breeding of range cattle. Goodnight managed the J A Ranch from 1879 to 1889, during which time it grew to encompass 700,000 acres of grassland subsisting 40,000 head of cattle. Still an active concern, the ranch possesses its original flavor, with some of the 1879 buildings still standing.
Private; not accessible to the public
NHL

BASTROP COUNTY
Bastrop
ALLEN-BELL HOUSE
1408 Church Street
c. 1855

The Allen-Bell House is a late Greek Revival residence distinguished by its unusual exterior wall sheathing. Walls are covered with vertical board and batten siding, and the battens are joined, both top and bottom, by arch-like cuts in the facia. One story in height, the house was originally L-shaped, but the later addition of a rear wing produced a V-shaped house, the center of which was eventually filled in completely. A portico covers the central entrance. It has four square columns with plinth bases and inset panels which repeat the design of the board and batten sheathing. The columns support a plain entablature and a box cornice.
Private; not accessible to the public

BASTROP COUNTY
Hills Prairie vicinity
HILL, ABRAHAM WILEY, HOUSE
5 miles southwest of Hills Prairie
1855

The Abraham Wiley Hill House is an excellent example of late Greek Revival domestic architecture in Texas. The two-story frame house has a gable roof and a two-story hexastyle portico on the main facade. Resting upon brick bases, the portico columns are tall and slender, emphasizing the vertical. Fluted pilasters mark all four corners of the house, and three of the four original brick chimneys still stand. The three-panel double front doors are flanked by plain wooden pilasters, and the entablature above repeats that of the main house. Abraham Hill (1816–1884) fought in the war for Texas independence and took part in the battle of San Jacinto (April 21, 1836).
Private; not accessible to the public
HABS

BEXAR COUNTY
San Antonio
THE ALAMO
Alamo Plaza
1718

Mission San Antonio de Valero was established by Spanish Franciscan friars in 1718, and construction of the present chapel was begun in 1744. Abandoned as a mission in 1793, it thereafter served intermittently as a fortress and military depot. Its primary significance came from the Texan Revolution battle on March 6, 1836, when Lieutenant Colonel William B. Travis' force of 188 men was annihilated. The group, which included James Bowie and Davy Crockett, was attempting to defend San Antonio against Mexican President Santa Anna's army of approximately 3,000. The battle cost Santa Anna many casualties and delayed his invasion for two weeks, thus providing a rallying point for Texas independence and valuable time for remaining Texan forces to organize their defenses. The Texans went on to victory with the cry, "Remember the Alamo!"
State
NHL; HABS

BEXAR COUNTY
San Antonio
EDWARD H. WHITE II MUSEUM
(HANGAR NINE)
Brooks Air Force Base
1918

Hangar Nine, now called the Edward H. White II Museum, is thought to be the oldest extant aircraft hangar at any United States military base. The federal government built Brooks Field during the final year of World War I as a training school for military aviators. It was first occupied for training on January 17, 1918, and all primary flight training took place here until 1928, when a second such center was established in California. The present frame hangar has a low bolted wood truss roof of modified gambrel form. Large sliding wooden doors open to the full width of the building. Edward H. White, father of Edward H. White II, the first American to walk in space, completed his flight training here in June, 1930. The hangar has been renamed in honor of the astronaut, who was born in San Antonio.
Federal

BEXAR COUNTY
San Antonio
ESPADA AQUEDUCT
Espada Road, just east of U.S. 281S
1731–1745

The Espada Dam, *Acéquia*, and Aqueduct were once a part of an integrated irrigation system that served the five missions in the San Antonio area. The remaining five-mile section begins at the Espada Dam on the San Antonio River in Mission Park Cemetery and parallels the river southward. In use from 1731 to 1745, the aqueduct is the only Spanish structure of its type remaining in the United States. The system, which is still functioning, illustrates the role of the Spanish missions in the agricultural history of the Southwest.
Private
NHL

BEXAR COUNTY
San Antonio
MISSION CONCEPCION
807 Mission Road
1731–1735

The Mission Nuestra Señora de la Purisima Concepción de Acuña was founded by Franciscan friars in east Texas, but conflict with the French and the Indians caused its transfer to San Antonio in 1731. The massive church building, designed in the Mexican Baroque style, features a broad western facade and massive twin bell towers. Mission Concepción, best preserved of all the Texas mission

units, has a full cruciform ground plan with altars in the north and south transepts as well as in the sanctuary at the east end. Original frescoes adorn some of the interior walls. The mission was secularized in 1793, and the church was completely abandoned by 1819. It was not used again for religious purposes until 1887. With the exception of minor repairs, the church and much of the adjacent convent remain as they were in the 18th century.
Private
NHL; HABS

BEXAR COUNTY
San Antonio
SAN JOSE MISSION NATIONAL HISTORIC SITE
6519 San Jose Drive
1720

Mission San Jose y San Miguel de Aguayo was established in 1720 by Captain Juan Valdez, lieutenant general of the Province of Texas, at the urging of Franciscan Fray Antonio Margil de Jesus. Throughout the 18th century the mission flourished, with a complex of buildings including Indian quarters, barracks, convents, mill and granary, carpenter shop, and blacksmith shop. Today the mission is regarded as an important example of Spanish mission architecture. It is an active church in the community.
Multiple public/private
NPS; 4.13 acres
HABS

BEXAR COUNTY
San Antonio
SPANISH GOVERNOR'S PALACE
105 Military Plaza
18th century

The Spanish Governor's Palace is the only remaining example of an aristocratic 18th-century Spanish residence in Texas. Although the exact date of construction is not known, the keystone over the elaborately carved main door bears the arms of the Hapsburgs and the date 1749. The palace served as headquarters and residence for the captain of the San Antonio de Bexar presidio, who was the ranking representative of the King of Spain in the absence of the governor, hence the name. The palace is U-shaped, and a rear wall encloses the central open area. Lime-plastered stone walls, which are three-feet thick, rise in a parapet above a flat roof. Considerably altered over the years, the Palace was restored in 1929-1930.
Municipal
NHL

BEXAR COUNTY
San Antonio
U.S. SAN ANTONIO ARSENAL
Bounded by S. Flores Street on the west, E. Arsenal Street on the south, the San Antonio River on the east, and private property on the north
1859-1949

The present arsenal complex contains six buildings which were constructed at various times. These are an office building, begun in 1858 and finished in 1860; the magazine, second building constructed on the grounds; the commanding officer's quarters, an Italianate house of the 1880's; the servants' quarters behind the commandant's house; a stable; and a storehouse. Confederate troops held the arsenal during the Civil War. After the war it reverted to federal control as a major supply base for the western frontier. The arsenal was operative in both World Wars.
Federal
HABS

BEXAR COUNTY
San Antonio
URSULINE CONVENT
300 Augusta Street
Mid-19th century

The Ursuline Academy of San Antonio was the result of concerted efforts to revitalize the Catholic Church in Texas. This effort was spearheaded by the Reverend John Mary Odin, vicar apostolic to Texas and later archbishop of New Orleans. Father Odin established a convent at Galveston in 1847, and four years later he brought a group of Ursulines to San Antonio. The school opened shortly thereafter. Buildings in the Academy complex are the first academy building, a two-story, *pise de terre* edifice building made of caliche (a calcium carbonate surface material); an addition to the academy building, a two-story, rectangular structure with a hip roof; a dormitory of masonry with hip roof, dormer window, a two-story gallery on the north facade, and surmounted by a square clock tower; a workshop and laundry; and the priest's house of late (1882) Gothic Revival style. Another cluster of buildings to the north has been demolished.
Private; not accessible to the public
HABS

BLANCO COUNTY (also in Gillespie County)
Johnson City
LYNDON B. JOHNSON NATIONAL HISTORIC SITE

The Lyndon B. Johnson National Historic Site contains two properties connected

with the early life of the thirty-sixth President of the United States: the site of his birth on the bank of the Pedernales River on August 27, 1908, and the house in Johnson City where he lived from 1914 until 1924. An approximate replica of the birthplace farmhouse has been reconstructed on the site of the original, and both it and the boyhood home have been furnished with Johnson family heirlooms. Both are open to the public.
Federal
NPS; 8.57 acres

BOWIE COUNTY
Texarkana
OFFENHAUSER INSURANCE BUILDING
State Line Avenue and 3rd Street
1901

The Offenhauser Insurance Building is an important commercial structure in downtown Texarkana. Frederick Wilhelm Offenhauser moved to Texas from Illinois as an employee of C. E. Hayden & Company. He also took a position with an insurance firm and eventually, in partnership with another man, opened his own business. After 1890 the name was F. W. Offenhauser & Company. The building is a three-story brick structure with inset, arcaded walkways on the north and west sides. A late 1870's bank building was incorporated into the newer building. Windows on the second and third floors have segmental brick arches and concrete lintels. The most unusual elevation faces east. It has two parallel sections which are not in the same plane but are connected by an oblique and angled wall.
Private

CAMERON COUNTY
Brownsville
FORT BROWN
1846, 1868

To establish its own advance position and thwart a Mexican attack during the Mexican War, General Zachary Taylor's army constructed large bastioned earthworks in March 1846 on the north side of the Rio Grande opposite Matamoros, Mexico. During the 1850's Fort Brown kept check on border disputes and protected Brownsville from hostile Indians. During the Civil War it played a key role in the contest for Brownsville, which was occupied by both Union and Confederate troops. Today mounds of earth define the outlines of the original earthen fort. Remodeling of the 1868 buildings has somewhat lessened the historical authenticity of the second Fort Brown.
Multiple public/private
NHL

CAMERON COUNTY
Brownsville
RESACA DE LA PALMA
BATTLEFIELD
> North edge of Brownsville on Parades
> Line Road
> 1846

The engagement between General Zachary Taylor's American forces and the Mexican Army, begun at Palo Alto, continued the next day, May 9, 1846, at Resaca de la Palma. The Mexicans were defeated and retreated across the Rio Grande, ending the military action in Texas in the Mexican War.
Private
NHL

CAMERON COUNTY
Brownsville vicinity
PALO ALTO BATTLEFIELD
> Junction of Farm Roads 1847 and
> 511, 6.3 miles north of Brownsville
> 1846

The battle of Palo Alto was the first of two important battles of the Mexican War fought on American soil. On May 8, 1846, General Zachary Taylor engaged the Mexican Army at Palo Alto in the first sizable battle of the war. The Mexican retreat toward the Rio Grande demonstrated the superiority of American arms, gained the United States prestige at home and abroad, and cleared the way for the invasion of Mexico. The site, still used as pasture land, has not changed materially since 1846.
Private; not accessible to the public
NHL

CHEROKEE COUNTY
Alto vicinity
GEORGE C. DAVIS SITE
> About 6 miles southwest of Alto on
> Tex. 21
> 700–1300

The George C. Davis Site is one of the major aboriginal sites in North America. It consists of two temple mounds, one burial mound, and the remains of an extensive village. The site was culturally affiliated with the Mississippian tradition, which is characterized by intensive agriculture, large, well-organized villages, flat-topped pyramids and the presence of many objects of skilled manufacture. Archeologists have found numerous artifacts at Davis, mostly fragments of earthenware vessels and simple lithic tools. The discovery of materials foreign to the Davis area (marine shells, copper, high quality flint, novaculite and galena) indicates that the occupants of the village had contact with groups in other locales.
State/private; not accessible to the public

COMAL COUNTY
New Braunfels
KLEIN, STEPHEN, HOUSE
> 131 S. Seguin Street
> 1846

Stephen Klein was one of many German immigrants to Texas in the 1840's. His one-story plus loft, stuccoed, *fachwerk* home has timber framing and limestone walls. There is a full width inset porch on the front and a lean-to at the rear. The tin roof is a modern replacement.
Private; not accessible to the public

COMAL COUNTY
New Braunfels
LINDHEIMER HOUSE
> 489 Comal Avenue
> c. 1852

The one-story plus loft Lindheimer House is *fachwerk* construction covered by stucco. *Fachwerk* is of medieval origin and employs a heavy timber frame with diagonal bracing. In this instance limestone rubble was used to fill the spaces. Such houses, lacking ornament, were frequently built by German emigrants. Ferdinand Lindheimer was a botanist and painter, and he incorporated a print shop into the rear of the house.
Private
HABS

CONCHO COUNTY
Paint Rock vicinity
PAINT ROCK INDIAN PICTOGRAPH
SITE
> 1 mile northwest of Paint Rock off
> U.S. 83
> Pre-Columbian to 18th century

Paint Rock is the most outstanding and extensive pictograph site in central Texas. The paintings appear along 1,000 feet of a limestone bluff on the north bank of the Concho River. Most figures are small (less than one foot high) and seem to have been painted individually rather than as part of a single large mural. Geometric shapes, animal and human figures, negative and positive hand prints are the subjects, and colors used are red, orange, yellow, black, and white.
Private; not accessible to the public

CROCKETT COUNTY
Sheffield vicinity
FORT LANCASTER
> 10 miles east of Sheffield on U.S. 290
> 1855–1860

Fort Lancaster was erected on Texas' western frontier to provide protection for settlers and travelers enroute to Califor-

nia. Strategically located in the Pecos River Valley, the fort was also situated on the old military road running between San Antonio and El Paso. The original portable shelters at the fort had been replaced by stone and adobe buildings by 1860. Ruins of 29 of these structures can be identified today, and the most prominent is the chimney of a soldiers' barracks. Fort Lancaster was abandoned in 1861, when Texas seceded from the Union. For a brief time in 1861 and 1862 the fort served as a Confederate garrison. It was abandoned until 1871 and reactivated then due to a Kiowa-Comanche uprising. Following cessation of the Indian troubles the fort was permanently closed (1873–1874).
State; not accessible to the public

DE WITT COUNTY
Cuero
DE WITT COUNTY COURTHOUSE
> Bounded by N. Gonzales, E. Live
> Oak, N. Clinton, and E. Courthouse
> Streets
> 1896, A. O. Watson

This three-story Richardsonian Romanesque courthouse was constructed of rusticated sandstone. It is basically square with four corner pavilions and a six-story tower. The main facade consists of a recessed, triple-bay section between flanking pavilions united by a connecting arcaded one-story porch. Squat clustered columns on the porch have Romanesque capitals and large connecting arches with rusticated voussoirs. All projecting corners have decorative quoins of narrow stones.
County

EL PASO COUNTY
El Paso
CHAMIZAL NATIONAL MEMORIAL
> 1848–1963

Chamizal National Memorial, established according to the provisions of the Chamizal Treaty of 1963, provides a memorial to the long history of cooperation between the United States and Mexico. Under the terms of the treaty, the Rio Grande, the international boundary between the two countries, is being re-routed to place all Mexican territory south of the river. The project will hopefully end the meandering of the river in the vicinity of El Paso, Texas. During the past 150 years it has flowed in innumerable channels, moving steadily south into Mexico. Each change of course has created problems for a stable international boundary. The memorial will feature not only the diplomatic and technical history of the settlement, but also international cultural and theatrical productions.
Federal; not accessible to the public
NPS; 55 acres

EL PASO COUNTY
El Paso
MAGOFFIN HOMESTEAD
1120 Magoffin Avenue
1875

The Magoffin Homestead is a one-story, U-shaped adobe house built around a central patio. An unusual feature is the elaborate wooden Victorian detailing on the windows and doors. Windows and doors (on the front wing) have pedimented lintels, and the pediments and returns are formed by a generous cyma reversa molding. There are flat, facia-board pilasters on each side of the openings. The principal entrance (north side) has double doors with a glazed upper panel and a molded, solid lower panel. This design is repeated in the sidelights. Joseph Magoffin (1837–1923), who built the house, was a successful businessman interested in street railways and public utilities and active in local and county politics.
Private; not accessible to the public

FAYETTE COUNTY
Winedale
WINEDALE INN COMPLEX
Off FM 1457
19th century

The Winedale Inn was first built (c. 1834) as a one-room frame structure with a loft. Sometime around 1850 the building was doubled in size. The loft was converted to a full second story, an identical section was added to the north, and a two-story gallery was constructed across the front. Inside the eight-room inn there are painted and stenciled motifs on the walls and ceilings. Other buildings in the complex are a log smokehouse and kitchen moved onto the property to replace the original ones; the Foursquare Barn, two double log houses under one roof; Hazel's Lone Oak, a one-story plus loft dogtrot house; the Theater Barn; the Lauderdale House, a 19th-century residence converted to a dormitory; the innkeeper's house; and the MacGregor House, a two-story late Greek Revival residence.
State

FISHER COUNTY
Noodle vicinity
STEADMAN, FOY, SITE
8.5 miles northwest of Noodle
Prehistoric

The Foy Steadman Site is one of four known Folsom occupation sites in America. Artifacts uncovered to date include Folsom points, scrapers, gravers, bifaces, and various types of flint flakes. The dates of similar artifacts from other sites suggest a possible occupation date of 8,000 to 10,000 years ago. Much of the 50–acre site has been utilized for farming and grazing. Located on the western section are the remains of a playa lake or low marshy area. It is hoped that archeological, geological, and paleontological studies will yield sufficient data to indicate the appearance of the site during the Folsom occupation.
Private; not accessible to the public

GALVESTON COUNTY
Galveston
ASHBEL SMITH BUILDING, OLD RED
914–916 Avenue B
1891

Old Red, or the Ashbel Smith Building, was the first medical school building of the University of Texas. Although the state approved the medical school in 1881, this building was not constructed for ten years, at which time it opened in conjunction with the John Sealy Hospital (1888–1889). Old Red is Romanesque Revival. The three-story brick edifice is topped by a hexagonal sectional roof. After the 1900 hurricane the original roof was replaced by the present ridge roof.
Public
HABS

GALVESTON COUNTY
Galveston
ASHTON VILLA (EL MINA SHRINE TEMPLE)
2328 Broadway
1858

Originally built as Ashton Villa by Colonel J. M. Brown, the Temple served as headquarters for the Confederate army and later the Union army after the battle of Galveston Bay. Brown was a prominent railroadman and later a purchasing agent in Mexico for the Confederacy. The three-story, Italian, brick structure has an overhanging cornice supported by ornate coupled brackets. There is a projecting central portico and the openings are crowned by carved lintels. During the 1890's a large wing was added to the east and later additions were made at the rear. The home was purchased by the Shriners in 1928, and it has been used as a meeting place ever since.
Private

GALVESTON COUNTY
Galveston
BISHOP'S PALACE (GRESHAM HOUSE)
1402 Avenue J (Broadway)
1887–1893, Nicholas J. Clayton

The Chateauesque Galveston Bishop's Palace was built for Walter Gresham, lawyer, legislator, and U.S. Congressman. This elaborate limestone dwelling has an unusual skyline formed by jutting towers, dormers, and gables. Round and polygonal bays project from all sides, and window and door trim is granite and sandstone. The most decorative stonework is concentrated near the roof line, and large cast iron griffins and stone finials cap the apexes of the glazed tile roof. In 1923 the Galveston-Houston diocese of the Roman Catholic Church purchased the house, which subsequently served as a bishop's residence.
Private
HABS

GALVESTON COUNTY
Galveston
SEALY, GEORGE, HOUSE
2424 Broadway
1887–1890

George Sealy was a wealthy Galveston banker, railroad entrepreneur, and businessman who had come to Texas from Pennsylvania in 1857. His spacious residence was designed in the neo-Renaissance style, two-and-one-half stories high with a full basement and hip roof. The exterior brick of the house is faced with a lighter, buff-colored brick, and sandstone blocks are used as accents. An arcade-like front gallery serves as an entrance porch leading up to the ornate four-paneled front doors. The tall brick chimneys consist of several flues combined into one stack, and the roof is tile. A Romanesque brick carriage house next to the main dwelling was erected in 1891 and served as a stable.
Private; not accessible to the public
HABS

GALVESTON COUNTY
Galveston
THE STRAND HISTORIC DISTRICT
Bounded on the north by Avenue A, on the east by 20th Street, on the south by an alley separating Avenues C and D, and on the west by the railroad passenger depot
1850–1900

The Strand was the principal commercial area of Galveston in the second half of the 19th century. Galveston entrepreneurs such as John Henry Hutchings, J. J. Hendley, Henry Rosenberg, and John

Sealy began buying property and constructing buildings in the decade before the Civil War. Galveston recovered rapidly from the war and by the 1870's was the Gulf terminus for the Missouri Pacific and the Atchison, Topeka, & Santa Fe railroads. A second building boom ensued, and the port of Galveston continued to grow. Architecture of the Strand encompasses Greek Revival, Beaux Arts, Gothic, and High Victorian styles. Notable buildings are the First National Bank, the J. S. Brown Building, the Old Sealy Building, the Merchants' Mutual Insurance Company, and the Washington Hotel.
Multiple public/private

GALVESTON COUNTY
Galveston
U.S. CUSTOMHOUSE (OLD GALVESTON CUSTOMHOUSE)
Southeast corner of 20th and Post Office (Avenue E) Streets
1858–1861, Ammi B. Young

Galveston was the leading 19th-century seaport and commercial center in Texas. Trade goods for Texas, Indian Territory, and parts of New Mexico and Louisiana were procured here. The Customhouse was a necessary offshoot of such business activity. Its rectangular brick walls are graced by a projecting double gallery on the west and inset double galleries on the north and south. The columns of the ground level are Ionic, and those above are Corinthian. All exterior ornament —columns, cornices, balustrades, dentils, entablature, and window architraves—is iron, cast in New York according to the architect's specifications.
Federal
HABS

GILLESPIE COUNTY
LYNDON B. JOHNSON NATIONAL HISTORIC SITE
Reference—see Blanco County

GILLESPIE COUNTY
Fredericksburg
FREDERICKSBURG HISTORIC DISTRICT
A 12–block-long section extending west from the confluence of Baron's and Town Creeks and about 4 blocks wide
Mid- and late 19th century

In 1842 an association of German noblemen was organized to encourage and finance German emigration to the Republic of Texas. Called the Adelsverein (or simply Verein), the group purchased land on the Comal River and founded the settlement of New Braunfels in 1845. A

second tract was acquired, and the following May the first settlers arrived, after a 16–day journey from New Braunfels, at the site of present-day Fredericksburg. The new town was named for Prince Frederick of Prussia, a member of the Adelsverein. Early structures were formed of logs and hides and later more permanent ones were built of stone and timber. In 1848 Fredericksburg became the county seat, and the population rose from 754 in 1850 to 2,703 by 1860. The present Vereins-Kirche is a 1930 reconstruction of an 1846 octagonal church destroyed in 1896. Most dwellings are masonry, either limestone ashlar or rubble. *Fachwerk* (heavy timber with wattle and daub nogging) buildings were common, and a good example is the Kammalach House (1873). The typical home was one-and-one-half stories with a front porch and rear ell and stood close to the street. Farmers in outlying areas often maintained Sunday houses or town residences. The present population is 5,000, and German is spoken.
Multiple public/private

GILLESPIE COUNTY
Fredericksburg
FREDERICKSBURG MEMORIAL LIBRARY (McDERMOTT BUILDING, GILLESPIE COUNTY COURTHOUSE)
Courthouse Square
1881–1882, Alfred Giles

The Gillespie County commissioners held a competition to select the best plan for a new courthouse, and San Antonio architect Alfred Giles won. The H-shaped limestone structure was designed with entrances on all four facades. Excellence of craftsmanship is evident in the elaborate heavy cornice with its large scroll-shaped modillions, in the ornamental ironwork along the roof, and in the four columned porches on each facade topped by delicate cast iron balustrades. Heavy double doors with raised panels set in molding were designed for the entrances and the upstairs courtroom. Copper locks and doorknobs were engraved with a hummingbird design. A new courthouse was completed in 1939, and the old one became an office building. It has recently been restored and houses the library and community meeting hall.
County

GOLIAD COUNTY
Goliad vicinity
PRESIDIO NUESTRA SENORA DE LORETO DE LA BAHIA
1 mile south of Goliad State Park on U.S. 183
1749

Presidio Loreto was moved from the Guadalupe River to its present site in 1749 in order that its garrison of Spanish soldiers could protect the nearby missions of Nuestra Señora del Espiritu Santo de Zuniga and Nuestra Señora del Rosario. Strategically located on the route linking the province of Texas with the rest of Mexico, the presidio was important in revolutionary efforts against Spain and later against Mexico. It was captured in 1812 by the Gutierrez-Magee expedition, a force of filibusterers organized in the United States who were fighting for Mexican independence. During the Texan Revolution, it was the headquarters for the command of Colonel James Walker Fannin. Nearby, after Fannin had surrendered to Mexican forces, he and 342 of his men were executed under direct orders of Mexican President Santa Anna on March 27, 1836.
Private
NHL; HABS

GONZALES COUNTY
Gonzales
KENNARD HOUSE
621 St. Louis Street
1895

This house is one of the few extant Queen Anne style dwellings in the state. An unusual mosaic of bright glass and pottery chips has been utilized in the pediments of the roof gables. Massing is irregular, and the high pitched roof has gabled ells. The two-story central front portico has shingled Romanesque arches on the first floor and an open colonnaded gallery above. A tall, three-story tower stands to the left of the entrance. It possesses a shingled Romanesque arcaded belvedere and a six-sided pyramidal roof.
Private; not accessible to the public.

GONZALES COUNTY
Gonzales vicinity
BRACHES HOME
12 miles southeast of Gonzales on U.S. 90 Alt.
1839–1842

The Braches Home was built by Bart McClure, first county judge of Gonzales County. It is a large two-story plus attic frame Greek Revival structure with an inset five-bay, two-story gallery across the

main facade. Columns of the gallery are square with edge molding strips and capitals. The entablature above the gallery contains a recessed architrave, and the balustrade at the second-floor level has stick balusters. A subsequent owner of the house, Charles Braches, represented Gonzales County in the lower house of the seventh congress of the Republic of Texas. Chimneys have been removed and the front doors replaced, but restoration work is planned.
Private; not accessible to the public

GUADALUPE COUNTY
Seguin
ERSKINE HOUSE NO. 1 (HOLLAMON HOUSE)
902 N. Austin Street
1855

This house, named for Michael Erskine, a Guadalupe County judge, is a two-story frame building with a series of one-story frame additions at the west side. The additions incorporate a one-story, stuccoed limestone structure, probably an outbuilding. The main house has a gable roof and an inset double gallery with five simple wooden posts and a wooden railing.
Private; not accessible to the public
HABS

GUADALUPE COUNTY
Seguin
SEBASTOPOL (ZORN HOUSE)
Northeast corner of W. Court and N. Erkel Streets
1850–1855

Sebastopol was built by Colonel J. W. Young for his sister Catherine LeGette. The house is unique in construction because it has a large, square water reservoir on the roof which provided insulation in winter and cooled the house in summer. Architectural detail includes square porch columns with molded capitals and bases as well as paneled double front doors with four lights above each panel, sidelights, and a transom. The house is concrete, T-shaped, and rests upon a raised basement.
Private

HALE COUNTY
Plainview
PLAINVIEW SITE
.5 mile west of the junction of U.S. 70 and 87
c. 7000 B.C.

Archeological excavations at the Plainview Site first demonstrated the antiquity of a specific kind of spear point commonly found on the surface throughout the plains region. Found with the bones of an extinct bison species, these points are associated with an early hunting group of Indians.
Private; not accessible to the public
NHL

HARRIS COUNTY
Houston
1884 HOUSTON COTTON EXCHANGE BUILDING
202 Travis Street
1884, Eugene Heiner

Houston became an important collection point for interior cotton during the early 1800's. In June of 1877 the local cotton men chartered the Houston Cotton Exchange and Board of Trade. Eugene Heiner was selected as architect for their new building. The structure, of red pressed brick, is elaborately decorated with white sandstone coping and trim and has arched windows, pilasters which run the height of the building, and a bracketed cornice capped by a plain brick parapet. In 1910 the fourth floor was added and the central entrance moved to one side.
Private; not accessible to the public

HARRIS COUNTY
Houston vicinity
SAN JACINTO BATTLEFIELD
22 miles east of Houston on Tex. 134
1836

On April 21, 1836, General Sam Houston's forces won the decisive engagement of the Texan Revolution at San Jacinto. It insured the ultimate independence of the Republic of Texas, which paved the way for annexation by the United States. This action in turn brought on the Mexican War and the acquisition by the United States of the entire Southwest and California. The dominant feature of the 500–acre area today is a 570–foot granite shaft commemorating Houston's victory. In the base of the monument is a museum of Texas history.
State
NHL

HILL COUNTY
Hillsboro
HILL COUNTY COURTHOUSE
Courthouse Square
1890, W. C. Dodson

Hill County was created in 1853, and this is the fourth courthouse to be erected. Its style is a regional version of French Second Empire. The main section of rusticated limestone is three stories high and has a seven-story central tower. Pilasters, columns, and trim around windows, doors, and cornice are banded dressed limestone. All four facades are identical, each with end pavilions and a central, raised portico. The main roof is hipped, but gable and mansard roofs cover the porticos and end pavilions. Four

---

pilasters with fanciful capitals and large brackets frame each entrance, and low relief patterns are carved in the brackets and the entablature they support.
County
HABS

HOUSTON COUNTY
Crockett
MONROE-CROOK HOUSE
707 E. Houston Street
1854

Armistead Thompson Monroe, a leading merchant of Crockett, built this one-and-one-half-story late Greek Revival cottage. It has a central hall plan with four rooms on the first floor, and a rear ell contains the kitchen. The central doorway is covered by a pedimented portico. Rather than capitals, the wooden columns of the portico have bracketed projections which form a transition at the entablature. The portico has a box cornice with bed mold and crown mold. All exterior walls are sheathed in clapboards.
County

HOUSTON COUNTY
Kennard vicinity
WESTERMAN MOUND
5.8 miles southeast of Kennard
Pre-Columbian

The country around the Westerman Mound was well-suited to the farming, hunting, and fishing of the early Caddoan peoples. This mound is attributed to them, although it does not resemble the large ceremonial centers constructed during the Alto Focus of the Gibson Aspect (800–1100 A.D.) of Caddoan culture. East of the area of the Westerman Mound are smaller ones not associated with the Gibson Aspect. Due to its affinity to the latter, the Westerman Mound may represent a special and perhaps temporal gap in the prehistory of the Neches River Valley.
Private; not accessible to the public

JACK COUNTY
Jacksboro vicinity
FORT RICHARDSON
South of Jacksboro on U.S. 281
1867

Fort Richardson was an important military post on the southwest frontier late in the period of Comanche and Kiowa Indian depredations. It blocked the path of Indian raids upon the Texas frontier or across the Rio Grande into Mexico. An 1871 massacre near Fort Richardson and the subsequent punishment of the Indian chiefs responsible created a stir on the frontier which culminated in the Red

River War of 1874. The part played by the fort and its troops in these events gave it national recognition. Several original stone buildings are extant: the commissary, bakery, guardhouse, morgue, officers' quarters, and hospital, which now houses a museum.
State
NHL

JEFF DAVIS COUNTY
Fort Davis
FORT DAVIS NATIONAL HISTORIC SITE
Junction of Tex. 17 and 118
1854

Fort Davis was established at a strategic spot in the Davis Mountains in 1854 to protect travelers on the road between San Antonio and El Paso, a section of the Overland Trail to California. With the outbreak of the Civil War, it was occupied for a few months by a small Confederate garrison and then abandoned. Reoccupied by Federal troops in 1867 and rebuilt afterwards, Fort Davis rose to peak strength and significance between 1879 and 1885. Although its men performed mostly routine duties such as patrolling, scouting, and escorting wagon trains and stage coaches, they played an important part in the 1879–1881 campaign against Chief Victorio and his Warm Springs Apaches —the last Indian war in Texas. The National Park Service has identified over 50 structures and sites, and portions of about 30 buildings have been either restored or stabilized. Seven of the surviving buildings are of cut red stone, the rest of adobe.
Federal/non-federal
NPS; 460 acres
HABS

JEFFERSON COUNTY
Beaumont
FRENCH HOME TRADING POST
2995 French Road
1845

John Jay French, a merchant and tanner, came to Texas from New York in the 1830's. He built this house for his family and used the large upstairs room as a trading post or store. The two-story frame residence has a gable roof, a shed-roofed front gallery, and an attached lean-to at the rear. Both front and rear doors are paneled and double with seven light sidelights. The chimney on the north side is not original. In addition to the trading post, French operated a tannery and mills for corn and grain.
Private

JEFFERSON COUNTY
Beaumont
McFADDIN HOUSE COMPLEX
1906 McFaddin
1906, Henry Conrad Mauer

Massiveness, irregularity of silhouette, and the combining of unrelated architectural details characterize the McFaddin House. Two stories high plus an attic, the house has a square plan with central projecting ells on each side. The hip roof has a balustraded deck, dormers with finials, gabled ells, and wide eaves supported by simple brackets. Stretching across the front of the house and about one-third of the way back on each side is a one-story, wraparound gallery with Ionic columns. Superimposed over this porch is a colossal Ionic portico with paired columns. Its entablature has a frieze of swags. There are decorative mullions in the doors, sidelights, and transom of the main entrance, which has an elaborate molded enframement with a segmentally arched transom and fluted pilasters. The carriage house looks like a residence except for its wide carriage door flanked by two giant bull's-eye windows.
Private; not accessible to the public

JEFFERSON COUNTY
Beaumont vicinity
LUCAS GUSHER, SPINDLETOP OIL FIELD
3 miles south of Beaumont on Spindletop Avenue
1901

The tapping of the Spindletop Oil Field by the Lucas Gusher opened the Texas Gulf coastal plain to commercial development and marked the beginning of the modern petroleum industry. By 1922 Texas was the third largest oil-producing state in the country, and by 1927, the largest. After the gusher "blew in" on January 10, 1901, a geyser of petroleum flowed uncapped for six days at an estimated rate of 75,000 barrels a day. The site is marked by a granite monument, near which are storage tanks built in 1901, a well pump, and a replica of a wooden derrick.
Private
NHL

KAUFMAN COUNTY
Terrell vicinity
PORTER, WALTER C., FARM
2 miles north of Terrell on Farm Road 986
1903

On the Walter C. Porter Farm the first cooperative farm demonstration took place on February 26, 1903. From this demonstration developed the Agricultural

Extension Service, which has influenced agriculture and rural life throughout the world. With the passage of the Smith-Lever Act of 1914, the scope of the work increased to include home economics and the betterment of rural life. Porter's sons still operate the 500–acre farm and use the original farm houses.
Private
NHL

KENEDY COUNTY (also in Kleberg, Nueces, and Willacy Counties)
Kingsville vicinity
KING RANCH
In and near Kingsville
1852

King Ranch is one of the best known cattle enterprises in the Southwest. It was founded by Richard King, who purchased a Spanish land grant of 75,000 acres on Santa Gertrudis Creek in 1852. By the middle of the 20th century, the ranch included 1,225,000 acres covering most of four counties. The largest ranch in the United States, it is still in operation and renowned for developing the Santa Gertrudis, a breed of large cattle which thrives in warm climates. The present white brick house and most of the other buildings date from 1912, although the 19th-century commissary survives.
Private
NHL

KLEBERG COUNTY
KING RANCH
Reference—see Kenedy County

LAMAR COUNTY
Paris
MAXEY, SAMUEL BELL, HOUSE
812 E. Church Street
1866–1867

The two-story, frame Maxey House is an example of a late Greek Revival residence that has architectural details heralding the Victorian style. Shaped like a square with an ell attached at the rear, the house has a hip roof with a balustraded deck. Details such as the cornice, windows, and porch are suggestive of the Victorian style. An unusual feature is the window treatment consisting of elaborate bracketed cornices with a transom-like division of the exterior shutters. Samuel Maxey (1825–1895), the original owner of the house, was a major general in the Civil War. When the war ended, Maxey returned to his home to practice law until elected to the United States Senate in 1875.
Public

LAMPASAS COUNTY
Lampasas
LAMPASAS COUNTY COURTHOUSE
Bounded by S. Live Oak, E. 4th, S.
Pecan, and E. 3rd Streets
1883, W. C. Dodson

Lampasas County, organized in 1856, has had only two courthouses. This one is Second Empire, the style W. C. Dodson employed for his other courthouses. The rectangular building has a mansard roof with a flat deck above it over the main section. All facades are ashlar, and smooth-faced ashlar is used for quoins, belt course, and window trim. Outside, the courthouse appears to have only two floors, but inside the upper level is actually divided to form a third floor. There are central projecting entrance pavilions on the northeast and southwest elevations, and the roof cornice is supported by console brackets. The tall clock tower has a mansard roof above a chamber containing louvered windows. The four clock faces have pedimented circular architraves and detached sills.
County; not accessible to the public

LAVACA COUNTY
Hallettsville
LAVACA COUNTY COURTHOUSE
Bounded by La Grange, 2nd, 3rd, and
Main Streets
1897, T. Heiner

The Lavaca County Courthouse is a Richardsonian Romanesque building strongly influenced by the Allegheny County Courthouse in Pittsburgh, Pennsylvania. The three-story building is of limestone and its plan is cruciform. The front arm of the cross is longer than the others and has an attached one-story porch with Romanesque arches. Topping the structure is a hip roof and heavy towers with pyramidal roofs and dormers flanking the side arms. A tall central tower has two-story slit-like windows with clock faces above, all contained in a tall arch. The top story of the tower has an open belvedere crowned with a four-part pyramidal roof. The courthouse has remained unaltered since its construction, except for general repairs made in 1936.
County

LAVACA COUNTY
Hallettsville
LAY-BOZKA HOUSE
205 Fairwinds
1878-1882

The Lay-Bozka House is one of a few surviving dwellings with a patterned shingle mansard roof. There is an unusual frosting of white wooden rope moldings and finials cresting the roof and roof dormers. Carpenter's lace and bead and spindle work adorn the front porch and the fanciful canopy above it. The ground story was built of locally quarried white sandstone, while the upper floor is cypress. James Lay, a Hallettsville physician, built the house.
Private; not accessible to the public

LEE COUNTY
Giddings
SCHUBERT HOUSE
183 Hampstead Street
1879

The Shubert House was built for August W. Schubert, a merchant. His two-story frame dwelling has a hip roof, corner pilasters, and a two-story, flat-roofed, two bay projecting porch. Four slender capped posts support the porch on both levels. There are sidelights and a transom around the main entrance and a dentil cornice under the eaveline. Schubert sold his home to Concordia College which owned it until 1900.
Private; not accessible to the public

LUBBOCK COUNTY
Lubbock vicinity
LUBBOCK LAKE SITE
North of Lubbock near the
intersection of Clovis Highway and
Loop 289
Pre-Columbian

The Lubbock Lake Site provided archeologists with the first material suitable for radio-carbon dating of the Folsom Complex. First excavated in 1948, 1950, and 1951, the Lubbock Lake area was a stratified kill site. At the lowest stratum were found bones of typical Pleistocene animals—muskox, mammoth, horse, camel, and bison. Stratum II contained flattened bison bones with which several characteristic Folsom points were associated. Altogether the site offers evidence of a 12,000–year period of use by men.
Municipal

MCLENNAN COUNTY
Waco
EARLE-NAPIER-KINNARD HOUSE
814 S. 4th Street
19th Century

The Earle-Napier-Kinnard House is a two-story, brick late Greek Revival mansion. The front facade is five bays wide with a three-bay attached two-story flat-roofed gallery. Evidence indicates that the one-story brick rear ell was the original portion of the house and was built by John Baylis Earle, who acquired title to the property in 1856. The exact date of construction is unknown, but in 1868 the property was conveyed to John S. Napier, who completed the house as it appears today. The Reverend D. C. Kinnard and his wife acquired the dwelling in the 1870's. In 1959 the house was restored, the back porch was enclosed, and additional bathrooms were added in that area. Today the house is operated as a house museum.
Private

MCLENNAN COUNTY
Waco
FORT HOUSE
503 E. 4th Street
Mid–19th century

The exact date of construction for the Fort House is not known, but it was built sometime between 1854 and 1868. Late Greek Revival in style, the house is two stories high and L-shaped in plan. There is a two-story, one-bay pedimented Ionic portico on the main facade, and a wide double gallery with square, classical columns extends along the rear and the ell. All windows have segmental arched brick hoodmolds, and there is a small wooden balcony above the main doorway. Colonel William Aldredge Fort was born in Alabama and came to Texas in 1854. He was a businessman who dabbled in farming and banking and owned Waco's first public transit system—a mule drawn streetcar.
Private

MCLENNAN COUNTY
Waco
WACO SUSPENSION BRIDGE
Across the Brazos River at Bridge
Street
1870

The Waco Suspension Bridge was the first bridge built across the Brazos River. It has a 475–foot span and two double cable towers of brick which have been stuccoed. Superimposed arches connect the two piers of each tower. Serving for almost 20 years as a private toll bridge, the Waco Bridge was conveyed to the city in 1889. A flood in 1885 damaged the east approach and a steel span replaced it. Most of the original crenellation and detail have been stuccoed over, but the bridge is still in use.
Municipal

MARION COUNTY
Jefferson
ALLEY-CARLSON HOUSE
501 Walker Street
Mid–19th century

The Alley-Carlson House exemplifies the mid–19th-century vernacular Greek Revival architecture of Jefferson. There are five bays on the main facade, and the centrally located entrance has two-panel, double wooden doors with sidelights and a transom. Covering three bays of the entrance is a tetrastyle portico with Greek Doric capitals. Inside, the main portion of the structure consists of a two-room, central hall block with a rear ell. A small board and batten structure behind the main house probably contained an outside kitchen and service rooms. Daniel N. Alley, builder of the house, was one of the founders of Jefferson.
Private
HABS

MARION COUNTY
Jefferson
BEARD HOUSE
212 N. Vale Street
1860–1870

The Beard House is an elaborately detailed, one-story frame residence with a low-pitched hip roof and attached front and side porches. Under the eaves is a wide box cornice with slender scroll brackets. Over the main entrance is a five-light transom, while the side entrance transom is oval and contains a unique snowflake-like carving. The porch columns are posts shaped like a Greek cross. They are smaller in scale than the house itself and their capitals are identical to the roof brackets. In 1900 the kitchen extension was added to the east wall.
Private; not accessible to the public

MARION COUNTY
Jefferson
EPPERSON-McNUTT HOUSE
409 S. Alley Street
19th century

This two-story, frame Italian villa is one of the few houses of its type in the region. It is an example of the transitory architecture which developed between the Greek Revival and the Victorian styles. Inside, on both floors, is a central hall with two rooms on each side. Benjamin H. Epperson, builder of the house, is most noted as his state's representative in the Supreme Court case of *Texas vs. White* (1869), in which it was decided that the Federal Union could not be dissolved. Thus the court declared the Civil War an act of rebellion on the part of the Confederate states.
Private
HABS

MARION COUNTY
Jefferson
EXCELSIOR HOTEL
Austin Street between Market and Vale Streets
Mid–19th century

The Excelsior Hotel has remained in continuous operation since it opened in the 1850's. It has been restored and now serves as a hotel and museum. The northeast wing is a two-story frame structure in the Classical Revival style. On the northeast (rear) elevation there is a roofed balcony with a wood railing extending the full length of the building. A two-story brick southwest wing was added in 1872.
Private
HABS

MARION COUNTY
Jefferson
JEFFERSON HISTORIC DISTRICT
Bounded roughly by Owens, Friou, Taylor, LaFayette, Market, Camp, Walnut extended, Polk, Vale, and Line Streets; and by a line parallel to and between Dixon and Walker Streets, and by a line north of and parallel to Dixon Street
19th century

Jefferson remains today much as it appeared in the 1880's. It is a quiet town of late Greek Revival residences and simple two-story commercial buildings located at the head of navigation on Cypress Bayou, a place where immigrants funneled into the interior after waiting to secure wagons, oxen, supplies, and tools. Wharves were built all along the bayou to handle the flood of river traffic; warehouses were erected, wholesale and retail stores did a booming business, and hotels were always full. After the Civil War an even greater wave of westward migration began. Steamboats were lined up at the wharves and endless wagon trains made up in Jefferson. Within the next 20 years activity virtually ceased. The railroad was not permitted to come through town, so other points of entry to the state were used, and the water level in the Red River above Shreveport became too low for steamboat traffic. Today Jefferson remains a sleepy, late 19th-century courthouse town. Most homes are one-story frame buildings with attached front porches. A few show Victorian influence (Koontz House, Bead House, Sedberry House), and the House of the Seasons is Italianate.
Multiple public/private
HABS

MARION COUNTY
Jefferson
JEFFERSON PLAYHOUSE
Northwest corner of Market and Henderson Streets
19th century

The Jefferson Playhouse was originally St. Mary's Catholic School (c. 1860) and Sinai Hebrew Synagogue (1876) when Jefferson, located on Big Cypress Bayou, was a center for passenger and commercial river traffic. The St. Mary's portion of the building is a two-story, Greek Revival structure, and the synagogue addition is done in the transitional style characteristic of the change from the late Greek Revival to the early Victorian periods. Minor interior changes and a modern rear addition were made in the structure since its abandonment as a school and synagogue.
Private
HABS

MARION COUNTY
Jefferson
THE MAGNOLIAS
209 E. Broadway
1868, 1873

The Magnolias is a one-and-one-half-story residence, strongly Greek Revival in character and indicating the popularity of this style in Texas long after its abandonment in the East. The frame residence is rectangular and has a rear ell and a five-bay front gallery. Slender, fluted, wooden Doric columns support the architrave, frieze, and cornice of the gallery. The main entrance has an unusual segmental arch-shaped one-light transom and wide paneled architrave, canted or beveled from the plane of the front facade to form a recessed opening. Two pilasters and an entablature terminate the door framing. The Magnolias was built by Dan Alley, an early Jefferson settler.
Private; not accessible to the public
HABS

MARION COUNTY
Jefferson
PERRY, CAPTAIN WILLIAM, HOUSE
Northwest corner of Walnut and Clarksville Streets
c. 1858

Captain William Perry, a native of New Hampshire, was involved in Jefferson's river trade with New Orleans. His home is a simple, rectangular frame dwelling devoid of ornament except for the area around the front door. The house has an unusual side hall plan, and the large front gable of the roof is treated as a pediment. A projecting front porch has two square columns with molded capitals, and the front door is composed of five molded

panels with a transom above. The house was moved to its present site in 1957.
Private

MARION COUNTY
Jefferson
PLANTERS BANK BUILDING
224 E. Austin Street

The Planters Bank Building is significant as one of the best remaining examples of 19th-century commercial architecture in Jefferson. It was one of the early warehouses built to handle Jefferson's booming river and railroad trade. Jefferson realtor and contractor John Speake constructed the two-story building. It has round-arched doorways on the first floor, segmental arched second-story windows, and French doors with fanlight transoms, features common to other commercial structures in the city. After 1870 it served as a bank.
Private; not accessible to the public

MARION COUNTY
Jefferson
PRESBYTERIAN MANSE
Northeast corner of Alley and Delta Streets
1839

Built as a private residence by General James Harrison Rogers, the structure was bought by the Cumberland Presbyterian Church in 1903 for use as a manse. It served in that capacity for a half century and is now a museum. The one-story frame house is considered to be the oldest home in Jefferson, A tetrastyle portico is carried around the entire building, and excellent examples of Greek Revival woodwork are visible, especially on the south portico and doorway. The principal entrance has been changed at least twice and an addition has been made to the main structure. A brick-floored porch was added to the north elevation in the last decade.
Private
HABS

MARION COUNTY
Jefferson
SEDBERRY HOUSE
211 N. Market Street
c. 1870

The Sedberry House is a Victorian version of the raised cottage common in Louisiana. It stands one story over a full raised brick basement. There is an attached porch on the main facade resting upon four brick piers with capitals. Victorian features are the tapered columns of the porch, tall narrow windows, small scroll brackets, and a steep front gable. The ornamental cast iron stairway and porch railing are of local design.
Private; not accessible to the public

MARION COUNTY
Jefferson
SINGLETON, CAPTAIN WILLIAM E., HOUSE
204 N. Soda Street
1870

The Singleton family acquired this house in 1885. Captain William E. Singleton was a Missourian who served in the Confederate Army before migrating to Texas. The frame residence is the only one of its type in Jefferson. A two-story, pedimented porch projects from the main facade. This porch and the sidelighted, paneled doors are Greek Revival features. Inside are two large rooms on either floor separated by a wide central hall. This plan evolved from earlier frontier dogtrot house.
Private; not accessible to the public
HABS

MARION COUNTY
Jefferson
U.S. POST OFFICE AND COURTS BUILDING
223 Austin Street
1888–1890

The combined Federal Courthouse and Post Office, typical of many small, period, government buildings throughout the West and Southwest, is Romanesque in style. The structure and foundations are of common bond brick, and the area which was formerly the public lobby of the post office is paved with six-inch by eight-inch marble slabs. The building is now a museum.
Private
HABS

MARION COUNTY
Jefferson
WOODS, PERRY, HOUSE (OLD LIGON PLACE)
502 Walker Street
19th century

This small frame residence has a central hall and two rooms on either side. The roof is framed as though the house were a central block flanked by end pavilions. Both pavilions have steeply pitched gabled ends with festooned bargeboards, and each contains a rounded window. The main entrance has carved double doors, transom, and sidelights and is covered by a flat-roofed portico. All windows are tall and narrow, extending from floor to ceiling.
Private; not accessible to the public
HABS

MARION COUNTY
Jefferson vicinity
FREEMAN PLANTATION HOUSE
.8 mile west of Jefferson on Route 49
c. 1850

William M. Freeman, an early Texas cotton planter and businessman, built this Greek Revival, raised cottage from materials produced on his plantation. Set on a brick basement which rises a full story above ground, the house has a central hall plan with four large chambers on each level. Interior carved paneling and woodwork are finely executed. The main entrance is reached by a broad flight of stairs rising to a tetrastyle portico supported by two-story, circular brick columns. Both house and portico are covered by a shallow hip roof. The two-story wing at the rear is an addition.
Private
HABS

MEDINA COUNTY
Castroville
CASTROVILLE HISTORIC DISTRICT
19th century

Ninety-six buildings are situated in the historic district, and all were constructed between 1844 and the 1880's. The community has a distinctly Alsatian character as most of the first settlers had emigrated from the Rhine Valley in Germany. Both railroad and industry bypassed the town, so it has not altered noticeably since the 19th century. The earliest houses were small, two-room and loft, stuccoed limestone structures with red tin or cypress shingled roofs. Kitchens were either attached at the rear under a shed roof or in a separate building. Several houses have galleries either set in under extensions of the roof or (in one-and-one-half-story residences) attached with a separate roof. Henri Castro (1786–1864), the founder of Castroville, was born in France. In 1842 he brought 27 boatloads of colonists to Texas. By 1847 the town had 700 inhabitants.
Multiple public/private
HABS

NACOGDOCHES COUNTY
Nacogdoches
OLD NACOGDOCHES UNIVERSITY BUILDING
Washington Square
1858–1859

Nacogdoches University, a non-sectarian institution of higher learning, was chartered on February 3, 1845. Only this building remains of all those originally constructed. It is a classic, temple-form Greek Revival edifice. The walls are brick,

and the main facade has a pedimented portico with four Tuscan columns. Sidelights and a transom surround the double doors of the main entrance, and the gable roof is highlighted by an octagonal, frame bell tower. The roof of the tower, an ogee curve, is topped by a carved wooden pineapple. Except for brief periods, the university remained in operation until 1895.
Municipal
HABS

NUECES COUNTY
KING RANCH
Reference—see Kenedy County

OLDHAM COUNTY
Vega vicinity
LANDERGIN MESA
East side of East Alamosa Creek, Mansfield Ranch
c. 1300–1450

The Landegin Mesa is a Panhandle culture ruin consisting of a series of buildings crowded together atop a steep-sided mesa. The Panhandle culture comprised a group of Indians showing both Plains and Pueblo influences. This is one of the largest, least damaged, and most spectacularly located ruins of this culture. It was occupied by a Plains village agricultural group which was using Pueblo architectural customs. There has been relatively little disturbance of the site.
Private; not accessible to the public
NHL

PARKER COUNTY
Weatherford
PARKER COUNTY COURTHOUSE
Courthouse Square
1884–1886, W. C. Dodson

Parker County was created in December, 1855, and this courthouse is the fourth to house the county government's offices. Built of rusticated limestone, the courthouse is a striking example of vernacular Second Empire architecture. A tall central tower is balanced by four corner pavilions with high mansard roofs. Both the central and end pavilions project slightly thus dividing the facades into five bays. The corners of the pavilions have ashlar pilasters, and the roofline has bracketed eaves.
County

POTTER COUNTY
Fritch vicinity
ALIBATES FLINT QUARRIES AND TEXAS PANHANDLE PUEBLO CULTURE NATIONAL MONUMENT
Southwest of Fritch on the Canadian River
c. 1000 B.C. to A.D. 1300

As early as 12,000 years ago Ice Age hunters were making spear points, knives, and other tools from variegated Alibates flint or agatized dolomite. Archeological excavations at the Alibates Flint Quarries indicated that they were used by Indians through late prehistoric times as a primary source of material for making tools. The Texas Panhandle Pueblo culture people, who began to occupy the area about A.D. 1300, built pueblos made of limestone slabs. Remaining today are flint chips, quarry blanks, and chipped stone artifacts.
Federal; not accessible to the public
NPS; 92.56 acres

ROBERTSON COUNTY
Calvert
HAMMOND HOUSE
Bounded by Burnet, China, Elm, and Hanna Streets
Late 1870's

The Gothic Revival Hammond House was originally built to be the Robertson County Courthouse. A crenellated parapet surrounds the low pitched roof. The plan of the two-story brick building is roughly that of a Latin cross, and the exterior is highlighted by ornamental buttresses and cast iron hoodmolds above the windows. There is a semi-attached dependency at the rear which once served as a jail, and an independent carriage house northeast of the main building. Calvert was the county seat of Robertson County from 1870 to 1879 when the town of Franklin was so designated. From 1885 until 1966 the building served as a residence.
Private

SAN AUGUSTINE COUNTY
San Augustine
CARTWRIGHT, MATTHEW, HOUSE
912 E. Main Street
1839

The Greek Revival Cartwright House was actually built for Isaac Campbell. Matthew Cartwright purchased the property in 1847. The dwelling is a rectangular, two-story structure with a five-bay facade, and a one-story portico shelters the front door. The portico columns are Doric and fluted. A very deep frieze and a narrower architrave make up the cornice, and both the architrave and the frieze are them-

selves divided. A mitered crown mold surmounts the box cornice. The extant end chimneys have inset panels and corbels. An ell, a wing, and a shed-roofed addition are attached to the main house. The one-story frame office nearby resembles the house in style; the Greek Revival school building is not original to the property.
Private; not accessible to the public

SAN AUGUSTINE COUNTY
San Augustine
CULLEN, EZEKIEL, HOUSE
207 S. Congress
1839

Ezekiel W. Cullen, lawyer, judge, and state representative, built this Greek Revival residence and occupied it for ten years. The house itself has unusual proportions, being very wide and only one story high. Four squat Doric columns support the heavy pedimented gable of the temple front. The pediment contains a wide, segmentally arched fanlight window, and there is a ballroom in the attic lighted by the gable-end fanlights and dormers in the north and south sides. Door and window moldings have bull's-eye medallions at the juncture of jamb and head.
Private
HABS

SHACKELFORD COUNTY
Albany vicinity
FORT GRIFFIN
15 miles north of Albany on U.S. 283
1867

Fort Griffin was one of a cordon of forts along the western frontier erected to protect settlers and provide troop escorts for the mail and for cattle drives. It became one of the most active forts in the Texas Panhandle, serving as a supply depot and departure point for campaigns against the Southern Plains Indians. Plans for the construction of many stone buildings were formulated, but only five were built. Approximately 40 wooden huts (measuring 8.5 by 13 feet), designed to house four men each, were built. Two of the hut sites were excavated in 1969. Only the powder magazine, sutler's store, administration building, bakery, chimney to an officer's house, a well, and a cistern, which were built completely of stone, remain standing. After a successful campaign in 1874–1875 against the Southern Plains Indians, Fort Griffin's importance diminished and it was abandoned in 1881. A museum has recently been built on the site and further restoration is being considered.
State

SHELBY COUNTY
Center
SHELBY COUNTY COURTHOUSE
Courthouse Square
1883–1885

Shelby County was created in 1836 and named for Isaac Shelby of Tennessee. Shelbyville was the most important town and county seat until 1866, when citizens voted to move the county government to Center. This courthouse replaced an earlier wooden structure which burned in 1882. It is a two-story brick building with a gable roof and 12 wall turrets resembling chimney stacks. Two-story entrance pavilions extend outward from the north and south elevations, each flanked by rounded turrets with buttressing. Brick string courses and denticulated tables mark the wall divisions horizontally and continue around the towers. The Shelby County Courthouse is one of the five oldest in the state.
County

SMITH COUNTY
Teaselville vicinity
DEWBERRY, COLONEL JOHN, HOUSE
1 mile north of Teaselville on FM 346
1954

The Dewberry House is a two-story frame dwelling raised on brick piers. It has a low-pitched gable roof with brick chimneys at the ends. There is a one-story gallery across the rear and a double pedimented one-bay gallery supported by tiers of square wooden columns with mitered capitals on the front. Pilasters mark the corners of the house. A stick balustrade encloses the upper gallery which is surmounted by a simple entablature. The main doorway and sidelights are as wide as the inside hall to allow prevailing breezes to cool the house.
Private; not accessible to the public
HABS

TARRANT COUNTY
Fort Worth
FLATIRON BUILDING
1000 Houston Street
1907, Sanguinet and Staats

The Flatiron Building was constructed of reinforced concrete over a steel frame and is faced with brick. It has the classic division of a two-story base supporting a five-story body capped by a well-proportioned and heavily ornamented cast iron cornice. The two wide facades are divided into bays by piers which extend to the arches at the top level in the manner of Louis Sullivan. Contrasting brick lozenges and

Modernistic designs at the second-floor and top levels decorate the exterior. The influence of the Chicago School is evident. Marshall R. Sanguinet and Carl Staats designed courthouses in Fort Worth, Wichita, and Galveston, the Houston City Hall, the Dallas Public Library, and countless banks.
Private

TARRANT COUNTY
Fort Worth
GULF, COLORADO & SANTA FE RAILROAD PASSENGER STATION
1601 Jones Street
1899

The Santa Fe Depot was built at the turn of the century and symbolized the prosperity which both Fort Worth and the Santa Fe Railroad hoped they could foster in the Southwest. The building was considered a monument to transportation progress. The Santa Fe tracks had been laid to Fort Worth by 1886 in the hope of countering Houston's control of upstate trade. The station is a two-story rectangular structure of red brick with white limestone trim. The first story has limestone inserted between the brick producing a banding effect, and the lines radiate into the window voussoirs. Diaper work appears between the first and second stories and between the second-floor arched end openings.
Private

TARRANT COUNTY
Fort Worth
KNIGHTS OF PYTHIAS BUILDING
315 Main Street
1901, Sanguinet and Staats

The red brick Knights of Pythias Building or Castle Hall is reminiscent of a European guildhall. The influence of the Low Countries architecture is evident in the steep pitch of the roof and the numerous gables. A store occupies the first floor, and there is a ballroom on the third. Founded in 1864, the Knights of Pythias Fraternal Order is a benevolent organization.
Private

TARRANT COUNTY
Fort Worth
TARRANT COUNTY COURTHOUSE
Bounded by Houston, Belknap, Weatherford, and Commerce Streets
1893–1895, Gunn and Curtis

The Tarrant County Courthouse was the third such structure erected. The first courthouse burned in 1876, and the second was razed in 1894. Constructed of red Texas granite, the courthouse is four stories high with central and end pavilions

and a central, domed clock tower. The main pavilion has slender paired columns, semicircular pediments, a balcony, and a Renaissance entablature. The exterior is rusticated, except the trim which is smooth. Iron cresting crowns the two side mansard roofs.
County

TOM GREEN COUNTY
San Angelo
FORT CONCHO
South edge of San Angelo
1867

Fort Concho was established as an army post for the protection of the Texas frontier. It was strategically located at the forks of the Concho River where most of the east-west trails converged to avoid the Staked Plains to the north and the desert to the south. It was also a point of departure for almost all southern travel for the far West. Troops from the fort took part in the campaigns against the Kiowa and Comanche Indians, 1870–1875. Several of the original buildings are extant, and associated artifacts are on exhibit.
Multiple public/private
NHL

TRAVIS COUNTY
Austin
BARKER HISTORY CENTER (OLD LIBRARY), UNIVERSITY OF TEXAS
South Mall, University of Texas campus
1910–1911, Cass Gilbert

Cass Gilbert agreed to design a library for the University of Texas if there would be "utter exclusion from the building of any feature of material or of ornament indigenous or identifiable to Texas. . . ." His plan consisted of two rectangles, one a reading room and art gallery, the other, a stack area. The resulting two-story building has cream colored limestone walls and a red tile roof with wide eaves. A wide architrave carved with plants and urns in low relief surrounds the paneled double doors of the main entrance. Polychrome terra cotta archivolts containing carved fruits and flowers appear around the second-story windows. There are iron grille balconies at each of these windows, and terra cotta medallions containing zodiac signs fill the spandrels between the window arches.
State

TRAVIS COUNTY
Austin
BREMOND BLOCK HISTORIC DISTRICT
> The block bounded by W. 8th Street, Guadalupe Street, W. 7th Street, and San Antonio Street; also the west side of San Antonio Street between W. 7th and W. 8th Streets and the south side of W. 7th Street from No. 315 to No. 610 Guadalupe Street
> 1850–1898

The Bremond Block Historic District contains 13 homes in a good state of repair which are typical, individually and collectively, of a Victorian neighborhood of the mid-to late 19th century. John Bremond, from whose family the block took its name, came to Austin from Philadelphia in 1845. All the houses, except one, in the district are cream-colored limestone or brick painted white. Notable among these are the Hale-Houston and B. J. Smith houses. Both are Greek Revival residences with five-bay front galleries and Doric columns. On San Antonio Street are the Walter Bremond and Catherine Robinson houses. The former has a mansard roof, segmentally arched openings with radiating voussoirs, and a wrought iron balcony on the facade. The latter house has a double four-bay gallery with giant Ionic columns, and a dentil cornice. The North-Evans Chateau was constructed of limestone rubble and remodeled in 1894 as a late Victorian castle with a crenellated roofline, Romanesque arched arcades, rusticated masonry, a tower, and buttressed retaining walls. The Eugene Bremond House is a one-story frame dwelling; the Pierre Bremond House is late Victorian with a low pitched hip roof, a double gallery on the front, and a tower on the west side.
Multiple public/private

TRAVIS COUNTY
Austin
CARRINGTON-COVERT HOUSE
> 1511 Colorado Street
> c. 1853–1857

The two-story, white limestone Carrington-Covert House was built for Leonidas Davis Carrington. Carrington was a merchant who made money in real estate speculation. The symmetrical facade contains a paneled double door with a fanlight and a round-arched opening marked by radiating and stepped voussoirs. A low pitched hip roof covers the house, and fine stonework is evident in the quoins, flat window arches, and sills. The walls themselves are 20 inches thick. Original fireplaces and staircase were removed about 1900.
State

TRAVIS COUNTY
Austin
DRISKILL HOTEL
> 117 E. 7th Street
> 1886, Joseph N. Preston and Son

From the day of its opening the Driskill Hotel has played an integral role in the cultural and political fabric of Texas. The first of many state functions hosted in the building was the 1877 inaugural ball for Governor Sul Ross. The hotel is a four-story Romanesque Revival building constructed of pressed brick dressed with white limestone. Carved finials capping the street facades are topped with limestone busts of the hotel's builder, Jesse Lincoln Driskill, and his two sons. The interior of the building has been extensively altered.
Private

TRAVIS COUNTY
Austin
FRENCH LEGATION
> 802 San Marcos Street
> 1840–1842

In 1836 Texas declared and won independence from Mexico and established a republic. Foreign nations were then invited to send representatives and establish diplomatic relations with the new nation. In 1840 France sent Alphonse de Saligny as her chargé d' affaires. The French Legation was built by Saligny to house himself and his retinue. It is a small, square, frame building that originally had four rooms, an attic, a cellar, and a porch. A stone kitchen was constructed west of the main house.
State
HABS

TRAVIS COUNTY
Austin
GETHSEMANE LUTHERAN CHURCH
> 1510 Congress Avenue
> 1883, August Swenson

In December, 1868, the first Swedish Lutheran religious service was held in Austin, and this service was the first of its kind in the state of Texas. The same congregation built the present Gethsemane Lutheran Church, a brick structure with Gothic Revival decorative elements. A tall central bell tower contains a lancet stained glass window and is topped by an ornately carved cupola and cross. Brick for the church came from the 1852 state capitol.
State
HABS

TRAVIS COUNTY
Austin
LITTLEFIELD HOUSE
> 24th Street and Whitis Avenue
> 1893–1894, James Wahrenberger

The central hall plan of the Littlefield House is disguised by the semicircular drawing room and bedroom on the west, the wraparound double veranda on the east, and the cylindrical library with its oriel and full turret above. Everywhere irregularity and asymmetry are emphasized. Two levels of polished, blue granite columns ornament the main entrance. Other columns and the railings of the two-story veranda are cast and wrought iron. The house itself is red-brown brick with red sandstone trim. Inside, all walls of the principal rooms have a high wood wainscot capped by an eight-inch strip of ornate pressed board. In most rooms there are plaster friezes at ceiling level, and all overdoors and mantels are elaborate. Colonel George W. Littlefield, for whom the house was built, was a cattle millionaire who dabbled in banking and real estate.
State

TRAVIS COUNTY
Austin
NEILL-COCHRAN HOUSE
> 2310 San Gabriel
> 1853

The Neill-Cochran House, though built for George W. Hill by master builder Abner Cook, takes its name from two subsequent owners. Its rough limestone rubble walls contrast strikingly with the smooth Greek Revival painted wooden detail. Six huge fluted Doric columns support a full entablature above the five-bay main facade. Hallmarks of Cook's work are apparent in the sidelighted doorway with tall transom and jamb pilasters that intersect the transom and support a high entablature, and in the bundled slats of the second-floor balcony railing which form an open diamond or crow's foot balustrade.
Private

TRAVIS COUNTY
Austin
THE OLD BAKERY
> 1006 Congress Avenue
> 1876

The builder and first owner of the Old Bakery was Charles Lundberg, a Swedish immigrant. In 1895 Lundberg's widow sold the business which continued to operate in the same building until 1966. The eclectic architecture of the bakery is highlighted by the gray-white limestone voussoirs, keystones, and moldings on the

476   TEXAS

tan brick facade. Living quarters for the baker and his family were on the second floor.
Municipal

TRAVIS COUNTY
Austin
OLD LAND OFFICE BUILDING
108 E. 11th Street
1857, Conrad C. Stremme

The Texas Land Office contains original maps, field notes, and papers pertaining to land grants and property sales. The three-story fireproof building has two-and-one-half-foot thick exterior walls of rubble stone masonry and two-foot interior walls of stone and brick masonry. Two stories high, plus an attic, the Land Office stands on a raised basement. End pavilions with crenellated parapets are attached at each side. All openings are round arched, and the building is impressive because of its massiveness and solidarity. In 1932 the office was reroofed and the outside walls stuccoed.
State

TRAVIS COUNTY
Austin
TEXAS GOVERNOR'S MANSION
1010 Colorado Street
1856

The Texas Governor's Mansion is a large and symmetrical Greek Revival residence which exhibits the creative workmanship of Abner Cook, the architect-builder. Six giant Ionic columns grace the main facade of the rectangular brick structure and support a second-story balcony. There is no pediment above the columns (a regional characteristic). Abner Cook was responsible for the wooden balustrade of the second-floor porch in which slender bundled slats form an open diamond pattern (crow's foot balusters). The sidelights and transom of the main entrance are unusual and are also the work of Cook. Additions have been made to the rear and one side. The property also includes a Victorian carriage house.
State
HABS

TRAVIS COUNTY
Austin
TEXAS STATE CAPITOL
Congress and 11th Streets
1882–1888, Elijah E. Myers

The present capitol is the second to stand on this spot. The earlier building burned in 1881 and was replaced by a new statehouse modeled after the national capitol. Exterior walls are red granite. The north and south wings are four stories high, the east and west wings, three sto-

ries. A massive dome surmounts the crossing of the two arms. The interior dome was made in Belgium, and it is topped by a statue of the goddess of liberty. A classical pediment crowns the entrance, and paired and single pilasters ornament all sides of the building. Inside, oak, pine, cedar, ash, cherry, and walnut woods have been used, and the hardware is bronze.
State

TRAVIS COUNTY
Austin
U.S. POST OFFICE (OLD POST OFFICE) AND FEDERAL BUILDING (O. HENRY HALL)
126 W. 6th Street
1878

The Post Office and Federal Building in Austin is a massive limestone ashlar structure which resembles, in some respects, an Italian palace of the 16th century. Its horizontal lines and massive form give the building this appearance. The only decorations are molding strips and a simplified cornice and balustrade. Attached to both ends of the central block are pavilions containing graduated openings in each bay. Segmental arches cover the openings on the first floor and those of the second-floor arcade.
State

TRAVIS COUNTY
Austin
WOODLAWN (PEASE MANSION)
6 Niles Road
1853

Abner Cook designed and built Woodlawn for James B. Shaw, but the house was owned for 100 years by Elisha M. Pease (a governor of Texas) and his family. The two-story, brick, Greek Revival house is distinguished by a two-story portico with six giant fluted Ionic columns. Above the main entrance is a balcony surrounded by a Cook balustrade in an openwork diamond (crow's foot) pattern. The doors at the center of both first and second stories have the characteristic Cook transom intersected by the pillars of the door jamb.
Private; not accessible to the public
HABS

TRAVIS COUNTY
Austin vicinity
LEVI ROCKSHELTER
On Lick Creek west of Tex. 71, about 27 miles west of Austin
Pre-Columbian

The Levi Rockshelter measures 120 feet long and its overhang averages about 15 feet. Excavations at the site have unearthed five distinct stratigraphic

archeological zones, and the lower four were deposited prior to the Archaic Period. The site is a stratified campsite and has yielded some artifact types previously unknown in Paleo-Indian cultures. Discovery of the rockshelter has extended the known geographical limits of several Paleo-American complexes and may define new foci for them.
Private; not accessible to the public

VAL VERDE COUNTY
Comstock vicinity
LOWER PECOS CANYON ARCHEOLOGICAL DISTRICT
12 miles west of Comstock on U.S. 90
Pre-Columbian

The Lower Pecos Canyon is characterized by steep rock walls containing numerous caves and rockshelters. The area is one of the richest in rock art in the world. A total of 71 separate archeological sites have been recorded and contain evidence of early bison hunters (of 10,000 years ago) and cultural debris from various periods of the Archaic peoples (7,000 years ago to proto-historic times just before Spanish contact). Artifacts recovered include basketry, matting, dart and arrow shafts, throwing sticks, rabbit fur robes, snares, and painted pebbles. The canyon is notable because such a variety of sites and materials has been found in so relatively small an area. The earliest rock paintings on the canyon walls may be 5,000 years old, and later art in the Red Monochrome style appears in several places covering the earlier Pecos River style.
Private

VAL VERDE COUNTY
Comstock vicinity
SEMINOLE CANYON ARCHEOLOGICAL DISTRICT
7 miles west of Comstock, south of U.S. 90
Pre-Columbian

Seminole Canyon is a six-mile tributary canyon of the Rio Grande. It lies in the approximate center of what is believed to be one of the richest pictograph areas in the world. Thousands of years of human occupation are represented by the cave paintings and the stratified midden debris. Caves and rockshelters have sheltered men since Paleo-Indian times and have preserved materials used through the Archaic Period (5,000 B.C. to 500 A.D.). Three of the most notable sites in the district are Coontail Spin Site, Fate Bell Shelter, and Panther Cave. The first is a rockshelter where sandals, cordage, projectile points, and matting have been recovered. At the second site a rich and extensive midden deposit has been found.

Panther Cave contains samples of a painting style identified as Lower Pecos River. Pictures date from prehistoric times and represent a magical or religious art.
Private; not accessible to the public

VAL VERDE COUNTY
Langtry vicinity
MILE CANYON (EAGLE NEST CANYON)
Northeast of Langtry off U.S. 90
Pre-Columbian

Mile Canyon is a meandering, steep to vertical-sided canyon which varies in depth from 80 to 200 feet and has a maximum width of 200 feet. Three major archeological sites in the canyon together constitute one of the most complete records of trans-Pecos Texas prehistory in the state. Bonfire Shelter, the first of the three, contains evidence of occupation by early man dating back more than 10,000 years. Mass bison kills took place here, and findings strongly suggest social groupings larger than extended families were present who planned and executed this sophisticated hunting technique. Extinct animal bones have also been found. Eagle Cave, a large rockshelter, is the second site. It measures 185 feet long, 87 feet deep, and has a roof extending 90 feet above the talus slope. This cave is one of the largest rockshelters in trans-Pecos Texas and contains aboriginal occupation debris which has been radiocarbon dated from 9,000 years ago to nearly historic times. Periods represented are Early, Middle, and Late Archaic. At one time there were many pictographs on the rear wall of the rockshelter, but only one panel is still clearly visible. The third site is Kelley Cave, a smaller rockshelter also containing a pictograph panel, one element of which is believed to be among the oldest in the area. Some archeological investigation has taken place.
Private; not accessible to the public

VICTORIA COUNTY
Inez vicinity
FORT ST. LOUIS SITE
About 13 miles south of Inez on Garcitas Creek
1685

Fort St. Louis was established by René Robert Cavelier, Sieur de La Salle, in February, 1685. La Salle used the fort as a base for exploration and as a defense against hostile natives. The site was abandoned in 1689, not to be occupied again until 1722. At this time the presidio of Nuestra Señora de Loreto was constructed on the same site. The presidio which replaced the wooden fort had a moat, four bastions, and a tower; it was moved to

another location in 1726. No visible remains of the fort (except concentrations of artifacts) can be seen.
Private; not accessible to the public

WALLER COUNTY
Hempstead vicinity
LIENDO
2 miles northeast of Hempstead off FM 1488
1853

Liendo, named for its original owner Jose Justo Liendo, was an extensive plantation located between the Houston-Galveston area and Austin. A later proprietor, Leonard W. Grace, constructed this late Greek Revival dwelling. The house is set on a raised basement of red brick obtained from the Brazos River. The five-bay main facade has identical entrances on both the first and second floors. A projecting two-story, pedimented gallery covers the central three bays of the front, and a lunette in the pediment contains a star and the construction date.
Private; not accessible to the public
HABS

WASHINGTON COUNTY
Brenham
PAMPELL-DAY HOUSE
409 W. Alamo Street
1844, 1875

The Pampell-Day House was built as two distinct sections. The older, which is now the rear wing, was a one-story, three-room dwelling of native pine with a long front gallery. In 1875 T. J. Pampell bought the house and added the two-story Victorian Gothic cottage, now the front section. There are three gables across the front and three at the rear, all with bargeboards, pendants, and carpenter's lace. The front doors are double and have a seven-light, stained glass transom and three sidelights on each side. Beneath the center gable on the main facade is a one-story, flat-roofed porch with capped posts and reverse curve brackets. J. Cochran Day was a later owner.
Private; not accessible to the public

WASHINGTON COUNTY
Brenham vicinity
HATFIELD PLANTATION
Northwest of Brenham off FM 912
c. 1853

Architecturally the Hatfield House is reminiscent of Virginia and Kentucky homes. It is a two-story dwelling with a partially raised basement and an attached, two-story, one-bay porch. The porch has a gable roof, and the eaves under the gable are bracketed. There are six panels on

each of the two front doors which have vertical sidelights and five-light transoms. The house is L-shaped and built of handmade brick with walls 13 inches thick. Present owners undertook restoration work in the 1960's using wood timbers, flooring, paneling, trim, and hardware taken from contemporary houses. Basil M. Hatfield (1811–1870) was a native of Kentucky who fought for Texas independence with the First Regiment of Texas Volunteers.
Private; not accessible to the public

WASHINGTON COUNTY
Gay Hill vicinity
THE RED HOUSE
Northwest of Gay Hill via Tex. 36 and FM 390
1852

The Red House is a late Greek Revival, four-room, two-story frame residence. Its second story is treated as a *piano nobile*, and the main entrance porch rests on tall brick piers. The roof is gabled. A one-room outbuilding of the same architectural design stands at the rear of the house. George Clark Red was a prominent physician and educator who came to Texas in 1845. He built the Red House and lived in it until 1876.
Private; not accessible to the public

WASHINGTON COUNTY
Independence
HOUSTON, MRS. SAM, HOUSE
FM 390, one block east of the intersection of FM 50
Early 1830's

This rectangular frame residence was built during the early period of Anglo settlement in Texas. It is two stories high and covered by a gable roof. There is a two-story, one-bay pedimented porch on the main facade and a stone chimney at each gable end. Sam Houston's widow and eight children lived here between 1863 and 1867. Sam Houston was commander-in-chief of the Texas Army during the Texas revolution of 1836, president of the Republic of Texas, U.S. Senator, and governor of Texas.
Private; not accessible to the public

WILLACY COUNTY
KING RANCH
Reference—see Kenedy County

WILLIAMSON COUNTY
Georgetown
TINNEN HOUSE
1220 Austin Street
1880

The Tinnen House, named for its second owner John Tinnen, is one of only a few truly Italianate frame dwellings in Texas where Italianate architecture was never as popular as Greek Revival. This house has been noticeably altered in places. The columns on the front porch are later additions, and the porch itself has probably also been changed. There may have been a balcony beneath the second-story tower window. Typical of Italianate architecture are the off-center tower, the segmentally arched windows, the wide bracketed eaves, and the low-pitched roof.
Private; not accessible to the public

WILLIAMSON COUNTY
Old Round Rock
INN AT BRUSHY CREEK (COLE HOUSE)
Taylor Exit of U.S. 79, off IH 35, west side
Mid–19th century

Settlers began coming to the Brushy Creek area just prior to the middle of the last century. The present inn was built on property originally owned and subdivided by a J. M. Harrell. The building was constructed some time between 1853 and 1863. It is a one-story, cut limestone Texas residence with a wide front gallery. The gallery has unusual square posts containing decorative molded panels. The gallery roof is flat.
Private

WILLIAMSON COUNTY
Round Rock vicinity
MERRELL, CAPTAIN NELSON, HOUSE
Northeast of Round Rock on U.S. 79
1870–1871

The Merrell House is a two-story, rectangular, coursed ashlar limestone dwelling with a gable roof. There is a deep five-bay double gallery on the main facade and a square frame cupola at the center of the roof. A one-story limestone ell is attached to the rear and contained the original kitchen and dining room. One-story porches were built across the rear and along the ell. Other buildings on the property are a barn (c. 1900), a hexagonal cistern, and the ruins of a smokehouse. Nelson Merrell was a prominent Austin landowner and farmer who came to Texas in 1837 from Ohio.
Private; not accessible to the public
HABS

WISE COUNTY
Decatur
ADMINISTRATION BUILDING, DECATUR BAPTIST COLLEGE
1602 S. Trinity Street
1892

Northwest Texas Baptist College was founded at Decatur in 1891, and the Administration Building was built the following year. It is a three-story limestone Victorian structure with Romanesque features. The complex hip roof is a backdrop for the numerous roof projections and heights. Strong, attenuated brackets support the cornices of the gables. The college went bankrupt within a few years because the supporting churches failed to pay their pledges. The Texas Baptist Convention eventually purchased the school, changing the name to Decatur Baptist Junior College, the first private junior college in the United States. The college was moved to Dallas in 1964, and the Administration Building was thereupon purchased by the Wise County Historical Society.
County

YOUNG COUNTY
Newcastle vicinity
FORT BELKNAP
1 mile south of junction of Tex. 24 and 251
1851

Fort Belknap was the key post in a chain of defenses established to protect the Texas frontier in the years of its most active advance, 1850 to 1856. During that period one-fifth of the United States Army attempted to defend Texas against raids by the Kiowa and Comanche Indians. Following evacuation of the state by federal troops in 1861, the Texas Frontier Regiment used Fort Belknap throughout the Civil War for operations against the Indians. It was discontinued as a permanent fort in 1867, and the only remaining original building is the arsenal, built in 1852. Others have been reconstructed in recent years.
County
NHL

YOUNG COUNTY
South Bend
HARRELL SITE
1 mile north of South Bend on the Brazos River
c. 1300–1600

The Harrell Site is the type site of the southernmost Plains village agricultural complex. It somewhat resembles the village cultures of central and western Oklahoma and possibly represents a group ancestral to the Wichita Indian tribes. Archeological evidence shows contacts with the Caddoan Indians to the east and the Pueblos to the west. The local agricultural practices may have had a northern origin, and the local people may have descended from an earlier local non-agricultural group. These facts make the Harrell Site significant in the study of the development of southern plains village life.
Private; not accessible to the public
NHL

SOUTH ELEVATION

Bishop's Palace, Galveston, Texas. *HABS*

Bonfire Shelter, Langtry, Texas. *David S. Dibble*

Parker County Courthouse,
Weatherford, Texas.
*Texas State Historical
Survey Committee*

Barker History Center, Austin, Texas.
Texas State Historical Survey Committee

Utah

Box Elder Stake Tabernacle, Brigham City, Utah.
Utah State Historical Society

Council Hall, Salt Lake City, Utah.
Utah Travel Council

Coke Oven, Old Irontown,
Little Pinto vicinity, Utah.
Kent Fairbanks for HABS

Beehive House, Salt Lake City, Utah. *LDS Church*

BEAVER COUNTY
Beaver
BEAVER COUNTY COURTHOUSE
90 E. Center Street
1876–1882

Beaver County was created by the Utah territorial legislature in 1855. Indian troubles delayed construction of the courthouse, and soon after its completion a fire partially destroyed the building (1889). Rebuilt shortly thereafter, the courthouse has been in use ever since. The two-story building is brick on a sandstone foundation and has a mansard roof broken by gables and a central clock tower. Overall dimensions (exclusive of the rear additions) are 39 feet by 55 feet. The window and entrance openings are elliptically arched with brick voussoirs and wood keystones. The courtroom occupies the front portion of the second floor; its ceiling is divided into nine coffers by beams, and there are acorn pendants at the intersections.
County
HABS

BOX ELDER COUNTY
Brigham City
BOX ELDER STAKE TABERNACLE
Main Street between 2nd and 3rd South Streets
c. 1876–1890; 1896 (rebuilt)

The original Box Elder Stake Tabernacle was built of fieldstone, measured 50 by 19 feet, and had a tower at each corner. Rebuilt after a fire gutted the interior, the tabernacle acquired 16 brick buttresses, each one topped by a steeple. A three-stage tower with a domed mansard roof was constructed above the principal entrance. The present building is brick and stone. Windows and doors have pointed arch openings.
Private
HABS

BOX ELDER COUNTY
Corinne
CORINNE METHODIST EPISCOPAL CHURCH
Corner of Colorado and S. 6th Streets

Corinne, the northernmost town on the first transcontinental rail line, was settled by Gentiles or non-Mormons. The town was laid out on the Union Pacific route in 1869 and incorporated in 1870. Both Catholics and Protestants settled here, but the first church to be organized was probably the Methodist. It is a one-story rectangle with brick walls. The wood frame vestibule and belfry are not original. Windows are lancet and the cornice is simple. The growth of Ogden and the development of alternate rail routes

reduced Corinne's population and importance. Today it is the center of a small farming community and important historically as a one-time Gentile enclave within Utah.
Private
HABS

BOX ELDER COUNTY
Promontory
GOLDEN SPIKE NATIONAL HISTORIC SITE
1869

Golden Spike National Historic Site contains the site where the last spike was driven on May 10, 1869, to complete the nation's first transcontinental railroad. The ceremony celebrated the completion of 1800 miles of railway in approximately six and a half years to form a junction of the Union Pacific from the east and the Central Pacific from the west. Construction followed the Railroad Act of 1862, which chartered and granted federal aid to the Union Pacific Railroad. This linking of West and East marked the beginning of a new era by the establishment of a practical means of trade, commerce, and political intercourse between the Atlantic and Pacific coasts.
Federal/non-federal
NPS; 1,542 acres

CARBON COUNTY (also in Emery, Grand, and Uintah counties)
Green River
DESOLATION CANYON
1869

John Wesley Powell (1834–1902) was born in New York State and spent most of his early life in Illinois. He attended Wheaton College (Illinois) and Oberlin College (Ohio) but received no degree from either. As a young man he developed a curiosity about nature which led to solitary expeditions on the Mississippi and Ohio rivers for the purpose of observing and collecting specimens of nature. As the captain of an artillery company during the Civil War, Powell lost his right forearm from a wound received at Shiloh. After the war he turned to exploring and led two expeditions (1869 and 1871) down the Green and Colorado rivers. The 1869 expedition of 11 men and four boats started from the point on the Green River where it is crossed by the Union Pacific Railroad. In Desolation Canyon the men saw a heretofore unexplored area of the United States and were confronted by dangers and natural wonders, frightening and at the same time awe-inspiring. Here the men gave enduring names to mountains, rapids, streams, and other natural landmarks that had never before been seen by

white men. Except for an occasional abandoned ranch, Desolation Canyon is virtually unchanged from its appearance in 1869. There are no permanent residents of the canyon.
Federal/private; not accessible to the public
NHL

EMERY COUNTY
Green River
DESOLATION CANYON
Reference—see Carbon County

GRAND COUNTY
Green River
DESOLATION CANYON
Reference—see Carbon County

IRON COUNTY
Cedar City vicinity
OLD IRONTOWN
About 22 miles west of Cedar City, 3 miles south of Utah 56
19th century

The development of Utah's iron and steel industry began in the fall of 1849 when an exploring party discovered Iron Mountain and the coal beds at nearby Cedar City. The Pioneer Iron Company and the Deseret Iron Company were founded to develop these resources. A third organization, the Union Iron Works, began operations in 1868 at the Old Irontown location on Pinto Creek. Several charcoal furnaces were built, one of which still remains. An "arastra" was constructed to prepare fine sand for furnace molds. This is also in fair condition. Stoves, irons, and milling equipment were made at the site. Reorganized in 1873 as the Great Western Iron and Manufacturing Company, the enterprise expanded to include an engine house, two furnaces, a foundry, a pattern shop, and offices. Today remnants of the foundry, a partial chimney, foundations, and walls are all the remaining evidence of a once-productive complex.
Private
HABS

MILLARD COUNTY
Cove Fort vicinity
COVE FORT
2 miles east of Int. 15 on Utah 4
1867

Mormon immigrants named the site Cove Creek and used it as a camping place. In 1860 Charles and Elliott Willden established a permanent residence called Willden's Fort. Indian hostilities later in the decade led Brigham Young to purchase the site on behalf of the Mormon community and erect a fort, which was completed in 1867. The protected structure thus erected was made of black volcanic rock laid with lime mortar. Walls measuring 18 feet from the base of the foundation were built in the shape of a square. Two sets of large hinged doors with sand between the planking, to prevent conflagration by flaming arrows, were hung on the east and west walls. Six apartments lined the north and south walls. The Mormon Church retained ownership of the fort until 1911.

Private

HABS

MILLARD COUNTY
Deseret vicinity
FORT DESERET
2 miles south of Deseret on Utah 257
1866

The first settlers came to the Pahvant Valley in 1860 and founded the town of Deseret. When the Black Hawk War broke out six years later, territorial governor Brigham Young advised all outlying settlements to construct fortifications. Fort Deseret was built of adobe mud with walls ten feet high and three feet wide at the base tapering to one and one-half feet at the top. Built as a square measuring 550 feet on a side, the fort had bastions at the northeast and southwest corners. Wind and rain have eroded the walls so that less than half remain standing, mainly the eastern portion. Fort Deseret is the only remaining adobe mud fort in Utah.

State

MILLARD COUNTY
Fillmore
UTAH TERRITORIAL CAPITOL
Center Street between Main and First West Streets
1852–1855, Truman O. Angell

Utah became a territory under the provisions of Henry Clay's Compromise of 1850. A capitol site was selected by a commission appointed by the territorial governor Brigham Young. The site chosen was Fillmore, centrally located in the territory. Although never completed and used only a short time, the capitol was planned as a large and impressive sandstone structure. The central section was to have been 60 feet square with four side wings measuring 60 by 40 feet. A central dome was planned but never executed, and only the south wing was actually built. The Utah territorial legislature met here in 1855, 1856, and 1858, after which the building was used sporadically and gradually fell into disrepair until given to the Daughters of Utah Pioneers (1927) and refurnished.

State

HABS

PIUTE COUNTY
Junction
PIUTE COUNTY COURTHOUSE
Main Street at Center Street
1903

Support for construction of the Piute Courthouse was difficult to muster in the sparsely populated county, and an earlier proposal for such a structure had been defeated in 1892. However, in 1902 John Morrill donated the lot for the building, and architect R. C. Watkins was selected to design it. It was constructed the following year of red-burnt brick by the builders, Young, Allen, and Morrill. The two-story building is Edwardian with arched windows and archways on both floors, small false towers in three corners, and a larger, more prominent tower on the southeast side.

County

SALT LAKE COUNTY
Salt Lake City
BEEHIVE HOUSE
67 E. South Temple Street
1854, Truman O. Angell

Brigham Young (1801–1877), second president of the Church of Jesus Christ of Latter-Day Saints and first governor of the state of Deseret—later Utah Territory—built and lived in the Beehive House until his death. For a short time it served as the official presidential residence before being restored by the Church in the late 1950's. The house is two stories high and surmounted by a cupola topped with a beehive, the traditional Mormon symbol of industry. A widow's walk on the roof and a two-storied gallery (railed above, open below) on two sides of the house are outstanding architectural features. In 1888 the rear section was rebuilt in three stories. The house has been restored in appearance to the time of Brigham Young's occupancy.

Private

SALT LAKE COUNTY
Salt Lake City
CATHEDRAL OF THE MADELEINE (ROMAN CATHOLIC)
331 East South Temple
1900–1909, C. M. Neuhausen and Bernard O. Mecklenburg

The Roman Catholic Cathedral of the Madeleine is built of gray sandstone on a granite block foundation. Architect C. M. Neuhausen was strongly influenced by the designs of H. H. Richardson, as evidenced by his use of rough-faced stone, round arches, and large building masses. Dimensions of the cathedral are 190 feet long,

103 feet wide at the transepts, and 100 feet from the ground to the ridge of the main roof. Sanctuary windows were designed by George Sotter of Pittsburgh, and the rose window is modeled after one in the cathedral in Toledo, Spain. Utah's mines and mineral resources were largely developed by Catholics, and the cathedral was built through their efforts under the direction of Bishop Lawrence Scanlon, who served from 1873 until 1915.

Private

SALT LAKE COUNTY
Salt Lake City
CHASE, ISAAC, MILL
Liberty Park, 6th Street East
1852, William Weeks

The Isaac Chase Mill is believed to be the only gristmill built by early Utah pioneers still standing on its original site. Previous to building this mill, Chase owned and operated an upright mill and a small crackling mill on the property. In 1854 Brigham Young bought into the Chase Mill, and by 1860 he had become sole owner. The mill was constructed of adobe blocks held together by clay mortar. Rectangular in shape (50 feet by 40 feet), the mill is two stories high and has a heavy timber framework. The brick chimney on the west wall is a later addition, and the first floor knotty pine wainscot was put on in 1959. Much original machinery from the mill, which ceased operating in the 1880's, remains.

Municipal/private

HABS

SALT LAKE COUNTY
Salt Lake City
THE COUNCIL HALL (OLD CITY HALL)
Capitol Hill, head of State Street
1864–1866, William H. Folsom

The Council Hall served as Salt Lake's city hall and the meeting place for the territorial legislature until 1894. Afterward it housed the police court and offices. In 1961–1962 the entire structure was dismantled, moved to its present site, and reconstructed with a minimum of modifications. The 60-foot-square red sandstone building contains a council hall on the second floor. Offices for the mayor, recorder, city treasurer, an alderman, the city attorney, and the adjutant general of the Nauvoo Legion (territorial militia) were also located within the Council Hall.

State

SALT LAKE COUNTY
Salt Lake City
DEVERAUX HOUSE (STAINES-JENNINGS MANSION)
334 West South Temple Street
1857, William Paul

Although much exterior decoration has been removed, the Deveraux House remains structurally sound and its basic lines have not been changed. The two-story residence has a mansard roof and the walls are brick masonry with a cement plaster exterior scored to resemble stone. A porch which extended across the south facade and around to the east side has been removed, as have the second-story roof balustrades and the metal roof cresting. Inside is heavy carved pine woodwork grained to simulate oak, mahogany, birds-eye maple, and marble. Much of the original wallpaper, which was handpainted to resemble oak grain, is intact. William Staines built the house and William Jennings, a later owner, named it Deveraux.
Private
HABS

SALT LAKE COUNTY
Salt Lake City
EMIGRATION CANYON
East edge of Salt Lake City on Utah 65
1847

Emigration Canyon forms the passage through the Wasatch Mountains to Salt Lake Valley traversed by Brigham Young and his Mormon followers in their journey from the Missouri Valley. From it Brigham Young allegedly stated, "This is the place"; for the valley lying before him he had seen in a vision as the destined home for his people. Just north of the mouth of the canyon on a bench of land overlooking the valley, the Mormons built Pioneer Monument in 1947 as a memorial to their forebears.
State
NHL

SALT LAKE COUNTY
Salt Lake City
FORT DOUGLAS
Fort Douglas Military Reservation
1862

The first military encampment subsequently called Camp Douglas, was made on this site in October, 1862. Temporary quarters for officers and men were erected in addition to a commandant's residence (stuccoed adobe), guardhouse, bakehouse, commissary, quartermaster tents, hospital, and stables. A year later these makeshift quarters were replaced with more permanent buildings. The camp was renamed Fort Douglas during the 1874–1876 rebuilding when the present Officers' Circle was constructed. Two other structures still standing from the previous century are the chapel (1883) and the camp theater (1864).
Federal
HABS

SALT LAKE COUNTY
Salt Lake City
GRANITE PAPER MILL
6900 Big Cottonwood Canyon Road
1880–1883, Henry Grow

Several factors contributed to the establishment of the Granite Paper Mill: the Mormon Church leaders' desire for independence, their policy of record keeping and extensive publication, and Mormon isolation. Printing of the *Deseret News*, managed by Thomas S. Taylor, began at the plant in 1883. Under the management of Charles J. Lambert up to five tons of paper were produced in an average 24-hour day. Fire broke out at the mill in 1893, destroying the roof structure and the papermaking machinery and thus ending the major effort by the Mormons to produce their own paper. The present frame structure with a hip roof was rebuilt on the original walls of the mill in 1927. The old mill is presently used as a private club.
Private
HABS

SALT LAKE COUNTY
Salt Lake City
KEITH-BROWN MANSION AND CARRIAGE HOUSE
529 East South Temple Street
1898–1900, Frederick Albert Hale

This three-story mansion of Sanpete limestone was built by David Keith, a Nova Scotia-born entrepreneur who helped establish the Silver King Coalition Mines Company. In partnership with Thomas Kearns, Keith published the Salt Lake *Tribune*. His large home has an eclectic exterior highlighted by four, massive, 24-foot Tuscan columns. Inside, through the lobby, one enters an octagonal room topped by a stained glass window and paneled in cherry wood. Two front parlors, an oval dining room, and a kitchen open off the two-story octagon. Second-floor rooms have been remodeled as offices but still retain their original fireplaces, chandeliers, and carved woodwork. The carriage house has undergone major remodeling inside, although the exterior is unaltered.
Private

SALT LAKE COUNTY
Salt Lake City
OTTINGER HALL
233 Canyon Road
1900

Salt Lake City established a paid fire department in October, 1833, with George M. Ottinger as its first chief. Under his leadership the Veterans-Volunteer Firemen's Association was organized in 1890. Ten years later Ottinger Hall was constructed as a meeting and social hall for the firemen. It is a two-story brick structure with a wood shingle roof and central bell tower. Today Ottinger Hall houses pioneer fire fighting equipment including Utah's first fire engine. The hall and its contents tell the story of early fire fighting in Salt Lake City.
Municipal

SALT LAKE COUNTY
Salt Lake City
ST. MARK'S EPISCOPAL CATHEDRAL
231 E. First South Street
1871, Richard Upjohn

St. Mark's is the oldest non-Mormon cathedral in Utah. The building was originally designed as a Latin cross with an east-west transept, although only part of the nave was built in 1871. The east transept was added in 1882, and the west transept and chancel, in 1902. This latter section was rebuilt in 1935 following a fire. In 1958 the original front was extended and a new vestibule and cloisters added. Building materials were sandstone, cutstone, and rubble. The nave windows have Gothic arches, while the gables contain rose windows. Inside, arched roof beams are supported on hammer beams and stone corbels.
Private
HABS

SALT LAKE COUNTY
Salt Lake City
SALT LAKE CITY AND COUNTY BUILDING
451 Washington Square
1891–1894, Proudfoot, Bird and Monheim

The many-turreted Salt Lake City and County Building, measuring 271 feet by 150 feet, is Romanesque Revival. Rising 72 feet above the ground, the Kyune sandstone walls are five stories high. The central tower measures 303 feet. During the early years of Utah's statehood the building served as the first state capitol (1896–1915). Presently county offices occupy the south half of the structure and city offices, the north. Extensive remodeling has taken place inside.
Municipal and county
HABS

SALT LAKE COUNTY
Salt Lake City
TEMPLE SQUARE
Temple, 1853–1893, Truman O.
Angell; Tabernacle, 1862–1867;
Assembly Hall, 1882

Temple Square best captures the essence of the Mormon achievement in building a "kingdom of Zion" in the Utah desert. The walled square symbolizes the strong cultural and religious individuality of the Mormons. Though the Temple dominates the square, the Tabernacle is an impressive monument to Mormon architectural and engineering skill. Its unsupported domed roof, one of the largest in the world, the organ, and the building's acoustical qualities are among its outstanding features. The Assembly Hall is devoted to nonsectarian religious, social, and intellectual uses.
Private
NHL; HABS

SALT LAKE COUNTY
Salt Lake City
UTAH STATE HISTORICAL SOCIETY
MANSION AND CARRIAGE HOUSE
603 E. South Temple Street
1900–1902, Carl M. Neuhausen

Millionaire Thomas Kearns had this house built while he was serving in the U.S. Senate (1901–1905). The architecture is basically Victorian with three Queen Anne corner towers and a classic style second-floor balcony and entrance porches topped by Palladian windows on the third floor. Building material is oolite marble. Other unusual exterior features are bracketed, segmental arch window pediments, carved finials at all roof points, and large, ornamental cartouche-like windows on the second floor flanking the central balcony. Inside, the craftsmanship is equally elaborate. Three governors have called the mansion home. The carriage house is presently occupied by the Utah Institute of Fine Arts.
State

SALT LAKE COUNTY
Salt Lake City
YOUNG, BRIGHAM, FOREST
FARMHOUSE
732 Ashton Avenue
1861–1863

Brigham Young established this farm in the 1850's, and the first house erected was a small adobe structure. The property became an experimental farm on which the first alfalfa in the valley was grown, mulberry trees were planted, a cocoonery was established to study silk production, and registered cattle were imported and bred. The frame residence has a stone foundation and was built in the shape of a double cross. There are two roof gables on each side and a single gable at each end. Young owned the farm until his death in 1877.
Private

SALT LAKE COUNTY
Salt Lake City
YOUNG, BRIGHAM, HOUSE (LION
HOUSE)
63 S. Temple Street
1856, Truman O. Angell and William
Ward

The Lion House was the home of Brigham Young until his death in 1877. After succeeding Joseph Smith as head of the Mormon Church in 1847, Young directed the mass migration of the Mormons to the Salt Lake Valley. He was first governor of the Territory of Utah, 1849–1857. His two-story house, patterned after a New England residence, is of plaster-covered adobe brick. The exterior is substantially unchanged, but the interior has been altered somewhat. On the first floor are several rooms with original furnishings and memorabilia.
Private
NHL

SALT LAKE COUNTY
Salt Lake City
Z. C. M. I. CAST IRON FRONT
(ZIONS COOPERATIVE MERCANTILE
INSTITUTE)
15 S. Main Street
1876, William H. Folsom and Obed
Taylor

The Zions Cooperative Mercantile Institute was formed in 1868. By 1880 it had 156 branch stores in 24 counties. The Salt Lake City store originally has a frontage of 50 feet and a depth of 318 feet. Most of the interior lighting came from skylights. The south (1880) and north (1901) sections were added to the central section later, but the entire facade appears uniform. Corinthian columns divide all windows. These columns are cast iron in the center and south sections and stamped sheet metal on the north end. There is a modillion cornice at each level and in the rake of the pediment. Much of the exterior ornament is light sheet metal over wood.
Private
HABS

SALT LAKE COUNTY
Salt Lake City vicinity
BINGHAM CANYON OPEN PIT
COPPER MINE
16 miles southwest of Salt Lake City
on Utah 48
1904

The Bingham Canyon Open Pit Copper Mine was the first open pit copper mine in the world and also the largest. The output from this mine lifted Utah from a minor copper-producing state to fourth by 1919. It still yields a high percentage of all United States copper production. Viewing facilities for visitors are provided on the west rim of the pit.
Private
NHL

SAN JUAN COUNTY
HOVENWEEP NATIONAL
MONUMENT
*Reference—see Montezuma County,
Colorado*

SAN JUAN COUNTY
Monticello vicinity
ALKALI RIDGE
25 miles southeast of Monticello on
secondary road, 10 miles east of
Recapture Creek on Utah 47
c. 900–1100

Excavations undertaken in 13 sites along Alkali Mesa closed the gap in the known development of the Pueblo Indian culture by defining the period known as Pueblo II, roughly 900–1100. In addition, the local development from the 600's into the 1200's has been shown to be a continual growth that was influenced by ideas of neighboring peoples. This is perhaps the area in which the ceremonial kiva developed.
Federal; not accessible to the public
NHL

SUMMIT COUNTY
Park City vicinity
KIMBALL STAGE STOP
NE 1/4 SW 1/4 sec. 20, T. 1 S., R. 4
E.
19th century

The Kimball Hotel-Stage Stop and Barns is one of the few remaining original stations of the Overland Stage. William H. Kimball constructed the two-story sandstone hotel in 1862. Besides housing overnight guests, it contained a large dining room, a bar, and a store. The hotel was well-known for its food and attracted notable guests such as Walt Whitman, Mark Twain, and Horace Greeley. The main structure is in good condition, and

two log barns built in the early 1860's still stand across the road. Much of the integrity of the stage complex remains, and plans for its development and restoration are being considered.
Private

TOOELE COUNTY
Wendover vicinity
DANGER CAVE
  1 mile east of Wendover on U.S. 40
  c. 9000 B.C. to A.D. 20

The archeological excavations of Danger Cave provide a clear picture of the life of the hunting and gathering peoples living in the desert environment of the Great Basin. Though no extinct animal remains have been found, the artifacts from the deep stratified deposits provide one of the more notable cross sections of long-term human development discovered west of the Continental Divide. The findings show that these people lived in an entirely different environment from that of the high plains Paleo Indian hunters.
Federal; not accessible to the public
NHL

UINTAH COUNTY
Green River
DESOLATION CANYON
Reference—see Carbon County

UTAH COUNTY
Fairfield
STAGECOACH INN
  c. 1858

John Carson settled in the Cedar Valley as early as 1855. The Stagecoach Inn was originally the Carson family dwelling converted to an inn. It is two stories high, L-shaped, and constructed of adobe. There is a frame addition on the west side. Carson, an elder in the Mormon Church, would not allow liquor to be served at the inn, which was the first stage stop west of Salt Lake City and a Pony Express stop (1860–1861). The hostelry ceased operating in 1947. Some of the original pine flooring and glass windows remain, and the fireplaces have been restored but are no longer used.
State
HABS

WASATCH COUNTY
Heber City
WASATCH STAKE TABERNACLE AND HEBER AMUSEMENT HALL
  Main Street at 100 North Street and 100 West Street corners
  1887–1889 (tabernacle), Alex Fortie; 1906–1908 (amusement hall)

The citizens of Heber City built the Wasatch Stake Tabernacle of local red sandstone. There is a central bell tower on the main facade which contains pointed-arch Gothic windows. Windows on the side elevations are segmentally arched, and the individual bays are separated by buttresses. The Heber Amusement Hall is also sandstone and is T-shaped. In 1917 a kitchen was added on the southwest corner, and an annex was built onto the west side in 1928. The one-story building has an excellent dance floor and is used for social and recreational functions.
Municipal
HABS

WASATCH COUNTY
Midway
WATKINS-COLEMAN HOUSE
  5 E. Main Street
  1869, John Watkins

John Watkins designed and built this home for his two wives. It is a one-and-one-half-story Gothic Revival residence with walls of hand pressed brick. Sandstone quoins mark the corners, and there are lacy bargeboards in the four main gables and the central dormer, all of which are topped by pointed finials. Some additions and minor alterations have been made.
Private
HABS

WASHINGTON COUNTY
Pine Valley
PINE VALLEY CHAPEL AND TITHING OFFICE
  Main and Grass Valley Streets
  19th century

Pine Valley Chapel and its adjacent Tithing Office is representative of the early Mormon Church situation. Since 1830, the "law of tithing," or donating ten percent of a person's income to the church, has been the economic practice of the Mormon Church. Tithing offices were generally built near the churches. Tithes of hay, grain, potatoes, vegetables, and other goods were brought to the office and receipts were issued for them. The stored goods were then passed out to the needy for worthy projects as the bishop directed. Pine Valley Chapel was designed

and built in 1868 by Ebenezer Bryce, a former shipbuilder from Australia. He assembled the frame walls on the ground, had them raised into position and joined by wooden pegs and rawhide. The inner walls and partitions were "hung" on the basic structure of ponderosa pine. To the east of the chapel stands the small red brick tithing office constructed in the 1880's.
Private

WASHINGTON COUNTY
St. George
OLD WASHINGTON COUNTY COURTHOUSE
  85 E. 100 North
  1876

The Old Washington County Courthouse was the only major public edifice built in the county during Utah's territorial period (1850–1896). St. George was settled in 1861 and became the county seat in 1863. The two-story brick courthouse was erected on a foundation of basalt rock. A cupola tops the structure, and within its tower is a gallows. The building ceased to serve as the county courthouse in 1960.
County
HABS

WASHINGTON COUNTY
St. George
ST. GEORGE TABERNACLE
  Intersection of Tabernacle and Main Streets
  19th century, Miles Romney

Ground for the Tabernacle was dedicated on June 1, 1863, but construction continued until 1877. A tabernacle was a meeting or assembly hall used primarily for church gatherings. From a distance the St. George Tabernacle looks like an eastern church of the colonial period. All materials for construction were produced locally except window panes, locks and hinges, and chandeliers. The tabernacle has walls of red sandstone and a tower on the east end of the gable roof which rises 140 feet. Inside, ceilings are 29 feet high. A gallery extends around three sides and is supported by solid turned columns. It is reached by two circular staircases. The ornate plaster of paris cornice contains dentils and bunches of grapes, a crop grown in this part of Utah.
Private
HABS

WASHINGTON COUNTY
St. George
YOUNG, BRIGHAM, WINTER HOME AND OFFICE
Corner of 2nd North and 1st West Streets
1874, Miles Romney

Brigham Young's Winter Home is located in Utah's southland. As early as 1856 missionaries had been sent to the Virgin River area to experiment with cotton production, and within five years the town of St. George was founded. Brigham Young (elected president of the Mormon Church in 1847) spent his winters in St. George from 1873 until his death in 1877. The dwelling is T-shaped and built of adobe brick. Bracketed cornices ornament the eaves of the gable roof, and there is a one-story, balustraded veranda on the south and east elevations. Inside, much of the original wood remains. Young's one-room office is also adobe with a sandstone foundation.
State
HABS

WASHINGTON COUNTY
Santa Clara
HAMBLIN, JACOB, HOME
Mid–19th century

Jacob Hamblin, a Mormon missionary to the Indians of southern Utah, may have come to the Santa Clara area as early as 1854. Three years later he was appointed president of all the southern Indian missions by Brigham Young. Hamblin's fellow missionaries built this two-story home for him, and he lived here until 1871, when he was called to work at nearby Kanab. The house was built into a hillside and has walls of local sandrock. Two porches run the full length of the house, which also has a gable roof and a rear shed extension.
State

WASHINGTON COUNTY
Silver Reef
WELLS FARGO AND COMPANY EXPRESS BUILDING
Main Street
1877

Silver Reef was a boom town for a brief eleven-year (1877–1888) period. Prosperity came as a result of the discovery of rarely found commercial quantity silver-bearing ore in sandstone formations. The population soared to 1,500, thus making Silver Reef the largest town in southern Utah. Major mining companies were the Leeds, Barbee and Walker, the Christy, and the Stormont. The one-story Wells Fargo Building is constructed of red sandstone, cut and tooled range ashlar at the front and coursed rubble at the sides and rear. The floor and roof are wood framed. There are four segmental arched doorways on the front and two on the rear. All openings could be closed with heavy steel shutters, most of which remain. Silver Reef's frame structures have largely disappeared. Only this building and the Rice Bank remain as reminders of a more prosperous time.
County
HABS

WASHINGTON COUNTY
Washington
WASHINGTON COTTON FACTORY
On U.S. 91 (Frontage Road West)
1865–1870

In 1865 Brigham Young and some Mormon settlers began construction of the sandstone factory which was expected to support and encourage the missionaries in the Washington County area. One floor was completed and operations began in 1867. Demand had increased by 1870, and two additional stories were built. At peak operation the factory produced 500 yards of cloth per day. By the end of the century the factory was plagued by problems, principal among which were locating a supply of cotton and wool and

finding a market for the goods. Some of the machinery was sold in 1910 and the remainder in 1914. The structure has served primarily as a warehouse since then.
Private

WEBER COUNTY
Ogden
BERTHA ECCLES COMMUNITY ART CENTER
2580 Jefferson Avenue
1893

This two-and-one-half-story Richardsonian Romanesque style house has exterior walls of brick and red sandstone. Characterizing features are the round-arched windows, the cylindrical towers with conical roofs, the steep-gabled wall dormers, and the eyebrow dormer in the roof. The design and material of the structure convey a sense of weight and massiveness. James C. Armstrong, first owner, sold the house to David Eccles in 1896. Eccles was a businessman with interests in lumber, land, railroads, banking, and sugar. His wife, Bertha Jensen Eccles, made the house a social and cultural center of Ogden.
Private

WEBER COUNTY
Ogden
GOODYEAR, MILES, CABIN
Tabernacle Square
1845

The first permanent white settlers in present-day Utah were trappers and traders. Miles Goodyear came west in 1836 and established himself on the banks of the Weber River. His stockaded cabin became a stopping place for California emigrants. It was built of cottonwood logs. The original floor was dirt, and the present foundation logs are replacements. Goodyear met the advance party of the first Mormon immigrants in July, 1847, and eventually sold to one of the settlers a land parcel constituting nearly all of Weber County. Goodyear's cabin is not on its construction site but is the oldest pioneer dwelling in Utah.
Private
HABS

Watkins-Coleman House, Midway, Utah.
Kent Fairbanks for HABS

Isaac Chase Mills,
Salt Lake City, Utah.
Kent Fairbanks for HABS

Fort Douglas, Salt Lake City, Utah.
Kent Fairbanks for HABS

Vermont

Wilder Barn, Plymouth Notch, Vermont.
William B. Pinney

Vermont State House, Montpelier, Vermont.
Vermont Development Department

Hubbardton Battlefield, Hubbardton, Vermont.
Vermont Development Department

ADDISON COUNTY
Addison
CHIMNEY POINT TAVERN
Vt. 125
1784

The first permanent settlers in the Chimney Point area were Frenchmen who came about 1730. Samuel de Champlain is credited with discovery of the site in 1609. The French built a substantial settlement here, but in 1759, fearful of attack, they burned their homes and barns and retreated to Canada. Nothing remained but blackened chimneys when the English arrived. Benjamin Paine built the Chimney Point Tavern the same year the town of Addison was organized. A later owner enclosed it in brick. It has two interior end chimneys and brick and frame (mid–19th-century) additions; the exterior porch on two sides was added in the 19th century. The taproom is little altered since construction.
State

ADDISON COUNTY
Middlebury
WILLARD, EMMA, HOUSE
Middlebury College Campus
1809

Emma Willard was a pioneer in the movement for female education in the United States. Her address to the New York legislature in 1819 has been termed the "Magna Carta of female education." Opening the Middlebury Female Seminary in 1814, she gradually expanded the conventional curriculum for young ladies by adding courses in mathematics, history, and languages. Her two-story brick house, where classes were once held, is now used by Middlebury College as an admissions office.
Private.
NHL

ADDISON COUNTY
Ripton vicinity
FROST, ROBERT, FARM (HOMER NOBLE FARM)
1 mile north of Vt. 125, 3 miles east of Ripton
1940–1963

Winner of four Pulitzer prizes and author of 11 volumes of poetry, Robert Frost is one of 20th-century America's most distinguished poets. In the fall of 1940 he purchased the Homer Noble Farm in the Green Mountains. Living and writing there in the summer and fall months until his death in 1963, Frost produced five volumes of poetry. *A Witness Tree* (1942) brought him his fourth Pulitzer Prize in 1943. Additional honors during this period include a medal awarded by Congress in 1962, his participation in the inau-

guration of President John F. Kennedy in 1961, and numerous fellowships and honorary degrees. The cabin which he occupied at this farm contains a number of Frost's personal belongings.
Private; accessible to the public by appointment only
NHL

BENNINGTON COUNTY
Bennington
BENNINGTON BATTLE MONUMENT
Monument Circle
1891

The Bennington Battle Monument is primarily commemorative, as the battle of Bennington (August 16, 1777) was fought in New York state. This 306–foot stone monolith contains an elevator (added in 1955) and over 400 steps. The monument is granite.
State

BENNINGTON COUNTY
South Shaftsbury
FROST, ROBERT, FARM (THE GULLY)
.25 mile east of U.S. 7 on Buck Hill Road
1790

Robert Frost, one of America's most distinguished 20th-century poets, spent his summers at The Gully from 1929 until the death of his wife in 1938. During this period Frost was awarded two Pulitzer prizes: one for *Collected Poems* in 1931 and the other for *A Further Range* in 1937. Many of the poems in the latter volume were written here: "Built-Soil," "A Record Stride," and "A Drumlin Woodchuck." During the period that The Gully served as his official residence (1929–1938), Frost held a position at Amherst College. The one-and-a-half-story Cape Cod farmhouse remains almost exactly as it was during the Frost occupancy.
Private; not accessible to the public
NHL

CALEDONIA COUNTY
Lyndon
OLD SCHOOLHOUSE BRIDGE
S. Wheelock Road
c. 1871

The Old Schoolhouse Covered Bridge is the only one in the state with covered walkways on both sides. The rectangular vehicle entrances are flanked by three-quarter arches at the eave line which support projections of the roof. It stands as built.
Municipal

CHITTENDEN COUNTY
Burlington
ETHAN ALLEN ENGINE COMPANY NO. 4
Church Street
1887

The Ethan Allen Engine Company building is three and one-half stories high, constructed of red sandstone and brick, and it has a 85–foot hose drying tower topped by an open belfry. The structure is in an unaltered condition except for weathering. Its original use was to house the equipment of a horse-drawn fire company and later, its motorized fire apparatus.
Municipal; not accessible to the public

CHITTENDEN COUNTY
Shelburne
THE *TICONDEROGA*
Shelburne Museum
1906

The *Ticonderoga* is the only extant and basically unchanged side-paddle-wheel lakeboat in the United States. From 1906 to 1953 the steamboat plied the waters of Lake Champlain as an excursion boat. The steel-hulled vessel is 120 feet long, with a beam of 57.5 feet. Its exterior has been restored, and the elaborate interior has been refurbished.
Private
NHL

GRAND ISLE COUNTY
Grand Isle
HYDE LOG CABIN
U.S. 2
1783

Jedidiah Hyde, Jr., built this one-and-one-half-story log cabin in the summer of 1783. It measures 20 by 25 feet and has an overhead loft and one interior end chimney. The chimney has been rebuilt, and the present roof is new. In 1952 the state of Vermont acquired the cabin and restored it using as much of the original materials as possible. The cabin has been moved from its construction site.
State

ORANGE COUNTY
Strafford
MORRILL, JUSTIN SMITH, HOMESTEAD
South of The Common
c. 1848

Justin Morrill introduced and directed final passage of legislation providing for land grant colleges. The Morrill Acts of 1862 and 1890 were among the most important actions taken by the federal

government in the field of higher education in the 19th century. While serving in the House of Representatives from 1855 to 1867 and in the Senate from 1867 to 1898, Morrill continued to retain his Strafford house. The house, Gothic Revival in style, contains many furnishings of the mid–19th century, including his extensive library.
Private; not accessible to the public
NHL; HABS

RUTLAND COUNTY
Castleton
CASTLETON MEDICAL COLLEGE BUILDING
South Street
1821

Castleton Medical College was founded in 1818 and continued to train doctors until 1861. It was the first proprietary degree granting medical college in the country. The two-story frame and clapboard Medical Building contained classroom, library, and laboratory space. An open arcaded cupola with attenuated columns stands atop the square central tower. The main facade features a dentil cornice above and within the central pediment. The structure does not stand on its original site.
Private

RUTLAND COUNTY
Hubbardton
HUBBARDTON BATTLEFIELD
Junction of Castleton-Hubbardton Road and Old Military Road to Mount Independence

American General Arthur St. Clair, retreating from Fort Ticonderoga, left a detachment consisting of a few hundred men from his rear guard unit at Hubbardton. These men had orders to slow the pursuing British in order to allow the remainder of the American army to escape. Soldiers from the British army commanded by General John Burgoyne fell upon the Americans during the early hours of July 7, 1777. They were led by General Simon Fraser and were better equipped and trained than their adversaries. However, the American delaying action was successful. Heavy casualties were inflicted upon the British, who abandoned the pursuit of St. Clair and retreated to Fort Ticonderoga. Three months later Burgoyne was forced to surrender his entire army at Saratoga. The battlefield site is being developed by the state of Vermont.
State

WASHINGTON COUNTY
Montpelier
VERMONT STATEHOUSE
State Street
1833–1838, Ammi B. Young; 1859

Completed in 1838, Vermont's Statehouse was severely damaged by fire in January, 1857. The interior was destroyed and had to be reconstructed, but the granite exterior walls and the hexastyle Doric portico survived. Ammi B. Young's original plans were generally followed in the rebuilding, although the structure was enlarged by the addition of one bay at each end of the facade. At this time the present high dome on a circular drum replaced the earlier, low, saucer dome. The Greek Doric columns of the portico are fluted. Inside, the Statehouse remains largely as it was in 1859.
State
NHL

WINDSOR COUNTY
Goulds Mill
EUREKA SCHOOLHOUSE
Charleston Road
Late 18th century

The Eureka Schoolhouse was used until 1900. It is a one-room building of hewn timber construction covered on the exterior with pine board siding cut to simulate stone blocks. The interior contains desks, maps, and books of the 19th century including two desks original to the building. The school is believed to be the oldest one in the state.
State

WINDSOR COUNTY
Plymouth
PLYMOUTH HISTORIC DISTRICT
The entire village of Plymouth; bounded on the east by East Mountain, on the south by Blueberry Hill and Soltudus Mountain, on the west by Mount Tom, and on the north by Wood Peak
Mid- to late 19th century

Plymouth retains the bucolic atmosphere of 19th-century rural Vermont. The village is also distinguished as the birthplace of President Calvin Coolidge. Fifteen buildings comprise the town, all are frame and date from the 1840's or later. Some of the significant structures are the Coolidge Birthplace (c. 1840); the Coolidge Homestead, where young Calvin Coolidge grew up; the Plymouth General Store, owned and operated by John Coolidge, the President's father; the Wilder House (c. 1830); the Brown House, a New England farm house built in 1868; the Plymouth Blacksmith Shop; the Plymouth church (1840); the Plymouth Cheese Fac-

tory, which is still operative; and the Plymouth schoolhouse.
Multiple state/private

WINDSOR COUNTY
Plymouth Notch
COOLIDGE, CALVIN, HOMESTEAD
Off Vt. 100 A
1876–1887

In this frame house Calvin Coolidge spent his boyhood years, 1876–1887. After graduation from Amherst College, he achieved prominence in Massachusetts as mayor of Northampton, state senator, lieutenant governor, and governor. He was Vice President in President Warren G. Harding's administration from 1921 to 1923, becoming President on Harding's death and was elected to the Presidency in 1924. He was visiting his early home on August 2, 1923, when word came of Harding's death. In the dining room at 2:37 A.M. the next morning, the oath of office as President of the United States was administered to Coolidge by his father, a justice of the peace.
State
NHL

WINDSOR COUNTY
Windsor
OLD CONSTITUTION HOUSE
16 N. Main Street
1777

On July 8, 1777, delegates from all sections of present-day Vermont met in this tavern building and adopted a constitution for the "free and independent state of Vermont." Vermont's constitution was the first in the nation to prohibit slavery and to establish universal manhood suffrage. The two-story frame tavern has interior end chimneys and an ell. Operated as a tavern until 1848, the building has been altered and does not stand on its original site.
State

WINDSOR COUNTY
Windsor
ROBBINS AND LAWRENCE ARMORY AND MACHINE SHOP
S. Main Street
1846

In the 1840's and 1850's the Robbins and Lawrence Company designed and produced machine tools that accelerated the Industrial Revolution in America by improving the production of interchangeable parts, which in turn stimulated mass production. Richard S. Lawrence, Frederick W. Howe, and Henry D. Stone, either individually or jointly, invented a profiling machine, a milling machine, and a universal milling machine. A brick ar-

mory housing some of the original machinery is all that remains of the once-flourishing factory.
Private
NHL

WINDSOR COUNTY
Woodstock
MARSH, GEORGE PERKINS, BOYHOOD HOME
54 Elm Street
1805–1807; 1885, Henry Hudson Holly

George Perkins Marsh, lawyer, diplomat, and philologist, made a significant con-

tribution to the conservation movement in America. His *Man and Nature or the Physical Geography as Modified by Human Behavior* (1864) opened up an area previously of little concern—the preservation of man's natural environment. Moreover, his writings significantly influenced sub-

sequent leaders of the conservation movement. This house later belonged to Frederick Billings, a well-known 19th-century philanthropist and railroad executive. The large, rambling mansion in the Queen Anne style bears little resemblance to the house as Marsh knew it.
Private; not accessible to the public
NHL

Virgin Islands

Government House, Christiansted National Historic Site,
Christiansted, St. Croix Island, Virgin Islands. *Jack E. Boucher for HABS*

Fort Christiansvaern,
Christiansted National Historic Site,
St. Croix, Virgin Islands.
Jack E. Boucher for HABS

Customhouse and Post Office, Christiansted National Historic Site,
Christiansted, St. Croix Island, Virgin Islands. *Jack E. Boucher for HABS*

ST. CROIX ISLAND
Christiansted
CHRISTIANSTED NATIONAL HISTORIC SITE
18th and 19th centuries

Christiansted was the capital of the Danish West Indies when "sugar was king," and St. Croix Island was an important example of Danish plantation society in the New World. The sugar empire, at its height in the early 19th century, declined steadily after 1820, and in 1916 Denmark agreed to sell her holdings in the West Indies to the United States. Approximately three city blocks on the Christiansted waterfront, including Fort Christiansvaern and such public buildings as the Danish Post Office and Customhouse, Steeple Building, and Government House, commemorate the colonial development of the Virgin Islands.
Federal
NPS; 27.15 acres
HABS

ST. CROIX ISLAND
Salt River Bay
COLUMBUS LANDING SITE
1493

The Columbus Landing Site is the earliest site now under the United States flag which is associated with Christopher Columbus. His skirmish with the Carib Indians here is the first recorded armed conflict between European explorers and American aborigines. The French conquered St. Croix in 1650 and held it for 45 years, during which time they built Fort Sale. Remains of the fort are undisturbed, and an associated aboriginal site has been extensively excavated.
Territorial; not accessible to the public
NHL

ST. THOMAS ISLAND
ST. THOMAS NATIONAL HISTORIC SITE
Charlotte Amalie
1680

St. Thomas National Historic Site contains Fort Christian, the oldest extant building in the Virgin Islands. Completed in 1680, the fort remains essentially the same as when it served as the hub of an early Danish settlement. Denmark, which had begun settling the Virgin Islands in the 1670's, retained possession until the United States purchased them in 1917. Fort Christian currently houses police and municipal offices.
Federal
NPS; 1.66 acres

Virginia

Adam Thoroughgood House, Virginia Beach, Virginia.
H. J. Sheely for NPS

Poplar Grove Mill, Williams vicinity, Virginia.
Virginia Chamber of Commerce

Hampton Institute, Hampton, Virginia. *Hampton Institute*

Annefield, Berryville vicinity, Virginia.
Phil Flournoy for Virginia Chamber of Commerce

ACCOMACK COUNTY
Accomac
ST. JAMES CHURCH
East side of Daugherty Road between
Back Street and Ocean Highway
1838

St. James Church is a one-story brick structure with a tetrastyle Greek Doric portico on the stuccoed, gable-end front. Over the portico is a Gothic bell tower. Each side of the building contains four tall, rectangular windows topped by rubbed-brick jack arches. St. James Church was built of materials salvaged from an earlier 18th-century church located nearby. The most outstanding feature of the church is its painted architectural decoration on the interior. This painting was done by a traveling artist soon after the church was built. It is sophisticated and finely executed trompe l'oeil with shadows and carefully worked-out perspective. A principal feature of the decoration is the painted reredos consisting of two pairs of Roman Doric pilasters supporting a plain entablature. The pilasters frame a painted, coffered tunnel vault at the end of which is a paneled door. Painted on the shallow, vaulted ceiling of the main part of the church are a false entablature, panels, and foliage imitative of plaster work. Imitation panels appear around the walls of the church.
Private

ACCOMACK COUNTY
Hallwood vicinity
WESSELLS ROOT CELLAR
.1 mile north of the intersection of
Routes 701 and 692
18th century

In 1768 William Wessells acquired 100 acres of land on which the present house and root cellar were later constructed. Shortly thereafter he probably built the root cellar and a dwelling (which burned in 1937). The root cellar is a rectangular brick structure covered by a steep gable roof. On the front gable is an unusual glazed header pattern of rather sophisticated craftsmanship. It is an unusual building of its type because most root cellars of the time were contained in the foundations of other buildings.
Private; not accessible to the public

ACCOMACK COUNTY
Metomkin Island vicinity
BOWMAN'S FOLLY
2.5 miles southeast of intersection of
Routes 652 and 13
c. 1815

Bowman's Folly combines a two-and-one-half-story, gable roofed main building with a one-and-one-half-story eastern wing plus outbuildings. The main house has brick ends laid in Flemish bond with two interior end chimneys. Both north and south facades are frame with a second-story Palladian window, five pedimented dormers, and a pedimented entranceway porch. A frame kitchen has been connected to the main house by a low hyphen and later frame wing. Other outbuildings include a frame dovecote and privy. Bowman's Folly was built by John Cropper, Jr. (1755–1821), to replace an earlier home which had burned.
Private; not accessible to the public
HABS

ACCOMACK COUNTY
Onancock
HOPKINS AND BROTHER STORE
Market Street
19th century

Hopkins and Brother Store is not on its original location. However, it has served as a commercial and maritime trading center of the Eastern Shore for over one hundred years. Founded in 1842 by Captain Stephen Hopkins, the business remained in the family until it was discontinued in 1965. When opened, the store served as a bank and a trading center. Business records for the store from 1842 to 1965 have been donated to the Virginia Historical Society.
Private

ACCOMACK COUNTY
Onancock
KERR PLACE
Northeast corner of Crockett Avenue
and Market Street
18th and 19th centuries

Kerr Place has been called the most elaborate Federal mansion on Virginia's Eastern Shore. The two-story brick house sits on a raised basement, and the central three bays project from the main block. The front entrances are crowned by fanlights, and a Federal style bracketed cornice follows the base of the roofline. Interior trim in all rooms is considered the most elaborate and formal found in any house on Virginia's Eastern Shore.
Private
HABS

ACCOMACK COUNTY
Pungoteague
ST. GEORGE'S CHURCH
Northwest side of Route 178, .3 mile
northeast of the intersection with
Route 180
c. 1738

The date of construction for St. George's Church is not definitely known. It was built in the shape of a Latin cross with a semicircular apse topped by a conical roof on the east end. A distinguishing and unusual feature was the hip gambrel roof. Damaged by Union soldiers in the Civil War, the church remained a roofless ruin until 1880, and very little of the 18th-century church is left. The north and south walls and the end bays of the east and west walls are original. A pedimented gable roof and simple belfry now cover the church, and the pediment, cornice, windows, and all other wood trim date from the post-Civil War renovation. St. George's is one of only two colonial churches on Virginia's Eastern Shore.
Private
HABS

ALBEMARLE COUNTY
Charlottesville vicinity
FARMINGTON
.9 mile west of the intersection of
Routes 250 and 29–250 Bypass
18th and 19th centuries

The original dwelling on the Farmington property was a two-story brick farmhouse, believed to have been completed before 1780. Five years later the estate was sold to George Divers, who, in 1802, asked his friend Thomas Jefferson to design an addition. Jefferson's proposals were for a large octagonal addition on the east facade. It features a two-story, tetrastyle, pedimented Tuscan portico, but there are some departures from the Jefferson drawings. The drawings showed no stone lintels above the triple-hung windows and no keystones around the circular windows. Jefferson apparently also wanted the full entablature to extend around the octagonal ends of the addition, although, on the building, only the modillion cornice does so. In 1929 Farmington became a country club, and Jefferson's two interior, two-story rooms of unequal size became one. Other changes have been made inside and out, and only the north wall remains unobscured by later building.
Private
HABS

ALBEMARLE COUNTY
Charlottesville vicinity
MONTICELLO
2 miles south of Charlottesville on
Va. 53
1770–1789, Thomas Jefferson

Thomas Jefferson served his country in many capacities: member of the Continental Congress, governor of Virginia, Secretary of State (1790–1793), Vice President (1797–1801) and President of the United States (1801–1809). In addition he was the author of the Declaration of Independence and founder and architect of the University of Virginia. Jefferson spent a

lifetime perfecting his mansion, which shows clearly many facets of his personality and intellect. As it stands today the house evidences many borrowings from Roman, Palladian, and 18th-century French designs. However, the manner in which these adapted elements are combined and the materials (red brick with wood trim) of which the house is built make it a very personal statement. Centered on both the east (main) facade and the west (garden) front are tetrastyle porticos with semicircular fanlights in the pediments, a favorite Jeffersonian motif. A domed octagonal third story rises above and behind the west portico. The interior, furnished as it was in Jefferson's day, employs all three of the principal Roman orders. On the ground floor the large entrance hall leads into a salon, and lateral halls lead to four rooms on either side. A dumbwaiter incorporated in the dining room mantel is but one of the many features of the interior expressing Jefferson's inventiveness.
Private
NHL; HABS

ALBEMARLE COUNTY
Covesville vicinity
REDLANDS
.1 mile east of the intersection of Routes 708 and 627
1798–1808

Taking its name from the red clay soil prevalent in that part of Albemarle County, Redlands plantation is still owned by the Carter family, who began construction of the house at the end of the 18th century. The two-story brick mansion is distinguished by the sophistication of its Adamesque woodwork, the most elaborate examples of which are found in the central drawing room. Except for the addition of dormer windows on the low hip roof and of a one-story Tuscan portico, the Federal-style exterior is unchanged.
Private
HABS

ALEXANDRIA (independent city)
ALEXANDRIA HISTORIC DISTRICT
Bounded roughly by the Capital Beltway on the south, Alfred and Patrick Streets on the west (with an extension westward along Prince Street), Oronoco and Princess Streets on the northwest and northeast respectively (with an extension northward along George Washington Memorial Parkway to the north city limits), and by the Potomac River on the east
Mid–18th to 19th century

From the mid–18th century until the Civil War the city of Alexandria served as the principal seaport and commercial center of northern Virginia. The historic district embraces nearly 100 blocks in the heart of the original town, and within its boundaries are numerous significant examples of Colonial and Federal architecture of great intrinsic as well as historic value. George Washington was one of the original surveyors of this district which consists of uniform rectangular blocks in a grid pattern. Portions of the historic district have been designated a National Historic Landmark.
Multiple public/private
NHL; HABS

ALEXANDRIA (independent city)
CARLYLE HOUSE
123 N. Fairfax Street
1752

The Carlyle House is significant architecturally as the only surviving mid-Georgian townhouse in Virginia designed on a five-part plan. It is a two-and-one-half-story rectangular structure which has been altered considerably in appearance and setting. Exterior wall surfaces, which were originally brick decorated at the corners by stone quoins, are now covered with scored stucco. The present hip roof and dormers probably replaced a shallower hip-on-hip roof without dormers. The original stone cornice remains on the entrance facade but has been replaced by a wooden one on the other three sides. Original sash has been replaced, the garden front entrance was restyled, and a neoclassic porch has been added across the Lee Street facade. The dependencies were removed in the 19th-century. Carlyle House was built for John Carlyle, one of the original incorporators of the city of Alexandria.
Private
HABS

ALEXANDRIA (independent city)
CHRIST CHURCH
Southeast corner of Cameron and Columbus Streets
1767–1773, James Wren

Alexandria's Christ Church is a little altered, continuously used, 18th-century, brick, late Georgian style church. The building is 60 feet long by 50 feet wide. Corners are emphasized by stone quoins painted white, and the east wall is highlighted by a two-tier Palladian window framed by a pediment. The interior wooden galleries were added between 1785 and 1800. The wood and brick belfry is an 1818 addition. Of all the comparable surviving houses of worship that date from the same period, Christ Church is the least altered.
Private
NHL; HABS

ALEXANDRIA (independent city)
GADSBY'S TAVERN
128 N. Royal Street
1752, 1792

One of the best-known inns in Virginia, Gadsby's Tavern comprises two adjoining buildings: the smaller City Tavern, which was built first, and the three-story brick building which was added 40 years later. Under both John Wise and John Gadsby, to whom Wise leased the tavern in 1794, the hostelry was renowned for both its hospitality and its architecture. Here George Washington recruited his first military command in 1754 in the campaign against the French and Indians. An important center of Virginia life, the tavern served as a political and social forum for the leading figures of the day.
Private
NHL; HABS

ALEXANDRIA (independent city)
THE LYCEUM
201 S. Washington Street
c. 1837

The Lyceum is a Greek Revival, two-story brick structure faced with scored stucco. The principal facade is composed of three widely spaced bays separated by pilasters, and the central bay has a projecting two-story, pedimented, tetrastyle Doric portico. The recessed front door is framed by two Doric pilasters supporting a full Doric entablature. On the rear facade is a shallow, one-story ell with a later, one-story wooden porch. Benjamin Hallowell founded the Lyceum in 1834 as a society for scholarly activity in the city of Alexandria. Meetings were first held in Hallowell's school, but eventually he purchased a lot on which the Lyceum building was constructed. The Lyceum continued as an active organization until the Civil War. After the war the society was dissolved and the building was converted into a residence.
Public; not accessible to the public at present
HABS

ALLEGHANY COUNTY
Covington vicinity
HUMPBACK BRIDGE
Over Dunlop Creek, .8 mile
southwest of the intersection of U.S.
60 and County Route 651
1835

The Humpback Bridge was built as part of
the James River and Kanawha Valley
Turnpike. It is the oldest remaining
covered bridge in Virginia and the only
one of its type in the country. Constructed
of hand-hewn oak timbers and held
together with locust pins, the bridge has
no middle support. The center floor and
roof are eight feet higher than the bridge
ends which discrepancy produces the
peculiar humped appearance. Both ends
of the bridge are supported by high stone
foundations.
State
HABS

AMELIA COUNTY
Chula vicinity
THE WIGWAM
8 miles northwest of Chula
18th and 19th centuries

The Wigwam is composed of two one-and-
one-half-story buildings set at right angles
to one another. It is thought that the rear
ell was constructed in the late 18th century and that the front section was added in
the early 19th century. Inside, the ell has
been altered, but the front section retains
much of its original woodwork sanded
down to a natural finish. The Wigwam was
the home of William Branch Giles
(1762–1830), Congressman, Senator, and
governor of Virginia.
Private; not accessible to the public
HABS

AMHERST COUNTY
Sweet Briar
SWEET BRIAR HOUSE
1 mile southwest of the intersection
of Routes 29 and 624
Early 19th century; 1851

The earliest portion of Sweet Briar House
was probably constructed in the first
quarter of the 19th century. It was then a
T-shaped, brick farmhouse with a hip roof
and a two-level pedimented portico and
exterior end chimneys. In 1830 the property was bought by Elijah Fletcher, a
newspaper publisher. He subsequently altered and enlarged the dwelling (1851) by
the addition of the two Italianate towers
and the present portico and veranda on
the main facade. Fletcher's daughter and
son-in-law, Mr. and Mrs. James Henry
Williams, later made plans to found a col-

lege in memory of their only child, who
died at 17. The college was established in
accordance with the provisions of Mrs.
Williams' will and chartered by the Commonwealth of Virginia in 1901. Today
Sweet Briar House serves as the president's house.
Private
HABS

APPOMATTOX COUNTY
Appomattox vicinity
**APPOMATTOX COURT HOUSE
NATIONAL HISTORICAL PARK**
3 miles northeast of Appomattox on
Va. 24
1865

At Appomattox Court House on April 9,
1865, General Robert E. Lee surrendered
his Army of Northern Virginia to General
Ulysses S. Grant. Although other Confederate armies had yet to surrender, the
Civil War had virtually ended. The two
commanders met at the house of Wilmer
McLean, where Lee accepted Grant's
generous surrender terms. The McLean
House, taken down in the 1890's, has
been reconstructed, and surviving
buildings have been restored.
Federal/non-federal
NPS; 972.01 acres
HABS

ARLINGTON COUNTY
Arlington
ARLINGTON HOUSE
Arlington National Cemetery
1802–1817, George Hadfield

George Washington Parke Custis, builder
of Arlington House, was the grandson of
Martha Washington. His daughter, Mary
Ann Randolph Custis, was married to
Robert E. Lee here in 1831. The mansion
was their home for most of their married
life. Here in 1861 Lee resigned his commission in the United States Army. In
1861 the Union Army seized Arlington to
fortify the approaches to Washington and
in 1864 converted it to a military cemetery. In 1882 George Washington Custis
Lee, son of Robert E. Lee, won compensation from the United States for his family's loss of the property. The Greek
Revival mansion, which contains
furnishings from Mount Vernon and personal effects of George Washington, has
since been restored.
Federal
NPS; 3.47 acres
HABS

AUGUSTA COUNTY (also in Nelson
County)
Waynesboro vicinity
SWANNANOA
.4 mile south of the intersection of
Routes 610 and 250
1913, Baskerville and Noland

Swannanoa was designed by the
Richmond architectural firm of Baskerville and Noland as a summer home for
Richmond railroad magnate, James
Dooley. The main house is built of white
Georgia marble in an Italian Renaissance
style of the 16th century. The facade is
composed of a three-story, five-bay center
section flanked by two protruding four-
story towers. At each corner of the facade
is a two-story pavilion. In the space
between the towers is a one-story vaulted
arcade which connects at either end with
an open gallery continuing around each
corner of the front.
Private

BATH COUNTY
Bacova vicinity
HIDDEN VALLEY (WARWICKTON)
1.1 miles north of the intersection of
Routes 621 and 39
1858

Hidden Valley, historically known as Warwickton, is a five-bay, two-story Georgian
brick residence adapted to the needs and
taste of a Greek Revival house builder.
Crowned by a hip roof, the house contains four interior end chimneys. The
pedimented tetrastyle portico employs
Greek Ionic capitals with fluted shafts.
Hidden Valley's main entranceway is a
close adaptation of a plate in Asher
Benjamin's *Practical House Carpenter*
(1835).
Federal; not accessible to the public
HABS

BEDFORD COUNTY
Bedford vicinity
THREE OTTERS
7 miles west of the intersection of
Routes 838 and 43
19th century

Nearly all the architectural detail of Three
Otters is based on plates in Asher
Benjamin's builder's handbook *The Practical House Carpenter*. Three Otters is a
non-temple-form Greek Revival house. It
has a low pitched hip roof which appears
flat, and a full Doric entablature in which
nearly all the metopes are single window
panes. Flat stuccoed panels between the
first- and second-floor windows greatly
reduce the ratio of solid to void. The main
entrance is sheltered by a small Greek

Doric portico topped by a balustraded deck. A similar portico adorns the asymmetrical rear elevation. Three Otters measures approximately 50 feet square and was built for Abel Beach Nichols, a merchant from Bridgeport, Connecticut. The original kitchen and pantry outbuilding is connected to the main house by a covered walkway, part of which has been incorporated into a two-story brick and frame addition.
Private; not accessible to the public
HABS

BEDFORD COUNTY
Lynchburg vicinity
POPLAR FOREST
.5 mile south of the intersection of Routes 661 and 460
Early 19th century, Thomas Jefferson

Thomas Jefferson built Poplar Forest as a country retreat. It is a brick, one-story building, octagonal in shape, and set on a high basement with tetrastyle pedimented Tuscan porticos on low arcades at the entrance and rear facades. The house burned in 1845, but the original floor plan has remained intact and all rebuilding was done according to Jefferson's plans. A kitchen, smokehouse, and two octagonal privies still stand.
Private
HABS

BOTETOURT COUNTY
Fincastle
FINCASTLE HISTORIC DISTRICT
Bounded by Back and Carper Streets on the north, by properties fronting on Hancock Street on the east, by Griffin Alley, the cemetery, and a line midway between Main Street and Murray Street on the south, and Catawba Street on the west
18th and 19th centuries

Fincastle was platted in 1770 and officially established as a town by an act of the Virginia Assembly in 1772. Today the town still retains the atmosphere of a small agricultural, courthouse community. The homogeneous scale of its buildings and the use of local materials help to unify the townscape. Significant individual buildings are the courthouse and the Methodist and Presbyterian churches, all Greek Revival in style, and St. Mark's Episcopal Church, which is Gothic Revival.
Multiple public/private
HABS

BUCKINGHAM COUNTY
Buckingham
BUCKINGHAM COURT HOUSE HISTORIC DISTRICT
Along Route 60, extending .3 mile east of the intersection of Routes 60 and 631
19th century

Built on a ridge between Bryant Creek and the Slate River, Buckingham Court House extends for slightly more than a half mile on either side of Route 60. The courthouse, a two-story temple-form building fronted by a pedimented, tetrastyle Doric portico, is located near the center of the district. Plans for the first courthouse (which was completed in 1823 and burned in 1869) were drawn by Thomas Jefferson. The building that replaced it is similar in size and style to its predecessor. Other noteworthy 19th-century structures in the historic district are the Buckingham Tavern, the Buckingham Inn, the Leach House, the Presbyterian manse, the Masonic Hall, West View (a house), a tavern, and another home, Rose Terrace. Although somewhat altered by the intrusion of a highway and construction of new buildings, Buckingham Court House retains much that was typical of a 19th-century courthouse village.
Multiple public/private
HABS

CAMPBELL COUNTY
Long Island vicinity
GREEN HILL
.3 mile south of the intersection of Routes 633 and 728
19th century

The Green Hill main house is a two-story, Flemish bond brick structure with a gable roof, modillion cornice, and two interior end chimneys. A central entrance on the five-bay facade has double doors topped by a double row transom. The one-story rear ell also has a gable roof with modillion cornice, and its brickwork resembles that of the main house. Interior woodwork in the main house is unusually good. Numerous outbuildings remain on the property among which are a brick duck house, an ice house, a kitchen, a stone laundry, a frame kitchen, and a frame slave dwelling. Advance buildings to the house are two log barns, ruins of a stone stable, a large tobacco barn, and a granary.
Private; not accessible to the public
HABS

CAROLINE COUNTY
Bowling Green vicinity
OLD MANSION
.4 mile south of intersection of Routes 2 (301) and 207
c.1670

The original front portion of the Old Mansion is a one-and-one-half-story brick house with dormers and a jerkinhead roof with exterior chimneys. A later front porch obscures the first floor facade of the structure, while a mid–18th century frame addition to the rear of the house is covered by a gambrel roof with shed dormers. Except for the removal of two partitions and a mantel, most all of the original interior features remain.
Private; not accessible to the public
HABS

CAROLINE COUNTY
Port Royal
PORT ROYAL HISTORIC DISTRICT
Bounded on the north by the intersection of Route 301 and the Rappahannock River; extending .1 mile east of the intersection of Routes T 1004 and T 1005, .1 mile west and .2 mile south of the intersection of Routes T 1003 and 301
18th and 19th centuries

The Port Royal Historic District encompasses 12 blocks. Contained therein are numerous 18th- and 19th-century homes and public buildings. Founded in 1744, Port Royal had an excellent harbor and was a major shipping port for tobacco. By the 19th century commercial activity lessened as the railroad superseded the rivers as the principal transportation artery. The character of Port Royal has changed little since the mid–19th century. Notable buildings are the 18th-century Fox's Tavern, the 19th-century Masonic Hall, and the 18th-century Brockenbrough House (all on King Street); the Hipkins-Carr House, the Gray House, with good late 18th-century woodwork, the Federal Lightfoot House, and the Greek Revival, temple-form St. Peter's Episcopal Church (Water Street). In all there are 35 structures of architectural or historic interest.
Multiple public/private
HABS

CAROLINE COUNTY
Port Royal vicinity
CAMDEN
.5 mile north of the intersection of Routes 686 and 17
1857–1859, Norris G. Starkwether

Camden, a two-story Italian villa house was built by William Carter Pratt. The exterior is frame covered with cypress siding

sanded to resemble stone. Norris G. Stark-wether, the architect, installed a central heating system (which was also designed to circulate cool air in summer), gas lights, and running water in every bedroom. There were also inside toilets and shower baths as well as tubs. A Union gunboat destroyed the upper story of Camden's tower in 1863; otherwise the house remains very much as built both inside and out. The land around the house contains a single house site probably occupied by one Indian family in the late 17th century. The site measures only 30 by 40 feet, but it has yielded a number of artifacts such as pottery, pieces of tobacco pipes, iron tools, and two silver medals.
Private; not accessible to the public
HABS

CHARLES CITY COUNTY
Charles City
CHARLES CITY COUNTY
COURTHOUSE
18th century

Charles City County originally consisted of land on both sides of the James River between James City and Henrico counties. In 1702, the county was divided into Prince George County (south of the James River) and Charles City County (north of the river). Charles City became the county seat in 1730, and it is believed that the courthouse was constructed soon thereafter. It is a one-story, T-shaped structure of brick laid in Flemish bond. Extensive alterations were made after the Civil War including the enclosure and installation of windows in the five-bay arcade on the front facade and the lowering of all other windows. A one-story front porch was added on the south side. Despite these changes, the Charles City County Courthouse is probably the most sophisticated example of the few surviving arcaded-front colonial courthouses in Virginia.
County
HABS

CHARLES CITY COUNTY
Charles City vicinity
GREENWAY
.6 mile west of the intersection of
Routes 5 and 155
Late 18th century

Greenway was built by Judge John Tyler, governor of Virginia (1808-1811) and father of John Tyler, tenth President of the United States. President Tyler lived in the house until his marriage and later returned while governor of Virginia (1825-1827). Greenway is a frame, one-and-one-half-story structure with beaded clapboarding and a wood cornered gable

roof with dormers. The brick foundation walls are primarily of Flemish bond, but evidence of occasional English bond suggests possible stages of growth not visible elsewhere.
Private; not accessible to the public
HABS

CHARLES CITY COUNTY
Charles City vicinity
SHERWOOD FOREST (JOHN TYLER HOUSE)
4 miles east of Charles City on Va. 5
1842–1862

John Tyler, President of the United States, lived at Sherwood Forest during the last 20 years of his life. After purchasing the estate in 1842, he added a covered colonnade to connect the main house with the kitchen and laundry and a corresponding wing to serve as a ballroom and private office. Before becoming President on the death of William Henry Harrison, Tyler had served Virginia as Congressman, governor, and United States Senator. His retirement at Sherwood Forest was disrupted by the Civil War, and he died in 1862 while serving the state of Virginia as a Confederate Congressman.
Private
NHL; HABS

CHARLES CITY COUNTY
Charles City vicinity
WESTOVER
7 miles west of Charles City on Va. 5
1730–1734

A noted example of early Georgian domestic architecture, Westover was built by William Byrd II, tobacco planter and founder of Richmond, Virginia. Flanked by a pair of one-and-a-half-story wings connected by passages, the central two-story rectangular mass has a hip roof. The pedimental entrance doors are decorative features of the exterior. Within, four large rooms are divided by a transverse hall. In addition to its architectural significance, Westover is historically important because of its association with Byrd's writings, which include *The History of the Dividing Line* and *A Journey to the Land of Eden*.
Private
NHL; HABS

CHARLES CITY COUNTY
Charles City vicinity
SHIRLEY
1.5 miles west of the intersection of
Routes 608 and 5
18th century

The plantation house at Shirley is a large, almost square, two-and-one-half-story brick building with a mansard roof, dor-

mers, and two interior chimneys. On both the land and river facades are tetrastyle, two-story pedimented porticos which were probably altered or rebuilt early in the 19th century. The house itself is brick, but the porticoed sides are covered with stucco. In the forecourt of the main house are two L-shaped stables, a kitchen, and an overseer's house. Shirley Plantation was part of a large tract of land patented by Edward Hill in 1660, and Anne Hill Carter, mother of Robert E. Lee, was born here in 1773.
Private
HABS

CHARLES CITY COUNTY
Hopewell vicinity
EPPES ISLAND
Between Eppes Creek and the James
River at the confluence of the James
and Appomattox rivers
17th, 18th, and 19th centuries

Eppes Island has been occupied by the Eppes family since 1624, and thus it may be considered the oldest family farm in Virginia still held by descendants of the original owner. By 1824 the Eppes family had bought out all other landowners on the island. The still visible field lines were at one time the property boundaries of separate farms which the Eppes family purchased and consolidated. Shirley Hundred village was located on the western side of the island near the present house. South of the house is a swamp containing a woodland and an Archaic Indian site. Slave quarters stand near the center of the island adjacent to the sites of other quarters. The two easternmost fields contain 18th-century house sites.
Private; not accessible to the public

CHARLOTTE COUNTY
Brookneal vicinity
STAUNTON HILL
1.4 miles southwest of the
intersection of County Route 619 and
Route 693
1848, John E. Johnson

Constructed of brick covered with pink stucco, Staunton Hill has a symmetrical two-story facade interrupted by a central three-story pavilion; the entire front is embellished with a one-story, Tudor style, gray marble veranda. The skyline of the house is broken by a crenellated parapet, clustered octagonal chimney pots, and octagonal crenellated towers at the corners of the central pavilion. The plan of the house is also symmetrical with a vaulted entrance hall separating the dining room from one of the parlors. Behind the entrance hall is the stair hall which contains a divided staircase. Staunton Hill was built

for Charles Bruce, son of James Bruce, a wealthy Virginia merchandiser.
Private; not accessible to the public
HABS

CHARLOTTESVILLE (independent city)
ROTUNDA, UNIVERSITY OF VIRGINIA
University of Virginia campus
1822–1826, Thomas Jefferson; 1898, Stanford White

Founded by Thomas Jefferson, the University of Virginia was granted its charter in 1819. Chosen a member of the first board of visitors, and elected rector, Jefferson helped mold the institution according to his enlightened educational principles. The visual expression of his ideals is still present in The Lawn and The Ranges, the "academic village" which he planned and which still forms the physical heart of the university. Dominating the composition is the Rotunda, adapted from the Pantheon of ancient Rome. Designed by Jefferson in 1821 and begun the next year, the building was finished only after its designer's death in 1826. It was intended to be the university's library, and served this purpose until 1938. In 1895 a fire broke out in the annex, which had been attached to the north facade in 1853, and rapidly spread to the Rotunda itself. Afterwards only the walls of the Rotunda remained. The Board of Visitors determined to rebuild the Rotunda, but not the annex, and engaged Stanford White to do the work. The interior was redesigned by White, who also modified the exterior proportions. Although remodeled, the Rotunda is still regarded as one of Jefferson's architectural masterpieces, and still dominates the university he founded.
State
NHL; HABS

CHARLOTTESVILLE (independent city)
UNIVERSITY OF VIRGINIA HISTORIC DISTRICT
Bounded on the north by University Avenue, on the south by Jefferson Park Avenue, on the east by Hospital Road, and on the west by McCormick Road
19th and 20th centuries, Thomas Jefferson and Stanford White

Throughout his public life Thomas Jefferson wished to found a university which would educate leaders for a democratic nation. Jefferson envisioned a community of scholars living and studying in an architecturally unified complex of buildings. His dream became a reality in 1817 with the laying of the cornerstone of the University of Virginia, which was chartered two years later by the General Assembly. Built according to Jefferson's design, the classrooms and professors' quarters were housed in 10 two-story pavilions aligned on either side of an elongated terraced court called The Lawn. As a focal point for this complex Jefferson chose a domed building, a scaled down version of the Pantheon, known now as the Rotunda, which was completed in 1827. In 1895 the Rotunda burned, and Stanford White was commissioned to rebuild it and to design additional classroom space and an auditorium. White's new buildings—Cocke, Rouss, and Cabell halls—are Neo-Classic Revival. Parallel to The Lawn buildings are additional rows of Jeffersonian edifices, known as East and West Ranges, which contained the original dining facilities. White also designed Garrett Hall. The Brooks Museum (1876, J. R. Thomas) and the University Chapel (1889) are also included in the historic district.
State
NHL; HABS

CHESTERFIELD COUNTY
Midlothian vicinity
BELLONA ARSENAL
.1 mile northwest of Route 673, 2 miles northwest of the intersection with Route 147
19th century

The original arsenal, constructed during the second decade of the 19th century, consisted of eight buildings: the main arsenal, two officers' quarters, four workshops, and the barracks. Major John Clarke established his Bellona Foundry in 1814, and was instrumental in arranging for the location of the arsenal nearby. By 1832 most production, specifically the repair of smaller arms, was discontinued. The complex was declared surplus property by the government five years later. Major Clarke's grandson bought the property in 1856 and leased the foundry and arsenal to the Confederacy in 1862. Remaining structures include only the powder magazine and three of the workshops, renovated and converted into a single residence in 1942.
Private
HABS

CHESTERFIELD COUNTY
Winterpock vicinity
EPPINGTON
1.6 miles south of intersection of Routes 621 and 602
Late 1760's

Built in the third quarter of the 18th-century, Eppington is a frame, Georgian manor house. The two-and-one-half-story, three-bay, central block, with a hip roof, is flanked on either side by one-story, two-bay wings which also have hip roofs. The house was built by Francis Eppes, a cousin, by marriage, of Thomas Jefferson. It was at Eppington that Jefferson's two daughters were reared, after the death of Mrs. Jefferson, and while Jefferson himself was minister to France.
Private; not accessible to the public
HABS

CLARKE COUNTY
Berryville vicinity
ANNEFIELD
.7 mile east of the intersection of Routes 633 and 652
c. 1790

Annefield stands on a knoll overlooking the rolling slopes of the lower Shenandoah Valley. Mathew Page, who left the worn-out fields of Hanover County for the fertile lands of western Virginia, built the hip-roofed structure in 1790. It is a well-proportioned mansion combining a basic mid–18th century house design with such Federal period features as a shallow roofline silhouette and Adamesque interior woodwork. The two-level, pedimented Ionic portico is noteworthy for its handsome Chinese Chippendale balustrade.
Private
HABS

CLARKE COUNTY
Berryville vicinity
FAIRFIELD
.2 mile east of the intersection of Routes 340 and 610
c. 1770

Fairfield is presently a five-part Palladian complex with a two-and-one-half-story hip-roofed central block. The walls are constructed of irregular native limestone ashlar, and the style of the complex is Georgian. Noticeable twentieth-century additions are the dormers on the central block, one-story attached dependencies at the ends of the complex, additions to the rear of the original one-story wings, and a screened, one-story porch on the garden side; the one-story portico on the entrance front was added in the 19th century. Warner Washington, a first cousin of George Washington's, built the house for his second wife.
Private; not accessible to the public
HABS

CLARKE COUNTY
Berryville vicinity
LONG BRANCH
.1 mile west of the intersection of
County Route 626 and Route 624
19th century, Benjamin Latrobe

Long Branch is one of the few existing
houses which Benjamin Latrobe is known
to have designed. The house was built for
Robert Carter Burwell and had already
been started by 1811, when Latrobe was
first consulted about the design. The
house itself is a rectangular, two-story
brick structure with seven bays on both
the front and rear facades. Both facades
are ornamented by two-story pedimented
porticos. The entire house is crowned by a
shallow deck-on-hip roof, and the deck is
surrounded by a balustrade enclosing a
central rectangular lantern.
Private; not accessible to the public
HABS

CLARKE COUNTY
Boyce vicinity
SARATOGA
.4 mile southeast of the intersection
of Routes 723 and 617
Late 18th century

Saratoga was built by Daniel Morgan
(1736–1802), a Revolutionary soldier who
settled in the Shenandoah Valley. The
house is a solid gray limestone residence
which combines Georgian architecture
with the native building skills of the valley's German settlers. Later additions to
the house are a frame porch at the rear,
the one-story brick wing on the southwest
wall, and a frame wing connecting the
stone kitchen to the house. Original outbuildings, besides the stone kitchen, are
the smokehouse, a stone shed, and a stone
dairy.
Private; not accessible to the public
HABS

CLARKE COUNTY
Millwood
MILLWOOD MILL
Southwest side of the intersection of
Routes 723 and 255
c. 1785

Millwood Mill was built by Colonel
Nathaniel Burwell (1750–1814) and
General Daniel Morgan (1736–1802) on
property belonging to Burwell. Once the
mill had been built and put into operation,
Burwell began to expand his industrial
operations in the area. In 1786 he built a
house to live in while workmen completed
his larger home, Carter Hall. Burwell also
constructed a tanyard, a tanner's house,
another mill, and later a distillery, all in
partnership with Morgan. The mill itself is

a two-story structure with gable roof and a
down slope basement. The first level of
the mill is stone with a frame second story
and an attic addition. Gears for running
the mill machinery came from an earlier
structure (c. 1750). Millwood Mill was
operative until 1943 and is presently undergoing restoration.
Private
HABS

CLARKE COUNTY
White Post vicinity
GREENWAY COURT
1 mile south of White Post on Va.
277
1762

The estate of Greenway Court was the
home of Thomas, Lord Fairfax from 1751
until his death in 1781. Lord Fairfax had
settled in Virginia in 1747. Here from
1762 until his death he maintained the
land office of his vast Northern Neck
proprietary, which he had inherited from
his mother. George Washington was once
employed as a surveyor on the Fairfax
grant. The limestone "estate office," still
in good condition, is the only extant building which dates from the period of Fairfax's occupancy. The hunting lodge which
served as his residence has been replaced
by a two-story brick farmhouse built in
1828.
Private; not accessible to the public
NHL; HABS

CULPEPER COUNTY
Rixeyville vicinity
LITTLE FORK CHURCH
Northeast corner of intersection of
Routes 624 and 726

Although relatively neglected at present,
Little Fork Church is one of the finest and
best preserved of Virginia's colonial
churches. The rectangular edifice is constructed of brick laid in Flemish bond.
Window and door openings, as well as the
corners of the building, are marked by
rubbed brick. The walls are capped by a
modillion cornice, above which is a hip
roof. The original reredos and some
original interior trim survive. Little Fork
Church was never a parish church, but
served only as a chapel of ease for those
living at a distance from their parish
church. After being used as a stable during the Civil War and later as a Methodist
church, it now serves again as a chapel of
ease for St. Mark's parish.
Private
HABS

CULPEPER COUNTY
Stevensburg vicinity
SALUBRIA
.8 mile east of the intersection of
Routes 3 and 663
18th century

Salubria is a two-story hip-roofed structure with two large corbel-capped chimneys on the interior ends. The architectural style is Georgian, and the basic
building material, brick. Segmental arches
crown the windows, main door, and basement openings.
Private; not accessible to the public
HABS

DANVILLE (independent city)
DANVILLE PUBLIC LIBRARY
975 Main Street
1857–1858

Although the interior has been considerably altered for use as a public library, this two-story structure remains one of
the outstanding examples of the Italian
Villa style in Virginia. Major William T.
Sutherland, a member of the Virginia
Convention of 1861, built the house and
was occupying it when Confederate President Jefferson Davis made a brief
stopover during his flight from Richmond
in April, 1865. At the Sutherland residence on April 4, Davis signed his last
official proclamation as president of the
Confederacy. The shallow hip roof of the
house, adorned by a bracketed cornice, is
crowned by a cupola. The asymmetrical
interior plan is characteristic of the
Italianate style.
Municipal
HABS

DINWIDDIE COUNTY
Dinwiddie vicinity
BURNT QUARTER
.7 mile southwest of the intersection
of Routes 627, 613, and 645
18th century

Burnt Quarter is the main house of a plantation complex built on land first patented
in the late 17th century. The center section of the three-part frame building is two
stories high and is covered with a hip roof,
while the two side sections, each one-and-
one-half stories high, are covered by gable
roofs. On April 1, 1865, the battle of Five
Forks was fought in the fields and woods
surrounding the house. During the battle
the house itself served as headquarters for
Union General Wesley Merritt and as a
hospital.
Private; not accessible to the public
HABS

DINWIDDIE COUNTY
Petersburg vicinity
FIVE FORKS BATTLEFIELD
12 miles west of Petersburg on
County Route 627 at Church Road
1865

The battle of Five Forks marked the turning point in General Ulysses S. Grant's long campaign to force General Robert E. Lee from the Richmond-Petersburg defenses. After failing to break through the Union siege line on March 25, 1865, Lee sent a scratch force under George Edward Pickett to Five Forks to keep Union forces from the Southside Railroad, his last supply line. On April 1 General Philip H. Sheridan swept through to cut the railroad. Thus, deprived of supplies, Lee was forced to withdraw from Richmond. He surrendered to Grant on April 9, 1865.
Private
NHL

DINWIDDIE COUNTY
Petersburg vicinity
MAYFIELD
Central State Hospital Grounds
Mid–18th century

Robert Ruffin is the earliest known owner of Mayfield, which was constructed sometime prior to 1769. The plantation residence is distinguished by an unusual jerkinhead roof pierced by dormer windows, and the Flemish bond masonry, with gauged flat arches, beveled watertable, and rubbed brick dressings is a fine example of colonial Virginia brickwork. During the siege of Petersburg in 1865, Mayfield was the scene of fierce fighting as Union soldiers sought to break the Confederate defense line. Removed a short distance from its original location, the house is undergoing restoration.
Private; not accessible to the public

DINWIDDIE COUNTY (also in Prince George County)
Petersburg vicinity
PETERSBURG NATIONAL
BATTLEFIELD
Southeast, south, and southwest of
Petersburg
1864–1865

The Confederate defeat at Five Forks and Petersburg on April 1–2, 1865, led to the fall of Richmond and the surrender of General Robert E. Lee's army to General Ulysses S. Grant. Dominating the southern and western approaches to Richmond through control of the railroads connecting the Confederate capital with the South, Petersburg in 1864 became a bastion of the Confederacy. Here for nearly 10 months Union soldiers of the armies of the Potomac and the James bat-

tled Confederate troops led by Generals Robert E. Lee and P. G. T. Beauregard before they smashed the Confederate right at Five Forks and compelled the evacuation of Petersburg. Near the battlefield site is Poplar Grove National Cemetery.
Federal/non-federal
NPS; 2,731 acres

DINWIDDIE COUNTY
Rowanta vicinity
WILLIAMSON SITE
.9 mile northeast of the intersection
of Routes 693 and 703
9000 B.C.

The approximately 20 acres covered by the Williamson Site have yielded fluted spear points, scrapers, knives, burins, hammers, and assorted debris, all indicating that the site was a quarry workshop. Paleo-Indians made tools and weapons here from chert, which is a rock resembling flint. Williamson Site is one of four Paleo-Indian workshops in the eastern United States.
Private

ESSEX COUNTY
Caret vicinity
BLANDFIELD
.7 mile east of the intersection of
Routes 624 and 17
18th century

Blandfield, on the Rappahannock River, was built of brick laid in Flemish bond. Mid-Georgian in style, the house consists of a two-story central block with flanking two-story dependencies connected to the center section by straight, one-story hyphens. These dependencies are placed at right angles to the central block which features a three-bay, pedimented central pavilion on both the land and river sides. Entirely surrounded by a modillion cornice and topped by a hip-on-hip roof with four interior chimneys, Blandfield was built by William Beverly (1696–1756) and named for his wife, Elizabeth Bland.
Private; not accessible to the public
HABS

ESSEX COUNTY
Loretto vicinity
ELMWOOD
.2 mile southwest of the intersection
of Routes 640 and 17
c. 1774

Elmwood was the plantation house of Muscoe Garnett (1736–1803), a member of the Essex Committee of Safety and one of the largest landowners in the county. The house measures 100 feet long by 30 feet deep, and the walls are laid in Flemish bond with a molded water table and a rubbed brick belt course. All windows, ex-

cept those of the first floor south, have gauged flat arches. A one-story porch originally hid the other windows. In 1852 Elmwood was extensively remodeled in the Italianate style, but the present owner is attempting to remove the later additions.
Private; not accessible to the public
HABS

FAIRFAX COUNTY
Accotink vicinity
POPE-LEIGHEY HOUSE
East of Accotink off U.S. 1
1940–1941, Frank Lloyd Wright

Frank Lloyd Wright was greatly concerned with the problem of providing middle income Americans with well-designed housing for minimum cost. The result of his search for an inexpensive and functionally practical dwelling was the U.S.-onian or Usonian house. The Pope-Leighey House is an example. It is one-story with neither basement nor attic, and all external features emphasize the horizontal. Wall construction is a wood sandwich, and primary materials are cypress, brick, and glass. The house is small in scale. The interior is not broken or divided into separate rooms but is instead a series of interpenetrating and overlapping spaces. Much of the furniture is built into the house. Endangered by a highway, the house was dismantled and reconstructed on the present site in 1965.
Private
HABS

FAIRFAX COUNTY
Accotink vicinity
WOODLAWN PLANTATION
.4 mile west of the intersection of
U.S. 1 and Route 235
1800–1805, Dr. William Thornton

Woodlawn Plantation was presented as a wedding gift to Eleanor Parke Custis by her guardian George Washington in 1799. The house was designed and built shortly thereafter as a two-story, five-part brick residence with end pavilions and connecting hyphens. A central cross gable and two jerkinheads break the roofline, and there are oval lights in all three front gables. Light-colored rectangular panels on the facade separate the first and second stories, and similar lintels ornament the windows on the central block.
Private
HABS

FAIRFAX COUNTY
Alexandria vicinity
GUNSTON HALL
15 miles south of Alexandria on Va.
242
1755–1758, William Buckland

Gunston Hall was the home of George Mason, a leading Revolutionary figure. Famous for his consitutional writings, including the Virginia Declaration of Rights (1776), Mason influenced many leaders in Virginia and on the national political scene. His gracefully proportioned one-and-one-half-story house has well-designed porches on both the land and the Potomac River sides. The interior is notable for its carved detail. The formal gardens have been restored.
State
NHL; HABS

FAIRFAX COUNTY
Alexandria vicinity
MOUNT VERNON
7 miles south of Alexandria on
George Washington Memorial
Parkway
1743, Augustine Washington

Mount Vernon was the home of George Washington, Commander-in-Chief of the Revolutionary forces and first President of the United States. Built by his half-brother Lawrence Washington, the estate came into Washington's possession in 1752. During his ownership, he enlarged the main house, built a complex of outbuildings, and landscaped the grounds during three periods of alteration: 1757–1758, 1773–1779, and 1784–1787. The rectangular mass of the two-story, frame, Georgian house is joined to the nearest outbuildings by curving arcades in a Palladian villa plan. The formal gardens and plantation dependencies are integrated portions of the composition. A full-length two-storied portico faces the Potomac River. The main block has a central hall plan with the flanking rooms grouped around twin chimney stacks. Washington returned to Mount Vernon following his retirement from the Presidency in 1797 and lived here until his death in 1799.
Private
NHL; HABS

FAIRFAX COUNTY
Chantilly vicinity
SULLY
.8 mile north of the intersection of
Routes 28 and 50
1794

The earliest portion of Sully is the center, two-story section which has two exterior brick end chimneys, a gable roof, and an interior side hall plan. A one-and-one-half-story east wing was added in 1799, and the one-story west wing, in the 1840's. The entire three-part frame farmhouse rests upon a local brownstone foundation. An interesting feature of the main section is its original, one-story porch on the south side which has scrolled work beneath the eaves and square columns supporting the roof. Richard Bland Lee, builder of Sully, was a younger brother of "Light Horse Harry" Lee and a member of the Continental Congress.
County
HABS

FAIRFAX COUNTY
Lorton
POHICK CHURCH
9201 Richmond Highway
1772

Pohick Church was completed in 1772, replacing an earlier 18th-century frame church of the same name. The structure is rectangular, two stories high, and crowned by a modillion cornice and a hip roof. The brick of the exterior is laid in Flemish bond with random glazed headers and has been entirely repointed. The lintels of the first floor windows are flat while those of the second floor are arched. Rubbed brick marks the jambs and arches of the windows. The exterior of Pohick Church has undergone several restorations. The window sills and portions of the roof and cornice have been renewed. Inside, only the cornice and a single baluster from the chancel rail are original. The remainder of the interior furnishings are a conjectural restoration installed largely between 1901 and 1916.
Private
HABS

FALLS CHURCH (independent city)
THE FALLS CHURCH
115 E. Fairfax Street
1767–1769

The original portion of the Falls Church is a 60–by–40–foot brick rectangle with two tiers of windows. Most of the wooden parts of the upper windows appear to be original, although the lower tier has been heavily restored. A modillion cornice and hip roof cover the structure, and the latter is also considered original. The windows and masonry of the east wall were demolished in 1959 for the addition of an enlarged chancel. This redesign has converted the original church into a nave for the new chancel. When first built, the interior of the Falls Church was similar to that of Pohick Church in Lorton, Virginia.
Private
HABS

FLUVANNA COUNTY
Bremo Bluff vicinity
BREMO
.9 mile north of the intersection of
Routes 15 and 656
Early 19th century

Bremo plantation possesses a notable group of architecturally significant structures designed by the builder himself, General John Hartwell Cocke. Reformer, soldier, and philanthropist as well as planter, Cocke sought the advice of Thomas Jefferson and other eminent contemporaries when he built the main house which was completed in 1820. It was the master-builder, John Neilson, however, who gave the house its final appearance. The brick residence has many of the features associated with Jefferson, such as the use of the Tuscan order in the portico, loggia, and side porches, the Chinese lattice railings on the esplanades, and the changes of ground level from one side of the complex to the other. Additional structures include the porticoed barn, the Greek Doric temperance monument, and two other residences, Bremo Recess and Upper Bremo.
Private; not accessible to the public
HABS

FLUVANNA COUNTY
Columbia
POINT OF FORK ARSENAL
West bank of the Rivanna River, 1.3
miles southeast of the intersection of
Routes 624 and 656
18th century

It is not known precisely when an arsenal was established at Point of Fork, but the earliest existing documents date from 1781, and in June of that year the arsenal was raided by the British, buildings were burned, and supplies destroyed. After the Revolution new buildings were erected on or near the sites of the original structures, and Point of Fork was operated as a state arsenal from 1783 until 1801, when it was abandoned in favor of a better situated arms factory at Richmond. The Point of Fork Arsenal site as rebuilt after the Revolution consisted of three or four large buildings of frame, brick, and stone, plus several houses, barns, and quarters for troops. The arsenal was used for the manufacture and repair of arms and equipment and as a stockpile of weapons for fighting the Indians on the frontier. In 1794 the arsenal supplied arms for the federal army, to the Virginia militia to suppress the Whiskey Rebellion in Pennsylvania, and for the Fallen Timbers campaign in Ohio. The ruins of two buildings may be seen today. The smaller ruin is 24 feet square and was originally vaulted into two rooms; the other ruin is

rectangular and was probably one of the "longhouse" arsenals mentioned in the records.
Private

FRANKLIN COUNTY
Rocky Mount vicinity
**BOOKER T. WASHINGTON
NATIONAL MONUMENT**
16 miles east of Rocky Mount on Va. 122
Mid–19th century

The eminent Negro educator Booker T. Washington was born here on the Burroughs plantation on April 5, 1856. As a slave boy he spent his childhood in a one-room cabin. After the Civil War Washington attended Hampton Institute, later teaching there from 1879 to 1881. Then he was selected to establish a Negro normal school in Alabama, the now-famous Tuskegee Institute. His early struggles are related in his autobiography, *Up From Slavery*. The 200–acre monument comprising the original plantation includes a replica of a slave cabin similar to the one in which Washington was born.
Federal
NPS; 217.93 acres

FREDERICK COUNTY (also in Warren County)
Middletown vicinity
**CEDAR CREEK BATTLEFIELD AND
BELLE GROVE**
On Int. 81 between Middletown and Strasburg
c. 1790

The battle of Cedar Creek took place on October 19, 1864, and involved 31,000 Union soldiers and approximately 18,000 Confederates. General Philip H. Sheridan defeated the Southern force led by General Jubal A. Early in the crucial struggle for the Shenandoah Valley, a major supply source for the South. Belle Grove, which served as General Sheridan's headquarters, was built by Isaac Hite, husband of Nelly Conway Madison, James Madison's sister. Originally the house was a one-story, seven-room structure with an attic and full basement. Sometime before 1820 the porticos and west wing were added by Major Hite. The house presently retains its pre-Civil War appearance.
Public/private (battlefield)
Private (house)
NHL; HABS

FREDERICKSBURG (independent city)
KENMORE
1201 Washington Avenue
Mid–18th century

Kenmore was built by Fielding Lewis, brother-in-law of George Washington, for his bride, Betty Washington. Lewis acquired the land in 1752. The exterior of Kenmore is plain but well-proportioned. The entrance facade is two stories high and five bays wide with a modillion cornice and a jerkinhead roof. Walls are laid in Flemish bond without rubbed or gauged brickwork. Two flanking dependencies have been reconstructed on their original foundations. Inside, the house retains most of its original paneling and woodwork, but it is the plasterwork which is most noteworthy. This was added after the house was completed and is found on the ceilings and chimney pieces of the drawing room, dining room, and library. Such work was exceedingly rare in 18th-century American houses. Fielding Lewis (1725–c. 1782) served in the Virginia House of Burgesses, was a member of a local committee of correspondence, and superintended the manufacture of small arms in Fredericksburg during the Revolution.
Private
HABS

FREDERICKSBURG (independent city)
MONROE LAW OFFICE
908 Charles Street
1758

From 1780 until 1783 James Monroe studied law with Thomas Jefferson. In 1786, somewhat disillusioned with politics, Monroe opened a law office which he occupied until he returned to the political scene in 1789. The eight years during which he served as President, 1817–1825, was a period of nationalism and attention to social and economic cohesion and development. Outstanding achievements of his administration included the acquisition of Florida from Spain in 1819 and the enunciation of the Monroe Doctrine in 1823. The law office is brick, one-and-one-half stories high. In 1961 a two-story wing was added to house a library and museum display.
State
NHL

FREDERICKSBURG (independent city)
RISING SUN TAVERN
1306 Caroline Street
1760, Charles Washington

Built by the youngest brother of George Washington, Rising Sun Tavern fulfilled an important function in 18th-century life as a political and social meeting place for lead-

ing figures of the day. The one-and-one-half-story frame building was a meeting place for colonial leaders on their way from the South to Philadelphia to attend the Continental Congress. Here in 1777 George Mason, George Wythe, Edmund Pendleton, Thomas Lee, and Thomas Jefferson outlined the bill that Jefferson later phrased as the Statute of Virginia for Religious Liberty. The Peace Ball, attended by George Washington, the Marquis de Lafayette, the Count de Rochambeau, and others to celebrate the Revolutionary victory at Yorktown, was held in 1781 in the assembly room which has since burned.
Private
NHL; HABS

GLOUCESTER COUNTY
Gloucester vicinity
ABINGDON GLEBE HOUSE
7 miles south of the intersection of Routes 17 and 615
18th century

The date of construction for the Abingdon Glebe House has not been recorded, although the building is known to have been standing in 1724. Very few of the early glebe houses remain in Virginia. Flemish bond brick with glazed headers was used on the facade of the T-shaped dwelling. One-story, hip-roofed end pavilions flank the central part of the house. The rear ell is thought to be an early addition as it is not bonded to the front portion of the house. Extensive renovation occurred in 1954. The exterior dormers, sash, and cornices were renewed, and a screen porch was added at the front.
Private; not accessible to the public
HABS

GLOUCESTER COUNTY
Gloucester vicinity
ROSEWELL
.3 mile south of the intersection of Route 644 and County Route 632
c. 1725–1744

Constructed of brick laid in Flemish bond with random glazed headers, Rosewell stood three stories above a high basement. The deck-on-hip roof was originally topped by two cupolas and four T-shaped chimneys with deep Portland stone caps. Belt courses above the first and second stories gave horizontal accents to the high walls. All of the windows were accentuated with gauged brick "bibs" and were topped by shallow rubbed brick segmental arches with finely carved Portland stone keystones. Rosewell was the seat of the Page family and most notably the home of John Page (1744–1808), a member of Congress (1789–1797) and governor of

Virginia (1802–1805). The house was significantly altered in 1838. All of the interior decoration except for the stairs was removed, and the original roof and cupolas were taken off and replaced by a gable roof. The house burned in 1916 and only sections of the walls remain.
Private; not accessible to the public
HABS

GLOUCESTER COUNTY
Gloucester vicinity
TODDSBURY
1.1 miles east of the intersection of Routes 622 and 14
17th and 18th centuries

This ancestral seat of the Todd family on the North River was patented in 1665 by Thomas Todd. The style of the interior woodwork indicates that the present house was constructed in the early 18th century, perhaps incorporating an earlier 17th-century residence. A steep gambrel roof pierced by dormer windows covers the T-shaped house, which remained in the hands of Todd descendants until the mid–19th century.
Private; not accessible to the public
HABS

GLOUCESTER COUNTY
White Marsh vicinity
ABINGDON CHURCH
.6 mile south of the intersection of Routes 17 and 614
c. 1755

The present Abingdon Church is the second to serve Abingdon parish, established in 1655. Its plan is a Latin cross, and the building has a gable roof, pedimented gable ends, and a modillion cornice. The brickwork is Flemish bond with glazed headers, and the three original doorways (west, north, and south) are framed by rubbed and molded brick designs. Much of the window sash is original. Inside, the church is dominated by a large wooden reredos consisting of a broken pediment with a pineapple set upon an urn at the center. Pews in the two transept galleries are original. New pews, floors for the aisles, a new pulpit, and a vesting room were installed after the Civil War. Some redecorating and repaneling was done in 1950.
Private
HABS

GOOCHLAND COUNTY
Goochland
GOOCHLAND COUNTY COURT SQUARE
East side of Route 6 (U.S. 522)
19th century

The Goochland County Courthouse, focal point of the court square, was erected in 1826. Its brick exterior, Tuscan pedimented portico, and temple form give evidence of the influence of Thomas Jefferson. Jefferson had no direct hand in designing the courthouse, but Dabney Cosby, one of the builders, had worked for Jefferson as a stone mason at the University of Virginia. The architecture is Roman Revival, of which Jefferson was a strong proponent. Windows on both floors retain most of their original sash. An addition was built in 1955 and attached to a courthouse annex in 1966. Inside, the building has been altered and renovated. The entire two-acre court square is surrounded by its original brick wall. Other structures on the square are the two-story, hip-roofed stone jail (1848) and a one-story brick clerk's office.
County
HABS

GOOCHLAND COUNTY
Manakin vicinity
TUCKAHOE
On the James River southeast of Manakin via secondary roads
Early 18th century

Tuckahoe is a Georgian, two-story frame house still in a plantation setting with a nearby complex of eight outbuildings. Much of the detail on the exterior of the house is original, such as the weatherboarding, the modillioned cornices, and heavily muntined sash with early glass. The interior detail is also original except for the fireplace mantels and one second-floor bedroom. The Tuckahoe property was first owned by William Randolph (1651–1711) of Turkey Island, who passed it on to his son Thomas (c. 1689–1730). A grandson of Thomas Randolph, Thomas Mann Randolph (1741–1793), fell heir to the land while an infant, so his guardian Peter Jefferson, father of the future President, lived on and took care of the property for him. The land remained in the Randolph family until 1830. The oldest portion of the U-shaped house (the north wing) may have been constructed as early as 1712. It was enlarged to its present form c. 1730. The original outbuildings are a brick kitchen, a tobacco house, a smokehouse, a storehouse, a barn, and three slave cabins.
Private; not accessible to the public
HABS

GOOCHLAND COUNTY
Rock Castle vicinity
ROCK CASTLE
On the east side of the southern end of Route 600
c. 1732

The land now called Rock Castle was patented in 1718 by Charles Fleming. A house was built prior to 1732, and the estate was inherited by Fleming's son, Tarleton. In 1843 Rock Castle was purchased by John Rutherfoord, governor of Virginia from 1841 to 1842. Rutherfoord's son built an Italianate front onto the 18th-century house which so altered and obscured the latter that it was not rediscovered until 1935. At that time the house was being dismantled to allow for the construction of a new one. Renamed the Queen Anne Cottage, the older house was moved several hundred feet and restored. It is a five-bay, one-and-one-half-story frame structure with clipped gable ends and two interior end chimneys. The unusual main entrance has an eight-panel door flanked on both sides by similar panels.
Private; not accessible to the public
HABS

GREENE COUNTY
Stanardsville
GREENE COUNTY COURTHOUSE
Northwest corner of Route 649, .1 mile south of the intersection with Route 33
1839

Greene County was formed in 1838 and named for Revolutionary General Nathanael Greene. The two-story brick courthouse has been altered only by the addition of a front portico in 1927–1928. Tuscan columns support a Roman Doric entablature which is continued around the entire building. Wide pilasters match the columns on the facade. The courthouse complex also contains a jail and clerk's office which is not original.
County
HABS

GREENE COUNTY
Stanardsville vicinity
OCTONIA STONE
1.7 miles northwest of the intersection of Routes 637 and 1001

The Octonia Stone marks the westernmost boundary of the 24,000–acre Octonia Grant. Virginia's Lieutenant Governor Alexander Spottswood made the grant on July 20, 1722, to eight men: Bartholomew Yates, Lewis Latane, John Robinson, Jeremiah Clowder, Harry Beverley, Christopher Robinson, William Stanard, and Edwin Thacker. The grant started

near the mouth of Laurell Run (Popular Run) on the Rapidan River in Orange County and extended to the foot of the Blue Ridge Mountains in Greene County. It was approximately two miles wide and twenty miles long. The Octonia Stone is part of a natural outcropping in a hayfield. A figure eight, composed of two circles, and a Roman Cross, standing atop the eight, are engraved upon the stone.
Private; not accessible to the public

HALIFAX COUNTY
South Boston vicinity
BERRY HILL
1.5 miles south of the intersection of Routes 659 and 682
c. 1839

The Greek Revival mansion Berry Hill represents the extensive remodeling of an earlier brick dwelling. Covered with stucco, the house is two-stories high, and its most impressive exterior feature is the octastyle Greek Doric portico across the front. Flanking the main house are two-matching, one-story outbuildings, the office and the schoolroom. Both are temple-form structures and have tetrastyle Greek Doric pedimented porticos.
Private; not accessible to the public
HABS

HAMPTON (independent city
FORT MONROE
Old Point Comfort
1819–1834

As the nearest continuously held Union stronghold to the Confederate capital, Fort Monroe played an important role in the Civil War. From its ramparts spectators watched the epic battle between the U.S.S. *Monitor* and the C.S.S. *Virginia*. Jefferson Davis was imprisoned here after the fall of the Confederacy. The original brick building is located in the center of the present headquarters of the Continental Army Command. Three casemates of the old fort have been converted into a museum.
Federal
NHL

HAMPTON (independent city)
FORT WOOL
On an island at the entrance to Hampton Roads between Willoughby Spit and Old Point Comfort
19th century

Fort Wool, originally named Fort Calhoun, was begun in 1819 as part of the coastal defense system devised by George Graham, Secretary of War under President James Madison. Work on the fort progressed until the Civil War, when fifty-two casemates were completed and a garrison of 187 men was stationed there. The garrison was removed in 1886, but the fort became reactivated during both World Wars. Original ramparts, consisting of a close-packed semi-circle of gun positions, still stand at the island's western end. Other sections of the fort have been altered or remodeled to accommodate modern guns.
State; not accessible to the public

HAMPTON (independent city)
HAMPTON INSTITUTE
.8 mile northwest of the intersection of Route 60 and Hampton Roads Bridge Tunnel
19th century

The town of Hampton became a gathering place for freedmen immediately after the Civil War. At the urging of the local Freedmen's Bureau chief, the American Missionary Society purchased 165 acres which form the nucleus of the present college. Opening in 1868, Hampton was chartered as a normal and industrial institute in 1870 and received college accreditation in 1932–1933. Today Hampton Institute occupies 200 acres and is composed of more than 100 buildings. Outstanding among these are the Mansion House (now the president's house), originally a plantation residence; Virginia Hall, designed by Richard Morris Hunt, a four-and-one-half-story structure that has little architectural ornament, but its steep-roofed center and end pavilions are French Renaissance in style; south of the Mansion House is Hunt's Academic Hall replacing an earlier building of his that was destroyed by fire; between Academic Hall and the Mansion House is the Romanesque style Memorial Church (designed by J. C. Cady), a rectangular brick building with an attached 150–foot, six-level campanile.
Private

HAMPTON (independent city)
ST. JOHN'S CHURCH
Northwest corner of W. Queen and Court Streets
Early 18th century

St. John's is the fourth structure to serve the Elizabeth City (or Hampton) Episcopal parish. Three earlier churches were constructed in the 17th century, and the present one (of which only the brick walls are original) dates from c. 1728. Internal decor is Victorian of the 1870's. St. John's is one of six remaining colonial churches in Virginia to have been built in the shape of a Latin cross. The brick tower at the northeast corner was added in 1901.
Private
HABS

HANOVER COUNTY
Ashland vicinity
FORK CHURCH
East side of Route 738 at the intersection with Route 685
18th century

Fork Church, built c. 1736–1740, is rectangular without transepts and has front and side doors. Its walls are laid in Flemish bond with glazed headers above a beveled water table which is laid in English bond. Rubbed brick decorates the jambs and segmental arches of the windows. The window sashes are little altered and retain some original glass. Inside, original fabric survives, although altered. The colonial pews were cut down in 1830, and the pulpit, also composed of colonial material, has been moved. The name Fork Church derives from the surrounding countryside which lies within a fork formed by the North and South Anna rivers which flow together to form the Pamunkey.
Private
HABS

HANOVER COUNTY
Ashland vicinity
SCOTCHTOWN (PATRICK HENRY HOUSE)
10 miles northwest of Ashland on Va. 685
1719, Charles Chiswell

Scotchtown is notable for its architecture as well as for its association with Patrick Henry, the Revolutionary leader, who lived here from 1771 until 1777. It was during those six years that Henry made his mark on American history in speeches such as his famous cry "liberty or death" at the Virginia Convention in 1775. Another noted occupant was Dolley Madison. The one-and-one-half-story frame house with jerkinhead roof and double massive center chimneys has recently been restored.
Private
NHL; HABS

HANOVER COUNTY
Hanover Court House
HANOVER COUNTY COURTHOUSE
Intersection of Routes 1006 and 301
c. 1735

Hanover County was created by an act of the Virginia Assembly in 1720. The courthouse was constructed about 15 years later and has been in continuous use ever since. One story high, the building is brick laid in Flemish bond with glazed headers. A steep hip roof surrounded by a modillion cornice tops the courthouse. The T-shaped structure contains a judge's chamber and a jury room in its arms and a courtroom in the center portion.
County
HABS

HANOVER COUNTY (also in Henrico
County and Richmond)
Richmond vicinity
**RICHMOND NATIONAL
BATTLEFIELD PARK**
1862–1865

Richmond became the capital of the Confederacy in May 1861. The North viewed
the city as the symbol of secession and as
a prime psychological objective. Of the
major drives launched on Richmond during the Civil War, two almost succeeded.
General George B. McClellan's Peninsula
campaign of 1862 came so close to
Richmond that Union aerial observers in
balloons could see the city's church spires.
In May 1864 General Ulysses S. Grant
moved south from Spotsylvania, maneu-
vering his way closer to Richmond. By
June 3, troops of the Army of the
Potomac and the Army of the James confronted Robert E. Lee's Army of Northern
Virginia at Cold Harbor. Grant's assaults
were beaten back with heavy losses. The
Federals then moved to the southeast and
crossed the James to attack Petersburg. In
the period from August, 1864, through
March, 1865, there was action along the
lines to the southeast of Richmond.
Richmond's fall on April 3, 1865, was fol-
lowed by Lee's surrender to Grant at Ap-
pomattox Court House on April 9.
Federal
NPS; 746.56 acres
HABS

HANOVER COUNTY
Richmond vicinity
**RUFFIN, EDMUND, PLANTATION
(MARLBOURNE)**
11 miles northeast of Richmond on
U.S. 360
1843

Edmund Ruffin was one of the foremost
opponents of the system of agriculture
practiced in the antebellum South, a
system which led to heavy soil exhaustion.
From 1814 to 1821 Ruffin experimented
in revitalizing his depleted lands with the
application of marl to the land. His success led to a significant increase in the
production of corn and wheat, and his
plantation became a laboratory for
agricultural experiments. Marlbourne includes Ruffin's house and family cemetery.
Private; not accessible to the public
NHL

HENRICO COUNTY
**RICHMOND NATIONAL
BATTLEFIELD PARK**
Reference—see Hanover County

HENRICO COUNTY
Richmond vicinity
MALVERN HILL
1.2 miles southeast of the intersection
of Routes 5 and 156
17th century

Malvern Hill was built by Thomas Cocke
(1639–1697), high sheriff of Henrico
County and a member of the Virginia
House of Burgesses. The house was
destroyed by fire (c. 1905) and only one
end wall and a chimney survive. Before
the fire Malvern Hill was a one-and-one-
half-story cruciform structure (one of the
few such houses known in Virginia)
covered by a steep gable roof. The surviving chimney (believed to have been part
of an earlier 17th-century frame house)
possesses what is perhaps the finest example of 17th-century brick diaper work in
the state. The battle of Malvern Hill (July
1, 1862), between Union and Confederate
forces, centered around the bluff on which
the ruin stands.
Private
HABS

HOPEWELL (independent city)
APPOMATTOX MANOR
At confluence of James and
Appomattox rivers, on the south bank
17th, 18th, and 19th centuries

The original Appomattox Manor House
was built in the 18th century on a land
grant made to Captain Francis Eppes in
1635. Several additions to the frame
house were made during the latter half of
the 19th century. A kitchen building in
the yard appears to have been a dependency to an earlier house. General Ulysses
S. Grant maintained his headquarters in
the manor house from June, 1864, until
April, 1865.
Private
HABS

ISLE OF WIGHT COUNTY
Benn's Church
ST. LUKE'S CHURCH
1682

St. Luke's Church is a 17th-century Virginia church in the Gothic style of
medieval English parish churches. The
brick church, begun in 1632 to replace an
earlier wooden building, was laid in
Flemish bond in a single nave plan with a
massive tower at the west end. Permanent
interior fittings and other additions were
made later in the century. Various
architectural changes were made during
the 18th century, but the church has
recently been restored, except for the late
19th-century stained glass windows.
Private
NHL; HABS

ISLE OF WIGHT COUNTY
Smithfield
OLD ISLE OF WIGHT COURTHOUSE
Northeast corner of Main and Mason
Streets
Mid–18th century

Smithfield was incorporated in 1752, and
the county government was subsequently
transferred there from a location two
miles west. Three brick buildings were
erected for county use: the courthouse,
jail, and clerk's office. The county seat
was permanently located in Isle of Wight
soon after 1800, and the old courthouse
was converted to a residence about 1812.
However, restoration work was begun in
1938, and the one-story, hip-roofed
courthouse now looks as it did in the 18th
century. At the rear is a apsidal ell, and
there is a full length, five-bay arcaded
porch across the front. The Federal doorway is a product of the 1812 conversion.
Inside is one large courtroom with the
former judge and jury rooms to either side
immediately behind the porch. The circular end of the courtroom originally contained the judge's bench.
Private
HABS

JAMES CITY COUNTY
Five Forks vicinity
POWHATAN
.8 mile north of the intersection of
Routes 615 and 5
18th century

Richard Taliaferro was the original patentee of the Powhatan lands. He is also believed to be the designer of the two-story
early Georgian residence. During the Civil
War fire gutted the house so only the
masonry portions are original. Restoration
took place in 1948, at which time the hip
roof was replaced. Powhatan has two massive, interior, T-shaped end chimneys. Its
brickwork exhibits the highest standards
of colonial craftsmanship. Walls are laid in
Flemish bond with glazed headers, while
the bevelled water table is done in English
bond. The windows of the facade exhibit a
typical Georgian characteristic: those on
the second floor are smaller than the ones
below.
Private; not accessible to the public
HABS

JAMES CITY COUNTY
Jamestown
JAMESTOWN NATIONAL HISTORIC
SITE
Jamestown Island
1607

Jamestown is the site of the first permanent English settlement in America.
The town which grew up here, and which

has long since disappeared, was the capital of the colony of Virginia during its first century of development, 1607–1698. In 1619 the first meeting of the House of Burgesses was held here, the first representative legislative assembly in the New World. Among the well-known persons associated with the colony's early years are Captain John Smith, John Rolfe, and his wife Pocahontas. With the exception of the Old Church Tower, which dates from the 1640's, there are no remains of the settlement above ground. Archeological excavations currently underway have uncovered foundations of houses and public buildings, remains of streets, and many small artifacts of the 17th-century settlement.
Private
NPS; 20.63 acres
HABS

JAMES CITY COUNTY (also in Williamsburg and in York County)
Jamestown vicinity
COLONIAL NATIONAL HISTORICAL PARK
17th and 18th centuries

Colonial National Historical Park includes Yorktown, Yorktown Battlefield, Jamestown Island, and the Colonial Parkway connecting these sites. Jamestown was the first permanent English Colony in the New World. The town remained the capital of Virginia for almost a century (1607–1698) before the capital was moved to Williamsburg. Yorktown, established in 1691, was the scene of the closing battle of the American Revolution and the surrender of Lord Charles Cornwallis on October 19, 1781. Many features of Yorktown and the battlefield have been preserved or reconstructed. The site includes Yorktown National Cemetery.
Federal/non-federal
NPS; 9,430 acres

JAMES CITY COUNTY
Williamsburg vicinity
CARTER'S GROVE
.2 mile southeast of the intersection of Routes 60 and 667
Mid–18th century

As originally built, Carter's Grove was a massive, two-story rectangular building crowned by a forty-five degree hip roof with splayed eaves. Flanking the main house were two one-and-one-half-story, free-standing dependencies. Few changes were made in the complex until a 1927–1928 renovation in which the owners attempted to give the structure a more grandiose appearance. The ridge of the main house roof was raised so rooms could be added at the attic level. Dormers were built onto the raised roof to light

these rooms. The two interior chimneys were raised in proportion to the roof. Brick hyphens were constructed to connect the main house with the dependencies; the roofs of the dependencies were raised, and their south fronts were extended to align with that of the main house. Interior woodwork has not been seriously altered, and it is considered by many authorities to be the most beautiful surviving example of the colonial period.
Private
NHL; HABS

KING GEORGE COUNTY
Comorn vicinity
MARMION
.8 mile northeast of the intersection of Routes 649 and 609
18th century

The date of Marmion's original construction is difficult to determine. The asymmetrical plan and window arrangement indicate that it was built in several stages. Marmion is a frame, two-story house with a clipped gable roof and two interior end chimneys having exposed shafts. Notable exterior woodwork appears on the modillion cornice, the architrave framings on the first level windows and doors, and the altered second floor windows. Surviving dependencies are a smokehouse, dairy, kitchen, and office. The east porch and north wing are later additions to the main house.
Private; not accessible to the public
HABS

KING GEORGE COUNTY
King George Court House vicinity
NANZATICO
1.8 miles south of the intersection of Routes 650 and 625
c. 1770

One of the most formal frame colonial mansions in Virginia, Nanzatico is a striking example of the architectural quality which was achieved by colonial craftsmen in timber construction. The engaged Ionic portico is a design feature unique in colonial Virginia. The architectural quality of the mansion and its several surviving dependencies makes it an important landmark.
Private
HABS

KING WILLIAM COUNTY
King William
KING WILLIAM COUNTY COURTHOUSE
Route 619, .1 mile north of the intersection of Route 619 and Va. 30
c. 1725

Characterized by its T-shape, steep hip roof, and modillion cornice, the King William Courthouse has served its original functional purpose since the 18th century. An unusual feature is the five-bay open arcade which extends across the entire facade. The rear of the building has been extended one bay, and an exterior end chimney added to the rear wall; the original wooden shingle roof has been replaced by a slate one.
County
HABS

KING WILLIAM COUNTY
Tunstall vicinity
ELSING GREEN
2.1 miles southwest of the intersection of Routes 632 and 623
18th and 19th centuries

Elsing Green, overlooking the Pamunkey River, is a two-story, U-shaped plantation house. On the river front the house is seven bays wide, and each side elevation has five bays including a center door. An interior fire in the 19th century destroyed most of the original woodwork. During the 1930's restoration work was undertaken. East of the main house is a one-and-one-half-story dependency (c. 1690) which was possibly the original plantation house. To the west is the restored kitchen, and a smokehouse and dairy have been rebuilt on their old foundations.
Private; not accessible to the public
HABS

KING WILLIAM COUNTY
West Point vicinity
CHELSEA
1.7 miles north of intersection of Chelsea Road and Route 30
c. 1706

Chelsea is a two-story, brick, T-shaped structure with a hip roof and a one-and-one-half-story gambrel roofed rear ell. The brickwork is Flemish bond. The interior of the rear ell has paneled rooms in the front section. Chelsea was built by Augustine Moore, a prominent planter.
Private; not accessible to the public
HABS

LANCASTER COUNTY
Kilmarnock vicinity
CHRIST CHURCH
3 miles south of Kilmarnock on Va. 3
1732

Christ Church, a significant example of ecclesiastical architecture in colonial Virginia, is well preserved in its plan, exterior design, and interior furnishings. Its history is linked with the Carter family, particularly Robert "King" Carter, whose tomb, together with those of his two wives, is a feature of the churchyard. Of early Georgian design, this cruciform plan brick building is covered by a gable roof with splayed eaves. Rubbed brick and cut stone are features used in the exterior door and window decorative elements. The interior woodwork of the pews, pulpit, sounding board, communion rail, and table matches the integrity and quality of the building.
Private
NHL; HABS

LANCASTER COUNTY
Lively vicinity
ST. MARY'S WHITECHAPEL
.1 mile northwest of the intersection
of Routes 354 and 201
17th, 18th, and 19th centuries

As early as 1661 the lower Northern Neck portion of Lancaster County contained an upper and lower parish which came to be known as St. Mary's Whitechapel and Christ Church respectively. A church stood on the site of the present St. Mary's as early as 1669, and it is believed that this structure provided the core for a cruciform 18th-century house of worship. The presently existing portions of St. Mary's Whitechapel were built as transepts in 1740–1741. In 1832 the nave and chancel were removed, and the resulting voids in the east and west walls were rebricked using the original materials. A brick patch on the south wall fills in a former round window, and patches on the north side result from alterations to an original and later doorways.
Private
HABS

LANCASTER COUNTY
Weems vicinity
COROTOMAN
South side of the intersection of
Routes 222 and 631
Early 18th century

Corotoman, when built, was perhaps the finest house in Virginia. It was built for Robert "King" Carter (1663–1732) early in the 18th century. In 1729 the house and all its contents were destroyed by fire, but

the site remains as one of great archeological promise. Bottles and other artifacts have already been recovered from the collapsed cellar.
Private; not accessible to the public

LEE COUNTY
CUMBERLAND GAP NATIONAL
HISTORICAL PARK
Reference—see Bell County, Kentucky

LEXINGTON (independent city)
BARRACKS, VIRGINIA MILITARY
INSTITUTE
North edge of Lexington on U.S. 11
Mid–19th century

Known as the "West Point of the South," the Virginia Military Institute was formally organized in 1839. The school attained significance as a contributor of leaders to the Confederate Army, the most notable being Thomas J. "Stonewall" Jackson. Since the Civil War Virginia Military Institute has continued to graduate outstanding military leaders such as General George C. Marshall. Part of the original barracks wall has been incorporated into the present cadet barracks, and a small building dating from 1848, formerly a tailor shop and hospital, is still in use.
State
NHL

LEXINGTON (independent city)
LEE CHAPEL, WASHINGTON AND
LEE UNIVERSITY
Washington and Lee University
campus
c. 1866

Lee Chapel, a Victorian Gothic brick building, commemorates the last period in the life of Robert E. Lee. From 1865 to 1870 he served as president of Washington College, later named Washington and Lee University. Under his leadership student enrollment increased, the curriculum was expanded, and the physical plant was greatly improved. The chapel houses not only the vault in which he and other members of his family are buried, but also the office which he used until his death in 1870.
Private
NHL; HABS

LOUDOUN COUNTY
Aldie
ALDIE HISTORIC DISTRICT
Extending .1 mile east of the
intersection of Routes 612 and 50, .1
mile west of the intersection of

Routes 50 and 732, and .2 mile north
and .3 mile south of Route 50
Early 19th century

The Aldie Mill complex contains a mill, a miller's house, and the home of Charles Fenton Mercer. Mercer settled here in 1803 and built the two-story brick residence which he named Aldie Manor. In 1804 Mercer obtained legal rights to erect a milldam on the Little River, and soon thereafter a large brick grist mill was put up by his slaves. A village grew up around the mill and was also called Aldie. The mill, which had twin overshot wheels, is a three-part structure. The two-story central section is flanked by a one-story building on the east and a two-story one on the west. One-story brick and frame hyphens with shed roofs connect the main block with the flanking dependencies. The mill (still in operation), miller's house, and manor house form an unusually complete, early 19th-century mill complex.
Multiple private

LOUDOUN COUNTY
Leesburg
LEESBURG HISTORIC DISTRICT
The area of the original town
centered at the intersection of U.S.
15 and Va. 9
18th and 19th centuries

Leesburg was established by the Virginia General Assembly in 1758 and designated as the Loudoun County seat. The community grew during the next 100 years, slowing down only after the Civil War. Consequently, the town possesses a large number of late 18th- and early 19th-century homes and commercial or public structures which have been fairly well maintained. Near the center of the district is the court square highlighted by the brick Classical Revival · courthouse completed in 1895. Other noteworthy buildings are the Laurel Brigade Inn (stone), the county office building (Greek Revival, c. 1844), and the Old Tavern (late 18th century).
Multiple public/private
HABS

LOUDOUN COUNTY
Leesburg vicinity
OAK HILL (JAMES MONROE HOUSE)
8 miles south of Leesburg on U.S. 15
1820–1823, James Hoban

Oak Hill was designed for President James Monroe, who had inherited the land in 1805. Monroe lived here until 1830, and existing records indicate that he outlined the ideas for the Monroe Doctrine in a letter written here. President of the United States during the "Era of Good Feeling,"

1817–1825, Monroe had served previously as a member of the Continental Congress, governor of Virginia, secretary of state, secretary of war, and minister to England and France. The brick house consists of a two-story, gable-roofed central portion with small one-room wings. Its most striking feature is the south portico, two stories high and supported by seven Doric pillars. Oak Hill has been altered since Monroe's time; however, several original outbuildings remain, including Monroe's Cottage.
Private; not accessible to the public
NHL

LOUDOUN COUNTY
Leesburg vicinity
OATLANDS
1 mile south of the intersection of
Routes 15 and 651
c. 1800

One of the most notable Federal style mansions in Virginia, Oatlands was built from designs credited to George Carter, its builder-owner. The house, of brick covered with stucco, is laid out in a five part plan. The Roman Corinthian portico, which extends the full width of the three-bay center section, was added in 1827 by Carter. An octagonal cupola was to have crowned the house but it is not known whether this feature was ever constructed. Also notable are the extensive formal gardens, laid out after 1803. Many of the early 19th-century outbuildings and quarters still stand.
Private
HABS

LOUDOUN COUNTY
Sterling vicinity
**BROAD RUN BRIDGE AND
TOLLHOUSE**
At the intersection of Routes 7 and
28 with Broad Run
c. 1820

In 1809 the Virginia General Assembly passed an act incorporating the Leesburg Turnpike Authority for the purpose of building a road from Leesburg to Alexandria. Sometime after 1820 the stone bridge over Broad Run was built. The bridge has a double span of arches supported by a central pier and massive abutments on either bank. The tollhouse connected with it is also stone, one-story, and was later enlarged by the addition of three wings. At the beginning of the Civil War the turnpike ceased to be a toll road.
Public (bridge)/private (tollhouse; not accessible to the public)

LOUDOUN COUNTY
Waterford
WATERFORD HISTORIC DISTRICT
A roughly pentagonal-shaped area following topographical features; measuring, from the intersection of Main and Second Streets, .9 mile to the northeast, 1.4 miles to the southeast, 1.2 miles to the southwest, 1.2 miles to the west, and .9 mile to the northwest
18th and 19th centuries

Situated 7 miles northwest of Leesburg, Waterford is the oldest settlement in Loudoun County. It was established by Quakers from Pennsylvania about 1730. The early 18th-century village was grouped around the first mill (c. 1730) and consisted of two-story, Georgian, frame and brick houses. In the middle and late 18th century, as the village expanded, several log houses were constructed as well as brick and frame row structures. Waterford reached its peak of development in the 1840's when it had more than 30 businesses, including three mills, and a population of more than 300. It remained essentially a Quaker community more closely tied to its Pennsylvania heritage than to its Virginia environment, and the sympathies of the villagers were with the North during the Civil War. Urbanization, the railroad, and even highway construction have bypassed Waterford, and thus it has remained a country village in a setting of rolling hills unspoiled by the intrusion of commercial and industrial elements. It is a rare example of an architecturally rich and little-altered early American village which is still viable in the 20th century.
Public/private
NHL; HABS

LOUISA COUNTY
Gordonsville vicinity
BOSWELL'S TAVERN
.1 mile southeast of intersection of
Routes 22 and 15
Mid–18th century

Boswell's Tavern was a well-known Virginia hostelry of the 18th century. The public portion is a three-bay, two-story gable-roofed frame building. Attached to the east is the innkeeper's quarters, originally a one-and-one-half-story wing which has been raised to two full stories. A modern one-story section has been added to the side and rear of the innkeeper's residence, and the pedimented porch is also not original. The stairway, wainscoting, and hat pegs of the public house survive from the 18th century as does the smokehouse. Recently renovated, the tavern is in good condition.
Private
HABS

LOUISA COUNTY
Gordonsville vicinity
HAWKWOOD
.5 mile west of the intersection of
Routes 617 and 15
1854–1855, Alexander Jackson Davis

Hawkwood, designed for planter Richard O. Morris, is one of only two Italian Villa designs by Davis which survives in virtually pristine condition. Of the six such structures still standing, two have been remodeled and two are not in the pure Italian Villa mode. Architecture of this type was characterized by picturesque asymmetry. The house itself is brick covered with stucco. Two one-story wings with hip roofs flank a projecting two-story pavilion with a gable end front. The south wing is surrounded on three sides by an arcaded veranda, and above the south wing is a three-story Italianate tower. A recent (1969) addition containing bedrooms and a garage was constructed at the rear of the north wing.
Private; not accessible to the public
HABS

LOUISA COUNTY
Trevilians vicinity
WESTEND
1.1 miles south of the intersection of
Routes 638 and 22
1849

Westend was built by Mrs. James Morris on land she had inherited from her husband. The overall appearance of the house is a temple-front central block with one-story wings on either side. Columns on the main facade (which have caps and bases of cast iron) are of the Tuscan order, and there is a one-story, four-column porch on the rear. The brick exterior of the house has been painted a light color to resemble stucco. Surviving outbuildings are slave dwellings, a smokehouse, and an office.
Private
HABS

LYNCHBURG (independent city)
THE ACADEMY OF MUSIC
522–526 Main Street
1905, E. G. Frye and Aubrey
Chesterman

The Academy of Music is one of a few surviving legitimate theaters dating from the turn of the century in Virginia. The three-story facade, which possesses a classical symmetry, has a rusticated ground floor and a second story with three central windows flanked on either side by double windows with projecting pediments. The three central windows on the third story are simple in design. Corinthian pilasters delimit the five bays of the upper two sto-

ries. The full range of classical decoration is found in the interior of the theater. The fine quality plaster work survives in excellent condition and retains, for the most part, its original color scheme. A painted ceiling of classical figures also is in a good state of repair as is the original, painted asbestos curtain which still hangs in front of the stage.
Private; not accessible to the public

LYNCHBURG (independent city)
POINT OF HONOR
112 Cabell Street
1806

Point of Honor was built by Dr. George Cabell (1766–1823), a Lychburg physician. The architect-builder is unknown, but the house resembles several Richmond town houses which in turn are close in appearance to designs by Benjamin H. Latrobe. Stuccoed brick covers the exterior of the two-story, Federal mansion; its facade is composed of a three-bay center section flanked by two octagonal end projections. Between the projections is a one-story Italianate porch, probably the original rebuilt. Point of Honor's interior contains exceptional period woodwork in its reception rooms. The door surround and mantel in the drawing room employ finely executed pineapple and tassel-and-swag motifs.
Municipal; not accessible to the public
HABS

MADISON COUNTY
Madison
MADISON COUNTY COURTHOUSE
U.S. 29
1828

A virtually untouched example of Jeffersonian architecture, this brick, two-story, temple-form courthouse was built by workmen who had also worked on the University of Virginia at nearby Charlottesville. The Tuscan pediment and entablature and the brick arcade are reminiscent of Jefferson's designs for the pavilions at the university. Although there have been minor modifications in the interior, the courtroom, gallery, and stairways have survived unchanged.
County
HABS

MATHEWS COUNTY
Hudgins vicinity
CRICKET HILL (FORT CRICKET HILL)
Northeast of Hudgins, .2 mile east of the intersection of Routes 669 and 223
1776

John Murray, last royal governor of Virginia, was driven out of Norfolk and set up a loyalist headquarters at Gwynn's Island in June 1776. Colonial troops commanded by General Andrew Lewis entrenched themselves on the mainland opposite the island. Their efforts were successful and Murray was dislodged from his position and set sail for England. Today what remains of the Cricket Hill earthworks faces Gwynn's Island for a distance of 150 yards and rises two feet above grade and four feet above high water.
Private; not accessible to the public

MATHEWS COUNTY
Williams vicinity
POPLAR GROVE MILL AND HOUSE
.5 mile southwest of the intersection of Routes 14 and 613
18th and 19th centuries

Poplar Grove Mill is tide operated. A mill has been located on the property since colonial times, but the present structure replaces one burned during the Civil War and was used until 1912. The mill is a two-story frame structure with a gable roof, and it stands on a narrow mole separating the millpond from the bay. Poplar Grove House, the miller's residence, is a five section house. The earliest portion is a one-and-one-half-story cottage built in Revolutionary times. It presently serves as an end wing.
Private; not accessible to the public
HABS

MECKLENBURG COUNTY
Clarksville vicinity
PRESTWOULD
1 mile north of Clarksville city limits
c. 1795

Prestwould occupies a commanding position on the high land overlooking the Roanoke River Valley. The mansion itself is a great rectangular stone ashlar structure, two stories high and crowned by a hip roof. The principal facade is seven bays wide and features a diminution of window size from the first floor to the second. Both the entrance and garden fronts possess nearly identical one-story porticos with Tuscan columns. The interiors of Prestwould are virtually unaltered. Built by Sir Peyton Skipwith, the house

took seven years to complete. The plantation house at Prestwould is surrounded by the original group of outbuildings.
Private
HABS

MONTGOMERY COUNTY
Blacksburg vicinity
SMITHFIELD
1 mile west of Blacksburg city limits
1773–1774

Built by William Preston, a member of the Virginia House of Burgesses (1768–1769), Smithfield is an architectural "transplant." Although located in the western portion of the state, the house is of a type and form found in the tidewater region. Of frame construction, the L-shaped building is one-and-one-half stories high and has recently been restored for exhibition.
Private
HABS

MONTGOMERY COUNTY
Elliston vicinity
FOTHERINGAY
1.4 miles south of the intersection of Routes 11 and 631
18th and 20th centuries

Fotheringay is a two-story brick structure situated on a knoll above the South Fork of the Roanoke River. Originally the house had only a three-bay facade, but in the late 1950's the south end was extended two more bays. The extension was added in the belief that the builder intended the house to have a symmetrical facade. Inside, original woodwork survives on both floors. Colonel George Hancock, father-in-law of William Clark of the Lewis and Clark Expedition, built the house sometime after 1796.
Private; not accessible to the public
HABS

NELSON COUNTY
SWANNANOA
Reference—see Augusta County

NEW KENT COUNTY
Tallysville vicinity
ST. PETER'S CHURCH
North side of County Route 642
18th century

St. Peter's Church represents the transition from the Gothic to the Classical style in Virginia ecclesiastical architecture. Built of brick early in the 18th century, St. Peter's measures 64 feet 4 inches by 28 feet 4 inches and is one-story high. The gable roof has curvilinear gable ends. Segmental arches appear over the windows and the open arches of the tower which was added in the mid–18th century to

replace an earlier wooden belfry. Much of the interior and exterior of the present church has been restored or replaced to what is thought to have been its original condition.
Private
HABS

NEW KENT COUNTY
Tunstall vicinity
HAMPSTEAD
1 mile northwest of the intersection of Routes 606 and 607
19th century

Conrade Webb (1778–1842) built this impressive and heavily ornamented Federal house in the 1820's. By the late 18th century the Webb family had acquired substantial acreage in New Kent County. The two-story dwelling has a hip roof, deck, and balustrades. Its size is emphasized by the elongation of the portico and the use of pilasters. The entablature consists of a plain architrave below a frieze of triglyphs and metopes and is completed by a projecting cornice with regulae. Both the entablature and the balustrading are carried around the entire building. Outbuildings are an 18th-century cottage, an ice house, and the ruins of a granary.
Private
HABS

NEWPORT NEWS (independent city)
DENBIGH PLANTATION
.2 mile southwest of the southern end of Lukas Creek Road
Mid–17th century and 18th century

The site of two Mathews Manor houses (17th century) and of the 18th-century Denbigh plantation house is a public park. Archeological investigations have provided information about Virginia plantation life between 1620 and 1670. Foundations are exposed, and evidences of early blacksmithing and other industrial activities have been found.
Private

NEWPORT NEWS (independent city)
HILTON VILLAGE
Bounded on the southwest by the James River, on the northwest by Post Street, on the northeast by the Chesapeake and Ohio Railroad tracks, and on the southeast by Hopkins Street
20th century, Francis Y. Joannes

Hilton Village is significant as one of the first planned communities financed with federal funds. The village was built to fill a specific need—a housing shortage—for the employees of the Newport News Shipbuilding Company during World War I. The project sponsors, the U.S. Shipping

Board and the Newport News Shipbuilding and Dry Dock Company, chose a site for the village which was near the shipyard and easily accessible by trolley. Hilton was the name of the only dwelling standing on the property at the time it was acquired. When completed the community provided housing for families of various income levels as well as planned play areas, a city square, stores, and land for schools, parks, and churches. All houses were of frame construction with either stucco or frame exteriors and steeply pitched slate roofs. There are single dwellings as well as double and row houses in the complex.
Private

NEWPORT NEWS (independent city)
JONES, MATTHEW, HOUSE
Fort Eustis Military Reservation, at MacAuliffe Avenue and James River Road intersection
18th and 19th centuries

The Matthew Jones House is one of the few medieval style Virginia houses still in existence. In design it resembles small English manor houses of 100 years earlier. The house was originally built as a one-story, gable-roofed dwelling with a central two-story enclosed porch and a one-story lean-to attached to the rear. The main part of the house was raised to two stories in the late 19th century, using bricks from an outbuilding. The brickwork of the original portion of the house is laid in Flemish bond with glazed headers above the water table and English bond below. Noteworthy features are the arched front door and the massive exterior end chimneys. Little, if any, of the interior woodwork survives because the inside was greatly altered when the second story was added.
Federal
HABS

NORFOLK (independent city)
MYERS, MOSES, HOUSE
Southwest corner of E. Freemason and N. Bank Streets
Late 18th century

The Norfolk home of Moses Myers, merchant, was one of the first brick houses built after the British destroyed the city in 1776. Federal in style, the town house features a pedimented gable end roof and a small aedicular type portico around the front door. A two-story octagonal ended wing was added in 1796; on the rear are a two-story service wing and an attached two-story kitchen. Inside, the interior is embellished by an Adam style ceiling decoration in the entrance hall. Much of the original furniture remains in the house.
Municipal
HABS

NORFOLK (independent city)
NORFOLK ACADEMY
420 Bank Street
1840, Thomas Ustick Walker

Although the Norfolk Academy Building was erected in 1840, the origins of the insituation may be traced back to 1728. The two-story structure has walls covered with stucco. An unfluted Greek Doric order is employed, but the form of the building is that of a Roman temple because it is on a raised podium and there are pilasters rather than free standing columns on the side elevations. Both the front and rear facades feature hexastyle pedimented porticos. Since 1915, when the Academy vacated the structure, it has been used as a court for the city. Presently it is occupied by the city's juvenile court.
Public
HABS

NORFOLK (independent city)
U.S. CUSTOMSHOUSE
101 E. Main Street
1852–1859, Ammi B. Young

The Norfolk Customshouse, built of granite and cast iron, is an early example of fireproof construction. Ammi B. Young was appointed Supervising Architect of the U.S. Office of Construction in 1852. His design for the Customshouse was that of a Roman temple with a pedimented Corinthian portico on the facade and Corinthian pilasters around the other three sides. An outstanding feature of the interior is a double staircase of open-work cast iron.
Federal
HABS

NORTHAMPTON COUNTY
Bridgetown
HUNGARS CHURCH
.2 mile east of the intersection of Routes 619 and 622
1742–1751

This church is the third to serve Hungars parish. The oldest was constructed about 1646, and a second, in 1681. There are four bays each in the north and south walls, and the one-story structure has a gable roof with a modillion cornice. Window and door openings are roundheaded and employ gauged rubbed brick and fluted brick tiles. In 1851 the west gable end was taken down and the overall length reduced from 92 feet to 74 feet 8 inches. Other alterations were made in 1892, 1922, 1950, and 1955.
Private
HABS

NORTHAMPTON COUNTY
Bridgetown vicinity
VAUCLUSE
1.8 miles south of the intersection of
Routes 619 and 657
Late 18th century

Purchased in 1768 by Arthur Upshur IV, the Vaucluse property belonged to the family until 1855. It is thought that the west end of the main block between the two chimneys, the oldest section, was built about 1784. This section is frame and stands on a Flemish bond brick foundation. An addition was constructed about 1829, and the annex connecting the house and kitchen dates from 1889. The long, two-story, square columned porch on the south side was added by the present owner.
Private; not accessible to the public
HABS

NORTHAMPTON COUNTY
Bridgetown vicinity
WINONA
.4 mile northeast of the intersection
of Routes 619 and 622
17th century

The date of this Eastern Shore farmhouse is uncertain, although it is thought to have been built by Mathew Patrick after 1681, when he acquired a reversionary interest in the property on which the house is situated. The original portion of Winona is a small, one-and-one-half-story brick structure with a gable roof and simple box cornice. The west wall of the house fell down several years ago and was replaced with clapboarding. A section of the north wall also fell and has been replaced by brick laid in five course American bond. A second one-story frame wing has recently been added to the west side of the house. Originally the house probably had dormers, but the present ones appear to be renewals. Winona is the only known 17th-century house in the country, other than Bacon's Castle, to have diagonally placed triple chimney stacks.
Private; not accessible to the public
HABS

NORTHAMPTON COUNTY
Cheapside vicinity
CUSTIS TOMBS
1.3 miles northwest of the
intersection of Routes 644 and 645

Two tombs remain in the Custis cemetery, those of Major General John Custis (1630–1696), progenitor of the Custis family in America, and of John Custis IV (c. 1679–c. 1750), his grandson. John Custis IV was the father of Daniel Parke Custis, Martha Washington's first husband, and the great-grandfather of

Mary Anne Randolph Custis, who married Robert E. Lee. The latter tomb is in a good state of preservation and still bears the name of the maker, William Colley of London. Skull motifs appear on it, and their use was rare in Virginia funerary sculpture. Arlington, the original home of the Custis family in America, stood near the graveyard.
Private

NORTHAMPTON COUNTY
Cheriton vicinity
EYRE HALL
1.6 miles north of the intersection of
Routes 13 and 680
18th century

Eyre Hall has evolved to its present state from an original one-and-one-half-story frame structure with four rooms and end chimneys. This house was eventually attached to a late 18th-century gambrel-roofed dwelling, and both sections are now two stories high. Eyre Hall was one of the major 18th-century plantation houses on Virginia's Eastern Shore. The house, its furnishings, the outbuildings, cemetery, and gardens have all survived remarkably intact.
Private; not accessible to the public
HABS

NORTHAMPTON COUNTY
Eastville vicinity
CASERTA
1 mile northwest of the intersection
of Route 630 and U.S. 13
19th century

Caserta is a rambling frame complex composed of a two-story main block with an attached one-and-one-half-story end wing and hyphen. No definite date of construction can be ascertained, although the wing is thought to be the older portion. The most interesting architectural feature of the house is the upward extension of the front pitch of the roof above the main block's western bay. This portion of the building projects at the rear as an ell. Inside it covers a three-story stairwell.
Private; not accessible to the public
HABS

NORTHAMPTON COUNTY
Eastville vicinity
PEAR VALLEY
.1 mile south of the intersection of
Routes 689 and 628
17th century

Pear Valley is a rare surviving example of the small yeoman cottage, virtually unchanged from its original medieval appearance and characterized by a high-pitched roof, a massive pyramidal end chimney, and a glazed header brick pat-

tern. Historians variously place its construction between the 1640's and the 1680's.
Private; not accessible to the public

NORTHAMPTON COUNTY
Franktown vicinity
GLEBE OF HUNGAR'S PARISH
1.3 miles northwest of the
intersection of Routes 622 and 619
17th and 18th centuries

Hungar's Parish Glebe stands on lands once belonging to the church of Hungar's Parish. From 1745 to 1850 ministers dwelled there. The house itself is brick, one and one-half stories with a steep gable roof and dormers. An earlier 17th-century home may have been incorporated into the glebe house, and the exact date of construction is unknown —anywhere from 1643 to 1745.
Private; not accessible to the public
HABS

NORTHAMPTON COUNTY
Jamesville vicinity
SOMMERS HOUSE
.2 mile southwest of the intersection
of Routes 183 and 691
18th century

Eastern Shore farmers owned small tracts of land rather than large plantations, and their homes reflected the size of their real estate holdings. The Sommers House is almost a cottage by modern standards. Its one and one-half stories are covered by a steep gable roof. Rubbed brick is employed at the corners and above most of the windows. A finely executed modillion cornice survives at the base of the roof, both front and rear. Originally the entrances, front and rear, were in the center bays.
Private; not accessible to the public
HABS

NORTHAMPTON COUNTY
Nassawadox vicinity
BROWNSVILLE
1.2 miles southeast of the intersection
of Routes 608 and 600
1806

Brownsville is a two-story brick house which serves as the main dwelling for a large farm. The walls of the house are laid in Flemish bond with white marble lintels over the windows. A main entrance on the land front is framed by a pedimented Doric portico with a Chinese railing. The one-and-one-half-story frame wing, built in 1809, is attached to the kitchen which was previously located farther from the house. Brownsville is noted for its interior Federal woodwork. Several outbuildings and the family burial ground surround the house.
Private; not accessible to the public

ORANGE COUNTY
Barboursville vicinity
BARBOURSVILLE
.5 mile south of intersection of
Routes 777 and 678
18th and 19th centuries, Thomas
Jefferson

Thomas Jefferson designed Barboursville for his friend James Barbour (1775–1842). A fire on Christmas Day, 1884, destroyed all but the exterior brick walls, the interior masonry partitions, and the portico columns. Jefferson's plans for the house were followed except that an octagonal dome, similar to that at Monticello, was omitted. Otherwise Barboursville closely resembled Jefferson's own home. Two service buildings (c. 1790) remain and serve as the present residence.
Private; not accessible to the public

ORANGE COUNTY
Orange vicinity
MAYHURST
.4 mile southwest of the intersection
of Routes 15 and 647
1860

Mayhurst is one of the outstanding examples of Victorian architecture in Virginia. Colonel John Willis, a great-nephew of President James Madison, completed the mansion in 1860. It is a frame, two-story structure set on an exposed brick basement. The exterior walls above the basement are scored to resemble ashlar stonework as at Mount Vernon. The shallow hip roof with a wide cornice supported by ornate paired brackets is repeated on a smaller scale in the cupola, which is topped by a carved wooden finial. During the winter of 1863–1864, when the Army of Northern Virginia was camped in Orange County, General A. P. Hill had his headquarters in the yard at Mayhurst.
Private; not accessible to the public
HABS

ORANGE COUNTY
Orange vicinity
MONTPELIER (JAMES MADISON
HOUSE)
4 miles west of Orange on Va. 20
c. 1760

For 76 years Montpelier was the home of James Madison, fourth President of the United States. Prior to his two terms as President, 1809–1817, Madison was a member of the Continental Congress and the House of Representatives and secretary of state, 1801–1809. His most enduring accomplishment was the work that led to the framing of the United States Constitution in 1789. The central portion of his house was built by his father, and Madison

carried out the landscaping and enlarged the house by adding a huge Doric portico and one-room wings on each side of the original portion. Both James and Dolley Madison are buried at Montpelier.
Private; not accessible to the public
NHL

PAGE COUNTY
Luray
AVENTINE HALL
143 S. Court Street
1852

Aventine Hall is a square, two-story, Greek Revival house crowned by a square cupola. The tetrastyle portico shelters a three-bay facade of the Corinthian order said to be modeled upon the Tower of the Winds in Athens. A Doric frieze and cornice, with water leaves in the metope rectangle, is continued around the entire house. Dismantled and moved from its original site in 1937, Aventine Hall was built by Peter Bock Borst, a Luray lawyer.
Private; not accessible to the public
HABS

PETERSBURG (independent city)
BATTERSEA
793 Appomattox Street
c. 1765–1770

Nineteenth-century alterations have given Battersea an Italianate feeling, but the mansion still remains one of Virginia's most sophisticated Palladian residences and follows Palladio's typical five-part plan of a central block with flanking wings. Strong circumstantial evidence ascribes Battersea to Thomas Jefferson but positive authentication of this has never been made. Colonel John Banister, a close friend of Jefferson's, built the house. The Chinese trellis stair is considered to be the finest of its type in the state.
Private; not accessible to the public
HABS

PETERSBURG (independent city)
CITY MARKET
Cockade Alley
1878–1879

The land on which the City Market stands was given in trust in 1806 to the city of Petersburg by Robert Bolling, a merchant. Bolling intended that the ground should always be the site of a market, and the present market building is the fourth to stand on this spot. It is an octagonal brick structure, 93 feet in diameter. Each side of the ground floor is divided into three arched bays composed of double Romanesque-style openings. Horizontally dividing the exterior walls and surrounding the entire building is a large metal

canopy supported by elaborate iron brackets. Above the canopy on each side were three arched windows, since bricked in. Crowning the hip roof is a low, octagonal cupola containing louvered arched windows.
Municipal
HABS

PETERSBURG (independent city)
EXCHANGE BUILDING
15–19 W. Bank Street
1841

In 1839 a group of local businessmen, desirous of having a building for the display and auction of tobacco and cotton, formed the Petersburg Exchange. They acquired property and commissioned the construction of a building on the site. The Greek Revival Exchange Building is two stories high and set on a raised basement. The entrance facade is five bays wide with a Doric portico in front of the three center bays. The side elevations also contain five bays which are widely spaced and separated by pilasters. A hip roof covers the structure and is topped by a large shallow dome with a lantern. Inside is a central, circular-domed room. The dome rests on an entablature supported by piers. Although the Exchange Building has served as a bank and a police court, the interior has not been radically altered.
Municipal
HABS

PITTSYLVANIA COUNTY
Chatham vicinity
LITTLE CHERRYSTONE
.1 mile north of the intersection of
Routes 703 and 832
Late 18th and early 19th centuries

The frame wing of Little Cherrystone was probably on the land when Thomas Hill Wooding acquired this tract in 1790. It was Wooding, a member of the Virginia House of Delegates between 1799 and 1821, who built the two-story brick addition at right angles to the earlier structure. The dentil cornice, fanlight doorway, and sunburst mantelpieces in the Federal style, later portion of Little Cherrystone, contrast with the simple lines of the older part, exemplifying the evolution of rural Virginia residential architecture.
Private
HABS

PORTSMOUTH (independent city)
DRYDOCK NO. 1
Norfolk Naval Shipyard
1827–1834

The Norfolk Naval Shipyard was established in 1767 and is the oldest in the

country. Large blocks of Massachusetts granite were used to construct the drydock. The sides are built up in a series of stepped tiers, and two flights of stairs lead up the landward end. Overall length of the drydock is 319.5 feet. No changes have been made since construction except to replace the original caisson. During the Civil War the Union steam frigate *Merrimac* was rebuilt here by the Confederate government as an ironclad, the C.S.S. *Virginia.*
Federal

PORTSMOUTH (independent city)
PORTSMOUTH COURTHOUSE (NORFOLK COUNTY COURTHOUSE)
Northeast corner of Court and High Streets
1846, William B. Singleton

Built as the Norfolk County Courthouse, the structure served in this capacity until 1960, when the county government moved to Great Bridge. It is Norfolk's oldest public building. Solid masonry in construction with lintels, sills, and a belt course of cut stone, the courthouse has gray painted brick walls and stands one story high above a ground-floor basement. The architecture is Greek Revival. A domed cupola with a drum and eight Greek Ionic columns has been removed.
Municipal
HABS

PORTSMOUTH (independent city)
PORTSMOUTH OLDE TOWNE HISTORIC DISTRICT
Bounded on the north by Crawford Parkway, on the south by London Street, on the east by the Elizabeth River, and extending .1 mile west of Washington Street

Portsmouth was founded in 1752, and ten years later the city limits were extended westward and encompassed all the present historic district. Most residences in the "Olde Towne" area are Greek Revival, although examples of earlier and later styles exist. Both brick and wood were used for construction. Peculiar to Portsmouth is the "basement house," so called because the dining and serving rooms were aboveground. Underground basements were impractical because the city is on low ground. Another characteristic of Portsmouth houses is a flight of wooden steps leading from the street to the main floor. Important houses in the historic district are the Watts House (1799), the Washington Reed and Bain houses (both Federal), the Grice-Neely House (Greek Revival), and the Nivison-Ball House (18th-century, probably the oldest in the district).
Multiple private

POWHATAN COUNTY
Powhatan Court House
POWHATAN COURT HOUSE HISTORIC DISTRICT
.2 mile north and south and .1 mile east and west of the intersection of Routes 13 and 300
19th century

The Powhatan County Courthouse and the several related buildings and private residences surrounding it form an attractive and relatively unaltered group of 19th-century structures. The courthouse was built in 1848–1849 and is a stuccoed, temple-form, Greek Revival edifice. Nearby are the 18th-century clerk's office, a one-story Italianate frame office building, and the early 19th-century former jail. On the west side of the town green is a late 18th-century, two-and-one-half-story brick tavern fronted by two level galleries.
Multiple public/private
HABS

POWHATAN COUNTY
Powhatan vicinity
BELMEAD
.5 mile northwest of the intersection of Routes 663 and 600
c. 1845, Alexander Jackson Davis

Belmead is a two-story, stuccoed brick residence with a gable roof and a three-story, central cross gable. A square tower hides the north end of the cross gable; corner piers, crenellations, belt courses, ground level Tudor-arched openings, and diamond-pane casement windows on the upper two levels lend a medieval flavor to the facade. Clusters of circular and polygonal chimney stacks and stepped gable ends break the roof line and enliven the facade of the house. Belmead was built for Philip St. George Cocke (1809–1861). Sold after the Civil War, the property passed eventually to Colonel Edward de Vaux Morrell and his wife Louise. In 1897 the Morrells gave Belmead to the Sisters of the Blessed Sacrament, and it became St. Emma's Industrial and Agricultural Institute.
Private

PRINCE EDWARD COUNTY
Briery vicinity
BRIERY CHURCH
.3 mile north of intersection of Routes 747 and 671
c. 1855, Robert Lewis Dabney

Briery Church, a Gothic Revival, board and batten structure was built in a T-shape. The vertical lines of the exterior are emphasized by a steep gable roof and overhanging eaves, by three cross gables

on the south front, and by simple finials on each gable end. All openings are lancet arches, and the windows have diamond panes. Inside, the long pine pulpit has lancet-arched recessed panels with a row of pendants hung from the top. The pine ceiling is constructed to give the appearance of vaulting. Briery Church is the third to serve its congregation. The first church was built about 1760, and it was replaced by a second structure in 1824.
Private

PRINCE EDWARD COUNTY
Hampden-Sydney
HAMPDEN-SYDNEY COLLEGE HISTORIC DISTRICT
Bounded approximately by the campus of Hampden-Sydney College
19th century

Hampden-Sydney Academy first opened its doors in 1776. Less than 20 years later the Virginia General Assembly incorporated the school as Hampden-Sydney College—a school "for the liberal education of youth. . ." The buildings which survive date from the 19th century, and the entire campus has retained much of its rural atmosphere. Representative of the college buildings are The Alamo (1817), a brick residence; Cushing Hall (1822, 1830), a classroom-dormitory; Penshurst (1830), a residence; Venable Hall (1823–1824, 1831), a dormitory, chapel, and library; Graham Hall (c. 1833), the original president's house; and College Church (1860), Greek Revival with brick walls and pilasters.
Private
HABS

PRINCE GEORGE COUNTY
PETERSBURG NATIONAL BATTLEFIELD
Reference—see Dinwiddie County

PRINCE GEORGE COUNTY
Brandon vicinity
BRANDON
West bank of the James River at the end of Route 611
18th century

Brandon Plantation comprises 4500 acres of woodland, pasture, and gardens. The main house is a seven-part brick structure with a two-story center section covered by a pyramidal roof. Flanking the center section are one-story wings with half hip roofs. Connecting this main section of the house to the two-story terminal wings are one-story hyphens. The terminal wings were originally free-standing, one-and-one-half-story dependencies. One outbuilding, a one-story blockhouse, survives.
Private; not accessible to the public
HABS

PRINCE GEORGE COUNTY
Hopewell vicinity
MERCHANT'S HOPE CHURCH
.5 mile west of the intersection of
Route 641 and Virginia 10
17th century

This church is notable for its age and its colonial brickwork. The small rectangular building is constructed of brick laid in Flemish bond with glazed headers above the water table and English bond below. The gable roof has splayed eaves with a modillion cornice, and the front gable end features a rubbed brick arched entranceway and gallery windows. Although most of the interior dates from 1870, the original Portland stone flooring tiles are intact. On one roof timber of the structure is the date 1657.
Private
HABS

PRINCE WILLIAM COUNTY
Dumfries
OLD HOTEL
U.S. 1
18th century

The Old Hotel is a two-story, rectangular structure with a facade of five-bays. The front wall is laid in all header bond with rusticated corner stone quoins, and the window openings are spanned by flat stone arches with superimposed keystones. Porches have been added, the original sash removed, and numerous changes have been made on the interior. The hotel is the last remaining Georgian building in Dumfries.
Private; not accessible to the public
HABS

PRINCE WILLIAM COUNTY
Manassas vicinity
**MANASSAS NATIONAL
BATTLEFIELD PARK**
1861–1862

Manassas was the scene of the first and second battles of Manassas, often called Bull Run, on July 21, 1861, and August 28–30, 1862. The first encounter, the opening battle of the Civil War, pitted General Irvin McDowell's unseasoned Union troops against ill-trained Confederates under General P. G. T. Beauregard. The Confederate victory was sparked by General Thomas J. Jackson's stand in which he gained by epithet "Stonewall." The second battle, also a Confederate victory, cleared the way for General Robert E. Lee's first invasion of the North.
Federal/non-federal
NPS; 3,108.87 acres
HABS

PRINCE WILLIAM COUNTY
Minnieville vicinity
BEL AIR
.9 mile west of Route 640
Mid–18th century

Bel Air is a one-and-one-half-story brick dwelling set on a high stone foundation. Alterations have been made all over the house, most noticeably on the brickwork and window openings of the north wall as well as changes in both the front and back porches. Mason Locke Weems (1759–1825), early biographer of George Washington, and his wife Frances occupied the house from 1809 through 1824 or 1825.
Private; not accessible to the public
HABS

PULASKI COUNTY
Radford vicinity
INGLES FERRY
.9 mile north of the intersection of
Routes 611 and 624
18th century

Ingles Ferry was begun in 1762 by William Ingles and continued to operate intermittently until 1948. Settlers moving west to Kentucky and Tennessee used the ferry to cross the New River. Ingles Ferry tavern, built in 1772, contained a store and public rooms, and stables and a ferry house also stood on the property. Across the river from the tavern stands Ingleside, a two-story frame house built in 1790.
Private; not accessible to the public

RICHMOND (independent city)
**RICHMOND NATIONAL
BATTLEFIELD PARK**
Reference—see Hanover County

RICHMOND (independent city)
BEERS, WILLIAM, HOUSE
1228 E. Broad Street
1839

This Greek Revival town house was built in 1839 by William Beers, a merchant tailor, and was owned by the Beers family until 1872. The only other family who lived here for any length of time was the Morris Nelson family, who owned the house from 1883 until 1909. In 1965 the house was acquired by the Medical College of Virginia, which now uses it for offices. Its location, on the corner of College and Broad streets, makes it an integral part of a group of historic buildings in the Medical College of Virginia area. The rectangular brick structure has three stories crowned by an Italianate, bracketed cornice and a shallow hip roof. Most of the interior features remain generally intact. The Beers House is the last early

house standing on Broad Street west of Shockoe Valley.
State; not accessible to the public
HABS

RICHMOND (independent city)
BELL TOWER
Capitol Square
1824

The Bell Tower is a square, three-story, Federal style brick structure which was originally built as a guardhouse for the Public Guard and as a signal tower. Above the first floor on each side the tower has a wide, recessed arch in which is set a rectangular window with a round window above. Crowning the tower is a simple cornice and a domed, arcaded, octagonal belvedere which houses the bell and which is surrounded by a wooden balustrade. Except for some repointing of the brickwork and replacement of the balustrade, the Bell Tower has remained virtually unchanged since its construction.
State
HABS

RICHMOND (independent city)
BRANCH BUILDING
1015 E. Main Street
c. 1866

The Branch Building was constructed on the site of an earlier structure that burned during the Confederate evacuation of Richmond in 1865. Although the side and rear walls are brick, the facade is cast iron. On the street level of the facade is a four-bay arcade with free-standing Corinthian columns on pedestals supporting semicircular arches. Offices still occupy the interior.
Private
HABS

RICHMOND (independent city)
CITY HALL
Bounded by 10th, Broad, 11th, and
Capitol Streets
1887–1894, Elijah E. Myers

The elaborate Gothic Revival Richmond City Hall was that city's first major post Civil War structure. It is four stories high and built of granite. The skyline of the City Hall is enlivened by a variety of ornamental gables, dormers, crockets, and chimneys. A seven-story clock tower at the northwest corner of the building is balanced by a four-story tower at the northeast corner. The interior is Gothic, and the principal feature is a four-story, skylit well surrounded by tiers of cloisters. A central staircase connects the major levels and surrounding it are the courtrooms, judicial chambers, and city offices.
Municipal

RICHMOND (independent city)
**DONNAN-ASHER IRON FRONT
BUILDING**
1207–1211 E. Main Street
c. 1866

Parts of Richmond were all but destroyed by fire following Confederate evacuation in the spring of 1865. During the next few years extensive rebuilding occurred. The Donnan-Asher Iron Front Building was constructed at that time. Four stories high and twelve bays wide, the building has brick side and rear walls and cast iron over brick on the facade. Corinthian columns and pilasters delineate the bays, and the facade is capped by an Italianate entablature. The windows in each bay are arched and divided into two sections. Architecturally the structure is High Victorian Italianate.
Private
HABS

RICHMOND (independent city)
EGYPTIAN BUILDING
Southwest corner, E. Marshall and
College Streets
1845, Thomas Stewart

In 1838 Hampden-Sydney College established a medical department in Richmond which was chartered by the state several years later as the Medical College of Virginia. The Egyptian Building, designed by the noted Greek Revival architect Thomas Stewart, was the first structure built especially for the new college. Completed in 1845, this exotic edifice was a radical departure from the current architectural traditions of the city. In 1939 the exterior of the building was renovated through the generosity of Bernard Baruch in memory of his father, who graduated from the Medical College of Virginia in 1862 and served as a Confederate surgeon during the Civil War. Unfortunately, none of the original interior survives. The Egyptian Building is the oldest medical college building in the South, and architecturally, it is generally considered to be the finest Egyptian Revival building in the Nation.
State
HABS

RICHMOND (independent city)
FIRST AFRICAN BAPTIST CHURCH
Northeast corner, College and E.
Broad Streets
1876

The First African Baptist Church is a brick, Greek Revival structure decorated with Doric pilasters which frame recessed panels. The entablature, containing modillions and dentils, is Roman Corinthian. The church originally housed one of the oldest Negro congregations in Virginia.

The building was sold to the Medical College of Virginia in 1955 and now houses offices and classrooms.
State

RICHMOND (independent city)
FIRST BAPTIST CHURCH
Northwest corner of 12th and E.
Broad Streets
1839–1841, Thomas U. Walter

Greek Revival in style, the First Baptist Church is a stuccoed, temple-form building with a portico using two fluted Doric columns. The bays of the sides are framed by Doric pilasters supporting a Doric entablature. The wing at the northeast corner of the building is a later addition but repeats the architectural detail of the original portion. A cupola which was over the portico has been removed. The congregation of the First Baptist Church was composed of the white membership of the old Baptist church at Broad and College Streets (thereafter known as the First African Baptist Church) and was the oldest Baptist congregation in Richmond. During the Civil War the building served as an emergency hospital for Confederate soldiers. In 1938 the congregation sold the church to the Medical College of Virginia, and it now serves as a student center.
State

RICHMOND (independent city)
HANCOCK-WIRT-CASKIE HOUSE
2 N. 5th Street
1808–1809

The Hancock-Wirt-Caskie House has an unusual facade composed of octagonal ended or three-sectioned bow front projections. The house itself is brick with a wooden two-story porch on the front. Other notable architectural details are a low pitched roof, deep eaves with narrow brackets, and the use of geometric shapes in the facade and the interior room arrangement. All original mantels have been replaced, but most wood and plaster trim remains as built.
Private
HABS

RICHMOND (independent city)
HOLLYWOOD CEMETERY
412 S. Cherry Street
Mid–19th century, John Notman

Hollywood Cemetery had become the most fashionable burying place in Richmond by 1860. The overall plan drawn up by Notman was followed closely with regard to plantings and roadways, although many of his architectural structures were not built. Among the well-known persons buried here are Presidents James Monroe and John Tyler, Matthew

Fontaine Maury, Jefferson Davis, and J. E. B. Stuart.
Private
HABS

RICHMOND (independent city)
**JAMES RIVER AND KANAWHA
CONNECTION LOCKS AND CANAL**
South of Cary Street, between 10th
and Jefferson Streets
1841–1854

The completion of these five great stone locks in 1854 provided a continuous water link between the James River and Kanawha Canal and the lower James, and thus an important commercial connection between piedmont and tidewater Virginia. The canal is constructed of granite blocks, generally measuring sixteen inches high and up to seventy-nine inches in length, which are cut in an ogive curve at the gate recesses to hold the gates in place against the water pressure. An irregular ashlar arched bridge built in 1860 spans the canal at one point. Canal traffic waned in the late 19th century, and today a portion of the locks are covered by a railroad trestle.
Municipal
HABS

RICHMOND (independent city)
JEFFERSON HOTEL
104 W. Main Street
1895, Carrère and Hastings

The Jefferson Hotel, a massive structure of buff brick and stone, displays several architectural styles reflecting its construction during the period of American eclecticism. The exterior is a successful blending of Italian Renaissance elements (a rusticated lower story, a central external loggia, and four rectangular towers), Palladian symmetry, and motifs associated with Spanish Baroque architecture such as the carved Plateresque decoration around third-story windows. The interior public rooms include the Pompeian Palm Court, the Louis XVI Grand Salon, and smaller rooms in various French styles. The interior was gutted by fire in 1901, but the exterior survives largely as it was originally designed. One basic change following the fire was the reconstruction of the wings on the southern end. These were rebuilt to run north and south instead of east and west to allow more light and air into the rooms. Among the fine appointments still contained in the building are an exceptional collection of late-19th-century academic paintings and a life-sized marble statue of Thomas Jefferson by Richmond sculptor Edward V. Valentine.
Private

RICHMOND (independent city)
KENT-VALENTINE HOUSE
    12 E. Franklin Street
    1845, 1904

Documented evidence indicates that Horace Kent had his Richmond home built from plans drawn by Isaiah Rogers of Boston. The Kent-Valentine House is the only identified and extant residential structure designed by Rogers. Exterior walls of the three-story dwelling are brick covered with stucco. The low hip roof has four interior end chimneys and a bracketed cornice. First-floor windows are floor length, and the almost square third-floor windows are "attic" type. Alterations were made in 1904, when the original one-story iron porch was removed, the present portico constructed, and the three-story bay expanded to five bays.
Private; not accessible to the public
HABS

RICHMOND (independent city)
LEIGH, BENJAMIN WATKINS, HOUSE
    1000 E. Clay Street
    1812–1816

The Benjamin Watkins Leigh House was built by John Wickham. Wickham's daughter, Julia, who married Benjamin Leigh, received the house from her father, and the couple made it their home. Benjamin Leigh, a lawyer and jurist, helped in the revision of the Virginia Constitution in 1831. He was an ardent supporter of states' rights and served in the U.S. Senate during the Jackson administration. After Leigh died, the property was sold. The house is now owned by the Medical College of Virginia and used for offices. The Italianate, bracketed cornice, Italianate front porch, and the three-story wing on the east side are later additions.
State; not accessible to the public
HABS

RICHMOND (independent city)
MAIN STREET STATION
    1520 E. Main Street
    1901, Wilson, Harris, and Richards

Richmond was the crossroads of the Seaboard Air Line and the Chesapeake & Ohio railroads. The station demonstrates the strong influence of the French Ecole des Beaux Arts on American architecture during the late 19th and early 20th centuries. Exterior brick walls are veneered with an unbonded tile resembling Roman brick, and the architectural decoration is executed in stone and terra cotta. The main facade is seven bays wide at ground level, and a five-bay rough hewn stone loggia with segmental arches frames the entrances. The steep hip roof has decorative bronze finials at either end, and there is a six-story clock tower at the southwest corner. Overall dimensions are 102 feet 5 inches by 63 feet.
Private

RICHMOND (independent city)
MARSHALL, JOHN, HOUSE
    9th and Marshall Streets
    1790

As Chief Justice, John Marshall presided over the United States Supreme Court during the formative years of American constitutional jurisprudence, 1801–1835. By his judicial opinions he contributed to the evolution of the federal government as a truly national government rather than a weak compact among sovereign states. Because Marshall owned this house for 45 years and spent much time in it, it is closely linked with the accomplishments of its owner. A square brick building originally containing six rooms and a basement, the house was altered in 1810 by the addition of a bedroom. A well-proportioned pedimented gable, modillioned cornice, and two small porches create the architectural quality of the exterior.
Municipal
NHL; HABS

RICHMOND (independent city)
MAUPIN-MAURY HOUSE
    1105 E. Clay Street
    1846

The Maupin-Maury House is a three-story Greek Revival town house. Its three-bay facade is plain except for a bead and reel molding under the cornice and a front porch with Ionic columns. The town house was built in 1846 by Dr. Socrates Maupin, one of the founders of the medical department at Hampden-Sydney College which became the Medical College of Virginia. In 1853 the house was sold to Robert H. Maury, a relative of Matthew Fontaine Maury, the oceanographer. The latter lived and worked in this house during the summer of 1861 while conducting experiments on an underwater torpedo.
Private; not accessible to the public
HABS

RICHMOND (independent city)
MONUMENT AVENUE HISTORIC DISTRICT
    Bounded on the southeast by a straight line running from the center of the block on Grace Street between Ryland and Lombardy Streets to the intersection of Birch Street and Park Avenue; on the southwest by Park Avenue to Belmont Avenue and then west in a straight line to the intersection of Roseneath Road and Wythe Avenue; on the northwest by a straight line from Wythe Avenue and Roseneath Road to Grace Street and Roseneath Road; and on the northeast by Grace Street
    19th and 20th centuries

Monument Avenue is a broad residential boulevard beginning at the termination of West Franklin Street and extending west for 14 blocks to Roseneath Road. Statues or memorials to great Confederate leaders have given the avenue its name, and the distinctive and unaltered period architecture has supplied character and atmosphere. Moving northwest along Monument Avenue the visitor encounters first an equestrian statue of J. E. B. Stuart (1907); then Jean Antoine Mercie's equestrian Robert E. Lee (1890); next, the Jefferson Davis Memorial (1907); a statue of "Stonewall" Jackson (1919); and, last, a memorial to Matthew Fontaine Maury (1929). One-hundred-thirty-foot-wide Monument Avenue is lined with Georgian Revival and Second Renaissance Revival town houses and terrace rows, and several Greek Revival churches. John Russell Pope, William Lawrence Bottomley, and Duncan Lee have all designed buildings in the district.
Multiple public/private

RICHMOND (independent city)
MONUMENTAL CHURCH
    1224 E. Broad Street
    1812–1814, Robert Mills

Monumental Church was erected on the site of the American French Academy which burned on December 26, 1811, during a theater performance. The church was built as a monument to the 72 people, including Gov. George William Smith, who died in the fire. The design of Monumental Church takes into account its dual function as a memorial to those who perished and as an Episcopal parish church. Thus the stone portico which shelters the monument almost appears to be a separate structure from the stuccoed church behind it. This portico is crowned by a triangular parapet, and its funereal quality is heightened by a frieze decorated with a series of lachrymatories. The two-story octagonal structure is crowned by a low dome topped by a lantern. Mills intended to add a spire to the rear side, but only the first stage was built. The interior contains box pews and a gallery across the rear. A two-story wing was added to the east side about 1840. The church no longer has an active parish.
State
HABS

RICHMOND (independent city)
MORSON'S ROW
219–223 Governor Street
1853

The three Victorian, Italianate town houses comprising Morson's Row were built by James Marion Morson as rental properties. All have three stories, flat roofs, and are made of brick although the facades are stuccoed. The row features heavy bracketed cornices, arched door frames, and molded consoled lintels above the windows. A distinctive architectural feature is the off-center, two-bay bow on each house which gives the row an undulating appearance. Another unusual feature is the difference in the levels of the houses caused by the grade of the lot. The interiors of all three houses retain original features such as mahogany doors and marble mantels.
Public/private; not accessible to the public
HABS

RICHMOND (independent city)
PUTNEY HOUSES
1010–1012 E. Marshall Street
1859

The Putney Houses were owned by Samuel and Stephen Putney, father and son, who resided here from 1862 until 1894. The Samuel Putney House at 1010 E. Marshall Street is a three-story, three-bay Italianate town house. Its scored stucco facade is crowned by an entablature with an unusual frieze containing panels and roundels. All of the front windows are topped by semicircular lintels supported on pilasters. The most noticeable exterior feature is the delicate cast iron porch across the first story. Not as elaborate as its neighbor, the Stephen Putney House next door is also three-storied and three-bayed. Its windows have plain lintels, and the fanlight of the off-center front door is surrounded by intricate carving. The most outstanding feature of this house is its two-story veranda of ornamental iron situated on the east side. Marble mantels and Victorian cornices of the interior are original.
Municipal
HABS

RICHMOND (independent city)
ST. JOHN'S CHURCH HISTORIC DISTRICT
    Bounded roughly by 22nd Street on the west, Marshall Street on the north, E. Franklin Street on the south, and 29th Street on the east

Originally called Richmond Hill or Indian Hill, St. John's Church Historic District grew up around St. John's Church. Here, in 1775, the Virginia Convention listened to Patrick Henry's ringing words, "Give me liberty or give me death." Settlement was slow due to the hilly topography, but gradually merchants whose stores stood on the banks of the James, built homes here. Today examples of almost all major 19th-century architectural styles, from Federal and Greek Revival to Victorian, are evident. Most dwellings are side hall plan town homes. The oldest existing rowhouse in Richmond, Carrington Row (2307–2311 E. Broad Street), is within the district and is Neo-Classical in style. By the 1950's the neighborhood had deteriorated greatly, but interested citizens formed the Historic Richmond Foundation and effected passage of municipal legislation creating the historic district.
Multiple public/private
HABS

RICHMOND (independent city)
ST. JOHN'S EPISCOPAL CHURCH
    E. Broad Street between 24th and
    25th Streets
    1740–1741

In St. John's Church on March 23, 1775, Patrick Henry delivered his famous "Liberty or Death" speech. Made at a meeting of Virginia's General Assembly, the address effected the passage of Henry's resolutions to put the colony into a state of defense. The church, built on land donated by Colonel William Byrd, was originally a simple rectangular building. It was first enlarged in 1772, at which time it assumed the proportions that existed at the time of Henry's speech.
Multiple municipal/private
NHL; HABS

RICHMOND (independent city)
ST. PAUL'S CHURCH
    815 E. Grace Street
    1845, Thomas B. Stewart

In the early 1840's a portion of the congregation of Richmond's Monumental Episcopal Church built a new church just west of their former house of worship. The lot chosen was adjacent to Capitol Square at the corner of Ninth and Grace streets. St. Paul's most outstanding exterior feature is its octastyle Greek Corinthian portico. Although Grecian motifs appear frequently, the building itself is constructed in the form of a Roman temple, as it is placed on a podium with pilasters between the side bays. The cupola surmounting the facade was originally topped by a 225-foot spire which has been removed and replaced by a small octagonal dome. The principal building material is stuccoed brick. Inside the church contains a finely executed series of Greek Corinthian columns around the choir and the semicircular apse. The nave, which retains its original pews, has a gallery around three sides and is crowned by a plaster relief ceiling. During services at St. Paul's on Sunday, April 2, 1865, President Jefferson Davis received word that Gen. Robert E. Lee could no longer hold Petersburg and that the government should evacuate Richmond.
Private
HABS

RICHMOND (independent city)
ST. PETER'S CHURCH
800 E. Grace Street
1834

St. Peter's Church is the oldest Roman Catholic church in Richmond. Roman Revival in style, the church is an elongated cruciform structure of stuccoed brick. The facade features a slender, pedimented portico with coupled columns. A finely executed Doric entablature surrounds the entire building. A stepped parapet hides the roof line on the facade, and the parapet is surmounted by an octagonal cupola. The interior of the church has not been altered extensively. The internal bays are divided by Doric pilasters with Ionic capitals. Other features are the shallow transepts and the semicircular apse.
Private
HABS

RICHMOND (independent city)
SHELTERING ARMS HOSPITAL
1008 E. Clay Street
1857

William H. Grant, a prominent tobacco manufacturer, built this mansion in 1857. The interior was greatly altered in 1892 when the house was acquired by the Sheltering Arms Hospital (a free hospital for all white residents in the Commonwealth of Virginia), but the basic elements of the original floor plan survive. With the conversion, extensive additions were made to the rear of the house, and a three-story wing was erected on the west side connecting it to the house next door. The hospital moved to a new location in 1965, and the property came under the control of the Medical College of Virginia, which now uses it for offices. A three-story, brick, Italianate town house, the building is one of the few houses of its period and type to have survived in downtown Richmond.
State; not accessible to the public

RICHMOND (independent city)
STEARNS IRON FRONT BUILDING
1007–1013 E. Main Street
c. 1865–1869

In 1865 Franklin Stearns, a Richmond businessman, purchased 1007–1013 E. Main Street and began construction of a commercial edifice. Completed four years later, the Stearns Iron Front Building is a cast iron, High Victorian Italianate row structure exhibiting a minimum proportion of solid (cast iron) to void (glass). All ground floor bays are separated by engaged Corinthian columns, and similar ones frame each window of the remaining three floors. Each window is round arched. A deep Italianate entablature crowns the facade; ornate brackets support the roof overhang and extend from beneath the cornice through the frieze. Cast iron garlands, rosebuds, and spiraling vines ornament the facade.
Private
HABS

RICHMOND (independent city)
U.S. POST OFFICE AND CUSTOMSHOUSE
1000 E. Main Street
1858, Ammi B. Young

Constructed of granite and Italianate in style, the U. S. Post Office and Customshouse was placed in the middle of the block between Bank and Main streets. The steep grade of the site necessitated a difference in elevation between the Main Street facade (three stories high) and the Bank Street side (two stories). The Bank Street entrance was framed by a central, one-story, triple-arch porch, one bay in depth. On the Main Street side the building had a rusticated basement. Quoins emphasized the corners, and the structure was crowned by a bracketed cornice and shallow-hip roof. In 1889 short wings were added to either side of the original building. Later one story was added to the structure as well as a large wing which extended to 10th Street. In 1930 further enlarging was done with the addition of an eastern wing, thus filling the entire block. None of the original interior survives. The U.S. Post Office and Customshouse was taken over by the Confederate government during the Civil War and used to house the Confederate treasury and the office of President Jefferson Davis. In 1867 when Davis was returned to Richmond to stand trial for treason, the trial was held in the district courtroom in the Customshouse.
Federal

RICHMOND (independent city)
VALENTINE MUSEUM
1005–1015 E. Clay Street
1812, 1840, 1870

The Valentine Museum, a repository for collections and archives important in Richmond and Virginia history, is housed in three separate buildings. The principal structure is the Wickham-Valentine House, a three-bay, two-story stuccoed house with a shallow hip roof. It was built by John Wickham, a Richmond lawyer who served as one of the defense counsel at the trial of Aaron Burr. Mann Valentine II, a collector of historic artifacts, purchased the house in 1882. At his death 10 years later, the house and collection were left to the city of Richmond to be maintained as a museum. The Gray-Valentine Houses, next to the Wickham-Valentine House, are a series of three Victorian town houses, three stories high, nine bays wide, and crowned by a heavy bracketed cornice. All three were built about 1870 and remodeled in 1938 to house part of the museum's collection. The Bransford-Cecil House, a Greek Revival dwelling built in 1840, was moved to its present site in 1954 and made a part of the museum complex. The plan of this house has been greatly altered, and only a few interior architectural features (window reveals and mantels) are original.
Private
HABS

RICHMOND (independent city)
VIRGINIA GOVERNOR'S MANSION
Capitol Square
1810–1813

In 1810 the Virginia General Assembly authorized $13,000 for the construction of a new gubernatorial residence to replace an earlier wooden house which had fallen into disrepair. The proposed dwelling was to stand near the site of the old one in the northeast corner of Capitol Square. Within three years the house was completed sufficiently for Gov. James Barbour to occupy it, and it has been the home of every Virginia governor since that time. The Governor's Mansion is a two-story, brick, Federal style building. The main facade is divided into five bays with the center one projecting slightly forward. The double front door is framed by sidelights and a transom embellished with ornate tracery. Less elaborate porches with Doric columns frame the side entrances. A one-story, semi-octagonal wing was added to the rear as a dining room in 1906, and the old dining room and drawing room were joined to form a ballroom across the end of the original portion of the house. A second story containing extra bedrooms

was built on this new wing in 1914–1915. Little of the original interior remains as the house was badly damaged by fire in 1926.
State
HABS

RICHMOND (independent city)
VIRGINIA STATE CAPITOL (CONFEDERATE CAPITOL)
Capitol Square
1785–1792, Thomas Jefferson and Louis Clerisseau

The design of the Virginia State Capitol was inspired by the Maison Carrée in Nîmes, France. From 1861 to 1865 it served as the Confederate Capitol, reverting to its original use after the fall of the Confederacy. The central portion of the Greek Revival building is unaltered, but wings were added and entrance steps constructed in 1904–1905. On the grounds are statues of noted Virginians, including the Washington Monument, executed by Thomas Crawford after a design by Robert Mills.
State
NHL

RICHMOND (independent city)
WHITE HOUSE OF THE CONFEDERACY (BROCKENBROUGH MANSION)
Clay and 12th Streets
1818

The Brockenbrough Mansion served as the South's Executive Mansion during the four-year period of Confederate President Jefferson Davis' residence in the Confederate capital. The house was seized by the victorious Union forces on April 3, 1865, and was held by the United States Government until 1870, when it was restored to Richmond. In 1893 the building was made into a museum of Civil War relics. Now called the Confederate Museum, it is an outstanding repository of Confederate memorabilia in the United States.
Private
NHL; HABS

RICHMOND (independent city)
WILLIAM J. CLARK LIBRARY AND BARCO-STEVENS HALL, VIRGINIA UNION UNIVERSITY
West side of Lombardy Street at the intersection with Brook Road
1939, Victor Bourgeois and Leo Stijnen

The library-gymnasium-classroom building was originally constructed as the Belgian Pavilion for the New York World's Fair. After the Fair the building was to be returned to Belgium, but the outbreak of World War II prevented this, and the

Belgian ambassador presented it to Virginia Union University in 1941. The U-shaped structure is one story high, flat roofed, and faced with red tiles above a black slate-faced water table. Its distinctive campanile-like tower is decorated on one corner by glass blocks and topped by a louvered lantern. Austere formalism, typical of the architectural modernism of the 1930's, marks the building as International in style.

Private

RICHMOND COUNTY
Ethel vicinity
MENOKIN
1.2 miles northwest of the
intersection of County Routes 690
and 621
1769

Menokin is a two-story structure built of local stone which has been stuccoed. The stone dressings include the elaborate quoins, belt course, and window and door trim. There is a belt course at the floor line as well as at the sill level of the second floor. The roof is hip-on-hip. Originally there were two dependencies, both of which were two stories. The interior of the house was constructed around a central hall plan with four rooms on each floor. Menokin was built as a home for Rebecca Taylor Lee and her husband Francis Lightfoot Lee.

Private; not accessible to the public
HABS

RICHMOND COUNTY
Tappahannock vicinity
SABINE HALL
1.4 miles south of intersection of
Routes 624 and 360
c. 1730

Sabine Hall, built by Landon Carter, son of Robert "King" Carter, is an early Georgian mansion constructed of brick laid in Flemish bond with random glazed headers. The principal facade is seven bays wide. The windows are highlighted by stone sills and stone lintels with projecting keystones. Sabine Hall is noted for its fully paneled central hall (18 feet by 48 feet). The east and west wings are not original.

Private; not accessible to the public
NHL; HABS

RICHMOND COUNTY
Warsaw vicinity
MOUNT AIRY
1 mile west of Warsaw on U.S. 360
1758–1762, John Ariss

One of the few major 18th-century plantation houses in Virginia to be built of stone, Mount Airy has continuously been the residence of the Tayloe family. It is an expression of the Palladian style in the colonies, with an abundance of stone detail. The entrance facade features a projecting pavilion of rusticated limestone with a full stone entablature. The dependent wings are connected to the main house by quadrant passages. Fire damaged the house in 1840, destroying the roof and some exterior trim; the interior was rebuilt in 1844.

Private; not accessible to the public
NHL; HABS

ROCKBRIDGE COUNTY
Lexington vicinity
TIMBER RIDGE PRESBYTERIAN CHURCH
.3 mile southwest of the intersection
of Routes 11 and 716
1755–1756

Since its organization in 1746 the congregation of Timber Ridge Presbyterian Church has had important associations with the development of the Valley of Virginia. Washington and Lee University traces its beginnings to Augusta Academy, at one time located at Timber Ridge and supported entirely by the church congregation. One of the early leaders of the congregation was John Houston, father of Sam Houston, the Texas patriot, who was born nearby. The only visible elements of the colonial edifice are portions of three of the stone walls and several roof timbers. The church was first altered in 1871 and completely remodelled in 1899–1900.

Private
HABS

ROCKBRIDGE COUNTY
Staunton vicinity
McCORMICK, CYRUS, FARM AND WORKSHOP
18 miles south of Staunton on U.S. 11
and County Route 606 at Walnut
Grove
Early 1800's

Of all the inventions that revolutionized agriculture during the first half of the 19th century, Cyrus McCormick's mechanical reaper (1834) was probably the most important. It made it possible for one man to harvest as much grain in a day as had required the labor of several men with the more primitive scythes and cradles. Both McCormick's workshop, a small log building on a high stone foundation, and his large brick farmhouse have been well preserved.

State
NHL

SHENANDOAH COUNTY
Middletown vicinity
FORT BOWMAN
.4 mile northeast of the intersection
of Routes 11 and 660
c. 1753

Fort Bowman illustrates the influence of Pennsylvania German architecture on the Shenandoah Valley. The house is a two-story, rectangular structure built of limestone and topped by a gable roof. All interior woodwork is original, but a kitchen wing and a wood and iron porch are later additions.

Private; not accessible to the public
HABS

SHENANDOAH COUNTY
New Market vicinity
NEW MARKET BATTLEFIELD PARK
1 mile north of the intersection of
Routes 11 and 211

The Northern campaign for Richmond in the spring of 1864 called for the advance of Union troops up the Shenandoah Valley to take possession of southwest Virginia. Commanded by Major General Franz Sigel, 6,500 Federal troops marched toward Staunton, a vital rail center controlled by Confederate forces under Major General John C. Breckinridge. His troops numbered about 5,000, including 247 cadets from the Virginia Military Institute. The battle of New Market took place on May 15, 1864, and the Southern soldiers successfully repulsed the more numerous enemy. New Market caused a delay in the Federals' advance, enabling crops to be harvested and the railroads to continue operation for five months. In October General Philip H. Sheridan broke Southern resistance at the battle of Cedar Creek. The 160–acre battlefield park contains the Bushong House, used by both sides as a hospital.

Private

SMYTH COUNTY
Marion vicinity
PRESTON HOUSE (HERONDON)
.1 mile south of the intersection of
Routes 645 and 11
1842

John Montgomery Preston built Herondon as an inn along the Wilderness Road, which ran from Kingsport, Tennessee, to Boonesborough, Kentucky. The house served this purpose until 1864, when it was converted to a private residence. Built of brick, the house is two stories high with a gable roof and twin interior end chimneys at both ends. Accenting the facade are rectangular plaster insets between the

stories and a complete Doric entablature. A rear, two-story brick ell appears to be contemporary with the main structure but is smaller in proportion.
Private; not accessible to the public
HABS

SPOTSYLVANIA COUNTY
Fredericksburg vicinity
FREDERICKSBURG AND SPOTSYLVANIA COUNTY BATTLEFIELDS MEMORIAL NATIONAL MILITARY PARK
Fredericksburg and the area in Spotsylvania County to the west and southwest
1862–1864

This park commemorates four major battles of the Civil War: Fredericksburg, Chancellorsville, the Wilderness, and Spotsylvania Court House. Included in the park is Fredericksburg National Cemetery. At Fredericksburg, strategically located between Washington, D.C., and Richmond, Virginia, Confederate troops under General Robert E. Lee defeated General A. E. Burnside, newly appointed commander of the Army of the Potomac, on December 11–13, 1862. At the battle of Chancellorsville in May 1863, Lee's forces turned back Federal troops under General Joseph Hooker and proceeded northward into Pennsylvania, only to be defeated by General George G. Meade at Gettysburg on July 1–3. The bloody battle of the Wilderness, May 5–7, 1864, was followed by the struggle in the vicinity of Spotsylvania Court House on May 9–19. There Union troops under General Ulysses S. Grant achieved a partial success that greatly weakened Lee's men. From Spotsylvania, Grant had Meade move his troops around Lee's right flank toward Richmond. Grant had begun his war of attrition.
Federal/non-federal
NPS; 3,672.15 acres

STAFFORD COUNTY
Brooke vicinity
POTOMAC CREEK SITE
1.8 miles southeast of the intersection of Routes 621 and 608
17th century

Potomac Creek Site has been identified as the Indian village of Patowomeke. Captain John Smith visited and described the village in 1608. Traders carried on business with the Indians here until 1630, and the village was finally abandoned about 1635.
Multiple/private

STAFFORD COUNTY
Falmouth
BELMONT (GARI MELCHERS HOME)
Early 1900's

Belmont was the home of Gari Melchers, landscape and portrait painter, from 1916 until his death in 1932. Melchers studied abroad and worked in the Netherlands for 15 years, gaining a reputation for his studies of Dutch life. He is well known for "The Arts of War" and "The Arts of Peace," painted for the Library of Congress. Belmont, a two-story frame building, and the fieldstone studio in which Melchers worked are maintained as a memorial and art center.
Private
NHL

STAFFORD COUNTY
Falmouth
FALMOUTH HISTORIC DISTRICT
Extending from the intersection of Routes 1 and 17, .3 mile north, .6 mile east, .2 mile south, and .3 mile west
18th and 19th centuries

Falmouth was laid out in 1727 on fifty acres along the Rappahannock River. Seven trustees assumed the responsibility of governing, and the town gradually became a leading mercantile center. Frame, brick, and stone buildings of the 18th and 19th centuries remain as evidence of past activity and prosperity. The residences are older than the commercial buildings which date from the 1800's. Falmouth's unique identity stems largely from its unusual setting on the riverbank and hillside.
Multiple public/private
HABS

STAFFORD COUNTY
Garrisonville vicinity
AQUIA CHURCH
.1 mile north of the intersection of Routes 1 and 610
1751

Aquia Church is a two-story brick structure with a hip roof and an unusual tower and cupola worked into the upper level of the entrance arm of the building. The exterior of the church is highlighted by the window keystones, corner quoins, and the three pedimented and rusticated doorways. The church walls are laid in Flemish bond with random glazed headers. Rubbed brick has been used on all window jambs and arches. Damaged by fire in 1754, Aquia Church was rebuilt three years later, and it is believed that only the present walls date from 1751. Inside, the church retains its original triple-tier pulpit, reredos, west gallery, and pews.
Private
HABS

STAUNTON (independent city)
MAIN BUILDING, WESTERN STATE HOSPITAL
Intersection of Routes 11 and 250
c. 1839, William Small

The Main Building or administration building of Western State Hospital is the oldest part of a six-structure complex. Greek Revival in style, the Main Building has five parts; the central portion is three stories high with a hip roof surmounted by an octagonal cupola. Two temple-form end pavilions are connected to the central structure by two-story hyphens. Inside, the building has been altered little, and original woodwork and hardware survive. Western State Hospital was founded in 1825 by an act of the state assembly. Those who were patients here were not considered dangerous to society and, in many cases, were thought to be curable.
Public

STAUNTON (independent city)
VIRGINIA SCHOOL FOR THE DEAF AND BLIND
Southeast side of intersection of E. Beverly Street and Pleasant Terrace
Mid–18th century, Robert Cory Long, Jr.

Although the Virginia General Assembly had passed an act in 1838 providing for the establishment of a state school for the deaf and blind, the main building was not completed until 1846. The monumental three-story brick structure is centered with a large hexastyle Greek Doric pedimented portico. Wings extend on either side of this portico, making the total length of the facade 182 feet. The imposing structure stands not only as one of the finest, albeit least known, of the country's major Greek Revival public buildings, but also as a focal point for one of the oldest and most distinguished deaf and blind schools in the United States.
State
HABS

STAUNTON (independent city)
WILSON, WOODROW, BIRTHPLACE
N. Coalter Street, between Beverly and Frederick Streets
1846

Thomas Woodrow Wilson, 28th President of the United States, was born in this Greek Revival manse in 1856. Before becoming President he served as a professor of history and government and as president of Princeton University. The political and economic reforms enacted at the request of Wilson's administration and his leadership of the country through the First World War cause many to regard Wilson as the President who led America politically into the 20th century. For his work in establishing the League of Nations, he was awarded the Nobel Peace Prize in 1919. Among the Wilson possessions on display here are the family Bible and the bookcase which Wilson bought with his first earnings.

Private

NHL; HABS

SURRY COUNTY
Bacon's Castle
BACON'S CASTLE
c. 1655

Bacon's Castle is distinguished by its association with an important event in Virginia's early history and by its architectural character. The house took its name from the episode in which supporters of the rebel Nathaniel Bacon seized and fortified the house in 1676. Among the earliest of the Virginia cross-plan houses, it is a two-story brick building laid in English bond and featuring curvilinear decorative end gables and large clustered triple chimneys.

Private; not accessible to the public

NHL; HABS

SURRY COUNTY
Jamestown vicinity
CHIPPOKES PLANTATION
  South bank of the James River
  between College Run and Lower
  Chippokes Creek, opposite
  Jamestown Island
  17th, 18th and 19th centuries

Chippokes Plantation consists of a 1,403-acre working farm located on the bluffs of the Cobham Bay section of the James River. In addition to the agricultural lands, the plantation contains woods and marshes. The buildings on the property include a one-and-one-half-story frame house built about 1810 in the vicinity of the 17th-century plantation house. The present main residence is a two-story, brick, Greek Revival house built about 1850. There are numerous outbuildings and farm dependencies. Chippokes Plantation was named for an early Indian chief who was friendly to the English. His lands included the present plantation. The first English owner of Chippokes Plantation was Captain William Powell, a shareholder in the Virginia Company of 1609.

State

SURRY COUNTY
Surry vicinity
FOUR MILE TREE
  .2 mile northeast of the intersection
  of Routes 618 and 610
  19th century

The Four Mile Tree Plantation House is a one-and-one-half-story brick structure with a hip-on-gambrel roof, pedimented dormers, and four interior end chimneys. In the 19th century the brick was stuccoed and scored to imitate ashlar. All openings, except the central entrance, were altered in the late 19th or early 20th century. The oldest interior woodwork in the house is in the central stair hall which probably dates from the first half of the 18th century. Four Mile Tree was the seat of the Brown family and was named for its distance from Jamestown.

Private

HABS

SURRY COUNTY
Surry vicinity
SMITH'S FORT
  .8 mile northeast of the intersection
  of Routes 31 and 620
  Early 17th century

John Smith is believed to have constructed the fort during the first two years of the Virginia colony's existence. The fortification consists of a mound intersecting the peninsula in two places, thus forming a triangle about 50 feet above the stream bank. Originally a palisade surmounted the mound, which was probably twice its present heights. The two exposed or seaward sides of the fort may have been protected by another wooden palisade.

Private; not accessible to the public

SUSSEX COUNTY
Grizzard vicinity
FORTSVILLE
  1.6 miles southeast of the intersection
  of Routes 612 and 611
  c. 1780–1820

Fortsville was the home of John Y. Mason (1799–1859), Congressman, Secretary of the Navy, Attorney General, and minister to France. He named the house for his wife, Mary Ann Fort. The dwelling is a three-part frame composition with a pedimented, gable-end main facade. Two shallow one-story wings flank the two-story center section. A fanlight in the pediment and the dentil and modillion cornice lend an air of sophistication to the entire dwelling. The one-story porch on the center section of the north facade may be original but has been altered. Fortsville is a country version of the Semple House in Williamsburg.

Private; not accessible to the public

HABS

SUSSEX COUNTY
Homeville vicinity
CHESTER
  .2 mile north of the intersection of
  Routes 625 and 35
  1773

The most unusual feature of this 18th-century colonial farmhouse are the pairs of coupled exterior chimney stacks at each end of the house which are joined by pent closets on both the first- and second-floor levels. Chester is a two-story frame dwelling covered by a gable roof. Off-center doors on the front and back facades reflect the interior side hall plan. Nearly all of the original interior woodwork survives.

Private; not accessible to the public

HABS

TAZEWELL COUNTY
Maiden Spring vicinity
INDIAN PAINTINGS
  2.7 miles south of intersection of
  Routes 610 and 19 (460)
  Pre-Columbian

Halfway up Paint Lick Mountain is a broad expanse of rock covered partially by Indian paintings. The surface upon which the paintings were done measures about 75 feet. Birds, horses, elk, deer, wolves, eagles, bows and arrows, women, and Indian warriors are depicted in locally available ocher. The meaning of the figures and their relation to one another is not known.

Private

VIRGINIA BEACH (independent city)
CAPE HENRY LIGHTHOUSE
  Atlantic Avenue at U.S. 60
  1792, John McComb, Jr.

The oil-burning lamps of Cape Henry Lighthouse, which stands at the entrance to Chesapeake Bay, were first lighted in October 1792. The first lighthouse to be erected by the federal government, it was in constant use until a new tower was erected nearby in 1881. The 90-foot-high stone building is faced with hammer-dressed stone. Though no longer in operation, the lighthouse remains as a landmark.

Private

NHL

VIRGINIA BEACH (independent city)
PEMBROKE MANOR
  1.5 miles east of the intersection of
  Routes 58, 627, and 647
  Mid–18th century

Flemish bond brick, a modillion cornice, and an unmolded belt course highlight the

facade of this Georgian house. The second floor windows have been enlarged, and the wooden segmental pediment above the door which is supported by pilasters is not original. Pembroke Manor was probably built by Jonathan Saunders and his wife Elizabeth Thoroughgood. The hip roof and two interior end chimneys are typical of the period.
Private; not accessible to the public
HABS

VIRGINIA BEACH (independent city)
THOROUGHGOOD HOUSE
4 miles east of Norfolk on Lynnhaven River
c. 1636–1640

One of the oldest houses in the English-speaking colonies, the Adam Thoroughgood House illustrates the central hall plan of 17th-century Virginia domestic architecture. The one-and-a-half-story brick house is laid in English and Flemish bond with a steep gabled roof. Its owner, Adam Thoroughgood, came to Virginia in 1621 as an indentured servant. After working off his indenture, he became a member of the House of Burgesses and a large landowner. His house has recently been restored to its 17th-century appearance.
Private
NHL; HABS

VIRGINIA BEACH (independent city)
WISHART-BOUSH HOUSE
.4 mile east of the intersection of Route 649 and Absalom Road
17th century

The Wishart-Boush House is one of the oldest extant brick dwellings in the United States. It is also an extraordinarily intact example of 17th century medieval design. The steep gable roof, massive T-shaped chimneys with steep tiled splays and belt courses, the segmental arched entranceways, and the brick corbels at either end of the eaves are all definite 17th-century characteristics. Inside, much of the original woodwork remains.
Private; not accessible to the public
HABS

WARREN COUNTY
CEDAR CREEK BATTLEFIELD AND BELLE GROVE
(see Frederick County)

WARREN COUNTY
Milldale
MOUNT ZION
.7 mile northeast of the intersection of Routes 624 and 639
1771–1772

Mount Zion's fieldstone facade is seven bays wide on the southwest and five bays on the northeast. Both sides have either a Palladian window or a Palladian-like arrangement of windows. Four interior end chimneys pierce the hip roof, which features a modillion cornice. The relationship between solids and voids, walls to windows, gives the house a fortresslike appearance.
Private; not accessible to the public
HABS

WASHINGTON COUNTY
Abingdon
ABINGDON BANK
225 E. Main Street
c. 1845

The Abingdon Bank is a resident-commercial building which combines neo-classical and Victorian design elements. Robert Preston, the first resident cashier, lived in one part of the house and the other contained the bank, counting room, and vault.
Private; not accessible to the public
HABS

WASHINGTON COUNTY
Abingdon
ABINGDON HISTORIC DISTRICT
Extending .1 mile north and south of Main Street (Route 11) and .3 mile northeast and southwest of the intersection of Main and Cummings Streets
18th and 19th centuries

Abingdon was established in 1778 and grew steadily through the first half of the next century. Today, Main Street of Abingdon is lined by domestic and commercial buildings typical of a rural Virginia town of the 19th century. An eight-and-one-half-block area constitutes the historic district. Buildings of particular note therein are the Abingdon Bank and Cashier's House, the Washington County Courthouse, the Virginia House (a 19th century hotel), the Dr. Pitts House, and the Martha Washington Inn.
Multiple public/private
HABS

WESTMORELAND COUNTY
Fredericksburg vicinity
GEORGE WASHINGTON BIRTHPLACE NATIONAL MONUMENT
38 miles east of Fredericksburg via Va. 218, U.S. 301, Va. 3 and 204
c. 1726

The site of the birthplace of George Washington was on a 150–acre tract of land fronting on Popes Creek which had been purchased by Augustine Washington in 1718. Born on February 22, 1732, the young Washington spent only his first three years here, but returned at the age of 11 to study surveying. The house, which burned during the Revolutionary War, is represented by a Memorial Mansion built in 1932. The mansion, in no sense a restoration, is a typical Virginia plantation house of the 18th century. Also within the monument are a commemorative granite shaft, a colonial-period frame kitchen, the family burial plot, and the site of the 1664 home of John Washington, George Washington's great-grandfather.
Federal
NPS; 393.68 acres

WESTMORELAND COUNTY
Lerty vicinity
STRATFORD HALL
3 miles north of Lerty on Va. 214
1725–1730

Stratford Hall, a notable example of early Georgian architecture, is well known as the birthplace of Robert E. Lee. Other prominent men who lived or were born here include two signers of the Declaration of Independence, several governors of Virginia, four members of the Virginia Convention of 1776, and several members of the Continental Congress. Constructed on an H-plan over a raised basement, Stratford contains a great central hall flanked by two four-room wings above which protrude twin sets of four chimney stacks. The house and remaining portions of the original 16,000–acre estate with formal gardens, walks, and shrubbery are well maintained.
Private
NHL; HABS

WESTMORELAND COUNTY
Tucker Hill vicinity
YEOCOMICO CHURCH
.5 mile southwest of Tucker Hill on Route 606
18th century

It has been assumed that the inscription "1706 IGI" on the south wall of the present church is its construction date. However, due to the highly irregular form of the structure and the variety of the brickwork pattern, it is difficult to determine whether the church had attained its present form by 1706 or whether it so evolved through alterations and additions made from the late 17th to the early 20th centuries. Laid out in an irregular T-shape, the church is covered by a steep gable roof with a pronounced splay at the eaves. Its blend of medieval and classical features makes it significant as an example of transitional colonial architecture. A highlight of the facade is the medieval style wicket door (the only surviving one of its kind in America) flanked by Doric pilasters.

Private
HABS

WILLIAMSBURG (independent city)
COLONIAL NATIONAL HISTORICAL PARK
Reference — See James City County

WILLIAMSBURG (independent city)
BRUTON PARISH CHURCH
Duke of Gloucester Street
1712–1715, Alexander Spotswood

Cruciform in style, Bruton Parish Church was for many years the court church of Virginia. It measures 75 feet by 28 feet with transept arms 14.5 feet long. Later, additional galleries were added and the chancel was lengthened by 25 feet (1752). At present a steep gable roof tops the church, and circular windows pierce the end walls of the chancel and the transepts. A square brick tower was built in 1769–1771. Inside, the church has been altered. Pews were cut down in 1829, and much of the original woodwork was removed ten years later. Restoration work began in 1905, and Colonial Williamsburg completed the project between 1938 and 1940.

Private
NHL; HABS

WILLIAMSBURG (independent city)
RANDOLPH, PEYTON, HOUSE
Intersection of Nicholson and N. England Streets
c. 1715, 1724 (east end)

Designed in the early Georgian style, the Peyton Randolph House is a rectangular, two-story frame house with gable roof, modillion cornice, and beaded clapboard siding. The house was erected in three stages between 1715 and 1725. The west end was constructed in 1715 or 1716. The east end was built separately, c. 1724, by Sir John Randolph, who later acquired the older house and united the two structures with a center section. The main rooms contain fine paneling and most of the interiors are original.

Private
NHL

WILLIAMSBURG (independent city)
SEMPLE, JAMES, HOUSE
South side of Frances Street between Blair and Walker Streets
c. 1770

The James Semple House, also known as the Randolph-Semple House, is an example of a Roman country house adapted for use as a frame town house. The dwelling is believed to have been designed by Thomas Jefferson because it so closely parallels his first drawing of Monticello, made about 1768. Also, the house is derived from a plate in Robert Morris' *Select Architecture* (London, 1757), a work seldom used in the colonies, but a favorite book of Jefferson's. The three-part composition is noted for its unusual facade. The center section is two-stories high and topped by a low pitched gable roof. Two tall chimneys frame the pediment which covers the full facade and is treated as a classical temple front.

Private; not accessible to the public
NHL; HABS

WILLIAMSBURG (independent city)
WILLIAMSBURG HISTORIC DISTRICT
Bounded by Francis, Waller, Nicholson, N. England, Lafayette, and Nassau Streets
1633

Williamsburg was originally settled as Middle Plantation, a palisade barrier against the Indians. It became the capital of Virginia in 1699 and continued its position of leadership until the capital was moved to Richmond in 1779. The College of William and Mary, founded here in 1693, is one of the oldest in the United States. Restoration of the historic district, begun in 1927, aims to accurately recreate the environment of 18th-century Williamsburg and to preserve the most significant portions of a planned historic colonial city.

Multiple municipal/private
NHL; HABS

WILLIAMSBURG (independent city)
WREN BUILDING, COLLEGE OF WILLIAM AND MARY
College of William and Mary campus
1702

The cornerstone of the Wren Building was laid in 1695, only two years after the College of William and Mary, the second oldest in the United States, was chartered. Four stories in height and 136 feet long, it was one of the largest buildings erected in the English colonies up to that time. U-shaped in plan, the central axis is accented by a round-arch portal, balcony, sharp-pitched gable, and cupola. The building originally housed the faculty and students and contained the chapel, dining hall, and classrooms. The main block and dining hall were completed in 1702. After a fire in 1705 the building was rebuilt, and the chapel wing was added in 1732. The building was restored in 1927, and it is within the Williamsburg Historic District, a National Historic Landmark.

State
NHL; HABS

WILLIAMSBURG (independent city)
WYTHE HOUSE
West side of the Palace Green
c. 1755, Richard Taliaferro

One of Virginia's finest Georgian brick townhouses, the Wythe House was the home of George Wythe (1726–1806), a member of the House of Burgesses, signer of the Declaration of Independence, mayor of Williamsburg, and the first professor of law in an American college (William and Mary). The chief features of the little-altered house are its simple lines and fine brickwork. The hip roof is pierced by two brick chimneys, and below the eave line is a modillion cornice.

Private
NHL

WINCHESTER (independent city)
HANDLEY LIBRARY
Northeast corner of Braddock and Piccadilly Streets
1908–1913, J. Stewart Barney and Henry Otis Chapman

Built through the generosity of Judge John Handley of Scranton, Pennsylvania, the Handley Library is one of the outstanding examples of Beaux Arts design in Virginia. Situated on a corner lot, the building is entered through a triple-arched portico set diagonally at the street intersection. The central room rises three stories and is covered with a tall dome, the dominant exterior feature of the building. On either side of the rotunda area are two wings which follow the line of the streets on which they front. In addition to its distinctive design, the building incorporates many advanced principles of construction. Glass floors aid in lighting the stack area, and the building is fireproof throughout.

Municipal

WINCHESTER (independent city)
JACKSON, THOMAS J., HEADQUARTERS
415 N. Braddock Street
1854

By the time of his death in 1863, Confederate General Thomas J. "Stonewall"

Jackson had firmly established himself as one of the leading military strategists of the Civil War. This Gothic Revival house served as Jackson's headquarters just prior to his famous Shenandoah Valley campaign of 1862. The campaign, which alarmed the Lincoln administration concerning the safety of the capital, effected the retreat of Union troops under General N. P. Banks to the Potomac River and the withdrawal of Union forces under Generals John C. Frémont and James Shields. Essentially unaltered, the house currently serves as a museum.
Private
NHL

WYTHE COUNTY
Max Meadows vicinity
FORT CHISWELL MANSION
U.S. 11, .6 mile east of the intersection with U.S. 52 and Va. 121
1839–1840

Fort Chiswell Mansion is a two-story brick dwelling. The blending of Roman and Greek Revival styles is evident in the two-story distyle portico and its two Greek Doric columns supporting a plain pediment. One-story Italianate bracketed porches adorn the front and west walls, while a two-story ell and frame gallery is attached to the rear. Notable are the step-gable ends which incorporate a pair of slightly projecting end chimneys. Other plantation buildings are a one-story brick kitchen and a brick smokehouse.
Private; not accessible to the public
HABS

WYTHE COUNTY
Max Meadows vicinity
SHOT TOWER
.1 mile west of intersection of Route 608 and U.S. 52
c. 1807

The Shot Tower was built by Thomas Jackson, owner of nearby lead mines, to manufacture commercial shot. Made of limestone, the Shot Tower stands 75 feet high, is square in shape, and has a pyramidal roof. The walls are two-and-one-half feet thick, while the base of the tower is twenty feet on a side. At the top of the tower on one side is a simple wooden balcony sheltering an entrance. When in operation the Shot Tower had interior winding wooden steps leading to a room containing a fireplace and chimney. Projecting earthward from this room was a shaft sunk 75 feet below the floor down which the molten metal was poured through a sieve. The metal fell the depth of the shaft into a kettle of water to be cooled.
Public
HABS

YORK COUNTY
COLONIAL NATIONAL HISTORICAL PARK
Reference—see James City County

YORK COUNTY
Lackey vicinity
LEE HOUSE, KISKIACK
2.4 miles northeast of intersection of Routes 238 and 168
17th century

Kiskiack is typical of the small brick farmhouses built in Virginia in the late 17th century. It is one-and-one-half stories high with a steep gable roof. All four walls are laid in Flemish bond with glazed headers above the beveled water table and English bond below. Various alterations and additions to the walls of the house have left scarred patches of brickwork, and the original fenestration has been changed on all but the gable ends. Everything but the masonry portions of the structure were destroyed by a fire in February, 1915. Henry Lee, first owner of the property on which Kiskiack was built, received patents to the land in 1641, 1650, and 1653.
Federal; not accessible to the public
HABS

YORK COUNTY
Yorktown
GRACE CHURCH
Intersection of Route 1003 and Main Street
c. 1697

The present Grace Church, originally called York-Hampton Parish Church, is thought to be the third to serve York parish (created in 1638). In 1706 York parish merged with Hampton parish, thus giving the church its earlier name. Grace Church is one of the few, if not the only, surviving colonial structures built of marl. Marl is soft when first cut but hardens upon exposure to the air. The church burned in 1814 and remained in ruins until 1848, when rebuilt without the north wing and covered with stucco. Damage was done to the interior during the Civil War, and the building was again unused for almost 10 years. The present belfry, western doorway, and circular window date from 1926. Grace Church possesses the second oldest set of communion silver in Virginia.
Private
HABS

Virginia State Capitol, Richmond, Virginia.
Virginia Chamber of Commerce

Handley Library, Winchester, Virginia.
Virginia Historic Landmarks Commission

Oatlands, Leesburg vicinity, Virginia.
Phil Flournoy for Virginia Chamber of Commerce

Egyptian Building, Richmond, Virginia.
Virginia Historic Landmarks Commission

Shirley, Charles City
County Courthouse vicinity, Virginia.
Virginia Historic Landmarks Commission

Washington

Schooner *Wawona*, Seattle, Washington. *Gordon Jones*

U.S.S. *Missouri*, Bremerton, Washington, *U.S. Navy*

St. Paul's Episcopal Church
Port Townsend, Washington.
Swearingen Studios

L. C. Smith Tower
Pioneer Square-Skid Road Historic District
Seattle, Washington.
Werner Leggenhager

CLARK COUNTY
Vancouver
FORT VANCOUVER NATIONAL HISTORIC SITE
1829

Fort Vancouver, built on its present site in 1829, has functioned in a variety of capacities. From establishment of the first fort in 1824 until 1849, this stockaded fur-trading post was headquarters for all activities of the Hudson's Bay Company west of the Rocky Mountains. It was the seat of British political authority for the Pacific Northwest, an area now comprising British Columbia, Washington, Oregon, Idaho, and western Montana. After the boundary settlement with Britain in 1846 the post declined. In 1849 the site became a United States Army camp, and it is still partly used as such. Little remains of the original post.
Federal/non-federal
NPS; 90 acres
HABS

FRANKLIN COUNTY
Lyons Ferry vicinity
MARMES ROCKSHELTER
1 mile north of Lyons Ferry on west side of Palouse River
c. 5600 B.C.

The Marmes Rockshelter is considered the most outstanding archeological site yet discovered in the Northwest. Excavations have revealed the earliest burials in the Northwest and possibly the earliest so far encountered in the western hemisphere. Geologically no other site offers better opportunity for dating and correlating the stratigraphic sequence with the record of human prehistory. Eight geological strata have been excavated, all of which contain cultural materials.
Federal
NHL

JEFFERSON COUNTY
Port Townsend
FOWLER, CAPTAIN ENOCH, HOUSE
Corner of Polk and Washington Streets

Captain Enoch S. Fowler was a native of Lubec, Maine. He first came to Puget Sound in 1852 and eventually settled in Port Townsend. Fowler built the first dock for large vessels in Port Townsend as well as the stone Leader Building. His home is believed to be the oldest frame residence in the town. It has a clapboard exterior and is two stories high with a gable roof and central chimney. The date of construction was sometime prior to 1865.
Private; not accessible to the public

JEFFERSON COUNTY
Port Townsend
CITY HALL
Water and Madison Streets
1891, Batwell and Patrick

Still the seat of government in Port Townsend, the City Hall has a basement jail and houses the Jefferson County Historical Museum. Built of brick with hewn stone belt courses and window lintels, the structure was three stories high when built. In 1945 a southwester severely damaged the corner tower at the south and the third floor roof. As a result both were removed.
Municipal

JEFFERSON COUNTY
Port Townsend
JAMES, FRANCIS WILCOX, HOUSE
Corner of Washington and Harrison Streets
1889

The James House is a substantial shingle style residence which has several unusual external features. The shingles are applied in several different patterns, usually coinciding with floor levels. The chimney rises two stories on the exterior and then disappears into a projecting eave. There are three-part bay and dormer windows on the south facade and elaborate carving on the front porch. Inside, the stairway is finished with wild cherry wood, and the entrance hall and master's suite have inlaid hardwood parquet floors.
Private

JEFFERSON COUNTY
Port Townsend
LEADER BUILDING (FOWLER BUILDING)
226 Adams Street
1874

Enoch S. Fowler was a sea captain from Maine who eventually settled in Port Townsend and opened a store. The Leader or Fowler Building which was built to house Captain Fowler's business is considered the oldest standing, two-story, all stone structure in the state of Washington. It is fashioned of local sandstone covered over in later years with cement to prevent deterioration. During Washington's territorial days the building served as the Jefferson County Courthouse and after 1892 became a Seaman's Bethel. The Leader Company, publishers of the *Port Townsend Leader*, moved into the building in 1916 and still occupies the ground floor. There are apartments on the second floor.
Private

JEFFERSON COUNTY
Port Townsend
MANRESA HALL (EISENBEIS CASTLE)
Sheridan Street
1892, 1928

Manresa Hall was built as a home for Charles Eisenbeis, the first mayor of Port Townsend. The house was constructed in two parts; the later portion was added by the Jesuits in 1928. Walls in the older section are brick 12 inches thick. Three turrets across the front give this part a castle-like appearance, and it is higher by a half story than the later additions. The brick exterior was covered with stucco in the late 1920's.
Private

JEFFERSON COUNTY
Port Townsend
OLD GERMAN CONSULATE (OLSON-HASTINGS HOUSE)
313 Walker
1890

The Queen Anne style Old German Consulate is a frame dwelling of two stories which has a three-story turret on the main facade. Its chimneys are distinctive, and there is a one-story wrap-around porch on the front. For a brief time early in the 20th century the German vice-consul, August Duddenhausen, executed minor business matters in the parlor of the house.
Private

JEFFERSON COUNTY
Port Townsend
POINT WILSON LIGHTHOUSE
On a point of land between Juan de Fuca Strait and Admiralty Inlet
1879

Any ship which leaves or enters Puget Sound is warned of the sandy shore off Point Wilson by this beacon. In clear weather there is no problem, but a fog signal is necessary in bad weather. The old oil lantern has been replaced by electricity and a modern foghorn installed. The light tower itself is octagonal.
Federal

JEFFERSON COUNTY
Port Townsend
ROTHSCHILD HOUSE
Taylor and Franklin Streets
1868

David C. H. Rothschild was a native of Bavaria who had gone to California in 1847. He eventually settled in Port Townsend, opened a store there, married, and built a home for his family. The frame dwelling is constructed of local materials, and it remained in the hands of the family

until deeded to the state of Washington. For this reason many pieces of furniture and articles of clothing belonging to the Rothschilds remain. There is flowered wallpaper in the parlor which has a gold background and one border of red velvet. Woodwork was grained by hand with a paint brush.
State

JEFFERSON COUNTY
Port Townsend
ST. PAUL'S EPISCOPAL CHURCH
Corner of Jefferson and Tyler Streets
1865

Port Townsend's first settlers arrived in February, 1852. Soon thereafter some members of the community felt the need of a religious organization, and an Episcopal parish was formed. Not for 13 years was a church erected to serve the parish. St. Paul's is a frame structure measuring 42 feet by 20 feet. The architecture is a local craftsmen's adaptation of Carpenter Gothic with pointed arch windows and steeply pitched roofs. In 1883 the church was moved to its present location, and the donation of a memorial window to be placed above the altar occasioned the rebuilding of the altar in the late 1890's.
Private

JEFFERSON COUNTY
Port Townsend
STARRETT HOUSE
744 Clay Street
1889

Also known as the House of the Four Seasons, the Starrett House is a large, rambling dwelling covered with elaborate carved wooden detail. Door pediments, window pediments, roof cornice, bargeboards, and dormers in the tower are intricately carved, and motifs such as stars, a sunrise, and winglike scrolls are numerous. On the ceiling of the domed entrance hall are murals by George Chapman representing the four seasons. Ceilings inside the house are 12 feet high, and the staircase in the entrance hall is a free-hung spiral which makes two complete turns. The house was built for George E. Starrett, a native of Maine who came to Port Townsend in 1885 and became a builder-contractor.
Private

KING COUNTY
Redmond vicinity
MARYMOOR PREHISTORIC INDIAN
SITE
6046 W. Lake Sammamish Parkway,
N.E.
Pre-Columbian

Current studies indicate a long prehistoric Indian occupation of the Marymoor Site. Location A, occupied principally during the Middle Period (3000 B.C. to A.D. 1000), may have been a reoccupied hunting camp. Location B, about 40 meters upstream from Location A, appears to reflect a more settled occupation in the Late Period (1000 to c. 1900). The relative dating is based primarily on the presence of ground-stone wood working tools at Location B and their absence at Location A, as well as on differences in projectile points from the two locations.
County

KING COUNTY
Seattle
ALASKA TRADE BUILDING (*UNION RECORD* BUILDING)
1915–1919 1st Avenue
1909, J. O. Taft

The Alaska Trade Building is important as the home of the Seattle *Union Record*, the only labor-owned daily newspaper in America. Begun in 1910 as a weekly, the paper had become a daily by April, 1918. By 1921 the paper's owners, the Central Labor Council and the local trade unions, had purchased the building at 1915 First Avenue. The *Union Record* was located here until it ceased publication in 1928. The newspaper was a powerful voice in the community and was effective in the labor movement because it provided a means of communication with non-labor elements. Persons associated with the *Union Record* were Harvey O'Connor, author; James A. Duncan of the Seattle school board; Professor Theresa McMahon of the University of Washington; Anna Louise Strong, author; the Rev. Sidney Strong; Robert Hesketh; Robert Harlan; Harry Ault; and R. W. Chaplin. The building itself is brick reinforced with steel and concrete, and it has been altered.
Private

KING COUNTY
Seattle
BUTTERWORTH BUILDING
1921 1st Avenue
1903, John Graham, Sr.

The Butterworth Building was designed for Edgar R. Butterworth, founder of E. R. Butterworth and Son, a well-known Seattle undertaking establishment. It is three stories high on the street facade and has a rusticated stone arcade at street level. The dentil cornice has elaborate consoles, and the roof above is decorated with a low stone balustrade. Four projecting pilasters highlight the second and third floors. The interior has recently been renovated for office use.
Private

KING COUNTY
Seattle
PIKE PLACE MARKET HISTORIC
DISTRICT
Along Pike Place between Western
and 1st Avenues
20th century

In 1907 when local farmers were licensed to sell their produce in Seattle, they chose a site on Pike Place near the water and soon put up a market building. Open stalls were erected around the market building, and eventually other timber and masonry structures were put up across Pike Place and on 1st Avenue. Expansion continued, and by the 1920's there were about 270 businesses, a local post office and library, and between 400 and 500 farmers selling produce. During the depression in the early 1930's, many businesses failed and the market shrank to approximately its present size. Today the market is a rambling collection of stalls, ramps, passageways, and stairways. Some of the architecturally notable structures are the Economy Market Building, the Corner Market Building, and the Market Hotel Building.
Multiple public/private

KING COUNTY
Seattle
PIONEER HALL
1642 43rd Avenue East
1910

Pioneer Hall was built with money donated to the city of Seattle by the descendant of an early pioneer family. The building was intended to serve as a meeting place for the Pioneer Association of the State of Washington, the Daughters of the Pioneers, and similar organizations. Two stories high and built of brick, the building still serves as a society meeting hall.
Private

KING COUNTY
Seattle
PIONEER SQUARE-SKID ROAD
HISTORIC DISTRICT
Starting at the intersection of Alaskan
Way Viaduct and Columbia Street
and proceeding east along Columbia
Street to the midpoint between 1st
and 2nd Avenues; proceed south to

Cherry Street, then east to the midpoint between 2nd and 3rd Avenues; then south to a point about 75 feet north of Washington Street, then east to 3rd Avenue South and south to a point about 75 feet south of Washington Street; proceed west to 2nd Avenue South, then south to the midpoint between S. Jackson and S. King Streets; west to the midpoint between Occidental Avenue South and 1st Avenue South; then south to S. King Street and west to 1st Avenue South; then south to a point about 125 feet south of S. King Street, then west to the Alaskan Way Viaduct and north to the intersection with Columbia Street
19th and 20th centuries

The first settlers, C. D. Boren, Arthur A. Denny, and William N. Bell, claimed land on the site of present-day Seattle in February, 1852. This area now constitutes most of the central business district and waterfront. The new town was named for a friendly chief of the Duwamish Indians. In March, 1853, Henry L. Yesler began operation of a steam sawmill at the corner of 1st Avenue and Yesler Way. Lumbering was to become Seattle's principal industry. Pioneer Square-Skid Road (so called because logs were skidded along it enroute to the sawmill) and the surrounding neighborhood constituted the heart of the growing city for more than 50 years. A fire swept the city in 1889 destroying most of the docks and other business establishments. Rebuilding took place, and one architect—Elmer H. Fisher—left his mark on the new downtown area. His work coupled with the new building restrictions (only brick, stone, and iron could be used) produced a homogeneity of style and construction which is evident today in the historic district. Structures worthy of notice are the Pioneer Building, the Maud Building, the Maynard and Mutual Life buildings, and the Smith Tower Annex.
Multiple public/private

KING COUNTY
Seattle
WAWONA
Seattle Police Harbor Patrol Dock, foot of Densmore Street
1897

The *Wawona* was built in Fairhaven, California, for the lumber firm of Dolbeer and Carson. The three-masted schooner was constructed entirely of wood and is powered by sail alone. She was engaged in the Pacific coast lumber trade until 1914, when the Robinson Fisheries Company of Anacortes, Washington, purchased her for a fishing vessel. Her last cod fishing cruise was in 1946, and, after unsuccessful at-

tempts to use the ship as a cruise boat and a cattle boat, she was purchased by a private group to be part of a maritime museum. The *Wawona*'s overall dimensions are 156 feet in length, 36 feet beam, and 12.3 feet depth.
Private

KITSAP COUNTY
Bainbridge Island
S. S. *SAN MATEO*
Eagle Harbor
1922

The S. S. *San Mateo* is the last steam-powered auto ferry remaining in the United States. It was built in 1922 by the Southern Pacific Golden Gate Ferries and operated on San Francisco Bay until 1940. The Puget Sound Navigation Company then purchased the boat and towed it to Seattle the following year. The *San Mateo* was acquired by the state of Washington in 1951 and is now retired from ferry service. The steel-hulled ship measures 230 feet by 63 feet and has a capacity of 55 vehicles and 659 passengers.
State

KITSAP COUNTY
Bremerton
U. S. S. *MISSOURI*
Puget Sound Naval Shipyard
20th century

The U. S. S. *Missouri* was built at the Brooklyn (New York) Naval Ship Yard and commissioned on June 11, 1944. Her length is 888 feet and beam, 108. She participated in actions supporting the seizure of Iwo Jima and Okinawa, carrier raids on Tokyo, Okinawa, Kyushu, and the Inland Sea, as well as the bombardments of Okinawa, Hokkaido, and Honshu. As the flagship of Admiral William F. Halsey, the *Missouri* was the scene of the official surrender ceremony between the Japanese government and the Allied Powers on September 2, 1945, ending World War II.
Federal

KITSAP COUNTY
Port Gamble
PORT GAMBLE HISTORIC DISTRICT
1853

Port Gamble was one of the earliest and most important lumber-producing centers on the Pacific coast. Still an active sawmill town, it exemplifies the mid–19th-century company-owned town. Still standing are some Greek Revival cottages, New England boxlike houses, Victorian houses, a church, a community center, and the company store. The sawmill and docks were rebuilt in 1926.
Private
NHL

KITTITAS COUNTY
Ellensburg vicinity
OLMSTEAD PLACE STATE PARK
4 miles east of Ellensburg near the Kittitas Highway
19th century

Olmstead Place was homesteaded in 1875 by Samuel Olmstead. He raised beef cattle here until 1892, when a Jersey dairy was established. His original cabin, built in 1875, remains as an outstanding example of squared timber construction. Olmstead used cottonwood logs from the Yakima River Canyon. Other historic buildings on the site include a dairy barn and granary (1892); a wagonshed (1894); a red barn used for hay storage (1908); and the Olmstead family house (1908). In 1968 the 219–acre farm was deeded to the Washington State Parks and Recreation Commission.
State

PACIFIC COUNTY
Chinook vicinity
CHINOOK POINT
5 miles southeast of Fort Columbia Historical State Park on U.S. 101
1792

The discovery of the Columbia River at Chinook Point by Captain Robert Gray climaxed a long search for the legendary Great River of the West and gave the United States a legitimate claim to the Northwest. Until the boundary settlement in 1846, Great Britain vied with the United States for possession of the Pacific Northwest.
State
NHL

PIERCE COUNTY
Tacoma
FORT NISQUALLY GRANARY
Point Defiance Park
1843

Fort Nisqually, the first permanent white settlement on Puget Sound, was originally located at Dupont, 15 miles south of Tacoma. The fortified trading post served as a communication and supply center for the Hudson's Bay Company's posts on the coast of British Columbia. The granary and factor's or agent's house were the only original buildings remaining in 1934, when they were moved to their present site. The one-story granary, measuring 20 by 31 feet, was constructed in the Canadian post-on-sill method, a type of log construction widely used by fur traders, missionaries, and settlers of the Pacific Northwest before 1846. It is the oldest extant frame structure in the state.
Municipal
NHL; HABS

Friday Harbor vicinity, San Juan Island
SAN JUAN ISLAND NATIONAL HISTORICAL PARK
1849–1872

San Juan Island National Historical Park will interpret the sites of American and British camps and commemorate the events which led to the peaceful settlement of the Oregon Territory boundary dispute in 1872. The Oregon Treaty of 1849 failed to settle the conflict concerning the water boundary between Vancouver Island, British Columbia, and the Oregon Territory of the United States. The situation reached a climax in the "Pig War of 1859," when hostilities almost began. The Treaty of Washington in 1871, which settled the dispute, marked the first time in United States history that there was no boundary quarrel with Britain. All that remains of the American camp now are the foundations of several buildings.

The British camp contains a two-story log blockhouse, a commissary, barracks, and other related buildings.
Federal/non-federal
NPS; 1,751.99 acres

Walla Walla vicinity
WHITMAN MISSION NATIONAL HISTORIC SITE
6 miles west of Walla Walla off U.S. 410
1836–1847

Whitman Mission National Historic Site is the place where Dr. and Mrs. Marcus Whitman ministered to the spiritual and physical needs of the Cayuse Indians until a handful of Indians massacred them and three other whites in 1847. On their 1836 journey over the Oregon Trail, Narcissa Whitman and Eliza Spalding became the first American women to cross the continent overland, a feat which encouraged many other families to follow. The present site embraces the mission grounds, the millpond, and the graves of the Whitmans as well as other victims of the 1847 massacre.
Federal
NPS; 98.15 acres

Bellingham
WHATCOM MUSEUM OF HISTORY AND ART
121 Prospect Street
1892, Alfred Lee

Built originally as the Bellingham City Hall, the Whatcom Museum of History and Art has served its present function since 1939. Today it is one of the few unaltered late Victorian public buildings remaining in the area. The exterior is red brick with local Chuckanut sandstone trim. The first floor and basement have been completely renovated, and the original hand carved wood staircase, paneling, and moldings have been refinished. An exterior central bell tower destroyed by fire in 1962 has not been rebuilt.
Municipal

Fort Vancouver National Historic Site, Vancouver, Washington, *NPS*

Pioneer Square-Skid Road Historic District,
Seattle, Washington, *Werner Leggenhager*

Old German Consulate
(Olson-Hastings House),
Port Townsend, Washington.
Swearingen Studios

West Virginia

Old Main, Bethany College, Bethany, West Virginia. *Frasier Smith*

South Charleston Mound,
South Charleston, West Virginia. *Fraiser Smith*

Graceland, Davis and Elkins College
Elkins, West Virginia. *Davis and Elkins College*

Wheeling Suspension Bridge,
Wheeling, West Virginia. *C. M. Lewis, S. J.*

BERKELEY COUNTY
Martinsburg
BOYDVILLE
601 S. Queen Street
1812

Boydville is a late Georgian home built of stone and covered on the exterior with stucco. The facade measures 120 feet in length, the main section is 44 feet deep, and the two wings are both 20 feet deep. A hip roof surmounts the five-bay central section which is marked by four end chimneys. Interior woodwork is well executed. All door frames and mantelpieces were hand carved in England and each has a different design. Original wallpaper brought from England in 1812 still adorns the central hallway. A few minor alterations have been made to the house. Outbuildings include a smokehouse, ice house, wash and tool houses, barn, and a law office.
Private

BERKELEY COUNTY
Martinsburg
STEPHEN, ADAM, HOUSE
309 E. John Street
1772–1789

The Adam Stephen House was the home of the founder of Martinsburg. It is built of limestone and the framing timbers are held together with wooden pegs. Stephen (1718–1791) was an officer in both the French and Indian War and in the Revolution and served in the Virginia House of Burgesses.
Municipal

BROOKE COUNTY
Bethany
OLD MAIN, BETHANY COLLEGE
Bethany College campus
1858–1872, James Keys Wilson and William Walter

Bethany College was founded in 1840 and is the oldest such institution in West Virginia. The man responsible was Alexander Campbell (1788–1866), founder of the Disciples of Christ. The collegiate Gothic style Old Main is one of a very few remaining buildings designed by James K. Wilson that have not been altered or modified beyond recognition. The facade of the building measures 420 feet in length, and its roofline is broken everywhere by towers, dormers, and turrets. There is a 122-foot central tower, and the window tracery, arches, and the door surrounds are stone. A chapel is located above the main entrance. The present Oglebay Hall (1911) replaced the literary societies' wing which burned in 1879, and Commencement Hall was rebuilt internally in 1924–1926.
Private

BROOKE COUNTY
Bethany vicinity
CAMPBELL, ALEXANDER, MANSION
East of Bethany on W. Va. 67
1793

Alexander Campbell (1788–1866), prominent educator and religious leader, was married in this house and lived here until his death. He was born in Ireland, the son of a preacher already established in America by 1809, when Alexander joined him. The younger Campbell founded Bethany College and was the organizer of a new religious sect, the Disciples of Christ. Built by Campbell's father-in-law John Brown, the house is frame on a limestone foundation, and the oldest section is on the eastern side. It had three rooms at ground level, three on the first floor, and three or four on the second floor. Two sections were subsequently added (one, c. 1836 and the other four years later), and some restoration work was done in 1940.
Private

JEFFERSON COUNTY (also in Washington County, Maryland)
Harpers Ferry
HARPERS FERRY NATIONAL HISTORICAL PARK
1733 (first settlement), 1859

At the confluence of the Shenandoah and Potomac rivers is Harpers Ferry, theater of important events from the early Federal period to the Civil War. In the 1790's Congress authorized establishment of a federal armory at the site. The area is best known, however, as the site of John Brown's raid in October 1859. His objective was to liberate the slaves by violence and set up a stronghold of free Negroes in the Appalachian Mountains. Though Brown's attack on the arsenal was unsuccessful, his death provided the abolitionist cause with a martyr. Because of its strategic location, the town changed hands numerous times during the Civil War.
Federal/non-federal
NPS; 517.75 acres
HABS

JEFFERSON COUNTY
Shepherdstown
SHEPHERD'S MILL
High Street
1734–1739

Shepherd's Mill marks the site of the state's earliest community's industry. As early as 1719 settlers arrived here and called their town Mecklenburg. After the Revolution the name was changed to Shepherdstown in honor of Thomas Shepherd, Sr., who built the original mill and also laid out building lots for homes.

The mill itself was at first a two-story structure of stone. The frame third story was added about 1880. Also on the property is a 1759 brick house erected by Abraham Shepherd to which a kitchen has been added. Equipment such as wheels and grinding burrs remain in the mill.
Private

KANAWHA COUNTY
Charleston
CRAIK-PATTON HOUSE (ELM GROVE)
1316 Lee Street
1830's

The Craik-Patton House is a Tuscan porticoed, Neo-Classical cottage with side wings. A steeply pitched roof tops the portico, and the original shingles have been replaced by sheet metal. The main doorway is flanked by pilasters supporting a full entablature. At the rear a gallery which was once open has been enclosed, and the house was moved to its present site in 1906. The Reverend James Craik built the cottage. It was purchased by George S. Patton, grandfather of Second World War General George S. Patton, in 1858.
Private

KANAWHA COUNTY
Dunbar
DUTCH HOLLOW WINE CELLARS
Dutch Hollow Road
Mid–19th century

Wine production was once a thriving industry in present-day West Virginia. The three surviving wine cellars were at one time owned by Thomas R. Friend, who was making wine on the premises in 1859. It is not known what variety of grape was grown by Friend, but he used the stone cellars for aging. Measurements of the three separate but contiguous vaults are 40 feet (wall length), 19 feet 4 inches (width in middle), and 14 feet (height in middle). Friend, a Southern sympathizer, left Kanawha County in 1861, and the cellars were not used again to produce wine.
Private; not accessible to the public

KANAWHA COUNTY
South Charleston
SOUTH CHARLESTON MOUND (CRIEL MOUND)
In a triangle formed by Oakes, MacCorkle, and 7th Avenue
Pre-Columbian

This prehistoric Indian burial mound is the second largest in West Virginia. It originally measured 525 feet in circumference and was 40 feet high. The mound was part of an elaborate earthworks system which once occupied bottom lands

on both sides of the Kanawha River. Archeological investigations by the Smithsonian Institution were undertaken in 1883–1885, at which time a number of skeletons and burial artifacts were found. Sometime prior to this the top of the mound had been leveled. It is now much reduced in size.
Municipal

MARSHALL COUNTY
Moundsville
GRAVE CREEK MOUND
Tomlinson and 9th Streets
c. 500 B.C.

Grave Creek Mound, one of the largest and oldest in the United States, is representative of the burial mound tradition of the Adena culture. Although this mound has been extensively excavated, its preservation is significant because few Adena sites are extant. The Adena culture paved the way for the slightly later Hopewell culture, which was noted for its large mounds and great earthwork structures.
State
NHL

MASON COUNTY
Point Pleasant
POINT PLEASANT BATTLEGROUND
Southwest corner of Main and 1st Streets

Point Pleasant, situated at the convergence of the Ohio and Kanawha rivers, was the scene of the principal engagement of Dunmore's War on October 10, 1774. Colonel Andrew Lewis, commanding 1,100 Colonial soldiers, fought with 800 to 1,000 Indians in an attempt to alter the western boundary of the frontier from the Allegheny Mountains to the Ohio River. His victory made Kentucky safer for settlement, and gave Americans a strategic foothold in this region during the Revolutionary War. The battle site is now a state park.
State

MINERAL COUNTY
Fort Ashby
FORT ASHBY
South Street
1755

Following Braddock's defeat in the battle of Monongahela (1755), Governor Robert Dinwiddie of Virginia gave orders for constructing a score of forts from the upper Potomac valleys to the Holston River in Tennessee. Fort Ashby, located on Patterson Creek, was named for its commander Captain John Ashby. The fort was surrounded by a stockade, and the present building served as a barracks. It consisted of a stone basement, a first floor divided into two sections by a large fireplace, and a single room on the second floor. Dimensions are 30 feet by 36 feet, and the outer walls are hewn logs chinked with lime and clay mortar. Outside doors are hung from wrought iron strap hinges. After the French and Indian War the barracks became a private home.
Private

MONONGALIA COUNTY
Cheat Neck vicinity
HENRY CLAY FURNACE
Southeast of Cheat Neck in Cooper's Rock State Forest

The Henry Clay Furnace was one of the earliest and most important in the Virginia (now West Virginia) iron smelting industry. Low grade native ore was employed, and the resulting iron was utilized chiefly by the cut nail industry. Built by Leonard Lamb for Tassie and Bissell between 1834 and 1836, the Clay Furnace may have continued to operate until 1868, when all the Cheat River ironworks ceased production. Externally the furnace resembles a truncated pyramid. The base is 30 feet square and the original height was approximately 34 feet. Ore, limestone, and charcoal were charged into the top of the furnace from a tramway which ran to the ore pits. The cold blast furnace was run by steam and produced about four tons of pig iron every 24 hours. Near the furnace was a water pit for cooling the melt. At peak activity the furnace complex employed about 200 men digging ore, making charcoal, and smelting iron, and a community of almost 500 people grew up close by.
State

MONONGALIA COUNTY
Morgantown
WADE, ALEXANDER, HOUSE
256 Prairie Street
1872–1904

As a teacher in West Virginia schools and superintendent of schools in Monongalia County, Alexander Wade developed a system of graduation in country schools which was widely adopted throughout the United States. Observing that rural children lost valuable time in enrolling and re-enrolling, Wade devised a system of grades, promotional examinations, and graduations. Its introduction in 1874 brought such favorable notice that in 1879 the National Education Association invited him to explain his program. Wade lived in this two-story brick house from 1872 until his death in 1904. It is essentially unchanged from his time.
Private; not accessible to the public
NHL

MORGAN COUNTY
CHESAPEAKE AND OHIO CANAL NATIONAL MONUMENT
Reference—see Allegany County, Maryland

OHIO COUNTY
Wheeling
INDEPENDENCE HALL
1524 Market Street
1859, Ammi B. Young; 1870, Alfred B. Mullett

In 1831 Wheeling (then in Virginia) was designated a U.S. port of entry. Completion of the Baltimore & Ohio Railroad as far as Wheeling (1852) so increased the commercial traffic that a customhouse was needed. Completed in April, 1859, the new federal building was gray sandstone and had tall, round-arched windows and belt courses dividing the three stories. Slight alterations (such as steepening the roofline) were made by Alfred B. Mullett. In June, 1861, representatives of the western Virginia counties met here and drew up a declaration of independence. A governor was elected, and the state assembly met in the former customhouse until June, 1863, when West Virginia was formally designated as a state. At that time the building reverted to its original use. A new federal building was constructed in 1907, and changes were made in the old customhouse by subsequent private owners. Presently the state is restoring Independence Hall to its Civil War appearance.
State
HABS

OHIO COUNTY
Wheeling
SHEPHERD HALL (MONUMENT PLACE)
Monument Place and Kruger Street
1798

This Georgian dwelling was built by Moses Shepherd, a wealthy citizen and mayor of Wheeling who gained prominence as a bridge builder on the National Road. The house is stone and has an elaborate recessed doorway flanked by wooden columns and surmounted by a pediment. The gable roof has dormers and stone end chimneys. An adjacent cottage was constructed about 100 years ago by a subsequent owner, and the porch on the east end is not original. Recent additions have been made to the rear of the house.
Private
HABS

OHIO COUNTY
Wheeling
WHEELING SUSPENSION BRIDGE
Across the Ohio River from 10th
Street, Wheeling, to Virginia Street,
Wheeling Island
Mid–19th century, Charles Ellet, Jr.;
1872, Washington A. Roebling

At the time of its completion this crossing
of the Ohio River was the longest suspension bridge in the world, and it is presently
believed to be the oldest existing cable
suspension highway bridge. Today the
structure retains the appearance of the
original, although in 1956 it was stripped
down to the towers, cables, and suspender
ropes and completely overhauled. In 1951
the bridge had a span of 1,010 feet from
tower summit to tower summit; the eastern tower measured 82 feet from the base
of the stonework upwards, while the
western towers measured 69.75 feet.
Flooring was supported by 12 iron cables
hung between the towers. Cables were
anchored by a succession of links in the
massive masonry walls and were 1,380
feet from fastening to fastening. The
highest level of the flooring lies immediately over the channel of the river,
about 93 feet above low water.
State
HABS

POCAHONTAS COUNTY
Hillsboro vicinity
BUCK, PEARL, HOUSE
Northeast of Hillsboro on U.S. 219
1858

The white frame house was built by a
Dutch refugee named Stulting who came
to America to avoid religious persecution.
His great-granddaughter, Pearl Buck, née
Sydenstricker, was born in the house on
June 26, 1892. Pearl Buck's parents were
Presbyterian missionaries to China, home
on a furlough at the time. One of Pearl
Buck's book's, *The Exile* (1936), describes
the childhood of her mother, Carrie Stulting Sydenstricker, spent in the Stulting
home. A six-room addition on the rear of
the house and the side porch on the
southwest are the only major alterations.
Private

POCAHONTAS COUNTY
Marlinton vicinity
DROOP MOUNTAIN BATTLEFIELD
On U.S. 219 about 14 miles south of
Marlinton

The battle of Droop Mountain was fought
on November 6, 1863. Federal troops
commanded by Brigadier General William
Averell were attempting to drive out all
Confederates from the Greenbrier Valley
as a first step toward their main objective:
severing the Virginia & Tennessee Railroad, a Southern lifeline in eastern Tennessee. Confederate General John Echols
and his 1,700 men were heavily outnumbered by the three or four thousand
Federals. Their defeat marked the end of
successful Southern action in West Virginia. The terrain today is densely wooded
and cut by deep ravines. Some trenches
are still visible along the northern boundary of the battlefield.
State

PUTNAM COUNTY
Buffalo
BUFFALO INDIAN VILLAGE SITE
Southwest of Buffalo off U.S. 35
Late 17th century

Cultural remains found at the Buffalo Village Site indicate that it was inhabited by
people of the Fort Ancient culture,
specifically the Shawnee. Remains of a
palisaded village, a ceremonial or council
center, and 575 burials have been
unearthed. The village was rectangular,
and the central ceremonial plaza had no
buildings on it. Ceremonial houses stood
around the plaza, and these were ringed
by three concentric rows of dwellings. Occupation dates are estimated as 1650 to
1700. The Shawnee Indians were known
to have two centers of settlement: a
southern group on the Savannah River
and a western group on the Cumberland.
This village on the Kanawha River may
represent a third group in a connecting
geographical concentration.
Private; not accessible to the public

RALEIGH COUNTY
Beckley
**WILDWOOD (GENERAL ALFRED
BECKLEY HOME)**
117 Laurel Terrace

The present Wildwood, home of Brigadier
General Alfred Beckley, was originally
constructed as a two-story log structure in
1835–1836. Beckley (1802–1888) remodeled the house in 1874 by adding
two rooms at the back with a loft or attic
above them. A graduate of West Point,
Beckley spent 12 years in the army and
later donated land in the town of Beckley
for a courthouse square, a school, church,
and jail, and half the building lots. Plans
are underway to restore the house to its
appearance in 1874 by removing the aluminum siding and reconstructing the
original front porch.
Private

RANDOLPH COUNTY
Elkins
**GRACELAND (HENRY GASSAWAY
DAVIS HOME)**
Davis and Elkins College campus
1892

Graceland is a massive stone and wood
turreted dwelling which was once the
home of Henry Gassaway Davis
(1823–1916). The basic building material
is West Virginia granite, although there is
some shingle work on third floor towers
and gables. The various towers, gables,
and chimneys form a highly irregular silhouette, and the entire house is rambling
in appearance and eclectic in style. Davis
was born in Maryland and worked several
years for the Baltimore & Ohio Railroad
as a brakeman, conductor, and station
agent. After the Civil War he undertook
the construction of a large railroad network in northern, central, and eastern
West Virginia. Together with his son-in-law, Stephen B. Elkins, he founded Elkins,
West Virginia, and was responsible for extending the West Virginia Central &
Pittsburgh Railroad (later the Western
Maryland Railroad) to Elkins. Davis was a
member of the Intercontinental Railway
Survey Commission, a co-founder of Davis
and Elkins College, and served as a state
senator and representative and a U.S.
Senator (1871–1883).
Private

TAYLOR COUNTY
Grafton
**ANDREW METHODIST CHURCH
(MOTHERS' DAY SHRINE)**
E. Main Street between St. John and
Luzader Streets

On May 10, 1908, a special service was
held in the Andrew Methodist Church
which heralded the beginning of the international Mother's Day celebration. Miss
Anna Jarvis was responsible for the service held to honor her mother, Mrs. Anna
Reeves Jarvis, and all mothers. Mrs. Jarvis
moved to nearby Webster in 1854 and
there organized the Mother's Day Work
clubs to combat health problems in the
area. Care was provided for families with
tubercular mothers, medicine was made
available to indigents, and milk inspection
was begun. Miss Jarvis' efforts to honor all
mothers were awarded national recognition in 1914, when Woodrow Wilson
signed a proclamation designating the
second Sunday in May as Mothers' Day.
Andrew Church is a two-story brick structure measuring 74.25 feet long by 44 feet
wide.
Private

Burning Springs
BURNING SPRINGS COMPLEX

Along the north bank of the Kanawha River from the confluence of Burning Springs Run

The world's second oil strike was made on the banks of the Little Kanawha River in 1860. Several wells were drilled along the riverbank, and Burning Spring (now Burning Springs) became a town of 5,000 people almost overnight. One well, drilled by the Rathbone brothers in the summer of 1860, produced 40 or 50 barrels of oil a day. Another important well was worked by Sherman D. Karns at the mouth of Burning Spring Run. He began production late in February, 1860. The Rathbone wells were located a few rods north of Burning Springs Run. Early in the 20th century the Mellon Oil Company drilled successfully in the same spot as the earlier wells. Confederate General William E. Jones destroyed the drilling operations on May 9, 1863, thus making Burning Springs the first military oil objective in the history of warfare.
Private

Point Pleasant Battlefield
Point Pleasant, West Virginia. *Frasier Smith*

Boydville, Martinsburg, West Virginia. *James W. Smallwood*

Pearl S. Buck House
Hillsboro, West Virginia. *Estep's Studio*

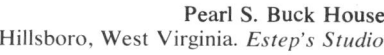

Wisconsin

Eagle Bluff Lighthouse, Fish Creek, Wisconsin. *Harmann Studios*

Rotunda of Wisconsin State Capitol,
Madison, Wisconsin.
McKillop Art Co.

Tallman House, Janesville, Wisconsin. *R. S. Sivesind*

Panther Intaglio Effigy Mound,
Fort Atkinson, Wisconsin.
Hoard's Dairyman

BROWN COUNTY
Green Bay
BAIRD LAW OFFICE
2630 S. Webster Avenue
1831

The Baird Law Office is a diminutive, Greek Revival, temple-form building, one of only two such known to remain in the state. It has a pedimented portico with two Ionic columns and two corner piers. There is a dentil cornice beneath the pediment. Built before Wisconsin became a territory, the building served as a law office for Henry S. Baird, who had been admitted to practice before the Michigan Territorial Court in 1824. Baird served as counsel for the Winnebago and Menominee Indians when they sold their lands (1830), as a territorial legislator (1836), attorney general for Wisconsin Territory (1836–1839), delegate to the Wisconsin constitutional convention (1846), and mayor of Green Bay (1861–1862).
Private

BROWN COUNTY
Green Bay
COTTON HOUSE
2632 S. Webster Avenue
1840

The Greek Revival Cotton House is two stories high and ornamented on the front by a two-story, distyle-*in-antis* portico. The house is frame and was built by Judge Joseph Penn Arndt for his son-in-law, Lieutenant John Cotton. In 1941 the house was moved one mile from the original site to its present location.
Private

BROWN COUNTY
Green Bay
HAZELWOOD
1008 S. Monroe Avenue
c. 1837, Joseph Jackson

Hazelwood was built for Morgan L. Martin, lawyer and legislator, who did the preliminary drafting of the Wisconsin constitution here in 1847. The house is Greek Revival with a Doric colonnaded porch front and back. One single-story wing remains as the north wing collapsed several years ago.
Multiple public/private

BROWN COUNTY
Green Bay
TANK COTTAGE
10th Avenue and 5th Street
1776, 1850

Originally built as a wattled cottage, the Tank Cottage is Wisconsin's oldest known surviving building. Clapboards were later placed over the walls of woven boughs covered by mud or clay plaster. Niels Otto Tank bought the cabin in 1850 and added wings at both ends. In 1908 the one-and-one-half-story cottage was moved to its present site.
Municipal

COLUMBIA COUNTY
Portage vicinity
FORT WINNEBAGO SURGEON'S QUARTERS
.1 mile east of the corporate city limits on Wis. 33
1818–1828

Constructed originally as a fur trader's home, this log building later served as a sutler's store and was converted in 1834 to a residence for the post surgeon. Fort Winnebago was established in 1828 to preserve peace with the Winnebago Indians and protect fur traders in the area. It was situated near the important portage between the Fox and Wisconsin rivers, part of the water route from Green Bay to Prairie du Chien. Fort Winnebago was garrisoned only until 1845, by which time the fur trade had disappeared, the Winnebago were removed from their lands, and the Wisconsin Territory had been created. The Surgeon's Quarters is the only remaining original structure. It is a U-shaped, gable-roofed log house with unusually refined exterior wooden trim. The corners of the house are covered with sawed boards, and there are raking cornices with wide frieze boards and cornice returns at the gable ends. In the early 1950's the quarters was restored using 1834 War Department plans.
Private

CRAWFORD COUNTY
Prairie du Chien
ASTOR FUR WAREHOUSE
Water Street, St. Feriole Island
c. 1835

French, British, and American occupation of Prairie du Chien shaped the settlement and development of the Old Northwest. Among the town's historic buildings is the Astor Warehouse, one of the American Fur Company's principal establishments. This stone building recalls the Astor empire and Prairie du Chien's prominence as a fur trading center.
Private
NHL

CRAWFORD COUNTY
Prairie du Chien
BRISBOIS, MICHAEL, HOUSE
Water Street, St. Feriole Island
1808

Illustrating Prairie du Chien's fur trading prominence is the Brisbois House, built of coursed ashlar by Michael Brisbois. This French Canadian came to Prairie du Chien in 1781 as one of its first permanent settlers. The two-and-a-half-story dwelling, which is reputed to have been his home, overlooks the Mississippi River and contains many original furnishings.
Private
NHL; HABS

CRAWFORD COUNTY
Prairie du Chien
DOUSMAN HOTEL
Water Street, St. Feriole Island
1864

Prairie du Chien's significance as a railroad center is illustrated by the Dousman Hotel, built by the Milwaukee & Mississippi Railroad to care for its passengers. After the Civil War the hotel was a stopping point for thousands of immigrants enroute to Minnesota and the Dakotas.
Private; not accessible to the public
NHL

CRAWFORD COUNTY
Prairie du Chien
SECOND FORT CRAWFORD
Bank of the Mississippi River
1829

Among Prairie du Chien's more historic buildings is the Second Fort Crawford. Originally located on St. Feriole Island, the fort was moved to its present site in 1829. It was abandoned in 1856, though temporarily reoccupied during the Civil War. The only remaining building, the restored post hospital, now houses a medical museum. During the period 1829–1833 the hospital was the scene of experiments by Dr. William Beaumont which contributed to the understanding of the digestive processes.
Private
NHL

CRAWFORD COUNTY
Prairie du Chien
VILLA LOUIS
St. Feriole Island
1843

The owner of Villa Louis, Hercules Louis Dousman, began his mercantile career in the employment of John Jacob Astor's American Fur Company in 1826. In subsequent years his interests expanded to include steamship and railroad transportation centered around the commercial heart of Prairie du Chien. His Georgian style house was remodeled to the Victorian style in 1872. On the grounds are Dousman's office, coach house, ice house, and preserve room.
State
NHL

DANE COUNTY
Madison
CAMP RANDALL
Camp Randall Memorial Park
1861-1865

Camp Randall was Wisconsin's largest and most active Civil War training ground. The land used by the State Agricultural Society as an exposition grounds was converted to a military camp in the spring of 1861 and named for Governor Alexander W. Randall. Exhibition halls became barracks and hospitals, and sheds were used as stables for horses. A small portion of the 50-acre camp has been retained as a memorial park. There is a granite arch above the east entrance of the training ground, and the park contains two statues and memorial plaques and markers.
State

DANE COUNTY
Madison
NORTH HALL, UNIVERSITY OF
WISCONSIN
University of Wisconsin campus
1851

Originating at the University of Wisconsin, the "Wisconsin Idea" was a vast expansion of the role of the state university, It was based on the concept that an enlightened public best insures a progressive nation. It became widely influential in the first decade of the 20th century. Extension work was begun at the university in 1885. Its farmers' institutions, short courses in farming, and summer schools greatly benefitted the agricultural population. Charles R. Van Hise, president of the university from 1905 to 1918, expanded the extension program and sought to involve faculty members more in legislative and regulatory affairs. North Hall, its first building, is a four-story sandstone structure now housing the department of political science.
State
NHL

DANE COUNTY
Madison
OLD SYNAGOGUE (SHAARE
SHOMAIN SYNAGOGUE)
E. Gorham Street at N. Butler Street
1863, August Kutzbock

Dimensions of Wisconsin's first synagogue are 28 feet by 51 feet. It is a one-story building with gable ends, foundation, and basement walls of tooled local sandstone while the sides, above floor level, are brick. Principal exterior features include an ornate battlemented facade with parapets; a circular, stone framed opening in the central elevation; a small, gable-roofed vestibule; round-arched windows;

and a denticulated doorway lintel. The cornice is composed of a series of Greek crosses. The doors and entrance steps are replacements, and the interior has been greatly altered. In the late 1840's the first Jew settled in Madison, and by 1856 there were 17 families in all. The synagogue served the Madison Jewish community until 1879. Since then it has housed various religious groups and business enterprises.
Municipal; not accessible to the public

DANE COUNTY
Madison
WISCONSIN STATE CAPITOL
Capitol Square
1906-1917, George Browne Post

Wisconsin's State Capitol is the third to occupy this site. Housed within are both legislative houses, the state supreme court, and all but one of the state's constitutional officers. During the early years of the 20th century Wisconsin led the nation in passage of progressive and innovative regulations pertaining to the process of state government. Notable among these were the first direct primary election law (1904) and the first state civil service system (1905). Legislation enacted in the present edifice includes the Workmen's Compensation Act and establishment of the Industrial Commission (1911), creation of the Public Service Commission (1931), and passage of the Unemployment Compensation Act (1932). The capitol is cruciform in plan, and each of the four wings terminates in a pedimented Corinthian portico. A central dome surmounts the crossing of the four arms and rests upon a barrel treated as a circular Corinthian arcade. Atop the dome is a gilded bronze statue by Daniel Chester French which symbolizes Wisconsin's motto "Forward." Other sculptors whose work adorns the capitol are Karl Bitter, Adolph A. Weinman, and Attilio Piccirilli. Exterior walls are white Bethel granite, while the inside employs numerous marbles, Wisconsin granite, and Kasota limestone.
State

DANE COUNTY
Maple Bluff
LA FOLLETTE, ROBERT M., HOME
733 Lakewood Boulevard
c. 1860

Trained as a lawyer, Robert M. LaFollette was the Progressive party candidate for the Presidency in 1924. He was a Republican member of the House of Representatives from 1885 to 1890. During his years as Wisconsin's governor, 1901-1905, he successfully sought help from academicians to enact government

reforms, thus breaking the grip of special interests in the State government. From 1906 until his death in 1925, he was a United States Senator, during which time he sponsored legislation dealing with financial reform. His two-story brick house, Maple Bluff, has undergone minor alterations.
Private
NHL

DOOR COUNTY
Fish Creek vicinity
EAGLE BLUFF LIGHTHOUSE
3.5 miles north of Fish Creek on
Shore Road, in Peninsula State Park
1868

The Eagle Bluff Lighthouse marks the east passage from Green Bay to Lake Michigan. Still in use today, the light has been converted to electricity. The light tower and keeper's house is two stories high with a gable roof. At the gable ends are ornamental finials which extend from the top level of the second-story windows through the roof; near the lower end of each finial is a horizontal supporting crosspiece attached to the verge boards forming an interesting piece of Gothic Revival ornament. The light tower is square and oriented diagonally to the keeper's house. The cupola containing the light is decagonal. Restoration work was undertaken in 1961-1963 using the original plans.
Federal/state

DOUGLAS COUNTY
Solon Springs vicinity
BRULE-ST. CROIX PORTAGE
About 3 miles northeast of Solon
Springs in Brule River State Forest
17th, 18th, and 19th centuries

This portage between the Brule and St. Croix rivers was used by explorers, fur traders, travelers, settlers, and missionaries from the late 17th through the mid-19th centuries. Daniel Greysolon, Sieur de Lhut (Du Luth), is credited with being the first white man to use the portage (1680). For the next two hundred years it was one of the most heavily traveled routes between Lake Superior and the Mississippi River.
State

GRANT COUNTY
Cassville vicinity
STONEFIELD
2.5 miles west of Cassville, on County
Route V V
1860's

Stonefield was the home of Nelson Dewey (1813-1889), first state governor of

Wisconsin. Dewey had been born in Connecticut and came to Wisconsin in 1836, the year it became a territory. His public career included the territorial assembly (1838), speaker of the assembly (1840), membership in the legislative council (1842), Grant County attorney, governor (1848–1852), and state senator (1853). The main house at Stonefield is brick and was largely rebuilt after a fire in 1873. A smokehouse and a two-story wine cellar of native limestone, both Gothic Revival in style, constitute the farm complex.
State

IOWA COUNTY
Mineral Point
PENDARVIS
114 Shake Rag Street
c. 1835

In the late 1820's rich deposits of lead ore were discovered on this hilly point of land dividing the branches of the Pecatonica River. Unemployed tin miners from Cornwall settled here and attempted to make this new town resemble villages in their homeland. The Cornish were skilled stonemasons, and their cottages display some of the finest stonework in the state. Three restored houses comprise Pendarvis. All were built about 1835. The first, Pendarvis House, is a small cottage with a gable roof and a chimney at each gable end. The front is faced with carefully fitted native buff limestone laid in coursed ashlar using minimal amounts of mortar. Stone on the sides and back is laid in random ashlar, and all walls are 18 to 20 inches thick. The second Cornish house is a two-story, gable-roofed cottage with a saltbox profile and a lean-to at the rear. The third house has a ground floor of stone which is topped by a two-and-one-half-story log section. A declining demand for lead and the lure of the California goldfields caused most of the miners to leave Mineral Point. By 1850 the town's heyday as a mining center was past.
Private
HABS

JEFFERSON COUNTY
Fort Atkinson
PANTHER INTAGLIO EFFIGY
MOUND
On Wis. 106 at the west corporate
city limits
Pre-Columbian

American Indians of the Effigy Mound culture excavated this mound for ceremonial purposes about 1000 A.D. Only one other intaglio effigy mound is known to exist anywhere in the world, and it is in Ontario, Canada. Ten other similar mounds were once known to exist in

Wisconsin, but all have been destroyed by cultivation. The Panther Intaglio Effigy Mound measures 100 feet long (originally 125 feet) and is oriented lengthwise in an east-west direction. The excavation is shallow and now covered with grass.
Municipal

JEFFERSON COUNTY
Lake Mills vicinity
AZTALAN
Near Lake Mills on Wis. 89, Aztalan
State Park
c. 1200–1300

A large stockaded temple mound site, Aztalan is the northernmost of the large Mississippian culture archeological sites. It is conjectured that it represents an intrusion of peoples from farther south, probably from the area of the Cahokia Mounds in Illinois. The site has been extensively excavated.
State
NHL

LAFAYETTE COUNTY
Belmont vicinity
FIRST CAPITOL (WISCONSIN
TERRITORIAL CAPITOL)
3 miles north and 1 mile west of
Belmont on County Trunk Route G
1836

The Territory of Wisconsin was created in 1837 and also included Iowa, Minnesota, parts of the Dakotas and disputed land in northern Illinois. A census was ordered by Henry Dodge, first territorial governor, and, on the basis of population and geography, Belmont was selected as the first capital. The legislature met here from October to December, but the choice was not a popular one, and at the end of the year Madison became the capital. An unpretentious, two-story, frame and clapboard structure served as the capitol. It has been restored using as much of the original material as possible.
State

MARINETTE COUNTY
Peshtigo
PESHTIGO FIRE CEMETERY
Oconto Avenue between Peck and
Ellis Avenues

The Peshtigo Cemetery was originally a small town cemetery containing graves from the 1850's and later. Then, on October 8, 1871, a tornado fire whipped through Peshtigo and its environs killing 800 or more people and completely destroying the town. In terms of lives lost, this was the worst forest fire disaster in the nation's history. A tornado fire is a series of rapidly spreading crown fires. The

crown fires create strong convection currents which develop tornado-like vortices. These vortices sweep along unpredictably, uproot trees, and hurl objects through the air for miles. The tragedy at Peshtigo caused government and private industry to reexamine their conservation and fire prevention methods and to slowly evolve improved ones. A mass grave for 350 unidentified victims of the holocaust is in the northwestern part of the cemetery.
Municipal

OCONTO COUNTY
Oconto
OCONTO SITE
Copper Culture State Park
c. 5000–4000 B.C.

The Oconto Site is a prehistoric burial ground where implements of the Old Copper culture have been found in association with human burials. The site provided what is thought to be an accurate date for the culture. If so, the Old Copper Complex may represent the earliest use of metals in the world, even though their use by these people later died out.
State
NHL

ROCK COUNTY
Janesville
TALLMAN HOUSE
440 N. Jackson Street
1857

The Tallman House was the home of William M. Tallman, a lawyer who made his money in real estate speculation. Three stories high with walls of buff-colored brick, the main house is rectangular in shape. A squat cupola with a wide cornice surmounts the low hip roof, and the main cornice, supported by carved brackets, is five feet wide. The frieze beneath the cornice contains alternate panels and windows. The columns and pilasters of the entrance portico have fluted shafts and elaborately carved capitals and bases. The front doors are carved walnut. A glassed-in porch on the southeast has unusual windows topped by horseshoe arches and an ornate frieze. First-floor windows have square tops, and those on the second floor are round-arched. Lintels and sills are cast iron.
Municipal

SAUK COUNTY
Baraboo
RINGLING BROTHERS CIRCUS HEADQUARTERS, RINGLINGVILLE
Bounded roughly by Water Street on the north, Brian Street on the east, Lynn Street on the south, and East Street on the west
1884–1918

The heyday of the American circus occurred between 1875 and 1920. It was during this period that the Ringling Brothers began their traveling show which eventually became the largest mobile entertainment combine in the world. The principal partners and operators of the Ringling Brothers Circus were Albert C., Otto, Alfred T., Charles, and John, all of whom grew up in Baraboo. In 1884 the brothers organized their first traveling circus. Eventually they were able to buy out competitors and increase the size of their own operation. By 1907 they absorbed their greatest rival, Barnum and Bailey, thus becoming the biggest combine circus in the world. Until 1919 the two circuses were operated separately but with their physical unification in that year as the Ringling Brothers, Barnum and Bailey Circus, the winter headquarters at Baraboo were abandoned. The buildings remained standing and were used as business establishments by the townspeople. In the mid-20th century interest in a circus museum was sparked, buildings purchased, and the museum opened on July 1, 1959. Structures within the complex include the Ring Barn, Elephant Barn, Camel Barn, a 20–car circus train, and a 600–foot railroad shop and storage barn.
State
NHL

WASHINGTON COUNTY
West Bend vicinity
LIZARD MOUND STATE PARK
3 miles northeast of West Bend on Wis. 144, then .33 mile east on County Route A
Pre-Columbian

During prehistoric times southern Wisconsin was occupied by a group of Indians who constructed low earthworks, three to four feet high, in conical and linear forms and resembling birds and animals. As a result of this practice the Indians are identified as belonging to the Effigy Mound culture. The mounds were used for burials and have yielded tools and weapons of bone, wood, stone, and occasionally copper. Apparently these people lived in small bands and fished, hunted, and farmed. There are 31 extant mounds in the park which vary in length and shape but are about three and one-half feet high. Lizard Mound is the most outstanding and measures 250 feet in length.
State

Pendarvis, Mineral Point, Wisconsin.
J. W. Winn for the State Historical Society of Wisconsin

Wyoming

Fort Laramie Bridge, Fort Laramie National Historic Site,
Fort Laramie vicinity, Wyoming. *William Edmund Barrett for HAER*

Officers' Quarters, Fort Fetterman,
Orpha vicinity, Wyoming.
Wyoming Recreation Commission

Father DeSmet's Prairie Mass Site
Daniels vicinity, Wyoming.
Bill Barnhart, Wyoming Recreation Commission

BIG HORN COUNTY
Kane vicinity
MEDICINE WHEEL
    Just north of U.S. 14 Alt., about 15
    miles east of Kane
    17th to 19th centuries

The Medicine Wheel is made of loose, irregularly-shaped, whitish, flat stones placed in a circle. The center hub is 3 feet high and 12 feet in diameter. Twenty-eight linear spokes varying from 70 to 75 feet in length radiate from the hub. The spokes are closed by an outer rim of stones. Five oblong stone cairns exist along the outer rim of the wheel. The wheel lies on the highest point of the western peak of Medicine Mountain. Its original purpose is not known, although many theories exist. Probably it had some religious significance.
Federal
NHL

CARBON COUNTY
Elk Mountain vicinity
FORT HALLECK
    NW 1/4 NE 1/4 NE 1/4 sec. 20, T. 20
    N., R. 81 W.
    1862–1866

Fort Halleck was established in the early years of the Civil War to protect the overland mail from Indian attacks. The post was named for Major General Henry W. Halleck. It consisted of a collection of log structures, huts and dugouts, flanking a parade ground. Abandoned in July, 1866, the fort site now serves as a ranch headquarters.
Private

CARBON COUNTY
Fort Fred Steele vicinity
FORT STEELE
    On the North Platte River at the point
    of the Union Pacific Railroad crossing
    19th century

Fort Steele was one of three forts set up to protect the railroad during its construction. It was also used as a supply post during the Army's wars with the Plains Indians. The site was chosen, and the fort established on June 30, 1868. The post was named for Maj. General Frederick Steele, a Civil War hero. Indian disturbances in the area were kept to a minimum, and Fort Steele exerted a stabilizing influence on the population. Abandoned by the Army on August 7, 1886, the fort site became a small civilian community along the transcontinental railroad. The Union Pacific trains still pass through, but the town and the fort are largely deserted. Parts of the original fort which are extant are the commanding officer's quarters, two large warehouses, a

powder magazine, and several smaller buildings.
Private

CARBON COUNTY (also in Natrona County)
Independence Rock vicinity
SUN, TOM, RANCH
    6 miles west of Independence Rock
    on Wyo. 220
    1872

The Tom Sun Ranch in the Sweetwater Valley of central Wyoming typifies the medium-sized ranching operations of the open range period. Tom Sun, a French Canadian frontiersman, became a respected pioneer cattleman, establishing operations on the Oregon Trail near Devil's Gate and Independence Rock. The present ranch house includes the original log building built by Sun and several outbuildings and corrals believed to be original.
Private; not accessible to the public
NHL

CARBON COUNTY
Rawlins vicinity
BRIDGER'S PASS
    SE 1/4 NW 1/4 sec. 8, T. 18 N., R. 89
    W.
    1850–1868

During the period of America's westward migration, Bridger's Pass, named for trapper and army scout Jim Bridger, was one of the most important passes over the continental divide. Bridger guided Captain Howard Stansbury and his men over the pass in 1850. Stansbury had been sent out by the federal government in 1849 to explore and survey the valley of the Great Salt Lake. His crossing of the divide through Bridger's Pass helped publicize the route for overland travel which increased steadily in the decade preceding the Civil War. In 1862 a section of the overland stage line was rerouted through Bridger's Pass, but, upon completion of the transcontinental railroad (1869), the stage line was forced to suspend operations. The pass then reverted to its original quiet natural setting.
Federal

CONVERSE COUNTY
Glenrock vicinity
GLENROCK BUFFALO JUMP
    About 2 miles west of Glenrock
    Interchange on Int. 25
    500–1750

The Glenrock Buffalo Jump is partly situated on a large, flat plateau which has abundant grass and water and which extends to the edge of a 40-foot bluff—the "jump-off" point. Below the bluff is a

talus slope. A large number of bones have been found in the soil of the talus slope. The buffalo jump dates from the Late Prehistoric period. The butchering site is believed to be at the base of the talus slope, but the area has not been excavated. Buffalo herds were driven over the cliff without the aid of horses. First, a herd of sufficient size had to be gathered and carefully driven to a point where it could be stampeded toward the jump-off. Most buffalo jumps have been destroyed by the recovery of bones for commercial use, and few have had adequate archeological work performed. The Glenrock Buffalo Jump is unique in being undisturbed, and plans are being made to conduct proper archeological investigations.
State/private

CONVERSE COUNTY
Orpha vicinity
FORT FETTERMAN
    Orpha County Road, .1 mile west of
    Orpha Road, 7 miles north of Int. 25
    1867–1882

Fort Fetterman was established as a military post in July, 1867, on the North Platte River at the crossroads of the Bozeman Trail and earlier overland routes. The fort was intended to provide protection against hostile Indians. Its strategic location caused it to become a supply base, headquarters, and marshalling point for army expeditions against the Indians of the northern plains. The post was named for Lieutenant Colonel William J. Fetterman, who was killed in an Indian battle near Fort Phil Kearny in December, 1866. Fort Fetterman was no longer needed once the power of the Indians was broken; it was abandoned in 1882. The site still contains two original structures, a log officers' quarters (now used as a museum and caretaker's house) and a rammed earth ordnance warehouse. Only foundations of the other buildings remain.
State

FREMONT COUNTY
Ethete
ST. MICHAEL'S MISSION
    19th and 20th centuries

The Wind River Indian Reservation was created by treaty with the Shoshone Indians in July, 1868. A military post, eventually named Fort Washakie, was established the following year. In 1878 the Northern Arapaho were allowed to winter at Wind River and have remained to the present time. The Reverend John Roberts, an Episcopal missionary, came to Fort Washakie in 1883 and within a few years

he started a small mission, St. Michael's, to serve the Arapaho. Construction of the present mission buildings took place between 1910 and 1917. Grouped around an oval, they are a schoolhouse, staff homes, a boys' and a girls' home, the child care center, post office, a bead shop, and the Church of Our Father's House. The mission is still in operation.
Private

FREMONT COUNTY
Fort Washakie vicinity
FORT WASHAKIE
Wind River Indian Reservation on U.S. 287
19th century

Fort Washakie was founded to protect the Bannock and Shoshone Indian reservations from attacks by wandering hostiles. It also served as a supply base for expeditions to Yellowstone National Park (which was established in 1872) and the Big Horn country. The fort was provided for in a treaty between the federal government and the Shoshone Indians signed at Fort Bridger on July 3, 1868. A series of camps at several locations were built before the permanent post was established on the present site in 1871. Originally called Camp Brown to honor Capt. Frederick H. Brown, killed at the Fetterman Massacre (December 26, 1866), the post was renamed in December 1878, after the Shoshone chief Washakie. Chief Washakie is buried in the post cemetery. The post was abandoned early in 1909 and became the property of the U.S. Department of the Interior's Bureau of Indian Affairs. The Shoshone share the reservation lands with the Arapaho.
Federal

FREMONT COUNTY
Moneta vicinity
CASTLE GARDENS PETROGLYPH SITE
About 28 miles south of Moneta on U.S. 20–26
Pre-Columbian to 19th century

The cliffs upon which the petroglyphs appear are 6 miles long and 1 mile wide with drawings scattered all along the vertical face which ranges from 10 to 100 feet high. A wide variety of forms appear, from simple to highly complex. The petroglyphs were executed with stone tools using techniques of pecking, rubbing, grinding, and fine-line incising. Particularly significant designs are figures of water turtles and recurrent circular shield motifs. All of the numerous rock formations created by wind and water erosion, when combined with the natural landscape, give the impression of a medieval castle surrounded by gardens—hence the name. The age and

specific meaning of these petroglyphs are not known.
Federal

FREMONT COUNTY
South Pass City
SOUTH PASS CITY
Sec. 20, T. 29 N., R. 100 W.
Late 19th century

South Pass City was laid out in 1867, when miners and adventurers began to pour into Wyoming's Sweetwater gold country. The town reached a peak of prosperity in 1870, but declined thereafter as mining activity petered out. During its heyday South Pass City served as county seat of Sweetwater County, and Wyoming's first female justice of the peace, Mrs. Esther Morris, presided over 34 cases there between February and November, 1870. Original buildings still standing are a store, bar and hotel, former Wells Fargo office, a dugout, and a log dwelling.
State/federal/private

FREMONT COUNTY
South Pass City vicinity
SOUTH PASS
About 10 miles southwest of South Pass City on Wyo. 28
1824

Of all the discoveries of Jedediah Smith in the West, South Pass (elevation 7550 feet) affected United States history the most. As the easiest passage through the Rocky Mountains, it was used more than any route by westbound settlers, inasmuch as the Oregon-California Trail crossed the continental divide here. The pass was significant not only in migration, but also in the fur trade, transportation, mining, exploration, and the establishment of effective claims to the Pacific Northwest.
Private
NHL

FREMONT COUNTY (also in Sublette County)
UNION PASS
On the continental divide, 12 miles west-southwest of Wind River Ranger Station (Shoshone National Forest), 16 miles north-northeast of Kendall Ranger Station (Bridger National Forest), 20 miles east-southeast of Goose Wing Ranger Station (Teton National Forest)
19th century

Union Pass is a strategically located passage through the mountains of northwestern Wyoming. The pass location, at an altitude of 9,210 feet, is really a hub or core area from which three great Wyoming mountain ranges rise in

gradually ascending elevations to heights of 13,000 feet or more—the Wind River Range to the southeast, the Gros Ventre Range to the west, and the Absaroka Range to the north. Union Pass, about 4,000 feet lower than the mountains surrounding it, offers an easy passageway among the headwaters of three great river systems—the Colorado, the Columbia, and the Missouri. On September 15, 1811, an overland expedition of John Jacob Astor's fur company led by Wilson Price Hunt became the first group of white men to cross the continental divide here. This expedition was traveling toward the mouth of the Columbia River. Prior to this time the pass had been frequently used by Indians, and it later became important in the Oregon fur trade.
Federal

GOSHEN COUNTY
Fort Laramie vicinity
FORT LARAMIE NATIONAL HISTORIC SITE
3 miles southwest of Fort Laramie
1834

Fort Laramie was established as a center for trade with the Indians of the northern plains in 1834. Situated on the Laramie River crossing of the California-Oregon Trail, it was purchased in 1849 for army use as a base for guarding the overland trails, controlling the Indians of the region, and extending American influence. A Pony Express station was located here in 1860–1861, and the post was a hub in the transportation and communications of the northern plains and mountains. Its troops were involved in numerous campaigns and treaties designed to pacify the northern Plains Indians. It was abandoned in 1890.
Federal/non-federal
NPS; 562.79 acres

GOSHEN COUNTY (also in Niobrara County)
Lusk vicinity
CHEYENNE-BLACK HILLS STAGE ROUTE AND RAWHIDE BUTTES AND RUNNING WATER STAGE STATIONS
1 mile west to about 15 miles southwest of Lusk
1876–1887

The Cheyenne-Black Hills Stage route linked Cheyenne and Deadwood, South Dakota. Thousands of passengers, tons of freight and express, and millions of dollars in gold passed over this trail until the advent of the railroad drove the stage line out of business. Both of the stage stations were typical of the road-ranches scattered throughout the west wherever stage lines existed. The Cheyenne-Deadwood Trail

ran to Fort Laramie, then north to Rawhide Buttes and Running Water. It served as a main artery to the Black Hills goldfields. Rawhide Springs, between the two stage stations, possessed water and grass in quantity and so became a favorite camping spot along the trail. The Cheyenne-Black Hills Stage Company carried mail to the Black Hills, and numerous robberies of gold and mail by armed desperadoes occurred along the route. The coming of the railroad brought an influx of settlers, but it meant the end of the stage line. Today the Running Water Station is marked only by stone ruins, but the Rawhide Buttes Station still stands and is used as a ranch.
Municipal/private

HOT SPRINGS COUNTY
Thermopolis vicinity
WOODRUFF CABIN SITE
26 miles northwest of Thermopolis, 18 miles west on County Route 0900 from the intersection with Wyo. 120
1871

The cabin of John Dwight Woodruff was the first recorded white man's dwelling in the Big Horn basin, the entire northwestern corner of Wyoming. Only the cabin site remains today, marked by a rock and mortar monument. From pictures it has been estimated that the cabin measured 12 feet wide by 20 feet long, was constructed of logs, and covered with several inches of dirt on the roof to absorb moisture. Woodruff used the cabin in the winter, spring, and early summer as a headquarters while trapping and prospecting. He eventually introduced both sheep and cattle into the area, and the cabin may have served as a ranch house. Woodruff sold his cabin in the early 1880's, and buildings of the Embar Ranch presently form a semicircle around the cabin site.
State

JOHNSON COUNTY
Story vicinity
FORT PHIL KEARNY AND ASSOCIATED SITES
On secondary road west of U.S. 87
1866

In and around Fort Phil Kearny the Sioux Indians fought successfully to prevent invasion of their hunting grounds by prospectors and wagon trains bound for the Montana gold fields. From 1866 to 1868 the fort was held under virtual siege as the focus of the Red Cloud War, which resulted in relinquishment of military control of the area and the abandonment of the Bozeman Trail. The natural setting of Fort Phil Kearny has suffered comparatively little encroachment. In 1938 a

peeled-log reproduction of an officers' quarters and a seven-foot slab stockade were erected here.
Multiple public/private
NHL

JOHNSON COUNTY
Sussex vicinity
FORT RENO
SE 1/4 SE 1/4 NW 1/4 sec. 33, T. 45 N., R. 78 W.
1865–1868

Fort Reno, established in August, 1865, as Fort Connor, was situated on the left bank of the Powder River. It was one of three forts (Fort Phil Kearny and Fort C. F. Smith) constructed by the Army to protect travelers along the Bozeman Trail. The Bozeman Trail ran along the eastern base of the Big Horn Mountains before turning east to Virginia City, and portions of it ran through a sacred hunting ground of the Sioux. A cottonwood stockade contained the quartermaster's and the commissary storehouses. Outside were two barracks, two officers' quarters, a post hospital, shops, teamsters' quarters, and two sutler's buildings. The fort was renamed (November, 1865) for General Jesse L. Reno, and in 1868 it was abandoned and later burned.
State

LARAMIE COUNTY
Cheyenne
ST. MARK'S EPISCOPAL CHURCH
1908 Central Avenue
1886–1888, Henry M. Congdon

St. Mark's Episcopal Church is the second structure of that name erected in Cheyenne. The first St. Mark's was built in 1868. The need for larger facilities caused the parish to embark upon a building program in the 1880's. The exterior is stone with pointed-arch windows and massive buttresses. Eleven of Wyoming's 26 governors have been members of St. Mark's congregation.
Private

LARAMIE COUNTY
Cheyenne
WYOMING GOVERNOR'S MANSION
300 E. 21st Street
1904

The Wyoming Governor's Mansion is a Georgian Revival brick house which originally contained a large drawing room and dining room, five bedrooms and a bath on the second floor, and three bedrooms and a bath on the third floor. Extensive interior remodeling was done in 1937. The Wyoming Executive Mansion has the distinction of being the first in the nation to have been occupied by a

woman, Nellie Tayloe Ross, governor from 1925 to 1927.
State

LARAMIE COUNTY
Cheyenne vicinity
FRANCIS E. WARREN AIR FORCE BASE
Bounds against the west side of Cheyenne, the two are roughly separated by Int. 25

The present Air Force base was established in 1867 as Fort David A. Russell. In 1930, upon the death in office of Senator Francis E. Warren, the post was renamed in his honor. Originally the federal government used Fort Russell, located at the eastern base of the Rocky Mountains, to protect the transcontinental railroad which ran through nearby Cheyenne. When the Indian wars were over, Fort Russell was considered important enough to be made a permanent post by the War Department (1885). In 1906 it was enlarged to brigade size, and in 1947 the name was changed a second time to Francis E. Warren Air Force Base. It is presently under the control of the Strategic Air Command. All buildings reflect the growth and changing role of the post. Most are red brick.
Federal

LINCOLN COUNTY
La Barge vicinity
NAMES HILL
On the Green River, 5 miles south of La Barge and just west of U.S. 189
19th century

Names Hill on the Green River is one of three places (Register Cliff on the North Platte and Independence Rock on the Sweetwater) along the Oregon-California Trail where emigrants carved their names or left messages and greetings for those following. In 1844 Jim Bridger, famous trapper and mountain man, left his name here. The earliest dated name is 1822, which is earlier than any dated inscription at either of the other two locations. Names Hill was a popular camping spot for westward moving emigrants.
State

NATRONA COUNTY
Casper vicinity
INDEPENDENCE ROCK
60 miles southwest of Casper on Wyo. 220

Called "the great registry of the desert," Independence Rock was a well-known natural landmark on the Oregon Trail. This oblong mass, over 1900 feet long and 850 feet wide, lies near the Sweetwater

River where the Oregon Trail first approaches it, making it a favorite stopping and resting place for travelers. The rock soon became famous because of the numerous names painted, carved, or written on its face. The landmark and its environs are little changed from that era.
Multiple state/private
NHL

NATRONA COUNTY
SUN, TOM, RANCH
Reference—see Carbon County

NIOBRARA COUNTY
CHEYENNE-BLACK HILLS STAGE ROUTE AND RAWHIDE BUTTES AND RUNNING WATER STAGE STATIONS
Reference—see Goshen County

NIOBRARA COUNTY
Van Tassell
FERDINAND BRANSTETTER POST NO. 1, AMERICAN LEGION
Lots 1 and 2, block 8, sec. 17, T. 31 N., R. 60 W.
20th century

The Ferdinand Branstetter Post No. 1 of the American Legion was the first such post organized in Wyoming and one of the four original posts organized in the United States. Charters for Van Tassell, Denver, St. Louis, and Washington, D.C., were signed on the same day. The structure which originally housed the Van Tassell post is no longer extant.
Private

PARK COUNTY
Cody vicinity
HORNER SITE
4 miles northeast of Cody on U.S. 20
c. 5000 B.C.

The Horner Site first yielded evidence that several distinctive weapons and tool types commonly found in the high plains region were all part of a single prehistoric flint tool industry of early hunter origin. These artifacts, which differed materially from each other, were all found in the same campsite. The site occupies a high flat terrace near the confluence of Sage Creek and the Shoshone River.
Private; not accessible to the public
NHL

PARK COUNTY
Wapiti vicinity
WAPITI RANGER STATION
Shoshone National Forest
1903

Wapiti Ranger Station was the first to be erected at federal expense. It is located within the area of the first national forest reserve, Yellowstone Timberland Reserve,

which was established by President Benjamin Harrison in 1891. Built as a supervisory ranger station for the Shoshone division of the reserve, the original still stands, though incorporated into the present station.
Federal
NHL

PLATTE COUNTY
Chugwater
SWAN LAND AND CATTLE COMPANY HEADQUARTERS
East side of Chugwater
1883

The Swan Land and Cattle Company was among the prominent foreign stock concerns that flourished in the American West during the heyday of the range cattle industry. Organized in Scotland, the company grazed more than 113,000 head of cattle on more than a million acres of grassland within three years. Turning to sheep in 1911, the Swan Company built sizable herds, reaching a peak of 112,000 head. Surviving buildings associated with the early days of the operation include the ranch house and barn (1876) and a store which housed the ranch commissary (1913).
Private, not accessible to the public
NHL

PLATTE COUNTY
Guernsey vicinity
OREGON TRAIL RUTS
South side of the North Platte River
.5 mile south of Guernsey
1841–1869

Worn from two to six feet into an eroded sandstone ridge, the Oregon Trail Ruts provide clear physical evidence of the route followed by those migrating westward across the plains. In 1841 the first wagon train moved over the Oregon Trail, and in ensuing years the trail became a clearly defined and deeply rutted road. With the completion of the Union Pacific Railroad in 1869, its use as an overland route to the Pacific rapidly declined.
State; not accessible to the public
NHL

PLATTE COUNTY
Guernsey vicinity
REGISTER CLIFF
NW 1/4 NW 1/4 sec. 7, T. 26 N., R. 65 W.
19th century

Register Cliff, a soft, chalky, limestone precipice, rises 100 feet above the valley floor on the south bank of the North Platte River. Settlers, trappers, scouts, and gold hunters moving west to California and Oregon left numerous dates and in-

scriptions here as tangible evidence of their passing. Register Cliff was the first night camp west of Fort Laramie. The earliest known date is July 14, 1829, and the majority of dated material falls within the peak travel years, 1840–1850. A number of graves have been discovered in the vicinity and are being protected.
State

SHERIDAN COUNTY
Sheridan
SHERIDAN INN
Broadway and 5th Street
1893, Thomas R. Kimball

When the Chicago, Burlington, & Quincy Railroad tracks reached Sheridan, the company constructed the Sheridan Inn. William F. "Buffalo Bill" Cody operated the hotel from 1894 to 1896, catering principally to a large clientele of sportsmen bound for the Big Horn Mountain country. Still in use today, the frame building has a piazza extending around two sides and a Buffalo Bill bar which retains its original features.
Private
NHL; HABS

SHERIDAN COUNTY
Sheridan
TRAIL END
400 Clarendon Avenue
1908–1913, William MacAlister

Trail End is typical of the substantial yet elaborate town houses built by wealthy cattlemen in the late 19th and early 20th centuries. The house itself is brick on a limestone foundation, and the architecture is Jacobean distinguished by ornate Baroque gables. Carved woodwork, polished wooden floors, brocade wall panels, rugs, velvet hangings and furniture of the owner's family decorate the interior. John B. Kendrick, builder of Trail End, was governor of Wyoming (1915–1917) and a U.S. Senator (1917–1933).
Private

SUBLETTE COUNTY
Daniel vicinity
FATHER DE SMET'S PRAIRIE MASS SITE
S 1/2 SE 1/4 sec. 36, T. 34 N., R. 111 W.
1840

On this site in 1840 Father Pierre-Jean De Smet celebrated the first recorded mass of the Roman Catholic Church in the northern Rocky Mountains. Father De Smet (1801–1873), a Belgian, came to America in 1821 and entered the novitiate of the Jesuit order. Ordained in 1827, he embarked upon his lifetime work as a mis-

sionary to the Indians eleven years later. The occasion for the prairie mass was the annual fur traders' rendezvous near present-day Daniel on the Upper Green River. A granite cross has been erected on the site, which is a broad, open plain atop a bluff overlooking the river valley. Father De Smet, affectionately called Blackrobe, became a well-known and trusted friend of the Plains and Pacific Northwest Indians and frequently acted as mediator when trouble broke out between tribes or between redman and white.
Public/private

SUBLETTE COUNTY
Daniel vicinity
UPPER GREEN RIVER RENDEZVOUS SITE

On Green River above and below Daniel
1824–1840

Of all the rendezvous sites connected with the Rocky Mountain fur trade, the most popular was that on the Green River. The rendezvous, instituted by General William Ashley, was an annual trading fair held each spring to which trappers, traders, and Indians came. The great supply caravans from St. Louis brought trade goods to exchange for the furs. Among the foremost figures who came were Kit Carson, Jedediah Smith, and Jim Bridger. The rendezvous area is in a natural state almost unchanged from the time when fur trappers gathered there.
Private
NHL

SUBLETTE COUNTY
Pinedale vicinity
FORT BONNEVILLE

NE 1/4 NE 1/4 sec. 30, R. 111 W., T. 34 N.
1832

Captain Benjamin Bonneville, on leave from the Army, headed west from Fort Osage (Missouri) with a party of 110 men and about 20 wagons. It was May, 1832, and Bonneville wished to investigate the possibilities of a fur trade venture in the northern Rockies. Arriving at the Green River in August, Bonneville set about constructing a stockade as protection against the hostile Blackfoot Indians. Evidently believing he had made an unwise choice of site, Bonneville abandoned the stockade soon after the first snowfall. Nothing remains above ground to reveal the dimensions or appearance of Fort Bonneville, but there are probably archeological remains to indicate general construction and shape.
Public/private

SUBLETTE COUNTY
UNION PASS
Reference—see Fremont County

SWEETWATER COUNTY
Granger
GRANGER STAGE STATION

NW 1/4 NW 1/4 NE 1/4 sec. 32, T. 19 N., R. 111 W.
c. 1856

A great westward migration to California and Oregon began in the 1840's. Wagons, cattle, and settlers crossed the country in great numbers, and trails and river fords came into being almost overnight. Such a crossing was located on Black's Fork near the site of the Granger Stage Station. Eventually Pony Express riders stopped here (1861–1862), and the Union Pacific Railroad laid tracks nearby in 1868. Only one original building remains today. It measures 56 feet by 22 feet, and the walls are stone and lime-sand mortar. None of the doors or windows is original.
State

SWEETWATER COUNTY
Green River
EXPEDITION ISLAND
1869, 1871

The town of Green River on the Union Pacific Railroad was the starting point for the two expeditions down the Green and Colorado rivers led by Maj. John Wesley Powell in 1869 and 1871. (*See* Desolation Canyon, Utah.) On these expeditions Powell completed the exploration of the last, large, unknown land area in the continental United States. No conclusive information has been found to indicate the precise campsite or embarkation point of the first expedition, but the second camped on Expedition Island and left from there May 22, 1871. Here the men prepared their specially designed boats for the arduous voyage ahead. In the absence of positive information as to the 1869 campsite, Expedition Island is recognized as the appropriate site to commemorate both trips.
Municipal
NHL

SWEETWATER COUNTY
Rock Springs vicinity
POINT OF ROCKS STAGE STATION

SW 1/4 SW 1/4 sec. 27, R. 101 W., T. 20 N.
Mid–19th century

Point of Rocks Stage Station served as a stop on the Overland Stage Line (from Atchison, Kansas, to Placerville, California) and as the junction of the Overland Trail and the Union Pacific Railroad (1868). When the railroad put the over-

land stage out of business, a shorter stage line began operating north from Point of Rocks to South Pass City and other settlements in the Sweetwater mining district. The building was constructed of native sandstone, and mud mortar was used to chink the walls.
State

TETON COUNTY
Jackson vicinity
MILLER CABIN

About 3 miles east of Jackson's central square along Main Street; follow northeast fork of road for 1 mile beyond city limits
1903–1912

Robert A. Miller settled on Flat Creek in 1885. His meadowland was well suited for hay production. Miller eventually helped to plat the town of Jackson. At the turn of the century Yellowstone Timber Land Reserve was created, and Miller was made the chief administrator of the Teton Division (one of four). Miller set up his headquarters at the cabin in 1903, two years before the establishment of the Forest Service within the U.S. Department of Agriculture. The cabin also served as the seat of administration for the first major federal refuge for a large species of North American wildlife—the Wapiti elk—which was started on 2,000 acres of Miller's original homestead. The Miller Cabin is really two cabins, both constructed of logs and typical of home construction during frontier times in the forested mountain valleys of the Northwest. The two cabins are only a few feet apart and belong to a single homesite. The original cabin was the first home of Robert Miller and was so used during the period connected with Miller's forest service. The larger, two-storied home was built later and was the headquarters for the wildlife refuge.
Federal

TETON COUNTY
Moose
MENOR'S FERRY

Across the Snake River just above park headquarters, Grand Teton National Park
1892–1927

Bill Menor homesteaded in the area of the present Menor's Ferry in 1892. He settled on the west bank of the Snake, whereas most settlers remained on the east side and used his ferry to reach the timber on the western bank. Menor was joined by his brother, Holiday, who assisted in the operation of the ferry. Both men had sold out and left the area by 1927. Two years later the ferry was acquired by the Rockefeller family. It was refurbished,

placed in working order, and turned over to the National Park Service in 1953. The ferry itself is large enough to carry a fully loaded wagon of logs plus a four-horse team. It was formed of two sharp-prowed boats across which the carrying platform was set at right angles. The ferry swung from a cable by means of two lines either one of which could be shortened while its opposite was lengthened by means of a windlass set on the platform and operated by the pilot. Thus the prows of the boat could be pointed at the angle desired, and the current itself carried the ferry across the stream.
Federal

UINTA COUNTY
Fort Bridger vicinity
FORT BRIDGER
    On Black's Fork of the Green River
    near the town of Fort Bridger
    19th century

Fort Bridger may be considered as one of the two most important forts in this area of the country with regard to overland migration, the other being Fort Laramie. Fort Bridger was named for fur trapper and mountain man Jim Bridger, who opened a trading post on the site in 1843. As time passed his trading post became a major resupply and outfitting point for emigrants, gold seekers, adventurers, and explorers, and a stopping place for friendly Indians. The Mormons acquired and held the fort from 1853 until 1857. In 1858 Fort Bridger became a U.S. Army post. During the 1860's it served as a Pony Express, overland telegraph, and overland stage station. When the Indians were finally subdued, the protection offered by the fort was no longer needed, and the post was abandoned on October 1, 1890.
State

UINTA COUNTY
Hilliard vicinity
PIEDMONT CHARCOAL KILNS
    14 miles northeast of Hilliard, NW
    1/4 SW 1/4 sec. 4, T. 14 N., R. 117
    W.
    1869

The Piedmont Charcoal Kilns were built to process charcoal for use in mining smelters. Union Pacific Railroad tracks were laid through the area in 1868, and Piedmont was a station on the line. Due to its proximity to Utah mines, the ease of transportation, and an abundant supply of timber, the site was an ideal location for a charcoal processing operation. Five conical native limestone kilns were constructed (only three and part of a fourth remain) in 1869 by Moses Byrne. Measuring 30 feet in circumference and 30 feet from the ground to the peak of the roof dome, each has one arched entrance eight feet high. The walls are two feet thick. Wood was placed in the kilns, a fire started, and the kilns sealed in such a way that the heat could be regulated. The wood smoldered slowly for several days, then the fire was allowed to die out, and the wood cooled before handling.
State

WESTON COUNTY
Newcastle vicinity
JENNEY STOCKADE
    NE 1/4 NW 1/4 sec. 7, T. 44 N., R.
    60 W.
    1875

The Jenney Stockade was constructed in the summer of 1875 as a headquarters and supply depot for an expedition to the Black Hills. Soldiers under the command of Lieutenant Colonel Richard I. Dodge joined forces at Fort Laramie with geologists and miners led by Professor Walter P. Jenney. In June construction began on Camp Jenney, which served during the summer as a supply center for all of the Black Hills area. That winter the stockade became a stopping place for gold seekers entering the Black Hills. By the summer of 1877 a cut-off on the Cheyenne (Wyo.) to Deadwood (S.D.) stage route was opened, and Jenney Stockade became a breakfast and supper stop for stagecoach passengers. The original waystation building has been moved to Newcastle.
Private

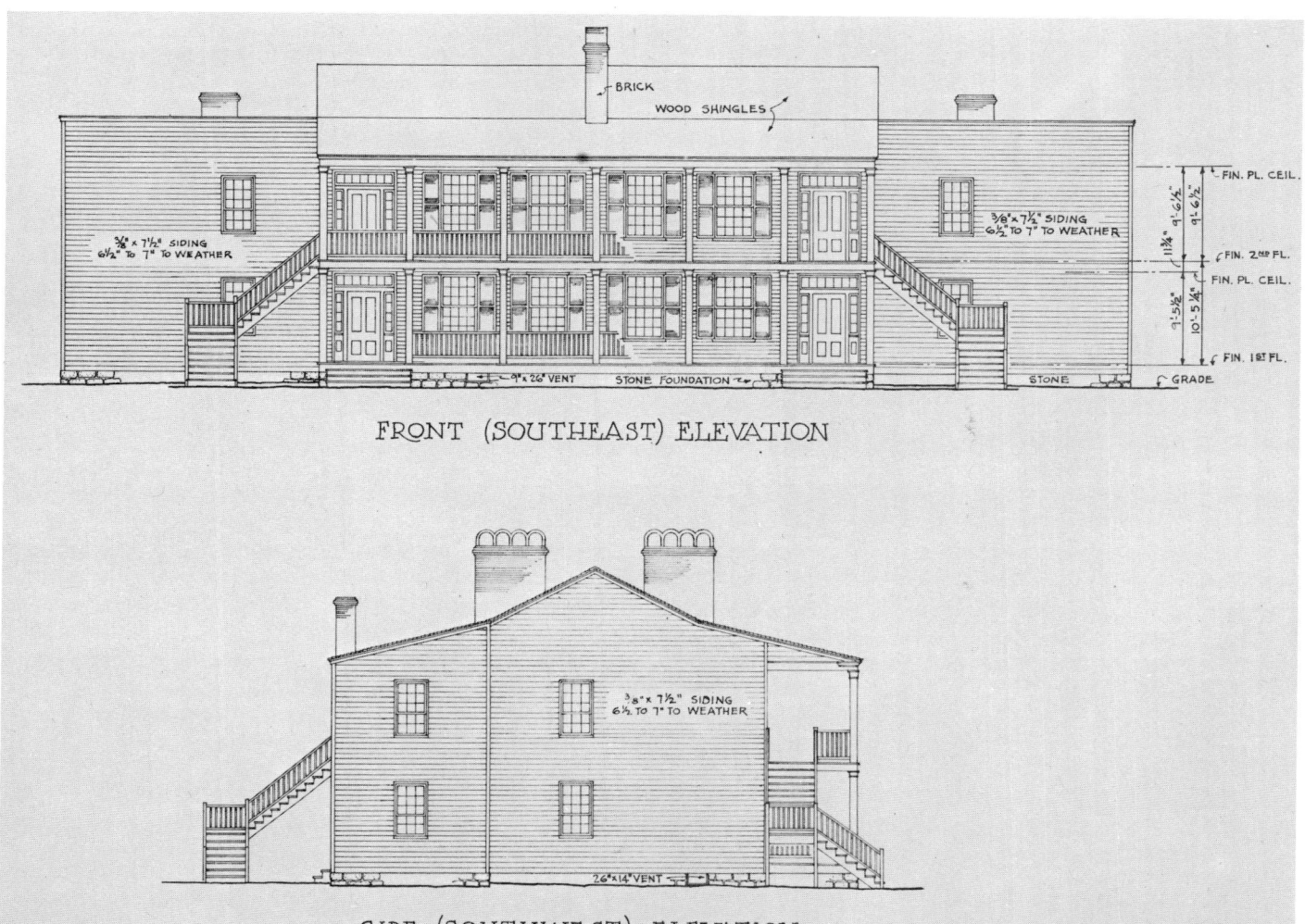

FRONT (SOUTHEAST) ELEVATION

3/8" x 7 1/2" SIDING
6 1/2" TO 7" TO WEATHER

BRICK
WOOD SHINGLES

3/8" x 7 1/2" SIDING
6 1/2" TO 7" TO WEATHER

FIN. PL. CEIL.

FIN. 2ND FL.

FIN. PL. CEIL.

FIN. 1ST FL.

9" x 26" VENT   STONE FOUNDATION   STONE   GRADE

SIDE (SOUTHWEST) ELEVATION
SCALE 1/8" = 1'-0"

3/8" x 7 1/2" SIDING
6 1/2" TO 7" TO WEATHER

2'6" x 1'4" VENT

Old Bedlam Fort Laramie National Historic Site,
Fort Laramie vicinity, Wyoming. *HABS*

Index

I

Ilium Building (Troy, N.Y.), 336
Illinois Capitol. *See* Old State Capitol
Illinois and Michigan Canal (locks and towpath) (Ill.), 137
Independence Hall (Philadelphia, Pa.), 401
Independence Hall (Wheeling, W.Va.), 548
Independence National Historical Park (Philadelphia, Pa.), 401
Independence Rock (Wyo.), 565–66
Indian Castle Church (N.Y.), 329
Indian Grinding Rock (Chaw'se) (Calif.), 37
Indian King Tavern (Creighton Tavern) (Haddonfield, N.J.), 301
Indian Knoll (Ky.), 165
Indian Mill (Ohio), 374
Indian Paintings (Va.), 531
Indian Village Site (Wittrock Area) (Iowa), 148
Infinity Archeological Site (Kans.), 157
Ingles Ferry (Va.), 524
Initial Point (Okla.), 380
Inn at Brushy Creek (Cole House) (Old Round Rock, Tex.), 478
Inscription House (cliff dwelling). *See* Navajo National Monument
Inscription Rock. *See* El Morro National Monument
Institute of the Pennsylvania Hospital (Philadelphia, Pa.), 401
Iolani Palace (Hawaiian statehouse) (Honolulu, Hawaii), 120
Iowa, Sac, and Fox Presbyterian Mission (Highland Presbyterian Mission) (Kans.), 154
Ipiutak Site (Alaska), 11
Iredell, James, House (Edenton, N.C.), 347
Irvin Hall, Highland Community Junior College (Highland, Kans.), 154
Irving, Washington, 340
Irving, Washington, House. *See* Sunnyside
Isle of Wight Courthouse. *See* Old Isle of Wight Courthouse
Itasca Bison Site (Minn.), 231
Ives, Thomas P., House (Providence, R.I.), 419
Ivy Green (Helen Keller Birthplace) (Tuscumbia, Ala.), 4
Ivy Hall (Cornelius Lowe House) (Piscataway, N.J.), 303
Iyatayet Site (Alaska), 11

J

J A Ranch (Tex.), 463
J. M. Wallace Archeological Site (Wardell Mounds) (Mo.), 261
Jabez S. Fitch House. *See* Brooks, Harold C., House

Jacinto Courthouse (Rienzi, Miss.), 243
Jackson, Andrew, 452
Jackson, Joseph: building by, 555
Jackson, Jesse, House (N.C.), 352
Jackson, Richard, House (Portsmouth, N.H.), 295
Jackson, Thomas J., Headquarters (Winchester, Va.), 533
Jackson County Jail and Marshal's House (Independence, Mo.), 257
Jackson Square (Place d'Armes, New Orleans, La.), 169
Jacksonport State Park (Jacksonport, Ark.), 30
Jacksonville Historic District (Ore.), 387
Jacobs Hall, Kentucky School for the Deaf (Danville, Ky.), 163
James, Francis Wilcox, House (Port Townsend, Wash.), 539
James Deering Estate. *See* Vizcaya
James River and Kanawha Canal. *See* James River and Kanawha Connection Locks and Canal
James River and Kanawha Connection Locks and Canal (Richmond, Va.), 525
Jamestown National Historic Site (Va.), 515
Jay, William: buildings by, 108
Jeffers Petroglyph Site (Minn.), 231
Jefferson, Thomas: and Bremo (Va.), 511; buildings by, 503, 506, 508, 511, 522, 528; career and accomplishments of, 503; and Farmington, 503; influence of on Goochland County Court Square, 513; and James Semple House, 533
Jefferson College (Washington, Miss.), 243
Jefferson Historic District (Jefferson, Tex.), 471
Jefferson Hotel (Richmond, Va.), 525
Jefferson Landing. *See* Lohman's Landing Building
Jefferson Memorial (Washington, D.C.), 86
Jefferson National Expansion Memorial National Historic Site (St. Louis, Mo.), 264
Jefferson Playhouse (Jefferson, Tex.), 471
Jeffries House. *See* Hansell, Augustine, House
Jenkins Ferry Battleground State Park (Ark.), 29
Jenney Stockade (Wyo.), 568
Jerome Historic District (Ariz.), 24
Joannes, Francis Y.: building by, 520
John Drayton House. *See* Drayton Hall
John Fitzgerald Kennedy National Historic Site (Brookline, Mass.), 207
John Jay House. *See* Gothic House
John Johnston Farm and Indian Agency. *See* Piqua Historical Area State Memorial
John Muir National Historic Site (Martinez, Calif.), 37
John Reynolds House. *See* Whitmarsh, Colonel Micah, House
Johnson, Andrew, 453

Johnson, John E.: building by, 507
Johnson, Sir William, 328
Johnson County Courthouse (Old Johnson County Courthouse) (Warrensburg, Mo.), 258
Johnson Hall (Johnstown, N.Y.), 328
Johnston, John, House (Sault Ste Marie, Mich.), 220
Johnston-Hay House (Macon, Ga.), 106
Johnstown Flood National Memorial (Pa.), 392
Jonathan Fisher Memorial (Blue Hill, Me.), 177
Jones, Edward C.: building by, 432
Jones, Harry Wild: building by, 232–33
Jones, Matthew, House (Newport News, Va.), 520
Jonesboro Historic District (Tenn.), 457
Jose de Jesus Vallejo Adobe. *See* California Nursery Company Guest House
Joseph (Nez Perce chief), 273
Joseph Henry Memorial. *See* Albany Academy
Joseph House (Columbus, Ga.), 112
Joy Homestead (Cranston, R.I.), 417
Juan De Anza House. *See* Anza House
Judah P. Benjamin Memorial. *See* Gamble, Robert, House
Judge Asa Holt House. *See* Cannonball House

K

Kamakahonu, Residence of King Kamehameha I (Hawaii), 119
Kamehameha I: 119, 120
Kanawha Canal. *See* James River and Kanawha Connection Locks and Canal
Kanawha Connection Locks. *See* James River and Kanawha Connection Locks and Canal
Karsner-Carroll House (Florence, Ala.), 5
Kaskaskia Village. *See* Old Kaskaskia Village
Kathio School Site. *See* Vineland Bay Site
Kathio Site (Vineland, Minn.), 234
Katz Building (Boley Building) (Kansas City, Mo.), 257
Kaunolu Village Site (Hawaii), 121
Kawaiahao Church and Mission Houses (Honolulu, Hawaii), 120
Keauhou Holua Slide (toboggan slide) (Hawaii), 119
Keet Seel (cliff dwelling). *See* Navajo National Monument
Keith-Brown Mansion and Carriage House (Salt Lake City, Utah), 485
Keller, Helen, Birthplace. *See* Ivy Green
Kelley, Jacob, House (S.C.), 432
Kelley, Oliver H., Homestead (Minn.), 237
Kelsey, Albert: building by, 88
Kenmore (house) (Fredericksburg, Va.), 512

U.S. GOVERNMENT PRINTING OFFICE : 1973 OLT–447–895

List of the Elements with Their Atomic Symbols and Atomic Weights

Name	Symbol	Atomic Number	Atomic Weight	Name	Symbol	Atomic Number	Atomic Weight
Actinium	Ac	89	227.028	Meitnerium	Mt	109	(268)
Aluminum	Al	13	26.9815	Mendelevium	Md	101	(258)
Americium	Am	95	(243)	Mercury	Hg	80	200.59
Antimony	Sb	51	121.757	Molybdenum	Mo	42	95.94
Argon	Ar	18	39.948	Neodymium	Nd	60	144.24
Arsenic	As	33	74.9216	Neon	Ne	10	20.1797
Astatine	At	85	(210)	Neptunium	Np	93	237.048
Barium	Ba	56	137.33	Nickel	Ni	28	58.69
Berkelium	Bk	97	(247)	Niobium	Nb	41	92.9064
Beryllium	Be	4	9.01218	Nitrogen	N	7	14.0067
Bismuth	Bi	83	208.9804	Nobelium	No	102	(259)
Bohrium	Bh	107	(264)	Osmium	Os	76	190.2
Boron	B	5	10.81	Oxygen	O	8	15.9994
Bromine	Br	35	79.904	Palladium	Pd	46	106.42
Cadmium	Cd	48	112.41	Phosphorus	P	15	30.9738
Calcium	Ca	20	40.078	Platinum	Pt	78	195.08
Californium	Cf	98	(251)	Plutonium	Pu	94	(244)
Carbon	C	6	12.011	Polonium	Po	84	(209)
Cerium	Ce	58	140.12	Potassium	K	19	39.0983
Cesium	Cs	55	132.905	Praseodymium	Pr	59	140.9077
Chlorine	Cl	17	35.4527	Promethium	Pm	61	(145)
Chromium	Cr	24	51.996	Protactinium	Pa	91	231.0399
Cobalt	Co	27	58.9332	Radium	Ra	88	226.0254
Copernicium	Cn	112	(285)	Radon	Rn	86	(222)
Copper	Cu	29	63.546	Rhenium	Re	75	186.207
Curium	Cm	96	(247)	Rhodium	Rh	45	102.9055
Darmstadtium	Ds	110	(271)	Roentgenium	Rg	111	(272)
Dubnium	Db	105	(262)	Rubidium	Rb	37	85.4678
Dysprosium	Dy	66	162.50	Ruthenium	Ru	44	101.07
Einsteinium	Es	99	(252)	Rutherfordium	Rf	104	(261)
Erbium	Er	68	167.26	Samarium	Sm	62	150.36
Europium	Eu	63	151.965	Scandium	Sc	21	44.9559
Fermium	Fm	100	(257)	Seaborgium	Sg	106	(266)
Fluorine	F	9	18.9984	Selenium	Se	34	78.96
Francium	Fr	87	(223)	Silicon	Si	14	28.0855
Gadolinium	Gd	64	157.25	Silver	Ag	47	107.8682
Gallium	Ga	31	69.72	Sodium	Na	11	22.98977
Germanium	Ge	32	72.61	Strontium	Sr	38	87.62
Gold	Au	79	196.9665	Sulfur	S	16	32.066
Hafnium	Hf	72	178.49	Tantalum	Ta	73	180.9479
Hassium	Hs	108	(269)	Technetium	Tc	43	(98)
Helium	He	2	4.00260	Tellurium	Te	52	127.60
Holmium	Ho	67	164.9304	Terbium	Tb	65	158.9254
Hydrogen	H	1	1.00794	Thallium	Tl	81	204.383
Indium	In	49	114.82	Thorium	Th	90	232.0381
Iodine	I	53	126.9045	Thulium	Tm	69	168.9342
Iridium	Ir	77	192.22	Tin	Sn	50	118.710
Iron	Fe	26	55.847	Titanium	Ti	22	47.88
Krypton	Kr	36	83.80	Tungsten	W	74	183.85
Lanthanum	La	57	138.9055	Uranium	U	92	238.0289
Lawrencium	Lr	103	(262)	Vanadium	V	23	50.9415
Lead	Pb	82	207.2	Xenon	Xe	54	131.29
Lithium	Li	3	6.941	Ytterbium	Yb	70	173.04
Lutetium	Lu	71	174.967	Yttrium	Y	39	88.9059
Magnesium	Mg	12	24.305	Zinc	Zn	30	65.39
Manganese	Mn	25	54.9380	Zirconium	Zr	40	91.224

Fundamentals of General, Organic, and Biological

CHEMISTRY

Fundamentals of General, Organic, and Biological

CHEMISTRY

Eighth Edition

John McMurry
Cornell University

David S. Ballantine
Northern Illinois University

Carl A. Hoeger
University of California, San Diego

Virginia E. Peterson
University of Missouri, Columbia

with contributions by
Sara Madsen

Editor-in-Chief: Jeanne Zalesky
Senior Acquisitions Editor: Chris Hess / Scott Dustan
Director of Development: Jennifer Hart
Product Marketing Manager: Elizabeth Ellsworth
Development Editor: Coleen Morrison
Program Manager: Sarah Shefveland
Project Manager: Beth Sweeten
Senior Media Producer: Jackie Jacob
Permissions Project Manager: William Opaluch
Permissions Specialist: Christina Simpson, QBS Learning
Program Management Team Lead: Kristen Flatham
Project Management Team Lead: David Zielonka
Production Management: Andrea Stefanowicz, Lumina Datamatics, Inc.
Compositor: Lumina Datamatics, Inc.
Design Manager: Mark Ong
Interior/Cover Designer: Tamara Newnam
Illustrators: Lachina
Photo Researcher: Eric Shrader
Operations Specialist: Maura Zaldivar-Garcia
Cover Photo Credit: *SEBASTIAN KAULITZKI/SPL/AGE Fotostock*

Library of Congress Cataloging-in-Publication Data
Fundamentals of general, organic, and biological chemistry / John McMurry, Cornell University
[and three others]; with contributions by Sara Madsen. — Eighth edition.
    pages cm
  Includes index.
    ISBN 978-0-13-401518-7
    ISBN 0-13-401518-5
  1. Chemistry—Textbooks.   I. McMurry, John. II. Madsen, Sara.
  QD31.3.M355 2017
  540—dc23
                                                            2015035819

2 16

www.pearsonhighered.com   ISBN 10: 0-13-401518-5; ISBN 13: 978-0-13-401518-7

About the Authors

 **John McMurry,** educated at Harvard and Columbia, has taught approximately 17,000 students in general and organic chemistry over a 30-year period. A professor of chemistry at Cornell University since 1980, Dr. McMurry previously spent 13 years on the faculty at the University of California at Santa Cruz. He has received numerous awards, including the Alfred P. Sloan Fellowship (1969–1971), the National Institute of Health Career Development Award (1975–1980), the Alexander von Humboldt Senior Scientist Award (1986–1987), and the Max Planck Research Award (1991).

 **David S. Ballantine** received his B.S. in Chemistry in 1977 from the College of William and Mary in Williamsburg, VA, and his Ph.D. in Chemistry in 1983 from the University of Maryland at College Park. After several years as a researcher at the Naval Research Labs in Washington, DC, he joined the faculty in the Department of Chemistry and Biochemistry of Northern Illinois University, where he has been a professor since 1989. He was awarded the Excellence in Undergraduate Teaching Award in 1998. Since then, he has served as the coordinator for the Introductory and General Chemistry programs, with responsibilities for supervision of supervising the laboratory teaching assistants. He served as the departmental director of undergraduate studies from 2008 to 2014 and is currently the associate dean for undergraduate affairs in the College of Liberal Arts and Sciences. He continues to teach in the Department of Chemistry and Biochemistry.

 **Carl A. Hoeger** received his B.S. in Chemistry from San Diego State University and his Ph.D. in Organic Chemistry from the University of Wisconsin–Madison in 1983. After a postdoctoral stint at the University of California–Riverside, he joined the Peptide Biology Laboratory at the Salk Institute in 1985, where he supervised the NIH Peptide Facility while doing basic research in the development of peptide agonists and antagonists. During this time, he also taught general, organic, and biochemistry at San Diego City College, Palomar College, and Miramar College. He joined the teaching faculty at University of California–San Diego (UCSD) in 1998. Dr. Hoeger has been teaching chemistry to undergraduates for 30 years, where he continues to explore the use of technology in the classroom; his current project involves the use of video podcasts as adjuncts to live lectures, along with the use of tablets to deliver real-time lectures with slide annotations. In 2004, he won the Barbara and Paul Saltman Distinguished Teaching Award from UCSD. He is deeply involved with both the general and organic chemistry programs at UCSD and has shared partial responsibility for the training and guidance of teaching assistants and new instructors in the Chemistry and Biochemistry department.

Virginia E. Peterson received her B.S. in Chemistry in 1967 from the University of Washington in Seattle and her Ph.D. in Biochemistry in 1980 from the University of Maryland at College Park. Between her undergraduate and graduate years, she worked in lipid, diabetes, and heart disease research at Stanford University. Following her Ph.D., she took a position in the Biochemistry Department at the University of Missouri in Columbia and is now professor emerita. When she retired in 2011, she had been the director of undergraduate advising for the department for 8 years and had taught both senior capstone classes and biochemistry classes for nonscience majors. Although retired, Dr. Peterson continues to advise undergraduates and teach classes. Awards include both the college-level and the university-wide Excellence in Teaching Award and, in 2006, the University's Outstanding Advisor Award and the State of Missouri Outstanding University Advisor Award. Dr. Peterson believes in public service and in 2003 received the Silver Beaver Award for service from the Boy Scouts of America. In retirement, she continues her public service activities by participating in a first-year medical student mentoring program and her more than 25-year commitment to the Boy Scouts of America as an active adult volunteer.

Sara K. Madsen received her B.S. in Chemistry at Central Washington University in Ellensburg, Washington, in 1988 and her Ph.D in Inorganic Chemistry at the University of Wyoming in 1998. She has been teaching since 2001. The beginning of her teaching career started with a one-semester survey course and moved from there to courses in general, organic, and biochemistry, general chemistry, organic and inorganic chemistry for undergraduates, and inorganic chemistry for graduate students. She loves helping students develop the connections between ideas and concepts and, above all, exposing their realization about how chemistry is involved in their program of study or professional path.

Brief Contents

Contents

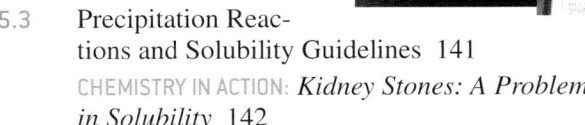

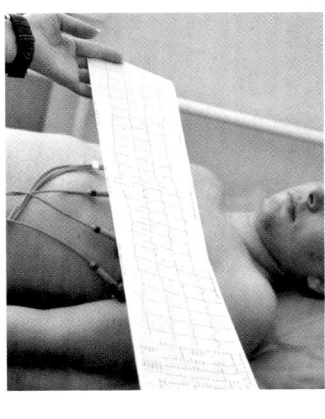

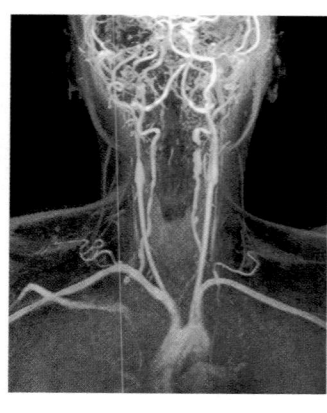

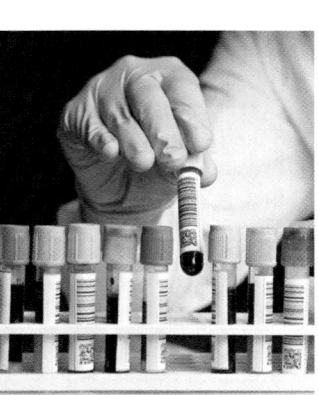

Features

Preface

This textbook and its related digital resources provide students in the allied health sciences with a needed background in chemistry and biochemistry while offering a general context for chemical concepts to ensure that students in other disciplines gain an appreciation of the importance of chemistry in everyday life.

To teach chemistry all the way from "What is an atom?" to "How do we get energy from glucose?" is a challenge. Throughout our general chemistry and organic chemistry coverage, the focus is on concepts fundamental to the chemistry of living things and everyday life. In our biochemistry coverage, we strive to meet the further challenge of providing a context for the application of those concepts in biological systems. Our goal is to provide enough detail for thorough understanding while avoiding so much detail that students are overwhelmed. Many practical and relevant examples are included to illustrate the concepts and enhance student learning.

The material covered is ample for a two-term introduction to general, organic, and biological chemistry. While the general and early organic chapters contain concepts that are fundamental to understanding the material in biochemistry, the later chapters can be covered individually and in an order that can be adjusted to meet the needs of the students and the duration of the course.

The writing style is clear and concise and punctuated with practical and familiar examples from students' personal experience. Art work, diagrams, and molecular models are used extensively to provide graphical illustration of concepts to enhance student understanding. Since the true test of knowledge is the ability to apply that knowledge appropriately, we include numerous worked examples that incorporate consistent problem-solving strategies.

Regardless of their career paths, all students will be citizens in an increasingly technological society. When they recognize the principles of chemistry at work not just in their careers but in their daily lives, they are prepared to make informed decisions on scientific issues based on a firm understanding of the underlying concepts.

New to This Edition

The major themes of this revision are active learning, an increased focus on clinical examples, updates based on current teaching and research findings, and digital innovations designed to engage and personalize the experience for students, all of which are accomplished in a variety of ways:

- **NEW! Chapter opening photos and vignettes** with an increased clinical focus have been added to provide a theme for each chapter and to strengthen connections between the concepts and applications in Chemistry in Action features in the chapter.
- **NEW! Chapters now have a more focused roadmap** that begins with specific learning objectives and ends with a summary study guide that addresses these initial goals and offers students targeted problems designed to help them assess their ability to understand those topics.
- **NEW! Hands-On Chemistry** boxes offer students an opportunity to solidify their understanding of chemistry through elementary experiments that can be safely done in their living spaces with household items. Many students strongly benefit from kinesthetic activities, and regardless of whether this is their "preferred" style, the evidence suggests that variety in exposure to concepts is by itself tremendously valuable.
- **NEW! Interactive Worked Examples** have been developed and are identified in the text with special icons, with video tutorials linked to the problem to help students master key concepts.
- **NEW! In-chapter questions have been added to the Chemistry in Action and Mastering Reactions** features to reinforce the connection between the chapter content and practical applications.

- **NEW! Concept Maps** have been added to most chapters, and others have been modified to draw connections between general, organic, and biological chemistry.
- **Updated Concept Links** offer visual reminders for students that indicate when new material builds on concepts from previous chapters or foreshadow related material that will be explained in more detail in future chapters.
- **Updated questions in the end-of-chapter section build on Concept Links** and require students to recall information learned in previous chapters.
- **Chemistry in Action** features (many with a clinical focus) extend the discussion of major chapter topics in new ways, providing students with enhanced perspective on core concepts relevant to their future careers.
- **All Learning Objectives tied to EOC problem sets:** Chapter summaries include a list of EOC problems that correspond to the learning objectives for a greater connection between problems and concepts.
- **NEW! Group Problems** at the end of every chapter are ideally used in class to get students to carefully think about higher level problems, such as how concepts fit together, or to put the concepts they have learned to use in a clinical application.
- **Chapters 1 and 2** have been restructured: Chapter 1 focuses on building math skills, while Chapter 2 focuses on matter, atomic structure, and the periodic table.
- **An expanded discussion of stereochemistry and chirality** has been moved to Chapter 14 to allow instructors and students more time to get used to this challenging topic before coming across it again in biochemistry. The concept of symmetry has also been introduced in this section.
- **Chapter 16 is now the chapter on amines**, allowing the discussion of organic bases and acids (Chapter 17) to flow together, whereas in the seventh edition, they were separated by the ketone and aldehyde chapter, which is now Chapter 15.
- **Chapter 20 is now the chapter on carbohydrates**, preceding the discussion of energy generation (now Chapter 21) and carbohydrate metabolism.
- **Chapter 25 is now the chapter on protein metabolism**, completing the discussions of metabolism before addressing DNA (Chapter 26) and Genomics (Chapter 27).

Organization

General Chemistry: Chapters 1–11 The introduction to elements, atoms, the periodic table, and the quantitative nature of chemistry (Chapters 1 and 2) is followed by chapters that individually highlight the nature of ionic and molecular compounds (Chapters 3 and 4). The next three chapters discuss chemical reactions and their stoichiometry, energies, rates, and equilibria (Chapters 5, 6, and 7). Topics relevant to the chemistry of life follow: Gases, Liquids, and Solids (Chapter 8); Solutions (Chapter 9); and Acids and Bases (Chapter 10). Nuclear Chemistry (Chapter 11) closes the general chemistry sequence.

Organic Chemistry: Chapters 12–17 These chapters concisely focus on what students must know in order to understand biochemistry. The introduction to hydrocarbons (Chapters 12 and 13) includes the basics of nomenclature, which is thereafter kept to a minimum. Discussion of functional groups with single bonds to oxygen, sulfur, or a halogen (Chapter 14) is followed by introducing aldehydes and ketones (Chapter 15), where a double bond between carbon and oxygen plays a key role in their chemistry. A short chapter on organic bases, the amines, which are so important to the chemistry of living things and drugs (Chapter 16) follows. Finally, the chemistry of carboxylic acids and their derivatives (esters and amides) is covered (Chapter 17), with a focus on similarities among the derivatives. Attention to the mechanisms by which organic reactions occur and the vernacular used to describe them has been retained in this edition. Stereochemistry, which is key to the understanding of how biological molecules function as they do, has been moved to Chapter 14 in this edition, allowing students more exposure to this complicated topic before reaching the biological chemistry section of this text.

Biological Chemistry: Chapters 18–29 Rather than proceeding through the complexities of protein, carbohydrate, lipid, and nucleic acid structure before getting to the roles of these compounds in the body, structure and function are integrated in this text. Protein structure (Chapter 18) is followed by enzyme and coenzyme chemistry (Chapter 19). Next, the structure and functions of common carbohydrates are introduced (Chapter 20). With enzymes and carbohydrates introduced, the central pathways and themes of biochemical energy production can be described (Chapter 21). If the time you have available to cover biochemistry is limited, stop with Chapter 21 and your students will have an excellent preparation in the essentials of metabolism. The following chapters cover more carbohydrate chemistry (Chapter 22), then lipid chemistry (Chapters 23 and 24), followed by protein and amino acid metabolism (Chapter 25). Next, we discuss nucleic acids and protein synthesis (Chapter 26) and genomics (Chapter 27). The last two chapters cover the function of hormones and neurotransmitters and the action of drugs (Chapter 28) and provide an overview of the chemistry of body fluids (Chapter 29).

Chapter-by-Chapter Changes

Coverage of General Chemistry

The major revisions in this section involve reorganization or revision of content to strengthen the connections between concepts and to provide a more focused coverage of specific concepts. Concept Maps, included in all general chemistry chapters, reinforce the relationship between topics.

Specific changes to chapters are provided below:

Chapter 1

- Content related to elements and the periodic table was moved to Chapter 2.
- Information on shape-memory alloys was added to the Chemistry in Action "Temperature Sensitive Materials" and the clinical information in the Chemistry in Action "Aspirin" and "A Measurement Example: Obesity and Body Fat" was updated.

Chapter 2

- Content from Chapter 1 on matter and the periodic table was moved to Chapter 2 to provide a more comprehensive and concentrated focus in the chapter.
- Information on the periodic table has been updated to reflect recent discoveries.
- A new Chemistry in Action, "Essential Elements and Group Chemistry," has been added. One Chemistry in Action was eliminated and "Are Atoms Real?" and "Atoms and Light" were revised to strengthen the connections between chapter content and clinical applications.

Chapter 3

- Sections have been reorganized to provide a more logical progression from ions and ion formation to the naming of ions and ionic compounds and finishing with the properties of ionic compounds. Coverage on the octet rule was also expanded and moved to earlier in the chapter.
- The Chemistry in Action "Salt" was streamlined to enhance clarity and relevancy to the student, and clinical information added.

Chapter 4

- Additional tables and text have been added, including a new Worked Example on coordinate covalent bonds, and some figures have been modified to enhance student learning of molecular models and molecular shape.
- Both the Chemistry in Action "VERY Big Molecules" and "Damascenone by Any Other Name Would Smell as Sweet" were updated with new clinical applications and photos.

Chapter 5

- Content from Section 5.3 from the seventh edition (Classes of Chemical Reactions) has been distributed to the individual sections dealing with the types of reactions: 5.3 (Precipitation Reactions), 5.4 (Neutralization Reactions), and 5.5 (Redox Reactions).
- Both Chemistry in Action were streamlined, and the Chemistry in Action "Batteries" was updated with relevant, new clinical applications.

Chapter 6

- The limiting reactant and percent yield discussion was expanded and clarified with new, specific examples to enhance student understanding.
- One Chemistry in Action was eliminated, and others were revised to strengthen the connections between chapter content and practical applications.

Chapter 7

- The quantitative aspects of spontaneity, entropy, enthalpy discussions (including the Worked Example) were revised to enhance clarity, and the Worked Example on drawing energy diagrams was simplified.
- One Chemistry in Action was eliminated, and the Chemistry in Action "Regulation of Body Temperature" was updated with new, practical applications.

Chapter 8

- The qualitative discussions on enthalpy and entropy in Section 8.1 were significantly streamlined.
- Section 8.13 from the seventh edition (Water: A Unique Liquid) has been deleted, and the content has been distributed to other sections to provide relevant examples for key concepts.
- The title to the last section (Section 8.14) was changed to "Change of State Calculations" to more clearly identify the focus for this section and to distinguish the content from the more general discussion on the changes of state of matter in Section 8.1.
- The Chemistry in Action "CO_2 as an Environmentally Friendly Solvent" was updated with new, cutting-edge information on supercritical fluids as they relate to allied health.

Chapter 9

- Section 9.3 (Solid Hydrates) was modified and converted into a new Chemistry in Action, "Solid Hydrates—Salt + Water."
- Section 9.10 from the seventh edition (Electrolytes in Body Fluids) has been modified in the eighth edition and combined with Section 9.9 (Ions in Solution: Electrolytes). References to gram-equivalents have been removed.
- The Chemistry in Action "Time-Release Drug Delivery Systems" was updated with new, clinical content.

Chapter 10

- Sections 10.1 (Acids and Bases in Aqueous Solution) and 10.3 (The Bronsted-Lowry Definition of Acids and Bases) have been combined to highlight the relationship between the various definitions of acids and bases.
- The information in Section 10.2 (Some Common Acids and Bases) has been condensed into Table 10.1.
- Section 10.7 (Measuring Acidity in Aqueous Solution: pH) and Section 10.9 (Laboratory Determinations of Acidity) have been combined to strengthen the connection between these concepts.
- Section 10.12 (Some Common Acid-Base Reactions) has been moved forward in the chapter, and Sections 10.10 (Buffer Solutions), 10.14 (Acidity and Basicity of

Salt Solutions), and 10.13 (Titrations) have been rearranged to improve the logical progression of these concepts.
- The Chemistry in Action "Acid Rain" was updated with new statistics, maps, and bar graphs.

- Section 11.6 (Radioactive Decay Series) was abbreviated and combined with Section 11.5 (Radioactive Half-Life). A new, additional Worked Example on half-lives was added as metadata indicated students struggled with this concept.
- Sections 11.8 (Detecting Radiation) and 11.9 (Measuring Radiation) were condensed and combined.

Coverage of Organic Chemistry

Since organic and biological chemistry are so tightly allied with one another, a major emphasis has been placed on the introduction of biologically significant molecules throughout the organic chapters in this edition. Emphasis on making the fundamental reactions that organic molecules undergo much clearer to the reader, with particular attention on those reactions encountered again in biochemical transformations has been retained in the Mastering Reactions feature boxes. This boxed feature discusses in relative depth the "how" behind a number of organic reactions. Mastering Reactions has been designed so that they may be integrated into an instructor's lecture or simply left out with no detriment to the material in the text itself, to accommodate those that do not wish to discuss the mechanisms of organic reactions. More emphasis on the use and evaluation of line-angle structure for organic molecules has been added, as this is incredibly important when discussing biomolecules. New to this edition is the inclusion of a more detailed examination of stereochemistry and chirality; its new placement at the end of Chapter 14 will allow students more time to grasp these concepts, but will also allow instructors who do not wish to discuss it to easily omit them. New and updated application features (Chemistry in Action) have been included in almost all the organic chapters, stressing the clinical aspects of the different classes of organic molecules and reflecting current understanding and research into the topics covered. Additionally, each chapter includes a new supplementary feature known as Integrated Worked Examples, which will provide students with tutor-like walkthroughs of topics and reactions they need to be familiar with before heading into the biological chemistry sections of this text.

Other specific changes to chapters are provided below:

- Several figures were revised and/or simplified for clarity and to enhance understanding. Art was added to help students synthesize complex topics where visuals were previously lacking.
- Table 12.1 has been reworked to highlight the atoms responsible for each functional group.
- Table 12.2 (Common Abbreviations in Organic Chemistry) has been added.
- A three-step mechanism (initiation, propagation, and termination) was added to the halogenation section along with a new Worked Example on drawing halogenated isomers; this Worked Example will be useful throughout the organic chapters in learning to draw isomers of other organic molecules.
- A new Chemistry in Action discussing biological methylation, "How Important Can a Methyl Group Really Be?," has been added, and the Chemistry in Action "Surprising Uses of Petroleum" was updated with new clinical information.
- There is an expanded functional group concept map that will aid in classifying functional groups; this will be included at the end of each of the organic chapters, with coloring added as each functional group family is discussed.

Chapter 13

- Expanded use and discussion of line structures has been added throughout.
- A new Chemistry in Action discussing biologically active alkynes, "Enediyne Antibiotics: A Newly Emerging Class of Antitumor Agents," has been added.

Chapter 14

- Table 14.1 (Common Alcohols and Their Uses) has been added, replacing and expanding on what was previously Section 14.3, making it easier for students to digest.
- A new and expanded discussion of stereochemistry and chirality has been added (Section 14.10), moving the introduction of these topics from Chapter 18 to a more appropriate location in the text.
- Two new Worked Examples, one on drawing alcohols, have been added.
- A new Chemistry in Action discussing the harm ethanol has on fetuses, "Fetal Alcohol Syndrome: Ethyl Alcohol as a Toxin," has been added.

Chapter 15

- Chapter 15, known previously as the amine chapter, now covers aldehydes and ketones.
- The section on common aldehydes and ketones has been shortened by the inclusion of Table 15.2 (Common Aldehydes and Ketones and Their Uses) making it easier for students to read.
- The Addition of Alcohols to Aldehydes and Ketones section was revised to clarify the distinction between hemiketals and hemiacetals.
- Worked Examples and problems have been modified to include the early introduction of carbohydrates.
- A new Chemistry in Action discussing anticancer drugs, "When Is Toxicity Beneficial?," has been added.

Chapter 16

- This is now the amine chapter, which was Chapter 15 in the seventh edition.
- The section on alkaloids has been simplified by the inclusion of Table 16.2 (Some Alkaloids and Their Properties) making it easier for students to digest the material.
- A new Worked Example on ammonium ions as acids has been included.
- A new Chemistry in Action discussing antidepressants, "Calming a Stormy Mind: Amines as Anti-Anxiety Medications," has been added.

Chapter 17

- The concept of pKa is discussed in Section 17.2; in addition, Table 17.2 now contains pKa values for the acids listed.
- Section 17.3 in the seventh edition has been expanded and converted into a new Chemistry in Action, "Medicinally Important Carboxylic Acids and Derivatives."
- The Worked Example on acid anhydrides has been removed and their coverage is limited in this edition.
- The Chemistry in Action "Medications, Body Fluids, and the 'Solubility Switch'" that was in Chapter 15 in the seventh edition has been updated and moved to the end of this chapter.

Coverage of Biological Chemistry

Biological chemistry, or biochemistry as professionals refer to the subject, is the chemistry of organisms and particularly chemistry at the cellular level—both inside and outside the cell. The foundations of biological chemistry are found in inorganic and organic chemistry, the first two major topics of this textbook. Biological chemistry integrates inorganic and organic chemistry in the study of biological molecules, many of which are large organic molecules with specific cellular roles. As you will see in the following chapters, biological molecules undergo the same reactions studied in the organic chemistry part of this book, and the fundamentals of inorganic chemistry are also important in cells.

Chapter 18

- The chapter was reorganized for a smoother flow that is more pedagogically sound. We now present an overview of proteins first, then discuss amino acids, peptides and peptide bonds, followed by protein structure and chemical properties. The one letter code for each amino acid was added to Table 18.3.
- The chirality discussion is limited to amino acids (the rest of this discussion moved to Chapter 14).
- Diagrams of the specific examples of the forces involved in tertiary protein structure were added.

Chapter 19

- Two new tables and a revised discussion enhance the "Enzyme Cofactors" section.
- The enzyme classification section has a new table describing each classification.
- The vitamins, minerals, and antioxidants section was streamlined for clarity.
- A Mastering Reactions on how to read biochemical reactions has been added.
- The Chemistry in Action "Enzymes in Medical Diagnosis" was updated to reflect current blood chemistry tests used in diagnosis of a heart attack.

Chapter 20

- This is now the carbohydrates chapter.
- Two new tables, one on important monosaccharides and another on disaccharides, make this content easy for students to digest. Both polysaccharides sections were streamlined and combined into one section.

Chapter 21

- This is now the generation of biological energy chapter.
- The first two sections were streamlined by reducing much of the review material from Chapter 7 (a Concept to Review link was added in place of lengthy narrative, directing students back to where they can review the material if necessary) and combined into one section.
- The citric acid cycle is now explained equation by equation with the description of each step directly above the equation for better student understanding.
- The section on reactive oxygen species has been converted into a new Chemistry in Action, "Reactive Oxygen Species and Antioxidant Vitamins."
- The discussion of "uncouplers" has been integrated into a new Chemistry in Action, "Metabolic Poisons."

Chapter 22

- The discussion of the steps in glycolysis was improved by explicitly splitting the descriptions of the reactions into individual steps.
- Most of the discussion of glucose metabolism in diabetes has been moved to a revised and now comprehensive Chemistry in Action "Diagnosis and Monitoring of Diabetes."

Chapter 23

- The Phospholipids and Glycolipids section was reorganized to ensure a smoother, more logical presentation of concepts.
- The Chemistry in Action "Lipids in the Diet" was updated to include some information from the deleted Chemistry in Action "Butter and Its Substitutes" as well as updated dietary and obesity statistics.

- The text discussion of eicosanoids was converted into a new Chemistry in Action, "Eicosanoids: Prostaglandins and Leucotrienes."

Chapter 24

- A clearer explanation of fatty acid activation and beta-oxidation is presented step-by-step with the appropriate biochemical reaction shown with each step's description.
- The discussion of energy yields from fat metabolism was converted into two sequential Worked Examples.
- The Chemistry in Action "Lipids and Atherosclerosis" was combined with information from the deleted Chemistry in Action "Fat Storage: A Good Thing or Not?" and updated to give a new Chemistry in Action, "Fat Storage, Lipids, and Atherosclerosis."

Chapter 25

- This chapter, Protein and Amino Acid Metabolism, was Chapter 27 in the seventh edition.
- The Chemistry in Action "The Importance of Essential Amino Acids and Effects of Deficiencies" on essential amino acids has been updated with new clinical information and streamlined.

Chapter 26

- Changes were made to the figure showing DNA replication to clarify copying of the opposite strands.
- The Chemistry in Action "Influenza: Variations on a Theme" now focuses on the nature of the common influenza viruses, primarily type A, and zoonotic pools for the mutating virus.

Chapter 27

- This chapter, "Genomics," was Chapter 26 in the seventh edition.
- The Chemistry in Action on the polymerase chain reaction has been shortened and streamlined.
- The Chemistry in Action "DNA Fingerprinting" has been updated to include PCR fingerprinting.

Chapter 28

- This chapter is now focused only on the messenger aspect of these peptides, amino acid derivatives, and steroids.
- Table 28.2, "Acetylcholine Drug Family" (therapeutic or poisonous), has been added to clarify this section for students.
- The steroid-abuse section was condensed to increase relevance for the student.

Chapter 29

- A new Chemistry in Action on common blood tests, "What's in Your Blood Test?," has been added and the Chemistry in Action "Blood–Brain Barrier" was updated with new clinical information.

Acknowledgments

Although this text is now in its eighth edition, each revision has aspired to improve the quality and accuracy of the content and emphasize its relevance to the student users. Achieving this goal requires the coordinated efforts of a dedicated team of editors and media experts. Without them, this textbook would not be possible.

On behalf of all my coauthors, I would like to thank Jeanne Zalesky (Editor in Chief), Chris Hess (Senior Acquisitions Editor) and Scott Dustan (Senior Acquisitions Editor) for building an excellent team for this project. Thanks also to Andrea Stefanowicz (Production Manager), Eric Schrader (Photo Researcher), Sarah Shefveland (Program Manager), and Lindsey Pruett (Editorial Assistant) for their attention to detail as we moved forward. Coleen Morrison, our developmental editor, deserves special recognition for providing invaluable feedback—her painstaking perusal of each chapter and her eye for details have contributed greatly to the accessibility and relevance of the text. Very special thanks also to Beth Sweeten, Senior Project Manager, who patiently guided the process and worked closely with us—thank you for your flexibility and dedication to the success of this project.

The value of this text has also been enhanced by the many individuals who have worked to improve the ancillary materials. Particular thanks to Emily Halvorson for her efforts to ensure the accuracy of the answers to problems provided in the text and Susan McMurry for her revisions to the solutions manual. Thanks to Kyle Doctor, Jackie Jakob, Sara Madsen and Dario Wong for their work on the media supplements. Thanks also to Margaret Trombley, Kristin Mayo, and Jayne Sportelli for their efforts to expand and improve MasteringChemistry™.

Finally, thank you to the many instructors and students who have used the seventh edition and have provided valuable insights and feedback to improve the accuracy of the current edition. We gratefully acknowledge the following reviewers for their contributions to the eighth edition.

Accuracy Reviewers of the Eighth Edition

Martin Wallace, *Butte College*
Erik Wasinger, *California State University, Chico*

Reviewers of the Eighth Edition

Pamela Abbott, *Lewis and Clark Community College–Godfrey*
Julie Abrahamson, *University of North Dakota*
Angela Allen, *Lenoir Community College*
Mary Alvarez, *Salt Lake Community College*
Vicki Audia, *Blue Ridge Community College*
Chris Bibeau, *Radford University*
Alan Bruha, *Lewis and Clark Community College–Godfrey*
Adam Brunet, *American International College*
Charmita Burch, *Georgia Gwinnett College*
Michael Finnegan, *Washington State University*
Luther Giddings, *Salt Lake Community College*
Karin Hassenrueck, *California State University–Northridge*
Lissa Huston, *Radford University*
Frederick Joslin, *Eastern Washington University*
Michael Julian, *Pulaski Technical College*
Ashley Lamm, *Eastern Washington University*
Gregory Marks, *Carroll University*
G. Patrick Meier, *Spokane Falls Community College*
Brenda Miller, *Ohio University, Chillicothe*
Joshua Mukhlall, *Queens College*
Melekeh Nasiri, *Woodland Community College*
Linda Nuss, *Sacramento City College*
Jackie Perry, *Southwestern Michigan College*
Elizabeth Pollock, *Stockton University*
Elizabeth S. Roberts-Kirchoff, *University of Detroit–Mercy*

David Rogers, *North Central Michigan College*
Mir Shamsuddin, *Loyola University*
Heather Sklenicka, *Rochester Community and Technical College*
Lucinda Spryn, *Thomas Nelson Community College*

Reviewers of the Previous Editions

Sheikh Ahmed, *West Virginia University*
Stanley Bajue, *CUNY–Medgar Evers College*
Daniel Bender, *Sacramento City College*
Dianne A. Bennett, *Sacramento City College*
Francis Burns, *Ferris State University*
Alfredo Castro, *Felician College*
Gezahegn Chaka, *Louisiana State University, Alexandria*
Michael Columbia, *Indiana University-Purdue University–Fort Wayne*
Lisa L. Crozier, *Northeast Wisconsin Technical Center*
Rajeev B. Dabke, *Columbus State University*
Robert P. Dixon, *Southern Illinois University, Edwardsville*
Danae R. Quirk Dorr, *Minnesota State University, Mankato*
Pamela S. Doyle, *Essex County College*
Marie E. Dunstan, *York College of Pennsylvania*
Karen L. Ericson, *Indiana University-Purdue University–Fort Wayne*
Charles P. Gibson, *University of Wisconsin, Oshkosh*
Luther Giddings, *Salt Lake Community College*
Arlene Haffa, *University of Wisconsin, Oshkosh*
Mildred V. Hall, *Clark State Community College*
Meg Hausman, *University of Southern Maine*
Ronald Hirko, *South Dakota State University*
L. Jaye Hopkins, *Spokane Community College*

Margaret Isbell, *Sacramento City College*
James T. Johnson, *Sinclair Community College*
Margaret G. Kimble, *Indiana University-Purdue University–Fort Wayne*
Grace Lasker, *Lake Washington Technical College*
Ashley Mahoney, *Bethel University*
Mohammad Mahroof, *Saint Cloud State University*
Gregory Marks, *Carroll University*
Matthew G. Marmorino, *Indiana University–South Bend*
Diann Marten, *South Central College–Mankato*
Barbara D. Mowery, *York College of Pennsylvania*
Tracey Arnold Murray, *Capital University*
Andrew M. Napper, *Shawnee State University*
Lisa Nichols, *Butte Community College*

Glenn S. Nomura, *Georgia Perimeter College*
Van Quach, *Florida State University*
Douglas E. Raynie, *South Dakota State University*
Paul D. Root, *Henry Ford Community College*
Victor V. Ryzhov, *Northern Illinois University*
Karen Sanchez, *Florida Community College–Jacksonville South*
Mir Shamsuddin, *Loyola University, Chicago*
Jeanne A. Stuckey, *University of Michigan*
John Sullivan, *Highland Community College*
Deborah E. Swain, *North Carolina Central University*
Susan T. Thomas, *University of Texas–San Antonio*
Richard Triplett, *Des Moines Area Community College*
Yakov Woldman, *Valdosta State University*

The authors are committed to maintaining the highest quality and accuracy and look forward to comments from students and instructors regarding any aspect of this text and supporting materials. Questions or comments should be directed to the lead coauthor.

David S. Ballantine
dballant@niu.edu

Active learning, an increased focus on clinical examples, updates based on current teaching and research findings, and digital innovations designed to engage and personalize students' experiences make the eighth edition of *Fundamentals of General, Organic, and Biological Chemistry* simply the best choice for students with a future in allied health.

NEW! Chapter-opening stories and visuals throughout the text have a greater clinical focus, providing even more relevance to allied health majors. Throughout the chapters, Learning Objectives follow each section head, and each chapter ends with a summary study guide offering students targeted problems designed to help them assess their ability to understand those topics.

CHEMISTRY IN ACTION boxes (many with a clinical focus) extend the discussion of major chapter topics in new ways, providing students with an enhanced perspective on core concepts relevant to their future careers. The final Chemistry in Action box in each chapter ties back to the chapter-opening topic, ensuring the clinical relevancy is woven throughout the chapter from beginning to end.

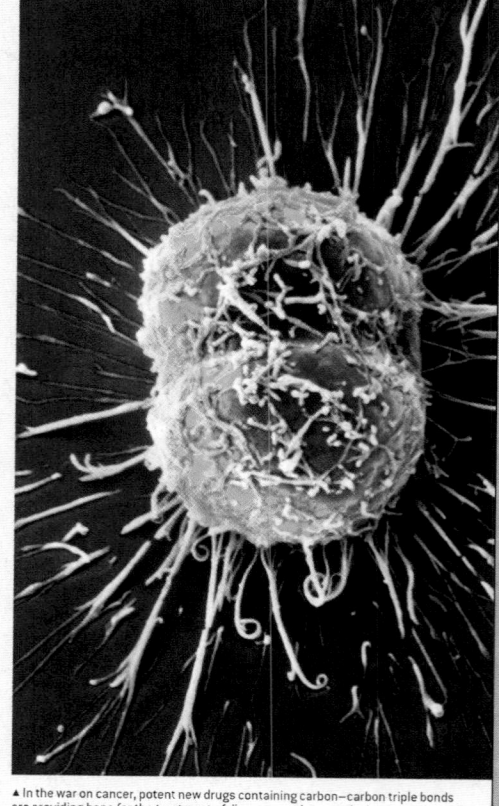

13

Alkenes, Alkynes, and Aromatic Compounds

CONTENTS

◀◀ CONCEPTS TO REVIEW

▲ In the war on cancer, potent new drugs containing carbon–carbon triple bonds are providing hope for the treatment of diseases such as cervical cancer.

Functional groups give organic molecules their characteristic physical, chemical, and biological properties. In Chapter 12, we examined the simplest hydrocarbons, alkanes, which provide the scaffolding upon which the complicated molecules responsible for life are built. Now we will look at the chemistry of molecules that contain carbon–carbon multiple bonds, or *unsaturated* hydrocarbons. While alkenes and aromatic systems are found in many naturally occurring biomolecules, alkynes are not as commonly observed. However, when

CHEMISTRY IN ACTION

↑ **Enediyne Antibiotics: A Newly Emerging Class of Antitumor Agents**

While we discuss alkynes only briefly in this chapter and this text as a whole, it is not because alkynes are not important in organic chemistry. Alkynes are not usually found in nature; however, when they are isolated from natural sources, such as plants and bacteria, they have unexpected physiological properties, including toxicity. For example, ichthyothereol, a trialkyne, isolated from the leaves of a small herb found in the Amazon and Central America, inhibits energy production in mitochondria, and while being toxic to fish, mice, and dogs, has no effect on humans. This has caused chemists to investigate what might happen if the alkyne function were introduced into other biologically active molecules, which has led to the discovery of pharmaceuticals such as Rasagiline, a monoamine oxidase inhibitor effective in treating Parkinson's disease. This compound, due to its neuroprotective nature, is also offering a novel approach to Alzheimer's drug therapy. Rasagiline seems to enhance memory and learning, while also improving mood, motivation, and age-related memory decline and provides a great lead for the discovery of new medicines to treat this debilitating disease. Due to successes such as Rasagiline, chemists and biochemists have intensified the hunt for naturally occurring alkynes. This expanding pursuit for new alkyne-containing natural products has led to the discovery of a very unlikely class of antitumor antibiotics known as the enediynes, which we first learned about at the beginning of the chapter. Initially discovered in a fermentation broth derived

from the bacteria *Micromonospora*, they represent a new chemical structure class for antibiotics.

Ichthyothereol

Rasagiline

The enediyne family of compounds represents the most potent antitumor agents known. The toxic nature of these compounds arises from their ability to cause scission of DNA strands in their target. The enediyne antibiotics fall into three basic families: the calicheamicins, the dynemicins (shown next), and the most complex of the group, the chromoproteins. All members have three distinct regions within them: (1) an anthraquinone-like portion; (2) a chemical "warhead" comprised of two triple bonds, conjugated through a double

Dynemicin A

bond, within a 9–10-membered ring; and (3) a "trigger." In Dynemicin A (shown above), that trigger is the three-membered epoxide ring (highlighted in red). The anthraquinone portion intercalates into the major groove of DNA; the trigger is then activated by some nucleophilic species (such as an oxygen, nitrogen, or sulfur atom) that attacks and then opens the epoxide ring. Once opened, the warhead undergoes a rearrangement reaction, producing an extremely reactive diradical species, which then induces the breakage of the DNA strands.

All of the enediynes are very toxic, as are all antitumor agents. One way to utilize them in the war on cancer would be to attach them to an antibody specifically prepared to target the tumor cells the doctor wishes to destroy. This method, known as

"immunotargeting," would allow the preparation of a "magic bullet," which would attack only the tumor cells and nothing else. One of the reasons that the enediyne antibiotics are so attractive is that they have activity against drug-resistant tumors. Many cancer cells have natural resistance to a number of the drugs usually used to treat them or will develop resistance over the course of a treatment. This, coupled with a lack of selectivity to antitumor agents (antitumor drugs affect all cells, not just cancer) is one of the major causes of the ineffectiveness of anticancer therapies. Compounds such as Dynemicin A and others discovered through studies of the enediynes could represent a new weapon in our assault on an old and deadly foe: cancer.

▶▶ The meaning of the wedged and dashed bonds will be clarified in Section 14.10 when we discuss stereochemistry.

CIA Problem 13.4 What beneficial properties of Rasagiline make it useful for the treatment of Alzheimer's disease?

CIA Problem 13.5 Why would attaching an enediyne-containing molecule to an antibody be an attractive way to treat cancer cells?

CIA Problem 13.6 What are the major causes of the ineffectiveness of anticancer therapies?

NEW! These boxes now include questions at the end of the narrative, designed specifically as engaging checkpoints to help students asses their understanding.

Active Learning Leads to Conceptual Understanding

Fundamentals of General, Organic, and Biological Chemistry has always provided a remarkably clear introduction to the broad subject of allied health chemistry in an appealing, applied, and precise manner. In the eighth edition, the authors make learning chemistry more active through features designed to get students doing chemistry.

HANDS-ON CHEMISTRY 3.1

Obtain a set of Lego building blocks and separate them **into groups** that are one, two, and three units long (if you do not have access to a physical set of blocks, visit www.buildwithchrome .com/builder). The blocks will represent anions and cations that have charges of 1, 2, and 3, respectively. If possible, try to have multiple colors within each group. Label the blocks in each group as follows:

—One unit long: Label as Na^+, K^+, Cl^-, and NO_3^-.
—Two units long: Label as Mg^{2+}, Ca^{2+}, Fe^{2+}, O^{2-}, and SO_4^{2-}.
—Three units long: Label as Al^{3+}, Fe^{3+}, N^{3-}, and PO_4^{3-}.

Try to have at least three blocks for each ion in a given group and, if possible, keep the colors consistent for a given ion; for example, let all Na^+ ions be black, all Cl^- ions be yellow, all O^{2-} ions be blue, and so on.

Using the blocks, assemble the following compound[s] matching anion and cation blocks. Starting with the ca[tion]

block, connect an anion on top of it. If the anion layer is not long enough for the two layers to match up exactly, add another anion of the same type beside it on top of the cation layer. If the anion layer extends over the end of the cation layer, add another cation to the bottom layer. When the cation and anion layers match exactly in length, count how many of the cation and anion blocks were necessary to determine the formula of the ionic compound.

Try building the compounds suggested next, or make up your own combinations. Just be sure that each compound has a cation and an anion!

a) Cation = Na^+ Anion = SO_4^{2-}
b) Cation = Fe^{2+} Anion = NO_3^-
c) Cation = Mg^{2+} Anion = PO_4^{3-}

NEW! **HANDS-ON CHEMISTRY** boxes offer students an opportunity to solidify their understanding of chemistry through elementary experiments that can be safely done in their home with household items. Many students strongly benefit from kinesthetic activities, and regardless of whether this is their preferred style, evidence suggests that variety in exposure to concepts is tremendously valuable.

HANDS-ON CHEMISTRY 19.1

Do food items contain active catalase? You can test this at home with samples of raw meat and vegetables. You will need clear (not colored), transparent glasses, 3% hydrogen peroxide (from a drugstore or grocery store), and a few 1 cm cubes of raw meat such as chicken liver or a bit of hamburger. Also cube some raw potato. Drop some of the raw meat in a glass with an inch or two of hydrogen peroxide in it. Using a different glass of hydrogen peroxide, do the same thing with potato cubes. What happened with the meat? With the potato? Does the amount of meat or potato used matter? Repeat your experiment with cooked meat and cooked potato. What happened?

Evolution of bubbles means catalase present in the sample was converting hydrogen peroxide to water and oxygen; the enzyme was active, in its native state and not denatured. If no significant amount of bubbles appeared, catalase was either absent or inactive. Based on the results of the trials with raw samples, was catalase absent or inactive? If inactive, why?

GROUP PROBLEMS

2.95 Look up one of the experiments by the scientists discussed in the Chemistry in Action on page 44, and explain how it contributed to our understanding of atomic structure.

2.96 Do a web search to identify each of the following elements/isotopes and indicate the number of neutrons, protons, and electrons in an atom of the element/isotope:

(a) A radioactive isotope used in cancer treatments? (There may be more than one answer!)

(b) The element having the greatest density.

(c) An element with $Z < 90$ that is *not* found in nature.

2.97 Tellurium ($Z = 52$) has a *lower* atomic number than iodine ($Z = 53$), yet it has a *higher* atomic weight (127.60 amu for Te vs. 126.90 amu for I). How is this possible? Can you find any other instances in the periodic table where two adjacent elements exhibit a similar behavior, that is, the element with the lower atomic number has a higher atomic mass?

2.98 Look again at the trends illustrated in Figures 2.3 and 2.4.

(a) How do the peaks/valleys correlate with locations in the periodic table?

(b) Are there other chemical properties that also exhibit periodic trends? What are they?

NEW! **GROUP PROBLEMS** at the end of every chapter are ideally used in class to get students to carefully think about higher level problems, such as how concepts fit together, or to put the concepts they have learned to use in a clinical application.

Integrated Learning Pathway

Chapters now have a more integrated narrative where Learning Objectives provide a starting point and are later revisited as capstones to the chapter in summary and question form.

Measurable **LEARNING OBJECTIVES** are listed as bullet points underneath each chapter section within the text.

18.2 Proteins and Their Functions: An Overview

Learning Objective:

• Describe the different functions of proteins and give an example for each function.

The word *protein* is a familiar one. Taken from the Greek *proteios*, meaning "primary," "protein" is an apt description for the biological molecules that are of primary importance to all living organisms. Approximately 50% of your body's dry weight is protein.

What roles do proteins play in living things? No doubt you are aware that a hamburger is produced from animal muscle protein and that we depend on our own muscle proteins for every move we make. But this is only one of many essential roles of proteins. They provide *structure* (keratin) and *support* (actin filaments) to tissues and organs throughout our bodies. As *hormones* (oxytocin) and *enzymes* (catalase), they control all aspects of metabolism. In body fluids, water-soluble proteins pick up other molecules for *storage* (casein) or *transport* (transferrin, Fe^{3+}). And the proteins of the immune system provide *protection* (Immunoglobulin G) against invaders such as bacteria and viruses. To accomplish their biological functions, which are summarized in Table 18.2, some proteins must be tough and fibrous, whereas others must be globular molecule, as you will see t protein in our metabolism.

SUMMARY REVISITING THE LEARNING OBJECTIVES

• **Describe the different functions of proteins and give an example for each function.** Proteins can be grouped by function such as structural, transport, etc. See Table 18.2 *(see Problems 1, 2, 40, and 41)*.

• **Describe and recognize the 20 alpha amino acid structures and their side chains.** Amino acids in body fluids have an ionized carboxylic acid group (—COO⁻), an ionized amino group (—NH₃⁺), and a side-chain R group bonded to a central carbon atom (the α-carbon). Twenty different amino acids occur in *proteins* (Table 18.3) *(see Problems 3–6, 38, and 42–45)*.

• **Categorize amino acids by the polarity or neutrality of the side chain and predict which are hydrophilic and which are hydrophobic.** Amino acid side chains have acidic or basic functional groups or neutral groups that are either polar or nonpolar. Side chains that form hydrogen bonds with water are hydrophilic; nonpolar side chains that do not form hydrogen bonds with water are hydrophobic *(see Problems 7–9, 50–51, 110, and 111)*.

• **Explain chirality and identify which amino acids are chiral.** All α-amino acids except glycine are chiral *(see Problems 10–12, 39, and 42–51)*.

• **Draw all ionic structures for an amino acid under acidic and basic conditions; identify the zwitterion.** The dipolar ion in which an amino group and a carboxylic acid group are both ionized is known as a zwitterion and the electrical charge on the molecule is zero. For each amino acid, there is a distinctive *isoelectric point*—the pH a

the numbers of positive and negative charges in a solution are equal. At a more acidic pH, all carboxylic acid groups are protonated; at a more basic pH, all amino groups are protonated *(see Problems 13, 14, 34, and 52–59)*.

• **Identify a peptide bond and explain how it is formed.** The amide bond formed between the carboxyl group of one amino acid with the amino group of a second amino acid is called a peptide bond *(see Problems 15–19, 36, and 60–65)*.

• **Draw and name a simple protein structure, given its amino acid sequence.** Peptides are named by combining the names of the amino acids. Amino acid sequences are often represented by using the three-letter or one-letter abbreviations for the amino acids in a left to right order *(see Problems 15–19, 36, and 60–65)*.

• **Identify the amino-terminal end and the carboxyl-terminal end of a simple protein (peptide) structure given its amino acid sequence.** Amino acid sequences are written with the amino group of the end amino acid on the left and the carboxyl group of the amino acid on the other end of the chain on the right *(see Problems 15–19, 36, and 60–65)*.

• **Define protein primary structure and explain how primary structures are represented.** Protein *primary structure* is the sequence in which the amino acids are connected by peptide bonds. Using formulas or amino acid abbreviations, the primary structures are written with the amino terminal end on the left and the carboxyl-

Each chapter concludes with a summary study guide section that restates the Learning Objectives for each section and lists problems students can do to practice the skills learned for each objective.

PROTEINS AND THEIR FUNCTIONS: AN OVERVIEW (SECTION 18.2)

18.40 Name four biological functions of proteins in the human body, and give an example of a protein for each function.

18.41 What kind of biological function would each of the following proteins perform?

(a) Human growth hormone   (b) Myosin

(c) Protease   (d) Myoglobin

AMINO ACIDS (SECTION 18.3)

18.42 What amino acids do the following abbreviations stand for? Draw the structure of each.

(a) Val   (b) Ser   (c) Glu

18.43 What amino acids do the following abbreviations stand for? Draw the structure of each.

(a) Ile   (b) Thr   (c) Gln

18.44 Name and draw the structures of the amino acids that fit the following descriptions:

(a) Contains a thiol group   (b) Contains a phenol group

18.45 Name and draw the structures of the amino acids that fit the following descriptions:

(a) Contains an isopropyl group

(b) Contains a secondary alcohol group

End-of-chapter problems tie back to chapter Learning Objectives, allowing students to test their knowledge of emphasized topics. Metadata, drawn from MasteringChemistry usage, on which problems students struggled with most was used to revise both in-chapter and end-of-chapter problems. Further revisions were made to end-of-chapter problems, where applicable, to increase clinical relevancy.

Personalize Learning with MasteringChemistry™

NEW! A strengthened relationship with MasteringChemistry helps students develop conceptual understanding before, during, and after class.

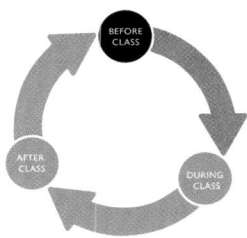

BEFORE CLASS

Chapter-specific quizzes and activities focus on important, hard-to-grasp chemistry concepts.

---

16 Aldehydes and Ketones | Chapter 16 Reading Quiz Question 1 | Resources ▼

Item Type: Reading Questions | Difficulty: 1 | Time: 1m | ✉ Contact the Publisher | Manage this Item: Standard View ▼

Chapter 16 Reading Quiz Question 1

Part A

Which of the following families of organic compounds is classified as a carbonyl compound?

○ ether
● alcohol
○ ester
○ amine

Submit Hints My Answers Give Up Review Part

Incorrect; Try Again; no points deducted

Alcohol contains an –OH group that is singly bonded to carbon. See (□ page 485).

Drawing Constitutional Isomers of hexane; C_6H_{14}

STRAIGHT CHAIN ALKANE

1st new constitutional isomer

same as →

NEW! **VIDEO TUTOR SOLUTIONS** offer students critical thinking strategies for each problem type presented in the text. These examples are accompanied by an analysis, which carefully describes the best approach for solving problems of each kind.

NEW! **DYNAMIC STUDY MODULES** help students study effectively on their own by continuously assessing their activity and performance in real time. Students initially answer a subset of questions, indicating their confidence level for each answer.

At the end of this and each subsequent subset, students are given explanations for any problems they missed as well as coaching that moves them toward conceptual understanding. This recursive process continues until students answer all questions in the module correctly and confidently. Dynamic Study Modules are available as graded assignments for use prior to class, and are accessible on smartphones, tablets, and computers.

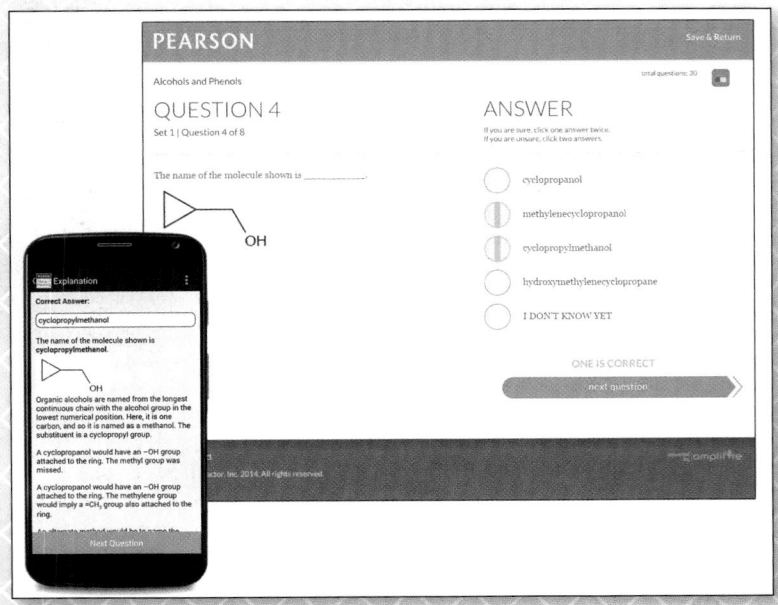

DURING CLASS

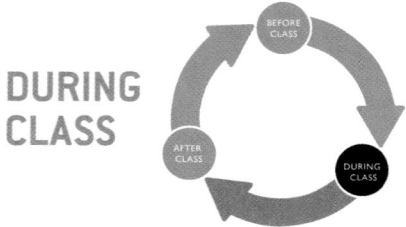

NEW! **LEARNING CATALYTICS**™ generates class discussion, guides your lecture, and promotes peer-to-peer learning with real-time analytics. MasteringChemistry with eText now provides Learning Catalytics—an interactive student response tool that uses students' smartphones, tablets, or laptops to engage them in more sophisticated tasks and thinking.

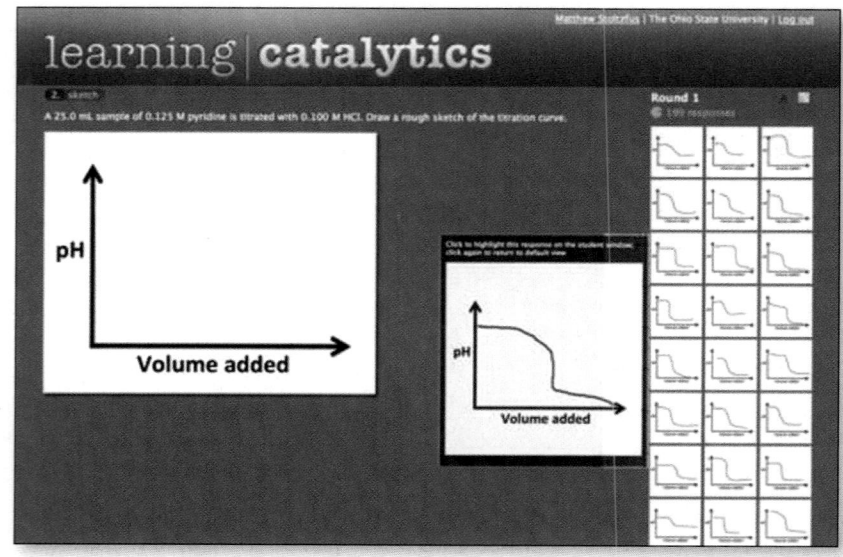

AFTER CLASS

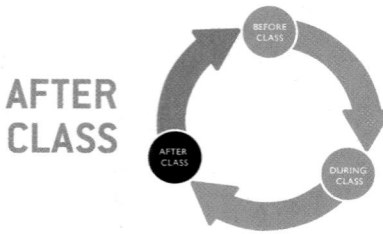

End-of-chapter problems within the textbook are available within MasteringChemistry™ and can be automatically graded and assigned for homework or practice. *New to this edition, 300 problems contain enhanced, wrong answer feedback.*

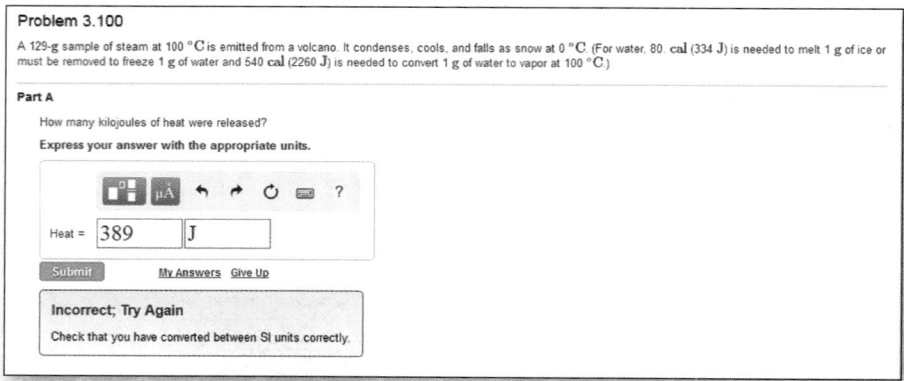

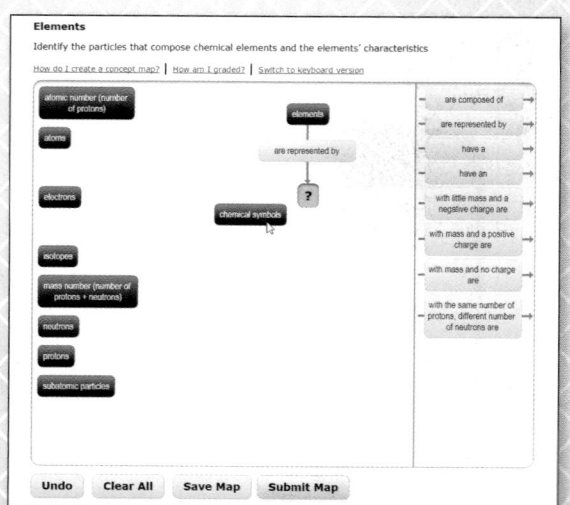

CONCEPT MAP ACTIVITIES

use interactive concept maps and related multiple-choice quiz questions to help students make connections between important concepts within each chapter.

Instructor and Student Resources

Name of Supplement	Available in Print	Available Online	Instructor or Student Supplement	Description
Instructor Resource Manual 0134283171 / 9780134283173		✓	Instructor	The IRM features lecture outlines with presentation suggestions, teaching tips, suggested in-class demonstrations, topics for classroom discussion, and answers to group problems.
TestGen Test Bank 013426147X / 9780134261478		✓	Instructor	The test bank has been updated to reflect revisions in this text, and contains more than 2,000 multiple choice, true/false, matching, and short answer questions.
Instructor's Resource Materials 0134261267 / 9780134261263		✓	Instructor	The Instructor Resource area provides the following downloadable resources: All illustrations, tables and photos from the text in JPEG format, and pre-built PowerPoint® Presentations (lecture–including Worked Examples, images).
Study Guide and Full Solutions Manual 0134261372 / 9780134261379	✓		Student	This manual, prepared by Susan McMurry, provides solutions to all problems in the text. It explains in detail how the answers to the in-text and end-of-chapter problems are obtained. It also contains chapter summaries, study hints, and self-tests for each chapter.

1

Matter and Measurements

CONTENTS

▲ The percentage of body fat can be determined by underwater immersion, which takes advantage of the differences in density of fat as compared to muscle and bone.

According to the U.S. Centers for Disease Control and Prevention, the U.S. population is suffering from a fat epidemic, with more than one-third (34.9% or 78.6 million) of U.S. adults characterized as obese. But how do we define obesity, and how is it measured? Obesity is defined as an excessive amount of body fat. But some body fat is important for good health, so how much body fat is healthy and how much is too much? What is fat, and how do we measure it? Body fat can be estimated using a Body Mass Index (BMI) as discussed later in the chapter, or can be measured directly using underwater immersion, or buoyancy testing, as illustrated in the photo above. The immersion tank uses buoyancy—a property related to the differences in density—to determine the percentage of body fat. Checking the observed buoyancy on a standard table then gives an estimation of body fat. Density is just one of the concepts we will explore in this chapter, as we learn about the properties of matter and the various forms that matter can take.

The ancient philosophers believed that all matter was composed of four fundamental substances—earth, air, fire, and water. We now know that matter is much more complex, made up of 91 naturally occurring fundamental substances, or elements, in millions of unique combinations. Everything you see, touch, taste, and smell is made of chemicals formed from these elements. Many chemicals occur naturally, but others are synthetic, including the plastics, fibers, and medicines that are so critical to modern life. Just as everything you see is made of chemicals, many of the natural changes you observe taking place around you are the result of *chemical reactions*—the change of one chemical into another. The crackling fire of a log burning in the fireplace, the color change of a leaf in the fall, and the changes that a human body undergoes as it grows and ages are all results of chemical reactions. To understand these and other natural processes, you must have a basic understanding of chemistry.

As you might expect, the chemistry of living organisms is complex, and it is not possible to understand all concepts without a proper foundation. Thus, we will gradually learn to connect the basic concepts, beginning in the first 11 chapters with a grounding in the scientific fundamentals that govern all of chemistry. Next, in the following six chapters, we look at the nature of the carbon-containing substances, or *organic chemicals,* that compose all living things. In the final 12 chapters, we apply what we have learned in the first part of the book to the study of biological chemistry.

We begin in Chapter 1 with an examination of the states and properties of matter. Since our knowledge of chemistry is based on observations and measurements, we include an introduction to the systems of measurement that are essential to our understanding of matter and its behavior.

1.1 Chemistry: The Central Science

Learning Objective:

• Identify properties of matter and differentiate between chemical and physical changes.

Chemistry is often referred to as "the central science" because it is essential to nearly all other sciences. In fact, as more and more is learned, the historical dividing lines between chemistry, biology, and physics are fading, and current research is more interdisciplinary. Figure 1.1 diagrams the relationship of chemistry and biological chemistry to other fields of scientific study.

Chemistry is the study of matter—its nature, properties, and transformations. **Matter,** in turn, is an all-encompassing word used to describe anything physically real—anything you can see, touch, taste, or smell. In more scientific terms, matter is anything that has mass and volume. Like all the other sciences, our knowledge of chemistry has developed by application of a process called the **scientific method.** The discovery of aspirin, for example, is a combination of serendipity and the scientific method: observation, evaluation of data, formation of a hypothesis, and the design of experiments to test the hypothesis and further our understanding (see the Chemistry in Action on p. 7). Advances in scientific knowledge are typically the result of this systematic approach; hypotheses can be tested by carefully designed experiments, modified based on the results of those experiments, and further tested to refine our understanding.

All of chemistry is based on the study of matter and the changes that matter undergoes. How might we describe different kinds of matter more specifically? Any characteristic used to describe or identify something is called a **property;** size, color,

Chemistry The study of the nature, properties, and transformations of matter.

Matter The physical material that makes up the universe; anything that has mass and occupies space.

Scientific method The systematic process of observation, hypothesis, and experimentation used to expand and refine a body of knowledge.

Property A characteristic useful for identifying a substance or object.

1

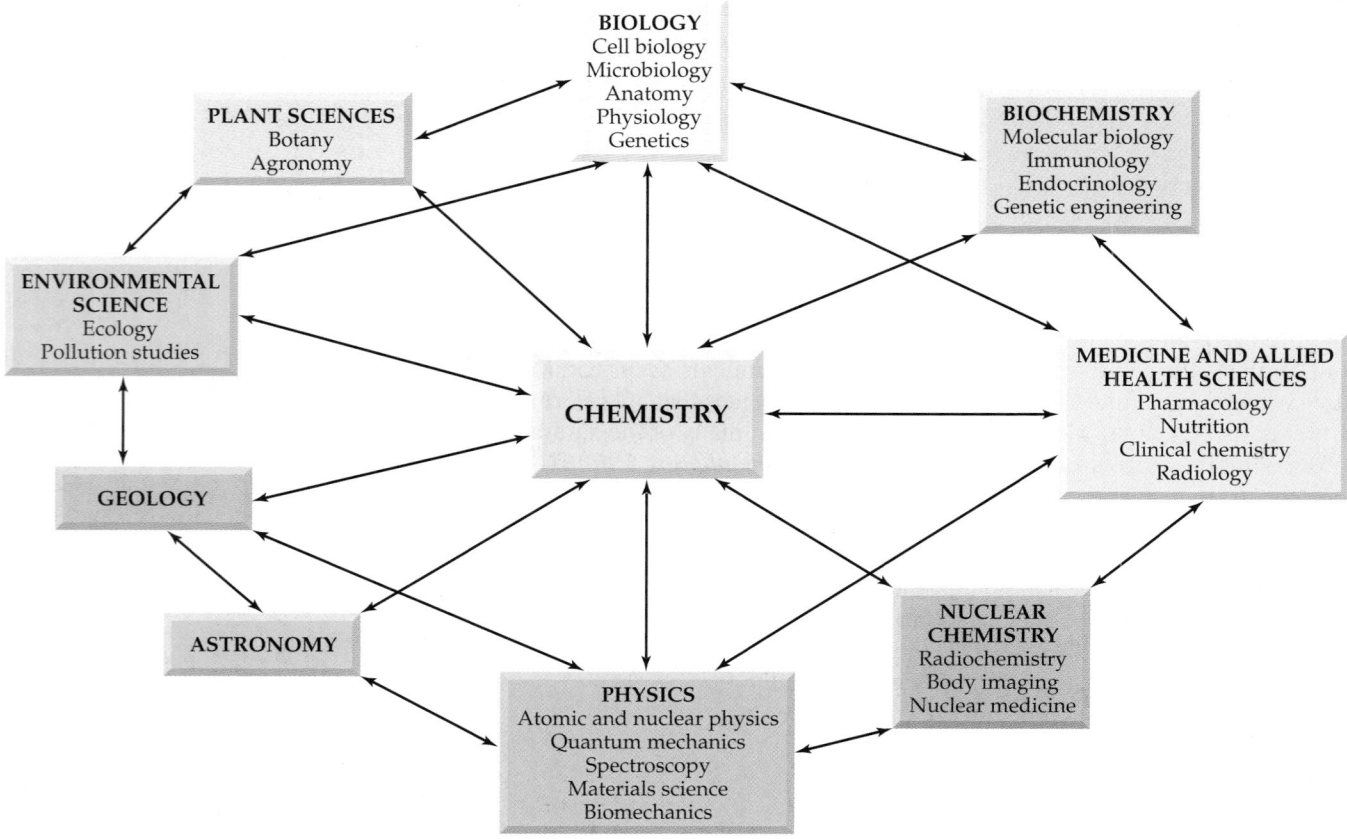

▲ **Figure 1.1**
Some relationships between chemistry—the central science—and other scientific and health-related disciplines.

and temperature are all familiar examples. Less familiar properties include *chemical composition,* which describes what matter is made of, and *chemical reactivity,* which describes how matter behaves. Rather than focusing on the properties themselves, it is often more useful to think about *changes* in properties. There are two types of changes: *physical* and *chemical.* A **physical change** is one that does not alter the identity of a substance, whereas a **chemical change** *does* alter a substance's identity. For example, the melting of solid ice to give liquid water is a physical change because the water changes only in form but not in chemical makeup. However, the rusting of an iron bicycle left in the rain is a chemical change because iron combines with oxygen and moisture from the air to give a new substance, rust.

Table 1.1 lists some chemical and physical properties of several familiar substances—water, table sugar (sucrose, a carbohydrate), and baking soda (sodium bicarbonate). Note in Table 1.1 that changes occurring when sugar and baking soda are heated are chemical changes because new substances are produced.

Physical change A change that does not affect the chemical makeup of a substance or object.

Chemical change A change in the chemical makeup of a substance.

Worked Example 1.1 Chemical vs. Physical Change

Identify each of the following as a chemical change or a physical change:

a) Sugar dissolving in water.

b) Sugar heated in a saucepan to make caramel.

ANALYSIS A physical change does not result in a change in the identity of the substance, whereas a chemical change results in the creation of a new substance with properties that are different than the original substance.

SOLUTION

a) Physical change: When sugar dissolves in water, the sugar and the water retain their identity. The water can be removed by evaporation, and the sugar can be recovered in its original form.

b) Chemical change: When sugar is heated in a saucepan, it melts and darkens and thickens into caramel. When cooled, the caramel clearly has significantly different properties (color, consistency) than the original sugar, indicating that a chemical change has occurred and a new substance has been formed.

Table 1.1 Some Properties of Water, Sugar, and Baking Soda

Water	Sugar (Sucrose)	Baking Soda (Sodium Bicarbonate)
Physical properties		
Colorless liquid	White crystals	White powder
Odorless	Odorless	Odorless
Melting point: 0 °C	Begins to decompose at 160 °C, turning black and giving off water.	Decomposes at 270 °C, giving off water and carbon dioxide.
Boiling point: 100 °C	—	—
Chemical properties		
Composition:*	Composition:*	Composition:*
11.2% hydrogen	6.4% hydrogen	27.4% sodium
88.8% oxygen	42.1% carbon	1.2% hydrogen
	51.5% oxygen	14.3% carbon
		57.1% oxygen
Does not burn.	Burns in air.	Does not burn.

Compositions are given by mass percent.

HANDS-ON CHEMISTRY 1.1

Look in the refrigerator or on the counter top in your home, apartment, or work place. If there is a bowl of fruit, onions, potatoes, etc., take a look at these items and compare what they would look like in the grocery store versus in their current location. Do you see mold? Is the flesh of the food soft, etc.? If so, would this be a physical change or a chemical change? What evidence can you cite to support your answer?

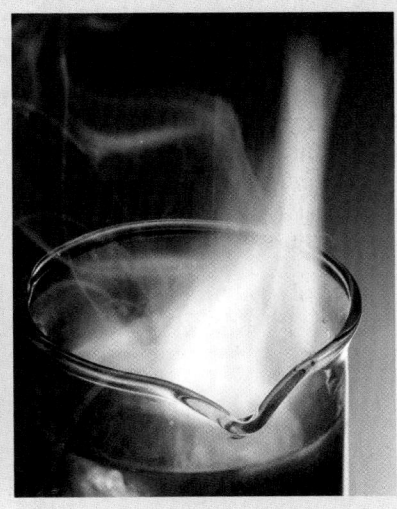

▲ Burning of potassium in water is an example of a chemical change.

1.2 States of Matter

Learning Objective:

• Identify the three states of matter and describe their properties.

Solid *(s)* A substance that has a definite shape and volume.

Liquid *(l)* A substance that has a definite volume but assumes the shape of its container.

Gas *(g)* A substance that has neither a definite volume nor a definite shape.

Matter exists in three forms: solid, liquid, and gas. A **solid** has a definite volume and a definite shape that does not change regardless of the container in which it is placed; for example, a wooden block, marbles, or a cube of ice all keep their volume and shape whether they are placed on a table or in a box. A **liquid,** by contrast, has a definite volume but an indefinite shape. The volume of a liquid, such as water, remains the same when it is poured into a different container, but its shape changes as it takes the shape of the container. A **gas** is different still, having neither a definite volume nor a definite shape. A gas expands to fill the volume and take the shape of any container it is placed in, such as the helium in a balloon or steam formed by boiling water (Figure 1.2).

▶ **Figure 1.2**
The three states of matter—solid, liquid, and gas.

(a) Ice: A solid has a definite volume and a definite shape independent of its container.

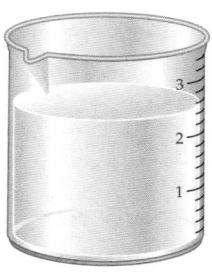

(b) Water: A liquid has a definite volume but a variable shape that depends on its container.

(c) Steam: A gas has both variable volume and shape that depend on its container.

State of matter The physical state of a substance as a solid *(s),* liquid *(l),* or gas *(g).*

Change of state The conversion of a substance from one state to another— for example, from liquid *(l)* to gas *(g).*

Many substances, such as water, can exist in all three phases, or **states of matter**—the solid state *(s),* the liquid state *(l),* and the gaseous state *(g)*—depending on the temperature. In general, a substance that is a solid can be converted to the liquid state if the temperature is increased sufficiently. Likewise, many liquids can be converted to the gaseous state by increasing the temperature even further. The conversion of a substance from one state to another is known as a **change of state.** The melting of a solid, the freezing or boiling of a liquid, and the condensing of a gas to a liquid are physical changes familiar to everyone.

Worked Example 1.2 Identifying States of Matter

Formaldehyde is a disinfectant, a preservative, and a raw material for the manufacturing of plastics. Its melting point is −92 °C, and its boiling point is −19.5 °C. Is formaldehyde a gas, a liquid, or a solid at room temperature (25 °C)? (Note: Room temperature in the Fahrenheit scale (°F), with which you may be more familiar, is around 78 °F. These two scales will be compared in Section 1.11.)

ANALYSIS The state of matter of any substance depends on its temperature. How do the melting point and boiling point of formaldehyde compare with room temperature?

SOLUTION
Room temperature (25 °C) is above the boiling point of formaldehyde (−19.5 °C), and so the formaldehyde is a gas.

PROBLEM 1.1

Pure acetic acid, which gives the sour taste to vinegar, has a melting point of 16.7 °C and a boiling point of 118 °C. Predict the physical state of acetic acid when the ambient temperature is 10 °C.

1.3 Classification of Matter

Learning Objective:

- Distinguish between mixtures and pure substances and classify pure substances as elements or compounds

The first question a chemist asks about an unknown substance is whether it is a pure substance or a mixture. Every sample of matter is one or the other. Separately, water and sugar are pure substances, but stirring some sugar into a glass of water creates a *mixture*.

What is the difference between a pure substance and a mixture? One difference is that a **pure substance** is uniform in its chemical composition and its properties all the way down to the microscopic level. Every sample of water, sugar, or baking soda, regardless of source, has the composition and properties listed in Table 1.1. A **mixture,** however, can vary in both composition and properties, depending on how it is made. A **homogeneous mixture** is a blend of two or more pure substances having a uniform composition at the microscopic level. Sugar dissolved in water is one example. You cannot always distinguish between a pure substance and a homogeneous mixture just by looking. The sugar–water mixture *looks* just like pure water but differs on a molecular level. The amount of sugar dissolved in a glass of water will determine the sweetness, boiling point, and other properties of the mixture. A **heterogeneous mixture,** by contrast, is a blend of two or more pure substances having nonuniform composition, such as a vegetable stew in which each spoonful is different. It is relatively easy to distinguish heterogeneous mixtures from pure substances.

Another difference between a pure substance and a mixture is that the components of a mixture can be separated without changing their chemical identities. For example, water can be separated from a sugar–water mixture by boiling the mixture to drive off the steam and then condensing the steam to recover the pure water. Pure sugar is left behind in the container.

Pure substances are classified into two groups: those that can undergo a chemical breakdown to yield simpler substances and those that cannot. A pure substance that cannot be broken down chemically into simpler substances is called an **element.** Examples include hydrogen, oxygen, aluminum, gold, and sulfur. At the time this book was printed, 118 elements had been identified, although only 91 of these occur naturally.

Any pure material that *can* be broken down into simpler substances by a chemical change is called a **chemical compound.** The term *compound* implies "more than one" (think "compound fracture"). A chemical compound, therefore, is formed by combining two or more elements to make a new substance. Water, for example, is a chemical compound consisting of hydrogen and oxygen; it can be chemically changed by passing an electric current through it to produce the elements hydrogen and oxygen). In Section 1.5, we will discuss chemical changes in more detail. Figure 1.3 summarizes the classification of matter into mixtures, pure compounds, and elements.

Pure substance A substance that has a uniform chemical composition throughout.

Mixture A blend of two or more substances, each of which retains its chemical identity.

Homogeneous mixture A uniform mixture that has the same composition throughout.

Heterogeneous mixture A nonuniform mixture that has regions of different composition.

LOOKING AHEAD ▶ We'll revisit the properties of mixtures in Section 9.1 when we discuss solutions. In Problem 1.2, that sour tasting vinegar is a 5% solution of acetic acid. Another state of matter that will be discussed is solutions in water, which are given the symbol *(aq)*.

Element A fundamental substance that cannot be broken down chemically into any simpler substance.

▶▶ Elements make up all the millions of other substances in the universe and are explored in the next section of this chapter (Section 1.4).

Chemical compound A pure substance that can be broken down into simpler substances by chemical reactions.

 Worked Example 1.3 Classifying Matter

Classify each of the following as a mixture or a pure substance. If a mixture, classify it as heterogeneous or homogeneous. If a pure substance, identify it as an element or a compound.

  (a) Vanilla ice cream   **(b)** Sugar

ANALYSIS Refer to the definitions of pure substances and mixtures. Is the substance composed of more than one kind of matter? Is the composition uniform?

SOLUTION

  (a) Vanilla ice cream is composed of more than one substance—cream, sugar, and vanilla flavoring. The composition appears to be uniform throughout, so this is a homogeneous mixture.

  (b) Sugar is composed of only one kind of matter—pure sugar. This is a pure substance. It can be converted to some other substance by a chemical change (see Table 1.1), so it is not an element. It must be a compound.

► **Figure 1.3**
A map for the classification of matter.

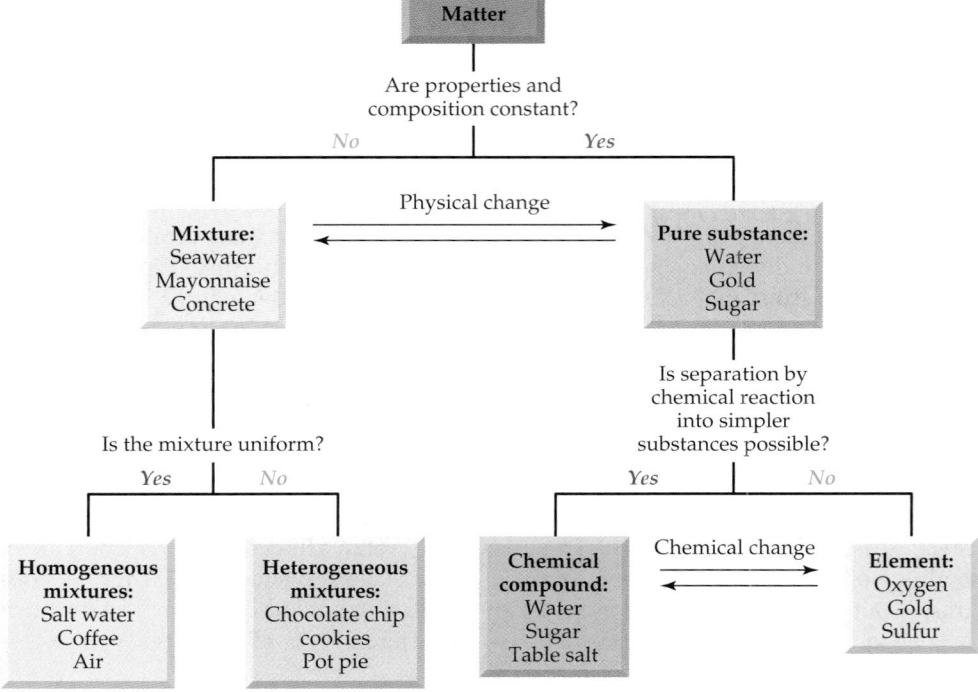

► **Figure 1.3**
A map for the classification of matter.

In fact, in Chapter 20, we will see that common table sugar is called sucrose; two other sugars, glucose and fructose, are chemically bonded to make one compound.

PROBLEM 1.2

Classify each of the following as a mixture or a pure substance. If a mixture, classify it as heterogeneous or homogeneous. If a pure substance, identify it as an element or a compound.

(a) Concrete   (b) The helium in a balloon

(c) A lead weight   (d) Wood

PROBLEM 1.3

Classify each of the following as a physical change or a chemical change:

(a) Dissolving sugar in water

(b) Producing carbon dioxide gas and solid lime by heating limestone

(c) Frying an egg

(d) The conversion of salicylic acid to acetylsalicylic acid (see the Chemistry in Action feature on the next page)

🔑 KEY CONCEPT PROBLEM 1.4 —————————————————

In the next image, red spheres represent element A and blue spheres represent element B. Identify the process illustrated in the image as a chemical change or a physical change. Also, identify the substance(s) on the left and the substance(s) on the right as pure substances or mixtures. Explain your answer.

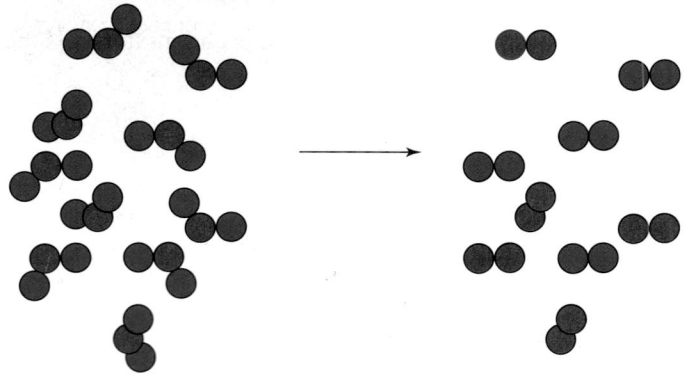

CHEMISTRY IN ACTION

☥ Aspirin—A Case Study

Acetylsalicylic acid (ASA), more commonly known as aspirin, is perhaps the first true wonder drug. It is a common staple in today's medicine chest, but its discovery can be traced back to 400 B.C. The ancient Greek physician Hippocrates pre-scribed the bark and leaves of the willow tree to relieve pain and fever. His knowledge of the therapeutic properties of these substances was derived through trial and error. In 1828, sci-entists isolated a bitter-tasting yellow extract, called salicin, from willow bark and identified salicin as the active ingredi-ent responsible for the observed medical effects. Salicin could be easily converted to salicylic acid (SA). SA, however, had an unpleasant taste and often caused stomach irritation and in-digestion. Further experiments were performed to convert SA to a substance that retained the therapeutic activity of SA but without the unpleasant side effects. Bayer marketed the new drug, now called aspirin, in water-soluble tablets.

But how does aspirin work? Once again, experimental data provided insights into the therapeutic activity of aspirin. In 1971, the British pharmacologist John Vane discovered that aspirin suppresses the body's production of prostaglandins, which are responsible for the pain and swelling that accom-pany inflammation. The discovery of this mechanism led to the development of new analgesic drugs.

Aspirin is classified as a *non*-steroidal *anti-i*nflammatory *d*rug (NSAID), but its therapeutic value goes well beyond reliev-ing aches and pains. Because aspirin also has anticoagulant activity, a daily, low-dose aspirin regimen (~100 mg) is recom-mended by many physicians to reduce the risks associated with cardiovascular disease—heart attacks and strokes. Its anti-inflammatory activity is also believed to reduce the risk of developing certain types of cancer, especially in patients who

▲ Hippocrates, the ancient Greek physician, prescribed a precursor of aspirin extracted from willow bark (above) to relieve pain.

suffer from chronic or persistent inflammation. For example, in a study of almost 20,000 women, the risk of ovarian cancer decreased by over 20% for women who followed a daily low-dose aspirin regimen, and that these benefits increased with long-term use. Individuals who followed the low-dose regimen for 5 years or more experienced lower incidence of colorectal cancers, and the 20-year risk of cancer death remained lower for a wide variety of other cancers, including stomach and esophageal cancers and adenocarcinomas—common malig-nant cancers that develop in the lungs, colon, and prostate.

CIA Problem 1.1   The active ingredient in aspirin, ASA, melts at 140 °C. Is it a solid or a liquid at room temperature?

CIA Problem 1.2   Do you think the conversion of SA to aspirin is a chemical change or a physical change? Give evidence to support your answer.

1.4   Chemical Elements and Symbols

Learning Objective:

• Identify the symbols and names of the common elements.

As of the date this book was printed, 118 chemical elements have been identified. Some are certainly familiar to you—for example, oxygen, helium, iron, aluminum, copper, and gold—but many others are probably unfamiliar—rhenium, niobium, thulium, and promethium. Rather than writing out the full names of elements, chemists use a short-hand notation in which elements are referred to by one- or two-letter symbols. The names and symbols of some common elements are listed in Table 1.2, and a complete alphabetical list is given inside the front cover of this book.

Note that all two-letter symbols have only their first letter capitalized, whereas the second letter is always lowercase. The symbols of most common elements are the first one or two letters of the elements' commonly used names, such as H (hydrogen) and Al (aluminum). Pay special attention, however, to the elements grouped in the last column to the right in Table 1.2. The symbols for these elements are derived from their original Latin names, such as Na for sodium, once known as *natrium*. The only way to learn these symbols is to memorize them; fortunately, they are few in number.

▶▶ Prostaglandins can be synthesized from arachidonic acid and have many biological effects, which are discussed in the Chemistry in Action feature in Chapter 23, p. 735. Aspirin can inhibit the formation of prostaglandins.

▶▶ We will discuss the creation of new elements by nuclear bombardment in Chapter 11. Many of these new sub-stances are used as medical diagnostic tracers or therapeutic agents.

Table 1.2 Names and Symbols for Some Common Elements

Elements with Symbols Based on Modern Names						Elements with Symbols Based on Latin Names	
Al	Aluminum	Co	Cobalt	N	Nitrogen	Cu	Copper *(cuprum)*
Ar	Argon	F	Fluorine	O	Oxygen	Au	Gold *(aurum)*
Ba	Barium	He	Helium	P	Phosphorus	Fe	Iron *(ferrum)*
Bi	Bismuth	H	Hydrogen	Pt	Platinum	Pb	Lead *(plumbum)*
B	Boron	I	Iodine	Rn	Radon	Hg	Mercury *(hydrargyrum)*
Br	Bromine	Li	Lithium	Si	Silicon	K	Potassium *(kalium)*
Ca	Calcium	Mg	Magnesium	S	Sulfur	Ag	Silver *(argentum)*
C	Carbon	Mn	Manganese	Ti	Titanium	Na	Sodium *(natrium)*
Cl	Chlorine	Ni	Nickel	Zn	Zinc	Sn	Tin *(stannum)*

▶ In Chapter 29, elements found in the human body will be discussed in greater detail along with body fluids.

Only 91 elements occur naturally; the remaining elements have been produced artificially by chemists and physicists. Each element has its own distinctive properties, and just about all of the first 95 elements have been put to use in some way that takes advantage of those properties. As indicated in Table 1.3, which shows the approximate elemental composition of the earth's crust and the human body, the naturally occurring elements are not equally abundant. Oxygen and silicon together account for nearly 75% of the mass in the earth's crust; oxygen, carbon, and hydrogen account for nearly all the mass of a human body.

Table 1.3 Elemental Composition of the Earth's Crust and the Human Body*

Earth's Crust		Human Body	
Oxygen	46.1%	Oxygen	61%
Silicon	28.2%	Carbon	23%
Aluminum	8.2%	Hydrogen	10%
Iron	5.6%	Nitrogen	2.6%
Calcium	4.1%	Calcium	1.4%
Sodium	2.4%	Phosphorus	1.1%
Magnesium	2.3%	Sulfur	0.20%
Potassium	2.1%	Potassium	0.20%
Titanium	0.57%	Sodium	0.14%
Hydrogen	0.14%	Chlorine	0.12%

Mass percent values are given.

Chemical formula A notation for a chemical compound using element symbols and subscripts to show how many atoms of each element are present.

▶ We'll learn more about the structure of atoms and how they form compounds in Chapter 2.

Just as elements combine to form chemical compounds, symbols are combined to produce **chemical formulas,** which use subscripts to identify how many *atoms* (the smallest fundamental units) of each element are in a given chemical compound. For example, the formula H_2O represents water, which contains two hydrogen atoms combined with one oxygen atom. Similarly, the formula CH_4 represents methane (natural gas), and the formula $C_{12}H_{22}O_{11}$ represents table sugar (sucrose). When no subscript is given for an element, as for carbon in the formula CH_4, a subscript of "1" is understood.

H_2O CH_4 $C_{12}H_{22}O_{11}$

2 H atoms   1 C atom   12 C atoms
1 O atom   4 H atoms   22 H atoms
                              11 O atoms

Those elements essential for human life are listed in Table 1.4. In addition to the well-known elements such as carbon, hydrogen, oxygen, and nitrogen, less familiar elements such as molybdenum and selenium are also important.

Table 1.4 Elements Essential for Human Life*

Element	Symbol	Function
Carbon	C	
Hydrogen	H	These four elements are present in all living organisms (Ch. 12–29).
Oxygen	O	
Nitrogen	N	
Arsenic	As	May affect cell growth and heart function.
Boron	B	Aids in the use of Ca, P, and Mg.
Calcium*	Ca	Necessary for growth of teeth and bones.
Chlorine*	Cl	Necessary for maintaining salt balance in body fluids (Ch. 29).
Chromium	Cr	Aids in carbohydrate metabolism (Ch. 22).
Cobalt	Co	Component of vitamin B_{12} (Ch. 19).
Copper	Cu	Necessary to maintain blood chemistry (Ch. 29).
Fluorine	F	Aids in the development of teeth and bones.
Iodine	I	Necessary for thyroid function (Ch. 28).
Iron	Fe	Necessary for oxygen-carrying ability of blood (Ch. 29).
Magnesium*	Mg	Necessary for bones, teeth, and muscle and nerve action (Ch. 28).
Manganese	Mn	Necessary for carbohydrate metabolism and bone formation (Ch. 22).
Molybdenum	Mo	Component of enzymes necessary for metabolism (Ch. 19).
Nickel	Ni	Aids in the use of Fe and Cu.
Phosphorus*	P	Necessary for growth of bones and teeth; present in DNA/RNA (Ch. 26).
Potassium*	K	Component of body fluids; necessary for nerve action (Ch. 28–29).
Selenium	Se	Aids vitamin E action and fat metabolism (Ch. 24).
Silicon	Si	Helps form connective tissue and bone.
Sodium*	Na	Component of body fluids; necessary for nerve and muscle action (Ch. 28–29).
Sulfur*	S	Component of proteins; necessary for blood clotting (Ch. 25 and 29).
Zinc	Zn	Necessary for growth, healing, and overall health.

*C, H, O, and N are present in most foods. Other elements listed vary in their distribution in different foods. Those marked with an asterisk are macronutrients, essential in the diet at more than 100 mg/day; the rest, other than C, H, O, and N, are micronutrients, essential at 15 mg or less per day.

▶▶ The elements listed in Table 1.4 are not present in our bodies in their free forms. Instead, they are combined into many thousands of different chemical compounds. We will talk about some compounds formed by metals in Chapter 3 and compounds formed by nonmetals in Chapter 4. The role that many of these elements play in biochemical functions will also be discussed in Chapters 19, 21, 25, 28, and 29.

PROBLEM 1.5

Match the names of the elements described below (a–f) with their elemental symbols (1–6).

(a) Sodium, a major component in table salt

(b) Tungsten, a metal used in light bulb filaments

(c) Strontium, used to produce brilliant red colors in fireworks

(d) Titanium, used in artificial hips and knee-replacement joints

(e) Fluorine, added to municipal water supplies to strengthen tooth enamel

(f) Tin, a metal used in solder

(1) W   (2) Na   (3) Sn   (4) F   (5) Ti   (6) Sr

PROBLEM 1.6

Identify the elements represented in each of the following chemical formulas and tell the number of atoms of each element:

(a) NH_3 (ammonia)

(b) $NaHCO_3$ (sodium bicarbonate)

(c) C_8H_{18} (octane, a component of gasoline)

(d) $C_6H_8O_6$ (vitamin C)

1.5 Chemical Reactions: Examples of Chemical Change

Learning Objective:

• Identify a chemical change as a chemical reaction.

Chemical reaction A process in which the identity and composition of one or more substances are changed.

Reactant A starting substance that undergoes change during a chemical reaction.

Product A substance formed as the result of a chemical reaction.

▶▶ We will discuss how reactions are classified in Chapter 5.

Chemists represent chemical changes using a symbolic shorthand notation called a **chemical reaction.** In writing this chemical change, the initial substances, or **reactants,** are written on the left; the new substances, or **products,** are written on the right. An arrow connects the two parts to indicate the chemical change or the chemical reaction. The conditions necessary to bring about the reaction are written above and below the arrow. Consider again the example of a chemical change discussed previously, in which electric current was passed through the reactant water (H_2O) to break it down into the products, the elements hydrogen (H_2) and oxygen (O_2). This chemical reaction can be expressed in words as shown next.

$$\underset{reaction}{\textit{A chemical}} \quad \overset{\text{Reactant}}{\text{Water}} \quad \xrightarrow[\text{current}]{\text{Electric}} \quad \overset{\text{Products}}{\text{Hydrogen} + \text{Oxygen}}$$

Chemists, however, find it more convenient to use chemical symbols to represent the elements and compounds involved in the reaction. This chemical reaction would more commonly be expressed as

$$H_2O(l) \quad \xrightarrow[\text{current}]{\text{Electric}} \quad H_2(g) + O_2(g)$$

Note that the reactants and products are represented using their chemical formulas, but that the physical states of the reactants and products are also indicated as a liquid *(l)* or gas *(g)*. The formation of gas bubbles is an indication that a chemical reaction has occurred.

If we take a quick look at another example of a chemical reaction in Figure 1.4, we can reinforce these ideas. The element *nickel* is a hard, shiny metal, and the compound *hydrogen chloride* is a colorless gas that dissolves in water to give a solution called *hydrochloric acid*. When pieces of nickel are added to hydrochloric acid in a test tube, the nickel slowly dissolves, the colorless solution turns green, and a gas bubbles out of the test tube. The change in color, the dissolving of the nickel, and the appearance of gas bubbles are indications that a chemical reaction is taking place.

Again, the overall reaction of nickel with hydrochloric acid can be written in words or represented in a shorthand notation using symbols to represent the elements or compounds involved as reactants and products, as shown below. The physical states of the reactants are indicated as solid *(s)* for Ni and the HCl as *(aq),* which means "aqueous," or "dissolved in water." The physical states of the products are *(aq)* for the nickel(II) chloride dissolved in water and *(g)* for the H_2 gas. If the water is evaporated away, the nickel(II) chloride product can be collected as a solid, also shown in Figure 1.4.

$$\overset{\text{Reactants}}{\overbrace{\text{Nickel} + \text{Hydrochloric acid}}} \quad \longrightarrow \quad \overset{\text{Products}}{\overbrace{\text{Nickel (II) chloride} + \text{Hydrogen}}}$$

$$\underset{(s)}{\text{Ni}} + \underset{(aq)}{2\,\text{HCl}} \quad \longrightarrow \quad \underset{(aq)}{\text{NiCl}_2} + \underset{(g)}{\text{H}_2}$$

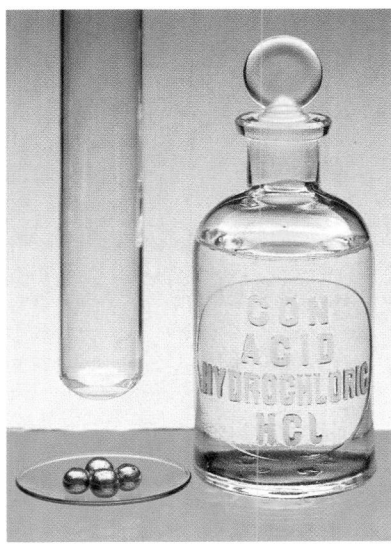
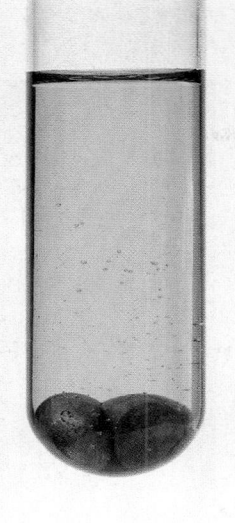

| (a) | (b) | (c) |

▲ Figure 1.4
Reactants and products of a chemical reaction.
(a) The reactants: Nickel (shown on the flat dish), an element that is a typical lustrous metal, and hydrochloric acid (in the bottle), a solution of the chemical compound hydrogen chloride in water. (b) The reaction: As the chemical reaction occurs, the colorless solution turns green when water-insoluble nickel metal slowly changes into the water-soluble chemical compound nickel(II) chloride. Hydrogen gas bubbles are produced and rise slowly through the green solution. (c) The product: Hydrogen gas can be collected as it bubbles from the solution and removal of water from the solution leaves behind the other product, a solid, green chemical compound known as nickel(II) chloride.

1.6 Physical Quantities: Units and Scientific Notation

Learning Objective:

- Write very large and very small numbers using scientific notation or units with appropriate numerical prefixes.

Our understanding of matter depends on our ability to measure the changes in physical properties associated with physical and chemical change. Mass, volume, temperature, density, and other physical properties that can be measured are called **physical quantities** and are described by both a number and a **unit** that defines the nature and magnitude of the number.

Physical quantity A physical property that can be measured.

Unit A defined quantity used as a standard of measurement.

Number   Unit

61.2 kilograms

Units of Measurement

The number alone is not much good without a unit. If you ask how much blood an accident victim has lost, the answer "three" would not tell you much. Three drops? Three milliliters? Three pints? Three liters? By the way, an adult human has only 5–6 liters of blood.

Any physical quantity can be measured in many different units. For example, a person's height might be measured in inches, feet, yards, centimeters, or many other units. To avoid confusion, scientists from around the world have agreed on a system of standard units, called by the French name *Système International d'Unites* (International System of Units), abbreviated *SI*. **SI units** for some common physical quantities

SI units Units of measurement defined by the International System of Units. Examples include kilograms, meters, and kelvins.

CHEMISTRY IN ACTION

✝ Mercury and Mercury Poisoning

Mercury, the only metallic element that is liquid at room temperature, has fascinated people for millennia. Much of the recent interest in mercury has concerned its toxicity, but mercury, in nontoxic forms, has a wide array of clinical uses. For example, the mercury compound Hg_2Cl_2 (called *calomel*) has a long history of medical use as a laxative, yet it is also used as a fungicide and rat poison. Dental amalgam, a solid alloy of elemental mercury, silver, tin, copper, and zinc, was used by dentists for many years to fill tooth cavities, with little or no adverse effects except in individuals with a hypersensitivity to mercury. Yet, exposure to elemental mercury *vapor* for long periods leads to mood swings, headaches, tremors, and loss of hair and teeth. The widespread use of mercuric nitrate, a mercury compound used to make the felt used in hats, exposed many hatters of the eighteenth and nineteenth centuries to toxic levels of mercury. The eccentric behavior displayed by hatters suffering from mercury poisoning led to the phrase "mad as a hatter."

Why is mercury more toxic in some forms than in others? It turns out that the toxicity of mercury and its compounds is related to solubility. Only soluble mercury compounds are highly toxic because they can be transported through the bloodstream to all parts of the body, where they react with different enzymes and interfere with various biological processes. Elemental mercury and insoluble mercury compounds become toxic only when converted into soluble compounds, reactions that are extremely slow in the body. Calomel, for example, is an insoluble mercury compound that passes through the body long before it is converted into any soluble compounds. Mercury alloys were considered safe for dental use because mercury does not evaporate readily from the alloys and it neither reacts with nor dissolves in saliva. Mercury vapor, however, remains in the lungs when breathed, until it is slowly converted into soluble compounds. Soluble organic forms of mercury can be particularly toxic. Trace amounts are found in nearly all

▲ Cinnabar, the dark red crystals in this photo, is a mineral comprised of mercury (Hg) and sulfur (S), and is one of the major commercial sources of elemental mercury.

seafood, but some larger species such as king mackerel and swordfish contain higher levels of mercury. Because mercury can affect the developing brain and nervous system of a fetus, pregnant women are often advised to avoid consuming them.

Recent events have raised new concerns regarding the safe use of mercury in some other applications. Perhaps the most controversial example is the use of thimerosal, an organic mercury compound, as a preservative in flu vaccines. Concerns about possible links between thimerosal and autism in children resulted in elimination of its use in 1999, although most scientific data seem to refute any connection. In response to these concerns, preservative-free versions of the influenza vaccine are available for use in infants, children, and pregnant women.

CIA Problem 1.3 Calomel (Hg_2Cl_2) is not toxic but methyl mercury chloride (CH_3HgCl) is highly toxic. What physical property explains this difference in toxicity?

are given in Table 1.5. Mass is measured in *kilograms* (kg), length is measured in *meters* (m), volume is measured in *cubic meters* (m^3), temperature is measured in *kelvins* (K), and time is measured in *seconds* (s).

SI units are closely related to the more familiar *metric units* used in all industrialized nations of the world except the United States, which uses the English system of units (inches, feet, ounces, pounds, etc.). One advantage of the SI system is that units are related by powers of 10. If you compare the SI and metric units shown in Table 1.5, you will find that the basic metric unit of mass is the *gram* (g) rather than the kilogram ($1\,g = 1/1000\,kg$), the metric unit of volume is the *liter* (L) rather than the cubic meter ($1\,L = 1/1000\,m^3$), and the metric unit of temperature is the *Celsius degree* (°C) rather than the kelvin. The meter is the unit of length, and the second is the unit of time in both systems. Although SI units are now preferred in scientific research, metric units are still used in some fields. You will probably find yourself working with both.

In addition to the units listed in Table 1.5, many other widely used units are derived from them. For instance, units of *meters per second* (m/s) are often used for *speed*—the distance covered in a given time. Similarly, units of *grams per cubic centimeter* (g/cm^3)

▶▶ The symbol °C means degrees Celsius, one of three temperature scales in common use, and will be discussed in Section 1.11. (Did you know that normal body temperature of 98.6 °F is 37.0 °C, when converting from Fahrenheit to the Celsius?)

Table 1.5 Some SI and Metric Units and Their Equivalents

Quantity	SI Unit (Symbol)	Metric Unit (Symbol)	Equivalents
Mass	Kilogram (kg)	Gram (g)	1 kg = 1000 g = 2.205 lb
Length	Meter (m)	Meter (m)	1 m = 3.280 ft
Volume	Cubic meter (m^3)	Liter (L)	1 m^3 = 1000 L = 264.2 gal
Temperature	Kelvin (K)	Celsius degree (°C)	See Section 1.11
Time	Second (s)	Second (s)	—

are often used for *density*—the mass of substance in a given volume. We will see other such derived units in future chapters.

One problem with any system of measurement is that the sizes of the units often turn out to be inconveniently large or small for the problem at hand. A biologist describing the diameter of a red blood cell (0.000 006 m) would find the meter to be an inconveniently large unit, but an astronomer measuring the average distance from the earth to the sun (150,000,000,000 m) would find the meter to be inconveniently small. For this reason, metric and SI units can be modified by prefixes to refer to either smaller or larger quantities. For instance, the SI unit for mass—the kilogram—differs by the prefix *kilo-* from the metric unit gram. *Kilo-* indicates that a kilogram is 1000 times as large as a gram:

$$1 \text{ kg} = (1000)(1 \text{ g}) = 1000 \text{ g}$$

Small quantities of active ingredients in medications are often reported in *milligrams* (mg). The prefix *milli-* shows that the unit gram has been divided by 1000, which is the same as multiplying by 0.001:

$$1 \text{ mg} = \left(\frac{1}{1000}\right)(1 \text{ g}) = (0.001)(1 \text{ g}) = 0.001 \text{ g}$$

A list of prefixes is given in Table 1.6, with the most common ones displayed in color. *Centi-* is seen most often in the length unit *centimeter* (1 cm = 0.01 m), and *deci-* is used most often in clinical chemistry, where the concentrations of blood components are given in milligrams per deciliter (1 dL = 0.1 L). These prefixes allow us to compare the magnitudes of different numbers by noting how the prefixes modify a common unit.

Table 1.6 Some Prefixes for Multiples of Metric and SI Units

Prefix	Symbol	Base Unit Multiplied By	Example
mega	M	1,000,000 = 10^6	1 megameter (Mm) = 10^6 m
kilo	k	1000 = 10^3	1 kilogram (kg) = 10^3 g
hecto	h	100 = 10^2	1 hectogram (hg) = 100 g
deka	da	10 = 10^1	1 dekaliter (daL) = 10 L
deci	d	0.1 = 10^{-1}	1 deciliter (dL) = 0.1 L
centi	c	0.01 = 10^{-2}	1 centimeter (cm) = 0.01 m
milli	m	0.001 = 10^{-3}	1 milligram (mg) = 0.001 g
micro	μ	0.000 001 = 10^{-6}	1 micrometer (μm) = 10^{-6} m
nano	n	0.000 000 001 = 10^{-9}	1 nanogram (ng) = 10^{-9} g
pico	p	0.000 000 000 001 = 10^{-12}	1 picogram (pg) = 10^{-12} g
femto	f	0.000 000 000 000 001 = 10^{-15}	1 femtogram (fg) = 10^{-15} g

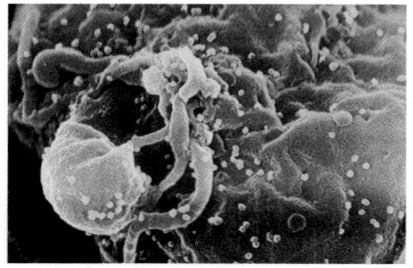

▲ The HIV-1 virus particles (in green) budding from the surface of a lymphocyte have an approximate diameter of 0.000 000 120 m.

▶ One approach for deactivating the HIV-1 virus is called *inhibition* and will be discussed in Chapter 19. How small would the inhibition agent have to be to fit in a specific location on the surface of the virus particle?

Scientific notation A number expressed as the product of a number between 1 and 10, times the number 10 raised to a power.

For example,

$$1 \text{ meter} = 10 \text{ dm} = 100 \text{ cm} = 1000 \text{ mm} = 1,000,000 \text{ } \mu\text{m}$$

Such comparisons will be useful when we start performing calculations involving units. It is worth noting that, as mentioned before, all the metric units displayed above are related by factors of 10. Note also in Table 1.6 that numbers having five or more digits to the right of the decimal point are shown with thin spaces every three digits for convenience—0.000 001, for example. This manner of writing numbers is becoming more common and will be used throughout this book.

Scientific Notation

Another way to solve the problem of representing very large or very small numbers is to use **scientific notation.** Rather than write very large or very small numbers in their entirety, it is more convenient to express them using *scientific notation*. A number is written in scientific notation as the product of a number between 1 and 10, times the number 10 raised to a power. Thus, 215 is written in scientific notation as 2.15×10^2:

$$215 = 2.15 \times 100 = 2.15(10 \times 10) = 2.15 \times 10^2$$

Notice that in this case, where the number is *larger* than 1, the decimal point has been moved *to the left* until it follows the first digit. The exponent on the 10 is positive and tells how many places we had to move the decimal point to position it just after the first digit:

$$215. = 2.15 \times 10^2$$

Decimal point is moved two places to the left, so exponent is 2.

To express a number *smaller* than one in scientific notation, we have to move the decimal point *to the right* until it follows the first digit. The number of places moved is the negative exponent of 10. For example, the number 0.002 15 can be rewritten as 2.15×10^{-3}:

$$0.002\ 15 = 2.15 \times \frac{1}{1000} = 2.15 \times \frac{1}{10 \times 10 \times 10} = 2.15 \times \frac{1}{10^3} = 2.15 \times 10^{-3}$$

$$0.002\ 15 = 2.15 \times 10^{-3}$$

Decimal point is moved three places to the right, so exponent is −3.

To convert a number written in scientific notation to standard notation, the process is reversed. For a number with a *positive* exponent, the decimal point is moved to the *right* a number of places equal to the exponent:

$$3.7962 \times 10^4 = 37,962$$

Positive exponent of 4, so decimal point is moved to the right four places.

For a number with a *negative* exponent, the decimal point is moved to the *left* a number of places equal to the exponent:

$$1.56 \times 10^{-8} = 0.000\ 000\ 015\ 6$$

Negative exponent of −8, so decimal point is moved to the left eight places.

Worked Example 1.4 Units and Scientific Notation

The HIV-1 virus particles seen in the margin photo on p. 14 are very small, on the order of 0.000 000 120 m in diameter. Express this value using scientific notation and using an appropriate numerical prefix to modify the basic unit.

ANALYSIS The number is significantly less than one, so when we convert to scientific notation we should have a number with a negative exponent. We can use the value of that exponent to identify the appropriate numerical prefix.

SOLUTION
To convert to scientific notation we have to move the decimal place to the right by seven places, so 0.000 000 120 m $= 1.20 \times 10^{-7}$ m. From Table 1.6, the closest numerical prefixes are *micro* (10^{-6}) or *nano* (10^{-9}). If we moved the decimal place six places to the right we would obtain:

$$0.000\ 000\ 120\ \text{m} = 0.120 \times 10^{-6}\ \text{m} = 0.120 \text{ micrometers } (\mu\text{m})$$

If we move the decimal place nine places to the right we obtain:

$$0.000\ 000\ 120\ \text{m} = 120 \times 10^{-9}\ \text{m} = 120 \text{ nanometers (nm)}.$$

PROBLEM 1.7

Give the full name of the following units and express the quantities in terms of the basic unit (e.g., 1 mL = 1 milliliter = 0.001 L):

(a) 1 cm   **(b)** 1 dg   **(c)** 1 km   **(d)** 1 μs   **(e)** 1 ng

1.7 Measuring Mass, Length, and Volume

Learning Objective:

- Name and correctly use the metric and SI units of measurement for mass, length, volume, and temperature and convert units appropriately.

The terms *mass* and *weight,* though often used interchangeably, really have quite different meanings. **Mass** is a measure of the amount of matter in an object, whereas **weight** is a measure of the gravitational pull that the earth, moon, or other large body exerts on an object. Clearly, the amount of matter in an object does not depend on location. Whether you are standing on the earth or standing on the moon, the mass of your body is the same. On the other hand, the weight of an object *does* depend on location. Your weight on earth might be 140 lb, but it would only be 23 lb on the moon because the pull of gravity there is only about one-sixth as great.

At the same location, two objects with identical masses have identical weights; that is, gravity pulls equally on both. Thus, the *mass* of an object can be determined by comparing the *weight* of the object to the weight of a known reference standard. Much of the confusion between mass and weight is simply due to a language problem: We speak of "weighing" when we really mean that we are measuring mass by comparing two weights. Figure 1.5 shows a two-pan balance in which the mass of objects are measured by comparison with the known masses of standard materials, such as brass weights.

One kilogram, the SI unit for mass, is equal to 2.205 lb—too large a quantity for many purposes in chemistry and medicine. Thus, smaller units of mass such as the gram, milligram (mg), and microgram (μg), are more commonly used. Table 1.7 shows the relationships between metric and common units for mass.

The meter is the standard measure of length, or distance, in both the SI and metric systems. One meter is 39.37 inches (about 10% longer than a yard), a length that is much too large for most measurements in chemistry and medicine. Other, more commonly used measures of length are the *centimeter* (cm; $1/100\ m$) and the *millimeter* (mm; $1/1000\ \text{m}$). One centimeter is a bit less than half an inch—0.3937 inch to be exact. A millimeter, in turn, is 0.03937 inch, or about the thickness of a dime. Table 1.8 lists the relationships of these units.

Volume is the amount of space occupied by an object. The SI unit for volume—the cubic meter, m^3—is so large that the liter ($1\ L = 0.001\ m^3 = 1\ dm^3$) is much more

Mass A measure of the amount of matter in an object.

Weight A measure of the gravitational force that the earth or other large body exerts on an object.

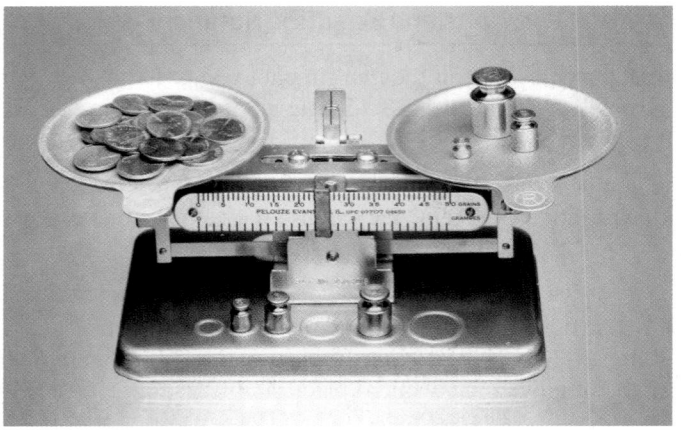

▲ Figure 1.5
The two-pan balance is used to measure the mass of objects, such as the pennies on the left pan, by comparing them with the mass of standard objects, such as the brass weights on the right pan.

Table 1.7 Units of Mass

Unit	Equivalent	Unit	Equivalent
1 kilogram (kg)	= 1000 grams = 2.205 pounds	1 ton	= 2000 pounds = 907.03 kilograms
1 gram (g)	= 0.001 kilogram = 1000 milligrams = 0.035 27 ounce	1 pound (lb)	= 16 ounces = 0.454 kilogram = 454 grams
1 milligram (mg)	= 0.001 gram = 1000 micrograms	1 ounce (oz)	= 0.028 35 kilogram = 28.35 grams = 28,350 milligrams
1 microgram (μg)	= 0.000 001 gram = 0.001 milligram		

Table 1.8 Units of Length

Unit	Equivalent
1 kilometer (km)	= 1000 meters = 0.6214 mile
1 meter (m)	= 100 centimeters = 1000 millimeters = 1.0936 yards = 39.37 inches
1 centimeter (cm)	= 0.01 meter = 10 millimeters = 0.3937 inch
1 millimeter (mm)	= 0.001 meter = 0.1 centimeter
1 mile (mi)	= 1.609 kilometers = 1609 meters
1 yard (yd)	= 0.9144 meter = 91.44 centimeters
1 foot (ft)	= 0.3048 meter = 30.48 centimeters
1 inch (in)	= 2.54 centimeters = 25.4 millimeters

commonly used in chemistry and medicine. One liter has the volume of a cube 10 cm (1 dm) on edge and is a bit larger than one U.S. quart. Each liter is further divided into 1000 *milliliters* (mL), with 1 mL being the size of a cube 1 cm on edge, or 1 cm^3. In fact, the milliliter is often called a *cubic centimeter* (cm^3 or cc) in medical work. Figure 1.6 shows the divisions of a cubic meter, and Table 1.9 shows the relationships among units of volume.

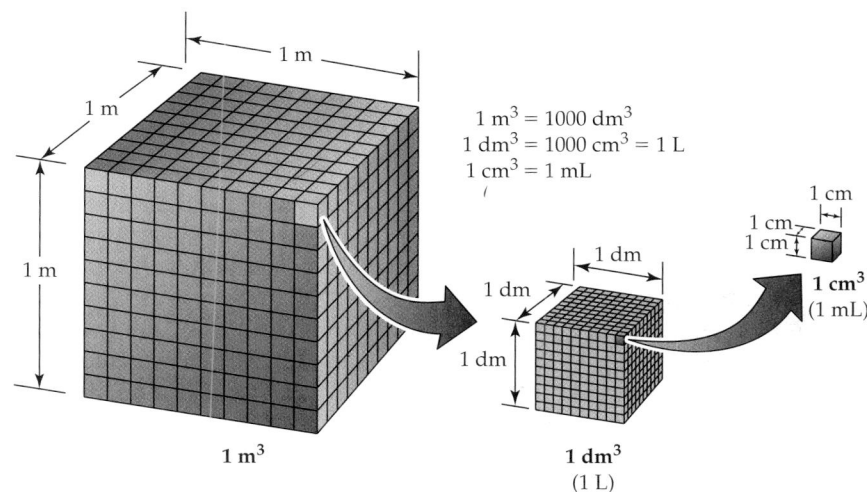

◄ Figure 1.6
A cubic meter is the volume of a cube 1 m on edge. Each cubic meter contains 1000 cubic decimeters (liters), and each cubic decimeter contains 1000 cubic centimeters (milliliters). Thus, there are 1000 mL in a liter and 1000 L in a cubic meter.

Table 1.9 Units of Volume

Unit	Equivalent
1 cubic meter (m^3)	= 1000 liters
	= 264.2 gallons
1 liter (L)	= 0.001 cubic meter
	= 1000 milliliters
	= 1.057 quarts
1 deciliter (dL)	= 0.1 liter
	= 100 milliliters
1 milliliter (mL)	= 0.001 liter
	= 1000 microliters
1 microliter (μL)	= 0.001 milliliter
1 gallon (gal)	= 3.7854 liters
1 quart (qt)	= 0.9464 liter
	= 946.4 milliliters
1 fluid ounce (fl oz)	= 29.57 milliliters

HANDS-ON CHEMISTRY 1.2

The mass of an object provides us with important information about its composition, that is, what elements it contains. But mass is not the only property that can be used to distinguish between objects. Consider the U.S. penny—its composition has changed significantly over time. For example, the penny was pure copper from 1793 to 1837, and then incorporated varying amounts of other metals (mainly zinc, nickel, and tin) from 1837 to 1982. Interestingly, in 1943, the penny was made mainly of zinc-coated steel because copper and zinc were needed for the war effort. From 1962 to 1982, the penny contained 95% copper and 5% zinc; after 1982, the composition changed to 2.5% copper and 97.5% zinc. The significant difference in composition can be seen in the different properties of pre-and post-1982 pennies.

To explore these differences, sort through your spare change jar and collect 10 pre-1982 and 10 post-1982 pennies and perform the following activities:

a. Collect two identical glasses or jars. Take the 10 pre-1982 pennies and drop them in the glass jar and listen to them as they hit the glass sides. Then, take the 10 post-1982 pennies and drop them in the glass jar and listen to them as they hit the glass sides. Do they sound different? (Note: If glasses or jars are not readily available, you can use a hard surface, like the kitchen counter.)

b. If a food scale is available, weigh 10 pre-1982 pennies and weigh 10 post-1982 pennies. Are their masses different? Which has more mass?

c. Find a pair of tin snips or heavy duty metal shears. Carefully cut a penny from each group in half. Is one penny easier to cut than the other? Which one is easier? Now look at the inside of the pennies. How are they different?

1.8 Measurement and Significant Figures

Learning Objective:

- Use significant figures and scientific notation to represent the precision of a measurement.

How much does a tennis ball weigh? If you put a tennis ball on an ordinary bathroom scale, the scale would probably register 0 lb (or 0 kg if you have a metric scale). If you placed the same tennis ball on a common laboratory balance, however, you might get a reading of 54.07 g. On an expensive analytical balance like those found in clinical and research laboratories, you might find the ball has a mass of 54.071 38 g. Clearly, the precision of your answer depends on the equipment used for the measurement.

Every experimental measurement, no matter how precise, has a degree of uncertainty to it because there is always a limit to the number of digits that can be determined. An analytical balance, for example, might reach its limit in measuring mass to the fifth decimal place, and weighing the tennis ball several times might produce slightly different readings, such as 54.071 39 g, 54.071 38 g, and 54.071 37 g. Also, different people making the same measurement might come up with slightly different answers. How, for instance, would you record the volume of the liquid shown in Figure 1.7? It is clear that the volume of liquid lies between 17.0 and 18.0 mL, but the exact value of the last digit must be estimated.

▲ The tennis ball weighs 54.07 g on this common laboratory balance, which is capable of determining mass to about 0.01 g.

To indicate the precision of a measurement, the value recorded should use all the digits known with certainty, plus one additional estimated digit that is usually considered uncertain by plus or minus 1 (written as ± 1). The total number of digits used to express such a measurement is called the number of **significant figures.** Thus, the quantity 54.07 g has four significant figures (5, 4, 0, and 7), and the quantity 54.071 38 g has seven significant figures. *Remember:* All but one of the significant figures are known with certainty; the last significant figure is only an estimate accurate to ± 1.

Significant figures The number of meaningful digits used to express a value.

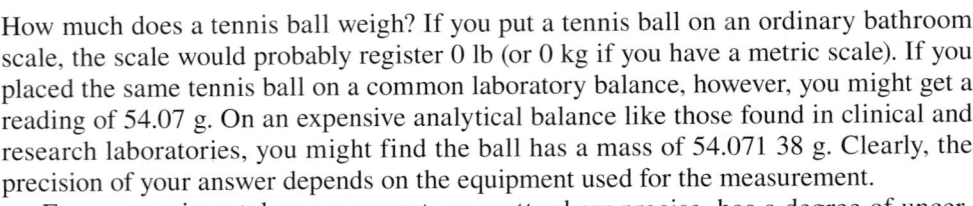

54.07 g   A mass between 54.06 g and 54.08 g ($\pm$0.01 g)

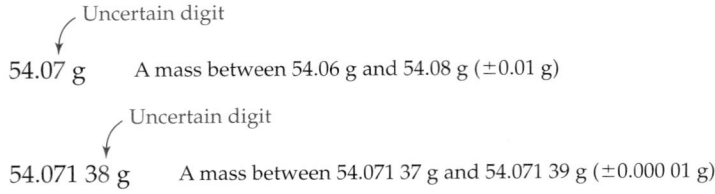

54.071 38 g   A mass between 54.071 37 g and 54.071 39 g ($\pm$0.000 01 g)

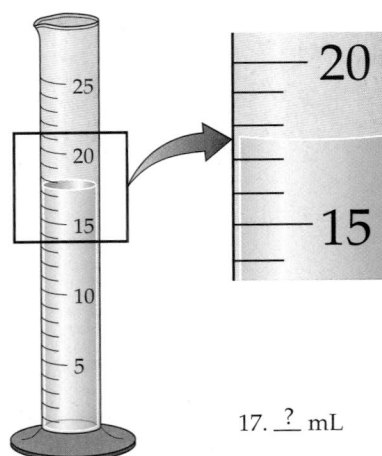

17. ? mL

▲ **Figure 1.7**
What is the volume of liquid in this graduated cylinder?

Deciding the number of significant figures in a given measurement is usually simple, but it can be troublesome when zeroes are involved. Depending on the circumstances, a zero might be significant or might be just a space filler to locate the decimal point. For example, how many significant figures does each of the following measurements have?

94.072 g	Five significant figures (9, 4, 0, 7, 2)
0.0834 cm	Three significant figures (8, 3, 4)
0.029 07 mL	Four significant figures (2, 9, 0, 7)
138.200 m	Six significant figures (1, 3, 8, 2, 0, 0)
23,000 kg	*Anywhere* from two (2, 3) to five (2, 3, 0, 0, 0) significant figures

The following rules are helpful for determining the number of significant figures when zeroes are present:

RULE 1: Zeroes in the middle of a number are like any other digit; they are always significant. Thus, 94.072 g has five significant figures.

RULE 2: Zeroes at the beginning of a number are not significant; they act only to locate the decimal point. Thus, 0.0834 cm has three significant figures, and 0.029 07 mL has four.

RULE 3: Zeroes at the end of a number and *after* the decimal point are significant. It is assumed that these zeroes would not be shown unless they were significant. Thus, 138.200 m has six significant figures. If the value were known to only four significant figures, we would write 138.2 m.

RULE 4: Zeroes at the end of a number and *before* an implied decimal point may or may not be significant. We cannot tell whether they are part of the measurement or whether they act only to locate the unwritten but implied decimal point. Thus, 23,000 kg may have two, three, four, or five significant figures. Adding a decimal point at the end would indicate that all five numbers are significant.

Often, however, a little common sense is useful. A temperature reading of 20 °C probably has two significant figures rather than one, because one significant figure would imply a temperature anywhere from 10 °C to 30 °C and would be of little use. Similarly, a volume given as 300 mL probably has three significant figures. On the other hand, a figure of 150,000,000 km for the distance between the earth and the sun has only two or three significant figures because the distance is variable. We will see a better way to deal with this problem in the next section.

▲ The number of seats in this auditorium is an exact number with an unlimited number of significant figures.

One final point about significant figures: some numbers, such as those obtained when counting objects and those that are part of a definition, are *exact* and effectively have an unlimited number of significant figures. Exact numbers are not measured and do not affect the number of significant figures in a calculated answer. Thus, a class might have *exactly* 32 students (not 31.9, 32.0, or 32.1), and 1 foot is defined to have *exactly* 12 inches.

Worked Example 1.5 Significant Figures of Measurements

How many significant figures do the following measurements have?

(a) 2730.78 m   (b) 0.0076 mL   (c) 3400 kg   (d) 3400.0 m²

ANALYSIS All nonzero numbers are significant; the number of significant figures will then depend on the status of the zeroes in each case. (Hint: Which rule applies in each case?)

SOLUTION

(a) Six (rule 1; Zeroes in the middle of a number are significant.)

(b) Two (rule 2; Leading zeroes after a decimal point are not significant.)

(c) Two, three, or four (rule 4; Trailing zeroes with no decimal point may or may not be significant.)

(d) Five (rule 3; Trailing zeroes are significant if a decimal point is included.)

PROBLEM 1.8

How many significant figures do the following measurements have?

(a) 3.45 m   (b) 0.1400 kg   (c) 10.003 L   (d) 35 cents

◉ KEY CONCEPT PROBLEM 1.9 ──────────────────

How would you record the temperature reading on the following Celsius thermometer? How many significant figures do you have in your answer?

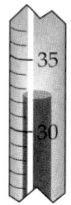

Scientific Notation and Significant Figures

Scientific notation is particularly helpful for indicating how many significant figures are present in a number that has zeroes at the end but to the left of a decimal point. If we read, for instance, that the distance from the earth to the sun is 150,000,000 km, we do not really know how many significant figures are indicated. Some of the zeroes might be significant, or they might merely act to locate the decimal point. Using scientific notation, however, we can indicate how many of the zeroes are significant. Rewriting 150,000,000 as 1.5×10^8 indicates two significant figures, whereas writing it as 1.500×10^8 indicates four significant figures. Scientific notation is not ordinarily used for numbers that are easily written, such as 10 or 175, although it is sometimes helpful in doing arithmetic.

▶▶ Rules for doing arithmetic with numbers written in scientific notation are reviewed in Appendix A.

Worked Example 1.6 Significant Figures and Scientific Notation

There are 1,760,000,000,000,000,000,000 molecules of sucrose (table sugar) in 1 g. Use scientific notation to express this number with four significant figures.

ANALYSIS Because the number is larger than 1, the exponent will be positive. You will have to move the decimal point 21 places to the left.

SOLUTION
The first four digits—1, 7, 6, and 0—are significant, meaning that only the first of the 19 zeroes is significant. Because we have to move the decimal point 21 places to the left to put it after the first significant digit, the answer is 1.760×10^{21}.

▲ How many molecules are in this 1 g pile of table sugar?

Worked Example 1.7 Scientific Notation

The rhinovirus responsible for the common cold has a diameter of 20 nm or 0.000 000 020 m. Express this number in scientific notation.

ANALYSIS The number is smaller than 1, and so the exponent will be negative. You will have to move the decimal point eight places to the right.

SOLUTION
There are only two significant figures because zeroes at the beginning of a number are not significant. We have to move the decimal point eight places to the right to place it after the first digit, so the answer is 2.0×10^{-8} m.

Worked Example 1.8 Scientific Notation and Unit Conversions

A clinical laboratory found that a blood sample contained 0.0026 g of phosphorus and 0.000 101 g of iron.
 (a) Give these quantities in scientific notation.
 (b) Give these quantities in the units normally used to report them—milligrams for phosphorus and micrograms for iron.

ANALYSIS Is the number larger or smaller than 1? How many places do you have to move the decimal point?

SOLUTION
 (a) 0.0026 g phosphorus $= 2.6 \times 10^{-3}$ g phosphorus

    0.000 101 g iron $= 1.01 \times 10^{-4}$ g iron

(b) We know from Table 1.6 that 1 mg $= 1 \times 10^{-3}$ g, where the exponent is -3. Expressing the amount of phosphorus in milligrams is straightforward because the amount in grams (2.6×10^{-3} g) already has an exponent of -3. Thus, 2.6×10^{-3} g $= 2.6$ mg of phosphorus.

$$(2.6 \times 10^{-3}\, \cancel{g})\left(\frac{1\ \text{mg}}{1 \times 10^{-3}\, \cancel{g}}\right) = 2.6\ \text{mg}$$

We know from Table 1.6 that 1 μg $= 1 \times 10^{-6}$ g where the exponent is -6. Expressing the amount of iron in micrograms thus requires that we restate the amount in grams so that the exponent is -6. We can do this by moving the decimal point six places to the right:

$$0.000\ 101\ \text{g iron} = 101 \times 10^{-6}\ \text{g iron} = 101\ \mu\text{g iron}$$

PROBLEM 1.10

Convert the following values to scientific notation:

(a) 0.058 g   (b) 46,792 m   (c) 0.006 072 cm   (d) 345.3 kg

PROBLEM 1.11

Convert the following values from scientific notation to standard notation:

(a) 4.885×10^4 mg   (b) 8.3×10^{-6} m   (c) 4.00×10^{-2} m

PROBLEM 1.12

Rewrite the following numbers in scientific notation as indicated:

(a) 630,000 with five significant figures
(b) 1300 with three significant figures
(c) 794,200,000,000 with four significant figures

1.9 Rounding Off Numbers

Learning Objective:

• Determine the appropriate number of significant figures in a calculated result and round off numbers in calculations involving measurements.

It often happens, particularly when doing arithmetic on a pocket calculator, that a quantity appears to have more significant figures than are really justified. For example, you might calculate the gas mileage of your car by finding that it takes 11.70 gallons of gasoline to drive 278 miles:

$$\text{Mileage} = \frac{\text{Miles}}{\text{Gallons}} = \frac{278\ \text{mi}}{11.70\ \text{gal}} = 23.760\ 684\ \text{mi/gal (mpg)}$$

Although the answer on a calculator has eight digits, your calculated result is really not as precise as it appears. In fact, as we will see next, your answer is good to only three significant figures and should be **rounded off** to 23.8 mi/gal.

How do you decide how many digits to keep? The full answer to this question is a bit complex and involves a mathematical treatment called *error analysis,* but for our purposes, a simplified procedure using just two rules is sufficient:

RULE 1: In carrying out a multiplication or division, the answer cannot have more significant figures than either of the original numbers. After all, if you do not know the number of miles you drove to better than three significant figures

Rounding off A procedure used for deleting nonsignificant figures.

(278 could mean 277, 278, or 279), you certainly cannot calculate your mileage to more than the same number of significant figures.

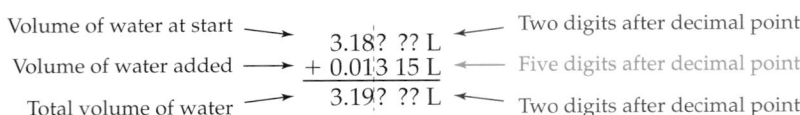

Three significant figures

Three significant figures

$$\frac{278 \text{ mi}}{11.70 \text{ gal}} = 23.8 \text{ mi/gal}$$

Four significant figures

RULE 2: In carrying out an addition or subtraction, the answer cannot have more digits after the decimal point than either of the original numbers. For example, if you have 3.18 L of water and you add 0.013 15 L more, you now have 3.19 L.

If you do not know the volume you started with past the second decimal place (it could be 3.17, 3.18, or 3.19), you cannot know the total of the combined volumes past the same decimal place.

▲ Calculators often display more digits than are justified by the precision of the data.

Volume of water at start → 3.18? ?? L ← Two digits after decimal point

Volume of water added → + 0.013 15 L ← Five digits after decimal point

Total volume of water → 3.19? ?? L ← Two digits after decimal point

If a calculation has several steps, it is generally best to round off at the end after all the steps have been carried out, keeping the number of significant figures determined by the least precise number in your calculations. Once you decide how many digits to retain for your answer, the rules for rounding off numbers are straightforward:

RULE 1: If the first digit you remove is four or less, drop it and all following digits. Thus, 2.4271 becomes 2.4 when rounded off to two significant figures because the first of the dropped digits (2) is four or less.

RULE 2: If the first digit you remove is five or greater, round the number up by adding a 1 to the digit to the left of the one you drop. Thus, 4.5832 becomes 4.6 when rounded off to two significant figures because the first of the dropped digits (8) is five or greater.

Worked Example 1.9 Significant Figures and Calculations: Addition /Subtraction

Suppose that you weigh 124 lb before dinner. How much will you weigh after dinner if you eat 1.884 lb of food?

ANALYSIS When performing addition or subtraction, the number of significant figures you report in the final answer is determined by the number of digits in the least precise number in the calculation.

SOLUTION
Your after-dinner weight is found by adding your original weight to the weight of the food consumed:

$$
\begin{array}{r}
124 \quad \text{lb} \\
1.884 \text{ lb} \\
\hline
125.884 \text{ lb (Unrounded)}
\end{array}
$$

Because the value of your original weight has no significant figures after the decimal point, your after-dinner weight also must have no significant figures after the decimal point. Thus, 125.884 lb must be rounded off to 126 lb.

Worked Example 1.10 Significant Figures and Calculations: Multiplication / Division

To make currant jelly, 13.75 cups of sugar was added to 18 cups of currant juice. How much sugar was added per cup of juice?

ANALYSIS For calculations involving multiplication or division, the final answer cannot have more significant figures than either of the original numbers.

SOLUTION
The quantity of sugar must be divided by the quantity of juice:

$$\frac{13.75 \text{ cups sugar}}{18 \text{ cups juice}} = 0.763\,888\,89 \frac{\text{cup sugar}}{\text{cup juice}} \text{ (Unrounded)}$$

The number of significant figures in the answer is limited to two by the quantity 18 cups in the calculation and must be rounded to 0.76 cup of sugar per cup of juice.

PROBLEM 1.13

Round off the following quantities to the indicated number of significant figures:
  (a) 2.304 g (three significant figures)
  (b) 188.3784 mL (five significant figures)
  (c) 0.008 87 L (one significant figure)
  (d) 1.000 39 kg (four significant figures)

PROBLEM 1.14

Carry out the following calculations, rounding each result to the correct number of significant figures:
  (a) 4.87 mL + 46.0 mL   **(b)** 3.4 × 0.023 g
  (c) 19.333 m − 7.4 m   **(d)** 55 mg − 4.671 mg + 0.894 mg
  (e) 62,911 ÷ 611

1.10 Problem Solving: Unit Conversions and Estimating Answers

Learning Objective:

• Use the factor-label method (conversion factors) to solve a problem and check the result to ensure that it makes sense chemically and physically.

Many activities in the laboratory and in medicine—measuring, weighing, preparing solutions, and so forth—require converting a quantity from one unit to another. For example: "These pills contain 1.3 grains of aspirin, but I need 200 mg. Is one pill enough?" Converting between units is not mysterious; we all do it every day. If you run nine laps around a 400 m track, for instance, you have to convert between the distance unit "lap" and the distance unit "meter" to find that you have run 3600 m (9 laps times 400 m / lap). If you want to find how many miles, you have to convert again to find that 3600 m = 2.237 mi.

The simplest way to carry out calculations involving different units is to use the **factor-label method.** In this method, a quantity in one unit is converted into an equivalent quantity in a different unit by using a **conversion factor** that expresses the relationship between units:

$$\text{Starting quantity} \times \text{Conversion factor} = \text{Equivalent quantity}$$

▲ Currency exchange between the US$ and euros is another activity that requires a unit conversion.

Factor-label method A problem-solving procedure in which equations are set up so that unwanted units cancel and only the desired units remain.

Conversion factor An expression of the numerical relationship between two units.

As an example, we learned from Table 1.8 that 1 km = 0.6214 mi. Writing this relationship as a fraction restates it in the form of a conversion factor, either kilometers per mile or miles per kilometer.

Since 1 km = 0.6214 mi, then:

Conversion factors between kilometers and miles

$$\frac{1 \text{ km}}{0.6214 \text{ mi}} = 1 \quad \text{or} \quad \frac{0.6214 \text{ mi}}{1 \text{ km}} = 1$$

Note that this and all other conversion factors are numerically equal to 1 because the value of the quantity above the division line (the numerator) is equal in value to the quantity below the division line (the denominator). Thus, multiplying by a conversion factor is equivalent to multiplying by 1 and so does not change the value of the quantity being multiplied.

These two quantities are the same.

$$\frac{1 \text{ km}}{0.6214 \text{ mi}} \quad \text{or} \quad \frac{0.6214 \text{ mi}}{1 \text{ km}}$$

These two quantities are the same.

The key to the factor-label method of problem solving is that units are treated like numbers and can thus be multiplied and divided (though not added or subtracted) just as numbers can. When solving a problem, the idea is to set up an equation so that all unwanted units cancel, leaving only the desired units. Usually, it is best to start by writing what you know and then manipulating that known quantity. For example, if you know there are 26.22 mi in a marathon and want to find how many kilometers that is, you could write the distance in miles and multiply by the conversion factor in kilometers per mile. The unit "mi" cancels because it appears both above and below the division line, leaving "km" as the only remaining unit.

$$26.22 \text{ mi} \times \frac{1 \text{ km}}{0.6214 \text{ mi}} = 42.20 \text{ km}$$

Starting quantity · Conversion factor · Equivalent quantity

The factor-label method gives the right answer only if the equation is set up so that the unwanted unit (or units) cancels. If the equation is set up in any other way, the units will not cancel and you will not get the right answer. Thus, if you selected the incorrect conversion factor (miles per kilometer) for the above problem, you would end up with an incorrect answer expressed in meaningless units:

$$\text{Incorrect } 26.22 \text{ mi} \times \frac{0.6214 \text{ mi}}{1 \text{ km}} = 16.29 \frac{\text{mi}^2}{\text{km}} \text{ Incorrect}$$

The main drawback to using the factor-label method is that it is possible to get an answer without really understanding what you are doing. It is therefore best when solving a problem to first think through a rough estimate, or *ballpark estimate,* as a check on your work. If your ballpark estimate is not close to the final calculated solution, there is a misunderstanding somewhere and you should think the problem through again. If, for example, you came up with the answer 5.3 cm³ when calculating the volume of a human cell, you should realize that such an answer could not possibly be right. Cells are too tiny to be distinguished with the naked eye, but a volume of 5.3 cm³ is about the size of a walnut. The Worked Examples 1.11, 1.12, and 1.13 at the end of this section show how to estimate the answers to simple unit-conversion problems.

The factor-label method and the use of ballpark estimates are techniques that will help you solve problems of many kinds, not just unit conversions. Problems sometimes seem complicated, but you can usually sort out the complications by analyzing the problem properly:

STEP 1: Identify the information given, including units.

STEP 2: Identify the information needed in the answer, including units.

STEP 3: Find the relationships between the known information and unknown answer, and plan a series of steps, including conversion factors, for getting from one to the other.

STEP 4: Solve the problem.

BALLPARK CHECK Make a ballpark estimate at the beginning and check it against your final answer to be sure the value and the units of your calculated answer are reasonable.

Worked Example 1.11 Factor Labels: Unit Conversions

Write conversion factors for the following pairs of units (use Tables 1.7–1.9):

(a) Deciliters and milliliters

(b) Pounds and grams

ANALYSIS Start with the appropriate equivalency relationship and rearrange to form conversion factors.

SOLUTION

(a) Since 1 dL = 0.1 L and 1 mL = 0.001 L, then $1 \text{ dL} = (0.1 \text{ L})\left(\dfrac{1 \text{ mL}}{0.001 \text{ L}}\right) = 100 \text{ mL}$. The conversion factors are

$$\frac{1 \text{ dL}}{100 \text{ mL}} \quad \text{and} \quad \frac{100 \text{ mL}}{1 \text{ dL}}$$

(b) $\dfrac{1 \text{ lb}}{454 \text{ g}}$ and $\dfrac{454 \text{ g}}{1 \text{ lb}}$

Worked Example 1.12 Factor Labels: Unit Conversions

(a) Convert 0.75 lb to grams.

(b) Convert 0.50 qt to deciliters.

ANALYSIS Start with conversion factors and set up equations so that units cancel appropriately.

SOLUTION

(a) Select the conversion factor from Worked Example 1.9(b) so that the "lb" units cancel and "g" remains:

$$0.75 \text{ lb} \times \frac{454 \text{ g}}{1 \text{ lb}} = 340 \text{ g}$$

(b) In this, as in many problems, it is convenient to use more than one conversion factor. As long as the unwanted units cancel correctly, two or more conversion factors can be strung together in the same calculation. In this case, we can convert first between quarts and milliliters and then between milliliters and deciliters:

$$0.50 \text{ qt} \times \frac{946.4 \text{ mL}}{1 \text{ qt}} \times \frac{1 \text{ dL}}{100 \text{ mL}} = 4.7 \text{ dL}$$

Worked Example 1.13 Factor Labels: Unit Conversions

A child is 21.5 inches long at birth. How long is this in centimeters?

ANALYSIS This problem calls for converting from inches to centimeters, so we will need to know how many centimeters are in an inch and how to use this information as a conversion factor.

—continued on next page

—continued from previous page

BALLPARK ESTIMATE It takes about 2.5 cm to make 1 in., and so it should take two and a half times as many centimeters to make a distance equal to approximately 20 in., or about 20 in. × 2.5 = 50 cm.

SOLUTION

STEP 1: **Identify given information.**	Length = 21.5 in.
STEP 2: **Identify answer and units.**	Length = ?? cm
STEP 3: **Identify conversion factor.**	1 in. = 2.54 cm ⟶ $\dfrac{2.54 \text{ cm}}{1 \text{ in.}}$
STEP 4: **Solve.** Multiply the known length (in inches) by the conversion factor so that units cancel, providing the answer (in centimeters)	21.5 i̶n̶. × $\dfrac{2.54 \text{ cm}}{1 \text{ i̶n̶.}}$ = 54.6 cm (Rounded off from 54.61)

BALLPARK CHECK How does this value compare with the ballpark estimate we made at the beginning? Are the final units correct? 54.6 cm is close to our original estimate of 50 cm.

Worked Example 1.14 Factor Labels: Concentration to Mass

A patient requires an injection of 0.012 g of a pain killer available as a 15 mg/mL solution. How many milliliters of solution should be administered?

ANALYSIS Knowing the amount of pain killer in 1 mL allows us to use the concentration as a conversion factor to determine the volume of solution that would contain the desired amount.

BALLPARK ESTIMATE One milliliter contains 15 mg of the pain killer, or 0.015 g. Since only 0.012 g is needed, a little less than 1.0 mL should be administered.

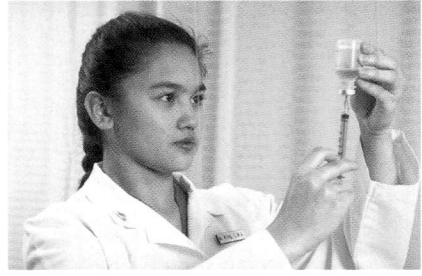

▲ How many milliliters should be injected?

SOLUTION

STEP 1: **Identify known information.**	Dosage = 0.012 g Concentration = 15 mg/mL
STEP 2: **Identify answer and units.**	Volume to administer = ?? mL
STEP 3: **Identify conversion factors.** Two conversion factors are needed. First, g must be converted to mg. Once we have the mass in mg, we can calculate mL using the conversion factor of mL/mg.	1 mg = .001 g ⟹ $\dfrac{1 \text{ mg}}{0.001 \text{ g}}$ 15 mg/mL ⟹ $\dfrac{1 \text{ mL}}{15 \text{ mg}}$
STEP 4: **Solve.** Starting from the desired dosage, we use the conversion factors to cancel units, obtaining the final answer in mL.	$(0.012 \text{ g̶}) \left(\dfrac{1 \text{ m̶g̶}}{0.001 \text{ g̶}} \right) \left(\dfrac{1 \text{ mL}}{15 \text{ m̶g̶}} \right)$ = 0.80 mL

BALLPARK CHECK Consistent with our initial estimate of a little less than 1 mL.

Worked Example 1.15 Factor Labels: Multiple Conversion Calculations

Administration of digitalis to control atrial fibrillation in heart patients must be carefully regulated because even a modest overdose can be fatal. To take differences between patients into account, dosages are sometimes prescribed in micrograms per kilogram of body weight (μg/kg). Thus, two people may differ greatly in weight, but both will receive the proper dosage. At a dosage of 20 μg/kg body weight, how many milligrams of digitalis should a 160 lb patient receive?

ANALYSIS Knowing the patient's body weight (in kg) and the recommended dosage (in μg/kg), we can calculate the appropriate amount of digitalis.

BALLPARK ESTIMATE Since a kilogram is roughly equal to 2 lb, a 160 lb patient has a mass of about 80 kg. At a dosage of 20 μg/kg, an 80 kg patient should receive 80 × 20 μg, or about 1600 μg of digitalis, or 1.6 mg.

SOLUTION

STEP 1: **Identify known information.**

STEP 2: **Identify answer and units.**

STEP 3: **Identify conversion factors.** Two conversions are needed. First, convert the patient's weight in pounds to weight in kg. The correct dose can then be determined based on μg digitalis/kg of body weight. Finally, the dosage in μg is converted to mg.

STEP 4: **Solve.** Use the known information and the conversion factors so that units cancel, obtaining the answer in mg.

Patient weight $= 160\,lb$
Prescribed dosage $= 20\,\mu g$ digitalis/kg body weight
Delivered dosage $= ??$ mg digitalis

$$1\,kg = 2.205\,lb \rightarrow \frac{1\,kg}{2.205\,lb}$$

$$1\,mg = (0.001\,g)\left(\frac{1\,\mu g}{10^{-6}\,g}\right) = 1000\,\mu g$$

$$160\,\cancel{lb} \times \frac{1\,\cancel{kg}}{2.205\,\cancel{lb}} \times \frac{20\,\cancel{\mu g}\ digitalis}{1\,\cancel{kg}} \times \frac{1\,mg}{1000\,\cancel{\mu g}}$$

$$= 1.5\,mg\ digitalis\ (Rounded\ off)$$

BALLPARK CHECK Close to our estimate of 1.6 mg.

PROBLEM 1.15

Write appropriate conversion factors and carry out the following conversions:

(a) $16.0\,oz = ?\,g$ (b) $2500\,mL = ?\,L$ (c) $99.0\,L = ?\,qt$

PROBLEM 1.16

Convert 0.840 qt to milliliters in a single calculation using more than one conversion factor.

PROBLEM 1.17

A patient is to receive 20 mg of methimazole, a drug used to treat hyperthyroid conditions. The drug is dissolved in solution containing 8 mg/mL. What volume of solution should be administered?

PROBLEM 1.18

Calculate the dosage in milligrams per kilogram body weight for a 135 lb adult who takes two aspirin tablets containing 0.324 g of aspirin each. Calculate the dosage for a 40 lb child who also takes two aspirin tablets.

1.11 Temperature, Heat, and Energy

Learning Objectives:

• Define the relationship between temperature and heat energy and convert temperatures between various temperature scales.

• Use temperature and specific heat to evaluate the flow of heat/energy in matter.

All chemical reactions are accompanied by a change in **energy,** which is defined in scientific terms as *the capacity to do work or supply heat* (Figure 1.8). Detailed discussion of the various kinds of energy will be included in Chapter 7, but for now we will look at the various units used to describe energy and heat, and how heat energy can be gained or lost by matter.

Temperature, the measure of the amount of heat energy in an object, is commonly reported either in Fahrenheit (°F) or Celsius (°C) units. The SI unit for reporting temperature, however, is the *kelvin* (K). (Note that we say only "kelvin," not "degrees kelvin.")

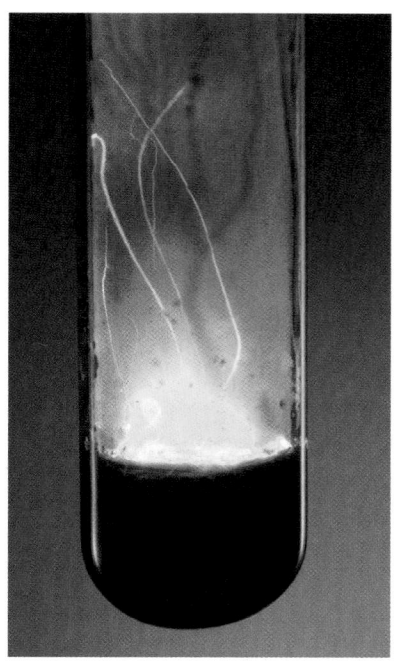

▲ Figure 1.8
The reaction of aluminum with bromine releases energy in the form of heat.
When the reaction is complete, the products undergo no further change.

Energy The capacity to do work or supply heat.

Temperature The measure of the amount of heat energy in an object.

The kelvin and the Celsius degree are the same size—both are 1/100 of the interval between the freezing point of water and the boiling point of water at atmospheric pressure. Thus, a change in temperature of 1 °C is equal to a change of 1 K. The only difference between the Kelvin and Celsius temperature scales is that they have different zero points. The Celsius scale assigns a value of 0 °C to the freezing point of water, but the Kelvin scale assigns a value of 0 K to the coldest possible temperature, sometimes called *absolute zero,* which is equal to −273.15 °C. Thus, 0 K = −273.15 °C, and +273.15 K = 0 °C. For example, a warm spring day with a temperature of 25 °C has a Kelvin temperature of 298 K (for most purposes, rounding off to 273 is sufficient).

$$\text{Temperature in °K} \;=\; \text{Temperature in °C} \,+\, 273.15$$

$$\text{Temperature in °C} \;=\; \text{Temperature in K} \,-\, 273.15$$

For practical applications in medicine and clinical chemistry, the Fahrenheit and Celsius scales are used almost exclusively. The Fahrenheit scale defines the freezing point of water as 32 °F and the boiling point of water as 212 °F, whereas 0 °C and 100 °C are the freezing and boiling points of water on the Celsius scale. Thus, it takes 180 °F to cover the same range encompassed by only 100 °C, and a Celsius degree is therefore exactly 180/100 = 9/5 = 1.8 times as large as a Fahrenheit degree. In other words, a change in temperature of 1.0 °C is equal to a change of 1.8 °F. Figure 1.9 gives a comparison of all three scales.

Converting between the Fahrenheit and Celsius scales is similar to converting between different units of length or volume, but is a bit more complex because two corrections need to be made—one to adjust for the difference in degree size and one to adjust for the different zero points. The degree-size correction is made by using the relationship 1 °C = 1.8 °F and 1 °F = (1/1.8) °C. The zero-point correction is made by

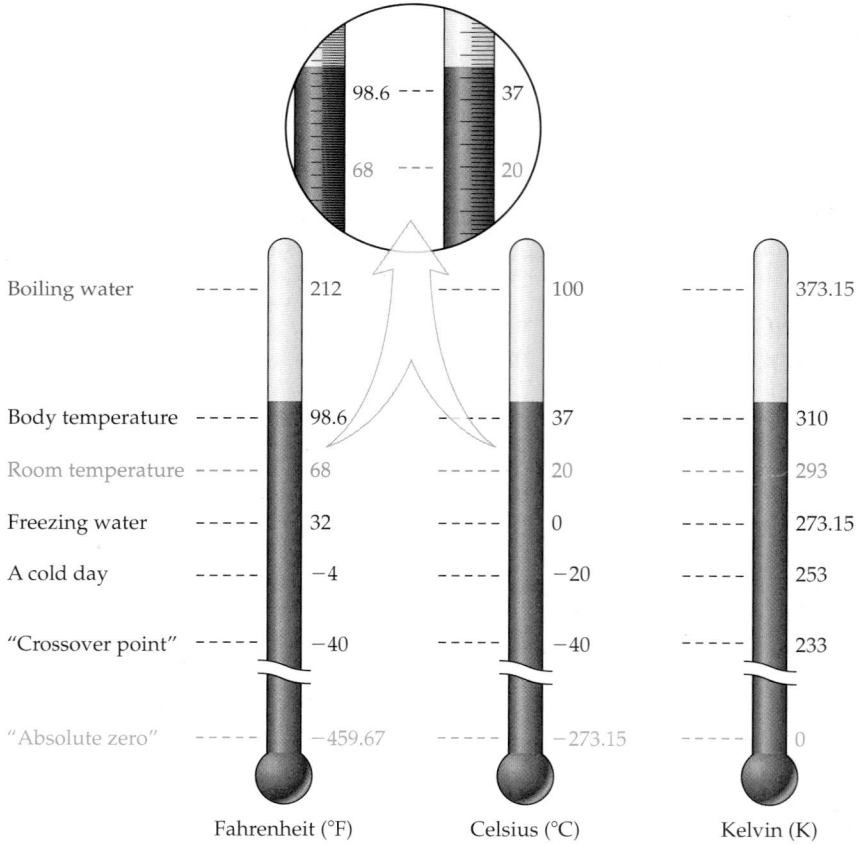

▲ **Figure 1.9**
A comparison of the Fahrenheit, Celsius, and Kelvin temperature scales.
One Celsius degree is 1.8 times the size of one Fahrenheit degree.

CHEMISTRY IN ACTION

☤ Temperature-Sensitive Materials

The physical properties of many materials change with the ambient temperature. Substances known as thermochromic materials change color as their temperature increases, and they change from the liquid phase to a semicrystalline-ordered state. These "liquid crystals" can be incorporated into plastics or paints and can be used to monitor temperature. For example, some meat packaging now includes a temperature strip that darkens when the meat is stored above a certain temperature, which makes the meat unsafe to eat. Hospitals and other medical facilities now routinely use strips that, when placed under the tongue or applied to the forehead, change color to indicate the patient's body temperature.

Other temperature-sensitive materials, called *shape-memory alloys* (SMAs), can be bent out of shape and will recover their original shape when heated above a certain temperature. These materials have many practical and clinical applications, including orthodontic wires that do not need to be tightened. The SMA is bent to fit into the orthodontic form, but once in the mouth its temperature increases and it contracts back to its original shape, applying constant force to align the teeth. SMAs are also used in stents. A collapsed stent can be inserted into an artery or vein; at body temperature the stent expands to its original shape and provides support for the artery or vein, improving blood flow.

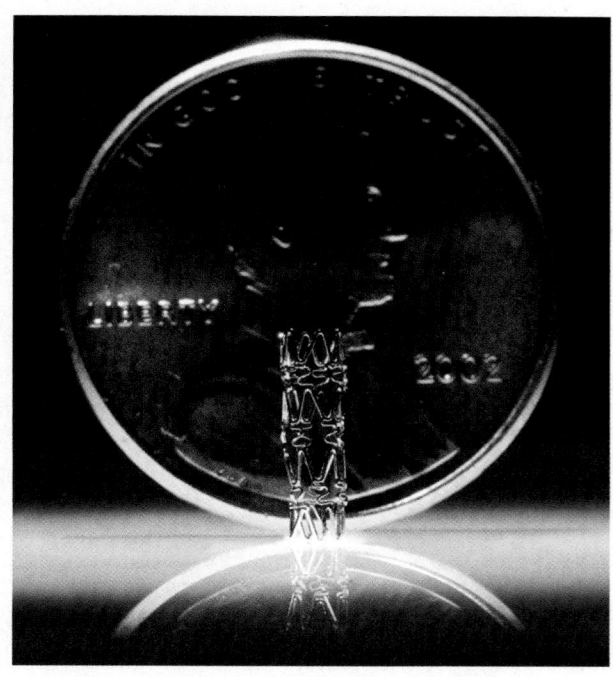

▲ This stent, made from shape memory alloy, can be collapsed for insertion into an artery. Once in position, it is expanded by application of heat to maintain the arterial opening.

CIA Problem 1.4 A thermochromic plastic chip included in a shipping container for beef undergoes an irreversible color change if the storage temperature exceeds 28 °F. What is this temperature on the Celsius and Kelvin scales?

CIA Problem 1.5 A temperature-sensitive bath toy undergoes several color changes in the temperature range from 37 °C to 47 °C. What is the corresponding temperature range on the Fahrenheit scale?

remembering that the freezing point is higher by 32 on the Fahrenheit scale than on the Celsius scale. These corrections are incorporated into the following formulas, which show the conversion methods:

$$\textit{Celsius to Fahrenheit:} \quad °F = \left(\frac{1.8\,°F}{°C} × °C \right) + 32\,°F$$

$$\textit{Fahrenheit to Celsius:} \quad °C = \left(\frac{°C}{1.8\,°F} \right) × (°F - 32\,°F)$$

Energy is represented in SI units by the unit *joule* (J; pronounced "jool"), but the metric unit *calorie* (cal) is still widely used in medicine. In this text we will present energy values in both units. One calorie is the amount of heat necessary to raise the temperature of 1 g of water by 1 °C. A *kilocalorie* (kcal), often called a *large calorie* (Cal) or *food calorie* by nutritionists, equals 1000 cal:

$$1000\,cal = 1\,kcal \qquad 1000\,J = 1\,kJ$$
$$1\,cal = 4.184\,J \qquad 1\,kcal = 4.184\,kJ$$

Not all substances have their temperatures raised to the same extent when equal amounts of heat energy are added. One calorie raises the temperature of 1 g of water by 1 °C but raises the temperature of 1 g of iron by 10 °C. The amount of heat needed

Specific heat The amount of heat that will raise the temperature of 1 g of a substance by 1 °C.

to raise the temperature of 1 g of a substance by 1 °C is called the **specific heat** of the substance. It is measured in units of $\text{cal}/(\text{g} \cdot {}^\circ\text{C})$.

$$\text{Specific heat} = \frac{\text{calories}}{\text{grams} \times {}^\circ\text{C}}$$

Specific heats vary greatly from one substance to another, as shown in Table 1.10. The specific heat of water, $1.00 \, \text{cal}/(\text{g} \cdot {}^\circ\text{C})$ or 4.184 J/g °C, is higher than that of most other substances, which means that a large transfer of heat is required to change the temperature of a given amount of water by a given number of degrees. One consequence is that the human body, which is about 60% water, is able to withstand changing outside conditions.

Knowing the mass and specific heat of a substance makes it possible to calculate how much heat must be added or removed to accomplish a given temperature change, as shown in Worked Example 1.17.

Table 1.10 Specific Heats of Some Common Substances

Substance	Specific Heat [cal/g°C]; [J/g°C]	
Ethanol	0.59	2.5
Gold	0.031	0.13
Iron	0.106	0.444
Mercury	0.033	0.14
Sodium	0.293	1.23
Water	1.00	4.18

$$\text{Heat (cal)} = \text{Mass (g)} \times \text{Temperature change } (\Delta \, {}^\circ\text{C}) \times \text{Specific heat} \left(\frac{\text{cal}}{\text{g} \cdot {}^\circ\text{C}} \right)$$

Worked Example 1.16 Temperature Conversions: Fahrenheit to Celsius

A body temperature above 107 °F can be fatal. What does 107 °F correspond to on the Celsius scale?

ANALYSIS Using the temperature (in °F) and the appropriate temperature conversion equation, we can convert from the Fahrenheit scale to the Celsius scale.

BALLPARK ESTIMATE Note that in Figure 1.9 the normal body temperature is 98.6 °F or 37 °C. A temperature of 107 °F is approximately 8 °F above normal; since 1 °C is nearly 2 °F then 8 °F is about 4 °C. Thus, the 107 °F body temperature is 41 °C.

SOLUTION

STEP 1: **Identify known information.**

STEP 2: **Identify answer and units.**

STEP 3: **Identify conversion factors.** We can convert from °F to °C using this equation.

STEP 4: **Solve.** Substitute the known temperature (in °F) into the equation.

Temperature = 107 °F

Temperature = ?? °C

$${}^\circ\text{C} = \left(\frac{{}^\circ\text{C}}{1.8 \, {}^\circ\text{F}} \right) ({}^\circ\text{F} - 32 \, {}^\circ\text{F})$$

$${}^\circ\text{C} = \left(\frac{{}^\circ\text{C}}{1.8 \, {}^\circ\text{F}} \right) (107 \, {}^\circ\text{F} - 32 \, {}^\circ\text{F}) = 42 \, {}^\circ\text{C}^*$$

(Rounded off from 41.666 667 °C)

BALLPARK CHECK Close to our estimate of 41 °C.

*It is worth noting that the 1.8 conversion factor in the equation is an exact conversion, and so it does not impact the number of significant figures in the final answer.

Worked Example 1.17 Specific Heat: Mass, Temperature, and Energy

Taking a bath might use about 95 kg of water. How much energy (in calories and Joules) is needed to heat the water from a cold 15 °C to a warm 40 °C?

ANALYSIS From the amount of water being heated (95 kg) and the amount of the temperature change (40 °C − 15 °C = 25 °C), the total amount of energy needed can be calculated by using specific heat [$1.00 \, \text{cal}/(\text{g} \cdot {}^\circ\text{C})$] as a conversion factor.

BALLPARK ESTIMATE The water is being heated by 25 °C (from 15 °C to 40 °C), and it therefore takes 25 cal to heat each gram. The tub contains nearly 100,000 g (95 kg is 95,000 g), and so it takes about 25 × 100,000 cal, or 2,500,000 cal, to heat all the water in the tub.

SOLUTION

STEP 1: **Identify known information.**

STEP 2: **Identify answer and units.**

STEP 3: **Identify conversion factors.** The amount of energy (in cal) can be calculated using the specific heat of water $(cal/g \cdot °C)$, and it will depend on both the mass of water (in g) to be heated and the total temperature change (in °C). In order for the units in specific heat to cancel correctly, the mass of water must first be converted from kg to g.

STEP 4: **Solve.** Starting with the known information, use the conversion factors to cancel unwanted units.

BALLPARK CHECK Close to our estimate of 2.5×10^6 cal.

Mass of water $= 95$ kg

Temperature change $= 40 °C - 15 °C = 25 °C$

Heat $= ??$ cal

Specific heat $= \dfrac{1.0 \text{ cal}}{g \cdot °C}$

$1 \text{ kg} = 1000 \text{ g} \rightarrow \dfrac{1000 \text{ g}}{1 \text{ kg}}$

$95 \text{ kg} \times \dfrac{1000 \text{ g}}{\text{kg}} \times \dfrac{1.00 \text{ cal}}{g \cdot °C} \times 25 °C = 2{,}400{,}000 \text{ cal}$

$= 2.4 \times 10^6 \text{ cal (or } 1.0 \times 10^7 \text{ J)}$

PROBLEM 1.19

The highest land temperature ever recorded was 136 °F in Al Aziziyah, Libya, on September 13, 1922. What is this temperature on the Kelvin scale?

PROBLEM 1.20

A patient exhibits a temperature of 39 °C. What is the body temperature of the patient in °F?

PROBLEM 1.21

Assuming that Coca-Cola has the same specific heat as water, how much energy in calories is removed when 350 g of Coca-Cola (about the contents of one 12 oz can) is cooled from room temperature (25 °C) to refrigerator temperature (3 °C)?

PROBLEM 1.22

What is the specific heat of aluminum if it takes 161 cal (674 J) to raise the temperature of a 75 g aluminum bar by 10.0 °C?

1.12 Density and Specific Gravity

Learning Objective:

• Define density and specific gravity and use these quantities in mass / volume calculations.

One further physical quantity that we will take up in this chapter is **density,** which relates the mass of an object to its volume. Density is usually expressed in units of grams per cubic centimeter (g/cm^3) for solids and grams per milliliter (g/mL) for liquids. Thus, if we know the density of a substance, we know both the mass of a given volume and the volume of a given mass. The densities of some common materials are listed in Table 1.11.

Density The physical property that relates the mass of an object to its volume; mass per unit volume.

$$\text{Density} = \frac{\text{Mass (g)}}{\text{Volume (mL or cm}^3)}$$

Although most substances contract when cooled and expand when heated, water behaves differently. Water contracts when cooled from 100 °C to 3.98 °C but below this temperature it begins to *expand* again. The density of liquid water is at its maximum of 1.0000 g / mL at 3.98 °C but decreases to 0.999 87 g / mL at 0 °C. When freezing occurs, the density drops still further to a value of 0.917 g / cm³ for ice at 0 °C. Since a

▲ The Galileo thermometer contains several weighted bulbs that rise or fall as the density of the liquid changes with temperature.

Specific gravity The density of a substance divided by the density of water at the same temperature.

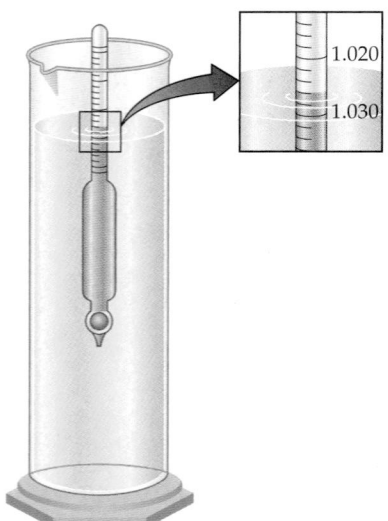

▲ **Figure 1.10**
A hydrometer for measuring specific gravity.
The instrument has a weighted bulb at the end of a calibrated glass tube. The depth to which the hydrometer sinks in a liquid indicates the liquid's specific gravity.

less dense substance will float on top of a more dense fluid, ice and any other substance with a density less than that of water will float in water. Conversely, any substance with a density greater than that of water will sink in water.

Table 1.11 Densities of Some Common Materials at 25 °C

Substance	Density*	Substance	Density*
Gases		Solids	
Helium	0.000 194	Ice (0 °C)	0.917
Air	0.001 185	Gold	19.3
		Human fat	0.94
Liquids		Cork	0.22–0.26
Water (3.98 °C)	1.0000	Table sugar	1.59
Urine	1.003–1.030	Balsa wood	0.12
Blood plasma	1.027		

*Densities are in g/cm^3 for solids and g/mL for liquids and gases. As noted in Section 1.7, $1\ mL\ =\ 1\ cm^3$.

Knowing the density of a liquid is useful because it is often easier to measure a liquid's volume rather than its mass. Suppose, for example, that you need 1.50 g of ethanol. Rather than use a dropper to weigh out exactly the right amount, it would be much easier to look up the density of ethanol (0.7893 g/mL at 20 °C) and measure the correct volume (1.90 mL) with a syringe or graduated cylinder. Thus, density acts as a conversion factor between mass (g) and volume (mL).

$$1.50\ \text{g ethanol} \times \frac{1\ \text{mL ethanol}}{0.7893\ \text{g ethanol}} = 1.90\ \text{mL ethanol}$$

For many purposes, ranging from winemaking to medicine, it is more convenient to use *specific gravity* than density. The **specific gravity** (sp gr) of a substance (usually a liquid) is simply the density of the substance divided by the density of water at the same temperature. Because all units cancel, specific gravity is unitless:

$$\text{Specific gravity} = \frac{\text{Density of substance}\ (\text{g}/\text{mL})}{\text{Density of water at the same temperature}\ (\text{g}/\text{mL})}$$

At typical temperatures, the density of water is very close to 1 g/mL. Thus, the specific gravity of a substance is numerically equal to its density and is used in the same way.

The specific gravity of a liquid can be measured using an instrument called a *hydrometer,* which consists of a weighted bulb on the end of a calibrated glass tube, as shown in Figure 1.10. The depth to which the hydrometer sinks when placed in a fluid indicates the fluid's specific gravity: the lower the bulb sinks, the lower the specific gravity of the fluid.

In medicine, a hydrometer called a *urinometer* is used to indicate the amount of solids dissolved in urine. Although the specific gravity of normal urine is about 1.003–1.030, conditions such as diabetes mellitus or a high fever cause an abnormally high urine specific gravity, indicating either excessive elimination of solids or decreased elimination of water. Abnormally low specific gravity is found in individuals using diuretics—drugs that increase water elimination.

Worked Example 1.18 Density: Mass-to-Volume Conversion

What volume of isopropyl alcohol (rubbing alcohol) would you use if you needed 25.0 g? The density of isopropyl alcohol is 0.7855 g/mL at 20 °C.

ANALYSIS The known information is the mass of isopropyl alcohol needed (25.0 g). The density (0.7855 g/mL) acts as a conversion factor between mass and the unknown volume of isopropyl alcohol.

BALLPARK ESTIMATE Because 1 mL of isopropyl alcohol contains only 0.7885 g of the alcohol, obtaining 1 g of alcohol requires almost 20% more than 1 mL, or about 1.2 mL. Therefore, a volume of about 25 × 1.2 mL = 30 mL is needed to obtain 25 g of alcohol.

SOLUTION

STEP 1: Identify known information.

STEP 2: Identify answer and units.

STEP 3: Identify conversion factors. Starting with the mass of isopropyl alcohol (in g), the corresponding volume (in mL) can be calculated using density (g/mL) as the conversion factor.

STEP 4: Solve. Starting with the known information, set up the equation with conversion factors so that unwanted units cancel.

BALLPARK CHECK Our estimate was 30 mL.

Mass of rubbing alcohol = 25.0 g
Density of rubbing alcohol = 0.7855 g/mL

Volume of rubbing alcohol = ?? mL

Density = g/mL → 1/density = mL/g

$$25.0 \text{ g alcohol} \times \frac{1 \text{ mL alcohol}}{0.7855 \text{ g alcohol}} = 31.8 \text{ mL alcohol}$$

PROBLEM 1.23

A sample of pumice, a porous volcanic rock, weighs 17.4 grams and has a volume of 27.3 cm³. If this sample is placed in a container of water, will it sink or will it float? Explain.

PROBLEM 1.24

Chloroform, once used as an anesthetic agent, has a density of 1.474 g/mL. What volume would you use if you needed 12.37 g?

PROBLEM 1.25

The sulfuric acid solution in an automobile battery typically has a specific gravity of about 1.27. Is battery acid more dense or less dense than pure water?

▲ The specific gravity of urine, measured by a urinometer, is used to diagnose conditions such as diabetes.

CHEMISTRY IN ACTION

⚕ A Measurement Example: Obesity and Body Fat

At the beginning of the chapter, we mentioned that some fat is good, but how much is too much and what are the health risks of too much body fat? The impacts of obesity include significant adverse health effects—heart disease, stroke, type 2 diabetes, and certain types of cancer—as well as annual medical costs related to obesity in excess of US$147 billion. Of particular concern is childhood obesity; the percentage of children aged 6–11 who were obese increased from 7% in 1980 to nearly 18% in 2012. For teenagers (ages 12–19), the increase was even more dramatic, from 5% to nearly 21% over the same period. In 2012, more than one-third of children and adolescents were overweight or obese.

At the beginning of the chapter, we learned that obesity is an excessive amount of body fat and one way to measure body fat is

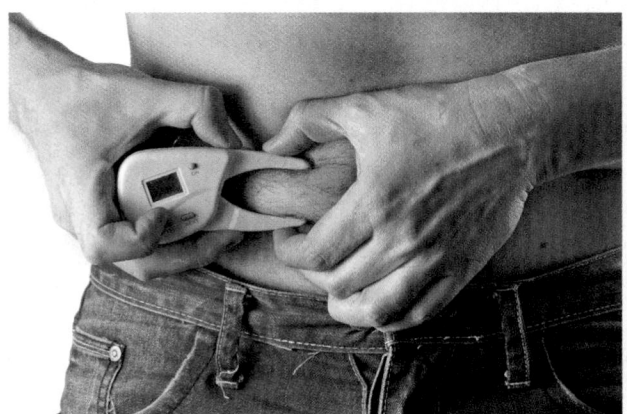

▲ A person's percentage body fat can be estimated by measuring the thickness of the fat layer under the skin.

through buoyancy testing. But obesity is also defined by reference to *body mass index* (BMI), which is equal to a person's mass in kilograms divided by the square of his or her height in meters. BMI can also be calculated by dividing a person's weight in pounds by the square of her or his height in inches multiplied by 703. For instance, someone 5 ft 7 in. (67 inches; 1.70 m) tall weighing 147 lb (66.7 kg) has a BMI of 23:

$$BMI = \frac{weight\ (kg)}{[\,height\ (m)\,]^2}, \quad or \quad \frac{weight\ (lb)}{[\,height\ (in.)\,]^2} \times 703$$

A BMI of 25 or above is considered overweight, and a BMI of 30 or above is obese. By these standards, approximately 61% of the U.S. population is overweight. Health professionals are concerned by the rapid rise in obesity in the United States because of the link between BMI and health problems. Many reports have documented the correlation between health and BMI, including a recent study on more than 1 million adults. The lowest death risk from any cause, including cancer and heart disease, is associated with a BMI between 22 and 24. Risk increases steadily as BMI increases, more than doubling for a BMI above 29.

An individual's percentage of body fat is most easily measured by the skinfold-thickness method. The skin at several locations on the arm, shoulder, and waist is pinched, and the thickness of the fat layer beneath the skin is measured with calipers. Comparing the measured results to those in a standard table gives an estimation of percentage body fat. As an alternative to skinfold measurement, a more accurate assessment of body fat can be made by underwater immersion, or buoyancy testing as we learned at the beginning of the chapter.

There is good news—campaigns to increase awareness of the negative effects of obesity and a renewed emphasis on healthy eating and exercise are producing results. The prevalence of obesity in children aged 2–5 years old decreased from 13.9% in 2004 to 8.4% in 2012.

Weight (lb)

	110	115	120	125	130	135	140	145	150	155	160	165	170	175	180	185	190	195	200
5'0"	21	22	23	24	25	26	27	28	29	30	31	32	33	34	35	36	37	38	39
5'2"	20	21	22	23	24	25	26	27	27	28	29	30	31	32	33	34	35	36	37
5'4"	19	20	21	21	22	23	24	25	26	27	27	28	29	30	31	32	33	33	34
5'6"	18	19	19	20	21	22	23	23	24	25	26	27	27	28	29	30	31	31	32
5'8"	17	17	18	19	20	21	21	22	23	24	24	25	26	27	27	28	29	30	30
5'10"	16	17	17	18	19	19	20	21	22	22	23	24	24	25	26	27	27	28	29
6'0"	15	16	16	17	18	18	19	20	20	21	22	22	23	24	24	25	26	26	27
6'2"	14	15	15	16	17	17	18	19	19	20	21	21	22	22	23	24	24	25	26
6'4"	13	14	15	15	16	16	17	18	18	19	19	20	21	21	22	23	23	24	24

(Height on left axis)

Body Mass Index (numbers in boxes)

CIA Problem 1.6 Calculate the BMI for an individual who is

(a) 5 ft 1 in. tall and weighs 155 lb
(b) 5 ft 11 in. tall and weighs 170 lb
(c) 6 ft 3 in. tall and weighs 195 lb

Which of these individuals is likely to have increased health risks?

CIA Problem 1.7 Liposuction is a technique for removing fat deposits from various areas of the body. How many liters of fat would have to be removed to result in a 5.0 lb weight loss? The density of human fat is 0.94 g/mL

SUMMARY REVISITING THE LEARNING OBJECTIVES

• **Identify properties of matter and differentiate between chemical and physical changes.** *Matter* is anything that has mass and occupies volume—that is, anything physically real. A *property* is any characteristic that can be used to describe or identify something: *physical* properties can be seen or measured without changing the chemical identity of the substance (i.e., color, melting point), while *chemical* properties can only be seen or measured when the substance undergoes a *chemical change,* such as a chemical reaction *(see Problems 33–35).*

• **Identify the three states of matter and describe their properties.** Matter can be classified by its physical state as *solid, liquid,* or *gas.* A solid has a definite volume and shape, a liquid has a definite volume but indefinite shape, and a gas has neither a definite volume nor a definite shape *(see Problems 26, 36–39, and 41).*

• **Distinguish between mixtures and pure substances and classify pure substances as elements or compounds.** Matter can also be classified by composition as being either *pure* or a *mixture.* Every pure substance is either an *element* or a *chemical compound.* Elements are fundamental substances that cannot be chemically changed into anything simpler. A chemical compound, by contrast, can be broken down by chemical change into simpler substances. Mixtures are composed of two or more pure substances and can be separated into component parts by physical means *(see Problems 40–43, 53, and 92).*

• **Identify the symbols and names of the common elements.** Elements are represented by one- or two-letter symbols, such as H for hydrogen, Ca for calcium, Al for aluminum, and so on. Most symbols are the first one or two letters of the element name, but some symbols are derived from Latin names—Na (sodium), for example *(see Problems 26, 27, 44–52, and 114).*

- **Identify a chemical change as a chemical reaction.** A chemical reaction is a symbolic representation of a chemical change. The starting materials (reactants) are on the left, the final materials (products) are on the right. An arrow is used to indicate a chemical change as reactants are converted to products, with reaction conditions written above/below the arrow. The reactants and products are identified using chemical symbols to represent the elements or compounds, and their physical states are indicated using appropriate abbreviations (s, l, g, aq) *(see Problems 34, 35, 42, 43, and 92).*

- **Write very large or very small numbers using scientific notation or units with appropriate numerical prefixes.** Measurements of small and large quantities are usually written in *scientific notation* as the product of a number between 1 and 10, times a power of 10. Numbers greater than 10 have a positive exponent, and numbers less than 1 have a negative exponent. For example, $3562 = 3.562 \times 10^3$, and $0.003\,91 = 3.91 \times 10^{-3}$ *(see Problems 55–58 and 67).*

- **Name and correctly use the metric and SI units of measurement for mass, length, volume, and temperature, and convert units appropriately.** A property that can be measured is called a *physical quantity* and is described by both a number and a label, or *unit*. The preferred units are either those of the International System of Units (*SI units*) or the *metric system*. Mass, the amount of matter an object contains, is measured in *kilograms* (kg) or *grams* (g). Length is measured in *meters* (m). Volume is measured in *cubic meters* (m^3) in the SI system and in *liters* (L) or *milliliters* (mL) in the metric system. Temperature is measured in *kelvins* (K) in the SI system and in *degrees Celsius* (°C) in the metric system. A measurement in one unit can be converted to another unit by multiplying by a *conversion factor* that expresses the exact relationship between the units. The conversion factor should be arranged so that the starting unit is canceled and the desired unit is carried over to the answer *(see Problems 54–56, 58, 67–77, 93, 94, 96–98, 103, 106, 110, and 115).*

- **Use significant figures and scientific notation to represent the precision of a measurement.** When measuring physical quantities or using them in calculations, it is important to indicate the exactness of the measurement by using significant figures or numbers to represent those decimal places that are known with certainty, plus one additional decimal place indicating the point at which the measured value is uncertain. For example, a mass that was recorded as 15.34 g has an uncertainty in the last decimal place of ±0.01 g *(see Problems 29–31, 59, 60, and 97).*

- **Determine the appropriate number of significant figures in a calculated result and round off numbers in calculations involving measurements.** For multiplication and division, the number of significant figures in the calculated result is the same as the number with the fewest significant figures involved in the calculation. For addition and subtraction, the number of significant figures in the calculated result is determined by the least precise decimal place for the numbers involved in the calculation. If necessary, the calculated result is *rounded off* to obtain the final answer to the correct number of *significant figures* *(see Problems 42, 43, 59–66, 101, and 105).*

- **Use the factor-label method (conversion factors) to solve a problem and check the result to ensure that it makes sense chemically and physically.** Problems are best solved by applying the *factor-label method* in which units can be multiplied and divided just as numbers can. The idea is to set up an equation so that all unwanted units cancel, leaving only the desired units. Usually it is best to start by identifying the known and needed information, then decide how to convert the known information to the answer, and finally check to make sure the answer is reasonable both chemically and physically *(see Problems 67–77, 96–101, 103–107, 112, and 113).*

- **Define the relationship between temperature and heat energy and be able to convert temperatures between various temperature scales.** *Temperature* is a measure of the amount of heat energy in an object. Temperature is reported using the Fahrenheit, Celsius, and Kelvin scales, with conversions between scales as shown on pages 28–29 *(see Problems 78, 91, 102, and 111).*

- **Use temperature and specific heat to evaluate the flow of heat/energy in matter.** Heat flows from a hot object to a cold object. The *specific heat* of a substance is the amount of heat necessary to raise the temperature of 1 g of the substance by 1 °C (1 cal/g °C or 4.184 J/g °C). Water has an unusually high specific heat, which helps our bodies to maintain an even temperature *(see Problems 79–84, 95, 104, 107, and 108).*

- **Define density and specific gravity and to use these quantities in mass/volume calculations.** *Density*, the physical property that relates mass to volume, is expressed in units of grams per milliliter (g/mL) for a liquid or grams per cubic centimeter (g/cm^3) for a solid. The *specific gravity* of a liquid is the density of the liquid divided by the density of water at the same temperature. Because the density of water is approximately 1 g/mL, specific gravity and density have the same numerical value *(see Problems 28, 32, 85–90, 102, 107, 109, 110, 115, and 116).*

KEY WORDS

Change of state, *p. 4*
Chemical change, *p. 2*
Chemical compound, *p. 5*
Chemical formula, *p. 8*
Chemical reaction, *p. 10*
Chemistry, *p. 1*
Conversion factor, *p. 23*
Density, *p. 31*
Element, *p. 5*

Energy, *p. 27*
Factor-label method, *p. 23*
Gas (g), *p. 4*
Heterogeneous mixture, *p. 5*
Homogeneous mixture, *p. 5*
Liquid (l), *p. 4*
Mass, *p. 15*
Matter, *p. 1*
Mixture, *p. 5*

Physical change, *p. 2*
Physical quantity, *p. 11*
Product, *p. 10*
Property, *p. 1*
Pure substance, *p. 5*
Reactant, *p. 10*
Rounding off, *p. 21*
Scientific method, *p. 1*
Scientific notation, *p. 14*

SI units, *p. 11*
Significant figures, *p. 18*
Solid (s), *p. 4*
Specific gravity, *p. 32*
Specific heat, *p. 30*
State of matter, *p. 4*
Temperature, *p. 27*
Unit, *p. 11*
Weight, *p. 15*

CONCEPT MAP: MATTER

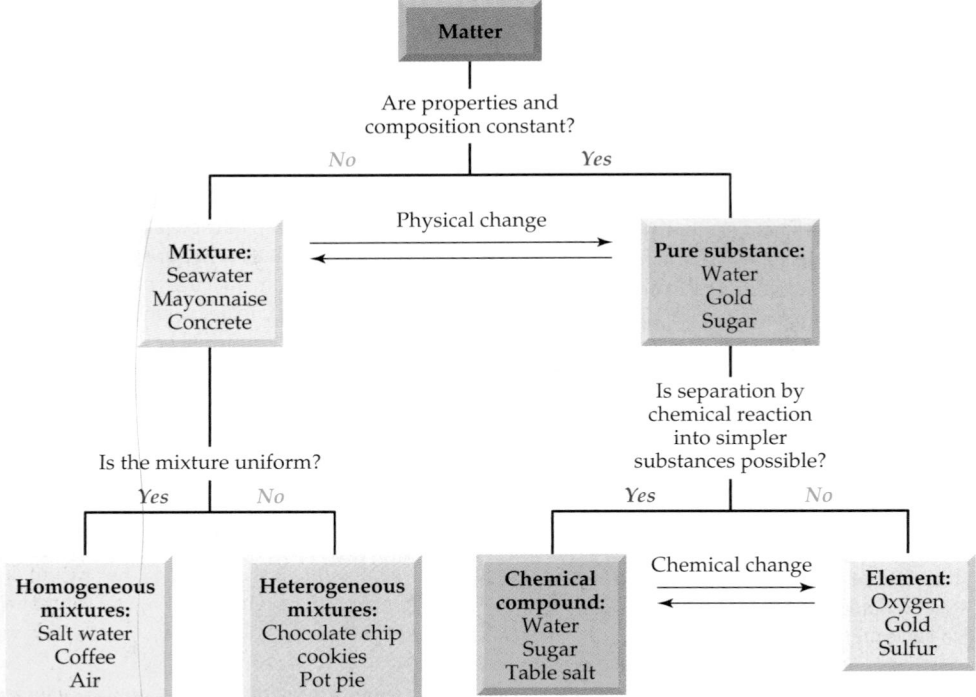

▲ **Figure 1.11 Concept Map.** Chemistry, like most subjects, makes more sense when presented in context. When we understand the connections between concepts, or how one idea leads to another, it becomes easier to see the "big picture" and to appreciate why a certain concept is important. A concept map is one way of illustrating those connections and providing a context for what we have learned and what we will be learning in later chapters. This concept map illustrates how we distinguish between the different types of matter and the types of changes that matter can undergo. As we continue exploring new topics, we will expand certain areas of this concept map or add new branches as needed.

⊙ UNDERSTANDING KEY CONCEPTS

The problems in this section are intended as a bridge between the Chapter Summary and the Additional Problems that follow. Primarily visual in nature, they are designed to help you test your grasp of the chapter's most important principles before attempting to solve quantitative problems. Answers to all Key Concept Problems are at the end of the book following the appendixes.

1.26 The six elements in blue at the far right of the periodic table are gases at room temperature. The red elements in the middle of the table are the so-called coinage metals. Identify each of these elements using the periodic table inside the front cover of this book.

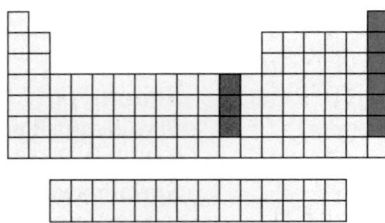

1.27 Identify the three elements indicated on the following periodic table. Do an Internet search to identify the common sources of these elements and some of their common uses or applications.

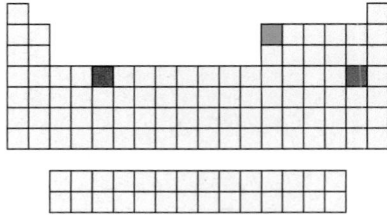

1.28 The radioactive element indicated on the following periodic table is used in smoke detectors. Identify it.

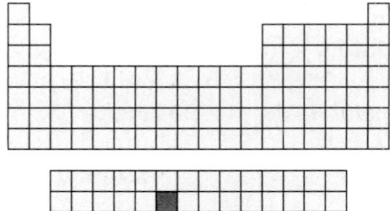

1.29 (a) What is the specific gravity of the following solution?
(b) How many significant figures does your answer have?
(c) Is the solution more dense or less dense than water?

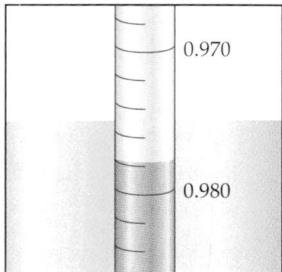

1.30   Assume that you have two graduated cylinders, one with a capacity of 5 mL (a) and the other with a capacity of 50 mL (b). Draw a line in each showing how much liquid you would add if you needed to measure 2.64 mL of water. Which cylinder do you think is more precise? Explain.

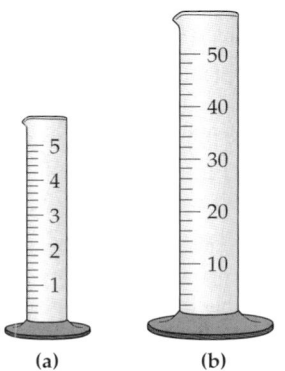

1.31   State the length of the pencil depicted in the accompanying figure in both inches and centimeters using appropriate numbers of significant figures.

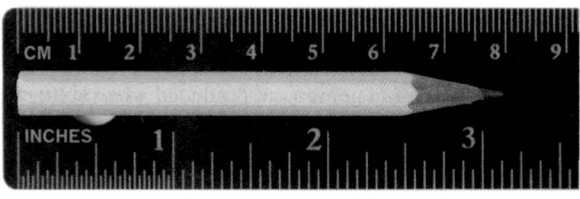

1.32   Assume that you are delivering a solution sample from a pipette. Figures (a) and (b) show the volume level before and after dispensing the sample, respectively. State the liquid level (in mL) before and after dispensing the sample, and calculate the volume of the sample.

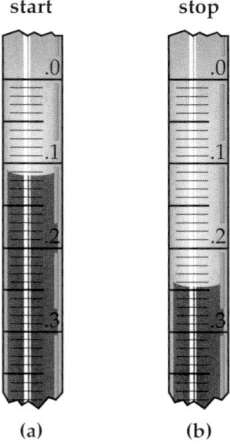

1.33   Assume that identical hydrometers are placed in ethanol (sp gr 0.7893) and in chloroform (sp gr 1.4832). In which liquid will the hydrometer float higher? Explain.

ADDITIONAL SECTION PROBLEMS

These exercises are divided into sections by topic. Each section begins with review and conceptual questions, followed by numerical problems of varying levels of difficulty. Many of the problems dealing with more difficult concepts or skills are presented in pairs, with each even-numbered problem followed by an odd-numbered one requiring similar skills. The final section consists of unpaired Conceptual Problems that draw on various parts of the chapter and, in future chapters, may even require the use of concepts from previous chapters. An additional feature in this edition is the incorporation of Group Questions that may sometimes require using resources other than the textbook and are suitable as small group activities. Answers to all even-numbered problems are given at the end of the book following the appendixes.

CHEMISTRY AND THE PROPERTIES OF MATTER (SECTION 1.1)

1.34   What is the difference between a physical change and a chemical change?

1.35   Which of the following is a physical change and which is a chemical change?

(a) Boiling water

(b) Decomposing water by passing an electric current through it

(c) Exploding of potassium metal when placed in water

(d) Breaking of glass

1.36   Which of the following is a physical change and which is a chemical change?

(a) Making lemonade (lemons + water + sugar)

(b) Frying eggs

(c) Burning a candle

(d) Whipping cream

(e) Leaves changing color

STATES AND CLASSIFICATION OF MATTER (SECTIONS 1.2, 1.3, AND 1.5)

1.37 Name and describe the three states of matter.

1.38 Name two changes of state and describe what causes each to occur.

1.39 Sulfur dioxide is a compound produced when sulfur burns in air. It has a melting point of $-72.7\,°C$ and a boiling point of $-10\,°C$. In what state does it exist at room temperature (298 K)? (Refer to Figure 1.9.)

1.40 Butane (C_4H_8) is an easily compressible gas used in cigarette lighters. It has a melting point of $-138.4\,°C$ and a boiling point of $-0.5\,°C$. Would you expect a butane lighter to work in winter when the temperature outdoors is 25 °F? Why or why not? (Refer to Figure 1.9.)

1.41 Classify each of the following as a mixture or a pure substance:

(a) Pea soup   (b) Seawater

(c) The contents of a propane tank

(d) Urine   (e) Lead

(f) A multivitamin tablet

1.42 Which of these terms, (i) mixture, (ii) solid, (iii) liquid, (iv) gas, (v) chemical element, (vi) chemical compound, applies to the following substances at room temperature?

(a) Gasoline   (b) Iodine

(c) Water   (d) Air

(e) Blood   (f) Sodium bicarbonate

(g) Gaseous ammonia   (h) Silicon

1.43 Hydrogen peroxide, often used in solutions to cleanse cuts and scrapes, breaks down to yield water and oxygen:

Hydrogen peroxide, $H_2O_2\,(aq) \rightarrow$
$$Hydrogen,\ H_2\,(g)\ +\ Oxygen,\ O_2\,(g)$$

(a) Identify the reactants and products.

(b) Which of the substances are chemical compounds, and which are elements?

1.44 When sodium metal is placed in water, the following change occurs:

Sodium, Na (s) + Water, $H_2O\,(l) \rightarrow$
$$Hydrogen,\ H_2\,(g)\ +\ Sodium\ hydroxide,\ NaOH\,(aq)$$

(a) Identify the reactants and products and their physical states

(b) Which of the substances are elements, and which are chemical compounds?

ELEMENTS AND THEIR SYMBOLS (SECTION 1.4)

1.45 What is the most abundant element in the earth's crust? In the human body? List the name and symbol for each.

1.46 What are the symbols for the following elements? Perform a web search to identify some of the common uses of the elements listed.

(a) Iodine   (b) Chromium

(c) Technetium   (d) Arsenic

(e) Barium

1.47 Supply the missing names or symbols for the elements in the spaces provided:

(a) N _____   (b) K _____

(c) Cl _____   (d) _____ Calcium

(e) _____ Phosphorus   (f) _____ Manganese

1.48 Correct the following statements.

(a) The symbol for bromine is BR.

(b) The symbol for manganese is Mg.

(c) The symbol for carbon is Ca.

(d) The symbol for potassium is Po.

1.49 Correct the following statements.

(a) Carbon dioxide has the formula CO2.

(b) Carbon dioxide has the formula Co_2.

(c) Table salt, NaCl, is composed of nitrogen and chlorine.

1.50 The amino acid, glycine, has the formula $C_2H_5NO_2$. Which elements are present in glycine? What is the total number of atoms represented by the formula?

1.51 Glucose, a form of sugar, has the formula $C_6H_{12}O_6$. Which elements are included in this compound, and how many atoms of each are present?

1.52 Write the formula for ibuprofen: 13 carbons, 18 hydrogens, and 2 oxygens. What are the common uses of ibuprofen?

1.53 The atmosphere consists of a number of permanent gases: oxygen (O_2), nitrogen (N_2), carbon dioxide (CO_2), water vapor (H_2O), and argon (Ar). Identify each substance as an element or a compound. Would you consider the atmosphere to be a heterogeneous or a homogeneous mixture?

PHYSICAL QUANTITIES: DEFINITIONS AND UNITS (SECTIONS 1.6 AND 1.7)

1.54 What is the difference between a physical quantity and a number?

1.55 What are the units used in the SI system to measure mass, volume, length, and temperature? In the metric system?

1.56 Give the full name of the following units:

(a) cc   (b) dm   (c) mm

(d) nL   (e) mg   (f) m^3

1.57 Write the symbol for the following units:

(a) nanogram   (b) centimeter

(c) microliter   (d) micrometer

(e) milligram

1.58 How many picograms are in 1 mg? In 35 ng?

1.59 How many microliters are in 1 L? In 20 mL?

SCIENTIFIC NOTATION, SIGNIFICANT FIGURES, AND ROUNDING OFF (SECTIONS 1.6, 1.8, AND 1.9)

1.60 Express the following numbers in scientific notation with the correct number of significant figures:

(a) 9457   (b) 0.000 07

(c) 20,000,000,000 (four significant figures)

(d) 0.012 345   (e) 652.38

1.61 Convert the following numbers from scientific notation to standard notation:

  (a) 5.28×10^3 **(b)** 8.205×10^{-2}

  (c) 1.84×10^{-5} **(d)** 6.37×10^4

1.62 How many significant figures does each of the following numbers have?

  (a) 237,401   **(b)** 0.300

  (c) 3.01   **(d)** 244.4

  (e) 50,000   **(f)** 660

1.63 How many significant figures are there in each of the following quantities?

  (a) Distance from New York City to Wellington, New Zealand, 14,397 km

  (b) Average body temperature of a crocodile, 25.6 °C

  (c) Melting point of gold, 1064 °C

  (d) Diameter of an influenza virus, 0.000 01 mm

  (e) Radius of a phosphorus atom, 0.110 nm

1.64 The diameter of the earth at the equator is 7926.381 mi.

  (a) Round off the earth's diameter to four significant figures, to two significant figures, and to six significant figures.

  (b) Express the earth's diameter in scientific notation.

1.65 Round off each of the numbers in Problem 1.63 to two significant figures and express them in scientific notation.

1.66 Carry out the following calculations, express each answer to the correct number of significant figures, and include units in the answers.

  (a) 9.02 g + 3.1 g

  (b) 88.80 cm + 7.391 cm

  (c) 362 mL − 99.5 mL

  (d) 12.4 mg + 6.378 mg + 2.089 mg

1.67 Carry out the following calculations, express the answers to the correct numbers of significant figures, and include units in the answers.

  (a) $5280 \dfrac{\text{ft}}{\text{mi}} \times 6.2\ \text{mi}$

  (b) 4.5 m × 3.25 m

  (c) $2.50\ \text{g} \div 8.3 \dfrac{\text{g}}{\text{cm}^3}$

  (d) 4.70 cm × 6.8 cm × 2.54 cm

UNIT CONVERSIONS AND PROBLEM SOLVING (SECTION 1.10)

1.68 Carry out the following conversions:

  (a) 3.614 mg to centigrams

  (b) 12.0 kL to megaliters

  (c) 14.4 μm to millimeters

  (d) 6.03×10^{-6} cg to nanograms

  (e) 174.5 mL to deciliters

  (f) 1.5×10^{-2} km to centimeters

1.69 Carry out the following conversions. Consult Tables 1.7–1.9 as needed.

  (a) 56.4 mi to kilometers and to megameters

  (b) 2.0 L to quarts and to fluid ounces

  (c) 7 ft 2.0 in. to centimeters and to meters

  (d) 1.35 lb to kilograms and to decigrams

1.70 Express the following quantities in more convenient units by using SI unit prefixes:

  (a) 9.78×10^4 g   **(b)** 1.33×10^{-4} L

  (c) 0.000 000 000 46 g   **(d)** 2.99×10^8 cm

1.71 Fill in the blanks to complete the equivalencies either with appropriate unit prefixes or with the appropriate scientific notation. The first blank is filled in as an example.

  (a) 125 km = 1.25×10^5 m

  (b) 6.285×10^3 mg = ____? ____ kg

  (c) 47.35 dL = 4.735 × ____? ____ mL

  (d) 67.4 cm = 6.7×10^{-4} ____? ____

1.72 The speed limit in Canada is 100 km/h.

  (a) How many miles per hour is this?

  (b) How many feet per second?

1.73 The muzzle velocity of a projectile fired from a 9 mm handgun is 1200 ft/s.

  (a) How many miles per hour is this?

  (b) How many meters per second?

1.74 The diameter of a red blood cell is 6×10^{-6} m.

  (a) How many centimeters is this?

  (b) How many red blood cells are needed to make a line 1 cm long? 1 in. long?

1.75 The Willis Tower in Chicago has an approximate floor area of 418,000 m². How many square feet of floor space is this?

1.76 A normal value for blood cholesterol is 200 mg/dL of blood. If a normal adult has a total blood volume of 5 L, how much total cholesterol is present?

1.77 The recommended daily dose of calcium for an 18-year-old male is 1200 mg. If 1.0 cup of whole milk contains 290 mg of calcium and milk is his only calcium source, how much milk should an 18-year-old male drink each day?

1.78 The white blood cell concentration in normal blood is approximately 12,000 cells/mm³ of blood. How many white blood cells does a normal adult with 5 L of blood have? Express the answer in scientific notation.

ENERGY, HEAT, AND TEMPERATURE (SECTION 1.11)

1.79 The boiling point of liquid nitrogen, used in the removal of warts and in other surgical applications, is −195.8 °C. What is this temperature in kelvins and in degrees Fahrenheit? (3.74 J/g °C)

1.80 Diethyl ether, a substance once used as a general anesthetic, has a specific heat of 0.895 cal/(g °C). How many calories and how many kilocalories of heat are needed to raise the temperature of 30.0 g of diethyl ether from 10.0 °C to 30.0 °C? How many joules and kilojoules?

1.81 Aluminum has a specific heat of $0.215 \text{ cal}/(\text{g} \,^\circ\text{C})$. When 25.7 cal (108.5 J) of heat is added to 18.4 g of aluminum at 20.0 °C, what is the final temperature of the aluminum?

1.82 Calculate the specific heat of copper if it takes 23 cal (96 J) to heat a 5.0 g sample from 25 °C to 75 °C.

1.83 The specific heat of fat is $0.45 \text{ cal}/(\text{g} \cdot {}^\circ\text{C})$ $(1.9 \text{ J}/\text{g} \,^\circ\text{C})$ and the density of fat is $0.94 \text{ g}/\text{cm}^3$. How much energy (in calories and joules) is needed to heat 10 cm^3 of fat from room temperature (25 °C) to its melting point (35 °C)?

1.84 A 150 g sample of mercury and a 150 g sample of iron are at an initial temperature of 25.0 °C. If 250 cal (1050 J) of heat is applied to each sample, what is the final temperature of each? (See Table 1.10.)

1.85 When 100 cal (418 J) of heat is applied to a 125 g sample, the temperature increases by 28 °C. Calculate the specific heat of the sample and compare your answer to the values in Table 1.10. What is the identity of the sample?

DENSITY AND SPECIFIC GRAVITY (SECTION 1.12)

1.86 Aspirin has a density of $1.40 \text{ g}/\text{cm}^3$. What is the volume in cubic centimeters of a tablet weighing 250 mg?

1.87 Gaseous hydrogen has a density of 0.0899 g/L at 0 °C. How many liters would you need if you wanted 1.0078 g of hydrogen?

1.88 What is the density of lead (in g/cm^3) if a rectangular bar measuring 0.500 cm in height, 1.55 cm in width, and 25.00 cm in length has a mass of 220.9 g?

1.89 What is the density of lithium metal (in g/cm^3) if a cube measuring 0.82 cm $\times$ 1.45 cm $\times$ 1.25 cm has a mass of 0.794 g?

1.90 Ethanol produced by fermentation has a specific gravity of 0.787 at 25 °C. What is the volume of 125 g of ethanol at this temperature? (The density of water at 25 °C is 0.997 g/mL.)

1.91 Ethylene glycol, commonly used as automobile antifreeze, has a specific gravity of 1.1088 at room temperature (25 °C). What is the mass of 1.00 L of ethylene glycol at this temperature?

CONCEPTUAL PROBLEMS

1.92 Another temperature scale is the Rankine scale. It represents an absolute temperature scale similar to the Kelvin scale, with a common absolute zero (i.e., 0.0 K = 0.0 °R). However, whereas a change of 1.0 K is the same as a change of 1.0 °C, a change of 1.0 °R is the same as 1.0 °F. Absolute zero on the Rankine scale equals −459.67 °F. Water freezes at 32 °F (or 0.0 °C) and boils at 212 °F (100.0 °C). Convert these temperatures to their equivalent temperatures on the Rankine scale.

1.93 A white solid with a melting point of 730 °C is melted. When electricity is passed through the resultant liquid, a brown gas and a molten metal are produced. Neither the metal nor the gas can be broken down into anything simpler by chemical means. Classify each—the white solid, the molten metal, and the brown gas—as a mixture, a compound, or an element.

1.94 Refer to the pencil in Problem 1.31. Using the equivalent values in Table 1.8 as conversion factors, convert the length measured in inches to centimeters. Compare the calculated length in centimeters to the length in centimeters measured using the metric ruler. How do the two values compare? Explain any differences.

1.95 Gemstones are weighed in carats, where 1 carat = 200 mg exactly. What is the mass in grams of the Hope diamond, the world's largest blue diamond, at 44.4 carats?

1.96 The relationship between the nutritional unit for energy and the metric unit is 1 Calorie = 1 kcal.

(a) One donut contains 350 Calories. Convert this to calories and joules.

(b) If the energy in one donut was used to heat 35.5 kg of water, calculate the increase in temperature of the water (in °C).

1.97 Drug dosages are typically prescribed in units of milligrams per kilogram of body weight. A new drug has a recommended dosage of 9 mg/kg.

(a) How many milligrams would a 130 lb woman have to take to obtain this dosage?

(b) How many 125 mg tablets should a 40 lb child take to receive the recommended dosage?

1.98 A clinical report gave the following data from a blood analysis: iron, 39 mg/dL; calcium, 8.3 mg/dL; cholesterol, 224 mg/dL. Express each of these quantities in grams per deciliter, writing the answers in scientific notation.

1.99 The Spirit of America Goodyear blimp has a volume of $2.027 \times 10^5 \text{ ft}^3$.

(a) Convert this volume to L.

(b) When in operation it is filled with helium gas. If the density of helium at room temperature is 0.179 g/L, calculate the mass of helium in the blimp.

(c) What is the mass of air occupying the same volume? The density of air at room temperature is 1.20 g/L.

1.100 Approximately 75 mL of blood is pumped by a normal human heart at each beat. Assuming an average pulse of 72 beats per minute, how many milliliters of blood are pumped in one day?

1.101 A doctor has ordered that a patient be given 15 g of glucose, which is available in a concentration of 50.00 g glucose/1000.0 mL of solution. What volume of solution should be given to the patient?

1.102 Reconsider the volume of the sample dispensed by pipette in Problem 1.32. Assuming that the solution in the pipette has a density of 0.963 g/mL, calculate the mass of solution dispensed in the problem to the correct number of significant figures.

1.103 Today, thermometers containing mercury are used less frequently than in the past because of concerns regarding the toxicity of mercury and because of its relatively high melting point (−39 °C). This means that mercury thermometers cannot be used in very cold environments because the mercury is a solid under such conditions. Alcohol thermometers, however, can be used over a temperature range from $-115\ °C$ (the melting point of alcohol) to $78.5\ °C$ (the boiling point of alcohol).

(a) What is the effective temperature range of the alcohol thermometer in $°F$?

(b) The densities of alcohol and mercury are $0.79\ g/mL$ and $13.6\ g/mL$, respectively. If the volume of liquid in a typical laboratory thermometer is $1.0\ mL$, what mass of alcohol is contained in the thermometer? What mass of mercury?

1.104 In a typical person, the level of blood glucose (also known as blood sugar) is about $85\ mg/100\ mL$ of blood. If an average body contains about 11 pints of blood, how many grams and how many pounds of glucose are present in the blood?

1.105 A patient is receiving $3000\ mL/day$ of a solution that contains $5\ g$ of dextrose (glucose) per $100\ mL$ of solution. If glucose provides $4\ kcal/g$ of energy, how many kilocalories per day is the patient receiving from the glucose?

1.106 A rough guide to fluid requirements based on body weight is $100\ mL/kg$ for the first $10\ kg$ of body weight, $50\ mL/kg$ for the next $10\ kg$, and $20\ mL/kg$ for weight over $20\ kg$. What volume of fluid per day is needed by a $55\ kg$ woman? Give the answer with two significant figures.

1.107 Chloral hydrate, a sedative and sleep-inducing drug, is available as a solution labeled $10.0\ gr/fluidram$. What volume in milliliters should be administered to a patient who is meant to receive $7.5\ gr$ per dose? ($1\ gr = 64.8\ mg$; $1\ fluidram = 3.72\ mL$)

1.108 When 1.0 tablespoon of butter is burned or used by our body, it releases $100\ kcal$ (100 food Calories or $418.4\ kJ$) of energy. If we could use all the energy provided, how many tablespoons of butter would have to be burned to raise the temperature of $3.00\ L$ of water from $18.0\ °C$ to $90.0\ °C$?

1.109 An archeologist finds a $1.62\ kg$ goblet that she believes to be made of pure gold. When $1350\ cal$ ($5650\ J$) of heat is added to the goblet, its temperature increases by $7.8\ °C$. Calculate the specific heat of the goblet. Is it made of gold? Explain.

1.110 In another test, the archeologist in Problem 1.109 determines that the volume of the goblet is $205\ mL$. Calculate the density of the goblet and compare it with the density of gold ($19.3\ g/mL$), lead ($11.4\ g/mL$), and iron ($7.86\ g/mL$). What is the goblet probably made of?

1.111 Imagine that you place a piece of cork measuring $1.30\ cm \times 5.50\ cm \times 3.00\ cm$ in a pan of water and that on top of the cork you place a small cube of lead measuring $1.15\ cm$ on each edge. The density of cork is $0.235\ g/cm^3$ and the density of lead is $11.35\ g/cm^3$. Will the combination of cork plus lead float or sink?

1.112 At a certain point, the Celsius and Fahrenheit scales "cross" and the numerical value of the Celsius temperature is the same as the numerical value of the Fahrenheit temperature. At what temperature does this crossover occur?

GROUP PROBLEMS

1.113 In the chapter, the conversion of currency was used as an example for unit conversion. Find out what the current monetary conversion rates are and convert US$500 into (a) euros, (b) British pounds, (c) rupees, and (d) Canadian dollars.

1.114 Look up the chemical formula for chloral hydrate mentioned in Problem 1.107. How many different elements are included in the compound, and how many atoms of each element?

1.115 The specific gravity of ethanol is 0.787, while the specific gravity of water is 1.0. Alcoholic beverages are a mixture of water and alcohol and have a specific gravity somewhere between 0.787 and 1.0 density of ethanol, Look up the average alcohol content, typically reported as % by volume, and the specific gravity of each of the following: 80 proof whiskey; red table wine; domestic beer.

1.116 Sulfuric acid (H_2SO_4, density $1.83\ g/mL$) is produced in larger amounts than any other chemical: Global production exceeded 230 million metric tonnes in 2012 and is projected to exceed 267 million tonnes by 2016. What was the volume of this amount (in liters) produced in 2012? What are the most common applications of sulfuric acid?

2

Atoms and the Periodic Table

CONTENTS

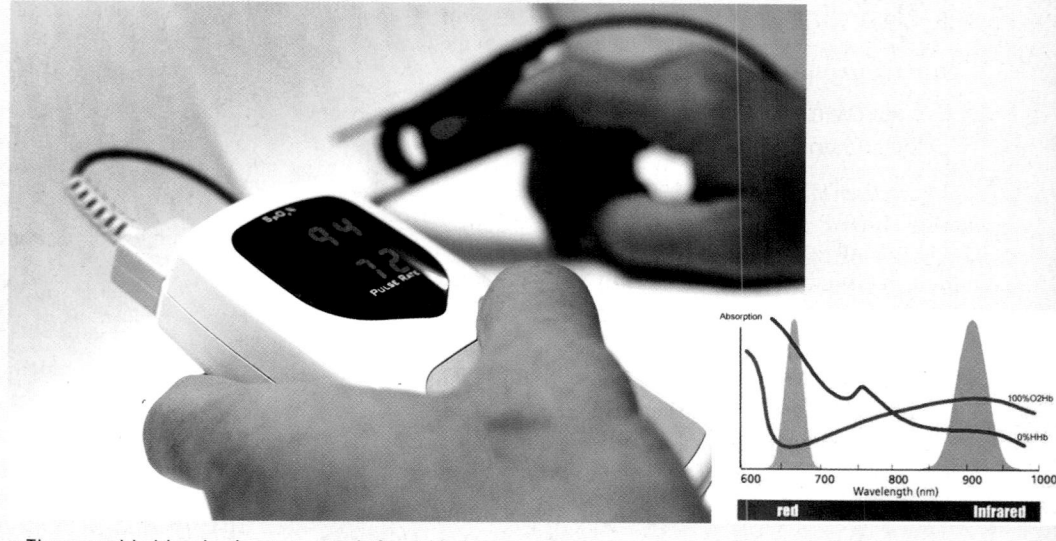

▲ The portable blood oximeter uses infrared light to measure the amount of oxygen dissolved in blood that is bound to hemoglobin, Hb (red line = oxygenated Hb; blue line = unoxygenated Hb), as indicated in the inserted graph. Results are reported as percent of saturation. This and related instruments, called spectrometers, take advantage of the ability of elements and compounds to interact with light of different wavelengths.

A patient visits his or her local clinic complaining of headaches and lethargy. A blood sample is taken and analyzed to determine the relative amounts of certain elements, including many metals identified as micronutrients or trace nutrients. Not enough iron, for example, could indicate anemia, while elevated levels of heavy metals, such as lead or cadmium, could be indicators of toxicity effects, such as headache or a feeling of fatigue. Knowing atomic structure and how elemental properties are related to the arrangement of electrons in a given atom allow us to identify and detect substances in the blood, including oxygen and essential nutrients, even at very low levels. Spectrometers, such as the portable blood oximeter featured above, measure the interaction of atoms or molecules with energy (such as a flame or light source) to determine the identity and concentrations of these substances, which should be in a certain range to ensure good health. As we will see in more detail in the Chemistry in Action feature on page 66, atoms will absorb or emit light of a specific wavelength based on the electron configuration and excitation in the atom. The color of the light can be used to determine the identity of certain elements, which can be used to determine the cause of the patient's symptoms.

Chemistry is studied on two levels. In the previous chapter, we learned about chemistry on the large-scale, or *macroscopic,* level, looking at the properties and transformations of matter that we can see and measure. We also introduced the elements that make up all matter and how we can use symbols to represent the many different elements and compounds of which matter is made. But what makes one element different from another? To answer that question, we need to look at the submicroscopic or atomic level, studying the behavior and properties of individual *atoms.* Although scientists have long been convinced of their existence, only within the past 20 years have powerful new instruments made it possible to see individual atoms. In this chapter, we will learn about modern atomic theory and how the structure of atoms influences macroscopic properties.

2.1 Atomic Theory and the Structure of Atoms

Learning Objective:

• Explain the major assumptions of atomic theory, and name and identify the properties of the subatomic particles that make up an atom.

Take a piece of aluminum foil, and cut it in two. Then, take one of the pieces and cut *it* in two, and so on. Assuming that you have extremely small scissors and extraordinary dexterity, how long can you keep dividing the foil? Is there a limit, or is matter infinitely divisible into ever smaller and smaller pieces? Historically, this argument dates as far back as the ancient Greek philosophers. Aristotle believed that matter could be divided infinitely, while Democritus argued (correctly) that there is a limit. The smallest and simplest bit that aluminum (or any other element) can be divided and still be identifiable as aluminum is called an **atom,** a word derived from the Greek *atomos,* meaning "indivisible."

Chemistry is built on four fundamental assumptions about atoms and matter, proposed by English scientist John Dalton in 1808, which together make up modern **atomic theory:**

• All matter is composed of atoms.
• Atoms of any given element share the same chemical properties while atoms of different elements have different properties.
• Chemical compounds consist of atoms combined in specific ratios. That is, only whole atoms can combine—one A atom with one B atom, or one A atom with two B atoms, and so on. The vast number of ways that atoms can combine with one another results in the enormous diversity in the substances around us.
• Chemical reactions change only the way that atoms are combined in compounds. The atoms themselves are unchanged and do not disappear.

Atoms are extremely small, ranging from about 7.4×10^{-11} m in diameter for a hydrogen atom to 5.24×10^{-10} m for a cesium atom. In mass, atoms vary from 1.67×10^{-24} g for hydrogen to 3.95×10^{-22} g for uranium, one of the heaviest naturally occurring atoms. It is difficult to appreciate just how small atoms are, although it might help if you realize that a fine pencil line is about 3 million atoms across and that even the smallest speck of dust contains about 10^{16} atoms. Our current understanding of atomic structure is the result of many experiments performed in the late 1800s and early 1900s (see Chemistry in Action on p. 44).

Atoms are composed of tiny **subatomic particles** called *protons, neutrons,* and *electrons.* A **proton** has a mass of $1.672\,622 \times 10^{-24}$ g and carries a positive $(+)$ electrical charge, a **neutron** has a mass similar to that of a proton $(1.674\,927 \times 10^{-24}\,\text{g})$ but is electrically neutral, and an **electron** has a mass that is only $1/1836$ of a proton $(9.109\,328 \times 10^{-28}\,\text{g})$ and carries a negative $(-)$ electrical charge. In fact, electrons are so much lighter than protons and neutrons that their mass is usually ignored. Table 2.1 compares the properties of the three fundamental subatomic particles.

Atom The smallest and simplest particle of an element.

Atomic theory A set of assumptions proposed by the English scientist John Dalton to explain the chemical behavior of matter.

LOOKING AHEAD We will further explore the topics of chemical compounds in Chapters 3 and 4 and chemical reactions in Chapters 5 and 6.

Subatomic particles Three kinds of fundamental particles from which atoms are made—protons, neutrons, and electrons.

Proton A positively charged subatomic particle.

Neutron An electrically neutral subatomic particle.

Electron A negatively charged subatomic particle.

Table 2.1 A Comparison of Subatomic Particles

Name	Symbol	Mass (Grams)	Mass (amu)	Charge (Charge Units)
Proton	p	$1.672\,622 \times 10^{-24}$	$1.007\,276$	$+1$
Neutron	n	$1.674\,927 \times 10^{-24}$	$1.008\,665$	0
Electron	e^-	$9.109\,328 \times 10^{-28}$	$5.485\,799 \times 10^{-4}$	-1

The masses of atoms and their constituent subatomic particles are so small when measured in grams that it is more convenient to express them on a *relative* mass scale. The basis for the relative atomic mass scale is an atom of carbon that contains six protons and six neutrons. Such an atom is assigned a mass of exactly 12 **atomic mass units (amu;** also called a *dalton* in honor of John Dalton), where $1\ \text{amu} = 1.660\,539 \times 10^{-24}$ g.

Atomic mass unit (amu) The unit for describing the mass of an atom; $1\ \text{amu} = \frac{1}{12}$ the mass of a carbon-12 atom.

▲ The relative size of a nucleus in an atom is the same as that of a pea in the middle of this stadium.

Nucleus The dense, central core of an atom that contains protons and neutrons.

Thus, for all practical purposes, both a proton and a neutron have a mass of 1 amu (Table 2.1). Hydrogen atoms are only about one-twelfth as heavy as carbon atoms and have a mass close to 1 amu, magnesium atoms are about twice as heavy as carbon atoms and have a mass close to 24 amu, and so forth.

Subatomic particles are not distributed at random throughout an atom. Rather, the protons and neutrons are packed closely together in a dense core called the **nucleus.** Surrounding the nucleus, the electrons move about rapidly through a large, mostly empty volume of space (Figure 2.1). Measurements show that the diameter of a nucleus is only about 10^{-15} m, whereas that of the atom itself is about 10^{-10} m. For comparison, if an atom were the size of a large domed stadium, the nucleus would be approximately the size of a small pea in the center of the playing field.

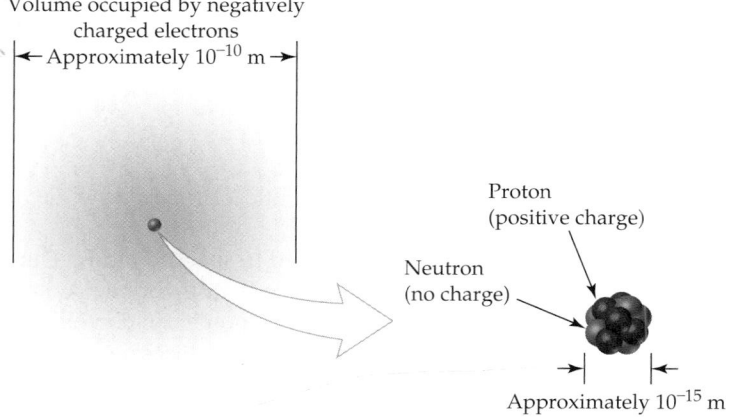

▲ **Figure 2.1**
The structure of an atom.
Protons and neutrons are packed together in the nucleus, whereas electrons move about in the large surrounding volume. Virtually all the mass of an atom is concentrated in the nucleus.

The structure of the atom is determined by an interplay of different attractive and repulsive forces. Because unlike charges attract one another, the negatively charged electrons are held near the positively charged nucleus. But because like charges repel one another, the electrons also try to get as far away from one another as possible, accounting for the relatively large volume they occupy.

▶ The positively charged protons in the nucleus also repel one another but are nevertheless held together by a unique attraction called the *nuclear strong force,* which we will discuss further in Chapter 11.

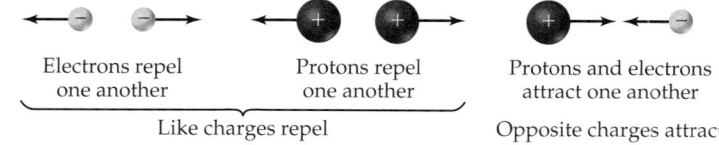

Electrons repel one another

Protons repel one another

Protons and electrons attract one another

Like charges repel

Opposite charges attract

CHEMISTRY IN ACTION

✛ Are Atoms Real?

Chemistry rests on the premise that matter is composed of the tiny particles we call atoms. Every chemical reaction and every physical law that governs the behavior of matter is explained by chemists in terms of atomic theory. But how do we know that atoms are real and not just an imaginary concept? And how do we know the structure of the atom?

The development of our understanding of atomic structure is another example of the scientific method at work, with several scientists contributing to our understanding of atomic structure. J. J. Thomson demonstrated that matter contained negatively charged particles that were 1000 times lighter than H^+, the lightest positively charged particles found in aqueous solution, and that the mass-to-charge ratio of these particles was the same regardless of the material used to produce the particles (Section 5.5 and Chapter 10). Ernest Rutherford deduced that an atom consists mostly of empty space (occupied by the negatively charged electrons) and that most of the mass and all of the positive charges are contained in a relatively small, dense region that he called the "nucleus."

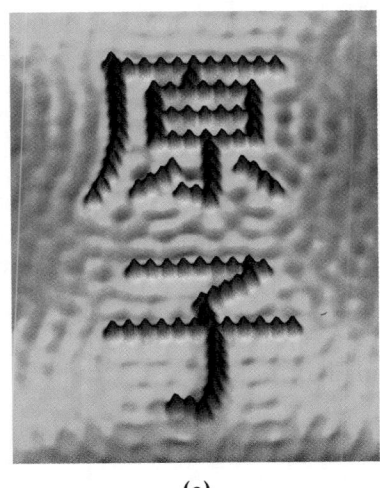
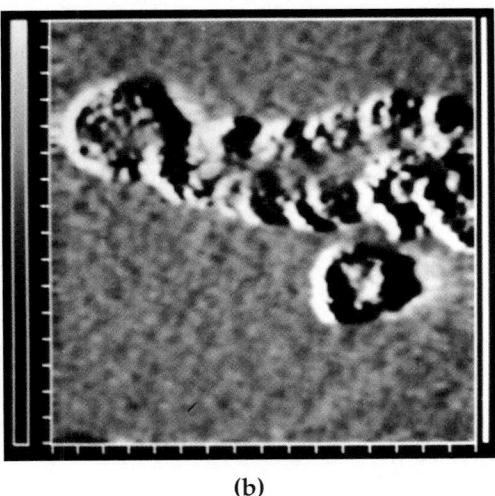

(a)	**(b)**

▲ (a) STM image of the Kanji characters for "atom" formed by iron atoms (radius = 126 pm) deposited on a copper metal surface. (b) STM image of DNA strand deposited on a graphite surface.

We can now actually "see" and manipulate individual atoms through the use of a device called a *scanning tunneling microscope,* or STM. With the STM, invented in 1981 by a research team at the IBM Corporation, magnifications of up to 10 million have been achieved, allowing chemists to look directly at atoms. The accompanying photograph shows a computer-enhanced representation of iron atoms that have been deposited on a copper surface.

Most early uses of the STM involved studies of surface chemistry, such as the events accompanying the corrosion of metals and the ordering of large molecules in polymers. More recently, however, the STM has been used to determine the structures of complex biological molecules, such as immunoglobulin G,

streptavidin, proteins and enzymes, and DNA, providing vital information about the structures and functions of these biomolecules. Modifications to the STM instrumentation have allowed imaging of these materials *in situ* (i.e., in their natural state) and also allowed scientists to manipulate individual molecules.

CIA Problem 2.1 What is the advantage of using an STM rather than a normal light microscope?

CIA Problem 2.2 For the Kanji character in the lower portion of figure (a):

(1) How wide is the character in terms of iron atoms?

(2) Given the radius of an iron atom is 126 pm, calculate the width of this character in centimeters.

2.2 Elements and Atomic Number

Learning Objective:

- Identify atoms of an element based on the number of protons in the nucleus.

All atoms contain proton, neutrons, and electrons, but how do we distinguish an atom of carbon from an atom of oxygen, or sodium? Each atom has a specific number of protons, neutrons, and electrons, and the identity of the element is determined by the number of protons within the nucleus, also called the element's **atomic number (Z).** Every element has a different number of protons within its nucleus, thus every element has a different atomic number. If we know the number of protons in an atom, we can identify the element. Any atom with six protons, for example, is a carbon atom because the atomic number for carbon is 6 ($Z = 6$).

Atoms are neutral and have no net charge because the number of positively charged protons in an atom is the same as the number of negatively charged electrons. Thus, the atomic number also equals the number of electrons in every atom of a given element. Hydrogen, $Z = 1$, has only 1 proton and 1 electron; carbon, $Z = 6$, has 6 protons and 6 electrons; sodium, $Z = 11$, has 11 protons and 11 electrons; and so on, up

Atomic number (Z) The number of protons in the nucleus of an atom of a given element.

LOOKING AHEAD ⇒ In a neutral atom, the number of electrons is equal to the number of protons. However, most elements can gain or lose electrons to form charged particles, called *ions,* which will be discussed in Chapter 3.

Mass number *(A)* The total number of protons and neutrons in an atom.

to the element with the largest known atomic number $(Z = 118)$. In a periodic table, elements are listed in order of increasing atomic number, beginning at the upper left and ending at the lower right.

The sum of the protons and neutrons in an atom is called the atom's **mass number** *(A).* For example, hydrogen atoms with 1 proton and no neutrons have mass number 1, carbon atoms with 6 protons and 6 neutrons have mass number 12, sodium atoms with 11 protons and 12 neutrons have mass number 23. Atomic number and mass number can be written using chemical symbols by showing the element's mass number *(A)* as a superscript and its atomic number *(Z)* as a subscript in front of the atomic symbol. For example, $^A_Z X$, where X represents the symbol for the element, A represents the mass number, and Z represents the atomic number.

Worked Example 2.1 Atomic Structure: Protons, Neutrons, and Electrons

Phosphorus has the atomic number $Z = 15$. How many protons, electrons, and neutrons are there in phosphorus atoms, which have mass number $A = 31$?

ANALYSIS The atomic number gives the number of protons, which is the same as the number of electrons, and the mass number gives the total number of protons plus neutrons.

SOLUTION
Phosphorus atoms, with $Z = 15$, have 15 protons and 15 electrons. To find the number of neutrons, subtract the atomic number from the mass number.

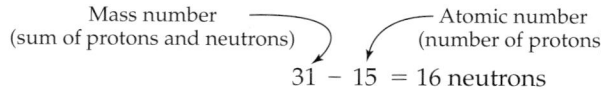

Mass number
(sum of protons and neutrons)   Atomic number
(number of protons)

$$31 - 15 = 16 \text{ neutrons}$$

Worked Example 2.2 Atomic Structure: Atomic Number and Atomic Mass

An atom contains 28 protons and has $A = 60$. Give the number of electrons and neutrons in the atom, and identify the element.

ANALYSIS The number of protons and the number of electrons are the same and are equal to the atomic number Z, 28 in this case. Subtracting the number of protons (28) from the total number of protons plus neutrons (60) gives the number of neutrons.

SOLUTION
The atom has 28 electrons and $60 - 28 = 32$ neutrons. The list of elements inside the front cover shows that the element with atomic number 28 is nickel (Ni).

PROBLEM 2.1

Use the list inside the front cover to identify the following elements:
- **(a)** $A = 186$, with 111 neutrons
- **(b)** $A = 59$, with 21 neutrons
- **(c)** $A = 127$, with 75 neutrons

2.3 Isotopes and Atomic Weight

Learning Objective:

- Write the symbols for different isotopes of an element, and use relative abundances and atomic masses of isotopes to calculate the average atomic weight of an element.

All atoms of a given element have the same number of protons, equal to the atomic number *(Z)* of that element; however, different atoms of an element can have different numbers of neutrons and, therefore, different mass numbers. Atoms with identical atomic numbers but different mass numbers are called **isotopes.** Hydrogen, for example, has three isotopes. The most abundant hydrogen isotope, called *protium,* has

Isotopes Atoms with identical atomic numbers but different mass numbers.

one proton but no neutrons and thus has a mass number of 1. A second hydrogen isotope, called *deuterium,* also has one proton, but has one neutron and a mass number
of 2; and a third isotope, called *tritium,* has two neutrons and a mass number of 3.

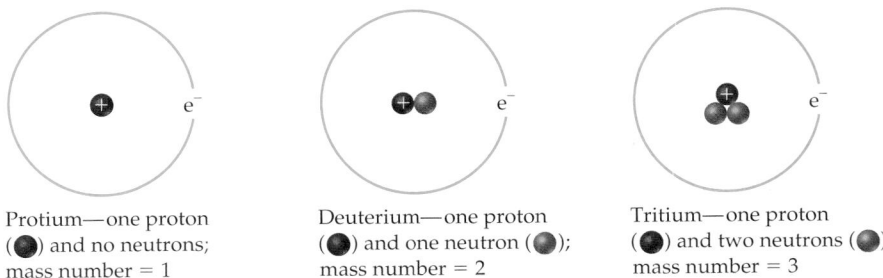

Protium—one proton
(⬤) and no neutrons;
mass number = 1

Deuterium—one proton
(⬤) and one neutron (⬤);
mass number = 2

Tritium—one proton
(⬤) and two neutrons (⬤);
mass number = 3

A specific isotope is represented by showing its mass number *(A)* as a superscript
and its atomic number *(Z)* as a subscript in front of the atomic symbol, for example, $^A_Z X$.
Thus, protium is $^1_1 H$, deuterium is $^2_1 H$, and tritium is $^3_1 H$.

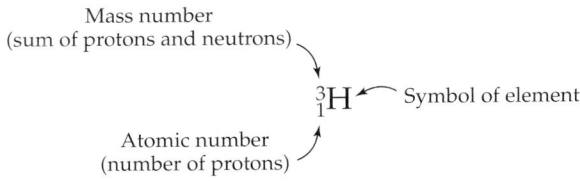

Mass number
(sum of protons and neutrons)

$^3_1 H$ Symbol of element

Atomic number
(number of protons)

Unlike the three isotopes of hydrogen, the isotopes of most elements do not have
distinctive names. Instead, the mass number of the isotope is given after the name of
the element. The $^{235}_{92} U$ isotope used in nuclear reactors, for example, is usually referred
to as uranium-235, or U-235.

Most naturally occurring elements are mixtures of isotopes. In a large sample of
naturally occurring hydrogen atoms, for example, 99.985% have mass number $A = 1$
(protium) and 0.015% have mass number $A = 2$ (deuterium). Therefore, it is useful to
know the *average* mass of the atoms in a large sample, a value called the element's
atomic weight. For hydrogen, the atomic weight is 1.008 amu. Atomic weights for all
elements are given on the inside of the front cover of this book.

To calculate the atomic weight of an element, the individual masses of the naturally occurring isotopes and the percent abundance of each must be known. The atomic
weight can then be calculated as the sum of the masses of the individual isotopes for
that element, or

$$\text{Atomic weight} = \Sigma [\,(\text{isotopic abundance}) \times (\text{isotopic mass})\,]$$

where the Greek symbol Σ indicates the mathematical summing of terms.

Chlorine, for example, occurs on earth as a mixture of 75.77% Cl-35 atoms
(mass = 34.97 amu) and 24.23% Cl-37 atoms (mass = 36.97 amu). This can also
be expressed in terms of fractional composition (i.e., 75.77% of all chlorine atoms is the
same as a fraction of 0.7577). The atomic weight is found by calculating the percentage
of the mass contributed by each isotope. For chlorine, the calculation is done in the following way (to four significant figures), giving an atomic weight of 35.45 amu:

Contribution from ^{35}Cl: $(0.7577)(34.97 \text{ amu}) = 26.4968 \text{ amu}$
Contribution from ^{37}Cl: $(0.2423)(36.97 \text{ amu}) = \underline{8.9578 \text{ amu}}$
Atomic weight $= 35.4546 = 35.45$ amu
(Rounded to four significant figures)

The final number of significant figures in this case (four) was determined by the
rounding rules presented in Chapter 1. Note that the final rounding to four significant
figures was not done until *after* the final answer was obtained.

▶ We will see that isotopes of the
same element have the same *chemical*
behavior (Chapter 5) but very different
nuclear behavior (Chapter 11). Tritium,
for example, is unstable and does not
occur naturally in significant amounts,
although it can be made in nuclear
reactors.

▶ We will discuss nuclear reactors in
Section 11.9.

Atomic weight The weighted average
mass of an element's atoms.

Worked Example 2.3 Average Atomic Mass: Weighted-Average Calculation

Gallium is a metal with a very low melting point—it will melt in the palm of your hand. It has two naturally occurring isotopes: 60.4% is Ga-69 (mass = 68.9257 amu) and 39.6% is Ga-71 (mass = 70.9248 amu). Calculate the atomic weight for gallium.

ANALYSIS We can calculate the average atomic mass for the element by summing up the contributions from each of the naturally occurring isotopes.

BALLPARK ESTIMATE The masses of the two naturally occurring isotopes of gallium differ by 2 amu (68.9 and 70.9 amu). Since slightly more than half of the Ga atoms are the lighter isotope (Ga-69), the average mass will be slightly less than halfway between the two isotopic masses; estimate = 69.8 amu.

SOLUTION

STEP 1: **Identify known information.**

Ga-69 (60.4% at 68.9257 amu)
Ga-71 (39.6% at 70.9248 amu)

STEP 2: **Identify the unknown answer and units.**

Atomic weight for Ga (in amu) = ?

STEP 3: **Identify conversion factors or equations.** This equation calculates the average atomic weight as a weighted average of all naturally occurring isotopes.

Atomic weight = $\sum [\,(\text{isotopic abundance}) \times (\text{isotopic mass})\,]$

STEP 4: **Solve.** Substitute known information and solve.

Atomic weight = (0.604) × (68.9257 amu) = 41.6311 amu
          + (0.396) × (70.9248 amu) = 28.0862 amu

Atomic weight = 69.7 amu (3 significant figures)

BALLPARK CHECK Our estimate (69.8 amu) is close!

Worked Example 2.4 Identifying Isotopes from Atomic Mass and Atomic Number

Identify element X in the symbol $^{194}_{78}X$ and give its atomic number, mass number, number of protons, number of electrons, and number of neutrons.

ANALYSIS The identity of the atom corresponds to the atomic number—78.

SOLUTION
Element X has Z = 78, which shows that it is platinum. (Look inside the front cover for the list of elements.) The isotope $^{194}_{78}\text{Pt}$ has a mass number of 194, and we can subtract the atomic number from the mass number to get the number of neutrons. This platinum isotope therefore has 78 protons, 78 electrons, and 194 − 78 = 116 neutrons.

PROBLEM 2.2

Potassium (K) has two naturally occurring isotopes: K-39 (93.12% mass = 38.9637 amu) and K-41 (6.88%; 40.9618 amu). Calculate the atomic weight for potassium. How does your answer compare with the atomic weight given in the list inside the front cover of this book?

PROBLEM 2.3

Bromine, an element present in compounds used as sanitizers and fumigants (for example, ethylene bromide), has two naturally occurring isotopes. Look up the mass numbers of the two naturally occurring isotopes of bromine, along with their percent abundance.

(a) Write the symbols for both isotopes.
(b) Using the masses and natural percent abundances, calculate the average molecular weight for bromine and compare your value to the value found in the periodic table on page 50.

HANDS-ON CHEMISTRY 2.1

Isotopes are used in many applications, including diagnosis and treatment of cancer and other diseases. In this activity, we will explore the structure of some isotopes of a specific element. Take two pieces of construction paper of different colors and cut each into about 25 pieces. Label each piece of one color with an "n" for neutron and each piece of the other color with a "p" for proton.

a. Distribute the pieces of construction paper into three piles as follows. Into pile 1, place six "p" and six "n" pieces. Into pile 2, place six "p" and seven "n" pieces.

Into pile 3, place six "p" and eight "n" pieces. How is each pile similar, and how are they different?

b. The three piles represent isotopes of a particular element. Which element? Write the atomic symbols for each isotope.

c. Look up the natural abundance of each isotope and calculate the average atomic mass for this element. How does your answer compare with the atomic weight given in the periodic table?

PROBLEM 2.4

An element used to sanitize water supplies has two naturally occurring isotopes with mass numbers of 35 and 37, and 17 electrons. Write the symbols for both isotopes, including their atomic numbers and mass numbers.

2.4 The Periodic Table

Learning Objective:

• Locate elements on the periodic table and classify them as metals, nonmetals, or metalloids based on their location.

Ten elements have been known since the beginning of recorded history: antimony (Sb), carbon (C), copper (Cu), gold (Au), iron (Fe), lead (Pb), mercury (Hg), silver (Ag), sulfur (S), and tin (Sn). It is worth noting that the symbols for many of these elements are derived from their Latin names, a reminder that they have been known since the time when Latin was the language used for all scholarly work. The first "new" element to be found in several thousand years was arsenic (As), discovered in about 1250. In fact, only 24 elements were known up to the time of the American Revolution in 1776.

As the pace of discovery quickened in the late 1700s and early 1800s, chemists began to look for similarities among elements that might make it possible to draw general conclusions. Numerous attempts were made in the mid-1800s to account for the similarities among groups of elements, but the great breakthrough came in 1869 when the Russian chemist Dmitri Mendeleev organized the elements in order of increasing mass and then organized elements into groups based on similarities in chemical behavior. His table is a forerunner of the modern **periodic table.** The table has boxes for each element that give the symbol, atomic number, and atomic mass of the element:

Periodic table A tabular format listing all known elements where the atomic symbol (top), name of the element (middle), and atomic mass (bottom) are given in each box that represents the element.

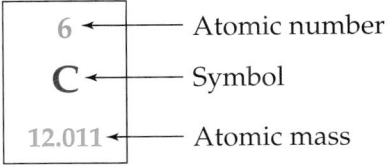

6 ← Atomic number

C ← Symbol

12.011 ← Atomic mass

The atomic masses for each element in the table are the average masses calculated based on the mass and percent abundance of the naturally occurring stable isotopes. The boxes are arranged in order of increasing atomic number, with the elements arranged in rows and columns as shown in Figure 2.2. An enormous amount of information is embedded in the periodic table, information that gives chemists the ability to explain known chemical behavior of elements and to predict new behavior.

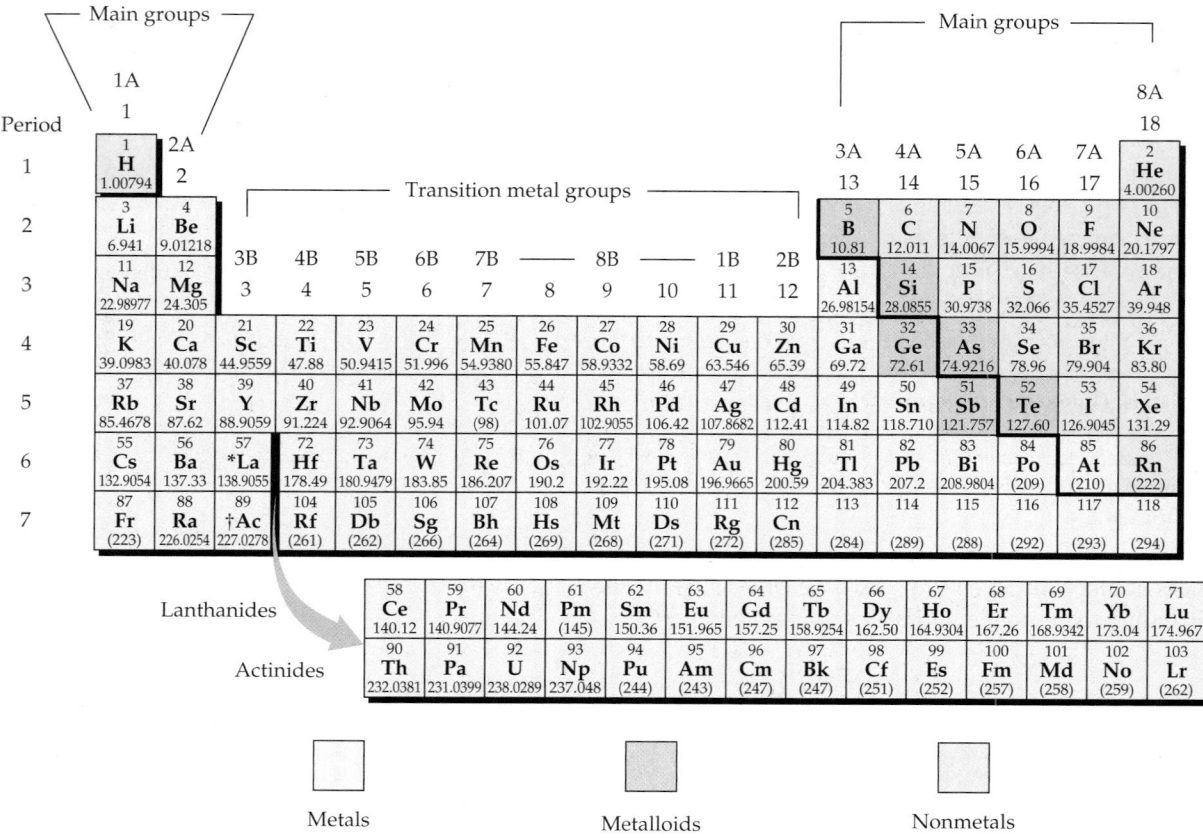

▲ **Figure 2.2**
The periodic table of the elements.
Elements are organized into groups, indicated with numbers and letters. Main group elements are in columns labeled 1A–8A, while the transition metal groups are in columns labeled 1B–8B. Elements to the left and bottom of the periodic table are classified as metals, while elements in the upper right portion are classified as nonmetals.

Metal A malleable element, with a lustrous appearance, that is a good conductor of heat and electricity.

Nonmetal An element that is a poor conductor of heat and electricity.

Metalloid An element whose properties are intermediate between those of a metal and a nonmetal.

One way of classifying the elements is by similarities in physical properties. Of the 118 currently known elements, 94 are classified as metals—aluminum, gold, copper, and zinc, for example. **Metals** are solid at room temperature (except for mercury), usually have a lustrous appearance when freshly cut, are good conductors of heat and electricity, and are malleable rather than brittle. That is, metals can be pounded into different shapes rather than shattering when struck. Note that metals occur on the left side of the periodic table.

Eighteen elements are **nonmetals.** All are poor conductors of heat and electricity. Eleven are gases at room temperature, six are brittle solids, and one is a liquid. Oxygen and nitrogen, for example, are gases present in air; sulfur is a solid found in large underground deposits. Bromine is the only liquid nonmetal. Note that nonmetals occur on the upper right side of the periodic table.

The **metalloids** are located in a zigzag band between the metals on the left and nonmetals on the right side of the periodic table. Although there is some debate as to which elements to include in this list, we include only six in this text: boron, silicon, arsenic, germanium, antimony, and tellurium. The metalloids are so named because their properties are intermediate between those of metals and nonmetals. Pure silicon, for example, has a lustrous or shiny surface, like a metal, but it is brittle, like a nonmetal, and its electrical conductivity lies between that of metals and nonmetals. Some chemistry texts identify polonium as a metalloid, but its chemical behavior and conductivity more closely resemble that of other metals. Others include astatine in the list, but this is purely academic: as a very rare and unstable element, it would be difficult to collect a sample of astatine large enough to obtain reliable data regarding its chemical and physical behavior.

(a)   (b)   (c)

▲ **Metals: Gold, zinc, and copper.**
(a) Known for its beauty, gold is very unreactive and is used primarily in jewelry and in electronic components. (b) Zinc, an essential trace element in our diets, has industrial uses ranging from the manufacture of brass, to roofing materials, to batteries. (c) Copper is widely used in electrical wiring, in water pipes, and in coins.

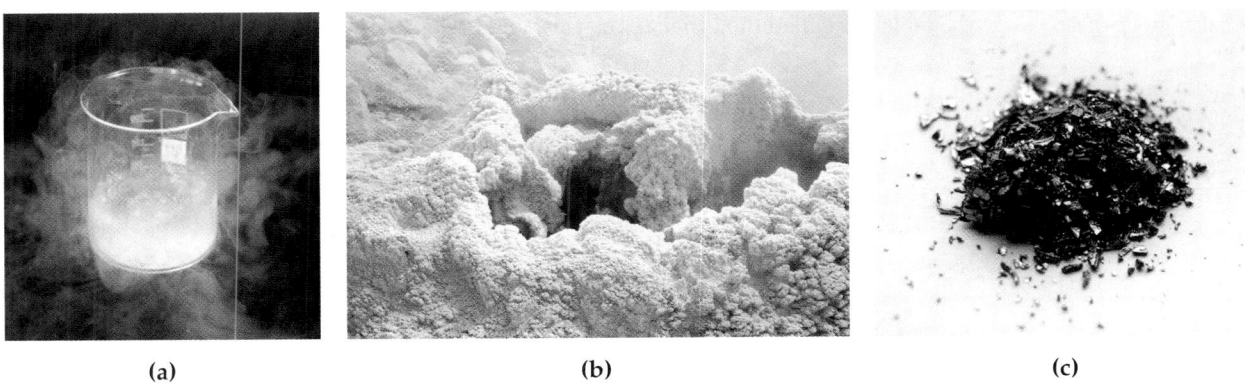

(a)   (b)   (c)

▲ **Nonmetals: Nitrogen, sulfur, and iodine.**
(a) Nitrogen, (b) sulfur, and (c) iodine are essential to all living things. Pure nitrogen, which constitutes almost 80% of air, is a gas at room temperature and does not condense to a liquid until it is cooled to −328 °C. Sulfur, a yellow solid, is found in large underground deposits in Texas and Louisiana. Iodine is a dark violet crystalline solid that was first isolated from seaweed.

(a)   (b)

▲ **Metalloids: Boron and silicon.**
(a) Boron is a strong, hard metalloid used in making the composite materials found in military aircraft. (b) Silicon is well known for its use in making computer chips.

Period One of the seven horizontal rows of elements in the periodic table.

Group One of the 18 vertical columns of elements in the periodic table.

Another way of classifying the elements in the periodic table is based on similarities in chemical behavior. Beginning at the upper left corner of the periodic table, elements are arranged by increasing atomic number into seven horizontal rows, called **periods,** and 18 vertical columns, called **groups.** When organized in this way, *the elements in a given group have similar chemical properties.* Lithium, sodium, potassium, and the other elements in group 1A behave similarly. Chlorine, bromine, iodine, and the other elements in group 7A behave similarly and so on throughout the table.

Note that different periods (rows) contain different numbers of elements. The first period contains only two elements, hydrogen and helium; the second and third periods each contain eight elements; the fourth and fifth periods each contain 18; the sixth and seventh periods contain 32. Note also that the 14 elements following lanthanum (the *lanthanides*) and the 14 following actinium (the *actinides*) are pulled out and shown below the others.

Main group element An element in one of the two groups on the left or the six groups on the right of the periodic table.

Transition metal element An element in one of the 10 smaller groups near the middle of the periodic table.

Inner transition metal element An element in one of the 14 groups shown separately at the bottom of the periodic table.

Groups are numbered in two ways, both shown in Figure 2.2. The two large groups on the far left and the six on the far right are called the **main group elements** and are numbered 1A through 8A. The 10 smaller groups in the middle of the table are called the **transition metal elements** and are numbered 1B through 8B. Alternatively, all 18 groups are numbered sequentially from 1 to 18. The 14 groups shown separately at the bottom of the table are called the **inner transition metal elements** and are not numbered.

PROBLEM 2.5

Locate aluminum in the periodic table and give its group number and period number.

PROBLEM 2.6

Identify the group 1B element in period five and the group 2A element in period four.

PROBLEM 2.7

There are five elements in group 5A of the periodic table. Identify them and give the period of each.

PROBLEM 2.8

The six metalloids are boron (B), silicon (Si), germanium (Ge), arsenic (As), antimony (Sb), and tellurium (Te). Locate them in the periodic table and tell where they appear with respect to metals and nonmetals.

PROBLEM 2.9

Locate the following elements in the periodic table, give the corresponding name for each, and classify them according to group (i.e., halogen, noble gas, alkali metal, etc.).

   (a) Ti   **(b)** Te   **(c)** Se   **(d)** Sc   **(e)** At   **(f)** Ar

2.5 Some Characteristics of Different Groups

Learning Objective:

• Classify elements and describe chemical behavior based on group membership.

To see why the periodic table has the name it does, look at the graph of atomic radius versus atomic number in Figure 2.3. The graph shows an obvious *periodicity*—a repeating rise-and-fall pattern. Beginning on the left with atomic number 1 (hydrogen), the sizes of the atoms increase to a maximum at atomic number 3 (lithium), then decrease to a minimum, then increase again to a maximum at atomic number 11 (sodium), then decrease, and

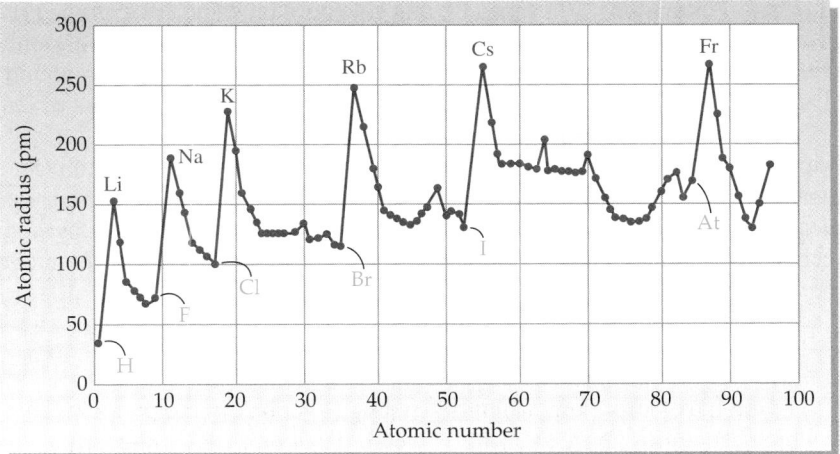

◄ **Figure 2.3**
A graph of atomic radius in picometers (pm) versus atomic number shows a periodic rise and fall pattern.
The maxima occur for atoms of the group 1A elements (Li, Na, K, Rb, Cs, and Fr in red); the minima occur for atoms of the group 7A elements (blue). Accurate data are not available for the group 8A elements.

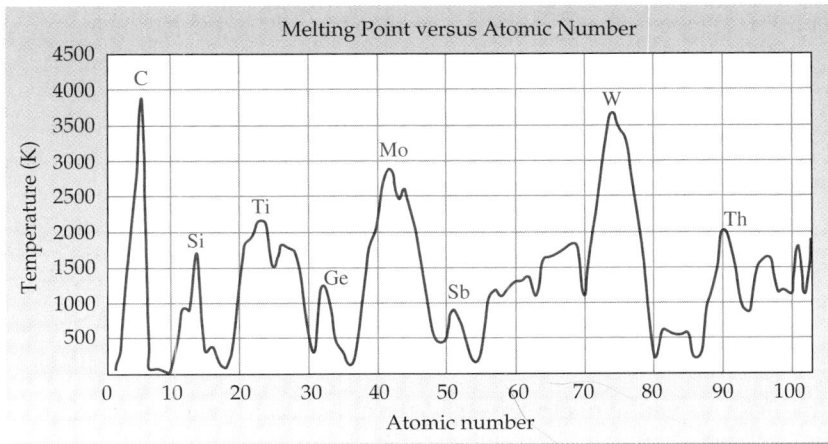

◄ **Figure 2.4**
A graph of melting point versus atomic number shows periodic properties similar to the trend in Figure 2.3.
While the maxima and minima are not as sharp as in Figure 2.3, the change in melting points of the elements still shows a similar periodic trend.

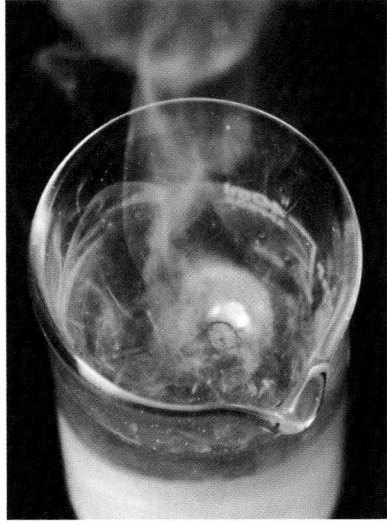

▲ Sodium, an alkali metal, reacts violently with water to yield hydrogen gas and an alkaline (basic) solution.

Alkali metal An element in group 1A of the periodic table.

Alkaline earth metal An element in group 2A of the periodic table.

so on. It turns out that the local maximum values occur for atoms of group 1A elements—Li, Na, K, Rb, Cs, and Fr—and the local minimum values occur for atoms of the group 7A elements.

There is nothing unique about the periodicity of atomic radii shown in Figure 2.3. The melting points of the first 100 elements, for example, exhibit similar periodic behavior, as shown in Figure 2.4, with a systematic trend of peaks and valleys as you progress through the elements in the periodic table. Many other physical and chemical properties can be plotted in a similar way with similar results. In fact, the various elements in a given group of the periodic table usually show remarkable similarities in many of their chemical and physical properties. Look at the following four groups, for example:

- **Group 1A—Alkali metals:** Lithium (Li), sodium (Na), potassium (K), rubidium (Rb), cesium (Cs), and francium (Fr) are shiny, soft metals with low melting points. All react rapidly (often violently) with water to form products that are highly alkaline, or basic—hence the name **alkali metals.** Because of their high reactivity, the alkali metals are never found in nature in the pure state but only in combination with other elements.
- **Group 2A—Alkaline earth metals:** Beryllium (Be), magnesium (Mg), calcium (Ca), strontium (Sr), barium (Ba), and radium (Ra) are also lustrous, silvery metals but are less reactive than their neighbors in group 1A. Like the alkali metals, the alkaline earths are never found in nature in the pure state.

Halogen An element in group 7A of
the periodic table.

Noble gas An element in group 8A of
the periodic table.

➤➤ Carbon, the element on which
life is based, is a group 4A nonmetal
near the top right of the periodic
table. Clustered near carbon are other
elements often found in living organisms, including oxygen, nitrogen,
phosphorus, and sulfur. We will look at
the subject of *organic chemistry*—the
chemistry of carbon compounds—
in Chapters 12–17 and move on to
biochemistry—the chemistry of living
things—in Chapters 18–29.

- **Group 7A—Halogens:** Fluorine (F), chlorine (Cl), bromine (Br), iodine (I), and
  astatine (At) are colorful and corrosive nonmetals. All are found in nature only in
  combination with other elements, such as with sodium in table salt (sodium chloride, NaCl). In fact, the group name **halogen** is taken from the Greek word *hals,*
  meaning salt.
- **Group 8A—Noble gases:** Helium (He), neon (Ne), argon (Ar), krypton (Kr),
  xenon (Xe), and radon (Rn) are colorless gases. The elements in this group were
  labeled the "noble" gases because of their lack of chemical reactivity—helium,
  neon, and argon do not combine with any other elements, whereas krypton and
  xenon combine with a very few.

PROBLEM 2.10

Locate (a) krypton, (b) strontium, (c) nitrogen, and (d) cobalt in the periodic table.
Indicate which categories apply to each: (i) metal, (ii) nonmetal, (iii) transition element, (iv) main group element, and (v) noble gas.

PROBLEM 2.11

For each of the following sets of elements, arrange in order of increasing atomic
radius:

  a) Na, Li, Rb, K   **b)** Li, O, C, F   **c)** Cl, Br, I, F

PROBLEM 2.12

For each set of elements presented in the previous problem, arrange in order of increasing melting point.

⌦ KEY CONCEPT PROBLEM 2.13 ——————————————————

Identify the elements whose nuclei are shown next. For each, tell its group number, its
period number, and whether it is a metal, nonmetal, or metalloid.

     (a)   (b)

    ● Neutron

    ● Proton

CHEMISTRY IN ACTION

✚ Essential Elements and Group Chemistry

In Chapter 1, we introduced the essential elements—elements
that are vital to good health and fitness. In this chapter, we
demonstrated how elements in a group exhibit similar chemical properties. As you might expect, the properties of a group
influence their role in the metabolism of an organism. As we
noted in Chapter 1, these elements are typically not present
in the body as free atoms but as ions or combined with other
elements in compounds (discussed in Chapter 3). Let's take a
look at some of the major players in the different groups:

1A. Alkali metals: Lithium (Li) plays no known physiological role in the body, but the apparent neurological effects
of the Li ion in many lithium compounds explains why they
are often used as mood stabilizing drugs. Sodium (Na) is
considered a macronutrient because of the vital role it plays
in regulation of blood volume and blood pressure and transmission of nerve impulses. Potassium (K), like sodium, is
also involved in neurological functions and nerve impulse
transmission, and a deficiency in K ions can lead to cardiac
dysfunctions.

2A. Alkaline earth metals: Magnesium (Mg) ions are important in many enzymatic processes, including energy production and DNA synthesis. Magnesium compounds also are used therapeutically as laxatives and to relieve the symptoms of fibromyalgia, migraines, and premenstrual syndrome. Calcium (Ca) is a major component in teeth and bones and also plays a role in neurotransmission and muscle contraction. An excess of calcium ions is the blood can lead to impaired kidney function and decreased absorption of other important minerals.

7A. Halogens: Fluorine (F) compounds have been added into toothpaste and municipal drinking water supplies to strengthen tooth enamel and increase dental health. Fluorine-containing drugs are used to lower cholesterol, as antidepressants, antibiotics, and anesthetics. Chlorine (Cl) ions play an important role in maintaining salt balance in bodily fluids. Bromine (Br) was initially thought to have no biological function; recent research indicates that it is necessary for tissue development. Iodine (I) is an essential trace element, primarily because of its role as a constituent in thyroxine, a thyroid hormone responsible for regulation of basal metabolism.

1–8B. Transition metals: Probably the most familiar essential transition metal is iron (Fe), a major component in hemoglobin that is responsible for oxygen transport in the blood. But many other transition metals are constituents of enzymes (biological catalysts), including chromium (Cr), cobalt (Co), copper (Cu), molybdenum (Mo), manganese (Mn), and zinc (Zn). Zinc, in particular, is recognized as an essential mineral important to public health. Zinc deficiencies in children are linked to delayed growth and sexual maturation, severe dermatitis, and diarrhea.

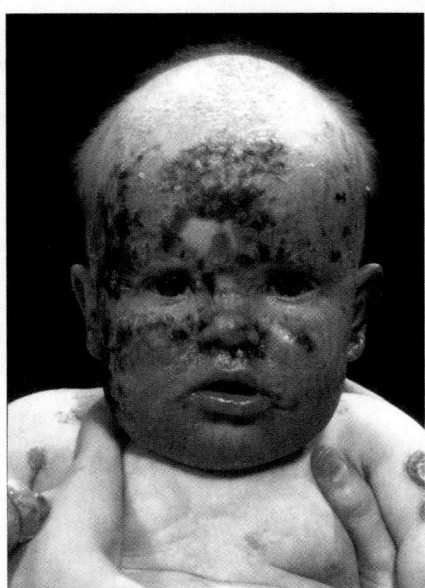

▲ This infant is suffering from acrodermatitis enteropathica, a skin condition resulting from an inability to metabolize zinc.

CIA Problem 2.3 Elements from other groups also play important biological roles. Identify each of the following:

a) A group 5A element that is a major component of cell membranes and bones.

b) A group 6A element that is involved in thyroid function and a constituent of enzymes involved in fat metabolism but is toxic in large doses.

CIA Problem 2.4 Locate and identify the group number for each of the transition metals mentioned earlier.

2.6 Electronic Structure of Atoms

Learning Objective:

• Describe the distribution of electrons into shells, subshells, and orbitals around the nucleus of an atom.

Why does the periodic table have the shape it does, with periods of different length? Why are periodic variations observed in atomic radii and in so many other characteristics of the elements? And why do elements in a given group of the periodic table show similar chemical behavior? These questions occupied the thoughts of chemists for more than 50 years after Mendeleev, and it was not until well into the 1920s that the answers were established. Today, we know that *the properties of the elements are determined by the arrangement of electrons in their atoms.*

Our current understanding of the electronic structure of atoms is based on the *quantum mechanical model,* developed by Austrian physicist Erwin Schrödinger in 1926. One of the fundamental assumptions of the model is that electrons have both particle-like and wave-like properties, and that the behavior of electrons can be described using a mathematical equation called a wave function. One consequence of this assumption is that electrons are not perfectly free to move about in an atom.

▲ Stairs are *quantized* because they change height in discrete amounts. A ramp, by contrast, is not quantized because it changes height continuously.

Shell (electron) A grouping of electrons in an atom according to energy.

Subshell (electron) A grouping of electrons in a shell according to the shape of the region of space they occupy.

Orbital A region of space within an atom where an electron in a given subshell can be found.

Instead, each electron is restricted to a certain region of space within the atom, depending on the energy level of the electron. Different electrons have different amounts of energy and thus occupy different regions within the atom. Furthermore, the energies of electrons are *quantized* or restricted to having only certain values.

To understand the idea of quantization, think about the difference between stairs and a ramp. A ramp is *not* quantized because it changes height continuously. Stairs, by contrast, *are* quantized because they change height only by a fixed amount. When you walk up a flight of stairs, you can put your foot on each step, but you cannot stand any place between the two steps. Conversely, on a ramp, you can step anywhere on the ramp you like. In the same way, the energy values available to electrons in an atom change only in steps rather than continuously.

The wave functions derived from the quantum mechanical model also provide important information about the location of electrons in an atom. Just as a person can be found by giving his or her address within a state, an electron can be found by giving its "address" within an atom. Furthermore, just as a person's address is composed of several successively narrower categories—city, street, and house number—an electron's address is also composed of successively narrower categories—*shell, subshell,* and *orbital,* which are defined by the quantum mechanical model.

The electrons in an atom are grouped around the nucleus into **shells,** like the layers in an onion, according to the energy of the electrons. The shell is designated using the letter n; $n = 1$ for the first shell (period 1), $n = 2$ for the second shell (period 2), and so on. The farther a shell is from the nucleus, the larger it is, the more electrons it can hold, the higher the energies of those electrons, and thus the easier they are to remove because they are the farthest away from the positively charged nucleus. The first shell (the one nearest the nucleus) can hold only 2 electrons, the second shell can hold 8, the third shell can hold 18, and the fourth shell can hold 32 electrons.

Shell number:	1	2	3	4
Electron capacity:	2	8	18	32

Within shells, electrons are further grouped into **subshells** of four different types, identified in order of increasing energy by the letters s, p, d, and f. The first shell has only one subshell, s. The second shell has two subshells: an s subshell and a p subshell. The third shell has an s, p, and d subshell. The fourth shell has an s, p, d, and f subshell. Of the four types, we will be concerned mainly with s and p subshells because most of the elements found in living organisms use only these. A specific subshell is symbolized by writing the number of the shell followed by the letter for the subshell. For example, the designation $3p$ refers to the p subshell in the third shell ($n = 3$). Note that the number of subshells in a given shell is equal to the shell number. For example, shell number 3 has three subshells (s, p, and d).

Finally, within each subshell, electrons are grouped into **orbitals,** regions of space within an atom where the specific electrons are most likely to be found. There are different numbers of orbitals within the different kinds of subshells. A given s subshell has only one orbital, a p subshell has three orbitals, a d subshell has five orbitals, and an f subshell has seven orbitals. Each orbital can hold only two electrons, which differ in a property known as *spin.* If one electron in an orbital has a clockwise spin, the other electron in the same orbital must have a counterclockwise spin. Since the number of orbitals in a shell increases as n increases, the number of electrons that can be placed in a shell also increases with n, as seen in Table 2.2. The following figure summarizes the configuration of shells, subshells, and orbitals.

Shell number:	1	2	3	4
Subshell designation:	s	s , p	s , p , d	s , p , d , f
Number of orbitals:	1	1 , 3	1 , 3 , 5	1 , 3 , 5 , 7

Table 2.2 Electron Distribution in Atoms

Shell Number:	1	2	3	4
Subshell designation:	s	s, p	s, p, d	s, p, d, f
Number of orbitals:	1	1, 3	1, 3, 5	1, 3, 5, 7
Number of electrons:	2	2, 6	2, 6, 10	2, 6, 10, 14
Total electron capacity:	2	8	18	32

In the quantum mechanical model, different orbitals have different shapes and orientations. Orbitals in s subshells are spherical regions centered about the nucleus, whereas orbitals in p subshells are roughly dumbbell-shaped regions where the nucleus is at the midpoint of the dumbbells (Figure 2.5). As shown in Figure 2.5b, the three p orbitals in a given subshell are oriented at right angles to one another.

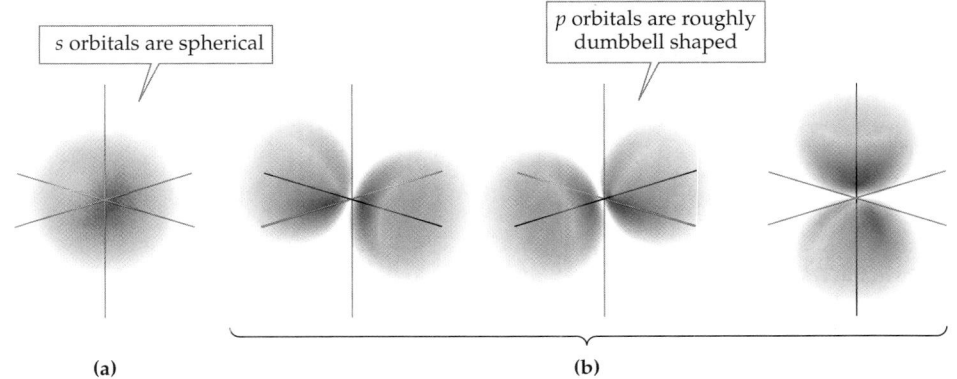

s orbitals are spherical

p orbitals are roughly dumbbell shaped

(a)   (b)

◄ **Figure 2.5**
The shapes of s and p orbitals.
(a) The s orbitals and (b) the p orbitals. The three p orbitals in a given subshell are oriented at right angles to one another. Each orbital can hold only two electrons.

The overall electron distribution within an atom is summarized in Table 2.2 and in the following list:

* The first shell has a maximum capacity of only two electrons. The two electrons have different spins and are in a single $1s$ orbital.
* The second shell has a maximum capacity of eight electrons. Two are in a $2s$ orbital, and 6 are in the three different $2p$ orbitals (two per $2p$ orbital).
* The third shell has a maximum capacity of 18 electrons. Two are in a $3s$ orbital, 6 are in three $3p$ orbitals, and 10 are in five $3d$ orbitals.
* The fourth shell has a maximum capacity of 32 electrons. Two are in a $4s$ orbital, 6 are in three $4p$ orbitals, 10 are in five $4d$ orbitals, and 14 are in seven $4f$ orbitals.

Worked Example 2.5 Atomic Structure: Electron Shells

How many electrons are present in an atom that has its first and second shells filled and has four electrons in its third shell? Name the element.

ANALYSIS The number of electrons in the atom is calculated by adding the total electrons in each shell. We can identify the element from the number of protons in the nucleus, which is equal to the number of electrons in the atom.

SOLUTION
The first shell of an atom holds two electrons in its $1s$ orbital, and the second shell holds eight electrons (two in a $2s$ orbital and six in three $2p$ orbitals). Thus, the atom has a total of $2 + 8 + 4 = 14$ electrons. Since the number of electrons is equal to the number of protons, the element's atomic number $Z = 14$ and must be silicon (Si).

PROBLEM 2.14

How many electrons are present in an atom in which the first and second shells and the $3s$ subshell are filled? Name the element.

HANDS-ON CHEMISTRY 2.2

This exercise is designed to help visualize the structure of the atom more closely. The manipulation of an onion will simulate the phenomenal behavior and properties of individual atoms.

a. Cut a medium-sized whole onion in half and remove the outer dry peeling/skin. If we consider the central kernel of the onion as the nucleus, each "layer" would then correspond to a shell containing varying numbers of electrons.

b. How many shells/layers are there in your onion? To which period in the periodic table does this correspond?

c. Note how far each layer is from the "nucleus." What does this imply about the relative attractive forces between each layer and the nucleus?

d. Now peel the successive layers of the onion. How big is the outermost layer compared with the inner layers? What does this imply about the number of electrons that can fit in each layer?

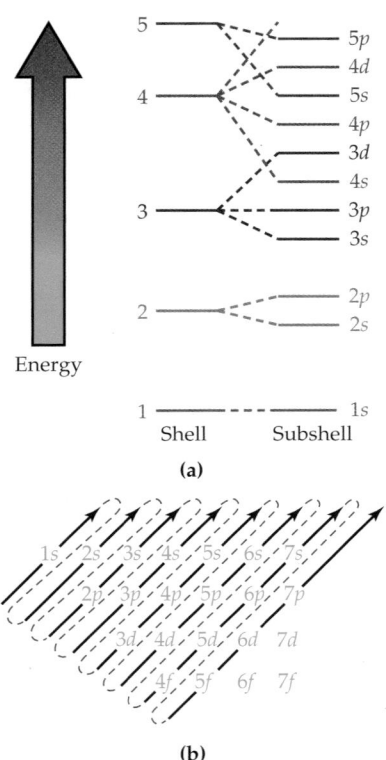

Energy

(a)

(b)

▲ **Figure 2.6**
Order of orbital energy levels.
(a) An energy-level diagram shows the order in which orbitals will be filled within each shell. Above the 3*p* level, there is some crossover of energies among orbitals in different shells.
(b) A simple scheme to remember the order in which the orbitals are filled.

Electron configuration The specific arrangement of electrons in an atom's shells and subshells.

Orbital diagram A representation of the electron distribution into orbitals, in which orbitals are indicated by a line or a box and electrons in each orbital are represented as arrows.

2.7 Electron Configurations

Learning Objective:

• Write the electronic configuration for an atom to describe how electrons are distributed into specific orbitals.

The exact arrangement of electrons in an atom's shells and subshells is called the atom's **electron configuration** and can be predicted by applying three rules:

RULE 1: Electrons occupy the lowest-energy orbitals available, beginning with 1*s*. Within each shell, the orbital energies increase in the order *s*, *p*, *d*, and *f*. For the first three periods, the order of energy is as follows: 1*s*, 2*s*, 2*p*, 3*s*, and 3*p*. Across shells, the orbital closer to the nucleus is lower in energy. For example, a 2*s* orbital has lower energy than a 3*s* orbital. As a result, above the 3*p* level the order of how shells are filled is not as straightforward. For example, the 4*s* orbital is lower in energy than the 3*d* orbitals and is therefore filled first. The energy level diagram and simple scheme shown in Figure 2.6 can be used to predict the order in which orbitals are filled. Neither of these diagrams need to be memorized, however, as you can also use the periodic table to determine the order in which orbitals are filled in relation to their placement, shown later in Section 2.8.

RULE 2: Each orbital can hold only two electrons, which must be of opposite spin.

RULE 3: Two or more orbitals with the same energy are each half-filled by one electron before any one orbital is completely filled by the addition of the second electron. For example, one electron is added to each of the three *p* orbitals before a second electron is added to fill an orbital.

Electron configurations of the first 20 elements are shown in Table 2.3. Notice that the number of electrons in each subshell is indicated by a superscript. For example, the notation $1s^2\,2s^2\,2p^6\,3s^2$ for magnesium means that magnesium atoms have two electrons in the first shell, eight electrons in the second shell, and two electrons in the third shell.

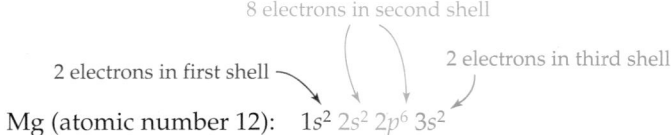

Mg (atomic number 12): $1s^2\,2s^2\,2p^6\,3s^2$

In additional to writing the configurations as shown above, we can also use **orbital diagrams.** In the written representation, the superscript in the notation $1s^1$ means that the 1*s* orbital is occupied by only one electron. In an orbital diagram, the 1*s* orbital is indicated by a line or a box and the single electron in this orbital is shown by a single arrow pointing up (↑). A single electron in an orbital is often referred to as being *unpaired*. Two electrons in an orbital are paired, with spins in opposite directions, so they are represented by two arrows pointing in opposite directions (one up, one down).

Table 2.3 Electron Configurations of the First 20 Elements

	Element	Atomic Number	Electron Configuration
H	Hydrogen	1	$1s^1$
He	Helium	2	$1s^2$
Li	Lithium	3	$1s^2\,2s^1$
Be	Beryllium	4	$1s^2\,2s^2$
B	Boron	5	$1s^2\,2s^2\,2p^1$
C	Carbon	6	$1s^2\,2s^2\,2p^2$
N	Nitrogen	7	$1s^2\,2s^2\,2p^3$
O	Oxygen	8	$1s^2\,2s^2\,2p^4$
F	Fluorine	9	$1s^2\,2s^2\,2p^5$
Ne	Neon	10	$1s^2\,2s^2\,2p^6$
Na	Sodium	11	$1s^2\,2s^2\,2p^6\,3s^1$
Mg	Magnesium	12	$1s^2\,2s^2\,2p^6\,3s^2$
Al	Aluminum	13	$1s^2\,2s^2\,2p^6\,3s^2\,3p^1$
Si	Silicon	14	$1s^2\,2s^2\,2p^6\,3s^2\,3p^2$
P	Phosphorus	15	$1s^2\,2s^2\,2p^6\,3s^2\,3p^3$
S	Sulfur	16	$1s^2\,2s^2\,2p^6\,3s^2\,3p^4$
Cl	Chlorine	17	$1s^2\,2s^2\,2p^6\,3s^2\,3p^5$
Ar	Argon	18	$1s^2\,2s^2\,2p^6\,3s^2\,3p^6$
K	Potassium	19	$1s^2\,2s^2\,2p^6\,3s^2\,3p^6\,4s^1$
Ca	Calcium	20	$1s^2\,2s^2\,2p^6\,3s^2\,3p^6\,4s^2$

As you read through the following electron configurations, check the atomic number and the location of each element in the periodic table (Figure 2.2). See if you can detect the relationship between electron configuration and position in the table.

- **Hydrogen ($Z = 1$):** The single electron in a hydrogen atom is in the lowest-energy, $1s$, level. The configuration can be represented in either of two ways:

$$\mathbf{H} \quad 1s^1 \quad \text{or} \quad \boxed{\uparrow}\;\;_{1s^1}$$

- **Helium ($Z = 2$):** The two electrons in helium are both in the lowest-energy, $1s$, orbital, and their spins are *paired,* as represented by up and down arrows ($\uparrow\downarrow$). Helium has a completely filled first shell ($n = 1$) of electrons.

$$\mathbf{He} \quad 1s^2 \quad \text{or} \quad \boxed{\uparrow\downarrow}\;\;_{1s^2}$$

- **Lithium ($Z = 3$):** Lithium has three electrons, so we must now use the orbitals in the second shell, starting with $2s$. Since electrons are always added to the lowest energy level first, the first two electrons fill the first shell. Next, the second shell begins to fill. The third electron goes into the $2s$ orbital and is unpaired:

$$\mathbf{Li} \quad 1s^2\,2s^1 \quad \text{or} \quad \boxed{\uparrow\downarrow}\;_{1s^2}\;\;\boxed{\uparrow}\;_{2s^1}$$

Because [He] has the configuration of a filled $1s^2$ orbital, it is sometimes substituted for the $1s^2$ orbital in depictions of electron pairing. Using this alternative shorthand notation, the electron configuration for Li is written [He] $2s^1$.

- **Beryllium ($Z = 4$):** For beryllium's four electrons, we continue to use the second shell. The three electrons are configured as they were for lithium, and the fourth electron pairs up to fill the $2s$ orbital:

$$\textbf{Be} \quad 1s^2\, 2s^2 \quad \text{or} \quad \boxed{\uparrow\downarrow}\ \boxed{\uparrow\downarrow} \quad \text{or} \quad [\text{He}]\, 2s^2$$
$$1s^2 \quad 2s^2$$

- **Boron ($Z = 5$), Carbon ($Z = 6$), Nitrogen ($Z = 7$):** The next three elements use the three $2p$ orbitals, one at a time. For boron, the fifth electron starts to fill the first $2p$ orbital. Carbon and nitrogen's sixth and seventh electron are placed in the next two orbitals, respectively (instead of filling the first p orbital). Note that representing the configurations with lines and arrows gives more information than the alternative written notations because the filling and pairing of electrons in individual orbitals within the p subshell is shown.

$$\textbf{B} \quad 1s^2\, 2s^2\, 2p^1 \quad \text{or} \quad \boxed{\uparrow\downarrow}\ \boxed{\uparrow\downarrow}\ \underbrace{\boxed{\uparrow\,|\,\,|\,\,}}_{2p^1} \quad \text{or} \quad [\text{He}]\, 2s^2\, 2p^1$$

$$\textbf{C} \quad 1s^2\, 2s^2\, 2p^2 \quad \text{or} \quad \boxed{\uparrow\downarrow}\ \boxed{\uparrow\downarrow}\ \underbrace{\boxed{\uparrow\,|\,\uparrow\,|\,\,}}_{2p^2} \quad \text{or} \quad [\text{He}]\, 2s^2\, 2p^2$$

$$\textbf{N} \quad 1s^2\, 2s^2\, 2p^3 \quad \text{or} \quad \boxed{\uparrow\downarrow}\ \boxed{\uparrow\downarrow}\ \underbrace{\boxed{\uparrow\,|\,\uparrow\,|\,\uparrow}}_{2p^3} \quad \text{or} \quad [\text{He}]\, 2s^2\, 2p^3$$

- **Oxygen ($Z = 8$), Fluorine ($Z = 9$), Neon ($Z = 10$):** Electrons now pair up one by one to fill the three $2p$ orbitals and fully occupy the second shell.

$$\textbf{O} \quad 1s^2\, 2s^2\, 2p^4 \quad \text{or} \quad \boxed{\uparrow\downarrow}\ \boxed{\uparrow\downarrow}\ \underbrace{\boxed{\uparrow\downarrow\,|\,\uparrow\,|\,\uparrow}}_{2p^4} \quad \text{or} \quad [\text{He}]\, 2s^2\, 2p^4$$

$$\textbf{F} \quad 1s^2\, 2s^2\, 2p^5 \quad \text{or} \quad \boxed{\uparrow\downarrow}\ \boxed{\uparrow\downarrow}\ \underbrace{\boxed{\uparrow\downarrow\,|\,\uparrow\downarrow\,|\,\uparrow}}_{2p^5} \quad \text{or} \quad [\text{He}]\, 2s^2\, 2p^5$$

$$\textbf{Ne} \quad 1s^2\, 2s^2\, 2p^6 \quad \text{or} \quad \boxed{\uparrow\downarrow}\ \boxed{\uparrow\downarrow}\ \underbrace{\boxed{\uparrow\downarrow\,|\,\uparrow\downarrow\,|\,\uparrow\downarrow}}_{2p^6}$$

Just as $[\text{He}]$ was used as a shorthand notation to indicate the closed-shell configuration $1s^2$, we may also use $[\text{Ne}]$ to represent the electron configuration for a completely filled set of orbitals in the second shell, or $1s^2 2s^2 2p^6$. Both helium and neon are noble gases and are located in Group 8A on the periodic table. All of electron configurations of the elements in one period can be written in shorthand using the noble gas that immediately precedes it in the periodic table.

- **Sodium to Calcium ($Z = 11 - 20$):** The pattern seen for lithium through neon is seen again for sodium ($Z = 11$) through argon ($Z = 18$) as the $3s$ and $3p$ subshells fill up. For elements having a third filled shell, we may use $[\text{Ar}]$ to represent a completely filled third shell. After argon, however, the first crossover in subshell energies occurs. As indicated in Figure 2.6, the $4s$ subshell is lower in energy than the $3d$ subshell and is filled first. Potassium ($Z = 19$) and calcium ($Z = 20$), therefore, have the following electron configurations:

$$\textbf{K} \quad 1s^2\, 2s^2\, 2p^6\, 3s^2\, 3p^6\, 4s^1 \text{ or } [\text{Ar}]4s^1 \qquad \textbf{Ca} \quad 1s^2\, 2s^2\, 2p^6\, 3s^2\, 3p^6\, 4s^2 \text{ or } [\text{Ar}]4s^2$$

After calcium we enter the transition metals, and the subsequent electrons for these elements would be placed into the next lowest energy orbitals, or the $3d$.

Worked Example 2.6 Atomic Structure: Electron Configurations

Show how the electron configuration of magnesium can be assigned.

ANALYSIS Magnesium, $Z = 12$, has 12 electrons to be placed in specific orbitals. Assignments are made by putting two electrons in each orbital, according to the order shown in Figure 2.6.

- The first two electrons are placed in the $1s$ orbital $(1s^2)$.
- The next two electrons are placed in the $2s$ orbital $(2s^2)$.
- The next six electrons are placed in the three available $2p$ orbitals $(2p^6)$.
- The remaining two electrons are both put in the $3s$ orbital $(3s^2)$.

SOLUTION
Magnesium has the configuration $1s^2 2s^2 2p^6 3s^2$ or $[\text{Ne}]3s^2$.

Worked Example 2.7 Electron Configurations: Orbital-Filling Diagrams

Write the electron diagram of phosphorus, $Z = 15$, using up and down arrows to show how the electrons in each orbital are paired.

ANALYSIS Phosphorus has 15 electrons, which occupy orbitals according to the order shown in Figure 2.6.

- The first two are paired and fill the first shell $(1s^2)$.
- The next eight fill the second shell $(2s^2 2p^6)$. All electrons are paired.
- The remaining five electrons enter the third shell, where two fill the $3s$ orbital $(3s^2)$ and three occupy the $3p$ subshell, one in each of the three p orbitals.

SOLUTION

PROBLEM 2.15

An element has completely filled $n = 1$ and $n = 2$ shells and has six electrons in the $n = 3$ shell. Identify the element and its major group (i.e., main group, transition, etc.). Is it a metal or a nonmetal? Identify the orbital in which the last electron is found.

PROBLEM 2.16

Write electron configurations for the following elements. (You can check your answers in Table 2.3.)

(a) C   (b) P   (c) Cl   (d) K

PROBLEM 2.17

For an atom containing 33 electrons, identify the incompletely filled subshell and show the paired and/or unpaired electrons in this subshell using up and down arrows.

⊙ KEY CONCEPT PROBLEM 2.18 ────────────

Identify the atom with the following orbital-filling diagram.

2.8 Electron Configurations and the Periodic Table

Learning Objective:

• Identify the valence shell electrons for an atom, and which subshell of electrons
(s, p, d, f) correlate with which groups in the periodic table.

s-**Block element** A main group
element that results from the filling of
an *s* orbital.

p-**Block element** A main group
element that results from the filling of
p orbitals.

d-**Block element** A transition metal
element that results from the filling of
d orbitals.

f-**Block element** An inner transition
metal element that results from the
filling of *f* orbitals.

How is an atom's electron configuration related to its chemical behavior, and why do
elements with similar behavior occur in the same group of the periodic table? As shown
in Figure 2.7, the periodic table can be divided into four regions, or *blocks,* of elements
according to the electron shells and subshells occupied by *the subshell filled last.*

• The main group 1A and 2A elements on the left side of the table (plus He) are
called the *s*-**block elements** because an *s* subshell is filled last in these elements.
• The main group 3A–8A elements on the right side of the table (except He) are the
p-**block elements** because a *p* subshell is filled last in these elements.
• The transition metals in the middle of the table are the *d*-**block elements** because a
d subshell is filled last in these elements.
• The inner transition metals detached at the bottom of the table are the *f*-**block
elements** because an *f* subshell is filled last in these elements.

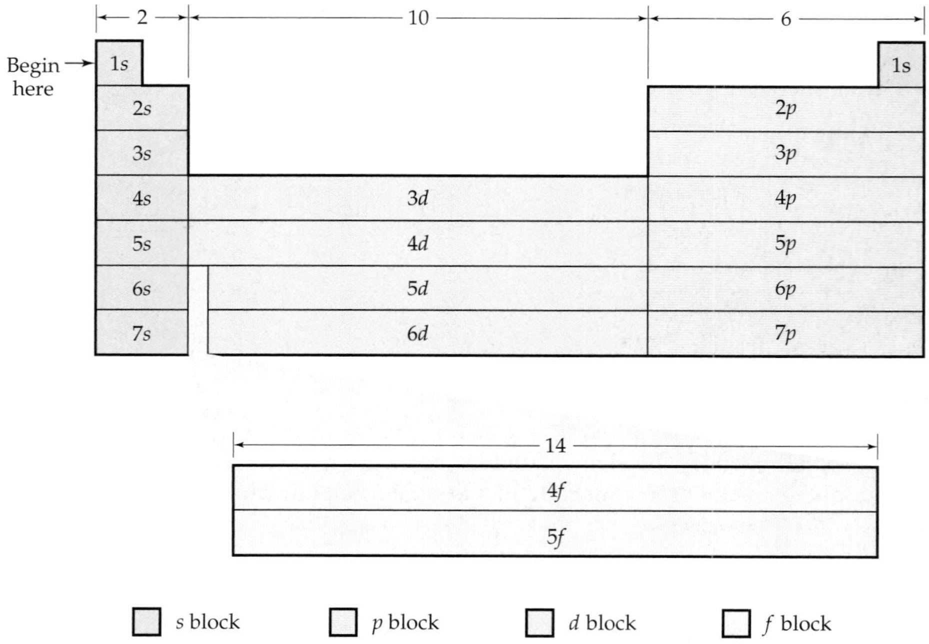

▶ **Figure 2.7**
**The blocks of elements in the
periodic table correspond to filling
the different types of subshells.**
Beginning at the top left and going
across successive rows of the periodic
table provides a method for remembering the order of orbital filling:
$1s \rightarrow 2s \rightarrow 2p \rightarrow 3s \rightarrow 3p \rightarrow 4s \rightarrow$
$3d \rightarrow 4p$, and so on.

Thinking of the periodic table as outlined in Figure 2.7 provides a simple way to remember the order of orbital filling shown previously in Figure 2.6. Beginning at the
top left corner of the periodic table, the first row contains only two elements (H and
He) because only two electrons are required to fill the *s* orbital in the first shell, $1s^2$.
The second row begins with two *s*-block elements (Li and Be) and continues with six *p*-
block elements (B through Ne), so electrons fill the next available *s* orbital (2*s*) and then
the first available *p* orbitals (2*p*). The third row is similar to the second row, so the 3*s*
and 3*p* orbitals are filled next. The fourth row again starts with 2 *s*-block elements
(K and Ca) but is then followed by 10 *d*-block elements (Sc through Zn) and 6 *p*-block
elements (Ga through Kr). Thus, the order of orbital filling is 4*s* followed by the first

available d orbitals ($3d$) followed by $4p$. Continuing through successive rows of the periodic table gives the entire filling order, identical to that shown in Figure 2.6.

$$1s \rightarrow 2s \rightarrow 2p \rightarrow 3s \rightarrow 3p \rightarrow 4s \rightarrow 3d \rightarrow 4p \rightarrow 5s \rightarrow$$
$$4d \rightarrow 5p \rightarrow 6s \rightarrow 4f \rightarrow 5d \rightarrow 6p \rightarrow 7s \rightarrow 5f \rightarrow 6d \rightarrow 7p$$

But why do the elements in a given group of the periodic table have similar properties? The answer emerges when you look at Table 2.4, which gives electron configurations for elements in the main groups 1A, 2A, 7A, and 8A. Focusing only on the electrons in the outermost shell, or **valence shell**, *elements in the same group of the periodic table have similar electron configurations in their valence shells.* The group 1A elements, for example, all have one **valence electron,** ns^1 (where n represents the number of the valence shell: $n = 2$ for Li, $n = 3$ for Na, $n = 4$ for K, and so on). The group 2A elements have two valence electrons (ns^2). The group 7A elements have seven valence electrons ($ns^2 \, np^5$). For example, fluorine (F) has the electron configuration of $1s^2 2s^2 2p^5$ (valence electrons in bold). The group 8A elements (except He) have eight valence electrons ($ns^2 \, np^6$). You might also notice that the group numbers from 1A through 8A give the numbers of valence electrons for the elements in each main group. It is worth noting that the valence electrons are those in the outermost shell (n)—not necessarily in the orbitals that were filled last!

Valence shell The outermost electron shell of an atom.

Valence electron An electron in the valence shell of an atom.

Table 2.4 Valence-Shell Electron Configurations for Groups 1A, 2A, 7A, and 8A Elements

Group	Element	Atomic Number	Valence-Shell Electron Configuration
1A	Li (lithium)	3	$2s^1$
	Na (sodium)	11	$3s^1$
	K (potassium)	19	$4s^1$
	Rb (rubidium)	37	$5s^1$
	Cs (cesium)	55	$6s^1$
2A	Be (beryllium)	4	$2s^2$
	Mg (magnesium)	12	$3s^2$
	Ca (calcium)	20	$4s^2$
	Sr (strontium)	38	$5s^2$
	Ba (barium)	56	$6s^2$
7A	F (fluorine)	9	$2s^2 \, 2p^5$
	Cl (chlorine)	17	$3s^2 \, 3p^5$
	Br (bromine)	35	$4s^2 \, 4p^5$
	I (iodine)	53	$5s^2 \, 5p^5$
8A	He (helium)	2	$1s^2$
	Ne (neon)	10	$2s^2 \, 2p^6$
	Ar (argon)	18	$3s^2 \, 3p^6$
	Kr (krypton)	36	$4s^2 \, 4p^6$
	Xe (xenon)	54	$5s^2 \, 5p^6$

What is true for the main group elements is also true for the other groups in the periodic table: atoms within a given group have the same number of valence electrons and have similar electron configurations. *Because the valence electrons are the most loosely held, they are the most important in determining an element's properties.* Similar electron configurations thus explain why the elements in a given group of the periodic table have similar chemical behavior.

▶▶ We have seen that elements in a given group have similar chemical behavior because they have similar valence electron configurations, and that many chemical properties exhibit periodic trends across the periodic table. The *chemical* behavior of nearly all the elements can be predicted based on their position in the periodic table, and this will be examined in more detail in Chapters 3 and 4. Similarly, the *nuclear* behavior of the different isotopes of a given element is related to the configuration of the nucleus (i.e., the number of neutrons and protons) and will be examined in Chapter 11.

Worked Example 2.8 Electron Configurations: Valence Electrons

Write the electron configuration for the following elements, using both the complete and the shorthand notations. Indicate which electrons are the valence electrons.

(a) Na   (b) Cl   (c) Zr

ANALYSIS Locate the row and the block in which each of the elements is found in Figure 2.7. The location can be used to determine the complete electron configuration and to identify the valence electrons.

SOLUTION

(a) Na (sodium) is located in the third row and in the first column of the s-block. Therefore, all orbitals up to the $3s$ are completely filled, and there is one electron in the $3s$ orbital.

$$\textbf{Na: } 1s^2\,2s^2\,2p^6\,\underline{3s^1} \quad \text{or} \quad [\text{Ne}]\,\underline{3s^1} \quad (\text{valence electrons are underlined})$$

(b) Cl (chlorine) is located in the third row and in the fifth column of the p-block. Therefore, there are five electrons in the $3p$ orbital.

$$\textbf{Cl: } 1s^2\,2s^2\,2p^6\,\underline{3s^2\,3p^5} \quad \text{or} \quad [\text{Ne}]\,\underline{3s^2\,3p^5}$$

(c) Zr (zirconium) is located in the fifth row and in the second column of the d-block. All orbitals up to the $4d$ are completely filled, and there are two electrons in the $4d$ orbitals. Note that the $4d$ orbitals are filled after the $5s$ orbitals in both Figures 2.6 and 2.7.

$$\textbf{Zr: } 1s^2\,2s^2\,2p^6\,3s^1\,3p^6\,4s^2\,3d^{10}\,4p^6\,\underline{5s^2\,4d^2} \quad \text{or} \quad [\text{Kr}]\,\underline{5s^2\,4d^2}$$

Worked Example 2.9 Electron Configurations: Valence-Shell Configurations

Using n to represent the number of the valence shell, write a general valence-shell configuration for the elements in group 6A.

ANALYSIS The elements in group 6A have six valence electrons. In each element, the first two of these electrons are in the valence s subshell, giving ns^2, and the next four electrons are in the valence p subshell, giving np^4.

SOLUTION
For group 6A, the general valence-shell configuration is $ns^2\,np^4$.

Worked Example 2.10 Electron Configurations: Inner Shells versus Valence Shell

How many electrons are in a tin atom? Give the number of electrons in each shell. How many valence electrons are there in a tin atom? Write the valence-shell configuration for tin.

ANALYSIS The total number of electrons will be the same as the atomic number for tin $(Z = 50)$. The number of valence electrons will equal the number of electrons in the valence shell.

SOLUTION
Checking the periodic table shows that tin (Sn) has atomic number 50 and is in group 4A. The number of electrons in each shell is

Shell number:	1	2	3	4	5
Number of electrons:	2	8	18	18	4

As expected from the group number, tin has four valence electrons. They are in the $5s$ and $5p$ subshells and have the configuration $5s^2\,5p^2$. Although there are f orbitals available in the $n = 4$ shell, the $5s$ orbital is of lower energy than the $4f$ orbitals, and so will fill first. Hence, there are only 18 electrons in the $n = 4$ shell.

PROBLEM 2.19

Write the electron configuration for the following elements, using both the complete and the shorthand notations. Indicate which electrons are the valence electrons.

   (a) F   **(b)** Al   **(c)** As

PROBLEM 2.20

Identify the group in which all the elements have the valence-shell configuration ns^2.

PROBLEM 2.21

For chlorine, identify the group number, give the number of electrons in each occupied shell, and write its valence-shell configuration.

⬤⬤ KEY CONCEPT PROBLEM 2.22 ————————————————————————

Identify the group number and write the general valence-shell configuration (e.g., ns^1 for group 1A elements) for the elements indicated in red in the following periodic table.

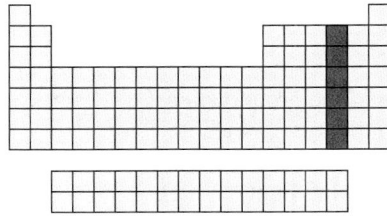

2.9 Electron-Dot Symbols

Learning Objective:

• Write Lewis dot symbols to represent the valence electrons for a given atom.

Valence electrons play such an important role in the behavior of atoms that it is useful to have a method for including them with atomic symbols. In an **electron-dot symbol** (also called Lewis symbols), dots are placed around the atomic symbol to indicate the number of valence electrons present. A group 1A atom, such as sodium, has a single dot; a group 2A atom, such as magnesium, has two dots; a group 3A atom, such as boron, has three dots; and so on.

   Table 2.5 gives electron-dot symbols for atoms of the first few elements in each main group. As shown, the dots are distributed around the four sides of the element symbol, singly at first until each of the four sides has one dot. As more electron dots are added they will form pairs, with no more than two dots on a side. Note that helium differs from other noble gases in having only two valence electrons rather than eight. Nevertheless, helium is considered a member of group 8A because its properties resemble those of the other noble gases and because its highest occupied subshell is filled ($1s^2$).

> **Electron-dot (Lewis) symbol** An atomic symbol with dots placed around it to indicate the number of valence electrons.

Table 2.5 Electron-Dot Symbols for Some Main Group Elements

1A	2A	3A	4A	5A	6A	7A	Noble Gases
H·							He:
Li·	·Be·	·Ḃ·	·Ċ·	·N̈:	·Ö:	·F̈:	:N̈e:
Na·	·Mg·	·Äl·	·S̈i·	·P̈:	·S̈:	·C̈l:	:Är:
K·	·Ca·	·Ġa·	·Ġe·	·Äs:	·S̈e:	·B̈r:	:K̈r:

Worked Example 2.11 Electron Configurations: Electron-Dot Symbols

Write the electron-dot symbol for any element X in group 5A.

ANALYSIS The group number, 5A, indicates five valence electrons. The first four are distributed singly around the four sides of the element symbol, and any additional are placed to form electron pairs.

SOLUTION

 (5 electrons)

PROBLEM 2.23

Write the electron-dot symbol for any element X in group 3A.

PROBLEM 2.24

Write electron-dot symbols for radon, lead, xenon, and radium.

PROBLEM 2.25

When an electron in a strontium atom drops from the excited state to the ground state, it emits red light, as explained in the following Chemistry in Action feature. When an electron in a copper atom drops from the excited state to the ground state, it emits blue light. What are the approximate wavelengths of the red light and the blue light? Which color is associated with higher energy?

CHEMISTRY IN ACTION

⚕ Atoms and Light

What we see as *light* is really a wave of energy moving through space. The shorter the length of the wave (the *wavelength*), the higher the energy; the longer the wavelength, the lower the energy.

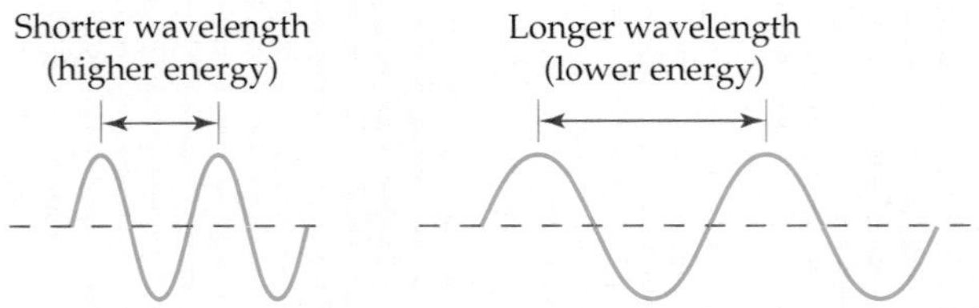

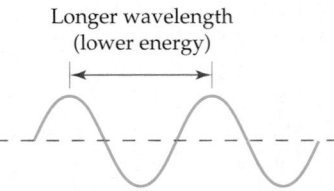

Shorter wavelength (higher energy)   Longer wavelength (lower energy)

What happens when a beam of electromagnetic energy collides with an atom? Remember that electrons are located in orbitals based on their energy levels. An atom with its electrons in their usual, lowest-energy locations is said to be in its *ground state*. If the amount of electromagnetic energy is just right, an electron can be kicked up from its usual energy level to a higher one. Energy from an electrical discharge or in the form of heat can also boost electrons to higher energy levels. With one of its electrons promoted to a higher energy, an atom is said to be *excited*. The excited state does not last long,

though, because the electron quickly drops back to its more stable, ground-state energy level, releasing its extra energy in the process. If the released energy falls in the range of visible light (400–800 nm), we can see the result. Many practical applications, from neon lights to fireworks, are the result of this phenomenon.

▲ This chest X ray equipment uses high energy, short wavelength electromagnetic radiation to generate diagnostic images.

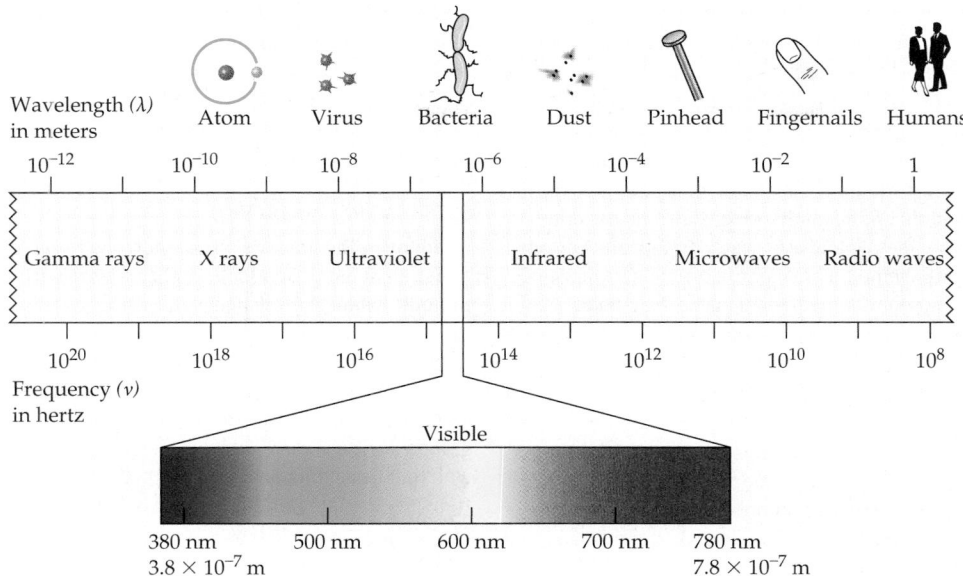

▲ The electromagnetic spectrum consists of a continuous range of wavelengths, with the familiar visible region accounting for only a small portion near the middle of the range.

The interaction of light with matter has many significant impacts. The UV radiation (200–350 nm) from the sun has enough energy to cause sunburn and, with chronic long-term exposure, can lead to skin cancers. Higher energy radiation (X rays) is used in many diagnostic applications, while even higher energies (gamma rays) can be used to kill cancer cells. In clinical applications, the concentration of certain biologically important metals in body fluids, such as blood or urine, is measured by sensitive instruments (such as the spectrophotometer mentioned at the beginning of this chapter), relying on the principle of electron excitation, where metal atoms will emit light of a specific wavelength corresponding to electronic transitions in the atom. These instruments measure the intensity of color produced in a flame by lithium (red), sodium (yellow), and potassium (violet), to determine the concentrations of these metals, which should be in a certain range to ensure good health. If the levels of these and other essential metals are outside the optimal range, it may be an indication of poor nutrition or certain diseases.

CIA Problem 2.5 Which type of electromagnetic energy in the following pairs is of higher energy?

(a) Infrared, ultraviolet

(b) Gamma waves, microwaves

(c) Visible light, X rays

CIA Problem 2.6 Why do you suppose ultraviolet rays from the sun are more damaging to the skin than visible light?

SUMMARY REVISITING THE CHAPTER LEARNING OBJECTIVES

• **Explain the major assumptions of atomic theory, and name and identify the properties of the subatomic particles that make up an atom.** All matter is composed of *atoms.* An atom is the smallest and simplest unit into which a sample of an element can be divided while maintaining the properties of the element. Atoms are made up of subatomic particles called *protons, neutrons,* and *electrons.* Protons have a positive electrical charge, neutrons are electrically neutral, and electrons have a negative electrical charge. The protons and neutrons in an atom are present in a dense, positively charged central region called the *nucleus.* Electrons are situated a relatively large distance away from the nucleus, leaving most of the atom as empty space *(see Problems 31–40, 83, 85, 89, and 95).*

• **Identify atoms of an element based on the number of protons in the nucleus.** Elements differ according to the number of protons their atoms contain, a value called the element's *atomic number* (Z). All atoms of a given element have the same number of protons and an equal number of electrons. The number of neutrons in an atom is not predictable but is generally equal to or greater than the number of protons. The total number of protons plus neutrons in an atom is called the atom's *mass number* (A) *(see Problems 43, 46, and 82).*

• **Write the symbols for different isotopes of an element and use relative abundances and atomic masses of isotopes to calculate the average atomic weight of an element.** The symbol for an atom is written using the symbol for the element (e.g., C for carbon), including the atomic number (Z) as a subscript on the left, and the atomic mass (A) as a superscript. An atom of carbon-12 (6 protons + 6 neutrons) would be represented as $^{12}_{6}C$. Atoms with identical numbers of protons and electrons but different numbers of neutrons are called *isotopes*. The atomic weight of an element is the weighted average mass of atoms of the element's naturally occurring isotopes *[see Problems 27, 40–49, 52, and 96]*.

- **Locate elements on the periodic table and classify them as metals, nonmetals, or metalloids based on their location.** The majority of elements are identified as metals and are located to the left/bottom of the periodic table. Only 18 elements are identified as nonmetals, and they are located to the upper right of the periodic table. Metalloids are located on a diagonal between the metals and nonmetals *[see Problems 26, 52–57, 86, and 88]*.

- **Classify elements and describe chemical behavior based on group membership.** Elements are organized into the *periodic table,* consisting of 7 rows, or *periods,* and 18 columns, or *groups.* The two columns on the left side of the table and the six columns on the right are called the *main group elements.* The 10 columns in the middle are the *transition metal groups,* and the 14 columns pulled out and displayed below the main part of the table are called the *inner transition metal groups [see Problems 27, 56–61, 80–82, 97, and 98]*.

- **Describe the distribution of electrons into shells, subshells, and orbitals around the nucleus of an atom.** The electrons surrounding an atom are grouped into layers, or *shells.* Within each shell, electrons are grouped into *subshells,* and within each subshell into *orbitals*—regions of space in which electrons are most likely to be found. The *s* orbitals are spherical, and the *p* orbitals are dumbbell-shaped. Each shell can hold a specific number of electrons. The first shell can hold 2 electrons, the second shell can hold 8 electrons, the third shell can hold 18 electrons, and so on *[see Problems 50, 51, and 62–69]*.

- **Write the electronic configuration for an atom to describe how electrons are distributed into specific orbitals.** The electron configuration of an element is predicted by assigning the element's electrons into shells and orbitals, beginning with the lowest-energy orbital. For example, the first shell can hold 2 electrons in an *s* orbital ($1s^2$); the second shell can hold 8 electrons in one *s* and three *p* orbitals ($2s^2 2p^6$); the third shell can hold 18 electrons in one *s,* three *p,* and five *d* orbitals ($3s^2 3p^6 3d^{10}$); and so on *[see Problems 29, 30, 68–74, 83, 84, 86, 87, and 90–94]*.

- **Identify the valence shell electrons for an atom, and which subshell of electrons (s, p, d, f) correlate with which groups in the periodic table.** The valence electrons for an atom are found in the outermost shell and correspond to the location of the element in the periodic table. The number of valence electrons for the main group elements corresponds to the group number. The valence electrons for the 1A and 2A elements are located in *s* orbitals, while the valence electrons for groups 3A–8A are in *p* orbitals. Electrons in the *d* orbitals are associated with the transition metals, while *f* orbitals are associated with the inner transition metals (lanthanide and actinide series). Within a given group in the table, elements have the same number of valence electrons in their valence shell and similar electron configurations *[see Problems 28, 53, 74–79, 84, 86–88, and 94]*.

- **Write Lewis dot symbols to represent the valence electrons for a given atom.** The number of valence electrons is determined by the location of the element in the periodic table. The Lewis dot symbol for an atom is written as the chemical symbol for the element (C for carbon) with the valence electrons represented as dots around the symbol. If there are only four (or fewer) valence electrons, they are written as single dots above, below, and to the left and right sides of the symbol. If there are more than four valence electrons, then the extra electrons are added to form electron pairs *[see Problems 78, 81, and 86]*.

KEY WORDS

Alkali metal, *p. 53*
Alkaline earth metal, *p. 53*
Atom, *p. 43*
Atomic mass unit (amu), *p. 43*
Atomic number (Z), *p. 45*
Atomic theory, *p. 43*
Atomic weight, *p. 47*
d-Block element, *p. 62*
Electron, *p. 43*
Electron configuration, *p. 58*

Electron-dot (Lewis) symbol, *p. 65*
f-Block element, *p. 62*
Group, *p. 52*
Halogen, *p. 54*
Inner transition metal element, *p. 52*
Isotopes, *p. 46*
Main group element, *p. 52*
Mass number (A), *p. 46*

Metal, *p. 50*
Metalloid, *p. 50*
Neutron, *p. 43*
Noble gas, *p. 54*
Nonmetal, *p. 50*
Nucleus, *p. 44*
Orbital, *p. 56*
Orbital diagram, *p. 58*
Periodic table, *p. 49*
p-Block element, *p. 62*
Period, *p. 52*

Proton, *p. 43*
s-Block element, *p. 62*
Shell (electron), *p. 56*
Subatomic particles, *p. 43*
Subshell (electron), *p. 56*
Transition metal element, *p. 52*
Valence electron, *p. 63*
Valence shell, *p. 63*

⊙▸ UNDERSTANDING KEY CONCEPTS

2.26 Where on the following outline of a periodic table do the indicated elements or groups of elements appear?

(a) Alkali metals   (b) Halogens

(c) Alkaline earth metals   (d) Transition metals

(e) Hydrogen   (f) Helium

(g) Metalloids

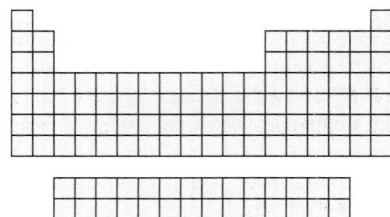

2.27 Is the element marked in red on the following periodic table likely to be a gas, a liquid, or a solid? What is the atomic number of the element in blue? Name at least one other element that is likely to be similar to the element in green.

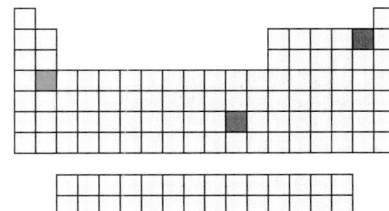

2.28 Use the following blank periodic table to show where the elements matching the following descriptions appear.

(a) Elements with the valence-shell electron configuration $ns^2 np^5$

(b) An element whose third shell contains two p electrons

(c) Elements with a completely filled valence shell

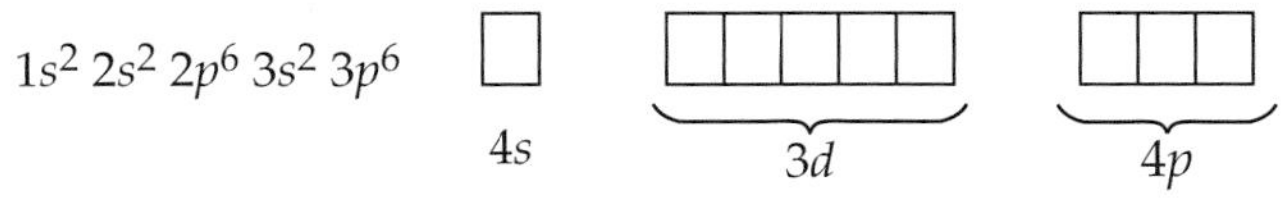

ADDITIONAL PROBLEMS

ATOMIC THEORY AND THE COMPOSITION OF ATOMS (SECTION 2.1–2.3)

2.31 What four fundamental assumptions about atoms and matter make up modern atomic theory?

2.32 How do atoms of different elements differ?

2.33 Find the mass in grams of one atom of the following elements:

(a) Bi, atomic weight 208.9804 amu

(b) Xe, atomic weight 131.29 amu

(c) He, atomic weight 4.0026 amu

2.34 Find the mass in atomic mass units of the following:

(a) 1 O atom, with a mass of 2.66×10^{-23} g

(b) 1 Br atom, with a mass of 1.31×10^{-22} g

2.35 What is the mass in grams of 6.022×10^{23} N atoms of mass 14.01 amu?

2.36 What is the mass in grams of 6.022×10^{23} O atoms of mass 16.00 amu?

2.37 How many O atoms of mass 15.99 amu are in 15.99 g of oxygen?

2.38 How many C atoms of mass 12.00 amu are in 12.00 g of carbon?

2.39 What are the names of the three subatomic particles? What are their approximate masses in atomic mass units, and what electrical charge does each have?

2.40 Where within an atom are the three types of subatomic particles located?

2.41 Give the number of neutrons in each naturally occurring isotope of argon: argon-36, argon-38, argon-40.

2.42 Give the number of protons, neutrons, and electrons in the following isotopes:

(a) Al-27

(b) $^{28}_{14}Si$

(c) B-11

(d) $^{115}_{47}Ag$

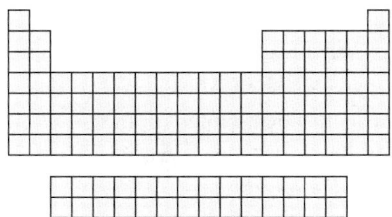

2.29 What atom has the following orbital-filling diagram?

$1s^2\ 2s^2\ 2p^6\ 3s^2\ 3p^6$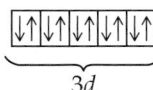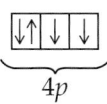

$\underbrace{\qquad}_{4s}\quad \underbrace{\qquad}_{3d}\quad \underbrace{\qquad}_{4p}$

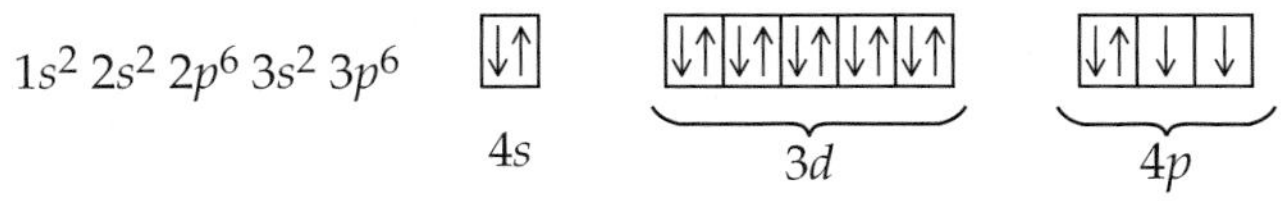

2.30 Use the following orbital-filling diagram to show the electron configuration for As:

$1s^2\ 2s^2\ 2p^6\ 3s^2\ 3p^6$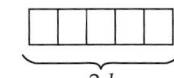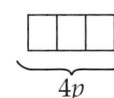

$\underbrace{\qquad}_{4s}\quad \underbrace{\qquad}_{3d}\quad \underbrace{\qquad}_{4p}$

2.43 Which of the following symbols represent isotopes of the same element? Explain.

(a) $^{19}_{9}X$

(b) $^{19}_{10}X$

(c) $^{21}_{9}X$

(d) $^{21}_{12}X$

2.44 Give the name and the number of neutrons in each isotope listed in Problem 2.43.

2.45 Write the symbols for the following isotopes:

(a) Its atoms contain 6 protons and 8 neutrons.

(b) Its atoms have mass number 39 and contain 19 protons.

(c) Its atoms have mass number 20 and contain 10 electrons.

2.46 Write the symbols for the following isotopes:

(a) Its atoms contain 50 electrons and 70 neutrons.

(b) Its atoms have $A = 56$ and $Z = 26$.

(c) Its atoms have $A = 226$ and contain 88 electrons.

2.47 One of the most widely used isotopes in medical diagnostics is technetium-99m (the m indicates that it is a *metastable* isotope). Write the symbol for this isotope, indicating both mass number and atomic number.

2.48 Naturally occurring copper is a mixture of 69.17% Cu-63 with a mass of 62.93 amu and 30.83% Cu-65 with a mass of 64.93 amu. What is the atomic weight of copper?

2.49 Naturally occurring lithium is a mixture of 92.58% Li-7 with a mass of 7.016 amu and 7.42% Li-6 with a mass of 6.015 amu. What is the atomic weight of lithium?

THE PERIODIC TABLE (SECTIONS 2.4–2.6)

2.50 Why does the third period in the periodic table contain eight elements?

2.51 Why does the fourth period in the periodic table contain 18 elements?

2.52 Americium, atomic number 95, is used in household smoke detectors. What is the symbol for americium? Is americium a metal, a nonmetal, or a metalloid?

2.53 What subshell is being filled for the metalloid elements?

2.54 Answer the following questions for the elements from scandium through zinc:
(a) Are they metals or nonmetals?
(b) To what general class of elements do they belong?
(c) What subshell is being filled by electrons in these elements?

2.55 Answer the following questions for the elements from cerium through lutetium:
(a) Are they metals or nonmetals?
(b) To what general class of elements do they belong?
(c) What subshell is being filled by electrons in these elements?

2.56 For (a) rubidium (b) tungsten, (c) germanium, and (d) krypton, which of the following terms apply? (i) metal, (ii) nonmetal, (iii) metalloid (iv) transition element, (v) main group element, (vi) noble gas, (vii) alkali metal, (viii) alkaline earth metal.

2.57 For (a) calcium, (b) palladium, (c) carbon, and (d) radon, which of the following terms apply? (i) metal, (ii) nonmetal, (iii) metalloid, (iv) transition element, (v) main group element, (vi) noble gas, (vii) alkali metal, (viii) alkaline earth metal.

2.58 Name an element in the periodic table that you would expect to be chemically similar to sulfur.

2.59 Name an element in the periodic table that you would expect to be chemically similar to potassium.

2.60 What elements in addition to lithium make up the alkali metal family?

2.61 What elements in addition to fluorine make up the halogen family?

ELECTRON CONFIGURATIONS (SECTIONS 2.6–2.9)

2.62 What is the maximum number of electrons that can go into an orbital?

2.63 What are the shapes and locations within an atom of s and p orbitals?

2.64 What is the maximum number of electrons that can go into the first shell? The second shell? The third shell?

2.65 What is the total number of orbitals in the third shell? The fourth shell?

2.66 How many subshells are there in the third shell? The fourth shell? The fifth shell?

2.67 How many orbitals would you expect to find in the last subshell of the fifth shell? How many electrons would you need to fill this subshell?

2.68 How many electrons are present in an atom with its $1s$, $2s$, and $2p$ subshells filled? What is this element?

2.69 How many electrons are present in an atom with its $1s$, $2s$, $2p$, $3s$, $3p$, and $4s$ subshells filled and with two electrons in the $3d$ subshell? What is this element?

2.70 Use arrows to show electron pairing in the valence p subshell of
(a) Sulfur　　　(b) Bromine　　　(c) Silicon

2.71 Use arrows to show electron pairing in the $5s$ and $4d$ orbitals of
(a) Rubidium　　　(b) Niobium　　　(c) Rhodium

2.72 Determine the number of unpaired electrons for each of the atoms in Problems 2.70 and 2.71.

2.73 Without looking back in the text, write the electron configurations for the following:
(a) Titanium $Z = 22$　　　(b) Phosphorus, $Z = 15$
(c) Argon, $Z = 18$　　　(d) Lanthanum, $Z = 57$

2.74 How many electrons does the element with $Z = 12$ have in its valence shell? Write the electron-dot symbol for this element.

2.75 How many valence electrons do group 4A elements have? Explain. Write a generic electron-dot symbol for elements in this group.

2.76 Identify the valence subshell occupied by electrons in beryllium and arsenic atoms.

2.77 What group in the periodic table has the valence-shell configuration $ns^2 np^3$?

2.78 Give the number of valence electrons and draw electron-dot symbols for atoms of the following elements:
(a) Kr　　　(b) C　　　(c) Ca
(d) K　　　(e) B　　　(f) Cl

2.79 Using n for the number of the valence shell and write a general valence-shell configuration for the elements in group 6A and in group 2A.

CONCEPTUAL PROBLEMS

2.80 What elements in addition to helium make up the noble gas family?

2.81 Hydrogen is placed in group 1A on many periodic charts, even though it is not an alkali metal. On other periodic charts, however, hydrogen is included with group 7A even though it is not a halogen. Explain. (Hint: Draw electron-dot symbols for H and for the 1A and 7A elements.)

2.82 What is the atomic number of the yet-undiscovered element directly below francium (Fr) in the periodic table?

2.83 Give the number of electrons in each shell for lead.

2.84 Identify the highest-energy occupied subshell in atoms of the following elements:
(a) Iodine　　　(b) Scandium
(c) Arsenic　　　(d) Aluminum

2.85 (a) What is the mass (in amu and in grams) of a single atom of Carbon-12?
(b) What is the mass (in grams) of 6.02×10^{23} atoms of Carbon-12?
(c) Based on your answer to part (b), what would be the mass of 6.02×10^{23} atoms of Sodium-23?

2.86 An unidentified element is found to have an electron configuration by shell of 2 8 18 8 2. To what group and period does this element belong? Is the element a metal or a nonmetal? How many protons does an atom of the element have? What is the name of the element? Write its electron-dot symbol.

2.87 Germanium, atomic number 32, is used in building semi-conductors for microelectronic devices, and has an electron configuration by shell of 2 8 18 4.

(a) Write the electronic configuration for germanium.

(b) In what shell and orbitals are the valence electrons?

2.88 Tin, atomic number 50, is directly beneath germanium (Problem 2.87) in the periodic table. What electron configuration by shell would you expect tin to have? Is tin a metal or a nonmetal?

2.89 A blood sample is found to contain 8.6 mg/dL of Ca. How many atoms of Ca are present in 8.6 mg? The atomic weight of Ca is 40.08 amu.

2.90 What is wrong with the following electron configurations?

(a) Ni $1s^2\, 2s^2\, 2p^6\, 3s^2\, 3p^6\, 3d^{10}$

(b) N $1s^2\, 2p^5$

(c) Si $1s^2\, 2s^2\, 2p$ ⟨↑↓⟩⟨ ⟩

(d) Mg $1s^2\, 2s^2\, 2p^6\, 3s$ ⟨↑↑⟩

2.91 Not all elements follow exactly the electron-filling order described in Figure 2.6. Atoms of which elements are represented by the following electron configurations?

(a) $1s^2\, 2s^2\, 2p^6\, 3s^2\, 3p^6\, 3d^5\, 4s^1$

(b) $1s^2\, 2s^2\, 2p^6\, 3s^2\, 3p^6\, 3d^{10}\, 4s^1$

(c) $1s^2\, 2s^2\, 2p^6\, 3s^2\, 3p^6\, 3d^{10}\, 4s^2\, 4p^6\, 4d^5\, 5s^1$

(d) $1s^2\, 2s^2\, 2p^6\, 3s^2\, 3p^6\, 3d^{10}\, 4s^2\, 4p^6\, 4d^{10}\, 5s^1$

2.92 What similarities do you see in the electron configurations for the atoms in Problem 2.91? How might these similarities explain their anomalous electron configurations?

2.93 Based on the identity of the elements whose electron configurations are given in Problem 2.91, write the electron configurations for the element with atomic number $Z = 79$.

2.94 What orbital is filled last in the most recently discovered element 117?

GROUP PROBLEMS

2.95 Look up one of the experiments by the scientists discussed in the Chemistry in Action on page 44, and explain how it contributed to our understanding of atomic structure.

2.96 Do a web search to identify each of the following elements/isotopes and indicate the number of neutrons, protons, and electrons in an atom of the element/isotope:

(a) A radioactive isotope used in cancer treatments. (There may be more than one answer!)

(b) The element having the greatest density.

(c) An element with Z < 90 that is *not* found in nature.

2.97 Tellurium $(Z = 52)$ has a *lower* atomic number than iodine $(Z = 53)$, yet it has a *higher* atomic weight (127.60 amu for Te vs. 126.90 amu for I). How is this possible? Can you find any other instances in the periodic table where two adjacent elements exhibit a similar behavior, that is, the element with the lower atomic number has a higher atomic mass?

2.98 Look again at the trends illustrated in Figures 2.3 and 2.4.

(a) How do the peaks/valleys correlate with locations in the periodic table?

(b) Are there other chemical properties that also exhibit periodic trends? What are they?

3

Ionic Compounds

CONTENTS

◀◀◀ CONCEPTS TO REVIEW

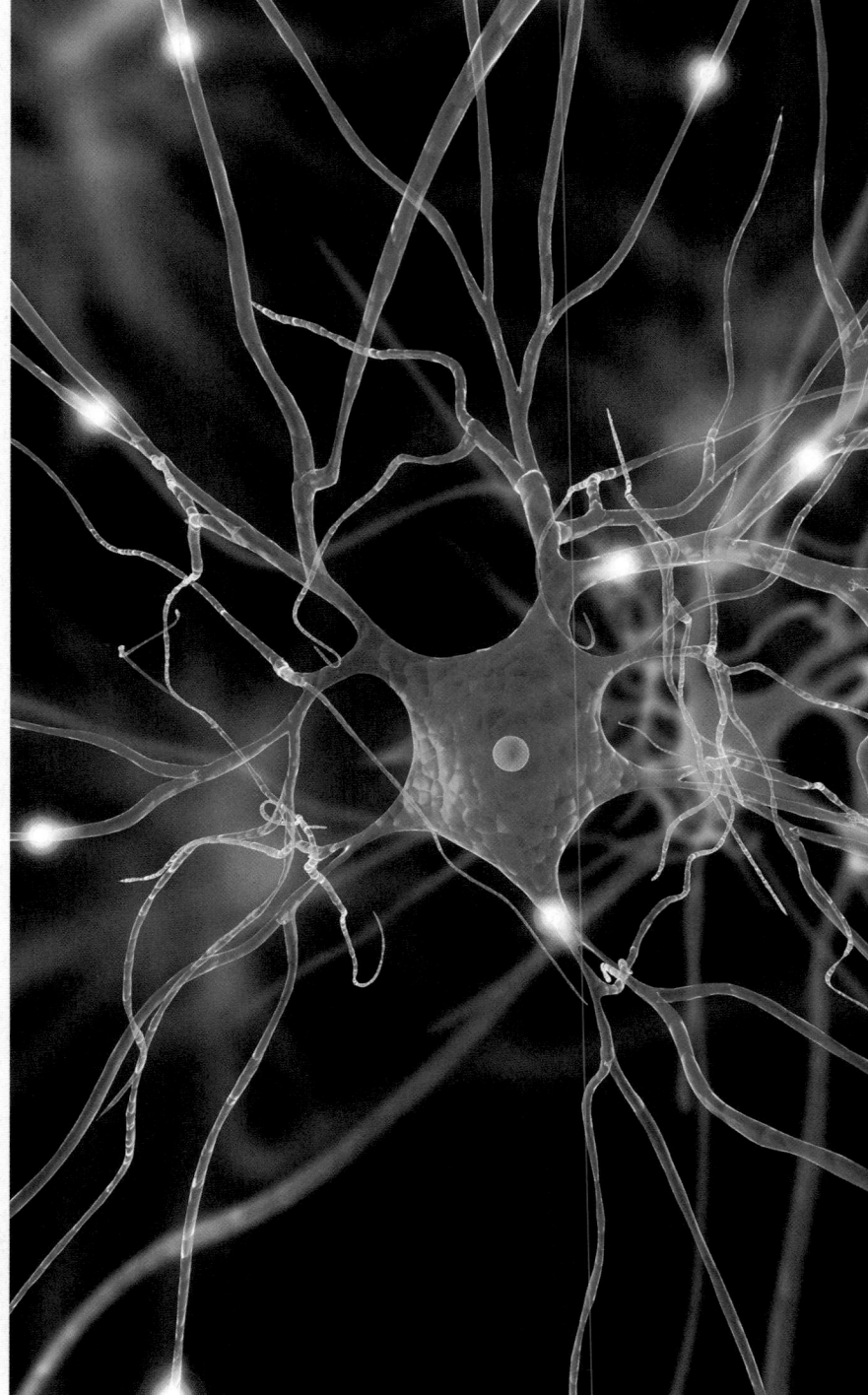

▲ Ions play critical roles in many cellular processes, including signal transmission between nerve cells as simulated above.

n previous chapters, we mentioned the importance of various elements for good health, identifying individual elements as *macro*nutrients (needed in large amounts) or *micro*nutrients (needed in lesser amounts). Of equal significance is the chemical form of the element; what is the chemical nature of the compounds in which an element is found? Many of these macro- and micronutrients, for example, exist as *ions,* or charged particles, and play critical roles in different cells within the body. Calcium ions, for example, are necessary for strong teeth and bones; sodium and potassium ions are necessary for signal transmission in nerve cells, such as those depicted in the artistic rendition in the chapter opening picture; and chloride ions are an important component of gastric juices found in the stomach. Disruptions in the transport or metabolism of these ions is linked to various diseases, including cystic fibrosis, neuropathy (chronic nerve pain), and osteoporosis, which we will discuss in greater detail in the Chemistry in Action feature on page 93.

There are more than 19 million known chemical compounds, ranging in size from small *diatomic* (two-atom) substances like carbon monoxide (CO) to deoxyribonucleic acid (DNA), which can contain several *billion* atoms linked together in a precise way. In the next two chapters, we will examine how atoms are held together in chemical compounds. We can describe the forces that hold atoms together as *chemical bonds.* All chemical bonds result from the electrical attraction between opposite charges—between positively charged nuclei and negatively charged electrons. As a result, the way that different elements form bonds is related to their different electron configurations and the changes that take place as each atom tries to achieve a more stable electron configuration. There are two types of chemical bonds: *ionic bonds* and *covalent bonds.* In this chapter, we look at how ions are formed, the ionic bonds that occur between ions of opposite charge, and at the behavior of ionic compounds. In the next chapter, we will look at covalent bonds.

3.1 Ions

Learning Objective:

• Describe ion formation processes and distinguish between anions and cations.

A general rule noted by early chemists is that metals, on the left side of the periodic table, tend to form compounds with nonmetals, on the right side of the table. The alkali metals of group 1A, for instance, react with the halogens of group 7A to form a variety of compounds. Sodium chloride (table salt), formed by the reaction of sodium with chlorine, is a familiar example. The names and chemical formulas of some other compounds containing elements from groups 1A and 7A include:

Potassium iodide, KI   Added to table salt to provide the iodide ion that is needed by the thyroid gland

Sodium fluoride, NaF   Added to many municipal water supplies to provide fluoride ion for the prevention of tooth decay

Sodium iodide, NaI   Used in laboratory scintillation counters to detect radiation (see Section 11.8)

The compositions and the properties of these alkali metal–halogen compounds are similar. For instance, the two elements always combine in a 1:1 ratio: one alkali metal atom for every halogen atom. Each compound has a high melting point (all are over 500 °C); each is a stable, white, crystalline solid; and each is soluble in water. Furthermore, a water solution containing each compound conducts electricity, a property that gives a clue as to the kind of chemical bond holding the atoms together.

Electricity can only flow through a medium containing charged particles that are free to move. The electrical conductivity of metals, for example, results from the movement of negatively charged electrons through the metal. But what charged particles might be present in the water solutions of alkali metal–halogen compounds? To answer this question, think about the composition of atoms. Atoms are electrically neutral because they contain equal numbers of protons and electrons. By gaining or losing one or more electrons, however, an atom can be converted into a charged particle called an **ion.**

Recall from Chapter 2 that the number of negative electrons in a neutral atom is equal to the number of positive protons in the nucleus of that atom. Therefore, the *loss* of one or more electrons from a neutral atom gives a *positively* charged ion called a **cation** (*cat*-ion). As we saw in Section 2.8, sodium and other alkali metal atoms have a single electron in their valence shell and an electron configuration symbolized as ns^1,

▲ A solution of sodium chloride in water conducts electricity, allowing the bulb to light.

Ion An electrically charged atom or group of connected atoms.

Cation A positively charged ion.

where n represents the shell number. By losing this electron, an alkali metal is converted to a positively charged cation with a stable noble gas configuration.

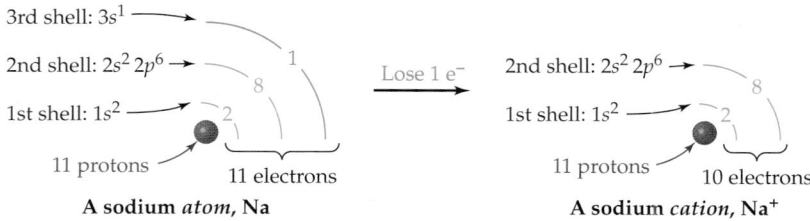

A sodium _atom_, Na   **A sodium _cation_, Na⁺**

Anion A negatively charged ion.

Conversely, the _gain_ of one or more electrons by a neutral atom gives a _negatively_ charged ion called an **anion** (_an_-ion). Chlorine and other halogen atoms have ns^2np^5 valence electrons and will readily gain an additional electron to fill their valence subshell with eight electrons, thereby forming negatively charged anions.

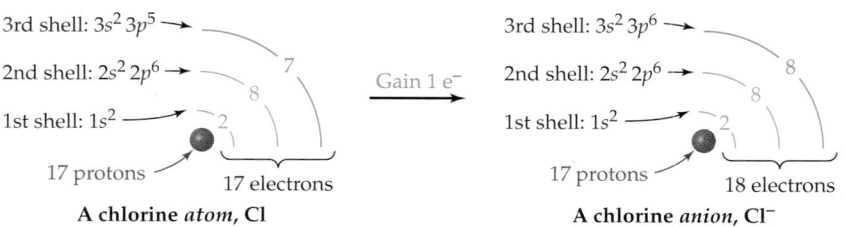

A chlorine _atom_, Cl   **A chlorine _anion_, Cl⁻**

The symbol for a cation is written by adding the positive charge as a superscript to the symbol for the element; an anion symbol is written by adding the negative charge as a superscript. If one electron is lost or gained, the charge is $+1$ or -1 but the number 1 is omitted in the notation, as in Na^+ and Cl^-. If two or more electrons are lost or gained, however, the charge is ± 2 or greater and the number _is_ used, as in Ca^{2+} and N^{3-}.

LOOKING AHEAD ▶▶ The tendency to gain or lose electrons is not limited to atoms in ionic compounds and forms the basis of an important class of chemical reactions (redox reactions), which will be discussed in Chapter 5.

In the sections that follow, we will discuss the reasons why metals tend to form cations and nonmetals tend to form anions, how we can predict the charges associated with the respective ions, and how these ions combine to form compounds.

PROBLEM 3.1

Magnesium atoms lose two electrons when they react. Write the symbol of the ion that is formed. Is it a cation or an anion?

PROBLEM 3.2

Sulfur atoms gain two electrons when they react. Write the symbol of the ion that is formed. Is it a cation or an anion?

🔑 KEY CONCEPT PROBLEM 3.3

Write the atomic symbol for the ion depicted here. Is it a cation or an anion?

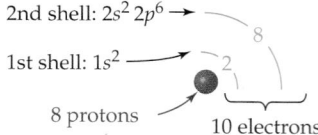

3.2 Ions and the Octet Rule

Learning Objective:

• Use the octet rule and electron configurations to explain the charge associated with ions.

We have seen that alkali metal atoms have a single valence-shell electron, ns^1. The electron-dot symbol X· is consistent with this valence electron configuration. Halogens, having seven valence electrons, ns^2np^5, can be represented using $:\ddot{X}\cdot$ as the electron-dot symbol. Noble gases can be represented as $:\ddot{X}:$, since they have eight valence electrons, ns^2np^6. Both the alkali metals and the halogens are extremely reactive, undergoing many chemical reactions and forming many compounds. The noble gases, however, are quite different. They are the least reactive of all elements.

Now look at sodium chloride and similar ionic compounds. When sodium or any other alkali metal reacts with chlorine or any other halogen, the metal transfers an electron from its valence shell to the valence shell of the halogen. Sodium thereby changes its valence-shell electron configuration from $2s^22p^63s^1$ in the atom to $2s^22p^6(3s^0)$ in the Na^+ ion, and chlorine changes from $3s^23p^5$ in the atom to $3s^23p^6$ in the Cl^- ion. *As a result, both sodium and chlorine gain noble gas electron configurations, with eight valence electrons.* The Na^+ ion has eight electrons in the $n = 2$ shell, matching the electron configuration of neon. The Cl^- ion has eight electrons in the $n = 3$ shell, matching the electron configuration of argon.

$$\underset{1s^2\,2s^2\,2p^6\,3s^1}{Na} \quad + \quad \underset{1s^2\,2s^2\,2p^6\,3s^2\,3p^5}{Cl} \quad \longrightarrow \quad \underset{\underbrace{1s^2\,2s^2\,2p^63s^0}_{\substack{Neon \\ configuration}}}{Na^+} \quad + \quad \underset{\underbrace{1s^2\,2s^2\,2p^6\,3s^2\,3p^6}_{\substack{Argon \\ configuration}}}{Cl^-}$$

$$Na\,\cdot \quad + \quad \cdot\ddot{\underset{\cdot\cdot}{Cl}}: \quad \longrightarrow \quad Na^+ \quad + \quad :\ddot{\underset{\cdot\cdot}{Cl}}:^-$$

Having eight valence electrons (filled s and p subshells) leads to stability and lack of chemical reactivity. In fact, observations of many chemical compounds have shown that main group elements frequently combine in such a way that each winds up with eight valence electrons, called an *electron octet*. This conclusion is summarized in a statement called the **octet rule.**

Octet rule   The tendency of atoms to gain or lose electrons to achieve a stable, noble gas configuration, that is, a completely filled subshell containing eight electrons.

Main group *metals* lose electrons to form cations and attain an electron configuration like that of the noble gas just *before* them in the periodic table. Main group *nonmetals* gain electrons to form anions and an electron configuration like that of the noble gas just *after* them in the periodic table. In both cases, the product ions have filled s and p subshells with eight electrons in their valence electron shell. We can use this tendency to explain why metals form cations and nonmetals form anions, as well as to predict the most likely charge of the ions that are formed.

Worked Example 3.1   Electron Configurations: Octet Rule for Cations

Write the electron configuration of magnesium $(Z = 12)$. Show how many electrons a magnesium atom must lose to form an ion with a filled shell (eight electrons) and write the configuration of the ion. Explain the reason for the ion's charge, and write the ion's symbol.

ANALYSIS Write the electron configuration of magnesium as described in Section 2.7 and count the number of electrons in the valence shell.

SOLUTION

Magnesium has the electron configuration $1s^22s^22p^63s^2$. Since the second shell contains an octet of electrons $(2s^22p^6)$ and the third shell is only partially filled $(3s^2)$, magnesium can achieve a valence-shell octet by losing the two electrons in the $3s$ subshell. The result is formation of a doubly charged cation, Mg^{2+}, with the neon configuration:

$$Mg^{2+} \qquad 1s^22s^22p^6 \text{ (Neon configuration or } [Ne])$$

A neutral magnesium atom has 12 protons and 12 electrons. With the loss of two electrons, there is an excess of two protons, accounting for the +2 charge of the ion, Mg^{2+}.

Worked Example 3.2 Electron Configurations: Octet Rule for Anions

How many electrons must a nitrogen atom, $Z = 7$, gain to attain a noble gas configuration? Write the electron-dot and ion symbols for the ion formed.

ANALYSIS Write the electron configuration of nitrogen, and identify how many more electrons are needed to reach a noble gas configuration.

SOLUTION

Nitrogen, a group 5A element, has the electron configuration $1s^2 2s^2 2p^3$. The second shell contains five electrons $(2s^2 2p^3)$ and needs three more to reach an octet. The result is formation of a triply charged anion, N^{3-}, with eight valence electrons, matching the neon configuration:

$$N^{3-} \qquad 1s^2 2s^2 2p^6 \quad \text{(Neon configuration)} \quad :\ddot{N}:^{3-}$$

PROBLEM 3.4

Write the electron configuration of potassium, $Z = 19$, and show how a potassium atom can attain a noble gas configuration.

PROBLEM 3.5

How many electrons must an aluminum atom, $Z = 13$, lose to attain a noble gas configuration? Write the symbol for the ion formed.

KEY CONCEPT PROBLEM 3.6

Which atom in the reaction depicted here gains electrons and which loses electrons? Draw the electron-dot symbols for the resulting ions.

$$X: + \cdot \ddot{Y} \cdot \longrightarrow ?$$

3.3 Ions of Some Common Elements

Learning Objective:

• Use the periodic table to predict the charge associated with ions of main group elements.

The periodic table is the key to understanding and remembering which elements form ions and which do not. As shown in Figure 3.1, atoms of elements in the same group tend to form ions of the same charge. The metals of groups 1A–3A, for example, form cations with charges identical to their group number (i.e., 1A elements form cations with +1 charge, etc.). The ions of these elements all have noble gas configurations as a

▶ **Figure 3.1**
Common ions formed by elements in the first four periods.
Ions important in biological chemistry are shown in magenta.

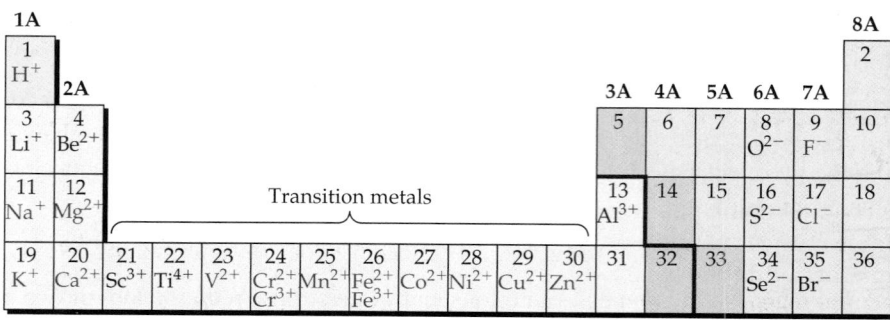

result of electron loss from their valence s subshells. (Note in the following equations that the electrons being lost are shown as products.)

Group 1A: $M \cdot \longrightarrow M^+ + e^-$

$(M = Li, Na, K, Rb, \text{ or } Cs)$

Group 2A: $M: \longrightarrow M^{2+} + 2e^-$

$(M = Be, Mg, Ca, Sr, Ba, \text{ or } Ra)$

Four of these ions, Na^+, K^+, Mg^{2+}, and Ca^{2+}, are present in body fluids, where they play extremely important roles in biochemical processes.

The only group 3A element commonly encountered in ionic compounds is aluminum, which forms Al^{3+} by loss of three electrons from its valence s and p subshells. Aluminum is not thought to be an essential element in the human diet, although it is known to be present in some organisms.

As we move to the right, elements in Group 4A would have to gain or lose too many electrons to achieve an octet. Therefore, the first three elements in groups 4A (C, Si, Ge) and 5A (N, P, As) do not ordinarily form cations or anions. The bonding of these elements is largely covalent and will be described in Chapter 4. Carbon, in particular, is the key element on which life is based. Together with hydrogen, nitrogen, phosphorus, and oxygen, carbon is present in all the essential biological compounds that we will be describing throughout the latter half of this book.

The group 6A elements, oxygen and sulfur, form ions having noble gas configurations, achieved by gaining two electrons:

Group 6A: $\cdot \ddot{\text{O}} \cdot + 2\,e^- \longrightarrow \,:\ddot{\text{O}}:^{2-}$

$\cdot \ddot{\text{S}} \cdot + 2\,e^- \longrightarrow \,:\ddot{\text{S}}:^{2-}$

The halogens can form ions by gaining one electron:

Group 7A: $\cdot \ddot{\text{X}}: + e^- \longrightarrow \,:\ddot{\text{X}}:^-$

$(X = F, Cl, Br, I)$

Transition metals lose electrons to form cations, some of which are present in the human body. The charges of transition metal cations are not as predictable as those of main group elements, however, because many transition metal atoms can lose one or more d electrons in addition to losing valence s electrons. For example, iron $(\ldots 3s^2 3p^6 3d^6 4s^2)$ forms Fe^{2+} by losing two electrons from the $4s$ subshell and also forms Fe^{3+} by losing an additional electron from the $3d$ subshell. Looking at the electron configuration for iron shows why the octet rule is limited to main group elements: transition metal cations generally do not have noble gas configurations because they would have to lose *all* their d electrons.

Important Points about Ion Formation and the Periodic Table:

- **Metals form cations by losing one or more electrons.**
  - Group 1A and 2A metals form +1 and +2 ions, respectively (e.g., Li^+ and Mg^{2+}), to achieve a noble gas configuration.
  - Transition metals can form cations of more than one charge (e.g., Fe^{2+} and Fe^{3+}) by losing a combination of valence-shell s electrons and inner-shell d electrons.
- **Reactive nonmetals form anions by gaining one or more electrons to achieve a noble gas configuration.**
  - Group 6A nonmetals oxygen and sulfur form the anions O^{2-} and S^{2-}.
  - Group 7A elements (the halogens) form -1 ions, for example, F^- and Cl^-.
- **Group 8A elements (the noble gases) are unreactive.**
- **Ionic charges of main group elements can be predicted using the group number and the octet rule.**
  - For 1A and 2A metals: cation charge = group number
  - For nonmetals in groups 5A, 6A, and 7A: anion charge = 8 − (group number)

Worked Example 3.3 Formation of Ions: Gain/Loss of Valence Electrons

Which of the following ions is likely to form?
 (a) S^{3-} **(b)** Si^{2+} **(c)** Sr^{2+}

ANALYSIS Count the number of valence electrons in each ion. For main group elements, only ions with a valence octet of electrons are likely to form.

SOLUTION

(a) Sulfur (S) is in group 6A, has six valence electrons, and needs only two more to reach an octet. Gaining two electrons gives an S^{2-} ion with a noble gas configuration but gaining three electrons does not. The S^{3-} ion is, therefore, unlikely to form.

(b) Silicon (Si) is a nonmetal in group 4A. Like carbon, it does not form ions because it would have to gain or lose too many electrons (four) to reach a noble gas electron configuration. The Si^{2+} ion does not have an octet and will not form.

(c) Strontium (Sr), a metal in group 2A, has only two outer-shell electrons and can lose both to reach a noble gas configuration. The Sr^{2+} ion has an octet and, therefore, forms easily.

PROBLEM 3.7

Iron is an important component of hemoglobin, a large biomolecule responsible for oxygen transport (Chapters 18 and 19). Find the common ions formed by iron in Figure 3.1. Which ion of iron is found in hemoglobin, and what is its electron configuration?

PROBLEM 3.8

Write symbols, both with and without electron dots, for the ions formed by the following processes:
 (a) Gain of two electrons by selenium
 (b) Loss of two electrons by barium
 (c) Gain of one electron by bromine

PROBLEM 3.9

Blood serum in healthy adults normally contains approximately 3.2 mg/mL of sodium ions (Na^+) and approximately 3.5 mg/mL of chloride ions (Cl^-). How many milliliters of blood serum would be needed to obtain 1.0 g of Na^+? To obtain 1.0 g of Cl^-?

3.4 Periodic Properties and Ion Formation

Learning Objective:

• Explain the formation of anions and cations based on periodic trends.

As we have seen, metals on the left side of the periodic table tend to lose electrons, whereas nonmetals on the right side of the periodic table tend to gain electrons. But how does this trend change as you move across a row in the periodic table and why? The answers are related to the ease with which an atom gains or loses an electron.

The ease with which an atom *loses* an electron to form a positively charged cation is measured by a property called the atom's **ionization energy,** defined as the energy required to remove one electron from a single atom in the gaseous state. Conversely, the ease with which an atom *gains* an electron to form a negatively charged anion is

Ionization energy The energy required to remove one valence electron from a single atom in the gaseous state.

measured by a property called **electron affinity,** defined as the energy released on adding an electron to a single atom in the gaseous state.

Electron affinity The energy released on adding an electron to a single atom in the gaseous state.

Ionization energy
(energy is added) $\text{Atom} + \text{Energy} \xrightarrow{\text{Lose } e^-} \text{Cation} + \text{Electron}$

Electron affinity
(energy is released) $\text{Atom} + \text{Electron} \xrightarrow{\text{Gain } e^-} \text{Anion} + \text{Energy}$

The relative magnitudes of ionization energies and electron affinities for elements in the first four rows of the periodic table are shown in Figure 3.2. Note the repeating pattern in Figure 3.2, beginning with small ionization energies for the 1A elements and a gradual increase as we move across a row, ending with very large ionization energies for the noble gases. Because ionization energy measures the amount of energy that must be *added* to pull an electron away from a neutral atom, the small values shown in Figure 3.2 for alkali metals (Li, Na, K) and other elements on the left side of the periodic table mean that these elements lose an electron easily. Conversely, the large values shown for halogens (F, Cl, Br) and noble gases (He, Ne, Ar, Kr) on the right side of the periodic table mean that these elements do not lose an electron easily. Another interesting feature in Figure 3.2 is the energy plateau after potassium (K). Remember from Chapter 2 that the electronic configuration for the fourth row transition metals is $4s^2 3d^x$; the ionization energy is related to the loss of a $4s$ electron, whose energy level remains fairly constant as you move across the row.

Electron affinities, in contrast, measure the amount of energy *released* when an atom gains an electron. Although electron affinities are small compared to ionization energies, the halogens nevertheless have the largest values and, therefore, gain an electron most easily, whereas metals have the smallest values and do not gain an electron easily.

Alkali metal $\begin{cases} \text{Small ionization energy—electron easily lost} \\ \text{Small electron affinity—electron not easily gained} \\ \textit{Net result: } \text{Cation formation is favored} \end{cases}$

Halogen $\begin{cases} \text{Large ionization energy—electron not easily lost} \\ \text{Large electron affinity—electron easily gained} \\ \textit{Net result: } \text{Anion formation is favored} \end{cases}$

As noted in Section 3.3 and illustrated in Figure 3.2, the main group elements near the *middle* of the periodic table—boron ($Z = 5$, group 3A), carbon ($Z = 6$, group 4A),

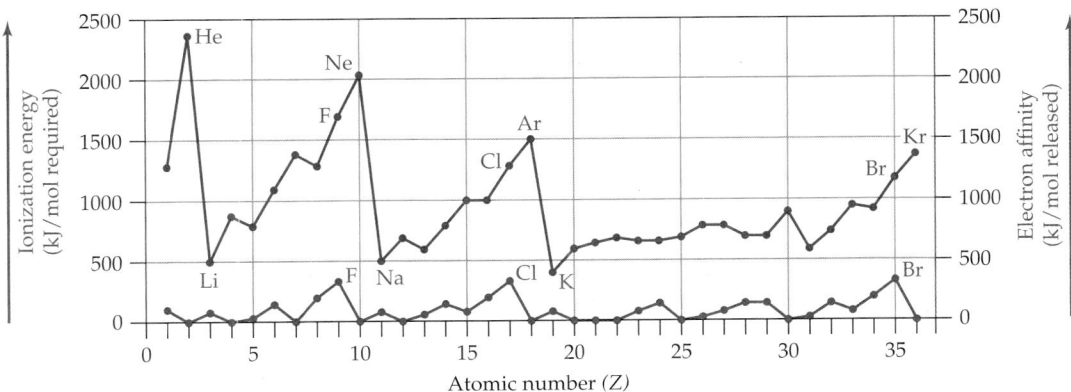

▲ Figure 3.2
Relative ionization energies (red) and electron affinities (blue) for elements in the first four rows of the periodic table.
Those elements having a value of zero for electron affinity do not accept an electron. Note that the alkali metals (Li, Na, K) have the lowest ionization energies and lose an electron most easily, whereas the halogens (F, Cl, Br) have the highest electron affinities and gain an electron most easily. The noble gases (He, Ne, Ar, Kr) neither gain nor lose an electron easily.

and nitrogen ($Z = 7$, group 5A)—neither lose nor gain electrons easily and thus do not readily form ions. In the next chapter, we will see that these elements tend to form covalent bonds instead.

Worked Example 3.4 Periodic Trends: Ionization Energy

Look at the periodic trends in Figure 3.2, and predict where the ionization energy of rubidium is likely to fall on the chart.

ANALYSIS Identify the group number of rubidium (group 1A), and find where other members of the group appear in Figure 3.2.

SOLUTION
Rubidium (Rb) is the alkali metal below potassium (K) in the periodic table. Since the alkali metals Li, Na, and K all have ionization energies near the bottom of the chart, the ionization energy of rubidium is probably similar.

Worked Example 3.5 Periodic Trends: Formation of Anions and Cations

Which element is likely to lose an electron more easily, Mg or S?

ANALYSIS Identify the group numbers of the elements, and find where members of those groups appear in Figure 3.2.

SOLUTION
Magnesium, a group 2A element on the left side of the periodic table, has a relatively low ionization energy and loses an electron easily. Sulfur, a group 6A element on the right side of the table, has a higher ionization energy and loses an electron less easily.

PROBLEM 3.10

Look at the periodic trend for ionization energies in Figure 3.2. How would you expect the ionization energies for Rb and Cs to compare with the other members of the 1A group? Look up these values to confirm your expectation.

PROBLEM 3.11

Which element in the following pairs is likely to lose an electron more easily?
  (a) Be or B   **(b)** Ca or Co   **(c)** Sc or Se

PROBLEM 3.12

Which element in the following pairs is likely to gain an electron more easily?
  (a) H or He   **(b)** S or Si   **(c)** Cr or Mn

3.5 Naming Monoatomic Ions

Learning Objective:

• Name common monoatomic anions and cations.

Main group metal cations in groups 1A, 2A, and 3A are named by identifying the metal, followed by the word *ion,* as in the following examples:

$$K^+ \qquad Mg^{2+} \qquad Al^{3+}$$
Potassium ion   Magnesium ion   Aluminum ion

It is sometimes a little confusing to use the same name for both a metal and its ion, and you may occasionally have to stop and think about what is meant. For example, it is common practice in nutrition and health-related fields to talk about sodium or potassium in the bloodstream. Because both sodium and potassium *metals* react violently with water, however, they cannot possibly be present in blood as neutral atoms. The references are to dissolved sodium and potassium *ions*.

Transition metals, such as iron or chromium, and many metals found in the *p*-block, such as tin and lead, can form more than one type of cation. To avoid confusion, a method is needed to differentiate between ions of these metals. Two systems are used. The first is an old system that gives the ion with the smaller charge the word ending *-ous* and the ion with the larger charge the word ending *-ic*.

CHEMISTRY IN ACTION

⚕ Salt

If you are like most people, you feel a little guilty about reaching for the salt shaker at mealtime. The notion that high salt intake and high blood pressure go hand in hand is surely among the most highly publicized pieces of nutritional lore ever to appear.

Although sodium is a macronutrient that we need—it plays a critical role in charge balance and ion transport in cell membranes—too much sodium has been linked to both hypertension and kidney ailments. Hypertension can be caused by a number of factors, including congenital conditions, reactions to some medications, and certain diseases, including thyroid problems. Regardless of the cause, hypertension can be aggravated by high salt consumption and, in extreme cases, must be controlled by medication and dietary restrictions. The recommended daily intake (RDI) for sodium is 2300 mg, which translates to roughly 4 g of salt. However, the average adult in most industrialized countries consumes over twice this amount, with most of it coming from processed foods.

What should an individual do? The best answer, as in so many things, is to use moderation and common sense. People with hypertension should make a strong effort to lower their sodium intake; others might be well advised to choose unsalted snacks, monitor their consumption of processed food, and read nutrition labels for sodium content.

CIA Problem 3.1 What is the RDI for sodium for adults, and what amount of table salt (in grams) contains this quantity of sodium?

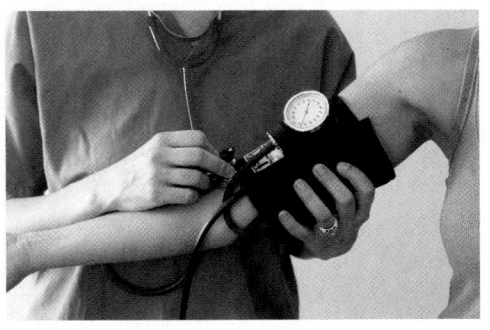

- ■ 5% added while cooking
- ■ 6% added while eating
- □ 12% from natural sources
- □ 77% from processed and prepared foods

CIA Problem 3.2 In the beginning of this chapter, we identified potassium iodide (KI) as an additive in table salt to provide the iodide ion needed by the thyroid. Look up the approximate amount of iodide in iodized salt and the daily adult intake of iodide recommended by the U.S. Food and Drug Administration (FDA).

The second is a newer system in which the charge on the ion is given as a Roman numeral in parentheses right after the metal name. For example:

	Cr^{2+}	Cr^{3+}
Old name:	Chrom*ous* ion	Chrom*ic* ion
New name:	Chromium(II) ion	Chromium(III) ion

We will generally emphasize the new system in this book, but it is important to understand both systems because the old system is often found on labels of commercially supplied chemicals. The small differences between the names in either system illustrate the importance of reading a name very carefully before using a chemical.

There are significant differences between compounds consisting of the same two elements but having different charges on the cation. In treating iron-deficiency anemia, for example, iron(II) compounds are preferable because the body absorbs them considerably better than iron(III) compounds.

The names of some common transition metal cations are listed in Table 3.1. Notice that the old names of the copper, iron, and tin ions are derived from their Latin names (*cuprum, ferrum,* and *stannum*).

Table 3.1 Names of Some Transition Metal Cations

Element	Symbol	Old Name	New Name
Chromium	Cr^{2+}	Chromous	Chromium(II)
	Cr^{3+}	Chromic	Chromium(III)
Copper	Cu^+	Cuprous	Copper(I)
	Cu^{2+}	Cupric	Copper(II)
Iron	Fe^{2+}	Ferrous	Iron(II)
	Fe^{3+}	Ferric	Iron(III)
Mercury	$*Hg_2^{2+}$	Mercurous	Mercury(I)
	Hg^{2+}	Mercuric	Mercury(II)
Tin	Sn^{2+}	Stannous	Tin(II)
	Sn^{4+}	Stannic	Tin(IV)

*This cation is composed of two mercury atoms, each of which has an average charge of +1.

Table 3.2 Names of Some Common Anions

Element	Symbol	Name
Bromine	Br^-	Bromide ion
Chlorine	Cl^-	Chloride ion
Fluorine	F^-	Fluoride ion
Iodine	I^-	Iodide ion
Oxygen	O^{2-}	Oxide ion
Sulfur	S^{2-}	Sulfide ion

Anions are named by replacing the ending of the element name with *-ide,* followed by the word *ion* (Table 3.2). For example, the anion formed by fluor*ine* is the fluor*ide* ion, and the anion formed by sul*fur* is the sul*fide* ion.

PROBLEM 3.13

Name the following ions:

(a) Cu^{2+} (b) F^- (c) Mg^{2+} (d) S^{2-}

PROBLEM 3.14

Write the symbols for the following ions:

(a) Silver(I) ion   (b) Iron(II) ion

(c) Cuprous ion   (d) Telluride ion

PROBLEM 3.15

Ringer's solution is used intravenously to adjust ion concentrations in body fluids. Look up the composition of Ringer's solution and identify the major ions it contains. Give the names and symbols of these ions (including the ionic charge).

3.6 Polyatomic Ions

Learning Objective:

- Identify the name, formula, and charge of common polyatomic ions.

Polyatomic ion An ion that is composed of more than one atom.

Ions that are composed of more than one atom are called **polyatomic ions.** Most polyatomic ions contain oxygen and another element, and their chemical formulas include subscripts to show how many of each type of atom are present. Sulfate ion, for example, is composed of one sulfur atom and four oxygen atoms and has a −2 charge: SO_4^{2-}. The atoms in a polyatomic ion are held together by covalent bonds, which will be discussed in Chapter 4, and the entire group of atoms acts as a single unit. A polyatomic ion is charged because it contains a total number of electrons different from the total number of protons in the combined atoms. For example, the individual atoms in the sulfate ion contribute 48 electrons—the S atom has 16 electrons, and the four O atoms contain 8 electrons each. The sulfate ion, however, has two extra electrons for a total of 50, hence the −2 charge.

The most common polyatomic ions are listed in Table 3.3. Note that the ammonium ion, NH_4^+, and the hydronium ion, H_3O^+, are the only cations; all the others are anions. These ions are encountered so frequently in chemistry, biology, and medicine that there is no alternative but to memorize their names and formulas. Fortunately, there are only a few of them.

Table 3.3   Some Common Polyatomic Ions

Name	Formula	Name	Formula
Hydronium ion	H_3O^+	Nitrate ion	NO_3^-
Ammonium ion	NH_4^+	Nitrite ion	NO_2^-
Acetate ion	$CH_3CO_2^-$	Oxalate ion	$C_2O_4^{2-}$
Carbonate ion	CO_3^{2-}	Permanganate ion	MnO_4^-
Hydrogen carbonate ion (bicarbonate ion)	HCO_3^-	Phosphate ion	PO_4^{3-}
Chromate ion	CrO_4^{2-}	Hydrogen phosphate ion (biphosphate ion)	HPO_4^{2-}
Dichromate ion	$Cr_2O_7^{2-}$	Dihydrogen phosphate ion	$H_2PO_4^-$
Cyanide ion	CN^-	Sulfate ion	SO_4^{2-}
Hydroxide ion	OH^-	Hydrogen sulfate ion (bisulfate ion)	HSO_4^-
Hypochlorite ion	OCl^-	Sulfite ion	SO_3^{2-}

Note in Table 3.3 that several pairs of ions—CO_3^{2-} and HCO_3^-, for example—are related by the presence or absence of a hydrogen ion, H^+. In such instances, the ion with the hydrogen is sometimes named using the prefix *bi-*. Thus, CO_3^{2-} is the carbonate ion, and HCO_3^- is the bicarbonate ion; similarly, SO_4^{2-} is the sulfate ion, and HSO_4^- is the bisulfate ion.

PROBLEM 3.16

Name the following ions:

(a) NO_3^- (b) CN^- (c) OH^- (d) HPO_4^{2-}

PROBLEM 3.17

Which of the biologically important ions (see the following Chemistry in Action feature) belong to Group 1A? To Group 2A? To the transition metals? To the halogens? Which are polyatomic?

CHEMISTRY IN ACTION

Biologically Important Ions

The human body requires many different ions for proper functioning. Several of these ions, such as Ca^{2+}, Mg^{2+}, and HPO_4^{2-}, are used as structural materials in bones and teeth in addition to having other essential functions. Although 99% of Ca^{2+} is contained in bones and teeth, small amounts in body fluids play a vital role in transmission of nerve impulses. Other ions, including essential transition metal ions such as Fe^{2+}, are required for specific chemical reactions in the body. And still others, such as K^+, Na^+, and Cl^-, are present in fluids throughout the body.

To maintain charge neutrality in solution, the total negative charge (from anions) must balance the total positive

(Continued)

charge (from cations). Several monatomic anions, and several polyatomic anions, especially HCO_3^- and HPO_4^{2-}, are present in body fluids where they help balance the cation charges.

Some of the most important ions and their functions are shown in the accompanying table.

Some Biologically Important Ions

Ion	Location	Function	Dietary Source
Ca^{2+}	Outside cell; 99% of Ca^{2+} is in bones and teeth as $Ca_3(PO_4)_2$ and $CaCO_3$	Bone and tooth structure; necessary for blood clotting, muscle contraction, and transmission of nerve impulses	Milk, whole grains, leafy vegetables
Fe^{2+}	Blood hemoglobin	Transports oxygen from lungs to cells	Liver, red meat, leafy green vegetables
K^+	Fluids inside cells	Maintain ion concentrations in cells; regulate insulin release and heartbeat	Milk, oranges, bananas, meat
Na^+	Fluids outside cells	Protect against fluid loss; necessary for muscle contraction and transmission of nerve impulses	Table salt, seafood
Mg^{2+}	Fluids inside cells; bone	Present in many enzymes; needed for energy generation and muscle contraction	Leafy green plants, seafood, nuts
Cl^-	Fluids outside cells; gastric juice	Maintain fluid balance in cells; help transfer CO_2 from blood to lungs	Table salt, seafood
HCO_3^-	Fluids outside cells	Control acid–base balance in blood	By-product of food metabolism
HPO_4^{2-}	Fluids inside cells; bones and teeth	Control acid–base balance in cells	Fish, poultry, milk

CIA Problem 3.3 Where are most of the calcium ions found in the body?

CIA Problem 3.4 Excess sodium ion is considered hazardous, but a certain amount is necessary for normal body functions. What is the purpose of sodium in the body?

3.7 Ionic Bonds

Learning Objective:

- Explain the nature of the ionic bonds holding ions together in ionic compounds.

Look again at the reaction between sodium and chlorine introduced in Section 3.2. When sodium reacts with chlorine, the product is sodium chloride, a compound completely unlike either of the elements from which it is formed. Sodium is a soft, silvery metal that reacts violently with water, and chlorine is a corrosive, poisonous, green gas (Figure 3.3a). When chemically combined, however, an electron is transferred from the sodium atom to the chlorine atom to produce our familiar table salt containing Na^+ ions and Cl^- ions. Because opposite electrical charges attract each other, the positive Na^+ ion and negative Cl^- ion are held together by an **ionic bond.**

Ionic bond The electrical attractions between ions of opposite charge in an ionic compound.

The product that results—sodium chloride (NaCl)—is electrically neutral because the positive charge of each Na^+ ion is balanced by the negative charge of each Cl^- ion. When a vast number of sodium atoms transfer electrons to an equally vast number of chlorine atoms, a visible crystal of sodium chloride results. In this crystal, equal numbers of Na^+ and Cl^- ions are packed together in a regular arrangement. Each positively charged Na^+ ion is surrounded by six negatively charged Cl^- ions, and each Cl^- ion is

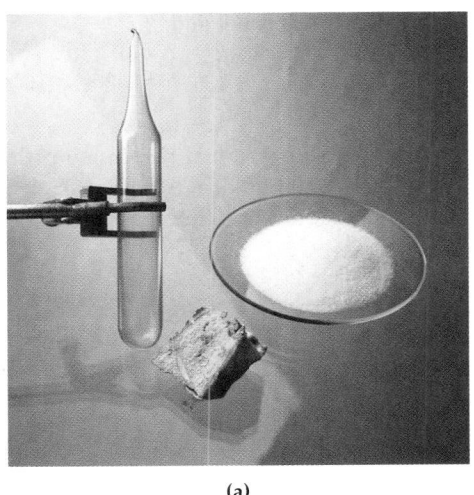

(a) (b)

◄ **Figure 3.3**
(a) Chlorine is a toxic green gas, sodium is a reactive metal, and sodium chloride is a harmless white solid. (b) Sodium metal burns with an intense yellow flame when immersed in chlorine gas, yielding white sodium chloride "smoke."

surrounded by six Na^+ ions (Figure 3.4). This packing arrangement allows each ion to be stabilized by the attraction of unlike charges on its six nearest-neighbor ions, while being as far as possible from ions of like charge.

▲ **Figure 3.4**
The arrangement of Na^+ and Cl^- ions in a sodium chloride crystal.
Each positively charged Na^+ ion is surrounded by six negatively charged Cl^- ions, and each Cl^- ion is surrounded by six Na^+ ions. The crystal is held together by ionic bonds—the attraction between oppositely charged ions that are formed by the transfer of electrons between atoms.

Because of the three-dimensional arrangement of ions in a sodium chloride crystal, we cannot speak of specific ionic bonds between specific pairs of ions. Rather, there are many ions attracted by ionic bonds to their nearest neighbors. We therefore speak of the whole NaCl crystal as being an **ionic solid** and of such compounds as being **ionic compounds.** The same is true of all compounds composed of ions.

Ionic solid A crystalline solid held together by ionic bonds.

Ionic compound A compound that contains ionic bonds.

3.8 Formulas of Ionic Compounds

Learning Objective:

• Determine the formula of ionic compounds based on the formulas and charges of the cations and anions.

Since all chemical compounds are neutral, it is relatively easy to figure out the formulas of ionic compounds. Once the ions are identified, all we need to do is decide how many ions of each type give a total charge of zero. Thus, the chemical formula of an ionic compound tells the ratio of anions and cations.

If the ions have the same charge, only one of each ion is needed:

$$K^+ \quad \text{and} \quad F^+ \quad \text{form} \quad KF$$
$$Ca^{2-} \quad \text{and} \quad O^{2-} \quad \text{form} \quad CaO$$

This makes sense when we look at how many electrons must be gained or lost by each atom in order to satisfy the octet rule. For the formation of KF and CaO, electrons must be transferred from the metals to the nonmetals to form their respective cations and anions. This process can be represented as:

$$K\cdot \; + \; \cdot\ddot{\underset{..}{F}}\!: \; \longrightarrow \; K^+ \; + \; :\ddot{\underset{..}{F}}\!:^-$$
$$\cdot Ca\cdot \; + \; \cdot\ddot{\underset{..}{O}}\cdot \; \longrightarrow \; Ca^{2+} \; + \; :\ddot{\underset{..}{O}}\!:^{2-}$$

For each case, the electrons being transferred are represented in red, and each of the product ions has an electron configuration equivalent to a noble gas (i.e., a complete octet). The charges on the anions and cations are equal, but opposite in sign, so the charges cancel. If the ions have different charges, however, unequal numbers of anions and cations must combine in order to have a net charge of zero. When potassium and oxygen combine, for example, it takes two K^+ ions to balance the -2 charge of the O^{2-} ion. Put another way, it takes two K atoms to provide the two electrons needed in order to complete the octet for the O atom:

$$2\,K\cdot \; + \; \cdot\ddot{\underset{..}{O}}\cdot \; \longrightarrow \; 2\,K^+ \; + \; :\ddot{\underset{..}{O}}\!:^{2-}$$
$$2\,K^+ \text{ and } O^{2-} \text{ form } K_2O$$

The situation is reversed when a Ca^{2+} ion reacts with a Cl^- ion. One Ca atom can provide two electrons; each Cl atom requires only one electron to achieve a complete octet. Thus, there is one Ca^{2+} cation for every two Cl^- anions:

$$\cdot Ca\cdot \; + \; 2\cdot\ddot{\underset{..}{Cl}}\!: \; \longrightarrow \; Ca^{2+} \; + \; 2:\ddot{\underset{..}{Cl}}\!:^-$$
$$Ca^{2+} \text{ and } 2\,Cl^- \text{ form } CaCl_2$$

It sometimes helps when writing the formulas for an ionic compound to remember that, when the two ions have different charges, the number of one ion is equal to the charge on the other ion. In magnesium phosphate, for example, the charge on the magnesium ion is $+2$ and the charge on the polyatomic phosphate ion is -3. Thus, there must be three magnesium ions with a total charge of $3 \times (+2) = +6$ and two phosphate ions with a total charge of $2 \times (-3) = -6$ for overall neutrality.

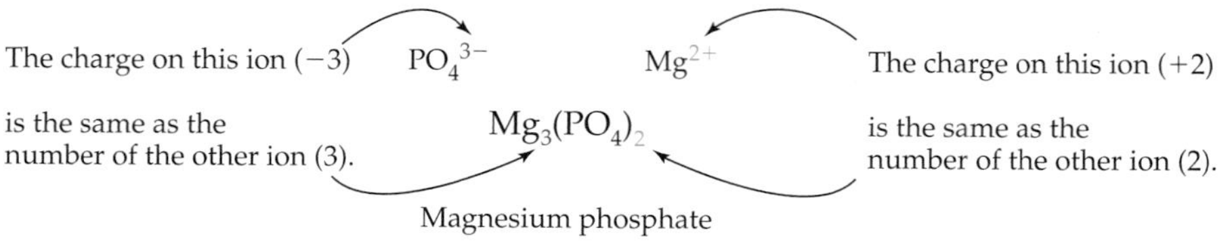

The charge on this ion (-3) $PO_4{}^{3-}$ $\qquad$ Mg^{2+} The charge on this ion ($+2$)

is the same as the number of the other ion (3). $\quad Mg_3(PO_4)_2 \quad$ is the same as the number of the other ion (2).

Magnesium phosphate

The formula of an ionic compound shows the lowest possible ratio of atoms in the compound and is thus known as a *simplest formula*. Because there is no such thing as a single neutral *particle* of an ionic compound, however, we use the term **formula unit** to identify the smallest possible neutral *unit* (Figure 3.5). For NaCl, the formula unit is one Na^+ ion and one Cl^- ion; for K_2SO_4, the formula unit is two K^+ ions and one $SO_4{}^{2-}$ ion; for CaF_2, the formula unit is one Ca^{2+} ion and two F^- ions; and so on.

Once the number and kinds of ions in a compound are known, the formula is written using the following rules:

Formula unit The formula that identifies the smallest neutral unit of an ionic compound.

- List the cation first and the anion second; for example, NaCl rather than ClNa.
- Do not write the charges of the ions; for example, KF rather than K^+F^-.
- Use parentheses around a polyatomic ion formula if it has a subscript; for example, $Al_2(SO_4)_3$ rather than Al_2SO_{43}.

One formula unit = (+1) + (−1) = 0

One formula unit = (+2) + (2)(−1) = 0

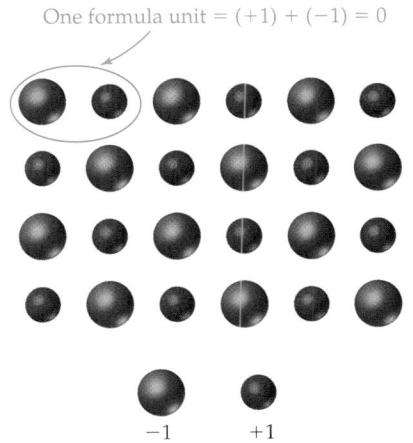
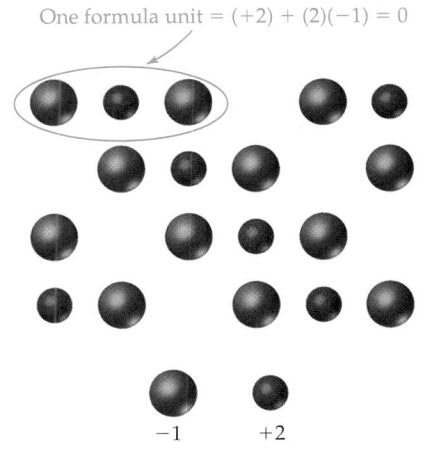

−1   +1

−1   +2

◄ **Figure 3.5**
Formula units of ionic compounds.
The sum of charges on the ions in a
formula unit equals zero.

Worked Example 3.6 Ionic Compounds: Writing Formulas

Write the formula for the compound formed by calcium ions and nitrate ions.

ANALYSIS Knowing the formula and charges on the cation and anion (Figure 3.1 and Table 3.3), we determine how many of each are needed to yield a neutral formula (zero charge) for the ionic compound.

SOLUTION
The two ions are Ca^{2+} and NO_3^-. Two nitrate ions, each with a −1 charge, will balance the +2 charge of the calcium ion.

$$Ca^{2+} \qquad \text{Charge} = 1 \times (+2) = +2$$
$$2NO_3^- \qquad \text{Charge} = 2 \times (-1) = -2$$

Since there are two ions, the nitrate formula must be enclosed in parentheses:

$$Ca(NO_3)_2 \qquad \text{Calcium nitrate}$$

PROBLEM 3.18

Write the formulas for the ionic compounds that are formed for each of the following ion combinations:

(a) Iodide ion and magnesium ion

(b) Oxide ion and aluminum ion

(c) Phosphate ion and Iron(II)

(d) Sulfate ion and Chromium(III)

PROBLEM 3.19

The ionic compound containing ammonium ion and carbonate ion gives off the odor of ammonia, a property put to use in smelling salts for reviving someone who has fainted. Write the formula for this compound.

PROBLEM 3.20

An *astringent* is a compound that causes proteins in blood, sweat, and other body fluids to coagulate, a property put to use in antiperspirants. Two safe and effective astringents are the ionic compounds of aluminum with sulfate ion and with acetate ion. Write the formulas of both.

KEY CONCEPT PROBLEM 3.21

Three ionic compounds are represented on this periodic table—red cation with red anion, blue cation with blue anion, and green cation with green anion. Give a likely formula for each compound.

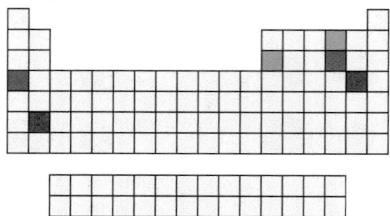

HANDS-ON CHEMISTRY 3.1

Obtain a set of Lego building blocks and separate them into groups that are one, two, and three units long (if you do not have access to a physical set of blocks, visit www.buildwithchrome.com/builder). The blocks will represent anions and cations that have charges of 1, 2, and 3, respectively. If possible, try to have multiple colors within each group. Label the blocks in each group as follows:

—*One unit long:* Label as Na^+, K^+, Cl^-, and NO_3^-.
—*Two units long:* Label as Mg^{2+}, Ca^{2+}, Fe^{2+}, O^{2-}, and SO_4^{2-}.
—*Three units long:* Label as Al^{3+}, Fe^{3+}, N^{3-}, and PO_4^{3-}.

Try to have at least three blocks for each ion in a given group and, if possible, keep the colors consistent for a given ion; for example, let all Na^+ ions be black, all Cl^- ions be yellow, all O^{2-} ions be blue, and so on.

Using the blocks, assemble the following compounds by matching anion and cation blocks. Starting with the cation

block, connect an anion on top of it. If the anion layer is not long enough for the two layers to match up exactly, add another anion of the same type beside it on top of the cation layer. If the anion layer extends over the end of the cation layer, add another cation to the bottom layer. When the cation and anion layers match exactly in length, count how many of the cation and anion blocks were necessary to determine the formula of the ionic compound.

Try building the compounds suggested next, or make up your own combinations. Just be sure that each compound has a cation and an anion!

a) Cation = Na^+ Anion = SO_4^{2-}
b) Cation = Fe^{2+} Anion = NO_3^-
c) Cation = Mg^{2+} Anion = PO_4^{3-}
d) Cation = Fe^{3+} Anion = O^{2-}

3.9 Naming Ionic Compounds

Learning Objective:

• Based on the cations and anions in the chemical formula, write the name of ionic compounds.

Ionic compounds are named by citing first the cation and then the anion, with a space between words. There are two kinds of ionic compounds, and the rules for naming them are slightly different.

Type I: Ionic compounds containing cations of main group elements (1A, 2A, aluminum). Since the charges on these cations do not vary, we do not need to specify the charge on the cation as discussed in Section 3.5. For example, NaCl is sodium chloride and $MgCO_3$ is magnesium carbonate.

Type II: Ionic compounds containing metals that can exhibit more than one charge. Since some metals, including the transition metals, often form more than one ion, we need to specify the charge on the cation in these compounds. Either the old *(-ous, -ic)* or the new (Roman numerals) system described in Section 3.5 can be used. Thus, $FeCl_2$ is called iron(II) chloride (or ferrous chloride) and $FeCl_3$ is called iron(III) chloride (or ferric chloride). Note that we do *not* name these compounds iron *di*chloride or iron *tri*chloride—once the charge on the metal is known, the number of anions needed to yield a neutral compound is also known and does not need to be included as part of the compound name. Table 3.4 lists some common ionic compounds and their uses.

Table 3.4 Some Common Ionic Compounds and Their Applications

Chemical Name (Common Name)	Formula	Applications
Ammonium carbonate	$(NH_4)_2CO_3$	Smelling salts
Calcium hydroxide (hydrated lime)	$Ca(OH)_2$	Mortar, plaster, whitewash
Calcium oxide (lime)	CaO	Lawn treatment, industrial chemical
Lithium carbonate (lithium)	Li_2CO_3	Treatment of bipolar disorder
Magnesium hydroxide (milk of magnesia)	$Mg(OH)_2$	Antacid
Magnesium sulfate (Epsom salts)	$MgSO_4$	Laxative, anticonvulsant
Potassium permanganate	$KMnO_4$	Antiseptic, disinfectant*
Potassium nitrate (saltpeter)	KNO_3	Fireworks, matches, and desensitizer for teeth
Silver nitrate	$AgNO_3$	Antiseptic, germicide
Sodium bicarbonate (baking soda)	$NaHCO_3$	Baking powder, antacid, mouthwash, deodorizer
Sodium hypochlorite	$NaOCl$	Disinfectant, active ingredient in household bleach
Zinc oxide	ZnO	Skin protection, in calamine lotion

*Antiseptics and disinfectants can also be harmful or toxic to nonharmful microorganisms but are used specifically to prevent infection from harmful microorganisms.

> Because the formula unit for an ionic compound must be neutral, we can unambiguously write the formula from the name of the compound and vice versa. As we shall see in Chapter 4, covalent bonding between atoms can produce a much greater variety of compounds. The rules for naming covalent compounds must be able to accommodate multiple combinations of elements (e.g., CO and CO_2).

Worked Example 3.7 Ionic Compounds: Formulas and Ionic Charges

Sodium and calcium both form a wide variety of ionic compounds. Write formulas for the following compounds:

(a) Sodium bromide and calcium bromide

(b) Sodium sulfide and calcium sulfide

(c) Sodium sulfate and calcium sulfate

(d) Sodium phosphate and calcium phosphate

ANALYSIS Using the formulas and charges for the cations and the anions (from Tables 3.2 and 3.3), we determine how many of each cation and anion are needed to yield a formula that is neutral.

SOLUTION

(a) The cations are sodium (Na) and calcium (Ca). Sodium, as a 1A metal would have a +1 charge (Na^+); calcium, as a 2A metal, would have a +2 charge (Ca^{2+}). The anion (bromide) is in group 7A and would have a −1 charge (Br^-). In order for the charges to be neutral, the respective compound formulas are $NaBr$ and $CaBr_2$.

(b) Again, the cations are Na^+ and Ca^{2+}. The anion (sulfide) is in group 6A and would have a −2 charge. The neutral formulas are Na_2S and CaS.

(c) The cations are Na^+ and Ca^{2+}. The anion (sulfate) is a polyatomic ion with a −2 charge (SO_4^{2-}). Neutral formulas = Na_2SO_4 and $CaSO_4$.

(d) Cations = Na^+ and Ca^{2+}. The anion (phosphate) is a polyatomic ion with −3 charge (PO_4^{3-}). Neutral formulas = Na_3PO_4 and $Ca_3(PO_4)_2$.

Worked Example 3.8 Naming Ionic Compounds

Name the following compounds using Roman numerals to indicate the charges on the cations where necessary:

(a) KF   **(b)** $MgCl_2$ **(c)** $AuCl_3$ **(d)** Fe_2O_3

ANALYSIS For main group metals, the charge is determined from the group number, and no Roman numerals are necessary. For transition metals, the charge on the metal can be determined from the total charge(s) on the anion(s).

—continued on next page

—continued from previous page

SOLUTION

(a) Potassium fluoride. No Roman numeral is necessary because a group 1A metal forms only one cation.

(b) Magnesium chloride. No Roman numeral is necessary because magnesium (group 2A) forms only Mg^{2+}.

(c) Gold(III) chloride. The three Cl^- ions require a +3 charge on the gold for a neutral formula. Since gold is a transition metal that can form other ions, the Roman numeral is necessary to specify the +3 charge.

(d) Iron(III) oxide. Because the three oxide anions (O^{2-}) have a total negative charge of −6, the two iron cations must have a total charge of +6. Thus, each is Fe^{3+}, and the charge on each is indicated by the Roman numeral (III).

PROBLEM 3.22

The compound Ag_2S is responsible for much of the tarnish found on silverware. Name this compound, and give the charge on the silver ion.

PROBLEM 3.23

Name the following compounds:

    (a) SnO_2 (b) $Ca(CN)_2$ (c) Na_2CO_3
    (d) Cu_2SO_4 (e) $Ba(OH)_2$ (f) $Fe(NO_3)_2$

PROBLEM 3.24

Write formulas for the following compounds:

    (a) Lithium phosphate   (b) Copper(II) carbonate
    (c) Aluminum sulfite   (d) Cuprous fluoride
    (e) Ferric sulfate   (f) Ammonium chloride

⊙ KEY CONCEPT PROBLEM 3.25 ————————————————————

The ionic compound calcium nitride is represented here. What is the formula for calcium nitride, and what are the charges on the calcium and nitride ions?

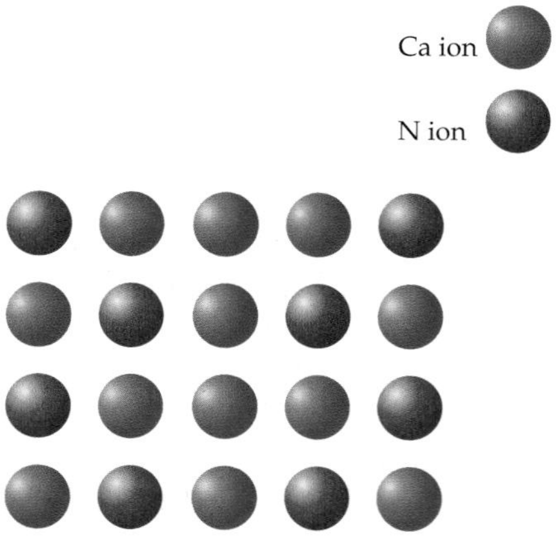

Ca ion ⬤

N ion ⬤

HANDS-ON CHEMISTRY 3.2

Using the same building block set from the previous Hands-On Chemistry activity, build the following compounds and identify the chemical formula. Refer to the names of common ions in Tables 3.1–3.3 as needed.

    a) Chromic phosphate
    b) Ferrous chloride
    c) Ferric nitrate
    d) Ammonium sulfite

3.10 Some Properties of Ionic Compounds

Learning Objective:

• Identify the properties of ionic compounds, and explain how the nature of the ionic bond is reflected in the physical properties of ionic compounds.

Like sodium chloride, ionic compounds are usually crystalline solids. Different ions vary in size and charge; therefore, they are packed together in crystals in different ways. The ions in each compound settle into a pattern that efficiently fills space and allows for maximum interaction with adjacent ions of opposite charge.

Because the ions in an ionic solid are held rigidly in place by attraction to their neighbors, they cannot move about. Once an ionic solid is dissolved in water, however, the ions can move freely, thereby making ionic compounds good conductors of electricity in a solution. Ionic compounds dissolve in water if the attraction between water and the ions overcomes the attraction of the ions for one another. Compounds like sodium chloride are very soluble in water and can be dissolved to make solutions of high concentration. Do not be misled, however, by the ease with which sodium chloride and other familiar ionic compounds dissolve in water. Many other ionic compounds, such as magnesium hydroxide or barium sulfate, are not water soluble, because the attractive forces between these ions and water is not sufficient to overcome the ionic attractions in the crystals.

Ionic compounds also have high melting and boiling points. The attractive force between oppositely charged cations and anions is extremely strong, so the ions need to gain a large amount of energy to overcome the attractions between one another. At higher boiling or melting points, more energy is needed. Sodium chloride, for example, melts at 801 °C and boils at 1413 °C; potassium iodide melts at 681 °C and boils at 1330 °C.

Despite the strength of ionic bonds, ionic solids shatter if struck sharply. A blow disrupts the orderly arrangement of cations and anions, forcing particles of like electrical charge closer together. The proximity of like charges creates repulsive energies that split the crystal apart.

▲ The melting point of sodium chloride is 801 °C.

PROBLEM 3.26

The melting points of NaCl, KCl, and RbCl are 801 °C, 770 °C, and 718 °C, respectively. Based on this, which compound exhibits the strongest ionic bonds, and which exhibits the weakest? How is this trend related to the relative size of the cations?

CHEMISTRY IN ACTION

Ionic Liquids

Imagine a substance that could help solve the problems of nuclear waste, make solar energy more efficient, and revolutionize the development of biomass-based renewable energies. When discussing ionic substances, most of us think of hard, crystalline materials like common table salt (see the Chemistry in Action feature on p. 81), with high melting points. But ionic liquids have very different properties, including low melting points, high viscosity, low-to-moderate electrical conductivity, and low volatility, which make them suitable for the varied uses described previously.

Although the details of the discovery of ionic liquids are in dispute, one of the first *room temperature ionic liquids* (or RTILs), ethylammonium nitrate, was synthesized in 1914 by Paul Walden. Most RTILs developed since then consist of a bulky, asymmetric organic cation (see Organic Chemistry in Chapters 12–19) combined with a variety of anions.

▲ Protic ionic liquids (PIL) are used to extract lignin from biomass (right) leaving behind the solid, energy-rich cellulose (left) to be converted into biofuels.

Bulky cations provide unique solvent properties, enabling them to dissolve substances that are not very soluble in more conventional solvents. Their low volatility also makes

(Continued)

them attractive as "green," or environmentally friendly, solvents. Consider the practice of using biomass as a fuel source. One common approach is to convert sugar or starch (from corn, beets, or cane sugar) into ethanol by the process of fermentation. But the major component of these and most other plants is cellulose. Cellulose is a polymer (see the Chemistry in Action feature on p. 121) composed of many sugars joined together in a long chain. Cellulose is chemically similar to starch but is neither highly soluble in most solvents nor subject to fermentation. RTILs can be used to dissolve cellulose at moderate temperatures and facilitate its breakdown into simple fermentable sugars. Most of the cellulose in biomass, however, is also combined with lignin—an integral component of the cell walls of plants. Lignin can be separated and removed from biomass by dissolving it in RTIL solutions, providing a simple and relatively inexpensive method for recovering cellulose for biofuel applications. At a volume of nearly 700 billion tons of the earth's biomass, cellulose represents an important renewable energy source. The ability to isolate and convert cellulose into fuel will certainly help meet our expanding energy needs.

CIA Problem 3.5 Most ionic substances are solids at room temperature. Explain why the RTILs discussed in this application are liquids rather than solids

CIA Problem 3.6 Ionic liquids are being evaluated for use in a moon-based spinning-liquid telescope. Which properties of ionic liquids make them particularly well suited for this application?

> In Chapter 10, we will look at the chemical behavior of acids and bases and their importance in many areas of chemistry. Acid–base chemistry is so significant that it requires a full chapter for adequate coverage. The importance of acids and bases will be evident as they reappear in later chapters related to organic and biochemistry.

3.11 H^+ and OH^- Ions: An Introduction to Acids and Bases

Learning Objective:

• Identify the ions associated with acids and bases.

Two of the most important ions we will be discussing in the remainder of this book are the hydrogen cation (H^+) and the hydroxide anion (OH^-). Since a hydrogen *atom* contains one proton and one electron, a hydrogen *cation* is simply a proton because it has lost its single electron. A hydroxide anion (OH^-), by contrast, is a polyatomic ion in which an oxygen atom is covalently bonded to a hydrogen atom (covalent bonds are discussed in Chapter 4). Although much of Chapter 10 is devoted to the chemistry of H^+ and OH^- ions, it is worth taking a preliminary look now.

Acid A substance that provides H^+ ions in water.

Base A substance that provides OH^- ions in water.

The importance of the H^+ cation and the OH^- anion is that they are fundamental to the concepts of *acids* and *bases*. In fact, one definition of an **acid** is a substance that provides H^+ ions when dissolved in water; for example, HCl, HNO_3, H_2SO_4, and H_3PO_4. One definition of a **base** is a substance that provides OH^- ions when dissolved in water; for example, NaOH, KOH, and $Ba(OH)_2$.

Hydrochloric acid (HCl), nitric acid (HNO_3), sulfuric acid (H_2SO_4), and phosphoric acid (H_3PO_4) are among the most common acids. When any of these substances is dissolved in water, H^+ ions are formed along with the corresponding anion (Table 3.5).

> The behavior of polyprotic acids, or acids that provide more than one H^+ ion per acid molecule, will be discussed in more detail in Chapter 10.

Different acids can provide different numbers of H^+ ions per acid molecule. Hydrochloric acid, for instance, provides one H^+ ion per acid molecule; sulfuric acid can provide two H^+ ions per acid molecule; and phosphoric acid can provide three H^+ ions per acid molecule.

Sodium hydroxide (NaOH; also known as *lye* or *caustic soda*), potassium hydroxide (KOH; also known as *caustic potash*), and barium hydroxide $[Ba(OH)_2]$ are examples of bases. When any of these compounds dissolves in water, OH^- anions go into solution along with the corresponding metal cation. Sodium hydroxide and potassium hydroxide provide one OH^- ion per formula unit; barium hydroxide provides two OH^- ions per formula unit, as indicated by its formula, $Ba(OH)_2$.

PROBLEM 3.27

Which of the following compounds are acids, and which are bases? Explain.

    (a) HF   **(b)** $Ca(OH)_2$ **(c)** LiOH   **(d)** HCN

Table 3.5 Some Common Acids and the Anions Derived from Them

Acids		Anions	
Acetic acid	CH_3COOH	Acetate ion	*CH_3COO^-
Carbonic acid	H_2CO_3	Hydrogen carbonate ion (bicarbonate ion)	HCO_3^-
		Carbonate ion	CO_3^{2-}
Hydrochloric acid	HCl	Chloride ion	Cl^-
Nitric acid	HNO_3	Nitrate ion	NO_3^-
Nitrous acid	HNO_2	Nitrite ion	NO_2^-
Phosphoric acid	H_3PO_4	Dihydrogen phosphate ion	$H_2PO_4^-$
		Hydrogen phosphate ion	HPO_4^{2-}
		Phosphate ion	PO_4^{3-}
Sulfuric acid	H_2SO_4	Hydrogen sulfate ion	HSO_4^-
		Sulfate ion	SO_4^{2-}

*Sometimes written $C_2H_3O_2^-$ or as $CH_3CO_2^-$.

▭ KEY CONCEPT PROBLEM 3.28

One of these pictures represents a solution of HCl and one represents a solution of H_2SO_4. Which is which?

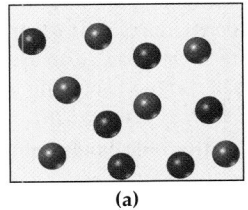 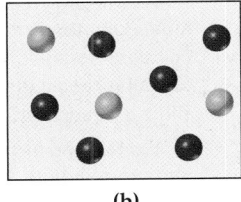

(a) (b)

CHEMISTRY IN ACTION

☤ Osteoporosis

At the beginning of the chapter we discussed the importance of dietary calcium ions for the formation of strong teeth and bones. Bone consists primarily of two components, one mineral and one organic. About 70% of bone is the ionic compound *hydroxyapatite,* $Ca_{10}(PO_4)_6(OH)_2$, called the *trabecular,* or spongy, bone. This mineral component is intermingled in a complex matrix with about 30% by mass of fibers of the protein *collagen,* called the *cortical,* or compact, bone. Hydroxyapatite gives bone its hardness and strength, whereas collagen fibers add flexibility and resistance to breaking.

Total bone mass in the body increases from birth until reaching a maximum in the mid 30s. By the early 40s, however, an age-related decline in bone mass begins to occur in both sexes. Bone density decreases, and the microarchitecture of bones is disrupted, resulting in weakening of bone structure, particularly in the wrists, hips, and spine. Should this thinning of bones become too great and the bones become too porous

and brittle, a clinical condition called osteoporosis can result. Osteoporosis is, in fact, the most common of all bone diseases, affecting approximately 25 million people in the United States. Approximately 1.5 million bone fractures each year are caused by osteoporosis, at an estimated health-care cost of $14 billion.

Although both sexes are affected by osteoporosis, the condition is particularly common in postmenopausal women, who undergo bone loss at a rate of 2–3% per year over and above that of the normal age-related loss. The cumulative lifetime bone loss, in fact, may approach 40–50% in women versus 20–30% in men. It has been estimated that half of all women over the age of 50 years will have an osteoporosis-related bone fracture at some point in their life. Other risk factors, in addition to sex, include being thin, being sedentary, having a family history of osteoporosis, smoking, and having a diet low in calcium.

No cure exists for osteoporosis, but treatment for its prevention and management includes estrogen-replacement

(Continued)

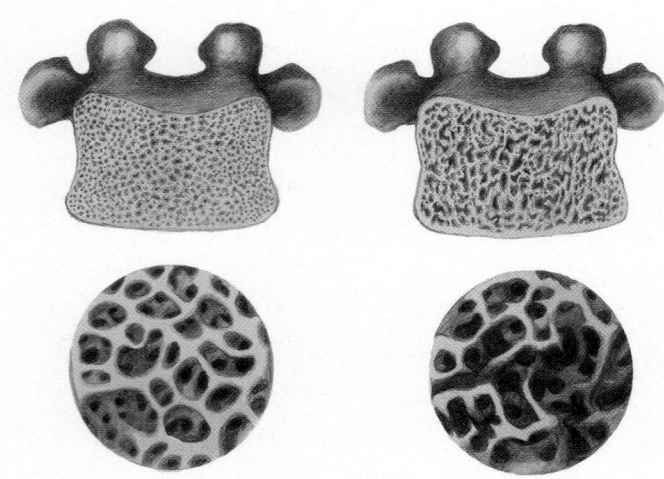

▲ These images represent a healthy vertebra (left) and one showing the effects of osteoporosis (right).

therapy for postmenopausal women as well as several approved medications called *bisphosphonates* that bind to the calcium in bone, slowing down bone loss by inhibiting the action of *osteoclasts*, or cells that break down bone tissue. Calcium supplements are also recommended, as is appropriate weight-bearing exercise. In addition, treatment with sodium fluoride is under active investigation and shows considerable promise. Fluoride ion reacts with hydroxyapatite to give *fluorapatite*, in which OH^- ions are replaced by F^-, increasing both bone strength and density.

$$Ca_{10}(PO_4)_6(OH)_2 + 2\,F^- \longrightarrow Ca_{10}(PO_4)_6F_2$$
Hydroxyapatite   Fluorapatite

CIA Problem 3.7 Name each ion in hydroxyapatite, $Ca_{10}(PO_4)_6(OH)_2$; give its charge; and show that the formula represents a neutral compound.

SUMMARY REVISITING THE CHAPTER LEARNING OBJECTIVES

• **Describe ion formation processes and distinguish between anions and cations.** Atoms are converted into *cations* by the loss of one or more electrons [resulting in a positive (+) charge] and into *anions* by the gain of one or more electrons [resulting in a negative (−) charge] *(see Problems 32, 33, 40–43, 46, 48, 49, 54, and 55)*.

• **Use the octet rule and electron configurations to explain the charge associated with ions.** A valence-shell electron configuration of eight electrons in filled *s* and *p* subshells leads to stability and lack of reactivity, as typified by the noble gases in group 8A. According to the *octet rule*, atoms of main group elements tend to form ions in which they have gained or lost the appropriate number of electrons to reach a stable electronic configuration of a noble gas *(see Problems 3, 37–39, 44, 45, 47, 78, 79, 84, and 86)*.

• **Use the periodic table to predict the charge associated with ions of main group elements.** The ionic charge can be predicted from the group number and the octet rule. For main group metals, the charge on the cation is equal to the group number. For nonmetals, the charge on the anion is equal to 8 − [group number] *(see Problems 29, 30, and 52–55)*.

• **Explain the formation of anions and cations based on periodic trends.** Periodic variations in *ionization energy,* the amount of energy that must be supplied to remove an electron from an atom, show that metals lose electrons more easily than nonmetals. As a result, metals usually form cations. Similar periodic variations in *electron affinity,* the amount of energy released on adding an electron to an atom, show that reactive nonmetals gain electrons more easily than metals. As a result, reactive nonmetals usually form anions *(see Problems 50–53, 56, 57, and 85)*.

• **Name common monoatomic anions and cations.** Cations have the same name as the metal from which they are derived. Monatomic anions have the name ending *-ide*. For metals that form more than one ion, a Roman numeral equal to the charge on the ion is added to the name of the cation. Alternatively, the ending *-ous* is added to the name of the cation with the lesser charge and the ending *-ic* is added to the name of the cation with the greater charge *(see Problems 58–61)*.

• **Identify the name, formula, and charge of common polyatomic ions.** Polyatomic ions consist of groups of atoms that are joined by covalent bonds (Chapter 4) but having an overall charge. The names, formulas, and charges of common polyatomic ions are summarized in Table 3.3 *(see Problems 62, 63, 88, and 89)*.

• **Explain the nature of the ionic bonds holding ions together in ionic compounds.** Ionic compounds are composed of cations and anions that are formed by the transfer of electrons; these ions are held together by *ionic bonds*, which result from the attraction between opposite electrical charges *(see Problems 48, 49, and 57)*.

• **Determine the formula of ionic compounds based on the formulas and charges of the cations and anions.** Ionic compounds must contain appropriate numbers of anions and cations to maintain overall neutrality, thereby providing a means of determining their chemical formulas *(see Problems 34–36, 64–67, and 70)*.

• **Based on the cations and anions in the chemical formula, write the name of ionic compounds.** To name an ionic compound, the cation name is given first, with the charge of the metal ion indicated if necessary. The name of the anion is given second using the *-ide* suffix as appropriate (for a monatomic anion) or the name of the polyatomic anion *(see Problems 68–73, 80, 82, 83, and 87–90)*.

• **Identify the properties of ionic compounds and explain how the nature of the ionic bond is reflected in the physical properties of ionic compounds.** Ionic compounds conduct electricity when dissolved in water because the charged particles (ions) act as mobile charge carriers. Ionic compounds are generally crystalline solids with high melting points and high boiling points because of the strong electrostatic attraction between ions in the solid state *(see Problems 49 and 50)*.

• **Identify the ions associated with acids and bases.** The hydrogen ion (H^+) and the hydroxide ion (OH^-) are among the most important ions in chemistry because they are fundamental to the idea of acids and bases. According to one common definition, an *acid* is a substance that yields H^+ ions when dissolved in water and a base is a substance that yields OH^- ions when dissolved in water *(see Problems 74–77 and 81)*.

CONCEPT MAP: ELECTROSTATIC FORCES

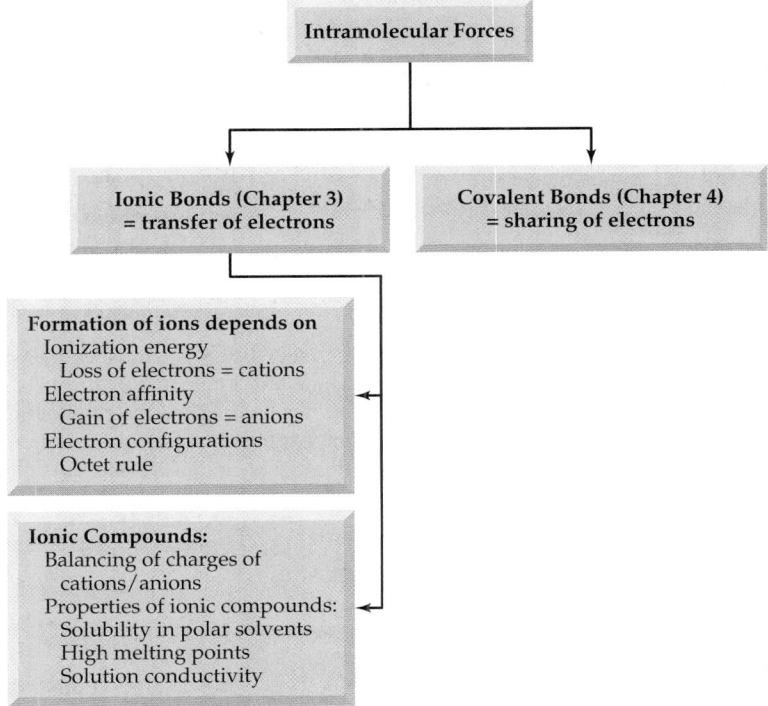

▲ **Figure 3.3 Concept Map.** As illustrated in this concept map, ionic bonds represent one type of intramolecular force holding elements together in compounds. Elements form ions by gaining or losing electrons to obtain a stable electronic configuration. The tendency to gain/lose electrons is reflected in the magnitude of the ionization energies or electron affinities of the elements. Properties of ionic compounds (high melting points, solubility in polar solvents, solution conductivity) are a consequence of the charges on the ions and the strong electrostatic attractions between ions.

KEY WORDS

Acid, *p. 92*	**Electron affinity,** *p. 79*	**Ionic bond,** *p. 84*	**Ionization energy,** *p. 78*
Anion, *p. 74*	**Formula unit,** *p. 86*	**Ionic compound,** *p. 85*	**Octet rule,** *p. 75*
Base, *p. 92*	**Ion,** *p. 73*	**Ionic solid,** *p. 85*	**Polyatomic ion,** *p. 82*
Cation, *p. 73*			

⊙━ UNDERSTANDING KEY CONCEPTS

3.29 Where on the blank outline of the periodic table are the following elements found?

    (a) Elements that commonly form only one type of cation

    (b) Elements that commonly form anions

    (c) Elements that can form more than one type of cation

    (d) Elements that do not readily form either anions or cations

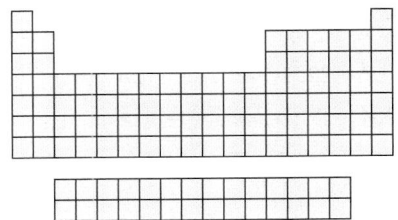

3.30 Where on the blank outline of the periodic table are the following elements found?

    (a) Elements that commonly form +2 ions

    (b) Elements that commonly form −2 ions

    (c) An element that forms a +3 ion

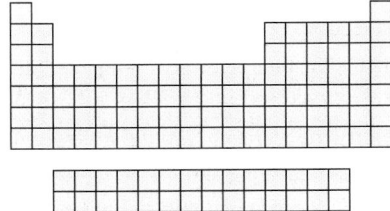

3.31 Write the symbols for the ions represented in the following drawings.

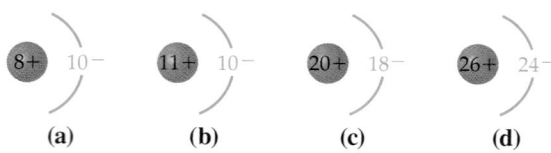

(a)   **(b)**   **(c)**   **(d)**

3.32 One of these drawings represents an Na atom, and one represents an Na$^+$ ion. Tell which is which, and explain why there is a difference in size.

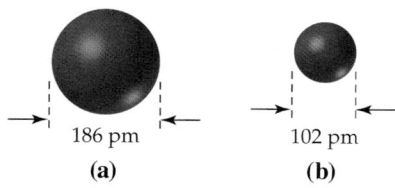

(a)   **(b)**

3.33 One of these drawings represents a Cl atom and one represents a Cl$^-$ ion. Tell which is which, and explain why there is a difference in size.

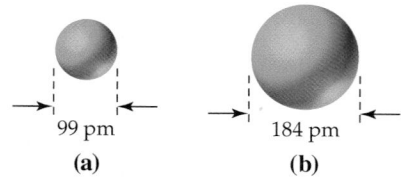

(a)   **(b)**

3.34 The elements in red in the periodic table can form cations having more than one charge. Write the formulas and names of the compounds that are formed between the red cations and the blue anions depicted in the periodic table.

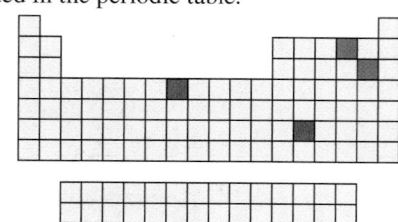

3.35 Each of these drawings (a)–(d) represents one of the following ionic compounds: PbBr$_2$, ZnS, CrF$_3$, and Al$_2$O$_3$. Which is which?

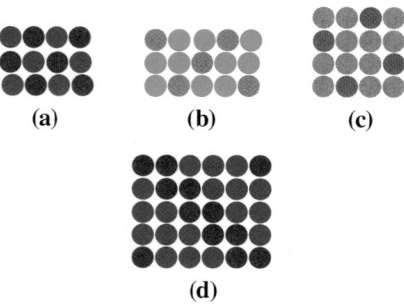

(a)   **(b)**   **(c)**

(d)

3.36 The ionic compound formed between chromium and oxygen is shown here. Name the compound and write its formula. (Hint: When naming the compound, remember that chromium is a transition metal cation and can have more than one possible charge.)

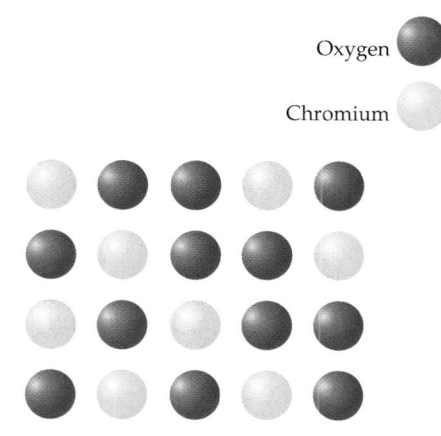

ADDITIONAL PROBLEMS

IONS AND THE OCTET RULE (SECTIONS 3.1 AND 3.2)

3.37 What is the *octet rule*?

3.38 What roles do the octet rule and the position of an element in the periodic table play in determining the charge on an ion?

3.39 Why do H and He not obey the octet rule?

3.40 Write the symbol for an ion that contains 34 protons and 36 electrons.

3.41 What is the charge of an ion that contains 21 protons and 19 electrons?

3.42 Identify the element X in the following ions and tell which noble gas has the same electron configuration.

(a) X^{2+}, a cation with 36 electrons

(b) X$^-$, an anion with 36 electrons

3.43 Element Z forms an ion Z^{3+}, which contains 31 protons. What is the identity of Z, and how many electrons does Z^{3+} have?

3.44 Write the electron configuration for the following ions:

(a) Rb$^+$ **(b)** Br$^-$ **(c)** S^{2-}

(d) Ba^{2+} **(e)** Al^{3+}

3.45 Based on the following atomic numbers and electronic configurations write the symbols for the following ions:

(a) Z = 20; $1s^2 \, 2s^2 \, 2p^6 \, 3s^2 \, 3p^6$

(b) Z = 8; $1s^2 \, 2s^2 \, 2p^6$

(c) Z = 22; $1s^2 \, 2s^2 \, 2p^6 \, 3s^2 \, 3p^6 \, 3d^2$

(d) Z = 19; $1s^2 \, 2s^2 \, 2p^6 \, 3s^2 \, 3p^6$

(e) Z = 13; $1s^2 \, 2s^2 \, 2p^6$

IONS AND IONIC BONDING (SECTION 3.3)

3.46 Write equations for loss or gain of electrons by atoms that result in formation of the following ions:

(a) Ca^{2+} (b) Au^+ (c) F^- (d) Cr^{3+}

3.47 Write electronic configurations and symbols for the ions formed by the following:

(a) Gain of three electrons by phosphorus

(b) Loss of one electron by lithium

(c) Loss of two electrons by cobalt

(d) Loss of three electrons by thallium

3.48 Tell whether each statement about ions is true or false. If a statement is false, explain why.

(a) A cation is formed by addition of one or more electrons to an atom.

(b) Group 4A elements tend to lose four electrons to yield ions with a +4 charge.

(c) Group 4A elements tend to gain four electrons to yield ions with a −4 charge.

(d) The individual atoms in a polyatomic ion are held together by covalent bonds.

3.49 Tell whether each statement about ionic solids is true or false. If a statement is false, explain why.

(a) Ions are randomly arranged in ionic solids.

(b) All ions are the same size in ionic solids.

(c) Ionic solids can often be shattered by a sharp blow.

(d) Ionic solids have low boiling points.

PERIODIC PROPERTIES AND ION FORMATION (SECTION 3.4)

3.50 Looking only at the periodic table, tell which member of each pair of atoms has the larger ionization energy and thus loses an electron less easily:

(a) Li and O   (b) Li and Cs

(c) K and Zn   (d) Mg and N

3.51 Looking only at the periodic table, tell which member of each pair of atoms has the larger electron affinity and thus gains an electron more easily:

(a) Li and S   (b) Ba and I

(c) Ca and Br

3.52 Which of the following ions are likely to form? Explain.

(a) Li^{2+} (b) K^- (c) Mn^{3+}

(d) Zn^{4+} (e) Ne^+

3.53 What is the charge on the cation formed from the following elements? For those elements that form more than one cation, indicate the ionic charges most commonly observed.

(a) Magnesium   (b) Tin

(c) Mercury   (d) Aluminum

3.54 Write the electron configurations of Cr^{2+} and Cr^{3+}.

3.55 Write the electron configurations of Co, Co^{2+}, and Co^{3+}.

3.56 Would you expect the ionization energy of Li^+ to be less than, greater than, or the same as the ionization energy of Li? Explain.

3.57 (a) Write equations for the loss of an electron by a K atom and the gain of an electron by a K^+ ion.

(b) What is the relationship between the equations?

(c) What is the relationship between the ionization energy of a K atom and the electron affinity of a K^+ ion?

SYMBOLS, FORMULAS, AND NAMES FOR IONS (SECTIONS 3.5 AND 3.6)

3.58 Name the following ions:

(a) S^{2-} (b) Sn^{2+} (c) Sr^{2+}

(d) Mg^{2+} (e) Au^+

3.59 Name the following ions in both the old and the new systems:

(a) Cr^{2+} (b) Fe^{3+} (c) Hg^{2+}

3.60 Write symbols for the following ions:

(a) Selenide ion   (b) Oxide ion

(c) Silver(I) ion

3.61 Write symbols for the following ions:

(a) Ferrous ion   (b) Tin(IV) ion

(c) Lead(II) ion   (d) Chromic ion

3.62 Write formulas for the following ions:

(a) Hydroxide ion   (b) Bisulfate ion

(c) Acetate ion   (d) Permanganate ion

(e) Hypochlorite ion   (f) Nitrate ion

(g) Carbonate ion   (h) Dichromate ion

3.63 Name the following ions:

(a) NO_2^- (b) CrO_4^{2-}

(c) NH_4^+ (d) HPO_4^{2-}

NAMES AND FORMULAS FOR IONIC COMPOUNDS (SECTIONS 3.8 AND 3.9)

3.64 Write the formula for the following substances:

(a) Sodium bicarbonate (baking soda)

(b) Potassium nitrate (a backache remedy)

(c) Calcium carbonate (an antacid)

(d) Ammonium nitrate (first aid cold packs)

3.65 Write the formula for the following compounds:

(a) Calcium hypochlorite, used as a swimming pool disinfectant

(b) Copper(II) sulfate, used to kill algae in swimming pools

(c) Sodium phosphate, used in detergents to enhance cleaning action

3.66 Complete the table by writing in the formula of the compound formed by each pair of ions:

	S^{2-}	Cl^-	PO_4^{3-}	CO_3^{2-}
Copper(II)	CuS			
Ca^{2+}				
NH_4^+				
Ferric ion				

3.67 Complete the table by writing in the formula of the compound formed by each pair of ions:

	O^{2-}	HSO_4^-	HPO_4^{2-}	$C_2O_4^{2-}$
K^+	K_2O			
Ni^{2+}				
NH_4^+				
Chromous				

3.68 Write the name of each compound in the table for Problem 3.66.

3.69 Write the name of each compound in the table for Problem 3.67.

3.70 Name the following substances:
(a) $MgCO_3$
(b) $Ca(CH_3CO_2)_2$
(c) $AgCN$
(d) $Na_2Cr_2O_7$

3.71 Name the following substances:
(a) $Fe(OH)_2$
(b) $KMnO_4$
(c) Na_2CrO_4
(d) $Ba_3(PO_4)_2$

3.72 Which of the following formulas is most likely to be correct for calcium phosphate?
(a) Ca_2PO_4
(b) $CaPO_4$
(c) $Ca_2(PO_4)_3$
(d) $Ca_2(PO_4)_2$

3.73 Fill in the missing information to give the correct formula for each compound:
(a) $Al_?(SO_4)_?$
(b) $(NH_4)_?(PO_4)_?$
(c) $Rb_?(SO_4)_?$

ACIDS AND BASES (SECTION 3.11)

3.74 What is the difference between an acid and a base?

3.75 Identify the following substances as either an acid or a base:
(a) H_2CO_3
(b) HCN
(c) $Mg(OH)_2$
(d) KOH

3.76 Write equations to show how the substances listed in Problem 3.75 give ions when dissolved in water.

3.77 Give the formula and the name of the anions for the acids in Problem 3.75. (Hint: The H^+ ion is the cation in the acids.)

CONCEPTUAL PROBLEMS

3.78 Explain why the hydride ion, H^-, has a noble gas configuration.

3.79 The H^- ion (Problem 3.78) is stable but the Li^- ion is not. Explain.

3.80 Many compounds containing a metal and a nonmetal are not ionic, yet they are named using the Roman numeral system for ionic compounds described in Section 3.5. Write the chemical formulas for the following such compounds.
(a) Chromium(VI) oxide
(b) Vanadium(V) chloride
(c) Manganese(IV) oxide
(d) Molybdenum(IV) sulfide

3.81 The arsenate ion has the formula AsO_4^{3-}. Write the formula of the corresponding acid that contains this anion. (Hint: The cation for the corresponding acid is H^+.)

3.82 The names given for the following compounds are incorrect. Write the correct name for each compound.
(a) Cu_3PO_4, copper(III) phosphate
(b) Na_2SO_4, sodium sulfide
(c) MnO_2, manganese(II) oxide
(d) $AuCl_3$, gold chloride
(e) $Pb(CO_3)_2$, lead(II) acetate
(f) Ni_2S_3, nickel(II) sulfide

3.83 The formulas given for the following compounds are incorrect. Write the correct formula for each compound.
(a) Cobalt(II) cyanide, $CoCN_2$
(b) Uranium(VI) oxide, UO_6
(c) Tin(II) sulfate, $Ti(SO_4)_2$
(d) Manganese(IV) oxide, MnO_4
(e) Potassium phosphate, K_2PO_4
(f) Calcium phosphide, CaP
(g) Lithium bisulfate, $Li(SO_4)_2$
(h) Aluminum hydroxide, $Al_2(OH)_3$

3.84 How many protons, electrons, and neutrons are in each of these ions?
(a) $^{16}O^{2-}$
(b) $^{89}Y^{3+}$
(c) $^{133}Cs^+$
(d) $^{81}Br^-$

3.85 Element X reacts with element Y to give a product containing X^{3+} ions and Y^{2-} ions.
(a) Is element X likely to be a metal or a nonmetal?
(b) Is element Y likely to be a metal or a nonmetal?
(c) What is the formula of the product?
(d) What groups of the periodic table are elements X and Y likely to be in?

3.86 Identify each of the ions having the following charges and electron configurations:
(a) X^{4+}; $[Ar] 4s^0 3d^3$
(b) X^+; $[Ar] 4s^0 3d^{10}$
(c) X^{4+}; $[Ar] 4s^0 3d^0$

GROUP QUESTIONS

3.87 The term "alum" refers to a group of ionic compounds that contain a monovalent cation (M⁺), a trivalent cation (M³⁺), and sulfate anions. Perform a web search to find:

(a) The chemical formulas of at least two different alum compounds.

(b) At least three common uses or applications of alum compounds.

3.88 One commercially available calcium supplement contains calcium gluconate. Look up the formula for calcium gluconate. Identify the charges on the calcium and gluconate ions. Are the calcium and gluconate ions monoatomic or polyatomic? Explain.

3.89 Borax is a common household and commercial chemical. Look up the chemical formula for borax. What is the anion in borax and the correct chemical name for the anion? (Hint: It is a polyatomic ion.)

3.90 Sodium fluoride reacts with hydroxyapatite to give fluorapatite, which increases both bone strength and density. Another fluoride compound is included in many toothpaste products to strengthen teeth enamel and prevent cavities. Do some research to identify this fluoride compound and give the name and formula of the compound.

4

Molecular Compounds

CONTENTS

◀◀ CONCEPTS TO REVIEW

▲ The opiate drugs derived from these poppy plants can produce very different physiological effects based on slight differences in chemical structures.

We saw in the preceding chapter that ionic compounds are crystalline solids composed of positively and negatively charged ions. Not all substances, however, are ionic. In fact, with the exception of table salt (NaCl), baking soda (NaHCO₃), lime for the garden (CaO), and a few others, most of the compounds we come into contact with on a daily basis are *not* crystalline, brittle, high-melting ionic solids. We are much more likely to encounter gases (like those in air), liquids (such as water), low-melting solids (such as butter), and flexible solids (like plastics). All these materials are composed of *molecules* rather than ions, all contain *covalent* bonds rather than ionic bonds, and all consist primarily of nonmetal atoms rather than metals.

As an example, consider the active ingredients in many over-the-counter drugs—they consist largely of the elements carbon, hydrogen, nitrogen, and oxygen. However, the myriad ways in which these elements can be combined lead to literally thousands of unique compounds with different chemical formulas, having different chemical and physical properties. In some cases, two compounds can have identical chemical formulas and structures but slightly different three-dimensional orientations of atoms in the compound that result in dramatically different behaviors. For example, dextromethorphan and levomethorphan have identical molecular formulas and are very similar to morphine and codeine—opiate drugs derived from the poppy plant. But very slight differences in the three-dimensional arrangement of atoms can affect the chemical and physiological behavior of these substances. Dextromethorphan, for example, is a safe and effective cough suppressant, whereas levomethorphan is a highly addictive opiate. In this chapter, we will explore the nature of covalent bonds, how they contribute to molecular shapes and properties, and some of the conventions used to name molecular compounds so that we can distinguish one from another.

4.1 Covalent Bonds

Learning Objectives:

- Describe the nature of covalent bonds and how they are formed.
- Differentiate between ionic and covalent bonds.

How do we describe the bonding in carbon dioxide, water, polyethylene, and the many millions of nonionic compounds that make up our bodies and much of the world around us? Simply put, the bonds in such compounds are formed by the sharing of electrons between atoms (unlike ionic bonds, which involve the complete transfer of electrons from one atom to another). The bond formed when atoms share electrons is called a **covalent bond,** and the group of atoms held together by covalent bonds is called a **molecule.** A single molecule of water, for example, contains two hydrogen atoms and one oxygen atom covalently bonded to one another. We might visualize a water molecule using a space-filling model as shown here:

Covalent bond A bond formed by sharing electrons between atoms.

Molecule A group of atoms held together by covalent bonds.

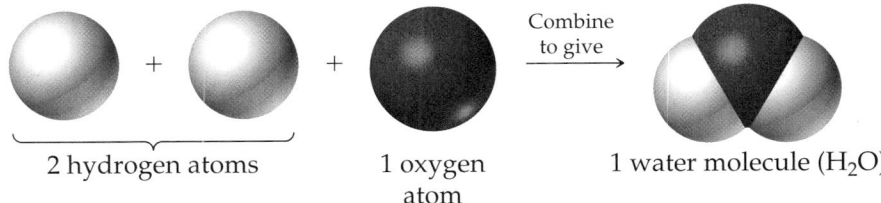

2 hydrogen atoms + 1 oxygen atom → Combine to give → 1 water molecule (H_2O)

Recall that according to the *octet rule* (Section 3.5), main group elements tend to undergo reactions that leave them with completed outer subshells with eight valence electrons (or two for hydrogen), so that they have a noble gas electron configuration. Although metals and reactive nonmetals can achieve an electron octet by gaining or losing an appropriate number of electrons to form ions, nonmetals can also achieve an electron octet by *sharing* an appropriate number of electrons in covalent bonds.

A simple example of how covalent bond formation occurs is the bond between two hydrogen atoms in a hydrogen molecule, H_2. Recall that a hydrogen *atom* consists of a positively charged nucleus and a single, negatively charged 1s valence electron, which we represent as H· using the electron-dot symbol. When two hydrogen atoms come together, electrostatic interactions occur. Some of these interactions are repulsive—the two positively charged nuclei repel each other, and the two negatively charged electrons repel each other. Other interactions, however, are attractive—each nucleus attracts both electrons, and each electron attracts both nuclei (Figure 4.1). Other factors, such as orbital energy levels and stable electronic configurations, contribute to making the attractive forces stronger than the repulsive forces, so that a covalent bond is formed and the hydrogen atoms stay together.

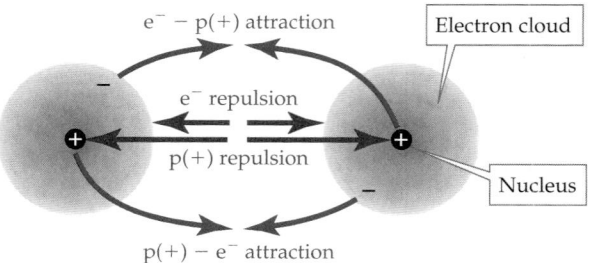

▲ **Figure 4.1**

A covalent H—H bond is the net result of attractive and repulsive forces.
The nucleus–electron attractions (blue arrows) are greater than the nucleus–nucleus and electron–electron repulsions (red arrows), resulting in a net attractive force that holds the atoms together to form an H_2 molecule.

In essence, the electrons act as a kind of "glue" to bind the two nuclei together into an H_2 molecule. Both nuclei are simultaneously attracted to the same electrons and are held together, much as two tug-of-war teams pulling on the same rope are held together.

Covalent bond formation in the H—H molecule can be visualized by imagining that the spherical $1s$ orbitals from the two individual atoms *overlap* and blend together to give an egg-shaped region in the H_2 molecule. Each hydrogen atom now "owns" one valence shell electron and "shares" one provided by the other H atom. The two electrons occupy the central region between the two H nuclei, giving both atoms a share in two valence electrons, and the $1s^2$ electron configuration of the noble gas helium. For simplicity, the shared pair of electrons in a covalent bond is often represented as a line between atoms. Thus, the symbols H—H, H:H, and H_2 all represent a hydrogen molecule.

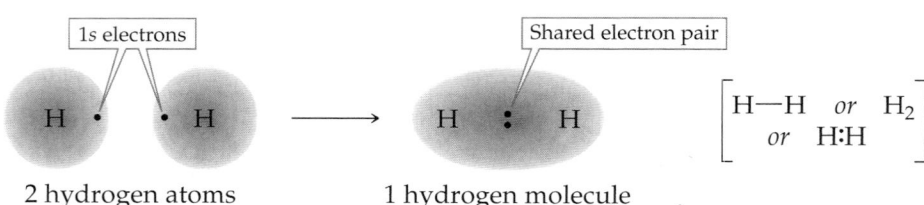

2 hydrogen atoms   1 hydrogen molecule

As you might imagine, the magnitudes of the various attractive and repulsive forces between nuclei and electrons in a covalent bond depend on how close the atoms are to each other. If the atoms are too far apart, the attractive forces are small and no bond exists. If the atoms are too close, the repulsive interaction between nuclei is so strong that it pushes the atoms apart. Thus, there is an optimum point where net attractive forces are maximized and where the H_2 molecule is most stable. This optimum distance between nuclei is called the **bond length** and is 74 pm (7.4×10^{-11} m) in the H_2 molecule. Typically, the bond length is slightly less than the sum of the atomic radii of the two atoms involved in the covalent bond.

As another example of covalent bond formation, look at the chlorine molecule, Cl_2. An individual chlorine atom has seven valence electrons and the valence-shell electron configuration $3s^2 3p^5$. Using the electron-dot symbols for the valence electrons, each Cl atom can be represented as $:\ddot{C}l\cdot$. The $3s$ orbital and two of the three $3p$ orbitals are filled by two electrons each, but the third $3p$ orbital holds only one electron. When two chlorine atoms approach each other, the unpaired $3p$ electrons are shared by both atoms in a covalent bond. Each chlorine atom in the resultant Cl_2 molecule now "owns" six outer-shell electrons and "shares" two more, giving each a valence-shell octet like that of the noble gas argon. We can represent the formation of a covalent bond between chlorine atoms as (where the red dots represent shared electrons once the bond is formed).

$$:\ddot{C}l\cdot \ + \ \cdot\ddot{C}l: \ \longrightarrow \ :\ddot{C}l:\ddot{C}l:$$

▲ The two teams are joined together because both are holding onto the same rope. In a similar way, two atoms are bonded together when both hold onto the same electrons.

Bond length The optimum distance between nuclei in a covalent bond.

Such bond formation can also be pictured as the overlap of the $3p$ orbitals containing the single electrons, with resultant formation of a region of high electron density between the nuclei.

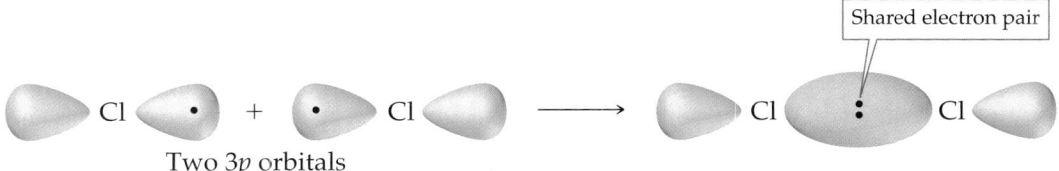

Two $3p$ orbitals

Shared electron pair

Similar to H_2 and Cl_2, other elements can achieve stable electron configurations by forming *diatomic* molecules (Figure 4.2): nitrogen (N_2) and oxygen (O_2) are colorless, odorless, nontoxic gases present in air; fluorine (F_2) is a pale yellow, highly reactive gas; bromine (Br_2) is a dark red, toxic liquid; and iodine (I_2) is a violet crystalline solid.

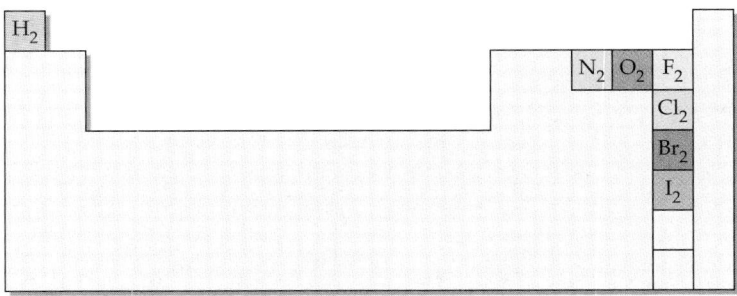

▲ Figure 4.2
Diatomic elements in the periodic table.

PROBLEM 4.1

Draw the iodine molecule using electron-dot symbols and indicate the shared electron pair. What noble gas configuration do the iodine atoms have in an iodine (I_2) molecule?

4.2 Covalent Bonds and the Periodic Table

Learning Objective:

• Predict the number of covalent bonds an atom will form based on its position in the periodic table.

Covalent bonds can form between unlike atoms as well as between like atoms, making possible a vast number of **molecular compounds.** Water molecules, for example, consist of two hydrogen atoms joined by covalent bonds to a single oxygen atom, H_2O; ammonia molecules consist of three hydrogen atoms covalently bonded to a nitrogen atom, NH_3; and methane molecules consist of four hydrogen atoms covalently bonded to a carbon atom, CH_4.

Molecular compound A compound that consists of atoms joined by covalent bonds to form molecules rather than ions.

H—Ö—H
Water, H_2O

H—N̈—H
|
H
Ammonia, NH_3

H
|
H—C—H
|
H
Methane, CH_4

Oxygen bonds to 2 hydrogen atoms.

Nitrogen bonds to 3 hydrogen atoms.

Carbon bonds to 4 hydrogen atoms.

Note that in all of these examples, each atom shares enough electrons to achieve a noble gas configuration: two electrons for hydrogen and octets for oxygen, nitrogen, and carbon. Hydrogen, with one valence electron $(\text{H} \cdot)$, needs one more electron to achieve a noble gas configuration (that of helium) and thus forms one covalent bond. Oxygen, with six valence electrons $(\cdot \ddot{\text{O}} \cdot)$, needs two more electrons to have an octet; this happens when oxygen forms two covalent bonds. Nitrogen, with five valence electrons $(\cdot \ddot{\text{N}} \cdot)$, needs three more electrons to achieve an octet and thus forms three covalent bonds. Carbon, with four valence electrons $(\cdot \dot{\text{C}} \cdot)$, needs four more electrons and thus forms four covalent bonds. Figure 4.3 summarizes the number of covalent bonds typically formed by common main group elements.

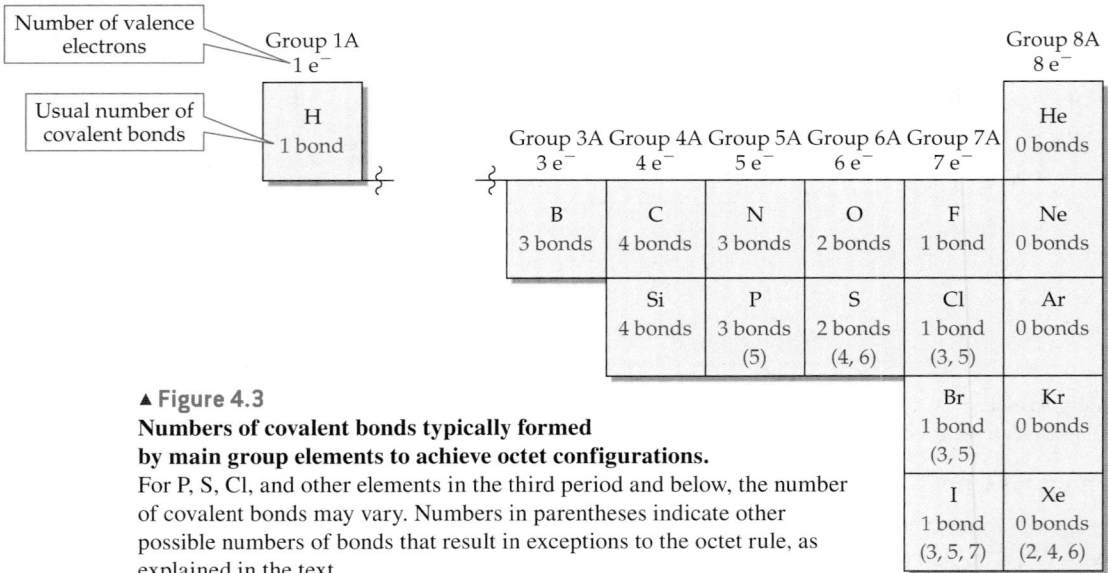

▲ **Figure 4.3**
Numbers of covalent bonds typically formed by main group elements to achieve octet configurations.
For P, S, Cl, and other elements in the third period and below, the number of covalent bonds may vary. Numbers in parentheses indicate other possible numbers of bonds that result in exceptions to the octet rule, as explained in the text.

The octet rule is a useful guideline, but it has numerous exceptions. Boron, for example, has only three valence electrons it can share $(\cdot \dot{\text{B}} \cdot)$ and thus often forms compounds in which it has only three covalent bonds and six electrons, such as BF_3. Exceptions to the octet rule are also seen with elements in the third row of the periodic table and below because these elements have vacant d orbitals that can be used for bonding. Phosphorus sometimes forms five covalent bonds (using 10 bonding electrons); sulfur sometimes forms four or six covalent bonds (using 8 and 12 bonding electrons, respectively); and chlorine, bromine, and iodine sometimes form three, five, or seven covalent bonds, respectively. Phosphorus and sulfur, for example, form molecules such as PCl_5, SF_4, and SF_6.

BF_3
Boron trifluoride
(6 valence electrons on B)

PCl_5
Phosphorus pentachloride
(10 valence electrons on P)

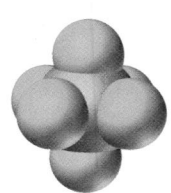

SF_6
Sulfur hexafluoride
(12 valence electrons on S)

Worked Example 4.1 Molecular Compounds: Octet Rule and Covalent Bonds

Using Figure 4.3, tell whether the following molecules are likely to exist.

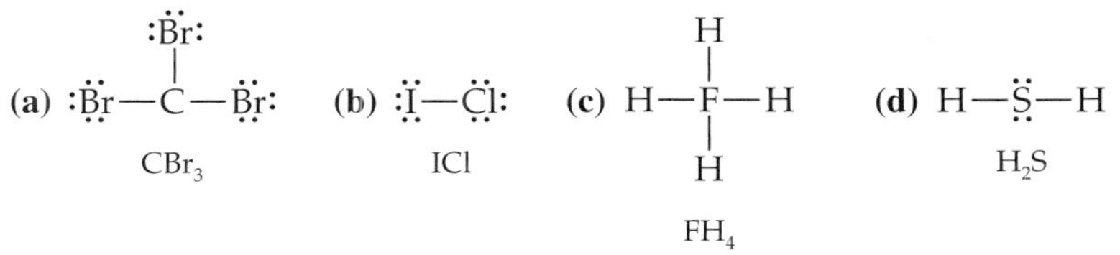

(a) $:\ddot{B}r:$
$\quad\quad\;\; |$
$:\ddot{B}r\!-\!C\!-\!\ddot{B}r:$
$\quad\quad$ CBr$_3$

(b) $:\ddot{I}\!-\!\ddot{C}l:$
$\quad\quad$ ICl

(c) $\quad\quad$ H
$\quad\quad\quad |$
$\quad$ H$-$F$-$H
$\quad\quad\quad |$
$\quad\quad\quad$ H
$\quad\quad$ FH$_4$

(d) H$-\ddot{S}-$H
$\quad\quad$ H$_2$S

ANALYSIS Count the number of covalent bonds formed by each element and see if the numbers correspond to those shown in Figure 4.3.

SOLUTION

(a) No. Carbon needs four covalent bonds to achieve a complete valence-shell octet but has only three in CBr$_3$.

(b) Yes. Both iodine and chlorine have achieved a complete octet by forming one covalent bond in ICl.

(c) No. Fluorine only needs one covalent bond to achieve an octet. It cannot form more than one covalent bond because it is in the second period and does not have valence *d* orbitals to use for bonding.

(d) Yes. Sulfur, which is in group 6A like oxygen, can achieve a complete valence-shell octet by forming two covalent bonds.

Worked Example 4.2 Molecular Compounds: Electron-Dot Symbols

Using electron-dot symbols, show the reaction between one hydrogen atom and one fluorine atom.

ANALYSIS The electron-dot symbols show the valence electrons for the hydrogen and fluorine atoms. A covalent bond is formed by the sharing of unpaired valence electrons between the two atoms so that each atom now has the electron configuration of a noble gas (helium in the case of hydrogen and neon in the case of fluorine).

SOLUTION

Draw the electron-dot symbols for the H and F atoms, showing the covalent bond as a shared electron pair.

$$H\cdot \; + \; \cdot\ddot{F}: \; \longrightarrow \; H\!:\!\ddot{F}:$$

Worked Example 4.3 Molecular Compounds: Predicting Number of Bonds

What are likely formulas for the following molecules?

(a) SiH$_2$Cl$_?$ **(b)** HBr$_?$ **(c)** PBr$_?$

ANALYSIS The numbers of covalent bonds needed to achieve a complete valence-shell octet for each element should be as indicated in Figure 4.3.

SOLUTION

(a) Silicon typically forms four bonds: SiH$_2$Cl$_2$

(b) Hydrogen forms only one bond: HBr

(c) Phosphorus typically forms three bonds: PBr$_3$

PROBLEM 4.2

How many covalent bonds are formed by each atom in the following molecules? Draw molecules using the electron-dot symbols and lines to show the covalent bonds.

(a) PH$_3$ **(b)** H$_2$Se   **(c)** HCl   **(d)** SiF$_4$

PROBLEM 4.3
What are likely formulas for the following molecules?

(a) $CH_2Cl_?$ **(b)** $BH_?$ **(c)** $NI_?$ **(d)** $SiCl_?$

4.3 Multiple Covalent Bonds

Learning Objective:

• Use the octet rule to determine when multiple covalent bonds (double and triple) will appear between two atoms.

The bonding in some molecules cannot be explained by the sharing of only two electrons between atoms. For example, the carbon and oxygen atoms in carbon dioxide (CO_2) and the nitrogen atoms in the N_2 molecule cannot have electron octets if only two electrons are shared:

UNSTABLE—Carbon has only 6 electrons; each oxygen has only 7.

UNSTABLE—Each nitrogen has only 6 electrons.

The only way the atoms in CO_2 and N_2 can have outer-shell electron octets is by sharing *more* than two electrons, resulting in the formation of *multiple* covalent bonds between two atoms. Only if the carbon atom shares four electrons with each oxygen atom do all atoms in CO_2 have electron octets, and only if the two nitrogen atoms share six electrons do both have electron octets. A bond formed by sharing two electrons (one pair) is a **single bond,** a bond formed by sharing four electrons (two pairs) is a **double bond,** and a bond formed by sharing six electrons (three pairs) is a **triple bond.** As you might expect, sharing more than two electrons increases the attractive forces between the two atoms and pulls them closer together. Hence, the bond length decreases in the order single bond > double bond > triple bond. Just as a single bond is represented by a single line between atoms, a double bond is represented by two lines between atoms and a triple bond by three lines:

Single bond A covalent bond formed by sharing one electron pair.

Double bond A covalent bond formed by sharing two electron pairs.

Triple bond A covalent bond formed by sharing three electron pairs.

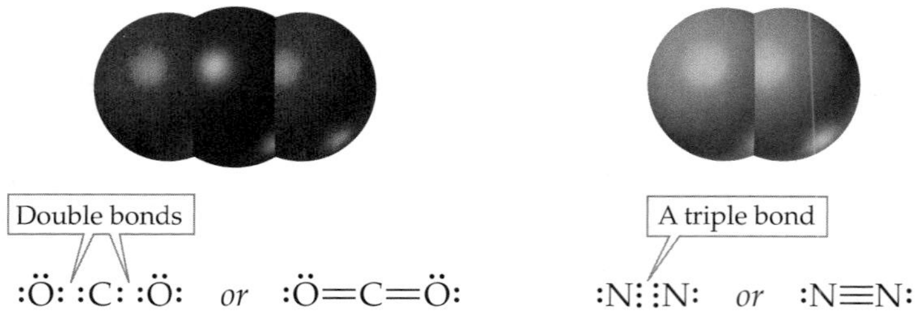

Double bonds

A triple bond

$:\ddot{O}::C::\ddot{O}:$ *or* $\ddot{O}=C=\ddot{O}:$ $:N::N:$ *or* $:N{\equiv}N:$

The carbon atom in CO_2 has two double bonds ($4e^-$ each) for a total of eight electrons. Each oxygen atom also has a complete octet: a double bond ($4e^-$) plus two sets of **lone pairs.** Similarly, formation of a triple bond in N_2 allows each nitrogen to obtain a complete octet: six electrons from the triple bond plus a lone pair.

Lone pair A pair of electrons that is not used for bonding.

Carbon, nitrogen, and oxygen are the elements most often present in multiple bonds. Carbon and nitrogen form both double and triple bonds; oxygen forms double bonds. Multiple covalent bonding is particularly common in *organic* molecules, which consist predominantly of the element carbon. For example, ethylene, a simple compound used commercially to induce ripening in fruit, has the formula C_2H_4. The only way for the two carbon atoms to have octets is for them to share four electrons in a carbon–carbon double bond.

LOOKING AHEAD ▶▶ In Chapters 12–18, we will explore the diverse chemistry of organic compounds containing multiple bonds between carbons and other atoms.

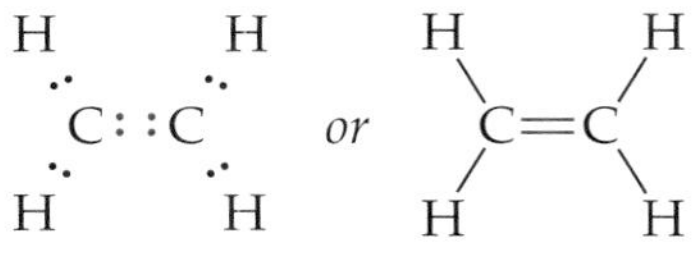

H H   H   H
 :. :.   \   /
  C : : C   *or*   C = C
 :. :.   /   \
H   H   H   H

Ethylene—the carbon atoms share
4 electrons in a double bond.

Another example, acetylene, the gas used in welding, has the formula C_2H_2. To achieve octets, the two carbons share six electrons in a carbon–carbon triple bond.

H : C ⦂⦂ C : H   *or*   H—C≡C—H

Acetylene—the carbon atoms share
6 electrons in a triple bond.

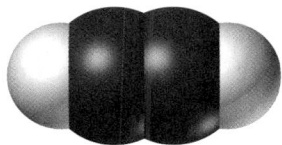

Note that in compounds with multiple bonds like ethylene and acetylene, each carbon atom still forms a total of four covalent bonds.

Worked Example 4.4 Molecular Compounds: Multiple Bonds

The compound 1-butene contains a multiple bond between two carbon atoms. In the following representation, however, only the connections between atoms are shown; the multiple bond is not specifically indicated. Identify the position of the multiple bond.

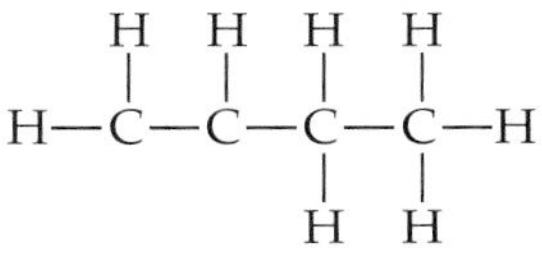

```
        H  H  H  H
        |  |  |  |
   H — C — C — C — C — H
        |  |  |  |
        H        H  H
```

1-Butene

ANALYSIS Look for two adjacent atoms that appear to have fewer than the typical number of covalent bonds and connect those atoms by a double or triple bond. Refer to Figure 4.3 to see how many bonds will typically be formed by hydrogen and carbon atoms in order to achieve a complete octet of valence-shell electrons.

SOLUTION

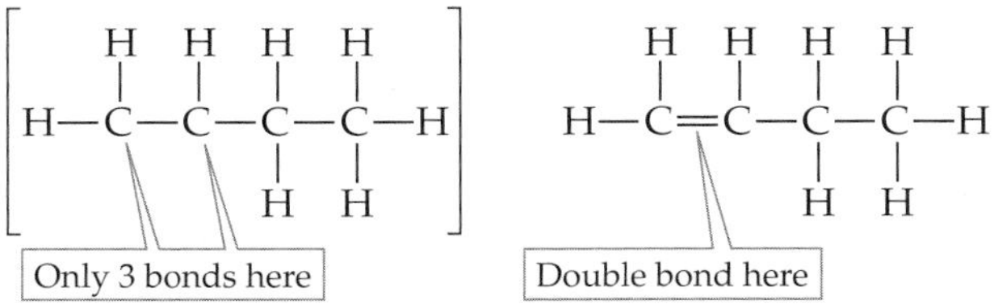

```
 ⎡      H  H  H  H    ⎤        H  H  H  H
 ⎢      |  |  |  |    ⎥        |  |  |  |
 ⎢ H — C — C — C — C — H ⎥   H — C = C — C — C — H
 ⎢      |  |  |  |    ⎥           |  |  |
 ⎣      H        H  H    ⎦              H  H
```

Only 3 bonds here   Double bond here

Worked Example 4.5 Multiple Bonds: Electron-Dot and Line Structures

Draw the oxygen molecule by (a) using the electron-dot symbols and (b) by using lines rather than dots to indicate covalent bonds.

ANALYSIS Each oxygen atom has six valence electrons and will tend to form two covalent bonds to reach an octet. Thus, each oxygen atom will need to share four electrons to form a double bond.

SOLUTION

:Ö::Ö: or   :Ö=Ö:

PROBLEM 4.4

Acetic acid, the organic constituent of vinegar, can be drawn using electron-dot symbols as shown next. How many outer-shell electrons are associated with each atom? Draw the structure using lines rather than dots to indicate covalent bonds.

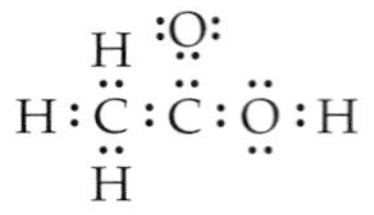

$$\begin{array}{cc} \text{H} & \ddot{\text{:O:}} \\ \text{H:\overset{..}{\underset{..}{C}}:\overset{..}{\underset{..}{C}}:\overset{..}{\underset{..}{O}}:H} \\ \text{H} & \end{array}$$

PROBLEM 4.5

Identify the positions of all double bonds in caffeine, a stimulant found in coffee and many soft drinks and as an additive in several over-the-counter drugs, such as aspirin.

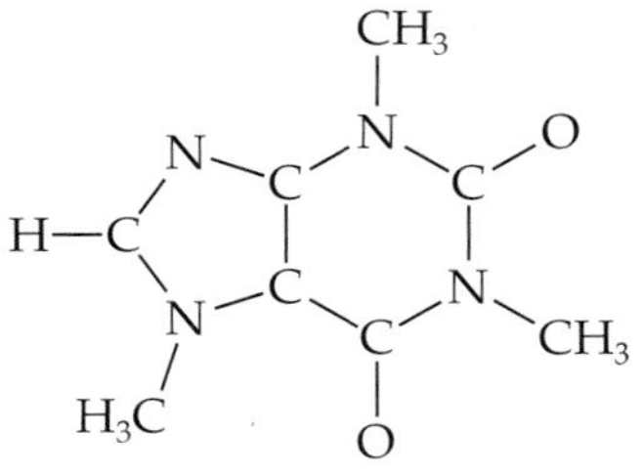

$$\begin{array}{c}
\text{CH}_3 \\
| \\
\text{N} \quad \text{N} \quad \text{O} \\
\text{H—C} \quad \text{C} \quad \text{C} \\
\text{N} \quad \text{C} \quad \text{N} \\
| \qquad \qquad \text{CH}_3 \\
\text{H}_3\text{C} \qquad \text{O}
\end{array}$$

4.4 Coordinate Covalent Bonds

Learning Objective:

- Identify coordinate covalent bonds in a molecule or polyatomic ion.

Coordinate covalent bond The covalent bond that forms when both electrons are donated by the same atom.

In the covalent bonds we have seen thus far, the shared electrons have come from different atoms. That is, the bonds result from the overlap of two singly occupied valence orbitals, one from each atom. Sometimes, though, a bond is formed by the overlap of a filled orbital on one atom with a vacant orbital on another atom so that both electrons come from the *same* atom. The bond that results in this case is called a **coordinate covalent bond.**

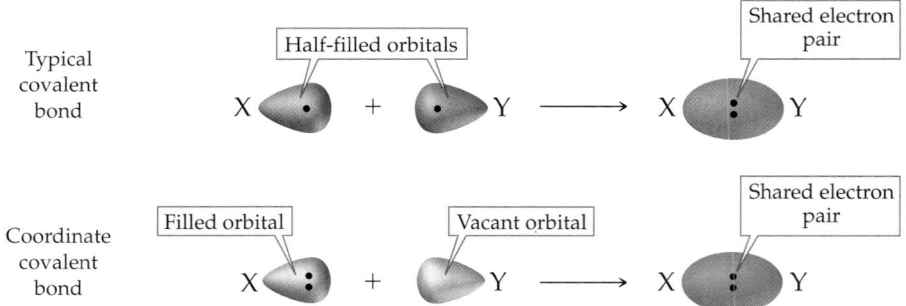

The ammonium ion, $NH_4{}^+$, is an example of a species with a coordinate covalent bond. When ammonia (NH_3) reacts in water solution with a hydrogen ion, H^+, the nitrogen atom donates two electrons from a filled valence orbital to form a coordinate covalent bond to the hydrogen ion which, due to the loss of its electron, has a vacant $1s$ orbital.

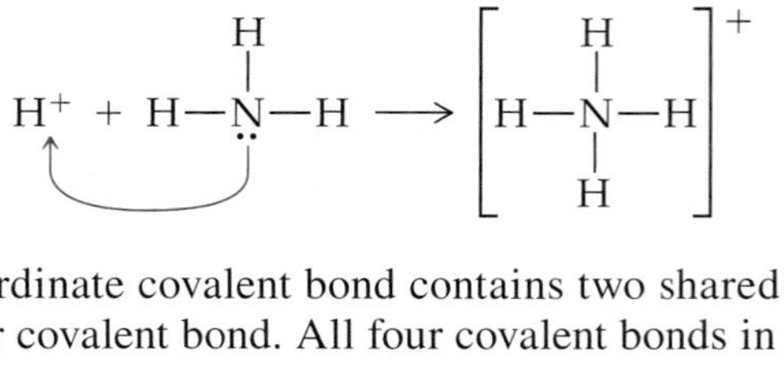

$$\text{H}^+ + \text{H—}\overset{\text{H}}{\underset{..}{\text{N}}}\text{—H} \longrightarrow \left[\text{H—}\overset{\text{H}}{\underset{\text{H}}{\text{N}}}\text{—H} \right]^+$$

Once formed, a coordinate covalent bond contains two shared electrons and is no different from any other covalent bond. All four covalent bonds in $NH_4{}^+$ are identical.

Note, however, that formation of a coordinate covalent bond often results in unusual bonding patterns, such as an N atom with four covalent bonds rather than the usual three, or an oxygen atom with three bonds rather than the usual two (H_3O^+). An entire class of substances is based on the ability of transition metals to form coordinate covalent bonds with nonmetals. Called *coordination compounds,* many of these substances have important roles in living organisms. For example, toxic metals can be removed from the bloodstream by the formation of water-soluble coordination compounds.

We will see in Chapter 19 that essential metal ions are held in enzyme molecules by coordinate covalent bonds.

Worked Example 4.6 Coordinate Covalent Bonds

Boron typically only forms three covalent bonds but can achieve a complete octet by forming coordinate covalent bonds. Illustrate the formation of BF_4^- by the reaction between BF_3 and F^-.

ANALYSIS A coordinate covalent bond is formed when a pair of electrons from one atom occupies an empty orbital on another atom.

SOLUTION
The reaction between BF_3 and F^- can be represented as follows:

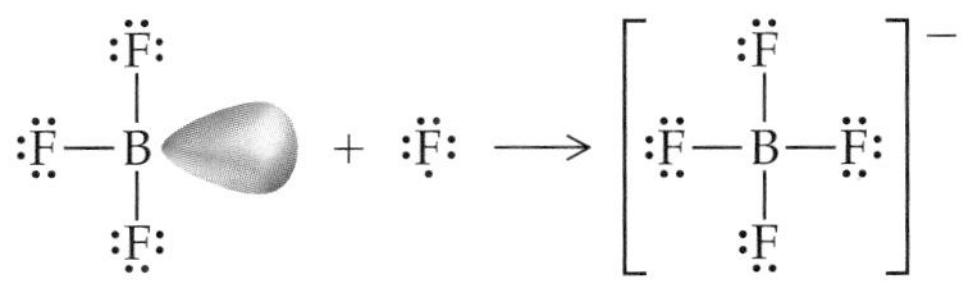

In this molecule, a coordinate covalent bond is formed when a pair of electrons from a filled valence orbital on the F^- ion occupies an empty valence orbital on the B atom in BF_3. As a result, the B atom now has four covalent bonds, three of which we would expect based on Figure 4.3.

PROBLEM 4.6

The BF_3 molecule can also react with NH_3 by formation of a coordinate covalent bond. Show the reaction and identify the coordinate covalent bond that is formed.

4.5 Characteristics of Molecular Compounds

Learning Objective:

• Distinguish structures, compositions, and properties of molecular compounds from those of ionic compounds.

We saw in Section 3.10 that ionic compounds have high melting and boiling points because the attractive forces between oppositely charged ions are so strong that the ions are held tightly together. But molecules are neutral, so there is no strong electrostatic attraction between molecules. There are, however, several weaker forces between molecules, called *intermolecular forces,* which we will look at in more detail in Chapter 8.

When intermolecular forces are very weak, molecules of a substance are so weakly attracted to one another that the substance is a gas at ordinary temperatures. If the forces are somewhat stronger, the molecules are pulled together into a liquid; and if the forces are still stronger, the substance becomes a molecular solid. Even so, the melting points and boiling points of molecular solids are usually lower than those of ionic solids because the intermolecular forces between molecules are weaker than the electrostatic attractive forces between ions.

In addition to having lower melting points and boiling points, molecular compounds differ from ionic compounds in other ways as well. Most molecular compounds are insoluble in water, for instance, because they have little attraction to the strongly polar water molecules. In addition, they do not conduct electricity when melted because they have no charged particles. Table 4.1 provides a comparison of the properties of ionic and molecular compounds.

Table 4.1 A Comparison of Ionic and Molecular Compounds

Ionic Compounds	Molecular Compounds
Smallest components are ions (eg., Na^+, Cl^-)	Smallest components are molecules (e.g., CO_2, H_2O)
Usually composed of metals combined with nonmetals	Usually composed of nonmetals combined with nonmetals
Crystalline solids	Gases, liquids, or low-melting-point solids
High melting points (e.g., NaCl = 801 °C)	Low melting points (H_2O = 0.0 °C)
High boiling points (above 700 °C) (e.g., NaCl = 1413 °C)	Low boiling points (e.g., H_2O = 100 °C; CH_3CH_2OH = 76 °C)
Conduct electricity when molten or dissolved in water	Do not conduct electricity
Many are water soluble	Relatively few are water soluble
Not soluble in organic liquids	Many are soluble in organic liquids

PROBLEM 4.7

Aluminum chloride ($AlCl_3$) has a melting point of 190 °C, whereas aluminum oxide (Al_2O_3) has a melting point of 2070 °C. Explain why the melting points of the two compounds are so different.

4.6 Molecular Formulas and Lewis Structures

Learning Objective:

• Interpret molecular formulas and draw Lewis structures for molecules.

Formulas such as H_2O, NH_3, and CH_4, which show the numbers and kinds of atoms in one molecule of a compound, are called **molecular formulas.** Though important, molecular formulas are limited in their use because they do not provide information about how the atoms in a given molecule are connected.

Much more useful are **structural formulas,** which use lines to show how atoms are connected, and **Lewis structures,** which show both the connections among atoms and the placement of unshared valence electrons. In a water molecule, for instance, the oxygen atom shares two electron pairs in covalent bonds with two hydrogen atoms and has two other pairs of valence electrons that are not shared in bonds. Such unshared pairs of valence electrons are called lone pairs. In an ammonia molecule, three electron pairs are used in bonding, and there is one lone pair. In methane, all four electron pairs are bonding.

Molecular formula A formula that shows the numbers and kinds of atoms in one molecule of a compound.

Structural formula A molecular representation that shows the connections among atoms by using lines to represent covalent bonds.

Lewis structure A molecular representation that shows both the connections among atoms and the locations of lone-pair valence electrons.

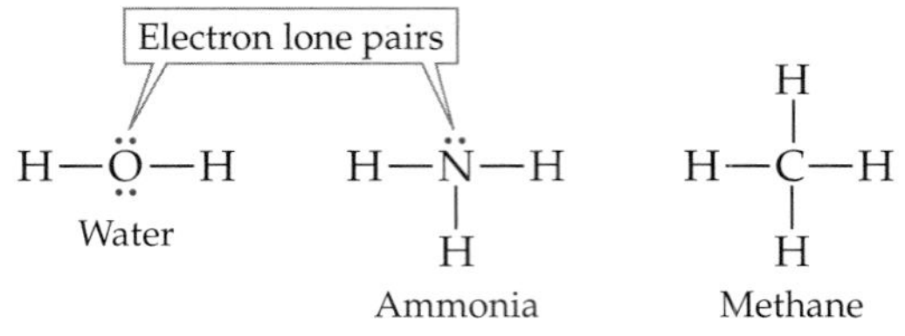

Note how a molecular formula differs from an ionic formula described previously in Section 3.9. A *molecular* formula gives the number of atoms that are combined in one molecule of a compound, whereas an *ionic* formula gives only a ratio of ions (Figure 4.4). The formula C_2H_4 for ethylene, for example, says that every ethylene molecule consists of two carbon atoms and four hydrogen atoms. The formula NaCl for sodium chloride, however, says only that there are equal numbers of Na$^+$ and Cl$^-$ ions in the crystal; the formula says nothing about how the ions interact with one another.

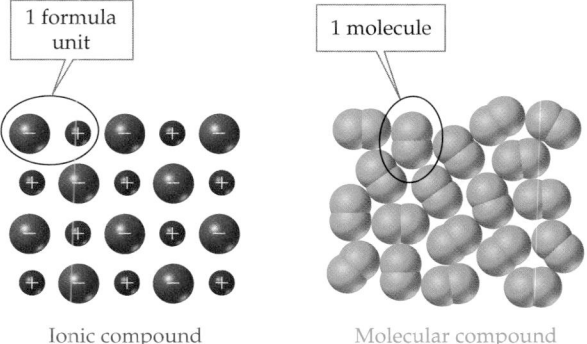

▲ **Figure 4.4**
The distinction between ionic and molecular compounds.
In ionic compounds, the smallest particle is an ion. In molecular compounds, the smallest particle is a molecule.

4.7 Drawing Lewis Structures

Learning Objective:

• Draw Lewis structures for molecules using their molecular formula and the octet rule.

To draw a Lewis structure, you first need to know the connections among atoms. Sometimes the connections are obvious. Water, for example, can only be H—O—H because only oxygen can be in the middle and form two covalent bonds. Other times, you will have to be told how the atoms are connected.

Two approaches are used for drawing Lewis structures once the connections are known. The first is particularly useful for organic molecules like those found in living organisms because the atoms follow common bonding patterns. The second approach is a more general, stepwise procedure that works for all molecules.

Lewis Structures for Molecules Containing C, N, O, X (Halogen), and H

As summarized in Figure 4.3, carbon, nitrogen, oxygen, halogen, and hydrogen atoms usually maintain consistent bonding patterns in order to achieve a valence-shell octet:

• C forms four covalent bonds and often bonds to other carbon atoms.
• N forms three covalent bonds and has one lone pair of electrons.
• O forms two covalent bonds and has two lone pairs of electrons.
• Halogens (X = F, Cl, Br, I) form one covalent bond and have three lone pairs of electrons.
• H forms one covalent bond.

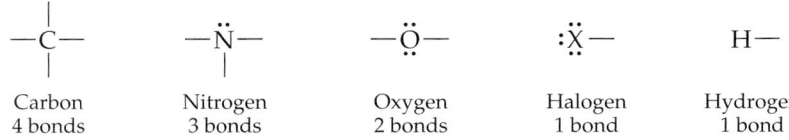

| Carbon 4 bonds | Nitrogen 3 bonds | Oxygen 2 bonds | Halogen 1 bond | Hydrogen 1 bond |

Relying on these common bonding patterns simplifies the writing of Lewis structures. In ethane (C_2H_6), a constituent of natural gas, for example, three of the four covalent bonds of each carbon atom are used in bonds to hydrogen, and the fourth is a carbon–carbon bond. There is no other arrangement in which all eight atoms can have their usual bonding patterns. In acetaldehyde (C_2H_4O), a substance used in manufacturing perfumes, dyes, and plastics, one carbon has three bonds to hydrogen, whereas the other has one bond to hydrogen and a double bond to oxygen.

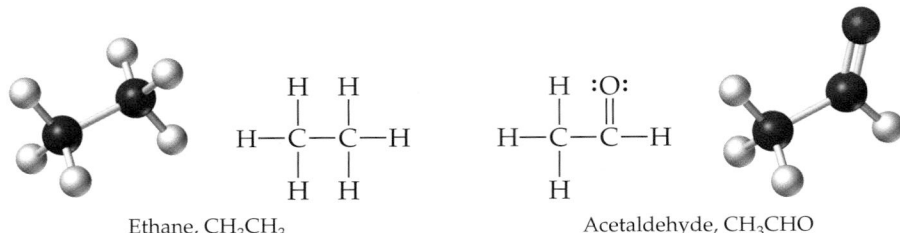

Ethane, CH_3CH_3 Acetaldehyde, CH_3CHO

Condensed structure A molecular representation in which bonds are not specifically shown but rather are understood by the order in which atoms are written.

▶▶ Condensed structures are used extensively to represent molecular structures in organic chemistry (Chapters 12–17).

Because Lewis structures are awkward for larger organic molecules, ethane is more frequently written as a **condensed structure** in which the bonds are not specifically shown. In its condensed form, ethane is CH_3CH_3, meaning that each carbon atom has three hydrogen atoms bonded to it (CH_3) and the two (CH_3) units are bonded to each other. In the same way, acetaldehyde can be written as CH_3CHO. Note that neither the lone-pair electrons nor the $C{=}O$ double bond in acetaldehyde is shown explicitly. You will get a lot more practice with such condensed structures in later chapters.

Many of the computer-generated pictures we will be using from now on will be *ball-and-stick models* rather than the space-filling models used previously. Space-filling models are more realistic, but ball-and-stick models do a better job of showing connections and molecular geometry. All models, regardless of type, use a consistent color such as that presented in Table 4.2

Table 4.2   Molecular Models Color Code

Element	Color	
H	White/ivory	⚪
C	Black	⚫
O	Red	⚫
N	Blue	⚫
S	Yellow	⚪
F	Light green	⚪
Cl	Dark green	⚪
Br	Brownish red	⚫
I	Purple	⚫

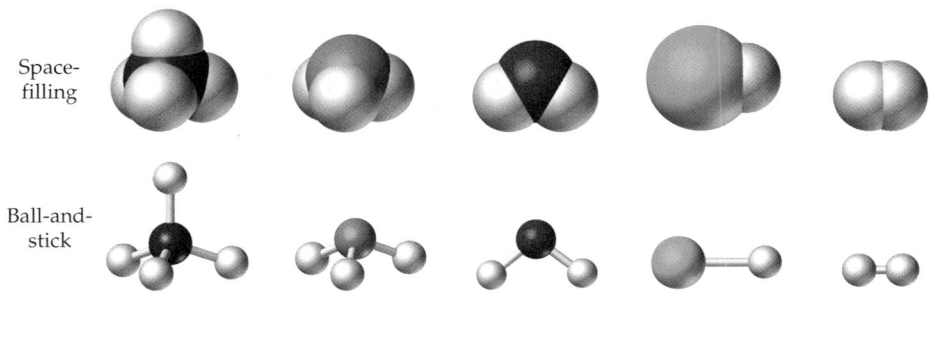

Space-filling

Ball-and-stick

A General Method for Drawing Lewis Structures

A Lewis structure can be drawn for any molecule or polyatomic ion by following a five-step procedure. Take PCl_3, for example, a substance in which three chlorine atoms surround the central phosphorus atom.

STEP 1: **Find the total number of valence electrons of all atoms in the molecule or ion.** In PCl_3, for example, phosphorus (group 5A) has five valence electrons and chlorine (group 7A) has seven valence electrons, giving a total of 26:

$$P + (3 \times Cl) = PCl_3$$
$$5e^- + (3 \times 7e^-) = 26e^-$$

For a polyatomic ion, add one electron for each negative charge or subtract one for each positive charge. In OH^-, the total is eight electrons (six from oxygen, one from hydrogen, plus one for the negative charge). In NH_4^+, the total is eight (five from nitrogen, one from each of four hydrogens, minus one for the positive charge).

STEP 2: **Draw a line between each pair of connected atoms to represent the two electrons in a covalent bond.** Remember that elements in the second row of the periodic table form the number of bonds discussed earlier in this section, whereas elements in the third row and beyond can use more than eight electrons and form more than the "usual" number of bonds (Figure 4.3). A particularly common pattern is that an atom in the third row (or beyond) occurs as the central atom in a cluster. In PCl$_3$, for example, the phosphorus atom is in the center with the three chlorine atoms bonded to it:

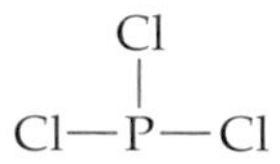

$$\text{Cl}$$
$$|$$
$$\text{Cl}—\text{P}—\text{Cl}$$

STEP 3: Using the remaining electrons, add lone pairs so that each atom connected to the central atom (except H) gets an octet. In PCl$_3$, six of the 26 valence electrons were used to make the covalent bonds. From the remaining 20 electrons, each Cl atom needs three lone pairs to complete the octet:

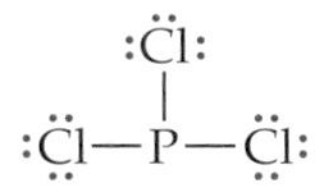

$$:\ddot{\text{Cl}}:$$
$$|$$
$$:\ddot{\text{Cl}}—\text{P}—\ddot{\text{Cl}}:$$

STEP 4: Place any remaining electrons in lone pairs on the central atom. In PCl$_3$, we have used 24 of the 26 available electrons—six in three single bonds and 18 in the three lone pairs on each chlorine atom. This leaves two electrons for one lone pair on phosphorus:

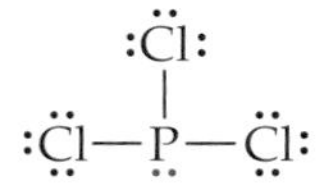

$$:\ddot{\text{Cl}}:$$
$$|$$
$$:\ddot{\text{Cl}}—\ddot{\text{P}}—\ddot{\text{Cl}}:$$

STEP 5: If the central atom does not yet have an octet after all electrons have been assigned, take a lone pair from a neighboring atom and form a multiple bond to the central atom. In PCl$_3$, each atom has an octet, all 26 available electrons have been used, and the Lewis structure is finished.

Worked Examples 4.7–4.9 show how to deal with cases where this fifth step is needed.

Worked Example 4.7 Multiple Bonds: Electron Dots and Valence Electrons

Draw a Lewis structure for the toxic gas hydrogen cyanide, HCN. The atoms are connected in the order shown in the preceding sentence.

ANALYSIS Follow the procedure outlined in the text.

SOLUTION

STEP 1: Find the total number of valence electrons.

$$H = 1, C = 4, N = 5 \text{ Total number of valence electrons} = 10$$

STEP 2: Draw a line between each pair of connected atoms to represent bonding electron pairs.

$$H—C—N \text{ 2 bonds} = 4 \text{ electrons, 6 electrons remaining}$$

STEP 3: Add lone pairs so that each atom (except H) has a complete octet.

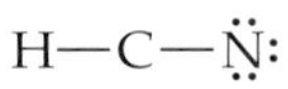

$$H—C—\ddot{\text{N}}:$$

STEP 4: All valence electrons have been used, and so Step 4 is not needed. H and N have filled valence shells but C does not.

STEP 5: If the central atom (C in this case) does not yet have an octet, use lone pairs from a neighboring atom (N) to form multiple bonds. This results in a triple bond between the C and N atoms, as shown in the following electron-dot and ball-and-stick representations:

$$H—C≡N:$$

We can check the structure by noting that all 10 valence electrons have been used (in four covalent bonds and one lone pair) and that each atom has the expected number of bonds (one bond for H, three for N, and four for C).

Worked Example 4.8 Lewis Structures: Location of Multiple Bonds

Draw a Lewis structure for vinyl chloride, C_2H_3Cl, a substance used in making polyvinyl chloride, or PVC, plastic.

ANALYSIS Since H and Cl form only one bond each, the carbon atoms must be bonded to each other, with the remaining atoms bonded to the carbons. With only four atoms available to bond with them, the carbon atoms cannot have four covalent bonds each unless they are joined by a double bond.

SOLUTION

STEP 1: The total number of valence electrons is 18, four from each of the two C atoms, one from each of the three H atoms, and seven from the Cl atom.

STEP 2: Place the two C atoms in the center and divide the four other atoms between them. The five bonds account for 10 valence electrons with eight remaining.

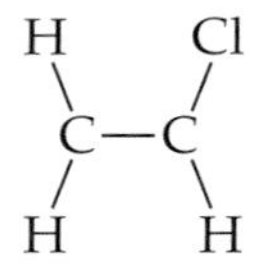

STEP 3: Place six of the remaining valence electrons around the Cl atom so that it has a complete octet and place the remaining two valence electrons on one of the C atoms (either C, it does not matter).

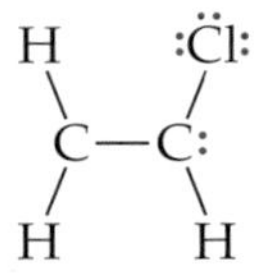

When all the valence electrons are distributed, the C atoms still do not have a complete octet; they each need four bonds but have only three.

STEP 5: The lone pair of electrons on the C atom can be used to form a double bond between the C atoms, giving each a total of four bonds (eight electrons). Placement of the double bond yields the Lewis structure and ball-and-stick model for vinyl chloride shown next.

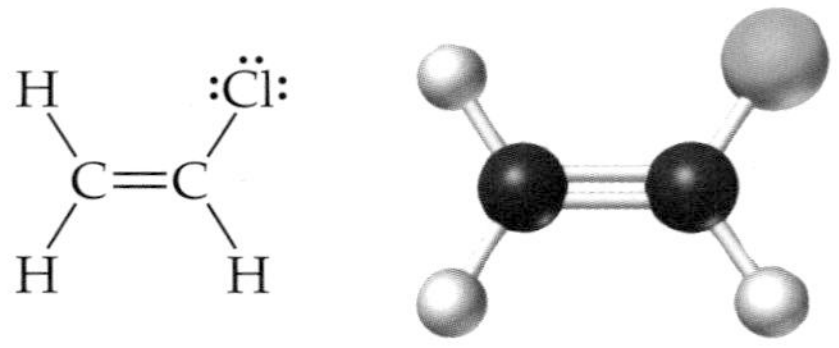

All 18 valence electrons are accounted for in six covalent bonds and three lone pairs, and each atom has the expected number of bonds.

Worked Example 4.9 Lewis Structures: Octet Rule and Multiple Bonds

Draw a Lewis structure for sulfur dioxide, SO_2. The connections are O—S—O.

ANALYSIS Follow the procedure outlined in the text.

SOLUTION

STEP 1: The total number of valence electrons is 18, six from each atom.

$$S + (2 \times O) = SO_2$$
$$6e^- + (2 + 6e^-) = 18e^-$$

STEP 2: O—S—O Two covalent bonds use four valence electrons.

STEP 3: :Ö—S—Ö: Adding three lone pairs to each oxygen atom to give each an octet uses 12 additional valence electrons.

STEP 4: $:\overset{..}{O}-S-\overset{..}{O}:$ The remaining two valence electrons are placed on sulfur, but sulfur still does not have an octet.

STEP 5: Moving one lone pair from a neighboring oxygen to form a double bond with the central sulfur gives sulfur an octet. It does not matter on which side the S=O bond is written.

$$:\overset{..}{O}-\underset{..}{S}=\overset{..}{O}:$$

NOTE: The Lewis structure for SO_2 includes a single bond to one O and a double bond to the other O. It doesn't matter which O has the double bond—both structures are equally acceptable. In reality, however, the S—O bonds in this molecule are actually closer to 1.5, an average between the two possible structures we could draw. This is an example of resonance structures or different Lewis structures that could be used to represent the same molecule.

PROBLEM 4.8

Methylamine, CH_5N, is responsible for the characteristic odor of decaying fish. Draw a Lewis structure of methylamine.

PROBLEM 4.9

Add lone pairs where appropriate to the following structures:

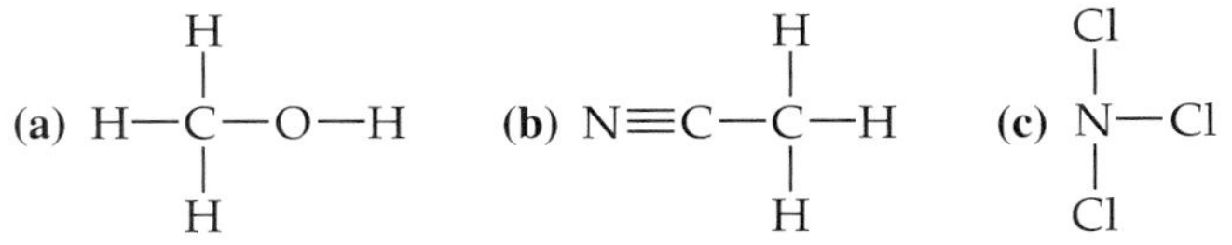

(a) H—C—O—H with H above and H below the C

(b) N≡C—C—H with H above and H below the second C

(c) N—Cl with Cl above and Cl below the N

> Because resonance structures don't always represent the true nature of the covalent bonds in compounds, chemists sometimes use different methods to represent bonding in molecules with resonance structures. Aromatic compounds, a class of organic compounds discussed in Section 13.8, are an important example of resonance structures in which the bonding patterns are represented using a "ring" of electrons rather than double bonds.

PROBLEM 4.10

Draw Lewis structures for the following:

(a) Phosgene, $COCl_2$, a poisonous gas

(b) Hypochlorite ion, OCl^-, present in many swimming pool chemicals

(c) Hydrogen peroxide, H_2O_2

(d) Sulfur dichloride, SCl_2

PROBLEM 4.11

Draw a Lewis structure for nitric acid, HNO_3. The nitrogen atom is in the center, and the hydrogen atom is bonded to an oxygen atom.

⚙ KEY CONCEPT PROBLEM 4.12 ─────────────────────────

The molecular model shown here is a representation of methyl methacrylate, a starting material used to prepare Lucite plastic. Only the connections between atoms are shown; multiple bonds are not indicated.

(a) What is the molecular formula of methyl methacrylate?

(b) Using the octet rule and bonding patterns from Figure 4.3 indicate the likely positions of the multiple bonds and lone pairs in methyl methacrylate.

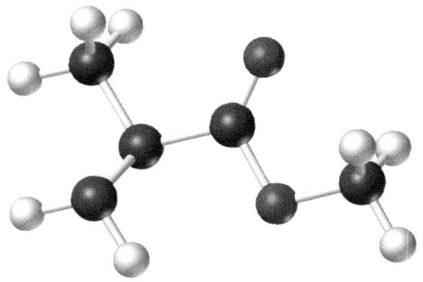

CHEMISTRY IN ACTION

✝ CO and NO: Pollutants or Miracle Molecules?

Carbon monoxide (CO) is a killer; everyone knows that. It is to blame for an estimated 3500 accidental deaths and suicides each year in the United States and is the number one cause of all deaths by poisoning. Nitric oxide (NO) is formed in combustion engines and reacts with oxygen to form nitrogen dioxide (NO_2), the reddish-brown gas associated with urban smog. What most people do not know, however, is that our bodies cannot function without these molecules. A startling discovery made in 1992 showed that CO and NO are key chemical messengers in the body, used by cells to regulate critical metabolic processes.

The toxicity of CO in moderate concentration is due to its ability to bind to hemoglobin molecules in the blood, thereby preventing the hemoglobin from carrying oxygen to tissues. The high reactivity of NO leads to the formation of compounds that are toxic irritants. However, low concentrations of CO and NO are produced in cells throughout the body. Both CO and NO are highly soluble in water and can diffuse from one cell to another, where they stimulate production of a substance called *guanylyl cyclase*. Guanylyl cyclase, in turn, controls the production of another substance called *cyclic guanosine monophosphate*, which regulates many cellular functions.

Levels of CO production are particularly high in certain regions of the brain, including those associated with long-term memory. Evidence from experiments with rat brains suggests that a special kind of cell in the brain's hippocampus is signaled by transfer of a molecular messenger from a neighboring cell. The receiving cell responds back to the signaling cell by releasing CO, which causes still more messenger molecules to be sent. After several rounds of this back-and-forth communication, the receiving cell undergoes some sort of change that becomes a memory. When CO production is blocked, possibly in response to a medical condition or exposure to certain toxic metals, long-term memories are no longer stored, and those memories that previously existed are erased. When CO production is stimulated, however, memories are again laid down.

NO controls a seemingly limitless range of functions in the body. The immune system uses NO to fight infections and tumors. It is also used to transmit messages between nerve cells

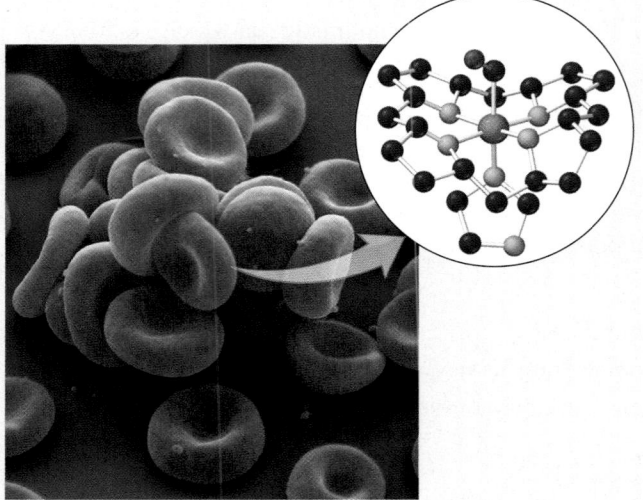

▲ Carbon monoxide (CO) in the air can be toxic because it can bind to hemoglobin and interfere with oxygen transport. But CO also plays an important role in many cellular functions, including signal transmission.

and is associated with the processes involved in learning and memory, sleeping, and depression. Its most advertised role, however, is as a *vasodilator,* a substance that allows blood vessels to relax and dilate. This discovery led to the development of a new class of drugs that stimulate production of enzymes called nitric oxide synthases (NOSs). These drugs can be used to treat conditions from erectile dysfunction (Viagra) to hypertension. Given the importance of NO in the fields of neuroscience, physiology, and immunology, it is not surprising that it was named "Molecule of the Year" in 1992.

CIA Problem 4.1 The CO molecule is highly reactive and will bind to the Fe^{2+} ion in hemoglobin and interfere with O_2 transport. What type of bond is formed between the CO molecule and the Fe^{2+} ion?

CIA Problem 4.2 Draw the Lewis dot structures for the molecules CO and NO. What is different about these structures compared with the general examples we have seen so far? How could these Lewis structures provide insight into the high chemical reactivity of these molecules?

PROBLEM 4.13

Molecular oxygen (O_2) is relatively stable, whereas ozone (O_3) is a very reactive compound. Draw a Lewis dot structure for ozone. Based on this structure and the bonding patterns in Figure 4.3, explain why ozone is so reactive.

4.8 The Shapes of Molecules

Learning Objective:

• Use Lewis structures to predict molecular geometry.

Look again at the computer-generated drawings of molecules introduced in the preceding section and compiled in Figure 4.5, and you will find that the molecules are shown with specific shapes. Acetylene is *linear,* water is *bent,* ammonia is *pyramid-shaped,* methane is *tetrahedral,* and ethylene chloride is flat, or *planar.* What determines such shapes? Why, for example, are the three atoms in water connected at an angle of 104.5° rather than in a straight line? Like so many other properties, molecular shapes are related to the numbers and locations of the valence electrons around atoms.

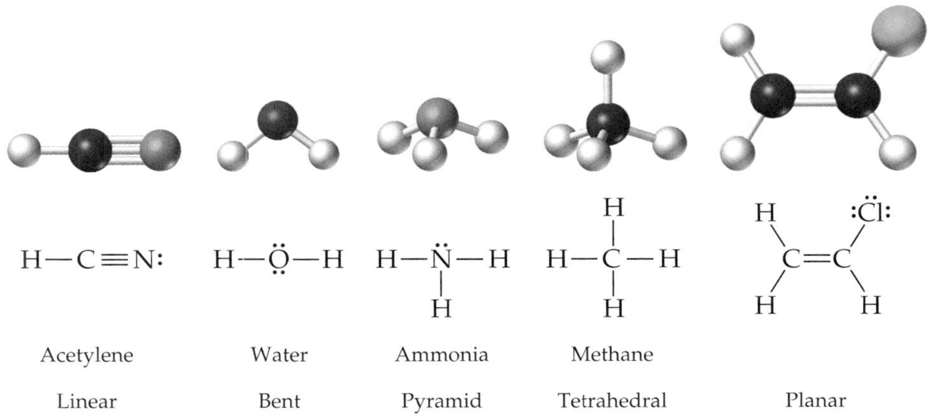

◄ **Figure 4.5**
Examples of the molecular geometries for molecules with two, three, and four valence electron charge clouds.

H—C≡N: H—Ö—H   H—N̈—H   H—C—H

| Acetylene | Water | Ammonia | Methane | |
| Linear | Bent | Pyramid | Tetrahedral | Planar |

Molecular shapes can be predicted by noting how many bonds and electron pairs surround individual atoms and applying what is called the **valence-shell electron-pair repulsion (VSEPR) model.** The basic idea of the VSEPR model is that the constantly moving valence electrons in bonds and lone pairs make up negatively charged clouds of electrons, which electrically repel one another. The clouds therefore tend to keep as far apart as possible, causing molecules to assume specific shapes. There are three steps to applying the VSEPR model:

Valence-shell electron-pair repulsion (VSEPR) model A method for predicting molecular shape by noting how many electron charge clouds surround atoms and assuming that the clouds orient as far away from one another as possible.

STEP 1: **Draw a Lewis structure of the molecule, and identify the atom whose geometry is of interest.** In a simple molecule like PCl_3 or CO_2, this is usually the central atom because it will determine the molecular geometry. In more complex molecules, the geometry around specific atoms will vary depending on the dot structure.

STEP 2: **Count the number of electron charge clouds surrounding the atom of interest.** The number of charge clouds is simply the total number of lone pairs plus connections to other atoms. It does not matter whether a connection is a single bond or a multiple bond because we are interested only in the *number* of charge clouds, not in how many electrons each cloud contains. The carbon atom in carbon dioxide, for instance, has two double bonds to oxygen (O=C=O), and thus has two charge clouds.

STEP 3: **Predict molecular shape by assuming that the charge clouds orient in space so that they are as far away from one another as possible.** How they achieve this favorable orientation depends on how many bonds and lone pairs there are, as summarized in Table 4.3.

If there are only two charge clouds, as occurs on the central atom of CO_2 (two double bonds) and HCN (one single bond and one triple bond), the clouds are farthest apart when they point in opposite directions. Thus, both HCN and CO_2 are linear molecules, with **bond angles** of 180°.

Bond angle The angle formed by three adjacent atoms in a molecule.

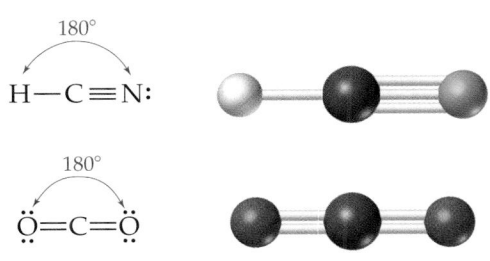

These molecules, with two bonding e⁻ clouds, are **linear,** with bond angles of 180°.

180°
H—C≡N:

180°
Ö=C=Ö

Table 4.3 Molecular Geometry Around Atoms with 2, 3, and 4 Charge Clouds

Number of Bonds	Number of Lone Pairs	Total Number of Charge Clouds	Molecular Geometry		Example
2	0	2		Linear	$O\!=\!C\!=\!O$
3	0	3		Trigonal planar	$\overset{H}{\underset{H}{}}C\!=\!O$
2	1			Bent	$\overset{O}{\underset{O}{}}S$
4	0	4		Tetrahedral	$H\!-\!\overset{\overset{H}{\vert}}{\underset{\underset{H}{\vert}}{C}}\!-\!H$
3	1			Pyramidal	$H\!-\!\overset{..}{\underset{\underset{H}{\vert}}{N}}\!-\!H$
2	2			Bent	$H\!-\!\overset{..}{\underset{H}{O}}$

When there are three charge clouds, as occurs on the central atom in formaldehyde (two single bonds and one double bond) and SO_2 (one single bond, one double bond, and one lone pair), the clouds will be farthest apart if they lie in a plane and point to the corners of an equilateral triangle. Thus, a formaldehyde molecule is trigonal planar, with all bond angles near 120°. Similarly, an SO_2 molecule has a trigonal planar arrangement of its three electron clouds, but one point of the triangle is occupied by a lone pair. As a result, the connection between the three atoms is therefore bent rather than linear as in CO_2, with an $O\!-\!S\!-\!O$ bond angle of approximately 120°.

A formaldehyde molecule, with three bonding e⁻ clouds, is **trigonal planar** with bond angles of roughly 120°.

An SO_2 molecule, with two bonding e⁻ clouds and one nonbonding lone pair, is **bent** with a bond angle of roughly 120°.

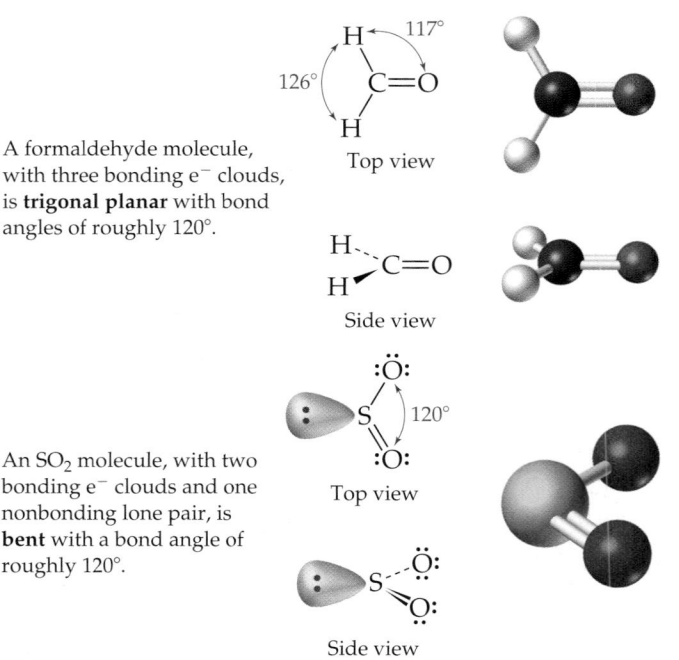

Top view

Side view

Top view

Side view

Note how the three-dimensional shapes of molecules like formaldehyde and SO_2 are shown. Solid lines are assumed to be in the plane of the paper, a dashed line recedes behind the plane of the paper away from the viewer, and a dark wedged line protrudes out of the paper toward the viewer. This standard method for showing three-dimensionality will be used throughout the rest of the book.

When there are four charge clouds, as occurs on the central atom in CH_4 (four single bonds), NH_3 (three single bonds and one lone pair), and H_2O (two single bonds and two lone pairs), the clouds can be farthest apart when they extend to the corners of a *regular tetrahedron*. As illustrated in Figure 4.6, a **regular tetrahedron** is a geometric solid whose four identical faces are equilateral triangles. The central atom is at the center of the tetrahedron, the charge clouds point to the corners, and the angle between lines drawn from the center to any two corners is 109.5°.

Regular tetrahedron A geometric figure with four identical triangular faces.

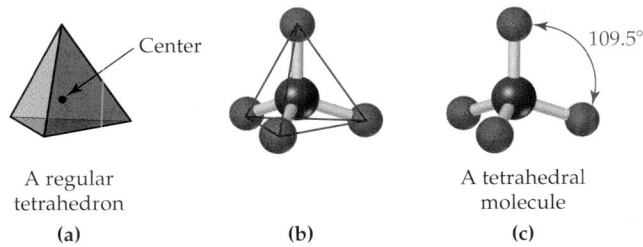

A regular		A tetrahedral
tetrahedron		molecule
(a)	(b)	(c)

▲ **Figure 4.6**
The tetrahedral geometry of an atom surrounded by four charge clouds.
The atom is located at the center of the regular tetrahedron, and the four charge clouds point toward the corners. The bond angle between the center and any two corners is 109.5°.

Because valence-shell electron octets are so common, a great many molecules have geometries based on the tetrahedron. In methane (CH_4), for example, the carbon atom has tetrahedral geometry with H—C—H bond angles of exactly 109.5°. In ammonia (NH_3), the nitrogen atom has a tetrahedral arrangement of its four charge clouds, but one corner of the tetrahedron is occupied by a lone pair, resulting in an overall pyramidal shape for the molecule. Similarly, water, which has two corners of the tetrahedron occupied by lone pairs, has an overall bent shape.

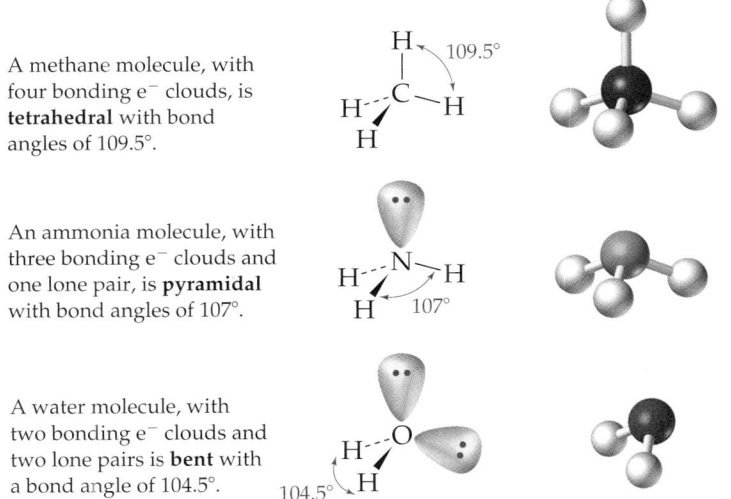

A methane molecule, with four bonding e⁻ clouds, is **tetrahedral** with bond angles of 109.5°.

An ammonia molecule, with three bonding e⁻ clouds and one lone pair, is **pyramidal** with bond angles of 107°.

A water molecule, with two bonding e⁻ clouds and two lone pairs is **bent** with a bond angle of 104.5°.

Note that the H—N—H bond angle in ammonia (107°) and the H—O—H bond angle in water (104.5°) are close to, but not exactly equal to, the ideal 109.5° tetrahedral value. The angles are diminished somewhat from their ideal value because the lone-pair charge clouds repel other electron clouds strongly and compress the rest of the molecule.

The geometry around atoms in larger molecules also derives from the shapes shown in Table 4.3. For example, each of the two carbon atoms in ethylene ($H_2C{=}CH_2$) has three charge clouds, giving rise to trigonal planar geometry. It turns out that the molecule as a whole is also planar, with H—C—C and H—C—H bond angles of approximately 120°.

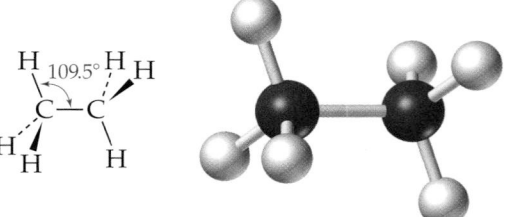

The ethylene molecule (three bonding e⁻ clouds on each carbon atom), is **planar,** with bond angles of 120°.

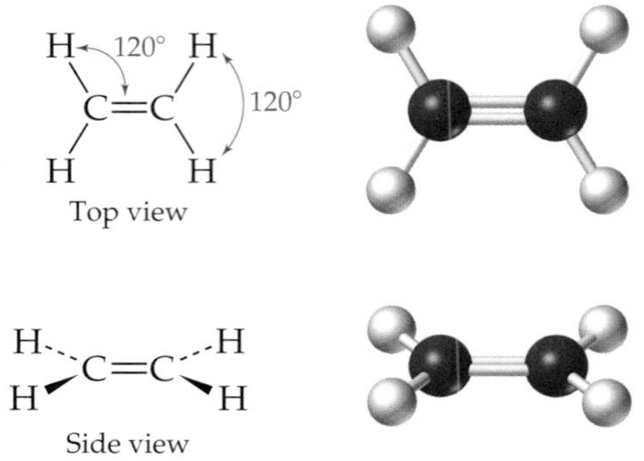

Top view

Side view

Carbon atoms bonded to four other atoms are each at the center of a tetrahedron, as shown here for ethane, H_3C—CH_3.

The ethane molecule (4 bonding e⁻ clouds) has **tetrahedral** carbon atoms, with bond angles of 109.5°.

Worked Example 4.10 Lewis Structures: Molecular Shape

What shape would you expect for the hydronium ion, H_3O^+?

ANALYSIS Draw the Lewis structure for the molecular ion, and count the number of charge clouds around the central oxygen atom; imagine the clouds orienting as far away from one another as possible.

SOLUTION
The Lewis structure for the hydronium ion shows that the oxygen atom has four charge clouds (three single bonds and one lone pair). The hydronium ion is therefore pyramidal with bond angles of approximately 109.5°.

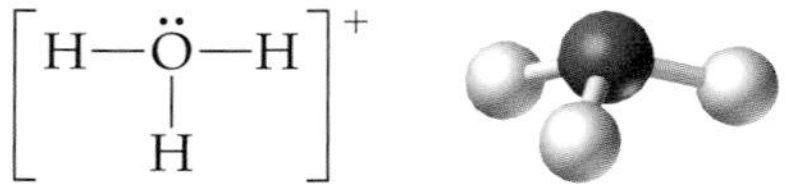

$$\left[H - \ddot{O} - H \atop H \right]^+$$

Worked Example 4.11 Lewis Structures: Charge Cloud Geometry

Predict the geometry around each of the carbon atoms in an acetaldehyde molecule, CH_3CHO.

ANALYSIS Draw the Lewis structure and identify the number of charge clouds around each of the central carbon atoms.

SOLUTION
The Lewis structure of acetaldehyde shows that the CH_3 carbon has four charge clouds (four single bonds) and the CHO carbon atom has three charge clouds (two single bonds, one double bond). Table 4.3 indicates that the CH_3 carbon is tetrahedral, but the CHO carbon is trigonal planar.

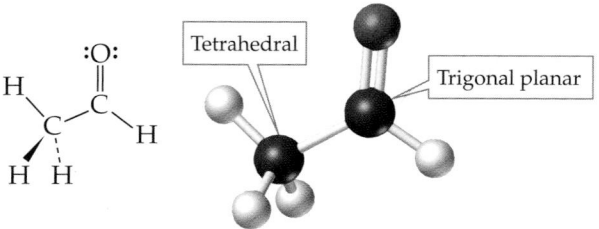

Tetrahedral

Trigonal planar

CHEMISTRY IN ACTION

⚕ VERY Big Molecules

How big can a molecule be? The answer is very, very big. The really big molecules in our bodies and in many items we buy are all polymers. Like a string of beads, a polymer is formed of many repeating units connected in a long chain. Each "bead" in the chain comes from a simple molecule that has formed chemical bonds at both ends, linking it to other molecules. The repeating units can be the same:

$$-a-a-a-a-a-a-a-a-a-a-a-a-a-$$

or they can be different. If different, they can be connected in an ordered pattern:

$$-a-b-a-b-a-b-a-b-a-b-a-b-$$

or in a random pattern:

$$-a-b-b-a-b-a-a-a-b-a-b-b-$$

Furthermore, the polymer chains can have branches, and the branches can have either the same repeating unit as the main chain or a different one:

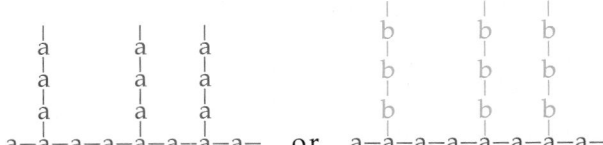

Still other possible variations include complex, three-dimensional networks of "cross-linked" chains. The rubber used in tires, for example, contains polymer chains connected by cross-linking atoms of sulfur to impart greater rigidity.

We all use synthetic polymers every day—we usually call them "plastics." Common synthetic polymers are made by connecting up to several hundred thousand smaller molecules together, producing giant polymer molecules with masses up to several million atomic mass units. Polyethylene, for example, is made by combining as many as 50,000 ethylene molecules to give a polymer with repeating units.

$$\text{Many } H_2C = CH_2 \longrightarrow -CH_2CH_2CH_2CH_2CH_2CH_2-$$
Ethylene   Polyethelene

The product is used in such items as chairs, toys, drain pipes, milk bottles, and packaging films. Other examples of polymers include the nylon used in clothing and pantyhose, molded hardware (nuts and bolts), and the Kevlar used in bulletproof vests.

Nature began to exploit the extraordinary variety of polymer properties long before humans did. In fact, despite great progress in recent years, there is still much to be learned about the polymers in living things. Carbohydrates and proteins are polymers, as are the giant molecules of deoxyribonucleic acid

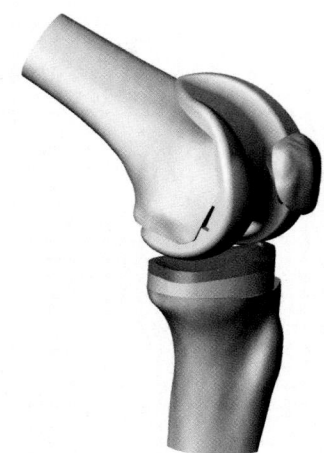

▲ The ultrahigh molecular weight polyethylene (UHMWPE) used as a lubricating interface in this artificial knee is made from the same basic polymer used for milk jugs and plastic shopping bags.

(DNA) that govern many cellular processes, including reproduction, in all organisms. Nature's polymer molecules, though, are more complex than any that chemists have yet created.

Polymers also find diverse applications in the fields of health and medicine, depending on their chemical and physical properties. Some polymers are absorbed or broken down by the body (i.e. are biodegradable) and are used as sutures or adhesives, for support of internal organs or tissue, or for controlled delivery of drugs. Other polymers are stable or inert and can retain their integrity for years. For example, Teflon and ultrahigh molecular weight polyethylene (UHMWPE) are highly durable low-friction polymer coatings used as lubricating interfaces in artificial joints.

▶▶ Carbohydrates are polymers composed of sugar molecules linked together in long chains (Chapter 20), whereas proteins are polymers of smaller molecules called amino acids (Chapter 18). DNA is a polymer of repeating nucleotide subunits, which is discussed in Chapter 26.

CIA Problem 4.3 Find the structure of Teflon (polytetrafluoroethylene). How is it similar to the structure of polyethylene, and how is it different?

CIA Problem 4.4 Polycarbonate, also known as plexiglass, has the basic repeating unit shown in the following figure. What is the geometry of the electron clouds for the carbon atoms labeled "a" and "b" in this structure?

PROBLEM 4.14

Boron typically only forms three covalent bonds because it only has three valence electrons but can form coordinate covalent bonds. Draw the Lewis structure for BF_4^- and predict the molecular shape of the ion.

PROBLEM 4.15

Predict shapes for the organic molecules chloroform, $CHCl_3$, and 1,1-dichloroethylene, $Cl_2C{=}CH_2$.

PROBLEM 4.16

Selenium and sulfur are in the same chemical family as oxygen. Hydrogen selenide (H_2Se) and hydrogen sulfide (H_2S) are both toxic gases having terrible odors. Draw Lewis structures and identify the shape of these compounds.

⊙☰ KEY CONCEPT PROBLEM 4.17 _____

Draw a structure corresponding to the molecular model of the amino acid methionine shown here, and describe the geometry around the indicated atoms. Refer to the color key in Table 4.2.

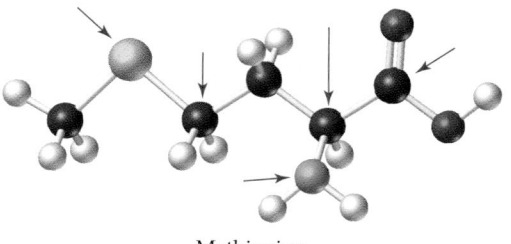

Methionine

4.9 Polar Covalent Bonds and Electronegativity

Learning Objective:

• Distinguish between polar covalent, nonpolar covalent, and ionic bonds using electronegativity.

Electrons in a covalent bond occupy the region between the bonded atoms. If the atoms are identical, as in H_2 and Cl_2, the electrons are attracted equally to both atoms and are shared equally. If the atoms are *not* identical, however, as in HCl, the bonding electrons are attracted more strongly by one atom than by the other and are shared unequally. Such bonds are said to be **polar covalent bonds.** In hydrogen chloride, for example, electrons spend more time near the chlorine atom than near the hydrogen atom. Although the molecule as a whole is neutral, the chlorine is more negative than the hydrogen, resulting in *partial* charges on the atoms. These partial charges are represented by placing a $\delta-$ (Greek lowercase *delta*) on the more negative atom and a $\delta+$ on the more positive atom.

A particularly helpful way of visualizing this unequal distribution of bonding electrons is to look at what is called an *electrostatic potential map,* which uses color to portray the calculated electron distribution in a molecule. In HCl, for example, the electron-poor hydrogen is blue and the electron-rich chlorine is reddish-yellow.

Polar covalent bond A bond in which the electrons are attracted more strongly by one atom than by the other.

| This end of the molecule is electron-poor and has a partial positive charge ($\delta+$). | This end of the molecule is electron-rich and has a partial negative charge ($\delta-$). |

$$\overset{\delta+}{H}{-}\overset{\delta-}{Cl}$$

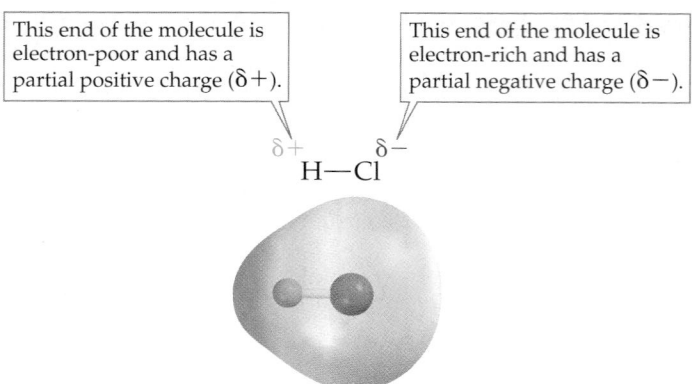

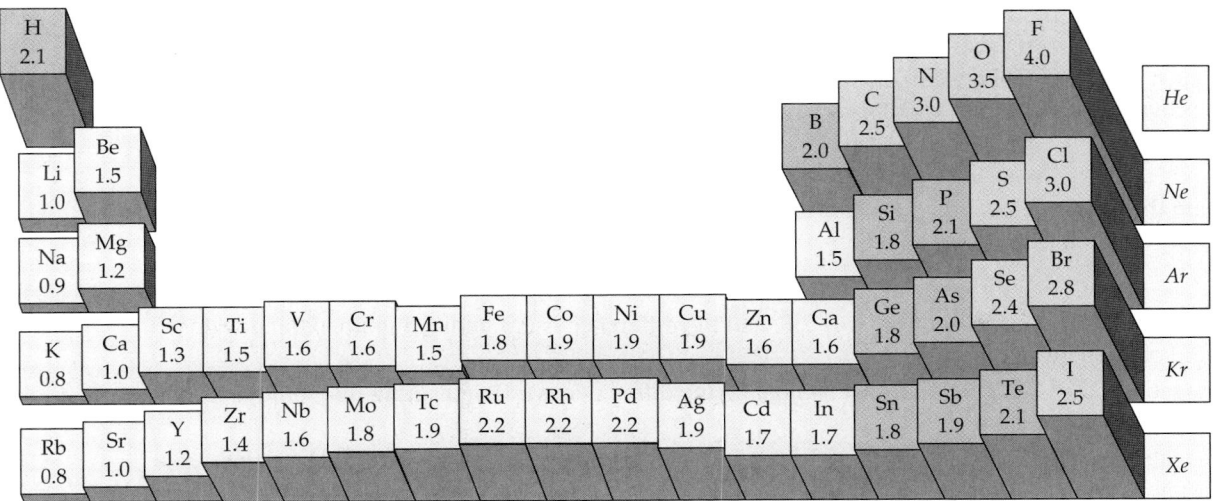

▲ **Figure 4.7**
Electronegativities of several main group and transition metal elements.
Reactive nonmetals at the top right of the periodic table are the most electronegative, and metals at the lower left are the least electronegative. The noble gases are not assigned values.

The ability of an atom to attract electrons in a covalent bond is called the atom's **electronegativity.** Fluorine, the most electronegative element, is assigned a value of four, and less electronegative atoms are assigned lower values, as shown in Figure 4.7. Metallic elements on the left side of the periodic table attract electrons only weakly and have lower electronegativities, whereas the halogens and other reactive nonmetal elements on the upper right side of the table attract electrons strongly and have higher electronegativities. Note in Figure 4.7 that electronegativity generally decreases going down the periodic table within a group.

Comparing the electronegativities of bonded atoms makes it possible to compare the polarities of bonds and to predict the occurrence of ionic bonding. Both oxygen (electronegativity 3.5) and nitrogen (3.0), for instance, are more electronegative than carbon (2.5). As a result, both C—O and C—N bonds are polar, with carbon at the positive end. The larger difference in electronegativity values shows that the C—O bond is the more polar of the two.

> **Electronegativity** The ability of an atom to attract electrons in a covalent bond.

> ➤➤ The values given in Figure 4.7 indicate that carbon and hydrogen have similar electronegativities. As a result, C—H bonds are nonpolar. We will see in Chapters 12–25 how this fact helps explain the properties of organic and biological compounds, all of which have carbon and hydrogen as their principal constituents.

Less polar ⟍   More polar ⟋
$\delta+$C—N$\delta-$ $\delta+$C—O$\delta-$
Electronegativity   Electronegativity
difference: difference:
$3.0 - 2.5 = 0.5$ $3.5 - 2.5 = 1.0$

As a rule of thumb, electronegativity differences of less than 0.5 (such as C—H) result in nonpolar covalent bonds, differences up to 1.9 (such as N—H and O—H) indicate increasingly polar covalent bonds, and differences of two or more indicate ionic bonds. The electronegativity differences show, for example, that the bond between carbon and fluorine is highly polar covalent, the bond between sodium and chlorine is largely ionic, and the bond between rubidium and fluorine is almost completely ionic.

Electronegativity Difference		Type of Bond
0—0.4	~	Covalent
0.5—1.9	~	Polar covalent
2.0 and above	~	Ionic

$\delta+$C—F$\delta-$ Na$^+$Cl$^-$ Rb$^+$F$^-$
Electronegativity
difference: 1.5   2.1   3.2

The partial charges associated with each end of the bond result in a **dipole,** meaning "two poles," similar to the "+" and "−" ends of a magnet. The larger the dipole associated with a bond, the more polar it is. Note, though, that there is no sharp dividing line between polar covalent and ionic bonds; most bonds fall somewhere between two extremes.

> **Dipole** A difference in charge (+ or −) associated with one end of a covalent bond compared with the other or one end of a molecule compared with another.

Worked Example 4.12 Electronegativity: Ionic, Nonpolar, and Polar Covalent Bonds

Predict whether each of the bonds between the following atoms would be ionic, polar covalent, or nonpolar covalent. If polar covalent, which atom would carry the partial positive and negative charges?

(a) C and Br   (b) Li and Cl   (c) N and H   (d) Si and I

ANALYSIS Compare the electronegativity values for the atoms and classify the nature of the bonding based on the electronegativity difference.

SOLUTION

(a) The electronegativity for C is 2.5 and for Br is 2.8, and the difference is 0.3, indicating nonpolar covalent bonding would occur between these atoms.

(b) The electronegativity for Li is 1.0 and for Cl is 3.0, and the difference is 2.0, indicating that ionic bonding would occur between these atoms.

(c) The electronegativity for N is 3.0 and for H is 2.5, and the difference is 0.5. Bonding would be polar covalent, with $N = \delta-$ and $H = \delta+$.

(d) The electronegativity for Si is 1.8 and for I is 2.5, and the difference is 0.7. Bonding would be polar covalent, with $I = \delta-$, and $Si = \delta+$.

PROBLEM 4.18

The elements H, N, O, P, and S are commonly bonded to carbon in organic compounds. Arrange these elements in order of increasing electronegativity.

PROBLEM 4.19

Use electronegativity differences to classify bonds between the following pairs of atoms as ionic, nonpolar covalent, or polar covalent. For those that are polar, use the symbols $\delta+$ and $\delta-$ to identify the location of the partial charges on the polar covalent bond.

(a) I and Cl   (b) Li and O
(c) Br and Br   (d) P and Br

4.10 Polar Molecules

Learning Objective:

• Predict polarity of molecules using electronegativity and molecular geometry (VSEPR).

Just as individual bonds can be polar, entire *molecules* can be polar if electrons are attracted more strongly to one part of the molecule than to another. Molecular polarity is due to the sum of all individual bond polarities and lone-pair contributions in the molecule and is often represented by an arrow pointing in the direction that electrons are displaced. The arrow is pointed at the negative end and is crossed at the positive end to resemble a plus sign, $(\delta+) \leftrightarrow (\delta-)$.

Molecular polarity depends on the shape of the molecule as well as the presence of polar covalent bonds and lone pairs. In water, for example, electrons are displaced away from the less electronegative hydrogen atoms toward the more electronegative oxygen atom so that the net polarity points between the two O—H bonds. In chloromethane, CH_3Cl, electrons are attracted from the carbon/hydrogen part of the molecule toward the electronegative chlorine atom so that the net polarity points along the C—Cl bond. Electrostatic potential maps show these polarities clearly, with electron-poor regions in blue and electron-rich regions in red.

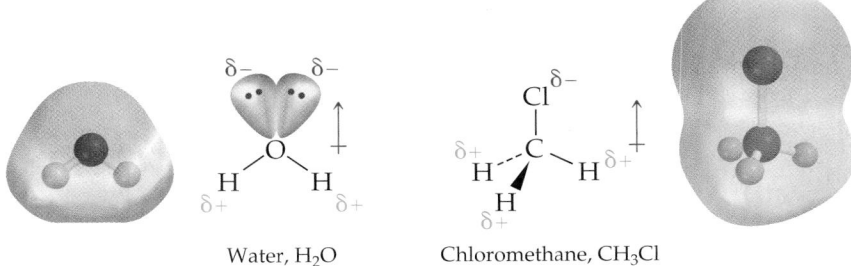

Water, H$_2$O   Chloromethane, CH$_3$Cl

Furthermore, just because a molecule has polar covalent bonds, it does not mean that the molecule is necessarily polar overall. Carbon dioxide (CO$_2$) and tetrachloromethane (CCl$_4$) molecules, for instance, have no net polarity because their symmetrical shapes cause the individual C=O and C—Cl bond polarities to cancel.

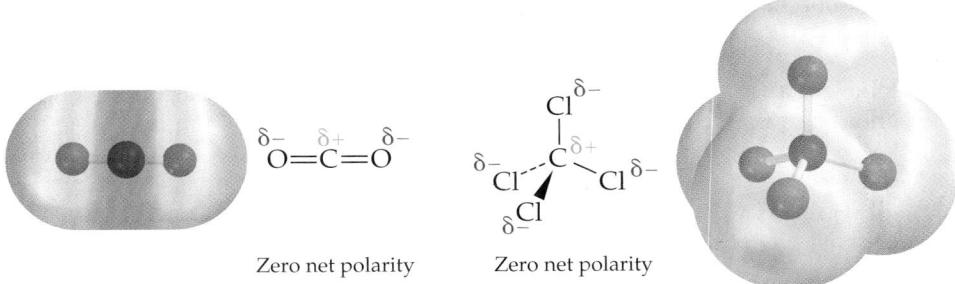

Zero net polarity   Zero net polarity

Polarity has a dramatic effect on the physical properties of molecules, particularly on melting points, boiling points, and solubilities. We will see numerous examples of such effects in subsequent chapters.

> ▶▶ The unique properties of water, which will be discussed in Chapter 8, result from its polarity and molecular geometry.

Worked Example 4.13 Electronegativity: Polar Bonds and Polar Molecules

Look at the structures of (a) hydrogen cyanide (HCN) and (b) vinyl chloride (H$_2$C=CHCl), described in Worked Examples 4.6 and 4.7; decide whether or not the molecules are polar, and show the direction of net polarity in each.

ANALYSIS Draw a Lewis structure for each molecule to find its shape, and identify any polar bonds using the electronegativity values in Figure 4.7. Then, decide on net polarity by adding the individual contributions.

SOLUTION

(a) The carbon atom in hydrogen cyanide has two charge clouds, making HCN a linear molecule. The C—H bond is relatively nonpolar, but the C≡N bonding electrons are pulled toward the electronegative nitrogen atom. In addition, a lone pair protrudes from nitrogen. Thus, the molecule has a net polarity.

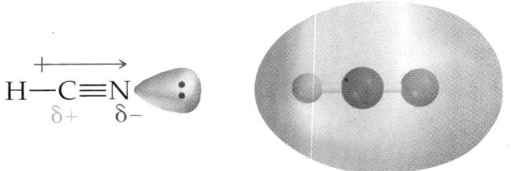

—continued on next page

—continued from previous page

(b) Vinyl chloride, like ethylene, is a planar molecule. The C—H and C=C bonds are nonpolar, but the C—Cl bonding electrons are displaced toward the electronegative chlorine. Thus, the molecule has a net polarity.

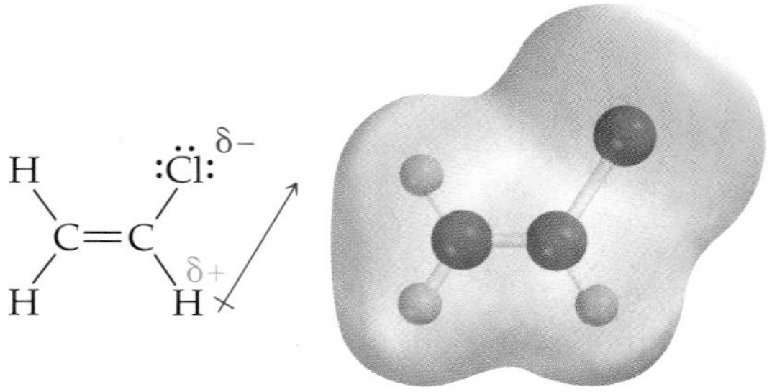

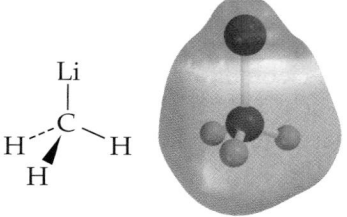

PROBLEM 4.20

Look at the molecular shape of formaldehyde (CH_2O) described on page 118, decide whether or not the molecule is polar, and show the direction of net polarity.

PROBLEM 4.21

Draw a Lewis structure for dimethyl ether (CH_3OCH_3), predict its shape, and tell whether or not the molecule is polar.

⊙━ KEY CONCEPT PROBLEM 4.22 _____

From this electrostatic potential map of methyllithium, identify the direction of net polarity in the molecule. Explain this polarity based on electronegativity values.

Methyllithium

HANDS-ON CHEMISTRY 4.1

Visualization of molecules can help us to understand their properties. Chemists typically do this with model kits or computer simulations, but we can approximate this by using toothpicks and gum drops or some other small, colored soft candy. We will let the toothpicks represent covalent bonds and the gum drops represent atoms of different elements. Try to find gum drops or candies with colors that match the color codes in Table 4.2.

a. We will start by building a methane molecule (CH_4). Take two tooth picks and one carbon atom (black gumdrop) and arrange them on the table like the figure to the right (in margin) to approximate a bond angle of 109.5°. Repeat this process twice more until you have your central C atom (black gumdrop) with four bonds oriented similarly to the tetrahedral methane molecule reproduced here.

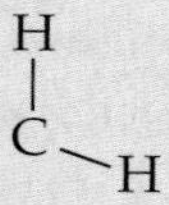

Finally, add white gum drops to the end of each of the four toothpicks to represent H atoms. Examine your methane model from various directions and orientations. Is it symmetrical? Refer to the electronegativity differences in Figure 4.7. Are the covalent bonds polar or nonpolar?

b. Now replace two of the H atoms with chlorine (green gum drops). Are the C—Cl bonds polar? Which end of each covalent bond is negative? Orient your molecule on the table top so that both Cl atoms are on the same side. Now look at the molecule as a whole. Where are the partial negative charges ($\delta-$) in the molecule? Is one side of the molecule more negative than the other? Is this molecule polar?

c. Now replace all four H atoms with Cl atoms, and answer the same questions as in Part b.

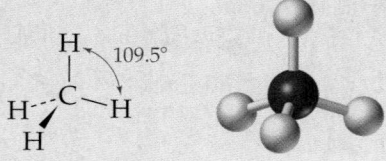

4.11 Naming Binary Molecular Compounds

Learning Objective:

- Name binary molecular compounds.

When two different elements combine, they form what is called a **binary compound.** The formulas of binary molecular compounds are usually written with the less electronegative element first. Thus, metals are always written before nonmetals, and a nonmetal farther left on the periodic table generally comes before a nonmetal farther right. For example,

Binary compound A compound formed by combination of two different elements.

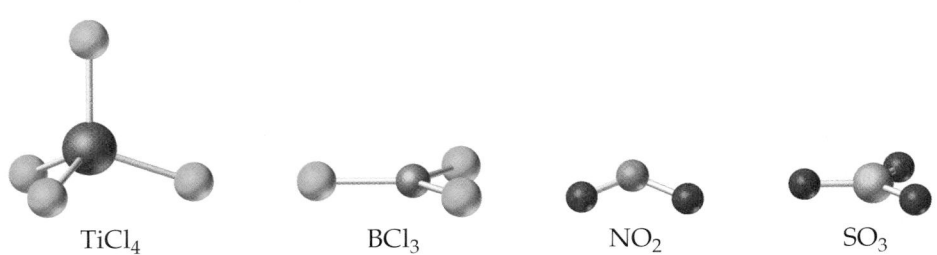

TiCl$_4$ BCl$_3$ NO$_2$ SO$_3$

as we learned in Section 3.8, the formulas of ionic compounds indicate the number of anions and cations necessary for a neutral formula unit, which depends on the charge on each of the ions. With molecular compounds, however, many combinations of atoms are possible, since nonmetals are capable of forming multiple covalent bonds. When naming binary molecular compounds, therefore, we must identify exactly how many atoms of each element are included in the molecular formula. The names of binary molecular compounds are assigned in two steps, using the prefixes listed in Table 4.4 to indicate the number of atoms of each element combined.

STEP 1: Name the first element in the formula, using a prefix if needed to indicate the number of atoms.

STEP 2: Name the second element in the formula, and modify by adding the -*ide* suffix as when naming anions (Section 3.5). Include numerical prefixes as appropriate.

The prefix *mono-,* meaning one, is omitted except where needed to distinguish between two different compounds with the same elements. For example, the two oxides of carbon are named carbon *mon*oxide for CO and carbon *di*oxide for CO$_2$. (Note that when the element name begins with a vowel, the last letter in the numerical prefix (if an "o" or an "a") is often deleted. For instance, we say *mon*oxide instead of *mono*oxide, and *pent*oxide instead of *penta*oxide.) Some examples follow:

Table 4.4 Numerical Prefixes Used in Chemical Names

Number	Prefix
1	mono-
2	di-
3	tri-
4	tetra-
5	penta-
6	hexa-
7	hepta-
8	octa-
9	nona-
10	deca-

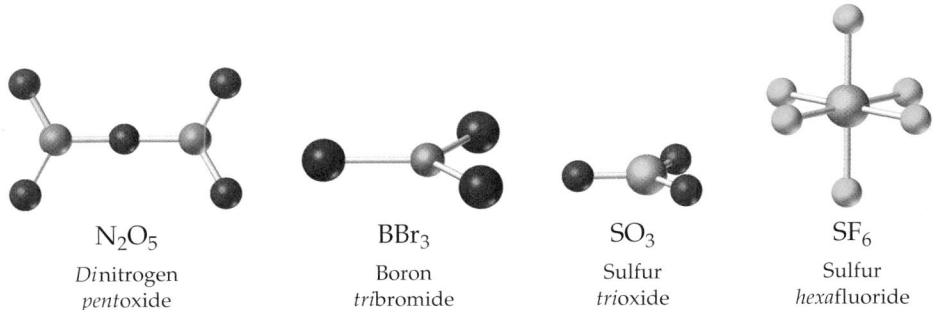

N$_2$O$_5$ BBr$_3$ SO$_3$ SF$_6$

*Di*nitrogen *pent*oxide   Boron *tri*bromide   Sulfur *tri*oxide   Sulfur *hexa*fluoride

Naming of molecular compounds can get complicated when more than two elements are present. This is particularly true for *organic compounds,* a class of molecular compounds composed largely of carbon (see examples in the Chemistry in Action on the following page). The rules for naming these compounds will be discussed in later chapters.

CHEMISTRY IN ACTION

✚ Damascenone by Any Other Name Would Smell as Sweet

What's in a name? According to Shakespeare's *Romeo and Juliet*, a rose by any other name would smell as sweet. Chemical names, however, often provoke less favorable responses: "It's unpronounceable;" "It's too complicated;" "It must be something bad."

But why are chemical names so complicated? The reason is obvious once you realize that there are more than 19 *million* known chemical compounds. The full name of a chemical compound has to include enough information to tell chemists the composition and structure of the compound. It is as if every person on earth had to have his or her own unique name that described height, hair color, and other identifying characteristics in sufficient detail to distinguish him or her from every other person. Consider, also, that subtle differences in structure can result in significant differences in chemical or physical properties. Geraniol, for example, is used as a flavor additive in the food industry, whereas citronellol is used in perfumes and insect repellants, such as citronella candles. The common names for these substances are easier to remember, but their *chemical* names give us precise information about their structural differences and similarities. Geraniol also known as *3,7-dimethylocta-2,6-dien-1-ol* differs from citronellol (or *3,7-dimethyloct-6-en-1-ol*) by only one double bond.

The three-dimensional orientation of atoms in a molecule is also important and must be reflected in the chemical name. As we saw in our chapter opener, many drugs and other biochemically active compounds exist in two forms that have identical molecular formulas but differ in the orientation of side groups around a single carbon atom—a property known as chirality that will be explored further in Chapters 14 and 20. L-Dopa, for example, is used to treat Parkinson's disease, whereas its counterpart (D-Dopa) has been linked to granulocytopenia, an immune system disorder. Similarly, one form of thalidomide is effective in treating morning sickness, whereas the other form causes birth defects. We learned at the beginning of the chapter that dextromethorphan is a cough suppressant in common over-the-counter remedies, whereas its counterpart, levomethorphan, is a highly addictive opiate.

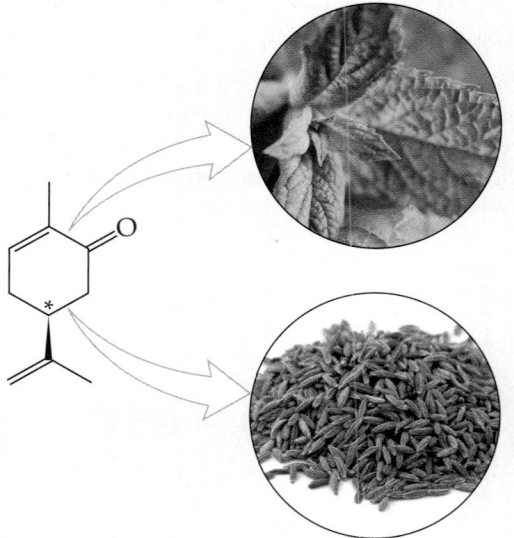

▲ The different aromas of L-carvone (spearmint) and D-carvone (cumin) result from variations in the 3-dimensional orientation of bonds around one carbon in carvone (indicated in the figure with a *).

Even carvone, one of the compounds that contribute to the aroma of roses, exists in multiple forms; L-carvone is perceived by smell receptors in the nose as spearmint, whereas D-carvone evokes the savory aroma of caraway or cumin. Molecular structure determines chemical behavior and biological activity, and the chemical name must specify that structure precisely—including the presence and location of multiple bonds and three-dimensional orientation.

CIA Problem 4.5   Why are many chemical names so complex?

CIA Problem 4.6   Geraniol, one of the components of rose oil has the basic structure represented here. Draw the structural formula for geraniol to include any multiple bonds, and then write the condensed structure for geraniol.

$$CH_3-\underset{\underset{H}{|}}{\overset{\overset{CH_3}{|}}{C}}-\underset{\underset{H}{|}}{\overset{\overset{H}{|}}{C}}-\underset{\underset{H}{|}}{\overset{\overset{H}{|}}{C}}-\underset{\underset{}{}}{\overset{\overset{CH_3}{|}}{C}}-\underset{\underset{H}{|}}{\overset{\overset{H}{|}}{C}}-\underset{\underset{H}{|}}{\overset{\overset{H}{|}}{C}}-OH$$

Worked Example 4.14 Naming Molecular Compounds

Name the following compounds:

(a) N_2O_3 (b) $GeCl_4$ (c) PCl_5

SOLUTION

(a) The first element is N (nitrogen) and there are two N atoms = *di*nitrogen; the second element is O (oxygen), which is modified with the *-ide* suffix. There are three O atoms = *tri*oxide. Put all of the elements together to get the molecule's name: Dinitrogen trioxide.

(b) Ge = germanium; Cl = chlorine, which is modified to chlor*ide*. There are four Cl atoms = *tetra*chloride; Germanium tetrachloride.

(c) P = Phosphorus; Cl = chlor*ide*. There are five Cl atoms = Phosphorus pentachloride.

Worked Example 4.15 Writing Formulas for Molecular Compounds

Write molecular formulas for the following compounds:

(a) Nitrogen triiodide   (b) Silicon tetrachloride   (c) Carbon disulfide

SOLUTION

(a) The first element is nitrogen (N), the "tri" prefix indicates "3," and iodide is derived from iodine (I) = NI_3

(b) Silicon is Si, "tetra" = 4, and chloride is derived from chlorine (Cl) = $SiCl_4$

(c) Carbon is C, "di" = 2, and sulfide is derived from sulfur (S) = CS_2

PROBLEM 4.23

Name the following compounds:

(a) S_2Cl_2 (b) ICl   (c) ICl_3

PROBLEM 4.24

Write formulas for the following compounds:

(a) Selenium tetrafluoride

(b) Diphosphorus pentoxide

(c) Bromine trifluoride

SUMMARY REVISITING THE CHAPTER LEARNING OBJECTIVES

- **Describe the nature of covalent bonds and how they are formed.** A covalent bond is formed by the sharing of electrons between atoms, and typically occurs when a singly occupied valence orbital on one atom overlaps a singly occupied valence orbital on another atom. The two electrons occupy both overlapping orbitals and belong to both atoms, thereby bonding the atoms together [see Problems 31, 34, 100, and 103].

- **Differentiate between ionic and covalent bonds.** A covalent bond is formed by the sharing of electrons between atoms rather than by the complete transfer of electrons from one atom to another [see Problems 31, 34, 100, and 103].

- **Predict the number of covalent bonds an atom will form based on its position in the periodic table.** Depending on the number of valence electrons, different atoms form different numbers of covalent bonds. In general, an atom shares enough electrons to reach a noble gas configuration. Hydrogen, for instance, forms one covalent bond because it needs to share one more electron to achieve the helium configuration $1s^2$ Carbon and other group 4A elements form four covalent bonds because they need to share four more electrons to reach an octet. In the same way, nitrogen and other group 5A elements form three covalent bonds, oxygen and other group 6A elements form two covalent bonds, and halogens (group 7A elements) form one covalent bond [see Problems 36, 37, 40, 49, 85, 88, 89, and 103].

- **Use the octet rule to determine when multiple covalent bonds (double and triple) will appear between two atoms.** The atoms in some molecules can satisfy the octet rule by sharing two electrons to form a single bond (such as C—C). In other molecules, some atoms have to share more than one pair of electrons to satisfy the octet rule. Atoms that share four electrons are joined by a double bond (such as O=O), and atoms that share six electrons are joined by a triple bond (such as N≡N) [see Problems 27–29, 33, 46, 49, and 98].

- **Identify coordinate covalent bonds in a molecule or polyatomic ion.** Alternatively, electron sharing can occur when a filled orbital containing an unshared, lone pair of electrons on one atom overlaps a vacant orbital on another atom to form a coordinate covalent bond [see Problems 32, 38, 39, 42, 43, 89, and 90].

- **Distinguish structures, compositions, and properties of molecular compounds from those of ionic compounds.** A group of atoms held together by covalent bonds or shared electron pairs is called a molecule. Molecular compounds can be gases, liquids, or low-melting solids. They usually have lower melting points and boiling points than ionic compounds, many are water insoluble, and they do not conduct electricity when melted or dissolved. By contrast, ionic compounds are formed by the transfer of electrons between atoms to form ions, which are held together by electrostatic attractions, or ionic bonds. Ionic compounds tend to be solids with high-melting point and are conductive when dissolved in solution [see Problems 27, 29, 41, 44, 45, 53, 54, 100, and 103].

- **Interpret molecular formulas and draw Lewis structures for molecules.** Formulas such as H_2O, NH_3, and CH_4, which show the numbers and kinds of atoms in a molecule, are called molecular formulas. More useful are Lewis structures, which show how atoms are connected in molecules. Covalent bonds are indicated as lines between atoms, and valence electron lone pairs are shown as dots [see Problems 30, 46, 52, 55–62, and 97].

- **Draw Lewis structures for molecules using their molecular formula and the octet rule.** Lewis structures are drawn by counting the total number of valence electrons in a molecule or polyatomic ion and then placing shared pairs (bonding) and lone pairs (nonbonding) so that all electrons are accounted for [see Problems 28, 35, 42, 43, 46–52, 55–62, 85, 86, 90, 93–96, 98, 99, 101, and 102].

- **Use Lewis structures to predict molecular geometry.** Molecules have specific shapes that depend on the number of electron charge clouds (bonds and lone pairs) surrounding the various atoms. These shapes can often be predicted using the VSEPR model. Atoms with two electron charge clouds adopt linear geometry, atoms with three charge clouds adopt trigonal planar geometry, and atoms with four charge clouds adopt tetrahedral geometry *(see Problems 25–27, 29, 63–68, 86, 87, 90, 93, and 99).*

- **Distinguish between polar covalent, nonpolar covalent, and ionic bonds using electronegativity.** Bonds between atoms are polar covalent if the bonding electrons are not shared equally between the atoms. The ability of an atom to attract electrons in a covalent bond is the atom's electronegativity and is highest for reactive nonmetal elements on the upper right of the periodic table and lowest for metals on the lower left. Comparing electronegativities allows prediction of whether a given bond is polar covalent, nonpolar covalent, or ionic *(see Problems 34, 69–76, 86, 89, 92, and 100).*

- **Predict polarity of molecules using electronegativity and molecular geometry (VSEPR).** Just as individual bonds can be polar, entire molecules can be polar if electrons are attracted more strongly to one part of the molecule than to another. Molecular polarity is due to the sum of all individual bond polarities and lone-pair contributions in the molecule *(see Problems 30, 34, 77–80, 87, and 91).*

- **Name binary molecular compounds.** When naming binary molecular compound, the less electronegative element (further to the left or further down in the periodic table) is named first. The name of the more electronegative element is modified by adding the *-ide* suffix and is then added to the compound name. Numerical prefixes are added as needed to indicate the number of each type of atom. For example, NO_2 is *nitrogen dioxide (see Problems 81–84, and 92).*

CONCEPT MAP: ELECTROSTATIC FORCES

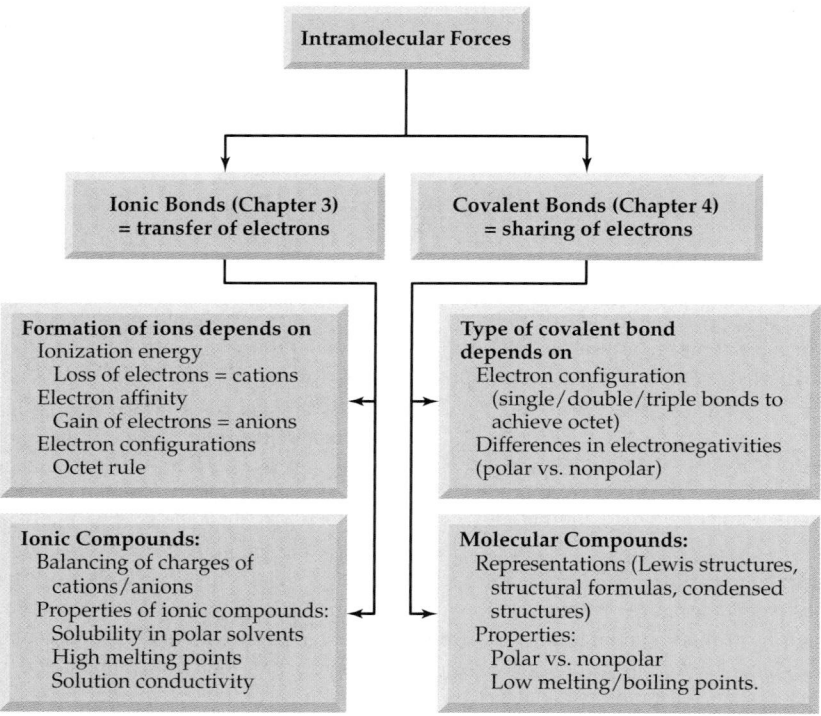

▲ **Figure 4.8 Concept Map.** As you can see from the concept map, the electronic structure of atoms discussed in Chapter 2 plays a critical role in the formation of ionic compounds (Chapter 3) or molecular compounds (Chapter 4). Furthermore, the nature of the attractive forces between particles (intermolecular versus intramolecular) plays a role in the physical and chemical behavior of substances discussed in later chapters.

KEY WORDS

Binary compound, *p. 127*	**Covalent bond,** *p. 101*	**Molecular compound,** *p. 103*	**Structural formula,** *p. 110*
Bond angle, *p. 117*	**Dipole,** *p. 123*	**Molecular formula,** *p. 110*	**Triple bond,** *p. 106*
Bond length, *p. 102*	**Double bond,** *p. 106*	**Molecule,** *p. 101*	**Valence-shell electron-pair**
Condensed structure, *p. 112*	**Electronegativity,** *p. 123*	**Polar covalent bond,** *p. 122*	**repulsion (VSEPR) model,**
Coordinate covalent	**Lewis structure,** *p. 110*	**Regular tetrahedron,** *p. 119*	*p. 117*
bond, *p. 108*	**Lone pair,** *p. 106*	**Single bond,** *p. 106*	

⚙ UNDERSTANDING KEY CONCEPTS

4.25   What is the geometry around the central atom in the following molecular models? (There are no "hidden" atoms; all atoms in each model are visible.)

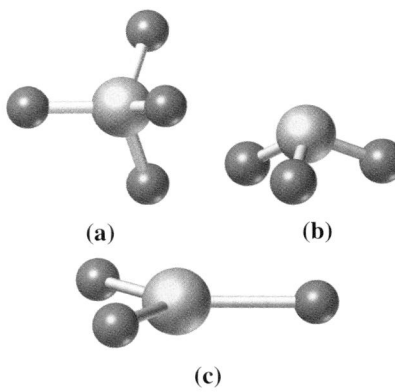

(a)   (b)

(c)

4.26   Three of the following molecular models have a tetrahedral central atom and one does not. Which is the odd one? (Note: Not all atoms and/or lone pairs may be visible in the models.)

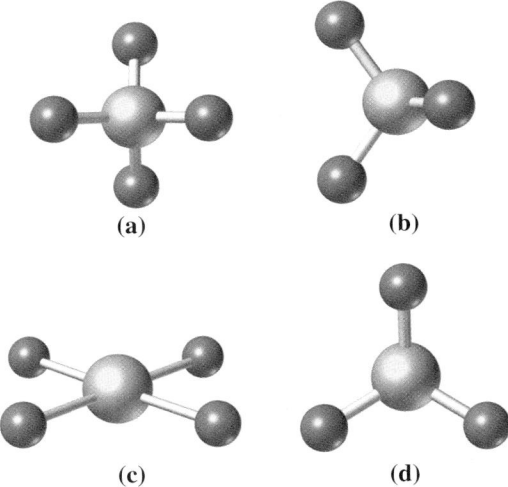

(a)   (b)

(c)   (d)

4.27   The ball-and-stick molecular model shown here is a representation of acetaminophen, the active ingredient in over-the-counter headache remedies such as Tylenol. The lines indicate only the connections between atoms not whether the bonds are single, double, or triple (red = O, gray = C, blue = N, ivory = H).

(a) What is the molecular formula of acetaminophen?

(b) Indicate the positions of the multiple bonds in acetaminophen.

(c) What is the geometry around each carbon and each nitrogen?

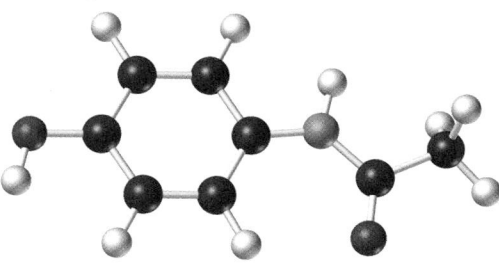

Acetaminophen

4.28   The atom-to-atom connections in vitamin C (ascorbic acid) are as shown here. Convert this skeletal drawing to a Lewis electron-dot structure for vitamin C by showing the positions of any multiple bonds and lone pairs of electrons.

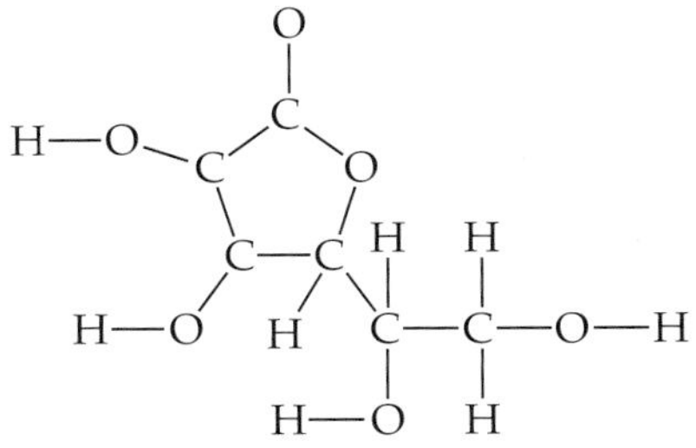

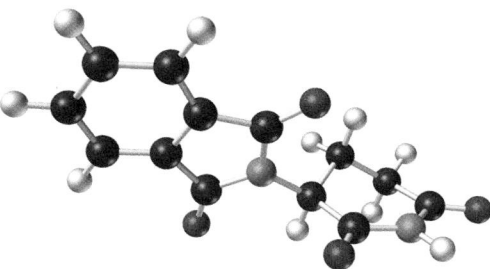

Vitamin C

4.29   The ball-and-stick molecular model shown here is a representation of thalidomide, a drug that has been approved for treating leprosy but causes severe birth defects when taken by expectant mothers. The lines indicate only the connections between atoms and not whether the bonds are single, double, or triple (red = O, gray = C, blue = N, ivory = H).

(a) What is the molecular formula of thalidomide?

(b) Indicate the positions of the multiple bonds in thalidomide.

(c) What is the geometry around each carbon and each nitrogen?

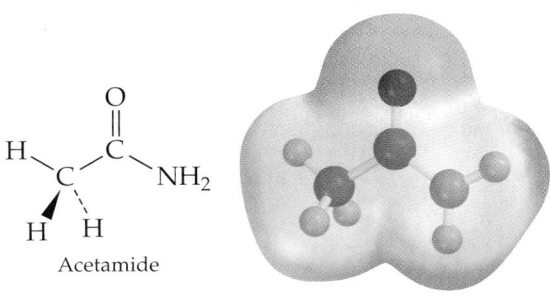

Thalidomide

4.30   Show the position of any electron lone pairs in this structure of acetamide, and indicate the electron-rich and electron-poor regions.

Acetamide

ADDITIONAL PROBLEMS

COVALENT BONDS AND MOLECULAR COMPOUNDS (SECTIONS 4.1–4.5)

4.31 What is a covalent bond, and how does it differ from an ionic bond?

4.32 What is a coordinate covalent bond, and how does it differ from a covalent bond?

4.33 When are multiple bonds formed between atoms and why?

4.34 Identify the bonds formed between the following pairs of atoms as either covalent or ionic.

(a) Aluminum and bromine

(b) Carbon and fluorine

(c) Cesium and iodine

(d) Zinc and fluorine

(e) Lithium and chlorine

4.35 Write electron-dot symbols to show the number of covalent bonds and the lone pairs of electrons in the molecules that are formed by reactions between the atoms in Problem 4.34.

4.36 Look up tellurium ($Z = 52$) in the periodic table and predict how many covalent bonds it is likely to form. Explain.

4.37 Look up antimony in the periodic table ($Z = 51$). How many covalent bonds would you expect it to form? Based on this information, which of the following antimony compounds is covalent and which is ionic: $SbCl_3$ or $SbCl_5$?

4.38 Which of the following contains a coordinate covalent bond? (Hint: How many covalent bonds would you expect the central atom (underlined) to form?)

(a) $\underline{Pb}Cl_2$ (b) $\underline{Cu}(NH_3)_4{}^{2+}$ (c) $\underline{N}H_4{}^+$

4.39 Which of the following contains a coordinate covalent bond? (Hint: How many covalent bonds would you expect the central atom (underlined) to form?)

(a) $H_2\underline{O}$ (b) $\underline{B}F_4{}^-$ (c) $H_3\underline{O}^+$

4.40 Tin forms both an ionic compound and a covalent compound with chlorine. The ionic compound is $SnCl_2$. Is the covalent compound more likely to be $SnCl_3$, $SnCl_4$, or $SnCl_5$? Explain.

4.41 A compound of gallium with chlorine has a melting point of 77 °C and a boiling point of 201 °C. Is the compound ionic or covalent? What is a likely formula?

4.42 Nitrous oxide, N_2O, has the following structure. Which bond in N_2O is a coordinate covalent bond? Explain.

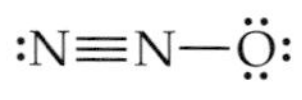

$$:N\equiv N-\overset{..}{\underset{..}{O}}:$$

Nitrous oxide

4.43 Thionyl chloride, $SOCl_2$, has the following structure. Which bond in $SOCl_2$ is a coordinate covalent bond?

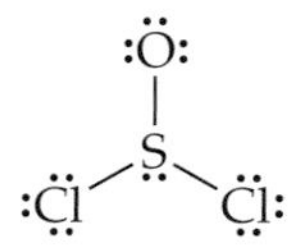

Thionyl chloride

STRUCTURAL FORMULAS (SECTION 4.6)

4.44 Distinguish between the following:

(a) A molecular formula and a structural formula

(b) A structural formula and a condensed structure

(c) A lone pair and a shared pair of electrons

4.45 Assume that you are given samples of two white crystalline compounds, one of them ionic and the other one covalent. Describe how you might tell which is which.

4.46 Determine the total number of valence electrons in the following molecules. If the molecule contains multiple bonds, indicate where the multiple bonds are located and whether they are double or triple bonds.

(a) N_2 (b) $NOCl$

(c) CH_3CH_2CHO (d) OF_2

4.47 Add lone pairs where appropriate to the following structures:

(a) $C\equiv O$ (b) CH_3SH

(c) 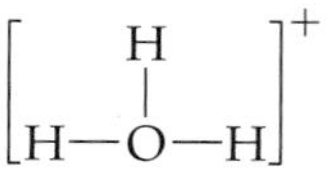 $\left[H-\overset{H}{\underset{|}{O}}-H\right]^+$ (d) 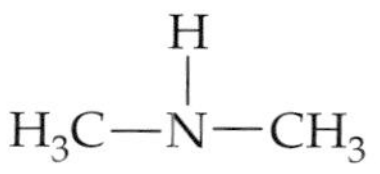 $H_3C-\overset{H}{\underset{|}{N}}-CH_3$

4.48 If a research paper appeared reporting the structure of a new molecule with formula C_2H_8, most chemists would be highly skeptical. Why?

4.49 Consider the following possible structural formulas for $C_3H_6O_2$. If a structure is not reasonable, explain what changes could be made to convert it to a reasonable structure.

(a) 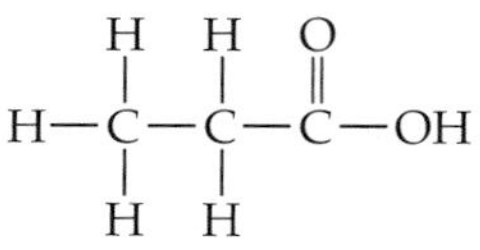 $H-\overset{\overset{\textstyle H}{|}}{\underset{\underset{\textstyle H}{|}}{C}}-\overset{\overset{\textstyle H}{|}}{\underset{\underset{\textstyle H}{|}}{C}}-\overset{\overset{\textstyle O}{\|}}{C}-OH$

(b) $H-\overset{\overset{\textstyle H}{|}}{\underset{\underset{\textstyle H}{|}}{C}}-\overset{\overset{\textstyle OH}{|}}{\underset{\underset{\textstyle OH}{|}}{C}}-H$ (c) $H-\overset{\overset{\textstyle H}{|}}{\underset{\underset{\textstyle H}{|}}{C}}-O-\overset{\overset{\textstyle H}{|}}{\underset{\underset{\textstyle H}{|}}{C}}-C=O$

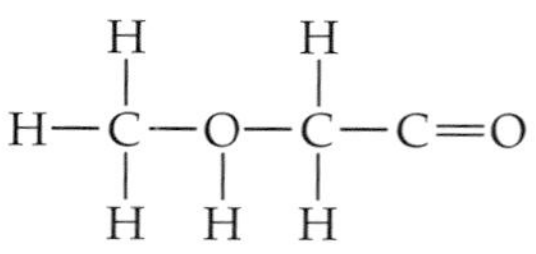

4.50 Convert the following Lewis structures into structural formulas in which lines replace the bonding electrons. Include the lone pairs.

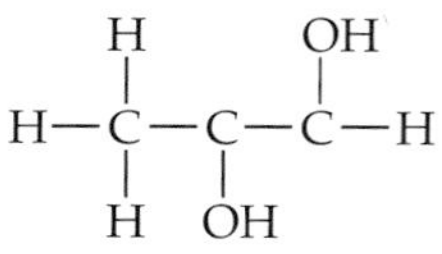

(a)  $H:\overset{..}{\underset{..}{O}}:\overset{..}{N}::\overset{..}{\underset{..}{O}}:$ (b) 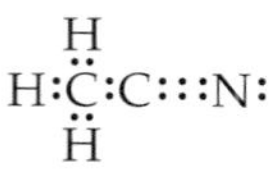 $H:\overset{\overset{\textstyle H}{..}}{\underset{\underset{\textstyle H}{}}{C}}:C:::N:$ (c) $H:\overset{..}{\underset{..}{F}}:$

4.51 Convert the following Lewis structure for the nitrate ion into a line structure that includes the lone pairs. Why does the nitrate ion have a −1 charge?

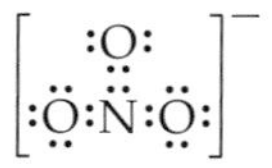

$$\left[:\overset{..}{\underset{..}{O}}:\overset{..}{N}:\overset{..}{\underset{..}{O}}:\right]^-$$
$$\overset{\overset{\textstyle :O:}{..}}{}$$

4.52 Convert the following structural formulas into condensed structures.

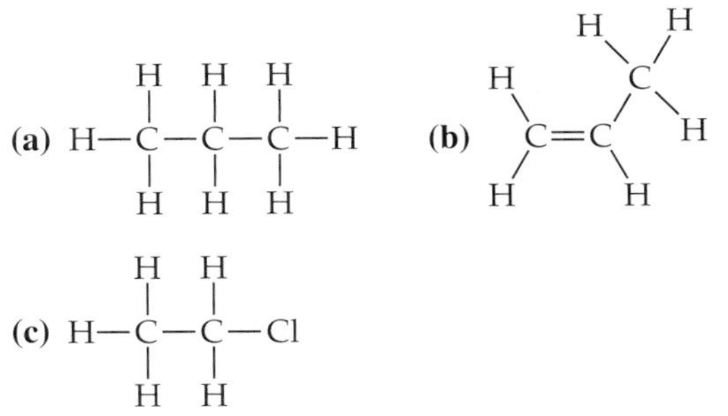

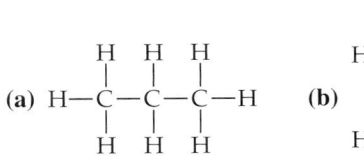

(a) **(b)**

(c)

4.53 Expand the following condensed structures into the correct structural formulas.

(a) $CH_3CH_2COCH(CH_3)_2$ **(b)** $CH_3CH_2COOCH_3$

(c) $CH_3CH_2OCH_2Cl$

4.54 Acetic acid is the major organic constituent of vinegar. Convert the following structural formula of acetic acid into a condensed structure similar to those shown in Problem 4.53.

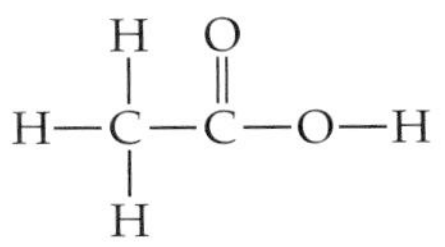

DRAWING LEWIS STRUCTURES (SECTION 4.7)

4.55 Draw a Lewis structure for the following molecules:

(a) SF_6 **(b)** $AlCl_3$

(c) CS_2 **(d)** SeF_4

(e) $BeCl_2$ (Note: This molecule does not follow the octet rule.)

(f) N_2O_4

4.56 Draw a Lewis structure for the following molecules:

(a) Nitrous acid, HNO_2 (H is bonded to an O atom)

(b) Sulfur trioxide, SO_3

(c) Acetaldehyde, CH_3CHO

4.57 Ethanol, or "grain alcohol," has the formula C_2H_6O and contains an O—H bond. Propose a structure for ethanol that is consistent with common bonding patterns.

4.58 Dimethyl ether has the same molecular formula as ethanol (Problem 4.57) but very different properties. Propose a structure for dimethyl ether in which the oxygen is bonded to two carbons.

4.59 Tetrachloroethylene, C_2Cl_4, is used commercially as a dry-cleaning solvent. Propose a structure for tetrachloroethylene based on the common bonding patterns expected in organic molecules. What kind of carbon–carbon bond is present?

4.60 Draw a Lewis structure for hydroxylamine, NH_2OH.

4.61 The carbonate ion, $CO_3{}^{2-}$, contains a double bond. Draw a Lewis structure for the ion and show why it has a charge of -2.

4.62 Draw a Lewis structure for the following polyatomic ions:

(a) Formate, $HCO_2{}^-$

(b) Sulfite, $SO_3{}^{2-}$

(c) Thiocyanate, SCN^-

(d) Phosphate, $PO_4{}^{3+}$

(e) Chlorite, $ClO_2{}^-$ (Chlorine is the central atom.)

MOLECULAR GEOMETRY (SECTION 4.8)

4.63 Predict the geometry and bond angles around atom A for molecules with the general formulas AB_3 and AB_2E, where B represents another atom and E represents an electron pair.

4.64 Predict the geometry and bond angles around atom A for molecules with the general formulas AB_4, AB_3E, and AB_2E_2, where B represents another atom and E represents an electron pair.

4.65 Sketch the three-dimensional shape of the following molecules:

(a) Methylamine, CH_3NH_2

(b) Iodoform, CHI_3

(c) Ozone, O_3

(d) Phosphorus pentachloride, PCl_5

(e) Chloric acid, $HClO_3$

4.66 Predict the three-dimensional shape of the following molecules:

(a) SiF_4 **(b)** CF_2Cl_2 **(c)** SO_3

(d) BBr_3 **(e)** NF_3

4.67 Predict the geometry around each carbon atom in the amino acid alanine.

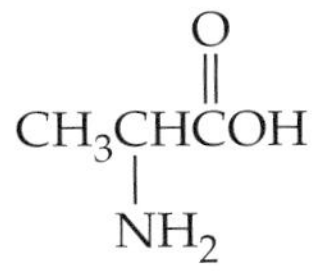

$$CH_3CHCOH$$

with O double bonded above C, and NH_2 below.

Alanine

4.68 Predict the geometry around each carbon atom in vinyl acetate, a precursor of the polyvinyl alcohol polymer used in automobile safety glass.

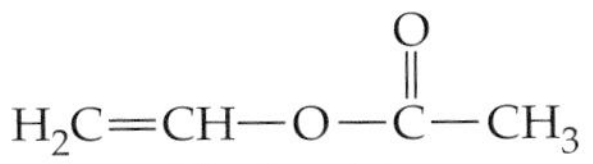

$$H_2C=CH-O-\overset{O}{\overset{\|}{C}}-CH_3$$

Vinyl acetate

POLARITY OF BONDS AND MOLECULES (SECTIONS 4.9 AND 4.10)

4.69 Where in the periodic table are the most electronegative elements found, and where are the least electronegative elements found?

4.70 Using Figure 4.7, predict the electronegativity of the yet-undiscovered element with $Z = 119$.

4.71 Look at the periodic table, and then order the following elements according to increasing electronegativity: K, Si, Be, O, B.

4.72 Look at the periodic table, and then order the following elements according to decreasing electronegativity: C, Ca, Cs, Cl, Cu.

4.73 Which of the following bonds are polar? If a bond is polar, identify the negative and positive ends of each bond by using $\delta+$ and $\delta-$.

(a) $I-Br$

(b) $O-H$

(c) $C-F$

(d) $N-C$

(e) $C-C$

4.74 Which of the following bonds are polar? If a bond is polar, identify the negative and positive ends of each bond by using $\delta+$ and $\delta-$.

(a) $O-Cl$

(b) $N-Cl$

(c) $P-H$

(d) $C-I$

(e) $C-O$

4.75 Based on electronegativity differences, would you expect bonds between the following pairs of atoms to be largely ionic or largely covalent?

(a) Be and F

(b) Ca and Cl

(c) O and H

(d) Be and Br

4.76 Arrange the following molecules in order of the increasing polarity of their bonds:

(a) HCl

(b) PH_3

(c) H_2O

(d) CF_4

4.77 Ammonia, NH_3, and phosphorus trihydride, PH_3, both have trigonal pyramid geometry. Which one is more polar? Explain.

4.78 Decide whether each of the compounds listed in Problem 4.76 is polar, and show the direction of polarity.

4.79 Carbon dioxide is a nonpolar molecule, whereas sulfur dioxide is polar. Draw Lewis structures for each of these molecules to explain this observation.

4.80 Water (H_2O) is more polar than hydrogen sulfide (H_2S). Explain.

NAMES AND FORMULAS OF MOLECULAR COMPOUNDS (SECTION 4.11)

4.81 Name the following binary compounds:

(a) PI_3

(b) $AsCl_3$

(c) P_4S_3

(d) Al_2F_6

(e) N_2O_5

(f) $AsCl_5$

4.82 Name the following compounds:

(a) SeO_2

(b) XeO_4

(c) N_2S_5

(d) P_3Se_4

4.83 Write formulas for the following compounds:

(a) Nitrogen dioxide

(b) Sulfur hexafluoride

(c) Bromine triiodide

(d) Dinitrogen trioxide

(e) Nitrogen triiodide

(f) Iodine heptafluoride

4.84 Write formulas for the following compounds:

(a) Silicon tetrachloride

(b) Sodium hydride

(c) Antimony pentafluoride

(d) Osmium tetroxide

CONCEPTUAL PROBLEMS

4.85 The discovery in the 1960s that xenon and fluorine react to form a molecular compound was a surprise to most chemists, because it had been thought that noble gases could not form bonds.

(a) Why was it thought that noble gases could not form bonds?

(b) Draw a Lewis structure of XeF_4 in which Xe is the central atom. How many electron clouds are there on the central atom?

(c) What type of bonds are the $Xe-F$ bonds? Explain.

4.86 Acetone, a common solvent used in some nail polish removers, has the molecular formula C_3H_6O and contains a carbon–oxygen double bond.

(a) Propose two Lewis structures for acetone.

(b) What is the geometry around the carbon atoms in each of the structures?

(c) Which of the bonds in each structure are polar?

4.87 Draw the structural formulas for two compounds having the molecular formula C_2H_4O. What is the molecular geometry around the carbon atoms in each of these molecules? Would these molecules be polar or nonpolar? (Hint: There is one double bond.)

4.88 The following formulas are unlikely to be correct. What is wrong with each?

(a) CCl_3

(b) N_2H_5

(c) H_3S

(d) C_2OS

4.89 Which of the following compounds contain ionic bonds? Which contain covalent bonds? Which contain coordinate covalent bonds? (A compound may contain more than one type of bond.)

(a) $BaCl_2$

(b) $Ca(NO_3)_2$

(c) BCl_4^-

(d) $TiBr_4$

4.90 The phosphonium ion, PH_4^+, is formed by reaction of phosphine, PH_3, with an acid.

(a) Draw the Lewis structure of the phosphonium ion.

(b) Predict its molecular geometry.

(c) Describe how a fourth hydrogen can be added to PH_3.

(d) Explain why the ion has a $+1$ charge.

4.91 Compare the trend in electronegativity seen in Figure 4.7 (p. 123) with the trend in electron affinity shown in Figure 3.2 (p. 79). What similarities do you see? What differences? Explain.

4.92 Name the following compounds. Be sure to determine whether the compound is ionic or covalent so that you use the proper rules.

(a) $CaCl_2$

(b) $TeCl_2$

(c) BF_3

(d) $MgSO_4$

(e) K_2O

(f) FeF_3

(g) PF_3

4.93 The sulfite ion (SO_3^{2-}) and sulfur trioxide (SO_3) have the same chemical formulas but different molecular geometries. Draw the Lewis dot structures and identify the molecular geometry of each.

4.94 Draw a Lewis structure for chloral hydrate, known in detective novels as "knockout drops." Indicate all lone pairs.

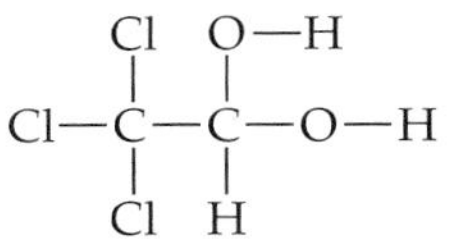

$$Cl-\underset{\underset{Cl}{|}}{\overset{\overset{Cl}{|}}{C}}-\underset{\underset{H}{|}}{\overset{\overset{O-H}{|}}{C}}-O-H \quad \text{Chloral hydrate}$$

4.95 The dichromate ion, $Cr_2O_7^{2-}$, has neither Cr—Cr nor O—O bonds. Draw a Lewis structure.

4.96 Oxalic acid, $H_2C_2O_4$, is a substance found in uncooked spinach leaves and other greens that can be poisonous at high concentrations (e.g., in raw rhubarb leaves). If oxalic acid has a C—C single bond and the H atoms are both connected to O atoms, draw its Lewis structure.

4.97 Identify the fourth row elements represented by "X" in the following compounds.

(a) 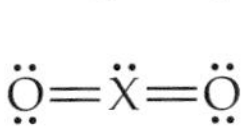 $\ddot{O}=\ddot{X}=\ddot{O}$ (b)  structure with F atoms bonded to X

4.98 Write Lewis structures for molecules with the following connections, showing the positions of any multiple bonds and lone pairs of electrons.

(a) 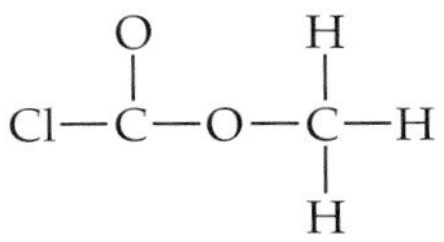 $Cl-\overset{\overset{O}{|}}{C}-O-\underset{\underset{H}{|}}{\overset{\overset{H}{|}}{C}}-H$ (b) 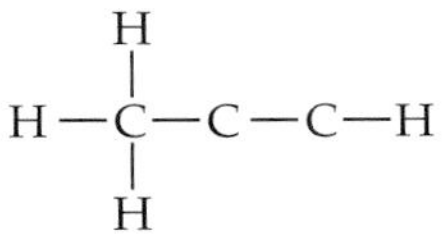 $H-\underset{\underset{H}{|}}{\overset{\overset{H}{|}}{C}}-C-C-H$

4.99 Electron-pair repulsion influences the shapes of polyatomic ions in the same way it influences neutral molecules. Draw electron-dot symbols and predict the shape of the ammonium ion, NH_4^+, the sulfate ion, SO_4^{2-}, and the phosphite ion, PO_3^{3-}.

GROUP PROBLEMS

4.100 Which of the following elements would you expect to form (i) diatomic molecules, (ii) mainly covalent bonds, (iii) mainly ionic bonds, and (iv) both covalent and ionic bonds? (More than one answer may apply; remember that some nonmetals can form ionic bonds with metals.) Explain your answers.

(a) Oxygen (b) Potassium
(c) Phosphorus (d) Iodine
(e) Hydrogen (f) Cesium

4.101 Hydrazine is a substance used to make rocket fuel. Look up the formula and propose a structure for hydrazine.

4.102 Dimethyl sulfoxide, also known as DMSO, is an important organic solvent often used for drug delivery since it readily penetrates the skin. Look up the formula for DMSO and write the Lewis dot structure. (Hint: There are no C—C bonds in the molecule.)

4.103 Titanium forms both molecular and ionic compounds with nonmetals, as, for example, $TiBr_4$ and TiO_2. Look up the melting points for these two compounds and use the information to identify which is ionic and which is molecular. Explain your answer in terms of electronegativities of the atoms involved in each compound.

5

Classification and Balancing of Chemical Reactions

CONTENTS

◀◀◀ CONCEPTS TO REVIEW

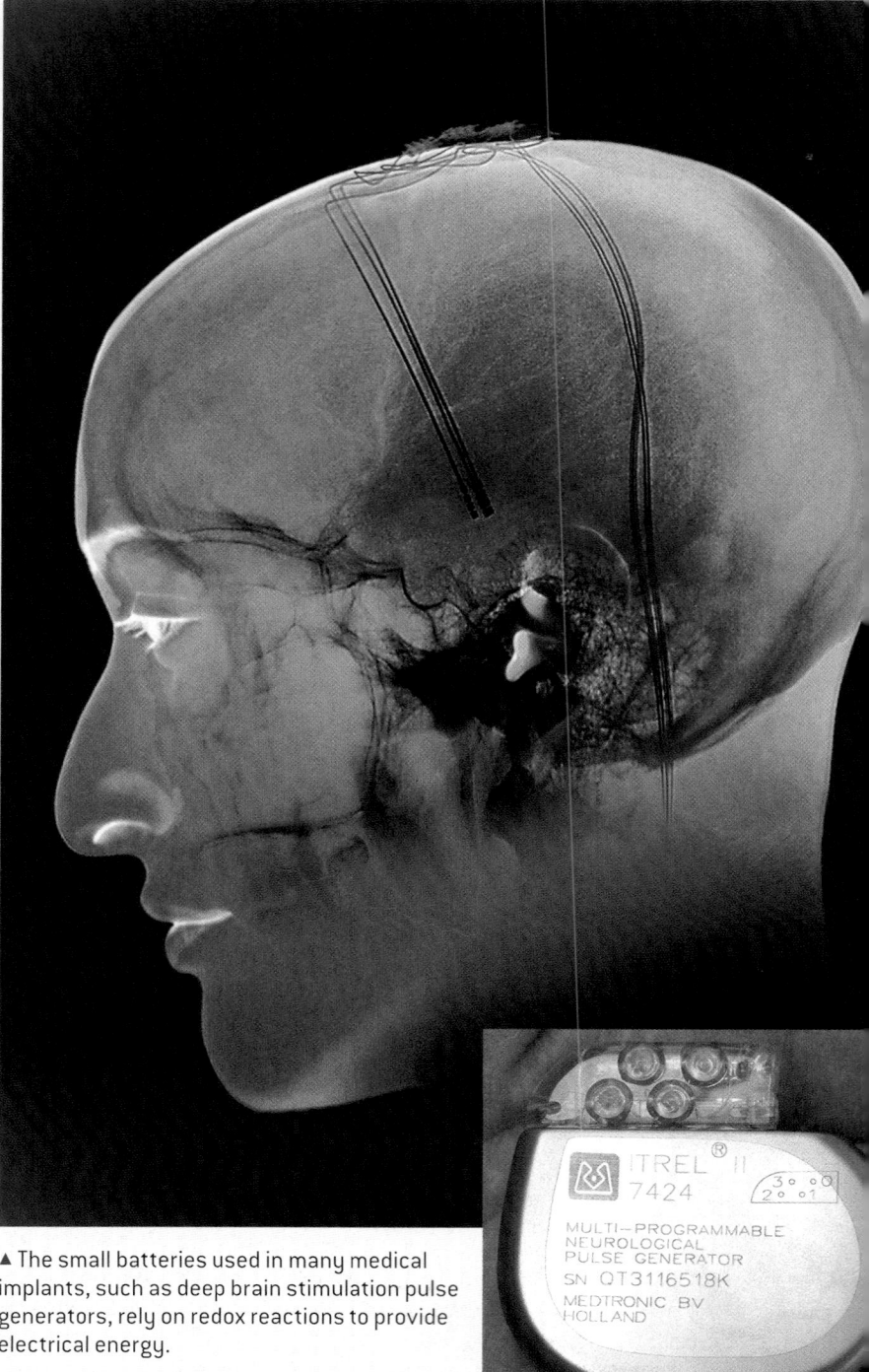

▲ The small batteries used in many medical implants, such as deep brain stimulation pulse generators, rely on redox reactions to provide electrical energy.

Advances in microelectronics made way for the development of small electronic devices for medical applications, such as pacemakers and insulin pumps. One of the more promising medical techniques involves "deep brain stimulation," in which a microdevice, called an implantable pulse generator (or IPG), provides electrical impulses to specific parts of the brain to either stimulate hormone production or inhibit abnormal nerve signals. This technique is used to treat conditions ranging from Parkinsons disease to Tourette's syndrome to clinical depression. What IPGs, pacemakers, and other electronic medical implants have in common is that they use small rechargeable batteries that use chemical reactions to generate the electricity needed to power the devices, as explained in the Chemistry in Action feature on page 150.

The study of how and why chemical reactions happen is a major part of chemistry, providing information that is both fascinating and practical. In this chapter, we will begin to look at chemical reactions, starting with a discussion of how to represent them in writing. We will then examine how to balance reactions and how to recognize different types or classes of chemical reactions.

5.1 Chemical Equations

Learning Objective:

• Understand the law of conservation of mass and how it applies to chemical equations.

One way to view chemical reactions is to think of them as "recipes." Like recipes, all the "ingredients" in a chemical equation and their relative amounts are given, as well as the amount of product that is produced. Take, for example, a recipe for making s'mores, a concoction of chocolate, marshmallows, and graham crackers:

$$\text{Graham crackers} + \text{Roasted marshmallows} + \text{Chocolate bars} \longrightarrow \text{S'mores}$$

This recipe, however, is simply a list of ingredients and gives no indication of the relative amounts of each ingredient, or how many s'mores we would obtain. A more detailed recipe would be

$$2 \text{ Graham crackers} + 1 \text{ Roasted marshmallow} + \tfrac{1}{4} \text{ Chocolate bar} \longrightarrow 1 \text{ S'more}$$

In this case, the relative amounts of each ingredient are given, as well as the amount of the final product.

Let us extend this analogy to a typical chemical reaction. When sodium bicarbonate, also known as baking soda, is heated in the range 50–100 °C, sodium carbonate, water, and carbon dioxide are produced. In words, we might write the reaction as

$$\text{Sodium bicarbonate} \xrightarrow{\text{Heat}} \text{Sodium carbonate} + \text{Water} + \text{Carbon dioxide}$$

Just as in the recipe, the starting materials and final products are listed. Replacing the chemical names with formulas converts the word description of this reaction into a **chemical equation:**

$$2 \underbrace{NaHCO_3}_{\text{Reactant}} \xrightarrow{\text{Heat}} \underbrace{Na_2CO_3 + H_2O + CO_2}_{\text{Products}}$$

To review the information regarding chemical reactions from Chapter 1, let us look at how this equation is written. The **reactants** are written on the left, the **products** are written on the right, and an arrow is placed between them to indicate a chemical change. Conditions necessary for the reaction to occur—heat in this particular instance—are often specified above the arrow. The substances that take part in chemical reactions may be solids, liquids, or gases, or they may be dissolved in a solvent. Ionic compounds, in particular, frequently undergo reactions in *aqueous solution*—that is, when they are dissolved in water. This information can be added to an equation by placing the appropriate abbreviations after the formulas:

(s)	(l)	(g)	(aq)
Solid	Liquid	Gas	Aqueous solution

Why is the number 2 placed before $NaHCO_3$ in the equation? The 2 is necessary because of a fundamental law of nature called the **law of conservation of mass,** which states that matter can neither be created nor destroyed in a chemical reaction.

The bonds between atoms in the reactants are rearranged to form new compounds in chemical reactions, but none of the atoms disappear and no new ones are formed.

Chemical equation An expression in which symbols and formulas are used to represent a chemical reaction.

Reactant A substance that undergoes change in a chemical reaction and is written on the left side of the reaction arrow in a chemical equation.

Product A substance that is formed in a chemical reaction and is written on the right side of the reaction arrow in a chemical equation.

Law of conservation of mass Matter is neither created nor destroyed in chemical reactions.

Balanced equation A chemical equation in which the numbers and kinds of atoms are the same on both sides of the reaction arrow.

Coefficient A number placed in front of a formula to balance a chemical equation.

As a consequence, chemical equations must be **balanced equations,** meaning that *the numbers and kinds of atoms must be the same on both sides of the reaction arrow.*

The numbers placed in front of formulas to balance equations are called **coefficients,** and they multiply all the atoms in a formula. Thus, the symbol "2 NaHCO₃" indicates two units of sodium bicarbonate (reactant), which contain 2 Na atoms, 2 H atoms, 2 C atoms, and 6 O atoms ($2 \times 3 = 6$, the coefficient times the subscript for O). Count the numbers of atoms on the right side of the equation to convince yourself that it is indeed balanced.

Thus, the decomposition of solid sodium bicarbonate can be written as

$$2\,NaHCO_3(s) \xrightarrow{\text{Heat}} Na_2CO_3(s) + H_2O(l) + CO_2(g)$$

5.2 Balancing Chemical Equations

Learning Objective:

• Balance chemical equations.

Just as a recipe indicates the appropriate amounts of each ingredient needed to make a given dish, a balanced chemical equation indicates the appropriate amounts of reactants needed to generate a given amount of product. Although balancing chemical equations often involves some trial and error, most reactions can be balanced by the following four-step approach:

STEP 1: **Write an unbalanced equation, using the correct formulas for all given reactants and products.** For example, hydrogen and oxygen must be written as H_2 and O_2, rather than as H and O, since we know that both elements exist as diatomic molecules. Remember that *the subscripts in chemical formulas cannot be changed in balancing an equation because doing so would change the identity of the substances in the reaction.*

STEP 2: **Add appropriate coefficients to balance the numbers of atoms of each element.** It helps to begin with elements that appear in only one compound or formula on each side of the equation, leaving elements that exist in elemental forms, such as oxygen and hydrogen, until last. For example, in the reaction of sulfuric acid with sodium hydroxide to give sodium sulfate and water, we might balance sodium first. We could do this by adding a coefficient of 2 for NaOH:

$$H_2SO_4 + NaOH \longrightarrow Na_2SO_4 + H_2O \quad \text{(Unbalanced)}$$
$$H_2SO_4 + 2\,NaOH \longrightarrow Na_2SO_4 + H_2O \quad \text{(Balanced for Na)}$$

Add this coefficient . . .   . . . to balance these 2 Na.

If a polyatomic ion appears on both sides of an equation, it can be treated as a single unit. For example, the sulfate ion (SO_4^{2-}) in our example is balanced because there is one on the left and one on the right:

$$H_2SO_4 + 2\,NaOH \longrightarrow Na_2SO_4 + H_2O \quad \text{(Balanced for Na and sulfate)}$$

One sulfate here . . .   . . . and one here.

At this point, the equation can be balanced for H and O by adding a coefficient of 2 for H₂O:

$$H_2SO_4 + 2\,NaOH \longrightarrow Na_2SO_4 + 2\,H_2O \quad \text{(Completely balanced)}$$

4 H and 2 O here.   4 H and 2 O here.

STEP 3: **Check the equation to make sure the numbers and kinds of atoms on both sides of the equation are the same.**

STEP 4: **Make sure the coefficients are reduced to their lowest whole-number values.**
For example, the equation

$$2 \, H_2SO_4 + 4 \, NaOH \longrightarrow 2 \, Na_2SO_4 + 4 \, H_2O$$

is balanced but can be simplified by dividing all coefficients by 2:

$$H_2SO_4 + 2 \, NaOH \longrightarrow Na_2SO_4 + 2 \, H_2O$$

Worked Example 5.1 Balancing Chemical Equations

Write a balanced chemical equation for the Haber process, an important industrial reaction in which elemental nitrogen and hydrogen combine to form ammonia.

SOLUTION

STEP 1: Write an unbalanced equation, using the correct formulas for all reactants and products.

$$N_2(g) + H_2(g) \longrightarrow NH_3(g)$$

By examination, we see that only two elements, N and H, need to be balanced. Both these elements exist in nature as diatomic gases, as indicated on the reactant side of the unbalanced equation.

STEP 2: Add appropriate coefficients to balance the numbers of atoms of each element. Remember that the subscript 2 in N_2 and H_2 indicates that these are diatomic molecules (i.e., 2 N atoms or 2 H atoms per molecule). Since there are 2 nitrogen atoms on the left, we must add a coefficient of 2 in front of the NH_3 on the right side of the equation to balance the equation with respect to N:

$$N_2(g) + H_2(g) \longrightarrow 2 \, NH_3(g)$$

Now we see that there are 2 H atoms on the left but 6 H atoms on the right. We can balance the equation with respect to hydrogen by adding a coefficient of 3 in front of the $H_2(g)$ on the left side:

$$N_2(g) + 3 \, H_2(g) \longrightarrow 2 \, NH_3(g)$$

STEP 3: Check the equation to make sure the numbers and kinds of atoms on both sides of the equation are the same.

On the left: $\quad (1 \times 2) \, N = 2 \, N \quad (3 \times 2) \, H = 6 \, H$

On the right: $\quad (2 \times 1) \, N = 2 \, N \quad (2 \times 3) \, H = 6 \, H$

STEP 4: Make sure the coefficients are reduced to their lowest whole-number values. In this case, the coefficients already represent the lowest whole-number values.

Worked Example 5.2 Balancing Chemical Equations

Natural gas (methane, CH_4) burns in oxygen to yield water and carbon dioxide (CO_2). Write a balanced equation for the reaction.

SOLUTION

STEP 1: Write the unbalanced equation, using correct formulas for all substances:

$$CH_4 + O_2 \longrightarrow CO_2 + H_2O \quad (\text{Unbalanced})$$

STEP 2: Since carbon appears in one formula on each side of the arrow, let us begin with that element. In fact, there is only 1 carbon atom in each formula, so the equation is already balanced for that element. Next, note that there are 4 hydrogen atoms on the left (in CH_4) and only 2 on the right (in H_2O). Placing a coefficient of 2 before H_2O gives the same number of hydrogen atoms on both sides:

$$CH_4 + O_2 \longrightarrow CO_2 + 2 \, H_2O \quad (\text{Balanced for C and H})$$

—continued on next page

—continued from previous page

Finally, look at the number of oxygen atoms. There are 2 on the left (in O_2) but 4 on the right (2 in CO_2 and 1 in each H_2O). If we place a 2 before the O_2, the number of oxygen atoms will be the same on both sides, but the numbers of other elements will not change:

$$CH_4 + 2\,O_2 \longrightarrow CO_2 + 2\,H_2O \quad (\text{Balanced for C, H, and O})$$

STEP 3: Check to be sure the numbers of atoms on both sides are the same.

On the left: 1 C   4 H $(2 \times 2)\,O = 4\,O$

On the right: 1 C $(2 \times 2)\,H = 4\,H$ $2\,O + 2\,O = 4\,O$

From CO_2 From 2 H_2O

STEP 4: Make sure the coefficients are reduced to their lowest whole-number values. In this case, the answer is already correct.

Worked Example 5.3 Balancing Chemical Equations

Sodium chlorate ($NaClO_3$) decomposes when heated to yield sodium chloride and oxygen, a reaction used to provide oxygen for the emergency breathing masks in airliners. Write a balanced equation for this reaction.

SOLUTION

STEP 1: The unbalanced equation is

$$NaClO_3 \longrightarrow NaCl + O_2$$

STEP 2: Both the Na and the Cl are already balanced, with only one atom of each on the left and right sides of the equation. There are 3 O atoms on the left but only 2 on the right. The O atoms can be balanced by placing a coefficient of 1½ in front of O_2 on the right side of the equation:

$$NaClO_3 \longrightarrow NaCl + 1½\,O_2$$

▲The oxygen in emergency breathing masks comes from heating sodium chlorate.

STEP 3: Checking to make sure the same number of atoms of each type occurs on both sides of the equation, we see 1 atom each of Na and Cl on both sides and 3 O atoms on both sides.

STEP 4: In this case, obtaining all coefficients in their smallest whole-number values requires that we multiply all coefficients by 2 to obtain:

$$2\,NaClO_3 \longrightarrow 2\,NaCl + 3\,O_2$$

Checking gives

On the left: 2 Na 2 Cl $(2 \times 3)\,O = 6\,O$

On the right: 2 Na 2 Cl $(3 \times 2)\,O = 6\,O$

PROBLEM 5.1

Ozone (O_3) is formed in the earth's upper atmosphere by the action of solar radiation on oxygen molecules (O_2). Write a balanced equation for the formation of ozone from oxygen.

PROBLEM 5.2

Balance the following equations:
(a) $Ca(OH)_2 + HCl \longrightarrow CaCl_2 + H_2O$
(b) $Al + O_2 \longrightarrow Al_2O_3$
(c) $CH_3CH_3 + O_2 \longrightarrow CO_2 + H_2O$
(d) $AgNO_3 + MgCl_2 \longrightarrow AgCl + Mg(NO_3)_2$

🔾 **KEY CONCEPT PROBLEM 5.3**

The following diagram represents the reaction of A (red spheres) with B_2 (blue spheres). Write a balanced equation for the reaction.

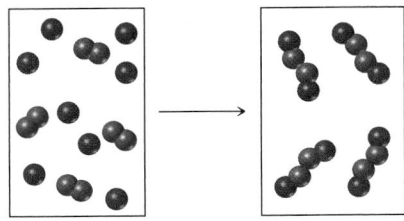

HANDS-ON CHEMISTRY 5.1

Look up a recipe for your favorite cookies. Using the list of ingredients and the expected yield (number of cookies), write a balanced equation to represent this process. Also, think about the units used to indicate the amount of each substance (teaspoon, cup, or ounce). What units would you use if all the ingredients had to be measured in the same unit?

5.3 Precipitation Reactions and Solubility Guidelines

Learning Objective:

- Apply solubility rules to predict if a precipitation reaction will occur, and write the appropriate balanced reaction.

One of the best ways to understand any subject is to look for patterns that help us categorize large amounts of information. When learning about chemical reactions, for instance, it is helpful to group the reactions of ionic compounds into three general classes: *precipitation reactions, acid-base neutralization reactions,* and *oxidation-reduction reactions.* We will study each of these three reaction classes in more detail in the next three sections, beginning here with precipitation reactions.

Precipitation reactions are processes in which an insoluble solid called a **precipitate** forms when reactants are combined in aqueous solution. Most precipitations take place when the anions and cations of two ionic compounds change partners. For example, an aqueous solution of lead(II) nitrate reacts with an aqueous solution of potassium iodide to yield an aqueous solution of potassium nitrate plus an insoluble yellow precipitate of lead iodide:

$$Pb(NO_3)_2\,(aq) + 2\,KI(aq) \longrightarrow 2\,KNO_3(aq) + PbI_2(s)$$

To predict whether a precipitation reaction will occur upon mixing aqueous solutions of two ionic compounds, you must know the **solubilities** of the potential products—how much of each compound will dissolve in a given amount of solvent at a given temperature. If a substance has a low solubility in water, then it is likely to precipitate from an aqueous solution. If a substance has a high solubility in water, then no precipitate will form.

Solubility is a complex matter, and it is not always possible to make correct predictions. As a rule of thumb, though, the following solubility guidelines for ionic compounds are useful.

Precipitate An insoluble solid that forms in solution during a chemical reaction.

Solubility The amount of a compound that will dissolve in a given amount of solvent at a given temperature.

▲ Reaction of aqueous $Pb(NO_3)_2$ with aqueous KI gives a yellow precipitate of PbI_2.

General Rules on Solubility

RULE 1: **A compound is probably soluble if it contains one of the following cations:**
- Group 1A cation: Li^+, Na^+, K^+, Rb^+, Cs^+
- Ammonium ion: NH_4^+

CHEMISTRY IN ACTION

⚕ Kidney Stones: A Problem in Solubility

One of the major pathways in the body for the breakdown of the nucleic acids—deoxyribonucleic acid (DNA) and ribonucleic acid (RNA)—is by conversion to a substance called *uric acid*, $C_5H_4N_4O_3$, so named because it was first isolated from urine in 1776. Most people excrete about 0.5 g of uric acid every day in the form of sodium urate, the salt that results from an acid-base reaction of uric acid. Unfortunately, the amount of sodium urate that dissolves in water (or urine) is fairly low—only about 0.07 mg/mL at the normal body temperature of 37 °C. When too much sodium urate is produced or mechanisms for its elimination fail, its concentration in blood and urine rises, and the excess sometimes precipitates in the joints to cause gout (see the Chemistry in Action in Chapter 25, p. 770) and in the kidneys as kidney stones.

▲ The limited solubility of uric acid and calcium oxalate can result in the formation of kidney stones measuring ~0.5 cm in diameter.

RULE 2: **A compound is probably soluble if it contains one of the following anions:**
- Halide: Cl^-, Br^-, and I^- except *Ag^+*, *Hg_2^{2+}*, and *Pb^{2+}* compounds
- Nitrate (NO_3^-), perchlorate (ClO_4^-), acetate $(CH_3CO_2^-)$, and sulfate (SO_4^{2-}) except *Ba^{2+}*, *Hg_2^{2+}*, and *Pb^{2+}* sulfates

If a compound does *not* contain at least one of the ions listed above, it is probably *not* soluble. Thus, Na_2CO_3 is soluble because it contains a group 1A cation, and $CaCl_2$ is soluble because it contains a halide anion. The compound $CaCO_3$, however, is probably *insoluble* because it contains none of the ions listed above. These same guidelines are presented in table form in Table 5.1.

Table 5.1 General Solubility Guidelines for Ionic Compounds in Water

Soluble	Exceptions
Ammonium compounds (NH_4^+)	None
Lithium compounds (Li^+)	None
Sodium compounds (Na^+)	None
Potassium compounds (K^+)	None
Nitrates (NO_3^-)	None
Perchlorates (ClO_4^-)	None
Acetates $(CH_3CO_2^-)$	None
Chlorides (Cl^-)	
Bromides (Br^-)	Ag^+, Hg_2^{2+}, and Pb^{2+} compounds
Iodides (I^-)	
Sulfates (SO_4^{2-})	Ba^{2+}, Hg_2^{2+}, and Pb^{2+} compounds

Let us try a problem. What will happen if aqueous solutions of sodium nitrate $(NaNO_3)$ and potassium sulfate (K_2SO_4) are mixed? To answer this question, look at the guidelines to find the solubilities of the two possible products, Na_2SO_4 and KNO_3. Because both have group 1A cations (Na^+ and K^+), both are water-soluble and no precipitation will occur. If aqueous solutions of silver nitrate $(AgNO_3)$ and sodium

Kidney stones are small crystals that precipitate in the kidney. Although often quite small, kidney stones cause excruciating pain when they pass through the ureter, the duct that carries urine from the kidney to the bladder. In some cases, complete blockage of the ureter occurs. Treatment or prevention of kidney stones depends on the underlying cause and the composition of the stones. The most common type of kidney stones consists of calcium oxalate, an insoluble ionic compound. High dietary intake of supplemental calcium by postmenopausal women is linked to increased incidents of kidney stones. Also, high intake of dietary oxalates, found in rhubarb, spinach, blueberries, and chocolate, can contribute to kidney stone formation.

Sodium urate–based kidney stones are linked to high dietary intake of animal protein, especially in foods such as liver, sardines, and shellfish. Drugs such as allopurinol can lower production of sodium urate by inhibiting the action of an enzyme called *xanthine oxidase,* thereby blocking a step in nucleic acid metabolism. In addition to dietary modification, kidney stones can be avoided by avoiding dehydration (i.e., increasing daily water consumption) and increasing dietary intake of citrates.

CIA Problem 5.1 Many kidney stones are formed by precipitation of oxalate by calcium. Show the balanced chemical equation for the precipitation of calcium oxalate, starting with calcium chloride ($CaCl_2$) and sodium oxalate ($Na_2C_2O_4$).

CIA Problem 5.2 Uric acid is formed in the body by the metabolism of purines. The reaction can be represented as $C_5H_4N_4$ (purine) $+ O_2 \longrightarrow C_5H_4N_4O_3$ (uric acid).

(a) Balance the reaction.
(b) What type of reaction is this?

carbonate (Na_2CO_3) are mixed, however, the guidelines predict that a precipitate of insoluble silver carbonate (Ag_2CO_3) will form.

$$2\, AgNO_3(aq) + Na_2CO_3(aq) \longrightarrow Ag_2CO_3(s) + 2\, NaNO_3(aq)$$

Worked Example 5.4 Chemical Reactions: Solubility Rules

Will a precipitation reaction occur when aqueous solutions of $CdCl_2$ and $(NH_4)_2S$ are mixed?

SOLUTION

Identify the two potential products, and predict the solubility of each using the guidelines in the text. In this instance, $CdCl_2$ and $(NH_4)_2S$ might give CdS and NH_4Cl. Since the guidelines predict that CdS is insoluble, a precipitation reaction will occur:

$$CdCl_2(aq) + (NH_4)_2S(aq) \longrightarrow CdS(s) + 2NH_4Cl(aq)$$

PROBLEM 5.4

Predict the solubility of the following compounds:
  (a) $CdCO_3$ **(b)** Na_2S **(c)** $PbSO_4$ **(d)** $(NH_4)_3PO_4$ **(e)** Hg_2Cl_2

PROBLEM 5.5

Predict whether a precipitation reaction will occur in the following situations. If a precipitation reaction occurs, write the balanced chemical equation for the reaction.

  (a) $NiCl_2(aq) + (NH_4)_2S(aq) \longrightarrow$ **(b)** $AgNO_3(aq) + CaBr_2(aq) \longrightarrow$

5.4 Acids, Bases, and Neutralization Reactions

Learning Objective:

• Predict the products of an acid-base neutralization reaction.

Acid-base neutralization reactions are processes in which an acid reacts with a base to yield water plus an ionic compound called a **salt.** We will look at both acids and bases in more detail in Chapter 10, but you might recall from Chapter 3 that we previously defined acids as compounds that produce H^+ ions and bases as compounds that produce OH^- ions when dissolved in water. Thus, a neutralization reaction removes H^+

Salt An ionic compound formed from reaction of an acid with a base.

◀◀◀ **CONCEPTS TO REVIEW** See
Section 3.11 for more discussion of acids
and bases.

Neutralization reaction The reaction
of an acid with a base.

and OH^- ions from solution and yields neutral H_2O. The reaction between hydrochloric acid and sodium hydroxide is a typical example:

$$HCl(aq) + NaOH(aq) \longrightarrow H_2O(l) + NaCl(aq)$$

When acids and bases are mixed in the correct proportion, both acidic and basic properties disappear because of a **neutralization reaction.** The most common kind of neutralization reaction occurs between an acid (generalized as HA) and a metal hydroxide (generalized as MOH) to yield water and a salt. The H^+ ion from the acid combines with the OH^- ion from the base to give neutral H_2O, whereas the anion from the acid (A^-) combines with the cation from the base (M^+) to give the salt.

$$A\ neutralization\ reaction: \quad \underset{\text{Acid}}{HA(aq)} + \underset{\text{Base}}{MOH(aq)} \longrightarrow \underset{\text{Water}}{H_2O(l)} + \underset{\text{A salt}}{MA(aq)}$$

Note that in the example involving HCl and NaOH, the "salt" produced is sodium chloride or common table salt. In a general sense, however, *any* ionic compound produced in an acid-base reaction is also called a salt. Other examples include potassium nitrate (KNO_3), magnesium bromide $(MgBr_2)$, and sodium sulfate (Na_2SO_4).

Another kind of neutralization reaction occurs between an acid and a carbonate (or bicarbonate) to yield water, a salt, and carbon dioxide. Hydrochloric acid reacts with potassium carbonate, for example, to give H_2O, KCl, and CO_2:

LOOKING AHEAD ▶▶▶Acids and bases
are enormously important in biological
chemistry. We will see in Chapter 18, for
instance, how acids and bases affect the
structure and properties of proteins.

$$2\ HCl(aq) + K_2CO_3(aq) \longrightarrow H_2O(l) + 2\ KCl(aq) + CO_2(g)$$

The reaction occurs because the carbonate ion (CO_3^{2-}) reacts initially with H^+ to yield H_2CO_3, which is unstable and immediately decomposes to give CO_2 plus H_2O.

Worked Example 5.5 Chemical Reactions: Acid-Base Neutralization

Write an equation for the neutralization reaction of aqueous HBr and aqueous $Ba(OH)_2$.

SOLUTION
The reaction of HBr with $Ba(OH)_2$ involves the combination of a proton (H^+) from the acid with OH^- from the base to yield water and a salt $(BaBr_2)$.

$$2\ HBr(aq) + Ba(OH)_2(aq) \longrightarrow 2\ H_2O(l) + BaBr_2(aq)$$

PROBLEM 5.6

Write and balance equations for the following acid-base neutralization reactions:

(a) $CsOH(aq) + H_2SO_4(aq) \longrightarrow$
(b) $Ca(OH)_2(aq) + CH_3CO_2H(aq) \longrightarrow$
(c) $NaHCO_3(aq) + HBr(aq) \longrightarrow$

HANDS-ON CHEMISTRY 5.2

Pour one-fourth cup of vinegar (containing acetic acid!)
into a large glass and fill the glass half-way with water.

1. Carefully waft the vapor above the solution to your
    nose. Can you smell the characteristic aroma of the
    vinegar/acetic acid?

2. Carefully add one antacid tablet (TUMS, Rolaids) or a
    teaspoon of baking soda (sodium bicarbonate) to the
    glass. What do you observe, and how is this evidence
    of a neutralization reaction? When the reaction stops,
    can you still smell the aroma of vinegar? If you add an-
    other antacid tablet, is there any further reaction?

5.5 Redox Reactions

Learning Objective:

- Recognize redox reactions, and identify the species being oxidized and reduced.

Oxidation-reduction (redox) reactions, the third and final category of reactions that we will discuss in this chapter, are more complex than precipitation and neutralization reactions. Redox reactions are processes in which electrons are transferred between reaction partners (atoms, molecules, ions). As a result of this transfer, the number of electrons assigned to individual atoms in the various reactants change. Look at the following examples and see if you can tell how they qualify as redox reactions. Copper metal reacts with aqueous silver nitrate to form silver metal and aqueous copper(II) nitrate; iron rusts in air to form iron(III) oxide; the zinc metal container on the outside of a battery reacts with manganese dioxide and ammonium chloride inside the battery to generate electricity and give aqueous zinc chloride plus manganese(III) oxide. Although these and many thousands of other reactions appear unrelated, all are examples of redox reactions.

> **Oxidation-reduction (redox) reaction** A reaction in which electrons are transferred from one atom to another.

$$Cu(s) + 2\,AgNO_3(aq) \longrightarrow 2\,Ag(s) + Cu(NO_3)_2(aq)$$

$$2\,Fe(s) + 3\,O_2(g) \longrightarrow Fe_2O_3(s)$$

$$Zn(s) + 2\,MnO_2(s) + 2\,NH_4Cl(s) \longrightarrow$$
$$ZnCl_2(aq) + Mn_2O_3(s) + 2\,NH_3(aq) + H_2O(l)$$

Historically, the word *oxidation* referred to the combination of an element with oxygen to yield an oxide, and the word *reduction* referred to the removal of oxygen from an oxide to yield the element. Today, though, the words have taken on a much broader meaning. An **oxidation** is now defined as the loss of one or more electrons by an atom, and a **reduction** is the gain of one or more electrons. Thus, an oxidation-reduction reaction, or redox reaction, is one in which *electrons are transferred from one atom to another.*

Fundamentally, all reactions involving covalent compounds are classified as redox reactions, because electrons are rearranged as bonds are broken and new bonds are formed. The discussion here, however, will focus mainly on reactions involving ionic substances.

> **Oxidation** The loss of one or more electrons by an atom.
>
> **Reduction** The gain of one or more electrons by an atom.

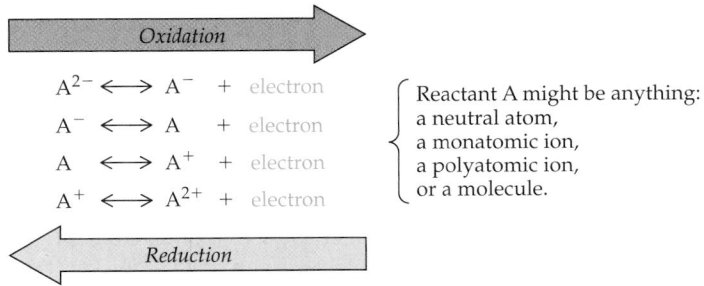

Take the reaction of copper with aqueous Ag^+ as an example, as shown in Figure 5.1. Copper metal gives an electron to each of two Ag^+ ions, forming Cu^{2+} and silver metal. Copper is oxidized in the process, and Ag^+ is reduced. You can follow the transfer of the electrons by noting that the charge on the copper increases from 0 to +2 when it loses two electrons, whereas the charge on Ag^+ decreases from +1 to 0 when it gains an electron.

Similarly, in the reaction of aqueous iodide ion with bromine, iodide ion gives an electron to bromine, forming iodine and bromide ion. Iodide ion is oxidized as its charge increases from −1 to 0, and bromine is reduced as its charge decreases from 0 to −1.

$$2\,I^-(aq) + Br_2(aq) \longrightarrow I_2(aq) + 2\,Br^-(aq)$$

+2 electrons = reduced!

−1 charge 0 charge 0 charge −1 charge

−2 electrons = oxidized!

As these examples show, oxidation and reduction always occur together. Whenever one substance loses an electron (is oxidized), another substance must gain that electron (be reduced). The substance that gives up an electron and causes the reduction—the

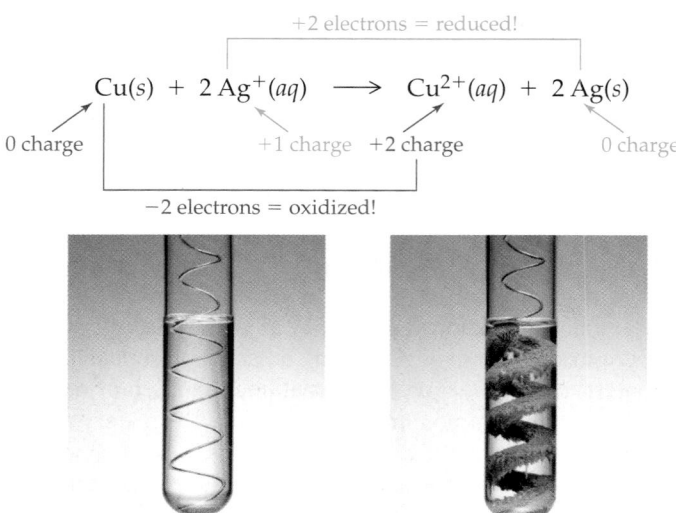

► **Figure 5.1**
The copper wire reacts with aqueous Ag^+ ion and becomes coated with metallic silver. At the same time, copper(II) ions go into solution, producing the blue color.

Reducing agent A reactant that causes a reduction in another reactant by giving up electron to it.

Oxidizing agent A reactant that causes an oxidation by taking electrons from another reactant.

copper atom in the reaction of Cu with Ag^+ and the iodide ion in the reaction of I^- with Br_2—is called a **reducing agent.** The substance that gains an electron and causes the oxidation—the silver ion in the reaction of Cu with Ag^+ and the bromine molecule in the reaction of I^- with Br_2—is called an **oxidizing agent.** The charge on the reducing agent increases during the reaction, and the charge on the oxidizing agent decreases.

Reducing agent	Loses one or more electrons
	Causes reduction
	Undergoes oxidation
	Becomes more positive (less negative)
	(May gain oxygen atoms)

Oxidizing agent	Gains one or more electrons
	Causes oxidation
	Undergoes reduction
	Becomes more negative (less positive)
	(May lose oxygen atoms)

Among the simplest of redox processes is the reaction of an element, usually a metal, with an aqueous cation to yield a different element and a different ion. Iron metal reacts with aqueous copper(II) ion, for example, to give iron(II) ion and copper metal. Similarly, magnesium metal reacts with aqueous acid to yield magnesium ion and hydrogen gas. In both cases, the reactant element (Fe or Mg) is oxidized, and the reactant ion (Cu^{2+} or H^+) is reduced.

$$Fe(s) + Cu^{2+}(aq) \longrightarrow Fe^{2+}(aq) + Cu(s)$$
$$Mg(s) + 2\,H^+(aq) \longrightarrow Mg^{2+}(aq) + H_2(g)$$

The reaction of a metal with water or aqueous acid (H^+) to release H_2 gas is a particularly important process. As you might expect based on the periodic properties discussed in Section 3.4, the alkali metals and alkaline earth metals (on the left side of the periodic table) are the most powerful reducing agents (electron donors), so powerful that they even react with pure water, in which the concentration of H^+ is very low. This is due in part to the fact that alkali metals and alkaline earth metals have low ionization energies. Ionization energy, which is a measure of how easily an element will lose an electron, tends to decrease as we move to the left and down in the periodic table. Thus, metals toward the middle of the periodic table, such as iron and chromium, have higher ionization energies and do not lose electrons as readily; they react only with aqueous acids but not with water. Those metals near the bottom right of the periodic table, such as platinum and gold, react with neither aqueous acid nor water. At the other extreme from the alkali metals, the reactive nonmetals at the top right of the periodic table have the highest ionization energies and are extremely weak reducing agents but powerful oxidizing agents (electron acceptors). This is, again, predictable based on the periodic property of electron affinity (Section 3.4), which becomes more energetically favored as we move up and to the right in the periodic table.

◄◄◄ The relationship between formation of ions and ionization energy/electronegativity was discussed in Chapter 3.

We can make a few generalizations about the redox behavior of metals and nonmetals.

1. In reactions involving metals and nonmetals, metals tend to lose electrons while nonmetals tend to gain electrons. The number of electrons lost or gained can often be predicted based on the position of the element in the periodic table. (Section 3.3)

2. In reactions involving nonmetals, the "more metallic" element (farther down and/or to the left in the periodic table) tends to lose electrons, and the "less metallic" element (up and/or to the right) tends to gain electrons.

Redox reactions involve almost every element in the periodic table, and they occur in a vast number of processes throughout nature, biology, and industry. Here are just a few examples:

- *Corrosion* is the deterioration of a metal by oxidation, such as the rusting of iron in moist air. The economic consequences of rusting are enormous: it has been estimated that up to one-fourth of the iron produced in the United States is used to replace bridges, buildings, and other structures that have been destroyed by corrosion.

- *Combustion* is the burning of a fuel by rapid oxidation with oxygen in air. Gasoline, fuel oil, natural gas, wood, paper, and other organic substances of carbon and hydrogen are the most common fuels that burn in air. Even some metals, though, will burn in air. Magnesium and calcium are examples.

$$CH_4(g) + 2\,O_2(g) \longrightarrow CO_2(g) + 2\,H_2O(l)$$

  Methane
  (natural gas)

$$2\,Mg(s) + O_2(g) \longrightarrow 2\,MgO(s)$$

- *Respiration* is the process of breathing and using oxygen for the many biological redox reactions that provide the energy required by living organisms. We will see in Chapters 21 and 22 that in the respiration process, energy is released from food molecules slowly and in complex, multistep pathways, but that the overall result is similar to that of the simpler combustion reactions. For example, the simple sugar glucose $(C_6H_{12}O_6)$ reacts with O_2 to give CO_2 and H_2O according to the following equation:

$$C_6H_{12}O_6 + 6\,O_2 \longrightarrow 6\,CO_2 + 6\,H_2O + Energy$$

  Glucose
  (a carbohydrate)

- *Bleaching* makes use of redox reactions to decolorize or lighten colored materials. Dark hair is bleached to turn it blond, clothes are bleached to remove stains, wood pulp is bleached to make white paper, and so on. The oxidizing agent used depends on the situation: hydrogen peroxide (H_2O_2) is used for hair, sodium hypochlorite (NaOCl) for clothes, and elemental chlorine for wood pulp, but the principle is always the same. In all cases, colored organic materials are destroyed by reaction with strong oxidizing agents.

- *Metallurgy,* the science of extracting and purifying metals from their ores, makes use of numerous redox processes. Worldwide, approximately 800 million tons of iron are produced each year by reduction of the mineral hematite, Fe_2O_3, with carbon monoxide.

Worked Example 5.6 Chemical Reactions: Redox Reactions

For the following reactions, indicate which atom is oxidized and which is reduced, based on the definitions provided in this section. Identify the oxidizing and reducing agents.

(a) $Cu(s) + Pt^{2+}(aq) \longrightarrow Cu^{2+}(aq) + Pt(s)$

(b) $2\,Mg(s) + CO_2(g) \longrightarrow 2\,MgO(s) + C(s)$

ANALYSIS The definitions for oxidation include a loss of electrons, an increase in charge, and a gain of oxygen atoms; reduction is defined as a gain of electrons, a decrease in charge, and a loss of oxygen atoms.

SOLUTION

(a) In this reaction, the charge on the Cu atom increases from 0 to 2+. This corresponds to a loss of two electrons. The Cu is therefore oxidized and acts as the reducing agent. Conversely, the Pt^{2+} ion undergoes a decrease in charge from 2+ to 0, corresponding to a gain of two electrons for the Pt^{2+} ion. The Pt^{2+} is reduced and acts as the oxidizing agent.

(b) In this case, the gain or loss of oxygen atoms is the easiest way to identify which atoms are oxidized and reduced. The Mg atom is gaining oxygen to form MgO; therefore, the Mg is being oxidized and acts as the reducing agent. The C atom in CO_2 is losing oxygen. Therefore, the C atom in CO_2 is being reduced, and so CO_2 acts as the oxidizing agent.

Worked Example 5.7 Chemical Reactions: Identifying Oxidizing/Reducing Agents

For the respiration and metallurgy examples discussed previously, identify the atoms being oxidized and reduced, and label the oxidizing and reducing agents.

ANALYSIS Again, using the definitions of oxidation and reduction provided in this section, we can determine which atom(s) are gaining/losing electrons or gaining/losing oxygen atoms.

SOLUTION

$$\textit{Respiration:} \quad C_6H_{12}O_6 + 6\,O_2 \longrightarrow 6\,CO_2 + 6\,H_2O$$

Because the charge associated with the individual atoms is not evident, we will use the definition of oxidation/reduction as the gaining/losing of oxygen atoms. In this reaction, there is only one reactant besides oxygen $(C_6H_{12}O_6)$, so we must determine *which* atom in the compound is changing. The ratio of carbon to oxygen in $C_6H_{12}O_4$ is 1:1, whereas the ratio in CO_2 is 1:2. Therefore, the C atoms are gaining oxygen and are oxidized; the $C_6H_{12}O_{16}$ is the reducing agent and O_2 is the oxidizing agent. Note that the ratio of hydrogen to oxygen in $C_6H_{12}O_6$ and in H_2O is 2:1. The H atoms are neither oxidized nor reduced.

$$\textit{Metallurgy:} \quad Fe_2O_3(s) + 3\,CO(g) \longrightarrow 2\,Fe(s) + 3\,CO_2(g)$$

The Fe_2O_3 is losing oxygen to form Fe(s); it is being reduced and acts as the oxidizing agent. In contrast, the CO is gaining oxygen to form CO_2; it is being oxidized and acts as the reducing agent.

Worked Example 5.8 Chemical Reactions: Identifying Redox Reactions

For the following reactions, identify the atom(s) being oxidized and reduced:

(a) $2\,Al(s) + 3\,Cl_2(g) \longrightarrow 2\,AlCl_3(s)$

(b) $C(s) + 2\,Cl_2(g) \longrightarrow CCl_4(l)$

ANALYSIS Again, there is no obvious increase or decrease in charge to indicate a gain or loss of electrons. Also, the reactions do not involve a gain or loss of oxygen. We can, however, evaluate the reactions in terms of the typical behavior of metals and nonmetals in reactions.

SOLUTION

(a) In this case, we have the reaction of a metal (Al) with a nonmetal (Cl_2). Because metals tend to lose electrons and nonmetals tend to gain electrons, we can assume that the Al atom is oxidized (loses electrons) and the Cl_2 is reduced (gains electrons).

(b) The carbon atom is the less electronegative element (farther to the left) and is less likely to gain an electron. The more electronegative element (Cl) will tend to gain electrons (be reduced).

Worked Example 5.9 Classifying Chemical Reactions

Classify the following as a precipitation, an acid-base neutralization, or a redox reaction.

(a) $Ca(OH)_2(aq) + 2 HBr(aq) \longrightarrow 2 H_2O(l) + CaBr_2(aq)$
(b) $Pb(ClO_4)_2(aq) + 2 NaCl(aq) \longrightarrow PbCl_2(s) + 2 NaClO_4(aq)$
(c) $2 AgNO_3(aq) + Cu(s) \longrightarrow 2 Ag(s) + Cu(NO_3)_2(aq)$

ANALYSIS One way to identify the class of reaction is to examine the products that form and match them with the descriptions for the types of reactions provided in this section. By a process of elimination, we can readily identify the appropriate reaction classification.

SOLUTION

(a) The products of this reaction are water and an ionic compound, or salt ($CaBr_2$). This is consistent with the description of an acid-base neutralization reaction.

(b) This reaction involves two aqueous reactants, $Pb(ClO_4)_2$ and NaCl, which combine to form a solid product, $PbCl_2$. This is consistent with a precipitation reaction.

(c) The products of this reaction are a solid, Ag(s), and an aqueous ionic compound, $Cu(NO_3)_2$. This does not match the description of a neutralization reaction, which would form *water* and an ionic compound. One of the products *is* a solid, but the reactants are not both aqueous compound; one of the reactants is *also* a solid (Cu). Therefore, this reaction would not be classified as a precipitation reaction. By the process of elimination, then, it must be a redox reaction.

PROBLEM 5.7

Classify each of the following as a precipitation, an acid-base neutralization, or a redox reaction.

(a) $AgNO_3(aq) + KCl(aq) \longrightarrow AgCl(s) + KNO_3(aq)$
(b) $2 Al(s) + 3 Br_2(l) \longrightarrow 2 AlBr_3(s)$
(c) $Ca(OH)_2(aq) + 2 HNO_3(aq) \longrightarrow 2 H_2O(l) + Ca(NO_3)_2(aq)$

PROBLEM 5.8

Identify the oxidized reactant, the reduced reactant, the oxidizing agent, and the reducing agent in the following reactions:

(a) $Fe(s) + Cu^{2+}(aq) \longrightarrow Fe^{2+}(aq) + Cu(s)$
(b) $Mg(s) + Cl_2(g) \longrightarrow MgCl_2(s)$
(c) $2 Al(s) + Cr_2O_3(s) \longrightarrow 2 Cr(s) + Al_2O_3(s)$

PROBLEM 5.9

Potassium, a silvery metal, reacts with bromine, a corrosive, reddish liquid, to yield potassium bromide, a white solid. Write the balanced equation, and identify the oxidizing and reducing agents.

CHEMISTRY IN ACTION

⚕ Batteries

A patient suffering from congestive heart failure receives an artificial mechanical heart, whereas another heart patient with arrythmia may receive a pacemaker or an implantable cardioverter defibrillator. A disabled veteran suffering from posttraumatic stress disorder (PTSD) receives a brain implant to monitor and control brain impulses affecting mood, whereas another patient uses a similar implant to send electrical impulses to control tremors associated with Parkinson's disease. A deaf person receives a cochlear implant to stimulate auditory sensation, whereas a patient experiencing vertigo associated with Meniere's disease may use a similar device to maintain equilibrium. What do all these scenarios have in common? They all utilize electronic implants that are powered by small batteries.

It is hard to imagine life without batteries: no cars (they do not start very easily without their batteries!), no flashlights, no hearing aids, no laptops, no radios, no cell phones, nor thousands of other things. Modern society could not exist without batteries.

Although they come in many types and sizes, all batteries work using redox reactions. In a typical redox reaction carried out in the laboratory—say, the reaction of zinc metal with Ag^+ to yield Zn^{2+} and silver metal—the reactants are simply mixed in a flask and electrons are transferred by direct contact between the reactants. In a battery, however, the two reactants are kept in separate compartments and the electrons are transferred through a wire running between them.

The common household battery used for flashlights and radios is the *dry cell,* developed in 1866. One reactant is a can of zinc metal, and the other is a paste of solid manganese

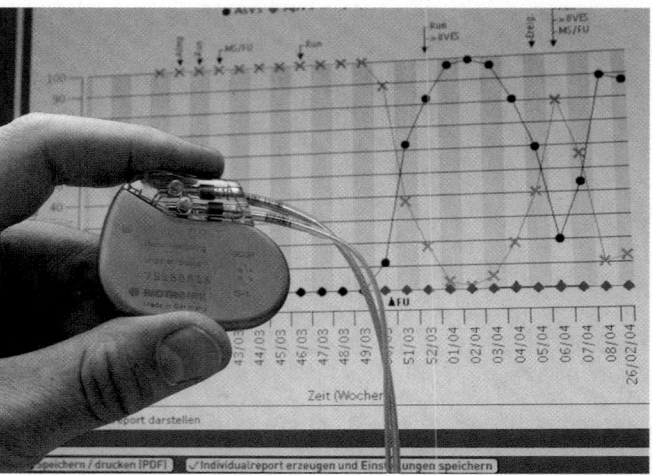

▲ This battery-powered pacemaker can run for 8 to 12 years, relaying cardiological data directly to doctors to monitor patients remotely.

dioxide. A graphite rod sticks into the MnO_2 paste to provide electrical contact, and a moist paste of ammonium chloride separates the two reactants. If the zinc can and the graphite rod are connected by a wire, zinc sends electrons flowing through the wire toward the MnO_2 in a redox reaction. The resultant electrical current can then be used to power a lightbulb or a radio. The accompanying figure shows a cutaway view of a dry-cell battery.

$$Zn(s) + 2\,MnO_2(s) + 2\,NH_4Cl(s) \longrightarrow$$
$$ZnCl_2(aq) + Mn_2O_3(s) + 2\,NH_3(aq) + H_2O(l)$$

Closely related to the dry-cell battery is the familiar *alkaline* battery, in which the ammonium chloride paste is replaced

5.6 Recognizing Redox Reactions

Learning Objective:

• Determine the oxidation number of an atom in a compound.

How can you tell when a redox reaction is taking place? When ions are involved, it is simply a matter of determining whether there is a change in the charges. For reactions involving metals and nonmetals, we can predict the gain or loss of electrons as discussed previously. When molecular substances are involved, though, it is not as obvious. Is the combining of sulfur with oxygen a redox reaction? If so, which partner is the oxidizing agent and which is the reducing agent?

$$S(s) + O_2(g) \longrightarrow SO_2(g)$$

One way to evaluate this reaction is in terms of the oxygen gain by sulfur, indicating that S atoms are oxidized and O atoms are reduced. But can we also look at this reaction in terms of the gain or loss of electrons by the S and O atoms? Because oxygen is more electronegative than sulfur, the oxygen atoms in SO_2 attract the electrons in the S—O bonds more strongly than sulfur does, giving the oxygen atoms a larger share of the electrons than sulfur. By extending the ideas of oxidation and reduction to an

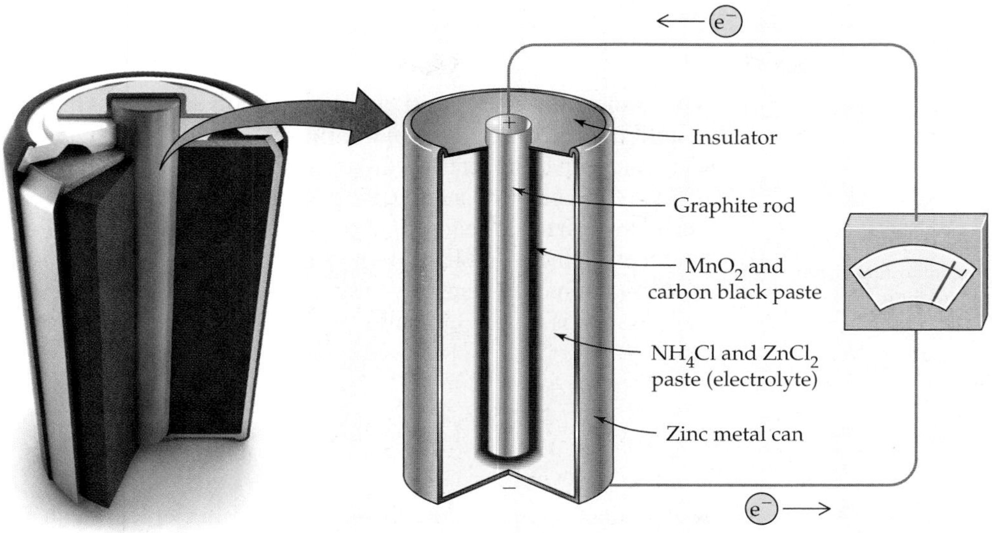

▲ A dry-cell battery. The cutaway view shows the two reactants that make up the redox reaction.

Labels in figure:
- Insulator
- Graphite rod
- MnO_2 and carbon black paste
- NH_4Cl and $ZnCl_2$ paste (electrolyte)
- Zinc metal can

by an alkaline, or basic, paste of NaOH or KOH. The alkaline battery has a longer life than the standard dry-cell battery because the zinc container corrodes less easily under basic conditions. The redox reaction is

$$Zn(s) + 2\,MnO_2(s) \longrightarrow ZnO(aq) + Mn_2O_3(s)$$

The batteries used in implanted medical devices such as pacemakers must be small, corrosion-resistant, reliable, and able to last up to 10 years. Nearly all pacemakers being implanted today—about 750,000 each year—use titanium-encased, lithium–iodine batteries, whose redox reaction is

$$2\,Li(s) + I_2(s) \longrightarrow 2\,LiI(aq)$$

CIA Problem 5.3 The rechargeable NiCd battery uses the following reaction:

$$2\,NiO(OH) + Cd + 2\,H_2O \longrightarrow 2\,Ni(OH)_2 + Cd(OH)_2$$

Which reactant is being oxidized and which is being reduced in this reaction?

CIA Problem 5.4 The redox reaction that provides energy for the lithium is

$$2\,Li(s) + I_2(s) \longrightarrow 2\,LiI(aq)$$

Identify which reactant is being oxidized and which is being reduced in this reaction.

increase or decrease in electron *sharing* instead of complete electron *transfer,* we can say that the sulfur atom is oxidized in its reaction with oxygen because it loses a share in some electrons, whereas the oxygen atoms are reduced because they gain a share in some electrons.

A formal system has been devised for keeping track of changes in electron sharing, and thus for determining whether atoms are oxidized or reduced in reactions. To each atom in a substance, we assign a value called an **oxidation number** (or *oxidation state*), which indicates whether the atom is neutral, electron-rich, or electron-poor. By comparing the oxidation number of an atom before and after a reaction, we can tell whether the atom has gained or lost shares in electrons. Note that *oxidation numbers do not necessarily imply ionic charges.* They are simply a convenient device for keeping track of electrons in redox reactions.

The rules for assigning oxidation numbers are straightforward:

• **An atom in its elemental state has an oxidation number of 0.**

◄◄ Electronegativity, or the propensity of an atom in a covalent bond to attract electrons, was introduced in Section 4.9.

Oxidation number A number that indicates whether an atom is neutral, electron-rich, or electron-poor.

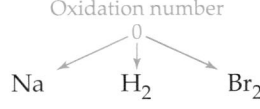

Oxidation number

Na H_2 Br_2 (each 0)

- **A monatomic ion has an oxidation number equal to its charge.**

- **In a molecular compound, an atom usually has the same oxidation number it would have if it were a monatomic ion.** Recall from Chapters 3 and 4 that the less electronegative elements (hydrogen and metals) on the left side of the periodic table tend to form cations, and the more electronegative elements (oxygen, nitrogen, and the halogens) near the top right of the periodic table tend to form anions. Hydrogen and metals, therefore, have positive oxidation numbers in most compounds, whereas reactive nonmetals generally have negative oxidation numbers. Hydrogen is usually +1, oxygen is usually −2, nitrogen is usually −3, and halogens are usually −1.

Review the Important Points about Ion Formation and the Periodic Table listed in Section 3.3.

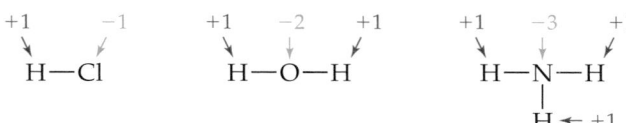

For compounds with more than one nonmetal element, such as SO_2, NO, or CO_2, the more electronegative element—oxygen in these examples—has a negative oxidation number and the less electronegative element has a positive oxidation number. Thus, in answer to the question posed at the beginning of this section, combining sulfur with oxygen to form SO_2 is a redox reaction because the oxidation number of sulfur increases from 0 to +4 and that of oxygen decreases from 0 to −2.

- **The sum of the oxidation numbers in a neutral compound is 0.** Using this rule, the oxidation number of any atom in a compound can be found if the oxidation numbers of the other atoms are known. In the SO_2 example just mentioned, each of the two O atoms has an oxidation number of −2, so the S atom must have an oxidation number of +4. In HNO_3, the H atom has an oxidation number of +1 and the strongly electronegative O atom has an oxidation number of −2, so the N atom must have an oxidation number of +5. In a polyatomic ion, the sum of the oxidation numbers equals the charge on the ion.

$$
\begin{array}{cccc}
^{+1} & ^{-2} & ^{+5} & ^{-2} \\
\searrow & \downarrow & \downarrow & \nearrow \\
H & - O & - N & = O
\end{array}
\qquad \text{Total} = 1 + 5 + 3(-2) = 0
$$

$$\underset{-2}{\overset{}{O}}$$

Worked Examples 5.10 and 5.11 show further instances of assigning and using oxidation numbers.

Worked Example 5.10 Redox Reactions: Oxidation Numbers

What is the oxidation number of the titanium atom in $TiCl_4$? Name the compound using a Roman numeral (Sections 3.5 and 3.9).

SOLUTION

Chlorine, a reactive nonmetal, is more electronegative than titanium and has an oxidation number of −1. Because there are four chlorine atoms in $TiCl_4$, the oxidation number of titanium must be +4. The compound is named titanium(IV) chloride. Note that the Roman numeral IV in the name of this molecular compound refers to the oxidation number +4 rather than to a true ionic charge.

Worked Example 5.11 Redox Reactions: Identifying Redox Reactions

Use oxidation numbers to show that the production of iron metal from its ore (Fe_2O_3) by reaction with charcoal (C) is a redox reaction. Which reactant has been oxidized, and which has been reduced? Which reactant is the oxidizing agent, and which is the reducing agent?

$$2\,Fe_2O_3(s) + 3\,C(s) \longrightarrow 4\,Fe(s) + 3\,CO_2(g)$$

SOLUTION

The idea is to assign oxidation numbers to both reactants and products and see if there has been a change. In the production of iron from Fe_2O_3, the oxidation number of Fe changes from +3 to 0, and the oxidation number of C changes from 0 to +4. Iron has thus been reduced (decrease in oxidation number), and carbon has been oxidized (increase in oxidation number). Oxygen is neither oxidized nor reduced because its oxidation number does not change. Carbon is the reducing agent, and Fe_2O_3 is the oxidizing agent.

$$\overset{+3\ -2}{2\,Fe_2O_3} + \overset{0}{3\,C} \longrightarrow \overset{0}{4\,Fe} + \overset{+4\ -2}{3\,CO_2}$$

PROBLEM 5.10

What are the oxidation numbers of the metal atoms in the following compounds? Name each, using the oxidation number as a Roman numeral.

(a) VCl_3 (b) $SnCl_4$ (c) CrO_3
(d) $Cu(NO_3)_2$ (e) $NiSO_4$

PROBLEM 5.11

Assign an oxidation number to each atom in the reactants and products shown here to determine which of the following reactions are redox reactions:

(a) $Na_2S(aq) + NiCl_2(aq) \longrightarrow 2\,NaCl(aq) + NiS(s)$
(b) $2\,Na(s) + 2\,H_2O(l) \longrightarrow 2\,NaOH(aq) + H_2(g)$
(c) $C(s) + O_2(g) \longrightarrow CO_2(g)$
(d) $2\,CO(g) + O_2(g) \longrightarrow 2\,CO_2(g)$
(e) $CuO(s) + 2\,HCl(aq) \longrightarrow CuCl_2(aq) + H_2O(l)$
(f) $2\,MnO_4^-(aq) + 5\,SO_2(g) + 2\,H_2O(l) \longrightarrow 2\,Mn^{2+}(aq) + 5\,SO_4^{2-}(aq) + 4\,H^+(aq)$

PROBLEM 5.12

For each of the reactions you identified as redox reactions in Problem 5.11, identify the oxidizing agent and the reducing agent.

5.7 Net Ionic Equations

Learning Objective:

• For ionic reactions, write the molecular, ionic, and net ionic reactions, and identify spectator ions.

In the equations we have been writing up to this point, all the substances involved in reactions have been written using their full formulas. In the precipitation reaction of lead(II) nitrate with potassium iodide mentioned in Section 5.3, for example, only the parenthetical *aq* indicated that the reaction actually takes place in aqueous solution, and nowhere was it explicitly indicated that ions are involved:

$$Pb(NO_3)_2(aq) + 2\,KI(aq) \longrightarrow 2\,KNO_3(aq) + PbI_2(s)$$

Ionic equation An equation in which ions are explicitly shown.

In fact, lead (II) nitrate, potassium iodide, and potassium nitrate dissolve in water to yield solutions of ions. Thus, it is more accurate to write the reaction as an **ionic equation,** in which all the ions are explicitly shown:

An ionic equation: $Pb^{2+}(aq) + 2 NO_3^-(aq) + 2 K^+(aq) + 2 I^-(aq) \longrightarrow$
$$2 K^+(aq) + 2 NO_3^-(aq) + PbI_2(s)$$

A look at this ionic equation shows that the NO_3^- and K^+ ions undergo no change during the reaction. They appear on both sides of the reaction arrow and act merely as **spectator ions,** that is, they are present but play no role. The actual reaction, when stripped to its essentials, can be described more simply by writing a **net ionic equation,** which includes only the ions that undergo change and ignores all spectator ions:

Spectator ion An ion that appears unchanged on both sides of a reaction arrow.

Net ionic equation An equation that does not include spectator ions.

Ionic equation: $Pb^{2+}(aq) + 2 \,\cancel{NO_3^-}(aq) + 2 \,\cancel{K^+(aq)} + 2 I^-(aq) \longrightarrow$
$$2 \,\cancel{K^+(aq)} + 2 \,\cancel{NO_3^-}(aq) + PbI_2(s)$$

Net ionic equation: $Pb^{2+}(aq) + 2 I^-(aq) \longrightarrow PbI_2(s)$

Note that a net ionic equation, like all chemical equations, must be balanced both for atoms and for charge, with all coefficients reduced to their lowest whole numbers. Note also that all compounds that do *not* give ions in solution—all insoluble compounds and all molecular compounds—are represented by their full formulas.

We can apply the concept of ionic equations to acid-base neutralization reactions and redox reactions as well. Consider the neutralization reaction between KOH and HNO_3:

$$KOH(aq) + HNO_3(aq) \longrightarrow H_2O(l) + KNO_3(aq)$$

Since acids and bases are identified based on the ions they form when dissolved in aqueous solutions, we can write an ionic equation for this reaction:

Ionic equation: $\cancel{K^+(aq)} + OH^- + H^+(aq) + \cancel{NO_3^-(aq)} \longrightarrow$
$$H_2O(l) + \cancel{K^+(aq)} + \cancel{NO_3^-(aq)}$$

Eliminating the spectator ions (K^+ and NO_3^-), we obtain the net ionic equation for the neutralization reaction:

Net ionic equation: $OH^-(aq) + H^+(aq) \longrightarrow H_2O(l)$

The net ionic equation confirms the basis of the acid-base neutralization; the OH^- from the base and the H^+ from the acid neutralize each other to form water.

Similarly, many redox reactions can be viewed in terms of ionic equations. Consider the reaction between $Cu(s)$ and $AgNO_3$ from Section 5.6:

$$Cu(s) + 2 AgNO_3(aq) \longrightarrow 2 Ag^+(aq) + Cu(NO_3)_2(aq)$$

The aqueous products and reactants can be written as dissolved ions:

Ionic equation: $Cu(s) + 2 Ag^+(aq) + 2 \,\cancel{NO_3^-(aq)} \longrightarrow$
$$2 Ag(s) + Cu^{2+}(aq) + 2 \,\cancel{NO_3^-(aq)}$$

Again, eliminating the spectator ions (NO_3^-), we obtain the net ionic equation for this redox reaction:

Net ionic equation: $Cu(s) + 2 Ag^+(aq) \longrightarrow 2 Ag(s) + Cu^{2+}(aq)$

It is now clear that the $Cu(s)$ loses two electrons and is oxidized, whereas each Ag^+ ion gains an electron and is reduced.

Worked Example 5.12 Chemical Reactions: Net Ionic Reactions

Write balanced net ionic equations for the following reactions:

(a) $AgNO_3(aq) + ZnCl_2(aq) \longrightarrow$

(b) $HCl(aq) + Ca(OH)_2(aq) \longrightarrow$

(c) $6\,HCl(aq) + 2\,Al(s) \longrightarrow 2\,AlCl_3(aq) + 3\,H_2(g)$

SOLUTION

(a) The solubility guidelines discussed in Section 5.3 predict that a precipitate of insoluble AgCl forms when aqueous solutions of Ag^+ and Cl^- are mixed. Writing all the ions separately gives an ionic equation, and eliminating spectator ions Zn^{2+} and NO_3^- gives the net ionic equation.

Ionic equation: $\quad 2\,Ag^+(aq) + 2\,\cancel{NO_3^-(aq)} + \cancel{Zn^{2+}(aq)} + 2\,Cl^-(aq) \longrightarrow$
$$2\,AgCl(s) + \cancel{Zn^{2+}(aq)} + 2\,\cancel{NO_3^-(aq)}$$

Net ionic equation: $\quad 2\,Ag^+(aq) + 2\,Cl^-(aq) \longrightarrow 2\,AgCl(s)$

The coefficients can all be divided by 2 to give

Net ionic equation: $\quad Ag^+(aq) + Cl^+(aq) \longrightarrow AgCl(s)$

A check shows that the equation is balanced for atoms and charge (zero on each side).

(b) Allowing the acid HCl to react with the base $Ca(OH)_2$ leads to a neutralization reaction. Writing the ions separately, and remembering to write a complete formula for water, gives an ionic equation. Then eliminating the spectator ions and dividing the coefficients by 2 gives the net ionic equation.

Ionic equation: $\quad 2\,H^+(aq) + 2\,\cancel{Cl^-(aq)} + \cancel{Ca^{2+}(aq)} + 2\,OH^-(aq) \longrightarrow$
$$2\,H_2O(l) + \cancel{Ca^{2+}(aq)} + 2\,\cancel{Cl^-(aq)}$$

Net ionic equation: $\quad H^+(aq) + OH^-(aq) \longrightarrow H_2O(l)$

A check shows that atoms and charges are the same on both sides of the equation.

(c) The reaction of Al metal with acid (HCl) is a redox reaction. The Al is oxidized, since the oxidation number increases from $0 \rightarrow +3$, whereas the H in HCl is reduced from $+1 \rightarrow 0$. We write the ionic equation by showing the ions that are formed for each aqueous ionic species. Eliminating the spectator ions yields the net ionic equation.

Ionic equation: $\quad 6\,H^+(aq) + 6\,\cancel{Cl^-(aq)} + 2\,Al(s) \longrightarrow$
$$2\,Al^{3+}(aq) + 6\,\cancel{Cl^-(aq)} + 3\,H_2(g)$$

Net ionic equation: $\quad 6\,H^+(aq) + 2\,Al(s) \longrightarrow 2\,Al^{3+}(aq) + 3\,H_2(g)$

A check shows that atoms and charges are the same on both sides of the equation.

PROBLEM 5.13

Write net ionic equations for the following reactions:

(a) $Zn(s) + Pb(NO_3)_2(aq) \longrightarrow Zn(NO_3)_2(aq) + Pb(s)$

(b) $2\,KOH(aq) + H_2SO_4(aq) \longrightarrow K_2SO_4(aq) + 2\,H_2O(l)$

(c) $2\,FeCl_3(aq) + SnCl_2(aq) \longrightarrow 2\,FeCl_2(aq) + SnCl_4(aq)$

PROBLEM 5.14

Identify each of the reactions in Problem 5.13 as an acid-base neutralization, a precipitation, or a redox reaction.

PROBLEM 5.15

For each reaction in Problem 5.13 that you identified as a redox reaction, determine the oxidation numbers for each of the products and reactants, and identify the substance that is oxidized and the substance that is reduced during the reaction.

SUMMARY REVISITING THE CHAPTER LEARNING OBJECTIVES

- **Understand the law of conservation of mass and how it applies to chemical equations.** Chemical equations must be *balanced*; in terms of the law of conservation of mass, that means the numbers and kinds of atoms must be the same in both the reactants and the products *(see Problems 16–19 and 22–24)*.

- **Balance chemical equations.** To balance an equation, *coefficients* are placed before formulas but the formulas themselves cannot be changed. Starting with the unbalanced equation, you add coefficients to balance elements that appear in only one compound on the reactants and products side and then move on to other elements. Balance atoms that appear in their elemental state last. To verify that the equation is balanced, count the atoms of each type on both the left and ride side of the equation. Finally, divide or multiply the coefficients by an appropriate factor to obtain the lowest whole numbers *(see Problems 17–19, 24–33, 59, 60, 62, 63, 69–71, and 73)*.

- **Apply solubility rules to predict if a precipitation reaction will occur, and write the appropriate balanced reaction.** *Precipitation reactions* are processes in which an insoluble solid called a *precipitate* is formed. Most precipitations take place when the anions and cations of two ionic compounds change partners. Solubility guidelines identify anions and cations that tend to form soluble or insoluble ionic compounds and are used to predict when precipitation will occur. If an insoluble anion is combined with an insoluble cation, a precipitation reaction will occur *(see Problems 20, 21, 34, 36–42, 45, 61, 62, and 66–68)*.

- **Predict the products of an acid-base neutralization reaction.** *Acid-base neutralization reactions* are processes in which acids produce H^+ ions and bases produce OH^- ions when dissolved in water; a neutralization reaction removes H^+ and OH^- ions from solution and yields neutral H_2O. The products of *acid-base neutralization reactions* are water plus an ionic compound called a *salt*. The acid provides the anion for the salt (e.g., Cl^- from HCl), whereas the base provides the cation for the salt (e.g., Na^+ from NaOH) *(see Problems 34, 35, 37, 38, 62, 71, 74, and 75)*.

- **Recognize redox reactions, and identify the species being oxidized and reduced.** *Oxidation-reduction (redox) reactions* are processes in which one or more electrons are transferred between reaction partners. An *oxidation* is defined as the loss of one or more electrons by an atom, and a *reduction* is the gain of one or more electrons. An *oxidizing agent* causes the oxidation of another reactant by accepting electrons, and a *reducing agent* causes the reduction of another reactant by donating electrons *(see Problems 34, 36–38, 47–50, 55–60, 62, 69, and 73)*.

- **Determine the oxidation number of an atom in a compound.** *Oxidation numbers* are assigned to atoms in reactants and products to provide a measure of whether an atom is neutral, electron-rich, or electron-poor. By comparing the oxidation number of an atom before and after reaction, we can tell whether the atom has gained or lost shares in electrons and thus whether a redox reaction has occurred *(see Problems 47–58, 63–65, and 72)*.

- **For ionic reactions, write the molecular, ionic, and net ionic reactions, and identify spectator ions.** The *net ionic equation* only includes those ions that are directly involved in the ionic reaction. These ions can be identified because they are found in different phases or compounds on the reactant and product sides of the chemical equation. The net ionic equation does not include *spectator ions*, which appear in the same state on both sides of the chemical equation *(see Problems 35, 36, 43, 44, and 66–68)*.

CONCEPT MAP: ELECTROSTATIC FORCES

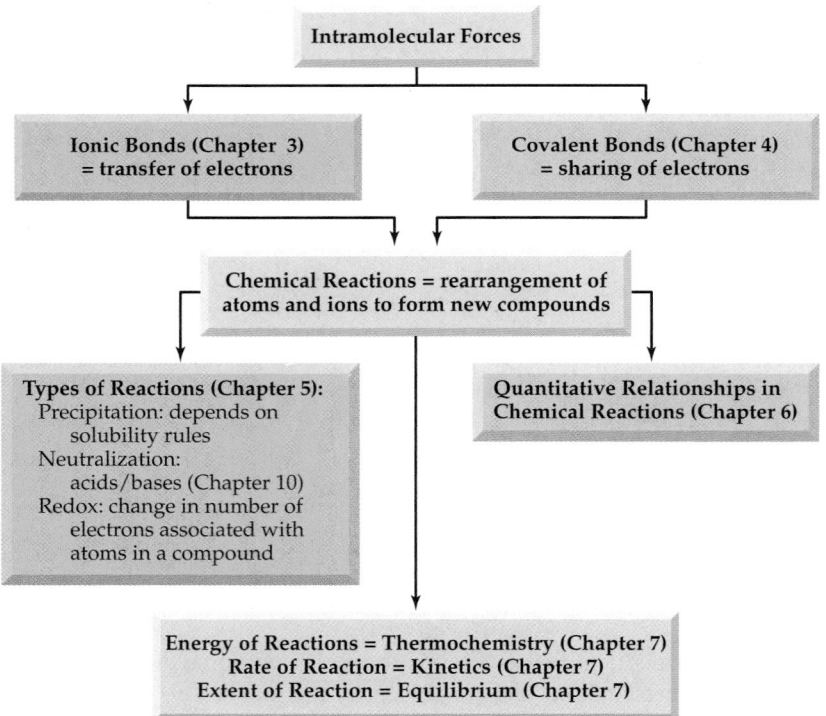

▲ **Figure 5.2 Concept Map.** By knowing the type of chemical reaction and the rules that govern the reaction, we can predict the products that will form and can balance the equation consistent with the law of conservation of mass.

KEY WORDS

Balanced equation, *p. 138*
Chemical equation, *p. 137*
Coefficient, *p. 138*
Ionic equation, *p. 154*
Law of conservation of mass, *p. 137*

Net ionic equation, *p. 154*
Neutralization reaction, *p. 144*
Oxidation, *p. 145*
Oxidation number, *p. 151*
Oxidation-reduction (redox) reaction, *p. 145*

Oxidizing agent, *p. 146*
Precipitate, *p. 141*
Product, *p. 137*
Reactant, *p. 137*
Reducing agent, *p. 146*

Reduction, *p. 145*
Salt, *p. 143*
Solubility, *p. 141*
Spectator ion, *p. 154*

⊙ UNDERSTANDING KEY CONCEPTS

5.16   Assume that the mixture of substances in drawing (a) undergoes a reaction. Which of the drawings (b)–(d) represent a product mixture consistent with the law of conservation of mass?

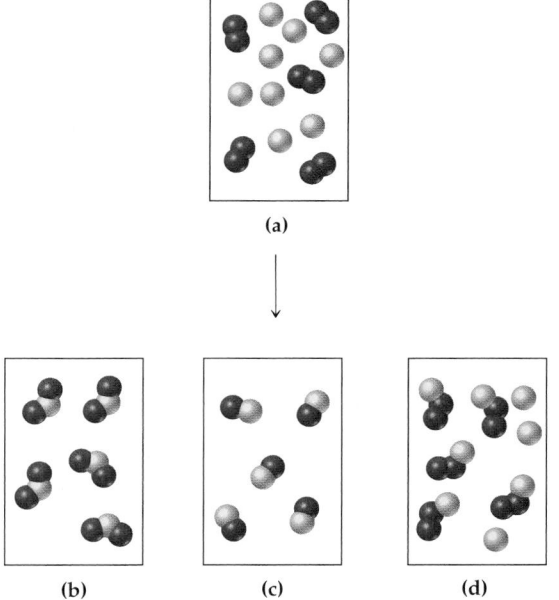

5.17   Reaction of A (green spheres) with B (blue spheres) is shown in the following diagram:

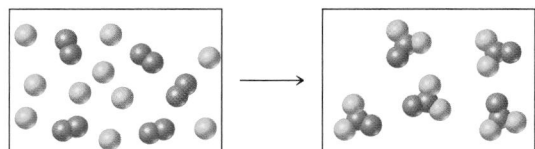

Which equation best describes the reaction?

(a) $A_2 + 2B \longrightarrow A_2B_2$

(b) $10A + 5B_2 \longrightarrow 5A_2B_2$

(c) $2A + B_2 \longrightarrow A_2B_2$

(d) $5A + 5B_2 \longrightarrow 5A_2B_2$

5.18   If blue spheres represent nitrogen atoms and red spheres represent oxygen atoms in the following diagrams, which box represents reactants and which represents products for the reaction $2NO(g) + O_2(g) \longrightarrow 2NO_2(g)$?

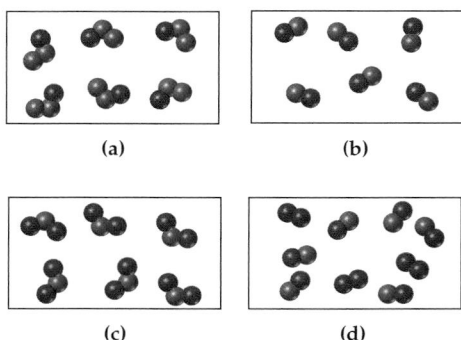

5.19   Assume that an aqueous solution of a cation (represented as red spheres in the diagram) is allowed to mix with a solution of an anion (represented as yellow spheres). Three possible outcomes are represented by boxes (1)–(3):

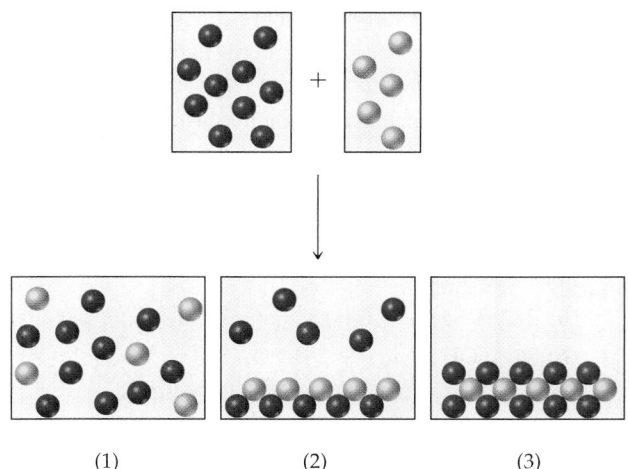

Which outcome corresponds to each of the following reactions?

(a) $2Na^+(aq) + CO_3^{2-}(aq) \longrightarrow$

(b) $Ba^{2+}(aq) + CrO_4^{2-}(aq) \longrightarrow$

(c) $2Ag^+(aq) + SO_3^{2-}(aq) \longrightarrow$

5.20   An aqueous solution of a cation (represented as blue spheres in the diagram) is allowed to mix with a solution of an anion (represented as green spheres) and the following result is obtained:

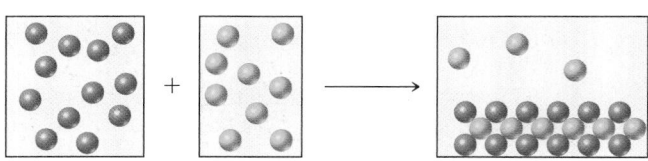

Which combinations of cation and anion, chosen from the following lists, are compatible with the observed results? Explain.

Cations: Na^+, Ca^{2+}, Ag^+, Ni^{2+}

Anions: Cl^-, CO_3^{2-}, CrO_4^{2-}, NO_3^-

5.21 A molecular view of two ionic solutions is presented right:

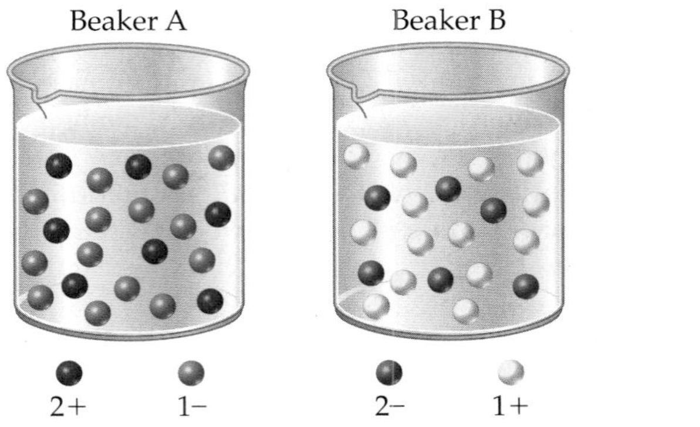

(a) Which compound is most likely dissolved in beaker A: KBr, $CaCl_2$, PbI_2, Na_2SO_4?

(b) Which compound is most likely dissolved in beaker B: Na_2CO_3, $BaSO_4$, $Cu(NO_3)_2$, $FeCl_3$?

(c) Identify the precipitate and spectator ions for any reaction that will result when beakers A and B are mixed.

Beaker A   Beaker B

2+   1-   2-   1+

ADDITIONAL PROBLEMS

BALANCING CHEMICAL EQUATIONS (SECTIONS 5.1 AND 5.2)

5.22 What is meant by the term "balanced equation"?

5.23 Why is it not possible to balance an equation by changing the subscript on a substance, say from H_2O to H_2O_2?

5.24 Write balanced equations for the following reactions:

(a) Hydrochloric acid reacts with calcium carbonate to form carbon dioxide and calcium chloride and water.

(b) Liquid bromine reacts with solid potassium metal to form solid potassium bromide.

(c) Gaseous propane (C_3H_8) burns in oxygen to form gaseous carbon dioxide and water vapor.

5.25 Balance the following equation for the synthesis of hydrazine, N_2H_4, a substance used as rocket fuel.

$$NH_3(g) + Cl_2(g) \longrightarrow N_2H_4(l) + NH_4Cl(s)$$

5.26 Which of the following equations are balanced? Balance those that need it.

(a) $2\,C_2H_6(g) + 5\,O_2(g) \longrightarrow 2\,CO_2(g) + 6\,H_2O(l)$

(b) $3\,Ca(OH)_2(aq) + 2\,H_3PO_4(aq) \longrightarrow Ca_3(PO_4)_2(aq) + 6\,H_2O(l)$

(c) $Mg(s) + O_2(g) \longrightarrow 2\,MgO(s)$

(d) $K(s) + H_2O(l) \longrightarrow KOH(aq) + H_2(g)$

5.27 Which of the following equations are balanced? Balance those that need it.

(a) $CaC_2 + 2\,H_2O \longrightarrow Ca(OH)_2 + C_2H_2$

(b) $C_2H_8N_2 + 2\,N_2O_4 \longrightarrow 2\,N_2 + 2\,CO_2 + 4\,H_2O$

(c) $3\,MgO + 2\,Fe \longrightarrow Fe_2O_3 + 3\,Mg$

(d) $N_2O \longrightarrow N_2 + O_2$

5.28 Balance the following equations:

(a) $Hg(NO_3)_2(aq) + LiI(aq) \longrightarrow LiNO_3(aq) + HgI_2(s)$

(b) $I_2(s) + Cl_2(g) \longrightarrow ICl_5(s)$

(c) $Al(s) + O_2(g) \longrightarrow Al_2O_3(s)$

(d) $CuSO_4(aq) + AgNO_3(aq) \longrightarrow Ag_2SO_4(s) + Cu(NO_3)_2(aq)$

(e) $Mn(NO_3)_3(aq) + Na_2S(aq) \longrightarrow Mn_2S_3(s) + NaNO_3(aq)$

5.29 Balance the following equations:

(a) $NO_2(g) + O_2(g) \longrightarrow N_2O_5(g)$

(b) $P_4O_{10}(s) + H_2O(l) \longrightarrow H_3PO_4(aq)$

(c) $B_2H_6(l) + O_2(g) \longrightarrow B_2O_3(s) + H_2O(l)$

(d) $Cr_2O_3(s) + CCl_4(l) \longrightarrow CrCl_3(s) + COCl_2(aq)$

(e) $Fe_3O_4(s) + O_2(g) \longrightarrow Fe_2O_3(s)$

5.30 When organic compounds are burned, they react with oxygen to form CO_2 and H_2O. Write balanced equations for the combustion reactions involving the following compounds. (Hint: When balancing combustion reactions, begin by balancing the C and H atoms first, and balance the O atoms last).

(a) C_4H_{10} (butane, used in lighters)

(b) C_2H_6O (ethyl alcohol, used in gasohol and as race car fuel)

(c) C_8H_{18} (octane, a component of gasoline)

5.31 When organic compounds are burned without enough oxygen, carbon monoxide is formed as a product instead of carbon dioxide. Write and balance the combustion reactions from Problem 5.30 using CO as a product instead of CO_2.

5.32 Hydrofluoric acid (HF) is used to etch glass (SiO_2). The products of the reaction are silicon tetrafluoride and water. Write the balanced chemical equation.

5.33 Write a balanced equation for the reaction of aqueous sodium carbonate (Na_2CO_3) with aqueous nitric acid (HNO_3) to yield CO_2, $NaNO_3$, and H_2O.

TYPES OF CHEMICAL REACTIONS (SECTIONS 5.3–5.5 AND 5.7)

5.34 Identify each of the following reactions as a precipitation, neutralization, or redox reaction:

(a) $Mg(s) + 2\,HCl(aq) \longrightarrow MgCl_2(aq) + H_2(g)$

(b) $KOH(aq) + HNO_3(aq) \longrightarrow KNO_3(aq) + H_2O(l)$

(c) $Pb(NO_3)_2(aq) + 2\,HBr(aq) \longrightarrow$
$\qquad\qquad\qquad PbBr_2(s) + 2\,HNO_3(aq)$

(d) $Ca(OH)_2(aq) + 2\,HCl(aq) \longrightarrow$
$\qquad\qquad\qquad 2\,H_2O(l) + CaCl_2(aq)$

5.35 Write balanced ionic equations and net ionic equations for the following reactions:

(a) Aqueous sulfuric acid is neutralized by aqueous potassium hydroxide.

(b) Aqueous magnesium hydroxide is neutralized by aqueous hydrochloric acid.

5.36 Write balanced ionic equations and net ionic equations for the following reactions:

(a) A precipitate of barium sulfate forms when aqueous solutions of barium nitrate and potassium sulfate are mixed.

(b) Zinc ion and hydrogen gas form when zinc metal reacts with aqueous sulfuric acid.

5.37 Identify each of the reactions in Problem 5.26 as a precipitation, neutralization, or redox reaction.

5.38 Identify each of the reactions in Problem 5.28 as a precipitation, neutralization, or redox reaction.

5.39 Which of the following substances are likely to be soluble in water?

(a) $ZnSO_4$ (b) $NiCO_3$

(c) $PbCl_2$ (d) $Ca_3(PO_4)_2$

5.40 Which of the following substances are likely to be soluble in water?

(a) Ag_2O (b) $Ba(NO_3)_2$

(c) $SnCO_3$ (d) Al_2S_3

5.41 Use the solubility guidelines in Section 5.3 to predict whether a precipitation reaction will occur when aqueous solutions of the following substances are mixed.

(a) $NaOH + HClO_4$

(b) $FeCl_2 + KOH$

(c) $(NH_4)_2SO_4 + NiCl_2$

5.42 Use the solubility guidelines in Section 5.3 to predict whether precipitation reactions will occur between the listed pairs of reactants. Write balanced equations for those reactions that should occur.

(a) $NaBr$ and $Hg_2(NO_3)_2$

(b) $CuCl_2$ and K_2SO_4

(c) $LiNO_3$ and $Ca(CH_3CO_2)_2$

(d) $(NH_4)_2CO_3$ and $CaCl_2$

(e) KOH and $MnBr_2$

(f) Na_2S and $Al(NO_3)_3$

5.43 Write net ionic equations for the following reactions:

(a) $Mg(s) + CuCl_2(aq) \longrightarrow MgCl_2(aq) + Cu(s)$

(b) $2\,KCl(aq) + Pb(NO_3)_2(aq) \longrightarrow$
$\qquad\qquad\qquad PbCl_2(s) + 2\,KNO_3(aq)$

(c) $2\,Cr(NO_3)_3(aq) + 3\,Na_2S(aq) \longrightarrow$
$\qquad\qquad\qquad Cr_2S_3(s) + 6\,NaNO_3(aq)$

5.44 Write net ionic equations for the following reactions:

(a) $2\,AuCl_3(aq) + 3\,Sn(s) \longrightarrow 3\,SnCl_2(aq) + 2\,Au(s)$

(b) $2\,NaI(aq) + Br_2(l) \longrightarrow 2\,NaBr(aq) + I_2(s)$

(c) $2\,AgNO_3(aq) + Fe(s) \longrightarrow$
$\qquad\qquad\qquad Fe(NO_3)_2(aq) + 2\,Ag(s)$

5.45 Complete the following precipitation reactions using balanced chemical equations:

(a) $FeSO_4(aq) + Sr(OH)_2(aq) \longrightarrow$

(b) $Na_2S(aq) + ZnSO_4(aq) \longrightarrow$

5.46 Write net ionic equations for each of the reactions in Problem 5.45.

REDOX REACTIONS AND OXIDATION NUMBERS (SECTIONS 5.5 AND 5.6)

5.47 Where in the periodic table are the best reducing agents found? The best oxidizing agents?

5.48 Where in the periodic table are the most easily reduced elements found? The most easily oxidized?

5.49 In each of the following, tell whether the substance gains electrons or loses electrons in a redox reaction:

(a) An oxidizing agent

(b) A reducing agent

(c) A substance undergoing oxidation

(d) A substance undergoing reduction

5.50 For the following substances, tell whether the oxidation number increases or decreases in a redox reaction:

(a) An oxidizing agent

(b) A reducing agent

(c) A substance undergoing oxidation

(d) A substance undergoing reduction

5.51 Assign an oxidation number to each element in the following compounds or ions:

(a) N_2O_5 (b) SO_3^{2-}

(c) CH_2O (d) $HClO_3$

5.52 Assign an oxidation number to the metal in the following compounds:

(a) $CoCl_3$ (b) $FeSO_4$ (c) UO_3

(d) CuF_2 (e) TiO_2 (f) SnS

5.53 Which element is oxidized and which is reduced in the following reactions?

(a) $Si(s) + 2\,Cl_2(g) \longrightarrow SiCl_4(l)$

(b) $Cl_2(g) + 2\,NaBr(aq) \longrightarrow Br_2(aq) + 2\,NaCl(aq)$

(c) $SbCl_3(s) + Cl_2(g) \longrightarrow SbCl_5(s)$

5.54 Which element is oxidized and which is reduced in the following reactions?

(a) $2 SO_2(g) + O_2(g) \longrightarrow 2 SO_3(g)$

(b) $2 Na(s) + Cl_2(g) \longrightarrow 2 NaCl(s)$

(c) $CuCl_2(aq) + Zn(s) \longrightarrow ZnCl_2(aq) + Cu(s)$

(d) $2 NaCl(aq) + F_2(g) \longrightarrow 2 NaF(aq) + Cl_2(g)$

5.55 Balance each of the following redox reactions:

(a) $Al(s) + H_2SO_4(aq) \longrightarrow Al_2(SO_4)_3(aq) + H_2(g)$

(b) $Fe(s) + Cl_2(g) \longrightarrow FeCl_3(s)$

(c) $CO(g) + I_2O_5(s) \longrightarrow I_2(s) + CO_2(g)$

5.56 Balance each of the following redox reactions:

(a) $N_2O_4(l) + N_2H_4(l) \longrightarrow N_2(g) + H_2O(g)$

(b) $CaH_2(s) + H_2O(l) \longrightarrow Ca(OH)_2(aq) + H_2(g)$

(c) $Al(s) + H_2O(l) \longrightarrow Al(OH)_3(s) + H_2(g)$

5.57 Identify the oxidizing agent and the reducing agent in Problem 5.55.

5.58 Identify the oxidizing agent and the reducing agent in Problem 5.56.

CONCEPTUAL PROBLEMS

5.59 Balance the following equations.

(a) The thermite reaction, used in welding:

$$Al(s) + Fe_2O_3(s) \longrightarrow Al_2O_3(l) + Fe(l)$$

(b) The explosion of ammonium nitrate:

$$NH_4NO_3(s) \longrightarrow N_2(g) + O_2(g) + H_2O(g)$$

5.60 Lithium oxide is used aboard the space shuttle to remove water from the atmosphere according to the equation:

$$Li_2O(s) + H_2O(g) \longrightarrow LiOH(s)$$

(a) Balance the chemical equation.

(b) Is this a redox reaction? Why or why not?

5.61 Look at the solubility guidelines in Section 5.3 and predict whether a precipitate forms when $CuCl_2(aq)$ and $Na_2CO_3(aq)$ are mixed. If so, write both the balanced equation and the net ionic equation for the process.

5.62 Balance the following equations and classify each as a precipitation, neutralization, or redox reaction:

(a) $Al(OH)_3(aq) + HNO_3(aq) \longrightarrow$
$Al(NO_3)_3(aq) + H_2O(l)$

(b) $AgNO_3(aq) + FeCl_3(aq) \longrightarrow$
$AgCl(s) + Fe(NO_3)_3(aq)$

(c) $(NH_4)_2Cr_2O_7(s) \longrightarrow Cr_2O_3(s) + H_2O(g) + N_2(g)$

(d) $Mn_2(CO_3)_3(s) \longrightarrow Mn_2O_3(s) + CO_2(g)$

5.63 White phosphorus (P_4) is a highly reactive form of elemental phosphorus that reacts with oxygen to form a variety of molecular compounds, including diphosphorus pentoxide.

(a) Write the balanced chemical equation for this reaction.

(b) Calculate the oxidation number for P and O on both sides of the reaction, and identify the oxidizing and reducing agents.

5.64 The transition metals form compounds with oxygen in which the metals have different oxidation states. Calculate the oxidation number for the transition metal in the following sets of compounds:

(a) Mn in MnO_2, Mn_2O_3, and $KMnO_4$

(b) Cr in CrO_2, CrO_3, and Cr_2O_3.

5.65 In the Breathalyzer test, blood alcohol is determined by reaction of the alcohol with potassium dichromate:

$$16 H^+(aq) + 2 Cr_2O_7{}^{2-}(aq) + C_2H_5OH(aq) \longrightarrow$$
$$4 Cr^{3+}(aq) + 2 CO_2(g) + 11 H_2O(l)$$

(a) Calculate the oxidation number of Cr in $Cr_2O_7{}^{2-}$.

(b) Calculate the oxidation number of C in C_2H_5OH and in CO_2.

(c) Identify the oxidizing agent and the reducing agent in this reaction.

5.66 Iron in drinking water is removed by precipitation of the Fe^{3+} ion by reaction with NaOH to produce iron(III) hydroxide. Write the balanced chemical equation and the net ionic equation for this reaction.

5.67 Hard water contains magnesium and calcium ions (Mg^{2+}, Ca^{2+}), which can precipitate out in hot water pipes and water heaters as carbonates. Write the net ionic equation for this reaction.

5.68 Pepto-Bismol, an antacid and antidiarrheal, contains bismuth subsalicylate, $C_7H_5BiO_4$. Some users of this product can experience a condition known as "black tongue," which is caused by the reaction of bismuth(III) ions with trace amounts of S^{2-} in saliva to form a black precipitate. Write the balanced net ionic equation for this precipitation reaction.

5.69 Iron is produced from iron ore by reaction with carbon monoxide:

$$Fe_2O_3(s) + CO(g) \longrightarrow Fe(s) + CO_2(g)$$

(a) Balance the chemical equation.

(b) Classify the reaction as a precipitation, neutralization, or redox reaction.

5.70 Balance the reaction for the synthesis of urea, commonly used as a fertilizer:

$$CO_2(g) + NH_3(g) \longrightarrow NH_2CONH_2(s) + H_2O(l)$$

5.71 Geologists identify carbonate minerals by reaction with acids. Dolomite, for example, contains magnesium carbonate, which reacts with hydrochloric acid by the following reaction:

$$MgCO_3(s) + HCl(aq) \longrightarrow$$
$$MgCl_2(aq) + CO_2(g) + H_2O(l)$$

(a) Balance the reaction and write the net ionic equation.

(b) Classify the reaction as a precipitation, neutralization, or redox reaction.

5.72 Iodine, used as an antiseptic agent, can be prepared in the laboratory by the following reaction:

$$2\,NaI(s)\,+\,2\,H_2SO_4(aq)\,+\,MnO_2(s)\,\longrightarrow$$
$$Na_2SO_4(aq)\,+\,MnSO_4(aq)\,+\,I_2(g)\,+\,2\,H_2O(l)$$

(a) Determine the oxidation number for the Mn and I on both sides of the equation.

(b) Identify the oxidizing and reducing agents.

GROUP PROBLEMS

5.73 High temperature combustion processes, such as in combustion engines and coal-fired power plants, can result in the reaction of nitrogen and sulfur with oxygen to form nitrogen oxides (NO_x) and sulfur oxides (SO_x), where x can vary. These NO_x and SO_x compounds subsequently undergo further reaction in the atmosphere to create acidic compounds that contribute to acid rain.

(a) Do some research to determine the common products that are formed (i.e., what are the values of x) for the reactions of N and S with oxygen. Write balanced equations for these reactions.

(b) What additional reactions do these NO_x and SO_x compounds undergo in the atmosphere that lead to the formation of acidic compounds? Write balanced equations for these reactions.

(c) Classify each of the reactions you identified in parts (a) and (b) (precipitation, neutralization, or redox) and explain your reason for each classification.

5.74 Milk of magnesia is an over-the-counter product that is used to neutralize excess stomach acid.

(a) Look up the active ingredient in milk of magnesia.

(b) Stomach acid is predominantly hydrochloric acid. Write the balanced chemical equation for the neutralization reaction between HCl and the active ingredient from part (a).

5.75 Many pharmaceuticals are marketed with the designation "HCl" appended to the name of the drug. What does the "HCl" mean? What type of reaction would be involved in converting a drug to the HCl form? What are the advantages of this form of the drug?

6

Chemical Reactions: Mole and Mass Relationships

CONTENTS

 CONCEPTS TO REVIEW

▲ These foods represent good sources of iron, an essential nutrient. A lack of dietary iron can cause anemia.

G ood health, in part, depends on a balanced diet containing adequate nutrients, vitamins, and minerals. For example, not enough iron can lead to anemia, not enough iodine can cause thyroid problems, and not enough vitamin C can cause diseases such as scurvy. The recommended daily allowances, or RDAs, of each vitamin and nutrient are set by regulatory groups such as the World Health Organization or the U.S. Department of Agriculture (USDA). The total allowances are based on the amounts needed to sustain the critical metabolic reactions in which these substances are involved. Foods such as red meats, beans, spinach, and dried fruits are rich in iron, a key component of hemoglobin, which is responsible for oxygen transport. Insufficient iron in the diet can cause fatigue and lethargy because of a lack of oxygen in the cells, which are symptoms of anemia, a condition that is explained in more detail in the Chemistry in Action feature on page 177 later in this chapter. But how do we know what amounts of iron and other nutrients are sufficient? To answer this question we need to be able to translate the molecular information—balanced chemical reactions and the relationships between reactants and products—into meaningful units that we can measure conveniently—mass!

Consider how these conversions are handled in the kitchen. When chefs prepare to cook a rice pudding, they do not count out individual grains of rice, or individual raisins, or individual sugar crystals. Rather, they measure out appropriate amounts of the necessary ingredients using more convenient units—such as cups or tablespoons. When chemists prepare chemical reactions, they use the same approach—they measure out grams of substances instead of individual molecules. From the mass of reactants, they can determine whether or not they have sufficient amounts of molecules to complete a reaction, and to calculate the mass of products they should obtain. In this chapter, we introduce the concept of the mole and its relationship to mass, and how chemists use the mole–mass relationship when studying the quantitative relationships between reactants and products.

6.1 The Mole and Avogadro's Number

Learning Objective:

• Define the mole, and calculate the molar mass of a compound from the molecular formula.

In the previous chapter, we learned how to use the balanced chemical equation to indicate what is happening at the molecular level during a reaction. Now, let us imagine a laboratory experiment: the reaction of ethylene (C_2H_4) with hydrogen chloride (HCl) to form ethyl chloride (C_2H_5Cl), a colorless, low-boiling liquid used by doctors and athletic trainers as a spray-on anesthetic. The reaction is represented as

$$C_2H_4(g) + HCl(g) \longrightarrow C_2H_5Cl(g)$$

In this reaction, one molecule of ethylene reacts with one molecule of hydrogen chloride to produce one molecule of ethyl chloride. How, though, can you be sure you have a one-to-one ratio of reactant molecules in your reaction flask? Since it is impossible to hand-count the number of molecules correctly, you must weigh them instead.

We do this every day with all kinds of small objects: Nails, nuts, and grains of rice are all weighed in bulk rather than counted individually. Consider a common example: You wish to construct a storage rack and need nuts and bolts. Let's assume that each nut weighs 1 g and each bolt weighs 63 g. Not wishing to count out each nut + bolt combination separately, you can take advantage of the mass ratios—if you weigh out 10 g of nuts and 630 g of bolts, you will have 10 of each item for a 1:1 ratio. Similarly, if you weigh out 1 pound of nuts, you will need 63 pounds of bolts for a 1:1 ratio of nuts to bolts. The same logic applies to the amounts of reactants needed for a balanced reaction.

But the weighing approach leads to another problem. How many *molecules* are there in 1 g of ethylene, hydrogen chloride, or any other substance? The answer depends on the identity of the substance—just as nuts and bolts have different masses, different molecules have different masses.

To determine how many molecules of a given substance are in a certain mass, it is helpful to define a quantity called *molecular weight*. Just as the *atomic weight* of an element is the average mass of the element's *atoms,* the **molecular weight (MW)** of a molecule is the average mass of a substance's *molecules*. Numerically, a substance's molecular weight (or **formula weight** for an ionic compound) is equal to the sum of the atomic weights for all the atoms in the molecule or formula unit.

For example, the molecular weight of ethylene (C_2H_4) is 28.0 amu, the molecular weight of HCl is 36.5 amu, and the molecular weight of ethyl chloride (C_2H_5Cl) is 64.5 amu. (The actual values are known more precisely but are rounded off here for convenience.)

Molecular weight (MW) The sum of atomic weights of all atoms in a molecule.

Formula weight The sum of atomic weights of all atoms in one formula unit of any compound, whether molecular or ionic.

◄◄ **CONCEPTS TO REVIEW** See Section 2.3 for a discussion of atomic weight.

For ethylene, C₂H₄:

Atomic weight of 2 C = 2 × 12.0 amu = 24.0 amu
Atomic weight of 4 H = 4 × 1.0 amu = 4.0 amu
MW of C_2H_4 = 28.0 amu

▲ These samples of sulfur, copper, mercury, and helium each contain 1 mol. Do they all have the same mass?

For hydrogen chloride, **HCl:**

$$\begin{array}{ll} \text{Atomic weight of H} & = 1.0 \text{ amu} \\ \underline{\text{Atomic weight of Cl} = 35.5 \text{ amu}} \\ \text{MW of HCl} & = 36.5 \text{ amu} \end{array}$$

For ethyl chloride, **C_2H_5Cl:**

$$\begin{array}{lll} \text{Atomic weight of 2 C} = 2 \times 12.0 \text{ amu} & = 24.0 \text{ amu} \\ \text{Atomic weight of 5 H} = 5 \times 1.0 \text{ amu} & = 5.0 \text{ amu} \\ \underline{\text{Atomic weight of Cl}} & = 35.5 \text{ amu} \\ \text{MW of } C_2H_5Cl & = 64.5 \text{ amu} \end{array}$$

How are molecular weights used? Since the mass ratio of one ethylene molecule to one HCl molecule is 28.0 to 36.5, the mass ratio of *any* given number of ethylene molecules to the same number of HCl molecules is also 28.0 to 36.5. In other words, a 28.0 to 36.5 *mass* ratio of ethylene and HCl always guarantees a 1:1 *number* ratio. *Samples of different substances always contain the same number of molecules or formula units whenever their mass ratio is the same as their molecular or formula weight ratio* (Figure 6.1).

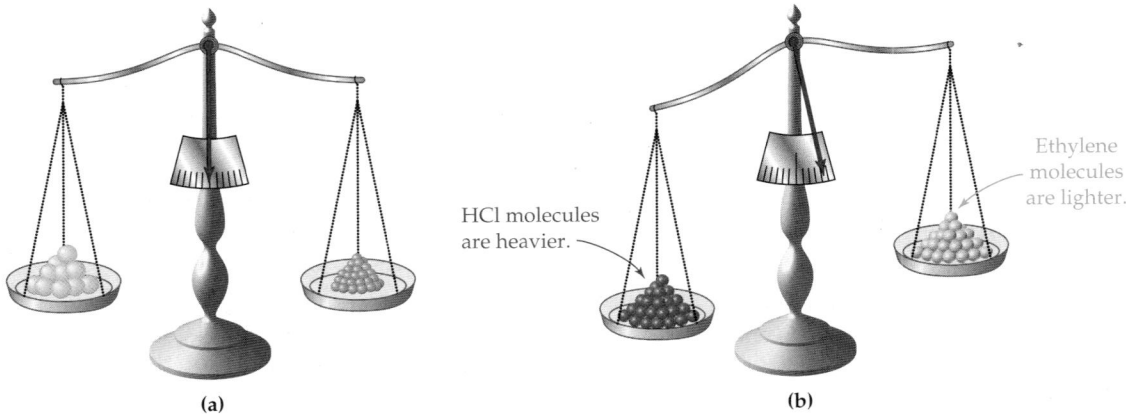

HCl molecules are heavier.

Ethylene molecules are lighter.

(a)   (b)

▲ **Figure 6.1**
(a) Because the yellow balls (left pan) are bigger than the green balls (right pan), you cannot get an equal number by taking equal weights. The same is true for atoms or molecules of different substances. (b) Equal numbers of ethylene and HCl molecules always have a mass ratio equal to the ratio of their molecular weights, 28.0 to 36.5.

A particularly convenient way to use this mass/number relationship for molecules is to measure amounts in grams that are numerically equal to molecular weights. If, for instance, you were to carry out your experiment with 28.0 g of ethylene and 36.5 g of HCl, you could be certain that you would have a 1:1 ratio of reactant molecules.

When referring to the vast numbers of molecules or formula units that take part in a visible chemical reaction, it is convenient to use a counting unit called a **mole,** abbreviated *mol.* One mole of any substance is the amount having a mass in grams—its **molar mass**—numerically equal to its molecular or formula weight in amu. One mole of ethylene has a mass of 28.0 g, 1 mole of HCl has a mass of 36.5 g, and 1 mole of ethyl chloride has a mass of 64.5 g.

Just how many molecules are there in a mole? Think back to Chapter 2 where we learned to calculate the number of atoms in a sample of an element given its weight in grams, the atomic mass of the atom, and a gram/amu conversion factor. In Problems 2.37 and 2.38, you (hopefully!) found that a 15.99 g sample of oxygen (atomic mass 15.99 amu) and a 12 g sample of carbon (atomic mass 12.00 amu) each contain 6.022×10^{23} atoms. One mole of any substance, therefore, contains 6.022×10^{23} formula units, a value called **Avogadro's number (N_A)** after the Italian scientist who first recognized the importance of the mass/number relationship in molecules. Avogadro's number of formula units of any substance—that is, one mole—has a mass in grams numerically equal to the molecular weight of the substance. Just as we use specific units when dealing with large numbers of other substances—a dozen eggs, a

Mole The amount of a substance whose mass in grams is numerically equal to its molecular or formula weight.

Molar mass The mass in grams of 1 mole of a substance, numerically equal to molecular weight.

Avogadro's number (N_A) The number of formula units in 1 mol of anything; 6.022×10^{23}.

ream of paper, a ton of coal—we use the mole as a convenient unit to refer to a specific number of atoms or molecules.

$$1 \text{ mol HCl} = 6.022 \times 10^{23} \text{ HCl molecules} = 36.5 \text{g HCl}$$
$$1 \text{ mol } C_2H_4 = 6.022 \times 10^{23} \text{ } C_2H_4 \text{ molecules} = 28.0 \text{ g } C_2H_4$$
$$1 \text{ mol } C_2H_5Cl = 6.022 \times 10^{23} \text{ } C_2H_5Cl \text{ molecules} = 64.5 \text{ g } C_2H_5Cl$$

How big is Avogadro's number? Our minds cannot really conceive of the magnitude of a number like 6.022×10^{23}, but the following comparisons will give you a sense of the scale.

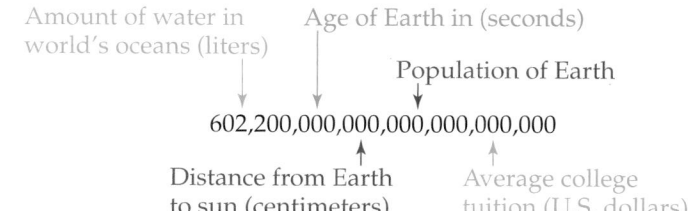

Avogadro's number: 602,200,000,000,000,000,000,000

Worked Example 6.1 Molar Mass and Avogadro's Number: Number of Molecules

Pseudoephedrine hydrochloride ($C_{10}H_{16}ClNO$) is a nasal decongestant commonly found in cold medication. (a) What is the molar mass of pseudoephedrine hydrochloride? (b) How many molecules of pseudoephedrine hydrochloride are in a tablet that contains a dose of 30.0 mg of this decongestant?

ANALYSIS We are given a mass and need to convert to a number of molecules. This is most easily accomplished by using the molar mass of pseudoephedrine hydrochloride calculated in part (a) as the conversion factor from mass to moles and realizing that this mass (in grams) contains Avogadro's number of molecules (6.022×10^{23}).

BALLPARK ESTIMATE The formula for pseudoephedrine contains 10 carbon atoms (each one of atomic weight 12.0 amu), so the molecular weight is greater than 120 amu, probably near 200 amu. Thus, the molecular weight should be near 200 g/mol. The mass of 30 mg of pseudoepinephrine HCl is less than the mass of 1 mol of this compound by a factor of roughly 10^4 (0.03 g versus 200 g), which means that the number of molecules should also be smaller by a factor of 10^4 (on the order of 10^{19} in the tablet versus 10^{23} in 1 mol).

SOLUTION

(a) The molecular weight of pseudoephedrine is found by summing the atomic weights of all atoms in the molecule as follows:

Atomic weight of 10 atoms of C:	10×12.011 amu $=$	120.11 amu
16 atoms of H:	16×1.00794 amu $=$	16.127 amu
1 atom of Cl:	1×35.4527 amu $=$	35.4527 amu
1 atom of N:	1×14.0067 amu $=$	14.0067 amu
1 atom of O:	1×15.9994 amu $=$	15.9994 amu
MW of $C_{10}H_{16}ClNO$	$= 201.6958$ amu $\longrightarrow$	201.70 g/mol

Remember that atomic mass in amu converts directly to molar mass in g/mol. Also, following the rules for significant figures from Sections 1.8 and 1.9, our final answer is rounded to the second decimal place.

(b) Since this problem involves unit conversions, we can use the step-wise solution introduced in Chapter 1.

STEP 1: Identify known information. We are given the mass of pseudoephedrine hydrochloride (in mg).	30.0 mg pseudoephedrine hydrochloride
STEP 2: Identify answer and units. We are looking for the number of molecules of pseudoephedrine hydrochloride in a 30 mg tablet.	?? = molecules

—continued on next page

—continued from previous page

STEP 3: Identify conversion factors. Since the molecular weight of pseudoephedrine hydrochloride is 201.70 amu, 201.70 g contains 6.022×10^{23} molecules. We can use this ratio as a conversion factor to convert from mass to molecules. We will also need to convert 30 mg to grams.

$$\frac{6.022 \times 10^{23} \text{ molecules}}{201.70 \text{ g}}$$

$$\frac{.001 \text{ g}}{1 \text{ mg}}$$

STEP 4: Solve. Set up an equation so that unwanted units cancel.

$$(30.0 \text{ mg pseudoephedrine hydrochloride}) \times \left(\frac{.001 \text{ g}}{1 \text{ mg}}\right) \times$$

$$\left(\frac{6.022 \times 10^{23} \text{ molecules}}{201.70 \text{ g}}\right)$$

$$= 8.96 \times 10^{19} \text{ molecules of pseudoephedrine hydrochloride}$$

BALLPARK CHECK Our estimate for the number of molecules was on the order of 10^{19}, which is consistent with the calculated answer.

Worked Example 6.2 Avogadro's Number: Atom to Mass Conversions

A tiny pencil mark just visible to the naked eye contains about 3×10^{17} atoms of carbon. What is the mass of this pencil mark in grams?

ANALYSIS We are given a number of atoms and need to convert to mass. The conversion factor can be obtained by realizing that the atomic weight of carbon in grams contains Avogadro's number of atoms (6.022×10^{23}).

BALLPARK ESTIMATE Since we are given a number of atoms that is six orders of magnitude less than Avogadro's number, we should get a corresponding mass that is six orders of magnitude less than the molar mass of carbon, which means a mass for the pencil mark of about 10^{-6} g.

SOLUTION

STEP 1: Identify known information. We know the number of carbon atoms in the pencil mark.

3×10^{17} atoms of carbon

STEP 2: Identify answer and units.

Mass of carbon $=$?? g

STEP 3: Identify conversion factors. The atomic weight of carbon is 12.01 amu, so 12.01 g of carbon contains 6.022×10^{23} atoms.

$$\frac{12.01 \text{ g carbon}}{6.022 \times 10^{23} \text{ atoms}}$$

STEP 4: Solve. Set up an equation using the conversion factors so that unwanted units cancel.

$$(3 \times 10^{17} \text{ atoms})\left(\frac{12.01 \text{ g carbon}}{6.022 \times 10^{23} \text{ atoms}}\right) = 6 \times 10^{-6} \text{ g carbon}$$

BALLPARK CHECK The answer is of the same magnitude as our estimate and makes physical sense.

PROBLEM 6.1

Calculate the molecular weight of the following substances:
   (a) Ibuprofen, $C_{13}H_{18}O_2$ (a drug used as for pain relief)
   (b) Phenobarbital, $C_{12}H_{12}N_2O_3$ (a drug used as a sedative, hypnotic, and antiseizure medication)

PROBLEM 6.2

How many molecules of ascorbic acid (vitamin C, $C_6H_8O_6$) are in a 500 mg tablet? (Hint: First calculate molar mass, then use it as a conversion factor to convert mass to moles).

PROBLEM 6.3

What is the mass in grams of 5.0×10^{20} molecules of aspirin $(C_9H_8O_4)$? (Hint: Using Avogadro's number, convert the number of molecules to moles.)

⊙━ KEY CONCEPT PROBLEM 6.4 ————————————————————————

What is the molecular weight of cytosine, a component of DNA (deoxyribonucleic acid)? (black = C, blue = N, red = O, white = H.)

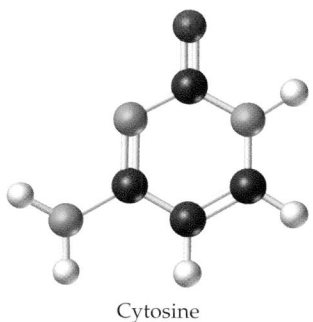

Cytosine

6.2 Gram–Mole Conversions

Learning Objective:

• Convert between mass and moles using the molar mass of a substance.

To ensure that we have the correct molecule to molecule (or mole to mole) relationship between reactants as specified by the balanced chemical equation, we can take advantage of the constant mass ratio between reactants. The mass in grams of 1 mol of any substance (i.e., Avogadro's number of molecules or formula units) is called the molar mass of the substance.

Molar mass = Mass of 1 mol of substance

= Mass of 6.022×10^{23} molecules (formula units) of substance

= Molecular (formula) weight of substance in grams

In effect, molar mass serves as a conversion factor between numbers of moles and mass. If you know how many moles you have, you can calculate their mass; if you know the mass of a sample, you can calculate the number of moles. Suppose, for example, we need to know how much 0.25 mol of water weighs. The molecular weight of H_2O is $(2 \times 1.0 \text{ amu}) + 16.0 \text{ amu} = 18.0 \text{ amu}$, so the molar mass of water is 18.0 g/mol. Thus, the conversion factor between moles of water and mass of water is 18.0 g/mol.

$$0.25 \text{ mol } H_2O \times \frac{\boxed{\text{Molar mass used as conversion factor}}}{\underset{\text{1 mol } H_2O}{\overset{18.0 \text{ g } H_2O}{}}} = 4.5 \text{ g } H_2O$$

Alternatively, suppose we need to know how many moles of water are in 27 g of water. The conversion factor is 1 mol/18.0 g.

$$27 \text{ g } H_2O \times \frac{\boxed{\text{Molar mass used as conversion factor}}}{\underset{18.0 \text{ g } H_2O}{\overset{1 \text{ mol } H_2O}{}}} = 1.5 \text{ mol } H_2O$$

Note that the 1 mol in the numerator is an exact number, so the number of significant figures in the final answer is based on the 27 g H_2O (2 significant figures). Worked Examples 6.3 and 6.4 give more practice in gram–mole conversions.

Worked Example 6.3 Molar Mass: Mole to Gram Conversion

The nonprescription pain relievers Advil and Nuprin contain ibuprofen $(C_{13}H_{18}O_2)$, whose molecular weight is 206.3 amu (Problem 6.1a). If all the tablets in a bottle of pain reliever together contain 0.082 mol of ibuprofen, what is the number of grams of ibuprofen in the bottle?

ANALYSIS We are given a number of moles and asked to find the mass. Molar mass is the conversion factor between the two.

BALLPARK ESTIMATE Since 1 mol of ibuprofen has a mass of about 200 g, 0.08 mol has a mass of about $0.08 \times 200\ g = 16\ g$.

SOLUTION

STEP 1: Identify known information.	0.082 mol ibuprofen in bottle
STEP 2: Identify answer and units.	mass ibuprofen in bottle = ?? g
STEP 3: Identify conversion factor. We use the molecular weight of ibuprofen to convert from moles to grams.	1 mol ibuprofen = 206.3 g $\dfrac{206.3\ g\ ibuprofen}{1\ mol\ ibuprofen}$
STEP 4: Solve. Set up an equation using the known information and conversion factor so that unwanted units cancel.	$0.082\ \cancel{mol\ C_{13}H_{18}O_2} \times \dfrac{206.3\ g\ ibuprofen}{1\ \cancel{mol\ ibuprofen}} = 17\ g\ C_{13}H_{18}O_2$

BALLPARK CHECK The calculated answer is consistent with our estimate of 16 g.

Worked Example 6.4 Molar Mass: Gram to Mole Conversion

The maximum dose of sodium hydrogen phosphate $(Na_2HPO_4$, MW $= 142.0$ molar mass$)$ that should be taken in one day for use as a laxative is 3.8 g. How many moles of sodium hydrogen phosphate, how many moles of Na^+ ions, and how many total moles of ions are in this dose?

ANALYSIS Molar mass is the conversion factor between mass and number of moles. The chemical formula Na_2HPO_4 shows that each formula unit contains 2 Na^+ ions and 1 HPO_4^{2-} ion.

BALLPARK ESTIMATE The maximum dose is about two orders of magnitude smaller than the molecular weight (approximately 4 g compared to 142 g). Thus, the number of moles of sodium hydrogen phosphate in 3.8 g should be about two orders of magnitude less than 1 mole. The number of moles of Na_2HPO_4 and total moles of ions, then, should be on the order of 10^{-2}.

SOLUTION

STEP 1: Identify known information. We are given the mass and molecular weight of Na_2HPO_4.	3.8 g Na_2HPO_4; MW $= 142.0$ amu
STEP 2: Identify answer and units. We need to find the number of moles of Na_2HPO_4 and the total number of moles of ions.	Moles of Na_2HPO = ?? mol Moles of Na^+ ions = ?? mol Total moles of ions = ?? mol
STEP 3: Identify conversion factor. We can use the molecular weight of Na_2HPO_4 to convert from grams to moles.	$\dfrac{1\ mol\ Na_2HPO_4}{142.0\ g\ Na_2HPO_4}$

STEP 4: **Solve.** We use the known information and conversion factor to obtain moles of Na_2HPO_4; since 1 mol of Na_2HPO_4 contains 2 mol of Na^+ ions and 1 mol of HPO_4^{2-} ions, we multiply these values by the number of moles in the sample.

$$3.8 \text{ g } Na_2HPO_4 \times \frac{1 \text{ mol } Na_2HPO_4}{142.0 \text{ g } Na_2HPO_4} = 0.027 \text{ mol } Na_2HPO_4$$

$$\frac{2 \text{ mol } Na^+}{1 \text{ mol } Na_2HPO_4} \times 0.027 \text{ mol } Na_2HPO_4 = 0.054 \text{ mol } Na^+$$

$$\frac{3 \text{ mol ions}}{1 \text{ mol } Na_2HPO_4} \times 0.027 \text{ mol } Na_2HPO_4 = 0.081 \text{ mol ions}$$

BALLPARK CHECK The calculated answers $(0.027 \text{ mol } Na_2HPO_4, 0.081 \text{ mol ions})$ are on the order of 10^{-2}, consistent with our estimate.

PROBLEM 6.5

How many moles of ethyl alcohol, C_2H_6O, are in a 10.0 g sample? How many grams are in a 0.10 mol sample of ethyl alcohol?

PROBLEM 6.6

Which weighs more, 5.00 g or 0.0225 mol of acetaminophen $(C_8H_9NO_2)$?

PROBLEM 6.7

A small kidney stone (Chemistry in Action on p. 142) might contain 0.50 g of uric acid $(C_5H_4N_4O_3)$. How many micromoles of uric acid are contained in this stone?

6.3 Mole Relationships and Chemical Equations

Learning Objective:

- Determine molar ratios of reactants and products using balanced chemical equations.

In a typical recipe, the amounts of ingredients needed are specified using a variety of units: The amount of flour, for example, is usually specified in cups, whereas the amount of salt or vanilla flavoring might be indicated in teaspoons. In chemical reactions, the appropriate unit to specify the relationship between reactants and products is the mole.

The coefficients in a balanced chemical equation tell how many *molecules,* and thus how many *moles,* of each reactant are needed and how many molecules, and thus, moles, of each product are formed. You can then use molar mass to calculate reactant and product masses. If, for example, you saw the following balanced equation for the industrial synthesis of ammonia, you would know that 3 mol of H_2 (3 mol $\times$ 2.0 g/mol = 6.0 g) are required for reaction with 1 mol of N_2 (28.0 g) to yield 2 mol of NH_3 (2 mol $\times$ 17.0 g/mol = 34.0 g).

This number of moles
of hydrogen . . .   . . . reacts with this number   to yield this number of
                         of moles of nitrogen . . .   moles of ammonia.

$$3 H_2 + 1 N_2 \longrightarrow 2 NH_3$$

The coefficients can be put in the form of *mole ratios,* which act as conversion factors when setting up factor-label calculations. In the ammonia synthesis, for example, the mole ratio of H_2 to N_2 is 3:1, the mole ratio of H_2 to NH_3 is 3:2, and the mole ratio of N_2 to NH_3 is 1:2.

$$\frac{3 \text{ mol } H_2}{1 \text{ mol } N_2} \quad \frac{3 \text{ mol } H_2}{2 \text{ mol } NH_3} \quad \frac{1 \text{ mol } N_2}{2 \text{ mol } NH_3}$$

Worked Example 6.5 shows how to set up and use mole ratios.

Worked Example 6.5 Balanced Chemical Equations: Mole Ratios

Rusting involves the reaction of iron with oxygen to form iron(III) oxide, Fe_2O_3:

$$4\,Fe(s) + 3\,O_2(g) \longrightarrow 2\,Fe_2O_3(s)$$

(a) What are the mole ratios of the product to each reactant and of the reactants to each other?
(b) How many moles of iron(III) oxide are formed by the complete oxidation of 6.2 mol of iron?

ANALYSIS AND SOLUTION

(a) The coefficients of a balanced equation represent the mole ratios.

$$\frac{2\text{ mol }Fe_2O_3}{4\text{ mol Fe}} \quad \frac{2\text{ mol }Fe_2O_3}{3\text{ mol }O_2} \quad \frac{4\text{ mol Fe}}{3\text{ mol }O_2}$$

(b) To find how many moles of Fe_2O_3 are formed, write down the known information—6.2 mol of iron—and select the mole ratio that allows the quantities to cancel, leaving the desired quantity.

$$6.2\,\cancel{\text{mol Fe}} \times \frac{2\text{ mol }Fe_2O_3}{4\,\cancel{\text{mol Fe}}} = 3.1\text{ mol }Fe_2O_3$$

Note that mole ratios are exact numbers and therefore do not limit the number of significant figures in the result of a calculation.

PROBLEM 6.8

(a) Balance the following equation, and tell how many moles of nickel will react with 9.81 mol of hydrochloric acid.

$$Ni(s) + HCl(aq) \longrightarrow NiCl_2(aq) + H_2(g)$$

(b) How many moles of $NiCl_2$ can be formed in the reaction of 6.00 mol of Ni and 12.0 mol of HCl?

PROBLEM 6.9

Plants convert carbon dioxide and water to glucose $(C_6H_{12}O_6)$ and oxygen in the process of photosynthesis. Write a balanced equation for this reaction, and determine how many moles of CO_2 are required to produce 15.0 mol of glucose.

6.4 Mass Relationships and Chemical Equations

Learning Objective:

- Using mole ratios, calculate the mass of product that can be formed from a given mass of reactant.

It is important to remember that the coefficients in a balanced chemical equation represent molecule to molecule (or mole to mole) relationships between reactants and products. Mole ratios make it possible to calculate the molar amounts of reactants and products, but actual amounts of substances used in the laboratory are weighed out in grams. Regardless of what units we use to specify the amount of reactants and/or products (mass, volume, number of molecules, and so on), the reaction always takes place on a mole to mole basis. Thus, we need to be able to carry out three kinds of conversions when doing chemical arithmetic.

- **Mole to mole conversions** are carried out using *mole ratios* as conversion factors. Worked Example 6.5 at the end of the preceding section is an example of this kind of calculation.

Use mole ratio as a conversion factor.

Moles of A (known) $\longrightarrow$ Moles of B (unknown)

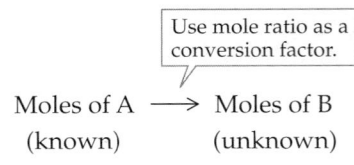

- **Mole to mass and mass to mole conversions** are carried out using *molar mass* as a conversion factor. Worked Examples 6.3 and 6.4 at the end of Section 6.2 are examples of this kind of calculation.

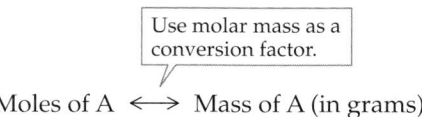

Moles of A $\longleftrightarrow$ Mass of A (in grams)

- **Mass to mass conversions** are frequently needed but cannot be carried out directly. If you know the mass of substance A and need to find the mass of substance B, you must first convert the mass of A into moles of A, then carry out a mole to mole conversion to find moles of B, and then convert moles of B into the mass of B (Figure 6.2).

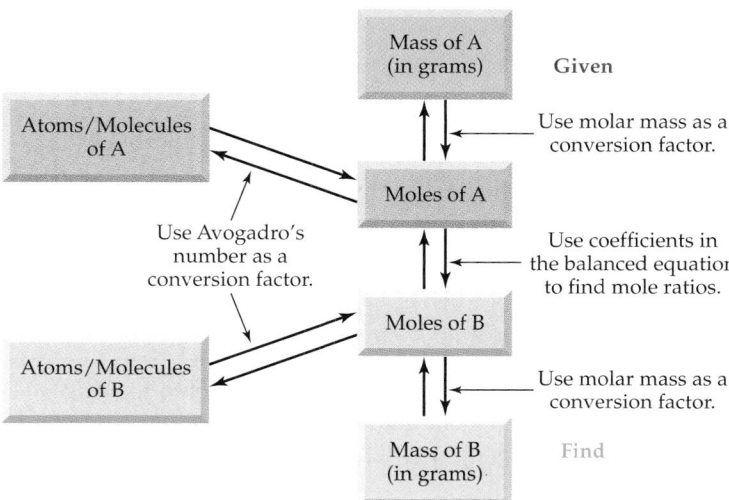

◄ **Figure 6.2**
A summary of conversions between moles, grams, and number of atoms or molecules for substances in a chemical reaction.
The numbers of moles tell how many molecules of each substance are needed, as given by the coefficients in the balanced equation; the numbers of grams tell what mass of each substance is needed.

Overall, there are four steps for determining mass relationships among reactants and products.

STEP 1: Write the balanced chemical equation.

STEP 2: Choose molar masses and mole ratios to convert the known information into the needed information.

STEP 3: Set up the factor-label expressions.

STEP 4: Calculate the answer and check the answer against the ballpark estimate you made before you began your calculations.

Worked Example 6.6 Mole Ratios: Mole to Mass Conversions

In the atmosphere, nitrogen dioxide reacts with water to produce NO and nitric acid, which contributes to pollution by acid rain.

$$3\,NO_2(g) + H_2O(l) \longrightarrow 2\,HNO_3(aq) + NO(g)$$

How many grams of HNO_3 are produced for every 1.0 mol of NO_2 that reacts? The molecular weight of HNO_3 is 63.0 amu.

ANALYSIS We are given the number of moles of a reactant and are asked to find the mass of a product. Problems of this sort always require working in moles and then converting to mass, as outlined in Figure 6.2.

BALLPARK ESTIMATE The molar mass of nitric acid is approximately 60 g/mol, and the coefficients in the balanced equation say that 2 mol of HNO_3 are formed for each 3 mol of NO_2 that undergo reaction. Thus, 1 mol of NO_2 should give about 2/3 mol HNO_3, or 2/3 mol × 60 g/mol = 40 g.

—continued on next page

—continued from previous page

SOLUTION

STEP 1: **Write balanced equation.**	$3\,NO_2(g) + H_2O(l) \longrightarrow 2\,HNO_3(aq) + NO(g)$
STEP 2: **Identify conversion factors.** We need a mole to mole conversion to find the number of moles of product, and then a mole to mass conversion to find the mass of product. For the first conversion, we use the mole ratio of HNO_3 to NO_2 as a conversion factor, and for the mole to mass calculation, we use the molar mass of HNO_3 (63.0 g/mol) as a conversion factor.	$\dfrac{2\;mol\;HNO_3}{3\;mol\;NO_2}$ $\dfrac{63.0\;g\;HNO_3}{1\;mol\;HNO_3}$
STEP 3: **Set up factor labels.** Identify appropriate mole ratio factor labels to convert moles NO_2 to moles HNO_3 and moles HNO_3 to grams.	$1.0\;\cancel{mol\;NO_2} \times \dfrac{2\;\cancel{mol\;HNO_3}}{3\;\cancel{mol\;NO_2}} \times \dfrac{63.0\;g\;HNO_3}{1\;\cancel{mol\;HNO_3}}$
STEP 4: **Solve.**	$= 42\;g\;HNO_3$

BALLPARK CHECK Our estimate was 40 g!

 Worked Example 6.7 Mole Ratios: Mass to Mole / Mole to Mass Conversions

The following reaction produced 0.022 g of calcium oxalate (CaC_2O_4). What mass of calcium chloride was used as reactant? (The molar mass of CaC_2O_4 is 128.1 g/mol, and the molar mass of $CaCl_2$ is 111.0 g/mol.)

$$CaCl_2(aq) + Na_2C_2O_4(aq) \longrightarrow CaC_2O_4(s) + 2\,NaCl(aq)$$

ANALYSIS Both the known information and that to be found are masses, so this is a mass to mass conversion problem. The mass of CaC_2O_4 is first converted into moles, a mole ratio is used to find moles of $CaCl_2$, and the number of moles of $CaCl_2$ is converted into mass.

BALLPARK ESTIMATE The balanced equation says that 1 mol of CaC_2O_4 is formed for each mole of $CaCl_2$ that reacts. Because the formula weights of the two substances are similar, it should take about 0.02 g of $CaCl_2$ to form 0.02 g of CaC_2O_4.

SOLUTION

STEP 1: **Write the balanced equation.**	$CaCl_2(aq) + Na_2C_2O_4(aq) \longrightarrow CaC_2O_4(s) + 2\,NaCl(aq)$
STEP 2: **Identify conversion factors.** Convert the mass of CaC_2O_4 into moles, use a mole ratio to find moles of $CaCl_2$, and convert the number of moles of $CaCl_2$ to mass. We will need three conversion factors.	mass CaC_2O_4 to moles: $\dfrac{1\;mol\;CaC_2O_4}{128.1\;g}$ moles CaC_2O_4 to moles $CaCl_2$: $\dfrac{1\;mol\;CaCl_2}{1\;mol\;CaC_2O_4}$ moles $CaCl_2$ to mass: $\dfrac{111.0\;g\;CaCl_2}{1\;mol\;CaCl_2}$
STEP 3: **Set up factor-labels.** We will need to perform gram to mole and mole to mole conversions to get from grams CaC_2O_4 to grams $CaCl_2$.	$0.022\;g\;\cancel{CaC_2O_4} \times \dfrac{1\;\cancel{mol\;CaC_2O_4}}{128.1\;g\;\cancel{CaC_2O_4}} \times$ $\dfrac{1\;\cancel{mol\;CaCl_2}}{1\;\cancel{mol\;CaC_2O_4}} \times \dfrac{111.0\;g\;CaCl_2}{1\;\cancel{mol\;CaCl_2}}$
STEP 4: **Solve.**	$= 0.019\;g\;CaCl_2$

BALLPARK CHECK The calculated answer (0.019 g) is consistent with our estimate (0.02 g).

PROBLEM 6.10

Hydrogen fluoride is one of the few substances that react with glass (which is made of silicon dioxide, SiO_2).

$$4\,HF(g) \;+\; SiO_2(s) \;\longrightarrow\; SiF_4(g) \;+\; 2\,H_2O(l)$$

(a) How many moles of HF will react completely with 9.90 mol of SiO_2?
(b) What mass of water (in grams) is produced by the reaction of 23.0 g of SiO_2?

PROBLEM 6.11

The tungsten metal used for filaments in light bulbs is made by reaction of tungsten(VI) oxide with hydrogen:

$$WO_3(s) \;+\; 3\,H_2(g) \;\longrightarrow\; W(s) \;+\; 3\,H_2O(g)$$

The above reaction was performed and produced 5.00 g of tungsten.
(a) How many moles of tungsten were formed?
(b) How many moles of tungsten(VI) oxide and hydrogen were required to produce the 5.00 g of tungsten?
(c) How many grams of tungsten(VI) oxide, and how many grams of hydrogen must you start with to prepare 5.00 g of tungsten? (For WO_3, MW = 231.8 amu.)

6.5 Limiting Reagent and Percent Yield

Learning Objective:

• Using mole ratios and the mass of reactants, calculate the theoretical yield and percent yield for a reaction.

All the calculations we have done in the past several sections have assumed that 100% of the reactants are converted to products. Only rarely is this the case in practice, though. Let us return to the recipe for s'mores presented in the previous chapter:

2 Graham crackers + 1 Roasted marshmallow + $\frac{1}{4}$ Chocolate bar $\longrightarrow$ 1 S'more

When you check your supplies, you find that you have 20 graham crackers, 8 marshmallows, and 3 chocolate bars. How many s'mores can you make? (Answer = 8!) You have enough graham crackers and chocolate bars to make more, but you will run out of marshmallows after you have made eight s'mores. In a similar way, when running a chemical reaction we do not always have the exact amounts of reagents to allow all of them to react completely. As a real example, consider a typical combustion reaction—such as a burning candle made of paraffin wax:

$$C_{31}H_{64}(s) \;+\; 47\,O_2(g) \;\longrightarrow\; 31\,CO_2(g) \;+\; 32\,H_2O(g) \;+\; heat$$

As long as there is a ready supply of oxygen and wax, the reaction will continue (i.e., the candle will continue to burn). However, if we cover the candle with a jar to limit the amount of oxygen, the candle will burn until all the available O_2 is consumed, and then the reaction would stop and the candle would go out. The reactant that is exhausted first in such a reaction (oxygen, in the case of the candle) is called the **limiting reagent.** The amount of product you obtain if the limiting reagent is completely consumed is called the **theoretical yield** of the reaction.

One way to identify the limiting reagent is to compare the mole ratio of reactants in the balanced chemical equation with the actual amounts of reactants available. Consider again the reaction of nitrogen with hydrogen to form ammonia.

$$N_2(g) \;+\; 3\,H_2(g) \;\longrightarrow\; 2\,NH_3(g)$$

Based on the balanced chemical equation, we know that the mole ratio of H_2 to N_2 is 3:1, or

$$\frac{3 \text{ moles } H_2}{1 \text{ mole } N_2} = 3.0$$

Limiting reagent The reactant that runs out first in any given reaction.

Theoretical yield The amount of product formed, assuming complete reaction of the limiting reagent.

Now, suppose you have 14.3 moles of H_2 and 4.5 moles of N_2; this ratio is $(14.3/4.5 = 3.18)$. The mole ratio is greater than the 3.0 from the balanced chemical equation, which implies that you have more H_2 than you need, or not enough N_2. So, nitrogen is the limiting reagent. Alternatively, you could use mole ratios to determine how much product (ammonia) could be formed by complete reaction of each reactant.

$$14.3 \text{ moles } H_2 \times \frac{2 \text{ moles } NH_3}{3 \text{ moles } H_2} = 9.53 \text{ moles } NH_3$$

$$4.5 \text{ moles } N_2 \times \frac{2 \text{ moles } NH_3}{1 \text{ mole } N_2} = 9.0 \text{ moles } NH_3*$$

Once all the available N_2 has reacted, only 9.0 mol of NH_3 has been produced and the reaction stops. Nitrogen is identified as the limiting reagent (*) because it "limits" the amount of product that can be formed.

Suppose that, while you are making s'mores, one of your eight marshmallows gets burned to a crisp. If this happens, the actual number of s'mores produced will be less than what you predicted based on the amount of starting materials. Similarly, chemical reactions do not always yield the exact amount of product predicted by the initial amount of reactants. More frequently, a majority of the reactant molecules behave as written, but other processes, called *side reactions,* also occur. For example, limiting the amount of O_2 in a combustion reaction may result in side reactions to produce carbon monoxide (CO) instead of carbon dioxide (CO_2). In addition, some of the product may be lost in handling. As a result, the amount of product actually obtained—the reaction's **actual yield**—is somewhat less than the theoretical yield. The amount of product actually obtained in a reaction is usually expressed as a **percent yield.**

Actual yield The amount of product actually formed in a reaction.

Percent yield The percentage of the theoretical yield actually obtained from a chemical reaction.

$$\text{Percent yield} = \frac{\text{Actual yield}}{\text{Theoretical yield}} \times 100$$

A reaction's actual yield is found by weighing the amount of product obtained. The theoretical yield is found by using the amount of limiting reagent in a mass to mass calculation like those illustrated in the preceding section (see Worked Example 6.7). Worked Examples 6.8–6.10 involve limiting reagent, percent yield, actual yield, and theoretical yield calculations.

Worked Example 6.8 Percent Yield

The combustion of acetylene gas (C_2H_2) produces carbon dioxide and water, as indicated in the following reaction:

$$2 C_2H_2(g) + 5 O_2(g) \longrightarrow 4 CO_2(g) + 2 H_2O(g)$$

When 26.0 g of acetylene is burned in sufficient oxygen for complete reaction, the theoretical yield of CO_2 is 88.0 g. Calculate the percent yield for this reaction if the actual yield is only 72.4 g CO_2.

ANALYSIS The percent yield is calculated by dividing the actual yield by the theoretical yield and multiplying by 100.

BALLPARK ESTIMATE The theoretical yield (88.0 g) is close to 100 g. The actual yield (72.4 g) is about 15 g less than the theoretical yield. The actual yield is thus about 15% less than the theoretical yield, so the percent yield is about 85%.

SOLUTION

$$\text{Percent yield} = \frac{\text{Actual yield}}{\text{Theoretical yield}} \times 100 = \frac{72.4 \text{ g } CO_2}{88.0 \text{ g } CO_2} \times 100 = 82.3$$

BALLPARK CHECK The calculated percent yield agrees very well with our estimate of 85%.

Worked Example 6.9 Mass to Mole Conversions: Limiting Reagent and Theoretical Yield

The element boron is produced commercially by the reaction of boric oxide with magnesium at high temperature.

$$B_2O_3(l) + 3\,Mg(s) \longrightarrow 2\,B(s) + 3\,MgO(s)$$

What is the theoretical yield of boron when 2350 g of boric oxide is reacted with 3580 g of magnesium? The molar masses of boric oxide and magnesium are 69.6 g/mol and 24.3 g/mol, respectively.

ANALYSIS To calculate theoretical yield, we first have to identify the limiting reagent. The theoretical yield in grams is then calculated from the amount of limiting reagent used in the reaction. The calculation involves the mass to mole and mole to mass conversions discussed in the preceding section.

SOLUTION

STEP 1: Identify known information. We have the masses and molar masses of the reagents.

2350 g B_2O_3, molar mass 69.6 g/mol
3580 g Mg, molar mass 24.3 g/mol

STEP 2: Identify answer and units. We are solving for the theoretical yield of boron.

Theoretical mass of B = ?? g

STEP 3: Identify conversion factors. We can use the molar masses to convert from masses to moles of reactants (B_2O_3, Mg). From moles of reactants, we can use mole ratios from the balanced chemical equation to find the number of moles of B produced, assuming complete conversion of a given reactant. B_2O_3 is the limiting reagent, since complete conversion of this reagent yields less product (67.6 mol B formed) than does complete conversion of Mg (98.0 mol B formed).

$$(2350\text{ g }B_2O_3) \times \frac{1\text{ mol }B_2O_3}{69.6\text{ g }B_2O_3} = 33.8\text{ mol }B_2O_3$$

$$(3580\text{ g Mg}) \times \frac{1\text{ mol Mg}}{24.3\text{ g Mg}} = 147\text{ mol Mg}$$

$$33.8\text{ mol }B_2O_3 \times \frac{2\text{ mol B}}{1\text{ mol }B_2O_3} = 67.6\text{ mol B*}$$

$$147\text{ mol Mg} \times \frac{2\text{ mol B}}{3\text{ mol Mg}} = 98.0\text{ mol B}$$

(*B_2O_3 is the limiting reagent because it yields fewer moles of B!)

STEP 4: Solve. Once the limiting reagent has been identified (B_2O_3), the theoretical amount of B that should be formed can be calculated using a mole to mass conversion.

$$67.6\text{ mol B} \times \frac{10.8\text{ g B}}{1\text{ mol B}} = 730\text{ g B}$$

Worked Example 6.10 Mass to Mole Conversion: Percent Yield

The reaction of ethylene with water to give ethyl alcohol (CH_3CH_2OH) occurs with 78.5% actual yield. How many grams of ethyl alcohol are formed by reaction of 25.0 g of ethylene? (For ethylene, MW = 28.0 amu; for ethyl alcohol, MW = 46.0 amu.)

$$H_2C{=}CH_2 + H_2O \longrightarrow CH_3CH_2OH$$

ANALYSIS Treat this as a typical mass relationship problem to find the amount of ethyl alcohol that can theoretically be formed from 25.0 g of ethylene, and then multiply the answer by 0.785 (the fraction of the theoretical yield actually obtained) to find the amount actually formed.

BALLPARK ESTIMATE The 25.0 g of ethylene is a bit less than 1 mol; since the percent yield is about 78%, a bit less than 0.78 mol of ethyl alcohol will form—perhaps about 3/4 mol, or 3/4 × 46 g = 34 g.

—continued on next page

—continued from previous page

SOLUTION

The theoretical yield of ethyl alcohol is as follows:

$$25.0 \text{ g ethylene} \times \frac{1 \text{ mol ethylene}}{28.0 \text{ g ethylene}} \times \frac{1 \text{ mol ethyl alcohol}}{1 \text{ mol ethylene}} \times \frac{46.0 \text{ g ethyl alcohol}}{1 \text{ mol ethyl alcohol}}$$

$$= 41.1 \text{ g ethyl alcohol}$$

and so the actual yield is as follows:

$$41.1 \text{ g ethyl alcohol} \times 0.785 = 32.3 \text{ g ethyl alcohol}$$

BALLPARK CHECK The calculated result (32.3 g) is close to our estimate (34 g).

PROBLEM 6.12

What is the theoretical yield of ethyl chloride in the reaction of 19.4 g of ethylene with 50 g of hydrogen chloride? What is the percent yield if 25.5 g of ethyl chloride is actually formed? (For ethylene, MW = 28.0 amu; for hydrogen chloride, MW = 36.5 amu; for ethyl chloride, MW = 64.5 amu.)

$$H_2C=CH_2 + HCl \longrightarrow CH_3CH_2Cl$$

PROBLEM 6.13

The reaction of ethylene oxide with water to give ethylene glycol (automobile antifreeze) occurs in 96.0% actual yield. How many grams of ethylene glycol are formed by reaction of 35.0 g of ethylene oxide? (For ethylene oxide, MW = 44.0 amu; for ethylene glycol, MW = 62.0 amu.)

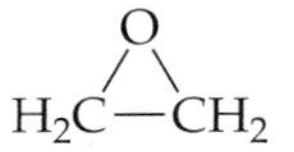

$$\overset{O}{\underset{H_2C-CH_2}{\triangle}} + H_2O \longrightarrow HOCH_2CH_2OH$$

Ethylene oxide   Ethylene glycol

⬛ KEY CONCEPT PROBLEM 6.14 ─────────────────────

Identify the limiting reagent in the reaction mixture shown next. The balanced reaction is as follows:

$$A_2 + 2 B_2 \longrightarrow 2 AB_2$$

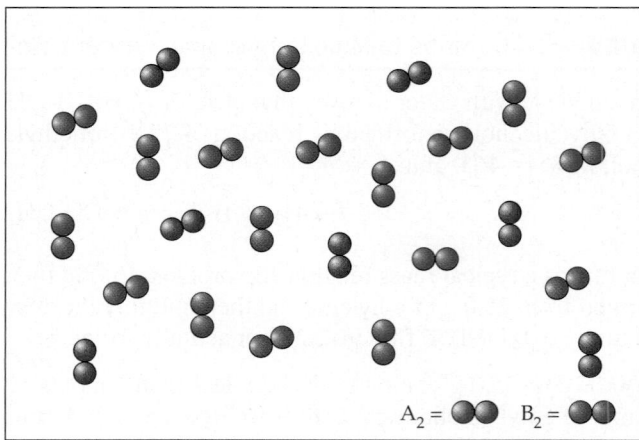

HANDS-ON CHEMISTRY 6.1

This activity illustrates the concepts of mole ratios and limiting reagents, and the product is a tasty snack. Assemble the following items: a packet of crackers, a jar of peanut butter, and a banana (or a chocolate bar that can be divided into sections). If the packet of crackers is small (less than 10), you can use the entire package; if you are using a box of crackers, remove a handful (but don't count them!) and place them in a pile. Then, peel the banana and cut it into slices and place them in a bowl; if you use a chocolate bar, divide it into sections. Finally, get a spoon, a plate, and the jar of peanut butter.

a. Assemble all the ingredients, and count how many crackers and banana slices (or chocolate sections) you have— we will assume that the jar of peanut butter represents a

sufficient amount for complete reaction. Now, make your "product" based on the following recipe (reaction):

2 Crackers + 1 Scoop of peanut butter + 1 Slice of banana (or section of chocolate) $\longrightarrow$ 1 Treat!

Scoop a small spoonful of peanut butter onto one of the crackers, add a banana slice or a piece of chocolate, and place the second cracker on top. Put the finished product on the plate. Continue making product until one of the ingredients/reagents runs out. Which ran out first? How many treats did you make?

b. Now, from the number of each ingredient and the "mole ratios" from the recipe, calculate the theoretical yield you would expect from complete reaction of each ingredient (crackers/banana slices/chocolate sections). How do your calculated yields compare to your actual yield?

CHEMISTRY IN ACTION

✝ Anemia—A Limiting Reagent Problem?

Anemia, which we first introduced in the opening of this chapter, is the most commonly diagnosed blood disorder, with symptoms typically including lethargy, fatigue, poor concentration, and sensitivity to cold. Although anemia has many causes, including genetic factors, the most common cause is insufficient dietary intake or absorption of iron.

Hemoglobin (abbreviated Hb), the iron-containing protein found in red blood cells, is responsible for oxygen transport throughout the body. Low iron levels in the body result in decreased production and incorporation of Hb into red blood cells. In addition, blood loss due to injury or to menstruation in women increases the body's demand for iron in order to replace lost Hb. In the United States, nearly 20% of women of child-bearing age suffer from iron-deficiency anemia compared to only 2% of adult men.

The recommended minimum daily iron intake is 8 mg for adult men and 18 mg for premenopausal women. One way to ensure sufficient iron intake is a well-balanced diet that includes iron-fortified grains and cereals, red meat, egg yolks, leafy green vegetables, tomatoes, and raisins. Vegetarians should pay extra attention to their diet, because the iron in fruits and vegetables is not as readily absorbed by the body as the iron in meat, poultry, and fish. Vitamin supplements containing folic acid and either ferrous sulfate or ferrous gluconate can decrease iron deficiencies, and vitamin C increases the absorption of iron by the body.

However, the simplest way to increase dietary iron may be to use cast iron cookware. Studies have demonstrated that the iron content of many foods increases when cooked in an iron pot. Other studies involving Ethiopian children showed that those who ate food cooked in iron cookware were less likely to suffer from iron-deficiency anemia than their playmates who ate similar foods prepared in aluminum cookware.

▲ Can cooking in cast iron pans decrease anemia?

CIA Problem 6.1 Dietary iron forms a 1:1 complex with hemoglobin (Hb), which is responsible for O_2 transport in the body based on the following equation:

$$Hb + 4\,O_2 \longrightarrow Hb(O_2)_4$$

How many moles of oxygen could be transported by the hemoglobin complex formed from 8 mg of dietary iron?

CIA Problem 6.2 Ferrous sulfate is one dietary supplement used to treat iron-deficiency anemia. What are the molecular formula and molecular weight of this compound? How many milligrams of iron are in 250 mg of ferrous sulfate?

CIA Problem 6.3 The recommended daily intake of iron is 8 mg for adult men and 18 mg for premenopausal women. Convert these masses of iron into moles.

LOOKING AHEAD ➤➤ We'll explore the role of hemoglobin in oxygen transport in greater detail in Chapter 9.

CONCEPT MAP: CHEMICAL REACTIONS (CHAPTERS 5 AND 6)

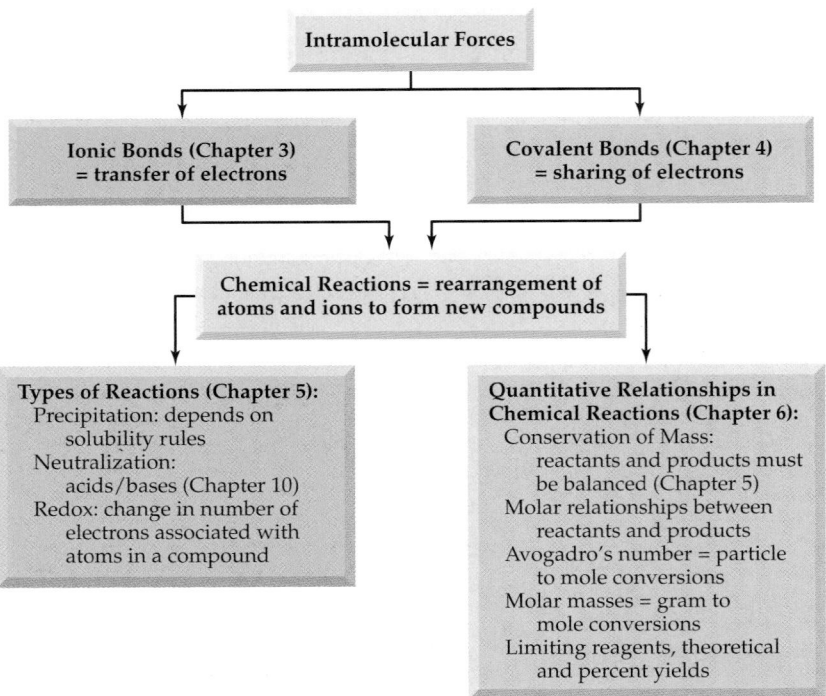

▲ **Figure 6.3 Concept Map.** As shown in this concept map, chemical reactions represent a rearrangement of the bonding forces within compounds as bonds in the reactants are broken and new bonds are formed to generate products. The quantitative relationships between reactants and products can be represented in terms of molar quantities or as masses, and these relationships can be used to determine limiting reagents and theoretical yields.

SUMMARY REVISITING THE CHAPTER LEARNING OBJECTIVES

• **Define the mole, and calculate molar mass of a compound from the molecular formula.** A *mole* refers to *Avogadro's number* (6.022×10^{23}) of formula units of a substance. One mole of any substance has a mass (*molar mass*) equal to the molecular or formula weight of the substance in grams *(see Problems 15, 20–34, 26–28, 31, 32, 35,55, and 71–74).*

• **Convert between mass and moles using the molar mass of a substance.** Because equal numbers of moles contain equal numbers of formula units, molar masses act as conversion factors between numbers of moles and masses in grams *(see Problems 19, 24, 25, 29, 30, 33–35, 44, 46–48, 56–60, 62, and 68–74).*

• **Determine molar ratios of reactants and products using balanced chemical equations.** The coefficients in a balanced chemical equation represent the numbers of moles of reactants and products in a reaction. Thus, the ratios of coefficients act as *mole ratios* that relate

amounts of reactants and/or products *(see Problems 16, 36–41, 43, 45–54, 56, 58–62, 66, 68–70, and 73).*

• **Using mole ratios, calculate the mass of product that can be formed from a given mass of reactant.** By using molar masses and mole ratios in factor-label calculations, unknown masses or molar amounts can be found from known masses or molar amounts *(see Problems 37–39, 41–54, 56, 57, 60, 61, 63–66, and 68).*

• **Using mole ratios and the mass of reactants, calculate the theoretical yield and percent yield for a reaction.** The *limiting reagent* is the reactant that runs out first. The *theoretical yield* is the calculated amount of product that would be formed based on the amount of the limiting reagent. The *actual yield* of a reaction is the amount of product obtained experimentally. The *percent yield* is the amount of product obtained divided by the amount theoretically possible and multiplied by 100% *(see Problems 17, 18, 49–54, and 64–67).*

KEY WORDS

Actual yield, *p. 174*	**Formula weight,** *p. 163*	**Mole,** *p. 164*	**Percent yield,** *p. 174*
Avogadro's number	**Limiting reagent,** *p. 173*	**Molecular weight (MW),**	**Theoretical yield,** *p. 173*
(N_A), *p. 164*	**Molar mass,** *p. 164*	*p. 163*	

⊙ UNDERSTANDING KEY CONCEPTS

6.15 Methionine, an amino acid used by organisms to make proteins, can be represented by the following ball-and-stick molecular model. Write the formula for methionine, and give its molecular weight (red = O, black = C, blue = N, yellow = S, white = H).

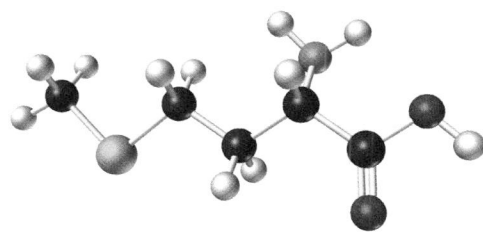

Methionine

6.16 The following diagram represents the reaction of A_2 (red spheres) with B_2 (blue spheres):

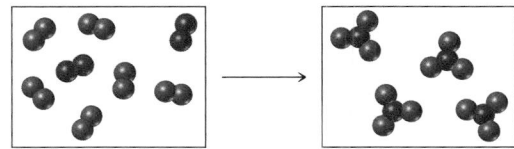

(a) Write a balanced equation for the reaction.

(b) How many moles of product can be made from 1.0 mol of A_2? From 1.0 mol of B_2?

6.17 Consider the balanced chemical equation: $2A + B_2 \longrightarrow 2AB$. Given the following reaction vessel, determine the theoretical yield of product.

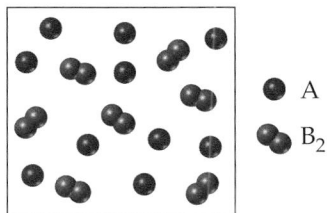

6.18 Consider the balanced chemical equation: $A_2 + 2 B_2 \longrightarrow 2 AB_2$. A reaction is performed with the initial amounts of A_2 and B_2 shown in part (a). The amount of product obtained is shown in part (b). Calculate the percent yield.

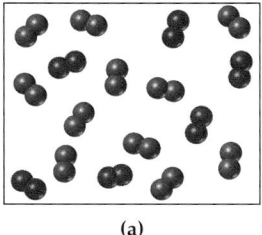

(a)

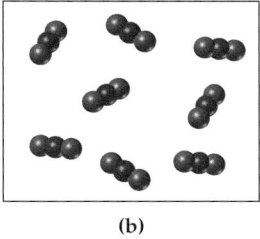

(b)

6.19 The following drawing represents the reaction of ethylene oxide with water to give ethylene glycol, a compound used as automobile antifreeze. What mass in grams of ethylene oxide is needed to react with 9.0 g of water, and what mass in grams of ethylene glycol is formed?

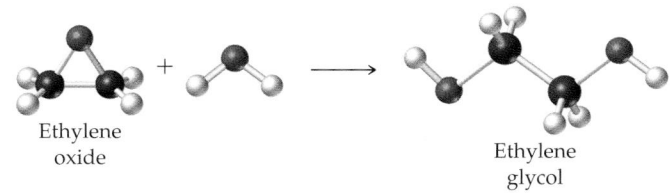

Ethylene oxide

Ethylene glycol

ADDITIONAL PROBLEMS

MOLAR MASSES AND MOLES (SECTIONS 6.1 AND 6.2)

6.20 What is a mole of a substance? How many molecules are in 1 mol of a molecular compound?

6.21 What is the difference between molecular weight and formula weight? Between molecular weight and molar mass?

6.22 How many Na^+ ions are in a mole of Na_2SO_4? How many SO_4^{2-} ions?

6.23 How many moles of ions are in 1.75 mol of K_2SO_4?

6.24 How many calcium atoms are in 16.2 g of calcium?

6.25 What is the mass in grams of 2.68×10^{22} atoms of uranium?

6.26 Calculate the molar mass of each of the following compounds:

(a) Calcium carbonate, $CaCO_3$

(b) Urea, $CO(NH_2)_2$

(c) Ethylene glycol, $C_2H_6O_2$

6.27 How many moles of carbon atoms are there in 1 mol of each compound in Problem 6.26?

6.28 How many atoms of carbon and how many grams of carbon are there in 1 mol of each compound in Problem 6.26?

6.29 Caffeine has the formula $C_8H_{10}N_4O_2$. If an average cup of coffee contains approximately 125 mg of caffeine, how many moles of caffeine are in one cup?

6.30 How many moles of aspirin, $C_9H_8O_4$, are in a 500 mg tablet?

6.31 What is the molar mass of diazepam (Valium), $C_{16}H_{13}ClN_2O$?

6.32 Calculate the molar masses of the following substances:

(a) Aluminum sulfate, $Al_2(SO_4)_3$

(b) Sodium bicarbonate, $NaHCO_3$

(c) Diethyl ether, $(C_2H_5)_2O$

(d) Penicillin V, $C_{16}H_{18}N_2O_5S$

6.33 How many moles are present in a 4.50 g sample of each compound listed in Problem 6.32?

6.34 How many grams are present in a 0.075 mol sample of each compound listed in Problem 6.32?

6.35 The principal component of many kidney stones is calcium oxalate, CaC_2O_4. A kidney stone recovered from a typical patient contains 8.5×10^{20} formula units of calcium oxalate. How many moles of CaC_2O_4 are present in this kidney stone? What is the mass of the kidney stone in grams?

MOLE AND MASS RELATIONSHIPS FROM CHEMICAL EQUATIONS (SECTIONS 6.2–6.4)

6.36 At elevated temperatures in an automobile engine, N_2 and O_2 can react to yield NO, an important cause of air pollution.

(a) Write a balanced equation for the reaction.

(b) How many moles of N_2 are needed to react with 7.50 mol of O_2?

(c) How many moles of NO can be formed when 3.81 mol of N_2 reacts?

(d) How many moles of O_2 must react to produce 0.250 mol of NO?

6.37 Ethyl acetate reacts with H_2 in the presence of a catalyst to yield ethyl alcohol.

$$C_4H_8O_2(l) + H_2(g) \longrightarrow C_2H_6O(l)$$

(a) Write a balanced equation for the reaction.

(b) How many moles of ethyl alcohol are produced by reaction of 1.5 mol of ethyl acetate?

(c) How many grams of ethyl alcohol are produced by reaction of 1.5 mol of ethyl acetate with H_2?

(d) How many grams of ethyl alcohol are produced by reaction of 12.0 g of ethyl acetate with H_2?

(e) How many grams of H_2 are needed to react with 12.0 g of ethyl acetate?

6.38 The active ingredient in milk of magnesia (an antacid) is magnesium hydroxide, $Mg(OH)_2$. A typical dose (one tablespoon) contains 1.2 g of $Mg(OH)_2$. Calculate (a) the molar mass of magnesium hydroxide and (b) the amount of magnesium hydroxide (in moles) in one teaspoon.

6.39 Ammonia, NH_3, is prepared for use as a fertilizer by reacting N_2 with H_2.

(a) Write a balanced equation for the reaction.

(b) How many moles of N_2 are needed for reaction to make 16.0 g of NH_3?

(c) How many grams of H_2 are needed to react with 75.0 g of N_2?

6.40 Hydrazine, N_2H_4, a substance used as rocket fuel, reacts with oxygen as follows:

$$N_2H_4(l) + O_2(g) \longrightarrow NO_2(g) + H_2O(g)$$

(a) Balance the equation.

(b) How many moles of oxygen are needed to react with 165 g of hydrazine?

(c) How many grams of oxygen are needed to react with 165 g of hydrazine?

6.41 One method for preparing pure iron from Fe_2O_3 is by reaction with carbon monoxide.

$$Fe_2O_3(s) + CO(g) \longrightarrow Fe(s) + CO_2(g)$$

(a) Balance the equation.

(b) How many grams of CO are needed to react with 3.02 g of Fe_2O_3?

(c) How many grams of CO are needed to react with 1.68 mol of Fe_2O_3?

6.42 Magnesium metal burns in oxygen to form magnesium oxide, MgO.

(a) Write a balanced equation for the reaction.

(b) How many grams of oxygen are needed to react with 25.0 g of Mg? How many grams of MgO will result?

(c) How many grams of Mg are needed to react with 25.0 g of O_2? How many grams of MgO will result?

6.43 Titanium metal is obtained from the mineral rutile, TiO_2. The process requires multiple steps, as shown in the following reactions:

$$TiO_2(s) + 2\,Cl_2(g) + 2\,C(s) \longrightarrow TiCl_4(s) + 2\,CO(g)$$
$$TiCl_4(s) + 2\,Mg(s) \longrightarrow Ti(s) + 2\,MgCl_2(s)$$

(a) Write mole ratios to show the relationship between the reactants and products for each reaction.

(b) How many moles of TiO_2 are needed to form one mole of titanium?

(c) How many kilograms of rutile are needed to produce 95 kg of Ti?

6.44 In the preparation of iron from hematite (Problem 6.43), how many moles of carbon monoxide are needed to react completely with 105 kg of Fe_2O_3?

6.45 The eruption of Mount St. Helens volcano in 1980 injected 4×10^8 kg of SO_2 into the atmosphere. If all this SO_2 was converted to sulfuric acid, how many moles of H_2SO_4 would be produced? How many kilograms?

6.46 The thermite reaction was used to produce molten iron for welding applications before arc welding was available. The thermite reaction is as follows:

$$Fe_2O_3(s) + 2\,Al(s) \longrightarrow Al_2O(s) + 2\,Fe(l)$$

How many moles of molten iron can be produced from 1.5 kg of iron(III) oxide? NaOH?

6.47 In closed environments, such as submarines, elevated levels of carbon dioxide can be toxic. Excess CO_2 is removed by scrubbers that take advantage of the reaction of CO_2 with soda lime, a mixture of sodium hydroxide and calcium hydroxide.

$$CO_2 + NaOH \longrightarrow NaHCO_3$$
$$CO_2 + Ca(OH)_2 \longrightarrow Ca(HCO_3)_2$$

How many moles of CO_2 could be removed from the air by 1.0 kg of NaOH? By 1.0 kg of $Ca(OH)_2$?

6.48 Diborane (B_2H_6) is a gas at room temperature that forms explosive mixtures with air. It reacts with oxygen according to the following equation:

$$B_2H_6(g) + 3\,O_2(g) \longrightarrow B_2O_3(s) + 3\,H_2O(l)$$

How many grams of diborane will react with 7.5 mol of O_2?

LIMITING REAGENT AND PERCENT YIELD (SECTION 6.5)

6.49 Once made by heating wood in the absence of air, methanol (CH_3OH) is now made by reacting carbon monoxide and hydrogen at high pressure.

$$CO(g) + 2\,H_2(g) \longrightarrow CH_3OH(l)$$

(a) If 25.0 g of CO is reacted with 6.00 g of H_2, which is the limiting reagent?

(b) How many grams of CH_3OH can be made from 10.0 g of CO if it all reacts?

(c) If 9.55 g of CH_3OH is recovered when the amounts in part (b) are used, what is the percent yield?

6.50 In Problem 6.40, hydrazine reacted with oxygen according to the following (unbalanced) equation:

$$N_2H_4(l) + O_2(g) \longrightarrow NO_2(g) + H_2O(g)$$

(a) If 75.0 kg of hydrazine are reacted with 75.0 kg of oxygen, which is the limiting reagent?

(b) How many kilograms of NO_2 are produced from the reaction of 75.0 kg of the limiting reagent?

(c) If 59.3 kg of NO_2 are obtained from the reaction in part (a), what is the percent yield?

6.51 Dichloromethane, CH_2Cl_2, the solvent used to decaffeinate coffee beans, is prepared by reaction of CH_4 with Cl_2.

(a) Write the balanced equation. (HCl is also formed.)

(b) How many grams of Cl_2 are needed to react with 50.0 g of CH_4?

(c) How many grams of dichloromethane are formed from 50.0 g of CH_4 if the percent yield for the reaction is 76%?

6.52 Cisplatin $[Pt(NH_3)_2Cl_2]$, a compound used in cancer treatment, is prepared by reaction of ammonia with potassium tetrachloroplatinate:

$$K_2PtCl_4 + 2\,NH_3 \longrightarrow 2\,KCl + Pt(NH_3)_2Cl_2$$

(a) How many grams of NH_3 are needed to react with 55.8 g of K_2PtCl_4?

(b) How many grams of cisplatin are formed from 55.8 g of K_2PtCl_4 if the percent yield for the reaction is 95%?

6.53 Nitrobenzene $(C_6H_5NO_2)$ is used in small quantities as a flavoring agent or in perfumes but can be toxic in large amounts. It is produced by reaction of benzene (C_6H_6) with nitric acid:

$$C_6H_6(l) + HNO_3(aq) \longrightarrow C_6H_5NO_2(l) + H_2O(l).$$

(a) Identify the limiting reagent in the reaction of 27.5 g of nitric acid with 75 g of benzene.

(b) Calculate the theoretical yield for this reaction.

6.54 Calculate the percent yield if 48.2 g of nitrobenzene is obtained from the reaction described in Problem 6.53.

CONCEPTUAL PROBLEMS

6.55 Batrachotoxin, $C_{31}H_{42}N_2O_6$, an active component of South American arrow poison, is so toxic that 0.05 μg can kill a person. How many molecules is this?

6.56 Zinc metal reacts with hydrochloric acid (HCl) according to the following equation:

$$Zn(s) + 2\,HCl(aq) \longrightarrow ZnCl_2(aq) + H_2(g)$$

(a) How many grams of hydrogen are produced if 15.0 g of zinc reacts?

(b) Is this a redox reaction? If so, tell what is reduced, what is oxidized, and identify the reducing and oxidizing agents.

6.57 When table sugar (sucrose, $C_{12}H_{22}O_{11}$) is heated, it decomposes to form C and H_2O.

(a) Write a balanced equation for the process.

(b) How many grams of carbon are formed by the breakdown of 60.0 g of sucrose?

(c) How many grams of water are formed when 6.50 g of carbon are formed?

6.58 Although Cu is not sufficiently active to react with acids, it can be dissolved by concentrated nitric acid, which functions as an oxidizing agent according to the following equation:

$$Cu(s) + 4\,HNO_3(aq) \longrightarrow$$
$$Cu(NO_3)_2(aq) + 2\,NO_2(g) + 2\,H_2O(l)$$

(a) Write the net ionic equation for this process.

(b) Is 35.0 g of HNO_3 sufficient to dissolve 5.00 g of copper?

6.59 The net ionic equation for the Breathalyzer test used to indicate alcohol concentration in the body is as follows:

$$16\,H^+(aq) + 2\,Cr_2O_7^{2-}(aq) + 3\,C_2H_6O(aq) \longrightarrow$$
$$3\,C_2H_4O_2(aq) + 4\,Cr^{3+}(aq) + 11\,H_2O(l)$$

(a) How many grams of $K_2Cr_2O_7$ must be used to consume 1.50 g of C_2H_6O?

(b) How many grams of $C_2H_4O_2$ can be produced from 80.0 g of C_2H_6O?

6.60 Ethyl alcohol is formed by enzyme action on sugars and starches during fermentation.

$$C_6H_{12}O_6 \longrightarrow 2\,CO_2 + 2\,C_2H_6O$$

If the density of ethyl alcohol is 0.789 g/mL, how many quarts can be produced by the fermentation of 100.0 lb of sugar?

6.61 Gaseous ammonia reacts with oxygen in the presence of a platinum catalyst to produce nitrogen monoxide and water vapor.

(a) Write a balanced chemical equation for this reaction.

(b) What mass of nitrogen monoxide would be produced by complete reaction of 17.0 g of ammonia?

6.62 Sodium hypochlorite, the primary component in commercial bleach, is prepared by bubbling chlorine gas through solutions of sodium hydroxide.

$$NaOH(aq) + Cl_2(g) \longrightarrow NaOCl(aq) + H_2O(l)$$

How many moles of sodium hypochlorite can be prepared from 32.5 g of NaOH?

6.63 Barium sulfate is an insoluble ionic compound swallowed by patients before having an X ray of their gastrointestinal tract.

(a) Write the balanced chemical equation for the precipitation reaction between barium chloride and sodium sulfate.

(b) What mass of barium sulfate can be produced by complete reaction of 27.4 g of Na_2SO_4?

6.64 The last step in the production of nitric acid is the reaction of nitrogen dioxide with water.

$$NO_2(g) + H_2O(l) \longrightarrow HNO_3(aq) + NO(g)$$

(a) Balance the chemical equation.

(b) If 65.0 g of nitrogen dioxide is reacted with excess water, calculate the theoretical yield.

(c) If only 43.8 g of nitric acid is obtained, calculate the percent yield.

6.65 Acetylsalicylic acid, the active ingredient in aspirin, is prepared from salicylic acid by reaction with acetic anhydride.

$$\underset{(\text{salicylic acid})}{C_7H_6O_3} + \underset{(\text{acetic anhydride})}{C_4H_6O_3} \longrightarrow \underset{(\text{acetylsalicylic acid})}{C_9H_8O_4} + \underset{(\text{acetic acid})}{C_2H_4O_2}$$

(a) Calculate the theoretical yield if 47 g of salicylic acid is reacted with 25 g of acetic anhydride.

(b) What is the percent yield if only 35 g is obtained?

6.66 Jewelry and tableware can be silver-plated by reduction of silver ions from a solution of silver nitrate. The net ionic equation is $Ag^+(aq) + e^- \longrightarrow Ag(s)$. How many grams of silver nitrate would be needed to plate 15.2 g of silver on a piece of jewelry?

6.67 Elemental phosphorus exists as molecules of P_4. It reacts with $Cl_2(g)$ to produce phosphorus pentachloride.

(a) Write the balanced chemical equation for this reaction.

(b) What mass of phosphorus pentachloride would be produced by the complete reaction of 15.2 g of P_4?

6.68 Lithium oxide is used aboard the International Space Station to remove water from the atmosphere according to the equation

$$Li_2O(s) + H_2O(g) \longrightarrow 2\,LiOH(s)$$

How many grams of must be carried on board to remove 80.0 kg of water?

6.69 One of the reactions used to provide thrust for the International Space Station involves the reaction of ammonium perchlorate with aluminum to produce $AlCl_3(s)$, $H_2O(g)$, and $NO(g)$.

(a) Write the balanced chemical equation for this reaction.

(b) How many moles of gas are produced by the reaction of 14.5 kg of ammonium perchlorate?

GROUP PROBLEMS

6.70 Calcium citrate, $Ca_3(C_6H_5O_7)_2$ (MW = 498.5 amu), is a common dietary supplement to provide calcium needed for strong teeth and bones.

(a) Look up the recommended daily dietary intake of calcium for adult men and premenopausal women.

(b) What mass of calcium citrate would be needed to provide the recommended daily intake of calcium?

6.71 Obtain a bottle of aspirin and identify the amount of active ingredient (acetylsalicylic acid, $C_9H_8O_4$) per tablet.

(a) How many moles of aspirin are in one tablet?

(b) How many aspirin molecules are there in one tablet?

6.72 Lovastatin, a drug used to lower serum cholesterol.

(a) Look up the molecular formula for Lovastatin and calculate the molar mass.

(b) How many moles of Lovastatin are present in a typical dose of one 10 mg tablet?

6.73 Pyrite, also known as fool's gold, is used commercially to produce SO_2 used in the production of paper products.

(a) What is the formula of pyrite, and what is its molar mass?

(b) How many moles of SO_2 can be produced from 1.0 kg of pyrite?

6.74 Look up the recommended daily intake of vitamin C (ascorbic acid, $C_6H_8O_6$).

(a) Obtain a bottle of a daily vitamin supplement. How many milligrams of vitamin C are contained per tablet?

(b) What percentage of the recommended daily dosage does this represent?

7

Chemical Reactions: Energy, Rates, and Equilibrium

CONTENTS

◀◀◀ CONCEPTS TO REVIEW

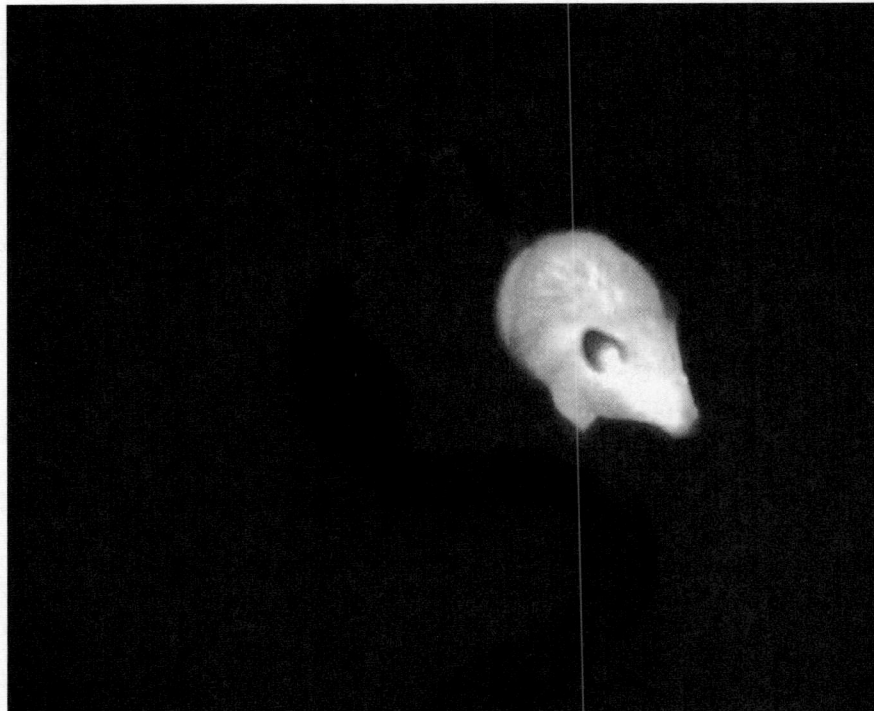

▲ This thermal image photo dramatically illustrates the differences between warm-blooded and cold-blooded animals. Warm-blooded animals use the heat generated by metabolic chemical reactions to maintain a constant body temperature.

Have you ever come across a snake or lizard warming itself on a rock in the sun? Lizards and other so-called cold-blooded animals are very active in warm weather but very sluggish in cool weather. Warm-blooded animals, including mammals, can remain very active in spite of environmental conditions. To maintain a fairly constant body temperature, they must consume substantial amounts of food and have developed complex mechanisms to generate heat when it is too cold or to cool down when it is too hot, which we will learn more about in the Chemistry in Action feature on p. 208. Still, other animals, such as bears, can lower their body temperature when food is scarce and go into hibernation. These substantial differences in animal behavior are all related to a complex system of biochemical reactions that are collectively known as metabolism. But in order to fully appreciate metabolic processes, we must examine chemical reactions, and the factors that control a reaction, in more detail.

In the two previous chapters, we began our study of reactions—reaction types, how to balance reactions, and the stoichiometric relationships between reactants and products—but we have yet to answer many questions about reactions. Why, for instance, do some reactions occur while others do not, or occur to a limited extent? Just because a balanced equation can be written does not mean it will take place. We can write a balanced equation for the reaction of gold with water, for example, but the reaction does not occur in practice—so your gold jewelry is safe in the shower.

Balanced but does not occur $2\,Au(s) + 3\,H_2O(l) \longrightarrow Au_2O_3(s) + 3\,H_2(g)$

Other reactions may proceed only partially, generating some products but leaving most of the original reactants unreacted. The amount of products that are formed can also be affected by other factors, including temperature. To understand chemical reactions more completely, several fundamental questions are commonly asked: Is energy released or absorbed when a reaction occurs? Is a given reaction fast or slow? Does a reaction continue until all reactants are converted to products, or is there a point beyond which no additional product forms? In this chapter, we will examine how reactions occur and identify the factors that affect both the rate and the extent of a reaction.

7.1 Energy and Chemical Bonds

Learning Objective:

- Distinguish between potential and kinetic energy.

There are two fundamental kinds of energy: *potential* and *kinetic*. **Potential energy** is stored energy. The water in a reservoir behind a dam, an automobile poised to coast downhill, and a coiled spring have potential energy waiting to be released. **Kinetic energy,** by contrast, is the energy of motion. When the water falls over the dam and turns a turbine, when the car rolls downhill, or when the spring uncoils and makes the hands on a clock move, the potential energy in each is converted to kinetic energy. Of course, once all the potential energy is converted, nothing further occurs. The water at the bottom of the dam, the car at the bottom of the hill, and the uncoiled spring no longer have potential energy and, thus, undergo no further change.

In chemical compounds, the attractive forces between ions or atoms are a form of potential energy, similar to the attractive forces between the poles of a magnet. When these attractive forces result in the formation of ionic or covalent bonds between ions or atoms, the potential energy is often converted into **heat**—a measure of the kinetic energy of the particles that make up the molecule. Breaking these bonds requires an input of energy.

In chemical reactions, some of the chemical bonds in the reactants must break (energy in) so that new bonds can form in the products (energy out). If the reaction products have less potential energy than the reactants, we say that the products are *more stable* than the reactants. The term "stable" is used in chemistry to describe a substance that has little remaining potential energy and consequently little tendency to undergo further change. Whether a reaction occurs, and how much energy or heat is associated with the reaction, depends on the difference in the amount of potential energy contained in the reactants and products.

Potential energy Stored energy.

Kinetic energy The energy of motion of an object in motion.

Heat A measure of the transfer of thermal energy.

PROBLEM 7.1

Classify each of the following as having potential or kinetic energy. For those identified as having potential energy, discuss how the potential energy would be realized by conversion to another form of energy.

- **(a)** gunpowder
- **(b)** a bullet in flight
- **(c)** a cell phone (lithium ion) battery
- **(d)** wind
- **(e)** a candy bar
- **(f)** spinning wind mill blades

7.2 Heat Changes during Chemical Reactions

Learning Objective:

- Identify chemical reactions as endothermic or exothermic and explain how the heats of reaction relate to the law of conservation of energy.

Why does chlorine react so easily with many elements and compounds but nitrogen does not? What dissimilarity between Cl_2 molecules and N_2 molecules accounts for their different reactivities? The answer is that the nitrogen–nitrogen triple bond is much *stronger* than the chlorine–chlorine single bond and cannot be broken as easily in chemical reactions.

The strength of a covalent bond is measured by its **bond dissociation energy,** defined as the amount of energy that must be absorbed to break the bond and separate the atoms in an isolated gaseous molecule. The greater the bond dissociation energy, the more stable the chemical bond between the atoms or ions. The triple bond in N_2, for example, has a

Bond dissociation energy The amount of energy that must be supplied to break a bond and separate the atoms in an isolated gaseous molecule.

bond dissociation energy of 226 kcal/mol (946 kJ/mol), whereas the single bond in chlorine has a bond dissociation energy of only 58 kcal/mol (243 kJ/mol):

$$:N:::N: + 226 \text{ kcal/mol} \longrightarrow :\dot{N}\cdot + \cdot\dot{N}:$$ N_2 bond dissociation energy = 226 kcal/mol (946 kJ/mol)

$$:\ddot{C}l:\ddot{C}l: + 58 \text{ kcal/mol} \longrightarrow :\ddot{C}l\cdot + \cdot\ddot{C}l:$$ Cl_2 bond dissociation energy = 58 kcal/mol (243 kJ/mol)

The greater stability of the triple bond in N_2 explains why nitrogen molecules are less reactive than Cl_2 molecules. Some typical bond dissociation energies are given in Table 7.1.

Table 7.1 Average Bond Dissociation Energies

Bond	Bond Dissociation Energy kcal/mol (kJ/mol)	Bond	Bond Dissociation Energy kcal/mol (kJ/mol)	Bond	Bond Dissociation Energy kcal/mol (kJ/mol)
C—H	99 (413)	N—H	93 (391)	C=C	147 (614)
C—C	83 (347)	N—N	38 (160)	C≡C	201 (839)
C—N	73 (305)	N—Cl	48 (200)	C=O*	178 (745)
C—O	86 (358)	N—O	48 (201)	O=O	119 (498)
C—Cl	81 (339)	H—H	103 (432)	N=O	145 (607)
Cl—Cl	58 (243)	O—H	112 (467)	O≡N	213 (891)
H—Cl	102 (427)	O—Cl	49 (203)	N≡N	226 (946)

*The C=O bond dissociation energies in CO_2 are 191 kcal/mol (799 kJ/mol).

Endothermic A process or reaction that absorbs heat.

Exothermic A process or reaction that releases heat.

A chemical change that absorbs heat, like the breaking of bonds, is **endothermic,** from the Greek words *endon* (within) and *therme* (heat), meaning that *heat* is required as a condition for reaction and would appear on the left side of the equation. The reverse of bond breaking is bond formation, a process that *releases* heat and is **exothermic,** from the Greek *exo* (outside), meaning that heat goes *out* and appears on the right side of the equation as a product. The amount of energy released in forming a bond is numerically the same as that absorbed in breaking it. When nitrogen atoms combine to give N_2, 226 kcal/mol (946 kJ/mol) of heat is released. Similarly, when chlorine atoms combine to give Cl_2, 58 kcal/mol (243 kJ/mol) of heat is released.

$$:\dot{N}\cdot + \cdot\dot{N}: \longrightarrow :N:::N: + 226 \text{ kcal/mol} \quad (946 \text{ kJ/mol}) \text{ heat released}$$
$$:\ddot{C}l\cdot + \cdot\ddot{C}l: \longrightarrow :\ddot{C}l:\ddot{C}l: + 58 \text{ kcal/mol} \quad (243 \text{ kJ/mol}) \text{ heat released}$$

For bond breakage and bond formation, the numerical value of the heat associated with the process is the same, but the direction of energy flow depends on the reaction. We indicate the direction of energy flow based on whether the energy is absorbed (gained) or released (lost) during the process. For endothermic processes, heat is absorbed (gained) and is indicated by a positive sign. For exothermic processes, heat is released (lost) and is indicated with a negative sign.

The same energy relationships that govern bond breaking and bond formation apply to every physical or chemical change. That is, the amount of heat transferred during a change in one direction is numerically equal to the amount of heat transferred during the change in the opposite direction. Only the *direction* of the heat transfer is different. This relationship reflects a fundamental law of nature called the *law of conservation of energy:*

Law of conservation of energy Energy can be neither created nor destroyed in any physical or chemical change.

If more energy could be released by an exothermic reaction than was consumed in its reverse, the law would be violated, and we could "manufacture" energy out of nowhere by cycling back and forth between forward and reverse reactions—a clear impossibility.

In every chemical reaction, some bonds in the reactants are broken, and new bonds are formed in the products. The difference between the heat energy absorbed in breaking bonds and the heat energy released in forming bonds is called the **heat of reaction** and is a quantity that we can measure. Heats of reaction that are measured when a reaction is held at constant pressure are represented by the abbreviation ΔH, where Δ (the Greek capital letter delta) is a general symbol used to indicate "a change in," and H is a quantity called **enthalpy.** Thus, the value of ΔH represents the **enthalpy change** that occurs during a reaction. The terms *enthalpy change* and *heat of reaction* are often used interchangeably, but we will generally use the latter term in this book.

Heat of reaction or Enthalpy change (ΔH) The difference between the energy of bonds broken in reactants and the energy of bonds formed in products.

Enthalpy (*H*) A measure of the amount of energy associated with substances involved in a reaction.

PROBLEM 7.2

Based on bond energies, which atmospheric gas in each pair do you think is more stable? Explain.

(a) O_2 or N_2 **(b)** CO or CO_2

7.3 Exothermic and Endothermic Reactions

Learning Objective:

• Use bond energies and stoichiometric relationships to calculate the enthalpy of a reaction and the total amount of heat consumed or produced.

When the total strength of the bonds formed in the products is *greater* than the total strength of the bonds broken in the reactants, the net result is that energy is released and the reaction is exothermic. All combustion reactions are exothermic; for example, burning 1 mol of methane releases 213 kcal (891 kJ) of energy in the form of heat. The heat released in an exothermic reaction can be thought of as a reaction product, and the heat of reaction ΔH is assigned a *negative* value, because overall, heat is *lost* during the reaction.

An exothermic reaction—negative ΔH

Heat is a product.

$$CH_4(g) + 2\,O_2(g) \longrightarrow CO_2(g) + 2\,H_2O(l) + 213 \text{ kcal (891 kJ)}$$

or

$$CH_4(g) + 2\,O_2(g) \longrightarrow CO_2(g) + 2\,H_2O(l) \qquad \Delta H = -213 \text{ kcal/mol } (-891 \text{ kJ/mol})$$

The heat of reaction can be calculated as the difference between the bond dissociation energies in the products and the bond dissociation energies of the reactants:

$$\Delta H = \Sigma\,(\text{Bond dissociation energies})_{\text{reactants}} - \Sigma\,(\text{Bond dissociation energies})_{\text{products}}$$

Look again at the reaction involving the combustion of methane. By determining the types of bonds and then counting the number of bonds of each type on each side of the chemical equation, we can use the average bond dissociation energies from Table 7.1 to estimate ΔH for the reaction.

Reactants	Bond Dissociation Energies (kcal/mol)	Products	Bond Dissociation Energies (kcal/mol)
(C—H) × 4	99 × 4 = 396 kcal	(C=O) × 2	191 × 2 = 382 kcal
(O=O) × 2	119 × 2 = 238 kcal	(H—O) × 4	112 × 4 = 448 kcal
Total:	= 634 kcal		= 830 kcal

$$\Delta H = (634 \text{ kcal})_{\text{reactants}} - (830 \text{ kcal})_{\text{products}} = -196 \text{ kcal}\,(-820 \text{ kJ})$$

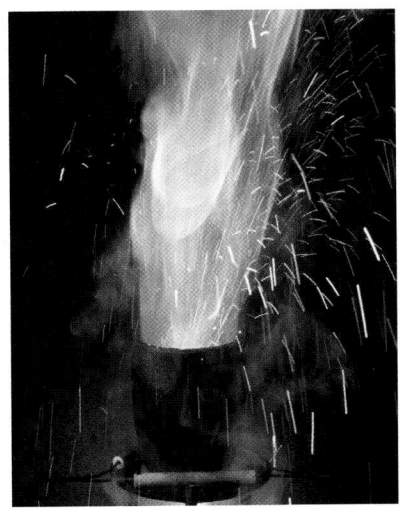

▲ The reaction between aluminum metal and iron(III) oxide, called the *thermite reaction,* is so strongly exothermic that it melts iron.

In this reaction, the input of energy needed to break the bonds in the reactants is less than the amount of energy released when forming bonds in the products. The excess energy is released as heat, and the reaction is exothermic (ΔH = negative).

Note that the bond energies in Table 7.1 are average values, and that actual bond energies may vary depending on the chemical environment in which the bond is found. The average C=O bond energy, for example, is 178 kcal/mol, but the actual value for the C=O bonds in the CO_2 molecule is 191 kcal/mol. The average C—H bond energy is 99 kcal/mol (413 kJ/mol), but in CH_3CH_3 the C—H bond dissociation energy is actually 101 kcal/mol (423 kJ/mol). Thus, the calculated ΔH for a reaction using average bond energies may differ slightly from the value obtained by experiment. For the combustion of methane, for example, the ΔH estimated from bond energies is −196 kcal/mol (−820 kJ/mol), while the value measured experimentally is −213 kcal/mol (−891 kJ/mol), a difference of about 9%.

Note that ΔH is in units of kilocalories or kilojoules per mole, where "per mole" means the reaction of *molar amounts of products and reactants as represented by the coefficients of the balanced equation*. Thus, the experimental value ΔH = −213 kcal/mol (−891 kJ/mol) refers to the amount of heat released when 1 mol (16.0 g) of methane reacts with 2 mol of O_2 to give 1 mol of CO_2 gas and 2 mol of liquid H_2O. If we were to double the amount of methane from 1 mol to 2 mol, the amount of heat released would also double.

The quantities of heat released in the combustion of several fuels, including natural gas (which is primarily methane), are compared in Table 7.2. The values are in kilocalories and kilojoules per gram to make comparisons easier. Based on the greater energy value (amount of energy per gram), you can see from the table why there is interest in the potential of hydrogen as a fuel.

When the total energy released upon bond formation in the products is *less* than the total energy added to break the bonds in the reactants, the net result is that energy is absorbed and the reaction is endothermic. The combination of nitrogen and oxygen to give nitrogen oxide (also known as nitric oxide), a gas present in automobile exhaust, is such a reaction. The heat added in an endothermic reaction is like a reactant, and ΔH is assigned a *positive* value because heat is *added*.

Table 7.2 Energy Values of Some Common Fuels

Fuel	Energy Value kcal/g (kJ/g)
Wood (pine)	4.3 (18.0)
Ethyl alcohol	7.1 (29.7)
Coal (anthracite)	7.4 (31.0)
Crude oil (Texas)	10.5 (43.9)
Gasoline	11.5 (48.1)
Natural gas	11.7 (49.0)
Hydrogen	34.0 (142)

An endothermic reaction—positive ΔH

Heat is a reactant.

$$N_2(g) + O_2(g) + 43 \text{ kcal (180 kJ)} \longrightarrow 2\,NO(g)$$

or

$$N_2(g) + O_2(g) \longrightarrow 2\,NO(g) \qquad \Delta H = +43 \text{ kcal/mol (+180 kJ/mol)}$$

Important Points about Heat Transfers and Chemical Reactions

- An exothermic reaction releases heat to the surroundings; ΔH is negative.
- An endothermic reaction absorbs heat from the surroundings; ΔH is positive.
- The reverse of an exothermic reaction is endothermic.
- The reverse of an endothermic reaction is exothermic.
- The amount of heat absorbed or released in the reverse of a reaction is equal to that released or absorbed in the forward reaction, but ΔH has the opposite sign.

Worked Examples 7.1–7.4 show how to calculate the amount of heat absorbed or released for reaction of a given amount of reactant. All that is needed is the balanced equation and its accompanying ΔH or the bond dissociation energies to permit calculation of ΔH. Mole ratios and molar masses are used to convert between masses and moles of reactants or products, as discussed in Sections 6.3 and 6.4.

Worked Example 7.1 Heat of Reaction from Bond Energies

Estimate the ΔH (in kcal/mol) for the reaction of hydrogen and oxygen to form water:

$$2\,H_2 + O_2 \longrightarrow 2\,H_2O \quad \Delta H = ?$$

ANALYSIS Use the individual bond energies from Table 7.1 to calculate the total bond energies of reactants and products. ΔH can then be calculated as

$$\Delta H = \Sigma\,(\text{Bond dissociation energies})_{\text{reactants}} - \Sigma\,(\text{Bond dissociation energies})_{\text{products}}$$

BALLPARK ESTIMATE The average H—H bond energy is ~100 kcal/mol, and the O=O bond energy is ~120 kcal/mol. Thus, the total energy needed to break reactant bonds is ~(200 + 120) = 320 kcal/mol. The O—H bonds are ~110 kcal/mol, so the total energy released when product bonds are formed is ~440 kcal/mol. Based on these estimates, ΔH ~120 kcal/mol.

SOLUTION

$$\begin{aligned}
\Delta H &= \Sigma\,(\text{Bond dissociation energies})_{\text{reactants}} - \Sigma\,(\text{Bond dissociation energies})_{\text{products}} \\
&= (2(H{-}H) + (O{=}O)) - (4(O{-}H)) \\
&= (2(103\,\text{kcal/mol}) + (119\,\text{kcal/mol})) - (4(112\,\text{kcal/mol})) = -123\,\text{kcal/mol}
\end{aligned}$$

BALLPARK CHECK Our estimate was −120 kcal/mol, within 3% of the calculated answer.

Worked Example 7.2 Heat of Reaction: Moles

Methane undergoes combustion with O_2 according to the following equation:

$$CH_4(g) + 2\,O_2(g) \longrightarrow CO_2(g) + 2\,H_2O(l) \quad \Delta H = -213\,\frac{\text{kcal}}{\text{mol CH}_4}$$

How much heat (in kcal and kJ) is released during the combustion of 0.35 mol of methane?

ANALYSIS Since the value of ΔH for the reaction (213 kcal/mol) is negative, it indicates the amount of heat released when 1 mol of methane reacts with O_2. We need to find the amount of heat released when an amount other than 1 mol reacts, using appropriate factor-label calculations to convert from our known or given units to kilocalories and then to kilojoules.

BALLPARK ESTIMATE Since 213 kcal is released for each mole of methane that reacts, 0.35 mol of methane should release about one-third of 213 kcal, or about 70 kcal. There are about 4 kJ per kcal, so 70 kcal is about 280 kJ.

SOLUTION
To find the amount of heat released (in kilocalories) by combustion of 0.35 mol of methane, we use a conversion factor of kcal/mol, and then we can convert to kilojoules using a kJ/kcal conversion factor (see Section 1.11):

$$0.35\;\text{mol CH}_4 \times \frac{-213\;\text{kcal}}{1\;\text{mol CH}_4} = -75\;\text{kcal}$$

$$-75\;\text{kcal} \times \left(\frac{4.184\;\text{kJ}}{\text{kcal}}\right) = -314\;\text{kJ}$$

The negative sign indicates that the 75 kcal (314 kJ) of heat is released.

BALLPARK CHECK The calculated answer is consistent with our estimate (70 kcal or 280 kJ).

Worked Example 7.3 Heat of Reaction: Mass to Mole Conversion

How much heat is released during the combustion of 7.50 g of methane (molar mass = 16.0 g/mol)?

$$CH_4(g) + 2 O_2(g) \longrightarrow CO_2(g) + 2 H_2O(l) \quad \Delta H = -213 \frac{kcal}{mol\ CH_4} = -891 \frac{kJ}{mol\ CH_4}$$

ANALYSIS We can find the moles of methane involved in the reaction by using the molecular weight in a mass to mole conversion, and then use ΔH to find the heat released.

BALLPARK ESTIMATE Since 1 mol of methane (molar mass = 16.0 g/mol) has a mass of 16.0 g, 7.50 g of methane is a little less than 0.5 mol. Thus, less than half of 213 kcal, or about 100 kcal (418 kJ), is released from combustion of 7.50 g.

SOLUTION
Going from a given mass of methane to the amount of heat released in a reaction requires that we first find the number of moles of methane by including molar mass (in mol/g) in the calculation and then converting moles to kilocalories or kilojoules:

$$7.50\ g\ CH_4 \times \frac{1\ mol\ CH_4}{16.0\ g\ CH_4} \times \frac{-213\ kcal}{1\ mol\ CH_4} = -99.8\ kcal$$

or

$$7.50\ g\ CH_4 \times \frac{1\ mol\ CH_4}{16.0\ g\ CH_4} \times \frac{-891\ kJ}{1\ mol\ CH_4} = -418\ kJ$$

The negative sign indicates that the 99.8 kcal (418 kJ) of heat is released.

BALLPARK CHECK Our estimate was -100 kcal (-418 kJ)!

 ## Worked Example 7.4 Heat of Reaction: Mole Ratio Calculations

How much heat is released in kcal and kJ when 2.50 mol of O_2 reacts completely with methane?

$$CH_4(g) + 2 O_2(g) \longrightarrow CO_2(g) + 2 H_2O(l) \quad \Delta H = -213 \frac{kcal}{mol\ CH_4} = -891 \frac{kJ}{mol\ CH_4}$$

ANALYSIS Since the ΔH for the reaction is based on the combustion of 1 mol of methane, we will need to perform a mole ratio calculation.

BALLPARK ESTIMATE The balanced equation shows that 213 kcal (891 kJ) is released for each 2 mol of oxygen that reacts. Thus, 2.50 mol of oxygen should release a bit more than 213 kcal, perhaps about 250 kcal (1050 kJ).

SOLUTION
To find the amount of heat released by combustion of 2.50 mol of oxygen, we include in our calculation a mole ratio based on the balanced chemical equation:

$$2.50\ mol\ O_2 \times \frac{1\ mol\ CH_4}{2\ mol\ O_2} \times \frac{-213\ kcal}{1\ mol\ CH_4} = -266\ kcal$$

or

$$2.50\ mol\ O_2 \times \frac{1\ mol\ CH_4}{2\ mol\ O_2} \times \frac{-891\ kJ}{1\ mol\ CH_4} = -1110\ kJ$$

The negative sign indicates that the 266 kcal (1110 kJ) of heat is released.

BALLPARK CHECK The calculated answer is close to our estimate (-250 kcal or -1050 kJ).

CHEMISTRY IN ACTION

⚕ Energy from Food

Any serious effort to lose weight usually leads to studying the caloric values of foods. Have you ever wondered how the numbers quoted on food labels are obtained?

All living organisms require fuel to produce the energy needed for daily activity. When the food consumed provides more energy than what is required, the "extra" energy is converted to potential energy in the form of body mass, usually fat. Conversely, when the energy expended during physical activity exceeds the amount provided from food intake, then the body taps into the potential energy stored as fat to meet the current demand. Food is "burned" in the body to yield H_2O, CO_2, and energy, just as natural gas is burned in furnaces to yield the same products. In fact, the "caloric value" of a food is just the heat of reaction for complete combustion of the food (minus a small correction factor). The value is the same whether the food is burned in the body or in the laboratory. One gram of protein releases 4 kcal, 1 g of table sugar (a carbohydrate) releases 4 kcal, and 1 g of fat releases 9 kcal (see table).

▲ These products are specially formulated to provide the energy needed for sustained physical activity.

Caloric Values of Some Foods

Substance, Sample Size	Caloric Value kcal (kJ)
Protein, 1 g	4 (17)
Carbohydrate, 1 g	4 (17)
Fat, 1 g	9 (38)
Alcohol, 1 g	7.1 (29.7)
Cola drink, 12 fl oz (369 g)	160 (670)
Apple, one medium (138 g)	80 (330)
Iceberg lettuce, 1 cup shredded (55 g)	5 (21)
White bread, 1 slice (25 g)	65 (270)
Hamburger patty, 3 oz (85 g)	245 (1030)
Pizza, 1 slice (120 g)	290 (1200)
Vanilla ice cream, 1 cup (133 g)	270 (1130)

The caloric value of a food is usually given in "Calories" (note the capital C), where 1 Cal = 1000 cal = 1 kcal = 4.184 kJ. To determine these values experimentally, a carefully dried and weighed food sample is placed together with oxygen in an instrument called a *calorimeter,* the food is ignited, the temperature change is measured, and the amount of heat given off is calculated from the temperature change. In the calorimeter, the heat from the food is released very quickly and the temperature rises dramatically. Clearly, though, something a bit different goes on when food is burned in the body, otherwise we would burst into flames after a meal!

It is a fundamental principle of chemistry that the total heat released or absorbed in going from reactants to products is the same, no matter how many reactions are involved. The body applies this principle by withdrawing energy from food a bit at a time in a long series of interconnected reactions rather than all at once in a single reaction. These and other reactions that are continually taking place in the body—called the body's *metabolism*—will be examined in later chapters.

CIA Problem 7.1 Which provides more energy, 1 g of carbohydrate or 1 g of fat?

CIA Problem 7.2 How many Calories (i.e., kilocalories) are in a 45.0 g (1.5 ounce) serving of potato chips if we assume that they are essentially 50% carbohydrate and 50% fats?

PROBLEM 7.3

In photosynthesis, green plants convert carbon dioxide and water into glucose $(C_6H_{12}O_6)$ according to the following equation:

$$6\,CO_2(g)\ +\ 6\,H_2O(l)\ \longrightarrow\ C_6H_{12}O_6(aq)\ +\ 6\,O_2(g)$$

(a) Estimate ΔH for the reaction using bond dissociation energies from Table 7.1. Give your answer in kcal/mol and kJ/mol. ($C_6H_{12}O_6$ has five C—C bonds, seven C—H bonds, seven C—O bonds, and five O—H bonds).

(b) Is the reaction endothermic or exothermic?

PROBLEM 7.4

The following equation shows the conversion of aluminum oxide (from the ore bauxite) to aluminum:

$$2\,Al_2O_3(s) \longrightarrow 4\,Al(s) + 3\,O_2(g) \quad \Delta H = +801\,kcal/mol\ (+3350\,kJ/mol)$$

(a) Is the reaction exothermic or endothermic?

(b) How many kilocalories are required to produce 1.00 mol of aluminum? How many kilojoules?

(c) How many kilocalories are required to produce 10.0 g of aluminum? How many kilojoules?

PROBLEM 7.5

How much heat is absorbed (in kilocalories and kilojoules) during production of 127 g of NO by the combination of nitrogen and oxygen?

$$N_2(g) + O_2(g) \longrightarrow 2\,NO(g) \quad \Delta H = +43\,kcal/mol\ (+180\,kJ/mol)$$

PROBLEM 7.6

Once consumed, the body metabolizes alcohol (ethanol, CH_3CH_2OH; MW $= 46$ g/mol) to carbon dioxide and water. The balanced reaction is: $CH_3CH_2OH + 3\,O_2 \longrightarrow 2\,CO_2 + 3\,H_2O$. Using the bond energies in Table 7.1, estimate the ΔH for this reaction in kcal/mol. How does it compare to the caloric value of alcohol (in Cal/g) given in the Chemistry in Action feature "Energy from Food" on p. 191?

HANDS-ON CHEMISTRY 7.1

Obtain an energy bar and look at the nutritional information included on the wrapper or label. How many grams of fat are included in each bar? How many grams of protein? How many grams of carbohydrate?

a. Using this information and the caloric values in the Chemistry in Action feature on p. 191, estimate the

total caloric value of the energy bar and compare your answer to the nutritional information on the wrapper.

b. Now obtain a typical candy bar and perform the same evaluation. How do the two bars compare in terms of total calories? In terms of composition?

▲ Events that lead to lower energy tend to occur spontaneously. Thus, water always flows *down* a waterfall, not up.

Spontaneous process A process or reaction that, once started, proceeds on its own without any external influence.

7.4 Why Do Chemical Reactions Occur? Free Energy

Learning Objective:

• Use enthalpy, entropy, and free energy to determine the spontaneity of a chemical reaction or process.

Events that lead to lower energy states tend to occur spontaneously. Water falls downhill, for instance, releasing its stored (potential) energy and reaching a lower-energy, more stable position. Similarly, a wound-up spring uncoils when set free. Applying this lesson to chemistry, the obvious conclusion is that exothermic processes—those that release heat energy—should be spontaneous. A log burning in a fireplace is just one example of a spontaneous reaction that releases heat. At the same time, endothermic processes, which absorb heat energy, should not be spontaneous. Often, these conclusions are correct, but not always. Many, but not all, exothermic processes take place spontaneously, and many, but not all, endothermic processes are nonspontaneous.

Before exploring the situation further, it is important to understand what the word "spontaneous" means in chemistry, which is not quite the same as in everyday language. A **spontaneous process** is one that, once started, proceeds on its own without any external influence. The change does not necessarily happen quickly, like a spring suddenly uncoiling or a car coasting downhill. It can also happen slowly, like the gradual rusting away of an abandoned bicycle. A *nonspontaneous process,* by contrast, takes place only in the presence of a continuous external influence. Energy must be continually expended to rewind a spring or push a car uphill. The reverse of a spontaneous process is always nonspontaneous.

As an example of a process that takes place spontaneously yet absorbs heat, think about what happens when you take an ice cube out of the freezer. The ice spontaneously melts to give liquid water above 0 °C, even though it *absorbs* heat energy from the surroundings. What this and other spontaneous endothermic processes have in common is *an increase in molecular disorder, or randomness.* When the solid ice melts, the H_2O molecules are no longer locked in position but are now free to move around randomly in the liquid water.

The amount of disorder in a system is called the system's **entropy,** symbolized by S and expressed in units of calories (or Joules) per mole-kelvin $[cal/(mol \cdot K)$ or $J/(mol \cdot K)]$. The greater the disorder, or randomness, of the particles in a substance or mixture, the larger the value of S (Figure 7.1). Gases have more disorder and therefore higher entropy than liquids because particles in the gas move around more freely than particles in the liquid. Similarly, liquids have higher entropy than solids. In chemical reactions, entropy increases when, for example, a gas is produced from a solid or when 2 mol of reactants split into 4 mol of products.

Entropy *(S)* A measure of the amount of molecular disorder in a system.

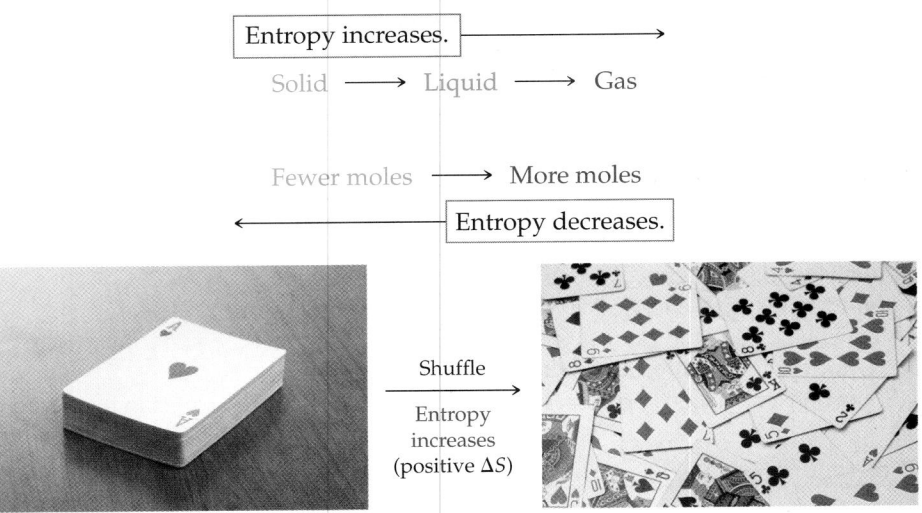

Shuffle
Entropy
increases
(positive ΔS)

◄ **Figure 7.1**
Entropy and values of *S*.
A new deck of cards, neatly stacked, has more order and lower entropy than the randomly shuffled and strewn cards on the right. The value of the entropy change, ΔS, for converting the system on the left to that on the right is positive because entropy increases.

The **entropy change (ΔS)** for a process has a *positive* value if disorder increases because the process adds disorder to the system. The melting of ice to give water is an example. Conversely, ΔS has a *negative* value if the disorder of a system decreases. The freezing of water to give ice is an example.

It thus appears that two factors determine the spontaneity of a chemical or physical change: the release or absorption of heat, ΔH, and the increase or decrease in entropy, ΔS. *To decide whether a process is spontaneous, both the enthalpy change and the entropy change must be taken into account.* We have already seen that a negative ΔH favors spontaneity, but what about ΔS? The answer is that an increase in molecular disorder (ΔS positive) favors spontaneity. A good analogy is the bedroom or office that seems to spontaneously become more messy over time (an increase in disorder, ΔS positive); to clean it up (a decrease in disorder, ΔS negative) requires an input of energy, a nonspontaneous process. Using our chemical example, the combustion of a log spontaneously converts large, complex molecules like lignin and cellulose (high molecular order, low entropy) into CO_2 and H_2O (a large number of small molecules with higher entropy). For this process, the level of disorder increases, and so ΔS is positive. The reverse process—turning CO_2 and H_2O back into cellulose—does occur in photosynthesis, but it requires a significant input of energy in the form of sunlight. Another useful example is complex living organisms; as highly ordered systems, they would have a large *negative* ΔS and would not be expected to occur spontaneously. However, remember that most living organisms consume large complex molecules as

Entropy change (ΔS) A measure of the increase in disorder ($\Delta S = +$) or decrease in disorder ($\Delta S = -$) as a chemical reaction or physical change occurs.

food and convert them to smaller molecules (CO_2, H_2O, etc.), a process that has a large *positive* ΔS and would favor spontaneity.

When enthalpy and entropy are both favorable (ΔH negative, ΔS positive), a process is spontaneous; when both are unfavorable, a process is nonspontaneous. Clearly, however, the two factors do not have to operate in the same direction. It is possible for a process to be *unfavored* by enthalpy (the process absorbs heat, and so, has a positive ΔH) and yet be *favored* by entropy (there is an increase in disorder, and so, ΔS is positive). The melting of an ice cube above 0 °C, for which $\Delta H = +1.44\ \text{kcal/mol}$ ($+6.02\ \text{kJ/mol}$) and $\Delta S = +5.26\ \text{cal/(mol·K)}$ ($+22.0\ \text{J/(mol·K)}$), is such a process. To take both heat of reaction (ΔH) and change in disorder (ΔS) into account when determining the spontaneity of a process, a quantity called the **free-energy change (ΔG),** is needed:

Free-energy change (ΔG) A measure of the change in free energy as a chemical reaction or physical change occurs.

Free-energy change

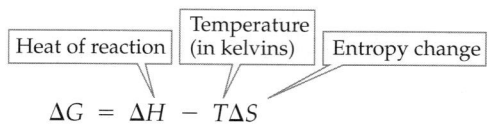

The value of the free-energy change, ΔG, determines spontaneity. A negative value for ΔG means that free energy is released and the reaction or process is spontaneous. Such events are said to be **exergonic.** A positive value for ΔG means that free energy must be added and the process is nonspontaneous. Such events are said to be **endergonic.**

Exergonic A spontaneous reaction or process that releases free energy and has a negative ΔG.

Endergonic A nonspontaneous reaction or process that absorbs free energy and has a positive ΔG.

LOOKING AHEAD ➤ In later chapters, we will see that a knowledge of free-energy changes is especially important for understanding how metabolic reactions work. Living organisms cannot raise their temperatures to convert nonspontaneous reactions into spontaneous reactions, so they must resort to other strategies, which we will explore in Chapter 21.

Important Points about Spontaneity and Free Energy

- A spontaneous process, once begun, proceeds without any external assistance and is exergonic; that is, free energy is released and it has a negative value of ΔG.
- A nonspontaneous process requires continuous external influence and is endergonic; that is, free energy is added and it has a positive value of ΔG.
- The value of ΔG for the reverse of a reaction is numerically equal to the value of ΔG for the forward reaction but has the opposite sign.
- Some nonspontaneous processes become spontaneous with a change in temperature.

Worked Example 7.5 Entropy Change of Processes

Does entropy increase or decrease in the following processes?

(a) Smoke from a cigarette disperses throughout a room rather than remaining in a cloud over the smoker's head.

(b) Water boils, changing from liquid to vapor.

(c) A chemical reaction occurs: $3\ H_2(g) + N_2(g) \longrightarrow 2\ NH_3(g)$

ANALYSIS Entropy is a measure of molecular disorder. Entropy increases when the products are more disordered than the reactants; entropy decreases when the products are less disordered than the reactants.

SOLUTION

(a) Entropy increases because smoke particles are more disordered when they are randomly distributed in the larger volume.

(b) Entropy increases because H_2O molecules have more freedom and disorder in the gas phase than in the liquid phase.

(c) Entropy decreases because 4 mol of reactant gas particles becomes 2 mol of product gas particles, with a consequent decrease in freedom and disorder.

PROBLEM 7.7

Does entropy increase or decrease in the following processes?

(a) Polymeric complex carbohydrates are metabolized by the body, converted into smaller simple sugars.

(b) Steam condenses on a glass surface.

(c) $2\ SO_2(g) + O_2(g) \longrightarrow 2\ SO_3(g)$

⦿⚡ KEY CONCEPT PROBLEM 7.8 ⎯⎯⎯⎯⎯⎯⎯⎯⎯⎯⎯⎯⎯⎯⎯⎯⎯⎯⎯⎯

The following diagram portrays a reaction of the type $A(s) \longrightarrow B(s) + C(g)$, where the different-colored spheres represent different molecular structures. Assume that the reaction has $\Delta H =$ negative.

(a) What is the sign of ΔS for the reaction?

(b) Is the reaction likely to be spontaneous at all temperatures, nonspontaneous at all temperatures, or spontaneous at some but nonspontaneous at others?

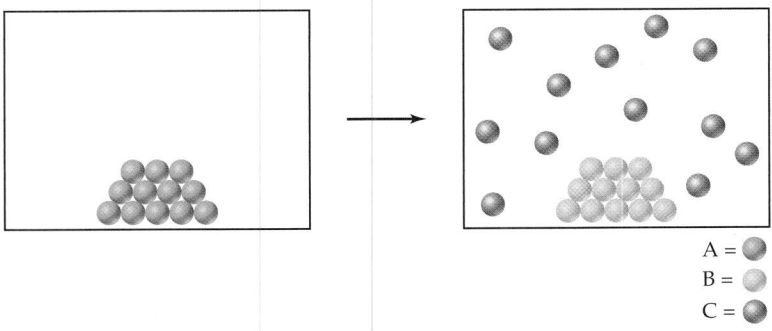

$A = $ ⬤
$B = $ ⬤
$C = $ ⬤

7.5 How Do Chemical Reactions Occur? Reaction Rates

Learning Objective:

• Use collision theory and reaction diagrams to explain the activation energy and free-energy change of a chemical reaction.

Just because a chemical reaction has a favorable free-energy change does not mean that it occurs rapidly. The value of ΔG tells us only whether a reaction *can* occur; it says nothing about how *fast* the reaction will occur or about the details of the molecular changes that take place during the reaction.

   For a chemical reaction to occur, reactant particles must collide, some chemical bonds have to break, and new bonds have to form. Not all collisions lead to products, however. One requirement for a productive collision is that the colliding molecules must approach each other with the correct orientation so that the atoms about to form new bonds can connect. In the reaction of ozone (O_3) with nitric oxide (NO) to give oxygen (O_2) and nitrogen dioxide (NO_2), for example, the two reactants must collide so that the nitrogen atom of NO strikes a terminal oxygen atom of O_3 (Figure 7.2).

   Another requirement for a reaction to occur is that the collision must take place with enough energy to break the appropriate bonds in the reactant. If the reactant particles are moving slowly, collisions might be too gentle to overcome the repulsion between electrons in the different reactants, and the particles will simply bounce apart. A reaction will only occur if the collisions between reactant molecules are sufficiently energetic.

Effective collision:

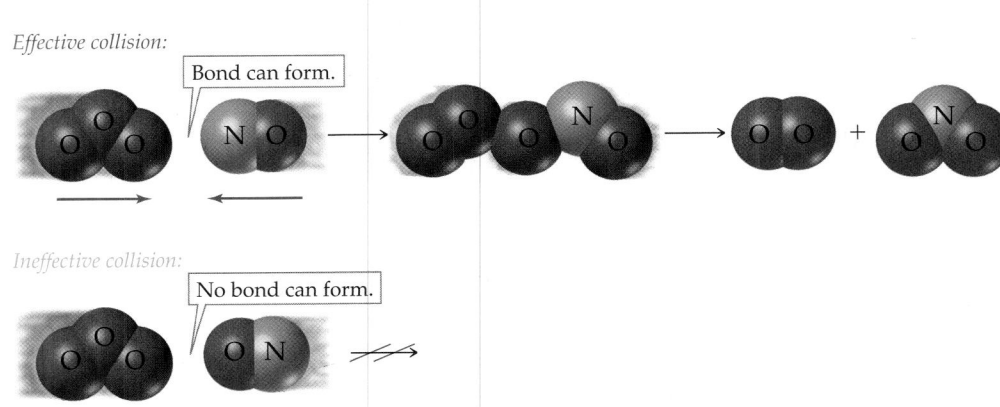

Ineffective collision:

◄ **Figure 7.2**

How do chemical reactions occur?
For a collision between NO and O_3 molecules to give O_2 and NO_2, the molecules must collide so that the correct atoms come into contact. No bond forms if the molecules collide with the wrong orientation.

For this reason, many reactions with a favorable free-energy change do not occur at room temperature. To get such a reaction started, energy (heat) must be added. The heat causes the reactant particles to move faster, thereby increasing both the frequency and the force of the collisions. We all know that matches burn, for instance, but we also know that they do not burst into flame until struck. The heat of friction provides enough energy for a few molecules to react. Once started, the reaction sustains itself as the energy released by reacting molecules gives other molecules enough energy to react.

The energy change that occurs during the course of a chemical reaction can be visualized in an energy diagram like that in Figure 7.3. At the beginning of the reaction (left side of the diagram), the reactants are at the energy level indicated. At the end of the reaction (right side of the diagram), the products are at a lower energy level than the reactants if the reaction is exergonic (Figure 7.3a) but higher than the reactants if the reaction is endergonic (Figure 7.3b).

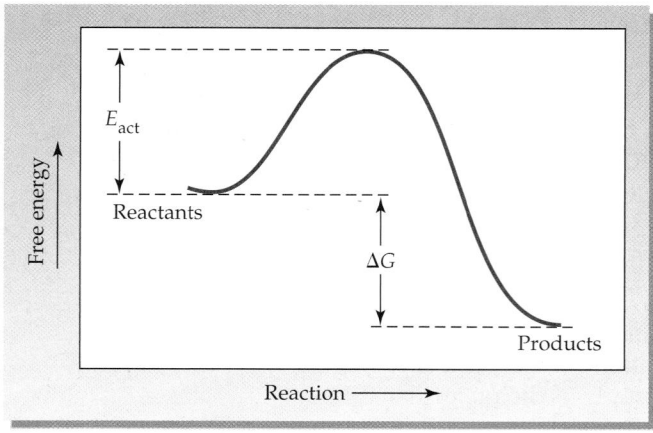

(a) An exergonic reaction

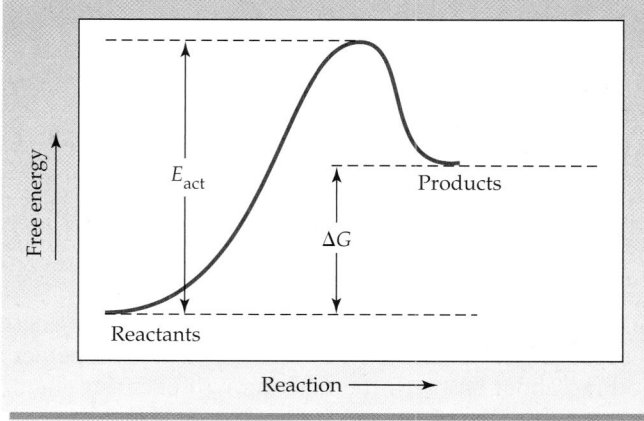

(b) An endergonic reaction

▲ **Figure 7.3**
Reaction energy diagrams show energy changes during a chemical reaction.
A reaction begins on the left and proceeds to the right. (a) In an exergonic reaction, the product energy level is lower than that of reactants. (b) In an endergonic reaction, the situation is reversed. The height of the barrier between reactant and product energy levels is the activation energy, E_{act}. The difference between reactant and product energy levels is the free-energy change, ΔG.

Activation energy (E_{act}) The amount of energy necessary for a reaction to occur; it determines the reaction rate.
Reaction rate A measure of how rapidly a reaction occurs; determined by E_{act}.

Lying between the reactants and the products is an energy "barrier" that must be surmounted. The height of this barrier represents the amount of energy the colliding particles must have for productive collisions to occur, an amount called the **activation energy (E_{act})** of the reaction. The size of the activation energy determines the **reaction rate,** or how fast the reaction occurs. Consider an example of rolling a handful of marbles over a bump in the rug—if the bump is small, a greater number of marbles will make it over the bump (i.e., progress to form products) than if the bump is large. Similarly for a chemical reaction, the lower the activation energy, the greater the number of productive collisions in a given amount of time, and the faster the reaction. Conversely, the higher the activation energy, the lower the number of productive collisions, and the slower the reaction.

Note that the size of the activation energy and the size of the free-energy change are unrelated. A reaction with a large E_{act} takes place very slowly even if it has a large negative ΔG. Every reaction is different; each has its own characteristic activation energy and free-energy change.

Worked Example 7.6 Energy of Reactions: Energy Diagrams

Consider the following energy diagram for a reaction. Is the reaction fast or slow? Is the reaction endergonic or exergonic? Would the reaction be spontaneous?

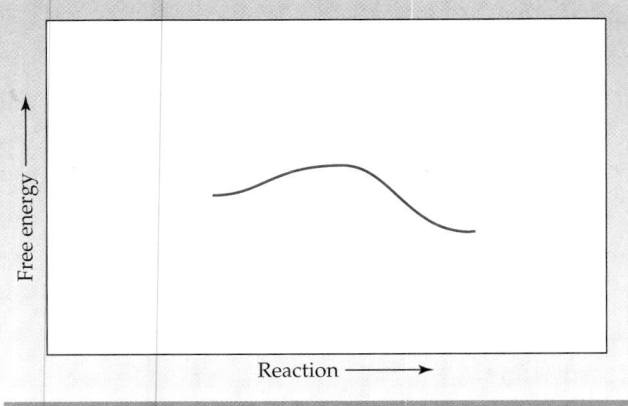

ANALYSIS The rate of the reaction is determined by the activation energy, E_{act}, while the free energy change (endergonic or exergonic) depends on the difference in free energy of the products compared to the reactants.

SOLUTION
The E_{act} for the reaction is small, as indicated in the following energy diagram, so we would expect the reaction to proceed rapidly. The free energy decreases slightly as the reaction proceeds from reactants to products, so ΔG is negative and the reaction is exergonic and spontaneous.

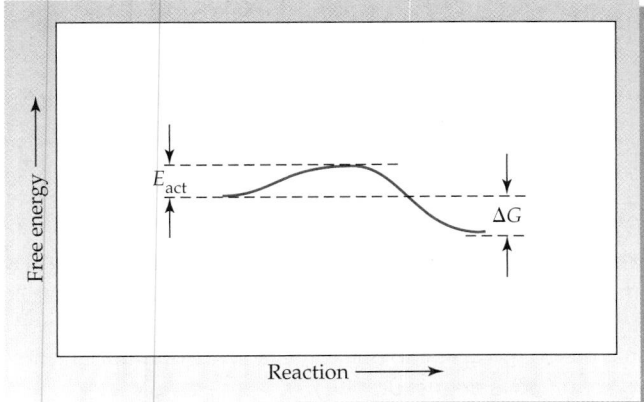

PROBLEM 7.9

The reaction between iron and oxygen to form rust occurs spontaneously. Based on your experience, does this reaction occur rapidly? What does this imply about the relative magnitudes of the activation energy and ΔG for the reaction? Explain.

7.6 Effects of Temperature, Concentration, and Catalysts on Reaction Rates

Learning Objective:

• Explain how temperature, concentration of reactants, and presence of a catalyst affect the rate of a reaction.

Several things can be done to help reactants over an activation energy barrier and thereby speed up a reaction. Let us look at some possibilities.

Temperature

One way to increase reaction rate is to add energy to the reactants by raising the temperature. With more energy in the system, the reactants move faster, so the frequency of collisions increases. Furthermore, the force with which collisions occur increases, making them more likely to overcome the activation barrier. As a rule of thumb, a 10 °C rise in temperature causes a reaction rate to double.

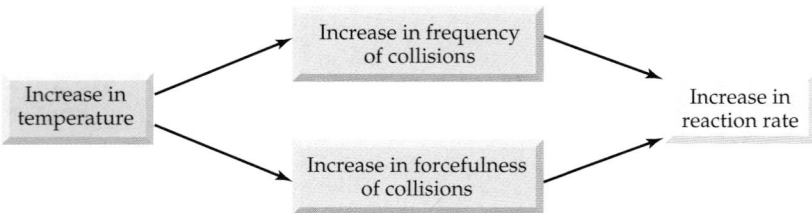

Concentration

Concentration A measure of the amount of a given substance in a mixture.

A second way to speed up a reaction is to increase the **concentrations** of the reactants. As the concentration increases, reactants are crowded together, and collisions between reactant molecules become more frequent. As the frequency of collisions increases, reactions between molecules become more likely. Flammable materials burn more rapidly in pure oxygen than in air, for instance, because the concentration of O_2 molecules is higher (air is approximately 21% oxygen). Hospitals must therefore take extraordinary precautions to ensure that no flames are used near patients receiving oxygen. Although different reactions respond differently to concentration changes, doubling or tripling a reactant concentration often doubles or triples the reaction rate.

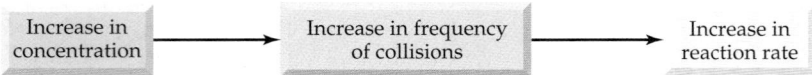

Catalysts

Catalyst A substance that speeds up the rate of a chemical reaction but is itself unchanged.

A third way to speed up a reaction is to add a **catalyst**—a substance that accelerates a chemical reaction but is itself unchanged in the process. For example, metals such as nickel, palladium, and platinum catalyze the addition of hydrogen to the carbon–carbon double bonds in vegetable oils to yield semisolid margarine. Without the metal catalyst, the reaction does not occur.

$$\underset{\substack{\text{A double bond in}\\\text{vegetable oil}}}{\overset{\text{H}\qquad\text{H}}{\text{C}=\text{C}}} \;+\; \text{H}_2 \;\;\xrightarrow[\text{catalyst}]{\text{Ni, Pd, or Pt}}\;\; \underset{\substack{\text{A single bond}\\\text{in margarine}}}{-\overset{\text{H}}{\underset{\text{H}}{\text{C}}}-\overset{\text{H}}{\underset{\text{H}}{\text{C}}}-}$$

A catalyst does not affect the energy level of either reactants or products. Rather, it increases reaction rate either by letting a reaction take place by an alternative set of reaction steps with a lower activation energy or by orienting the reacting molecules appropriately. In a reaction energy diagram, the catalyzed reaction has a lower activation energy (Figure 7.4). A catalyzed reaction releases (or absorbs) the same amount of energy as an uncatalyzed reaction; it simply occurs more rapidly.

In addition to their widespread use in industry, we also rely on catalysts to reduce the air pollution created by exhaust from automobile engines. The catalytic converters in most automobiles are tubes packed with catalysts of two types (Figure 7.5). One catalyst accelerates the complete combustion of hydrocarbons and CO in the exhaust to give CO_2 and H_2O and the other decomposes NO to N_2 and O_2.

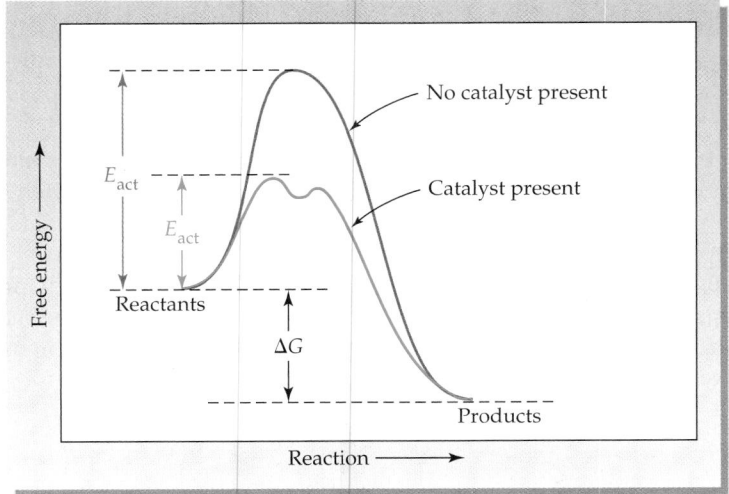

◄ **Figure 7.4**
A reaction energy diagram for a reaction in the presence (green curve) and absence (blue curve) of a catalyst.
The catalyzed reaction has a lower (E_{act}) because it uses an alternative pathway (represented by the multiple bumps in the green line) with a lower energy barrier.

▷▷ The thousands of biochemical reactions continually taking place in our bodies are catalyzed by large protein molecules called *enzymes,* which promote reactions by controlling the orientation of the reacting molecules. Since almost every reaction is catalyzed by its own specific enzyme, the study of enzyme structure, activity, and control is a central part of biochemistry. We will look more closely at enzymes and how they work in Chapter 19.

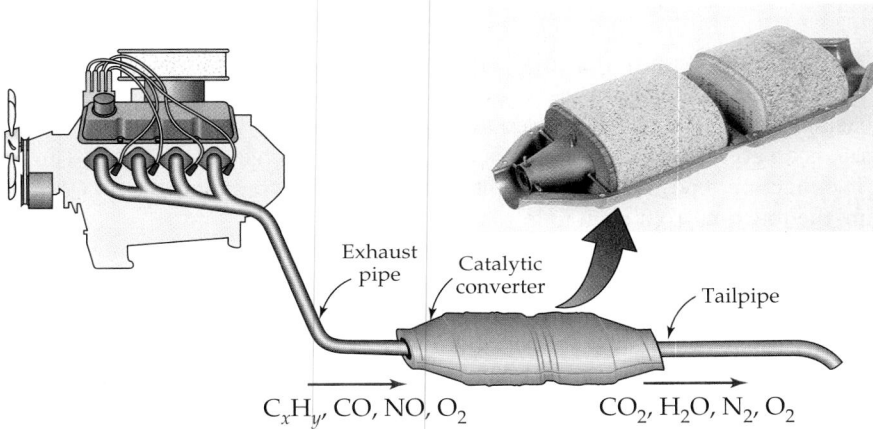

▲ **Figure 7.5**
A catalytic converter.
The exhaust gases from an automobile pass through a two-stage catalytic converter. In one stage, carbon monoxide and unburned hydrocarbons are converted to CO_2 and H_2O. In the second stage, NO is converted to N_2 and O_2.

Table 7.3 summarizes the effects of changing conditions on reaction rates.

Table 7.3 Effects of Changes in Reaction Conditions on Reaction Rates

Change	Effect
Concentration	Increase in reactant concentration increases rate. Decrease in reactant concentration decreases rate.
Temperature	Increase in temperature increases rate. Decrease in temperature decreases rate.
Catalyst added	Increases reaction rate.

PROBLEM 7.10

Ammonia is synthesized industrially by reaction of nitrogen and hydrogen according to the equation $3\,H_2(g) + N_2(g) \longrightarrow 2\,NH_3(g)$. The free-energy change for this reaction is $\Delta G = -3.8\,\text{kcal/mol}\ (-16\,\text{kJ/mol})$, yet this reaction does not readily occur at room temperature. List three ways to increase the rate of this reaction.

7.7 Reversible Reactions and Chemical Equilibrium

Learning Objective:

• Define chemical equilibrium for reversible reactions.

Many chemical reactions result in the complete conversion of reactants into products. When sodium metal reacts with chlorine gas, for example, both are entirely consumed. The sodium chloride product is so much more stable than the reactants that, once started, the reaction keeps going until it is complete.

What happens, though, when the reactants and products are of approximately equal stability? This is the case, for example, in the reaction of acetic acid (the main organic constituent of vinegar) with ethyl alcohol to yield ethyl acetate, a solvent used in nail-polish remover and glue.

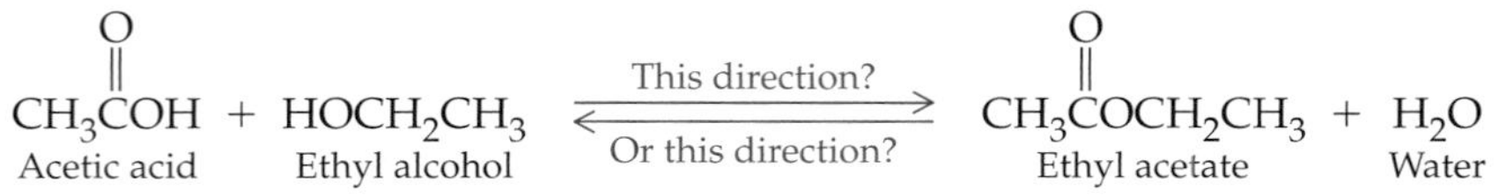

$$\underset{\text{Acetic acid}}{CH_3\overset{\overset{\displaystyle O}{\|}}{C}OH} + \underset{\text{Ethyl alcohol}}{HOCH_2CH_3} \underset{\text{Or this direction?}}{\overset{\text{This direction?}}{\rightleftharpoons}} \underset{\text{Ethyl acetate}}{CH_3\overset{\overset{\displaystyle O}{\|}}{C}OCH_2CH_3} + \underset{\text{Water}}{H_2O}$$

Reversible reaction A reaction that can go in either direction, from products to reactants or reactants to products.

Imagine the situation if you mix acetic acid and ethyl alcohol. The two begin to form ethyl acetate and water. But as soon as ethyl acetate and water form, they begin to go back to acetic acid and ethyl alcohol. Such a reaction, which easily goes in either direction, is a **reversible reaction** and is indicated by a double arrow ($\rightleftharpoons$) in equations. The reaction read from left to right as written is referred to as the *forward reaction,* and the reaction from right to left is the *reverse reaction.*

Now, suppose you mix some ethyl acetate and water. The same thing occurs: as soon as small quantities of acetic acid and ethyl alcohol form, the reaction in the other direction begins to take place. No matter which pair of reactants is mixed together, both reactions occur until ultimately the concentrations of reactants and products reach constant values and undergo no further change. At this point, the reaction vessel contains all four substances—acetic acid, ethyl acetate, ethyl alcohol, and water—and the reaction is in a state of **chemical equilibrium.**

Chemical equilibrium A state in which the rates of forward and reverse reactions are the same.

Since the reactant and product concentrations undergo no further change once equilibrium is reached, you might conclude that the forward and reverse reactions have stopped. That is not the case, however. The forward reaction takes place rapidly at the beginning of the reaction but then slows down as reactant concentrations decrease. At the same time, the reverse reaction takes place slowly at the beginning but then speeds up as product concentrations increase (Figure 7.6). Ultimately, the forward and reverse rates become equal and change no further.

Chemical equilibrium is an active, dynamic condition. All substances present are continuously being made and unmade at the same rate, so their concentrations are constant at equilibrium. As an analogy, think of two floors of a building connected by up and down escalators. If the number of people moving up is the same as the number of people moving down, the numbers of people on each floor remain constant. *Individual people* are continuously changing from one floor to the other, but the *total populations* of the two floors are in equilibrium. In complex biological systems, many reactions may be linked together to establish an equilibrium, called *homeostasis,* in which certain conditions such as body temperature or pH of blood are maintained at optimal levels.

Note that it is not necessary for the concentrations of reactants and products at equilibrium to be equal (just as it is not necessary for the numbers of people on two floors connected by escalators to be equal). Equilibrium can be reached at any point between pure products and pure reactants. The extent to which the forward or reverse reaction is favored over the other is a characteristic property of a given reaction under given conditions.

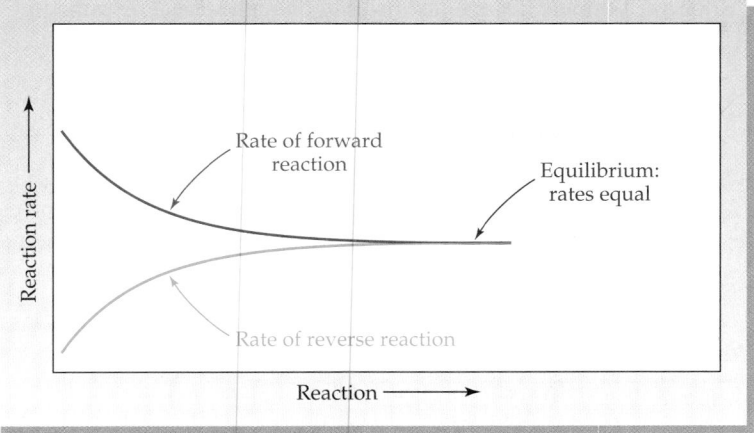

▲ **Figure 7.6**
Reaction rates in an equilibrium reaction.
The forward rate is large initially but decreases as the concentrations of reactants drop. The reverse rate is small initially but increases as the concentrations of products increase. At equilibrium, the forward and reverse reaction rates are equal.

7.8 Equilibrium Equations and Equilibrium Constants

Learning Objective:

• Define the equilibrium constant *(K)*, and use the value of *K* to predict the extent of reaction.

Remember that the rate of a reaction depends on the number of collisions between molecules (Section 7.5), and that the number of collisions in turn depends on concentration, that is, the number of molecules in a given volume (Section 7.6). For a reversible reaction, then, the rates of both the forward *and* the reverse reactions must depend on the concentration of reactants and products, respectively. When a reaction reaches equilibrium, the rates of the forward and reverse reactions are equal, and the concentrations of reactants and products remain constant. We can use this fact to obtain useful information about a reaction.

Let us look at the details of a specific equilibrium reaction. Suppose that you allow various mixtures of sulfur dioxide and oxygen to come to equilibrium with sulfur trioxide at a temperature of 727 °C and then measure the concentrations of all three gases in the mixtures.

$$2\,SO_2(g) + O_2(g) \rightleftharpoons 2\,SO_3(g)$$

▲ When the number of people moving up is the same as the number of people moving down, the number of people on each floor remains constant, and the two populations are in equilibrium.

In one experiment, we start with only 1.00 mol of SO_2 and 1.00 mol of O_2 in a 1.00 L container. In other words, the initial concentrations of reactants are 1.00 mol/L. When the reaction reaches equilibrium, we have 0.0620 mol/L of SO_2, 0.538 mol/L of O_2, and 0.938 mol/L of SO_3. In another experiment, we start with 1.00 mol/L of SO_3. When this reaction reaches equilibrium, we have 0.150 mol/L of SO_2, 0.0751 mol/L of O_2, and 0.850 mol/L of SO_3. In both cases, we see that there is substantially more product (SO_3) than reactants when the reaction reaches equilibrium, regardless of the starting conditions. Is it possible to predict what the equilibrium conditions will be for any given reaction?

As it turns out, the answer is YES! No matter what the original concentrations were, and no matter what concentrations remain at equilibrium, we find that a constant numerical value is obtained if the equilibrium concentrations are substituted into the expression

$$\frac{[SO_3]^2}{[SO_2]^2[O_2]} = \text{constant at a given temperature}$$

The square brackets in this expression indicate the concentration of each substance expressed as moles per liter. Using the equilibrium concentrations for each of the experiments previously described, we can calculate the value and verify that it is constant:

Experiment 1. $\quad \dfrac{[SO_3]^2}{[SO_2]^2[O_2]} = \dfrac{(0.938 \text{ mol/L})^2}{(0.0620 \text{ mol/L})^2(0.538 \text{ mol/L})} = 425$

Experiment 2. $\quad \dfrac{[SO_3]^2}{[SO_2]^2[O_2]} = \dfrac{(0.850 \text{ mol/L})^2}{(0.150 \text{ mol/L})^2(0.0751 \text{ mol/L})} = 428$

At a temperature of 727 °C, the actual value of the constant is 429. Within experimental error, the ratios of product and reactant concentrations for the two experiments at equilibrium yield the same result. Numerous experiments like those just described have led to a general equation that is valid for any reaction. Consider a general reversible reaction:

$$a\text{A} + b\text{B} + \ldots \rightleftharpoons m\text{M} + n\text{N} + \ldots$$

where A, B, . . . are reactants; M, N, . . . are products; and $a, b, \ldots, m, n, \ldots$ are coefficients in the balanced equation. At equilibrium, the composition of the reaction mixture obeys the following *equilibrium equation,* where K is the **equilibrium constant.**

Equilibrium constant *(K)* Value obtained at a given temperature from the ratio of the concentrations of products and reactants, each raised to a power equal to its coefficient in the balanced equation.

Equilibrium equation $\qquad K = \dfrac{[M]^m[N]^n \cdots}{[A]^a[B]^b \cdots}$

— Product concentrations
— Reactant concentrations

Equilibrium constant

The equilibrium constant K is the number obtained by multiplying the equilibrium concentrations of the products and dividing by the equilibrium concentrations of the reactants, with the concentration of each substance raised to a power equal to its coefficient in the balanced equation. If we take another look at the reaction between sulfur dioxide and oxygen, we can now see how the equilibrium constant was obtained:

$$2\,SO_2(g) + O_2(g) \rightleftharpoons 2\,SO_3(g)$$

$$K = \frac{[SO_3]^2}{[SO_2]^2\,[O_2]}$$

Note that if there is no coefficient for a reactant or product in the reaction equation, it is assumed to be 1. The value of K varies with temperature, but a temperature of 25 °C is assumed unless otherwise specified—and units are usually omitted.

For reactions that involve pure solids or liquids, these pure substances are omitted when writing the equilibrium constant expression. To explain why, consider the decomposition of limestone:

▶ The practice of omitting pure substances in the equilibrium constant expression will be utilized in Chapter 10 when we discuss equilibria involving acids and bases.

$$CaCO_3(s) \longrightarrow CaO(s) + CO_2(g)$$

Writing the equilibrium constant expression for this reaction as the concentration of products over the concentration of reactions would yield

$$K = \frac{[CaO][CO_2]}{[CaCO_3]}$$

Consider the solids CaO and $CaCO_3$. Their concentrations (in mol/L) can be calculated from their molar masses and densities at a given temperature. For example, the concentration of CaO at 25 °C can be calculated as

$$\frac{\left(3.25 \ \frac{\text{g CaO}}{\text{cm}^3}\right) \cdot \left(\frac{1000 \ \text{cm}^3}{L}\right)}{56.08 \ \frac{\text{g Cao}}{\text{mol Cao}}} = 58.0 \ \frac{\text{mol CaO}}{L}$$

The ratio of products over reactants would change if CO_2 was added to or removed from the reaction. The concentration of CaO, however, is the same whether we have 10 g or 500 g. Adding solid CaO will not change the ratio of products over reactants. Since the concentration of solids is independent of the amount of solid present, these concentrations are omitted and the expression for K becomes

$$K = \frac{[\text{CaO}][\text{CO}_2]}{[\text{CaCO}_3]} = [\text{CO}_2]$$

The value of the equilibrium constant indicates the position of a reaction at equilibrium. If the forward reaction is favored, the product term $[M]^m[N]^n$ (numerator) is larger than the reactant term $[A]^a[B]^b$ (denominator), and the value of K is larger than one. If instead the reverse reaction is favored, $[M]^m[N]^n$ is smaller than $[A]^a[B]^b$ at equilibrium, and the value of K is smaller than one.

For a reaction such as the combination of hydrogen and oxygen to form water vapor, the equilibrium constant is enormous (3.1×10^{81}), showing how greatly the formation of water is favored. Equilibrium is effectively nonexistent for such reactions, and the reaction is described as *going to completion*.

On the other hand, the equilibrium constant is very small for a reaction such as the combination of nitrogen and oxygen at 25 °C to give NO (4.7×10^{-31}), showing what we know from observation—that N_2 and O_2 in the air do not combine noticeably at room temperature:

$$N_2(g) + O_2(g) \rightleftharpoons 2 \ NO(g) \quad K = \frac{[NO]^2}{[N_2][O_2]} = 4.7 \times 10^{-31}$$

When K is close to 1, say between 10^3 and 10^{-3}, significant amounts of both reactants and products are present at equilibrium. An example is the reaction of acetic acid with ethyl alcohol to give ethyl acetate (Section 7.7). For this reaction, $K = 3.4$.

$$CH_3CO_2H + CH_3CH_2OH \rightleftharpoons CH_3CO_2CH_2CH_3 + H_2O$$
$$K = \frac{[CH_3CO_2CH_2CH_3][H_2O]}{[CH_3CO_2H][CH_3CH_2OH]} = 3.4$$

We can summarize the meaning of equilibrium constants in the following way:

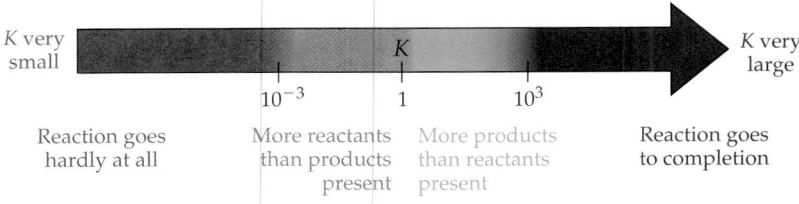

K much smaller than 0.001	Only reactants are present at equilibrium; essentially no reaction occurs.
K between 0.001 and 1	More reactants than products are present at equilibrium.
K between 1 and 1000	More products than reactants are present at equilibrium.
K much larger than 1000	Only products are present at equilibrium; reaction goes essentially to completion.

Worked Example 7.7 Writing Equilibrium Equations

The first step in the industrial synthesis of hydrogen is the reaction of steam with methane to give carbon monoxide and hydrogen. Write the equilibrium equation for the reaction.

$$H_2O(g) + CH_4(g) \rightleftharpoons CO(g) + 3 H_2(g)$$

ANALYSIS The equilibrium constant K is the number obtained by multiplying the equilibrium concentrations of the products (CO and H_2) and dividing by the equilibrium concentrations of the reactants (H_2O and CH_4), with the concentration of each substance raised to the power of its coefficient in the balanced equation.

SOLUTION

$$K = \frac{[CO][H_2]^3}{[H_2O][CH_4]}$$

Worked Example 7.8 Equilibrium Equations: Calculating K

In the reaction of Cl_2 with PCl_3, the concentrations of reactants and products were determined experimentally at equilibrium and found to be 7.2 mol/L for PCl_3, 7.2 mol/L for Cl_2, and 0.050 mol/L for PCl_5.

$$PCl_3(g) + Cl_2(g) \rightleftharpoons PCl_5(g)$$

Write the equilibrium equation, and calculate the equilibrium constant for the reaction. Which reaction is favored, the forward one or the reverse one?

ANALYSIS All the coefficients in the balanced equation are 1, so the equilibrium constant equals the concentration of the product, PCl_5, divided by the product of the concentrations of the two reactants, PCl_3 and Cl_2. Insert the values given for each concentration, and calculate the value of K.

BALLPARK ESTIMATE At equilibrium, the concentration of the reactants (7.2 mol/L for each reactant) is higher than the concentration of the product (0.05 mol/L), so we expect a value of K less than 1.

SOLUTION

$$K = \frac{[PCl_5]}{[PCl_3][Cl_2]} = \frac{0.050 \text{ mol/L}}{(7.2 \text{ mol/L})(7.2 \text{ mol/L})} = 9.6 \times 10^{-4}$$

The value of K is less than 1, so the reverse reaction is favored. Note that units for K are omitted.

BALLPARK CHECK Our calculated value of K is just as we predicted: $K < 1$.

PROBLEM 7.11

Write equilibrium equations for the following reactions:

(a) $N_2O_4(g) \rightleftharpoons 2 NO_2(g)$
(b) $2 H_2S(g) + O_2(g) \rightleftharpoons 2 S(s) + 2 H_2O(g)$
(c) $2 BrF_5(g) \rightleftharpoons Br_2(g) + 5 F_2(g)$

PROBLEM 7.12

Do the following reactions favor reactants or products at equilibrium? Give relative concentrations at equilibrium.

(a) Sucrose(aq) + $H_2O(l)$ $\rightleftharpoons$ Glucose(aq) + Fructose(aq) $K = 1.4 \times 10^5$
(b) $NH_3(aq)$ + $H_2O(l)$ $\rightleftharpoons$ $NH_4^+(aq)$ + $OH^-(aq)$ $K = 1.6 \times 10^{-5}$
(c) $Fe_2O_3(s)$ + $3 CO(g)$ $\rightleftharpoons$ $2 Fe(s)$ + $3 CO_2(g)$ K (at 727 °C) = 24.2

PROBLEM 7.13

For the reaction $H_2(g) + I_2(g) \rightleftharpoons 2 HI(g)$, equilibrium concentrations at 25 °C are $[H_2] = 0.0510$ mol/L, $[I_2] = 0.174$ mol/L, and $[HI] = 0.507$ mol/L. What is the value of K at 25 °C?

🔵 **KEY CONCEPT PROBLEM 7.14**

The following diagrams represent two similar reactions that have achieved equilibrium:

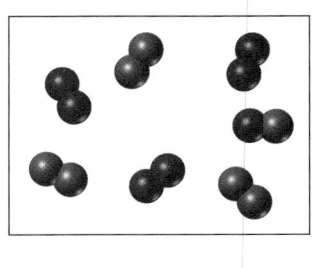   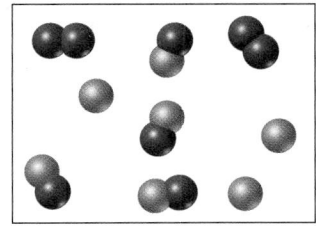

$$A_2 + B_2 \longrightarrow 2\,AB \qquad\qquad A_2 + 2B \longrightarrow 2\,AB$$

(a) Write the expression for the equilibrium constant for each reaction.
(b) Calculate the value for the equilibrium constant for each reaction.

7.9 Le Châtelier's Principle: The Effect of Changing Conditions on Equilibria

Learning Objective:

• Use Le Châtelier's principle to predict the effect of changes in temperature, pressure, and concentrations on an equilibrium reaction.

The effect of a change in reaction conditions on chemical equilibrium is predicted by a general rule called *Le Châtelier's principle.*

Le Châtelier's principle When a stress is applied to a system at equilibrium, the equilibrium shifts to relieve the stress.

The word "stress" in this context means any change in concentration, pressure, volume, or temperature that disturbs the original equilibrium and causes the rates of the forward and reverse reactions to become temporarily unequal.

We saw in Section 7.6 that reaction rates are affected by changes in temperature and concentration and by addition of a catalyst. But what about equilibria? Are they similarly affected? The answer is that changes in concentration, temperature, and pressure *do* affect equilibria, but that addition of a catalyst does not (except to reduce the time it takes to reach equilibrium). The change caused by a catalyst affects forward and reverse reactions equally so that equilibrium concentrations are the same in both the presence and the absence of the catalyst.

Effect of Changes in Concentration

Let us look at the effect of a concentration change by considering the reaction of CO with H_2 to form CH_3OH (methanol). Once equilibrium is reached, the concentrations of the reactants and product are constant, and the forward and reverse reaction rates are equal.

$$CO(g) + 2\,H_2(g) \rightleftharpoons CH_3OH(g)$$

What happens if the concentration of CO is increased? To relieve the stress of added CO, according to Le Châtelier's principle, the extra CO must be used up. In other words, the rate of the forward reaction must increase to consume CO. Think of the CO added on the left as "pushing" the equilibrium to the right:

$$\overset{\displaystyle [CO \longrightarrow]}{CO(g) + 2\,H_2(g) \rightleftharpoons CH_3OH(g)}$$

Of course, as soon as more CH_3OH forms, the reverse reaction also speeds up, some CH_3OH converts back to CO and H_2. Ultimately, the forward and reverse reaction rates adjust until they are again equal, and equilibrium is reestablished. At this new equilibrium state, the value of $[H_2]$ is lower because some of the H_2 reacted with the added CO and the value of $[CH_3OH]$ is higher because CH_3OH formed as the reaction was driven to the right by the addition of CO. The changes offset each other, however, so that the value of the equilibrium constant K remains constant.

$$CO(g) + 2 H_2(g) \rightleftharpoons CH_3OH(g)$$

If this increases . . .   . . . then this decreases . . .   . . . and this increases . . .

. . . but this remains constant. $K = \dfrac{[CH_3OH]}{[CO][H_2]^2}$

What happens if CH_3OH is added to the reaction at equilibrium? Some of the methanol reacts to yield CO and H_2, making the values of $[CO]$, $[H_2]$, and $[CH_3OH]$ higher when equilibrium is reestablished. As before, the value of K does not change.

If this increases . . .

$$CO(g) + 2 H_2(g) \rightleftharpoons CH_3OH(g)$$

. . . then this increases . . .   . . . and this increases . . .

. . . but this remains constant. $K = \dfrac{[CH_3OH]}{[CO][H_2]^2}$

Alternatively, we can view chemical equilibrium as a *balance* between the free energy of the reactants (on the left) and the free energy of the products (on the right). Adding more reactants tips the balance in favor of the reactants. In order to restore the balance, reactants must be converted to products, or the reaction must shift to the right. If, instead, we remove reactants, then the balance is too heavy on the product side and the reaction must shift left, generating more reactants to restore balance.

▶ Equilibrium represents a balance between the free energy of reactants and products. Adding reactants (or products) to one side upsets the balance, and the reaction will proceed in a direction to restore the balance.

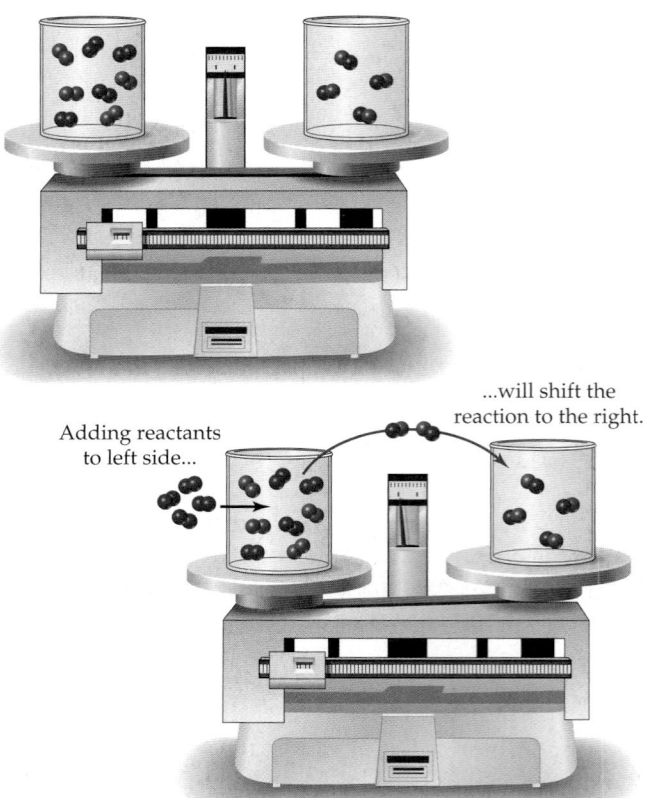

Adding reactants to left side...

...will shift the reaction to the right.

Finally, what happens if a reactant is continuously supplied or a product is continuously removed? Because the concentrations are continuously changing, equilibrium can never be reached. As a result, it is sometimes possible to force a reaction to produce large quantities of a desirable product even when the equilibrium constant is unfavorable. Take the reaction of acetic acid with ethanol to yield ethyl acetate, for example. As discussed in the preceding section, the equilibrium constant K for this reaction is 3.4, meaning that substantial amounts of reactants and products are both present at equilibrium. If, however, the ethyl acetate is removed as soon as it is formed, the production of more and more product is forced to occur, in accord with Le Châtelier's principle.

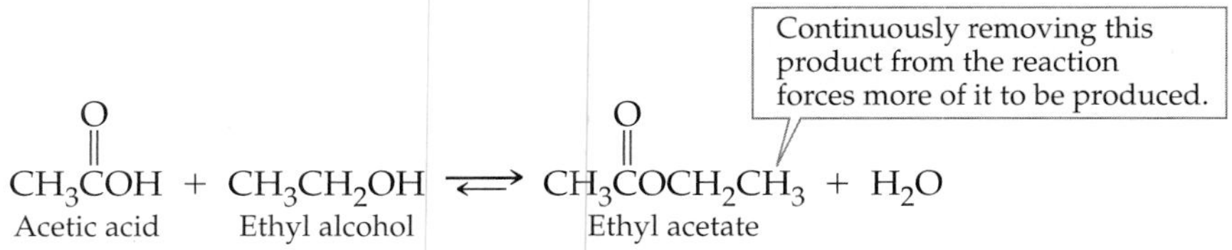

Metabolic reactions sometimes take advantage of this effect, with one reaction prevented from reaching equilibrium by the continuous consumption of its product in a further reaction.

Effect of Changes in Temperature and Pressure

We noted in Section 7.2 that the reverse of an exothermic reaction is always endothermic. Equilibrium reactions are therefore exothermic in one direction and endothermic in the other. Le Châtelier's principle predicts that an increase in temperature will cause an equilibrium to shift in favor of the endothermic reaction so the additional heat is absorbed. Conversely, a decrease in temperature will cause an equilibrium to shift in favor of the exothermic reaction so additional heat is released. In other words, you can think of heat as a reactant or product whose increase or decrease stresses an equilibrium just as a change in reactant or product concentration does.

Endothermic reaction   Favored by increase in temperature
(Heat is absorbed)

Exothermic reaction   Favored by decrease in temperature
(Heat is released)

In the exothermic reaction of N_2 with H_2 to form NH_3, for example, raising the temperature favors the reverse reaction, which absorbs the heat:

$$[\longleftarrow \qquad\qquad\qquad \text{Heat}]$$
$$N_2(g) + 3\,H_2(g) \rightleftharpoons 2\,NH_3(g) + \text{Heat}$$

We can also use the balance analogy to predict the effect of temperature on an equilibrium mixture; again, we can think of heat as a reactant or product. Increasing the temperature of the reaction is the same as adding heat to the left side (for an endothermic reaction) or to the right side (for an exothermic reaction). The reaction then proceeds in the appropriate direction to restore "balance" to the system.

What about changing the pressure? Pressure influences an equilibrium only if one or more of the substances involved is a gas. As predicted by Le Châtelier's principle, increasing the pressure (by decreasing the volume) in such a reaction shifts the equilibrium in the direction that decreases the number of molecules in the gas phase and thus, decreases the pressure. For the ammonia synthesis, decreasing the volume *increases* the concentration of reactants and products but has a greater effect on the reactant side of the equilibrium since there are more moles of gas phase reactants. Increasing the pressure, therefore, favors the forward reaction because 4 mol of gas is converted to 2 mol of gas.

$$[\text{Pressure} \longrightarrow]$$
$$\underbrace{N_2(g) + 3\,H_2(g)}_{\text{4 mol of gas}} \rightleftharpoons \underbrace{2\,NH_3(g)}_{\text{2 mol of gas}}$$

CHEMISTRY IN ACTION

✚ Regulation of Body Temperature

Living organisms are highly complex systems that use chemical reactions to produce the energy needed for daily activity. Many of these reactions occur very slowly—if at all—at normal body temperature, so organisms use several different strategies discussed in this chapter to obtain the energy they need and to function optimally. For example, the rates of slow reactions are increased by using biocatalysts, otherwise known as enzymes (Chapter 19). Le Châtelier's principle is used for regulation of critical processes, including oxygen transport (Chemistry in Action "Breathing and Oxygen Transport," p. 264) and blood pH (Chemistry in Action "Buffers in the Body: Acidosis and Alkalosis," p. 321). As mentioned in the beginning of the chapter, maintaining "normal" body temperature is crucial for mammals and other warm-blooded animals and is one of the conditions regulated by homeostasis. If the body's thermostat is unable to maintain a temperature of 37 °C, the rates of the many thousands of chemical reactions that take place constantly in the body will change accordingly, with potentially disastrous consequences.

If, for example, a skater fell through the ice of a frozen lake, *hypothermia* could soon result. Hypothermia is a dangerous state that occurs when the body is unable to generate enough heat to maintain normal temperature. All chemical reactions in the body slow down because of the lower temperature, energy production drops, and death can result. Slowing the body's reactions can also be used to advantage, however. During open-heart surgery, the heart is stopped and maintained at about 15 °C, while the body, which receives oxygenated blood from an external pump, is cooled to 25–32 °C. In this case, the body is receiving oxygenated blood from an external pump in an operating chamber under medical supervision. If hypothermia occurred due to some other environmental condition, the heart would slow down, respiration would decrease, and the body would not receive sufficient oxygen and death would result.

Conversely, a marathon runner on a hot, humid day might become overheated, and *hyperthermia* could result. Hyperthermia, also called *heat stroke,* is an uncontrolled rise in temperature as the result of the body's inability to lose sufficient heat. Chemical reactions in the body are accelerated at higher temperatures, the heart struggles to pump blood faster to supply increased oxygen, and brain damage can result if the body temperature rises above 41 °C.

Body temperature is maintained both by the thyroid gland and by the hypothalamus region of the brain, which

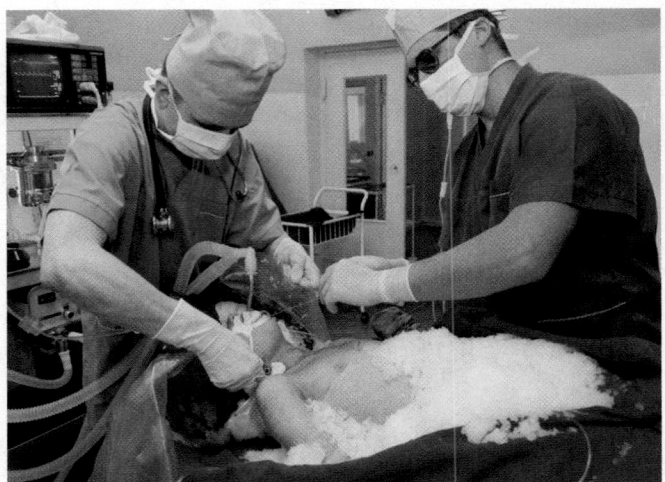

▲ The body is cooled to 25–32 °C by immersion in ice prior to open-heart surgery to slow down metabolism.

act together to regulate metabolic rate. When the body's environment changes, temperature receptors in the skin, spinal cord, and abdomen send signals to the hypothalamus, which contains both heat-sensitive and cold-sensitive neurons.

Stimulation of the heat-sensitive neurons on a hot day causes a variety of effects: Impulses are sent to stimulate the sweat glands, dilate the blood vessels of the skin, decrease muscular activity, and reduce metabolic rate. Sweating cools the body through evaporation; approximately 540 cal (2260 J) is removed by evaporation of 1.0 g of sweat. Dilated blood vessels cool the body by allowing more blood to flow close to the surface of the skin, where heat is removed by contact with air. Decreased muscular activity and a reduced metabolic rate cool the body by lowering internal heat production. Stimulation of the cold-sensitive neurons on a cold day also causes a variety of effects: The hormone epinephrine is released to stimulate metabolic rate; peripheral blood vessels contract to decrease blood flow to the skin and prevent heat loss; and muscular contractions increase to produce more heat, resulting in shivering and "goosebumps."

CIA Problem 7.3 Which body organs help to regulate body temperature?

CIA Problem 7.4 What is the purpose of blood vessel dilation?

The effects of changing reaction conditions on equilibria are summarized in Table 7.4.

Table 7.4 Effects of Changes in Reaction Conditions on Equilibria

Change	Effect
Concentration	Increase in reactant concentration or decrease in product concentration favors forward reaction. Increase in product concentration or decrease in reactant concentration favors reverse reaction.
Temperature	Increase in temperature favors endothermic reaction. Decrease in temperature favors exothermic reaction.
Pressure	Increase in pressure favors side with fewer moles of gas. Decrease in pressure favors side with more moles of gas.
Catalyst added	Equilibrium reached more quickly; value of K unchanged.

▶ In Chapter 21, we will see how Le Châtelier's principle is exploited to keep chemical "traffic" moving through the body's metabolic pathways. It often happens that one reaction in a series is prevented from reaching equilibrium because its product is continuously consumed in another reaction.

Worked Example 7.9 Le Châtelier's Principle and Equilibrium Mixtures

Nitrogen reacts with oxygen to give NO:

$$N_2(g) + O_2(g) \rightleftharpoons 2\,NO(g) \quad \Delta H = +43\,\text{kcal/mol} \;(+180\,\text{kJ/mol})$$

Explain the effects of the following changes on reactant and product concentrations:

(a) Increasing temperature

(b) Increasing the concentration of NO

(c) Adding a catalyst

SOLUTION

(a) The reaction is endothermic (positive ΔH), so increasing the temperature favors the forward reaction. The concentration of NO will be higher at equilibrium.

(b) Increasing the concentration of NO, a product, favors the reverse reaction. At equilibrium, the concentrations of both N_2 and O_2, as well as that of NO, will be higher.

(c) A catalyst accelerates the rate at which equilibrium is reached, but the concentrations at equilibrium do not change.

PROBLEM 7.15

Is the yield of SO_3 at equilibrium favored by a higher or lower pressure? By a higher or lower temperature?

$$2\,SO_2(g) + O_2(g) \rightleftharpoons 2\,SO_3(g) \quad \Delta H = -47\,\text{kcal/mol}$$

PROBLEM 7.16

What effect do the listed changes have on the position of the equilibrium in the reaction of carbon with hydrogen?

$$C(s) + 2\,H_2(g) \rightleftharpoons CH_4(g) \quad \Delta H = -18\,\text{kcal/mol} \;(-75\,\text{kJ/mol})$$

(a) Increasing temperature

(b) Increasing pressure by decreasing volume

(c) Allowing CH_4 to escape continuously from the reaction vessel

PROBLEM 7.17

As we exercise, our bodies metabolize glucose, converting it to CO_2 and H_2O, to supply the energy necessary for physical activity. The simplified reaction is:

$$C_6H_{12}O_6(aq) + 6\,O_2(g) \longrightarrow 6\,CO_2(g) + 6\,H_2O(l) + 678\,\text{kcal}\,(2840\,\text{kJ})$$

An individual weighing 150 pounds jogging at 5 mph for 30 minutes would burn 272 kcal. How many moles of glucose would need to be metabolized to generate this required energy?

SUMMARY REVISITING THE CHAPTER LEARNING OBJECTIVES

- **Distinguish between potential and kinetic energy.** Energy can be classified as *potential energy* (energy that is stored) or as *kinetic energy* (energy in motion). Energy can be interconverted from one form to another.

- **Identify chemical reactions as endothermic or exothermic, and explain how the heats of reaction relate to the law of conservation of energy.** The law of conservation of energy states that energy can neither be created nor destroyed during a reaction. Energy can be converted from chemical or potential energy to heat and vice versa. Reactions that absorb heat (convert thermal energy to bond energies) are called *endothermic*, whereas reactions that release heat (convert bond energies to heat) are called *exothermic* [see Problems 26–30, 67, 68, and 77].

- **Use bond energies and stoichiometric relationships to calculate the enthalpy of a reaction and the total amount of heat consumed or produced.** The strength of a covalent bond is measured by its *bond dissociation energy*, the amount of energy that must be supplied to break the bond in an isolated gaseous molecule. For any reaction, the heat released or absorbed by changes in bonding is called the *heat of reaction* or *enthalpy change* (ΔH). If the total strength of the bonds formed in a reaction is greater than the total strength of the bonds broken, then heat is released (negative ΔH) and the reaction is *exothermic*. If the total strength of the bonds formed in a reaction is less than the total strength of the bonds broken, then heat is absorbed (positive ΔH) and the reaction is *endothermic* [see Problems 23–26, 67–69, 72, 74, 76–78, and 80].

- **Use enthalpy, entropy, and free energy to determine the spontaneity of a chemical reaction or process.** *Spontaneous reactions* are those that, once started, continue without external influence; nonspontaneous reactions require a continuous external influence. Spontaneity depends on two factors: the amount of heat absorbed or released in a reaction (ΔH) and the *entropy change* (ΔS), which measures the change in molecular disorder in a reaction. Spontaneous reactions are favored by a release of heat (negative ΔH) and/or an increase in disorder (positive ΔS). The *free-energy change* ΔG takes both factors into account, according to the equation $\Delta G = \Delta H - T\,\Delta S$. A negative value for ΔG indicates spontaneity, and a positive value for ΔG indicates nonspontaneity [see Problems 18–20, 22, and 31–40].

- **Use collision theory and reaction diagrams to explain the activation energy and free-energy change of a chemical reaction.** A chemical reaction occurs when reactant particles collide with proper orientation and sufficient energy to break bonds in reactants. The exact amount of collision energy necessary is called the *activation energy* (E_{act}). A high activation energy results in a slow reaction because few collisions occur with sufficient force, whereas a low activation energy results in a fast reaction. The relationship between activation energy and the relative energies of reactants and products is illustrated using a *reaction diagram* [see Problems 21, 41–43, 46–48, and 75].

- **Explain how temperature, concentration of reactants, and presence of a catalyst affect the rate of a reaction.** Reaction rates can be increased by raising the temperature, by raising the concentrations of reactants, or by adding a *catalyst*, which accelerates a reaction without itself undergoing any change [see Problems 44–48, 57, and 80].

- **Define chemical equilibrium for reversible reactions.** A reaction that can occur in either the forward or reverse direction is *reversible* and will ultimately reach a state of *chemical equilibrium*. At equilibrium, the forward and reverse reactions occur at the same rate, and the concentrations of reactants and products are constant [see Problems 49 and 50].

- **Define the equilibrium constant (K), and use the value of K to predict the extent of reaction.** Every reversible reaction has a characteristic *equilibrium constant* (K), given by an *equilibrium equation* that can be derived from the balanced chemical equation as shown:

For the reaction: $a\text{A} + b\text{B} + \cdots \rightleftarrows m\text{M} + n\text{N} + \cdots$

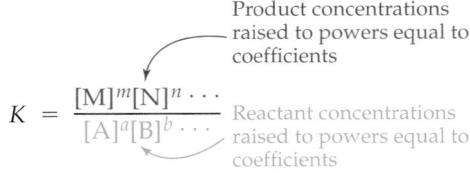

$$K = \frac{[\text{M}]^m[\text{N}]^n \cdots}{[\text{A}]^a[\text{B}]^b \cdots}$$

Product concentrations raised to powers equal to coefficients

Reactant concentrations raised to powers equal to coefficients

[see Problems 51–58 and 69].

- **Use Le Châtelier's principle to predict the effect of changes in temperature, pressure, and concentrations on an equilibrium reaction.** Le Châtelier's principle states that when a stress is applied to a system in equilibrium, the equilibrium shifts so that the stress is relieved. Applying this principle allows prediction of the effects of changes in temperature, pressure, and concentration [see Problems 59–66, 70, 73, 79, and 80].

KEY WORDS

Activation energy (E_{act}), *p. 196*	**Endothermic,** *p. 186*	**Exergonic,** *p. 194*	**Le Châtelier's principle,** *p. 205*
Bond dissociation energy, *p. 185*	**Enthalpy (H),** *p. 187*	**Exothermic,** *p. 186*	**Potential energy,** *p. 185*
Catalyst, *p. 198*	**Enthalpy change (ΔH),** *p. 187*	**Free-energy change (ΔG),** *p. 194*	**Reaction rate,** *p. 196*
Chemical equilibrium, *p. 200*	**Entropy (S),** *p. 193*	**Heat,** *p. 185*	**Reversible reaction,** *p. 200*
Concentration, *p. 198*	**Entropy change (ΔS),** *p. 193*	**Heat of reaction,** *p. 187*	**Spontaneous process,** *p. 192*
Endergonic, *p. 194*	**Equilibrium constant (K),** *p. 202*	**Kinetic energy,** *p. 185*	
		Law of conservation of energy, *p. 186*	

CONCEPT MAP: CHEMICAL REACTIONS: ENERGY, RATES, AND EQUILIBRIUM

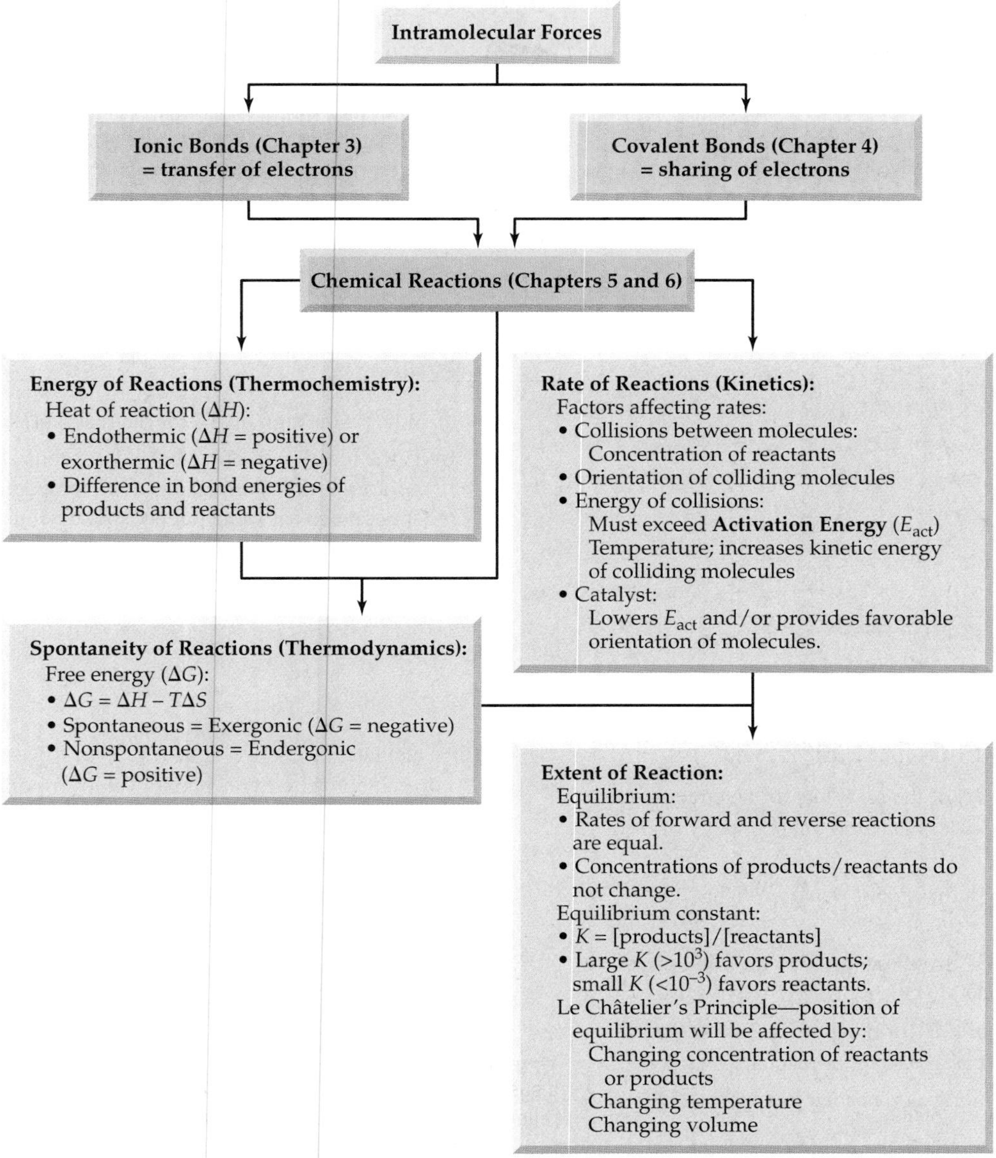

Intramolecular Forces

Ionic Bonds (Chapter 3)
= transfer of electrons

Covalent Bonds (Chapter 4)
= sharing of electrons

Chemical Reactions (Chapters 5 and 6)

Energy of Reactions (Thermochemistry):
Heat of reaction (ΔH):
- Endothermic (ΔH = positive) or
  exothermic (ΔH = negative)
- Difference in bond energies of
  products and reactants

Rate of Reactions (Kinetics):
Factors affecting rates:
- Collisions between molecules:
  Concentration of reactants
- Orientation of colliding molecules
- Energy of collisions:
  Must exceed **Activation Energy** (E_{act})
  Temperature; increases kinetic energy
  of colliding molecules
- Catalyst:
  Lowers E_{act} and/or provides favorable
  orientation of molecules.

Spontaneity of Reactions (Thermodynamics):
Free energy (ΔG):
- $\Delta G = \Delta H - T\Delta S$
- Spontaneous = Exergonic (ΔG = negative)
- Nonspontaneous = Endergonic
  (ΔG = positive)

Extent of Reaction:
Equilibrium:
- Rates of forward and reverse reactions
  are equal.
- Concentrations of products/reactants do
  not change.
Equilibrium constant:
- K = [products]/[reactants]
- Large K ($>10^3$) favors products;
  small K ($<10^{-3}$) favors reactants.
Le Châtelier's Principle—position of
  equilibrium will be affected by:
    Changing concentration of reactants
      or products
    Changing temperature
    Changing volume

▲ **Figure 7.7 Concept Map.** We discussed the fundamentals of chemical reactions in Chapters 5 and 6. In this chapter, we looked at the heats of reaction, rates of reaction, spontaneity of reactions, and the extent of reaction as indicated by the equilibrium constant, K. These concepts, and the connections between them and previous concepts, are shown here.

▱ UNDERSTANDING KEY CONCEPTS

7.18   What are the signs of ΔH, ΔS, and ΔG for the spontaneous conversion of a crystalline solid into a gas? Explain.

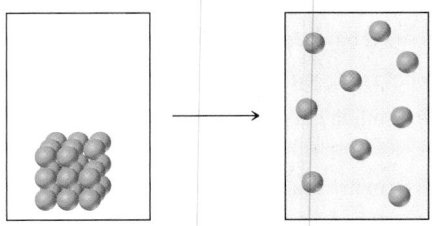

7.19   What are the signs of ΔH, ΔS, and ΔG for the spontaneous condensation of a vapor to a liquid? Explain.

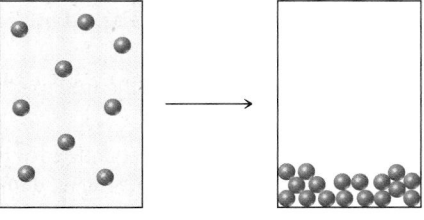

7.20   Consider the following spontaneous reaction of A_2 molecules (red) and B_2 molecules (blue):

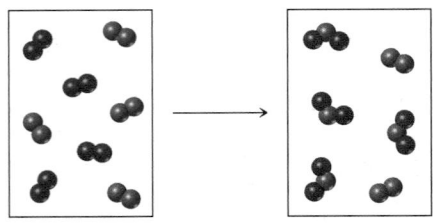

(a) Write a balanced equation for the reaction.

(b) What are the signs of ΔH, ΔS, and ΔG for the reaction? Explain.

7.21   Two curves are shown in the following energy diagram:

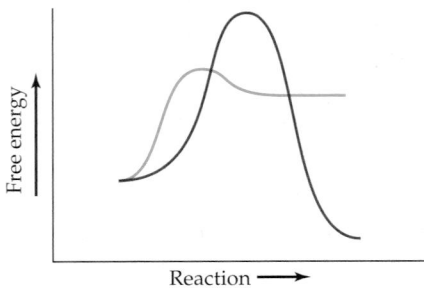

(a) Which curve represents the faster reaction, and which the slower?

(b) Which curve represents the spontaneous reaction, and which the nonspontaneous?

7.22   The following diagram portrays a reaction of the type $A(s) \longrightarrow B(g) + C(g)$, where the different-colored spheres represent different molecular structures. Assume that the reaction has $\Delta H = +9.1 \text{ kcal/mol} (+38.1 \text{ kJ/mol})$.

(a) What is the sign of ΔS for the reaction?

(b) Is the reaction likely to be spontaneous at all temperatures, nonspontaneous at all temperatures, or spontaneous at some but nonspontaneous at others?

ADDITIONAL PROBLEMS

ENTHALPY AND HEAT OF REACTION (SECTIONS 7.1–7.3)

7.23   Is the total enthalpy *(H)* of the reactants for an endothermic reaction greater than or less than the total enthalpy of the products?

7.24   What is meant by the term *heat of reaction*? What other name is a synonym for this term?

7.25   The vaporization of Br_2 from the liquid to the gas state requires 7.4 kcal/mol (31.0 kJ/mol).

(a) What is the sign of ΔH for this process? Write a reaction showing heat as a product or reactant.

(b) How many kilocalories are needed to vaporize 5.8 mol of Br_2?

(c) How many kilojoules are needed to evaporate 82 g of Br_2?

7.26   Converting liquid water to solid ice releases 1.44 kcal/mol (6.02 kJ/mol).

(a) What is the sign of ΔH for this process? Write a reaction showing heat as a product or reactant.

(b) How many kilojoules are released by freezing 2.5 mol of H_2O?

(c) How many kilocalories are released by freezing 32 g of H_2O?

(d) How many kilocalories are absorbed by melting 1 mol of ice?

7.27   Acetylene $(H-C \equiv C-H)$ is the fuel used in welding torches.

(a) Write the balanced chemical equation for the combustion reaction of 1 mol of acetylene with $O_2(g)$ to produce $CO_2(g)$ and water vapor.

(b) Estimate ΔH for this reaction (in kJ/mol) using the bond energies listed in Table 7.1.

(c) Calculate the energy value (in kJ/g) for acetylene. How does it compare to the energy values for other fuels in Table 7.2?

7.28   Nitrogen in air reacts at high temperatures to form NO_2 according to the following reaction: $N_2 + 2 O_2 \longrightarrow 2 NO_2$

(a) Draw structures for the reactant and product molecules indicating single, double, and triple bonds.

(b) Estimate ΔH for this reaction (in kcal and kJ) using the bond energies from Table 7.1.

7.29   Glucose, also known as "blood sugar" when measured in blood, has the formula $C_6H_{12}O_6$.

(a) Write the equation for the combustion of glucose with O_2 to give CO_2 and H_2O.

(b) If 3.8 kcal (16 kJ) is released by combustion of each gram of glucose, how many kilocalories are released by the combustion of 1.50 mol of glucose? How many kilojoules?

(c) What is the minimum amount of energy (in kJ) a plant must absorb to produce 15.0 g of glucose?

7.30   During the combustion of 5.00 g of octane, C_8H_{18}, 239.5 kcal (1002 kJ) is released.

(a) Write a balanced equation for the combustion reaction.

(b) What is the sign of ΔH for this reaction?

(c) How much energy (in kJ) is released by the combustion of 1.00 mol of C_8H_{18}?

(d) How many grams and how many moles of octane must be burned to release 450.0 kcal?

(e) How many kilojoules are released by the combustion of 17.0 g of C_8H_{18}?

ENTROPY AND FREE ENERGY (SECTION 7.4)

7.31 Which of the following processes results in an increase in entropy of the system?

(a) A drop of ink spreading out when it is placed in water

(b) Steam condensing into drops on windows

(c) Constructing a building from loose bricks

7.32 For each of the following processes, specify whether entropy increases or decreases. Explain each of your answers.

(a) Assembling a jigsaw puzzle

(b) $I_2(s) + 3 F_2(g) \longrightarrow 2 IF_3(g)$

(c) A precipitate forming when two solutions are mixed

(d) $C_6H_{12}O_6(aq) + 6 O_2(g)6 \longrightarrow CO_2(g) + 6 H_2O(g)$

(e) $CaCO_3(s) \longrightarrow CaO(s) + CO_2(g)$

(f) $Pb(NO_3)_2(aq) + 2 NaCl(aq) \longrightarrow$
$PbCl_2(s) + 2 NaNO_3(aq)$

7.33 What two factors affect the spontaneity of a reaction?

7.34 What is the difference between an exothermic reaction and an exergonic reaction?

7.35 Why are most spontaneous reactions exothermic?

7.36 Under what conditions might a reaction be endothermic but exergonic? Explain.

7.37 For the reaction
$NaCl(s) \xrightarrow{Water} Na^+(aq) + Cl^-(aq),$
$\Delta H = +1 \text{ kcal/mol } (+4.184 \text{ kJ/mol})$

(a) Is this process endothermic or exothermic?

(b) Does entropy increase or decrease in this process?

(c) Table salt (NaCl) readily dissolves in water. Explain, based on your answers to parts (a) and (b).

7.38 For the reaction $2 Hg(l) + O_2(g) \longrightarrow 2 HgO(s),$
$\Delta H = -43 \text{ kcal/mol } (-180 \text{ kJ/mol}).$

(a) Does entropy increase or decrease in this process? Explain.

(b) Under what conditions would you expect this process to be spontaneous?

7.39 The reaction of gaseous H_2 and liquid Br_2 to give gaseous HBr has $\Delta H = -17.4 \text{ kcal/mol } (-72.8 \text{ kJ/mol})$ and $\Delta S = 27.2 \text{ cal/(mol·K)} (114 \text{ J/(mol·K)}).$

(a) Write the balanced equation for this reaction.

(b) Does entropy increase or decrease in this process?

(c) Is this process spontaneous at all temperatures? Explain.

(d) What is the value of ΔG (in kcal and kJ) for the reaction at 300 K?

7.40 The following reaction is used in the industrial synthesis of polyvinyl chloride (PVC) polymer:
$Cl_2(g) + H_2C=CH_2(g) \longrightarrow ClCH_2CH_2Cl(l)$
$\Delta H = -52 \text{ kcal/mol } (-218 \text{ kJ/mol})$

(a) Is ΔS positive or negative for this process?

(b) Is this process spontaneous at all temperatures? Explain.

RATES OF CHEMICAL REACTIONS (SECTIONS 7.5 AND 7.6)

7.41 What is the activation energy of a reaction?

7.42 Which reaction is faster, one with $E_{act} = +10 \text{ kcal/mol}$ $(+41.8 \text{ kJ/mol})$ or one with $E_{act} = +5 \text{ kcal/mol}$ $(+20.9 \text{ kJ/mol})$? Explain.

7.43 How does the rate of the forward reaction compare to the rate of the reverse reaction for an endergonic reaction? For an exergonic reaction? Explain.

7.44 Why does increasing concentration generally increase the rate of a reaction?

7.45 What is a catalyst, and what effect does it have on the activation energy of a reaction?

7.46 If a catalyst changes the activation energy of a forward reaction from 28.0 kcal/mol to 23.0 kcal/mol, what effect does it have on the reverse reaction?

7.47 For the reaction $C(s, \text{diamond}) \longrightarrow C(s, \text{graphite}),$
$\Delta G = -0.693 \text{ kcal/mol } (-2.90 \text{ kJ/mol}) \text{ at } 25 \text{ °C}.$

(a) According to this information, do diamonds spontaneously turn into graphite?

(b) In light of your answer to part (a), why can diamonds be kept unchanged for thousands of years?

7.48 The reaction between hydrogen gas and carbon to produce the gas known as ethylene is:
$2 H_2(g) + 2 C(s) \longrightarrow H_2C=CH_2(g),$
$\Delta G = +16.3 \text{ kcal/mol } (+68.2 \text{ kJ/mol}) \text{ at } 25 \text{ °C}.$

(a) Is this reaction spontaneous at 25 °C?

(b) Would it be reasonable to try to develop a catalyst for the reaction run at 25 °C? Explain.

CHEMICAL EQUILIBRIA (SECTIONS 7.7 AND 7.8)

7.49 What is meant by the term "chemical equilibrium"? Must amounts of reactants and products be equal at equilibrium?

7.50 Why do catalysts not alter the amounts of reactants and products present at equilibrium?

7.51 Write the equilibrium constant expressions for the following reactions:

(a) $2 CO(g) + O_2(g) \rightleftharpoons 2 CO_2(g)$

(b) $Mg(s) + HCl(aq) \rightleftharpoons MgCl_2(aq) + H_2(g)$

(c) $HF(aq) + H_2O(l) \rightleftharpoons H_3O^+(aq) + F^-(aq)$

(d) $S(s) + O_2(g) \rightleftharpoons SO_2(g)$

7.52 Write the equilibrium constant expressions for the following reactions.

(a) $S_2(g) + 2 H_2(g) \rightleftharpoons 2 H_2S(g)$

(b) $H_2S(aq) + Cl_2(aq) \rightleftharpoons S(s) + 2 HCl(aq)$

(c) $Br_2(g) + Cl_2(g) \rightleftharpoons 2 BrCl(g)$

(d) $C(s) + H_2O(g) \rightleftharpoons CO(g) + H_2(g)$

7.53 For the reaction $N_2O_4(g) \rightleftharpoons 2 NO_2(g)$, the equilibrium concentrations at 25 °C are $[NO_2] = 0.0325 \text{ mol/L}$ and $[N_2O_4] = 0.147 \text{ mol/L}.$

(a) What is the value of K at 25 °C? Are reactants or products favored?

7.54 For the reaction $2\,CO(g) + O_2(g) \rightleftharpoons 2\,CO_2(g)$, the equilibrium concentrations at a certain temperature are $[CO_2] = 0.11\,mol/L$, $[O_2] = 0.015\,mol/L$, and $[CO] = 0.025\,mol/L$.

(a) Write the equilibrium constant expression for the reaction.

(b) What is the value of K at this temperature? Are reactants or products favored?

7.55 Use your answer from Problem 7.53 to calculate the following:

(a) $[N_2O_4]$ at equilibrium when $[NO_2] = 0.0250\,mol/L$

(b) $[NO_2]$ at equilibrium when $[N_2O_4] = 0.0750\,mol/L$

7.56 Use your answer from Problem 7.54 to calculate the following:

(a) $[O_2]$ at equilibrium when $[CO_2] = 0.18\,mol/L$ and $[CO] = 0.0200\,mol/L$

(b) $[CO_2]$ at equilibrium when $[CO] = 0.080\,mol/L$ and $[O_2] = 0.520\,mol/L$

7.57 Would you expect to find relatively more reactants or more products for the reaction in Problem 7.53 if the pressure is raised by decreasing the volume? Explain.

7.58 Would you expect to find relatively more reactants or more products for the reaction in Problem 7.54 if the pressure is lowered by increasing the volume?

LE CHÂTELIER'S PRINCIPLE (SECTION 7.9)

7.59 Oxygen can be converted into ozone by the action of lightning or electric sparks:

$$3\,O_2(g) \rightleftharpoons 2\,O_3(g)$$

For this reaction, $\Delta H = +68\,kcal/mol$ ($+285\,kJ/mol$) and $K = 2.68 \times 10^{-29}$ at 25 °C.

(a) Is the reaction exothermic or endothermic?

(b) Are the reactants or the products favored at equilibrium?

(c) Explain the effect on the equilibrium of

(1) Increasing pressure by decreasing volume

(2) Increasing the concentration of $O_2(g)$

(3) Increasing the concentration of $O_3(g)$

(4) Adding a catalyst

(5) Increasing the temperature

7.60 Hydrogen chloride can be made from the reaction of chlorine and hydrogen:

$$Cl_2(g) + H_2(g) \longrightarrow 2\,HCl(g)$$

For this reaction, $K = 26 \times 10^{33}$ and $\Delta H = -44\,kcal/mol$ ($-184\,kJ/mol$) at 25 °C.

(a) Is the reaction endothermic or exothermic?

(b) Are the reactants or the products favored at equilibrium?

(c) Explain the effect on the equilibrium of

(1) Increasing pressure by decreasing volume

(2) Increasing the concentration of $HCl(g)$

(3) Decreasing the concentration of $Cl_2(g)$

(4) Increasing the concentration of $H_2(g)$

(5) Adding a catalyst

7.61 When the following equilibria are disturbed by increasing the pressure, does the concentration of reaction products increase, decrease, or remain the same?

(a) $2\,CO_2(g) \rightleftharpoons 2\,CO(g) + O_2(g)$

(b) $N_2(g) + O_2(g) \rightleftharpoons 2\,NO(g)$

(c) $Si(s) + 2\,Cl_2(g) \rightleftharpoons SiCl_4(g)$

7.62 For the following equilibria, use Le Châtelier's principle to predict the direction of the reaction when the pressure is increased by decreasing the volume of the equilibrium mixture.

(a) $C(s) + H_2O(g) \rightleftharpoons CO(g) + H_2(g)$

(b) $2\,H_2(g) + O_2(g) \rightleftharpoons 2\,H_2O(g)$

(c) $2\,Fe(s) + 3\,H_2O(g) \rightleftharpoons Fe_2O_3(s) + 3\,H_2(g)$

7.63 The reaction $CO(g) + H_2O(g) \rightleftharpoons CO_2(g) + H_2(g)$ has $\Delta H = -9.8\,kcal/mol$ ($-41\,kJ/mol$). Does the amount of H_2 in an equilibrium mixture increase or decrease when the temperature is decreased?

7.64 The reaction $3\,O_2(g) \rightleftharpoons 2\,O_3(g)$ has $\Delta H = +68\,kcal/mol$ ($+285\,kJ/mol$). Does the equilibrium constant for the reaction increase or decrease when the temperature increases?

7.65 The reaction $H_2(g) + I_2(g) \rightleftharpoons 2\,HI(g)$ has $\Delta H = -2.2\,kcal/mol$ ($-9.2\,kJ/mol$). Will the equilibrium concentration of HI increase or decrease when

(a) I_2 is added?

(b) H_2 is removed?

(c) A catalyst is added?

(d) The temperature is increased?

7.66 The reaction $Fe^{3+}(aq) + Cl^-(aq) \rightleftharpoons FeCl^{2+}(aq)$ is endothermic. How will the equilibrium concentration of $FeCl^{2+}$ change when

(a) $Fe(NO_3)_3$ is added?

(b) Cl^- is precipitated by addition of $AgNO_3$?

(c) The temperature is increased?

(d) A catalyst is added?

CONCEPTUAL PROBLEMS

7.67 For the unbalanced combustion reaction shown, 1 mol of ethanol, C_2H_5OH, releases 327 kcal (1370 kJ):

$$C_2H_5OH + O_2 \longrightarrow CO_2 + H_2O$$

(a) Write a balanced equation for the combustion reaction.

(b) What is the sign of ΔH for this reaction?

(c) How much heat (in kilocalories) is released from the combustion of 5.00 g of ethanol?

(d) How many grams of C_2H_5OH must be burned to raise the temperature of 500.0 mL of water from 20.0 °C to 100.0 °C? (The specific heat of water is $1\,cal/g \cdot °C$ or $4.184\,J/g \cdot °C$. See Section 1.11.)

(e) If the density of ethanol is 0.789 g/mL, calculate the combustion energy of ethanol in kilocalories/milliliter and kilojoules/milliliter

7.68 For the production of ammonia from its elements, $\Delta H = -22\,kcal/mol$ ($-92\,kJ/mol$).

(a) Is this process endothermic or exothermic?

(b) How much energy (in kilocalories and kilojoules) is involved in the production of 0.700 mol of NH_3?

7.69 Magnetite, an iron ore with formula Fe_3O_4, can be reduced by treatment with hydrogen to yield iron metal and water vapor.

(a) Write the balanced equation.

(b) This process requires 36 kcal (151 kJ) for every 1.00 mol of Fe_3O_4 reduced. How much energy (in kilocalories and kilojoules) is required to produce 55 g of iron?

(c) How many grams of hydrogen are needed to produce 75 g of iron?

(d) This reaction has $K = 2.3 \times 10^{-18}$. Are the reactants or the products favored?

7.70 Hemoglobin (Hb) reacts reversibly with O_2 to form HbO_2, a substance that transfers oxygen to tissues:

$$Hb(aq) + O_2(aq) \rightleftharpoons HbO_2(aq)$$

Carbon monoxide (CO) is attracted to Hb 140 times more strongly than O_2 and establishes another equilibrium.

(a) Explain, using Le Châtelier's principle, why inhalation of CO can cause weakening and eventual death.

(b) Still another equilibrium is established when both O_2 and CO are present:

$$Hb(CO)(aq) + O_2(aq) \rightleftharpoons HbO_2(aq) + CO(aq)$$

Explain, using Le Châtelier's principle, why pure oxygen is often administered to victims of CO poisoning.

7.71 Urea is a metabolic waste product that decomposes to ammonia and water according to the following reaction:

$$NH_2CONH_2 + H_2O \longrightarrow 2\,NH_3 + CO_2.$$

(a) Draw the Lewis structure for urea.

(b) Estimate ΔH (in kcal and kJ) for this reaction using the bond energies from Table 7.1.

7.72 For the evaporation of water, $H_2O(l) \longrightarrow H_2O(g)$, at 100 °C, $\Delta H = +9.72\,\text{kcal/mol}\,(+40.7\,\text{kJ/mol})$.

(a) How many kilocalories are needed to vaporize 10.0 g of $H_2O(l)$?

(b) How many kilojoules are released when 10.0 g of $H_2O(g)$ is condensed?

7.73 Ammonia reacts slowly in air to produce nitrogen monoxide and water vapor:

$$NH_3(g) + O_2(g) \rightleftharpoons NO(g) + H_2O(g) + \text{Heat}$$

(a) Balance the equation.

(b) Write the equilibrium equation.

(c) Explain the effect on the equilibrium of

(1) Raising the pressure

(2) Adding $NO(g)$

(3) Decreasing the concentration of NH_3

(4) Lowering the temperature

7.74 Methanol, CH_3OH, is used as race car fuel.

(a) Write the balanced equation for the combustion reaction of methanol with O_2 to form CO_2 and H_2O.

(b) $\Delta H = -174\,\text{kcal/mol}\,(-728\,\text{kJ/mol})$ methanol for the process. How many kilocalories are released by burning 1.85 mol of methanol?

(c) How many kilojoules are released by burning 50.0 g of methanol?

7.75 Sketch an energy diagram for a system in which the forward reaction has $E_{\text{act}} = +25\,\text{kcal/mol}\,(+105\,\text{kJ/mol})$ and the reverse reaction has $E_{\text{act}} = +35\,\text{kcal/mol}\,(+146\,\text{kJ/mol})$.

(a) Is the forward process endergonic or exergonic?

(b) What is the value of ΔG for the reaction?

7.76 The thermite reaction (photograph, p. 187), in which aluminum metal reacts with iron(III) oxide to produce a spectacular display of sparks, is so exothermic that the product (iron) is in the molten state:

$$2\,Al(s) + Fe_2O_3(s) \longrightarrow 2\,Al_2O_3(s) + 2\,Fe(l)$$
$$\Delta H = -202.9\,\text{kcal/mol}\,(-848.9\,\text{kJ/mol})$$

(a) How much heat is released (in kilojoules) when 0.255 mol of Al is used in this reaction?

(b) How much heat (in kilocalories) is released when 5.00 g of Al is used in the reaction?

7.77 How much heat (in kilocalories) is evolved or absorbed in the reaction of 1.00 g of Na with H_2O? Is the reaction exothermic or endothermic?

$$2\,Na(s) + 2\,H_2O(l) \longrightarrow 2\,NaOH(aq) + H_2(g)$$
$$\Delta H = -88.0\,\text{kcal/mol}\,(-368\,\text{kJ/mol})$$

GROUP PROBLEMS

7.78 Obtain a package of your favorite snack food and examine the nutritional information on the label. Confirm the caloric value listed by using the conversions listed in the table in the Chemistry in Action feature "Energy from Food" (p. 191). Alternatively, you can use the estimates for caloric value for a given food as provided in the table.

(a) Do some research to find out the amount of calories associated with typical physical activities (e.g., walking or jogging, riding a bicycle, swimming laps).

(b) How long would you have to engage in each of the physical activities to burn the calories contained in your snack?

7.79 Most living organisms use glucose in cellular metabolism to produce energy, but blood glucose levels that are too high can be toxic. Do a little research on the role of insulin in the regulation of blood glucose. Explain the process in terms of Le Châtelier's principle.

7.80 Ammonia is an important chemical used in the production of fertilizer. Industrial production of ammonia from atmospheric nitrogen is difficult because of the energy required to cleave the N–N triple bond. Consider the balanced reaction of ammonia: $N_2(g) + 3\,H_2(g) \longrightarrow 2\,NH_3(g)$. This reaction has a value of $K = 4.3 \times 10^{-2}$ at 25 °C.

(a) Estimate the ΔH for this reaction using bond energies. Is the process endothermic or exothermic?

(b) Using Le Châtelier's principle, identify three ways you might increase the production of ammonia.

(c) Do some research on the Haber–Bosch process, developed in the early 1900s. What methods did this process use to increase production of ammonia (i.e., shift the equilibrium to the right)?

8

Gases, Liquids, and Solids

CONTENTS

◀◀◀ CONCEPTS TO REVIEW

▲ Aloe vera gel, extracted from the leaves of the succulent ornamental plant using supercritical fluid extraction, has many uses in cosmetics and alternative medicine.

Carbon dioxide is a gas at room temperature and is a significant component of the Earth's atmosphere. You may also be familiar with "dry ice," which is solid CO_2, and which evaporates directly to the gas phase. But have you ever seen "liquid" carbon dioxide? As a matter of fact, CO_2 can exist in a liquid-like state, known as a supercritical fluid, under conditions of elevated pressures and temperature. As you will learn in more detail in the Chemistry in Action on page 246 of this chapter, this unique state of matter has physical properties that make it particularly well suited for applications such as extracting potentially therapeutic natural products from plants—such as aloe vera, featured in the photo above. Supercritical fluid is also used for removing caffeine from coffee beans, cleaning and sterilizing medical implants, and for processing drugs to produce microencapsulated drug delivery systems. But what are the characteristic properties of supercritical fluids and the other different states of matter, and how are those properties related to molecular structure?

In the previous seven chapters, we dealt with matter at the atomic level. We have seen that all matter is composed of atoms, ions, or molecules; these particles are in constant motion; atoms combine to make compounds using chemical bonds; and physical and chemical changes are accompanied by the release or absorption of energy. Furthermore, we have distinguished between ionic and covalent compounds and between polar and nonpolar substances. In this chapter, we will concentrate on the large-scale behavior of visible amounts of matter, and how that behavior is related to molecular structure and affected by external factors such as temperature and pressure.

8.1 States of Matter and Their Changes

Learning Objective:

- Identify phase changes as endothermic or exothermic, and predict how a change in temperature will affect a phase change.

Matter exists in any of three phases, or *states*—solid, liquid, or gas. The state in which a compound exists under a given set of conditions depends on the relative strength of the attractive forces between particles compared to the kinetic energy of the particles. Kinetic energy (Section 7.1) is energy associated with motion and is related to the temperature of the substance. In gases, the attractive forces between particles are very weak compared to their kinetic energy, so the particles move about freely, are far apart, and have almost no influence on one another. In liquids, the attractive forces between particles are stronger, pulling the particles close together but still allowing them considerable freedom to move about. In solids, the attractive forces are much stronger than the kinetic energy of the particles, so the atoms, molecules, or ions are held in a specific arrangement and can only vibrate in place (Figure 8.1).

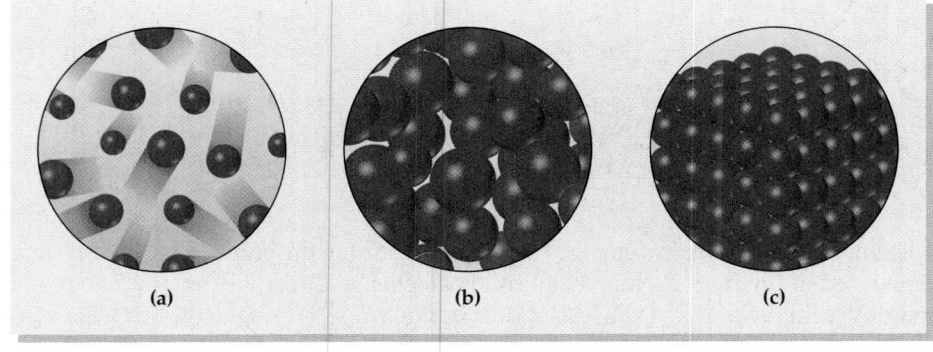

(a)   (b)   (c)

◄ **Figure 8.1**

A molecular comparison of gases, liquids, and solids.
(a) In gases, the particles feel little attraction for one another and are free to move about randomly. (b) In liquids, the particles are held close together by attractive forces but are free to slide over one another. (c) In solids, the particles are strongly attracted to one another. They can move slightly but are held in a fairly rigid arrangement with respect to one another.

The transformation of a substance from one state to another is called a *phase change* or a **change of state.** Every change of state is reversible and, like all chemical and physical processes, is characterized by changes in enthalpy and entropy.

The enthalpy change ΔH is a measure of the heat absorbed or released during a given change of state. The magnitude of ΔH depends on the attractive forces between molecules; as heat is absorbed, the kinetic energy of molecules increases until it is sufficient to overcome the forces of attraction. In the melting of a solid to a liquid, for example, heat is absorbed and ΔH is positive (endothermic). In the reverse process—the freezing of a liquid to a solid—the potential energy of attractive forces between molecules is converted to thermal energy; heat is released and ΔH is negative (exothermic). Look at the change between ice and water, for instance:

Change of state The change of a substance from one state of matter (gas, liquid, or solid) to another.

◄◄◄ **CONCEPTS TO REVIEW** Review Sections 7.3 and 7.4 to brush up on these concepts.

Melting: $H_2O(s) \longrightarrow H_2O(l)$ $\Delta H = +1.44 \text{ kcal/mol or } +6.02 \text{ kJ/mol}$

Freezing: $H_2O(l) \longrightarrow H_2O(s)$ $\Delta H = -1.44 \text{ kcal/mol or } -6.02 \text{ kJ/mol}$

The entropy change ΔS is a measure of the change in molecular disorder or free-dom that occurs during a process. In the melting of a solid to a liquid, for example, disorder increases because particles gain freedom of motion, so ΔS is positive. In the reverse process—the freezing of a liquid to a solid—disorder decreases as particles are locked into position, so ΔS is negative. Look at the change between ice and water:

Melting: $H_2O(s) \longrightarrow H_2O(l)$ $\Delta S = +5.26 \text{ cal}/(\text{mol}\cdot\text{K})$ or $+22.0 \text{ J}/(\text{mol}\cdot\text{K})$

Freezing: $H_2O(l) \longrightarrow H_2O(s)$ $\Delta S = -5.26 \text{ cal}/(\text{mol}\cdot\text{K})$ or $-22.0 \text{ J}/(\text{mol}\cdot\text{K})$

Melting point (mp) The tempera-ture at which solid and liquid are in equilibrium.

Boiling point (bp) The tempera-ture at which liquid and gas are in equilibrium.

The enthalpy and entropy associated with phase changes are contrary; the melting of ice, for instance, is unfavored by a positive ΔH but favored by a positive ΔS. Similarly, the freezing of water is favored by a negative ΔH but is unfavored by a negative ΔS. The exact temperature at which these two factors (ΔH and ΔS) exactly balance out is called the **melting point (mp)** and represents the temperature at which solid and liquid coexist in equilibrium. In the corresponding change from a liquid to a gas, the two states are in equilibrium at the **boiling point (bp).**

▶ **Figure 8.2**
Changes of state.
The changes are endothermic from bottom to top and exothermic from top to bottom.

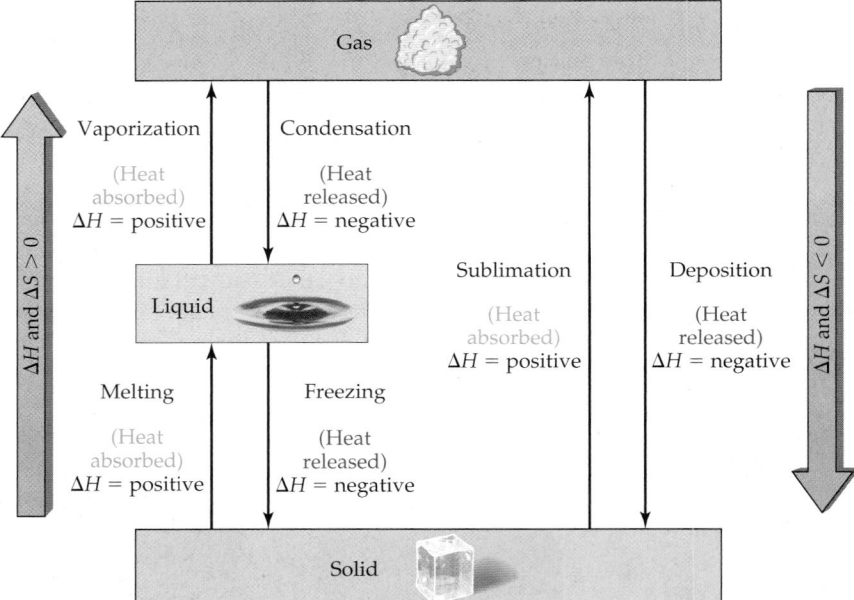

The names and enthalpy changes associated with the different changes of state are summarized in Figure 8.2. Note that a solid can change directly to a gas without going through the liquid state—a process called *sublimation*. Dry ice (solid CO_2) at atmo-spheric pressure, for example, changes directly to a gas without melting.

PROBLEM 8.1

The change of state from liquid H_2O to gaseous H_2O has $\Delta H = +9.72 \text{ kcal}/\text{mol}$ ($+40.7 \text{ kJ}/\text{mol}$) and $\Delta S = -26.1 \text{ cal}/(\text{mol}\cdot\text{K})[-109 \text{ J}/(\text{mol}\cdot\text{K})]$.

(a) Is the change from liquid to gaseous H_2O favored or unfavored by ΔH? By ΔS?

(b) What are the values of ΔH and ΔS (in kcal/mol and kJ/mol) for the change from gaseous to liquid H_2O?

8.2 Intermolecular Forces

Learning Objective:

• Identify the different types of intermolecular attractive forces, and predict the predomi-nant forces responsible for the physical properties of a given substance.

What determines whether a substance is a gas, a liquid, or a solid at a given temperature? Why does rubbing alcohol evaporate much more readily than water? Why do molecular compounds have lower melting points than ionic compounds? To answer these and a great many other such questions, we need to look into the nature of **intermolecular forces**—the forces that act *between different molecules* rather than within an individual molecule.

In gases, the intermolecular forces are negligible, so the gas molecules act independently of one another. In liquids and solids, however, intermolecular forces are strong enough to hold the molecules in close contact. As a general rule, the stronger the intermolecular forces in a substance, the more difficult it is to separate the molecules, and the higher the melting and boiling points of the substance.

There are three major types of intermolecular forces: *London dispersion, dipole–dipole,* and *hydrogen bonding.* Collectively, these attractive forces are also known as **van der Waals forces,** and we will discuss each in turn.

> **Intermolecular forces** Forces that act between molecules or discrete atoms and hold them close to one another. Also called **van der Waals forces**.

London Dispersion Forces

All molecules, regardless of structure, experience *London dispersion forces.* **London dispersion forces** are caused by the constant motion of electrons within molecules. Take even a simple nonpolar molecule like Br_2, for example. Averaged over time, the distribution of electrons throughout the molecule is uniform, but at any given *instant* there may be more electrons at one end of the molecule than at the other (Figure 8.3). At that instant, the molecule has a short-lived polarity. Electrons in neighboring molecules are attracted to the positive end of the polarized molecule, resulting in a polarization of the neighbor and creation of an attractive London dispersion force that holds the molecules together. As a result, Br_2 is a liquid at room temperature rather than a gas.

> **London dispersion force** The short-lived attractive force due to the constant motion of electrons within molecules.

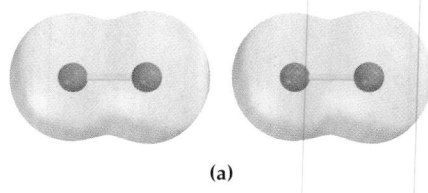

(a)

$\delta-$ $\delta+$ $\delta-$ $\delta+$

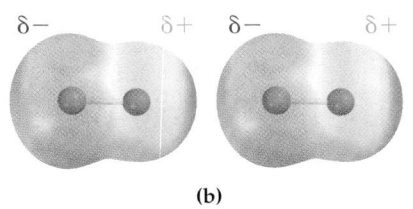

(b)

> ◄ **Figure 8.3**
> (a) Averaged over time, the electron distribution in a Br_2 molecule is symmetrical. (b) At any given instant, however, the electron distribution may be unsymmetrical, resulting in a temporary polarity that induces a complementary polarity in neighboring molecules.

London dispersion forces are the only intermolecular force available to nonpolar molecules; they are relatively weak—in the range 0.5–2.5 kcal/mol (2–10 kJ/mol)—but they increase with molecular weight and amount of surface area available for interaction between molecules. The larger the molecular weight, the more electrons there are moving about and the greater the temporary polarization of a molecule. The larger the amount of surface contact, the greater the close interaction between different molecules.

The effect of surface area on the magnitude of London dispersion forces can be seen by comparing a roughly spherical molecule with a flatter, more linear one having the same molecular weight. Both 2,2-dimethylpropane and pentane, for instance, have the same formula (C_5H_{12}), but the nearly spherical shape of 2,2-dimethylpropane allows for less surface contact with neighboring molecules than does the more linear shape of pentane (Figure 8.4). As a result, London dispersion forces are smaller for 2,2-dimethylpropane, molecules are held together less tightly, and the boiling point is correspondingly lower: 9.5 °C for 2,2-dimethylpropane versus 36 °C for pentane.

Dipole–Dipole Forces

Many molecules contain polar covalent bonds and may therefore have a permanent net molecular polarity. In such cases, the positive and negative ends of different molecules are attracted to one another by what is called a **dipole–dipole force** (Figure 8.5).

> **Dipole–dipole force** The attractive force between positive and negative ends of polar molecules.

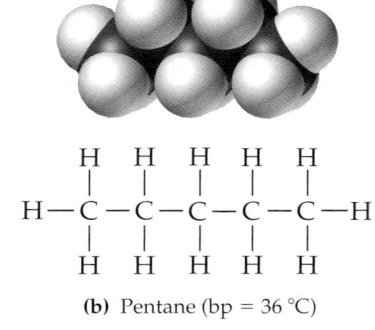

(a) 2,2-Dimethylpropane (bp = 9.5 °C)

(b) Pentane (bp = 36 °C)

▲ Figure 8.4
London dispersion forces.
More compact molecules like 2,2-dimethylpropane have smaller surface areas, weaker London dispersion forces, and lower boiling points. By comparison, flatter, less compact molecules like pentane have larger surface areas, stronger London dispersion forces, and higher boiling points.

▲ **Figure 8.5**
Dipole–dipole forces.
The positive and negative ends of polar molecules are attracted to one another by dipole–dipole forces. As a result, polar molecules have higher boiling points than nonpolar molecules of similar size.

◀◀ Recall from Sections 4.9 and 4.10 that a polar covalent bond is one in which the electrons are attracted more strongly by one atom than by the other.

◀◀ Recall from Section 4.9 how molecular polarities can be visualized using electrostatic potential maps.

Dipole–dipole forces are typically stronger than London dispersion forces, with average strengths on the order of 1 kcal/mol (4 kJ/mol). Although still significantly weaker than covalent bonds, which have bond strengths on the order of 70–100 kcal/mol (300–400 kJ/mol, see Table 7.1), the effects of dipole–dipole forces are, nevertheless, important. This is demonstrated by observing the difference in boiling points between polar and nonpolar molecules. Butane, for instance, is a nonpolar molecule with a molecular weight of 58 amu and a boiling point of −0.5 °C, whereas acetone has the same molecular weight yet boils 57 °C higher because it is polar.

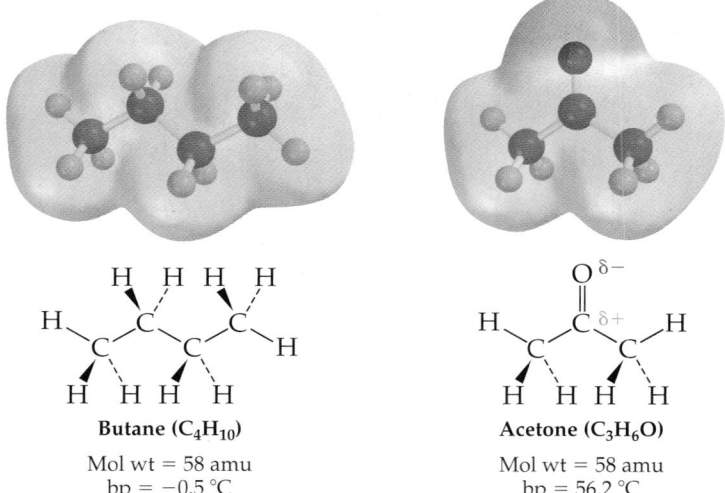

Butane (C_4H_{10})
Mol wt = 58 amu
bp = −0.5 °C

Acetone (C_3H_6O)
Mol wt = 58 amu
bp = 56.2 °C

Hydrogen Bonds

In many ways, hydrogen bonding is responsible for life on earth. It causes water to be a liquid rather than a gas at ordinary temperatures, and it is the primary intermolecular force that holds huge biomolecules in the shapes needed to play their essential roles in biochemistry. Deoxyribonucleic acid (DNA) and keratin (Figure 8.6), for instance, are long molecular chains that form an α-helix, held in place largely due to hydrogen bonding.

A **hydrogen bond** is an attractive interaction between an H-bond acceptor (an electronegative O or N atom having unshared electron pairs) and an H-bond donor (a positively polarized hydrogen atom bonded to another electronegative atom (N, O, or F). For example, hydrogen bonds occur in both water and ammonia (see example at top of next page).

Hydrogen bond The attraction between a hydrogen atom bonded to an electronegative atom (N, O, or F) and another nearby electronegative N or O atom. While O and N atoms bonded to C can act as H-bond acceptors, F atoms bonded to C rarely act as H-bond acceptors.

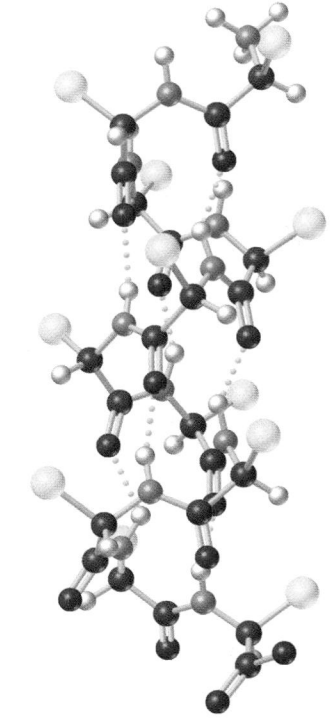

Hydrogen bonding is really just a special kind of dipole–dipole interaction. The O—H, N—H, and F—H bonds are highly polar, with a partial positive charge on the hydrogen and a partial negative charge on the electronegative atom. In addition, the hydrogen atom has no inner-shell electrons to act as a shield around its nucleus, and it is small, so it can be approached closely. As a result, the dipole–dipole attractions involving positively polarized hydrogens are unusually strong, and hydrogen bonds result. Water, in particular, is able to form a vast three-dimensional network of hydrogen bonds because each H_2O molecule has two hydrogens and two electron pairs (Figure 8.7).

▲ Figure 8.7
Hydrogen bonding in water.
The intermolecular attraction in water is especially strong because each oxygen atom has two lone pairs and two hydrogen atoms, allowing the formation of as many as four hydrogen bonds per molecule. Individual hydrogen bonds are constantly being formed and broken.

Hydrogen bonds can be quite strong, with energies up to 10 kcal/mol (40 kJ/mol). To see the effect of hydrogen bonding, look at Table 8.1, which compares the boiling

Table 8.1 Boiling Points for Binary Hydrogen Compounds of Some Second-Row and Third-Row Elements

Compound	bp (C)
CH_4	−161.5
NH_3	−33.3
H_2O	100.0
HF	19.5
SiH_4	−111.9
PH_3	−87.7
H_2S	−59.6
HCl	−84.2

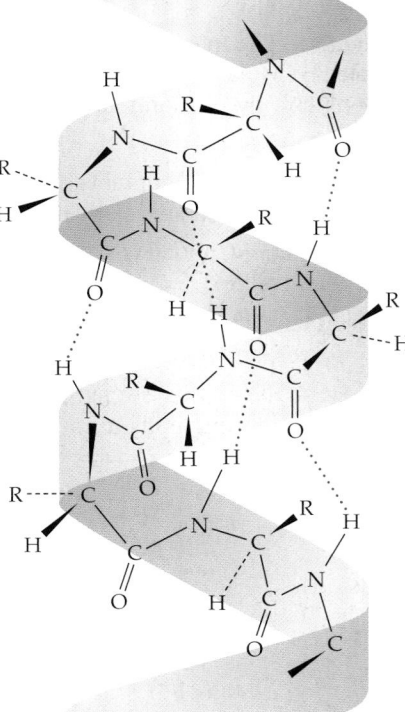

▲ Figure 8.6
The α-helical structure of keratin results from hydrogen bonding along the amino acid backbone of the molecule. Hydrogen bonding is represented by gray dots in the ball-and-stick model on the left and red dots in the molecular structure on the right.

points of binary hydrogen compounds of second-row elements with their third-row counterparts. Because NH_3, H_2O, and HF molecules are held tightly together by hydrogen bonds, an unusually large amount of energy must be added to separate them in the boiling process. As a result, the boiling points of NH_3, H_2O, and HF are much higher than the boiling points of their second-row neighbor CH_4 and of related third-row compounds.

A summary and comparison of the various kinds of intermolecular forces are shown in Table 8.2.

LOOKING AHEAD ➤ Dipole–dipole forces, London dispersion forces, and hydrogen bonds are traditionally called "intermolecular forces" because of their influence on the properties of molecular compounds. But these same forces can also operate between different parts of a very large molecule. In this context, they are often referred to as "noncovalent interactions." In later chapters, we will see how noncovalent interactions determine the shapes of biologically important molecules such as proteins and nucleic acids.

Table 8.2 A Comparison of Intermolecular Forces

	Strength	Characteristics
London dispersion	Weak (0.5–2.5 kcal/mol, 2–10 kJ/mol)	Occurs between all molecules; strength depends on size
Dipole–dipole	Weak (1 kcal/mol, 4 kJ/mol)	Occurs between polar molecules
Hydrogen bond	Moderate (2–10 kcal/mol, 8–40 kJ/mol)	Occurs between molecules with O—H, N—H, and/or F—H bonds

 Worked Example 8.1 Identifying Intermolecular Forces: Polar vs. Nonpolar

Identify the intermolecular forces that influence the properties of the following compounds. Based on your answers, arrange the three molecules in order of increasing boiling point.
 (a) Methane, CH_4 **(b)** HCl   **(c)** CH_3COOH

ANALYSIS The intermolecular forces will depend on the molecular structure, what type of bonds are in the molecule (polar or non-polar), and how the bonds are arranged. The boiling point will depend on the relative strength of the predominant intermolecular forces for each compound.

SOLUTION
 (a) Since methane contains only C—H bonds, it is a nonpolar molecule; it has only London dispersion forces, which are relatively weak since methane is a small molecule.

 (b) The H—Cl bond is polar, so this is a polar molecule; it has both dipole–dipole forces and London dispersion forces.

 (c) Acetic acid is a polar molecule with an O—H bond. Thus, it has dipole–dipole forces, London dispersion forces, and hydrogen bonds.

Based on the relative strengths of the predominant intermolecular forces for each compound, we would expect the boiling point to increase from $CH_4 < HCl < CH_3COOH$.

PROBLEM 8.2

Would you expect the boiling points to increase or decrease in the following series? Explain.
 (a) Kr, Ar, Ne   **(b)** Cl_2, Br_2, I_2

PROBLEM 8.3

Which of the following compounds form hydrogen bonds?

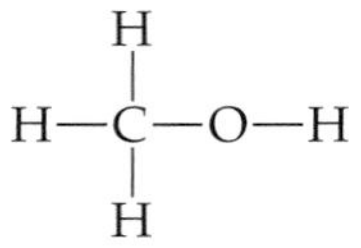

Methyl alcohol
(a)

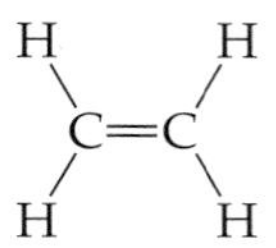

Ethylene
(b)

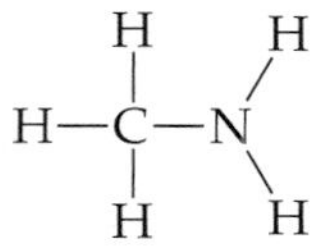

Methylamine
(c)

PROBLEM 8.4

Identify the intermolecular forces (dipole–dipole, London dispersion, hydrogen bonding) that influence the properties of the following compounds:

(a) Ethane, CH_3CH_3

(b) Ethyl alcohol, CH_3CH_2OH

(c) Ethyl chloride, CH_3CH_2Cl

8.3 Gases and the Kinetic–Molecular Theory

Learning Objective:

• Use the kinetic–molecular theory to explain the behavior of gases.

Gases behave quite differently from liquids and solids. Gases, for instance, have low densities and are easily compressed to a smaller volume when placed under pressure, a property that allows them to be stored in large tanks. Liquids and solids, by contrast, are much more dense and much less compressible. Furthermore, gases undergo a far larger expansion or contraction when their temperature is changed than do liquids and solids.

The behavior of gases can be explained by a group of assumptions known as the **kinetic–molecular theory of gases.** We will see in the next several sections how the following assumptions account for the observable properties of gases:

Kinetic–molecular theory of gases A group of assumptions that explain the behavior of gases.

• **A gas consists of many particles, either atoms or molecules, moving about at random with no attractive forces between them.** Because of this random motion, different gases mix together quickly.

• **The amount of space occupied by the gas particles themselves is much smaller than the amount of space between particles.** Most of the volume taken up by gases is empty space, accounting for the ease of compression and low densities of gases.

• **The average kinetic energy of gas particles is proportional to the Kelvin temperature.** Thus, gas particles have more kinetic energy and move faster as the temperature increases. (In fact, gas particles move much faster than you might suspect. The average speed of a helium atom at room temperature and atmospheric pressure is approximately 1.36 km/s, or 3000 mi/h, nearly that of a rifle bullet.)

• **Collisions of gas particles, either with other particles or with the wall of their container, are elastic; that is, no energy is lost during collisions so the total kinetic energy of the particles is constant.** The pressure of a gas against the walls of its container is the result of collisions of the gas particles with the walls. The more collisions and the more forceful each collision, the higher the pressure.

A gas that obeys all the assumptions of the kinetic–molecular theory is called an **ideal gas.** In practice, though, there is no such thing as a perfectly ideal gas. All gases behave somewhat differently than predicted when, at very high pressures or very low temperatures, their particles get closer together and interactions between particles become significant. As a rule, however, most real gases display nearly ideal behavior under normal conditions.

Ideal gas A gas that obeys all the assumptions of the kinetic–molecular theory.

8.4 Pressure

Learning Objective:

• Define pressure, and convert between units of pressure.

We are all familiar with the effects of air pressure. When you fly in an airplane, the change in air pressure against your eardrums as the plane climbs or descends can cause a painful "popping." When you pump up a bicycle tire, you increase the pressure of air against the inside walls of the tire until the tire feels hard.

In scientific terms, **pressure (P)** is defined as a force *(F)* per unit area *(A)* pushing against a surface; that is, $P = F/A$. In the bicycle tire, for example, the pressure you feel is the force of air molecules colliding with the inside walls of the tire. The units

Pressure (P) The force per unit area pushing against a surface.

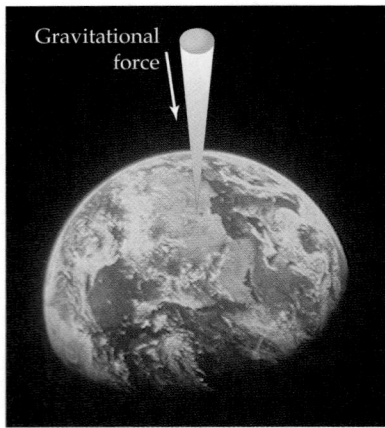

▲ **Figure 8.8**
Atmospheric pressure.
A column of air weighing 14.7 lb presses down on each square inch of Earth's surface at sea level, resulting in what we call atmospheric pressure.

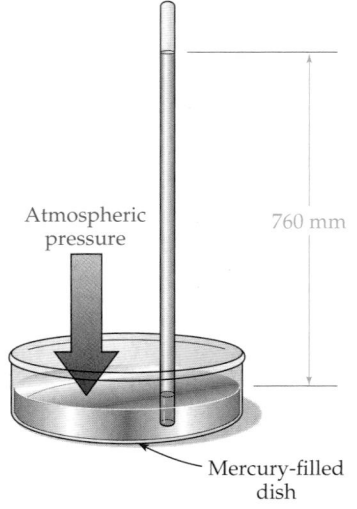

▲ **Figure 8.9**
Measuring atmospheric pressure.
A mercury barometer measures atmospheric pressure by determining the height of a mercury column in a sealed glass tube. The downward pressure of the mercury in the column is exactly balanced by the outside atmospheric pressure, which presses down on the mercury in the dish and pushes it up into the column.

you probably use for tire pressure are pounds per square inch (psi), where 1 psi is equal to the pressure exerted by a 1-pound object resting on a 1-square inch surface.

On Earth, we are under pressure from the atmosphere, the blanket of air pressing down on us (Figure 8.8). Atmospheric pressure is not constant, however; it varies slightly from day to day depending on the weather, and it also varies with altitude. Due to gravitational forces, the density of air is greatest at the earth's surface and decreases with increasing altitude. As a result, air pressure is greatest at the surface: It is about 14.7 psi at sea level but only about 4.7 psi on the summit of Mt. Everest.

One of the most commonly used units of pressure is the *millimeter of mercury,* abbreviated *mmHg* and often called a *torr* (after the Italian physicist Evangelista Torricelli). This unusual unit dates back to the early 1600s when Torricelli made the first mercury *barometer.* As shown in Figure 8.9, a barometer consists of a long, thin tube that is sealed at one end, filled with mercury, and then inverted into a dish of mercury. Some mercury runs from the tube into the dish until the downward pressure of the mercury in the column is exactly balanced by the outside atmospheric pressure, which presses down on the mercury in the dish and pushes it up into the column. The height of the mercury column varies depending on the altitude and weather conditions, but standard atmospheric pressure at sea level is defined to be exactly 760 mm.

Gas pressure inside a container is often measured using an open-ended *manometer,* a simple instrument similar in principle to the mercury barometer. As shown in Figure 8.10, an open-ended manometer consists of a U-tube filled with mercury, with one end connected to a gas-filled container and the other end open to the atmosphere. The difference between the heights of the mercury levels in the two arms of the U-tube indicates the difference between the pressure of the gas in the container and the pressure of the atmosphere. If the gas pressure inside the container is less than atmospheric pressure, the mercury level is higher in the arm connected to the container (Figure 8.10a). If the gas pressure inside the container is greater than atmospheric, the mercury level is higher in the arm open to the atmosphere (Figure 8.10b).

In the Systéme International (SI) system, (Section 2.1) the unit for pressure is named the *pascal* (Pa), where 1 Pa = 0.007500 mmHg (or 1 mmHg = 133.32 Pa). Measurements in pascals are becoming more common, and many clinical laboratories have made the switchover. Higher pressures are often still given in *atmospheres* (atm), where 1 atm = 760 mmHg exactly.

$$\text{Pressure units: } 1 \text{ atm} = 760 \text{ mmHg} = 14.7 \text{ psi} = 101,325 \text{ Pa}$$
$$1 \text{ mmHg} = 1 \text{ torr} = 133.32 \text{ Pa}$$

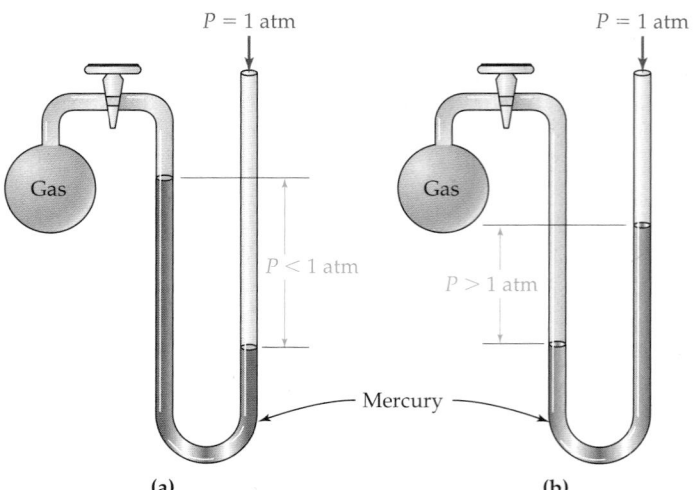

▲ **Figure 8.10**
 Open-ended manometers for measuring pressure in a gas-filled bulb.
(a) When the pressure in the gas-filled container is lower than atmospheric pressure, the mercury level is higher in the arm open to the container. (b) When the pressure in the container is higher than atmospheric pressure, the mercury level is higher in the arm open to the atmosphere.

Worked Example 8.2 Unit Conversions (Pressure): psi, Atmospheres, and Pascals

A typical bicycle tire is inflated with air to a pressure of 55 psi. How many atmospheres is this? How many pascals?

ANALYSIS Using the starting pressure in psi, the pressure in atmospheres and pascals can be calculated using the equivalent values in appropriate units as conversion factors.

SOLUTION

STEP 1: Identify known information.

Pressure = 55 psi

STEP 2: Identify answer and units.

Pressure = ?? atm = ?? pascals

STEP 3: Identify conversion factors. Using equivalent values in appropriate units, we can obtain conversion factors to convert to atmospheres and pascals.

$$14.7 \text{ psi} = 1 \text{ atm} \rightarrow \frac{1 \text{ atm}}{14.7 \text{ psi}}$$

$$14.7 \text{ psi} = 101{,}325 \text{ Pa} \rightarrow \frac{101{,}325 \text{ Pa}}{14.7 \text{ psi}}$$

STEP 4: Solve. Use the appropriate conversion factors to set up an equation in which unwanted units cancel.

$$(55 \text{ psi}) \times \left(\frac{1 \text{ atm}}{14.7 \text{ psi}} \right) = 3.7 \text{ atm}$$

$$(55 \text{ psi}) \times \left(\frac{101{,}325 \text{ Pa}}{14.7 \text{ psi}} \right) = 3.8 \times 10^5 \text{ Pa}$$

Worked Example 8.3 Unit Conversions (Pressure): mmHg to Atmospheres

The pressure in a closed flask is measured using a manometer. If the mercury level in the arm open to the sealed vessel is 23.6 cm higher than the level of mercury in the arm open to the atmosphere, what is the gas pressure (in atm) in the closed flask?

ANALYSIS Since the mercury level is higher in the arm open to the flask, the gas pressure in the flask is lower than atmospheric pressure (1 atm = 760 mmHg). We can convert the difference in the level of mercury in the two arms of the manometer from mmHg to atmospheres to determine the difference in pressure.

BALLPARK ESTIMATE The height difference (23.6 cm) is about one-third the height of a column of Hg that is equal to 1 atm (or 76 cmHg). Therefore, the pressure in the flask should be about 0.33 atm lower than atmospheric pressure, or about 0.67 atm.

SOLUTION
Since the height difference is given in cmHg, we must first convert to mmHg, and then to atmospheres. The result is the difference in gas pressure between the flask and the open atmosphere (1 atm).

$$(23.6 \text{ cmHg}) \left(\frac{10 \text{ mmHg}}{\text{cmHg}} \right) \left(\frac{1 \text{ atm}}{760 \text{ mmHg}} \right) = 0.311 \text{ atm}$$

The pressure in the flask is calculated by subtracting this difference from 1 atm:

$$1 \text{ atm} - 0.311 \text{ atm} = 0.689 \text{ atm}$$

BALLPARK CHECK This result agrees well with our estimate of 0.67 atm.

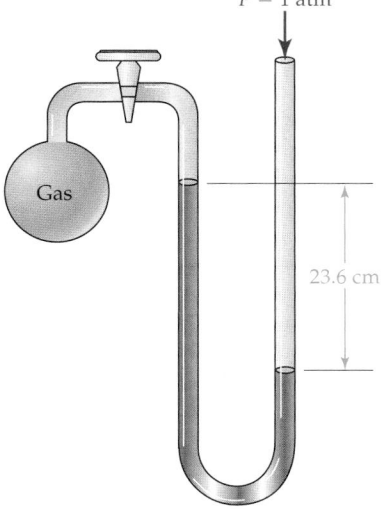

PROBLEM 8.5

The air pressure outside a jet airliner flying at 35,000 ft is about 0.289 atm. Convert this pressure to mmHg, psi, and pascals.

PROBLEM 8.6

A typical automobile tire is inflated with air to a pressure of 32 psi. Convert this pressure to atm, mmHg, and pascals.

CHEMISTRY IN ACTION

✚ Greenhouse Gases and Global Warming

The mantle of gases surrounding the earth is far from the uniform mixture you might expect, consisting of layers that vary in composition and properties at different altitudes. The ability of the gases in these layers to absorb radiation is responsible for life on earth as we know it.

The *stratosphere*—the layer extending from about 12 km up to 50 km altitude—contains the ozone layer that is responsible for absorbing harmful ultraviolet (UV) radiation. The greenhouse effect refers to the warming that occurs in the *troposphere*, the layer extending from the surface of Earth up to about 12 km altitude, as gases absorb radiant energy. Much of the radiant energy reaching Earth's surface from the sun is reflected back into space, but some is absorbed by atmospheric gases, particularly those referred to as *greenhouse gases* (GHGs)—water vapor, carbon dioxide, and methane. This absorbed radiation warms the atmosphere and acts to maintain a relatively stable temperature of 15 °C (59 °F) at Earth's surface. Without the greenhouse effect, the average surface temperature would be about −18 °C (0 °F)—a temperature so low that Earth would be frozen and unable to sustain life.

The basis for concern about the greenhouse effect is the fear that human activities over the past century have disturbed Earth's delicate thermal balance. Should increasing amounts of radiation be absorbed, increased atmospheric heating will result, and global temperatures will continue to rise.

Measurements show that the concentration of atmospheric CO_2 has been rising in the past 150 years, from an estimated 290 parts per million (ppm) in 1850 to current levels approaching 400 ppm. The increase in CO_2 levels is largely because of the increased burning of fossil fuels and correlates with a concurrent increase in average global temperatures. The latest Assessment Report of the Intergovernmental Panel on Climate Change (IPCC) (AR5) approved at the 40th session of the IPCC in November 2014 concluded that "[W]arming of the climate system is unequivocal, and since the 1950s, many of the observed changes are unprecedented over decades to millennia. The atmosphere and ocean have warmed, the amounts of snow and ice have diminished, and sea levels have risen." With regard to future risks and impacts, they concluded, "Continued emission of greenhouse gases will cause further warming and long-lasting changes in all components of the climate system, increasing the likelihood of severe, pervasive, and irreversible impacts for people and ecosystems."[1] Increased international concerns about the political and economic impacts of global climate change prompted development of the Kyoto Protocol to the United Nations Framework Convention on Climate Change (UNFCCC). Under the protocol, countries commit to a reduction in the production and emission of GHGs, including CO_2, methane, and chlorofluorocarbons (CFCs). To date, however, many signatories to the original agreement have failed to reach their emission reduction targets due to economic and political pressures.

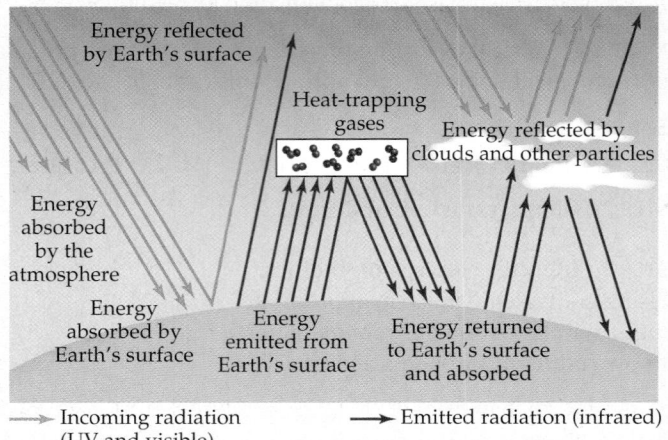

▲ GHGs trap heat reflected from the earth's surface, resulting in the increase in surface temperatures known as global warming.

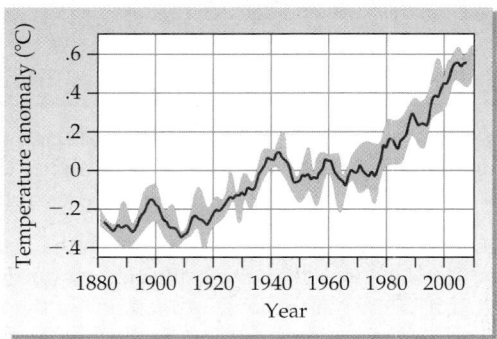

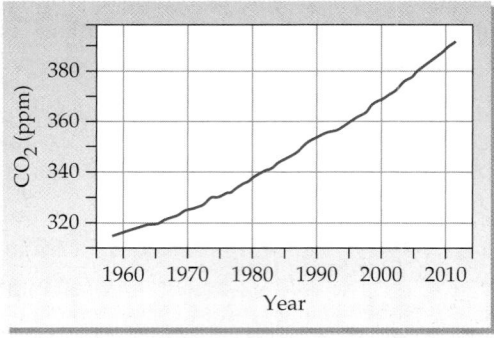

▲ Concentrations of atmospheric CO_2 and global average temperatures have increased dramatically in the past 150 years because of increased fossil fuel use, causing serious changes in Earth's climate system.

However, environmental concerns have resulted in market pressures to develop sustainable and renewable energy sources as well as more efficient technologies, such as hybrid electric vehicles.

CIA Problem 8.1 What evidence is there that global warming is occurring

CIA Problem 8.2 What are the three most important GHGs?

---

[1]*IPCC, 2014: Climate Change 2014: Synthesis Report. Contribution of Working Groups I, II, and III to the Fifth Assessment Report of the Intergovernmental Panel on Climate Change [Core Writing Team, R.K. Pachauri and L.A. Meyer (eds.)]. IPCC, Geneva, Switzerland, pp. 151.*

PROBLEM 8.7

A local weather station reports the barometric pressure as 29.5 inHg (inches of Hg). Convert this pressure to torr and to atm.

KEY CONCEPT PROBLEM 8.8 ————————————————

Using the image in the margin, what is the pressure of the gas inside the following manometer (in mmHg) if outside pressure is 750 mmHg?

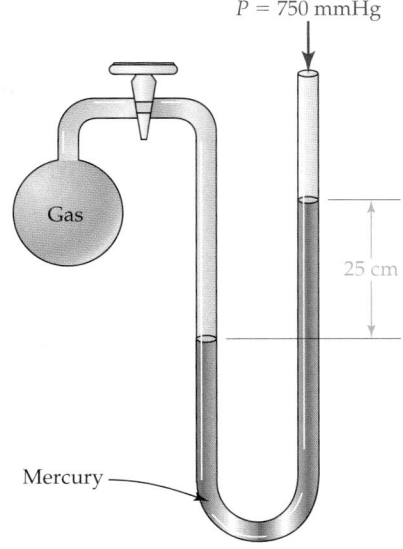

8.5 Boyle's Law: The Relation between Volume and Pressure

Learning Objective:

• Use Boyle's law to calculate the changes in pressure or volume of a gas at a given temperature.

The physical behavior of all gases is much the same, regardless of identity. Helium and chlorine, for example, are completely different in their *chemical* behavior but are very similar in many of their physical properties. Observations of many different gases by scientists in the 1700s led to the formulation of the **gas laws,** which make it possible to predict the influence of pressure *(P),* volume *(V),* temperature *(T),* and molar amount *(n)* on any gas or mixture of gases. We will begin by looking at *Boyle's law,* which describes the relation between volume and pressure.

Imagine that you have a sample of gas inside a cylinder that has a movable plunger at one end (Figure 8.11). What happens if you double the pressure on the gas by pushing the plunger down, while keeping the temperature constant? Since the gas particles are forced closer together, the volume of the sample decreases.

Gas laws A series of laws that predict the influence of pressure *(P),* volume *(V),* and temperature *(T)* on any gas or mixture of gases.

▶ **Figure 8.11**
Boyle's law.
The volume of a gas decreases proportionately as its pressure increases. For example, if the pressure of a gas sample is doubled, the volume is halved.

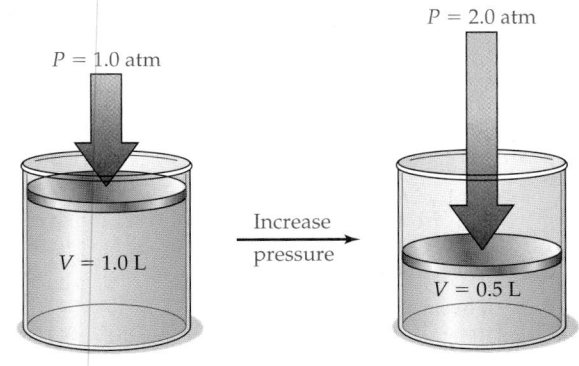

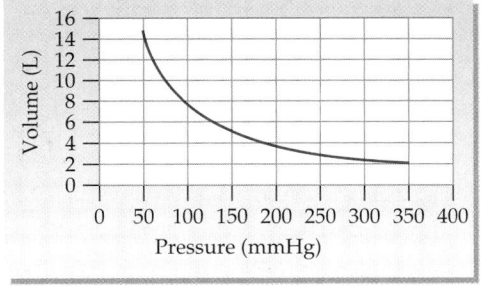

(a)

According to **Boyle's law,** the volume of a fixed amount of gas at a constant temperature is inversely proportional to its pressure, meaning that volume and pressure change in opposite directions. As pressure goes up, volume goes down; as pressure goes down, volume goes up (Figure 8.12). This observation is consistent with the kinetic–molecular theory. Since most of the volume occupied by gases is empty space, gases are easily compressed into smaller volumes. Since the average kinetic energy remains constant, the number of collisions must increase as the interior surface area of the container decreases, leading to an increase in pressure.

Boyle's law The volume of a gas is inversely proportional to its pressure for a fixed amount of gas at a constant temperature. That is, *P* times *V* is constant when the amount of gas *n* and the temperature *T* are kept constant. (The symbol $\propto$ means "is proportional to," and *k* denotes a constant value.)

$$\text{Volume } (V) \propto \frac{1}{\text{Pressure } (P)}$$

$$\text{or} \quad PV = k \quad (\text{A constant value})$$

Because $P \times V$ is a constant value for a fixed amount of gas at a constant temperature, the starting pressure (P_1) times the starting volume (V_1) must equal the

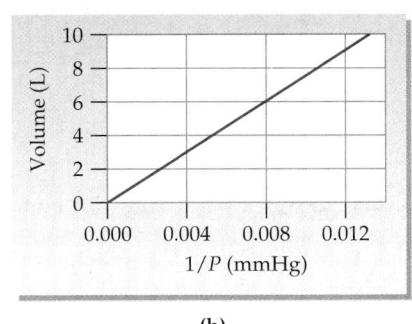

(b)

▲ **Figure 8.12**
Boyle's law.
Pressure and volume are inversely related. Graph (a) demonstrates the decrease in volume as pressure increases, whereas graph (b) shows the linear relationship between *V* and $1/P$.

final pressure (P_2) times the final volume (V_2). Thus, Boyle's law can be used to find the final pressure or volume when the starting pressure or volume is changed.

Since $P_1V_1 = k$ and $P_2V_2 = k$

then $P_1V_1 = P_2V_2$

so $P_2 = \dfrac{P_1V_1}{V_2}$ and $V_2 = \dfrac{P_1V_1}{P_2}$

As an example of Boyle's law behavior, think about what happens every time you breathe. Between breaths, the pressure inside your lungs is equal to atmospheric pressure. When inhalation takes place, your diaphragm lowers and the rib cage expands, increasing the volume of the lungs and thereby decreasing the pressure inside them (Figure 8.13). Air must then move into the lungs to equalize their pressure with that of the atmosphere. When exhalation takes place, the diaphragm rises and the rib cage contracts, decreasing the volume of the lungs and increasing pressure inside them. Now gases move out of the lungs until pressure is again equalized with the atmosphere.

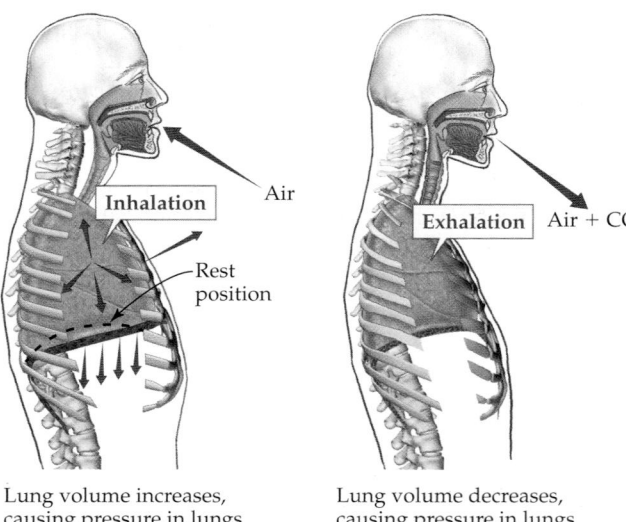

Lung volume increases, causing pressure in lungs to *decrease*. Air flows *in*.

Lung volume decreases, causing pressure in lungs to *increase*. Air flows *out*.

▲ **Figure 8.13**
Boyle's law in breathing.
During inhalation, the diaphragm moves down and the rib cage moves up and out, thus increasing lung volume, decreasing pressure, and drawing in air. During exhalation, the diaphragm moves back up, lung volume decreases, pressure increases, and air moves out.

Worked Example 8.4 Using Boyle's Law: Finding Volume at a Given Pressure

In a typical automobile engine, the fuel/air mixture in a cylinder is compressed from 1.0 atm to 9.5 atm. If the uncompressed volume of the cylinder is 750 mL, what is the volume when fully compressed?

ANALYSIS This is a Boyle's law problem because the volume and pressure in the cylinder change but the amount of gas and the temperature remain constant. According to Boyle's law, the pressure of the gas times its volume is constant:

$$P_1V_1 = P_2V_2$$

Knowing three of the four variables in this equation, we can solve for the unknown.

BALLPARK ESTIMATE Since the pressure *increases* approximately 10-fold (from 1.0 atm to 9.5 atm), the volume must *decrease* to approximately one-tenth, from 750 mL to about 75 mL.

▲ A cut-away diagram of an internal combustion engine shows movement of pistons during expansion and compression cycles.

SOLUTION

STEP 1: Identify known information. Of the four variables in Boyle's law, we know P_1, V_1, and P_2.

STEP 2: Identify answer and units.

STEP 3: Identify equation. In this case, we simply substitute the known variables into Boyle's law and rearrange to isolate the unknown.

STEP 4: Solve. Substitute the known information into the equation. Make sure units cancel so that the answer is given in the units of the unknown variable.

BALLPARK CHECK Our estimate was 75 mL.

$$P_1 = 1.0 \text{ atm}$$
$$V_1 = 750 \text{ mL}$$
$$P_2 = 9.5 \text{ atm}$$

$$V_2 = ?? \text{ mL}$$

$$P_1 V_1 = P_2 V_2 \implies V_2 = \frac{P_1 V_1}{P_2}$$

$$V_2 = \frac{P_1 V_1}{P_2} = \frac{(1.0 \text{ atm})(750 \text{ mL})}{(9.5 \text{ atm})} = 79 \text{ mL}$$

CHEMISTRY IN ACTION

✚ Blood Pressure

Having your blood pressure measured is a quick and easy way to get an indication of the state of your circulatory system. Although blood pressure varies with age, a normal adult male has a reading near 120/80 mmHg, and a normal adult female has a reading near 110/70 mmHg. Abnormally high values signal an increased risk of heart attack and stroke.

Pressure varies greatly in different types of blood vessels. Usually, though, measurements are carried out on arteries in the upper arm as the heart goes through a full cardiac cycle. *Systolic pressure* is the maximum pressure developed in the artery just after contraction, as the heart forces the maximum amount of blood into the artery. *Diastolic pressure* is the minimum pressure that occurs at the end of the heart cycle.

Blood pressure is most often measured by a *sphygmomanometer*, a device consisting of a squeeze bulb, a flexible cuff, and a mercury manometer. (1) The cuff is placed around the upper arm over the brachial artery and inflated by the squeeze bulb to about 200 mmHg pressure, an amount great enough to squeeze the artery shut and prevent blood flow. Air is then slowly released from the cuff, and pressure drops (2). As cuff pressure reaches the systolic pressure, blood spurts through the artery, creating a turbulent tapping sound that can be heard through a stethoscope. The pressure registered on the manometer at the moment the first sounds are heard is the systolic blood pressure.

(3) Sounds continue until the pressure in the cuff becomes low enough to allow diastolic blood flow. (4) At this point, blood flow becomes smooth, no sounds are heard, and a diastolic blood pressure reading is recorded on the manometer. Readings are usually recorded as systolic/diastolic, for example,

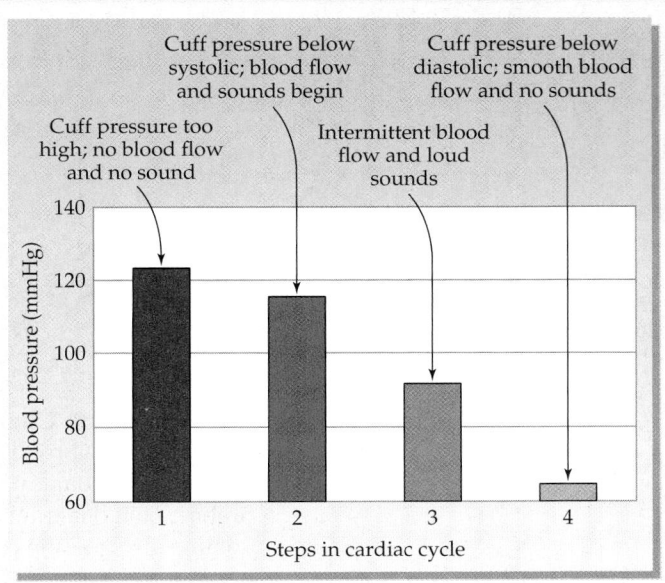

▲ The sequence of events during blood pressure measurement, including the sounds heard.

120/80. The accompanying figure shows the sequence of events during measurement.

CIA Problem 8.3 What is the difference between a systolic and a diastolic pressure reading? Is a blood pressure of 180/110 within the normal range?

CIA Problem 8.4 Convert the blood pressure reading in CIA Problem 8.3 to atm.

CIA Problem 8.5 Convert the blood pressure reading in CIA Problem 8.3 from mmHg to inHg. Now look up the ambient barometric pressure (inHg). How do they compare?

PROBLEM 8.9

An oxygen cylinder used for breathing has a volume of 5.0 L at 90 atm pressure. What is the volume of the same amount of oxygen at the same temperature if the pressure is 1.0 atm? (Hint: Would you expect the volume of gas at this pressure to be greater than or less than the volume at 90 atm?)

PROBLEM 8.10

A sample of hydrogen gas at 273 K has a volume of 3.2 L at 4.0 atm pressure. What is the volume if the pressure is increased to 10.0 atm? If the pressure is decreased to 0.70 atm?

8.6 Charles's Law: The Relation between Volume and Temperature

Learning Objective:

• Use Charles's law to calculate changes in volume of a gas as a function of temperature.

Imagine that you again have a sample of gas inside a cylinder with a plunger at one end. What happens if you double the sample's kelvin temperature while letting the plunger move freely to keep the pressure constant? The gas particles move with twice as much energy and collide twice as forcefully with the walls. To maintain a constant pressure, the volume of the gas in the cylinder must double (Figure 8.14).

▲ The volume of the gas in the balloon increases as it is heated, causing a decrease in density and allowing the balloon to rise.

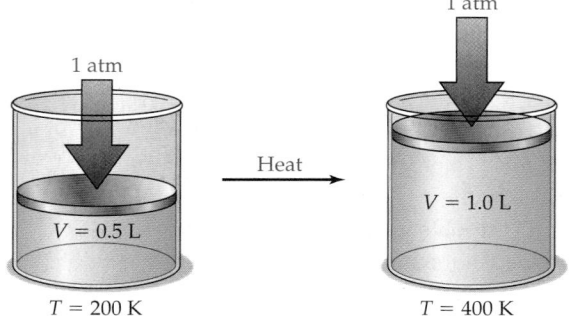

◀ **Figure 8.14**
Charles's law.
The volume of a gas is directly proportional to its kelvin temperature at constant n and P. If the kelvin temperature of the gas is doubled, its volume doubles.

According to **Charles's law,** the volume of a fixed amount of gas at constant pressure is directly proportional to its kelvin temperature. Note the difference between *directly* proportional in Charles's law and *inversely* proportional in Boyle's law. Directly proportional quantities change in the same direction—as temperature goes up or down, volume also goes up or down (Figure 8.15).

Charles's law The volume of a gas is directly proportional to its kelvin temperature for a fixed amount of gas at a constant pressure. That is, V divided by T is constant when n and P are held constant.

$$V \propto T \quad (\text{In kelvins})$$

$$\text{or } \frac{V}{T} = k \quad (\text{A constant value})$$

$$\text{or } \frac{V_1}{T_1} = \frac{V_2}{T_2}$$

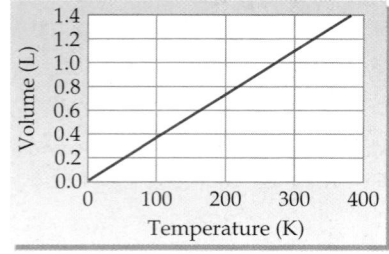

▲ **Figure 8.15**
Charles's law.
Volume is directly proportional to the kelvin temperature for a fixed amount of gas at a constant pressure. As the temperature goes up, the volume also goes up.

This observation is consistent with the kinetic–molecular theory. As temperature increases, the average kinetic energy of the gas molecules increases, as does the energy of molecular collisions with the interior surface of the container. The volume of the container must increase to maintain a constant pressure. As an example of Charles's law, think about what happens when a hot-air balloon is inflated. Heating causes the air inside to expand and fill the balloon. The air inside the balloon is less dense than the air outside the balloon, creating the buoyancy effect.

Worked Example 8.5 Using Charles's Law: Finding Volume at a Given Temperature

An average adult inhales a volume of 0.50 L of air with each breath. If the air is warmed from room temperature ($20\,°C = 293\text{ K}$) to body temperature ($37\,°C = 310\text{ K}$) while in the lungs, what is the volume of the air
exhaled?

ANALYSIS This is a Charles's law problem because the volume and temperature of the air change while the
amount and pressure remain constant. Knowing three of the four variables, we can rearrange Charles's law to
solve for the unknown.

BALLPARK ESTIMATE Charles's law predicts an increase in volume directly proportional to the increase in temperature from 273 K to 310 K. The increase of less than 20 K represents a relatively small change compared to
the initial temperature of 273 K. A 10% increase, for example, would be equal to a temperature change of
27 K; so a 20-K change would be less than 10%. We would therefore expect the volume to increase by less
than 10%, from 0.50 L to a little less than 0.55 L.

SOLUTION

STEP 1: Identify known information. Of the
four variables in Charles's law, we know T_1, V_1,
and T_2.

STEP 2: Identify answer and units.

STEP 3: Identify equation. Substitute the known
variables into Charles's law and rearrange to isolate
the unknown.

STEP 4: Solve. Substitute the known information
into Charles's law; check to make sure units cancel.

$$T_1 = 293\text{ K}$$
$$V_1 = 0.50\text{ L}$$
$$T_2 = 310\text{ K}$$

$$V_2 = ??\text{ L}$$

$$\frac{V_1}{T_1} = \frac{V_2}{T_2} \Rightarrow V_2 = \frac{V_1 T_2}{T_1}$$

$$V_2 = \frac{V_1 T_2}{T_1} = \frac{(0.50\text{ L})(310\text{ K})}{293\text{ K}} = 0.53\text{ L}$$

BALLPARK CHECK This is consistent with our estimate!

PROBLEM 8.11

A sample of chlorine gas has a volume of 0.30 L at 273 K and 1 atm pressure. What
temperature (in °C) would be required to increase the volume to 1.0 L? To decrease the
volume to 0.20 L?

HANDS-ON CHEMISTRY 8.1

Take a balloon and blow it up until it is about six inches in
diameter. Then place it in the refrigerator or freezer. After about
10 minutes, remove it from the refrigerator and estimate its diameter. How much has it changed? Now run the balloon under
hot water for a few minutes, and estimate its diameter. Explain
the changes you observed in terms of the kinetic–molecular
theory and using Charles's law. (Note: Instead of placing the
balloon in the refrigerator / freezer, it can be run under cold
water.)

8.7 Gay-Lussac's Law: The Relation between Pressure and Temperature

Learning Objective:

• Use Gay-Lussac's law to calculate changes in pressure of a gas as a function of
temperature.

Imagine next that you have a fixed amount of gas in a sealed container whose volume
remains constant. What happens if you double the temperature (in kelvins)? The gas
particles move with twice as much energy and collide with the walls of the container
with twice as much force. Thus, the pressure in the container doubles. According to

Gay-Lussac's law, the pressure of a fixed amount of gas at constant volume is directly proportional to its Kelvin temperature. As temperature goes up or down, pressure also goes up or down (Figure 8.16).

▶ **Figure 8.16**
Gay-Lussac's law.
Pressure is directly proportional to the temperature in kelvins for a fixed amount of gas: (a) At a constant volume, doubling the absolute temperature would also double the pressure; (b) the increase in pressure is directly proportional to absolute temperature.

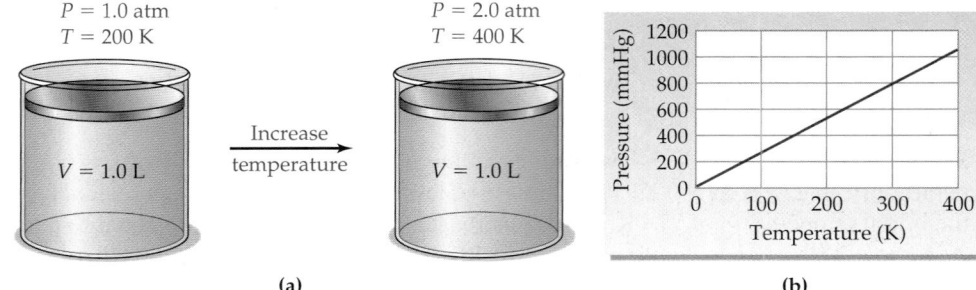

(a)   (b)

Gay-Lussac's law The pressure of a gas is directly proportional to its Kelvin temperature for a fixed amount of gas at a constant volume. That is, P divided by T is constant when n and V are held constant.

$$P \propto T \quad (\text{In kelvins})$$

$$\text{or } \frac{P}{T} = k \quad (\text{A constant value})$$

$$\text{or } \frac{P_1}{T_1} = \frac{P_2}{T_2}$$

According to the kinetic–molecular theory, the kinetic energy of molecules is directly proportional to absolute temperature. As the average kinetic energy of the molecules increases, the energy of collisions with the interior surface of the container increases, causing an increase in pressure. As an example of Gay-Lussac's law, think of what happens when an aerosol can is thrown into an incinerator. As the can gets hotter, pressure builds up inside and the can explodes (hence the warning statement on aerosol cans).

Worked Example 8.6 Using Gay-Lussac's Law: Finding Pressure at a Given Temperature

What does the inside pressure become if an aerosol can with an initial pressure of 4.5 atm is heated in a fire from room temperature (20 °C) to 600 °C?

ANALYSIS This is a Gay-Lussac's law problem because the pressure and temperature of the gas inside the can change while its amount and volume remain constant. We know three of the four variables in the equation for Gay-Lussac's law and can find the unknown by substitution and rearrangement.

BALLPARK ESTIMATE Gay-Lussac's law states that pressure is directly proportional to temperature. Since the Kelvin temperature increases approximately threefold (from about 300 K to about 900 K), we expect the pressure to also increase by approximately threefold, from 4.5 atm to about 14 atm.

SOLUTION

STEP 1: Identify known information. Of the four variables in Gay-Lussac's law, we know P_1, T_1, and T_2. (Note that T must be in kelvins.)

$P_1 = 4.5 \text{ atm}$
$T_1 = 20\,°\text{C} = 293 \text{ K}$
$T_2 = 600\,°\text{C} = 873 \text{ K}$

STEP 2: Identify answer and units.

$P_2 = \text{?? atm}$

STEP 3: Identify equation. Substituting the known variables into Gay-Lussac's law, we rearrange to isolate the unknown.

$$\frac{P_1}{T_1} = \frac{P_2}{T_2} \Rightarrow P_2 = \frac{P_1 T_2}{T_1}$$

STEP 4: Solve. Substitute the known information into Gay-Lussac's law; check to make sure units cancel.

$$P_2 = \frac{P_1 T_2}{T_1} = \frac{(4.5 \text{ atm})(873 \text{ K})}{293 \text{ K}} = 13 \text{ atm}$$

BALLPARK CHECK Our estimate was 14 atm.

PROBLEM 8.12

Driving on a hot day causes tire temperature to rise. What is the pressure inside an automobile tire at 45 °C if the tire has a pressure of 30 psi at 15 °C? Assume that the volume and amount of air in the tire remain constant.

8.8 The Combined Gas Law

Learning Objective:

- Use the combined gas law to determine changes in pressure, temperature, or volume of a gas.

Since PV, V/T, and P/T all have constant values for a fixed amount of gas, these relationships can be merged into a **combined gas law,** which holds true whenever the amount of gas is fixed.

Combined gas law $\dfrac{PV}{T} = k$ (A constant value)

$$\text{or } \frac{P_1 V_1}{T_1} = \frac{P_2 V_2}{T_2}$$

If any five of the six quantities in this equation are known, the sixth quantity can be calculated. Furthermore, if any of the three variables T, P, or V is constant, that variable drops out of the equation, leaving behind Boyle's law, Charles's law, or Gay-Lussac's law. As a result, *the combined gas law is the only equation you need to remember for a fixed amount of gas.* Worked Example 8.8 gives a sample calculation.

Since $\qquad \dfrac{P_1 V_1}{T_1} = \dfrac{P_2 V_2}{T_2}$

At constant T: $\quad \dfrac{P_1 V_1}{T} = \dfrac{P_2 V_2}{T}$ gives $P_1 V_1 = P_2 V_2$ (Boyle's law)

At constant P: $\quad \dfrac{PV_1}{T_1} = \dfrac{PV_2}{T_2}$ gives $\dfrac{V_1}{T_1} = \dfrac{V_2}{T_2}$ (Charles's law)

At constant V: $\quad \dfrac{P_1 V}{T_1} = \dfrac{P_2 V}{T_2}$ gives $\dfrac{P_1}{T_1} = \dfrac{P_2}{T_2}$ (Gay-Lussac's law)

Worked Example 8.7 Using the Combined Gas Law: Finding Temperature

A 6.3 L sample of helium gas stored at 25 °C and 1.0 atm pressure is transferred to a 2.0 L tank and maintained at a pressure of 2.8 atm. What temperature is needed to maintain this pressure?

ANALYSIS This is a combined gas law problem because pressure, volume, and temperature change while the amount of helium remains constant. Of the six variables in this equation, we know P_1, V_1, T_1, P_2, and V_2, and we need to find T_2.

BALLPARK ESTIMATE Since the volume goes down by a little more than a factor of about 3 (from 6.3 L to 2.0 L) and the pressure goes up by a little less than a factor of about 3 (from 1.0 atm to 2.8 atm), the two changes roughly offset each other, and so the temperature should not change much. Since the volume-decrease factor (3.2) is slightly greater than the pressure-increase factor (2.8), the temperature will drop slightly ($T \propto V$).

SOLUTION

STEP 1: Identify known information. Of the six variables in the combined gas law, we know P_1, V_1, T_1, P_2, and V_2 (As always, T must be converted from Celsius degrees to kelvins.)

$P_1 = 1.0$ atm, $P_2 = 2.8$ atm
$V_1 = 6.3$ L, $V_2 = 2.0$ L
$T_1 = 25\,°C = 298$ K

—continued on next page

—continued from previous page

STEP 2: Identify answer and units.

$T_2 = $?? kelvin

STEP 3: Identify the equation. Substitute the known variables into the equation for the combined gas law and rearrange to isolate the unknown.

$$\frac{P_1 V_1}{T_1} = \frac{P_2 V_2}{T_2} \Rightarrow T_2 = \frac{P_2 V_2 T_1}{P_1 V_1}$$

STEP 4: Solve. Solve the combined gas law equation for T_2, check to make sure units cancel.

$$T_2 = \frac{P_2 V_2 T_1}{P_1 V_1} = \frac{(2.8 \text{ atm})(2.0 \text{ L})(298 \text{ K})}{(1.0 \text{ atm})(6.3 \text{ L})} = 260 \text{ K} (\Delta T = 2.38\,°C)$$

BALLPARK CHECK The relatively small decrease in temperature (38 °C, or 13% compared to the original temperature) is consistent with our prediction.

PROBLEM 8.13

A weather balloon is filled with helium to a volume of 275 L at 22 °C and 752 mmHg. The balloon ascends to an altitude where the pressure is 480 mmHg and the temperature is −32 °C. What is the volume of the balloon at this altitude?

◯▭ KEY CONCEPT PROBLEM 8.14 ————————————————————

A balloon is filled under the initial conditions indicated in the following figure. If the pressure is then increased to 2 atm while the temperature is increased to 50 °C, which balloon on the right, (a) or (b), represents the new volume of the balloon?

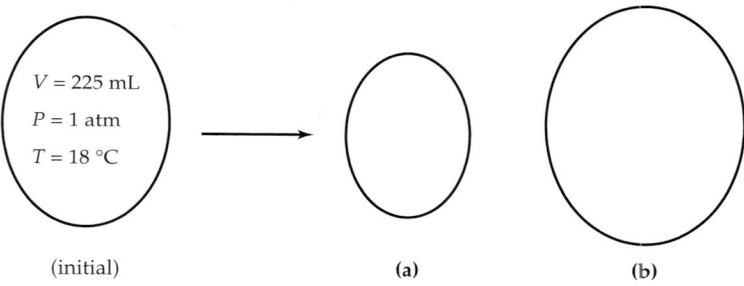

$V = 225$ mL
$P = 1$ atm
$T = 18\,°C$

(initial)   (a)   (b)

8.9 Avogadro's Law: The Relation between Volume and Molar Amount

Learning Objective:

• Use Avogadro's law to calculate the volume for a given number of moles of a gas.

Here, we look at a gas law that takes changes in amount of gas into account. Imagine that you have two different volumes of a gas at the same temperature and pressure. How many moles does each sample contain? According to **Avogadro's law,** the volume of a gas is directly proportional to its molar amount at a constant pressure and temperature (Figure 8.17). A sample that contains twice the molar amount has twice the volume.

Avogadro's law The volume of a gas is directly proportional to its molar amount at a constant pressure and temperature. That is, V divided by n is constant when P and T are held constant.

$$\text{Volume } (V) \propto \text{ Number of moles } (n)$$

or $\dfrac{V}{n} = k$ (A constant value; the same for all gases)

or $\dfrac{V_1}{n_1} = \dfrac{V_2}{n_2}$

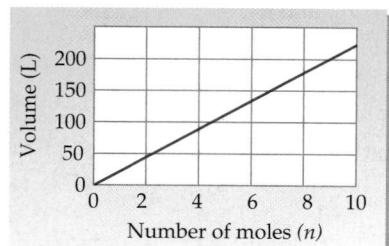

▲ **Figure 8.17**
Avogadro's law.
Volume is directly proportional to the molar amount, n, at a constant temperature and pressure. As the number of moles goes up, the volume also goes up.

Because the particles in a gas are so tiny compared to the empty space surrounding them, there is no interaction among gas particles as proposed by the kinetic–molecular theory. As a result, the chemical identity of the particles does not matter and the value of the constant k in the equation $V/n = k$ is the same for all gases. It is therefore possible to compare the molar amounts of *any* two gases simply by comparing their volumes at the same temperature and pressure.

Notice that the *values* of temperature and pressure do not matter; it is only necessary that T and P be the same for both gases. To simplify comparisons of gas samples, however, it is convenient to define a set of conditions called **standard temperature and pressure (STP),** which specifies a temperature of 0 °C (273 K) and a pressure of 1 atm (760 mmHg).

At STP, 1 mol of any gas (6.02×10^{23} particles) has a volume of 22.4 L, a quantity called the **standard molar volume** (Figure 8.18).

Standard temperature and pressure (STP) 0 °C (273.15 K); 1 atm (760 mmHg)

Standard molar volume Volume of one mole of any ideal gas at STP, 22.4 L/mol.

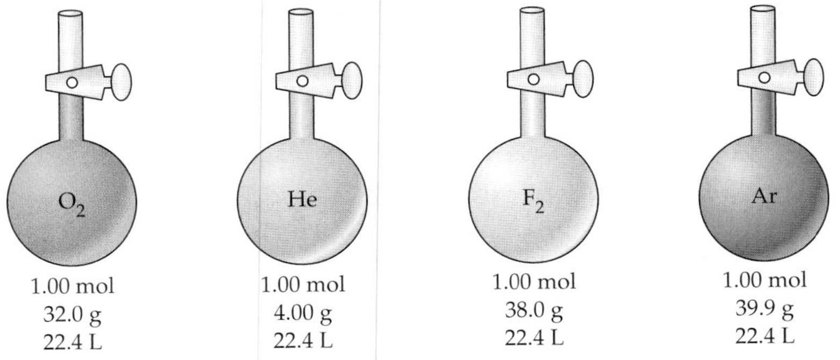

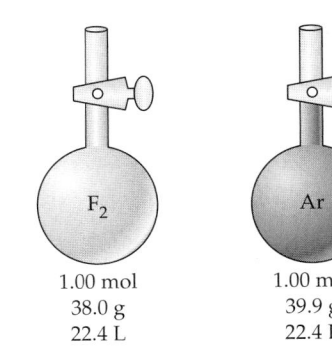

◄ **Figure 8.18**
Avogadro's law.
Each of these 22.4 L bulbs contains 1.00 mol of gas at 0 °C and 1 atm pressure. Note that the volume occupied by 1 mol of gas is the same even though the mass (in grams) of 1 mol of each gas is different.

O_2
1.00 mol
32.0 g
22.4 L

He
1.00 mol
4.00 g
22.4 L

F_2
1.00 mol
38.0 g
22.4 L

Ar
1.00 mol
39.9 g
22.4 L

Worked Example 8.8   Using Avogadro's Law: Finding Moles in a Given Volume at STP

Use the standard molar volume of a gas at STP (22.4 L) to find how many moles of air at STP are in a room measuring 4.11 m wide by 5.36 m long by 2.58 m high.

ANALYSIS We first find the volume of the room and then use standard molar volume as a conversion factor to find the number of moles.

SOLUTION

STEP 1: Identify known information. We are given the room dimensions.

Length = 5.36 m
Width = 4.11 m
Height = 2.58 m

STEP 2: Identify answer and units.

Moles of air = ?? mol

STEP 3: Identify the equation. The volume of the room is the product of its three dimensions. Once we have the volume (in m³), we can convert to liters and use the molar volume at STP as a conversion factor to obtain moles of air.

Volume = $(4.11 \text{ m})(5.36 \text{ m})(2.58 \text{ m})$ = 56.8 m³

$$= 56.8 \text{ m}^3 \times \frac{1000 \text{ L}}{1 \text{ m}^3} = 5.68 \times 10^4 \text{ L}$$

$$1 \text{ mol} = 22.4 \text{ L} \rightarrow \frac{1 \text{ mol}}{22.4 \text{ L}}$$

STEP 4: Solve. Use the room volume and the molar volume at STP to set up an equation, making sure unwanted units cancel.

$$5.68 \times 10^4 \text{ L} \times \frac{1 \text{ mol}}{22.4 \text{ L}} = 2.54 \times 10^3 \text{ mol}$$

PROBLEM 8.15

How many moles of methane gas, CH_4, are in a 1.00×10^5 L storage tank at STP? How many grams of methane is this? How many grams of carbon dioxide gas could the same tank hold?

8.10 The Ideal Gas Law

Learning Objective:

• Use the ideal gas law to calculate the pressure, temperature, volume, or number of moles of an ideal gas.

The relationships among the four variables P, V, T, and n for gases can be combined into a single expression called the **ideal gas law.** If you know the values of any three of the four quantities, you can calculate the value of the fourth.

Ideal gas law $\quad \dfrac{PV}{nT} = R \quad (\text{A constant value})$

$\quad$ or $PV = nRT$

Gas constant (R) The constant R in the ideal gas law, $PV = nRT$.

The constant R in the ideal gas law (instead of the usual k) is called the **gas constant.** Its value depends on the units chosen for pressure, with the two most common values being

For P in atmospheres: $\quad R = 0.0821 \dfrac{\text{L} \cdot \text{atm}}{\text{mol} \cdot \text{K}}$

For P in millimeters Hg: $\quad R = 62.4 \dfrac{\text{L} \cdot \text{mmHg}}{\text{mol} \cdot \text{K}}$

In using the ideal gas law, it is important to choose the value of R having pressure units that are consistent with the problem and, if necessary, to convert volume into liters and temperature into kelvins.

Table 8.3 summarizes the various gas laws, and Worked Examples 8.10 and 8.11 show how to use the ideal gas law.

Table 8.3 A Summary of the Gas Laws

	Gas Law	Variables	Constant
Boyle's law	$P_1V_1 = P_2V_2$	P, V	n, T
Charles's law	$V_1/T_1 = V_2/T_2$	V, T	n, P
Gay-Lussac's law	$P_1/T_1 = P_2/T_2$	P, T	n, V
Combined gas law	$P_1V_1/T_1 = P_2V_2/T_2$	P, V, T	n
Avogadro's law	$V_1/n_1 = V_2/n_2$	V, n	P, T
Ideal gas law	$PV = nRT$	P, V, T, n	R

Worked Example 8.9 Using the Ideal Gas Law: Finding Moles

How many moles of air are in the lungs of an average person with a total lung capacity of 3.8 L? Assume that the person is at 1.0 atm pressure and has a normal body temperature of 37 °C.

ANALYSIS This is an ideal gas law problem because it asks for a value of n when P, V, and T are known: $n = PV/RT$. The volume is given in the correct unit of liters, but temperature must be converted to kelvins.

SOLUTION

STEP 1: Identify known information. We know three of the four variables in the ideal gas law.

$P = 1.0$ atm
$V = 3.8$ L
$T = 37\,°C = 310$ K

STEP 2: Identify answer and units.

Moles of air, $n = $?? mol

STEP 3: **Identify the equation.** Knowing three of the four variables in the ideal gas law, we can rearrange and solve for the unknown variable, n. Note: Because pressure is given in atmospheres, we use the value that is expressed in atm:

$$PV = nRT \implies n = \frac{PV}{RT}$$

$$R = 0.0821 \frac{L \cdot atm}{mol \cdot K}$$

STEP 4: **Solve.** Substitute the known information and the appropriate value of R into the ideal gas law equation and solve for n.

$$n = \frac{PV}{RT} = \frac{(1.0 \text{ atm})(3.8 \text{ L})}{\left(0.0821 \dfrac{L \cdot atm}{mol \cdot K}\right)(310 \text{ K})} = 0.15 \text{ mol}$$

Worked Example 8.10   Using the Ideal Gas Law: Finding Pressure

Methane gas is sold in steel cylinders with a volume of 43.8 L containing 5.54 kg. What is the pressure in atmospheres inside the cylinder at a temperature of 20.0 °C (293.15 K)? The molar mass of methane (CH_4) is 16.0 g/mol.

ANALYSIS This is an ideal gas law problem because it asks for a value of P when V, T, and n are given. Although not provided directly, enough information is given so that we can calculate the value of n $(n = g/MW)$.

SOLUTION

STEP 1: **Identify known information.** We know two of the four variables in the ideal gas law—V and T—and can calculate the third, n, from the information provided.

$$V = 43.8 \text{ L}$$
$$T = 37 \text{ °C} = 310 \text{ K}$$

STEP 2: **Identify answer and units.**

Pressure, P = ?? atm

STEP 3: **Identify equation.** First, calculate the number of moles, n, of methane in the cylinder by using molar mass (16.0 g/mol) as a conversion factor. Then use the ideal gas law to calculate the pressure.

$$n = (5.54 \text{ kg methane})\left(\frac{1000 \text{ g}}{1 \text{ kg}}\right)\left(\frac{1 \text{ mol}}{16.0 \text{ g}}\right) = 346 \text{ mol methane}$$

$$PV = nRT \implies P = \frac{nRT}{V}$$

STEP 4: **Solve.** Substitute the known information and the appropriate value of R into the ideal gas law equation and solve for P.

$$P = \frac{nRT}{V} = \frac{(346 \text{ mol})\left(0.0821 \dfrac{L \cdot atm}{mol \cdot K}\right)(293 \text{ K})}{43.8 \text{ L}} = 190 \text{ atm}$$

PROBLEM 8.16

An aerosol spray can of deodorant with a volume of 350 mL contains 3.2 g of propane gas (C_3H_8) as propellant. What is the pressure in the can at 20 °C?

PROBLEM 8.17

A helium gas cylinder of the sort used to fill balloons has a volume of 180 L and a pressure of 2200 psi (150 atm) at 25 °C. How many moles of helium are in the tank? How many grams?

◯▣ KEY CONCEPT PROBLEM 8.18 ────────────────────

Show the approximate level of the movable piston in drawings (a) and (b) after the indicated changes have been made to the initial gas sample (assume a constant pressure of 1 atm).

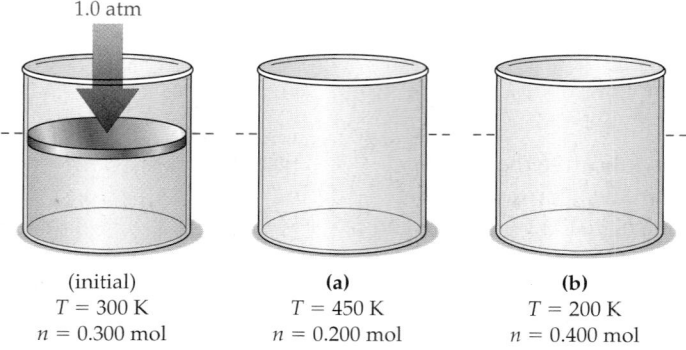

(initial)	(a)	(b)
$T = 300\ K$	$T = 450\ K$	$T = 200\ K$
$n = 0.300\ \text{mol}$	$n = 0.200\ \text{mol}$	$n = 0.400\ \text{mol}$

8.11   Partial Pressure and Dalton's Law

Learning Objective:

- Use Dalton's law to calculate the partial pressure or the number of moles of a gas in a mixture.

According to the kinetic–molecular theory, each particle in a gas acts independently of all others because there are no attractive forces between them and they are so far apart. To any individual particle, the chemical identity of its neighbors is irrelevant. Thus, *mixtures* of gases behave the same as pure gases and obey the same laws.

Dry air, for example, is a mixture of about 21% oxygen, 78% nitrogen, and 1% argon by volume, which means that 21% of atmospheric air pressure is caused by O_2 molecules, 78% by N_2 molecules, and 1% by Ar atoms. The contribution of each gas in a mixture to the total pressure of the mixture is called the **partial pressure** of that gas. According to **Dalton's law,** the total pressure exerted by a gas mixture (P_{total}) is the sum of the partial pressures of the components in the mixture.

Dalton's law: $P_{total} = P_{gas\ 1} + P_{gas\ 2} + P_{gas\ 3}$

In dry air at a total air pressure of 760 mmHg, the partial pressure caused by the contribution of O_2 is $0.21 \times 760\ \text{mmHg} = 160\ \text{mmHg}$, the partial pressure of N_2 is $0.78 \times 760\ \text{mmHg} = 593\ \text{mmHg}$, and that of argon is 7 mmHg. *The partial pressure exerted by each gas in a mixture is the same pressure that the gas would exert if it were alone.* Put another way, the pressure exerted by each gas depends on the frequency of collisions of its molecules with the walls of the container. However, this frequency does not change when other gases are present because the different molecules have no influence on one another.

To represent the partial pressure of a specific gas, we add the formula of the gas as a subscript to P, the symbol for pressure. You might see the partial pressure of oxygen represented as P_{O_2}, for instance. Moist air inside the lungs at 37 °C and atmospheric pressure has the following average composition at sea level. Note that P_{total} is equal to atmospheric pressure, 760 mmHg.

$$P_{total} = P_{N_2} + P_{O_2} + P_{CO_2} + P_{H_2O}$$
$$= 573\ \text{mmHg} + 100\ \text{mmHg} + 40\ \text{mmHg} + 47\ \text{mmHg}$$
$$= 760\ \text{mmHg}$$

The composition of air does not change appreciably with altitude, but the total pressure decreases rapidly. The partial pressure of oxygen in air therefore decreases with increasing altitude, and it is this change that leads to difficulty in breathing at high elevations.

Partial pressure The contribution of a given gas in a mixture to the total pressure.

Worked Example 8.11 Using Dalton's Law: Finding Partial Pressures

Humid air on a warm summer day is approximately 20% oxygen, 75% nitrogen, 4% water vapor, and 1% argon. What is the partial pressure of each component if the atmospheric pressure is 750 mmHg?

ANALYSIS According to Dalton's law, the partial pressure of any gas in a mixture is equal to the percent concentration of the gas times the total gas pressure (750 mmHg). In this case,

$$P_{total} = P_{O_2} + P_{N_2} + P_{H_2O} + P_{Ar}$$

SOLUTION

Oxygen partial pressure (P_{O_2}): $\quad 0.20 \times 750\ \text{mmHg} = 150\ \text{mmHg}$
Nitrogen partial pressure (P_{N_2}): $\quad 0.75 \times 750\ \text{mmHg} = 560\ \text{mmHg}$
Water vapor partial pressure (P_{H_2O}): $\quad 0.04 \times 750\ \text{mmHg} = 30\ \text{mmHg}$
Argon partial pressure (P_{Ar}): $\quad 0.01 \times 750\ \text{mmHg} = 8\ \text{mmHg}$
Total pressure $= 748\ \text{mmHg} \longrightarrow 750\ \text{mmHg}$ (rounding to two significant figures!)

Note that the sum of the partial pressures must equal the total pressure (within rounding error).

PROBLEM 8.19

Assuming a total pressure of 9.5 atm, what is the partial pressure of each component in the mixture of 98% helium and 2.0% oxygen breathed by deep-sea divers? How does the partial pressure of oxygen in diving gas compare with its partial pressure in normal air?

PROBLEM 8.20

Determine the percent composition of air in the lungs from the following composition in partial pressures: $P_{N_2} = 573\ \text{mmHg}$, $P_{O_2} = 100\ \text{mmHg}$, $P_{CO_2} = 40\ \text{mmHg}$, and $P_{H_2O} = 47\ \text{mmHg}$; all at 37 °C and 1 atm pressure.

PROBLEM 8.21

The atmospheric pressure on the top of Mt. Everest, an altitude of 29,035 ft, is only 265 mmHg. What is the partial pressure of oxygen in the lungs at this altitude (assuming that the percent O_2 is the same as in dry air)?

KEY CONCEPT PROBLEM 8.22

Using the image in the margin, assume that you have a mixture of He (blue spheres) and Xe (green spheres) at 300 K. The total pressure of the mixture is 750 mmHg. What are the partial pressures of each of the gases?

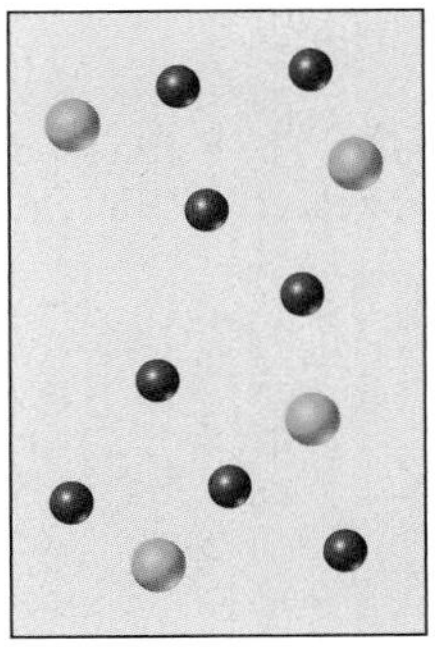

8.12 Liquids

Learning Objective:

- Identify how the vapor pressure, boiling point, and surface tension of liquids are related to temperature and intermolecular forces.

Molecules are in constant motion in the liquid state, just as they are in gases. If a molecule happens to be near the surface of a liquid, and if it has enough energy, it can break free of the liquid and escape into the gas state, called **vapor.** In an open container, the now gaseous molecule will wander away from the liquid, and the process will continue until all the molecules escape from the container (Figure 8.19a). This, of course, is what happens during *evaporation*. We are all familiar with puddles of water evaporating after a rainstorm.

If the liquid is in a closed container, the situation is different because the gaseous molecules cannot escape. Thus, the random motion of the molecules occasionally brings them back into the liquid. After the concentration of molecules in the gas state has increased sufficiently, the number of molecules reentering the liquid becomes equal

Vapor The gas molecules are in equilibrium with a liquid.

to the number escaping from the liquid (Figure 8.19b). At this point, a dynamic equilibrium exists, exactly as in a chemical reaction at equilibrium. Evaporation and condensation take place at the same rate, and the concentration of vapor in the container is constant as long as the temperature does not change.

Once molecules have escaped from the liquid into the gas state, they are subject to all the gas laws previously discussed. In a closed container at equilibrium, for example, the vapor molecules will make their own contribution to the total pressure of gases above the liquid according to Dalton's law (Section 8.11). We call this contribution the **vapor pressure** of the liquid.

Vapor pressure The partial pressure of vapor molecules in equilibrium with a liquid.

▶ **Figure 8.19**
The transfer of molecules between liquid and gas states.
(a) Molecules escape from an open container and drift away until the liquid has entirely evaporated. (b) Molecules in a closed container cannot escape. Instead, they reach an equilibrium in which the rates of molecules leaving the liquid and returning to the liquid are equal, and the concentration of molecules in the gas state is constant.

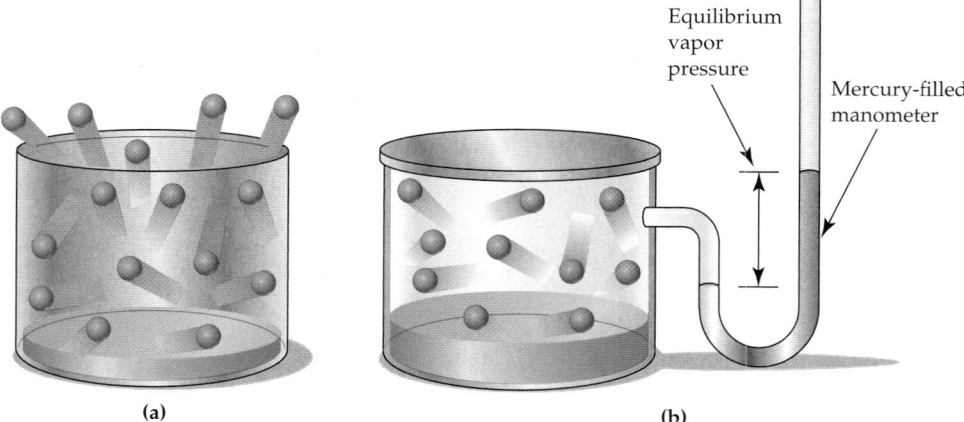

Vapor pressure depends on both temperature and the chemical identity of a liquid. As the temperature rises, molecules become more energetic and more likely to escape into the gas state. Thus, vapor pressure rises with increasing temperature until ultimately it becomes equal to the pressure of the atmosphere. At this point, bubbles of vapor form under the surface and force their way to the top, giving rise to the violent action observed during a vigorous boil. At an atmospheric pressure of exactly 760 mmHg, boiling occurs at the **normal boiling point.**

Normal boiling point The boiling point at a pressure of exactly 1 atm.

The vapor pressure and boiling point of a liquid will also depend on the intermolecular forces (discussed in Section 8.2) at work between liquid molecules. Ether molecules, for example, can engage in dipole–dipole interactions, which are weaker than the hydrogen bonds formed between water molecules. As a result, ether exhibits a higher vapor pressure at a given temperature and a lower boiling point than water, as seen in Figure 8.20.

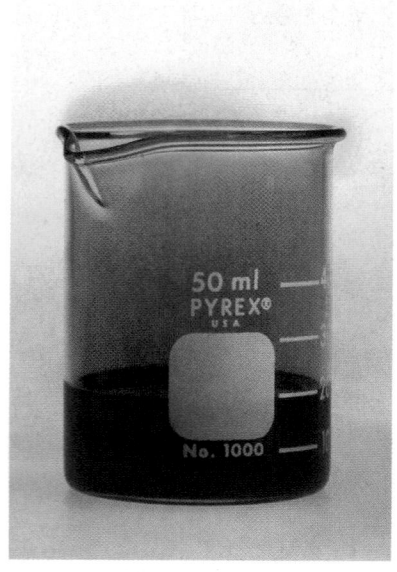

▲ Because bromine is colored, it is possible to see its gaseous reddish vapor above the liquid.

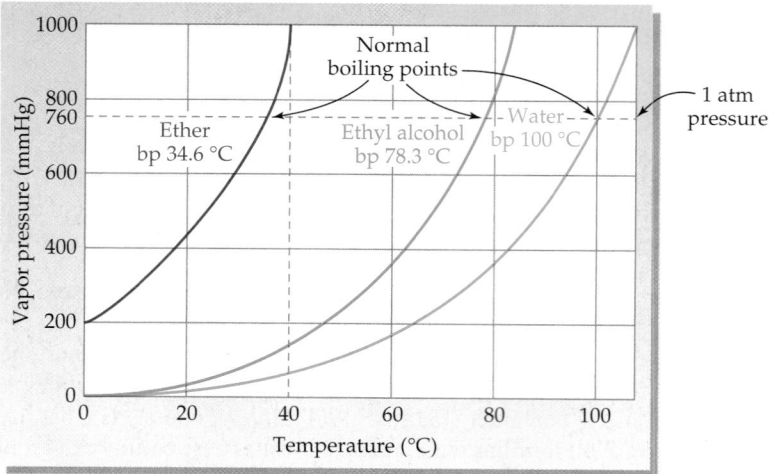

▲ **Figure 8.20**
A plot of the change of vapor pressure with temperature for ethyl ether, ethyl alcohol, and water.
At a liquid's boiling point, its vapor pressure is equal to atmospheric pressure. Commonly reported boiling points are those at 760 mmHg.

If atmospheric pressure is higher or lower than normal, the boiling point of a liquid changes accordingly. At high altitudes, for example, atmospheric pressure is lower than at sea level, and boiling points are also lower. On top of Mt. Everest (29,035 ft; 8850 m), atmospheric pressure is about 245 mmHg and the boiling temperature of water is only 71 °C. If the atmospheric pressure is higher than normal, the boiling point is also higher. This principle is used in strong vessels known as *autoclaves,* in which water at high pressure is heated to the temperatures needed for sterilizing medical and dental instruments (170 °C).

Many familiar properties of liquids can be explained by the intermolecular forces just discussed. We all know, for instance, that some liquids, such as water or gasoline, flow easily when poured, whereas others, such as motor oil or maple syrup, flow sluggishly.

The measure of a liquid's resistance to flow is called its *viscosity.* Not surprisingly, viscosity is related to the ease with which individual molecules move around in the liquid and thus to the intermolecular forces present. Substances such as gasoline, which have small, nonpolar molecules, experience only weak intermolecular forces and have relatively low viscosities, whereas more polar substances such as glycerin $[C_3H_5(OH)_3]$ experience stronger intermolecular forces and so have higher viscosities.

Another familiar property of liquids is *surface tension,* the resistance of a liquid to spreading out and increasing its surface area. Water beading up on a newly waxed car and the ability of a water strider to walk on water are both due to surface tension.

The difference between the intermolecular forces experienced by molecules at the surface of the liquid and those experienced by molecules in the interior causes surface tension. Molecules in the interior of a liquid are surrounded and experience maximum intermolecular forces, whereas molecules at the surface have fewer neighbors and feel weaker forces. Surface molecules are therefore less stable, and the liquid acts to minimize their number by minimizing the surface area (Figure 8.21).

▲ A bench-top autoclave, used to sterilize medical and dental instruments.

▲ Surface tension allows a water strider to walk on water without penetrating the surface.

◄◄◄ Recall from Section 1.11 that specific heat is the amount of heat required to raise the temperature of 1g of a substance by 1 °C.

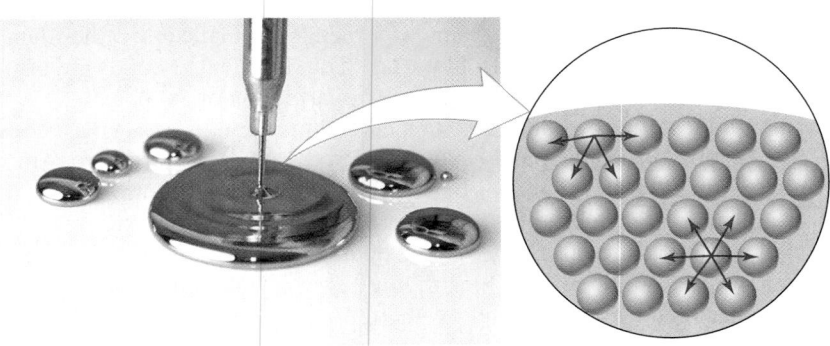

◄ **Figure 8.21**
Surface tension.
Surface tension is caused by the different forces experienced by molecules in the interior of a liquid and those on the surface. Molecules on the surface are less stable because they feel fewer attractive forces, so the liquid acts to minimize their number by minimizing surface area.

8.13 Solids

Learning Objective:

• Distinguish between the different types of solids and explain their physical properties.

A brief look around us reveals that most substances are solids rather than liquids or gases. It is also obvious that there are many different kinds of solids. Some, such as iron and aluminum, are hard and metallic; others, such as sugar and table salt, are crystalline and easily broken; and still others, such as rubber and many plastics, are soft and amorphous.

The most fundamental distinction between solids is that some are crystalline and some are amorphous. A **crystalline solid** is one whose particles—whether atoms, ions, or molecules—have an ordered arrangement extending over a long range. This order on the atomic level is also seen on the visible level because crystalline solids usually have flat faces and distinct angles.

Crystalline solid A solid whose atoms, molecules, or ions are rigidly held in an ordered arrangement.

▲ Crystalline solids, such as pyrite (left) and fluorite (right), have flat faces and distinct angles. The octahedral shape of pyrite and the cubic shape of fluorite reflect similarly ordered arrangements of particles at the atomic level.

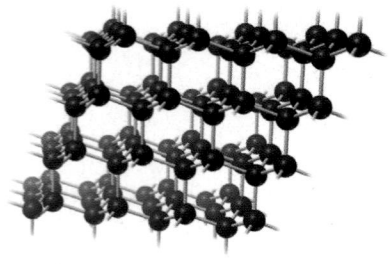

▲ **Figure 8.22**
Diamond.
Diamond is a covalent network solid—one very large molecule of carbon atoms linked by covalent bonds.

Amorphous solid A solid whose particles do not have an orderly arrangement.

Crystalline solids can be further categorized as ionic, molecular, covalent network, or metallic. *Ionic solids* are those like sodium chloride, whose constituent particles are ions. A crystal of sodium chloride is composed of alternating Na^+ and Cl^- ions ordered in a regular three-dimensional arrangement held together by ionic bonds (see Figure 3.4). *Molecular solids* are those like sucrose or ice, whose constituent particles are molecules held together by the intermolecular forces discussed in Section 8.2. *Covalent network solids* are those like diamond (Figure 8.22) or quartz (SiO_2), whose atoms are linked together by covalent bonds into a giant three-dimensional array. In effect, a covalent network solid is one *very* large molecule.

Metallic solids, such as silver or iron, can be viewed as vast three-dimensional arrays of metal cations immersed in a sea of electrons that are free to move about. This continuous electron sea acts both as a glue to hold the cations together and as a mobile carrier of charge to conduct electricity. Furthermore, the fact that bonding attractions extend uniformly in all directions explains why metals are malleable rather than brittle. When a metal crystal receives a sharp blow, no spatially oriented bonds are broken; instead, the electron sea simply adjusts to the new distribution of cations.

An **amorphous solid,** by contrast with a crystalline solid, is one whose constituent particles are randomly arranged and have no ordered long-range structure. Amorphous solids often result when liquids cool before they can achieve internal order or when their molecules are large and tangled together, as happens in many polymers. Glass is an amorphous solid, as are tar, the gemstone opal, and some hard candies. Amorphous solids differ from crystalline solids by softening over a wide temperature range rather than having sharp melting points and by shattering to give pieces with curved rather than planar faces. Table 8.4 gives a summary of the different types of solids and their characteristics.

Table 8.4 Types of Solids

Substance	Smallest Unit	Interparticle Forces	Properties	Examples
Ionic solid	Ions	Attraction between positive and negative ions	Brittle and hard; high melting point; crystalline	NaCl, KI, $Ca_3(PO_4)_2$
Molecular solid	Molecules	Intermolecular forces	Soft; low to moderate melting point; crystalline	Ice, wax, frozen CO_2, all solid organic compounds
Covalent network	Atoms	Covalent bonds	Very hard; very high melting point; crystalline	Diamond, quartz (SiO_2), tungsten carbide (WC)
Metal or alloy	Metal atoms	Metallic bonding (attraction between metal ions and surrounding mobile electrons)	Lustrous; soft (Na) to hard (Ti); high melting point; crystalline	Elements (Fe, Cu, Sn, . . .), bronze (CuSn alloy), amalgams (Hg+ other metals)
Amorphous solid	Atoms, ions, or molecules (including polymer molecules)	Any of the above	Noncrystalline; no sharp melting point; able to flow (may be very slow); curved edges when shattered	Glasses, tar, some plastics

Most substances are more dense as solids than as liquids because molecules are more closely packed in the solid than in the liquid state. Water, however, is unique. Liquid water has a maximum density of 1.000 g/mL at 3.98 °C but then becomes *less* dense as it cools. When it freezes, its density decreases still further to 0.917 g/mL.

As water freezes, each molecule is locked into position by hydrogen bonding to four other water molecules (Figure 8.23). The resulting structure has more open space than liquid water, accounting for its lower density. As a result, ice floats on liquid water, and lakes and rivers freeze from the top down. If the reverse were true, fish would be killed in winter as they became trapped in ice at the bottom.

▶▶ Water has other unique properties, including a high heat of vaporization and the highest specific heat of any liquid. The high ΔH_{vap}, is of particular importance in regulating body temperature by dissipating heat generated by metabolic processes (Chapters 21 and 22).

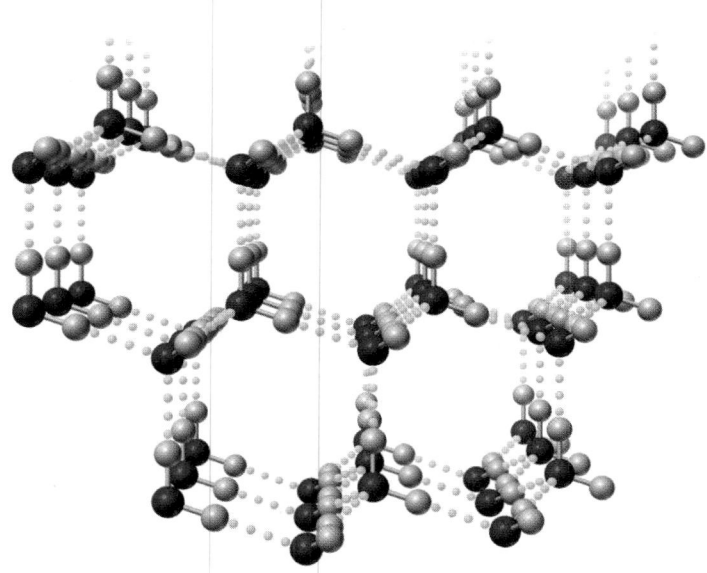

◀ **Figure 8.23**
Ice.
Ice consists of individual H_2O molecules held rigidly together in an ordered manner by hydrogen bonds. The open, cage-like crystal structure shows why ice is less dense than liquid water.

8.14 Changes of State Calculations

Learning Objective:

• Calculate the total amount of heat associated with changes in physical states of a substance.

What happens when a solid is heated? As more and more energy is added, molecules begin to stretch, bend, and vibrate more vigorously, and atoms or ions wiggle about with more energy. Finally, if enough energy is added and the motions become vigorous enough, particles start to break free from one another and the substance starts to melt. Addition of more heat continues the melting process until all particles have broken free and are in the liquid phase. The quantity of heat required to completely melt a substance once it reaches its melting point is called its **heat of fusion.** After melting is complete, further addition of heat causes the temperature of the liquid to rise.

The change of a liquid into a vapor proceeds in the same way as the change of a solid into a liquid. When you first put a pan of water on the stove, all the added heat goes into raising the temperature of the water. Once the water reaches its boiling point, further absorbed heat goes into freeing molecules from their neighbors as they escape into the gas state. The quantity of heat needed to completely vaporize a liquid once it reaches its boiling point is called its **heat of vaporization.** A liquid with a low heat of vaporization, like rubbing alcohol (isopropyl alcohol), evaporates rapidly and is said to be *volatile.* If you spill a volatile liquid on your skin, you will feel a cooling effect as it evaporates because it is absorbing heat from your body.

Heat of fusion The quantity of heat required to completely melt 1 g of a substance once it has reached its melting point.

Heat of vaporization The quantity of heat needed to completely vaporize 1 g of a liquid once it has reached its boiling point.

It is important to know the difference between heat that is added or removed to change the *temperature* of a substance and heat that is added or removed to change the *phase* of a substance. Remember that temperature is a measure of the kinetic energy in a substance (see Section 7.1). When a substance is above or below its phase-change temperature (i.e., melting point or boiling point), adding or removing heat will simply change the kinetic energy and, hence, the temperature of the substance. The amount of heat needed to produce a given temperature change was presented previously (Section 1.11) but is worth presenting again here.

$$\text{Heat (cal or J)} = \text{Mass (g)} \times \text{Temperature change (°C)} \times \text{Specific heat} \left(\frac{\text{cal or J}}{\text{g} \times \text{°C}} \right)$$

In contrast, when a substance is at its phase-change temperature, heat that is added is being used to overcome the intermolecular forces holding particles in that phase. The temperature remains constant until *all* particles have been converted to the next phase. The energy needed to complete the phase change depends only on the amount of the substance and the heat of fusion (for melting) or the heat of vaporization (for boiling).

$$\text{Heat (cal or J)} = \text{Mass (g)} \times \text{Heat of fusion} \left(\frac{\text{cal or J}}{\text{g}} \right)$$

$$\text{Heat (cal or J)} = \text{Mass (g)} \times \text{Heat of vaporization} \left(\frac{\text{cal or J}}{\text{g}} \right)$$

If the intermolecular forces are strong then large amounts of heat must be added to overcome these forces and the heats of fusion and vaporization will be large. Table 8.5 gives a list of heats of fusion and heats of vaporization for some common substances. Butane, for example, has a small heat of vaporization since the predominant intermolecular forces in butane (dispersion) are relatively weak. Water, on the other hand, has a particularly high heat of vaporization because of its unusually strong hydrogen bonding interactions. Thus, water evaporates more slowly than many other liquids, takes a long time to boil away, and absorbs more heat in the process. A so-called *heating curve*, which indicates the temperature and state changes as heat is added, is shown in Figure 8.24.

Table 8.5 Melting Points, Boiling Points, Heats of Fusion, and Heats of Vaporization of Some Common Substances

Substance	Melting Point (°C)	Boiling Point (°C)	Heat of Fusion cal/g (J/g)	Heat of Vaporization cal/g (J/g)
Ammonia	−77.7	−33.4	84.0 (351)	327 (1370)
Butane	−138.4	−0.5	19.2 (80.3)	92.5 (387)
Ether	−116	34.6	23.5 (98.3)	85.6 (358)
Ethyl alcohol	−117.3	78.5	26.1 (109)	200 (837)
Isopropyl alcohol	−89.5	82.4	21.4 (89.5)	159 (665)
Sodium	97.8	883	14.3 (59.8)	492 (2060)
Water	0.0	100.0	79.7 (333)	540 (2260)

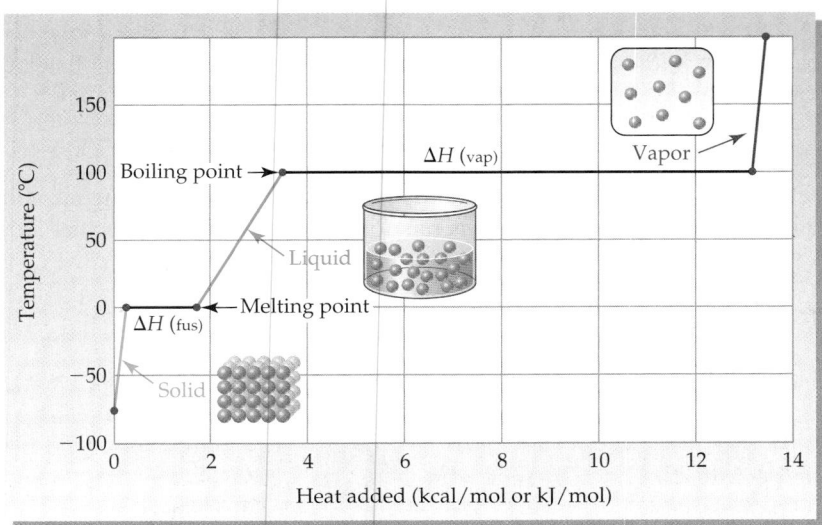

A heating curve for water, showing the temperature and state changes that occur when heat is added. The horizontal lines at 0 °C and 100 °C represent the heat of fusion and heat of vaporization, respectively. The sloped lines represent temperature changes resulting from absorbed heat relative to the specific heat of the substance in a given phase.

Worked Example 8.12   Heat of Fusion: Calculating Total Heat of Melting

Naphthalene, an organic substance often used in mothballs, has a heat of fusion of 35.7 cal/g (149 J/g) and a molar mass of 128.0 g/mol. How much heat in kilocalories is required to melt 0.300 mol of naphthalene?

ANALYSIS   The heat of fusion tells how much heat is required to melt 1 g. To find the amount of heat needed to melt 0.300 mol, we need a mole-to-mass conversion.

BALLPARK ESTIMATE   Naphthalene has a molar mass of 128.0 g/mol, so 0.300 mol has a mass of about one-third this amount, or about 40 g. Approximately 35 cal or 150 J is required to melt 1 g, so we need about 40 times this amount of heat or $35 \times 40 = 1400 \, \text{cal} = 1.4 \, \text{kcal}$ or $150 \times 40 = 6000 \, \text{J} = 6.0 \, \text{kJ}$.

SOLUTION

STEP 1: Identify known information. We know heat of fusion (cal/g) and the number of moles of naphthalene.

Heat of fusion = 35.7 cal/g or 149 J/g
Moles of naphthalene = 0.300 mol

STEP 2: Identify answer and units.

Heat = ?? cal or J

STEP 3: Identify conversion factors. First, convert moles of naphthalene to grams using the molar mass (128 g/mol) as a conversion factor. Then use the heat of fusion as a conversion factor to calculate the total heat necessary to melt the mass of naphthalene.

$(0.300 \, \text{mol naphthalene}) \left(\dfrac{128.0 \, \text{g}}{1 \, \text{mol}} \right) = 38.4 \, \text{g naphthalene}$

Heat of fusion = 35.7 cal/g or 149 J/g

STEP 4: Solve. Multiplying the mass of naphthalene by the heat of fusion then gives the answer.

$(38.4 \, \text{g naphthalene}) \left(\dfrac{35.7 \, \text{cal}}{1 \, \text{g naphthalene}} \right) = 1370 \, \text{cal} = 1.37 \, \text{kcal}$ or

$(38.4 \, \text{g naphthalene}) \left(\dfrac{149 \, \text{J}}{1 \, \text{g naphthalene}} \right) = 5720 \, \text{J} = 5.72 \, \text{J}$

BALLPARK CHECK   The calculated result agrees with our estimate (1.4 kcal or 6.0 kJ)

PROBLEM 8.23

How much heat in kilocalories is required to (a) melt and (b) boil 1.50 mol of isopropyl alcohol (rubbing alcohol; molar mass = 60.0 g/mol)? The heat of fusion and heat of vaporization of isopropyl alcohol are given in Table 8.5.

PROBLEM 8.24

How much heat in kilojoules is released by the condensation of 2.5 mol of steam? The heat of vaporization is given in Table 8.5.

PROBLEM 8.25

Compare the ΔH_{vap} values for water, isopropyl alcohol, ether, and ammonia, and order them from lowest to highest. Explain the rank order based on intermolecular attractive forces.

CHEMISTRY IN ACTION

✚ CO₂ as an Environmentally Friendly Solvent

As noted in the chapter opener, most of us are familiar with CO_2 as an atmospheric gas, and as solid "dry ice," but how can CO_2 be a solvent?

Consider the two factors that determine the physical state of a substance: temperature and pressure. In the solid state, molecules are packed closely together and do not have enough kinetic energy to overcome the intermolecular forces. If we increase the temperature, however, we increase the kinetic energy so that the molecules can move apart and produce a phase change to either a liquid or a gas. In the gas state, molecules are too far apart to interact, but increasing the pressure will force molecules closer together and, eventually, intermolecular attractions between molecules will cause them to condense into a liquid or solid state. This dependence of the physical state on temperature and pressure is represented by a *phase diagram,* such as the one shown here for CO_2.

The *supercritical state* is intermediate between liquid and gas. The molecules are too far apart to be truly a liquid, yet they are too close together to be truly a gas. Supercritical CO_2 exists above the *critical point.* Above 72.8 atm, the pressure is high enough to prevent molecules from expanding into the gas state; above 31.2 °C, the molecules have too much kinetic energy to condense into the liquid state.

Because open spaces already exist between CO_2 molecules, it is energetically easy for dissolved molecules to slip in, and supercritical CO_2 is therefore an extraordinarily good solvent. Among its many applications, supercritical CO_2 is used in the beverage and food-processing industries to decaffeinate coffee beans and to obtain spice extracts from vanilla, pepper, cloves, nutmeg, and other seeds. In the cosmetics and perfume industry, fragrant oils are extracted from flowers using supercritical CO_2. It is also used in the cleaning and sterilization of medical implants; because supercritical CO_2 has very low surface tension, it can permeate all the cracks and crevices in implant devices and afterward simply evaporates leaving no residue.

In the pharmaceutical industry, it can be used for both the extraction and processing of pharmacologically active compounds. Extraction of therapeutic natural products is accomplished without the use of organic solvents so the

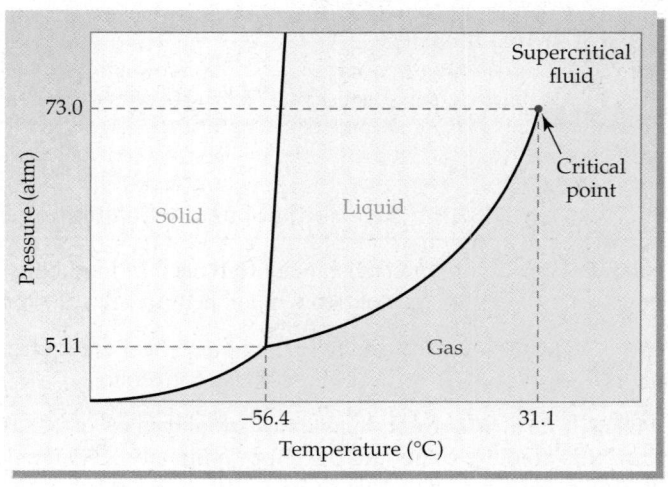

product contains no residual solvent impurities. Supercritical fluids (SCFs) are also used in processing of drugs; rapid recrystallization of drug compounds from SCF solvents produces much smaller particles with high surface areas, which can be absorbed more readily by the body and are more suitable for microencapsulated and aerosol delivery systems.

Perhaps the most impactful application is the use of carbon dioxide for dry-cleaning clothes, thereby replacing environmentally harmful chlorinated solvents with an alternative that is nontoxic and nonflammable. Industrial processes using CO_2 are designed as closed systems so that the CO_2 is recaptured after use and continually recycled. No organic solvent vapors are released into the atmosphere and no toxic liquids seep into groundwater supplies, as can occur with current procedures using chlorinated organic solvents. The future looks bright for this new "green" technology.

CIA Problem 8.6 What is a supercritical fluid?

CIA Problem 8.7 What are the environmental advantages of using supercritical CO_2 in place of chlorinated organic solvents?

CIA Problem 8.8 The physical state of CO_2 depends on the temperature and pressure. In what state would you expect to find CO_2 at 50 atm and 25 °C?

SUMMARY REVISITING THE CHAPTER LEARNING OBJECTIVES

- **Identify phase changes as endothermic or exothermic, and predict how a change in temperature will affect a phase change.** Melting occurs when a solid is converted to a liquid; vaporization occurs when a liquid is converted to a gas; sublimation occurs when a solid is converted to a gas. These physical changes are endothermic (absorb heat, $\Delta H > 0$) and involve an increase in entropy ($\Delta S > 0$). Freezing occurs when a liquid is converted to a solid; condensation occurs when a gas is converted to a liquid; deposition occurs when a gas is converted to a solid. These physical changes are exothermic (release heat, $\Delta H < 0$) and involve a decrease in entropy ($\Delta S < 0$). Identify the different types of intermolecular forces, and predict the predominant forces responsible for the physical properties of a given compound (see Problems 27, 28, 36, 37, and 114).

- **Identify the different types of intermolecular attractive forces, and predict the predominant forces responsible for the physical properties of a given substance.** There are three major types of *intermolecular forces*, which act to hold molecules near one another in solids and liquids. *London dispersion forces* occur between all molecules as a result of temporary molecular polarities due to unsymmetrical electron distribution. These forces increase in strength with molecular weight and with the surface area of molecules. *Dipole–dipole forces* are the electrical attractions that occur between polar molecules. *Hydrogen bonding,* the strongest of the three intermolecular forces, occurs between a hydrogen atom bonded to O, N, or F and a nearby O, N, or F atom (see Problems 34–37, 93, 109, and 113).

- **Use the kinetic–molecular theory to explain the behavior of gases.** According to the *kinetic–molecular theory of gases,* the physical behavior of gases can be explained by assuming that they consist of particles moving rapidly at random, separated from other particles by great distances, and colliding without loss of energy. The kinetic energy of gas particles is directly proportional to absolute temperature (Kelvin scale). Gas pressure is the result of molecular collisions with a surface (see Problems 29, 40, 41, and 100).

- **Define pressure, and convert between units of pressure.** Pressure is defined as *force/area* ($P = F/A$). Common units for pressure are *pounds per square inch (psi), atmospheres (atm), torr (or mmHg),* and *pascals (Pa).* The relationship between these units is 1 atm = 760 mmHg = 14.7 psi = 101,325 Pa (see Problems 30, 38, 39, and 42–45).

- **Use Boyle's law to calculate the changes in pressure or volume of a gas at a given temperature.** *Boyle's law* says that the volume of a fixed amount of gas at constant temperature is inversely proportional to its pressure ($P_1V_1 = P_2V_2$) (see Problems 26, 32, and 46–51).

- **Use Charles's law to calculate changes in volume of a gas as a function of temperature.** *Charles's law* says that the volume of a fixed amount of gas at constant pressure is directly proportional to its Kelvin temperature ($V_1/T_1 = V_2/T_2$). (see Problems 26, 27, and 52–57).

- **Use Gay-Lussac's law to calculate changes in pressure of a gas as a function of temperature.** *Gay-Lussac's law* says that the pressure of a fixed amount of gas at constant volume is directly proportional to its Kelvin temperature ($P_1/T_1 = P_2/T_2$) (see Problems 58–61).

- **Use the combined gas law to determine changes in pressure, temperature, or volume of a gas.** Boyle's law, Charles's law, and Gay-Lussac's law together give the *combined gas law* ($P_1V_1/T_1 = P_2V_2/T_2$), which applies to changing conditions for a fixed quantity of gas (see Problems 26, 32, and 62–67).

- **Use Avogadro's law to calculate the volume for a given number of moles of a gas.** *Avogadro's law* says that equal volumes of gases at the same temperature and pressure contain the same number of moles ($V_1/n_1 = V_2/n_2$) (see Problems 32, 68–75, 101, 107, and 111).

- **Use the ideal gas law to calculate the pressure, temperature, volume, or number of moles of an ideal gas.** The four gas laws together give the *ideal gas law, PV = nRT,* which relates the effects of temperature, pressure, volume, and molar amount. If three of the four variables are specified, the fourth can be calculated using the ideal gas law. At 0 °C and 1 atm pressure, called *standard temperature and pressure (STP),* 1 mol of any gas (6.02×10^{23} molecules) occupies a volume of 22.4 L (see Problems 76–85, 102–106, 108, and 110).

- **Use Dalton's law to calculate the partial pressure or the number of moles of a gas in a mixture.** The amount of pressure exerted by an individual gas in a mixture is called the *partial pressure* of the gas. According to *Dalton's law,* the total pressure exerted by the mixture is equal to the sum of the partial pressures of the individual gases and is proportional to the mole fraction of the gas in the mixture (see Problems 33, 86–89, and 112).

- **Identify how the vapor pressure, boiling point, and surface tension of liquids are related to temperature and intermolecular forces.** As a liquid is heated, molecules escape from the surface of a liquid until an equilibrium is reached between liquid and gas, resulting in a *vapor pressure* of the liquid. At a liquid's *boiling point,* its vapor pressure equals atmospheric pressure, and the entire liquid is converted into gas. The vapor pressure of a liquid is inversely related to the strength of the intermolecular forces of attraction between molecules; the boiling point of a liquid is directly related to the strength of the intermolecular forces (see Problems 28, 90, 92, 93, and 109).

- **Distinguish between the different types of solids and explain their physical properties.** Solids are either crystalline or amorphous. *Crystalline solids* are those whose constituent particles have an ordered arrangement; *amorphous solids* lack internal order and do not have sharp melting points. There are several kinds of crystalline solids: *Ionic solids* are those such as sodium chloride, whose constituent particles are ions. *Molecular solids* are those such as ice, whose constituent particles are molecules held together by intermolecular forces. *Covalent network solids* are those such as diamond, whose atoms are linked together by covalent bonds into a giant three-dimensional array. *Metallic solids,* such as silver or iron, also consist of large arrays of atoms, but their crystals have metallic properties such as electrical conductivity (see Problems 96–99).

- **Calculate the total amount of heat associated with changes in physical states of a substance.** When a solid is heated, particles begin to move around freely at the *melting point,* and the substance becomes liquid. The amount of heat necessary to melt a given amount of solid at its melting point is its *heat of fusion.* The amount of heat necessary to vaporize a given amount of liquid at its boiling point is called its *heat of vaporization* (see Problems 31, 91, 94, 95, 98, and 99).

CONCEPT MAP: GASES, LIQUIDS, AND SOLIDS

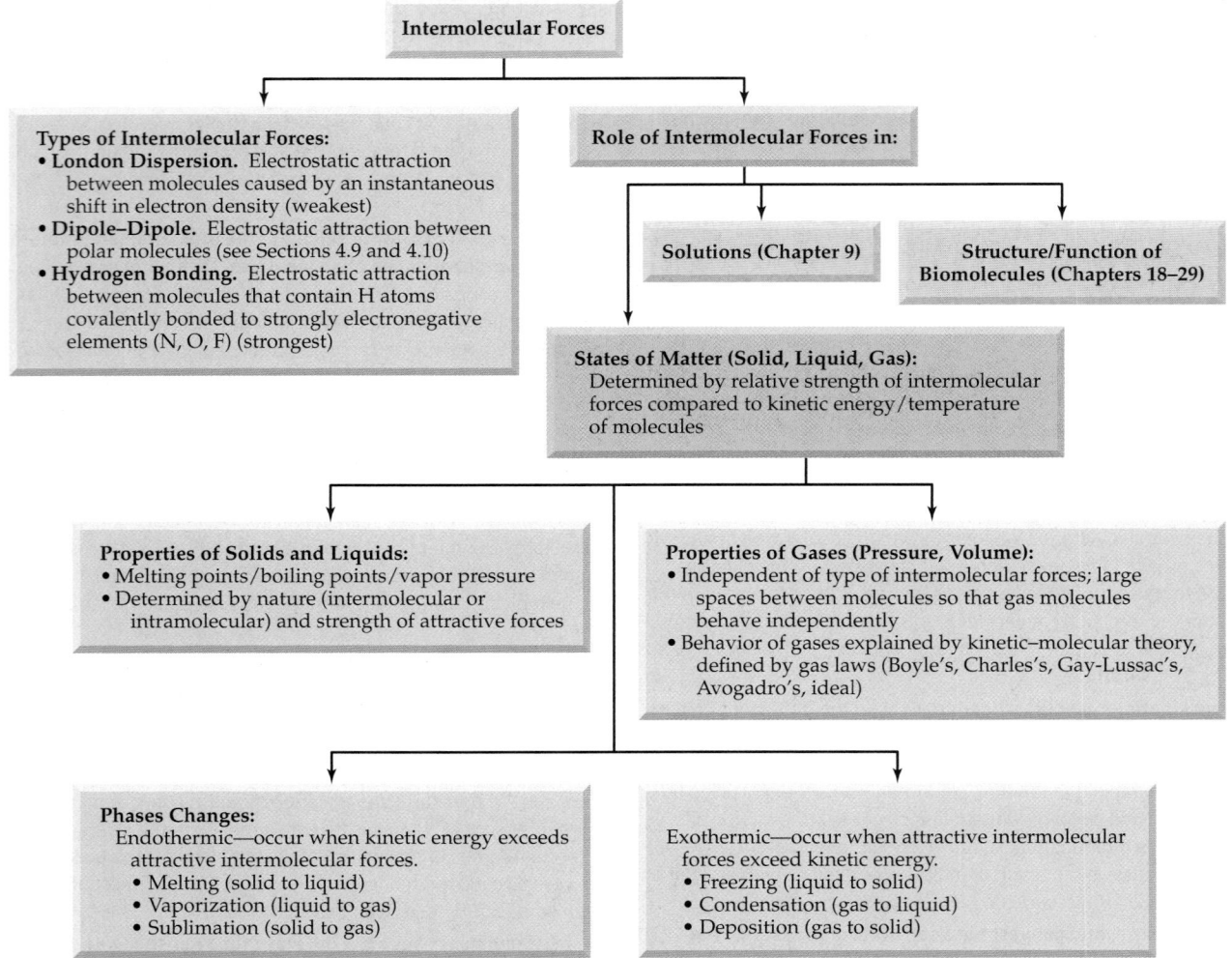

▲ **Figure 8.25 Concept Map.** The physical state of matter (solid, liquid, gas) depends on the strength of the intermolecular forces between molecules compared to the kinetic energy of the molecules. When the kinetic energy (i.e., temperature) is greater than the forces holding molecules in a given state, then a phase change occurs. Thus, the physical properties of matter (melting and boiling points, etc.) depend on the strength of the intermolecular forces between molecules, which depend on chemical structure and molecular shape. These relationships are reflected in the map above.

KEY WORDS

⟦📷⟧ UNDERSTANDING KEY CONCEPTS

8.26 Assume that you have a sample of gas in a cylinder with a movable piston, as shown in the following drawing:

Redraw the apparatus to show what the sample will look like after the following changes:

(a) The temperature is increased from 300 K to 450 K at constant pressure.

(b) The pressure is increased from 1 atm to 2 atm at constant temperature.

(c) The temperature is decreased from 300 K to 200 K and the pressure is decreased from 3 atm to 2 atm.

8.27 Assume that you have a sample of gas at 350 K in a sealed container, as represented in part (a). Which of the drawings (b)–(d) represents the gas after the temperature is lowered from 350 K to 150 K and if the gas has a boiling point of 200 K? Which drawing represents the gas at 150 K if the gas has a boiling point of 100 K?

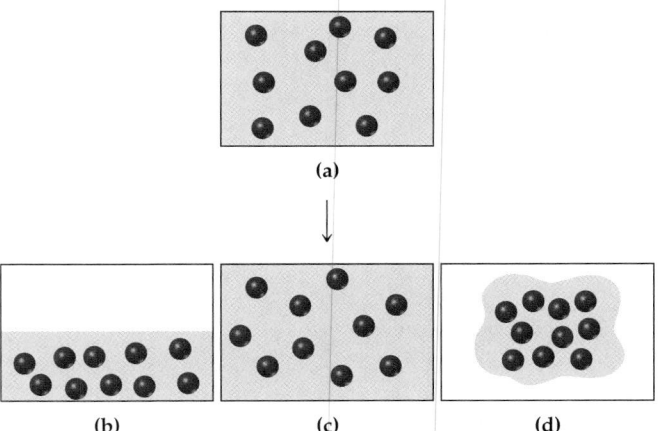

8.28 Assume that drawing (a) represents a sample of H_2O at 200 K. Which of the drawings (b)–(d) represents what the sample will look like when the temperature is raised to 300 K?

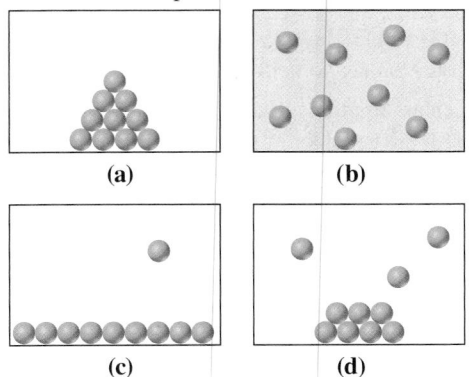

8.29 Three bulbs, two of which contain different gases and one of which is empty, are connected as shown in the following drawing:

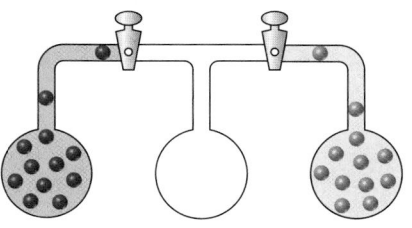

Redraw the apparatus to represent the gases after the stopcocks are opened and the system is allowed to come to equilibrium.

8.30 Redraw the following open-ended manometer to show what it would look like when stopcock A is opened.

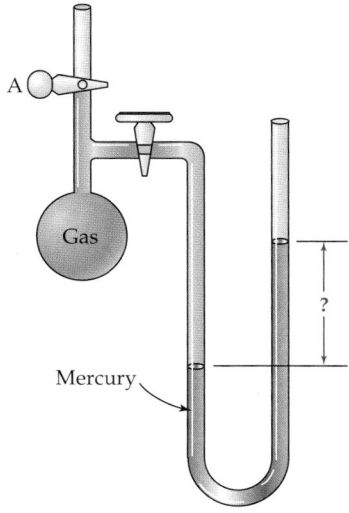

8.31 The following graph represents the heating curve of a hypothetical substance:

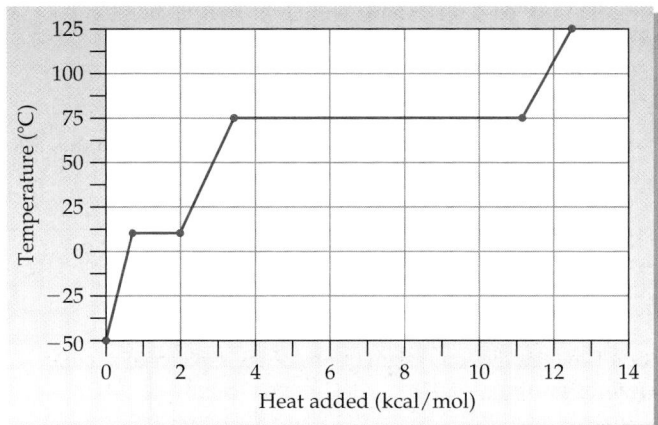

(a) What is the melting point of the substance?

(b) What is the boiling point of the substance?

(c) Approximately what is the heat of fusion for the substance in kcal/mol?

(d) Approximately what is the heat of vaporization for the substance in kcal/mol?

8.32 Show the approximate level of the movable piston in drawings (a)–(c) after the indicated changes have been made to the gas.

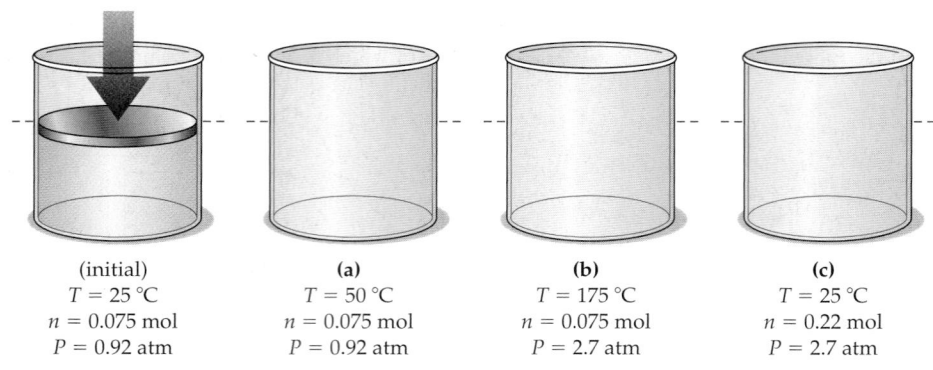

(initial)	(a)	(b)	(c)
$T = 25\,°C$	$T = 50\,°C$	$T = 175\,°C$	$T = 25\,°C$
$n = 0.075$ mol	$n = 0.075$ mol	$n = 0.075$ mol	$n = 0.22$ mol
$P = 0.92$ atm	$P = 0.92$ atm	$P = 2.7$ atm	$P = 2.7$ atm

8.33 The partial pressure of the blue gas in the container represented in the picture is 240 mmHg. What are the partial pressures of the yellow and red gases? What is the total pressure inside the container?

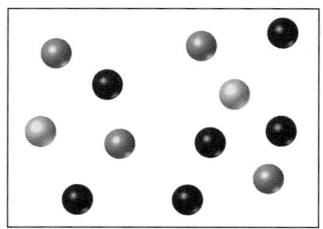

ADDITIONAL PROBLEMS

INTERMOLECULAR FORCES (SECTIONS 8.1 AND 8.2)

8.34 What characteristic must a compound have to experience the following intermolecular forces?

(a) London dispersion forces

(b) Dipole–dipole forces

(c) Hydrogen bonding

8.35 Identify the predominant intermolecular force in each of the following substances.

(a) N_2 (b) HCN   (c) CCl_4

(d) NH_3 (e) CH_3Cl (f) CH_3COOH

8.36 Dimethyl ether (CH_3OCH_3) and ethanol (C_2H_5OH) have the same formula (C_2H_6O), but the boiling point of dimethyl ether is $-25\,°C$ while that of ethanol is $78\,°C$. Explain this difference in boiling points.

8.37 Iodine is a solid at room temperature $(mp = 113.5\,°C)$ while bromine is a liquid $(mp = -7\,°C)$. Explain this difference in terms of intermolecular forces.

GASES AND PRESSURE (SECTIONS 8.3 AND 8.4)

8.38 How is 1 atm of pressure defined?

8.39 List four common units for measuring pressure.

8.40 What are the four assumptions of the kinetic–molecular theory of gases?

8.41 How does the kinetic–molecular theory of gases explain gas pressure?

8.42 Convert the following values into mmHg:

(a) Standard pressure   (b) 25.3 psi

(c) 7.5 atm   (d) 28.0 in. Hg

(e) 41.8 Pa

8.43 Atmospheric pressure at the top of Mt. Whitney in California is 440 mmHg.

(a) How many atmospheres is this?

(b) How many pascals is this?

8.44 What is the pressure (in mmHg) inside a container of gas connected to a mercury-filled, open-ended manometer of the sort shown in Figure 8.10 when the level in the arm connected to the container is 17.6 cm lower than the level in the arm open to the atmosphere and the atmospheric pressure reading outside the apparatus is 754.3 mmHg? What is the pressure inside the container in atmospheres?

8.45 What is the pressure (in atmospheres) inside a container of gas connected to a mercury-filled, open-ended manometer of the sort shown in Figure 8.10 when the level in the arm connected to the container is 28.3 cm higher than the level in the arm open to the atmosphere, and the atmospheric pressure reading outside the apparatus is 1.021 atm? What is the pressure in mmHg?

BOYLE'S LAW (SECTION 8.5)

8.46 What is Boyle's law, and what variables must be kept constant for the law to hold?

8.47 Which assumptions of the kinetic–molecular theory explain the behavior of gases described by Boyle's law? Explain your answer.

8.48 The pressure of gas in a 600.0 mL cylinder is 65.0 mmHg. What is the new volume when the pressure is increased to 385 mmHg?

8.49 The volume of a balloon is 2.85 L at 1.00 atm. What pressure is required to compress the balloon to a volume of 1.70 L?

8.50 The use of CFCs as refrigerants and propellants in aerosol cans has been discontinued as a result of concerns about the ozone layer. If an aerosol can contained 350 mL of CFC gas at a pressure of 5.0 atm, what volume would this gas occupy at 1.0 atm?

8.51 A balloon occupies a volume of 1.25 L at sea level where the ambient pressure is 1 atm. What volume would the balloon occupy at an altitude of 35,000 ft, where the air pressure is only 220 mmHg?

CHARLES'S LAW (SECTION 8.6)

8.52 What is Charles's law, and what variables must be kept constant for the law to hold?

8.53 Which assumptions of the kinetic–molecular theory explain the behavior of gases described by Charles's law? Explain your answer.

8.54 A hot-air balloon has a volume of 960 L at 291 K. To what temperature (in °C) must it be heated to raise its volume to 1200 L, assuming the pressure remains constant?

8.55 A hot-air balloon has a volume of 875 L. What is the original temperature of the balloon if its volume changes to 955 L when heated to 56 °C?

8.56 A gas sample has a volume of 185 mL at 38 °C. What is its volume at 97 °C?

8.57 A balloon has a volume of 43.0 L at 25 °C. What is its volume at 2.8 °C?

GAY-LUSSAC'S LAW (SECTION 8.7)

8.58 What is Gay-Lussac's law, and what variables must be kept constant for the law to hold?

8.59 Which assumptions of the kinetic–molecular theory explain the behavior of gases described by Gay-Lussac's law? Explain your answer.

8.60 A glass laboratory flask is filled with gas at 25 °C and 0.95 atm pressure, sealed, and then heated to 117 °C. What is the pressure inside the flask?

8.61 An aerosol can has an internal pressure of 3.85 atm at 25 °C. What temperature is required to raise the pressure to 18.0 atm?

COMBINED GAS LAW (SECTION 8.8)

8.62 A gas has a volume of 2.84 L at 1.00 atm and 0 °C. At what temperature does it have a volume of 7.50 L at 520 mmHg?

8.63 A compressed-air tank carried by scuba divers has a volume of 6.80 L and a pressure of 120 atm at 20 °C. What is the volume of air in the tank at 0 °C and 1.00 atm pressure (STP)?

8.64 When H_2 gas was released by the reaction of HCl with Zn, the volume of H_2 collected was 75.4 mL at 23 °C and 748 mmHg. What is the volume of the H_2 at 0 °C and 1.00 atm pressure (STP)?

8.65 What is the effect on the volume of a gas if you simultaneously:
(a) Halve its pressure and double its Kelvin temperature?
(b) Double its pressure and double its Kelvin temperature?

8.66 What is the effect on the pressure of a gas if you simultaneously:
(a) Halve its volume and double its Kelvin temperature?
(b) Double its volume and halve its Kelvin temperature?

8.67 A small cylinder of helium gas used for filling balloons has a volume of 2.30 L and a pressure of 1850 atm at 25 °C. How many balloons can you fill if each one has a volume of 1.5 L and a pressure of 1.25 atm at 25 °C?

AVOGADRO'S LAW AND STANDARD MOLAR VOLUME (SECTION 8.9)

8.68 Explain Avogadro's law using the kinetic–molecular theory of gases.

8.69 What conditions are defined as STP?

8.70 How many molecules are in 1.0 L of O_2 at STP? How may grams of O_2?

8.71 How many moles of gas are in a volume of 48.6 L at STP?

8.72 What is the mass of CH_4 in a sample that occupies a volume of 16.5 L at STP?

8.73 Assume that you have 1.75 g of the deadly gas hydrogen cyanide, HCN. What is the volume of the gas at STP?

8.74 A typical room is 4.0 m long, 5.0 m wide, and 2.5 m high. What is the total mass of the oxygen in the room assuming that the gas in the room is at STP and that air contains 21% oxygen and 79% nitrogen?

8.75 What is the total volume and number of moles of nitrogen in the room described in Problem 8.74?

IDEAL GAS LAW (SECTION 8.10)

8.76 What is the ideal gas law?

8.77 How does the ideal gas law differ from the combined gas law?

8.78 Which sample contains more molecules: 2.0 L of Cl_2 at STP or 3.0 L of CH_4 at 300 K and 1150 mmHg? Which sample weighs more?

8.79 Which sample contains more molecules: 2.0 L of CO_2 at 300 K and 500 mmHg or 1.5 L of N_2 at 57 °C and 760 mmHg? Which sample weighs more?

8.80 If 2.3 mol of He has a volume of 0.15 L at 294 K, what is the pressure in atm? In psi?

8.81 If 3.5 mol of O_2 has a volume of 27.0 L at a pressure of 1.6 atm, what is its temperature in degrees Celsius?

8.82 If 15.0 g of CO_2 gas has a volume of 0.30 L at 310 K, what is its pressure in mmHg?

8.83 If 20.0 g of N_2 gas has a volume of 4.00 L and a pressure of 6.0 atm, what is its temperature in degree Celsius?

8.84 If 18.0 g of O_2 gas has a temperature of 350 K and a pressure of 550 mmHg, what is its volume?

8.85 How many moles of a gas will occupy a volume of 0.55 L at a temperature of 347 K and a pressure of 2.5 atm?

DALTON'S LAW AND PARTIAL PRESSURE (SECTION 8.11)

8.86 What is meant by *partial pressure*?

8.87 What is Dalton's law?

8.88 If the partial pressure of oxygen in air at 1.0 atm is 160 mmHg, what is its partial pressure on the summit of Mt. Whitney, where atmospheric pressure is 440 mmHg? Assume that the percent oxygen is the same.

8.89 Scuba divers who suffer from decompression sickness are treated in hyperbaric chambers using heliox (21% oxygen, 79% helium) at pressures up to 120 psi. Calculate the partial pressure of O_2 (in mmHg) in a hyperbaric chamber under these conditions.

LIQUIDS (SECTIONS 8.12 AND 8.14)

8.90 What is the vapor pressure of a liquid?

8.91 What is a liquid's heat of vaporization?

8.92 What is the effect of pressure on a liquid's boiling point?

8.93 Which of the following substances would you expect to have the higher vapor pressure: CH_3OH or CH_3Cl? Explain.

8.94 The heat of vaporization of water is 9.72 kcal/mol.
  (a) How much heat (in kilocalories) is required to vaporize 3.00 mol of H_2O?
  (b) How much heat (in kilocalories) is released when 320 g of steam condenses?

8.95 Patients with a high body temperature are often given "alcohol baths." The heat of vaporization of isopropyl alcohol (rubbing alcohol) is 159 cal/g. How much heat is removed from the skin by the evaporation of 190 g (about half a cup) of isopropyl alcohol?

SOLIDS (SECTION 8.13)

8.96 What is the difference between an amorphous and a crystalline solid?

8.97 List three kinds of crystalline solids, and give an example of each.

8.98 The heat of fusion of acetic acid, the principal organic component of vinegar, is 45.9 cal/g. How much heat (in kilocalories) is required to melt 1.75 mol of solid acetic acid?

8.99 The heat of fusion of sodium metal is 630 cal/mol. How much heat (in kilocalories) is required to melt 262 g of sodium?

CONCEPTUAL PROBLEMS

8.100 Use the kinetic–molecular theory to explain why gas pressure increases if the temperature is raised and the volume is kept constant.

8.101 Hydrogen and oxygen react according to the equation $2\,H_2(g) + O_2(g) \longrightarrow 2\,H_2O(g)$. According to Avogadro's law, how many liters of hydrogen are required to react with 2.5 L of oxygen at STP?

8.102 If 3.0 L of hydrogen and 1.5 L of oxygen at STP react to yield water, how many moles of water are formed? What gas volume does the water have at a temperature of 100 °C and 1 atm pressure?

8.103 Approximately 240 mL/min of CO_2 is exhaled by an average adult at rest. Assuming a temperature of 37 °C and 1 atm pressure, how many moles of CO_2 is this?

8.104 How many grams of CO_2 are exhaled by an average resting adult in 24 hours? (See Problem 8.103.)

8.105 When fully inflated, a hot-air balloon has a volume of 1.6×10^5 L at an average temperature of 375 K and 0.975 atm. Assuming that air has an average molar mass of 29 g/mol, what is the density of the air in the hot-air balloon? How does this compare with the density of air at STP?

8.106 A 10.0 g sample of an unknown gas occupies 14.7 L at a temperature of 25 °C and a pressure of 745 mmHg. How many moles of gas are in the sample? What is the molar mass of the gas?

8.107 One mole of any gas has a volume of 22.4 L at STP. What are the molecular weights of the following gases, and what are their densities in grams per liter at STP?
  (a) CH_4 **(b)** CO_2 **(c)** O_2

8.108 Gas pressure outside the space shuttle is approximately 1×10^{-14} mm Hg at a temperature of approximately 1 K. If the gas is almost entirely hydrogen atoms (H, not H_2), what volume of space is occupied by 1 mol of atoms? What is the density of H gas in atoms per liter?

8.109 Ethylene glycol, $C_2H_6O_2$, has one OH bonded to each carbon.
  (a) Draw the Lewis dot structure of ethylene glycol.
  (b) Draw the Lewis dot structure of chloroethane, C_2H_5Cl.
  (c) Chloroethane has a slightly higher molar mass than ethylene glycol but a much lower boiling point (3 °C versus 198 °C). Explain.

8.110 Isooctane, C_8H_{18}, is the component of gasoline from which the term *octane rating* derives.
  (a) Write a balanced equation for the combustion of isooctane to yield CO_2 and H_2O.
  (b) Assuming that gasoline is 100% isooctane and that the density of isooctane is 0.792 g/mL, what mass of CO_2 (in kilograms) is produced each year by the annual U.S. gasoline consumption of 4.6×10^{10} L?
  (c) What is the volume (in liters) of this CO_2 at STP?

GROUP PROBLEMS

8.111 Imagine that you have two identical containers, one containing hydrogen at STP and the other containing oxygen at STP. How can you tell which is which without opening them?

8.112 A rule of thumb for scuba diving is that the external pressure increases by 1 atm for every 10 m of depth. A diver using a compressed air tank is planning to descend to a depth of 25 m.

(a) What is the external pressure at this depth? (Remember that the pressure at sea level is 1 atm.)

(b) Assuming that the tank contains 20% oxygen and 80% nitrogen, what is the partial pressure of each gas in the diver's lungs at this depth?

8.113 Obtain an aerosol can and read the list of ingredients. Some of the ingredients are "active" (e.g., the substance used as a deodorant or a lubricant) while others are listed as "inert." For aerosol products, one of the inert ingredients is typically used as a propellant to provide the pressure necessary to disperse the active ingredients as an aerosol.

(a) For your aerosol product, identify the inert ingredient used as the propellant and research its physical properties (melting point and boiling point).

(b) Discuss how the physical properties make it suitable for the aerosol application.

8.114 Obtain phase diagrams for water and carbon dioxide.

(a) Based on the phase diagram for water, explain how it is possible to skate on ice, that is, solid water.

(b) Would it be possible to skate on "dry ice," that is, solid CO_2?

8.115 The increase in atmospheric CO_2 levels has been correlated with the combustion of fossil fuels (see the Chemistry in Action "Greenhouse Gases and Global Warming" on p. 226). How would the atmospheric CO_2 levels be affected by a shift to corn-based ethanol or some other biomass-based fuel? Explain.

9

Solutions

CONTENTS

◀◀◀ CONCEPTS TO REVIEW

▲ Controlled-release medications provide significant benefits for the treatment of many conditions, including attention deficit-hyperactivity disorder (ADHD). Development of appropriate drug delivery systems requires consideration of many factors discussed in this chapter, including drug solubility and osmosis.

Have you ever taken medication for motion sickness or for allergy relief or to relieve chronic pain? While the biological activity of these drugs is often complex, and a topic for later chapters, the delivery systems used to control the release of these drugs in the body are equally complex. Some drugs taken for relief of acute asthma or extreme pain must be fast acting. Other pharmaceuticals, for treatment of conditions such as attention deficit hyperactivity disorder (ADHD) and diabetes, are more beneficial if delivered in controlled doses over extended periods of time. An effective drug delivery system must consider many factors: How soluble is it? What concentration of the drug in the blood is necessary to provide a therapeutic response without toxic side effects? How can the release of the drug be controlled to provide the optimal dose?

To date, we have discussed the properties of pure substances, but to answer the questions raised in the introduction we need to examine how different substances interact to form mixtures, which we call *solutions*. Specifically, we will address how solutions are formed, how we can express quantitatively the amounts of substances in the solution, and how the properties of solutions differ from those of pure substances.

9.1 Mixtures and Solutions

Learning Objective:

- Distinguish between heterogeneous and homogeneous mixtures and between solutions and colloids.

As we saw in Section 1.3, a *mixture* is an intimate combination of two or more substances, both of which retain their chemical identities. Mixtures can be classified as either *heterogeneous* or *homogeneous,* as indicated in Figure 9.1, depending on their appearance. In heterogeneous mixtures, the mixing is not uniform and the mixtures have regions of different composition. Rocky Road ice cream, for example, is a heterogeneous mixture, with something different in every spoonful. Mixing *is* uniform in homogenous mixtures, and they have the same composition throughout. Seawater, a homogeneous mixture of soluble ionic compounds in water, is an example.

Homogeneous mixtures are further classified as either *solutions* or *colloids,* according to the size of their particles. **Solutions,** the most important class of homogeneous mixtures, contain particles the size of a typical ion or small molecule—roughly 0.1–2 nm in diameter. **Colloids,** such as milk and fog, are also homogeneous in appearance but contain larger particles than solutions—in the range 2–500 nm diameter. Many common over-the-counter medications, such as Milk of Magnesia and PeptoBismol, are colloidal suspensions.

Liquid solutions, colloids, and heterogeneous mixtures can be distinguished in several ways. For example, liquid solutions are transparent (although they may be colored). Colloids may appear transparent if the particle size is small, but they have a murky or opaque appearance if the particle size is larger. Neither solutions nor small-particle colloids separate on standing, and the particles in both are too small to be removed by filtration. Heterogeneous mixtures and large-particle colloids, also known as "suspensions," are murky or opaque and their particles will slowly settle on prolonged standing. House paint is one example.

Table 9.1 gives some examples of solutions, colloids, and heterogeneous mixtures. It is interesting to note that blood has characteristics of all three. About 45% by volume of blood consists of suspended red and white cells, which settle slowly on standing; the remaining 55% is *plasma,* which contains ions in solution and colloidal protein molecules.

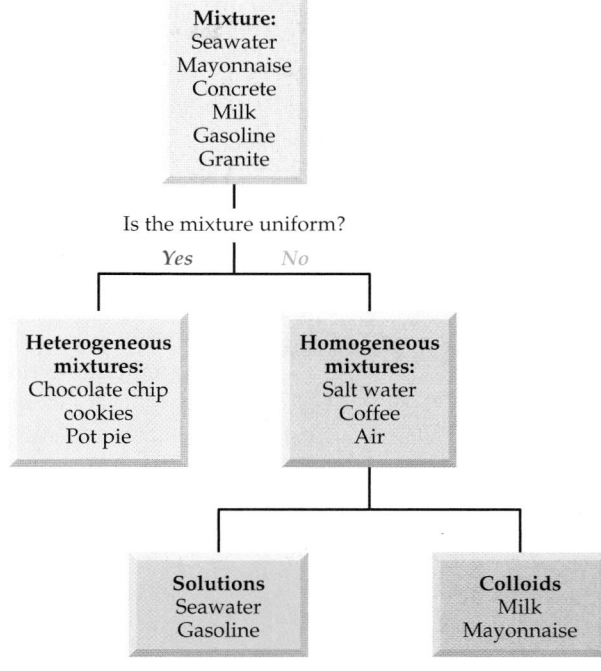

▲ **Figure 9.1**
Classification of mixtures.
The components in heterogeneous mixtures are not uniformly mixed, and the composition varies with location within the mixture. In homogeneous mixtures, the components are uniformly mixed at the molecular level.

Solution A homogeneous mixture that contains particles the size of a typical ion or small molecule.

Colloid A homogeneous mixture that contains particles that range in diameter from 2 to 500 nm.

Table 9.1 Some Characteristics of Solutions, Colloids, and Heterogeneous Mixtures

Type of Mixture	Particle Size	Examples	Characteristics
Solution	<2.0 nm	Air, seawater, gasoline, wine	Transparent to light; does not separate on standing; nonfilterable
Colloid	2.0–500 nm	Butter, milk, fog, pearl	Often murky or opaque to light; does not separate on standing; nonfilterable
Heterogeneous	>500 nm	Blood, paint, aerosol sprays	Murky or opaque to light; separates on standing; filterable

Although we usually think of solids dissolved in liquids when we talk about solutions, solutions actually occur in all three phases of matter (Table 9.2). Metal alloys like 14-karat gold (58% gold with silver and copper) and brass (10–40% zinc with copper), for instance, are solutions of one solid with another. For solutions in which a gas or solid is dissolved in a liquid, the dissolved substance is called the **solute** and the liquid is called the **solvent.** In seawater, for example, the dissolved salts would be the solutes and water would be the solvent. When one liquid is dissolved in another, the minor component is usually considered the solute and the major component is the solvent.

Solute A substance that is dissolved in a solvent.

Solvent The substance in which another substance (the solute) is dissolved.

Table 9.2 Some Different Types of Solutions

Type of Solution	Example
Gas in gas	Air (O_2, N_2, Ar, and other gases)
Gas in liquid	Seltzer water (CO_2 in water)
Gas in solid	H_2 in palladium metal
Liquid in liquid	Gasoline (mixture of hydrocarbons)
Liquid in solid	Dental amalgam (mercury in silver)
Solid in liquid	Seawater (NaCl and other salts in water)
Solid in solid	Metal alloys such as 14-karat gold (Au, Ag, and Cu)

PROBLEM 9.1

Classify the following liquid mixtures as heterogeneous or homogeneous. Further classify each homogeneous mixture as a solution or colloid.

(a) Orange juice with pulp   (b) Apple juice

(c) Hand lotion   (d) Tea

9.2 The Solution Process

Learning Objective:

• Predict whether a solution is likely to form based on the relative polarity and intermolecular forces between solute and solvent.

What determines whether a substance is soluble in a given liquid? Solubility depends primarily on the strength of the attractions between solute and solvent particles relative to the strengths of the attractions within the pure substances. Ethyl alcohol is soluble in water, for example, because hydrogen bonding (Section 8.2) is nearly as strong between water and ethyl alcohol molecules as it is between water molecules alone or ethyl alcohol molecules alone.

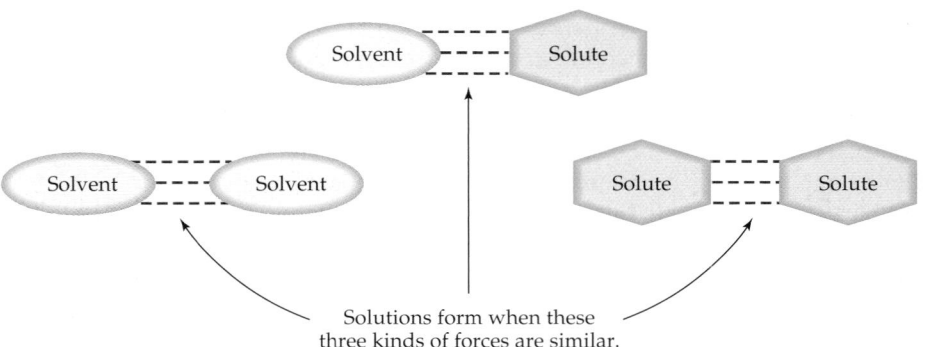

Solutions form when these three kinds of forces are similar.

LOOKING AHEAD ▶▶ Many compounds consisting largely of carbon, hydrogen, and oxygen are called organic compounds because they were originally derived from living organisms. We will study the chemistry of organic compounds in Chapters 12–18, 21, and 23.

A good rule of thumb for predicting solubility is that "like dissolves like," meaning that substances with similar intermolecular forces form solutions with one another, whereas substances with different intermolecular forces do not (Section 8.2).

Polar solvents dissolve polar and ionic solutes; nonpolar solvents dissolve nonpolar solutes. Thus, a polar, hydrogen-bonding compound like water dissolves ethyl alcohol and sodium chloride, whereas a nonpolar organic compound like hexane (C_6H_{14}) dissolves other nonpolar organic compounds like fats and oils. Water and oil, however, do not dissolve one another, as summed up by the old saying, "Oil and water don't mix." The intermolecular forces between water molecules are so strong that after an oil–water mixture is shaken, the water layer re-forms, squeezing out the oil molecules.

Water solubility is not limited to ionic compounds and ethyl alcohol. Many polar organic substances, such as sugars, amino acids, and even some proteins, dissolve in water. In addition, small, moderately polar organic molecules such as chloroform ($CHCl_3$) are soluble in water to a limited extent. When mixed with water, a small amount of the organic compound dissolves, but the remainder forms a separate liquid layer. As the number of carbon atoms in organic molecules increases, though, water solubility decreases.

The process of dissolving an ionic solid in a polar liquid is shown in Figure 9.2 for sodium chloride. When NaCl crystals are put in water, ions at the crystal surface come into contact with polar water molecules. Positively charged Na^+ ions are attracted to the negatively polarized oxygen of water, and negatively charged Cl^- ions are attracted to the positively polarized hydrogens. The combined forces of attraction between an ion and several water molecules pull the ion away from the crystal, exposing a

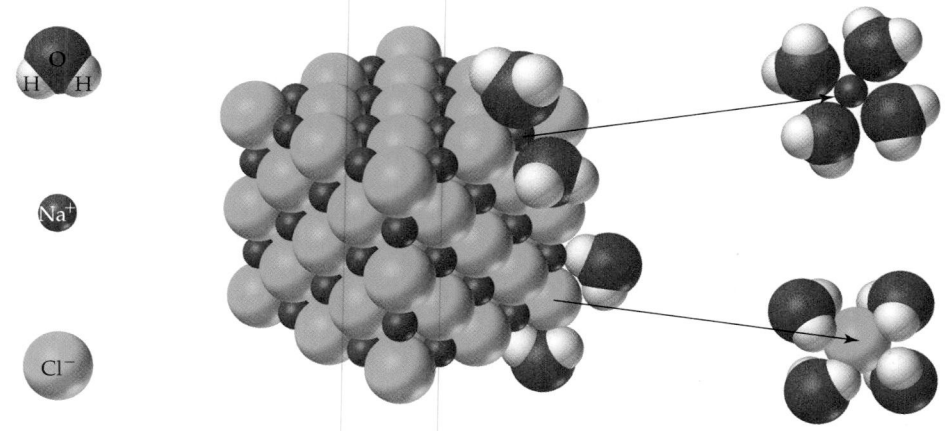

◀ **Figure 9.2**
Dissolution of a NaCl crystal in water.
Polar water molecules surround the individual Na⁺ and Cl⁻ ions at an exposed edge or corner, pulling them from the crystal surface into solution and surrounding them. Note how the negatively polarized oxygens of water molecules cluster around Na⁺ ions and the positively polarized hydrogens cluster around Cl⁻ ions.

fresh surface, until ultimately the crystal dissolves. Once in solution, Na^+ and Cl^- ions are completely surrounded by solvent molecules, a phenomenon called **solvation** (or, specifically for water, *hydration*). The water molecules form a loose shell around the ions, stabilizing them by electrical attraction.

Solvation The clustering of solvent molecules around a dissolved solute molecule or ion.

The dissolution of a solute in a solvent is a physical change, because the solution components retain their chemical identities. When sugar dissolves in water, for example, the individual sugar and water molecules still have the same chemical formulas as in the pure or undissolved state. Like all chemical and physical changes, the dissolution of a substance in a solvent has associated with it a heat change, or *enthalpy* change (Section 7.2). Some substances dissolve exothermically, releasing heat and warming the resultant solution, whereas other substances dissolve endothermically, absorbing heat and cooling the resultant solution. Calcium chloride, for example, *releases* 19.4 kcal/mol (81.2 kJ/mol) of heat energy when it dissolves in water, but ammonium nitrate (NH_4NO_3) *absorbs* 6.1 kcal/mol (25.5 kJ/mol) of heat energy. Athletes and others take advantage of both situations when they use instant hot packs or cold packs to treat injuries. Both hot and cold packs consist of a pouch of water and a dry chemical, such as $CaCl_2$ or $MgSO_4$ for hot packs and NH_4NO_3 for cold packs. Squeezing the pack breaks the pouch and the solid dissolves, either raising or lowering the temperature.

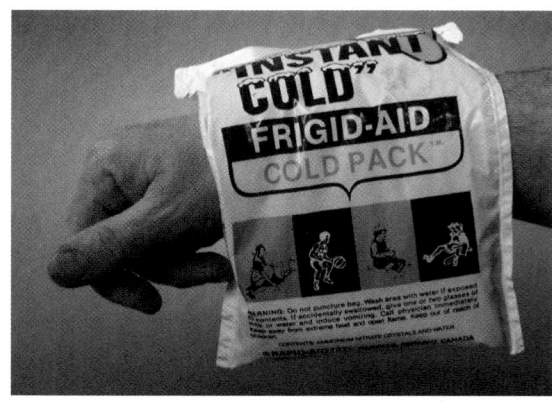

▲ Instant cold packs used to treat muscle strains and sprains often take advantage of the endothermic enthalpy of a solution of salts such as ammonium nitrate.

Worked Example 9.1 Formation of Solutions

Which of the following pairs of substances would you expect to form solutions?
(a) Carbon tetrachloride (CCl_4) and hexane (C_6H_{14}).
(b) Octane (C_8H_{18}) and methyl alcohol (CH_3OH).

ANALYSIS Identify the kinds of intermolecular forces in each substance (Section 8.2). Substances with similar intermolecular forces tend to form solutions.

SOLUTION

(a) Hexane contains only C—H and C—C bonds, which are nonpolar. Carbon tetrachloride contains polar C—Cl bonds, but they are distributed symmetrically in the tetrahedral molecule so that it too is nonpolar. The major intermolecular force for both compounds is London dispersion forces, so they will form a solution.

(b) Octane contains only C—H and C—C bonds and so is nonpolar; the major intermolecular force is dispersion. Methyl alcohol contains polar C—O and O—H bonds; it is polar and forms hydrogen bonds. The intermolecular forces for the two substances are so dissimilar that they do not form a solution.

CHEMISTRY IN ACTION

✝ Solid Hydrates—Salt + Water

If you add salt to water, you would expect it to dissolve and form a solution. But some ionic compounds attract water strongly enough to hold on to water molecules even when crystalline, forming what are called *solid hydrates*. For example, the plaster of Paris used to make decorative objects and casts for broken limbs is calcium sulfate hemihydrate, $CaSO_4 \cdot \frac{1}{2}H_2O$. The dot between $CaSO_4$ and $\frac{1}{2}H_2O$ in the formula indicates that for every two $CaSO_4$ formula units in the crystal there is also one water molecule present.

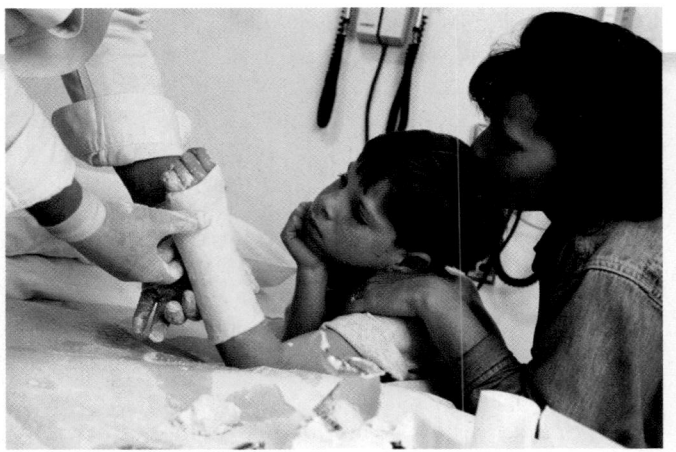

$$CaSO_4 \cdot \frac{1}{2}H_2O \quad \text{A solid hydrate}$$

After being ground up and mixed with water to make plaster, $CaSO_4 \cdot \frac{1}{2}H_2O$ gradually changes into the crystalline dihydrate $CaSO_4 \cdot 2H_2O$, known as *gypsum*.

During the change, the plaster hardens and expands in volume, causing it to fill a mold or shape itself closely around a broken limb. Still other ionic compounds attract water so strongly that they pull water vapor from humid air to become hydrated. Compounds that show this behavior, such as calcium chloride $(CaCl_2)$, are called hygroscopic and are often used as drying agents. You might have noticed a small bag of a hygroscopic compound (probably silica gel, SiO_2) included in the packing material of a new MP3 player, camera, or other electronic device to keep humidity low during shipping. These and other ionic compounds that are handled primarily as hydrates are listed in the following table.

Some Common Solid Hydrates

Formula	Name	Uses
$AlCl_3 \cdot 6H_2O$	Aluminum chloride hexahydrate	Antiperspirant
$CaSO_4 \cdot 2H_2O$	Calcium sulfate dihydrate (gypsum)	Cements, wallboard molds
$CaSO_4 \cdot \frac{1}{2}H_2O$	Calcium sulfate hemihydrate (plaster of Paris)	Casts, molds
$CuSO_4 \cdot 5H_2O$	Copper(II) sulfate pentahydrate (blue vitriol)	Pesticide, germicide, topical fungicide
$MgSO_4 \cdot 7H_2O$	Magnesium sulfate heptahydrate (epsom salts)	Laxative, anticonvulsant
$NaB_4O_7 \cdot 10H_2O$	Sodium tetraborate decahydrate (borax)	Cleaning compounds, fireproofing agent
$Na_2S_2O_3 \cdot 5H_2O$	Sodium thiosulfate pentahydrate (hypo)	Photographic fixer

CIA Problem 9.1 Write the formula of sodium sulfate decahydrate, known as Glauber's salt and used as a laxative.

CIA Problem 9.2 What mass of Glauber's salt must be used to provide 1.00 mol of sodium sulfate?

PROBLEM 9.2

Which of the following pairs of substances would you expect to form solutions?

(a) CCl_4 and water
(b) Benzene (C_6H_6) and $MgSO_4$
(c) Hexane (C_6H_{14}) and heptane (C_7H_{16})
(d) Ethyl alcohol (C_2H_5OH) and heptanol $(C_7H_{15}OH)$

9.3 Solubility

Learning Objective:

• Define the properties of a solution, including miscibility, saturation, and solubility.

We learned in Section 9.2 that ethyl alcohol is soluble in water because hydrogen bonding is nearly as strong between water and ethyl alcohol molecules as it is between water molecules alone or ethyl alcohol molecules alone. So similar are the forces in this particular case, in fact, that the two liquids are **miscible** or mutually soluble in all pro-portions. Ethyl alcohol will continue to dissolve in water no matter how much is added.

Most substances, however, reach a solubility limit beyond which no more will dis-solve in solution. Imagine, for instance, that you are asked to prepare a saline solution (aqueous NaCl). You might measure out some water, add solid NaCl, and stir the mix-ture. Dissolution occurs rapidly at first but then slows down as more and more NaCl is added. Eventually the dissolution stops because an equilibrium is reached when the numbers of Na^+ and Cl^- ions leaving a crystal and going into solution are equal to the numbers of ions returning from solution to the crystal. At this point, the solution is said to be **saturated.** A maximum of 35.8 g of NaCl will dissolve in 100 mL of water at 20 °C. Any amount above this limit simply sinks to the bottom of the container and sits there.

The equilibrium reached by a saturated solution is like the equilibrium reached by a reversible reaction (Section 7.7). Both are dynamic situations in which no *ap-parent* change occurs because the rates of forward and backward processes are equal. Solute particles leave the solid surface and reenter the solid from solution at the same rate.

The maximum amount of a substance that will dissolve in a given amount of a sol-vent at a given temperature, usually expressed in grams per 100 mL (g/100 mL), is called the substance's **solubility.** Solubility is a characteristic property of a specific solute–solvent combination, and different substances have greatly differing solubilities. Only 9.6 g of sodium hydrogen carbonate will dissolve in 100 mL of water at 20 °C, for instance, but 204 g of sucrose will dissolve under the same conditions.

Miscible Mutually soluble in all proportions.

Saturated solution A solution that contains the maximum amount of dissolved solute at equilibrium.

$$Solid\ solute \underset{Crystallize}{\overset{Dissolve}{\rightleftarrows}} Solution$$

Solubility The maximum amount of a substance that will dissolve in a given amount of solvent at a specified temperature.

9.4 The Effect of Temperature on Solubility

Learning Objective:

• Determine the effect of temperature changes on the solubility of a solute in a solution.

As anyone who has ever made tea or coffee knows, temperature often has a dramatic effect on solubility. The compounds in tea leaves or coffee beans, for instance, dissolve easily in hot water but not in cold water. The effect of temperature is different for every substance, however, and is usually unpredictable. As shown in Figure 9.3a, the solubili-ties of most molecular and ionic solids increase with increasing temperature, but the

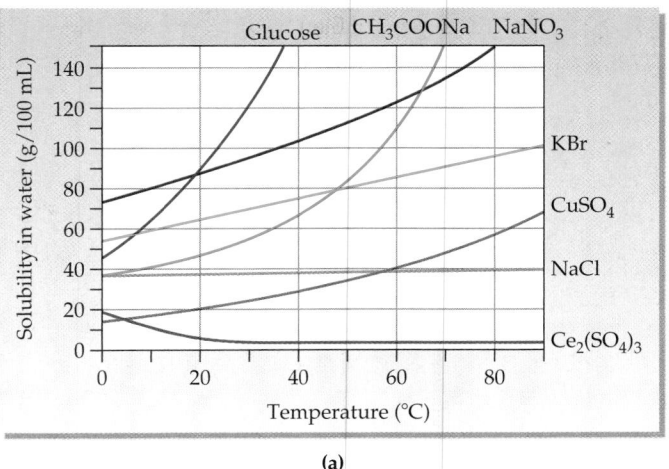

(a)

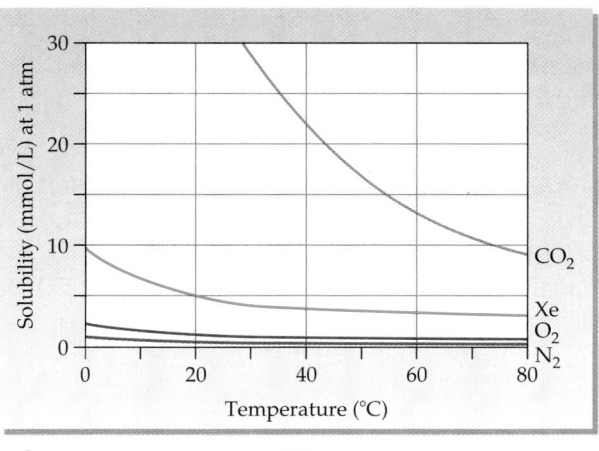

(b)

▲ **Figure 9.3**
Solubilities of some (a) solids and (b) gases in water as a function of temperature.
Most solid substances become more soluble as temperature rises (although the exact relationship is usually complex), whereas the solubility of gases decreases.

▲ **Figure 9.4**
A supersaturated solution of sodium acetate in water.
When a tiny seed crystal is added, larger crystals rapidly grow and precipitate from the solution until equilibrium is reached.

solubilities of others (NaCl) are almost unchanged, and the solubilities of still others $[Ce_2(SO_4)_3]$ decrease with increasing temperature.

Solids that are more soluble at high temperature than at low temperature can sometimes form **supersaturated solutions,** which contain even more solute than a saturated solution. Suppose, for instance, that a large amount of a substance is dissolved at a high temperature. As the solution cools, the solubility decreases and the excess solute should precipitate to maintain equilibrium. But if the cooling is done very slowly, and if the container stands quietly, crystallization might not occur immediately and a supersaturated solution might result. Such a solution is unstable, however, and precipitation can occur dramatically when a tiny seed crystal is added to initiate crystal growth or when the container is disturbed (Figure 9.4).

Unlike solids, the influence of temperature on the solubility of gases *is* predictable: Addition of heat decreases the solubility of most gases, as seen in Figure 9.3b (helium is the only common exception). One result of this temperature-dependent decrease in gas solubility can sometimes be noted in a stream or lake near the outflow of warm water from an industrial operation. As water temperature increases, the concentration of dissolved oxygen in the water decreases, killing fish that cannot tolerate the lower oxygen levels.

Worked Example 9.2 Solubility of Gases: Effect of Temperature

From the following graph of solubility versus temperature for O_2, estimate the concentration of dissolved oxygen in water at 25 °C and at 35 °C. By what percentage does the concentration of O_2 change?

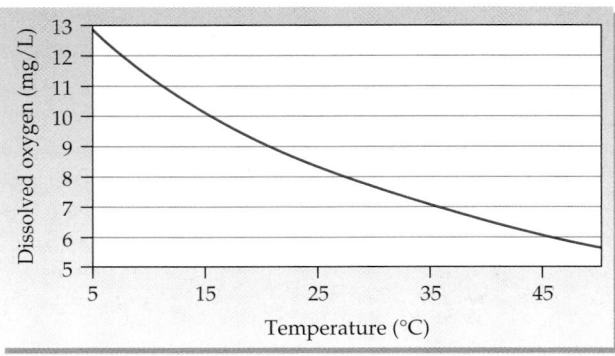

ANALYSIS The solubility of O_2 (on the *y*-axis) can be determined by finding the appropriate temperature (on the *x*-axis) and extrapolating. The percent change is calculated as

$$\frac{(\text{Solubility at } 25\,°C) - (\text{Solubility at } 35\,°C)}{(\text{Solubility at } 25\,°C)} \times 100$$

SOLUTION
From the graph, we estimate that the solubility of O_2 at 25 °C is approximately 8.3 mg/L and at 35 °C is 7.0 mg/L. The percent change in solubility is

$$\frac{8.3 - 7.0}{8.3} \times 100 = 16$$

Supersaturated solution A solution that contains more than the maximum amount of dissolved solute; a nonequilibrium situation.

PROBLEM 9.3

A solution is prepared by dissolving 12.5 g of KBr in 20 mL of water at 60 °C (see Figure 9.3). Is this solution saturated, unsaturated, or supersaturated? What will happen if the solution is cooled to 10 °C?

9.5 The Effect of Pressure on Solubility: Henry's Law

Learning Objective:

• Determine the effect of a change in pressure on the solubility of a gas in solution.

Pressure has virtually no effect on the solubility of a solid or liquid, but it has a strong effect on the solubility of a gas. According to **Henry's law,** the solubility (or concentration) of a gas in a liquid is directly proportional to the partial pressure of the gas over the liquid. If the partial pressure of the gas doubles, solubility doubles; if the gas pressure is halved, solubility is halved (Figure 9.5).

◀◀◀ **CONCEPTS TO REVIEW** Recall from Section 8.11 that each gas in a mixture exerts a partial pressure independent of other gases present (Dalton's law of partial pressures).

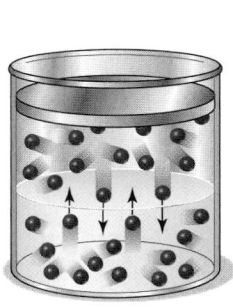 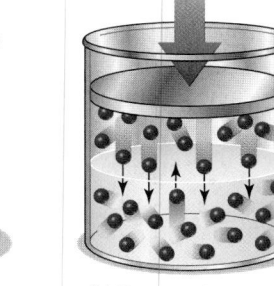 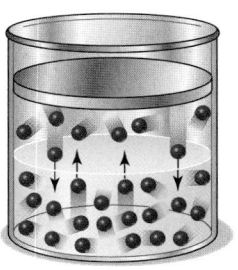

| (a) Equilibrium | (b) Pressure increase | (c) Equilibrium restored |

◀ **Figure 9.5**
Henry's law.
The solubility of a gas is directly proportional to its partial pressure. An increase in pressure causes more gas molecules to enter solution until equilibrium is restored between the dissolved and undissolved gas.

Henry's law   The solubility (or concentration) of a gas is directly proportional to the partial pressure of the gas if the temperature is constant. That is, concentration *(C)* divided by pressure *(P)* is constant when *T* is constant, or

$$\frac{C}{P_{gas}} = k \quad \text{(At a constant temperature)}$$

Henry's law can be explained using Le Châtelier's principle. In the case of a saturated solution of a gas in a liquid, an equilibrium exists whereby gas molecules enter and leave the solution at the same rate. When the system is stressed by increasing the pressure of the gas, more gas molecules go into solution to relieve that increase. Conversely, when the pressure of the gas is decreased, more gas molecules come out of solution to relieve the decrease.

◀◀◀ Le Châtelier's principle states that when a system at equilibrium is placed under stress, the equilibrium shifts to relieve that stress (Section 7.9).

As an example of Henry's law in action, think about the fizzing that occurs when you open a bottle of soft drink or champagne. The bottle is sealed under greater than 1 atm of CO_2 pressure, causing some of the CO_2 to dissolve. When the bottle is opened, however, CO_2 pressure drops and gas comes fizzing out of solution.

[Pressure increases ⟶]
Gas + Solvent ⇌ Solution

Writing Henry's law in the form $P_{gas} = C/k$ shows that partial pressure can be used to express the concentration of a gas in a solution, a practice especially common in health-related sciences. Table 9.3 gives some typical values and illustrates the convenience of having the same unit for concentration of a gas in both air and blood. Compare the oxygen partial pressures in saturated alveolar air (air in the lungs) and in arterial blood, for instance. The values are almost the same because the gases dissolved in blood come to equilibrium with the same gases in the lungs.

If the partial pressure of a gas over a solution changes while the temperature is constant, the new solubility of the gas can be found easily. Because C/P is a constant value at constant temperature, Henry's law can be restated to show how one variable changes if the other changes.

$$\frac{C_1}{P_1} = \frac{C_2}{P_2} = k \quad \text{(Where } k \text{ is constant at a fixed temperature)}$$

Worked Example 9.3 gives an illustration of how to use this equation.

Table 9.3 Partial Pressures and Normal Gas Concentrations in Body Fluids

	Partial Pressure (mmHg)			
Sample	P_{N_2}	P_{O_2}	P_{CO_2}	P_{H_2O}
Inspired air (dry)	597	159	0.3	3.7
Alveolar air (saturated)	573	100	40	47
Expired air (saturated)	569	116	28	47
Arterial blood	573	95	40	
Venous blood	573	40	45	
Peripheral tissues	573	40	45	

Worked Example 9.3 Solubility of Gases: Henry's Law

At a partial pressure of oxygen in the atmosphere of 159 mmHg, the solubility of oxygen in blood is 0.44 g/100 mL. What is the solubility of oxygen in blood at 26,000 ft, where the partial pressure of O_2 is 56 mmHg?

ANALYSIS According to Henry's law, the solubility of the gas divided by its pressure is constant.

$$\frac{C_1}{P_1} = \frac{C_2}{P_2}$$

Of the four variables in this equation, we know P_1, C_1, and P_2, and we need to find C_2.

BALLPARK ESTIMATE The pressure drops by a factor of about 3 (from 159 mmHg to 56 mmHg). Since the ratio of solubility to pressure is constant, the solubility must also drop by a factor of 3 (from 0.44 g/100 mL to about 0.15 g/100 mL).

SOLUTION

STEP 1: Identify known information. We have values for P_1, C_1, and P_2.

$P_1 = 159$ mmHg
$C_1 = 0.44$ g/100 mL
$P_2 = 56$ mmHg

STEP 2: Identify answer and units. We are looking for the solubility of O_2 (C_2) at a partial pressure P_2.

Solubility of O_2, $C_2 = $?? g/100 mL

STEP 3: Identify conversion factors or equations. In this case, we restate Henry's law to solve for C_2.

$$\frac{C_1}{P_1} = \frac{C_2}{P_2} \Rightarrow C_2 = \frac{C_1 P_2}{P_1}$$

STEP 4: Solve. Substitute the known values into the equation and calculate C_2.

$$C_2 = \frac{C_1 P_2}{P_1} = \frac{(0.44 \text{ g}/100 \text{ mL})(56 \text{ mmHg})}{159 \text{ mmHg}} = 0.15 \text{ g}/100 \text{ mL}$$

BALLPARK CHECK The calculated answer matches our estimate.

PROBLEM 9.4

At 20 °C and a partial pressure of 760 mmHg, the solubility of CO_2 in water is 0.169 g/100 mL. What is the solubility of CO_2 at 2.5×10^4 mmHg?

PROBLEM 9.5

At a total atmospheric pressure of 1.00 atm, the partial pressure of CO_2 in air is approximately 4.0×10^{-4} atm. Using the data in Problem 9.4, what is the solubility of CO_2 in an open bottle of seltzer water at 20 °C?

9.6 Units of Concentration

Learning Objective:

• Define units of concentration, and calculate the concentration of a solute in solution.

Although we speak casually of a solution of, say, orange juice as either "dilute" or "concentrated," laboratory work usually requires an exact knowledge of a solution's concentration. As indicated in Table 9.4, there are several common methods for expressing concentration. The units differ, but all the methods describe how much solute is present in a given quantity of solution.

Table 9.4 Some Units for Expressing Concentration

Concentration Measure	Solute Measure	Solution Measure
Percent		
Mass/mass percent, (m/m)%	Mass (g)	Mass (g)
Volume/volume percent, (v/v)%	Volume*	Volume*
Mass/volume percent, (m/v)%	Mass (g)	Volume (mL)
Parts per million, ppm	Parts*	10^6 parts*
Parts per billion, ppb	Parts*	10^9 parts*
Molarity, M	Moles	Volume (L)

*Any units can be used as long as they are the same for both solute and solution.

Let us look at each of the concentration measures listed in Table 9.4 individually, beginning with *percent concentrations.*

Percent Concentrations

Percent concentrations express the amount of solute in 100 units of solution. The amount of solute and the amount of solution can be represented in units of mass or volume. For solid solutions, such as a metal alloy, concentrations are typically expressed as **mass/mass percent concentration, (m/m)%.**

$$(m/m)\% \text{ concentration} = \frac{\text{Mass of solute (g)}}{\text{Mass of solution (g)}} \times 100$$

mass/mass percent concentration, (m/m)% Concentration expressed as the number of grams of solute per 100 g of solution.

For example, the mass percent of copper in a red-gold ring that contains 19.20 g of gold and 4.80 g of copper would be calculated as

$$(m/m)\% \text{ Cu} = \frac{\text{mass of Cu (g)}}{\text{mass of Cu (g)} + \text{mass of Au (g)}} \times 100$$

$$= \frac{4.80 \text{ g}}{4.80 \text{ g} + 19.20 \text{ g}} \times 100 = 20.0$$

The concentration of a solution made by dissolving one liquid in another is often given by expressing the volume of solute as a percentage of the volume of final solution—the **volume/volume percent concentration, (v/v)%.**

$$(v/v)\% \text{ concentration} = \frac{\text{Volume of solute (mL)}}{\text{Volume of solution (mL)}} \times 100$$

volume/volume percent concentration, (v/v)% Concentration expressed as the number of milliliters of solute dissolved in 100 mL of solution.

For example, if 10.0 mL of ethyl alcohol is dissolved in enough water to give 100.0 mL of solution, the ethyl alcohol concentration is $(10.0 \text{ mL}/100.0 \text{ mL}) \times 100 = 10.0\% \text{ (v/v)}$.

A third common method for expressing percent concentration is to give the number of grams (mass) as a percentage of the number of milliliters (volume) of the final solution—called the **mass/volume percent concentration, (m/v)%.**

mass/volume percent concentration, (m/v)% Concentration expressed as the number of grams of solute per 100 mL of solution.

CHEMISTRY IN ACTION

✝ Breathing and Oxygen Transport

Like all other animals, humans need oxygen. When we breathe, the freshly inspired air travels through the bronchial passages and into the lungs. The oxygen then diffuses through the delicate walls of the approximately 150 million alveolar sacs of the lungs and into arterial blood, which transports it to all body tissues.

. Only about 3% of the oxygen in blood is dissolved; the rest is chemically bound to *hemoglobin* molecules, large proteins with *heme* groups embedded in them. Each hemoglobin molecule contains four heme groups, and each heme group contains an iron atom that is able to bind one O_2 molecule. Thus, a single hemoglobin molecule can bind up to four molecules of oxygen. The entire system of oxygen transport and delivery in the body depends on the pickup and release of O_2 by hemoglobin (Hb) according to the following series of equilibria:

$$O_2(\text{lungs}) \rightleftharpoons O_2(\text{blood}) \quad (\text{Henry's law})$$
$$Hb + 4\,O_2(\text{blood}) \rightleftharpoons Hb(O_2)_4$$
$$Hb(O_2)_4 \rightleftharpoons Hb + 4O_2(\text{cell})$$

The delivery of oxygen depends on the concentration of O_2 in the various tissues, as measured by partial pressure (P_{O_2}, Table 9.3). The amount of oxygen carried by hemoglobin at any given value of P_{O_2} is usually expressed as a percent saturation and can be found from the curve shown in the accompanying figure. When $P_{O_2} = 100$ mmHg, the saturation in the lungs is 97.5%, meaning that each hemoglobin is carrying close to its maximum of four O_2 molecules. When $P_{O_2} = 26$ mmHg, however, the saturation drops to 50%.

So, how does the body ensure that enough oxygen is available to the various tissues? When large amounts of oxygen are needed—during a strenuous workout, for example—oxygen is released from hemoglobin to the hardworking, oxygen-starved muscle cells, where P_{O_2} is low. Increasing the supply of oxygen to the blood (by breathing harder and faster) shifts all the equilibria toward the right, according to Le Châtelier's principle (Section 7.9), to supply the additional O_2 needed by the muscles.

What about people living at high altitudes? In Leadville, CO, for example, where the altitude is 10,156 ft, the P_{O_2} in the lungs is only about 68 mmHg. Hemoglobin is only 90% saturated with O_2 at this pressure, meaning that less oxygen is available for delivery to the tissues. The body responds by producing erythropoietin (EPO), a hormone that stimulates the bone marrow to produce more red blood cells and hemoglobin molecules. The increase in Hb provides more capacity for O_2 transport and drives the Hb + O_2 equilibria to the right.

World-class athletes use the mechanisms of increased oxygen transport associated with higher levels of hemoglobin

▲ At high altitudes, the partial pressure of oxygen in the air is too low to saturate hemoglobin sufficiently. Additional oxygen is therefore needed.

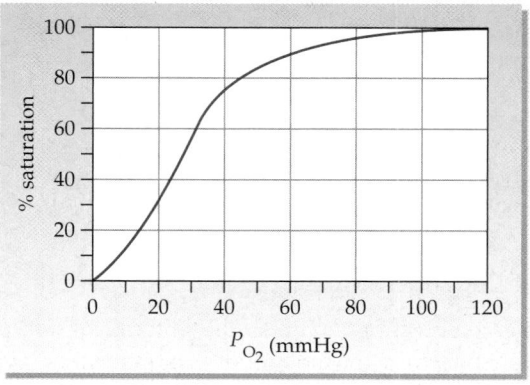

▲ An oxygen-carrying curve for hemoglobin. The percent saturation of the oxygen binding sites on hemoglobin depends on the partial pressure of oxygen P_{O_2}.

to enhance their performance. High-altitude training centers have sprung up, with living and training regimens designed to increase blood EPO levels. Unfortunately, some athletes have also tried to "cheat" by using injections of EPO and synthetic analogs and "blood doping" to boost performance. This has led the governing bodies of many sports federations, including the Olympic Committee, to start testing for such abuse.

CIA Problem 9.3 How does the body increase oxygen availability at high altitude?

CIA Problem 9.4 The height of Mt. Kilimanjaro in Africa is 5895 m (19,340 ft). The atmospheric pressure at this altitude is 374 mmHg. Assuming that the atmosphere is 18% oxygen (by volume), calculate the partial pressure of O_2, and determine the percent saturation of O_2 in blood.

Mathematically, $(m/v)\%$ concentration is found by taking the number of grams of solute per milliliter of solution and multiplying by 100.

$$(\mathbf{m/v})\% \textbf{ concentration} = \frac{\text{Mass of solute (g)}}{\text{Volume of solution (mL)}} \times 100$$

For example, if 15 g of glucose is dissolved in enough water to give 100 mL of solution, the glucose concentration is 15 g/100 mL or 15% (m/v).

$$\frac{15 \text{ g glucose}}{100 \text{ mL solution}} \times 100 = 15\% \text{ (m/v)}$$

To prepare 100 mL of a specific mass/volume solution, the weighed solute is dissolved in just enough solvent to give a final volume of 100 mL, not in an initial volume of 100 mL solvent. (If the solute is dissolved in 100 mL of solvent, the final volume of the solution will likely be a bit larger than 100 mL, since the volume of the solute is included.) In practice, the appropriate amount of solute is weighed and placed in a *volumetric flask,* as shown in Figure 9.6. Enough solvent is then added to dissolve the solute, and further solvent is added until an accurately calibrated final volume is reached. The solution is then shaken until it is uniformly mixed. Worked Examples 9.4–9.7 illustrate how percent concentrations can be calculated for a solution, or how the percent concentration can be used as a conversion factor to determine the amount of solute in a given amount of solution.

(a)

(b)

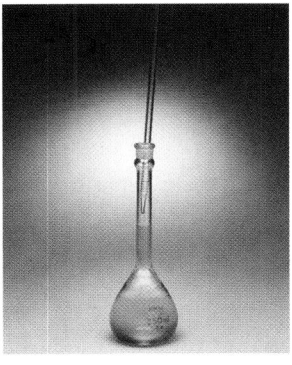
(c)

◄ **Figure 9.6**
Preparing a solution of known mass/volume percent concentration, (m/v)%.
(a) A measured number of grams of solute is placed in a volumetric flask. (b) Enough solvent is added to dissolve the solute by swirling. (c) Further solvent is carefully added until the calibration mark on the neck of the flask is reached, and the solution is shaken until uniform.

Worked Example 9.4 Mass Percent as Conversion Factor: Mass of Solution to Mass of Solute

The percentage of gold in jewelry is typically reported in carats, with 24 carats representing 100% gold. A sample of 18-carat gold would contain 18 g of gold in 24 g of metal, which would equal a $(m/m)\%$ of 75%. Calculate the mass of gold in a 5.05 g ring that is 18-carat gold.

ANALYSIS We are given a concentration and the total mass of the sample solution (the gold alloy in the ring), and we need to find the mass of gold by rearranging the equation for $(m/m)\%$ concentration.

BALLPARK ESTIMATE A 75% (m/m) solution contains 75 g for every 100 g of solution, so 10 g contains 7.5 g. The mass of the ring is a little more than 5 g (or half of 10 g) so the amount of gold in the ring will be slightly more than half of 7.5 g, or ∼3.8 g gold.

SOLUTION

$$(5.05 \text{ g})\left(\frac{75 \text{ g Au}}{100 \text{ g solution}}\right) = 3.79 \text{ g Au}$$

BALLPARK CHECK The calculated answer is consistent with our estimate of 3.8 g gold.

Worked Example 9.5 Volume Percent as Conversion Factor: Volume of Solution
to Volume of Solute

How many milliliters of methyl alcohol are needed to prepare 75 mL of a 5.0% (v/v) solution?

ANALYSIS We are given a solution volume (75 mL) and a concentration (5.0% (v/v), meaning 5.0 mL solute/100 mL solution). The concentration acts as a conversion factor for finding the amount of methyl alcohol needed.

BALLPARK ESTIMATE A 5% (v/v) solution contains 5 mL of solute in 100 mL of solution, so the amount of solute in 75 mL of solution must be about three-fourths of 5 mL, which means between 3 and 4 mL.

SOLUTION

$$(75 \text{ mL solution})\left(\frac{5.0 \text{ mL methyl alcohol}}{100 \text{ mL solution}}\right) = 3.8 \text{ mL methyl alcohol}$$

BALLPARK CHECK The calculated answer is consistent with our estimate of between 3 and 4 mL.

Worked Example 9.6 Solution Concentration: Mass/Volume Percent

A solution of heparin sodium, an anticoagulant for blood, contains 1.8 g of heparin sodium dissolved to make a final volume of 15 mL of solution. What is the mass/volume percent concentration of this solution?

ANALYSIS Mass/volume percent concentration is defined as the mass of the solute in grams divided by the volume of solution in milliliters and multiplied by 100.

BALLPARK ESTIMATE The mass of solute (1.8 g) is smaller than the volume of solvent (15 mL) by a little less than a factor of 10. The weight/volume percent should thus be a little greater than 10%.

SOLUTION

$$(\text{m/v})\% \text{ concentration} = \frac{1.8 \text{ g heparin sodium}}{15 \text{ mL}} \times 100 = 12\%(\text{m/v})$$

BALLPARK CHECK The calculated (m/v)% is reasonably close to our original estimate of 10%.

Worked Example 9.7 Mass/Volume Percent as Conversion Factor: Volume to Mass

How many grams of NaCl are needed to prepare 250 mL of a 1.5% (m/v) saline solution?

ANALYSIS We are given a concentration and a volume, and we need to find the mass of solute by rearranging the equation for (m/v)% concentration.

BALLPARK ESTIMATE The desired (m/v)% value, 1.5%, is between 1 and 2%. For a volume of 250 mL, we would need 2.5 g of solute for a 1% (m/v) solution and 5.0 g of solute for a 2% solution. Thus, for our 1.5% solution, we need a mass midway between 2.5 and 5.0 g, or about 3.8 g.

SOLUTION

Since $(\text{m/v})\% = \dfrac{\text{Mass of solute in g}}{\text{Volume of solution in mL}} \times 100$

then Mass of solute in grams $= \dfrac{(\text{Volume of solution in mL})[(\text{m/v})]\%}{100}$

$$= \frac{(250)(1.5\%)}{100} = 3.75 \text{ g} = 3.8 \text{ g NaCl}$$

(2 significant figures)

BALLPARK CHECK The calculated answer matches our estimate.

PROBLEM 9.6

A metal alloy contains 15.8% nickel (m/m)%. What mass of the metal alloy would contain 36.5 g of nickel?

PROBLEM 9.7

How would you use a 500.0 mL volumetric flask to prepare a 7.5% (v/v) solution of acetic acid in water?

PROBLEM 9.8

In clinical lab reports, some concentrations are given in mg/dL. Convert a Ca^{2+} concentration of 8.6 mg/dL to mass/volume percent.

PROBLEM 9.9

What amounts of solute or solvent are needed to prepare the following solutions?
  (a) Mass of glucose needed to prepare 125.0 mL of 16% (m/v) glucose ($C_6H_{12}O_6$).
  (b) Volume of water needed to prepare a 2.0% (m/v) KCl solution using 1.20 g KCl.

Parts per Million (ppm) or Parts per Billion (ppb)

The concentration units mass/mass percent (m/m)%, volume/volume percent (v/v)%, and mass/volume percent (w/v)% can also be defined as *parts per hundred* (pph) since 1% means one item per 100 items. When concentrations are very small, as often occurs in dealing with trace amounts of pollutants or contaminants, it is more convenient to use **parts per million (ppm)** or **parts per billion (ppb).** The "parts" can be in any unit of either mass or volume as long as the units of both solute and solvent are the same.

Parts per million (ppm) Number of parts per one million (10^6) parts.

Parts per billion (ppb) Number of parts per one billion (10^9) parts.

$$ppm = \frac{\text{Mass of solute (g)}}{\text{Mass of solution (g)}} \times 10^6 \quad or \quad \frac{\text{Volume of solute (mL)}}{\text{Volume of solution (mL)}} \times 10^6$$

$$ppb = \frac{\text{Mass of solute (g)}}{\text{Mass of solution (g)}} \times 10^9 \quad or \quad \frac{\text{Volume of solute (mL)}}{\text{Volume of solution (mL)}} \times 10^9$$

To take an example, the maximum allowable concentration in air of the organic solvent benzene (C_6H_6) is currently set by government regulation at 1 ppm. A concentration of 1 ppm means that if you take a million "parts" of air in any unit—say, mL—then one of those parts is benzene vapor and the other 999,999 parts are other gases.

$$1 \text{ ppm} = \frac{1 \text{ mL}}{1,000,000 \text{ mL}} \times 10^6$$

Because the density of water is approximately 1.0 g/mL at room temperature, 1.0 L (or 1000 mL) of an aqueous solution weighs 1000 g. Therefore, when dealing with very dilute concentrations of solutes dissolved in water, ppm is equivalent to mg solute/L solution, and ppb is equivalent to μg solute/L solution. To demonstrate that these units are equivalent, the conversion from ppm to mg/L is as follows:

$$1 \text{ ppm} = \left(\frac{1 \text{ g solute}}{10^6 \text{ g solution}}\right)\left(\frac{1 \text{ mg solute}}{10^{-3} \text{ g solute}}\right)\left(\frac{10^3 \text{ g solution}}{1 \text{ L solution}}\right) = \frac{1 \text{ mg solute}}{1 \text{ L solution}}$$

Worked Example 9.8 ppm as Conversion Factor: Mass of Solution to Mass of Solute

The maximum allowable concentration of chloroform, $CHCl_3$, in drinking water is 100 ppb. What is the maximum amount (in grams) of chloroform allowed in a glass containing 400 g (400 mL) of water?

ANALYSIS We are given a solution amount (400 g) and a concentration (100 ppb). This concentration of 100 ppb means

$$100 \text{ ppb} = \frac{\text{Mass of solute (g)}}{\text{Mass of solution (g)}} \times 10^9$$

This equation can be rearranged to find the mass of solute.

—continued on next page

—continued from previous page

BALLPARK ESTIMATE A concentration of 100 ppb means there are 100×10^{-9} g (1×10^{-7} g) of solute in 1 g of solution. In 400 g of solution, we should have 400 times this amount, or $400 \times 10^{-7} = 4 \times 10^{-5}$ g.

SOLUTION

$$\text{Mass of solute (g)} = \frac{\text{Mass of solution (g)}}{10^9} \times 100 \text{ ppb}$$

$$= \frac{400 \text{ g}}{10^9} \times 100 \text{ ppb} = 4 \times 10^{-5} \text{ g (or 0.04 mg)}$$

BALLPARK CHECK The calculated answer matches our estimate.

PROBLEM 9.10

What is the concentration in ppm of sodium fluoride in tap water that has been fluoridated by the addition of 32 mg of NaF for every 20 kg of solution?

PROBLEM 9.11

The maximum amounts of lead and copper allowed in drinking water are 0.015 mg/kg for lead and 1.3 mg/kg for copper. Express these values in parts per million, and tell the maximum amount of each (in grams) allowed in 100 g of water.

Mole/Volume Concentration: Molarity

We saw in Chapter 6 that the various relationships between amounts of reactants and products in chemical reactions are calculated in *moles* (Sections 6.1–6.3). Thus, the most generally useful means of expressing concentration in the laboratory is **molarity (M),** the number of moles of solute dissolved per liter of solution. For example, a solution made by dissolving 1.00 mol (58.5 g) of NaCl in enough water to give 1.00 L of solution has a concentration of 1.00 mol/L, or 1.00 *M*. The molarity of any solution is found by dividing the number of moles of solute by the number of liters of solution (solute + solvent).

Molarity (M) Concentration expressed as the number of moles of solute per liter of solution.

$$\textbf{Molarity (M)} = \frac{\text{Moles of solute}}{\text{Liters of solution}}$$

Note that a solution of a given molarity is prepared by dissolving the solute in enough solvent to give a *final* solution volume of 1.00 L, not by dissolving it in an *initial* volume of 1.00 L. If an initial volume of 1.00 L was used, the final solution volume might be a bit larger than 1.00 L because of the additional volume of the solute. In practice, solutions are prepared using a volumetric flask, as shown previously in Figure 9.6.

Molarity can be used as a conversion factor to relate the volume of a solution to the number of moles of solute it contains. If we know the molarity and volume of a solution, we can calculate the number of moles of solute. If we know the number of moles of solute and the molarity of the solution, we can find the solution's volume.

$$\text{Molarity} = \frac{\text{Moles of solute}}{\text{Volume of solution (L)}}$$

$$\text{Moles of solute} = \text{Molarity} \times \text{Volume of solution}$$

$$\text{Volume of solution} = \frac{\text{Moles of solute}}{\text{Molarity}}$$

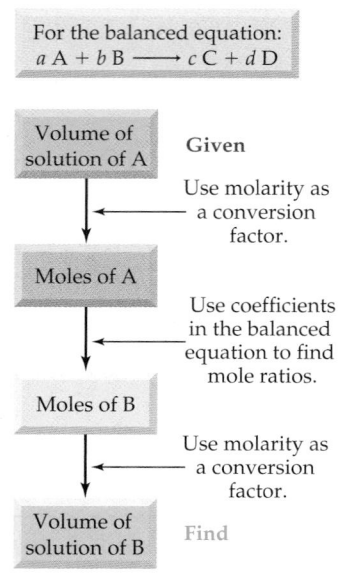

▲ **Figure 9.7**
Molarity and conversions.
A flow diagram summarizing the use of molarity for conversions between solution volume and moles to find quantities of reactants and products for chemical reactions in solution.

The flow diagram in Figure 9.7 shows how molarity is used in calculating the quantities of reactants or products in a chemical reaction, and Worked Examples 9.10 and 9.11 show how the calculations are done. Note that Problem 9.14 employs *millimolar* (mM) concentrations, which are useful in health-care fields for expressing low concentrations such as are often found in body fluids (1 mM = 0.001 *M*).

Worked Example 9.9 Solution Concentration: Molarity

What is the molarity of a solution made by dissolving 2.355 g of sulfuric acid (H_2SO_4) in water and diluting to a final volume of 50.0 mL? The molar mass of H_2SO_4 is 98.1 g/mol.

ANALYSIS Molarity is defined as moles of solute per liter of solution: $M = $ mol/L. Thus, we must first find the number of moles of sulfuric acid by doing a mass to mole conversion and then divide the number of moles by the volume of the solution.

BALLPARK ESTIMATE The molar mass of sulfuric acid is about 100 g/mol, so 2.355 g is roughly 0.025 mol. The volume of the solution is 50.0 mL, or 0.05 L, so we have about 0.025 mol of acid in 0.05 L of solution, which is a concentration of about 0.5 M.

SOLUTION

STEP 1: Identify known information. We know the mass of sulfuric acid and the final volume of solution.

Mass of H_2SO_4 = 2.355 g
Volume of solution = 50.0 mL

STEP 2: Identify answer including units. We need to find the molarity *(M)* in units of moles per liter.

$$\text{Molarity} = \frac{\text{Moles } H_2SO_4}{\text{Liters of solution}}$$

STEP 3: Identify conversion factors and equations. We know both the amount of solute and the volume of solution, but first we must make two conversions: convert mass of H_2SO_4 to moles of H_2SO_4, using molar mass as a conversion factor, and convert volume from milliliters to liters.

$$(2.355 \text{ g } H_2SO_4)\left(\frac{1 \text{ mol } H_2SO_4}{98.1 \text{ g } H_2SO_4}\right) = 0.0240 \text{ mol } H_2SO_4$$

$$(50.0 \text{ mL})\left(\frac{1 \text{ L}}{1000 \text{ mL}}\right) = 0.0500 \text{ L}$$

STEP 4: Solve. Substitute the moles of solute and volume of solution into the molarity expression.

$$\text{Molarity} = \frac{0.0240 \text{ mol } H_2SO_4}{0.0500 \text{ L}} = 0.480 \ M$$

BALLPARK CHECK The calculated answer is close to our estimate, which was 0.5 M.

Worked Example 9.10 Molarity as Conversion Factor: Molarity to Mass

A blood concentration of 0.065 M ethyl alcohol (EtOH) is sufficient to induce a coma. At this concentration, what is the total mass of alcohol (in grams) in an adult male whose total blood volume is 5.6 L? The molar mass of ethyl alcohol is 46.0 g/mol. (Refer to the flow diagram in Figure 9.7 to identify which conversions are needed.)

ANALYSIS We are given a molarity (0.065 M) and a volume (5.6 L), which allows us to calculate the number of moles of alcohol in the blood. A mole to mass conversion then gives the mass of alcohol.

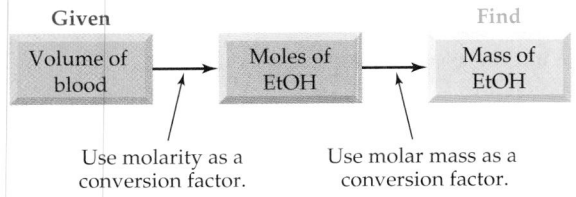

SOLUTION

$$(5.6 \text{ L blood})\left(\frac{0.065 \text{ mol EtOH}}{1 \text{ L blood}}\right) = 0.36 \text{ mol EtOH}$$

$$(0.36 \text{ mol EtOH})\left(\frac{46.0 \text{ g EtOH}}{1 \text{ mol EtOH}}\right) = 17 \text{ g EtOH}$$

Worked Example 9.11 Molarity as Conversion Factor: Molarity to Volume

In our stomachs, gastric juice that is about 0.1 M in HCl aids in digestion. How many milliliters of gastric juice will react completely with an antacid tablet that contains 500 mg of magnesium hydroxide? The molar mass of $Mg(OH)_2$ is 58.3 g/mol, and the balanced equation is

$$2\,HCl(aq) + Mg(OH)_2(aq) \longrightarrow MgCl_2(aq) + 2\,H_2O(l)$$

ANALYSIS We are given the molarity of HCl and need to find the volume. We first convert the mass of $Mg(OH)_2$ to moles and then use the coefficients in the balanced equation to find the moles of HCl that will react. Once we have the moles of HCl and the molarity in moles per liter, we can find the volume.

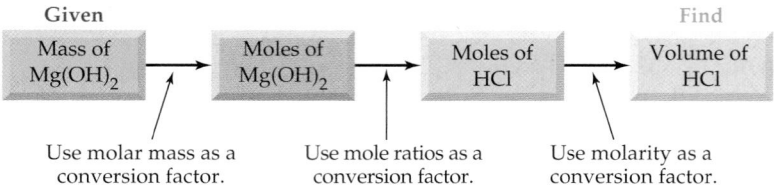

SOLUTION

$$[500\text{ mg Mg(OH)}_2]\left(\frac{1\text{ g}}{1000\text{ mg}}\right)\left[\frac{1\text{ mol Mg(OH)}_2}{58.3\text{ g Mg(OH)}_2}\right] = 0.008\,58\text{ mol Mg(OH)}_2$$

$$[0.00858\text{ mol Mg(OH)}_2]\left[\frac{2\text{ mol HCl}}{1\text{ mol Mg(OH)}_2}\right]\left(\frac{1\text{ L HCl}}{0.1\text{ mol HCl}}\right) = 0.2\text{ L }(200\text{ mL})$$

PROBLEM 9.12

What is the molarity of a solution that contains 50.0 g of vitamin B_1 hydrochloride (molar mass = 337 g/mol) in 160 mL of solution?

PROBLEM 9.13

How many moles of solute are present in the following solutions?

(a) 175 mL of 0.35 M $NaNO_3$

(b) 480 mL of 1.4 M HNO_3

PROBLEM 9.14

The concentration of cholesterol ($C_{27}H_{46}O$) in blood is approximately 5.0 mM. How many grams of cholesterol are in 250 mL of blood?

PROBLEM 9.15

Calcium carbonate reacts with HCl according to the following equation:

$$2\,HCl(aq) + CaCO_3(aq) \longrightarrow CaCl_2(aq) + H_2O(l) + CO_2(g)$$

(a) How many moles of HCl are in 65 mL of 0.12 M HCl?

(b) What mass of calcium carbonate (in grams) is needed for complete reaction with the HCl in (a)?

9.7 Dilution

Learning Objective:

• Use dilution factors to calculate molarities or volumes of dilute solutions prepared from concentrated solutions.

Many solutions, from orange juice to chemical reagents, are stored in high concentrations and then prepared for use by *dilution*—that is, by adding additional solvent to lower the concentration. For example, you might make up 1/2 gal of orange juice by adding water to a canned concentrate. In the same way, you might buy a medicine or chemical reagent as a concentrated solution and dilute it before use.

The key fact to remember about dilution is that the amount of *solute* remains constant; only the *volume* is changed by adding more solvent. If, for example, the initial and final concentrations are given in molarity, then we know that the number of moles of solute is the same both before and after dilution and can be determined by multiplying molarity times volume.

$$\text{Number of moles} = \text{Molarity (mol/L)} \times \text{Volume (L)}$$
$$M = \text{moles/volume}$$

Because the number of moles remains constant, we can set up the following equation, where M_c and V_c refer to the concentrated solution (before dilution), and M_d and V_d refer to the solution after dilution.

$$\text{Moles of solute} = M_c V_c = M_d V_d$$

This equation can be rewritten to solve for M_d, the concentration of the solution after dilution.

$$M_d = M_c \times \frac{V_c}{V_d}, \quad \text{where} \quad \frac{V_c}{V_d} \quad \text{is a } \textit{dilution factor.}$$

The equation shows that the concentration after dilution (M_d) can be found by multiplying the initial concentration (M_c) by a **dilution factor,** which is simply the ratio of the initial and final solution volumes (V_c/V_d). If, for example, the solution volume *increases* by a factor of 5, from 10 mL to 50 mL, then the concentration must *decrease* to one-fifth of its initial value because the dilution factor is 10 mL/50 mL, or 1/5. Worked Example 9.12 shows how to use this relationship for calculating dilutions.

Dilution factor The ratio of the initial and final solution volumes (V_c/V_d).

The relationship between concentration and volume can also be used to find what volume of initial solution to start with to achieve a given dilution.

$$\text{Since} \quad M_c V_c = M_d V_d,$$
$$\text{then} \quad V_c = V_d \times \frac{M_d}{M_c}.$$

In this case, V_c is the initial volume that must be diluted to prepare a less concentrated solution with volume V_d. The initial volume is found by multiplying the final volume (V_d) by the ratio of the final and initial concentrations (M_d/M_c). For example, to decrease the concentration of a solution to one-fifth its initial value, the initial volume must be one-fifth the desired final volume. Worked Example 9.13 gives a sample calculation.

Although the preceding discussion and the following Worked Examples use concentration units of molarity, the dilution equation can be generalized to allow for the use of other concentration units. A more general equation would be $C_c V_c = C_d V_d$, where C refers to other concentration units, such as ppm, or m/v%.

Worked Example 9.12 Dilution of Solutions: Concentration

What is the final concentration if 75 mL of a 3.5 *M* glucose solution is diluted to a volume of 450 mL?

ANALYSIS The number of moles of solute is constant, so

$$M_c V_c = M_d V_d$$

Of the four variables in this equation, we know the initial concentration M_c (3.5 *M*), the initial volume V_c (75 mL), and the final volume V_d (450 mL), and we need to find the final concentration M_d.

BALLPARK ESTIMATE The volume increases by a factor of 6, from 75 mL to 450 mL, so the concentration must decrease by a factor of 6, from 3.5 *M* to about 0.6 *M*.

—continued on next page

—continued from previous page

SOLUTION

Solving the above equation for M_d and substituting in the known values gives

$$M_d = \frac{M_c V_c}{V_d} = \frac{(3.5 \text{ M glucose})(75 \text{ mL})}{450 \text{ mL}} = 0.58 \text{ M glucose}$$

BALLPARK CHECK The calculated answer is close to our estimate of 0.6 M.

Worked Example 9.13 Dilution of Solutions: Volume

Aqueous NaOH can be purchased at a concentration of 1.0 M. How would you use this concentrated solution to prepare 750 mL of 0.32 M NaOH?

ANALYSIS The number of moles of solute is constant, so

$$M_c V_c = M_d V_d$$

Of the four variables in this equation, we know the initial concentration M_c (1.0 M), the final volume V_d (750 mL), and the final concentration M_d (0.32 M), and we need to find the initial volume V_c.

BALLPARK ESTIMATE We want the solution concentration to decrease by a factor of about 3, from 1.0 M to 0.32 M, which means we need to dilute the 1.0 M solution by a factor of 3. This means the final volume must be about three times greater than the initial volume. Because our final volume is to be 750 mL, we must start with an initial volume of about 250 mL.

SOLUTION

Solving the above equation for V_1 and substituting in the known values gives

$$V_c = \frac{V_d M_d}{M_c} = \frac{(750 \text{ mL})(0.32 \text{ M})}{1.0 \text{ M}} = 240 \text{ mL}$$

To prepare the desired solution, dilute 240 mL of 1.0 M NaOH with water to make a final volume of 750 mL.

BALLPARK CHECK The calculated answer (240 mL) is reasonably close to our estimate of 250 mL.

PROBLEM 9.16

Aqueous ammonia is commercially available at a concentration of 16.0 M. How much of the concentrated solution would you use to prepare 500.0 mL of a 1.25 M solution?

PROBLEM 9.17

The Environmental Protection Agency has set the limit for arsenic in drinking water at 0.010 ppm. To what volume would you need to dilute 1.5 L of water containing 5.0 ppm arsenic to reach the acceptable limit?

9.8 Ions in Solution: Electrolytes

Learning Objectives:

• Identify solutes as strong electrolytes, weak electrolytes, or nonelectrolytes.
• Calculate equivalents for an ionic solute in solution.

◄◄ As we learned in Section 3.1, electricity can only flow through a medium containing charged particles that are free to move.

Look at Figure 9.8, which shows a light bulb connected to a power source through a circuit that is interrupted by two metal strips dipped into a beaker of liquid. When the strips are dipped into pure water, the bulb remains dark, but when they are dipped into an aqueous NaCl solution, the circuit is closed and the bulb lights. This simple demonstration shows that ionic compounds in aqueous solution can conduct electricity.

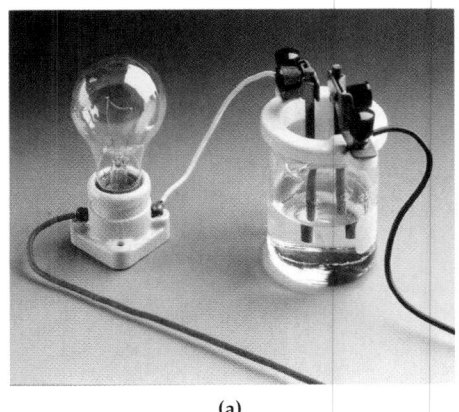 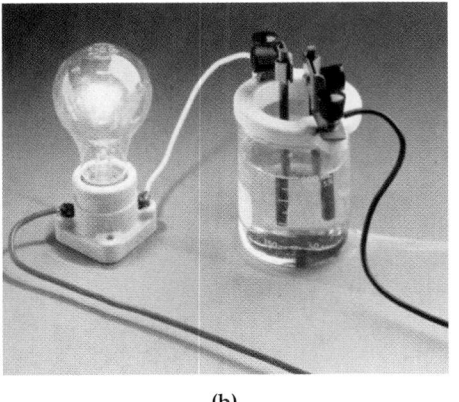

(a)   (b)

A simple demonstration shows that electricity can flow through a solution of ions.
(a) With pure water in the beaker, the circuit is incomplete, no electricity flows, and the bulb does not light.
(b) With a concentrated NaCl solution in the beaker, the circuit is complete, electricity flows, and the light bulb glows.

Substances like NaCl that conduct an electric current when dissolved in water are called **electrolytes.** Conduction occurs because negatively charged Cl^- anions migrate through the solution toward the metal strip connected to the positive terminal of the power source, whereas positively charged Na^+ cations migrate toward the strip connected to the negative terminal. As you might expect, the ability of a solution to conduct electricity depends on the concentration of ions in solution. Distilled water contains virtually no ions and is nonconducting, ordinary tap water contains low concentrations of dissolved ions (mostly Na^+, K^+, Mg^{2+}, Ca^{2+}, and Cl^-) and is weakly conducting, and a concentrated solution of NaCl is strongly conducting.

Ionic substances like NaCl that ionize completely when dissolved in water are called **strong electrolytes,** and molecular substances like acetic acid (CH_3CO_2H) that are only partially ionized are **weak electrolytes.** Molecular substances like glucose that do not produce ions when dissolved in water are **nonelectrolytes.**

Electrolyte A substance that produces ions and therefore conducts electricity when dissolved in water.

Strong electrolyte A substance that ionizes completely when dissolved in water.

Weak electrolyte A substance that is only partly ionized in water.

Nonelectrolyte A substance that does not produce ions when dissolved in water.

Strong electrolyte; completely ionized

$$NaCl(s) \xrightarrow[\text{in water}]{\text{Dissolve}} Na^+(aq) + Cl^-(aq)$$

Weak electrolyte; partly ionized

$$CH_3CO_2H(l) \underset{\text{in water}}{\overset{\text{Dissolve}}{\rightleftharpoons}} CH_3CO_2^-(aq) + H^+(aq)$$

Nonelectrolyte; not ionized

$$Glucose(s) \underset{\text{in water}}{\overset{\text{Dissolve}}{\rightleftharpoons}} Glucose(aq)$$

But what happens if strong electrolytes, such as NaCl and KBr, are dissolved in the same solution? Because the cations (K^+ and Na^+) and anions (Cl^- and Br^-) are all mixed together and no reactions occur between them, an identical solution could just as well be made from KCl and NaBr. Thus, we can no longer speak of having a NaCl + KBr solution; we can only speak of having a solution with four different ions in it.

A similar situation exists for blood and other body fluids, which contain many different anions and cations. Since they are all mixed together, it is difficult to "assign" specific cations to specific anions or to talk about specific ionic compounds. Instead, we are interested only in individual ions and in the total numbers of positive and negative charges. To discuss such mixtures, we use a new term—*equivalents* of ions. For ions, one **equivalent (Eq)** is equal to the number of ions that carry 1 mol of charge.

The number of equivalents of a given ion per liter of solution can be found by multiplying the molarity of the ion (moles per liter) by the charge on the ion. Because ion concentrations in body fluids are often low, clinical chemists find it more convenient to talk about *milliequivalents* of ions rather than equivalents. One milliequivalent (mEq) of an ion is one-hundredth of an equivalent. For example, the normal concentration of Na^+ in blood is 0.14 Eq/L, or 140 mEq/L.

Equivalent (Eq) For ions, the amount equal to 1 mol of charge.

$$1 \text{ mEq} = 0.001 \text{ Eq} \qquad 1 \text{ Eq} = 1000 \text{ mEq}$$

CHEMISTRY IN ACTION

✝ Electrolytes, Fluid Replacement, and Sports Drinks

Electrolytes are essential in many physiological processes, and significant deviations from the blood electrolyte levels listed in the following table can be potentially life-threatening if not addressed quickly. Heavy and continuous diarrhea from conditions such as cholera can result in dehydration and very low sodium levels in the body (hyponatremia). Restoration of electrolytes can be accomplished by oral rehydration therapy (ORT). The introduction of ORT in developing countries decreased infant mortality from diarrhea, which had previously been the leading cause of death in children under 5 years of age. A typical ORT solution contains sodium (75 mEq/L), potassium (75 mEq/L), chloride (65 mEq/L), citrate (10 mEq/L), and glucose (75 mmol/L). Heavy sweating during strenuous exercise can also lead to dehydration and loss of electrolytes.

▲ An athlete places labels on electrolyte solutions for easy identification. These solutions will be distributed at hydration stations for his use during a long-distance competition.

Concentrations of Major Electrolytes in Blood Plasma

Cation	Concentration (mEq/L)
Na^+	136–145
Ca^{2+}	4.5–6.0
K^+	3.6–5.0
Mg^{2+}	3

Anion	Concentration (mEq/L)
Cl^-	98–106
HCO_3^-	25–29
SO_4^{2-} and HPO_4^{2-}	2

If water and electrolytes are not replaced, dehydration, hyperthermia and heat stroke, dizziness, nausea, muscle cramps, impaired kidney function, and other difficulties ensue. As a rule of thumb, a sweat loss equal to 5% of body weight—about 3.5 L for a 150 lb person—is the maximum amount that can be safely allowed for a well-conditioned athlete.

Plain water works perfectly well to replace sweat during short bouts of activity, but a carbohydrate–electrolyte beverage, or "sports drink," is much superior for rehydrating during and after longer activity in which substantial amounts of electrolytes have been lost. While some sports drinks are little more than overpriced sugar–water solutions, others are carefully formulated and highly effective for fluid replacement. Nutritional research has shown that a serious sports drink should meet the following criteria.

- The drink should contain 6–8% of soluble complex carbohydrates (about 15 g per 8 oz serving) and only a small amount of simple sugar for taste. The complex carbohydrates, which usually go by the name "maltodextrin," provide a slow release of glucose into the bloodstream to provide a steady source of energy and enhance the absorption of water from the stomach.
- The drink should contain electrolytes to replenish those lost in sweat, about 100 mg sodium, 100 mg potassium, and 25 mg magnesium per 8 oz serving.
- The drink should be noncarbonated because carbonation can cause gastrointestinal upset during exercise, and it should not contain caffeine, which acts as a diuretic.
- The drink should taste good so the athlete will want to drink it. Thirst is a poor indicator of fluid requirements, and most people will drink less than needed unless a beverage is flavored.

In addition to complex carbohydrates, electrolytes, and flavorings, some sports drinks also contain vitamin A (as beta-carotene), vitamin C (ascorbic acid), and selenium, which act as antioxidants to protect cells from damage. Some drinks also contain the amino acid glutamine, which appears to lessen lactic acid buildup in muscles and thus helps muscles bounce back more quickly after an intense workout.

CIA Problem 9.5 What are the major electrolytes in sweat, and what are their approximate concentrations in mEq/L?

CIA Problem 9.6 Why is a sport drink more effective than plain water for rehydration after extended exercise?

CIA Problem 9.7 A typical sport drink for electrolyte replacement contains 20 mEq/L of Na^+ and 10 mEq/L of K^+ ions. Convert these concentrations to m/v%.

Worked Example 9.14 Equivalents as Conversion Factors: Volume to Mass

The normal concentration of Ca^{2+} in blood is 5.0 mEq/L. How many milligrams of Ca^{2+} are in 1.00 L of blood?

ANALYSIS We are given a volume and a concentration in milliequivalents per liter, and we need to find an amount in milligrams. Thus, we need to calculate the equivalents/mol (or mEq/mmol) for Ca^{2+} and then use concentration and molar mass (g/mol or mg/mmol) as conversion factors between volume and mass, as indicated in the following flow diagram:

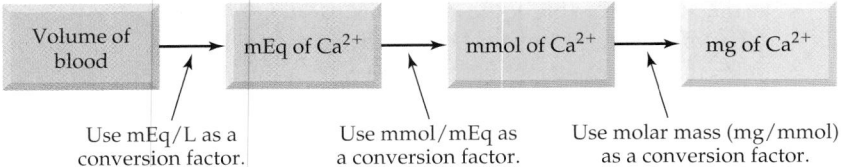

Use mEq/L as a conversion factor.   Use mmol/mEq as a conversion factor.   Use molar mass (mg/mmol) as a conversion factor.

BALLPARK ESTIMATE The molar mass of calcium is 40.08 g/mol, and the calcium ion carries a charge of 2+. Thus, 1 millimole of Ca^{2+} (40 mg) equals about 2 mEq, and 1.0 mEq would correspond to about 0.50 mmol, or 20 mg. This means that the 5.0 mEq of Ca^{2+} ions in 1.00 L of blood corresponds to a mass of 5.0 mEq $Ca^{2+} \times 20$ mg/mEq $= 100$ mg Ca^{2+}.

SOLUTION

$$(1.00 \text{ L blood})\left(\frac{5.0 \text{ mEq } Ca^{2+}}{1.0 \text{ L blood}}\right)\left(\frac{40.08 \text{ mg } Ca^{2+}}{2 \text{ mEq } Ca^{2+}}\right) = 100 \text{ mg } Ca^{2+}$$

BALLPARK CHECK The calculated answer (100 mg of Ca^{2+} in 1.00 L of blood) matches our estimate.

PROBLEM 9.18

How many grams are in 1 Eq of the following ions? How many grams in 1 mEq?

(a) K^+ **(b)** Br^- **(c)** Mg^{2+} **(d)** SO_4^{2-} **(e)** Al^{3+} **(f)** PO_4^{3-}

PROBLEM 9.19

The typical concentration of Mg^{2+} in blood is 3 mEq/L. How many milligrams of Mg^{2+} are in 250 mL of blood?

9.9 Properties of Solutions

Learning Objective:

• Calculate the colligative properties of boiling-point elevation and freezing-point depression for a solution.

The properties of solutions are similar in many respects to those of pure solvents, but there are also some interesting and important differences. One such difference is that solutions have higher boiling points than the pure solvents; another is that solutions have lower freezing points. Pure water boils at 100.0 °C and freezes at 0.0 °C, for example, but a 1.0 M solution of NaCl in water boils at 101.0 °C and freezes at −3.7 °C.

The elevation of boiling point and the lowering of freezing point for a solution as compared with a pure solvent are examples of **colligative properties**—properties that depend on the *concentration* of a dissolved solute but not on its chemical identity. Other colligative properties are a lower vapor pressure for a solution compared with the pure solvent and *osmosis,* the migration of solvent molecules through a semipermeable membrane.

Colligative property A property of a solution that depends only on the number of dissolved particles not on their chemical identity.

Colligative Properties

• Vapor pressure is lower for a solution than for a pure solvent.
• Boiling point is higher for a solution than for a pure solvent.

- Freezing point is lower for a solution than for a pure solvent.
- Osmosis occurs when a solution is separated from a pure solvent by a semi-permeable membrane.

Vapor-Pressure Lowering in Solutions

We learned in Section 8.12 that the vapor pressure of a liquid depends on the equilibrium between molecules entering and leaving the liquid surface. Only those molecules at the surface of the liquid that are sufficiently energetic will evaporate. If, however, some of the liquid (solvent) molecules at the surface are replaced by other (solute) particles that do not evaporate, then the rate of evaporation of solvent molecules decreases and the vapor pressure of a solution is lower than that of the pure solvent (Figure 9.9). Note that the *identity* of the solute particles is irrelevant—only their concentration matters.

▶ **Figure 9.9**
Vapor-pressure lowering of solution.
(a) The vapor pressure of a solution is lower than (b) the vapor pressure of the pure solvent because fewer solvent molecules are able to escape from the surface of the solution.

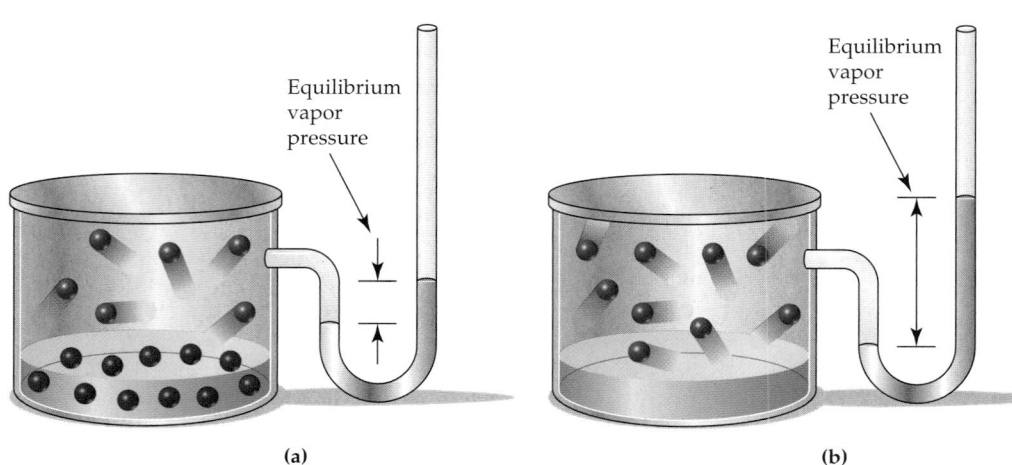

(a)   (b)

Boiling-Point Elevation of Solutions

One consequence of the vapor-pressure lowering for a solution is that the boiling point of the solution is higher than that of the pure solvent. Recall from Section 8.12 that boiling occurs when the vapor pressure of a liquid reaches atmospheric pressure. But because the vapor pressure of a solution is lower than that of the pure solvent at a given temperature, the solution must be heated to a higher temperature for its vapor pressure to reach atmospheric pressure. Figure 9.10 shows a close-up plot of vapor pressure versus temperature for pure water and for a 1.0 M NaCl solution. The vapor pressure of pure water reaches atmospheric pressure (760 mmHg) at 100.0 °C, but the vapor pressure of the NaCl solution does not reach the same point until 101.0 °C.

For each mole of solute particles added, regardless of chemical identity, the boiling point of 1 kg of water is raised by 0.51 °C, or

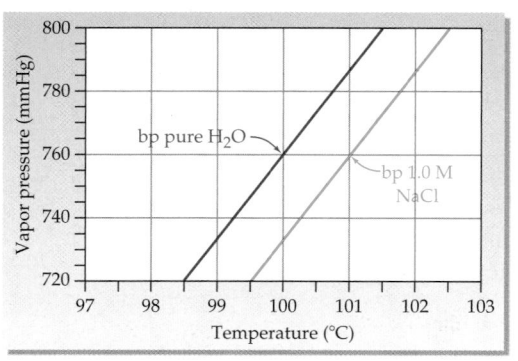

▲ **Figure 9.10**
Vapor pressure and temperature.
A close-up plot of vapor pressure versus temperature for pure water (red curve) and for a 1.0 M NaCl solution (blue curve). Pure water boils at 100.0 °C, but the solution does not boil until 101.0 °C.

$$\Delta T_{\text{boiling}} = \left(0.51\,^{\circ}\text{C}\,\frac{\text{kg water}}{\text{mol particles}}\right)\left(\frac{\text{mol particles}}{\text{kg water}}\right)$$

The addition of 1 mol of a molecular substance like glucose to 1 kg of water therefore raises the boiling point from 100.0 °C to 100.51 °C. The addition of 1 mol of NaCl per kilogram of water, however, raises the boiling point by 2 × 0.51 °C = 1.02 °C because the solution contains 2 mol of solute particles—Na^+ and Cl^- ions.

Worked Example 9.15 Properties of Solutions: Boiling-Point Elevation

What is the boiling point of a solution of 0.75 mol of KBr in 1.0 kg of water?

ANALYSIS The boiling point increases 0.51 °C for each mole of solute per kilogram of water. Since KBr is a strong electrolyte, there are 2 moles of ions (K^+ and Br^-) for every 1 mole of KBr that dissolves.

BALLPARK ESTIMATE The boiling point will increase about 0.5 °C for every 1 mol of ions in 1 kg of water. Since 0.75 mol of KBr produce 1.5 mol of ions, the boiling point should increase by (1.5 mol ions) × (0.5 °C/mol ions) = 0.75 °C.

SOLUTION

$$\Delta T_{\text{boiling}} = \left(0.51\,°C\,\frac{\text{kg water}}{\text{mol ions}}\right)\left(\frac{2\ \text{mol ions}}{1\ \text{mol KBr}}\right)\left(\frac{0.75\ \text{mol KBr}}{1.0\ \text{kg water}}\right) = 0.77\,°C$$

The normal boiling point of pure water is 100 °C, so the boiling point of the solution increases to 100.77 °C.

BALLPARK CHECK The 0.77 °C increase is consistent with our estimate of 0.75 °C.

PROBLEM 9.20

A solution is prepared by dissolving 0.67 mol of $MgCl_2$ in 0.50 kg of water.
  (a) How many moles of ions are present in solution?
  (b) What is the change in the boiling point of the aqueous solution?

PROBLEM 9.21

When 1.0 mol of HF is dissolved in 1.0 kg of water, the boiling point of the resulting solution is 100.5 °C. Is HF a strong or weak electrolyte? Explain.

◉ KEY CONCEPT PROBLEM 9.22

The diagram to the right shows plots of vapor pressure versus temperature for a solvent and a solution.
  (a) Which curve represents the pure solvent and which the solution?
  (b) What is the approximate boiling-point elevation for the solution?
  (c) What is the approximate concentration of the solution in mol/kg, if 1 mol of solute particles raises the boiling point of 1 kg of solvent by 3.63 °C?

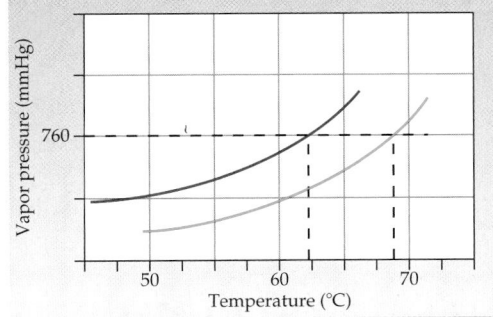

Freezing-Point Depression of Solutions

Just as solutions have lower vapor pressure and consequently higher boiling points than pure solvents, they also have lower freezing points. Motorists in cold climates take advantage of this effect when they add "antifreeze" to the water in automobile cooling systems. Antifreeze is a nonvolatile solute, usually ethylene glycol ($HOCH_2CH_2OH$), that is added in sufficient concentration to lower the freezing point below the lowest expected outdoor temperature. In the same way, salt sprinkled on icy roads lowers the freezing point of ice below the road temperature and thus causes ice to melt.

Freezing-point depression has much the same cause as vapor-pressure lowering and boiling-point elevation. Solute molecules are dispersed between solvent molecules throughout the solution, thereby making it more difficult for solvent molecules to come together and organize into ordered crystals.

For each mole of nonvolatile solute particles, the freezing point of 1 kg of water is lowered by 1.86 °C, or

$$\Delta T_{\text{freezing}} = \left(-1.86\,°C\,\frac{\text{kg water}}{\text{mol particles}}\right)\left(\frac{\text{mol particles}}{\text{kg water}}\right)$$

Thus, addition of 1 mol of antifreeze to 1 kg of water lowers the freezing point from 0.00 °C to −1.86 °C, and addition of 1 mol of NaCl (2 mol of particles) to 1 kg of water lowers the freezing point from 0.00 °C to −3.72 °C.

Worked Example 9.16 Properties of Solutions: Freezing-Point Depression

The cells of a tomato contain mostly an aqueous solution of sugar and other substances. If a typical tomato freezes at −2.5 °C, what is the concentration of dissolved particles in the tomato cells (in moles of particles per kg of water)?

ANALYSIS The freezing point decreases by 1.86 °C for each mole of solute dissolved in 1 kg of water. We can use the decrease in freezing point (2.5 °C) to find the amount of solute per kg of water.

BALLPARK ESTIMATE The freezing point will decrease by about 1.9 °C for every 1 mol of solute particles in 1 kg of water. To lower the freezing point by 2.5 °C (about 30% more) will require about 30% more solute, or 1.3 mol.

SOLUTION

$$\Delta T_{freezing} = -2.5\,°C$$

$$= \left(-1.86\,°C\,\frac{kg\ water}{mol\ solute\ particles}\right)\left(\frac{??\ mol\ solute\ particles}{1.0\ kg\ water}\right)$$

We can rearrange this expression to

$$(-2.5\,°C)\left(\frac{1}{-1.86\,°C}\,\frac{mol\ solute\ particles}{kg\ water}\right) = 1.3\,\frac{mol\ solute\ particles}{kg\ water}$$

BALLPARK CHECK The calculated answer agrees with our estimate of 1.3 mol/kg.

PROBLEM 9.23

What is the freezing point of a solution of 1.0 mol of glucose in 1.0 kg of water?

PROBLEM 9.24

When 0.5 mol of a certain ionic substance is dissolved in 1.0 kg of water, the freezing point of the resulting solution is −2.8 °C. How many ions does the substance give when it dissolves?

HANDS-ON CHEMISTRY 9.1

Place about 4–5 cups of cold water in a small pot and set in on the stove. Turn on the heat and monitor the temperature of the water every few minutes with a thermometer that can be read to the nearest 1 °C.

a. Note the temperature when you see bubbles start to form—are you at the boiling point? What is responsible for the formation of bubbles? (see Section 9.4 and Figure 9.3b)

b. As the water temperature approaches 100 °C, what happens to the bubbles? When boiling occurs, record the temperature of the water.

c. Remove the pot from the stove and carefully add half a cup of salt to the water, and stir until it is completely dissolved. Return the pot to the stove and reheat until the water again begins to boil. How does the boiling point temperature of the salt solution compare to the boiling point of pure water? Is this consistent with Figure 9.10?

9.10 Osmosis and Osmotic Pressure

Learning Objective:

- Calculate the osmotic pressure of a solution and predict the direction of solvent flow across a semipermeable membrane due to osmosis.

Certain materials, including those that make up the membranes around living cells, are *semipermeable*. They allow water and other small molecules to pass through, but they block the passage of large solute molecules or ions. When a solution and a pure solvent, or two solutions of different concentration, are separated by a semipermeable membrane, solvent molecules pass through the membrane in a process called **osmosis.** Although the passage of solvent through the membrane takes place in both directions, passage from the pure solvent side to the solution side is favored and occurs more often. As a result, the amount of liquid on the pure solvent side decreases, the amount of liquid on the solution side increases, and the concentration of the solution decreases.

    For the simplest explanation of osmosis, let us look at what happens on the molecular level. As shown in Figure 9.11, a solution inside a bulb is separated by a semipermeable membrane from pure solvent in the outer container. Solvent molecules in the outer container, because of their somewhat higher concentration, approach the membrane more frequently than do molecules in the bulb, thereby passing through more often and causing the liquid level in the attached tube to rise.

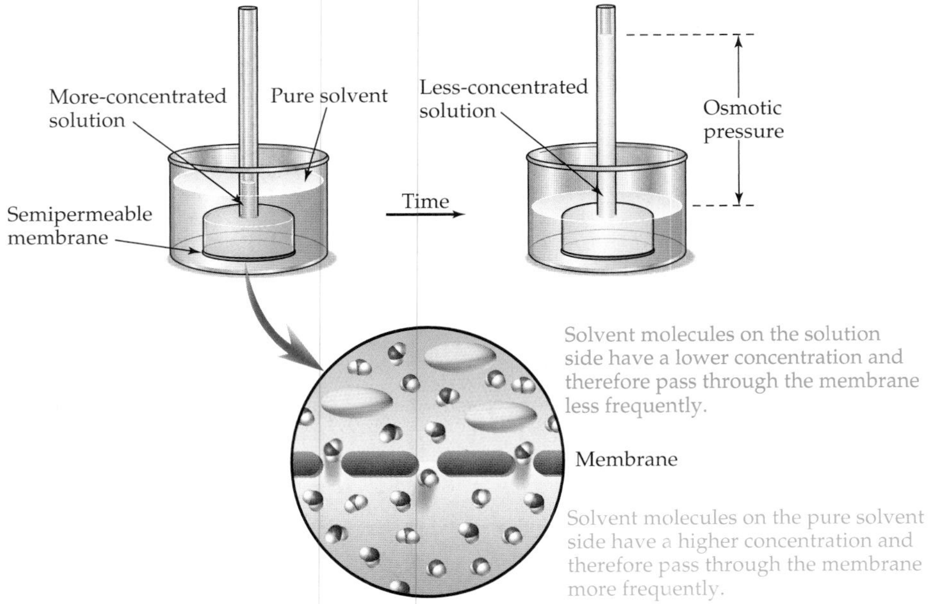

Osmosis The passage of solvent through a semipermeable membrane separating two solutions of different concentration.

◄ **Figure 9.11**
The phenomenon of osmosis.
A solution inside the bulb is separated from pure solvent in the outer container by a semipermeable membrane. Solvent molecules in the outer container have a higher concentration than molecules in the bulb and therefore pass through the membrane more frequently. The liquid in the tube therefore rises until an equilibrium is reached. At equilibrium, the osmotic pressure exerted by the column of liquid in the tube is sufficient to prevent further net passage of solvent.

As the liquid in the tube rises, its increased weight creates an increased pressure that pushes solvent back through the membrane until the rates of forward and reverse passage become equal and the liquid level stops rising. The amount of pressure necessary to achieve this equilibrium is called the **osmotic pressure** (π) of the solution and can be determined from the following expression:

$$\pi = \left(\frac{n}{V}\right)RT$$

where n is the number of moles of particles in the solution, V is the solution volume, R is the gas constant (Section 8.10), and T is the absolute temperature of the solution. Note the similarity between this equation for the osmotic pressure of a solution and the equation for the pressure of an ideal gas, $P = (n/V)RT$. In both cases, the pressure has units of atmospheres.

    Osmotic pressures can be extremely high, even for relatively dilute solutions. The osmotic pressure of a 0.15 M NaCl solution at 25 °C, for example, is 7.3 atm, a value that supports a difference in water level of approximately 250 ft!

Osmotic pressure The amount of external pressure that must be applied to a solution to prevent the net movement of solvent molecules across a semipermeable membrane.

Osmolarity (osmol/L) The sum of the molarities of all dissolved particles (osmol) in 1.0 liter of solution.

As with other colligative properties, the amount of osmotic pressure depends only on the concentration of solute particles, not on their identity. Thus, it is convenient to use a new unit, *osmolarity,* to describe the concentration of particles in solution. The **osmolarity (osmol/L)** of a solution is equal to the number of moles of dissolved particles (ions or molecules) per liter of solution. A 0.2 *M* glucose solution, for instance, has an osmolarity of 0.2 osmol/L, but a 0.2 *M* solution of NaCl has an osmolarity of 0.4 osmol/L because it contains 0.2 mol of Na^+ ions and 0.2 mol of Cl^- ions.

Osmosis is particularly important in living organisms because the membranes around cells are semipermeable. The fluids both inside and outside cells must therefore have the same osmolarity to prevent buildup of osmotic pressure and consequent rupture of the cell membrane.

Isotonic Having the same osmolarity.

In blood, the plasma surrounding red blood cells has an osmolarity of approximately 0.30 osmol/L and is said to be **isotonic** with (i.e., has the same osmolarity as) the cell contents. If the cells are removed from plasma and placed in 0.15 *M* NaCl (called *physiological saline solution*), they are unharmed because the osmolarity of the saline solution (0.30 osmol/L) is the same as that of plasma. If, however, red blood cells are placed in pure water or in any solution with an osmolarity much lower than 0.30 osmol/L (a **hypotonic** solution), water passes through the membrane into the cell, causing the cell to swell up and burst, a process called *hemolysis.*

Hypotonic Having an osmolarity *less than* the surrounding blood plasma or cells.

Hypertonic Having an osmolarity *greater than* the surrounding blood plasma or cells.

Finally, if red blood cells are placed in a solution having an osmolarity greater than the cell contents (a **hypertonic** solution), water passes out of the cells into the surrounding solution, causing the cells to shrivel, a process called *crenation.* Figure 9.12 shows red blood cells under all three conditions: isotonic, hypotonic, and hypertonic. Therefore, it is critical that any solution used intravenously be isotonic to prevent red blood cells from being destroyed.

▶ **Figure 9.12**
Red blood cells.
In an isotonic solution the blood cells are normal in appearance (a), but the cells in a hypotonic solution (b) are swollen because of water gain, and those in a hypertonic solution (c) are shriveled because of water loss.

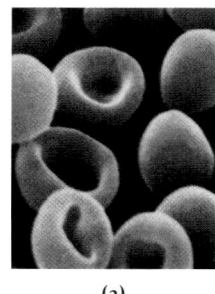  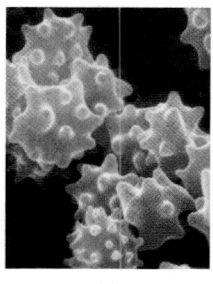

(a) (b) (c)

Worked Example 9.17 Properties of Solutions: Osmolarity

The solution of glucose commonly used intravenously has a concentration of 5.0% (m/v) glucose. What is the osmolarity of this solution? The molar mass of glucose is 180 g/mol.

ANALYSIS Since glucose is a molecular substance that does not give ions in solution, the osmolarity of the solution is the same as the molarity. Recall from Section 9.7 that a solution of 5.0% (m/v) glucose has a concentration of 5.0 g glucose per 100 mL of solution, which is equivalent to 50 g per liter of solution. Thus, finding the molar concentration of glucose requires a mass to mole conversion.

BALLPARK ESTIMATE One liter of solution contains 50 g of glucose (MW = 180 g/mol). Thus, 50 g of glucose is equal to a little more than 0.25 mol, so a solution concentration of 50 g/L is equal to about 0.25 osmol/L, or 0.25 *M*.

SOLUTION

STEP 1: Identify known information. We know the (m/v)% concentration of the glucose solution.

$$5.0\%(m/v) = \frac{5.0 \text{ g glucose}}{100 \text{ mL solution}} \times 100\%$$

STEP 2: Identify answer and units. We are looking for osmolarity, which in this case is equal to the molarity of the solution because glucose is a molecular substance and does not dissociate into ions.

Osmolarity = Molarity = ?? mol/liter

STEP 3: Identify conversion factors. The $(m/v)\%$ concentration is defined as grams of solute per 100 mL of solution, and molarity is defined as moles of solute per liter of solution. We will need to convert from milliliters to liters and then use molar mass to convert grams of glucose to moles of glucose.

$$\frac{\text{g glucose}}{100 \text{ mL}} \times \frac{1000 \text{ mL}}{\text{L}} \longrightarrow \frac{\text{g glucose}}{\text{L}}$$

$$\frac{\text{g glucose}}{\text{L}} \times \frac{1 \text{ mol glucose}}{180 \text{ g glucose}} \longrightarrow \frac{\text{moles glucose}}{\text{L}}$$

STEP 4: Solve. Starting with the $(m/v)\%$ glucose concentration, we first find the number of grams of glucose in 1 L of solution and then convert to moles of glucose per liter.

$$\left(\frac{5.0 \text{ g glucose}}{100 \text{ mL solution}}\right)\left(\frac{1000 \text{ mL}}{1 \text{ L}}\right) = \frac{50 \text{ g glucose}}{\text{L solution}}$$

$$\left(\frac{50 \text{ g glucose}}{1 \text{ L}}\right)\left(\frac{1 \text{ mol}}{180 \text{ g}}\right) = 0.28 \text{ } M \text{ glucose} = 0.28 \text{ osmol}$$

BALLPARK CHECK The calculated osmolarity is reasonably close to our estimate of 0.25 osmol/L.

Worked Example 9.18 Properties of Solutions: Osmolarity

What mass of NaCl is needed to make 1.50 L of a 0.300 osmol/L solution? The molar mass of NaCl is 58.44 g/mol.

ANALYSIS Since NaCl is an ionic substance that produces 2 mol of ions (Na^+, Cl^-) when it dissociates, the osmolarity of the solution is twice the molarity. From the volume and the osmolarity we can determine the moles of NaCl needed and then perform a mole to mass conversion.

SOLUTION

STEP 1: Identify known information. We know the volume and the osmolarity of the final NaCl solution.

$$V = 1.50 \text{ L}$$

$$0.300 \text{ osmol/L} = \left(\frac{0.300 \text{ mol ions}}{\text{L}}\right)$$

STEP 2: Identify answer and units. We are looking for the mass of NaCl.

$$\text{Mass of NaCl} = \text{?? g}$$

STEP 3: Identify conversion factors. Starting with osmolarity in the form (moles NaCl/L), we can use volume to determine the number of moles of solute. We can then use molar mass for the mole to mass conversion.

$$\left(\frac{\text{moles NaCl}}{\text{L}}\right) \times (\text{L}) = \text{moles NaCl}$$

$$(\text{moles NaCl}) \times \left(\frac{\text{g NaCl}}{\text{moles NaCl}}\right) = \text{g NaCl}$$

STEP 4: Solve. Use the appropriate conversions, remembering that NaCl produces two ions per formula unit, to find the mass of NaCl.

$$\left(\frac{0.300 \text{ mol ions}}{\text{L}}\right)\left(\frac{1 \text{ mol NaCl}}{2 \text{ mol ions}}\right)(1.50 \text{ L}) = 0.225 \text{ mol NaCl}$$

$$(0.225 \text{ mol NaCl})\left(\frac{58.44 \text{ g NaCl}}{\text{mol NaCl}}\right) = 13.1 \text{ g NaCl}$$

PROBLEM 9.25

What is the osmolarity of the following solutions?

(a) 0.35 M KBr

(b) 0.15 M glucose $+$ 0.05 M K_2SO_4

PROBLEM 9.26

A typical oral rehydration solution (ORS) for infants contains 90 mEq/L Na^+, 20 mEq/L K^+, 110 mEq/L Cl^-, and 2.0% (m/v) glucose $(MW = 180 \text{ g/mol})$.

(a) Calculate the concentration of each ORS component in units of molarity.

(b) What is the osmolarity of the solution, and how does it compare with the osmolarity of blood plasma?

HANDS-ON CHEMISTRY 9.2

Obtain two clear glasses and two stalks of celery.
If you do not have celery, some lettuce leaves will do. Fill both glasses about three quarters full with fresh water. Add about 2 teaspoons of salt to one glass and stir until it is dissolved. Place one celery stalk (or a large piece of lettuce) in each glass.

a. After about 15–30 minutes, check on the celery/lettuce in each glass. Do they appear different? In what ways?

b. Based on your observations, explain what has occurred based on osmotic flow.

9.11 Dialysis

Learning Objective:

• Distinguish between osmosis and dialysis, and discuss dialysis applications.

Dialysis is similar to osmosis, except that the pores in a dialysis membrane are larger than those in an osmotic membrane so that both solvent molecules and small solute particles can pass through, but large colloidal particles such as proteins cannot pass. (The exact dividing line between a "small" molecule and a "large" one is imprecise, and dialysis membranes with a variety of pore sizes are available.) Dialysis membranes include animal bladders, parchment, and cellophane.

Perhaps the most important medical use of dialysis is in artificial kidney machines, where *hemodialysis* is used to cleanse the blood of patients whose kidneys malfunction (Figure 9.13). Blood is diverted from the body and pumped through a long cellophane dialysis tube suspended in an isotonic solution formulated to contain many of the same components as blood plasma. These substances—glucose, NaCl, $NaHCO_3$, and KCl—have the same concentrations in the dialysis solution as they do in blood so that they have no net passage through the membrane.

▶ **Figure 9.13**
Operation of a hemodialysis unit used for purifying blood.
Blood is pumped from an artery through a coiled semipermeable membrane of cellophane. Small waste products pass through the membrane and are washed away by an isotonic dialysis solution.

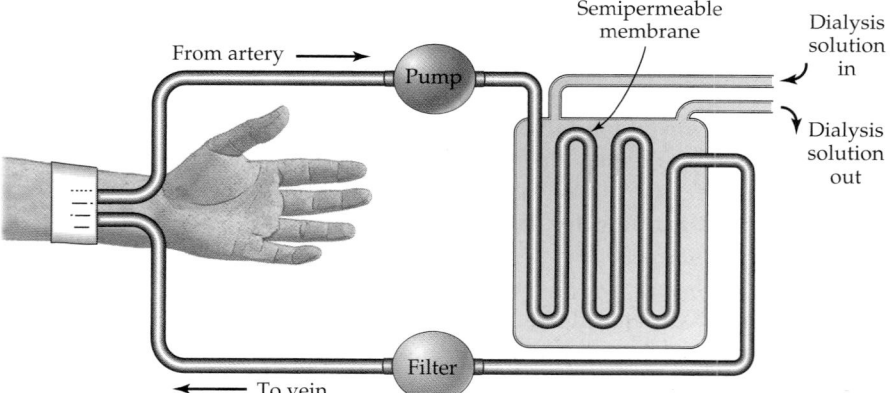

Small waste materials such as urea pass through the dialysis membrane from the blood to the solution side where they are washed away, but cells, proteins, and other important blood components are prevented from passing through the membrane because of their larger size. In addition, the dialysis fluid concentration can be controlled so that imbalances in electrolytes are corrected. The wash solution is changed every two hours, and a typical hemodialysis procedure lasts for four to seven hours.

As previously noted, colloidal particles are too large to pass through a semipermeable membrane. Protein molecules, in particular, do not cross semipermeable membranes and thus play an essential role in determining the osmolarity of body fluids. The distribution of water and solutes across the capillary walls that separate blood plasma from the fluid surrounding cells is controlled by the balance between blood pressure and osmotic pressure. The pressure of blood inside the capillary tends to push water out of the plasma (filtration), but the osmotic pressure of colloidal protein molecules tends to draw water into the plasma (reabsorption). The balance between the two processes

CHEMISTRY IN ACTION

⚕ Timed-Release Drug Delivery Systems

There is much more in most medications than medicine. Even something as simple as a generic aspirin tablet contains a binder to keep it from crumbling, a filler to bring it to the right size and help it disintegrate in the stomach, and a lubricant to keep it from sticking to the manufacturing equipment. Timed-release medications are even more complex.

The widespread use of timed-release medication dates from the introduction of Contac decongestant in 1961. The original idea was simple: tiny beads of medicine were encapsulated by coating them with varying thicknesses of a slow-dissolving polymer. Those beads with a thinner coat dissolve and release their medicine more rapidly; those with a thicker coat dissolve more slowly. Combining the right number of beads with the right thicknesses into a single capsule makes possible the gradual release of medication over a predictable time.

The technology of timed-release medications has become much more sophisticated in recent years, and the kinds of medications that can be delivered have become more numerous, as mentioned in the opening paragraph to this chapter. Slow-dissolving polymer coatings have been replaced by an insoluble porous polymer matrix; the drug is embedded in the matrix and slowly dissolves and diffused out of the holes. The release rate can be controlled by modifying the size of the pores in the matrix. Other delivery systems utilize polymer tablets with a porous membrane on one side and a laser-drilled hole on the other. As stomach fluids diffuse through the porous membrane, the drug is forced out the laser-drilled hole on the other side. After the entire drug dose has been delivered over a period of several hours, the insoluble matrix or tablet passes through the digestive system and is excreted.

Similar technology has been incorporated into transdermal patches to deliver drugs directly by diffusion through the skin. These patches use the osmotic effect to force a drug from its reservoir. Useful only for drugs that do not dissolve in water, the device is divided into two compartments, one containing medication covered by a perforated membrane and the other containing a hygroscopic material (p. 258) covered by a semipermeable membrane. As moisture from the air diffuses through the membrane into the compartment with the hygroscopic material, the buildup of pressure squeezes the medication out of the other compartment through tiny holes. Popular uses of transdermal patches include nicotine patches to reduce cigarette cravings, hormonal patches to treat menopausal symptoms or for contraception, opioid medications to provide long-term pain relief, and patches to treat motion sickness.

CIA Problem 9.8 What is the purpose of the hygroscopic material in the transdermal patch illustrated in the figure to the right?

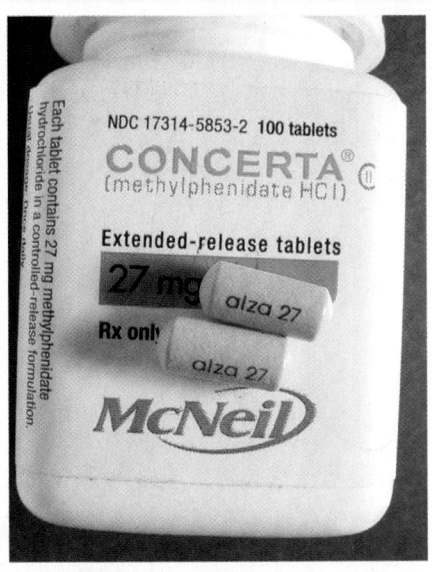

▲ This time-release medication uses a semipermeable membrane and osmotic pressure to deliver controlled amounts of a drug to treat ADHD.

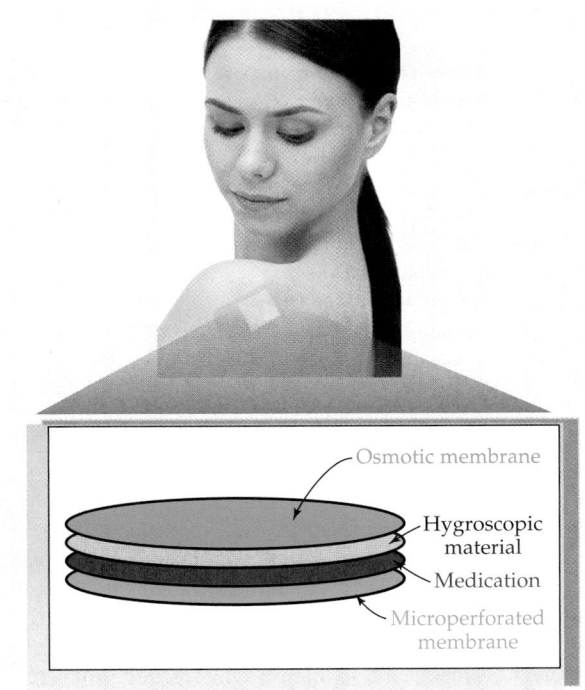

CIA Problem 9.9 Which of the following polymers would be more appropriate for use as a hygroscopic material? Explain your choice.

Polyethylene $(-[CH_2-CH_2]_n-)$ or
nylon $(-[CO(CH_2)_4CONH(CH_2)_6NH]_n-)$

▶ **Figure 9.14**
The delivery of oxygen and nutrients to the cells and the removal of waste products are regulated by osmosis.

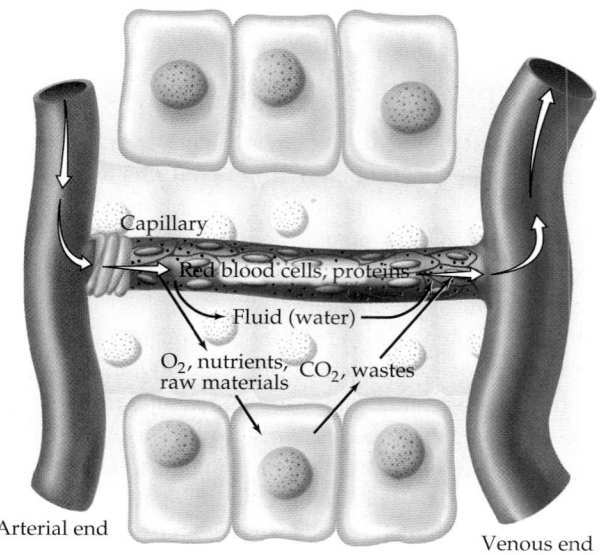

Capillary

Red blood cells, proteins

Fluid (water)

O_2, nutrients, raw materials CO_2, wastes

Arterial end

Venous end

varies with location in the body (see Figure 9.14). At the arterial end of a capillary, where blood pumped from the heart has a higher pressure, filtration is favored. At the venous end, where blood pressure is lower, reabsorption is favored, causing waste products from metabolism to enter the bloodstream, to be removed by the kidneys.

SUMMARY REVISITING THE CHAPTER LEARNING OBJECTIVES

- **Distinguish between heterogeneous and homogeneous mixtures and between solutions and colloids.** Mixtures are classified as either *heterogeneous,* if the mixing is nonuniform, or *homogeneous,* if the mixing is uniform. *Solutions* are homogeneous mixtures that contain particles the size of ions and molecules (<2.0 nm diameter), whereas larger particles (2.0–500 nm diameter) are present in *colloids* [see Problems 32, 33, and 36].

- **Predict whether a solution is likely to form based on the relative polarity and intermolecular forces between solute and solvent.** The general rule for solution formation is "like dissolves like"; polar solutes will tend to be soluble in polar solvents, whereas nonpolar solutes will be soluble in nonpolar solvents. In other words, substances tend to be mutually soluble when their intermolecular forces are similar [see Problems 34, 35, 37, and 92].

- **Define the properties of a solution, including miscibility, saturation, and solubility.** *Miscibility* refers to the tendency of two substances to be completely soluble in any proportions. The maximum amount of one substance (the *solute*) that can be dissolved in another (the *solvent*) is called the substance's *solubility.* Saturation is determined by the amount of solute dissolved compared to the substances maximum solubility. When the maximum amount of a given solute is dissolved, the solution is *saturated* [see Problems 34, 35, 37–40, 92, and 96].

- **Determine the effect of temperature changes on the solubility of a solute in a solution.** The solubility in water of a solid often increases with temperature, but the solubility of a gas decreases with temperature [see Problems 38, 39, and 100].

- **Determine the effect of a change in pressure on the solubility of a gas in solution.** Pressure significantly affects gas solubilities, which are directly proportional to their partial pressure over the solution [Henry's law] [see Problems 42, 43, and 100].

- **Define units of concentration, and calculate the concentration of a solute in solution.** The concentration of a solution can be expressed in several ways, including molarity, weight/weight percent composition, weight/volume percent composition, and parts per million (or billion). Osmolarity is used to express the total concentration of dissolved particles (ions and molecules). Molarity, which expresses concentration as the number of moles of solute per liter of solution, is the most useful method when calculating quantities of reactants or products for reactions in aqueous solution [see Problems 40–43, 49–60, 83–92, 94, 95, 97, and 98].

- **Use dilution factors to calculate molarities or volumes of dilute solutions prepared from concentrated solutions.** A dilution is carried out by adding more solvent to an existing solution. Only the amount of solvent changes; the amount of solute remains the same. Thus, the molarity times the volume of the dilute solution is equal to the molarity times the volume of the concentrated solution: $M_c V_c = M_d V_d$ [see Problems 31, 44–48, 61–66, and 87].

- **Identify solutes as strong electrolytes, weak electrolytes, or nonelectrolytes.** Substances that form ions when dissolved in water and whose water solutions therefore conduct an electric current are called *electrolytes.* Substances that ionize completely in water are *strong electrolytes,* those that ionize partially are *weak electrolytes,* and those that do not ionize are *nonelectrolytes* [see Problems 28, 29, 67, 68, 82, and 95].

- **Calculate equivalents for ionic solutes in solution.** Body fluids contain small amounts of many different electrolytes, whose concentrations are expressed as moles of ionic charge, or *equivalents,* per liter [see Problems 67–74, 86, and 98].

- **Calculate the colligative properties of boiling-point elevation and freezing-point depression for a solution.** In comparing a solution to a pure solvent, the solution has a lower vapor pressure at a given temperature, a higher boiling point, and a lower melting point. Called *colligative properties,* these effects depend only on the number of dissolved particles, not on their chemical identity. The colligative properties of aqueous solutions can be calculated as described in Section 9.9 [see Problems 28–30, 75–78, 95, and 99].

- **Calculate the osmotic pressure of a solution and predict the direction of solvent flow across a semipermeable membrane due to osmosis.** *Osmosis* occurs when solutions of different concentration are separated by a semipermeable membrane that allows solvent molecules to pass but blocks the passage of solute ions and molecules. Solvent flows from the more dilute side to the more concentrated side until sufficient *osmotic pressure* builds up and stops the flow. An effect similar to osmosis occurs when membranes of larger pore size are used. *Osmotic pressure* (π) can be calculated as $\pi = (n/V)RT$ *(see Problems 27, 79–84, and 98).*

- **Distinguish between osmosis and dialysis, and discuss dialysis applications.** An effect similar to osmosis occurs when membranes of larger pore size are used. In *dialysis,* the membrane allows the passage of solvent and small dissolved molecules but prevents passage of proteins and larger particles. Dialysis is commonly used to remove metabolic waste products from blood *(see Problem 101).*

CONCEPT MAP: SOLUTIONS

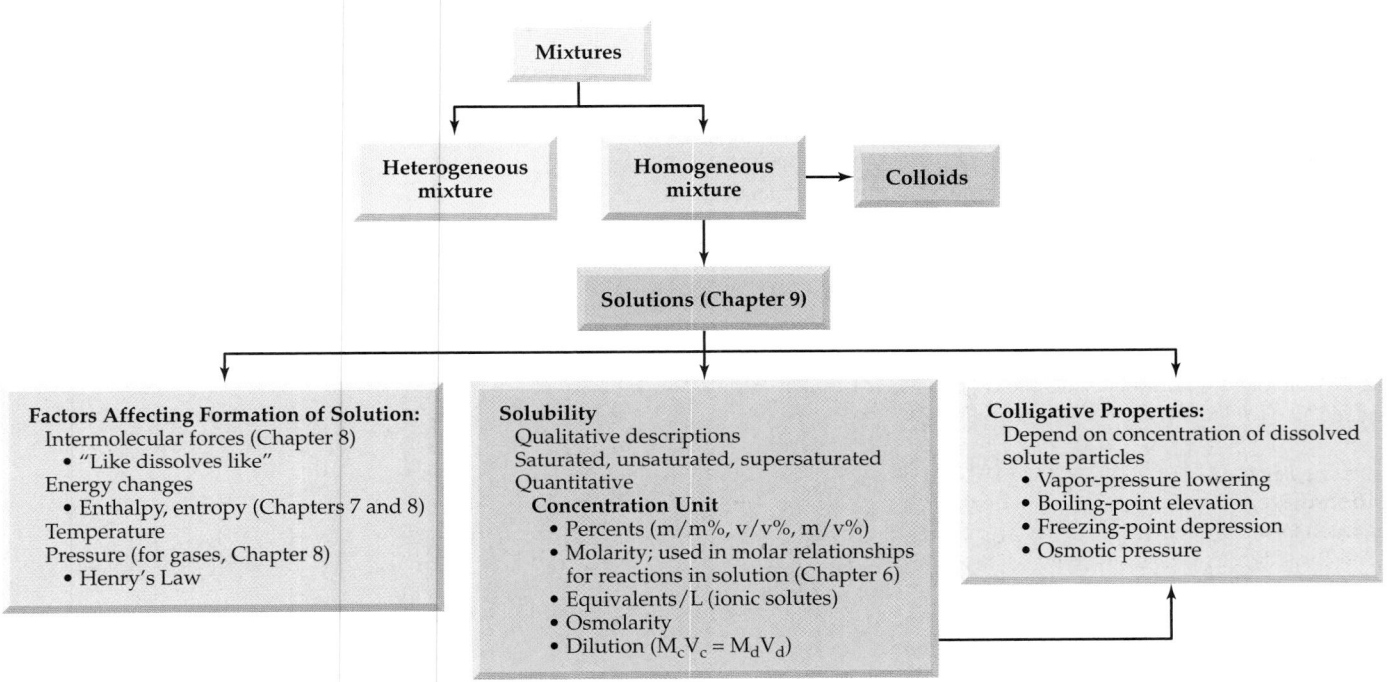

▲ **Figure 9.15 Concept Map.** Formation of a solution depends on many factors, including the attractive forces between solute and solvent particles, temperature, and pressure (gases). The extent to which a solute dissolves in solution can be expressed either qualitatively or using quantitative concentration units. The most common concentration unit in chemical applications is molarity (moles of solute/L solution), which is also useful in quantitative relationships involving reactions that take place in solution. Colligative properties of solution, including boiling and freezing points, will vary with the amount of solute dissolved in solution. These relationships are illustrated in this concept map.

KEY WORDS

Colligative property,
  p. 275
Colloid, *p. 255*
Dilution factor, *p. 271*
Electrolyte, *p. 273*
Equivalent (Eq), *p. 273*
Henry's law, *p. 261*
Hypertonic, *p. 280*
Hypotonic, *p. 280*
Isotonic, *p. 280*

Mass/mass percent
  concentration, (m/m)%,
  p. 263
Mass/volume percent
  concentration, (m/v)%,
  p. 263
Miscible, *p. 259*
Molarity (*M*), *p. 268*
Nonelectrolyte, *p. 273*
Osmolarity (osmol/L), *p. 280*

Osmosis, *p. 279*
Osmotic pressure, *p. 279*
Parts per billion (ppb), *p. 267*
Parts per million (ppm),
  p. 267
Saturated solution, *p. 259*
Solubility, *p. 259*
Solute, *p. 255*
Solution, *p. 255*
Solvation, *p. 257*

Solvent, *p. 255*
Strong electrolyte, *p. 273*
Supersaturated solution,
  p. 260
Volume/volume percent
  concentration, (v/v)%,
  p. 263
Weak electrolyte, *p. 273*

☞ UNDERSTANDING KEY CONCEPTS

9.27 Assume that two liquids are separated by a semipermeable membrane, with pure solvent on the right side and a solution of a solute on the left side. Make a drawing that shows the situation after equilibrium is reached.

Before equilibrium

9.28 When 1 mol of HCl is added to 1 kg of water, the boiling point increases by 1.0 °C, but when 1 mol of acetic acid, CH_3CO_2H, is added to 1 kg of water, the boiling point increases by only 0.5 °C. Explain.

9.29 HF is a weak electrolyte and HBr is a strong electrolyte. Which of the curves in the figure represents the change in the boiling point of an aqueous solution when 1 mole of HF is added to 1 kg of water, and which represents the change when 1 mol of HBr is added?

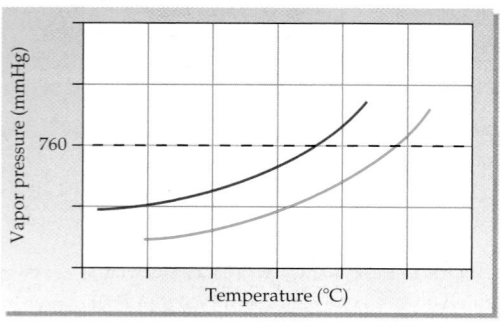

9.30 Assume that you have two full beakers, one containing pure water (blue) and the other containing an equal volume of a 10% (w/v) solution of glucose (green). Which of the drawings (a)–(c) best represents the two beakers after they have stood uncovered for several days and partial evaporation has occurred? Explain.

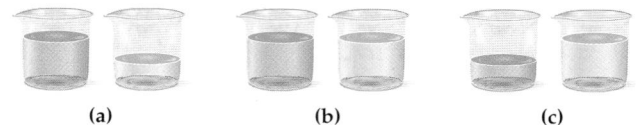

(a)   (b)   (c)

9.31 A beaker containing 150.0 mL of 0.1 M glucose is represented by (a). Which of the drawings (b)–(d) represents the solution that results when 50.0 mL is withdrawn from (a) and then diluted by a factor of 4?

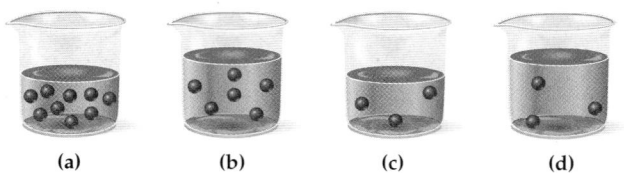

(a)   (b)   (c)   (d)

ADDITIONAL PROBLEMS

SOLUTIONS AND SOLUBILITY (SECTIONS 9.1–9.5)

9.32 What is the difference between a homogeneous mixture and a heterogeneous one?

9.33 How can you tell a solution from a colloid?

9.34 What characteristic of water allows it to dissolve ionic solids?

9.35 Why does water not dissolve motor oil?

9.36 Which of the following are solutions?
   (a) Italian salad dressing
   (b) Rubbing alcohol
   (c) Algae in pond water
   (d) Mouthwash

9.37 Based on the predominant intermolecular forces, which of the following pairs of liquids are likely to be miscible?
   (a) H_2SO_4 and H_2O **(b)** C_8H_{18} and C_6H_6
   (c) CH_2Cl_2 and H_2O **(d)** CS_2 and CCl_4

9.38 The solubility of NH_3 gas in water at an NH_3 pressure of 760.0 mmHg and 25 °C is 51.8 g/100 mL and 27.0 g/100 mL at 50 °C.
   (a) What is the solubility of NH_3 if its partial pressure is reduced to 225.0 mmHg?
   (b) How many moles of NH_3 would be released from 1.0 L of a saturated NH_3 solution if the temperature was increased from 25 to 50 °C?

9.39 The solubility of CO_2 gas in water is 0.15 g/100 mL at a CO_2 pressure of 760 mmHg.
   (a) What is the solubility of CO_2 in a soft drink (which is mainly water) that was bottled under a CO_2 pressure of 4.5 atm?
   (b) An atmospheric concentration of 380 ppm, CO_2 corresponds to a partial pressure of 0.00038 atm. What percentage of the CO_2 originally dissolved in the solution in part (a) remains in solution after the soft drink reaches equilibrium with the ambient atmosphere?

(c) One bottle of soda is stored in a refrigerator at 3 °C, and another is stored at room temperature (25 °C). If both bottles are opened simultaneously, which one would exhibit greater carbonation (i.e., bubbles)? Explain.

CONCENTRATION AND DILUTION OF SOLUTIONS (SECTIONS 9.6 AND 9.7)

9.40 Is a solution highly concentrated if it is saturated? Is a solution saturated if it is highly concentrated?

9.41 How is mass/volume percent concentration defined and for what types of solutions is it typically used?

9.42 How is molarity defined?

9.43 How is volume/volume percent concentration defined and for what types of solutions is it typically used?

9.44 A 750.0 mL bottle of Listerine is of a 21% (v/v) ethyl alcohol.

(a) What is the volume (in mL) of ethyl alcohol in the bottle?

(b) If the density of ethyl alcohol is 0.789 g/mL and the molar mass is 46.07 g/mol, calculate the molarity of ethyl alcohol in Listerine.

9.45 A dilute aqueous solution of boric acid, H_3BO_3, is often used as an eyewash. How would you prepare 500.0 mL of a 0.50% (m/v) boric acid solution?

9.46 Describe how you would prepare 250 mL of a 0.10 M NaCl solution.

9.47 Describe how you would prepare 1.50 L of a 7.50% (m/v) $Mg(NO_3)_2$ solution.

9.48 What is the mass/volume percent concentration of the following solutions?

(a) 0.078 mol KCl in 75 mL of solution

(b) 0.044 mol sucrose ($C_{12}H_{22}O_{11}$) in 380 mL of solution

9.49 The concentration of glucose in blood is approximately 90 mg/100 mL. What is the mass/volume percent concentration of glucose? What is the molarity of glucose?

9.50 How many moles of each substance are needed to prepare the following solutions?

(a) 50.0 mL of 8.0% (m/v) KCl (MW = 74.55 g/mol)

(b) 200.0 mL of 7.5% (m/v) acetic acid (MW = 60.05 g/mol)

9.51 Which of the following solutions is more concentrated?

(a) 0.50 M KCl or 5.0% (m/v) KCl

(b) 2.5% (m/v) $NaHSO_4$ or 0.025 M $NaHSO_4$

9.52 If you had only 23 g of KOH remaining in a bottle, how many milliliters of 10.0% (m/v) solution could you prepare? How many milliliters of 0.25 M solution?

9.53 Over-the-counter hydrogen peroxide (H_2O_2) solutions are 3% (m/v). What is this concentration in moles per liter?

9.54 The lethal dosage of potassium cyanide (KCN) in rats is 10 mg KCN per kilogram of body weight. What is this concentration in parts per million?

9.55 What is the molarity of the following solutions?

(a) 12.5 g $NaHCO_3$ in 350.0 mL solution

(b) 45.0 g H_2SO_4 in 300.0 mL solution

(c) 30.0 g NaCl dissolved to make 500.0 mL solution

9.56 How many grams of solute are in the following solutions?

(a) 200 mL of 0.30 M acetic acid, CH_3CO_2H

(b) 1.50 L of 0.25 M NaOH

(c) 750 mL of 2.5 M nitric acid, HNO_3

9.57 How many milliliters of a 0.75 M HCl solution do you need to obtain 0.0040 mol of HCl?

9.58 Nalorphine, a relative of morphine, is used to combat withdrawal symptoms in heroin users. How many milliliters of a 0.40% (m/v) solution of nalorphine must be injected to obtain a dose of 1.5 mg?

9.59 A flask containing 450 mL of 0.50 M H_2SO_4 was accidentally knocked to the floor. How many grams of $NaHCO_3$ do you need to put on the spill to neutralize the acid according to the following equation?

$$H_2SO_4(aq) + 2\,NaHCO_3(aq) \longrightarrow Na_2SO_4(aq) + 2\,H_2O(l) + 2\,CO_2(g)$$

9.60 Sodium thiosulfate ($Na_2S_2O_3$), the major component in photographic fixer solution, reacts with silver bromide to dissolve it according to the following reaction:

$$AgBr(s) + 2\,Na_2S_2O_3(aq) \longrightarrow Na_3Ag(S_2O_3)_2(aq) + NaBr(aq)$$

(a) How many moles of $Na_2S_2O_3$ would be required to react completely with 0.450 g of AgBr?

(b) How many mL of 0.02 M $Na_2S_2O_3$ contain this number of moles?

9.61 What is the final volume of an orange juice prepared from 100.0 mL of orange juice concentrate if the final juice is to be 20.0% of the strength of the original?

9.62 What is the final volume of NaOH solution prepared from 100.0 mL of 0.500 M NaOH if you wanted the final concentration to be 0.150 M?

9.63 An aqueous solution that contains 285 ppm of potassium nitrate (KNO_3) is being used to feed plants in a garden. What volume of this solution is needed to prepare 2.0 L of a solution that is 75 ppm in KNO_3?

9.64 What is the concentration of a NaCl solution, in (m/v)%, prepared by diluting 65 mL of a saturated solution, which has a concentration of 37 (m/v)%, to 480 mL?

9.65 Concentrated (12.0 M) hydrochloric acid is sold for household and industrial purposes under the name "muriatic acid." How many milliliters of 0.500 M HCl solution can be made from 25.0 mL of 12.0 M HCl solution?

9.66 Dilute solutions of $NaHCO_3$ are sometimes used in treating acid burns. How many milliliters of 0.100 M $NaHCO_3$ solution are needed to prepare 750.0 mL of 0.0500 M $NaHCO_3$ solution?

ELECTROLYTES (SECTION 9.8)

9.67 What is an electrolyte?

9.68 Give an example of a strong electrolyte and a nonelectrolyte.

9.69 What does it mean when we say that the concentration of Ca^{2+} in blood is 3.0 mEq/L?

9.70 What is the total anion concentration (in mEq/L) of a solution that contains 5.0 mEq/L Na^+, 12.0 mEq/L Ca^{2+}, and 2.0 mEq/L Li^+?

9.71 Kaochlor, a 10% (m/v) KCl solution, is an oral electrolyte supplement administered for potassium deficiency. How many milliequivalents of K^+ are in a 30 mL dose?

9.72 Calculate the mass needed for each of the following ion equivalents:

    (a) 0.25 Eq Ca^{2+} **(b)** 75 mEq K^+

    (c) 199 mEg SO_4^{2-} **(d)** 0.65 Eq PO_4^{3-}

9.73 The concentration of Cl^- ion in blood is approximately 100 mEq/L. How many milliliters of blood would be needed to obtain 1.0 g of Cl^- ions?

9.74 Normal blood contains 3 mEq/L of Mg^{2+}. How many milligrams of Mg^{2+} are present in 150.0 mL of blood?

PROPERTIES OF SOLUTIONS (SECTION 9.9)

9.75 Which lowers the freezing point of 2.0 kg of water more, 0.20 mol NaOH or 0.20 mol Ba(OH)$_2$? Both compounds are strong electrolytes. Explain.

9.76 Which solution has the higher boiling point, 0.500 *M* glucose or 0.300 *M* KCl? Explain.

9.77 Methanol, CH_3OH, is sometimes used as an antifreeze for the water in automobile windshield washer fluids. How many moles of methanol must be added to 5.00 kg of water to lower its freezing point to $-10.0\ °C$? (For each mole of solute, the freezing point of 1 kg of water is lowered 1.86 °C.)

9.78 Hard candy is prepared by dissolving pure sugar and flavoring in water and heating the solution to boiling. What is the boiling point of a solution produced by adding 650 g of cane sugar (molar mass 342.3 g/mol) to 1.5 kg of water? (For each mole of nonvolatile solute, the boiling point of 1 kg of water is raised 0.51 °C.)

OSMOSIS (SECTION 9.10)

9.79 Why do red blood cells swell up and burst when placed in pure water?

9.80 What does it mean when we say that a 0.15 *M* NaCl solution is isotonic with blood, whereas distilled water is hypotonic?

9.81 Which of the following solutions has the higher osmolarity?

    (a) 0.25 *M* KBr or 0.20 *M* Na$_2$SO$_4$

    (b) 0.30 *M* NaOH or 3.0% (m/v) NaOH

9.82 Which of the following solutions will give rise to a greater osmotic pressure at equilibrium: 5.00 g of NaCl in 350.0 mL water or 35.0 g of glucose in 400.0 mL water? For NaCl, MW = 58.5 amu; for glucose, MW = 180 amu.

9.83 A pickling solution for preserving food is prepared by dissolving 270 g of NaCl in 3.8 L of water. Calculate the osmolarity of the solution.

9.84 An isotonic solution must be approximately 0.30 osmol/L. How much KCl is needed to prepare 175 mL of an isotonic solution?

CONCEPTUAL PROBLEMS

9.85 Uric acid, the principal constituent of some kidney stones, has the formula $C_5H_4N_4O_3$. In aqueous solution, the solubility of uric acid is only 0.067 g/L. Express this concentration in (m/v)%, in parts per million, and in molarity.

9.86 Emergency treatment of cardiac arrest victims sometimes involves injection of a calcium chloride solution directly into the heart muscle. How many grams of $CaCl_2$ are administered in an injection of 5.0 mL of a 5.0% (m/v) solution? How many milliequivalents of Ca^{2+}?

9.87 Nitric acid, HNO_3, is available commercially at a concentration of 16 *M*.

    (a) What volume would you need to obtain 0.150 mol HNO_3?

    (b) To what volume must you dilute this volume of HNO_3 from part (a) to prepare a 0.20 *M* solution?

9.88 One test for vitamin C (ascorbic acid, $C_6H_8O_6$) is based on the reaction of the vitamin with iodine:

$$C_6H_8O_6(aq) + I_2(aq) \longrightarrow C_6H_6O_6(aq) + 2\ HI(aq)$$

    (a) A 25.0 mL sample of a fruit juice requires 13.0 mL of 0.0100 *M* I_2 solution for reaction. How many moles of ascorbic acid are in the sample?

    (b) What is the molarity of ascorbic acid in the fruit juice?

    (c) The Food and Drug Administration recommends that 60 mg of ascorbic acid be consumed per day. How many milliliters of the fruit juice in part (a) must a person drink to obtain the recommended dosage?

9.89 A typical dosage of statin drugs for the treatment of high cholesterol is 10 mg. Assuming a total blood volume of 5.0 L, calculate the (m/v)% concentration of drug in the blood in units of g/100 mL.

9.90 Assuming the density of blood in healthy individuals is approximately 1.05 g/mL, report the concentration of drug in Problem 9.89 in units of ppm.

9.91 In all 50 states, a person with a blood alcohol concentration of 0.080% (v/v) is considered legally drunk. What volume of total alcohol does this concentration represent, assuming a blood volume of 5.0 L?

9.92 Ammonia, NH_3, is very soluble in water (51.8 g/L at 20 °C and 760 mmHg).

    (a) Show how NH_3 can hydrogen bond to water.

    (b) What is the solubility of ammonia in water in moles per liter?

9.93 Cobalt(II) chloride, a blue solid, can absorb water from the air to form cobalt(II) chloride hexahydrate, a pink solid. The equilibrium is so sensitive to moisture in the air that $CoCl_2$ is used as a humidity indicator.

(a) Write a balanced equation for the equilibrium. Be sure to include water as a reactant to produce the hexahydrate.

(b) How many grams of water are released by the decomposition of 2.50 g of cobalt(II) chloride hexahydrate?

9.94 How many milliliters of 0.150 M $BaCl_2$ are needed to react completely with 35.0 mL of 0.200 M Na_2SO_4? How many grams of $BaSO_4$ will be formed?

9.95 Many compounds are only partially dissociated into ions in aqueous solution. Trichloroacetic acid (CCl_3CO_2H), for instance, is partially dissociated in water according to the equation

$$CCl_3CO_2H\,(aq) \longrightarrow H^+(aq) + CCl_3CO_2^-\,(aq)$$

For a solution prepared by dissolving 1.00 mol of trichloroacetic acid in 1.00 kg of water, 36.0% of the trichloroacetic acid dissociates to form H^+ and $CCl_3CO_2^-$ ions.

(a) What is the total concentration of dissolved ions and molecules in 1 kg of water?

(b) What is the freezing point of this solution? (The freezing point of 1 kg of water is lowered 1.86 °C for each mole of solute particles.)

GROUP PROBLEMS

9.96 Hyperbaric chambers, which provide high pressures (up to 6 atm) of either air or pure oxygen, are used to treat a variety of conditions, ranging from decompression sickness in deep-sea divers to carbon monoxide poisoning. Look up the solubility of O_2, N_2, CO, and CO_2 in water at standard temperature and pressure (1 atm, 25 °C).

(a) Explain the trends in relative solubility for these gases. (Refer to Section 8.2 and Section 9.2)

(b) Explain how elevated pressures in a hyperbaric chamber be used to treat decompression sickness (excess N_2 in blood) and carbon monoxide poisoning. (Refer to Section 7.9 and Section 9.5)

9.97 Look up the maximum concentrations set by the U.S. Environmental Protection Agency for lead and cadmium in drinking water.

(a) What are these concentrations in milligrams per liter? In moles/L?

(b) Based on your answers to part (a), which is more toxic? Explain your answer.

(c) How many liters of water contaminated at this maximum level must you drink to consume 1.0 μg of lead? To consume 1.0 μg of cadmium?

9.98 Look up the composition of *Ringer's solution* used in the treatment of burns and wounds.

(a) What is the molarity of each component?

(b) What is the osmolarity of the solution? Is it hypertonic, isotonic, or hypotonic with blood plasma (0.30 osmol)? Discuss possible medicinal reasons for the osmolarity of the solution.

9.99 To prevent accumulation of ice on roads and sidewalks, many municipalities (and home-owners) will apply de-icing compounds to "melt" the ice by lowering the freezing point.

(a) Obtain a package of de-icing compound/mixture and identify the ingredients or look up the composition. Are the compounds ionic or molecular? Discuss possible reasons for the use of these compounds and for the specific compounds used in the formulations.

(b) Some de-icing compositions include dyes or colored compounds called indicators. Why?

9.100 Many carbonate minerals are insoluble in water and appear in water pipes as "scale."

(a) What is "scale"? What are the solubilty equilibria involved in scale formation?

(b) Why is scale formation typically only a problem in hot water pipes?

9.101 Research information related to dialysis and answer the following questions:

(a) What is the difference between hemodialysis and peritoneal dialysis?

(b) In hemodialysis, which substances diffuse out of the blood and into the dialysate (the solution used to remove waste products)? Which substances flow from the dialysate into the blood?

(c) Why is the level of bicarbonate in the dialysate set at a slightly higher level than in normal blood?

10

Acids and Bases

CONTENTS

◀◀◀ CONCEPTS TO REVIEW

▲ This young woman is experiencing shortness of breath from respiratory alkalosis, a result of anxiety-related hyperventilation. Breathing into a paper bag restores the balance of blood gases CO_2 and O_2, and returns the blood pH to an appropriate level.

A group of teenagers at a rock concert experiences a collective fainting spell. A woman taking high doses of aspirin for chronic pain appears disoriented and is having trouble breathing. A man with type 1 diabetes complains of tiredness and stomach pains. An athlete who recently completed a highly strenuous workout suffers from muscle cramps and nausea. A patient on an HIV drug regimen experiences increasing weakness and numbness in the hands and feet. What do all these individuals have in common? Just like the young woman in the opening photograph, they are all experiencing symptoms related to fluctuations in blood pH, conditions referred to as acidosis (low pH) or alkalosis (high pH). The concepts of acids and bases were introduced in previous chapters, but to fully appreciate the significance of blood pH and the means by which it is controlled physiologically, we need to explore further the behavior of acids and bases. Specifically, in this chapter, we will examine the differences between strong and weak acids and bases, the reactions of acids and bases, and the role of acids and bases in solutions called *buffers*.

10.1 Acids and Bases: Definitions

Learning Objective:

- Define the behavior of acids and bases in solution, and identify conjugate acid-base pairs.

Acids! The word evokes images of dangerous, corrosive liquids that eat away everything they touch. Although a few well-known substances such as sulfuric acid (H_2SO_4) do indeed fit this description, most acids are relatively harmless. In fact, many acids, such as ascorbic acid (vitamin C), are necessary for life. We have already learned a few facts about acids and bases in previous chapters:

- An acid is a substance that produces hydrogen ions, H^+, when dissolved in water. (Section 3.11)
- A base is a substance that produces hydroxide ions, OH^-, when dissolved in water. (Section 3.11)
- The neutralization reaction of an acid with a base yields water plus a *salt,* an ionic compound composed of the cation from the base and the anion from the acid. (Section 5.4)

The above definitions of acids and bases from Section 3.11 were proposed in 1887 by the Swedish chemist Svante Arrhenius and are useful for many purposes. The definitions are limited, however, because they refer only to reactions that take place in aqueous solutions. (We will see shortly how the definitions can be broadened.) Another issue is that the H^+ ion is so reactive it does not exist in water. Instead, H^+ reacts with H_2O to give the **hydronium ion,** H_3O^+, as mentioned in Section 3.11. When gaseous HCl dissolves in water, for instance, H_3O^+ and Cl^- are formed. As described in Section 4.9, electrostatic potential maps show that the hydrogen of HCl is positively polarized and electron-poor (blue), whereas the oxygen of water is negatively polarized and electron-rich (red):

Hydronium ion The H_3O^+ ion, formed when an acid reacts with water.

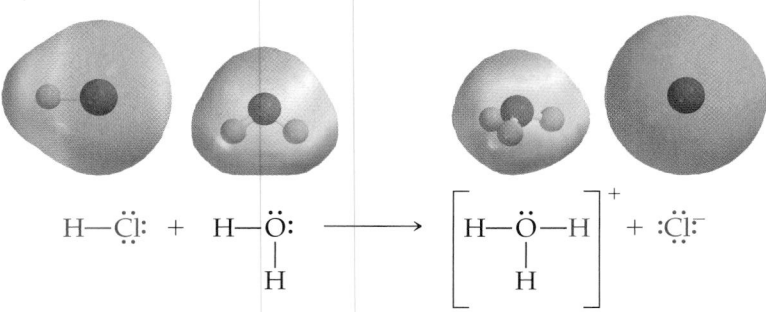

Thus, the Arrhenius definition was updated to acknowledge that an acid yields H_3O^+ in water rather than H^+; however, the notations H_3O^+ and $H^+(aq)$ are often used interchangeably.

The Arrhenius definition of a base is obvious in some cases, but what about substances in which the hydroxide ions are not obvious? It is important to realize that the OH⁻ ions "produced" by the base can come from either of two sources. Metal hydroxides, such as NaOH, KOH, and $Ba(OH)_2$, are ionic compounds that already contain OH⁻ ions and merely release those ions when they dissolve in water. But, metal oxides can also react with water to generate OH⁻ ions. In addition, some molecular compounds, such as ammonia, are not ionic and contain no OH⁻ ions in their structure. Nonetheless, they can act as bases to produce OH⁻ ions in reactions with water.

The Arrhenius definition of acids and bases applies only to processes that take place in an aqueous solution. A far more general definition was proposed in 1923 by the Danish chemist Johannes Brønsted and the English chemist Thomas Lowry. A **Brønsted–Lowry acid** is any substance that is able to give a hydrogen ion, H^+, to another molecule or ion. A hydrogen *atom* consists of a proton and an electron, so a hydrogen *ion*, H^+, is simply a proton. Thus, we often refer to acids as *proton donors*. The reaction need not occur in water, and a Brønsted–Lowry acid need not give appreciable concentrations of H_3O^+ ions in water.

Different acids can supply different numbers of H^+ ions, as we saw in Section 3.11. Acids with one proton to donate, such as HCl or HNO_3, are called *monoprotic acids;* H_2SO_4 is a *diprotic acid* because it has two protons to donate, and H_3PO_4 is a *triprotic acid* because it has three protons to donate. Notice that the acidic H atoms (i.e., the H atoms that are donated as protons) are bonded to electronegative atoms, such as chlorine or oxygen.

> **Brønsted–Lowry acid** A substance that can donate a hydrogen ion, H^+, to another molecule or ion.

H—Cl

Hydrochloric acid
(monoprotic)

Nitric acid
(monoprotic)

Sulfuric acid
(diprotic)

Phosphoric acid
(triprotic)

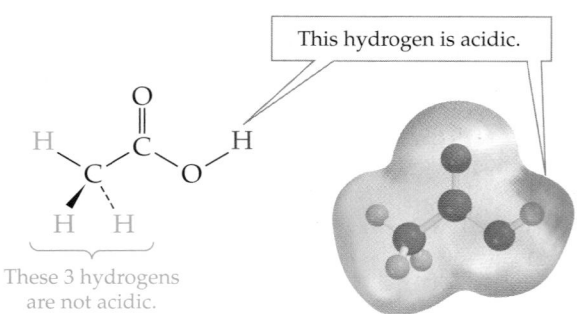

This hydrogen is acidic.

These 3 hydrogens are not acidic.

Acetic acid (CH_3CO_2H), an example of an organic acid, actually has a total of four hydrogens, but only the one bonded to the electronegative oxygen is positively polarized and therefore acidic. The three hydrogens bonded to carbon are not acidic. Most organic acids are similar in that they contain many hydrogen atoms, but only the one in the —CO_2H group (blue in the electrostatic potential map) is acidic.

Acetic acid will react with water to produce H_3O^+ ions (Arrhenius acid definition) by donating a proton (Brønsted–Lowry acid definition) to water, as shown:

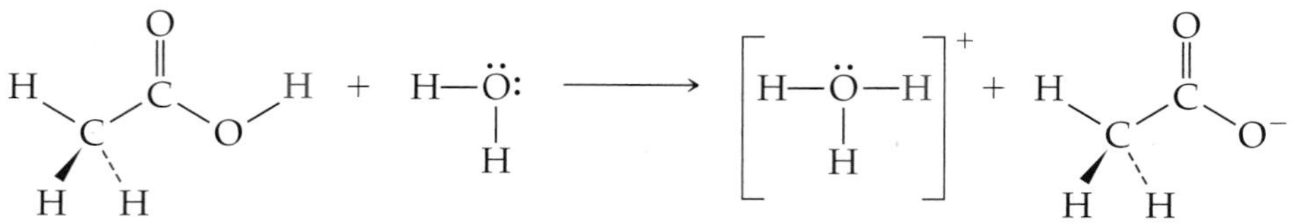

> **Brønsted–Lowry base** A substance that can accept H^+ ions from an acid.

Whereas a Brønsted–Lowry acid is a substance that *donates* H^+ ions, a **Brønsted–Lowry base** is a substance that *accepts* H^+ ions from an acid. Ammonia will react with water to produce OH⁻ ions (Arrhenius base definition) by accepting a proton (Brønsted–Lowry base definition), as shown:

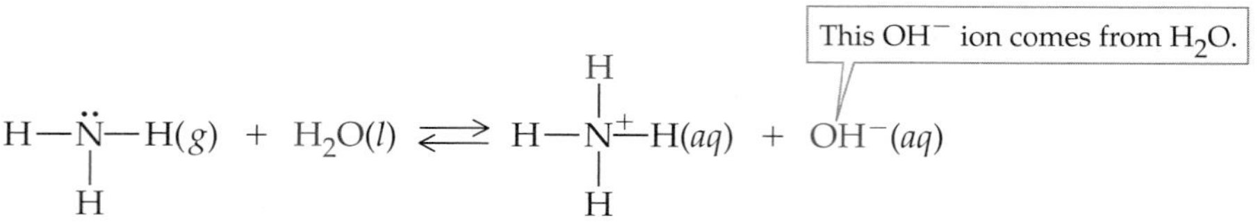

This OH⁻ ion comes from H_2O.

As with the acids, reactions involving Brønsted–Lowry bases need not occur in water, and the Brønsted–Lowry base need not give appreciable concentrations of OH^- ions in water. Gaseous NH_3, for example, acts as a base to accept H^+ from gaseous HCl and yield the ionic solid $NH_4^+ \ Cl^-$:

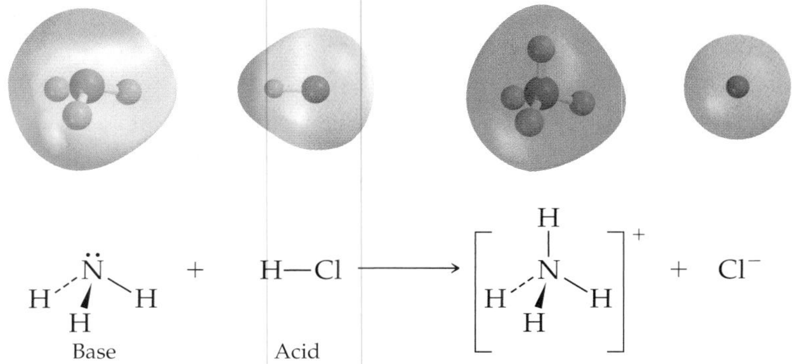

Putting the acid and base definitions together, *an acid-base reaction is one in which a proton is transferred*. The general reaction between proton-donor acids and proton-acceptor bases can be represented as

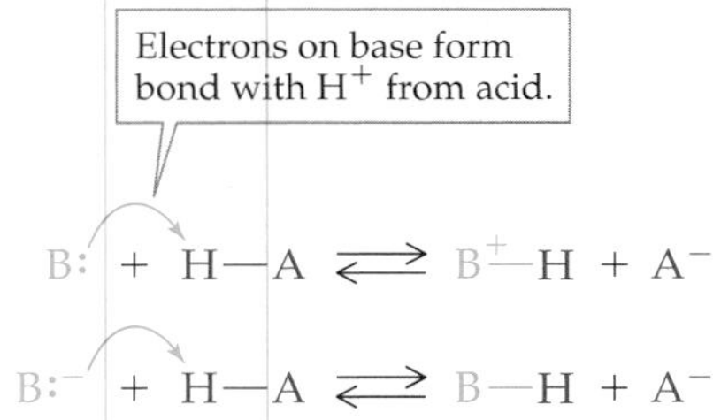

Electrons on base form bond with H^+ from acid.

where the abbreviation HA represents a Brønsted–Lowry acid and B: or B:$^-$ represents a Brønsted–Lowry base. Notice in these acid-base reactions that both electrons in the product B—H bond come from the base, as indicated by the curved arrow flowing from the electron pair of the base to the hydrogen atom of the acid. Thus, the B—H bond that forms is a coordinate covalent bond. In fact, a Brønsted–Lowry base *must* have such a lone pair of electrons; without them, it could not accept H^+ from an acid.

A base can either be neutral (B:) or negatively charged (B:$^-$). If the base is neutral, then the product has a positive charge (BH$^+$) after H^+ has been added. Ammonia is an example:

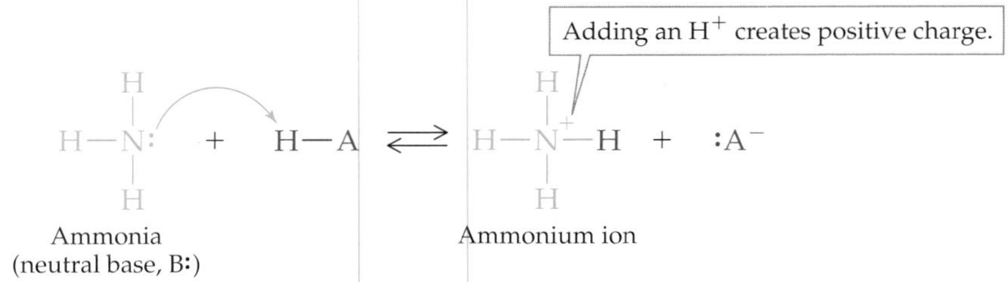

Adding an H^+ creates positive charge.

Ammonia (neutral base, B:)   Ammonium ion

If the base is negatively charged, then the product is neutral (BH). Hydroxide ion is an example:

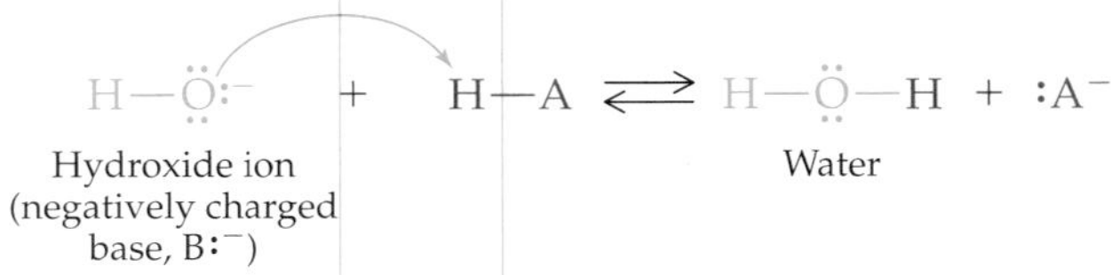

Hydroxide ion (negatively charged base, B:$^-$)   Water

◀◀◀ **CONCEPTS TO REVIEW** Recall from Section 4.4 that a coordinate covalent bond is one where both electrons are donated by the same atom.

An important consequence of the Brønsted–Lowry definitions is that the *products* of an acid-base reaction can also behave as acids and bases. Many acid-base reactions are reversible, although in some cases the equilibrium constant for the reaction is quite large. For example, suppose we have as a forward reaction an acid HA donating a proton to a base B to produce A⁻. This product A⁻ is a base because it can act as a proton acceptor in the reverse reaction. At the same time, the product BH⁺ acts as an acid because it may donate a proton in the reverse reaction:

◄◄ When the equilibrium constant for a reaction is greater than 1, the forward reaction is favored. When the equilibrium constant is less than 1, the reverse reaction is favored (Section 7.8).

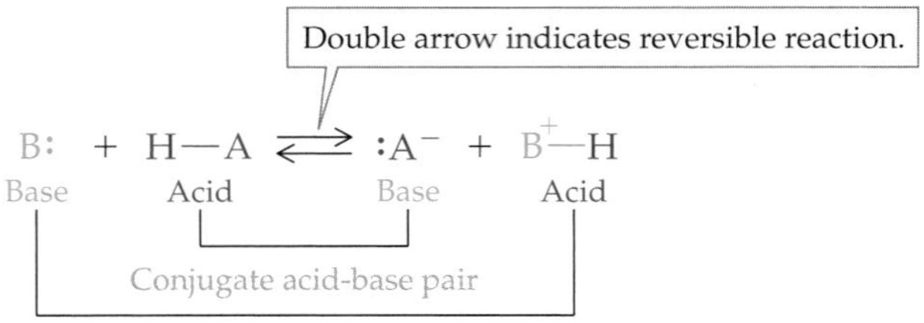

| Double arrow indicates reversible reaction. |

$$B: \ + \ H-A \ \rightleftharpoons \ :A^- \ + \ B^+\!-H$$

Base   Acid   Base   Acid

Conjugate acid-base pair

Conjugate acid-base pair Two substances whose formulas differ by only a hydrogen ion, H^+.

Conjugate base The substance formed by loss of H^+ from an acid.

Conjugate acid The substance formed by addition of H^+ to a base.

Pairs of chemical species such as B, BH⁺ and HA, A⁻ are called **conjugate acid-base pairs.** They are species that are found on opposite sides of a chemical reaction whose formulas differ by only one H^+. Thus, the product anion A⁻ is the **conjugate base** of the reactant acid HA, and HA is the **conjugate acid** of the base A⁻. Similarly, the reactant B is the conjugate base of the product acid BH⁺, and BH⁺ is the conjugate acid of the base B. The number of protons in a conjugate acid-base pair is always one greater than the number of protons in the base of the pair. To give some examples, acetic acid and acetate ion, the hydronium ion and water, and the ammonium ion and ammonia all make conjugate acid-base pairs:

$$
\begin{aligned}
\text{Conjugate acids} \left\{
\begin{array}{l}
CH_3COH \rightleftharpoons H^+ + CH_3CO^- \\
H_3O^+ \rightleftharpoons H^+ + H_2O \\
NH_4^+ \rightleftharpoons H^+ + NH_3
\end{array}
\right\} \text{Conjugate bases}
\end{aligned}
$$

Worked Example 10.1 Acids and Bases: Identifying Brønsted–Lowry Acids and Bases

Identify each of the following as a Brønsted–Lowry acid or base:

(a) $PO_4{}^{3-}$ (b) $HClO_4$ (c) CN^-

ANALYSIS A Brønsted–Lowry acid must have a hydrogen that it can donate as H^+, and a Brønsted–Lowry base must have an atom with a lone pair of electrons that can bond to H^+. Typically, a Brønsted–Lowry base is an anion derived by loss of H^+ from an acid.

SOLUTION

(a) The phosphate anion $\left(PO_4{}^{3-}\right)$ has no proton to donate, so it must be a Brønsted–Lowry base. It is derived by loss of 3 H^+ ions from phosphoric acid, H_3PO_4.

(b) Perchloric acid $\left(HClO_4\right)$ is a Brønsted–Lowry acid because it can donate an H^+ ion.

(c) The cyanide ion $\left(CN^-\right)$ has no proton to donate, so it must be a Brønsted–Lowry base. It is derived by loss removal of an H^+ ion from hydrogen cyanide, HCN.

Worked Example 10.2 Acids and Bases: Identifying Conjugate Acid-Base Pairs

Write formulas for
(a) The conjugate acid of the cyanide ion, CN^-
(b) The conjugate base of perchloric acid, $HClO_4$

ANALYSIS A conjugate acid is formed by adding H^+ to a base; a conjugate base is formed by removing H^+ from an acid.

SOLUTION
(a) HCN is the conjugate acid of CN^-
(b) ClO_4^- is the conjugate base of $HClO_4$.

PROBLEM 10.1

Which of the following are Brønsted–Lowry acids?
(a) HCO_2H (b) H_2S (c) $SnCl_2$

PROBLEM 10.2

Which of the following are Brønsted–Lowry bases?
(a) SO_3^{2-} (b) Ag^+ (c) F^-

PROBLEM 10.3

Write formulas for:
(a) The conjugate acid of HS^- (b) The conjugate acid of PO_4^{3-}
(c) The conjugate base of H_2CO_3 (d) The conjugate base of NH_4^+

⊙▬ KEY CONCEPT PROBLEM 10.4 ─────────────────────

For the reaction shown here, identify the Brønsted–Lowry acids, bases, and conjugate acid-base pairs.

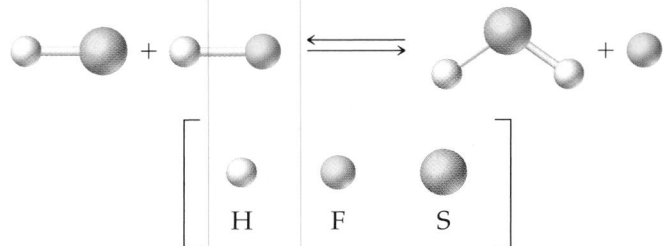

10.2 Acid and Base Strength

Learning Objective:

* Identify substances as strong or weak acids or bases, and predict the direction of the proton transfer reaction based on the relative strength of the acids and bases involved.

Some acids and bases must be handled with caution because these substances are caustic or corrosive; contact with skin can cause severe burns. Other acids and bases are present in a variety of foods and consumer products. Acids generally have a sour taste, and nearly every sour food contains an acid: Lemons, oranges, and grapefruit contain citric acid, for instance, and sour milk contains lactic acid. Bases are not so obvious in foods, but most of us have them stored under the kitchen or bathroom sink. Bases are present in many household cleaning agents, from perfumed bar soap, to ammonia-based

▲ Common household cleaners typi-cally contain bases (NaOH, NH₃). Soap is manufactured by the reaction of vegetable oils and animal fats with the bases NaOH and KOH.

window cleaners, to the substance you put down the drain to dissolve hair, grease, and other materials that clog it.

Some of the most common acids and bases are listed in Table 10.1. You should learn their names and formulas, because we will refer to them often throughout this chapter and the rest of the text.

Table 10.1 Common Acids and Bases

Common Acids	Information/Applications
Sulfuric acid, H_2SO_4	• The most important raw material in the chemical and pharmaceutical industries. • Over 45 million tons are prepared in the United States annually. • Used in the preparation of phosphate fertilizers, and is the acid found in automobile batteries.
Hydrochloric acid, HCl (*also* muriatic acid)	• Industrial applications include cleaning metal surfaces and manufacturing high-fructose corn syrup. • Component of "stomach acid" in the digestive systems of most mammals.
Phosphoric acid, H_3PO_4	• Used in the manufacturing of phosphate fertilizers, and as an additive in foods and toothpastes. • The tart taste of many soft drinks is due to the presence of phosphoric acid.
Nitric acid, HNO_3	• Strong oxidizing agent. • Used in the manufacturing of ammonium nitrate fertilizer and military explosives. • Contact with skin leaves a characteristic yellow coloration due to reaction with skin proteins.
Acetic acid, CH_3CO_2H	• Primary organic constituent of vinegar. • Occurs in all living cells. • Used in many industrial processes such as the preparation of solvents, lacquers, and coatings.
Common Bases	Information/Applications
Sodium hydroxide, NaOH (*also* caustic soda or lye)	• Most commonly used of all bases. • Industrially, used in the production of aluminum from its ore and in the production of glass; It is also used to manufacture soap from animal fat. • Drain cleaners often contain NaOH because it reacts with the fats and proteins found in grease and hair.
Calcium hydroxide, $Ca(OH)_2$ (*also* slaked lime)	• Made industrially by treating lime (CaO) with water. • A major component of mortars and cements. • Aqueous solution of $Ca(OH)_2$ often called *limewater*.
Magnesium hydroxide, $Mg(OH)_2$	• Aqueous suspensions called *milk of magnesia*. • Used as an additive in foods and toothpaste. • Component in many over-the-counter antacids such as Rolaids, Mylanta, and Maalox.
Ammonia, NH_3	• Used primarily as a fertilizer. • Other industrial applications include the manufacturing of pharmaceuticals and explosives. • Dilute solutions of ammonia are frequently used around the house as a glass cleaner.

Some acids and bases, such as sulfuric acid (H_2SO_4), hydrochloric acid (HCl), or sodium hydroxide (NaOH), are highly corrosive. They react readily and, in contact with skin, can cause serious burns. Other acids and bases are not nearly as reactive. Acetic acid (CH_3COOH, the major component in vinegar) and phosphoric acid (H_3PO_4) are found in many food products. Why are some acids and bases relatively "safe," while others must be handled with extreme caution? The answer lies in how easily they dissociate in water to produce the active ions for an acid (H^+) or a base (OH^-).

As indicated in Table 10.2, acids differ in their ability to give up a proton. The six acids at the top of the table are **strong acids,** meaning that they give up a proton

Strong acid An acid that gives up H^+ easily and completely dissociates in water.

easily and completely **dissociate,** or split apart into ions, in water. Those remaining are **weak acids,** meaning that they give up a proton with difficulty and do not completely dissociate in water. In a similar way, the conjugate bases at the top of the table are **weak bases** because they have little affinity for a proton, and the conjugate bases at the bottom of the table are **strong bases** because they have a strong affinity for a proton.

Dissociation The splitting apart of an acid in water to give H^+ and an anion.

Weak acid An acid that gives up H^+ with difficulty and does not completely dissociate in water.

Table 10.2 Relative Strengths of Acids and Conjugate Bases

Increasing acid strength		Acid		Conjugate base			Increasing base strength
	Strong acids: 100% dissociated	Perchloric acid	$HClO_4$	ClO_4^-	Perchlorate ion	Little or no reaction as bases	
		Sulfuric acid	H_2SO_4	$H_2SO_4^-$	Hydrogen sulfate ion		
		Hydriodic acid	HI	I^-	Iodide ion		
		Hydrobromic acid	HBr	Br^-	Bromide ion		
		Hydrochloric acid	HCl	Cl^-	Chloride ion		
		Nitric acid	HNO_3	NO_3^-	Nitrate ion		
		Hydronium ion	H_3O^+	H_2O	**Water**		
	Weak acids	Hydrogen sulfate ion	HSO_4^-	SO_4^{2-}	Sulfate ion	Very weak bases	
		Phosphoric acid	H_3PO_4	$H_2PO_4^-$	Dihydrogen phosphate ion		
		Nitrous acid	HNO_2	NO_2^-	Nitrite ion		
		Hydrofluoric acid	HF	F^-	Fluoride ion		
		Acetic acid	CH_3COOH	CH_3COO^-	Acetate ion		
	Very weak acids	Carbonic acid	H_2CO_3	HCO_3^-	Bicarbonate ion	Weak bases	
		Dihydrogen phosphate ion	$H_2PO_4^-$	HPO_4^{2-}	Hydrogen phosphate ion		
		Ammonium ion	NH_4^+	NH_3	Ammonia		
		Hydrocyanic acid	HCN	CN^-	Cyanide ion		
		Bicarbonate ion	HCO_3^-	CO_3^{2-}	Carbonate ion		
		Hydrogen phosphate ion	HPO_4^{2-}	PO_4^{3-}	Phosphate ion		
		Water	H_2O	OH^-	**Hydroxide ion**	Strong base	

Note that diprotic acids, such as sulfuric acid H_2SO_4, undergo two stepwise dissociations in water. The first dissociation yields HSO_4^- and occurs to the extent of nearly 100%, so H_2SO_4 is a strong acid. The second dissociation yields SO_4^{2-} and takes place to a much lesser extent because separation of a positively charged H^+ from the negatively charged HSO_4^- anion is difficult. Thus, HSO_4^- is a weak acid:

$$H_2SO_4(l) + H_2O(l) \longrightarrow H_3O^+(aq) + HSO_4^-(aq)$$
$$HSO_4^-(aq) + H_2O(l) \rightleftharpoons H_3O^+(aq) + SO_4^{2-}(aq)$$

Perhaps the most striking feature of Table 10.2 is the inverse relationship between acid strength and base strength. **The stronger the acid, the weaker its conjugate base; the weaker the acid, the stronger its conjugate base.** HCl, for example, is a strong acid, so Cl^- is a very weak base. H_2O, however, is a very weak acid, so OH^- is a strong base.

Why is there an inverse relationship between acid strength and base strength? To answer this question, think about what it means for an acid or base to be strong or weak. A strong acid, HA, is one that readily gives up a proton, meaning that its conjugate base A^- has little affinity for the proton. But this is exactly the definition of a weak base—a substance that has little affinity for a proton. As a result, the reverse

Weak base A base that has only a slight affinity for H^+ and holds it weakly.

Strong base A base that has a high affinity for H^+ and holds it tightly.

reaction occurs to a lesser extent, as indicated by the size of the forward and reverse arrows in the reaction:

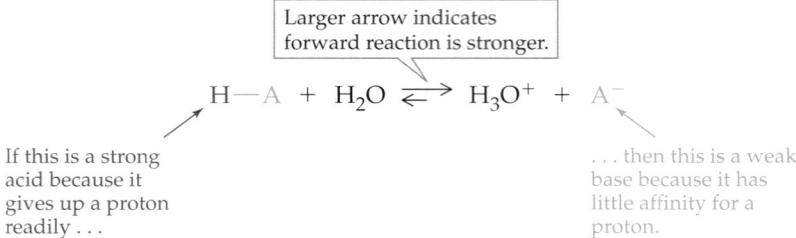

| Larger arrow indicates forward reaction is stronger. |

$$H\!-\!A \;+\; H_2O \;\rightleftharpoons\; H_3O^+ \;+\; A^-$$

If this is a strong acid because it gives up a proton readily . . .

. . . then this is a weak base because it has little affinity for a proton.

In the same way, a weak acid is one that gives up a proton with difficulty, meaning that its conjugate base has a high affinity for the proton. But this is just the definition of a strong base—a substance that has a high affinity for the proton. The reverse reaction now occurs more readily.

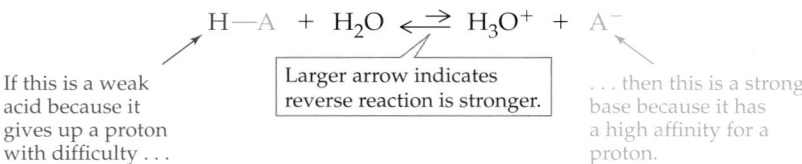

$$H\!-\!A \;+\; H_2O \;\rightleftharpoons\; H_3O^+ \;+\; A^-$$

If this is a weak acid because it gives up a proton with difficulty . . .

| Larger arrow indicates reverse reaction is stronger. |

. . . then this is a strong base because it has a high affinity for a proton.

Knowing the relative strengths of different acids as shown in Table 10.2 makes it possible to predict the direction of proton-transfer reactions. *An acid-base proton-transfer equilibrium always favors reaction of the stronger acid with the stronger base and formation of the weaker acid and base.* That is, the proton always leaves the stronger acid (whose weaker conjugate base cannot hold the proton) and always ends up in the weaker acid (whose stronger conjugate base holds the proton tightly). Put another way, in a contest for the proton, the stronger base always wins.

$$\text{Stronger acid} \;+\; \text{Stronger base} \;\rightleftharpoons\; \text{Weaker base} \;+\; \text{Weaker acid}$$

To try out this rule, compare the reactions of acetic acid with water and with hydroxide ion. The idea is to write the equation, identify the acid on each side of the arrow, and then decide which acid is stronger and which is weaker. For example, the reaction of acetic acid with water to give acetate ion and hydronium ion is favored in the reverse direction, because acetic acid is a weaker acid than H_3O^+:

$$\underset{\substack{\text{Acetic acid}\\\text{Weaker acid}}}{CH_3\overset{\overset{\displaystyle O}{\|}}{C}OH} \;+\; H_2O \;\rightleftharpoons\; \underset{\text{Acetate ion}}{CH_3\overset{\overset{\displaystyle O}{\|}}{C}O^-} \;+\; \underset{\substack{\text{Hydronium ion}\\\text{Stronger acid}}}{H_3O^+}$$

Reverse reaction is favored.

This base holds the proton less tightly . . .   . . . than this base does.

On the other hand, the reaction of acetic acid with hydroxide ion to give acetate ion and water is favored in the forward direction, because acetic acid is a stronger acid than H_2O:

$$\underset{\substack{\text{Acetic acid}\\\text{Stronger acid}}}{CH_3\overset{\overset{\displaystyle O}{\|}}{C}OH} \;+\; OH^- \;\rightleftharpoons\; \underset{\text{Hydroxide ion}}{CH_3\overset{\overset{\displaystyle O}{\|}}{C}O^-} \;+\; \underset{\substack{\text{Acetate ion}\\\text{Weaker acid}}}{H_2O}$$

Forward reaction is favored.

This base holds the proton more tightly . . .   . . . than this base does.

CHEMISTRY IN ACTION

⚕ GERD—Too Much Acid or Not Enough?

Strong acids are very caustic substances that can dissolve even metals, and no one would think of ingesting them. However, the major component of the gastric juices secreted in the stomach is hydrochloric acid—a strong acid—and the acidic environment in the stomach is vital to good health and nutrition.

Stomach acid is essential for the digestion of proteins and for the absorption of certain micronutrients, such as calcium, magnesium, iron, and vitamin B_{12}. It also creates a sterile environment in the gut by killing yeast and bacteria that may be ingested. If these gastric juices leak up into the esophagus, the tube through which food and drink enter the stomach, they can cause the burning sensation in the chest or throat known as either heartburn or acid indigestion. Persistent irritation of the esophagus is known as gastro-esophageal reflux disease (GERD) and, if untreated, can lead to more serious health problems.

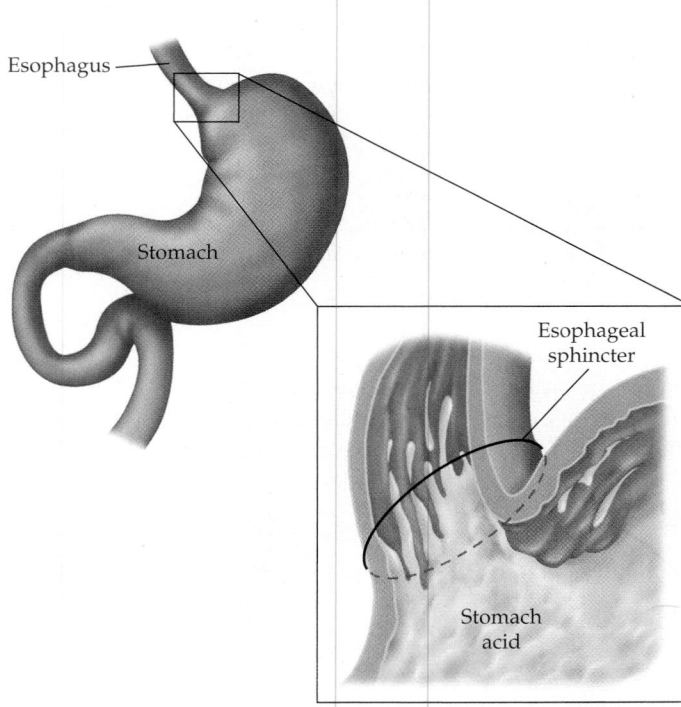

▲ The burning sensation and other symptoms associated with GERD are caused by the reflux of the acidic contents of the stomach into the esophagus.

Hydrogen ions and chloride ions are secreted separately from the cytoplasm of parietal cells lining the stomach and then combine to form HCl that is usually close to 0.10 M. The HCl is then released into the stomach cavity, where the concentration is diluted to about 0.01–0.001 M. Unlike the esophagus, the stomach is coated by a thick mucus layer that protects the stomach wall from damage by this caustic solution.

Those who suffer from acid indigestion can obtain relief by using over-the-counter antacids, such as TUMS or

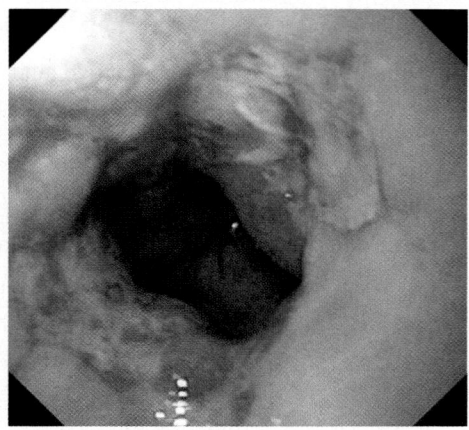

▲ If not treated, GERD can cause ulcers and scarring of esophageal tissue.

Rolaids (see Section 10.8, p. 311). Chronic conditions such as GERD, however, are often treated with prescription medications. GERD can be treated by two classes of drugs. Proton-pump inhibitors (PPI), such as Prevacid and Prilosec, prevent the production of the H^+ ions in the parietal cells, while H_2-receptor blockers (Tagamet, Zantac, and Pepcid) prevent the release of stomach acid into the lumen. Both drugs effectively decrease the production of stomach acid to ease the symptoms of GERD.

Ironically, GERD can also be caused by not having enough stomach acid—a condition known as *hypochlorhydria*. The valve that controls the release of stomach contents to the small intestine is triggered by acidity. If this valve fails to open because the stomach is not acidic enough, the contents of the stomach can be churned back up into the esophagus.

CIA Problem 10.1   The concentration of HCl when released to the stomach cavity is diluted to between 0.01 and 0.001 M.

 (a) Which of the two concentration of HCl cited above would require more antacid for neutralization? How much more?

 (b) Write a balanced equation for the neutralization of stomach acid by $NaHCO_3$.

 (c) How many grams of $NaHCO_3$ are required to neutralize 15.0 mL of a solution having a pH of 1.8?

CIA Problem 10.2   What are the functions of the acidic gastric juices in the stomach?

CIA Problem 10.3   Hydrochloric acid is the primary component of gastric juice in the stomach. The reaction between hydrochloric acid and the carbonate ion, the primary active ingredient in antacid tablets such as TUMS, can be written as

$$HCl(aq) + CO_3^{2-}(aq) \rightleftharpoons HCO_3^-(aq) + Cl^-(aq)$$

Identify the conjugate acid-base pairs in the reaction, and rewrite the arrows in the reaction to indicate if the forward or reverse reaction is favored.

Worked Example 10.3 Acid/Base Strength: Predicting Direction of H-transfer Reactions

Write a balanced equation for the proton-transfer reaction between phosphate ion (PO_4^{3-}) and water, and determine in which direction the equilibrium is favored.

ANALYSIS Look in Table 10.2 to see the relative acid and base strengths of the species involved in the reaction. The acid-base proton-transfer equilibrium will favor reaction of the stronger acid and formation of the weaker acid.

SOLUTION
Phosphate ion is the conjugate base of a weak acid (HPO_4^{2-}) and is, therefore, a relatively strong base. Table 10.2 shows that HPO_4^{2-} is a stronger acid than H_2O, and OH^- is a stronger base than PO_4^{3-}, so the reaction is favored in the reverse direction:

$$PO_4^{3-}(aq) \quad + \quad H_2O(l) \rightleftharpoons HPO_4^{3-}(aq) \quad + \quad OH^-(aq)$$

Weaker base   Weaker acid   Stronger acid   Stronger base

PROBLEM 10.5

Use Table 10.2 to identify the stronger acid in the following pairs:

(a) H_2O or NH_4^+ (b) H_2SO_4 or CH_3CO_2H (c) HCN or H_2CO_3

PROBLEM 10.6

Use Table 10.2 to identify the stronger base in the following pairs:

(a) F^- or Br^- (b) OH^- or HCO_3^-

PROBLEM 10.7

Write a balanced equation for the proton-transfer reaction between a hydrogen phosphate ion and a hydroxide ion. Identify each conjugate acid-base pair, and determine in which direction the equilibrium is favored.

PROBLEM 10.8

Write a balanced equation for the proton transfer reaction between hydrofluoric acid (HF) and ammonia (NH_3). Identify each conjugate acid-base pair, and rewrite the equilibrium arrows to indicate if the forward or reverse reaction is favored.

🔑 KEY CONCEPT PROBLEM 10.9

From this electrostatic potential map of the amino acid alanine, identify the most acidic hydrogens in the molecule:

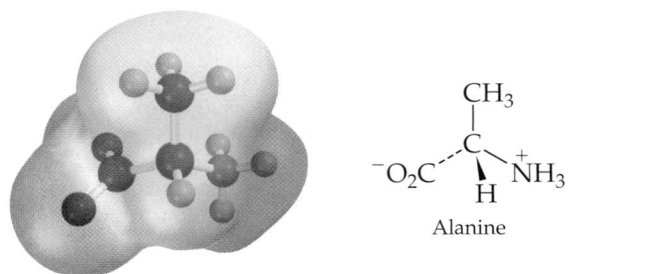

Alanine

10.3 Acid Dissociation Constants

Learning Objective:

• Write the expression for the acid dissociation constant (K_a), and use the value of K_a as a predictor of acid strength.

The reaction of a weak acid with water, like any chemical equilibrium, can be described by an equilibrium equation (Section 7.8), where square brackets indicate the concentrations of the enclosed species in molarity (moles per liter).

For the reaction $HA(aq) + H_2(l) \rightleftharpoons H_3^+(aq) + A^-(aq)$

we have $K = \dfrac{[H_3O^+][A^-]}{[HA][H_2O]}$

Because water is a solvent as well as a participant for the reaction, its concentration is essentially constant and has no effect on the equilibrium. Therefore, we usually put the equilibrium constant K and the water concentration $[H_2O]$ together to make a new constant called the **acid dissociation constant (K_a).** The acid dissociation constant is simply the hydronium ion concentration $[H_3O^+]$ times the conjugate base concentration $[A^-]$ divided by the undissociated acid concentration $[HA]$:

Acid dissociation constant $K_a = K[H_2O] = \dfrac{[H_3O^+][A^-]}{[HA]}$

> **Acid dissociation constant (K_a)** The equilibrium constant for the dissociation of an acid (HA), equal to $[H^+][A^-]/[HA]$.

For a strong acid, the H_3O^+ and A^- concentrations are much larger than the HA concentration, so K_a is very large. In fact, the K_a values for strong acids such as HCl are so large that it is difficult and not very useful to measure them. For a weak acid, however, the H_3O^+ and A^- concentrations are smaller than the HA concentration, so K_a is small. Table 10.3 gives K_a values for some common acids and illustrates several important points:

- Strong acids have K_a values much greater than 1 because dissociation is favored.
- Weak acids have K_a values much less than 1 because dissociation is not favored.
- Donation of each successive H^+ from a polyprotic acid is more difficult than the one before it, so K_a values become successively lower (see K_a values for phosphoric acid in Table 10.3).
- Most organic acids, which contain the $-COOH$ group, have K_a values near 10^{-5}.

Table 10.3   Some Acid Dissociation Constants, K_a, at 25 °C

Acid	K_a	Acid	K_a
Hydrofluoric acid (HF)	3.5×10^{-4}	*Polyprotic acids*	
Hydrocyanic acid (HCN)	4.9×10^{-10}	Sulfuric acid	
Ammonium ion (NH_4^+)	5.6×10^{-10}	H_2SO_4	Large
		HSO_4^-	1.2×10^{-2}
Organic acids		Phosphoric acid	
Formic acid (HCOOH)	1.8×10^{-4}	H_3PO_4	7.5×10^{-3}
Acetic acid (CH_3COOH)	1.8×10^{-5}	$H_2PO_4^-$	6.2×10^{-8}
Propanoic acid (CH_3CH_2COOH)	1.3×10^{-5}	HPO_4^{2-}	2.2×10^{-13}
		Carbonic acid	
Ascorbic acid (vitamin C)	7.9×10^{-5}	H_2CO_3	4.3×10^{-7}
		HCO_3^-	5.6×10^{-11}

PROBLEM 10.10

Benzoic acid ($C_6H_5CO_2H$) has $K_a = 6.5 \times 10^{-5}$ and citric acid ($C_6H_8O_7$) has $K_a = 7.2 \times 10^{-4}$. Which is the stronger conjugate base, benzoate ($C_6H_5CO_2^-$) or citrate ($C_6H_7O_7^-$)?

10.4   Water as Both an Acid and a Base

Learning Objectives:

- Identify the role of water as an acid or a base in hydrolysis reactions.
- Use the ion product constant for water (K_w) to calculate the relative concentrations of H_3O^+ and OH^- ions in aqueous solution.

Water is neither an acid nor a base in the Arrhenius sense because it does not contain appreciable concentrations of either H_3O^+ or OH^-. In the Brønsted–Lowry sense, however, water can act as *both* an acid and a base. When in contact with a base, water reacts as a Brønsted–Lowry acid and *donates* a proton to the base. In its reaction with ammonia, for example, water donates H^+ to ammonia to form the ammonium ion:

$$NH_3 + H_2O \longrightarrow NH_4^+ + OH^-$$

Ammonia   Water   Ammonium ion   Hydroxide ion
(base)   (acid)   (acid)   (base)

When in contact with an acid, water reacts as a Brønsted–Lowry base and *accepts* H^+ from the acid. This, of course, is exactly what happens when an acid such as HCl dissolves in water, as discussed in Section 10.1.

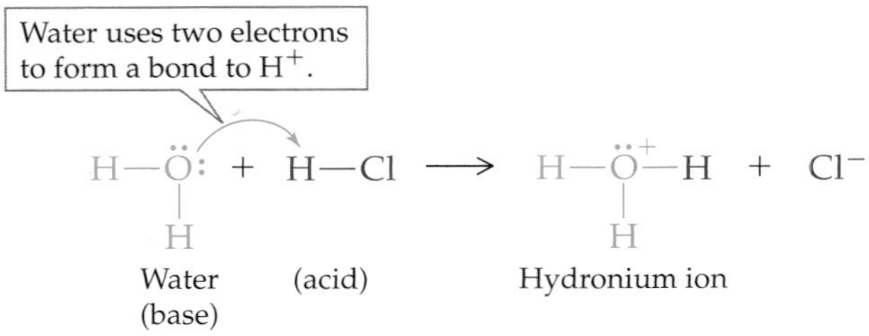

Water uses two electrons to form a bond to H^+.

$$H{-}\overset{..}{\underset{H}{O}}{:} + H{-}Cl \longrightarrow H{-}\overset{..}{\underset{H}{O}}^+{-}H + Cl^-$$

Water   (acid)   Hydronium ion
(base)

Amphoteric A substance that can react as either an acid or a base.

Substances like water, which can react as either an acid or a base depending on the circumstances, are said to be **amphoteric** (am-pho-**tare**-ic). When water acts as an acid, it donates H^+ and becomes OH^-; when it acts as a base, it accepts H^+ and becomes H_3O^+. (Note: HCO_3^-, $H_2PO_4^-$, and HPO_4^{2-} are also amphoteric.)

Dissociation of Water

We have learned how water can act as an acid when a base is present and as a base when an acid is present. But what about when no other acids or bases are present? In this case, one water molecule acts as an acid while another water molecule acts as a base, reacting to form the hydronium and hydroxide ions:

$$H_2O(l) + H_2O(l) \rightleftharpoons H_3O^+(aq) + OH^-(aq)$$

Because each dissociation reaction yields one H_3O^+ ion and one OH^- ion, the concentrations of the two ions are identical. Also, the equilibrium arrows indicate that this reaction favors reactants, so that not many H_3O^+ and OH^- ions are present at equilibrium. At 25 °C, the concentration of each is $1.00 \times 10^{-7} M$. We can write the equilibrium constant expression for the dissociation of water as

$$K = \frac{[H_3O^+][OH^-]}{[H_2O][H_2O]}$$

where $[H_3O^+] = [OH^-] = 1.00 \times 10^{-7} M$ (at 25 °C)

◀◀◀ Refer to discussion of equilibria involving pure liquids and solids in Section 7.8.

Ion-product constant for water (K_w) The product of the H_3O^+ and OH^- molar concentrations in water or any aqueous solution ($K_w = [H_3O^+][OH^-] = 1.00 \times 10^{-14}$).

As a pure substance the concentration of water is essentially constant. We can therefore put the water concentrations $[H_2O]$ together to make a new equilibrium constant called the **ion-product constant for water (K_w)**, which is simply the H_3O^+ concentration times the OH^- concentration. At 25 °C, $K_w = 1.00 \times 10^{-14}$.

Ion-product constant for water $K_w = K[H_2O][H_2O]$
$$= [H_3O^+][OH^-]$$
$$= 1.0 \times 10^{-14} \quad (\text{at } 25 \text{ °C})$$

The importance of the equation $K_w = [H_3O^+][OH^-]$ is that it applies to all aqueous solutions, not just to pure water. Since the product of $[H_3O^+]$ times $[OH^-]$ is always constant for any solution, we can determine the concentration of one species if we know the concentration of the other. If an acid is present in solution, for instance, so that $[H_3O^+]$ is large, then $[OH^-]$ must be small. If a base is present in solution so that $[OH^-]$ is large, then $[H_3O^+]$ must be small. For example, for a 0.10 M HCl solution, we know that $[H_3O^+] = 0.10\,M$ because HCl is 100% dissociated. Thus, we can calculate that $[OH^-] = 1.0 \times 10^{-13}\,M$:

$$\text{Since}\quad K_w \times [H_3O^+][OH^-] = 1.00 \times 10^{-14}$$

$$\text{we have}\quad [OH^-] = \frac{K_w}{[H_3O^+]} = \frac{1.00 \times 10^{-14}}{0.10} = 1.0 \times 10^{-13}\,M$$

Similarly, for a 0.10 M NaOH solution, we know that $[OH^-] = 0.10\,M$, so $[H_3O^+] = 1.0 \times 10^{-13}\,M$:

$$[H_3O^+] = \frac{K_w}{[OH^-]} = \frac{1.00 \times 10^{-14}}{0.10} = 1.0 \times 10^{-13}\,M$$

Solutions are identified as acidic, neutral, or basic (*alkaline*) according to the value of their H_3O^+ and OH^- concentrations:

Acidic solution: $[H_3O^+] > 10^{-7}\,M$ and $[OH^-] < 10^{-7}\,M$
Neutral solution: $[H_3O^+] = 10^{-7}\,M$ and $[OH^-] = 10^{-7}\,M$
Basic solution: $[H_3O^+] < 10^{-7}\,M$ and $[OH^-] > 10^{-7}\,M$

Worked Example 10.4 Water Dissociation Constant: Using K_w to Calculate $[OH^-]$

Milk has an H_3O^+ concentration of $4.5 \times 10^{-7}\,M$. What is the value of $[OH^-]$? Is milk acidic, neutral, or basic?

ANALYSIS The OH^- concentration can be found by dividing K_w by $[H_3O^+]$. An acidic solution has $[H_3O^+] > 10^{-7}\,M$, a neutral solution has $[H_3O^+] = 10^{-7}\,M$, and a basic solution has $[H_3O^+] < 10^{-7}\,M$.

BALLPARK ESTIMATE Since the H_3O^+ concentration is slightly *greater* than $10^{-7}\,M$, the OH^- concentration must be slightly *less* than $10^{-7}\,M$, on the order of 10^{-8}.

SOLUTION

$$[OH^-] = \frac{K_w}{[H_3O^+]} = \frac{1.00 \times 10^{-14}}{4.5 \times 10^{-7}} = 2.2 \times 10^{-8}\,M$$

Milk is slightly acidic because its H_3O^+ concentration is slightly larger than $1 \times 10^{-7}\,M$.

BALLPARK CHECK The OH^- concentration is of the same order of magnitude as our estimate.

PROBLEM 10.11

Identify the following solutions as either acidic or basic. What is the value of $[OH^-]$ in each?

(a) Household ammonia, $[H_3O^+] = 3.1 \times 10^{-12}\,M$
(b) Vinegar, $[H_3O^+] = 4.0 \times 10^{-3}\,M$

10.5 Measuring Acidity in Aqueous Solution: The pH Scale

Learning Objective:

• Calculate the pH of a solution from the H_3O^+ or OH^- concentration, and use the pH scale as an indication of the relative acidity/basicity of a solution.

In many fields, from medicine to chemistry to winemaking, it is necessary to know the exact concentration of H_3O^+ or OH^- in a solution. If, for example, the H_3O^+ concentration in blood varies only slightly from a value of $4.0 \times 10^{-8}\,M$, death can result.

Although correct, it is nevertheless awkward, or in some instances inconvenient, to refer to low concentrations of H_3O^+ using molarity. Fortunately, there is an easier way to express and compare H_3O^+ concentrations—the *pH scale*.

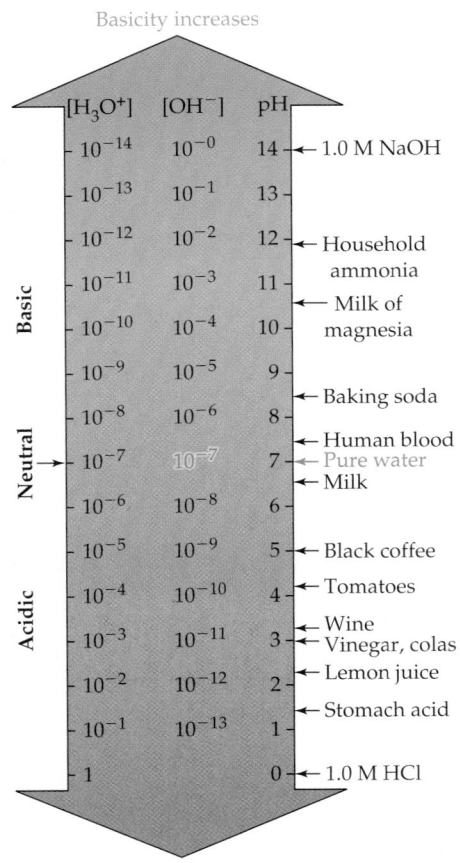

▲ **Figure 10.1**
The pH scale and the pH values of some common substances.
A low pH corresponds to a strongly acidic solution, a high pH corresponds to a strongly basic solution, and a pH of 7 corresponds to a neutral solution.

p function The negative common logarithm of some variable, $pX = -\log(X)$.

pH A measure of the acid strength of a solution; the negative common logarithm of the H_3O^+ concentration.

Acid-base indicator A dye that changes color depending on the pH of a solution.

▶ **Figure 10.2**
Finding pH.
(a) The color of universal indicator in solutions of known pH from 1 to 12.
(b) Testing pH with a paper strip. Comparing the color of the strip with the code on the package gives the approximate pH.

The pH of an aqueous solution is a number, usually between 0 and 14, that indicates the H_3O^+ concentration of the solution. A pH smaller than 7 indicates an acidic solution, a pH larger than 7 indicates a basic solution, and a pH of exactly 7 indicates a neutral solution. The pH scale and pH values of some common substances are shown in Figure 10.1.

Mathematically, a **p function** is defined as the negative common logarithm of some variable. The **pH** of a solution, therefore, is the negative common logarithm of the H_3O^+ concentration:

$$pH = -\log[H^+](\text{or}[H_3O^+])$$

If you have studied logarithms, you may remember that the common logarithm of a number is the power to which 10 must be raised to equal the number. The pH definition can therefore be restated as

$$[H_3O^+] = 10^{-pH}$$

For example, in neutral water at 25 °C, where $[H_3O^+] = 1 \times 10^{-7} M$, the pH is 7; in a strong acid solution where $[H_3O^+] = 1 \times 10^{-1} M$, the pH is 1; and in a strong base solution where $[H_3O^+] = 1 \times 10^{-14} M$, the pH is 14:

Acidic solution: pH < 7, $[H_3O^+] > 1 \times 10^{-7} M$
Neutral solution: pH = 7, $[H_3O^+] = 1 \times 10^{-7} M$
Basic solution: pH > 7, $[H_3O^+] < 1 \times 10^{-7} M$

Keep in mind that the pH scale covers an enormous range of acidities because it is a *logarithmic* scale, which involves powers of 10 (Figure 10.2). A change of only 1 pH unit means a 10-fold change in $[H_3O^+]$, a change of 2 pH units means a 100-fold change in $[H_3O^+]$, and a change of 12 pH units means a change of 10^{12} (a trillion) in $[H_3O^+]$.

To get a feel for the size of the quantities involved, think of a typical backyard swimming pool, which contains about 100,000 L of water. You would have to add only 0.10 mol of HCl (3.7 g) to lower the pH of the pool from 7.0 (neutral) to 6.0, but you would have to add 10,000 mol of HCl (370 kg!) to lower the pH of the pool from 7.0 to 1.0.

The pH of water is an important indicator of water quality in applications ranging from swimming pool and spa maintenance to municipal water treatment. There are several ways to measure the pH of a solution. The simplest but least accurate method is to use an **acid-base indicator,** a dye that changes color depending on the pH of the solution. For example, the well-known dye *litmus* is red below pH 4.8 but blue above pH 7.8 and the indicator *phenolphthalein* (fee-nol-THAY-lean) is colorless below pH 8.2 but red above pH 10. To make pH determination particularly easy, test kits are available that contain a mixture of indicators known as *universal indicator* to give approximate pH measurements in the range 2–10 (Figure 10.2a). Also available are rolls of "pH paper," which make it possible to determine pH simply by putting a drop of solution on the paper and comparing the color that appears to the color on a calibration chart (Figure 10.2b).

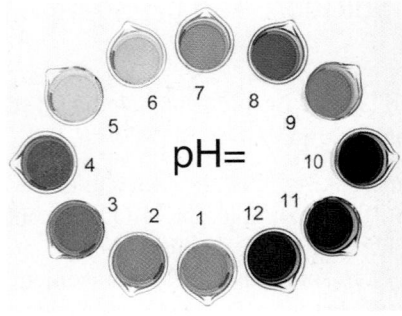

(a)

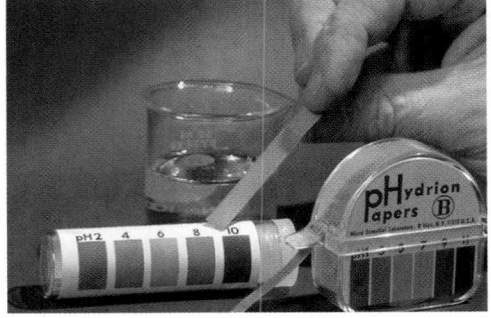

(b)

A much more accurate way to determine pH uses an electronic pH meter like the one shown in Figure 10.3. Electrodes are dipped into the solution, and the pH is read from the meter.

The logarithmic pH scale is a convenient way of reporting the relative acidity of solutions, but using logarithms can also be useful when calculating H_3O^+ and OH^- concentrations. Remember that the equilibrium between H_3O^+ and OH^- in aqueous solutions is expressed by K_w, where

$$K_w = [H_3O^+][OH^-] = 1 \times 10^{-14} \quad (\text{at } 25\ ^\circ\text{C})$$

If we convert this equation to its negative logarithmic form, we obtain

$$-\log(K_w) = -\log[H_3O^+] - \log[OH^-]$$
$$-\log(1 \times 10^{-14}) = -\log[H_3O^+] - \log[OH^-]$$
$$or \quad 14.00 = pH + pOH$$

The logarithmic form of the K_w equation can simplify the calculation of solution pH from OH^- concentration, as demonstrated in Worked Example 10.7.

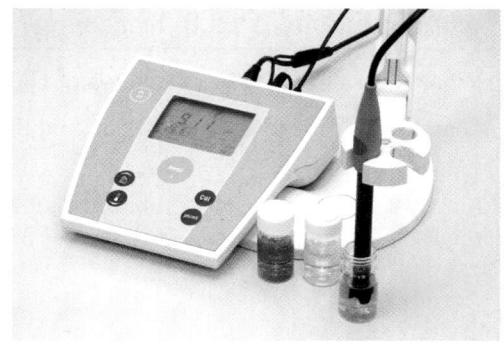

▲ **Figure 10.3**
Using a pH meter to obtain an accurate reading of pH.
Is the blue solution acidic or basic?

Worked Example 10.5   Measuring Acidity: Calculating pH from $[H_3O^+]$

The H_3O^+ concentration in coffee is about $1 \times 10^{-5}\,M$. What pH is this?

ANALYSIS The pH is the negative common logarithm of the H_3O^+ concentration: $pH = -\log[H_3O^+]$.

SOLUTION
Since the common logarithm of $1 \times 10^{-5}\,M$ is –5.0, the pH is 5.0.

Worked Example 10.6   Measuring Acidity: Calculating $[H_3O^+]$ from pH

Lemon juice has a pH of about 2. What $[H_3O^+]$ is this?

ANALYSIS In this case, we are looking for the $[H_3O^+]$, where $[H_3O^+] = 10^{-pH}$.

SOLUTION
Since pH = 2.0, $[H_3O^+] = 10^{-2} = 1 \times 10^{-2}\,M$.

Worked Example 10.7   Measuring Acidity: Using K_w to Calculate $[H_3O^+]$ and pH

A cleaning solution is found to have $[OH^-] = 1 \times 10^{-3}\,M$. What is the pH?

ANALYSIS To find pH, we must first find the value of $[H_3O^+]$ by using the equation $[H_3O^+] = K_w/[OH^-]$. Alternatively, we can calculate the pOH of the solution and then use the logarithmic form of the K_w equation: pH + pOH = 14.00.

SOLUTION
Rearranging the K_w equation, we have

$$[H_3O^+] = \frac{K_w}{[OH^-]} = \frac{1.00 \times 10^{-14}}{1 \times 10^{-3}} = 1 \times 10^{-11}\,M$$
$$pH = -\log(1 \times 10^{-11}) = 11.0$$

Using the logarithmic form of the K_w equation, we have

$$pH = 14.0 - pOH = 14.0 - (-\log[OH^-])$$
$$pH = 14.0 - (-\log(1 \times 10^{-3}))$$
$$pH = 14.0 - 3.0 = 11.0$$

Worked Example 10.8 Measuring Acidity: Calculating pH of Strong Acid Solutions

What is the pH of a 0.01 M solution of HCl?

ANALYSIS To find pH, we must first find the value of $[H_3O^+]$.

SOLUTION
Since HCl is a strong acid (Table 10.1), it is 100% dissociated, and the H_3O^+ concentration is the same as the HCl concentration: $[H_3O^+]$ = 0.01 M, or $1 \times 10^{-2}\,M$, and pH = 2.0.

PROBLEM 10.12

Calculate the pH of the solutions in Problem 10.11.

PROBLEM 10.13

Give the hydronium ion and hydroxide ion concentrations of solutions with the following values of pH. Which of the solutions is most acidic? Which is most basic?

(a) pH 13.0   (b) pH 3.0   (c) pH 8.0

PROBLEM 10.14

Which solution would have the higher pH: 0.010 M HNO_2 or 0.010 M HNO_3? Explain.

10.6 Working with pH

Learning Objective:

• Calculate pH from $[H_3O^+]$ or $[OH^-]$, and calculate $[H_3O^+]$ from pH.

Converting between pH and H_3O^+ concentration is easy when the pH is a whole number, but how do you find the H_3O^+ concentration of blood, which has a pH of 7.4, or the pH of a solution with $[H_3O^+]$ = $4.6 \times 10^{-3}\,M$? Sometimes it is sufficient to make an estimate. The pH of blood (7.4) is between 7 and 8, so the H_3O^+ concentration of blood must be between 1×10^{-7} and $1 \times 10^{-8}\,M$. To be exact about finding pH values, though, requires a calculator.

Converting from pH to $[H_3O^+]$ requires finding the *antilogarithm* of the negative pH, which is done on many calculators with an "INV" key and a "log" key. Converting from $[H_3O^+]$ to pH requires finding the logarithm, which is commonly done with a "log" key and an "exp" or "EE" key for entering exponents of 10. Consult your calculator instructions if you are not sure how to use these keys. Remember that the sign of the number given by the calculator must be changed from minus to plus to get the pH.

The H_3O^+ concentration in blood with pH = 7.4 is

$$[H_3O^+] = antilog(-7.4) = 4 \times 10^{-8}\,M$$

The pH of a solution with $[H_3O^+]$ = $4.6 \times 10^{-3}\,M$ is

$$pH = -\log(4.6 \times 10^{-3}) = -(-2.34) = 2.34$$

If instead of $[H_3O^+]$ we are given $[OH^-]$, then we must first use the relationship $K_w = [H_3O^+][OH^-]$; if $[OH^-]$ is known, we can rearrange to solve for the hydronium ion concentration and then calculate pH. Alternatively, we can calculate pOH and use the logarithmic form of K_w as discussed in the previous section:

$$14.00 = pH + pOH$$

A note about significant figures: an antilogarithm contains the same number of significant figures as the original number has to the right of the decimal point. A logarithm contains the same number of digits to the right of the decimal point as the number of significant figures in the original number.

$$\text{antilog}(-7.4) = 4 \times 10^{-8} \qquad \log(4.6 \times 10^{-3}) = -2.34$$

| 1 digit after decimal point | 1 digit | | 2 digits | 2 digits after decimal point |

Worked Example 10.9 Working with pH: Converting a pH to $[H_3O^+]$

Soft drinks usually have a pH of approximately 3.1. What is the $[H_3O^+]$ concentration in a soft drink?

ANALYSIS To convert from a pH value to an $[H_3O^+]$ concentration requires using the equation $[H_3O^+] = 10^{-pH}$, which requires finding an antilogarithm on a calculator.

BALLPARK ESTIMATE Because the pH is between 3.0 and 4.0, the $[H_3O^+]$ must be between 1×10^{-3} and 1×10^{-4}. A pH of 3.1 is very close to 3.0, so the $[H_3O^+]$ must be just slightly below $1 \times 10^{-3}\,M$.

SOLUTION
Entering the negative pH on a calculator (-3.1) and pressing the "INV" and "log" keys gives the answer 7.943×10^{-4}, which must be rounded off to 8×10^{-4} because the pH has only one digit to the right of the decimal point.

BALLPARK CHECK The calculated $[H_3O^+]$ of $8 \times 10^{-4}\,M$ is between $1 \times 10^{-3}\,M$ and $1 \times 10^{-4}\,M$ and, as we estimated, just slightly below $1 \times 10^{-3}\,M$. (Remember, 8×10^{-4} is 0.8×10^{-3}.)

Worked Example 10.10 Working with pH: Calculating pH for Strong Acid Solutions

What is the pH of a $0.0045\,M$ solution of $HClO_4$?

ANALYSIS Finding pH requires first finding $[H_3O^+]$ and then using the equation $pH = -\log[H_3O^+]$. Since $HClO_4$ is a strong acid (see Table 10.1), it is 100% dissociated, and so the H_3O^+ concentration is the same as the $HClO_4$ concentration.

BALLPARK ESTIMATE Because $[H_3O^+] = 4.5 \times 10^{-3}\,M$ is close to midway between $1 \times 10^{-2}\,M$ and $1 \times 10^{-3}\,M$, the pH must be close to the midway point between 2.0 and 3.0. (Unfortunately, because the logarithm scale is not linear, trying to estimate the midway point is not a simple process.)

SOLUTION
$[H_3O^+] = 0.0045\,M = 4.5 \times 10^{-3}\,M$. Taking the negative logarithm gives $pH = 2.35$.

BALLPARK CHECK The calculated pH is consistent with our estimate.

Worked Example 10.11 Working with pH: Calculating pH for Strong Base Solutions

What is the pH of a $0.0032\,M$ solution of NaOH?

ANALYSIS Since NaOH is a strong base, the OH^- concentration is the same as the NaOH concentration. Starting with the OH^- concentration, finding pH requires either using the K_w equation to find $[H_3O^+]$ or calculating pOH and then using the logarithmic form of the K_w equation.

BALLPARK ESTIMATE Because $[OH^-] = 3.2 \times 10^{-3}\,M$ is close to midway between $1 \times 10^{-2}\,M$ and $1 \times 10^{-3}\,M$, the pOH must be close to the midway point between 2.0 and 3.0. Subtracting the pOH from 14 would therefore yield a pH between 11 and 12.

SOLUTION

$$[OH^-] = 0.0032\,M = 3.2 \times 10^{-3}\,M$$

$$[H_3O^+] = \frac{K_w}{(3.2 \times 10^{-3})} = 3.1 \times 10^{-12}\,M$$

—continued on next page

—continued from previous page

Taking the negative logarithm gives pH $= -\log(3.1 \times 10^{-12}) = 11.51$. Alternatively, we can calculate pOH and subtract from 14.00 using the logarithmic form of the K_w equation. For $[\text{OH}^-] = 0.0032\ M$,

$$\text{pOH} = -\log(3.2 \times 10^{-3}) = 2.49$$
$$\text{pH} = 14.00 - 2.49 = 11.51$$

Since the given OH^- concentration included two significant figures, the final pH includes two significant figures beyond the decimal point.

BALLPARK CHECK The calculated pH is consistent with our estimate.

CHEMISTRY IN ACTION

Acid Rain

As the water that evaporates from oceans and lakes condenses into raindrops, it dissolves small quantities of gases from the atmosphere. Under normal conditions, rain is slightly acidic, with a pH close to 5.6, because of atmospheric CO_2 that dissolves to form carbonic acid:

$$CO_2(aq) + H_2O(l) \rightleftharpoons H_2CO_3(aq) \rightleftharpoons$$
$$HCO_3^-(aq) + H_3O^+(aq)$$

In recent decades, however, the acidity of rainwater in many industrialized areas of the world has increased by a factor of over 100, to a pH between 3 and 3.5.

The primary cause of this so-called *acid rain* is industrial and automotive pollution. Each year, large power plants and smelters pour millions of tons of sulfur dioxide (SO_2) gas into the atmosphere, where some is oxidized by air to produce sulfur trioxide (SO_3). Sulfur oxides then dissolve in rain to form dilute sulfurous acid (H_2SO_3) and sulfuric acid (H_2SO_4):

$$SO_2(g) + H_2O(l) \longrightarrow H_2SO_3(aq)$$
$$SO_3(g) + H_2O(l) \longrightarrow H_2SO_4(aq)$$

Nitrogen oxides produced by the high-temperature reaction of N_2 with O_2 in coal-burning plants and in automobile engines further contribute to the problem. Nitrogen dioxide (NO_2) dissolves in water to form dilute nitric acid (HNO_3) and nitric oxide (NO):

$$3\,NO_2(g) + H_2O(l) \longrightarrow 2\,HNO_3(aq) + NO(g)$$

Oxides of both sulfur and nitrogen have always been present in the atmosphere, produced by such natural sources as volcanoes and lightning bolts, but their amounts have increased dramatically over the last century because of industrialization. The result is a notable decrease in the pH of rainwater in more densely populated regions, including Europe and the eastern United States.

Many processes in nature require such a fine pH balance that they are dramatically upset by the shift that has

▲ This limestone statue adorning the Rheims Cathedral in France has been severely eroded by acid rain.

occurred in the pH of rain. Some watersheds contain soils that have the ability to neutralize acidic compounds in acid rain. Other areas, such as the northeastern United States and eastern Canada, where neutralizing capacity is poor, have experienced negative ecological effects. Acid rain releases aluminum salts from soil, and the ions then wash into streams. The low pH and increased aluminum levels are so toxic to fish and other organisms that many lakes and streams in these areas are devoid of aquatic life. Massive tree die-offs have occurred throughout central and eastern Europe as acid rain has lowered the pH of the soil and has leached nutrients from leaves.

Fortunately, acidic emissions in the United States have been greatly reduced in recent years as a result of the Clean Air Act Amendments of 1990, and cap-and-trade programs such as the Clean Air Interstate Rule (CAIR) and the Acid Rain

PROBLEM 10.15

Identify the following solutions as acidic or basic, estimate $[H_3O^+]$ and $[OH^-]$ values for each, and rank them in order of increasing acidity:

(a) Saliva, pH = 6.5   (b) Pancreatic juice, pH = 7.9

(c) Orange juice, pH = 3.7   (d) Wine, pH = 3.5

PROBLEM 10.16

Calculate the pH of the following solutions and report it to the correct number of significant figures:

(a) Seawater with $[H_3O^+] = 5.3 \times 10^{-9} M$

(b) A urine sample with $[H_3O^+] = 8.9 \times 10^{-6} M$

PROBLEM 10.17

What is the pH of a 0.0025 M solution of HCl?

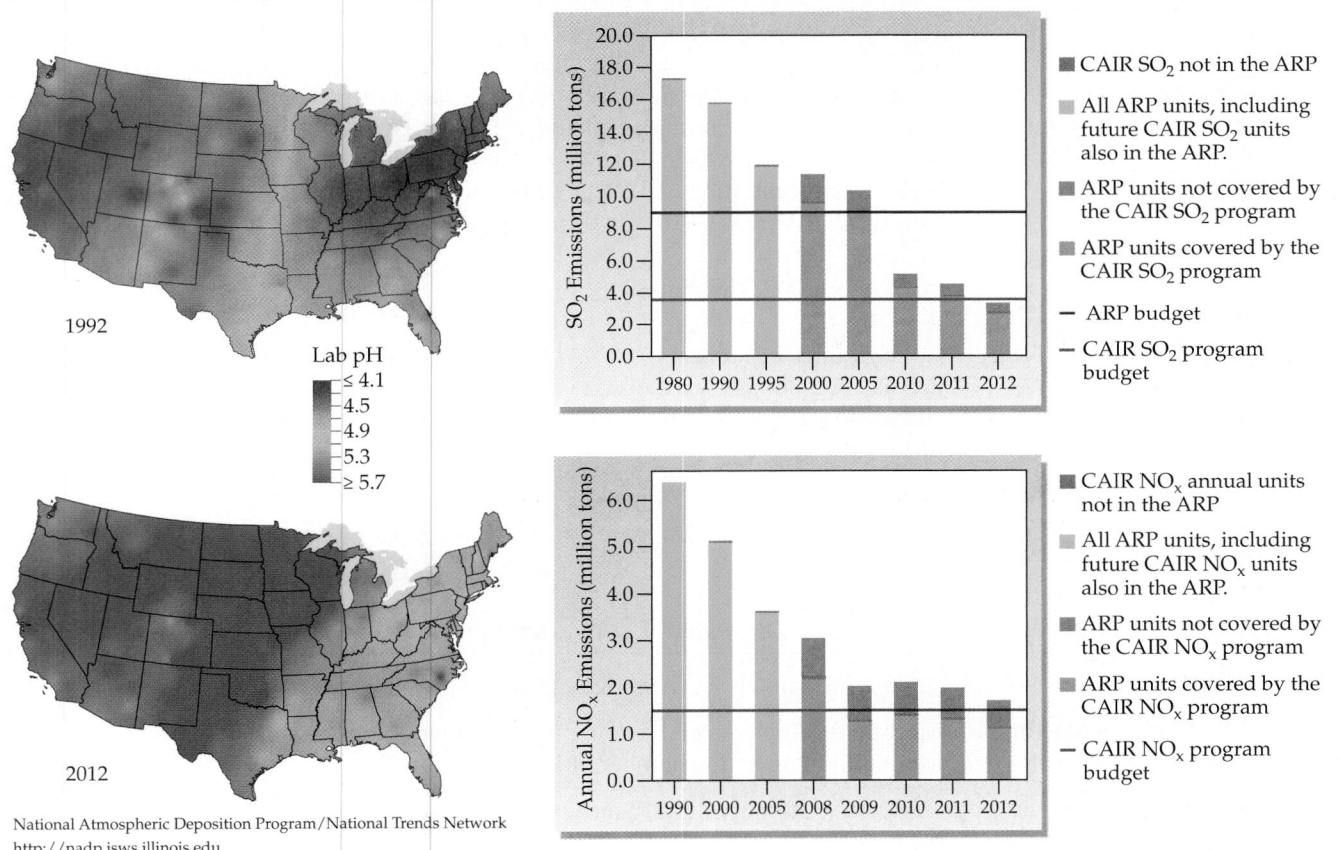

National Atmospheric Deposition Program/National Trends Network
http://nadp.isws.illinois.edu

▲ As illustrated on the pH maps (left side of figure), the decreased incidence of acid rain from 1992 to 2012 strongly correlates with decreases in SO_2 and NO_2 emissions over this same time frame (right side of figure).

Program (ARP) designed to reduce SO_2 and NO_x emissions from power plants. Emissions of SO_2 from participating industries decreased from 9.8 million tons in 2005 to 2.8 million tons in 2012, a decrease of 68%. Emissions of NO_x decreased by 53% over the same period. While these legislative actions have resulted in significant reductions in the United States, acid rain is a growing concern in many newly industrialized nations, including China and India.

CIA Problem 10.4 Rain typically has a pH of about 5.6. What is the H_3O^+ concentration in rain?

CIA Problem 10.5 Acid rain with a pH as low as 1.5 has been recorded in West Virginia.

(a) What is the H_3O^+ concentration in this acid rain?

(b) How many grams of HNO_3 must be dissolved to make 25 L of solution that has a pH of 1.5?

10.7 Acid and Base Equivalents

Learning Objective:

• Define normality (i.e., equivalent ion concentrations) for acids and bases, and the relationship between units of normality and molarity.

We said in Section 9.10 that it is sometimes useful to think in terms of ion *equivalents* (Eq) when we are primarily interested in an ion itself rather than the compound that produced the ion. For similar reasons, it can also be useful to consider acid or base equivalents.

When dealing with ions, the property of interest was the charge on the ion. Therefore, 1 Eq of an ion was defined as the number of ions that carry 1 mol of charge. For acids and bases, the property of interest is the number of H^+ ions (for an acid) or the number of OH^- ions (for a base) per formula unit. Thus, 1 **equivalent of acid** contains 1 mol of H^+ ions, and 1 **equivalent of base** contains 1 mol of OH^- ions.

Using acid-base equivalents has a practical advantage when only the acidity or basicity of a solution is of interest rather than the identity of the acid or base. *One equivalent of any acid neutralizes one equivalent of any base.* Because acid-base equivalents are so useful, clinical chemists sometimes express acid and base concentrations in *normality* rather than molarity. The **normality (N)** of an acid or base solution is defined as the number of equivalents (or milliequivalents) of acid or base per liter of solution. For example, a solution made by dissolving 49.0 g of H_2SO_4 (or 0.50 mol) in water to give 1.0 L of solution has a concentration of 1.0 Eq/L, which is 1.0 N. Similarly, a solution that contains 0.010 Eq/L of acid is 0.010 N and has an acid concentration of 10 mEq/L:

Equivalent of acid Amount of an acid that contains 1 mole of H^+ ions.

Equivalent of base Amount of base that contains 1 mole of OH^- ions.

Normality (N) A measure of acid (or base) concentration expressed as the number of acid (or base) equivalents per liter of solution.

$$\text{Normality (N)} = \frac{\text{Equivalents of acid or base}}{\text{Liters of solution}}$$

The values of molarity *(M)* and normality (N) are the same for monoprotic acids, such as HCl, but are not the same for diprotic or triprotic acids. For any acid or base, normality is always equal to molarity times the number of H^+ or OH^- ions produced per formula unit:

Normality of acid $=$ (Molarity of acid) $\times$ (Number of H^+ ions produced per formula unit)

Normality of base $=$ (Molarity of base) $\times$ (Number of OH^- ions produced per formula unit)

Worked Example 10.12 Equivalents: Mass to Equivalent Conversion for Diprotic Acid

How many equivalents are in 3.1 g of the diprotic acid H_2S? The molar mass of H_2S is 34.0 g.

ANALYSIS The number of acid or base equivalents is calculated by doing a gram to mole conversion using molar mass as the conversion factor and then multiplying by the number of H^+ ions produced.

BALLPARK ESTIMATE The 3.1 g is a little less than 0.10 mol of H_2S. Since it is a diprotic acid, (two H^+ per mole), this represents a little less than 0.2 Eq of H_2S.

SOLUTION

$$(3.1 \text{ g } H_2S)\left(\frac{1 \text{ mol } H_2S}{34.0 \text{ g } H_2S}\right)\left(\frac{2 \text{ Eq } H_2S}{1 \text{ mol } H_2S}\right) = 0.18 \text{ Eq } H_2S$$

BALLPARK CHECK The calculated value of 0.18 is consistent with our prediction of a little less than 0.2 Eq of H_2S.

Worked Example 10.13 Equivalents: Calculating Equivalent Concentrations

What is the normality of a solution made by diluting 6.5 g of H_2SO_4 to a volume of 200 mL? What is the concentration of this solution in milliequivalents per liter? The molar mass of H_2SO_4 is 98.0 g.

ANALYSIS Calculate how many equivalents of H_2SO_4 are in 6.5 g by using the molar mass of the acid as a conversion factor and then determine the normality of the acid.

SOLUTION

STEP 1: Identify known information. We know the molar mass of H_2SO_4, the mass of H_2SO_4 to be dissolved, and the final volume of solution.

MW of H_2SO_4 = 98.0 g/mol
Mass of H_2SO_4 = 6.5 g
Volume of solution = 200 mL

STEP 2: Identify answer including units. We need to calculate the normality of the final solution.

Normality = ?? (equiv./L)

STEP 3: Identify conversion factors. We will need to convert the mass of H_2SO_4 to moles, and then to equivalents of H_2SO_4. We will then need to convert volume from mL to L.

$$(6.5 \text{ g } H_2SO_4)\left(\frac{1 \text{ mol } H_2SO_4}{98.0 \text{ g } H_2SO_4}\right)\left(\frac{2 \text{ Eq } H_2SO_4}{1 \text{ mol } H_2SO_4}\right)$$
$$= 0.132 \text{ Eq } H_2SO_4 \text{ (Don't round yet!)}$$
$$(200 \text{ mL})\left(\frac{1 \text{ L}}{1000 \text{ mL}}\right) = 0.200 \text{ L}$$

STEP 4: Solve. Dividing the number of equivalents by the volume yields the normality.

$$\frac{0.132 \text{ Eq } H_2SO_4}{0.200 \text{ L}} = 0.66 \text{ N}$$

The concentration of the sulfuric acid solution is 0.66 N, or 660 mEq/L.

PROBLEM 10.18

How many equivalents are in the following?
 (a) 5.0 g HNO_3 (b) 12.5 g $Ca(OH)_2$ (c) 4.5 g H_3PO_4

PROBLEM 10.19

What are the normalities of the solutions if each sample in Problem 10.18 is dissolved in water and diluted to a volume of 300.0 mL?

10.8 Some Common Acid-Base Reactions

Learning Objective:
• Write balanced chemical equations for the common reactions of acids and bases.

Among the most common Brønsted–Lowry acid-base reactions are those of an acid with hydroxide ion, an acid with bicarbonate or carbonate ion, and an acid with ammonia or a related nitrogen-containing compound. Let us look briefly at each of the three types.

Reaction of Acids with Hydroxide Ion

One equivalent of an acid reacts with 1 Eq of a metal hydroxide to yield water and a salt in a neutralization reaction:

$$HCl(aq) + KOH(aq) \longrightarrow H_2O(l) + KCl(aq)$$
(acid) (base) (water) (salt)

◀◀ In Section 5.4, we discussed neutralization reactions, and noted that the products were water, and a salt—an ionic compound formed from reaction of an acid with a base.

Such reactions are usually written with a single arrow because their equilibria lie far to the right and they have very large equilibrium constants ($K = 5 \times 10^{15}$; Section 7.8). The net ionic equation (Section 5.7) for all such reactions makes clear why acid-base equivalents are useful and why the properties of the acid and base disappear in neutralization reactions: The equivalent ions for the acid (H^+) and the base (OH^-) are used up in the formation of water.

$$H^+(aq) + OH^-(aq) \longrightarrow H_2O(l)$$

PROBLEM 10.20

Maalox, an over-the-counter antacid, contains aluminum hydroxide, $Al(OH)_3$, and magnesium hydroxide, $Mg(OH)_2$. Write balanced equations for the reaction of both with stomach acid (HCl).

Reaction of Acids with Bicarbonate and Carbonate Ion

Bicarbonate ion reacts with acid by accepting H^+ to yield carbonic acid, H_2CO_3. Similarly, carbonate ion accepts two protons in its reaction with acid. Carbonic acid is unstable, however, rapidly decomposing to carbon dioxide gas and water:

$$H^+(aq) + HCO_3^-(aq) \longrightarrow [H_2CO_3(aq)] \longrightarrow H_2O(l) + CO_2(g)$$
$$2\,H^+(aq) + CO_3^{2-}(aq) \longrightarrow [H_2CO_3(aq)] \longrightarrow H_2O(l) + CO_2(g)$$

Most metal carbonates are insoluble in water—marble, for example, is almost pure calcium carbonate, $CaCO_3$ —but they nevertheless react easily with aqueous acid. In fact, geologists often test for carbonate-bearing rocks by putting a few drops of aqueous HCl on the rock and watching to see if bubbles of CO_2 form (Figure 10.4). This reaction is also responsible for the damage to marble and limestone artwork caused by acid rain (see the Chemistry in Action "Acid Rain" on p. 308). The most common application involving carbonates and acid, however, is the use of antacids that contain carbonates, such as TUMS or Rolaids, to neutralize excess stomach acid.

▲ Figure 10.4
Marble.
Marble, which is primarily $CaCO_3$, releases bubbles of CO_2 when treated with hydrochloric acid.

PROBLEM 10.21

Write a balanced equation for each of the following reactions:
(a) $HCO_3^-(aq) + H_2SO_4(aq) \longrightarrow$?   **(b)** $CO_3^{2-}(aq) + HNO_3(aq) \longrightarrow$?

Reaction of Acids with Nitrogen-Containing Compounds

Acids react with ammonia to yield ammonium salts, such as ammonium chloride, NH_4Cl, most of which are water-soluble:

$$NH_3(aq) + HCl(aq) \longrightarrow NH_4Cl(aq)$$

Living organisms contain a group of compounds called *amines*, which contain nitrogen atoms bonded to carbon. Amines react with acids just as ammonia does, yielding water-soluble salts. Methylamine, for example, an organic compound found in rotting fish, reacts with HCl:

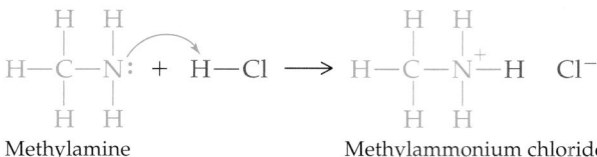

Methylamine   Methylammonium chloride

LOOKING AHEAD ▶▶ In Chapter 16, we will see that amines occur in all living organisms, both plant and animal, as well as in many pharmaceutical agents. Amines called amino acids form the building blocks from which proteins are made, as we will see in Chapter 18.

PROBLEM 10.22

What products would you expect from the reaction of ammonia and sulfuric acid in aqueous solution?

$$2\,NH_3(aq) + H_2SO_4(aq) \longrightarrow$$?

PROBLEM 10.23

Show how ethylamine $(C_2H_5NH_2)$ reacts with hydrochloric acid to form an ethylammonium salt.

HANDS-ON CHEMISTRY 10.1

Assemble the following materials: vinegar (a 5% solution of acetic acid), baking soda (sodium bicarbonate), a tall glass, a candle, and matches. Note: if you do not have baking soda, some antacid tablets containing calcium or magnesium carbonate will serve the same purpose.

1. Light the candle and place it on a clean, uncluttered surface.
2. Pour about ¼ cup of vinegar into the tall glass.
3. Slowly add about a tablespoon of baking soda, a little at a time. What do you observe? Try to avoid having the

reaction solution bubble up higher than half the height of the glass. Based on the reactions discussed in this section, identify the gas that was produced in this reaction.

4. Now pick up the glass and position it about 5 inches above the candle flame. Tilt the glass so that the gas that has collected in the glass can flow out onto the candle flame. (Be careful not to allow any solution to pour from the glass.) What happens to the flame? How does this confirm the identity of the gas produced in the reaction?

10.9 Acidity and Basicity of Salt Solutions

Learning Objective:

• Predict whether a salt solution will be acidic, basic, or neutral.

It is tempting to think of all salt solutions as neutral; after all, they come from the neutralization reaction between an acid and a base. In fact, salt solutions can be neutral, acidic, or basic, depending on the ions present, because some ions react with water to produce H_3O^+ and some ions react with water to produce OH^-. To predict the acidity of a salt solution, it is convenient to classify salts according to the acid and base from which they are formed in a neutralization reaction. The classification and some examples are given in Table 10.4.

Table 10.4 Acidity and Basicity of Salt Solutions

Anion Derived from Acid That Is:	Cation Derived from Base That Is:	Solution	Example
Strong	Weak	Acidic	NH_4Cl, NH_4NO_3
Weak	Strong	Basic	$NaHCO_3$, KCH_3CO_2
Strong	Strong	Neutral	$NaCl$, KBr, $Ca(NO_3)_2$
Weak	Weak	More information needed	

The general rule for predicting the acidity or basicity of a salt solution is that the stronger partner from which the salt is formed dominates. That is, a salt formed from a strong acid and a weak base yields an acidic solution because the strong acid dominates; a salt formed from a weak acid and a strong base yields a basic solution because the base dominates; and a salt formed from a strong acid and a strong base yields a neutral solution because neither acid nor base dominates. Here are some examples.

Salt of Strong Acid + Weak Base ⟶ Acidic Solution

A salt such as NH_4Cl, which can be formed by reaction of a strong acid (HCl) with a weak base (NH_3), yields an acidic solution. The Cl^- ion does not react with water, but the NH_4^+ ion is a weak acid that gives H_3O^+ ions:

$$NH_4^+(aq) + H_2O(l) \rightleftharpoons NH_3(aq) + H_3O^+(aq)$$

Salt of Weak Acid + Strong Base ⟶ Basic Solution

A salt such as sodium bicarbonate, which can be formed by reaction of a weak acid (H_2CO_3) with a strong base (NaOH), yields a basic solution. The Na^+ ion does not react with water, but the HCO_3^- ion is a weak base that gives OH^- ions:

$$HCO_3^-(aq) + H_2O(l) \rightleftharpoons H_2CO_3(aq) + OH^-(aq)$$

Salt of Strong Acid + Strong Base ⟶ Neutral Solution

A salt such as NaCl, which can be formed by reaction of a strong acid (HCl) with a strong base (NaOH), yields a neutral solution. Neither the Cl^- ion nor the Na^+ ion reacts with water.

Salt of Weak Acid + Weak Base

Both cation and anion in this type of salt react with water, so we cannot predict whether the resulting solution will be acidic or basic without quantitative information. The ion that reacts to the greater extent with water will govern the pH—it may be either the cation or the anion.

Worked Example 10.14 Acidity and Basicity of Salt Solutions

Predict whether the following salts produce an acidic, basic, or neutral solution:
(a) $BaCl_2$ (b) NaCN   (c) NH_4NO_3

ANALYSIS Look in Table 10.2 to see the classification of acids and bases as strong or weak.

SOLUTION

(a) $BaCl_2$ gives a neutral solution because it is formed from a strong acid (HCl) and a strong base $[Ba(OH)_2]$.

(b) NaCN gives a basic solution because it is formed from a weak acid (HCN) and a strong base (NaOH).

(c) NH_4NO_3 gives an acidic solution because it is formed from a strong acid (HNO_3) and a weak base (NH_3).

PROBLEM 10.24

Predict whether the following salts produce an acidic, basic, or neutral solution:
(a) K_2SO_4 (b) Na_2HPO_4 (c) MgF_2 (d) NH_4Br

10.10 Buffer Solutions

Learning Objective:

• Identify a buffer, and calculate the pH of a buffer solution.

Much of the body's chemistry depends on maintaining the pH of blood and other fluids within narrow limits. This is accomplished through the use of **buffers**—combinations of substances that act together to prevent a drastic change in pH.

Buffer A combination of substances that act together to prevent a drastic change in pH; usually a weak acid and its conjugate base.

Most buffers are mixtures of a weak acid and a roughly equal concentration of its conjugate base—for example, a solution that contains 0.10 M acetic acid and 0.10 M acetate ion. If a small amount of OH^- is added to a buffer solution, the pH increases, but not by much because the acid component of the buffer neutralizes the added OH^-. If a small amount of H_3O^+ is added to a buffer solution, the pH decreases, but again not by much because the conjugate base component of the buffer neutralizes the added H_3O^+.

To see why buffer solutions work, look at the equation for the acid dissociation constant of an acid HA.

For the reaction: $HA(aq) + H_2O(l) \rightleftharpoons A^-(aq) + H_3O^+(aq)$

we have $K_a = \dfrac{[H_3O^+][A^-]}{[HA]}$

Rearranging this equation shows that the value of $[H_3O^+]$, and thus the pH, depends on the ratio of the undissociated acid concentration to the conjugate base concentration, $[HA]/[A^-]$:

$$[H_3O^+] = K_a\frac{[HA]}{[A^-]}$$

In the case of the acetic acid–acetate ion buffer, for instance, we have

$$CH_3CO_2H(aq) + H_2O(l) \rightleftharpoons H_3O^+(aq) + CH_3CO_2^-(aq)$$
$$(0.10\,M) \qquad\qquad\qquad\qquad\qquad (0.10\,M)$$

and $[H_3O^+] = K_a\dfrac{[CH_3CO_2H]}{[CH_3CO_2^-]}$

Initially, the pH of the 0.10 M acetic acid–0.10 M acetate ion buffer solution is 4.74. When acid is added, most will be removed by reaction with $CH_3CO_2^-$. The equilibrium reaction shifts to the left, and as a result the concentration of CH_3CO_2H increases and the concentration of $CH_3CO_2^-$ decreases. As long as the changes in $[CH_3CO_2H]$ and $[CH_3CO_2^-]$ are relatively small, however, the ratio of $[CH_3CO_2H]$ to $[CH_3CO_2^-]$ changes only slightly, and there is little change in the pH.

When base is added to the buffer, most will be removed by reaction with CH_3CO_2H. The equilibrium shifts to the right, and so the concentration of CH_3CO_2H decreases and the concentration of $CH_3CO_2^-$ increases. Here too, though, as long as the concentration changes are relatively small, there is little change in the pH.

The ability of a buffer solution to resist changes in pH when acid or base is added is illustrated in Figure 10.5. Addition of 0.010 mol of H_3O^+ to 1.0 L of pure water changes the pH from 7 to 2, and addition of 0.010 mol of OH^- changes the pH from 7 to 12. A similar addition of acid to 1.0 L of a 0.10 M acetic acid–0.10 M acetate ion buffer, however, changes the pH from only 4.74 to 4.68, and addition of base changes the pH from only 4.74 to 4.85.

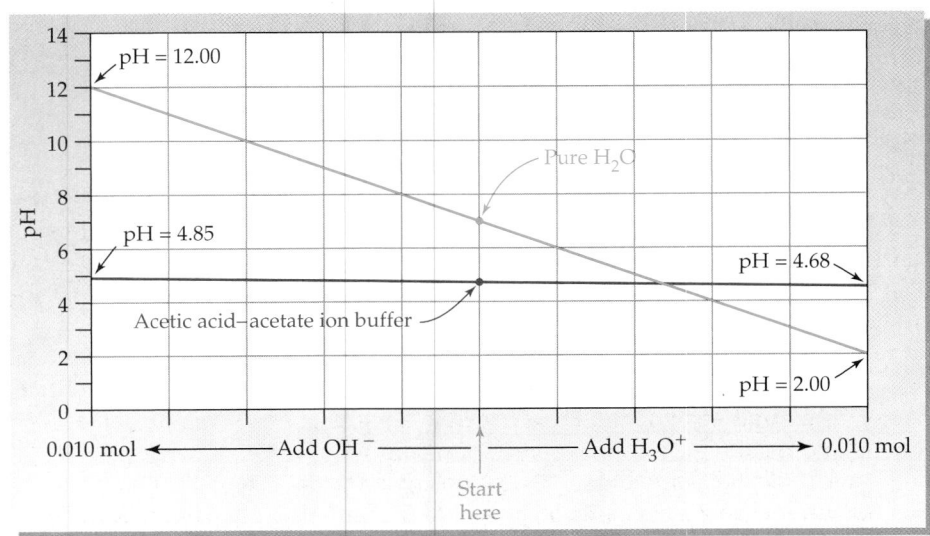

◄ **Figure 10.5**
A comparison of the change in pH.
When 0.010 mol of strong acid (H_3O^+) or 0.00 mol of strong base (OH^-) are added to 1.0 L of pure water with an initial pH of 7.00, the pH of the solution varies between 12.00 (basic) and 2.000 (acidic) as indicated by the blue line. When the same amounts of strong acid or base is added to a 0.10 M acetic acid buffer solution having an initial pH of 4.74, the pH of the solution varies only between 4.85 and 4.68 (red line).

As we did with K_w, we can convert the rearranged K_a equation to its logarithmic form to obtain

$$pH = pK_a - \log\left(\frac{[HA]}{[A^-]}\right)$$

$$\text{or}\quad pH = pK_a + \log\left(\frac{[A^-]}{[HA]}\right)$$

Henderson–Hasselbalch equation The logarithmic form of the K_a equation for a weak acid, used in applications involving buffer solutions.

This expression is known as the **Henderson–Hasselbalch equation** and is very useful in buffer applications, particularly in biology and biochemistry. Examination of the Henderson–Hasselbalch equation provides useful insights into how to prepare a buffer and into the factors that affect the pH of a buffer solution.

The effective pH range of a buffer will depend on the pK_a of the acid HA and on the relative concentrations of HA and conjugate base A^-. In general, the most effective buffers meet the following conditions:

- The pK_a for the weak acid should be close to the desired pH of the buffer solution.
- The ratio of $[HA]$ to $[A^-]$ should be close to 1, so that neither additional acid nor additional base changes the pH of the solution dramatically.
- The molar amounts of HA and A^- in the buffer should be approximately 10 times greater than the molar amounts of either acid or base you expect to add so that the ratio $[A^-]/[HA]$ does not undergo a large change.

The pH of body fluids is maintained by three major buffer systems. Two of these buffers, the carbonic acid–bicarbonate ($H_2CO_3 - HCO_3^-$) system and the dihydrogen phosphate–hydrogen phosphate ($H_2PO_4 - HPO_4^{2-}$) system, depend on weak acid–conjugate base interactions exactly like those of the acetate buffer system described previously:

> In Chapter 29, we will see how the regulation of blood pH by the bicarbonate buffer system is particularly important in preventing *acidosis* and *alkalosis*.

$$H_2CO_3(aq) + H_2O(l) \rightleftharpoons HCO_3^-(aq) + H_3O^+(aq) \qquad pK_a = 6.37$$
$$H_2PO_4^-(aq) + H_2O(l) \rightleftharpoons HPO_4^{2-}(aq) + H_3O^+(aq) \qquad pK_a = 7.21$$

The third buffer system depends on the ability of proteins to act as either proton acceptors or proton donors at different pH values.

Worked Example 10.15 Buffers: Selecting a Weak Acid for a Buffer Solution

Which of the organic acids in Table 10.3 would be the most appropriate for preparing a pH 4.15 buffer solution?

ANALYSIS The pH of the buffer solution depends on the pK_a of the weak acid. Remember that $pK_a = -\log(K_a)$.

SOLUTION
The K_a and pK_a values for the four organic acids in Table 10.3 are tabulated below. The ascorbic acid $(pK_a = 4.10)$ will produce a buffer solution closest to the desired pH of 4.15.

Organic Acid	K_a	pK_a
Formic acid (HCOOH)	1.8×10^{-4}	3.74
Acetic acid (CH_3COOH)	1.8×10^{-5}	4.74
Propanoic acid (CH_3CH_2COOH)	1.3×10^{-5}	4.89
Ascorbic acid (vitamin C)	7.9×10^{-5}	4.10

Worked Example 10.16   Buffers: Calculating the pH of a Buffer Solution

What is the pH of a buffer solution that contains 0.100 M HF and 0.120 M NaF? The K_a of HF is 3.5×10^{-4}, and so $pK_a = 3.46$.

ANALYSIS The Henderson–Hasselbalch equation can be used to calculate the pH of a buffer solution:

$$pH = pK_a + \log\left(\frac{[F^-]}{[HF]}\right).$$

BALLPARK ESTIMATE If the concentrations of F^- and HF were equal, the log term in our equation would be zero, and the pH of the solution would be equal to the pK_a for HF, which means pH = 3.46. However, since the concentration of the conjugate base ($[F^-] = 0.120\ M$) is slightly higher than the concentration of the conjugate acid ($[HF] = 0.100\ M$), then the pH of the buffer solution will be slightly higher (more basic) than the pK_a.

SOLUTION

$$pH = pK_a + \log\left(\frac{[F^-]}{[HF]}\right)$$

$$pH = 3.46 + \log\left(\frac{0.120}{0.100}\right) = 3.46 + 0.08 = 3.54$$

BALLPARK CHECK The calculated pH of 3.54 is consistent with the prediction that the final pH will be slightly higher than the pK_a of 3.46.

Worked Example 10.17   Buffers: Measuring the Effect of Added Base on pH

What is the pH of 1.00 L of the 0.100 M hydrofluoric acid–0.120 M fluoride ion buffer system described in Worked Example 10.16 after 0.020 mol of NaOH is added?

ANALYSIS Initially, the 0.100 M HF–0.120 M NaF buffer has pH = 3.54, as calculated in Worked Example 10.16. The added base will react with the acid as indicated in the neutralization reaction,

$$HF(aq) + OH^-(aq) \longrightarrow H_2O(l) + F^-(aq)$$

which means $[HF]$ decreases and $[F^-]$ increases. With the pK_a and the concentrations of HF and F^- known, pH can be calculated using the Henderson–Hasselbalch equation.

BALLPARK ESTIMATE After the neutralization reaction, there is more conjugate base (F^-) and less conjugate acid (HF), and so we expect the pH to increase slightly from the initial value of 3.54.

SOLUTION
When 0.020 mol of NaOH is added to 1.00 L of the buffer, the HF concentration *decreases* from 0.100 M to 0.080 M as a result of an acid–base reaction. At the same time, the F^- concentration *increases* from 0.120 M to 0.140 M because additional F^- is produced by the neutralization. Using these new values gives

$$pH = 3.46 + \log\left(\frac{0.140}{0.080}\right) = 3.46 + 0.24 = 3.70$$

The addition of 0.020 mol of base causes the pH of the buffer to rise only from 3.54 to 3.70.

BALLPARK CHECK The final pH, 3.70, is slightly more basic than the initial pH of 3.54, consistent with our prediction.

PROBLEM 10.25

What is the pH of 1.00 L of the 0.100 M hydrofluoric acid–0.120 M fluoride ion buffer system described in Worked Example 10.16 after 0.020 mol of HNO_3 is added?

PROBLEM 10.26

The ammonia/ammonium buffer system is sometimes used to optimize polymerase chain reactions (PCR) used in DNA studies. The equilibrium for this buffer can be written as

$$NH_4^+(aq) + H_2O(l) \rightleftharpoons H_3O^+(aq) + NH_3(aq)$$

Calculate the pH of a buffer that contains 0.050 M ammonium chloride and 0.080 M ammonia. The K_a of ammonium is 5.6×10^{-10}.

PROBLEM 10.27

What is the ratio of bicarbonate ion to carbonic acid ($[HCO_3^-]/[H_2CO_3]$) in blood plasma that has a pH of 7.40? (see the Chemistry in Action "Buffers in the Body: Acidosis and Alkalosis" on p. 321).

⊂▭ **KEY CONCEPT PROBLEM 10.28** _____

A buffer solution is prepared using CN^- (from NaCN salt) and HCN in the amounts indicated in the margin. The K_a for HCN is 4.9×10^{-10}. Calculate the pH of the buffer solution.

10.11 Titration

Learning Objective:

- Use balanced neutralization reactions and titration data to determine the total acid or base concentration of a solution.

Determining the pH of a solution gives the solution's H_3O^+ concentration but not necessarily its total acid concentration. That is because the two are not the same thing. The H_3O^+ concentration gives only the amount of acid that has dissociated into ions, whereas total acid concentration gives the sum of dissociated plus undissociated acid. In a 0.10 *M* solution of acetic acid, for instance, the total acid concentration is 0.10 *M*, yet the H_3O^+ concentration is only 0.0013 *M* (pH = 2.89) because acetic acid is a weak acid that is only about 1% dissociated.

The total acid or base concentration of a solution can be found by carrying out a **titration** procedure, as shown in Figure 10.6. Let us assume, for instance, that we want to find the acid concentration of an HCl solution. (Likewise, we might need to find the base concentration of an NaOH solution.) We begin by measuring out a known volume of the HCl solution and adding an acid-base indicator. Next, we fill a calibrated glass tube called a *buret* with an NaOH solution of known concentration, and we slowly add the NaOH to the HCl until neutralization is complete (the *end point*), identified by a color change in the indicator.

Reading from the buret gives the volume of the NaOH solution that has reacted with the known volume of HCl. Knowing both the concentration and volume of the NaOH solution then allows us to calculate the molar amount of NaOH, and the coefficients in the balanced equation allow us to find the molar amount of HCl that has been neutralized. Dividing the molar amount of HCl by the volume of the HCl solution gives the concentration. The calculation thus involves mole–volume conversions just like those done in Section 9.6. Figure 10.7 shows a flow diagram of the strategy, and Worked Example 10.18 shows how to calculate total acid concentration.

When the titration involves a neutralization reaction in which one mole of acid reacts with one mole of base, such as that shown in Figure 10.7, then the moles of acid and base needed for complete reaction can be represented as

$$M_{acid} \times V_{acid} = M_{base} \times V_{base}$$

When the coefficients for the acid and base in the balanced neutralization reaction are not the same, such as in the reaction of a diprotic acid (H_2SO_4) with a monoprotic

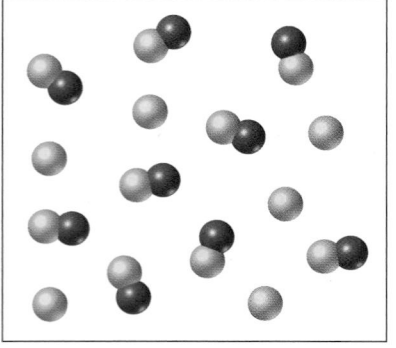

⬤⬤ = HCN   ⬤ = CN^-

Titration A procedure for determining the total acid or base concentration of a solution.

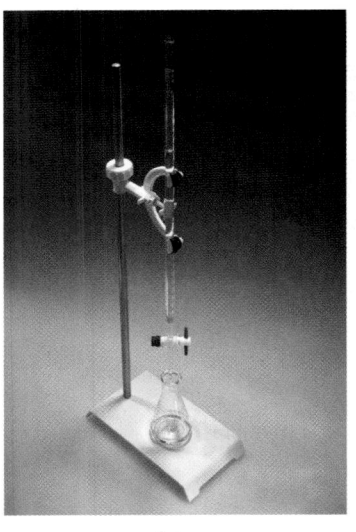
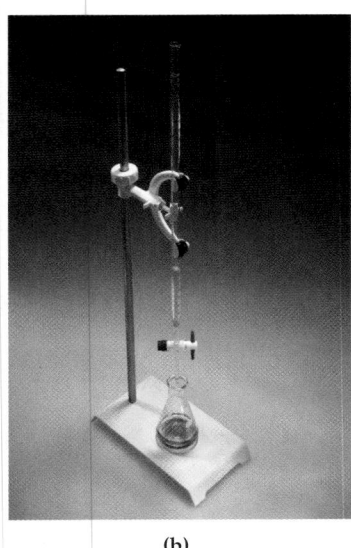

(a)　　　　　　　　　　(b)　　　　　　　　　　(c)

▲ Figure 10.6
Titration of an acid solution of unknown concentration with a base solution of known concentration.
(a) A measured volume of the acid solution is placed in the flask along with an indicator. (b) The base of known concentration is then added from a buret until the color change of the indicator shows that neutralization is complete (the *end point*). (c) Volume of base is calculated by difference, based on the initial and final volumes in the buret, measured at the meniscus.

base (NaOH), then we can use equivalents of acid and base instead of moles, and normality instead of molarity:

$$(\text{Eq})_{\text{acid}} = (\text{Eq})_{\text{base}}$$
$$N_{\text{acid}} \times V_{\text{acid}} = N_{\text{base}} \times V_{\text{base}}.$$

We can convert between normality and molarity as described in Section 10.7.

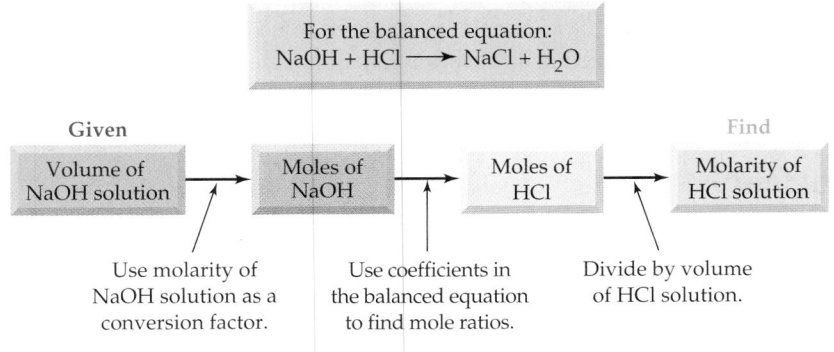

◄ Figure 10.7
A flow diagram for an acid-base titration.
This diagram summarizes the calculations needed to determine the concentration of an HCl solution by titration with an NaOH solution of known concentration. The steps are similar to those shown in Figure 9.7.

Worked Example 10.18 Titrations: Calculating Total Acid Concentration

When a 5.00 mL sample of household vinegar (dilute aqueous acetic acid) is titrated, 44.5 mL of 0.100 M NaOH solution is required to reach the end point. What is the acid concentration of the vinegar in moles per liter, equivalents per liter, and milliequivalents per liter? The neutralization reaction is

$$\text{CH}_3\text{CO}_2\text{H}(aq) + \text{NaOH}(aq) \longrightarrow \text{CH}_3\text{CO}_2^- \text{Na}^+(aq) + \text{H}_2\text{O}(l)$$

ANALYSIS To find the molarity of the vinegar, we need to know the number of moles of acetic acid dissolved in the 5.00 mL sample. Following a flow diagram similar to Figure 10.7, we use the volume and molarity of NaOH to find the number of moles. From the chemical equation, we use the mole ratio to find the number of moles of acid, and then divide by the volume of the acid solution. Because acetic acid is a monoprotic acid, the normality of the solution is numerically the same as its molarity.

—continued on next page

—continued from previous page

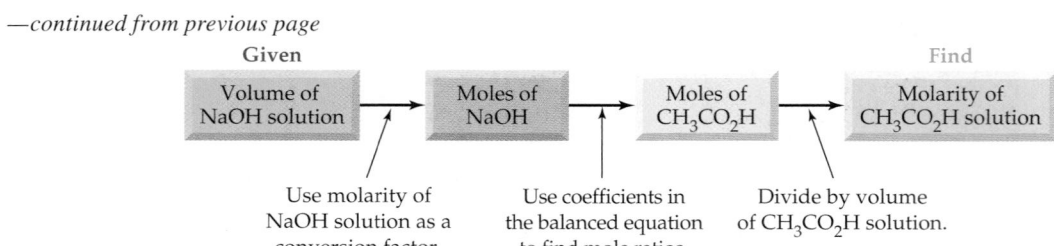

Given   Find

BALLPARK ESTIMATE The 5.00 mL of vinegar required nearly nine times as much NaOH solution (44.5 mL) for complete reaction. Since the neutralization stoichiometry is 1:1, the molarity of the acetic acid in the vinegar must be nine times greater than the molarity of NaOH, or approximately 0.90 M.

SOLUTION

Substitute the known information and appropriate conversion factors into the flow diagram, and solve for the molarity of the acetic acid:

$$(44.5 \text{ mL NaOH}) \left(\frac{0.100 \text{ mol NaOH}}{1000 \text{ mL}} \right) \left(\frac{1 \text{ mol CH}_3\text{CO}_2\text{H}}{1 \text{ mol NaOH}} \right) \times \left(\frac{1}{0.00500 \text{ L}} \right) = 0.890 \text{ M CH}_3\text{CO}_2\text{H}$$

$$= 0.890 \text{ N CH}_3\text{CO}_2\text{H}$$

Expressed in milliequivalents, this concentration is

$$\frac{0.890 \text{ Eq}}{\text{L}} \times \frac{1000 \text{ m Eq}}{1 \text{ Eq}} = 890 \text{ m Eq/L}$$

BALLPARK CHECK The calculated result (0.890 M) is very close to our estimate of 0.90 M.

PROBLEM 10.29

A titration is carried out to determine the concentration of the acid in an old bottle of aqueous HCl whose label has become unreadable. What is the HCl concentration if 58.4 mL of 0.250 M NaOH is required to titrate a 20.0 mL sample of the acid?

PROBLEM 10.30

How many milliliters of 0.150 M NaOH are required to neutralize 50.0 mL of 0.200 M H_2SO_4? The balanced neutralization reaction is:

$$H_2SO_4(aq) + 2 \text{ NaOH}(aq) \longrightarrow Na_2SO_4(aq) + 2 H_2O(l).$$

PROBLEM 10.31

A 21.5 mL sample of a KOH solution of unknown concentration requires 16.1 mL of 0.150 M H_2SO_4 solution to reach the end point in a titration.

    (a) How many moles of H_2SO_4 were necessary to reach the end point? How many equivalents?

    (b) What is the molarity of the KOH solution?

PROBLEM 10.32

Titration of a 50.00 mL sample of acid rain required 9.30 mL of 0.0012 M NaOH to reach the end point. What was the total $[H_3O^+]$ in the rain sample? What was the pH?

CHEMISTRY IN ACTION

⚕ Buffers in the Body: Acidosis and Alkalosis

Remember the diverse clinical cases introduced at the beginning of the chapter? All those individuals—the teenagers, the athlete, the diabetic patient, and the individuals taking aspirin or HIV medication—were all experiencing symptoms resulting from fluctuations in blood pH that produced clinical conditions known as *acidosis* (pH < 7.35) or *alkalosis* (pH > 7.45).

Each of the fluids in our bodies has a pH range suited to its function, as shown in the accompanying table. The stability of cell membranes, the shapes of huge protein molecules that must be folded in certain ways to function, and the activities of enzymes are all dependent on appropriate H_3O^+ concentrations. Blood plasma and the interstitial fluid surrounding cells, which together compose one-third of body fluids, have a slightly basic pH with a normal range of 7.35–7.45. The highly complex series of reactions and equilibria that take place throughout the body are very sensitive to pH—variations of even a few tenths of a pH unit can produce severe physiological symptoms.

▲ Hyperventilation, the rapid breathing due to excitement or stress, removes CO_2 and increases blood pH resulting in respiratory alkalosis.

pH of Body Fluids

Fluid	pH
Blood plasma	7.4
Interstitial fluid	7.4
Cytosol	7.0
Saliva	5.8–7.1
Gastric juice	1.6–1.8
Pancreatic juice	7.5–8.8
Intestinal juice	6.3–8.0
Urine	4.6–8.0
Sweat	4.0–6.8

Maintaining the pH of blood serum in its optimal range is accomplished by the carbonic acid–bicarbonate buffer system (Section 10.10), which depends on the relative amounts of CO_2 and bicarbonate dissolved in the blood. Because carbonic acid is unstable and therefore in equilibrium with CO_2 and water, there is an extra step in the bicarbonate buffer mechanism:

$$CO_2(aq) + H_2O(l) \rightleftharpoons H_2CO_3(aq) \rightleftharpoons HCO_3^-(aq) + H_3O^+(aq)$$

As a result, the bicarbonate buffer system is intimately related to the elimination of CO_2, which is continuously produced in cells and transported to the lungs to be exhaled. Anything that significantly shifts the balance between dissolved CO_2 and HCO_3^- can upset these equilibria and raise or lower the pH. How does this happen, and how does the body compensate?

The relationships between the bicarbonate buffer system, the lungs, and the kidneys are shown in the figure on the next page. Under normal circumstances, the reactions shown in the figure are in equilibrium. Addition of excess acid (red arrows) causes formation of H_2CO_3 and results in lowering of H_3O^+ concentration. Removal of acid (blue arrows) causes formation of more H_3O^+ by dissociation of H_2CO_3. The maintenance of pH by this mechanism is supported by a reserve of bicarbonate ions in body fluids. Such a buffer can accommodate large additions of H_3O^+ before there is a significant change in the pH.

Additional backup to the bicarbonate buffer system is provided by the kidneys. Each day a quantity of acid equal to that produced in the body is excreted in the urine. In the process, the kidney returns HCO_3^- to the extracellular fluids, where it becomes part of the bicarbonate reserve.

Respiratory acidosis can be caused by a decrease in respiration, which leads to a buildup of excess CO_2 in the blood and a corresponding decrease in pH. This could be caused by a blocked air passage due to inhaled food—removal of the blockage restores normal breathing and a return to the optimal pH. *Metabolic acidosis* results from an excess of other acids in the blood that reduce the bicarbonate concentration. High doses of aspirin (acetylsalicylic acid, Section 17.5), for example, increase the hydronium ion concentration and decrease the pH. Strenuous exercise generates excess lactate in the muscles, which is released into the bloodstream (Section 22.9). The liver converts lactate into glucose, which is the body's major source of energy; this process consumes bicarbonate ions, which decreases the pH. Some HIV drug therapies can damage cellular mitochondria (Section 21.2), resulting in a buildup of lactic acid in the cells and bloodstream. In the case of a person with diabetes, lack of insulin causes the body to start burning fat, which generates ketones and keto acids (Chapter 15), organic compounds that lower the blood pH.

The body attempts to correct acidosis by increasing the rate and depth of respiration—breathing faster "blows off" CO_2, shifting the CO_2–bicarbonate equilibrium to the left and

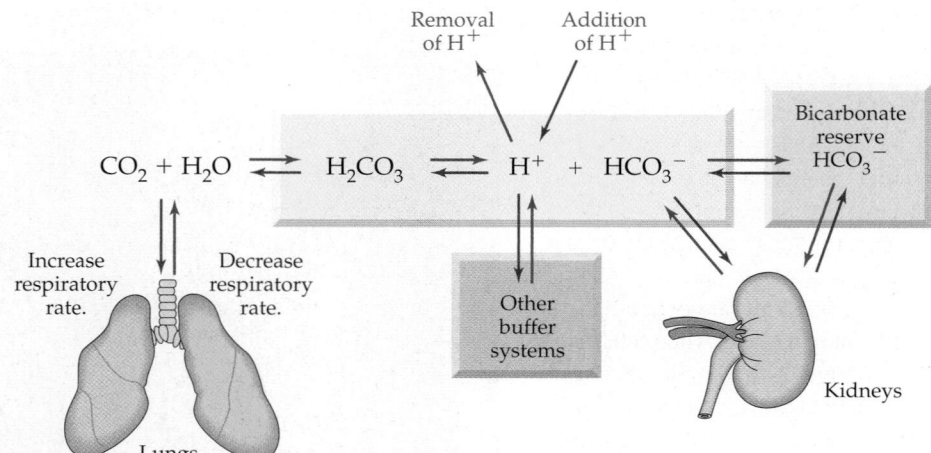

raising the pH. The net effect is rapid reversal of the acidosis. Although this may be sufficient for cases of respiratory acidosis, it provides only temporary relief for metabolic acidosis. A long-term solution depends on removal of excess acid by the kidneys, which can take several hours.

What about our teenage fans? In their excitement they have hyperventilated—their increased breathing rate has removed too much CO_2 from their blood and they are suffering from *respiratory alkalosis*. The body responds by "fainting" to

decrease respiration and restore the CO_2 levels in the blood. When they regain consciousness, they will be ready to rock once again.

CIA Problem 10.6 Metabolic acidosis is often treated by administering bicarbonate intravenously. Explain how this treatment can increase blood plasma pH.

CIA Problem 10.7 Which body fluid is most acidic? Which is most basic?

SUMMARY REVISITING THE CHAPTER LEARNING OBJECTIVES

• **Define the behavior of acids and bases in solution, and identify conjugate acid-base pairs.** According to the *Brønsted–Lowry definition,* an acid is a substance that donates a hydrogen ion (a proton, H^+) and a base is a substance that accepts a hydrogen ion. Thus, the generalized reaction of an acid with a base involves the reversible transfer of a proton: B: $+$ H—A $\rightleftharpoons$ A:$^-$ $+$ H—B$^+$. In aqueous solution, water acts as a base and accepts a proton from an acid to yield a *hydronium ion,* H_3O^+. Reaction of an acid with a metal hydroxide, such as KOH, yields water and a salt; reaction with bicarbonate ion (HCO_3^-) or carbonate ion (CO_3^{2-}) yields water, a salt, and CO_2 gas; and reaction with ammonia yields an ammonium salt. The two substances that are related by the gain or loss of a proton in an acid-base reaction are called a *conjugate acid-base pair (see Problems 34–36, 39–41, 43, 46–49, 102, 106, 109, and 111).*

• **Identify substances as strong or weak acids or bases, and predict the direction of the proton transfer reaction based on the relative strength of the acids and bases involved.** Different acids and bases differ in their ability to give up or accept a proton. A *strong acid* gives up a proton easily and is 100% *dissociated* in aqueous solution; a *weak acid* gives up a proton with difficulty, is only slightly dissociated in water, and establishes an equilibrium between dissociated and undissociated forms. Similarly, a *strong base* accepts and holds a proton readily, whereas a *weak base* has a low affinity for a proton and establishes an equilibrium in aqueous solution. A proton-transfer reaction always takes place in the direction that favors formation of the weaker acid *(see Problems 34–36, 38–41, 44, and 45).*

• **Write the expression for the acid dissociation constant (K_a), and use the value of K_a as a predictor of acid strength.** The exact strength of an acid is defined by an *acid dissociation constant,* K_a: For the reaction HA $+$ H_2O $\rightleftharpoons$ H_3O^+ $+$ A$^-$

we have $K_a = \dfrac{[H_3O^+][A^-]}{[HA]}$ *(see Problems 35, 50, 55, 56, 71, and 102).*

• **Use the ion product constant for water (K_w) to calculate the relative concentrations of H_3O^+ and OH^- ions in aqueous solution.** Water is *amphoteric;* that is, it can act as either an acid or a base. Water also dissociates slightly into H_3O^+ ions and OH^- ions; the product of whose concentrations in any aqueous solution is the *ion-product constant for water,* $K_w = [H_3O^+][OH^-] = 1.00 \times 10^{-14}$ at 25 °C *(see Problems 51, 61, 62, and 64–66).*

• **Calculate the pH of a solution from the H_3O^+ or OH^- concentration, and use the pH scale as an indication of the relative acidity/basicity of a solution.** The acidity or basicity of an aqueous solution is given by its *pH,* defined as the negative logarithm of the hydronium ion concentration, $[H_3O^+]$. A pH below 7 means an acidic solution; a pH equal to 7 means a neutral solution; and a pH above 7 means a basic solution *(see Problems 52, 53, 61, 64, 98, 99, 102, and 108).*

• **Calculate pH from $[H_3O^+]$ and $[OH^-]$, and calculate $[H_3O^+]$ from pH.** The pH of a solution is defined as pH $= -\log[H_3O^+]$. To determine hydronium ion concentration from a measured pH, the antilog function (or inverse log) would be used: $[H_3O^+] = 10^{-pH}$ *(see Problems 53, 54, 57–62, and 64–66).*

• **Define normality (i.e., equivalent ion concentrations) for acids and bases, and the relationship between units of normality and molarity.** Normality is a concentration unit defined as Eq./L. For acids, an equivalent is defined as the amount of acid that can produce one mole of H_3O^+ ions. For bases, an equivalent is defined as the amount of base that can produce one mole of OH^- ions. The relationship between the two concentration units is Normality = Molarity × (Equiv. /mole) *(see Problems 33, 42, 82–95, and 104).*

• **Write balanced chemical equations for the common reactions of acids and bases.** Reactions between acids and bases typically involve direct reaction of the H_3O^+ and the OH^- ions to form water and a salt. However, acids can react with carbonate (CO_3^{2-}) compounds to form CO_2, and with NH_3 to form ammonium salts (see Section 10.8) *(see Problems 33, 36, 67–70, 79, 81, and 107–111).*

• **Predict whether a salt solution will be acidic, basic, or neutral.** The salt formed by the neutralization of a strong acid and strong base forms a neutral solution. The salt formed by the neutralization of a weak acid and a strong base forms a basic solution. The salt formed by the neutralization of a strong acid and a weak base forms an acidic solution *(see Problems 72, 73, 96, 97, and 111).*

• **Identify a buffer, and calculate the pH of a buffer solution.** The pH of a solution can be controlled through the use of a *buffer* that acts to remove either added H_3O^+ ions or added OH^- ions. Most buffer solutions consist of roughly equal amounts of a weak acid and its conjugate base. If the relative concentrations of the weak acid and its conjugate base are known, the pH can be calculated using the *Henderson–Hasselbalch equation* (see Section 10.10) *(see Problems 71, 74–81, 103, and 105).*

• **Use balanced neutralization reactions and titration data to determine the total acid or base concentration of a solution.** Acid (or base) concentrations are determined in the laboratory by *titration* of a solution of unknown concentration with a base (or acid) solution of known strength until an indicator signals that neutralization is complete *(see Problems 37, 86, 92–95, 101, 104, and 108).*

CONCEPT MAP: ACIDS AND BASES

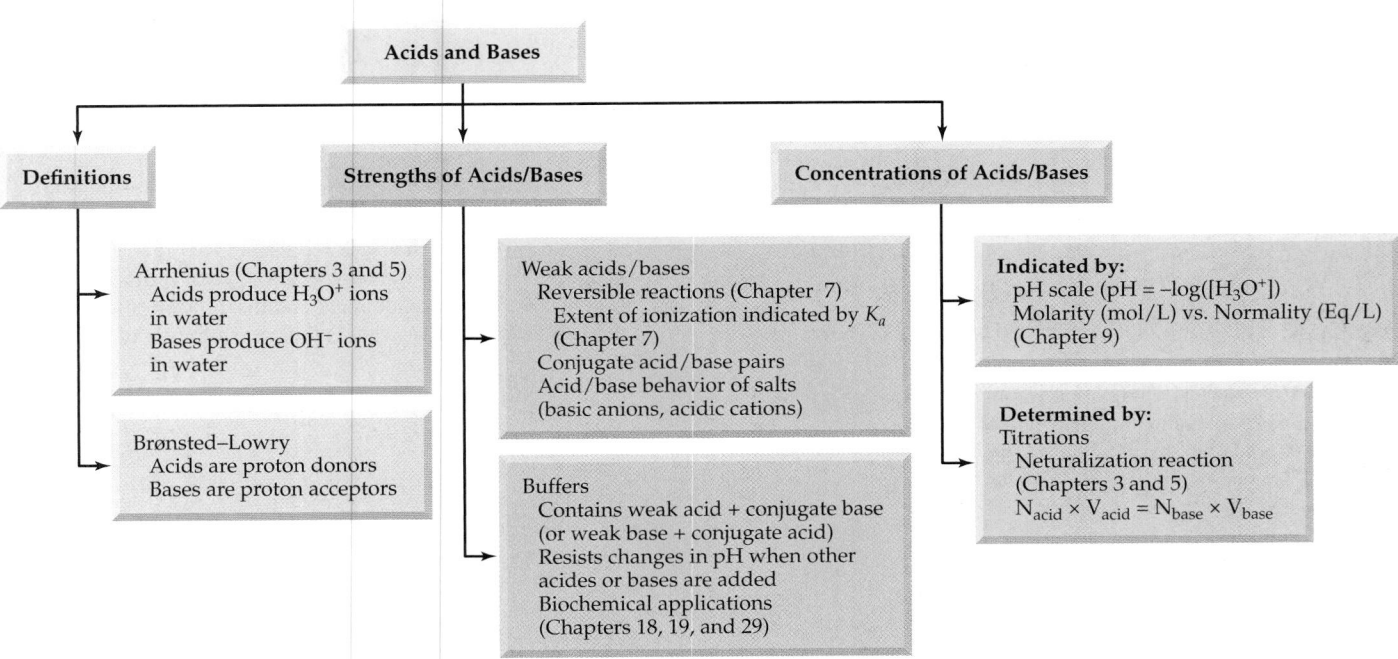

▲ **Figure 10.8 Concept Map.** Acids and bases play important roles in many chemical and biochemical processes, and many common substances are classified as acids or bases. Acid and base behavior is related to the ability to exchange protons, or to form H_3O^+ or OH^- ions, respectively, in water. Strong acids and bases ionize completely in aqueous solution, while weak acids/bases ionize only partially and establish an equilibrium with their conjugates. The relationship between these concepts and some of their practical and/or quantitative applications are illustrated in this concept map.

KEY WORDS

Acid dissociation constant (K_a), *p. 301*
Acid-base indicator, *p. 304*
Amphoteric, *p. 302*
Brønsted–Lowry acid, *p. 292*
Brønsted–Lowry base, *p. 292*

Buffer, *p. 314*
Conjugate acid, *p. 294*
Conjugate acid-base pair, *p. 294*
Conjugate base, *p. 294*
Dissociation, *p. 297*
Equivalent of acid, *p. 310*

Equivalent of base, *p. 310*
Henderson–Hasselbalch equation, *p. 316*
Hydronium ion, *p. 291*
Ion-product constant for water (K_w), *p. 302*
Normality (N), *p. 310*

p function, *p. 304*
pH, *p. 304*
Strong acid, *p. 296*
Strong base, *p. 297*
Titration, *p. 318*
Weak acid, *p. 297*
Weak base, *p. 297*

⬤ UNDERSTANDING KEY CONCEPTS

10.33 An aqueous solution of OH^-, represented as a blue sphere, is allowed to mix with a solution of an acid H_nA, represented as a red sphere. Three possible outcomes are depicted by boxes (1)–(3), where the green spheres represent A^{n-}, the anion of the acid:

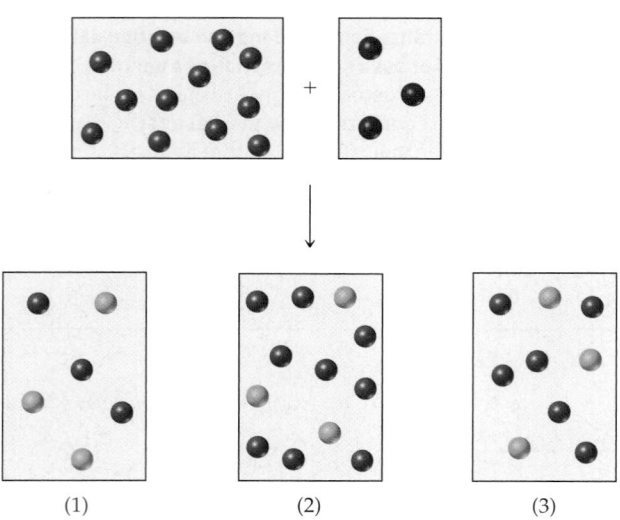

(1)   (2)   (3)

Which outcome corresponds to the following reactions?

(a) $HF + OH^- \longrightarrow H_2O + F^-$

(b) $H_2SO_3 + 2 OH^- \longrightarrow 2 H_2O + SO_3^{2-}$

(c) $H_3PO_4 + 3 OH^- \longrightarrow 3 H_2O + PO_4^{3-}$

10.34 Electrostatic potential maps of acetic acid (CH_3CO_2H) and ethyl alcohol (CH_3CH_2OH) are shown. Identify the most acidic hydrogen in each, and tell which of the two is likely to be the stronger acid.

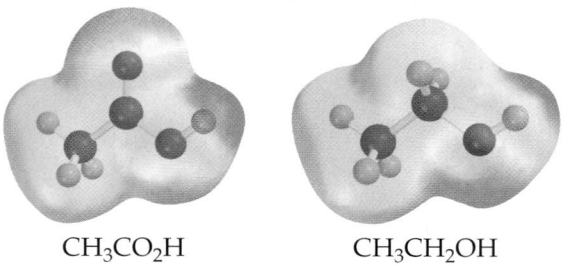

CH₃CO₂H   CH₃CH₂OH

10.35 The following pictures represent aqueous acid solutions. Water molecules are not shown.

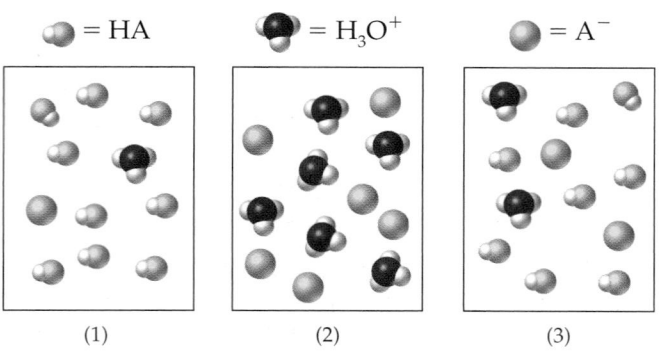

⬤ = HA   ⬤ = H_3O^+ ⬤ = A^-

(1)   (2)   (3)

(a) Which picture represents the weakest acid?

(b) Which picture represents the strongest acid?

(c) Which picture represents the acid with the smallest value of K_a?

10.36 The following pictures represent aqueous solutions of a diprotic acid H_2A. Water molecules are not shown.

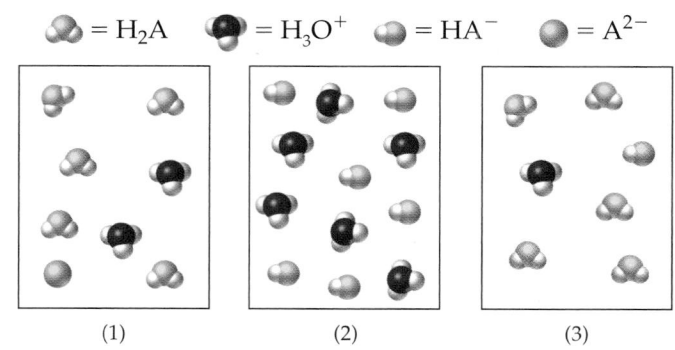

⬤ = H_2A ⬤ = H_3O^+ ⬤ = HA^- ⬤ = A^{2-}

(1)   (2)   (3)

(a) Which picture represents a solution of a weak diprotic acid?

(b) Which picture represents an impossible situation?

10.37 Assume that the red spheres in the buret represent H_3O^+ ions, the blue spheres in the flask represent OH^- ions, and you are carrying out a titration of the base with the acid. If the volumes in the buret and the flask are identical and the concentration of the acid in the buret is 1.00 M, what is the concentration of the base in the flask?

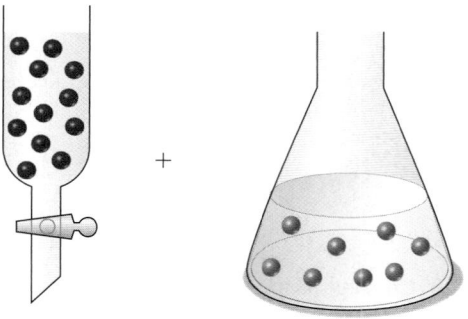

ADDITIONAL PROBLEMS

ACIDS AND BASES (SECTIONS 10.1 AND 10.2)

10.38 What happens when a strong acid such as HBr is dissolved in water?

10.39 What happens when a weak acid such as CH_3CO_2H is dissolved in water?

10.40 What happens when a strong base such as KOH is dissolved in water?

10.41 What happens when a weak base such as NH_3 is dissolved in water?

10.42 What is the difference between a monoprotic acid and a diprotic acid? Give an example of each.

10.43 What is the difference between H^+ and H_3O^+?

10.44 Which of the following are strong acids? Look at Table 10.2 if necessary.

(a) $HClO_4$ (b) H_2CO_3 (c) H_3PO_4

(d) NH_4^+ (e) HI   (f) $H_2PO_4^-$

10.45 Which of the following are weak bases? Look at Table 10.2 if necessary.

(a) NH_3 (b) $Ca(OH)_2$ (c) HPO_4^{2-}

(d) LiOH   (e) CN^- (f) NH_2^-

10.46 Identify the following substances as a Brønsted–Lowry base, a Brønsted–Lowry acid, or neither:

(a) HCN   (b) $CH_3CO_2^-$ (c) $AlCl_3$

(d) H_2CO_3 (e) Mg^{2+} (f) $CH_3NH_3^+$

10.47 Label the Brønsted–Lowry acids and bases in the following equations, and tell which substances are conjugate acid-base pairs.

(a) $CO_3^{2-}(aq) + HCl(aq) \longrightarrow HCO_3^-(aq) + Cl^-(aq)$

(b) $H_3PO_4(aq) + NH_3(aq) \longrightarrow$
$$H_2PO_4^-(aq) + NH_4^+(aq)$$

(c) $NH_4^+(aq) + CN^-(aq) \rightleftharpoons NH_3(aq) + HCN(aq)$

(d) $HBr(aq) + OH^-(aq) \longrightarrow H_2O(l) + Br^-(aq)$

(e) $H_2PO_4^-(aq) + N_2H_4(aq) \rightleftharpoons$
$$HPO_4^{2-}(aq) + N_2H_5^+(aq)$$

10.48 Write the formulas of the conjugate acids of the following Brønsted–Lowry bases:

(a) $ClCH_2CO_2^-$ (b) C_5H_5N

(c) SeO_4^{2-} (d) $(CH_3)_3N$

10.49 Write the formulas of the conjugate bases of the following Brønsted–Lowry acids:

(a) HCN   (b) $(CH_3)_2NH_2^+$

(c) H_3PO_4 (d) $HSeO_3^-$

ACID AND BASE STRENGTH: K_a AND pH (SECTIONS 10.3–10.6)

10.50 How is K_a defined? Write the equation for K_a for the generalized acid HA.

10.51 How is K_w defined, and what is its numerical value at 25 °C?

10.52 How is pH defined?

10.53 A solution of 0.10 M HCl has a pH = 1.00, whereas a solution of 0.10 M CH_3COOH has a pH = 2.88. Explain.

10.54 Calculate $[H_3O^+]$ for the 0.10 M CH_3COOH solution in Problem 10.53. What percent of the weak acid is dissociated?

10.55 Write the expressions for the acid dissociation constants for the three successive dissociations of phosphoric acid, H_3PO_4, in water.

10.56 Based on the K_a values in Table 10.3, rank the following solutions in order of increasing pH: 0.10 M HCOOH, 0.10 M HF, 0.10 M H_2CO_3, 0.10 M HSO_4^-, 0.10 M NH_4^+.

10.57 The electrode of a pH meter is placed in a sample of urine, and a reading of 7.9 is obtained. Is the sample acidic, basic, or neutral? What is the concentration of H_3O^+ in the urine sample?

10.58 A 0.10 M solution of the deadly poison hydrogen cyanide, HCN, has a pH of 5.2. Calculate the $[H_3O^+]$ of the solution. Is HCN a strong or a weak acid?

10.59 Human sweat can have a pH ranging from 4.0 to 6.8. Calculate the range of $[H_3O^+]$ in normal human sweat. How many orders of magnitude does this range represent?

10.60 Saliva has a pH range of 5.8–7.1. Approximately what is the H_3O^+ concentration range of saliva?

10.61 What is the approximate pH of a 0.02 M solution of a strong monoprotic acid? Of a 0.02 M solution of a strong base, such as KOH?

10.62 Calculate the pOH of each solution in Problems 10.57–10.61.

10.63 Without using a calculator, match the H_3O^+ concentrations of the following solutions, (a)–(d), to the corresponding pH, i–iv:

(a) Fresh egg white: $[H_3O^+] = 2.5 \times 10^{-8}\ M$

(b) Apple cider: $[H_3O^+] = 5.0 \times 10^{-4}\ M$

(c) Household ammonia: $[H_3O^+] = 2.3 \times 10^{-12}\ M$

(d) Vinegar (acetic acid): $[H_3O^+] = 4.0 \times 10^{-3}\ M$

i. pH = 3.30

ii. pH = 2.40

iii. pH = 11.64

iv. pH = 7.60

10.64 What are the OH^- concentration and pOH for each solution in Problem 10.63? Rank the solutions according to increasing acidity.

10.65 What are the H_3O^+ and OH^- concentrations of solutions that have the following pH values?

(a) pH 4   (b) pH 11   (c) pH 0

(d) pH 1.38   (e) pH 7.96

10.66 About 12% of the acid in a 0.10 M solution of a weak acid dissociates to form ions. What are the H_3O^+ and OH^- concentrations? What is the pH of the solution?

REACTIONS OF ACIDS AND BASES (SECTION 10.8)

10.67 The hydrogen-containing anions of many polyprotic acids are amphoteric. Write equations for HCO_3^- and $H_2PO_4^-$ acting as bases with the strong acid HCl and as acids with the strong base NaOH.

10.68 Write balanced equations for proton-transfer reactions between the listed pairs. Indicate the conjugate pairs, and determine the favored direction for each equilibrium.

(a) HCl and PO_4^{3-}
(b) HCN and SO_4^{2-}
(c) $HClO_4$ and NO_2^-
(d) CH_3O^- and HF

10.69 Sodium bicarbonate $(NaHCO_3)$, also known as baking soda, is a common home remedy for acid indigestion and is also used to neutralize acid spills in the laboratory. Write a balanced chemical equation for the reaction of sodium bicarbonate with

(a) Gastric juice (HCl)

(b) Sulfuric acid (H_2SO_4)

10.70 Refer to Section 10.8 to write balanced equations for the following acid-base reactions:

(a) $LiOH + HNO_3 \longrightarrow$
(b) $BaCO_3 + HI \longrightarrow$
(c) $H_3PO_4 + KOH \longrightarrow$
(d) $Ca(HCO_3)_2 + HCl \longrightarrow$
(e) $Ba(OH)_2 + H_2SO_4 \longrightarrow$
(f) $NH_3 + HCl \longrightarrow$

10.71 Rearrange the equation you wrote in Problem 10.50 to solve for $[H_3O^+]$ in terms of K_a.

SALTS AND BUFFERS (SECTIONS 10.9 AND 10.10)

10.72 For each of the following salts, indicate if the solution would be acidic, basic or neutral.

(a) NH_4Cl
(b) KBr
(c) Na_2CO_3
(d) $NaCH_3CO_2$

10.73 Which salt solutions in problem 10.72 could be used to prepare a buffer solution? In each case, indicate which acid or base must be added to create the buffer solution.

10.74 What are the two components of a buffer system? How does a buffer work to hold pH nearly constant?

10.75 Which system would you expect to be a better buffer: $HNO_3 + Na^+ NO_3^-$, or $CH_3CO_2H + CH_3CO_2^- Na^+$? Explain.

10.76 The pH of a buffer solution containing 0.10 M acetic acid and 0.10 M sodium acetate is 4.74.

(a) Write the Henderson–Hasselbalch equation for this buffer.

(b) Write the equations for reaction of this buffer with a small amount of HNO_3 and with a small amount of NaOH.

10.77 Which of the following buffer systems would you use if you wanted to prepare a solution having a pH of approximately 9.5?

(a) 0.08 M $H_2PO_4^-$/0.12 M HPO_4^{2-}

(b) 0.08 M NH_4^+/0.12 M NH_3

10.78 What is the pH of a buffer system that contains 0.200 M hydrocyanic acid (HCN) and 0.150 M sodium cyanide (NaCN)? The pK_a of hydrocyanic acid is 9.31.

10.79 Consider 1.00 L of the buffer system described in Problem 10.78.

(a) What are the $[HCN]$ and $[CN^-]$ after 0.020 mol of HCl is added? What is the pH?

(b) What are the $[HCN]$ and $[CN^-]$ after 0.020 mol of NaOH is added? What is the pH?

10.80 What is the pH of a buffer system that contains 0.15 M NH_4^+ and 0.10 M NH_3? The pK_a of NH_4^+ is 9.25.

10.81 How many moles of NaOH must be added to 1.00 L of the solution described in Problem 10.80 to increase the pH to 9.25? (Hint: What is the $[NH_3]/[NH_4^+]$ when the pH $=$ pK_a?)

CONCENTRATIONS OF ACID AND BASE SOLUTIONS (SECTIONS 10.7 AND 10.11)

10.82 What does it mean when we talk about acid *equivalents* and base *equivalents*?

10.83 How does normality compare to molarity for monoprotic and polyprotic acids?

10.84 Identify the number of equivalents per mole for each of the following acids and bases.

(a) HNO_3
(b) H_3PO_4
(c) KOH
(d) $Mg(OH)_2$

10.85 What mass of each of the acids and bases in Problem 10.84 is needed to prepare 500 mL of 0.15 N solution?

10.86 How many milliliters of 0.0050 N KOH are required to neutralize 25 mL of 0.0050 N H_2SO_4? To neutralize 25 mL of 0.0050 M H_2SO_4?

10.87 How many equivalents are in 75.0 mL of 0.12 M H_2SO_4 solution? In 75.0 mL of a 0.12 M H_3PO_4 solution?

10.88 How many equivalents of an acid or base are in the following?

(a) 0.25 mol $Mg(OH)_2$
(b) 2.5 g $Mg(OH)_2$
(c) 15 g CH_3CO_2H

10.89 What mass of citric acid (triprotic, $C_6H_5O_7H_3$) contains 152 mEq of citric acid?

10.90 What are the molarity and the normality of a solution made by dissolving 5.0 g of $Ca(OH)_2$ in enough water to make 500.0 mL of solution?

10.91 What are the molarity and the normality of a solution made by dissolving 25 g of citric acid (triprotic, $C_6H_5O_7H_3$) in enough water to make 800 mL of solution?

10.92 Titration of a 12.0 mL solution of HCl requires 22.4 mL of 0.12 M NaOH. What is the molarity of the HCl solution?

10.93 How many equivalents are in 15.0 mL of 0.12 M $Ba(OH)_2$ solution? What volume of 0.085 M HNO_3 is required to reach the end point when titrating 15.0 mL of this solution?

10.94 Titration of a 10.0 mL solution of NH_3 requires 15.0 mL of 0.0250 M H_2SO_4 solution. What is the molarity of the NH_3 solution?

10.95 If 35.0 mL of a 0.100 N acid solution is needed to reach the end point in titration of 21.5 mL of a base solution, what is the normality of the base solution?

10.96 For the titrations discussed in Problems 10.92 and 10.93, what is the pH of the solution at the equivalence point (acidic, basic, or neutral)? Explain.

10.97 For the titration discussed in Problem 10.94, what is the pH of the solution at the equivalence point (acidic, basic, or neutral)? Explain.

CONCEPTUAL PROBLEMS

10.98 A solution is prepared by bubbling 15.0 L of $HCl(g)$ at 25 °C and 1 atm into 250.0 mL of water.

    (a) Assuming all the HCl dissolves in the water, how many moles of HCl are in solution?

    (b) What is the pH of the solution?

10.99 The dissociation of water into H_3O^+ and OH^- ions depends on temperature. At 0 °C the $[H_3O^+] = 3.38 \times 10^{-8}\ M$, at 25 °C the $[H_3O^+] = 1.00 \times 10^{-7}\ M$, and at 50 °C the $[H_3O^+] = 2.34 \times 10^{-7}\ M$.

    (a) Calculate the pH of water at 0 °C and 50 °C.

    (b) What is the value of K_w at 0 °C and 50 °C?

    (c) Is the dissociation of water endothermic or exothermic?

10.100 The active ingredient in aspirin is acetylsalicylic acid (MW = 180.2 g/mol). An aspirin tablet was dissolved in water and titrated with 0.100 M NaOH. If the titration required 13.87 mL of NaOH to reach the phenolphthalein endpoint, how many milligrams of acetylsalicylic acid were in the tablet?

10.101 How many milliliters of 0.50 M NaOH solution are required to titrate 40.0 mL of a 0.10 M H_2SO_4 solution to an end point?

10.102 Which solution contains more acid, 50 mL of a 0.20 N HCl solution or 50 mL of a 0.20 N acetic acid solution? Which has a higher hydronium ion concentration? Which has a lower pH?

10.103 One of the buffer systems used to control the pH of blood involves the equilibrium between $H_2PO_4^-$ and HPO_4^{2-}. The pK_a for $H_2PO_4^-$ is 7.21.

    (a) Write the Henderson–Hasselbalch equation for this buffer system.

    (b) What HPO_4^{2-} to $H_2PO_4^-$ ratio is needed to maintain the optimum blood pH of 7.40?

10.104 A 0.15 N solution of HCl is used to titrate 30.0 mL of a $Ca(OH)_2$ solution of unknown concentration. If 140.0 mL of HCl is required, what is the normality of the $Ca(OH)_2$ solution? What is the molarity?

10.105 Which of the following combinations produces an effective buffer solution? Assuming equal concentrations of each acid and its conjugate base, calculate the pH of each buffer solution.

    (a) NaF and HF   **(b)** $HClO_4$ and $NaClO_4$

    (c) NH_4Cl and NH_3 **(d)** KBr and HBr

10.106 One method of analyzing ammonium salts is to treat them with NaOH and then heat the solution to remove the NH_3 gas formed.

$$NH_4^+(aq) + OH^-(aq) \longrightarrow NH_3(g) + H_2O(l)$$

    (a) Label the Brønsted–Lowry acid-base pairs.

    (b) If 2.86 L of NH_3 at 60 °C and 755 mmHg is produced by the reaction of NH_4Cl, how many grams of NH_4Cl were in the original sample?

10.107 One method of reducing acid rain is "scrubbing" the combustion products before they are emitted from power plant smoke stacks. The process involves addition of an aqueous suspension of lime (CaO) to the combustion chamber and stack, where the lime reacts with SO_2 to give calcium sulfite $(CaSO_3)$: $CaO(aq) + SO_2(g) \longrightarrow CaSO_3(aq)$

    (a) How much lime (in grams) is needed to remove 1 mol of SO_2?

    (b) How much lime (in kilograms) is needed to remove 1 kg of SO_2?

10.108 Sodium oxide, Na_2O, reacts with water to give NaOH.

    (a) Write a balanced equation for the reaction.

    (b) What is the pH of the solution prepared by allowing 1.55 g of Na_2O to react with 500.0 mL of water? Assume that there is no volume change.

    (c) How many milliliters of 0.0100 M HCl are needed to neutralize the NaOH solution prepared in (b)?

GROUP PROBLEMS

10.109 Obtain a package of Alka-Seltzer, an antacid, from the local drug store:

    (a) List the ingredients.

    (b) Why does Alka-Seltzer foam and bubble when dissolved in water? Which ingredient is the antacid?

    (c) Write the reaction responsible for the formation of bubbles, and the reaction responsible for the antacid activity.

10.110 Research the composition of "smelling salts"—a product that is used to rouse people who have lost consciousness.

    (a) What are the primary components?

    (b) What are the chemical reactions that generate the "active" component?

10.111 Many allergy medications contain antihistamines, compounds that contain amine groups (R-NH_2, where R refers to an organic functional group). Would you expect these compounds to be acidic, basic or neutral? Explain.

    (a) One over-the-counter product lists the active ingredient as "diphenhydramine HCl." What does this designation mean?

    (b) Write the acid-base reaction to illustrate how this compound is produced. When this product is dissolved in water would you expect the solution be acidic, basic, or neutral? Explain.

11

Nuclear
Chemistry

CONTENTS

◄◄◄ CONCEPTS TO REVIEW

A. Atomic Theory
(Section 2.1)

B. Elements and Atomic Number
(Section 2.2)

C. Isotopes
(Section 2.3)

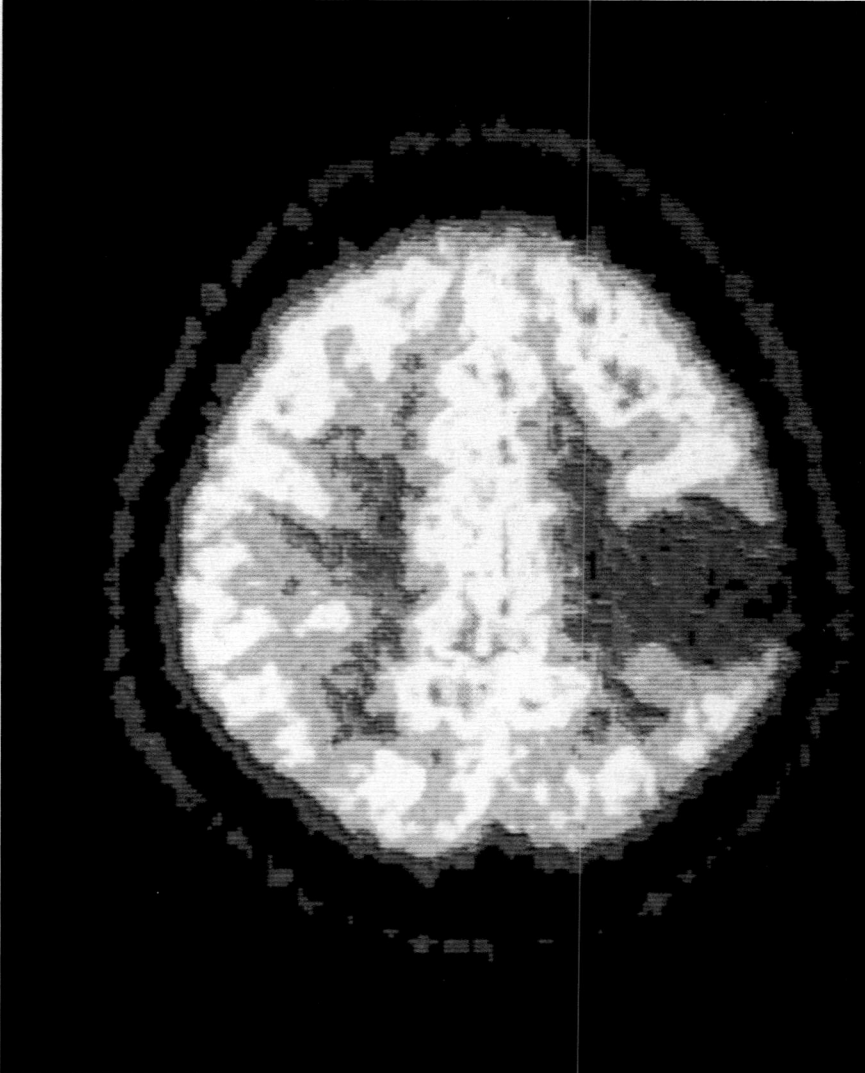

▲ This positron emission tomography (PET) scan takes advantage of the properties of radioactive isotopes to produce an image of a brain tumor. PET scans can also allow physicians to determine if a tumor is benign or malignant, and avoid unnecessary surgery.

A patient complaining of headaches and blurred vision on one side is referred to a regional research hospital for diagnostic tests. Thirty years ago, the standard diagnostic tool would have been X-ray imaging, but the use of 3-D *positron emission tomography* (PET) scans is becoming increasingly common. One advantage of PET technology is the ability to generate a 3-D image of tumors and body organs, including the brain, which enables physicians to more accurately diagnose the cause of medical symptoms. PET scans, and many other medical diagnostic techniques discussed in this chapter and in the Chemistry in Action "Body Imaging" on page 347, take advantage of the unique properties of radioisotopes—nuclei that undergo spontaneous nuclear decay reactions. Radioisotopes have practical applications far beyond medical diagnostics, including use in smoke detectors, in the determination of the age of archeological artifacts and geological formations, and as sources of energy in nuclear power plants.

But what is a "nuclear" reaction, and how is it different from the chemical reactions we have examined previously? In all of the reactions we have discussed thus far, only the *bonds* between atoms have changed; the chemical identities of atoms themselves have remained unchanged. Anyone who reads the paper or watches television knows, however, that atoms *can* change, often resulting in the conversion of one element into another. Atomic weapons, nuclear energy, and radioactive radon gas in our homes are all topics of societal importance, and all involve *nuclear chemistry*—the study of the properties and reactions of atomic nuclei.

11.1 Nuclear Reactions

Learning Objective:

• Identify reactants and products of nuclear reactions as elements, isotopes, or subatomic particles.

Recall from Section 2.2 that an atom is characterized by its *atomic number, Z,* and its *mass number, A.* The atomic number, written below and to the left of the element symbol, gives the number of protons in the nucleus and identifies the element. The mass number, written above and to the left of the element symbol, gives the total number of **nucleons,** a general term for both protons (p) and neutrons (n). The most common isotope of carbon, for example, has 12 nucleons: 6 protons and 6 neutrons: $^{12}_{6}C$.

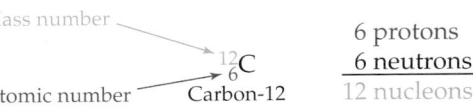

Mass number · · · · · · · · · · 6 protons
$^{12}_{6}C$ · · · · · · · · · · · · · · 6 neutrons
Atomic number · · · Carbon-12 · · · 12 nucleons

Atoms with identical atomic numbers but different mass numbers are called *isotopes,* and the nucleus of a specific isotope is called a **nuclide.** Thirteen isotopes of carbon are known—two occur commonly (^{12}C and ^{13}C) and one (^{14}C) is produced in small amounts in the upper atmosphere by the action of neutrons from cosmic rays on ^{14}N. The remaining 10 carbon isotopes have been produced artificially. Only the two commonly occurring isotopes are stable indefinitely; the others undergo spontaneous **nuclear reactions,** which change their nuclei. Carbon-14, for example, is an unstable isotope that slowly decomposes and is converted to nitrogen-14 plus an electron, a process we can write as

$$^{14}_{6}C \longrightarrow ^{14}_{7}N + ^{0}_{-1}e$$

The electron is often written as $^{0}_{-1}e$, where the superscript 0 indicates that the mass of an electron is essentially zero when compared with that of a proton or neutron, and the subscript -1 indicates that the charge is -1. (The subscript in this instance is not a true atomic number; in Section 11.4 the purpose of representing the electron this way will become clear.)

Nuclear reactions, such as the spontaneous decay of ^{14}C, are different from chemical reactions in several ways:

• A *nuclear* reaction involves a change in an atom's nucleus, usually producing a different element. A *chemical* reaction, by contrast, involves only a change in distribution of the outer-shell electrons around the atom and never changes the nucleus itself or produces a different element.
• Different isotopes of an element have essentially the same behavior in chemical reactions but often have completely different behavior in nuclear reactions.
• The rate of a nuclear reaction is unaffected by a change in temperature or pressure or by the addition of a catalyst.
• The nuclear reaction of an atom is essentially the same whether it is in a chemical compound or in an uncombined, elemental form.
• The energy change accompanying a nuclear reaction can be up to several million times greater than that accompanying a chemical reaction. The nuclear transformation of 1.0 g of uranium-235 releases 3.4×10^{8} kcal (1.4×10^{9} kJ), for example, whereas the chemical combustion of 1.0 g of methane releases only 12 kcal (50 kJ).

Nucleon A general term for both protons and neutrons.

◀◀ **CONCEPTS TO REVIEW** The different isotopes of an atom each have the same number of protons and only differ in their number of neutrons (Section 2.3).

Nuclide The nucleus of a specific isotope of an element.

Nuclear reaction A reaction that changes an atomic nucleus, usually causing the change of one element into another.

11.2 The Discovery and Nature of Radioactivity

Learning Objective:

• Identify the different types of radiation and the properties of each type.

The discovery of *radioactivity* dates to the year 1896 when the French physicist Henri Becquerel made a remarkable observation. While investigating the nature of phosphorescence—the luminous glow of some minerals and other substances that remains when the lights are suddenly turned off—Becquerel happened to place a sample of a uranium-containing mineral on top of a photographic plate that had been wrapped in black paper and put in a drawer to protect it from sunlight. On developing the plate, Becquerel was surprised to find a silhouette of the mineral. He concluded that the mineral was producing some kind of unknown radiation, which passed through the paper and exposed the photographic plate.

Radioactivity The spontaneous emission of radiation from a nucleus.

Marie Sklodowska Curie and her husband, Pierre, began a series of investigations into this new phenomenon, which they termed **radioactivity.** They found that the source of the radioactivity was the element uranium (U) and that two previously unknown elements, which they named polonium (Po) and radium (Ra), were also radioactive. For these achievements, Becquerel and the Curies shared the 1903 Nobel Prize in physics.

Further work on radioactivity by the English scientist Ernest Rutherford established that there were at least two types of radiation, which he named *alpha* (α) and *beta* (β) after the first two letters of the Greek alphabet. Shortly thereafter, a third type of radiation was found and named for the third Greek letter, *gamma* (γ).

Subsequent studies showed that when the three kinds of radiation are passed between two plates with opposite electrical charges, each is affected differently. Alpha radiation bends toward the negative plate and must therefore have a positive charge. Beta radiation, by contrast, bends toward the positive plate and must have a negative charge, whereas gamma radiation does not bend toward either plate and has no charge (Figure 11.1).

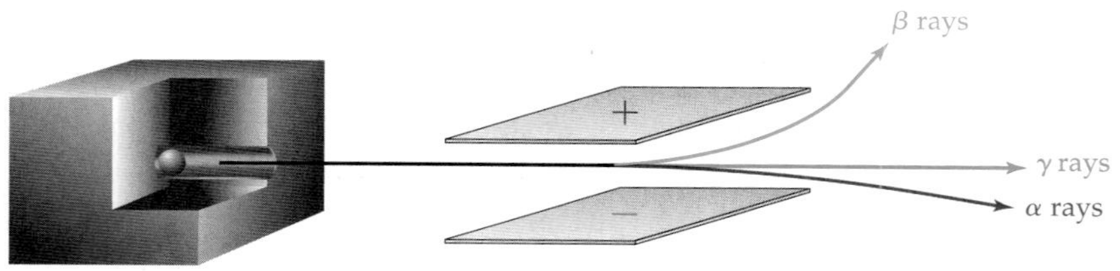

▶ **Figure 11.1**
The effect of an electric field on α, β, γ radiation.
The radioactive source in the shielded box emits radiation, which passes between the two electrically charged plates. Alpha radiation is deflected toward the negative plate, β radiation is deflected toward the positive plate, and γ radiation is not deflected.

Gamma (γ) radiation Radioactivity consisting of high-energy light waves.

Beta (β) particle An electron (e^-), emitted as radiation.

Alpha (α) particle A helium nucleus (He^{2+}), emitted as α radiation.

Another difference among the three kinds of radiation soon became apparent when it was discovered that α and β radiations are composed of small particles with a measurable mass, whereas **gamma (γ) radiation** consists of high-energy electromagnetic waves and has no mass. Rutherford was able to show that a **beta (β) particle** is an electron (e^-) and that an **alpha (α) particle** is actually a helium nucleus, He^{2+}. (Recall that a helium *atom* consists of two protons, two neutrons, and two electrons. When the two electrons are removed, the remaining helium nucleus, or α particle, has only the two protons and two neutrons.).

Yet a third difference among the three kinds of radiation is their penetrating power. Because of their relatively large mass, α particles move slowly (up to about one-tenth the speed of light) and can be stopped by a few sheets of paper or by the top layer of skin. Beta particles, because they are much lighter, move at up to nine-tenth the speed of light and have about 100 times the penetrating power of α particles. A block of wood or heavy protective clothing is necessary to stop β radiation, which can otherwise penetrate the skin and cause burns and other damage. Gamma rays move at the speed of light (3.00×10^8 m/s) and have about 1000 times the penetrating power of α particles. A lead block several inches thick is needed to stop γ radiation, which can otherwise penetrate and damage the body's internal organs.

◀◀◀ See the Chemistry in Action "Atoms and Light" on p. 66 in Chapter 2 for a discussion of gamma rays and the rest of the electromagnetic spectrum.

Table 11.1 summarizes the characteristics of the three kinds of radiation. Note that an α particle, even though it is an ion with a +2 charge, is usually written using the symbol $_2^4$He without the charge. A β particle is usually written $_{-1}^0$e, as noted previously.

Table 11.1 Characteristics of α, β, and γ Radiation

Type of Radiation	Symbol	Charge	Composition	Mass (AMU)	Velocity	Relative Penetrating Power
Alpha	α, $_2^4$He	+2	Helium nucleus	4	Up to 10% speed of light	Low (1)
Beta	β, $_{-1}^0$e	−1	Electron	1/1823	Up to 90% speed of light	Medium (100)
Gamma	γ, $_0^0\gamma$	0	High-energy radiation	0	Speed of light (3.00×10^8 m/s)	High (1000)

11.3 Stable and Unstable Isotopes

Learning Objective:

- Identify natural isotopes, and distinguish between stable and unstable isotopes.

Every element in the periodic table has at least one radioactive isotope, or **radioisotope,** and more than 3300 radioisotopes are known. Their radioactivity is the result of having unstable nuclei, although the exact causes of this instability are not fully understood. Radiation is emitted when an unstable radioactive nucleus, or **radionuclide,** spontaneously changes into a more stable one.

For elements in the first few rows of the periodic table, stability is associated with a roughly equal number of neutrons and protons (Figure 11.2). Hydrogen, for example, has stable $_1^1$H (protium) and $_1^2$H (deuterium) isotopes, but its $_1^3$H isotope (tritium) is radioactive. As elements get heavier, the number of neutrons relative to protons in stable nuclei increases. Lead-208 ($_{82}^{208}$Pb), for example, the most abundant stable isotope of lead, has 126 neutrons and 82 protons in its nuclei. Nevertheless, of the 35 known isotopes of lead, only 3 are stable whereas 32 are radioactive. In fact, there are only 264 stable isotopes among all the elements. All isotopes of elements with atomic numbers higher than that of bismuth (83) are radioactive.

Most of the more than 3300 known radioisotopes have been made in high-energy particle accelerators by reactions that will be described in Section 11.8. Such isotopes are called **artificial radioisotopes** because they are not found in nature. All isotopes of the transuranium elements (those heavier than uranium) are artificial. The much smaller number of radioactive isotopes found in Earth's crust, such as $_{92}^{238}$U, are called **natural radioisotopes.**

Aside from their radioactivity, different radioisotopes of the same element have the same chemical properties as stable isotopes, which accounts for their great usefulness as *tracers* (see the Chemistry in Action "Medical Uses of Radioactivity" on p. 338). A chemical compound tagged with a radioactive atom undergoes exactly the same reactions as its nonradioactive counterpart. The difference is that the tagged compound can be located with a radiation detector and its location determined, as discussed in the Chemistry in Action "Body Imaging" on page 347.

Radioisotope A radioactive isotope.

Radionuclide The nucleus of a radioactive isotope.

Artificial radioisotope Radioactive isotopes not found in nature.

Natural radioisotopes Radioactive isotopes that occur naturally and are found in Earth's crust.

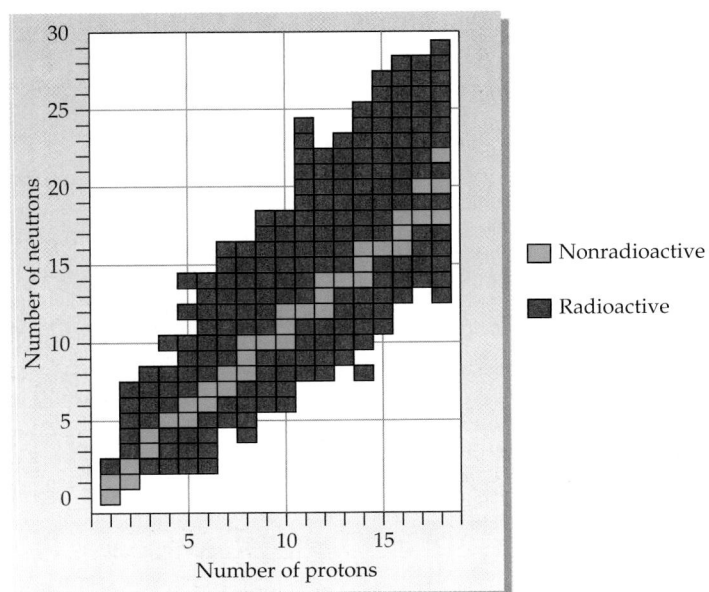

► **Figure 11.2**

A plot of the numbers of neutrons and protons for known isotopes of the first 18 elements.

Stable (nonradioactive) isotopes of these elements have equal or nearly equal numbers of neutrons and protons.

11.4 Nuclear Decay

Learning Objective:

- Write and balance nuclear reactions involving alpha, beta, and positron emission modes of radioactive decay.

Think for a minute about the consequences of α and β radiation. If radioactivity involves the spontaneous emission of a small particle from an unstable atomic nucleus, then the nucleus itself must undergo a change. With that understanding of radioactivity came the startling discovery that atoms of one element can change into atoms of another element, something that had previously been thought impossible. The spontaneous emission of a particle from an unstable nucleus is called **nuclear decay,** or *radioactive decay,* and the resulting change of one element into another is called **transmutation.**

Nuclear decay: Radioactive element $\longrightarrow$ New element $+$ Emitted particle

Nuclear decay The spontaneous emission of a particle from an unstable nucleus.

Transmutation The change of one element into another.

Alpha Emission

When an atom of uranium-238 ($^{238}_{92}$U) emits an α particle (i.e., $^{4}_{2}$He), the nucleus loses 2 protons and 2 neutrons. Because the number of protons in the nucleus has now changed from 92 to 90, the *identity* of the atom has changed from uranium to thorium. Furthermore, since the total number of nucleons has decreased by 4, uranium-238 has become thorium-234 ($^{234}_{90}$Th) (Figure 11.3).

Note that the equation for a nuclear reaction is not balanced in the usual chemical sense because the kinds of atoms are not the same on both sides of the arrow. Instead, we say that a nuclear equation is balanced when the number of nucleons on both sides of the equation is the same and when the sums of the charges on the nuclei plus any ejected subatomic particles (protons or electrons) are same on both sides of the equation. In the decay of $^{238}_{92}$U to give $^{4}_{2}$He and $^{234}_{90}$Th, for example, there are 238 nucleons and 92 nuclear charges on both sides of the nuclear equation.

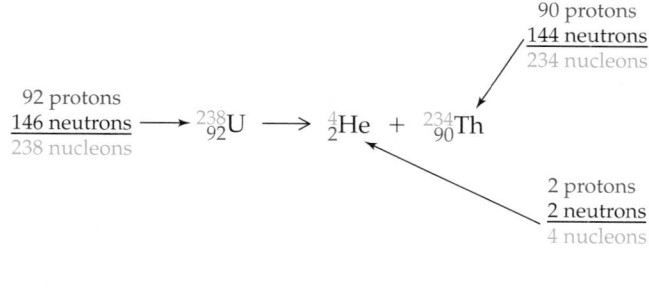

▶ **Figure 11.3**
Alpha emission.
Emission of an α particle from an atom of uranium-238 produces an atom of thorium-234.

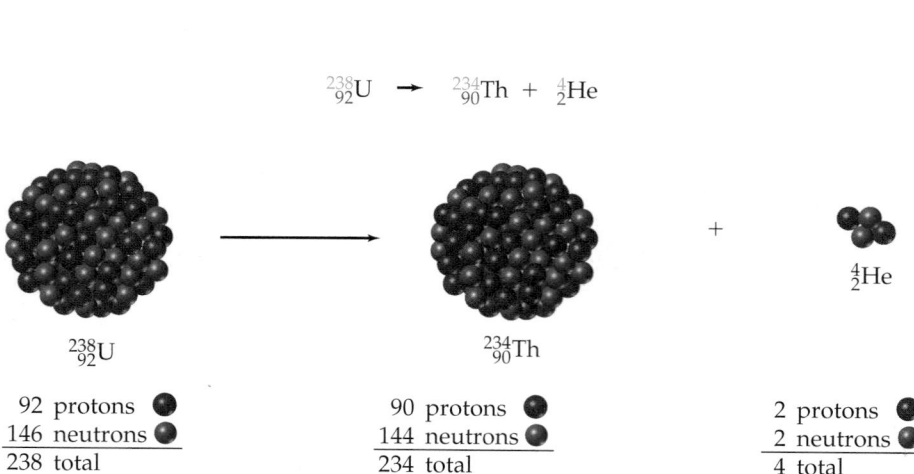

Worked Example 11.1 Balancing Nuclear Reactions: Alpha Emission

Polonium-208 is one of the α emitters studied by Marie Curie. Write the equation for the α decay of polonium-208, and identify the element formed.

ANALYSIS Look up the atomic number of polonium (84) in the periodic table, and write the known part of the nuclear equation, using the standard symbol for polonium-208:

$$^{208}_{84}\text{Po} \longrightarrow {}^{4}_{2}\text{He} + ?$$

Then, calculate the mass number and atomic number of the product element, and write the final equation.

SOLUTION

The mass number of the product is $208 - 4 = 204$, and the atomic number is $84 - 2 = 82$. A look at the periodic table identifies the element with atomic number 82 as lead (Pb).

$$^{208}_{84}\text{Po} \longrightarrow {}^{4}_{2}\text{He} + {}^{204}_{82}\text{Pb}$$

Check your answer by making sure that the mass numbers and atomic numbers on the two sides of the equation are balanced:

Mass numbers: $208 = 4 + 204$ Atomic numbers: $84 = 2 + 82$

PROBLEM 11.1

High levels of radioactive radon-222 ($^{222}_{86}\text{Rn}$) have been found in many homes built on radium-containing rock, leading to the possibility of health hazards. What product results from α emission by radon-222?

PROBLEM 11.2

What isotope of radium (Ra) is converted into radon-222 by α emission?

Beta Emission

Whereas α emission leads to the loss of two protons and two neutrons from the nucleus, β emission involves the *decomposition* of a neutron to yield an electron and a proton. This process can be represented as

$$^{1}_{0}\text{n} \longrightarrow {}^{1}_{1}\text{p} + {}^{0}_{-1}\text{e}$$

where the electron ($^{0}_{-1}\text{e}$) is ejected as a β particle, and the proton is retained by the nucleus. Note that the electrons emitted during β radiation come from the *nucleus* and not from the occupied orbitals surrounding the nucleus. The decomposition of carbon-14 to form nitrogen-14 in Section 11.1 is an example of beta decay.

The net result of β emission is that the atomic number of the atom increases by one because there is a new proton. The mass number of the atom remains the same, however, because a neutron has changed into a proton, leaving the total number of nucleons unchanged. For example, iodine-131 ($^{131}_{53}\text{I}$), a radioisotope used in detecting thyroid problems, undergoes nuclear decay by β emission to yield xenon-131 ($^{131}_{54}\text{Xe}$):

53 protons / 78 neutrons / 131 nucleons $\longrightarrow$ $^{131}_{53}\text{I}$

$$^{131}_{53}\text{I} \longrightarrow {}^{131}_{54}\text{Xe} + {}^{0}_{-1}\text{e}$$

$^{131}_{54}\text{Xe}$: 54 protons / 77 neutrons / 131 nucleons

$^{0}_{-1}\text{e}$: 0 nucleons, but -1 charge

Note that the superscripts (mass numbers) are balanced in this equation because a β particle has a mass near zero, and the subscripts are balanced because a β particle has a charge of -1.

Worked Example 11.2 Balancing Nuclear Reactions: Beta Emission

Write a balanced nuclear equation for the β decay of chromium-55.

ANALYSIS Write the known part of the nuclear equation:

$$^{55}_{24}\text{Cr} \longrightarrow ^{0}_{-1}\text{e} + ?$$

Then calculate the mass number and atomic number of the product element, and write the final equation.

SOLUTION

The mass number of the product stays at 55, and the atomic number increases by 1, $24 + 1 = 25$, so the product is manganese-55.

$$^{55}_{24}\text{Cr} \longrightarrow ^{0}_{-1}\text{e} + ^{55}_{25}\text{Mn}$$

Check your answer by making sure that the mass numbers and atomic numbers on the two sides of the equation are balanced:

Mass numbers: $55 = 0 + 55$ Atomic numbers: $24 = -1 + 25$

PROBLEM 11.3

Strontium-89 is a short-lived β emitter often used in the treatment of bone tumors. Write a nuclear equation for the decay of strontium-89.

PROBLEM 11.4

Write nuclear equations for the formation of each of the following nuclides by β emission.

   (a) $^{3}_{2}\text{He}$ **(b)** $^{210}_{83}\text{Bi}$ **(c)** $^{20}_{10}\text{Ne}$

Gamma Emission

Emission of γ rays, unlike the emission of α and β particles, causes no change in mass or atomic number because γ rays are simply high-energy electromagnetic waves. Although γ emission can occur alone, it usually accompanies α or β emission as a mechanism for the new nucleus that results from a transmutation to release some extra energy.

Since γ emission affects neither mass number nor atomic number, it is often omitted from nuclear equations. Nevertheless, γ rays are of great importance. Their penetrating power makes them by far the most dangerous kind of external radiation for humans and also makes them useful in numerous medical applications. Cobalt-60, for example, is used in cancer therapy as a source of penetrating γ rays that kill cancerous tissue.

$$^{60}_{27}\text{Co} \longrightarrow ^{60}_{28}\text{Ni} + ^{0}_{-1}\text{e} + ^{0}_{0}\gamma$$

Positron Emission

Positron A "positive electron," which has the same mass as an electron but a positive charge.

In addition to α, β, and γ radiation, there is another common type of radioactive decay process called *positron emission*, which involves the conversion of a proton in the nucleus into a neutron plus an ejected **positron**, $^{0}_{1}\text{e}$ or β^{+}. A positron, which can be thought of as a "positive electron," has the same mass as an electron but a positive charge. This process can be represented as

$$^{1}_{1}\text{p} \longrightarrow ^{1}_{0}\text{n} + ^{0}_{1}\text{e}$$

The result of positron emission is a decrease in the atomic number of the product nucleus because a proton has changed into a neutron, but no change in the mass number. Potassium-40, for example, undergoes positron emission to yield argon-40, a nuclear reaction important in geology for dating rocks. Note once again that the sum of the two subscripts on the right of the nuclear equation $(18 + 1 = 19)$ is equal to the subscript in the $^{40}_{19}K$ nucleus on the left.

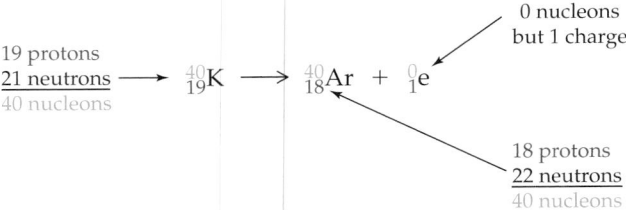

Electron Capture

Electron capture, symbolized E.C., is a process in which the nucleus captures an inner-shell electron from the surrounding electron cloud, thereby converting a proton into a neutron, and energy is released in the form of gamma rays. The mass number of the product nucleus is unchanged, but the atomic number decreases by one, just as in positron emission. The conversion of mercury-197 into gold-197 is an example:

> **Electron capture (E.C.)** A process in which the nucleus captures an inner-shell electron from the surrounding electron cloud, thereby converting a proton into a neutron.

$$\underset{\substack{80 \text{ protons} \\ 117 \text{ neutrons} \\ 197 \text{ nucleons}}}{^{197}_{80}Hg} + \underset{\substack{\text{Inner-shell} \\ \text{electron}}}{^{0}_{-1}e} \longrightarrow \underset{\substack{79 \text{ protons} \\ 118 \text{ neutrons} \\ 197 \text{ nucleons}}}{^{197}_{79}Au}$$

Do not plan on using this reaction to get rich, however. Mercury-197 is not one of the naturally occurring isotopes of Hg and is typically produced by transmutation reactions as discussed in Section 11.8.

In Figure 11.2, we see that most of the stable isotopes of the lighter elements have nearly the same number of neutrons and protons. With this fact in mind, we can often predict the most likely decay mode: unstable isotopes that have more protons than neutrons are more likely to undergo β decay to convert a proton to a neutron, whereas unstable isotopes having more neutrons than protons are more likely to undergo either positron emission or electron capture to convert a neutron to a proton. Also, the very heavy isotopes $(Z > 83)$ will most likely undergo α-decay to lose both neutrons and protons to decrease the atomic number. Characteristics of the five kinds of radioactive decay processes are summarized in Table 11.2.

Table 11.2 A Summary of Radioactive Decay Processes

Process	Symbol	Change in Atomic Number	Change in Mass Number	Change in Number of Neutrons
α emission	^4_2He or α	-2	-4	-2
β emission	$^0_{-1}e$ or $\beta^{-}*$	$+1$	0	-1
γ emission	$^0_0\gamma$ or γ	0	0	0
Positron emission	^0_1e or $\beta^{+}*$	-1	0	$+1$
Electron capture	E.C.	-1	0	$+1$

*Superscripts are used to indicate the charge associated with the two forms of beta decay; β^-, or a beta particle, carries a -1 charge, while β^+, or a positron, carries a $+1$ charge.

Worked Example 11.3   Balancing Nuclear Reactions: Electron Capture, Positron Emission

Write balanced nuclear equations for the following processes:

(a) Electron capture by polonium-204: $^{204}_{84}Po + ^{0}_{-1}e \longrightarrow ?$

(b) Positron emission from xenon-118: $^{118}_{54}Xe \longrightarrow ^{0}_{1}e + ?$

—*continued on next page*

—continued from previous page

ANALYSIS The key to writing nuclear equations is to make sure that the number of nucleons is the same on both sides of the equation and that the number of charges is the same.

SOLUTION

(a) In electron capture, the mass number is unchanged and the atomic number decreases by one, giving bismuth-204: $^{204}_{84}\text{Po} + ^{0}_{-1}\text{e} \longrightarrow ^{204}_{83}\text{Bi}$.

Check your answer by making sure that the number of nucleons and the number of charges are the same on both sides of the equation:

Mass number: $204 + 0 = 204$ Atomic number: $84 + (-1) = 83$

(b) In positron emission, the mass number is unchanged and the atomic number decreases by one, giving iodine-118: $^{118}_{54}\text{Xe} \longrightarrow ^{0}_{1}\text{e} + ^{118}_{53}\text{I}$.

CHECK!

Mass number: $118 = 0 + 118$ Atomic number: $54 = 1 + 53$

PROBLEM 11.5

Write nuclear equations for positron emission from the following radioisotopes:

(a) $^{38}_{20}\text{Ca}$ **(b)** $^{118}_{54}\text{Xe}$ **(c)** $^{79}_{37}\text{Rb}$

PROBLEM 11.6

Write nuclear equations for the formation of the following radioisotopes by electron capture:

(a) $^{62}_{29}\text{Cu}$ **(b)** $^{110}_{49}\text{In}$ **(c)** $^{81}_{35}\text{Br}$

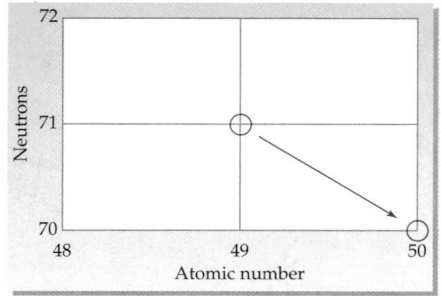

🔑 KEY CONCEPT PROBLEM 11.7

The red arrow in the graph (see margin) indicates the changes that occur in the nucleus of an atom during a nuclear reaction. Identify the isotopes involved as product and reactant, and name the type of decay process.

11.5 Radioactive Half-Life

Learning Objective:

• Determine the half-life of a radioactive isotope, and use the half-life to calculate the fraction of the isotope remaining as a function of time.

The rate of radioactive decay varies greatly from one radioisotope to another. Some radioisotopes, such as uranium-238, decay at a barely perceptible rate over billions of years, but others, such as carbon-17, decay within thousandths of a second.

Half-life ($t_{1/2}$) The amount of time required for one-half of a radioactive sample to decay.

Rates of nuclear decay are measured in units of **half-life ($t_{1/2}$)**, defined as the amount of time required for one-half of a radioactive sample to decay. For example, the half-life of iodine-131 is 8.021 days. If today, you have 1.000 g of $^{131}_{53}\text{I}$, then 8.021 days from now, you will have only 50% of that amount (0.500 g) because one-half of the sample will have decayed into $^{131}_{54}\text{Xe}$. After 8.021 more days (16.063 days total), you will have only 25% (0.250 g) of your original $^{131}_{53}\text{I}$ sample; after another 8.021 days (24.084 days total), you will have only 12.5% (0.125 g); and so on. Each passage of a half-life causes the decay of one-half of whatever sample remains. The half-life of any particular isotope is the same no matter what the size of the sample, the temperature, or any other external conditions. There is no known way to slow down, speed up, or otherwise change the characteristics of radioactive decay.

$$1.000 \text{ g } ^{131}_{53}\text{I} \xrightarrow[\text{days}]{8} 0.500 \text{ g } ^{131}_{53}\text{I} \xrightarrow[\text{days}]{8} 0.250 \text{ g } ^{131}_{53}\text{I} \xrightarrow[\text{days}]{8} 0.125 \text{ g } ^{131}_{53}\text{I} \longrightarrow$$

	One half-life	Two half-lives (16 days total)	Three half-lives (24 days total)
100%	50% remaining	25% remaining	12.5% remaining

The fraction of radioisotope remaining after the passage of each half-life is represented by the curve in Figure 11.4 and can be calculated as

$$\text{fraction remaining} = (0.5)^n$$

where n is the number of half-lives that have elapsed.

One of the better known half-life applications is radiocarbon dating to determine the age of archaeological artifacts. The method is based on the slow and constant production of radioactive carbon-14 atoms in the upper atmosphere by bombardment of nitrogen atoms with neutrons from cosmic rays. Carbon-14 atoms combine with oxygen to yield $^{14}CO_2$, which slowly mixes with ordinary $^{12}CO_2$ and is then incorporated into plants during photosynthesis. When these plants are eaten by animals, carbon-14 enters the food chain and is distributed evenly throughout all living organisms.

As long as a plant or animal is living, a dynamic equilibrium is established in which the organism excretes or exhales the same amount of ^{14}C that it takes in. As a result, the ratio of ^{14}C to ^{12}C in the living organism is the same as that in the atmosphere—about one part in 10^{12}. When the plant or animal dies, however, it no longer takes in more ^{14}C. Thus, the $^{14}C/^{12}C$ ratio in the organism slowly decreases as ^{14}C undergoes radioactive decay. At 5730 years (one ^{14}C half-life) after the death of the organism, the $^{14}C/^{12}C$ ratio has decreased by a factor of 2; at 11,460 years after death, the $^{14}C/^{12}C$ ratio has decreased by a factor of 4; and so on. By measuring the amount of ^{14}C remaining in the traces of any once-living organism, archaeologists can determine how long ago the organism died. The accuracy of the technique lessens as a sample gets older, but artifacts with an age of 1000–20,000 years can be dated with reasonable accuracy.

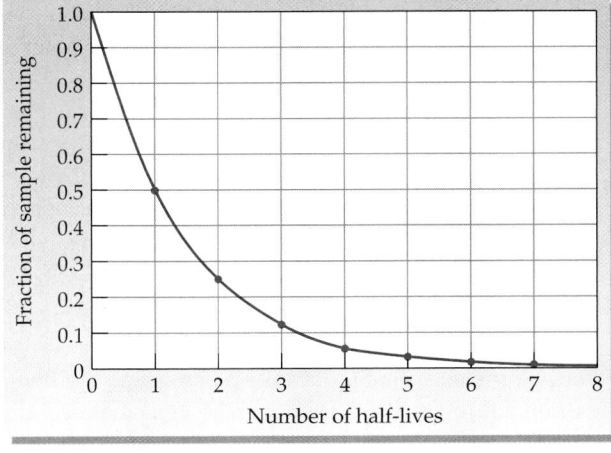

▲ **Figure 11.4**
The decay of a radioactive nucleus over time.
All nuclear decays follow this curve, whether the half-lives are measured in years, days, minutes, or seconds. That is, the fraction of sample remaining after one half-life is 0.50, the fraction remaining after two half-lives is 0.25, the fraction remaining after three half-lives is 0.125, and so on.

Table 11.3 gives the half-lives of some useful radioisotopes. As you might expect, radioisotopes that are used internally for medical applications have fairly short half-lives so that they decay rapidly and do not remain in the body for prolonged periods.

Often, decay of a radioisotope produces a stable nucleus, but sometimes the product nucleus is itself radioactive and undergoes further decay. In fact, some of the heavier radioactive nuclei undergo an extended **decay series** of nuclear disintegrations before they ultimately reach a nonradioactive product. Uranium-238, for example, undergoes a series of 14 sequential nuclear reactions, ultimately stopping at lead-206 (Figure 11.5).

One of the intermediate radionuclides in the uranium-238 decay series is radon-222, a gas. Rocks, soil, and building materials that originally contained uranium are sources of radon-222, which can seep through cracks in basements and get into the air inside homes and other buildings. Radon-222 undergoes α decay to form a solid product, polonium-218, which also undergoes α decay. If radon-222 is inhaled, potential exposure to α radiation can damage lung tissue.

Decay series A sequential series of nuclear disintegrations leading from a heavy radioisotope to a nonradioactive product.

Table 11.3 Half-Lives of Some Useful Radioisotopes

Radioisotope	Symbol	Radiation	Half-Life	Use
Tritium	$^{3}_{1}H$	β	12.33 years	Biochemical tracer
Carbon-14	$^{14}_{6}C$	β	5730 years	Archaeological dating
Sodium-24	$^{24}_{11}Na$	β	14.959 hours	Examining circulation
Phosphorus-32	$^{32}_{15}P$	β	14.262 days	Leukemia therapy
Potassium-40	$^{40}_{19}K$	β, β^+	1.277×10^9 years	Geological dating
Cobalt-60	$^{60}_{27}Co$	β, γ	5.271 years	Cancer therapy
Arsenic-74	$^{74}_{33}As$	β^+	17.77 days	Locating brain tumors
Technetium-99m*	$^{99m}_{43}Tc$	γ	6.01 hours	Brain scans
Iodine-131	$^{131}_{53}I$	β	8.021 days	Thyroid therapy
Uranium-235	$^{235}_{92}U$	α, γ	7.038×10^8 years	Nuclear reactors

*The m in technetium-99m stands for metastable, meaning that the nucleus undergoes γ emission but does not change its mass number or atomic number.

CHEMISTRY IN ACTION

⚕ Medical Uses of Radioactivity

The origins of nuclear medicine date from 1901, when the French physician Henri Danlos first used radium in the treatment of a tubercular skin lesion. Since that time, the use of radioactivity has become a crucial part of modern medical care, both diagnostic and therapeutic. Current nuclear techniques can be grouped into three classes: (1) in vivo procedures, (2) radiation therapy, and (3) imaging procedures. The first two are described here, and the third one is described on page 347 in the Chemistry in Action "Body Imaging."

In Vivo Procedures

In vivo studies—those that take place inside the body—are carried out to assess the functioning of a particular organ or body system. A *radiopharmaceutical* agent is administered, and its path in the body—whether absorbed, excreted, diluted, or concentrated—is determined by analysis of blood or urine samples. Such compounds are called *tracers,* because their location or distribution can be tracked by monitoring the decay of the radioisotope incorporated in the radiopharmaceutical agent.

Among the many *in vivo* procedures utilizing radioactive agents is a simple method for the determination of whole-blood volume, a common indicator used in the diagnosis of congestive heart failure, hypertension, and renal failure. A known quantity of red blood cells labeled with radioactive chromium-51 is injected into the patient and allowed to circulate to be distributed evenly throughout the body. After a suitable interval, a blood sample is taken and blood volume is calculated by comparing the concentration of labeled cells in the blood with the quantity of labeled

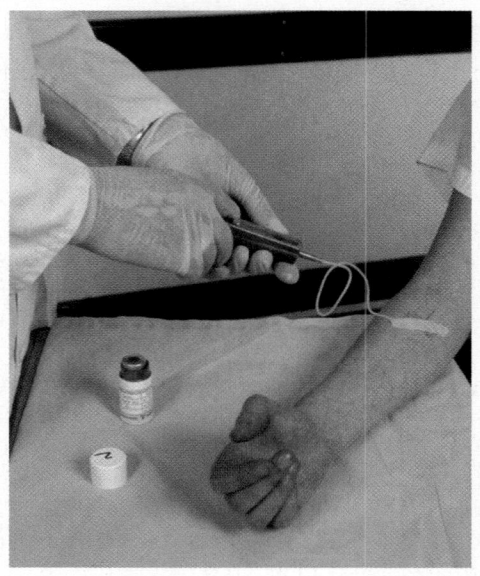

▲ A person's blood volume can be found by injecting a small amount of radioactive chromium-51 and measuring the dilution factor.

cells injected. This and similar procedures are known as *isotope dilution* and are described by

$$R_{sample} = R_{tracer}\left(\frac{W_{sample}}{W_{system} + W_{tracer}}\right)$$

where R_{sample} is the counting rate (a measure of radioactivity) of the analyzed sample, R_{tracer} is the counting rate of the tracer added to the system, and W refers to either the mass or volume of the analyzed sample, added tracer, or total system as indicated.

▶ **Figure 11.5**
The decay series from $^{238}_{92}U$ to $^{206}_{82}Pb$. Each isotope except for the last is radioactive and undergoes nuclear decay. The long slanted arrows represent α emissions, and the short horizontal arrows represent β emissions.

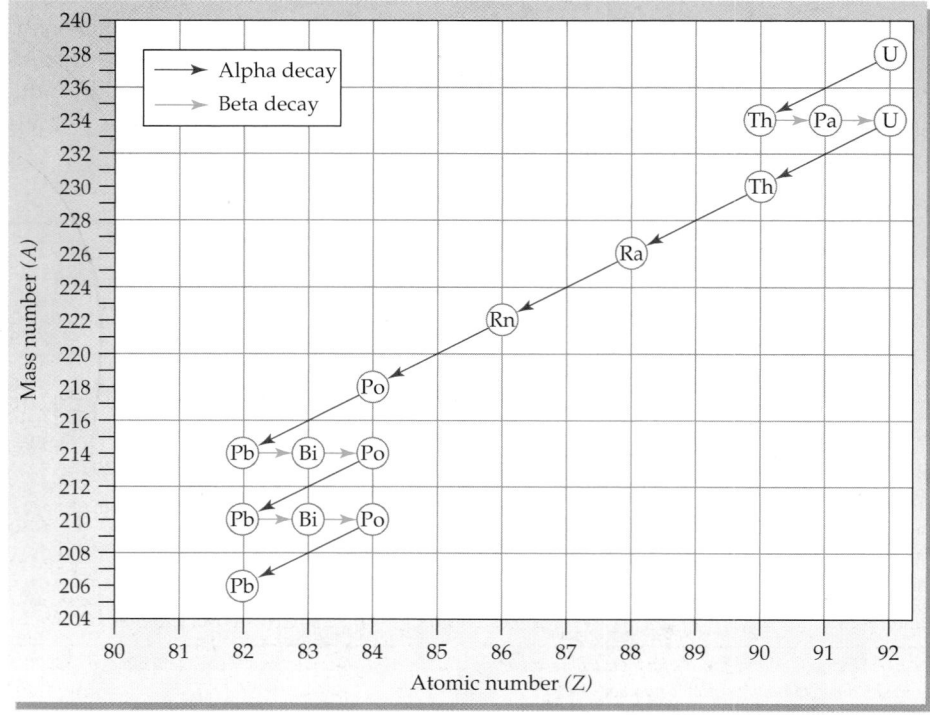

▲ Lasers are used to align and focus the neutron beam with the location of a patient's tumor at a neutron beam therapy facility at Fermilab.

Therapeutic Procedures

Therapeutic procedures—those in which radiation is purposely used as a weapon to kill diseased tissue—involve either external or internal sources of radiation. External radiation therapy for the treatment of cancer is often carried out with γ rays emanating from a cobalt-60 source. The highly radioactive source is shielded by a thick lead container and has a small opening directed toward the site of the tumor. By focusing the radiation beam on the tumor, the tumor receives the full exposure whereas exposure of surrounding parts of the body is minimized. Nevertheless, enough healthy tissue is affected so that most patients treated in this manner suffer the effects of radiation sickness discussed in Section 11.7.

Internal radiation therapy is a much more selective technique than external therapy. In the treatment of thyroid disease, for example, a radioactive substance such as iodine-131 is administered. This powerful β emitter is incorporated into the iodine-containing hormone thyroxine, which concentrates in the thyroid gland. Because β particles penetrate no farther than several millimeters, the localized ^{131}I produces a high radiation dose that destroys only the surrounding diseased tissue. To treat some tumors, such as those in the female reproductive system, a radioactive source is placed physically close to the tumor for a specific amount of time.

Boron neutron-capture therapy (BNCT) is a relatively new technique in which boron-containing drugs are administered to a patient and concentrate in the tumor site. The tumor is then irradiated with a neutron beam from a nuclear reactor. The boron absorbs a neutron and undergoes transmutation to produce an α particle and a lithium nucleus. These highly energetic particles have very low penetrating power and can kill nearby tumor tissue while sparing the healthy surrounding tissue. Because one disadvantage of BNCT is the need for access to a nuclear reactor, this treatment is available only in limited locations.

CIA Problem 11.1 What are the three main classes of techniques used in nuclear medicine? Give an example of each.

CIA Problem 11.2 A 2 mL solution containing 1.25 μCi/mL is injected into the bloodstream of a patient. After dilution, a 1.00 mL sample is withdrawn and found to have an activity of 2.6 $\times$ 10^{-4} μCi. Calculate total blood volume.

▶ Worked Example 11.4 Nuclear Reactions: Half-Life

Phosphorus-32, a radioisotope used in leukemia therapy, has a half-life of about 14 days. Approximately what percentage of a sample remains after eight weeks?

ANALYSIS Determine how many half-lives have elapsed. For an integral number of half-lives, we can multiply the starting amount (100%) by 1/2 for each half-life that has elapsed.

SOLUTION
Since one half-life of $^{32}_{15}$P is 14 days (two weeks), eight weeks represents four half-lives. The fraction that remains after eight weeks is thus

Four half-lives

$$\text{Final percentage} = 100\% \times (0.5)^4 = 100\% \times \left(\tfrac{1}{2} \times \tfrac{1}{2} \times \tfrac{1}{2} \times \tfrac{1}{2}\right)$$
$$= 100\% \times \tfrac{1}{16} = 6.25\%$$

Worked Example 11.5 Nuclear Reactions: Half-Life

As noted in Table 11.3, iodine-131 has a half-life of about eight days. Approximately what fraction of a sample remains after 20 days?

ANALYSIS Determine how many half-lives have elapsed. For a non-integral number (i.e., fraction) of half-lives, use the equation below to determine the fraction of radioisotope remaining.

$$\text{fraction remaining} = (0.5)^n$$

BALLPARK ESTIMATE Since the half-life of iodine-131 is eight days, an elapsed time of 20 days is 2.5 half-lives. The fraction remaining should be between 0.25 (fraction remaining after two half-lives) and 0.125 (fraction remaining after three half-lives). Since the relationship between the number of half-lives and fraction remaining is not linear (see Figure 11.4), the fraction remaining will not be exactly halfway between these values but instead will be slightly closer to the lower fraction, say 0.17.

SOLUTION

$$\text{fraction remaining} = (0.5)^n = (0.5)^{2.5} = 0.177$$

BALLPARK CHECK The fraction remaining is close to our estimate of 0.17.

Worked Example 11.6 Nuclear Reactions: Half-Life

For the phosphorus-32 radioisotope discussed in Worked Example 11.4, how long would it take for 85% of the ^{32}P to decay? (Note: $t_{1/2} = 14$ days.)

ANALYSIS If 85% of the original ^{32}P has decayed, then 15% remains. Knowing the fraction remaining (15%) the half-life relationship can be rearranged to solve for n (i.e., the number of half-lives). Multiplying n by 14 days yields the time required.

BALLPARK ESTIMATE Using exact half-lives as an estimate, we know that 25% would remain after two half-lives, and 12.5% would remain after three half-lives. Therefore, an elapsed time between two half-lives (28 days) and three half-lives (42 days) would be necessary. Since 15% is pretty close to 12.5% (three half-lives) the actual time is only slightly less than 42 days, so an estimate of 37 days is reasonable.

SOLUTION
Knowing the fraction remaining, we rearrange the half-life equation and solve for n. Because there is an exponential term involved, the mathematical solution can be simplified by applying the inverse function (i.e., a log function) to both sides, and rearranging:

$$\text{fraction remaining} = 0.15 = (0.5)^n$$
$$\log(0.15) = \log(0.5)^n$$
$$\log(0.15) = n\log(0.5)$$
$$-0.824 = n(-0.301)$$
$$n = (-0.824/-0.301) = 2.74 \text{ half-lives}$$

The time required is (14 days × 2.74) = 38.3 (38 days), close to our estimate.

PROBLEM 11.8

The half-life of carbon-14, an isotope used in archaeological dating, is 5730 years. What percentage of $^{14}_6C$ remains in a sample estimated to be 17,000 years old?

PROBLEM 11.9

A 1.00 mL sample of red blood cells containing chromium-51 as a tracer was injected into a patient. After several hours, a 5.00 mL sample of blood was drawn and its activity compared to the activity of the injected tracer sample. If the collected sample activity was 0.10% of the original tracer, calculate the total blood volume of the patient (see the Chemistry in Action "Medical Uses of Radioactivity," p. 338).

PROBLEM 11.10

The first four radioisotopes in Table 11.3 are included in Figure 11.2. They all undergo β decay.

  (a) Locate the position of these radioisotopes in Figure 11.2.

  (b) Write the balanced decay reactions for these radioisotopes, and locate the position of the product nuclei in Figure 11.2.

KEY CONCEPT PROBLEM 11.11

What is the half-life of the radionuclide that shows the decay curve indicated in the graph (see margin)?

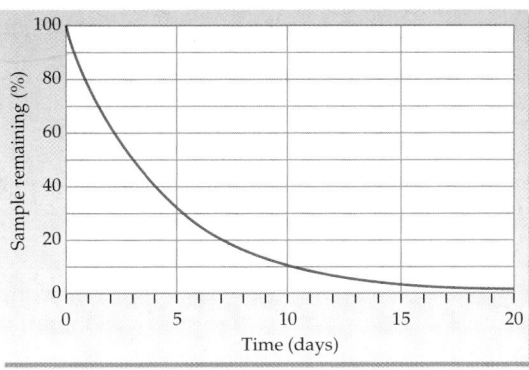

11.6 Ionizing Radiation

Learning Objective:

• Identify the types of ionizing radiation, and calculate the radiation intensity as a function of distance from the radiation source.

High-energy radiation of all kinds is often grouped together under the name **ionizing radiation.** This includes not only α particles, β particles, and γ rays but also *X rays* and *cosmic rays.* **X rays** are like γ rays; they have no mass and consist of high-energy electromagnetic radiation. The only difference between them is that the energy of X rays is somewhat less than that of γ rays (see the Chemistry in Action "Atoms and Light" in Chapter 2). **Cosmic rays** are not rays at all but are a mixture of high-energy particles that shower Earth from outer space. They consist primarily of protons, along with some α and β particles.

The interaction of any kind of ionizing radiation with a molecule knocks out an orbital electron, converting the atom or molecule into an extremely reactive ion:

$$\text{Molecule} \xrightarrow[\text{radiation}]{\text{ionizing}} \text{Ion} + e^-$$

This reactive ion can react with other molecules nearby, creating still other fragments that can cause further reactions. In this manner, a large dose of ionizing radiation can destroy the delicate balance of chemical reactions in living cells, ultimately causing the death of an organism.

A small dose of ionizing radiation may not cause visible symptoms but can nevertheless be dangerous if it strikes a cell nucleus and damages the genetic machinery inside. The resultant changes might lead to a genetic mutation, to cancer, or to cell death. The nuclei of rapidly dividing cells, such as those in bone marrow, the lymph system, the lining of the intestinal tract, or an embryo, are the most readily damaged. Because cancer cells are also rapidly dividing they are highly susceptible to the effects of ionizing radiation, which is why radiation therapy is an effective treatment for many types of cancer (see the Chemistry in Action "Medical Uses of Radioactivity" on p. 338). Table 11.4 summarizes some properties of ionizing radiation.

Ionizing radiation A general name for high-energy radiation of all kinds.

X rays Electromagnetic radiation with an energy somewhat less than that of γ rays.

Cosmic rays A mixture of high-energy particles—primarily of protons and various atomic nuclei—that shower Earth from outer space.

Table 11.4 Some Properties of Ionizing Radiation

Type of Radiation	Energy Range*	Penetrating Distance in Water**
α	3–9 MeV	0.02–0.04 mm
β	0–3 MeV	0–4 mm
X	100 eV–10 keV	0.01–1 cm
γ	10 keV–10 MeV	1–20 cm

*The energies of subatomic particles are often measured in electron volts (eV): $1\ eV = 6.703 \times 10^{-19}\ cal$, or $2.805 \times 10^{-18}\ J$.
**Distance at which one-half of the radiation is stopped.

The effects of ionizing radiation on the human body vary with the energy of the radiation, its distance from the body, the length of exposure, and the location of the source outside or inside the body. When coming from outside the body, γ rays and X rays are potentially more harmful than α and β particles because they pass through clothing and skin and into the body's cells. Alpha particles are stopped by clothing and skin, and β particles are stopped by wood or several layers of clothing. These types of radiation are much more dangerous when emitted within the body, however, because all their radiation energy is given up to the immediately surrounding tissue. Alpha emitters are especially hazardous internally and are almost never used in medical applications.

Health professionals who work with X rays or other kinds of ionizing radiation protect themselves by surrounding the source with a thick layer of lead or other dense material. Protection from radiation is also afforded by controlling the distance between the worker and the radiation source because radiation intensity *(I)* decreases with the square of the distance from the source. The intensities of radiation at two different distances, 1 and 2, are given by the equation

$$\frac{I_1}{I_2} = \frac{d_2{}^2}{d_1{}^2}$$

For example, suppose a source delivers 16 units of radiation at a distance of 1.0 m. Doubling the distance to 2.0 m decreases the radiation intensity to one-fourth:

$$\frac{16 \text{ units}}{I_2} = \frac{(2\text{ m})^2}{(1\text{ m})^2}$$

$$I_2 = 16 \text{ units} \times \frac{1 \text{ m}^2}{4 \text{ m}^2} = 4 \text{ units}$$

Worked Example 11.7 Ionizing Radiation: Intensity versus Distance from the Source

If a radiation source gives 75 units of radiation at a distance of 2.4 m, at what distance does the source give 25 units of radiation?

ANALYSIS Radiation intensity *(I)* decreases with the square of the distance *(d)* from the source according to the equation

$$\frac{I_1}{I_2} = \frac{d_2{}^2}{d_1{}^2}$$

We know three of the four variables in this equation (I_1, I_2, and d_1), and we need to find d_2.

BALLPARK ESTIMATE In order to decrease the radiation intensity from 75 units to 25 units (a factor of 3), the distance must *increase* by a factor of $\sqrt{3} = 1.7$. Thus, the distance should increase from 2.4 m to about 4 m.

SOLUTION

STEP 1: **Identify known information.** We know three of the four variables.

$I_1 = 75$ units
$I_2 = 25$ units
$d_1 = 2.4$ m

STEP 2: **Identify answer and units.**

$d_2 = $??? m

STEP 3: **Identify equation.** Rearrange the equation relating intensity and distance to solve for d_2.

$$\frac{I_1}{I_2} = \frac{d_2{}^2}{d_1{}^2}$$

$$d_2{}^2 = \frac{I_1 d_1{}^2}{I_2} \implies d_2 = \sqrt{\frac{I_1 d_1{}^2}{I_2}}$$

STEP 4: **Solve.** Substitute in known values so that unwanted units cancel.

$$d_2 = \sqrt{\frac{(75 \text{ units})(2.4\text{ m})^2}{(25 \text{ units})}} = 4.2 \text{ m}$$

BALLPARK CHECK The calculated result is consistent with our estimate of about 4 m.

PROBLEM 11.12

A β-emitting radiation source gives 250 units of radiation at a distance of 4.0 m. At what distance does the radiation drop to one-tenth its original value?

11.7 Detecting and Measuring Radiation

Learning Objective:

* Identify methods for detecting radiation and the units used to measure radiation exposure.

Small amounts of naturally occurring radiation have always been present, but people have been aware of it only within the past 100 years. The problem is that radiation is invisible. We cannot see, hear, smell, touch, or taste radiation, no matter how high the dose. We can, however, detect radiation by taking advantage of its ionizing properties.

The simplest device for detecting exposure to radiation is the photographic film badge worn by people who routinely work with radioactive materials. The film is protected from exposure to light, but any other radiation striking the badge causes the film to fog (remember Becquerel's discovery). At regular intervals, the film is developed and compared with a standard to indicate the radiation exposure.

The most versatile method for measuring radiation in the laboratory is the *scintillation counter,* a device in which a substance called a *phosphor* emits a flash of light when struck by radiation. The number of flashes are counted electronically and converted into an electrical signal.

▲ This photographic film badge is a common device for monitoring radiation exposure.

Perhaps the best-known method for detecting and measuring radiation is the *Geiger counter,* an argon-filled tube containing two electrodes (Figure 11.6). The inner walls of the tube are coated with an electrically conducting material and given a negative charge, and a wire in the center of the tube is given a positive charge. As radiation enters the tube through a thin window, it strikes and ionizes argon atoms, which briefly conduct a tiny electric current between the walls and the center electrode. The passage of the current is detected, amplified, and used to produce a clicking sound or to register on a meter. The more radiation that enters the tube, the more frequent the clicks. Geiger counters are useful for seeking out a radiation source in a large area and for gauging the intensity of emitted radiation.

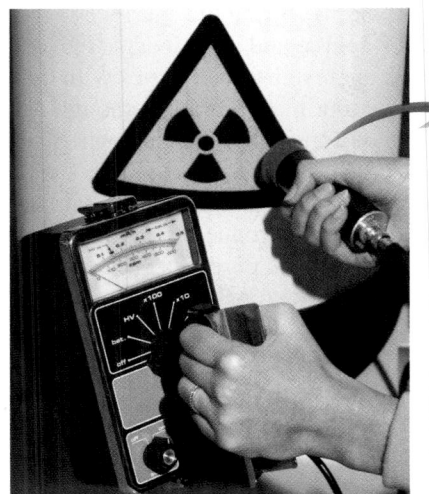

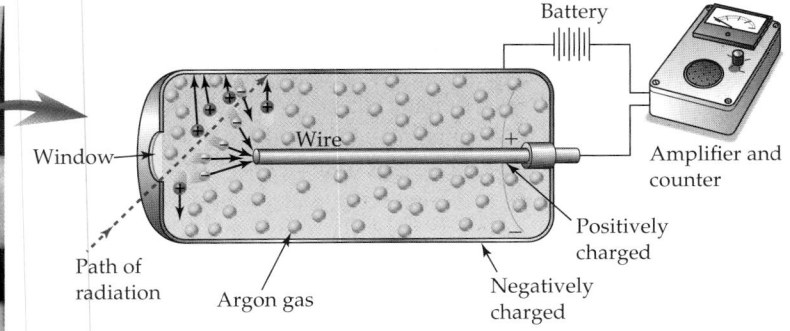

▲ **Figure 11.6**
A Geiger counter for measuring radiation.
As radiation enters the tube through a thin window, it ionizes argon atoms and produces electrons that conduct a tiny electric current between the walls and the center electrode. The current flow then registers on the meter.

Measuring Radiation

Radiation intensity is expressed in different ways, depending on what characteristic of the radiation is measured (Table 11.5). Some units measure the number of nuclear decay events, while others measure exposure to radiation or the biological consequences of radiation.

Table 11.5 Common Units for Measuring Radiation

Unit	Quantity Measured	Description
Curie (Ci)	Decay events	Amount of radiation equal to 3.7×10^{10} disintegrations per second
Roentgen (R)	Ionizing intensity	Amount of radiation producing 2.1×10^9 charges per cubic centimeter of dry air
Rad	Energy absorbed per gram of tissue	1 rad = 1 R
Rem	Tissue damage	Amount of radiation producing the same damage as 1 R of X rays
Sievert (Sv)	Tissue damage	1 Sv = 100 rem

- **Curie** The *curie* (Ci), the *millicurie* (mCi), and the *microcurie* (μCi) measure the number of radioactive disintegrations occurring each second in a sample. One curie is the decay rate of 1 g of radium, equal to 3.7×10^{10} disintegrations per second; 1 mCi = 0.001 Ci = 3.7×10^7 disintegrations per second; and 1 μCi = 0.000 001 Ci = 3.7×10^4 disintegrations per second.

  The dosage of a radioactive substance administered orally or intravenously is usually given in millicuries. To calculate the size of a dose, it is necessary to determine the decay rate of the isotope solution per milliliter. Because the emitter concentration is constantly decreasing as it decays, the activity must be measured immediately before administration. Suppose, for example, that a solution containing iodine-131 for a thyroid-function study is found to have a decay rate of 0.020 mCi/mL and the dose administered is to be 0.050 mCi. The amount of the solution administered must be

$$\frac{0.05 \text{ mCi}}{\text{Dose}} \times \frac{1 \text{ mL } ^{131}\text{I solution}}{0.020 \text{ mCi}} = 2.5 \text{ mL } ^{131}\text{I solution/dose}$$

- **Roentgen** The *roentgen* (R) is a unit for measuring the ionizing intensity of γ or X radiation. In other words, the roentgen measures the capacity of the radiation for affecting matter. One roentgen is the amount of radiation that produces 2.1×10^9 units of charge in 1 cm^3 of dry air at atmospheric pressure. Each collision of ionizing radiation with an atom produces one ion, or one unit of charge.
- **Rad** The *rad* (radiation absorbed dose) is a unit for measuring the energy absorbed per gram of material exposed to a radiation source and is defined as the absorption of 1×10^{-5} J of energy per gram. The energy absorbed varies with the type of material irradiated and the type of radiation. For most purposes, though, the roentgen and the rad are so close that they can be considered identical when used for X rays and γ rays: 1 R = 1 rad.
- **Rem** The *rem* (roentgen equivalent for man) measures the amount of tissue damage caused by radiation. One rem is the amount of radiation that produces the same effect as 1 R of X rays. Rems are the preferred units for medical purposes because they measure equivalent doses of different kinds of radiation. The rem is calculated as

$$\text{Rems} = \text{rads} \times \text{RBE}$$

where RBE is a *relative biological effectiveness* factor, which takes into account the differences in energy and of the different types of radiation. Although the actual biological effects of radiation depend greatly on both the source and the energy of the radiation, the RBE of X rays, γ rays, and β particles are essentially equivalent (RBE = 1), while the accepted RBE for α particles is 20. For example, 1 rad of α radiation causes 20 times more tissue damage than 1 rad of γ rays, but 1 rem of α radiation and 1 rem of γ rays cause the same amount of damage. Thus, the rem takes both ionizing intensity and biological effect into account, whereas the rad deals only with intensity.

- **SI Units** In the SI system, the *becquerel* (Bq) is defined as one disintegration per second. The SI unit for energy absorbed is the *gray* (Gy; 1 Gy = 100 rad). For radiation dose, the SI unit is the *sievert* (Sv), which is equal to 100 rem.

The biological consequences of different radiation doses are given in Table 11.6. Although the effects seem frightening, the average radiation dose received annually by most people is only about 0.62 rem. Typical sources and percentage contribution to average background exposure are provided in Figure 11.7. About 50% of this *background radiation* comes from natural sources (rocks and cosmic rays); the remaining 50% comes from consumer products and from medical procedures such as X rays. The amount due to emissions from nuclear power plants and to fallout from testing of nuclear weapons in the 1950s is barely detectable.

Table 11.6 Biological Effects of Short-Term Radiation on Humans

Dose (rem)	Biological Effects
0–25	No detectable effects
25–100	Temporary decrease in white blood cell count
100–200	Nausea, vomiting, longer-term decrease in white blood cells
200–300	Vomiting, diarrhea, loss of appetite, listlessness
300–600	Vomiting, diarrhea, hemorrhaging, eventual death in some cases
Above 600	Eventual death in nearly all cases

CHEMISTRY IN ACTION

Irradiated Food

The idea of irradiating food to kill harmful bacteria is not new; it goes back almost as far as the earliest studies on radiation. Not until the 1940s did serious work get under way, however, when U.S. Army scientists found that irradiation increased the shelf-life of ground beef. Nevertheless, widespread civilian use of the technique has been a long time in coming, spurred on in recent years by outbreaks of food poisoning that resulted in several deaths.

The principle of food irradiation is simple: exposure of contaminated food to ionizing radiation—usually γ rays produced by cobalt-60 or cesium-137—destroys the genetic material of any bacteria or other organisms present, thereby killing them. Irradiation will not, however, kill viruses or prions, the cause of "mad-cow" disease. The amount of radiation depends on the desired effect. For example, to delay ripening of fruit may require a dose of 0.25–0.75 kGy, while sterilization of packaged meat requires a much higher dose of 25–70 kGy. The food itself undergoes little if any change when irradiated and does not itself become radioactive. The only real argument against food irradiation, in fact, is that it is *too* effective. Knowing that irradiation will kill nearly all harmful organisms, a food processor might be tempted to cut back on normal sanitary practices!

Food irradiation has been implemented to a much greater extent in Europe than in the United States. The largest marketers of irradiated food are Belgium, France, and the Netherlands, which irradiate between 10,000 and 20,000 tons of food per year. Currently, over 40 countries permit food irradiation and over 500,000 metric tons of food are treated annually worldwide. One of the major concerns in the United States is the possible generation of *radiolytic products,* compounds formed in food by exposure to ionizing radiation which some consumers fear may introduce radioactivity or degrade the nutritional value of the food. The U.S. Food and Drug Administration, after

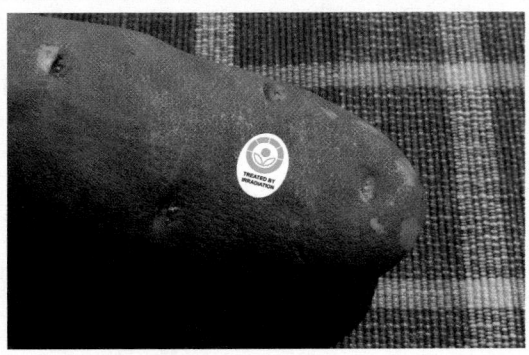

▲ Irradiating food kills bacteria and extends shelf life. Most irradiated food products are labeled with the Radura symbol (in green) to inform the public that the food product was exposed to radiation.

studying the matter extensively, has declared that food irradiation is safe and irradiated food products are nutritionally sound. Spices, fruits, pork, and vegetables were approved for irradiation in 1986, followed by poultry in 1990 and red meat, particularly ground beef, in 1997. In 2000, approval was extended to whole eggs and sprouting seeds. Should the food industry adopt irradiation of meat as its standard practice, occurrences of *Escherichia coli* and *salmonella* contaminations, resulting in either massive product recalls or serious health concerns for consumers will become a thing of the past.

CIA Problem 11.3 What is the purpose of food irradiation, and how does it work?

CIA Problem 11.4 What kind of radiation is used to treat food?

CIA Problem 11.5 A typical food irradiation application for the inhibition of sprout formation in potatoes applies a dose of 0.20 kGy. What is this dose in units of rem if the radiation is predominantly γ rays? If it is predominantly α particles? (Hint: 1 Gy = 100 rad)

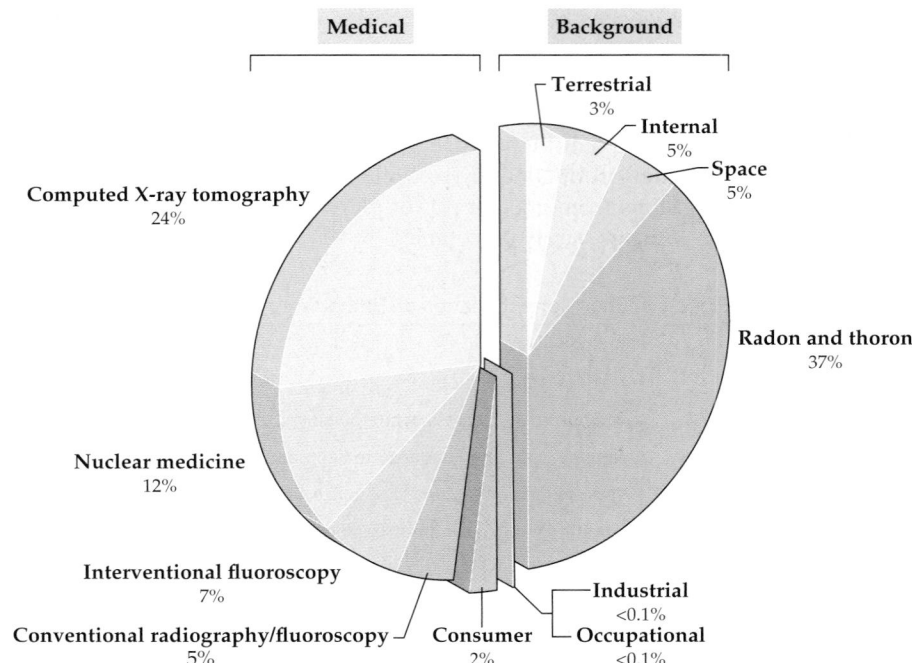

▶ Figure 11.7
Average Radiation Exposure Sources.
This pie chart illustrates the sources of radiation exposure, expressed as percent of total average exposure. The greatest sources of radiation exposure are natural, background sources (radon, terrestrial, food) and medical applications.

PROBLEM 11.13

A solution of selenium-75, a radioisotope used in the diagnosis of pancreatic disease, is found just prior to administration to have an activity of 44 μCi/mL. If 3.98 mL were delivered intravenously to the patient, what dose of Se-75 (in μCi) did the patient receive?

PROBLEM 11.14

A typical chest X ray exposes a patient to an effective dose of 0.02 mSv. How many rem is this, and how many chest X rays would a patient have to receive before biological effects would be observed? (The limit from Table 11.6 is >25 rem.)

11.8 Artificial Transmutation

Learning Objective:

• Write and balance equations for nuclear transmutation reactions.

Very few of the approximately 3300 known radioisotopes occur naturally. Most are made from stable isotopes by **artificial transmutation,** the change of one atom into another brought about by nuclear bombardment reactions.

When an atom is bombarded with a high-energy particle, such as a proton, a neutron, an α particle, or even the nucleus of another element, an unstable nucleus is created in the collision. A nuclear change then occurs, and a different element is produced. For example, transmutation of ^{14}N to ^{14}C occurs in the upper atmosphere when neutrons produced by cosmic rays collide with atmospheric nitrogen. In the collision, a neutron dislodges a proton (^{1}H) from the nitrogen nucleus as the neutron and nucleus fuse together:

$$^{14}_{7}\text{N} + ^{1}_{0}\text{n} \longrightarrow ^{14}_{6}\text{C} + ^{1}_{1}\text{H}$$

Artificial transmutation can lead to the synthesis of entirely new elements never before seen on Earth. In fact, all the *transuranium elements*—those elements with atomic numbers greater than 92—have been produced by bombardment reactions. For example, plutonium-241 (^{241}Pu) can be made by bombardment of uranium-238 with α particles:

$$^{238}_{92}\text{U} + ^{4}_{2}\text{He} \longrightarrow ^{241}_{94}\text{Pu} + ^{1}_{0}\text{n}$$

Plutonium-241 is itself radioactive, with a half-life of 14.35 years, decaying by β emission to yield americium-241, which in turn, decays by α emission with a half-life

Artificial transmutation The change of one atom into another brought about by a nuclear bombardment reaction.

▲ Smoke detectors contain a small amount of americium-241. The α particles emitted by this radioisotope ionize the air within the detector, causing it to conduct a tiny electric current. When smoke enters the chamber, conductivity drops and an alarm is triggered.

of 432.2 years. (If the name *americium* sounds vaguely familiar, it is because this radioisotope is used in smoke detectors.)

$$^{241}_{94}\text{Pu} \longrightarrow {}^{241}_{95}\text{Am} + {}^{0}_{-1}\text{e}$$

Note that all the equations just given for artificial transmutations are balanced. The sum of the mass numbers and the sum of the charges are the same on both sides of each equation.

CHEMISTRY IN ACTION

✝ Body Imaging

We are all familiar with the appearance of a standard X-ray image, produced when X rays pass through the body and the intensity of the radiation that exits is recorded on film. X-ray imaging is, however, only one of a host of noninvasive imaging techniques that are now in common use.

Among the most widely used imaging techniques are those that give diagnostic information about the health of various parts of the body by analyzing the distribution pattern of a radioactively tagged substance in the body. A radiopharmaceutical agent that is known to concentrate in a specific organ or other body part is injected into the body, and its distribution pattern is monitored by an external radiation detector such as a γ ray camera. Depending on the medical condition, a diseased part might concentrate more of the radiopharmaceutical than normal and thus show up on the film as a radioactive hot spot against a cold background. Alternatively, the diseased part might concentrate less of the radiopharmaceutical than normal and thus show up as a cold spot on a hot background.

Among the radioisotopes most widely used for diagnostic imaging is technetium-99*m,* whose short half-life of only six hours minimizes the patient's exposure to radioactivity. Enhanced body images, such as the brain scan shown in the accompanying photograph, are an important tool in the diagnosis of cancer and many other medical conditions.

Several other techniques now used in medical diagnosis are made possible by *tomography,* a technique in which computer processing allows production of images through "slices" of the body. In X-ray tomography, commonly known as *CAT* or *CT* scanning (computerized tomography), the X-ray source and an array of detectors move rapidly in a circle around a patient's body, collecting up to 90,000 readings. CT scans can detect structural abnormalities such as tumors without the use of radioactive materials.

Combining tomography with radioisotope imaging gives cross-sectional views of regions that concentrate a radioactive substance. We learned of one such technique, PET, in the opening of this chapter. PET utilizes radioisotopes that emit positrons and ultimately yield γ rays. Oxygen-15, nitrogen-13, carbon-11, and fluorine-18 are commonly used for PET because they can be readily incorporated into many physiologically active compounds. An ${}^{18}\text{F}$-labeled glucose derivative, for instance, is useful for imaging brain regions that respond to various stimuli. The disadvantage of PET scans is that the necessary radioisotopes are so short-lived that they must be

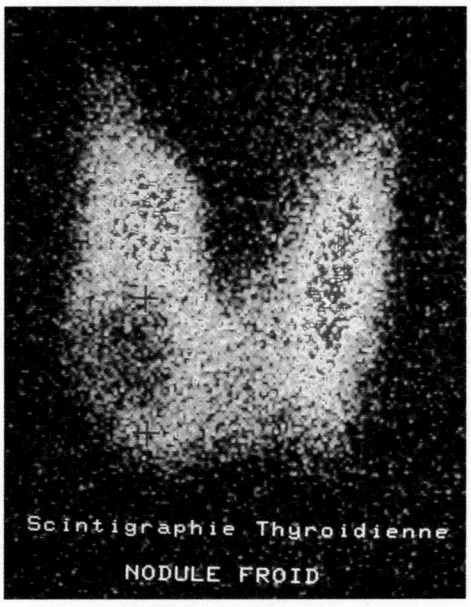

▲ A scintillation image obtained using I-131 indicates the presence of a "cold" thyroid nodule (lower left). A cold nodule, composed of tissue that does not absorb I-131, has a higher probability of being cancerous.

produced on-site immediately before use. The cost of PET is therefore high, because a hospital must install and maintain the necessary nuclear facility.

Magnetic resonance imaging (MRI) is a medical imaging technique that uses powerful magnetic and radio-frequency fields to interact with specific nuclei in the body (usually the nuclei of hydrogen atoms) to generate images in which the contrast between soft tissues is much better than that seen with CT. The original name for this technique was *nuclear* magnetic resonance imaging, but the *nuclear* was eliminated because in the public mind this word conjured up negative images of ionizing radiation. Ironically, MRI does not involve any nuclear radiation at all.

CIA Problem 11.6 What are the advantages of CT and PET relative to conventional X rays?

CIA Problem 11.7 What advantages does MRI have over CT and PET imaging?

CIA Problem 11.8 Technetium-99*m* (Tc-99*m*) is used extensively in diagnostic applications, including PET scans. The half-life of Tc-99*m* is six hours. How long will it take for the Tc-99*m* activity to decrease to 0.1% of its original activity?

Worked Example 11.8 Balancing Nuclear Reactions: Transmutation

Californium-246 is formed by bombardment of uranium-238 atoms. If 4 neutrons are also formed, what particle is used for the bombardment?

ANALYSIS First, write an incomplete nuclear equation incorporating the known information:

$$^{238}_{92}U + ? \longrightarrow {}^{246}_{98}Cf + 4^1_0n$$

Then find the numbers of nucleons and charges necessary to balance the equation. In this instance, there are 238 nucleons on the left and $246 + 4 = 250$ nucleons on the right, so the bombarding particle must have $250 - 238 = 12$ nucleons. Furthermore, there are 92 nuclear charges on the left and 98 on the right, so the bombarding particle must have $98 - 92 = 6$ protons.

SOLUTION
The missing particle is $^{12}_6C$.

$$^{238}_{92}U + {}^{12}_6C \longrightarrow {}^{246}_{98}Cf + 4\,^1_0n$$

PROBLEM 11.15

What isotope results from α decay of the americium-241 in smoke detectors?

PROBLEM 11.16

The element berkelium, first prepared at the University of California at Berkeley in 1949, is made by α bombardment of $^{241}_{95}Am$. Two neutrons are also produced during the reaction. What isotope of berkelium results from this transmutation? Write a balanced nuclear equation.

PROBLEM 11.17

Write a balanced nuclear equation for the reaction of argon-40 with a proton:

$$^{40}_{18}Ar + {}^1_1H \longrightarrow ? + {}^1_0n$$

11.9 Nuclear Fission and Nuclear Fusion

Learning Objective:

• Write and balance equations for nuclear fission and nuclear fusion reactions.

In the preceding section, we learned that particle bombardment of various elements causes artificial transmutation and results in the formation of new, usually heavier elements. Under very special conditions with a very few isotopes, however, different kinds of nuclear events occur. Certain very heavy nuclei can split apart, and certain very light nuclei can fuse together. The two resultant processes—**nuclear fission** for the fragmenting of heavy nuclei and **nuclear fusion** for the joining together of light nuclei—have changed the world since their discovery in the late 1930s and early 1940s.

The huge amounts of energy that accompany these nuclear processes are the result of mass-to-energy conversions and are predicted by Einstein's equation

$$E = mc^2$$

where E = energy, m = mass change associated with the nuclear reaction, and c = the speed of light $(3.0 \times 10^8 \text{ m/s})$. Based on this relationship, a mass change as small as 1 µg results in a release of 2.15×10^4 kcal $(9.00 \times 104 \text{ kJ})$ of energy!

Nuclear fission When heavy nuclei fragment into lighter nuclei.

Nuclear fusion When lighter nuclei combine to form a heavier nuclide.

Nuclear Fission

Uranium-235 is the only naturally occurring isotope that undergoes nuclear fission. When this isotope is bombarded by a stream of relatively slow-moving neutrons, its nucleus splits to give isotopes of other elements. The split can take place in more than 400 ways, and more than 800 different fission products have been identified. One of the more frequently occurring pathways generates barium-142 and krypton-91, along with two additional neutrons plus the one neutron that initiated the fission:

$$\,_{0}^{1}\text{n} + \,_{92}^{235}\text{U} \longrightarrow \,_{56}^{142}\text{Ba} + \,_{36}^{91}\text{Kr} + 3\,_{0}^{1}\text{n}$$

As indicated by the balanced nuclear equation above, *one* neutron is used to initiate fission of a ^{235}U nucleus, but *three* neutrons are released. Thus, a nuclear **chain reaction** can be started: one neutron initiates one fission that releases three neutrons. Those three neutrons initiate three new fissions that release nine neutrons. The nine neutrons initiate nine fissions that release 27 neutrons, and so on at an ever-faster pace (Figure 11.8). It is worth noting that the neutrons produced by fission reactions are highly energetic. They possess penetrating power greater than α and β particles, but less than γ rays. In a nuclear fission reactor, the neutrons must first be slowed down to allow them to react. If the sample size is small, many of the neutrons escape before initiating additional fission events, and the chain reaction stops. If a sufficient amount of ^{235}U is present, however—an amount called the **critical mass**—then the chain reaction becomes self-sustaining. Under high-pressure conditions that confine the ^{235}U to a small volume, the chain reaction occurs so rapidly that a nuclear explosion results. For ^{235}U, the critical mass is about 56 kg, although the amount can be reduced to approximately 15 kg by placing a coating of ^{238}U around the ^{235}U to reflect back some of the escaping neutrons.

An enormous quantity of heat is released during nuclear fission—the fission of just 1.0 g of uranium-235 produces 3.4×10^8 kcal (1.4×10^9 kJ) for instance. This heat can be used to convert water to steam, which can be harnessed to turn huge generators and produce electric power. Although the United States, France, and Japan are responsible for nearly 50% of all nuclear power generated worldwide, only about 19% of the

Chain reaction A reaction that, once started, is self-sustaining.

Critical mass The minimum amount of radioactive material needed to sustain a nuclear chain reaction.

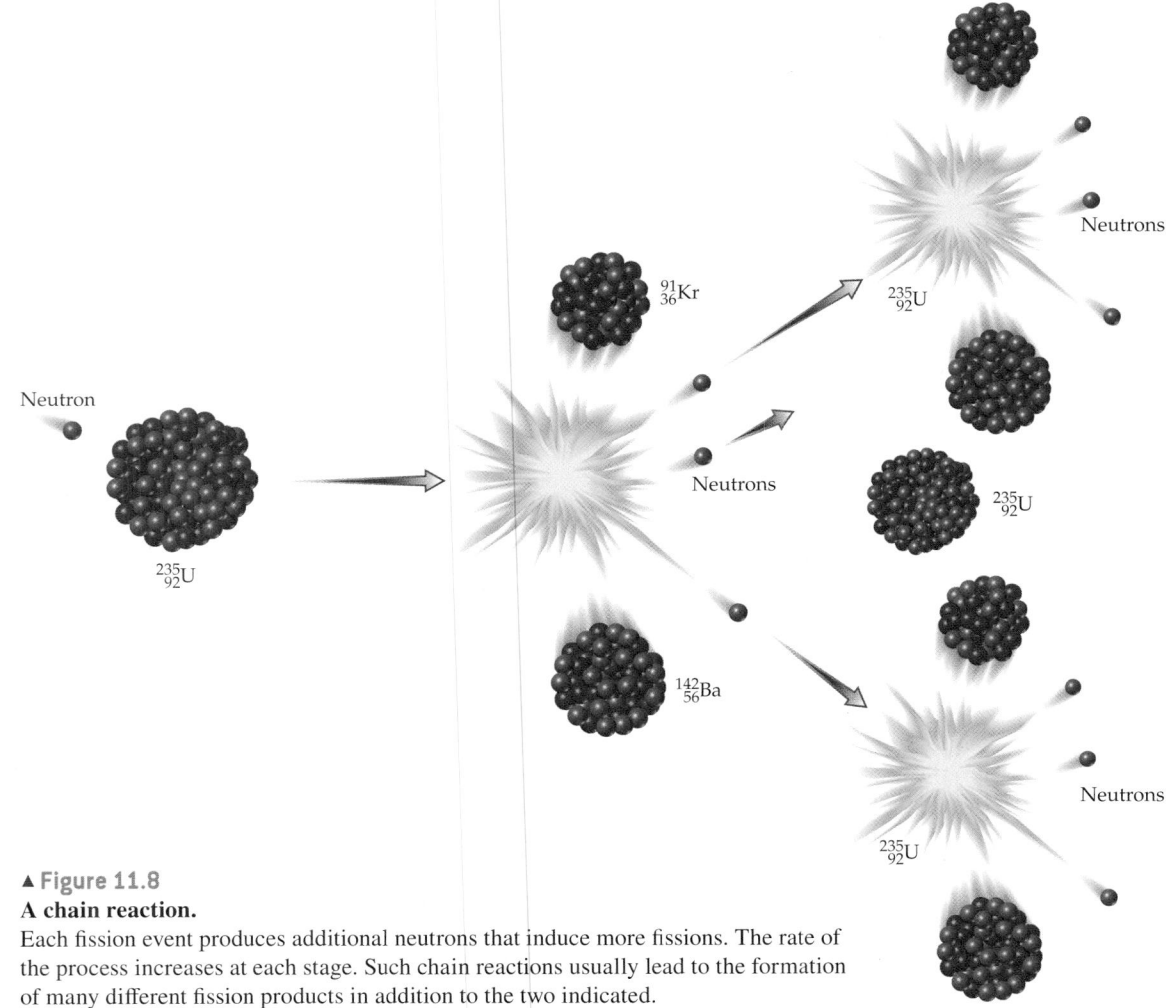

▲ **Figure 11.8**
A chain reaction.
Each fission event produces additional neutrons that induce more fissions. The rate of the process increases at each stage. Such chain reactions usually lead to the formation of many different fission products in addition to the two indicated.

electricity consumed in the United States is nuclear-generated. In France, nearly 80% of electricity is generated by nuclear power plants.

Two major objections that have caused much public debate about nuclear power plants are safety and waste disposal. Although a nuclear explosion is not possible under the conditions that typically exist in a power plant, there is a serious potential radiation hazard should an accident rupture the containment vessel holding the nuclear fuel and release radioactive substances to the environment. There have been several such instances in the past 35 years, most notably Three Mile Island in Pennsylvania (1979), Chernobyl in the Ukraine (1986), and the more recent Fukushima reactor damaged by a tsunami in Japan (2011). Perhaps even more important is the problem posed by disposal of radioactive wastes from nuclear plants. Many of these wastes have such long half-lives that hundreds or even thousands of years must elapse before they will be safe for humans to approach. How to dispose of such hazardous materials safely is an unsolved problem.

PROBLEM 11.18

What other isotope besides tellurium-137 is produced by nuclear fission of uranium-235?

$$^{235}_{92}\text{U} + ^{1}_{0}\text{n} \longrightarrow ^{137}_{52}\text{Te} + 2\,^{1}_{0}\text{n} + ?$$

PROBLEM 11.19

Uranium-238 is not used as a nuclear power source because it does not undergo nuclear fission. However, it can absorb a neutron and then undergo a series of β decays to produce plutonium-239, which is fissionable and can also be used as a nuclear fuel. Complete the following nuclear reaction:

$$^{238}_{92}\text{U} + ^{1}_{0}n \longrightarrow \text{??} \xrightarrow{\beta} \text{??} \xrightarrow{\beta} ^{239}_{94}\text{Pu}$$

Nuclear Fusion

Just as heavy nuclei such as ^{235}U release energy when they undergo *fission*, very light nuclei such as the isotopes of hydrogen release enormous amounts of energy when they undergo *fusion*. In fact, it is just such a fusion reaction of hydrogen nuclei to produce helium that powers our sun and other stars. Among the processes thought to occur in the sun are those in the following sequence leading to helium-4:

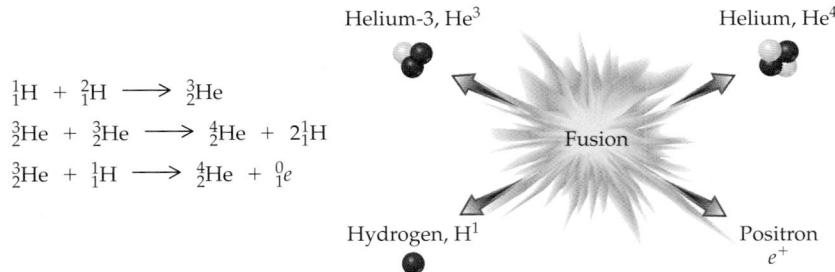

$$^{1}_{1}\text{H} + ^{2}_{1}\text{H} \longrightarrow ^{3}_{2}\text{He}$$

$$^{3}_{2}\text{He} + ^{3}_{2}\text{He} \longrightarrow ^{4}_{2}\text{He} + 2\,^{1}_{1}\text{H}$$

$$^{3}_{2}\text{He} + ^{1}_{1}\text{H} \longrightarrow ^{4}_{2}\text{He} + ^{0}_{1}e$$

Helium-3, He³   Helium, He⁴

Fusion

Hydrogen, H¹   Positron e^+

Under the conditions found in stars, where the temperature is on the order of 2×10^7 K and pressures approach 10^5 atmospheres, nuclei are stripped of all their electrons and have enough kinetic energy that nuclear fusion readily occurs. The energy of our sun, and all the stars, comes from thermonuclear fusion reactions in their core that fuse hydrogen and other light elements, transmuting them into heavier elements. On Earth, however, the necessary conditions for nuclear fusion are not easily created. For more than 50 years, scientists have been trying to create the necessary conditions for fusion in laboratory reactors, including the Tokamak Fusion Test Reactor (TFTR) at Princeton, New Jersey, and the Joint European Torus (JET) at Culham, England. Recent advances in reactor design have raised hopes that a commercial fusion reactor will be realized within the next 20 years.

If the dream becomes reality, controlled nuclear fusion can provide the ultimate cheap, clean power source. The fuel is deuterium (^2H), available in the oceans in limitless amounts, and there are few radioactive by-products.

⊙⊐ KEY CONCEPT PROBLEM 11.20 ⎯⎯⎯⎯⎯⎯⎯⎯⎯⎯⎯⎯⎯⎯⎯⎯⎯⎯⎯⎯

One of the possible reactions for nuclear fusion involves the collision of 2 deuterium nuclei. Complete the reaction by identifying the missing particle:

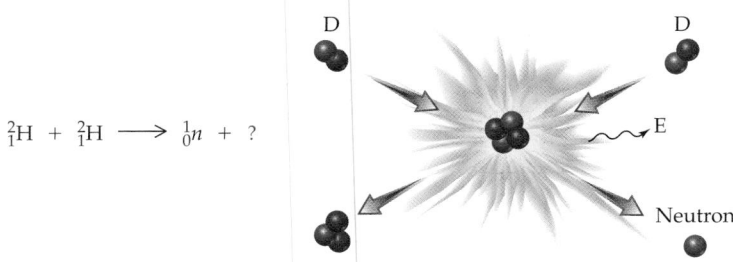

$$_1^2H + {}_1^2H \longrightarrow {}_0^1n + ?$$

HANDS-ON CHEMISTRY 11.1

Nuclear power plants provide about 20% of the electricity used in the United States. Nuclear reactors also serve as energy sources for U.S. Navy ships, including aircraft carriers and submarines. Perform a web search and respond to the following items:

a. Compare and contrast the two nuclear power sources (land-based vs. naval).

b. Locate a web site that provides a virtual tour of a nuclear power plant (such as at www.edfenergy.com /energyfuture/key-info/nuclear-power-plants /interactive-tour powered?) and identify the key components.

SUMMARY REVISITING THE CHAPTER LEARNING OBJECTIVES

• **Identify reactants and products of nuclear reactions as elements, isotopes, or subatomic particles.** A *nuclear reaction* is one that changes an atomic nucleus, causing the change of one element or isotope into another. Isotopes are atoms of a given element that have different atomic masses. Subatomic particles (protons, neutrons, electrons) can also be included as products or reactants in nuclear reactions *(see Problems 22, 24–27, 36, 37, 40, 41, and 44–53)*.

• **Identify the different types of radiation and the properties of each type.** *Radioactivity* is the spontaneous emission of radiation from the nucleus of an unstable atom. The three major kinds of radiation are called *alpha* (α), *beta* (β), and *gamma* (γ). Alpha radiation consists of helium nuclei, small particles containing 2 protons and 2 neutrons ($_2^4He$); β radiation consists of electrons ($_{-1}^0e$); and γ radiation consists of high-energy light waves. Every element in the periodic table has at least one radioactive isotope, or *radioisotope* *(see Problems 22, 25, 27, 29, 30–32, 40, 41, 44–47, 49, 75, 76, and 86)*.

• **Identify natural isotopes, and distinguish between stable and unstable isotopes.** *Natural* isotopes are found in the earth's crust, for elements with atomic numbers $Z \leq 92$. Stable isotopes are naturally occurring isotopes that do not undergo spontaneous radioactive decay *(see Problems 24, 26, 27, and 39)*.

• **Write and balance nuclear reactions involving alpha, beta, and positron emission modes of radioactive decay.** Loss of an α particle leads to a new atom whose atomic number is 2 less than that of the starting atom. Loss of a β particle leads to an atom whose atomic number is 1 greater than that of the starting atom:

$$\alpha \text{ emission: } _{92}^{238}U \longrightarrow {}_{90}^{234}Th + {}_2^4He$$
$$\beta \text{ emission: } _{53}^{131} \longrightarrow {}_{54}^{131}Xe + {}_{-1}^0e$$

A nuclear reaction is balanced when the sum of the *nucleons* (protons and neutrons) is the same on both sides of the reaction arrow and when the sum of the charges on the nuclei plus any ejected subatomic particles is the same *(see Problems 22, 24–27, 44–53, 59, 75–78, 81, and 83)*.

• **Determine the half-life of a radioactive isotope, and use the half-life to calculate the fraction of the isotope remaining as a**

function of time. The rate of a nuclear reaction is expressed in units of *half-life* ($t_{1/2}$), where one half-life is the amount of time necessary for one half of the radioactive sample to decay. The fraction of an isotope remaining after a given amount of time can be expressed as (fraction remaining $= (0.5)^n$), where n = number of half-lives *(see Problems 21, 23, 28, 29, 54–59, 71, 77, and 79)*.

• **Identify the types of ionizing radiation, and calculate the radiation intensity as a function of distance from the radiation source.** High-energy radiation of all types—α particles, β particles, γ rays, and X rays—is called *ionizing radiation*. When any of these kinds of radiation strikes an atom, it dislodges an orbital electron and gives a reactive ion that can be lethal to living cells. Gamma rays and X rays are the most penetrating and most harmful types of external radiation; α and β particles are the most dangerous types of internal radiation because of their high energy and the resulting damage to surrounding tissue. Radiation intensity (I) decreases with the square of the distance from the source *(see Problems 33–37, 63, 65, 70, 78, 80, and 81)*.

• **Identify methods for detecting radiation and the units used to measure radiation exposure.** Radiation intensity is expressed in different ways according to the property being measured. The *curie* (*CI*) measures the number of radioactive disintegrations per second in a sample; the *roentgen* (*R*) measures the ionizing ability of radiation. The *rad* measures the amount of radiation energy absorbed per gram of tissue; and the *rem* measures the amount of tissue damage caused by radiation. Radiation effects become noticeable with a human exposure of 25 rem and become lethal at an exposure above 600 rem *(see Problems 60–69, 73, and 74)*.

• **Write and balance equations for nuclear transmutation reactions.** *Transmutation* is the change of one element into another brought about by a nuclear reaction. Most known radioisotopes do not occur naturally but are made by bombardment of an atom with a high-energy particle. In the ensuing collision between particle and atom, a nuclear change occurs and a new element is produced by *artificial transmutation* *(see Problems 38, 39, 48, 50, 51, 53, 84, 87, and 88)*.

• **Write and balance equations for nuclear fission and nuclear fusion reactions.** With a very few isotopes, including $^{235}_{92}U$, the nucleus is split apart by neutron bombardment to give smaller fragments. A large amount of energy is released during this *nuclear fission*, leading to use of the reaction for generating electric power. *Nuclear fusion* results when small nuclei such as those of tritium (^3_1H) and deuterium (^2_1H) combine to give a heavier nucleus *(see Problems 42, 43, 48, 78, 84, and 85)*.

CONCEPT MAP: SOLUTIONS

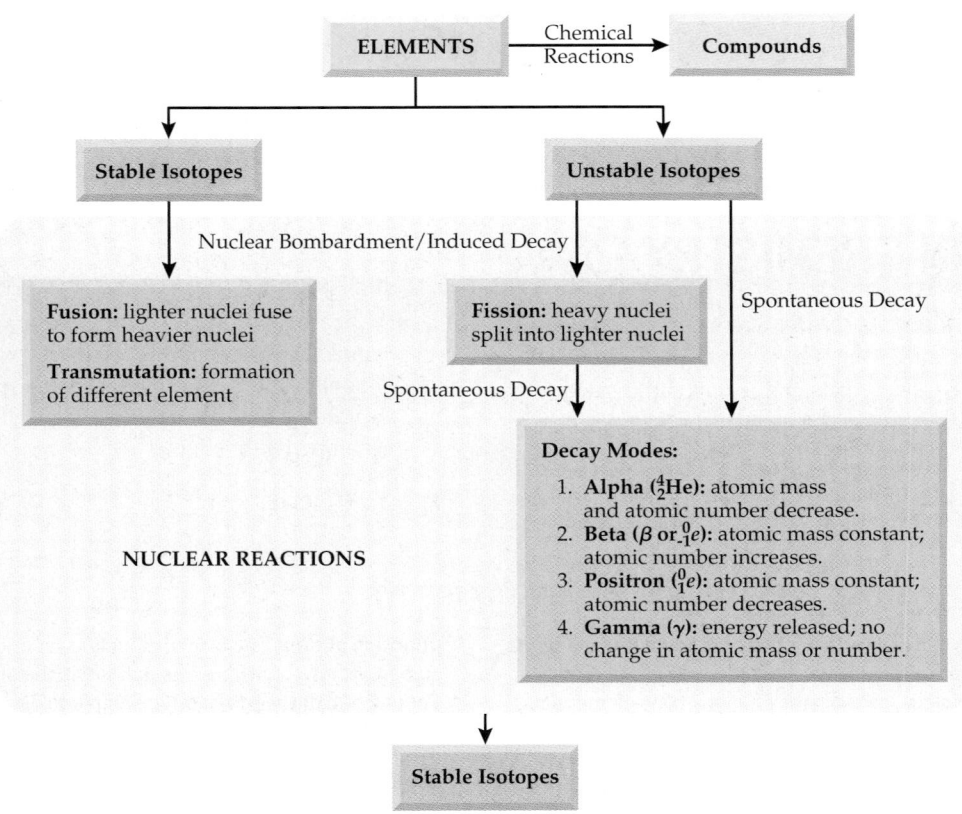

▲ **Figure 11.9 Concept Map.** Nuclear reactions involve changes in the composition of the nucleus of an atom, usually resulting in a change in the identity of the element. Some isotopes are stable, while other isotopes undergo spontaneous radioactive decay. Nuclei of a given element can also undergo transmutation, a nuclear reaction in which a nucleus is bombarded with light nuclei or subatomic particles to create a different nucleus.

KEY WORDS

Alpha (α) particle, *p. 330*	**Cosmic rays,** *p. 341*	**Ionizing radiation,** *p. 341*	**Nuclide,** *p. 329*
Artificial radioisotopes, *p. 331*	**Critical mass,** *p. 349*	**Natural radioisotopes,** *p. 331*	**Positron,** *p. 334*
Artificial transmutation, *p. 346*	**Decay series,** *p. 337*	**Nuclear decay,** *p. 332*	**Radioactivity,** *p. 330*
	Electron capture (E.C.), *p. 335*	**Nuclear fission,** *p. 348*	**Radioisotope,** *p. 331*
Beta (β) particle, *p. 330*	**Gamma (γ) radiation,** *p. 330*	**Nuclear fusion,** *p. 348*	**Radionuclide,** *p. 331*
Chain reaction, *p. 349*	**Half-life ($t_{1/2}$)** *p. 336*	**Nuclear reaction,** *p. 329*	**Transmutation,** *p. 332*
		Nucleon, *p. 329*	**X rays,** *p. 341*

⬛ UNDERSTANDING KEY CONCEPTS

11.21 Magnesium-28 decays by β emission to give aluminum-28. If yellow spheres represent $^{28}_{12}Mg$ atoms and blue spheres represent $^{28}_{13}Al$ atoms, how many half-lives have passed in the following sample?

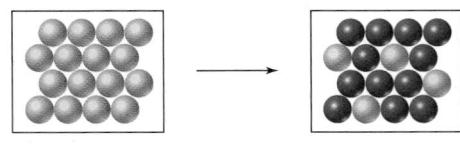

11.22 Write a balanced nuclear equation to represent the decay reaction described in Problem 11.21.

11.23 Refer to Figure 11.4 and then make a drawing similar to those in Problem 11.21 representing the decay of a sample of $^{28}_{12}Mg$ after approximately four half-lives have passed.

11.24 Write the symbol of the isotope represented by the following drawing. Blue spheres represent neutrons and red spheres represent protons. Based on Figure 11.2, would you expect this to be a stable or an unstable isotope?

11.25 Shown in the following graph is a portion of the decay series for plutonium-241 ($^{241}_{94}$Pu). The series has two kinds of arrows: shorter arrows pointing right and longer arrows pointing left. Which arrow corresponds to an α emission, and which to a β emission? Explain.

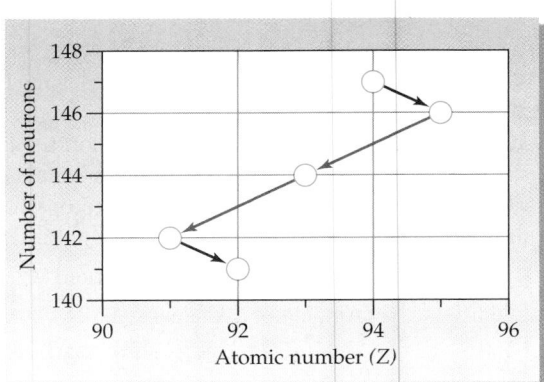

11.26 Identify and write the symbol for each of the five nuclides in the decay series shown in Problem 11.25.

11.27 Identify the isotopes involved, and tell the type of decay process occurring in the following nuclear reaction:

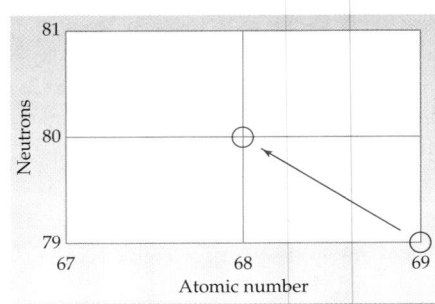

ADDITIONAL PROBLEMS

RADIOACTIVITY (SECTIONS 11.1–11.4 AND 11.6)

11.30 What does it mean to say that a substance is radioactive?

11.31 Describe how α radiation, β radiation, γ radiation, positron emission, and electron capture differ.

11.32 List three of the five ways in which a nuclear reaction differs from a chemical reaction.

11.33 What happens when ionizing radiation strikes an atom in a chemical compound?

11.34 How does ionizing radiation lead to cell damage?

11.35 What are the main sources of background radiation?

11.36 How can a nucleus emit an electron during β decay when there are no electrons present in the nucleus to begin with?

11.37 What is the difference between an α particle and a helium atom?

NUCLEAR DECAY AND TRANSMUTATION
(SECTIONS 11.4, 11.8, AND 11.9)

11.38 What does it mean to say that a nuclear equation is balanced?

11.39 What are transuranium elements, and how are they made? Are they stable or unstable?

11.28 What is the half-life of the radionuclide that shows the following decay curve?

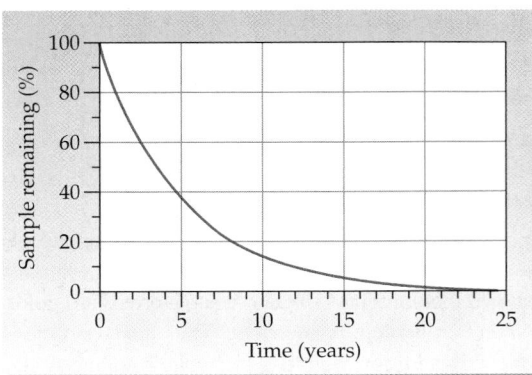

11.29 What is wrong with the following decay curve? Explain.

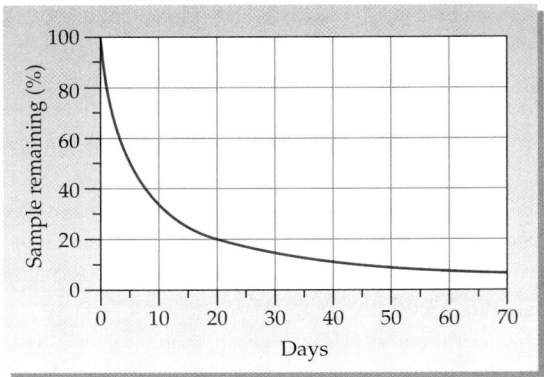

11.40 What happens to the mass number and atomic number of an atom that emits an α particle? A β particle?

11.41 What happens to the mass number and atomic number of an atom that emits a γ ray? A positron?

11.42 How does nuclear fission differ from normal radioactive decay?

11.43 What characteristic of uranium-235 fission causes a chain reaction?

11.44 What products result from radioactive decay of the following β emitters?

(a) $^{35}_{16}$S   (b) $^{24}_{10}$Ne   (c) $^{90}_{38}$Sr

11.45 What radioactive nuclides will produce the following products following α decay?

(a) $^{186}_{76}$Os   (b) $^{204}_{85}$At   (c) $^{241}_{94}$Pu

11.46 Identify the starting radioisotopes needed to balance each of these nuclear reactions:

(a) ? + $^4_2$He $\longrightarrow$ $^{113}_{49}$In   (b) ? + $^4_2$He $\longrightarrow$ $^{13}_7$N + $^1_0$n

11.47 Identify the radioisotope product needed to balance each of these nuclear reactions:

(a) $^{26}_{11}$Na $\longrightarrow$? + $^0_{-1}$e   (b) $^{212}_{83}$Bi $\longrightarrow$? + $^4_2$He

11.48 Balance the following equations for the nuclear fission of $^{235}_{92}U$:

(a) $^{235}_{92}U + ^1_0n \longrightarrow ^{160}_{62}Sm + ^{72}_{30}Zn + ?\,^1_0n$

(b) $^{235}_{92}U + ^1_0n \longrightarrow ^{87}_{35}Br + ? + 3\,^1_0n$

11.49 Complete the following nuclear equations and identify each as α decay, β decay, positron emission, or electron capture:

(a) $^{126}_{50}Sn \longrightarrow ? + ^{126}_{51}Sb$ (b) $^{210}_{88}Ra \longrightarrow ? + ^{206}_{86}Rn$

(c) $^{76}_{36}Kr + ? \longrightarrow ^{76}_{35}Br$

11.50 For centuries, alchemists dreamed of turning base metals into gold. The dream finally became reality when it was shown that mercury-198 can be converted into gold-198 when bombarded by neutrons. What small particle is produced in addition to gold-198? Write a balanced nuclear equation for the reaction.

11.51 Cobalt-60 (half-life = 5.3 years) is used to irradiate food, to treat cancer, and to disinfect surgical equipment. It is produced by irradiation of cobalt-59 in a nuclear reactor. It decays to nickel-60. Write nuclear equations for the formation and decay reactions of cobalt-60.

11.52 Bismuth-212 attaches readily to monoclonal antibodies and is used in the treatment of various cancers. This bismuth-212 is formed after the parent isotope undergoes a decay series consisting of four α decays and one β decay (the decays could be in any order). What is the parent isotope for this decay series?

11.53 Meitnerium-266 ($^{266}_{109}Mt$) was prepared in 1982 by bombardment of bismuth-209 atoms with iron-58. What other product must also have been formed? Write a balanced nuclear equation for the transformation.

HALF-LIFE (SECTION 11.5)

11.54 What does it mean when we say that strontium-90, a waste product of nuclear power plants, has a half-life of 28.8 years?

11.55 How many half lives must pass for the mass of a radioactive sample to decrease to 35% of the original mass? To 10%?

11.56 Selenium-75, a β emitter with a half-life of 120 days, is used medically for pancreas scans.

(a) Approximately how long would it take for a 0.050 g sample of selenium-75 to decrease to 0.010 g?

(b) Approximately how much selenium-75 would remain from a 0.050 g sample that has been stored for one year? (Hint: How many half-lives are in one year?)

11.57 Approximately how long would it take a sample of selenium-75 to lose 75% of its radioactivity? To lose 99%? (See Problem 11.56.)

11.58 The half-life of mercury-197 is 64.1 hours. If a patient undergoing a kidney scan is given 5.0 ng of mercury-197, how much will remain after 7 days? After 30 days?

11.59 Gold-198, a β emitter used to treat leukemia, has a half-life of 2.695 days. The standard dosage is about 1.0 mCi/kg body weight.

(a) What is the product of the β emission of gold-198?

(b) How long does it take a 30.0 mCi sample of gold-198 to decay so that only 3.75 mCi remains?

(c) How many millicuries are required in a single dosage administered to a 70.0 kg adult?

MEASURING RADIOACTIVITY (SECTION 11.7)

11.60 Describe how a Geiger counter works.

11.61 Describe how a film badge works.

11.62 Describe how a scintillation counter works.

11.63 Why are rems the preferred units for measuring the health effects of radiation?

11.64 Approximately what amount (in rems) of short-term exposure to radiation produces noticeable effects in humans?

11.65 Match each unit in the left column with the property being measured in the right column:

1. curie   (a) Ionizing intensity of radiation

2. rem   (b) Amount of tissue damage

3. rad   (c) Number of disintegrations per second

4. roentgen   (d) Amount of radiation per gram of tissue

11.66 Technetium-99m is used for radioisotope-guided surgical biopsies of certain bone cancers. A patient must receive an injection of 28 mCi of technetium-99m 6–12 hours before surgery. If the activity of the solution is 15 mCi/mL, what volume should be injected?

11.67 Sodium-24 is used to study the circulatory system and to treat chronic leukemia. It is administered in the form of saline (NaCl) solution, with a therapeutic dosage of 180 μCi/kg body weight.

(a) What dosage (in mCi) would be administered to a 68 kg adult patient?

(b) How many milliliters of a 6.5 mCi/mL solution are needed to treat a 68 kg adult?

11.68 A selenium-75 source is producing 300 rem at a distance of 2.0 m?

(a) What is its intensity at 16 m?

(b) What is its intensity at 25 m?

11.69 If a radiation source has an intensity of 650 rem at 1.0 m, what distance is needed to decrease the intensity of exposure to below 25 rem, the level at which no effects are detectable?

CONCEPTUAL PROBLEMS

11.70 Film badge dosimeters typically include filters to target specific types of radiation. A film badge is constructed that includes a region containing a tin foil filter, a region containing a plastic film filter, and a region with no filter. Which region monitors exposure to α-radiation? Which monitors exposure to β-radiation? Which monitors γ-radiation? Explain.

11.71 Some dried beans with a $^{14}C/^{12}C$ ratio one-eighth of the current value are found in an old cave. How old are the beans?

11.72 Harmful chemical spills can often be cleaned up by treatment with another chemical. For example, a spill of H_2SO_4 might be neutralized by addition of $NaHCO_3$. Why is it that the harmful radioactive wastes from nuclear power plants cannot be cleaned up as easily?

11.73 Why is a scintillation counter or Geiger counter more useful for determining the existence and source of a new radiation leak than a film badge?

11.74 A Geiger counter records an activity of 28 counts per minute (cpm) when located at a distance of 10 m. What will be the activity (in cpm) at a distance of 5 m?

11.75 Most of the stable isotopes for elements lighter than Ca-40 have equal numbers of protons and neutrons in the nucleus. What would be the most probable decay mode for an isotope that had more protons than neutrons? More neutrons than protons?

11.76 Technetium-99m, used for brain scans and to monitor heart function, is formed by decay of molybdenum-99.

(a) By what type of decay does ^{99}Mo produce ^{99m}Tc?

(b) Molybdenum-99 is formed by neutron bombardment of a natural isotope. If one neutron is absorbed and there are no other by-products of this process, from what isotope is ^{99}Mo formed?

11.77 The half-life of technetium-99m (Problem 11.76) is 6.01 hours. If a sample with an initial activity of 15 μCi is injected into a patient, what is the activity in 24 hours, assuming that none of the sample is excreted?

11.78 Plutonium-238 is an α emitter used to power batteries for heart pacemakers.

(a) Write the balanced nuclear equation for this emission.

(b) Why is a pacemaker battery enclosed in a metal case before being inserted into the chest cavity?

11.79 Sodium-24, a beta-emitter used in diagnosing circulation problems, has a half-life of 15 hours.

(a) Write the balanced nuclear equation for this emission.

(b) What fraction of sodium-24 remains after 50 hours?

11.80 High levels of radioactive fallout after the 1986 accident at the Chernobyl nuclear power plant in what is now Ukraine resulted in numerous miscarriages in humans and many instances of farm animals born with severe defects. Why are embryos and fetuses particularly susceptible to the effects of radiation?

11.81 Iodine-131 is a radioactive isotope used to treat thyroid conditions.

(a) What is the mode of radioactive decay for I-131? Write a balanced nuclear reaction to illustrate.

(b) The half-life of I-131 is eight days. What fraction of I-131 remains after four weeks? After eight weeks?

11.82 What are the main advantages of nuclear fission relative to nuclear fusion as an energy source? What are the drawbacks?

11.83 Although turning lead into gold in a nuclear reactor is technologically feasible (Problem 11.50), it is not economical. It is far easier to convert gold into lead. The process involves a series of neutron bombardments, and can be summarized as

$$^{197}_{79}\text{Au} + ?\,^{1}_{0}n \longrightarrow ^{204}_{82}\text{Pb} + ?\,^{0}_{-1}e$$

How many neutrons and β particles are involved?

11.84 Balance the following transmutation reactions:

(a) $^{253}_{99}\text{Es} + ? \longrightarrow ^{256}_{101}\text{Md} + ^{1}_{0}n$

(b) $^{250}_{98}\text{Cf} + ^{11}_{5}\text{B} \longrightarrow ? + 4\,^{1}_{0}n$

11.85 Boron is used in *control rods* for nuclear reactors because it can absorb neutrons to keep a chain reaction from becoming supercritical, and decays by emitting α particles (i.e., a He-4 nucleus). Balance the equation by supplying the missing product:

$$^{10}_{5}\text{B} + ^{1}_{0}n \longrightarrow ? + ^{4}_{2}\text{He}$$

11.86 Thorium-232 decays by a 10-step series, ultimately yielding lead-208. How many α particles and how many β particles are emitted?

11.87 Californium-246 is formed by bombardment of uranium-238 atoms. If four neutrons are formed as by-products, what particle is used for the bombardment?

11.88 The most recently discovered element 117 (Ununseptium, Uus) was synthesized by nuclear transmutation reactions in which berkelium-249 was bombarded with calcium-48. Two isotopes of Uus were identified:

$$^{48}_{20}\text{Ca} + ^{249}_{97}\text{Bk} \longrightarrow ^{294}_{117}\text{Uus} + ?\,^{1}_{0}n$$
$$^{48}_{20}\text{Ca} + ^{249}_{97}\text{Bk} \longrightarrow ^{293}_{117}\text{Uus} + ?\,^{1}_{0}n$$

How many neutrons are produced in each reaction?

GROUP PROBLEMS

11.89 One way to demonstrate the dose factor of ionizing radiation (penetrating distance × ionizing energy) is to think of radiation as cookies. Imagine that you have four cookies—an α cookie, a β cookie, a γ cookie, and a neutron cookie. Which one would you eat, which would you hold in your hand, which would you put in your pocket, and which would you throw away? Explain your reasoning.

11.90 One approach for treating cancerous tumors is **B**oron **N**eutron **C**apture **T**herapy (BNCT). Perform an internet search on BNCT and answer the following:

(a) How is boron introduced to the tumors?

(b) How are neutrons generated and directed to the tumor site?

(c) What nuclear reactions occur? What are the products of the nuclear reaction, and why is this a particularly effective treatment for tumors?

11.91 The nuclear disasters at the Chernobyl nuclear power plant disaster in 1986 and in Fukushima in 2011 resulted in significant releases of radioactive nuclear materials into the environment. Perform a web search to find information about one or both of these disasters and answer the following questions:

(a) What was the primary nuclear fuel? What other radioactive materials besides the fuel were released during the accident?

(b) What is the estimated amount of radioactive material released into the environment, and in what form was it released?

(c) How much additional radiation exposure would be expected for a person living near the power plant? How much additional radiation exposure would be expected for someone living at a considerable distance from the plant? How do these levels compare to the average background radiation dose for the average person? Express your answer as a percentage.

12

Introduction to Organic Chemistry: Alkanes

CONTENTS

◀◀◀ CONCEPTS TO REVIEW

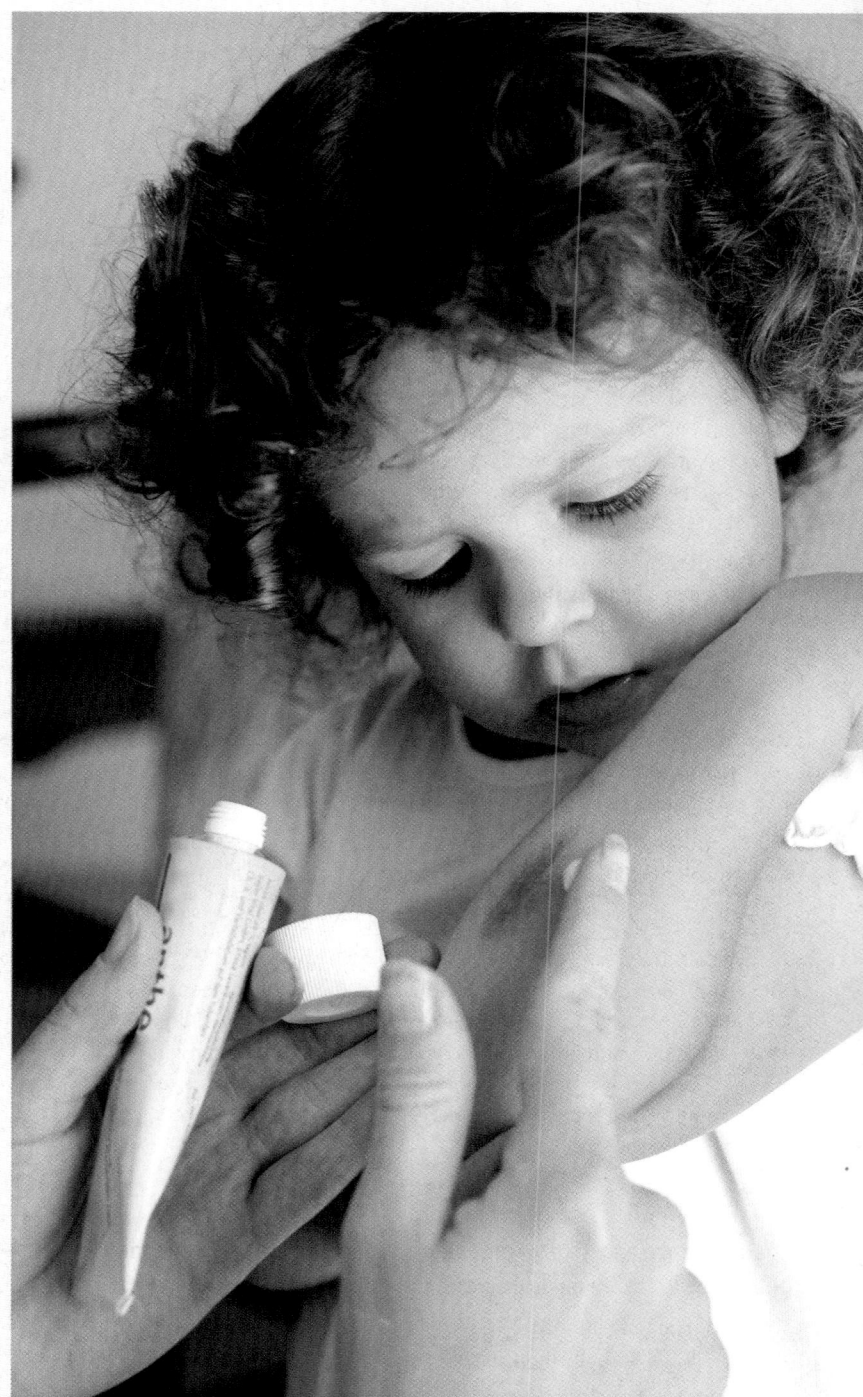

▲ As a mother attends to her daughter's scrape, organic chemistry aids in the healing process, in the form of the antibiotic cream she is using.

Think back to the days when you first learned to ride a bike; at some time you undoubtedly fell off and scraped an elbow or knee. Your mom or dad came to the rescue, picking you up, dusting you off, and putting some antibacterial ointment and a bandage on your scrape. Or think of the times you went camping or to the beach and your lips got so chapped that the lip balm you had so fortuitously brought with you felt like it saved your life. Both of these instances are examples of organic chemistry at work. Organic chemistry impacts your life on a daily basis and is the foundation upon which biochemistry, the chemistry of life, is built. In Chapters 12–17 of this book, we will discuss organic chemistry, then later, in Chapters 18–29, the biochemistry that is built upon it. We will look at how organic molecules form, the reactions they undergo, and how those molecules, with their unique shapes, structures, and chemistries, affect our bodies and those of other living organisms.

The term *organic chemistry* was first introduced to describe the study of compounds derived from living organisms, whereas *inorganic chemistry* was used to refer to the study of compounds obtained from minerals. Scientists long believed that organic compounds could only be obtained from a living source; this concept, known as *vitalism,* hindered the study of these types of molecules because vitalist chemists believed that organic materials could not be synthesized from inorganic components. In 1828, Friedrich Wöhler prepared an organic compound, urea, from an inorganic salt, ammonium cyanate, disproving the theory of vitalism and truly pioneering the field of organic chemistry. Since compounds from living sources contain carbon as their primary component, organic chemistry is now defined as the study of carbon-based compounds.

Carbon is special because it can readily form strong bonds with both other carbon atoms and atoms of other elements (primarily hydrogen, oxygen, nitrogen, and halogens) to produce long chains and rings of organic compounds. Only carbon is able to form such a diverse and immense array of compounds; chemists have discovered or prepared more than 18 million organic compounds (versus less than 2 million inorganic compounds), the simplest class of which are called the hydrocarbons, or *alkanes,* compounds composed of only carbon and hydrogen connected by single bonds.

So, how does any of this relate to a scraped knee or chapped lips? While hydrocarbons themselves are important from an industrial and energy standpoint (being responsible for waxes, lubricants, and fuels, so-called *petrochemicals*), their biological and medical significance is sometimes lost at first glance. One of the hydrocarbon products obtained from petroleum is *petrolatum* (petroleum jelly; commonly known as Vaseline). This product is the footing upon which many medically useful ointments are based. Neosporin, a common antibiotic cream, is composed of a mixture of three different antibiotics in a petrolatum-based matrix. Lip balms (such as ChapStick or Carmex) also heavily rely on the presence of petroleum jelly for their healing properties, which, because of their *hydrophobic* nature, seal moisture in allowing the chapped skin to heal quickly. In fact, petroleum jelly alone, with no additives, is believed to be just as effective as either antibiotic ointments or lip balms in promoting the healing of wounded or dry skin. We will learn more about petrochemicals and petroleum jelly in the Chemistry in Action on page 394. As you can see, hydrocarbons play such a fundamental role in our everyday world it is appropriate that we begin our study of organic chemistry with alkanes.

12.1 The Nature of Organic Molecules

Learning Objective:

- Identify the general structural characteristics of organic molecules, in particular, the tetravalent nature of carbon and the different ways in which it can be expressed.

Let us begin our study of **organic chemistry**—the chemistry of carbon compounds— by reviewing what we have learned in earlier chapters about covalent bonds and molecular compounds and seeing how this applies to organic molecules in general (as you go through this section, take note of the three-dimensional shapes these molecules possess):

- **Carbon is tetravalent; it always forms four bonds** (Section 4.2). With the four valence electrons it already possesses, carbon has the ability to pick up four more from other atoms to fill out its octet. In the organic compound methane, for example, carbon is connected to four hydrogen atoms, with each hydrogen donating its valence electron to carbon to fill out its octet. Because it has groups attached to the carbon, methane is both tetrahedral (Section 4.8) and tetravalent.

Organic chemistry The study of carbon compounds.

◀◀ **CONCEPTS TO REVIEW** Recall that a bond is formed when two electrons are shared between atoms.

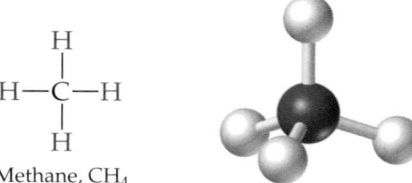

Methane, CH_4

- **Organic molecules, which are primarily composed of nonmetals, have covalent bonds** (Section 4.2). In ethane, for example, the bonds result from the sharing of two electrons, either between two C atoms or a C and an H atom.

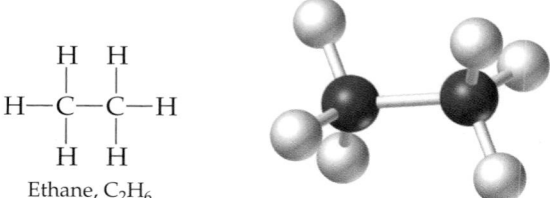

Ethane, C_2H_6

- **Carbon forms multiple covalent bonds by sharing more than two electrons with a neighboring atom** (Section 4.3). In ethylene, for example, the two carbon atoms share four electrons to form a double bond; in acetylene (also called ethyne), the two carbons share six electrons to form a triple bond. Notice, however, that each carbon still possesses an octet: in ethylene, four shared between the two carbons and two each shared with the hydrogens; in acetylene, six shared between the carbons and two with the hydrogen. The carbons in ethylene and acetylene are not tetrahedral, but they are tetravalent.

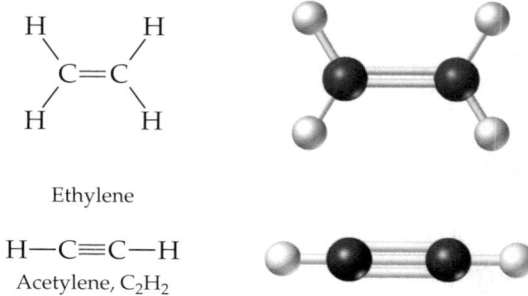

Ethylene

$$H-C{\equiv}C-H$$
Acetylene, C_2H_2

In general, we can make the following statements:

A group is any atom or collection of atoms attached to the carbon.

1. A carbon that has four groups attached will be tetrahedral (e.g., methane or ethane);
2. A carbon that has three groups attached will be trigonal planar (e.g., ethylene);
3. A carbon that has two groups attached will be linear (e.g., acetylene).

- **When carbon bonds to a more electronegative element, polar covalent bonds result** (Section 4.9). C—H bonds are considered nonpolar, as are most C—C bonds; however, if you replace a hydrogen with an oxygen or a halogen, for example, a polar covalent bond results. In chloromethane, for example, the electronegative chlorine atom attracts electrons more strongly than carbon, resulting in polarization of the C—Cl bond so that carbon and hydrogens have a partial positive charge, $\delta+$, and chlorine has a partial negative charge, $\delta-$. It is useful to think of polar covalent bonds in this manner, as it will later help to explain their reactivity. In electrostatic potential maps (Section 4.9), the chlorine atom is therefore in the red region of the map and the carbon atom in the blue region.

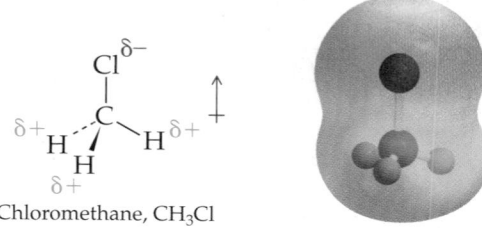

Chloromethane, CH_3Cl

- **Organic molecules have specific three-dimensional shapes** (Section 4.8). For example, when carbon is bonded to four atoms, as in methane, CH_4, the bonds are oriented toward the four corners of a regular tetrahedron with carbon in the center. Such three-dimensionality is commonly shown using normal lines for bonds in the plane of the page, dashed lines for bonds receding behind the page, and wedged lines for bonds coming out of the page.

- In addition to carbon, most **organic molecules always contain hydrogen and often also contain nitrogen and oxygen** (Section 4.7). Nitrogen can form single, double, and triple bonds to carbon, whereas oxygen can form single and double bonds. Hydrogen can only form single bonds to carbon because hydrogen can only hold two electrons in its valence shell:

$$
\begin{array}{lll}
C{-}N & C{-}O & C{-}H \\
C{=}N & C{=}O & \\
C{\equiv}N & &
\end{array}
$$

Covalent bonding makes organic compounds quite different from the inorganic compounds we have been concentrating on up to this point. For example, inorganic compounds such as NaCl have high melting points and high boiling points because they consist of a large network of oppositely charged ions held together by strong electrical attractions. By contrast, organic compounds consist of atoms joined by covalent bonds, forming individual molecules. Because the organic molecules are attracted to one another only by weak nonionic intermolecular forces, organic compounds generally have lower melting and boiling points than inorganic salts. As a result, many simple organic compounds are liquids or low melting solids at room temperature, and a few are gases.

Other important differences between organic and inorganic compounds include solubility and electrical conductivity. Whereas many inorganic compounds dissolve in water to yield solutions of ions that conduct electricity, most organic compounds are insoluble in water, and almost all of those that are soluble do not conduct electricity. Only small polar organic molecules, such as glucose and ethyl alcohol, or large molecules with many polar groups, such as some proteins, interact with water molecules through both dipole–dipole interactions and/or hydrogen bonding and, thus, dissolve in water. This lack of water solubility for organic compounds has important practical consequences, varying from the difficulty in removing greasy dirt and cleaning up environmental oil spills to drug delivery, the ability of getting a drug to its target organ or tissue.

◀◀◀ Other unique properties of ionic compounds are discussed in Section 3.10

◀◀◀ Recall from Section 8.2 the various intermolecular forces: dipole–dipole forces, London dispersion forces, and hydrogen bonds.

◀◀◀ Section 9.9 explores how anions and cations in solution conduct electric current.

◀◀◀ Recall from Section 9.2 that a compound is only soluble when the intermolecular forces between solvent and solute are comparable in strength to the intermolecular forces of the pure solvent or solute.

▲ Oil spills can be a serious environmental problem because oil is insoluble in water.

LOOKING AHEAD ▶▶▶ The interior of a living cell is largely a water solution that contains many hundreds of different compounds. In Section 23.7, we will see how cells use membranes composed of water-insoluble organic molecules to enclose their watery interiors and to regulate the flow of substances across the cell boundary.

12.2 Families of Organic Molecules: Functional Groups

Learning Objectives:

- Define functional group.
- Identify the functional groups in organic molecules.

More than 18 *million* organic compounds are described in scientific literature, each with unique chemical and physical properties, and many also having unique biological properties (both desired and undesired). How can we ever understand them all?

Chemists have learned through experience that organic compounds can be classified into families according to their structural features, and that the chemical behavior of family members is often predictable based on their specific grouping of atoms. As a result, the millions of compounds can be sorted into just a few general families of organic compounds with simple chemical patterns.

Functional group An atom or group of atoms within a molecule that has a characteristic physical and chemical behavior.

The structural features that allow us to classify organic compounds into distinct chemical families are called **functional groups.** A functional group is an atom or group of atoms that has a characteristic physical and chemical behavior. Each functional group is always part of a larger molecule, and a molecule may have more than one class of functional group present, as we shall soon see. An important property of functional groups is that a given functional group *tends to undergo the same types of reactions in every molecule that contains it.* Once a functional group undergoes a chemical reaction it quite often changes the chemical behavior of the entire molecule. For example, the carbon–carbon double bond is a common functional group. Ethylene (C_2H_4), the simplest compound with a carbon–carbon double bond, undergoes many chemical reactions similar to those of oleic acid ($C_{18}H_{34}O_2$), a much larger and more complex compound that also contains a carbon double bond. Both, for example, react with hydrogen gas in the same manner, as shown in Figure 12.1. We will see in Chapter 13 that the double bond reacts with water and acid to produce alcohols; in doing so a molecule that is completely insoluble in water (such as ethylene) is converted to one that shows a substantial increase in its water solubility (ethyl alcohol). These identical reactions with hydrogen are typical: *The chemistry of an organic molecule is primarily determined by the functional groups it contains, not by its size or complexity.*

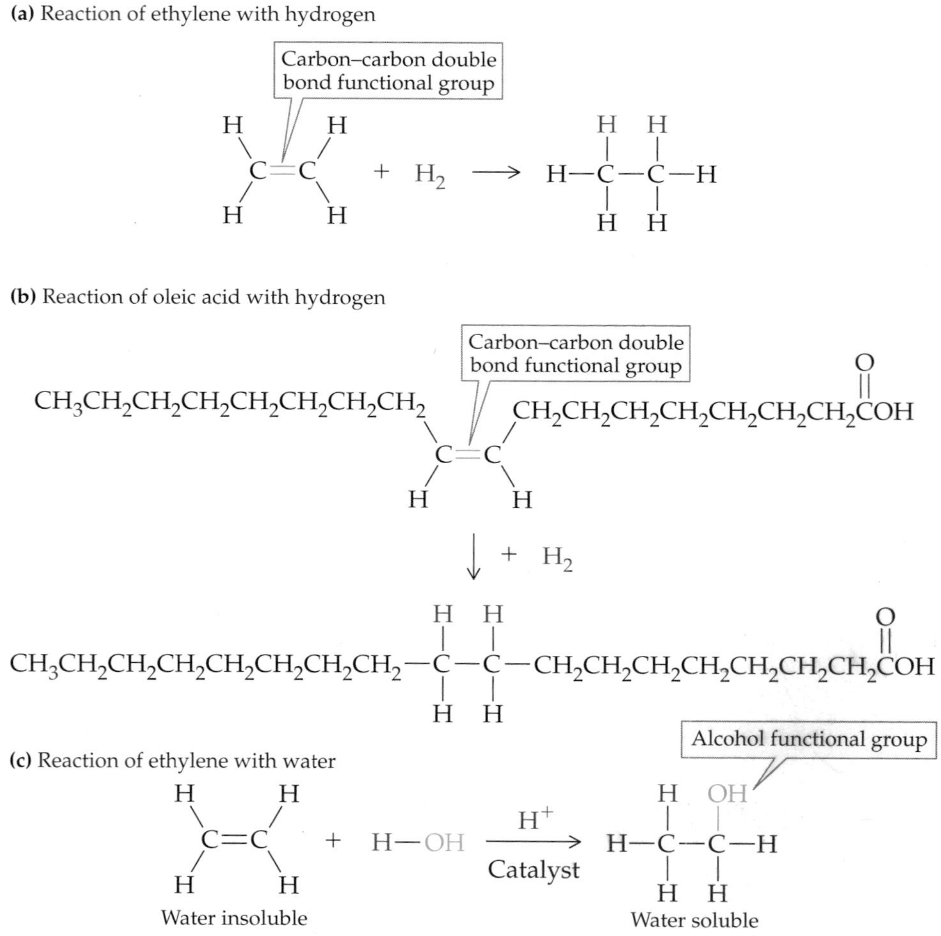

▶ **Figure 12.1**
The reactions of (a) ethylene and (b) oleic acid with hydrogen; reaction of (c) ethylene with water in the presence of acid. The carbon–carbon double-bond functional group adds 2 hydrogen atoms in both cases, regardless of the complexity of the rest of the molecule.

Table 12.1 lists some of the most important families of organic molecules and their distinctive functional groups. Compounds that contain a $C{=}C$ double bond functional group, for instance, are in the *alkene* family, compounds that have an $-OH$ group bound to a tetravalent carbon are in the *alcohol* family, and so on. To aid in identifying the organic functional groups you will encounter, we have included an Organic Functional Group Concept Map (Figure 12.5) at the end of this chapter; it should be used in

Table 12.1 Some Important Families of Organic Molecules

Family Name	Functional Group Structure*	Simple Example	Line Structure	Name Suffix
Alkane (Chapter 12)	No readily reactive bonds. Contains only C—H and C—C single bonds	$CH_3CH_2CH_3$ Propane	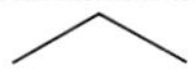	-ane
Alkene (Chapter 13)	C=C	$H_2C=CH_2$ Ethylene	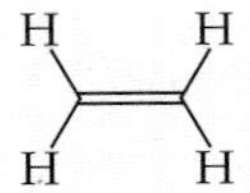	-ene
Alkyne (Chapter 13)	—C≡C—	$H-C≡C-H$ Acetylene (Ethyne)	 H————H	-yne
Aromatic (Chapter 13)	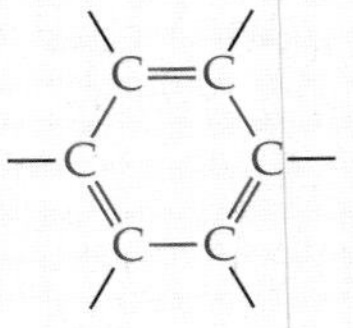 C=C ring	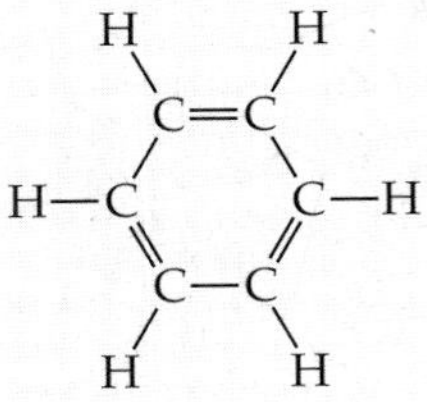 Benzene	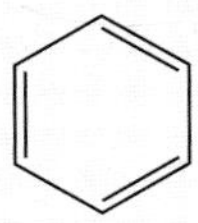	None
Alkyl halide (Chapters 12, 14)	—C—X (X = F, Cl, Br, I)	CH_3CH_2Cl Ethyl chloride	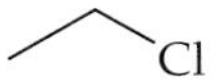 Cl	None
Alcohol (Chapter 14)	—C—O—H	CH_3CH_2OH Ethyl alcohol (Ethanol)	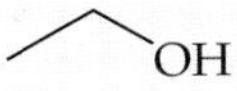 OH	-ol
Ether (Chapter 14)	—C—O—C—	$CH_3CH_2-O-CH_2CH_3$ Diethyl ether	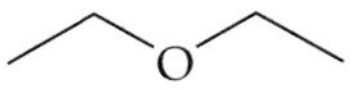 O	None
Amine (Chapter 16)	—C—N	$CH_2CH_3NH_2$ Ethylamine	 NH_2	-amine
Aldehyde (Chapter 15)	—C—C—H (C=O)	CH_3-C-H (C=O) Acetaldehyde (Ethanal)	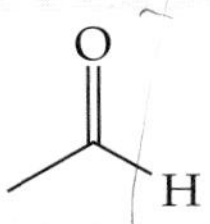 H	-al
Ketone (Chapter 15)	—C—C—C— (C=O)	CH_3-C-CH_3 (C=O) Acetone	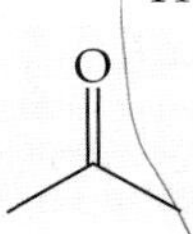	-one
Carboxylic acid (Chapter 17)	—C—C—OH (C=O)	CH_3-C-OH (C=O) Acetic acid	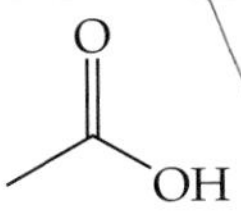 OH	-ic acid
Anhydride (Chapter 17)	—C—C—O—C—C— (two C=O)	$CH_3-C-O-C-CH_3$ (two C=O) Acetic anhydride	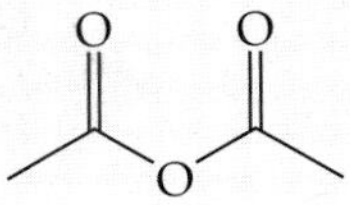	None
Ester (Chapter 17)	—C—C—O—C— (C=O)	$CH_3-C-O-CH_3$ (C=O) Methyl acetate	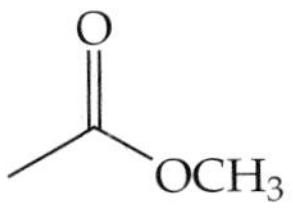 OCH_3	-ate
Amide (Chapter 17)	—C—C—NH_2, —C—C—N—H, —C—C—N— (C=O)	CH_3-C-NH_2 (C=O) Acetamide	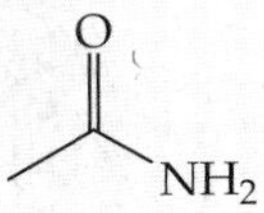 NH_2	-amide
Thiol (Chapter 14)	—C—SH	CH_3CH_2SH Ethyl thiol	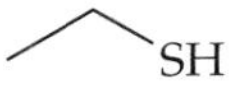 SH	None
Disulfide (Chapter 14)	C—S—S—C	CH_3SSCH_3 Dimethyl disulfide	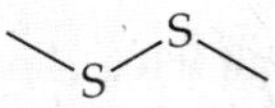 S—S	None
Sulfide (Chapter 14)	C—S—C	$CH_3CH_2SCH_3$ Ethyl methyl sulfide	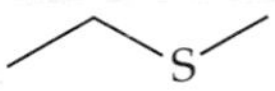 S	None

The bonds shown in RED refer to the functional group of interest and the atoms required.

*The bonds whose connections are not specified are assumed to be attached to carbon or hydrogen atoms in the rest of the molecule.

conjunction with Table 12.1. Also at the end of each organic chemistry chapter you will find a summary of functional group reactions discussed in that chapter. You will find Table 12.1, Figure 12.5, and these Functional Group Summaries helpful as you proceed through the remainder of this text.

Much of the chemistry discussed in this and the next five chapters is the chemistry of the families listed in Table 12.1, so it is best to learn the names and become familiar with their structures now. Note that they fall into four groups:

Hydrocarbon An organic compound that contains only carbon and hydrogen.

- The first four families in Table 12.1 are **hydrocarbons,** organic compounds that contain only carbon and hydrogen. *Alkanes* have only single bonds and contain no functional groups. As we will see later in this chapter, the absence of functional groups makes alkanes relatively unreactive. *Alkenes* contain a carbon–carbon double-bond functional group; *alkynes* contain a carbon–carbon triple-bond functional group; and *aromatic* compounds contain a six-membered benzene ring of carbon atoms with three alternating double bonds.
- The next four families in Table 12.1 have functional groups that contain only single bonds and have a carbon atom bonded to an electronegative atom. *Alkyl halides* have a carbon–halogen bond; *alcohols* have a carbon–oxygen bond; *ethers* have two carbons bonded to the same oxygen; and *amines* have a carbon–nitrogen bond.
- The next six families in Table 12.1 have functional groups that contain a carbon–oxygen double bond: *aldehydes, ketones, carboxylic acids, anhydrides, esters,* and *amides.*
- The remaining three families in Table 12.1 have functional groups that contain sulfur: *thioalcohols* (known simply as *thiols*), *sulfides,* and *disulfides.* These three families play an important role in protein function (Chapter 18).
- Many of the organic molecules we will come across in later chapters (in particular the biochemistry chapters) will have more than one functional group present in the same molecule (see, e.g., for the amino acids Section 18.3). When this is the case, we will classify the molecule as chemically belonging to multiple functional group families; from a biological and medical standpoint these molecules are quite often classified according their biologically relevant function (e.g., neurotransmitters (Sections 28.5 to 28.7) or nucleic acids (Section 26.2).

Worked Example 12.1 Molecular Structures: Identifying Functional Groups

To which family of organic compounds do the following compounds belong? Explain.

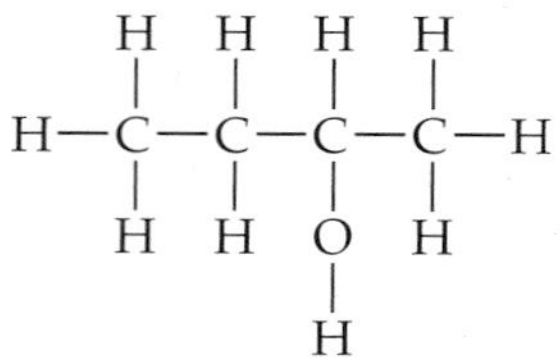

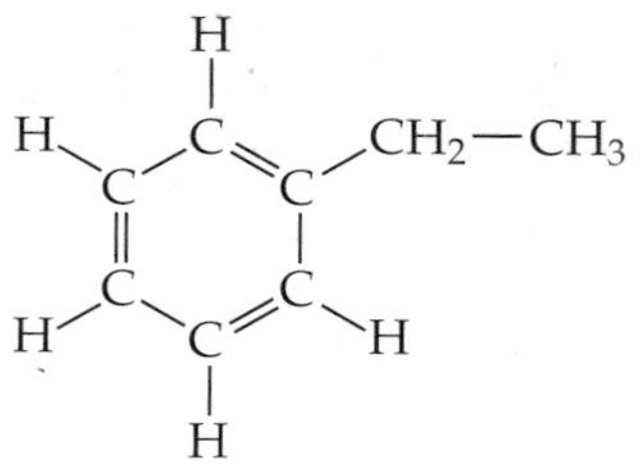

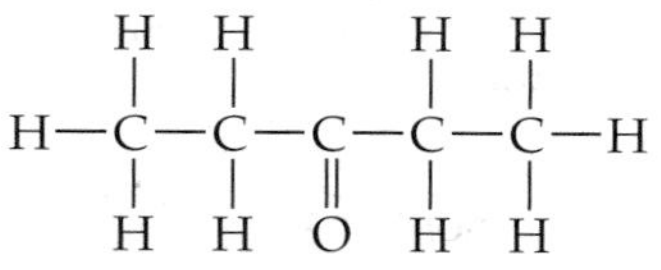

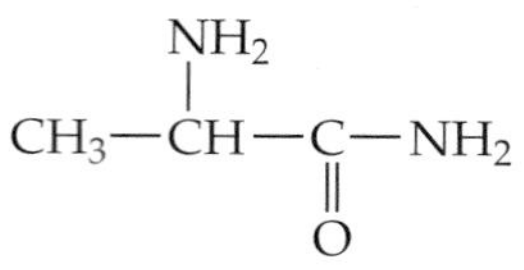

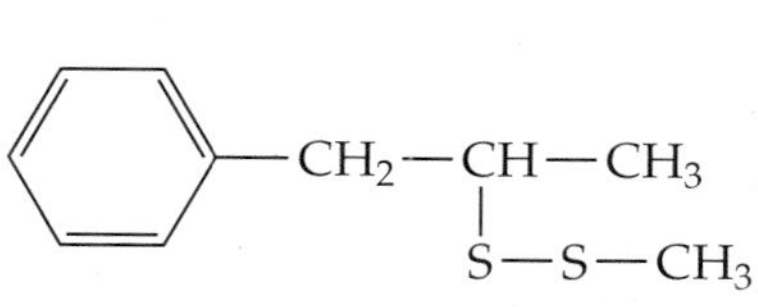

ANALYSIS Use the Organic Functional Group Concept Map (Figure 12.5, see end of chapter) and Table 12.1 to identify each functional group, and name the corresponding family to which the compound belongs. Begin by determining what elements are present and whether multiple bonds are present.

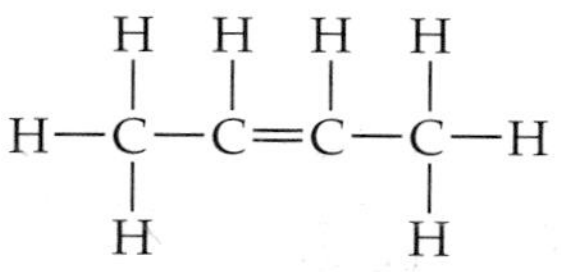

SOLUTION

(a) This compound contains only carbon and hydrogen atoms, so it is a *hydrocarbon*. There is only one carbon–carbon double bond, so it is an *alkene*.

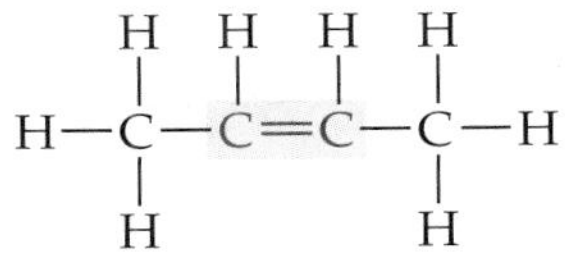

$$\begin{array}{cccc} H & H & H & H \\ | & | & | & | \\ H-C-C{=}C-C-H \\ | & & & | \\ H & & & H \end{array}$$

(b) This compound contains an oxygen and has only single bonds. The presence of the O—H group bonded to tetravalent carbon identifies this compound as an *alcohol*.

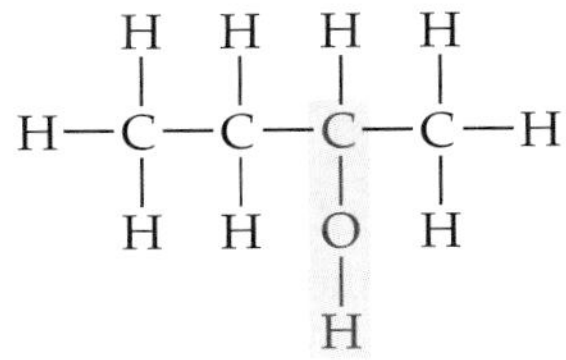

$$\begin{array}{cccc} H & H & H & H \\ | & | & | & | \\ H-C-C-C-C-H \\ | & | & | & | \\ H & H & O & H \\ & & | \\ & & H \end{array}$$

(c) This compound also contains only carbon and hydrogen atoms, which identifies it as a *hydrocarbon*. It has three double bonds in a ring. The six-membered carbon ring with alternating double bonds also identifies this compound as an *aromatic* hydrocarbon compound.

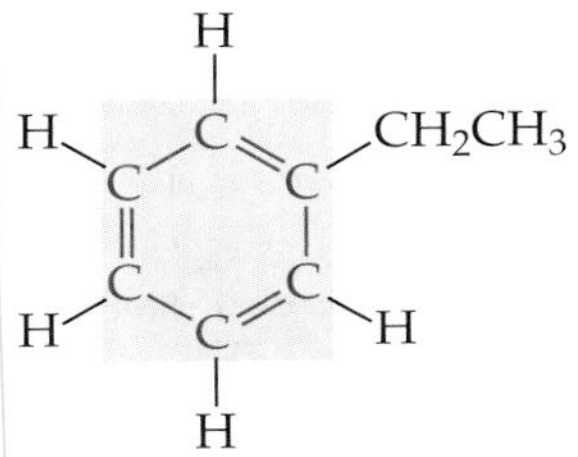

(d) This molecule contains an oxygen that is double bonded to a carbon (a *carbonyl group*, discussed in Chapter 16), and there is no singly bound oxygen or nitrogen also connected to the carbon. The carbon–oxygen double bond is connected to two other carbons (as opposed to a hydrogen) that identifies this compound as a *ketone*.

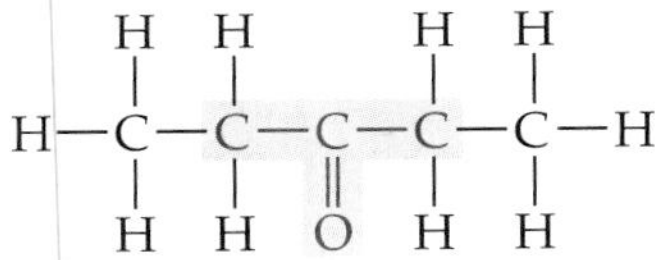

$$\begin{array}{ccccc} H & H & & H & H \\ | & | & & | & | \\ H-C-C-C-C-C-H \\ | & | & \| & | & | \\ H & H & O & H & H \end{array}$$

(e) Here, we have an example of a molecule belonging to multiple functional group families. This molecule contains oxygen and nitrogen in addition to carbon and hydrogen, so it is not a hydrocarbon. The presence of the carbonyl group further classifies this molecule, but here we run into a problem: one —NH₂ is attached to the carbonyl but the other —NH₂ is not. This leads us to conclude that there are two functional groups present: an *amide* and an *amine*.

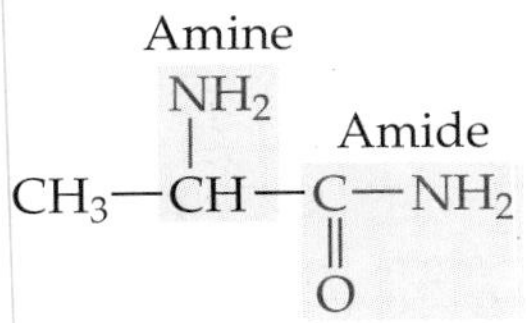

Amine
$$NH_2$$
Amide
$$CH_3-CH-C-NH_2$$
$$\|$$
$$O$$

> We will see in Chapter 16 that while the NH₂ of an amine produces a basic molecule, the NH₂ of an amide does not, and that amides, despite having a nitrogen in them, are nonbasic (Chapter 17).

(f) This molecule also contains two functional groups: a ring containing alternating carbon–carbon single and double bonds as well as an S—S group. From our concept map, we trace the double bond to indicate we have an aromatic hydrocarbon, while the sulfurs indicate the presence of a disulfide.

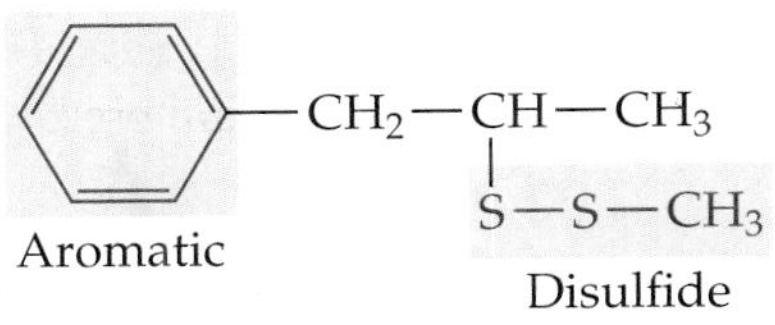

Aromatic
$$-CH_2-CH-CH_3$$
$$|$$
$$S-S-CH_3$$
Disulfide

Worked Example 12.2 Molecular Structures: Drawing Functional Groups

Given the family of organic compounds to which the compound belongs, propose structures for compounds having the following chemical formulas.
(a) An amine having the formula C_2H_7N
(b) An alkyne having the formula C_3H_4
(c) An ether having the formula $C_4H_{10}O$

ANALYSIS Identify the functional group for each compound from Table 12.1. Once the atoms in this functional group are eliminated from the chemical formula, the remaining structure can be determined. (Remember that each carbon atom forms four bonds, nitrogen forms three bonds, oxygen forms two bonds, and hydrogen forms only one bond.)

SOLUTION

(a) Amines have a $C-NH_2$ group. Eliminating these atoms from the formula leaves 1 C atom and 5 H atoms. Since only the carbons are capable of forming more than one bond, the 2 C atoms must be bonded together. The remaining H atoms are then bonded to the carbons until each C has 4 bonds.

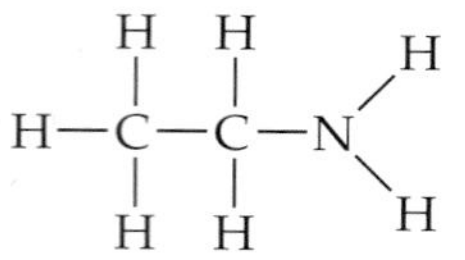

(b) The alkynes contain a $C\equiv C$ bond. This leaves 1 C atom and 4 H atoms. Attach this C to one of the carbons in the triple bond, and then distribute the H atoms until each carbon has a full complement of four bonds.

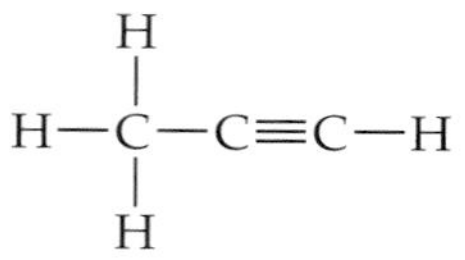

(c) The ethers contain a $C-O-C$ group. Eliminating these atoms leaves 2 C atoms and 10 H atoms. The C atoms can be distributed on either end of the ether group, and the H atoms are then distributed until each carbon atom has a full complement of four bonds.

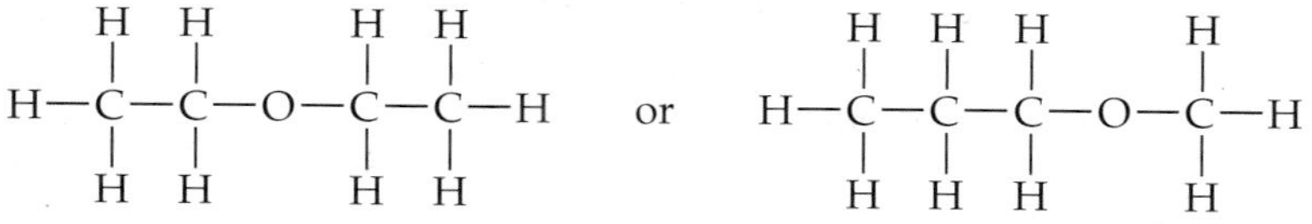

PROBLEM 12.1

Locate and identify the functional groups in (a) propylene glycol, one of the major ingredients used in electronic cigarettes; (b) glutaric acid, produced in the body during the metabolism of lysine and tryptophan; (c) lactic acid, from sour milk; and (d) phenylalanine, an amino acid found in proteins.

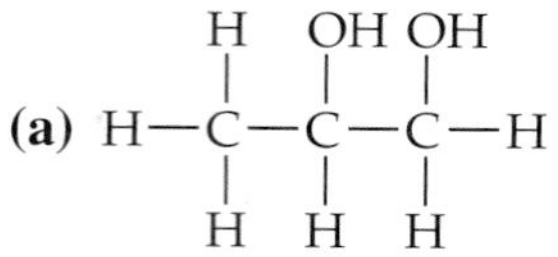

(a) Propylene glycol

(b) Glutaric acid

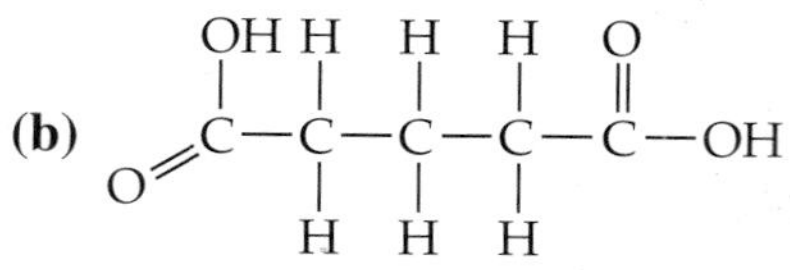

(c) lactic acid

(d) phenylalanine

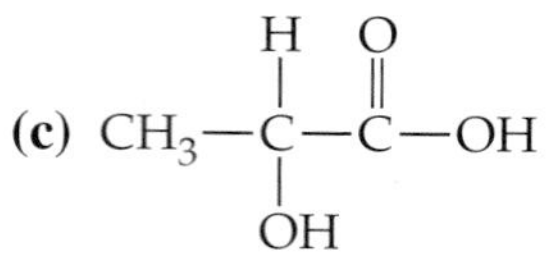

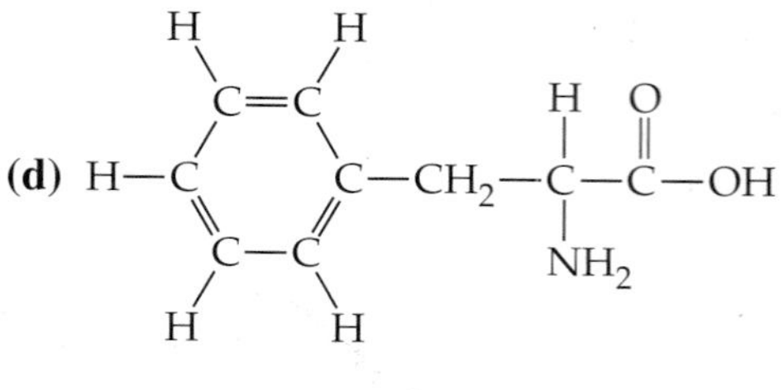

PROBLEM 12.2

Draw structures for molecules that fit the following descriptions:
(a) C_3H_6O containing an aldehyde functional group
(b) C_3H_6O containing a ketone functional group
(c) $C_3H_6O_2$ containing a carboxylic acid functional group

HANDS-ON CHEMISTRY 12.1

To see how much organic chemistry impacts your daily life, let's take a look at some of the common products that you should have around your home and see what is "organic" in them. You will need to have an internet connection to fully carry out this activity.

a. Let's begin by looking at a simple substance found in almost every pantry: vinegar. Vinegar is simply diluted acetic acid. Look up the structure of acetic acid and draw it. Circle the functional group in it. What other food products can you find that contain vinegar? You may want to look in your refrigerator as well as your pantry.

b. Other common organic compounds found in a home are citric acid, folic acid, dextrose, and thiamine. Look up the structures of each of these and draw them, circling and

identifying as many functional groups present as you can. Do any of these four compounds go by a more recognizable name? If so, what? See if you can find at least one food item than contains one or more of these in it. Canned items such as soups are a good place to start. Some of them may be listed as their salt forms (like citrate, folate, thiamine mononitrate, etc). You may have to make a trip to the store to complete this. Provide at least one role the compound plays in the item in which it is present.

c. In the chapter opener, the antibiotic ointment Neosporin was mentioned. What are the three antibiotics found in it? Look up the structures of each of these and draw them, circling and identifying as many functional groups present as you can.

12.3 The Structure of Organic Molecules: Alkanes and Their Isomers

Learning Objective:

• Recognize structural (constitutional) isomers and functional group isomers.

Hydrocarbons that contain only single bonds belong to the family of organic molecules called **alkanes.** Alkanes are most commonly found and used as fuels; the tank of gas found on a backyard barbecue is usually the hydrocarbon propane. Imagine how 1 carbon and 4 hydrogens can combine, and you will realize there is only one possibility: methane, CH_4. Now, imagine how 2 carbons and 6 hydrogens can combine—only ethane, CH_3CH_3, is possible. Likewise, with the combination of 3 carbons with 8 hydrogens—only propane, $CH_3CH_2CH_3$, is possible. The general rule for *all* hydrocarbons except methane is that each carbon *must* be bonded to at least one other carbon. The carbon atoms bond together to form the "backbone" of the compound, with the hydrogens on the periphery. The general formula for alkanes is C_nH_{2n+2}, where n is the number of carbons in the compound.

Alkane A hydrocarbon that has only single bonds.

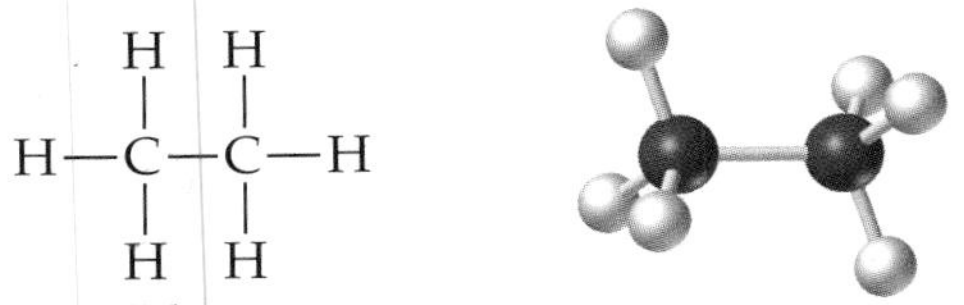

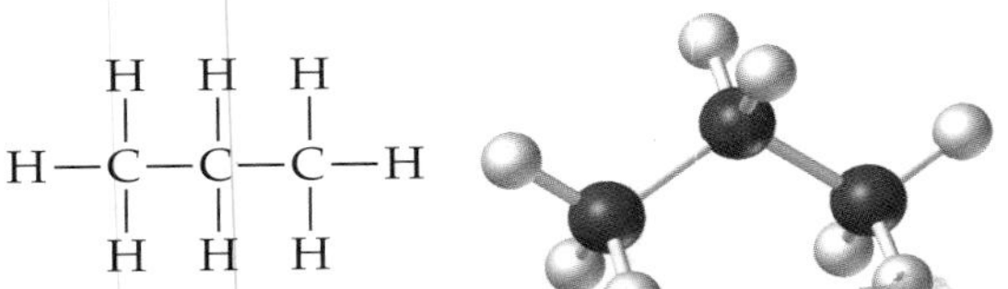

Isomers Compounds with the same molecular formula but different structures.

In alkanes, as the number of carbons becomes greater than three, the ability to form *isomers* arises. Compounds that have the same molecular formula but different structural formulas are called **isomers** of one another. For example, there are two ways in which molecules that have the formula C_4H_{10} can be formed. The 4 carbons can either be joined in a continuous row or have a branched arrangement:

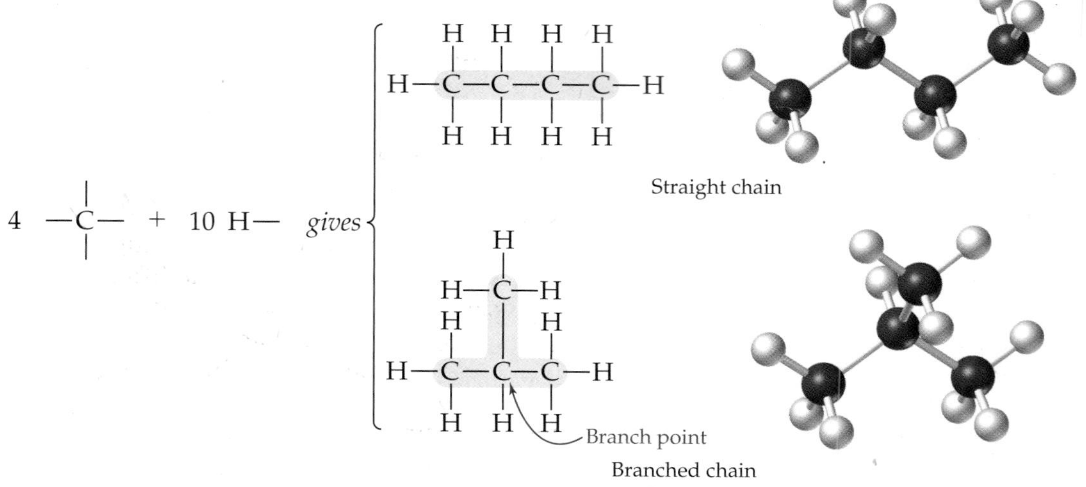
4 —C— + 10 H— gives
Straight chain
Branch point
Branched chain

The same is seen with the molecules that have the formula C_5H_{12}, for which three isomers are possible.

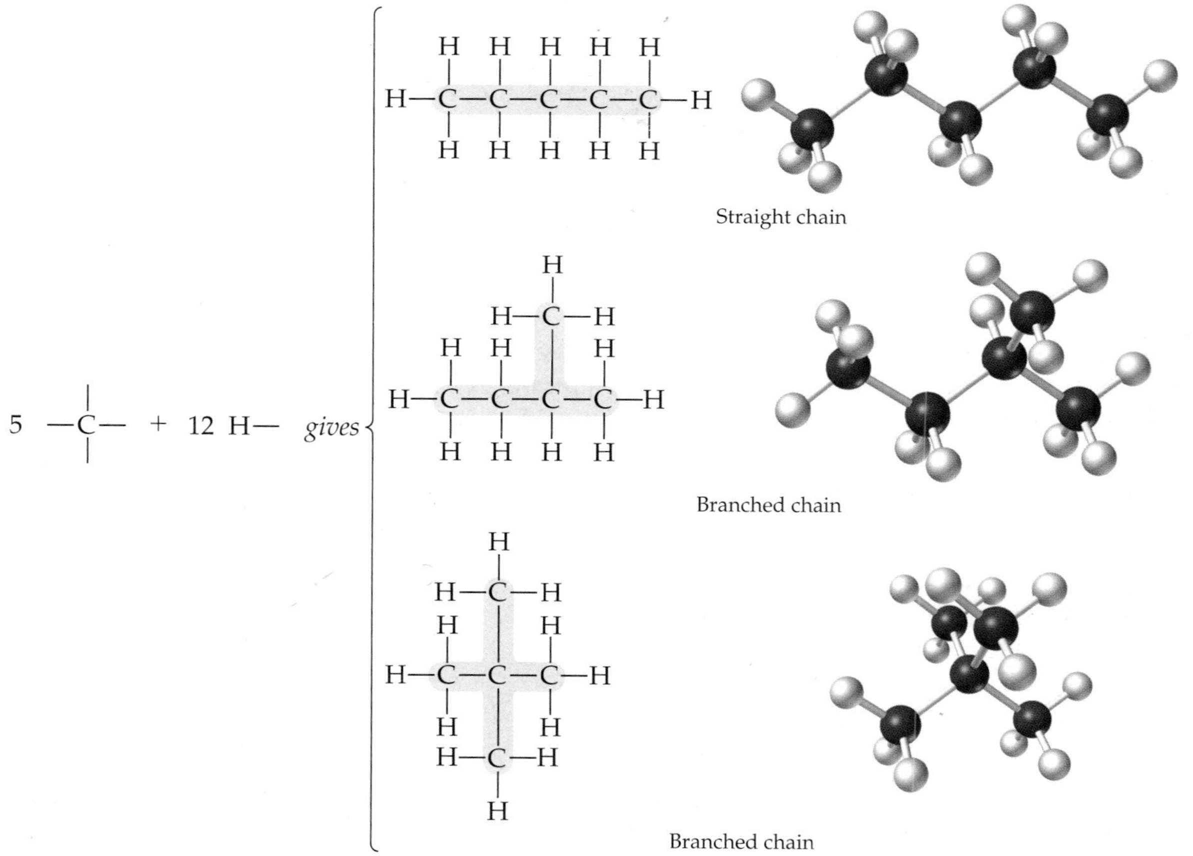
5 —C— + 12 H— gives
Straight chain
Branched chain
Branched chain

Compounds with all their carbons connected in a continuous chain are called **straight-chain alkanes;** those with a branching connection of carbons are called **branched-chain alkanes.** Note that in a straight-chain alkane, you can draw a line through all the carbon atoms without lifting your pencil from the paper. In a branched-chain alkane, however, you must either lift your pencil from the paper or retrace your steps to draw a line through all the carbons.

The two isomers of C_4H_{10} and the three isomers of C_5H_{12} shown above are **constitutional (or structural) isomers**—compounds with the same molecular formula but with different connections among their constituent atoms. Needless to say, the number of possible alkane isomers grows rapidly as the number of carbon atoms increases.

Constitutional isomers of a given molecular formula are chemically distinct from one another. They have different structures, physical properties (such as melting and boiling points), and potentially different physiological properties. When the molecular formula contains atoms other than carbon and hydrogen, the constitutional isomers obtained can also be **functional group isomers:** isomers that differ in both molecular connection and family classification. In these cases, the differences between isomers can be dramatic. For example, ethyl alcohol and dimethyl ether both have the formula C_2H_6O, but ethyl alcohol is a liquid with a boiling point of 78.5 °C and dimethyl ether is a gas with a boiling point of 23 °C. While ethyl alcohol is a depressant of the central nervous system, dimethyl ether is a nontoxic compound with anesthetic properties at high concentrations. Clearly, molecular formulas by themselves are not very useful in organic chemistry; knowledge of structures is also necessary.

Straight-chain alkane An alkane that has all its carbons connected in a row.

Branched-chain alkane An alkane that has a branching connection of carbons.

Constitutional isomers Compounds with the same molecular formula but different connections among their atoms. Also known as structural isomers.

Functional group isomer Isomers having the same chemical formula but belonging to different chemical families due to differences in bonding; ethyl alcohol and dimethyl ether are examples of functional group isomers.

Ethyl alcohol
C_2H_6O

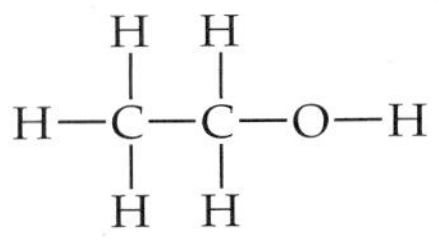

Dimethyl ether
C_2H_6O

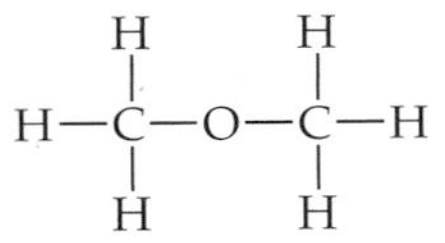

▶ Worked Example 12.3 Molecular Structures: Drawing Isomers

Draw all isomers that have the formula C_6H_{14}.

ANALYSIS Knowing that all the carbons must be bonded together to form the molecule, find all possible arrangements of the 6 carbon atoms. Begin with the isomer that has all 6 carbons in a straight chain, then draw the isomer that has 5 carbons in a straight chain, using the remaining carbon to form a branch, then repeat for the isomer having 4 carbons in a straight chain and 2 carbons in branches. Once each carbon backbone is drawn, arrange the hydrogens around the carbons to complete the structure. (Remember that each carbon can only have *four* bonds total.)

SOLUTION

The straight-chain isomer contains all 6 carbons bonded to form a chain with no branches. The branched isomers are drawn by starting with either a 5-carbon chain or a 4-carbon chain and by adding the extra carbons as branches in the middle of the chain. Hydrogens are added until each carbon has a full complement of four bonds.

—continued on next page

—continued from previous page

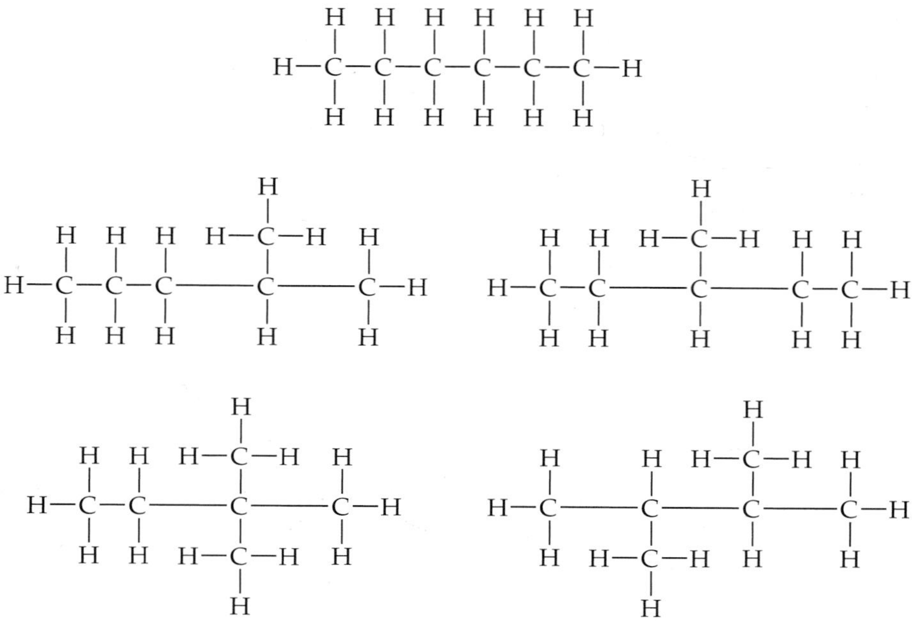

$$H-\overset{\displaystyle H}{\underset{\displaystyle H}{C}}-\overset{\displaystyle H}{\underset{\displaystyle H}{C}}-\overset{\displaystyle H}{\underset{\displaystyle H}{C}}-\overset{\displaystyle H}{\underset{\displaystyle H}{C}}-\overset{\displaystyle H}{\underset{\displaystyle H}{C}}-\overset{\displaystyle H}{\underset{\displaystyle H}{C}}-H$$

PROBLEM 12.3

Draw the straight-chain isomer with the formula **(a)** C_7H_{16} and **(b)** C_9H_{20}.

PROBLEM 12.4

There are two branched-chain isomers with the formula C_7H_{16}, where the longest chain in the molecule is six carbons long. Draw them.

12.4 Drawing Organic Structures

Learning Objectives:

- Draw structural, condensed, and line formulas for simple chemical compounds.
- Convert any given structural, condensed, or line formula into its corresponding alternative.

Drawing structural formulas that show every atom and every bond in a molecule is both time-consuming and awkward, even for relatively small molecules. Much easier is the use of **condensed structures,** which are simpler but still show the essential information about which functional groups are present and how atoms are connected. In condensed structures, C—C and C—H single bonds are not necessarily shown; rather, they are "understood." If a carbon atom has three hydrogens bonded to it, we write CH_3 (or H_3C if needed; this is only done in special cases); if the carbon has two hydrogens bonded to it, we write CH_2; and so on. For example, the 4-carbon, straight-chain alkane called butane and its branched-chain isomer (2-methylpropane), both of which have the formula C_4H_{10} can be written as the following condensed structures:

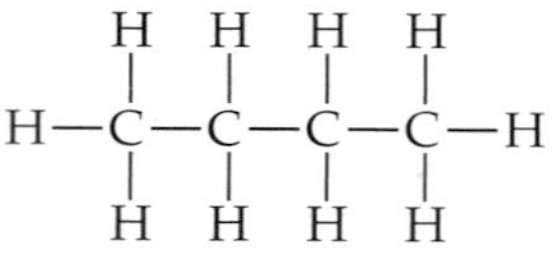

Condensed structure A shorthand way of drawing structures in which C—C and C—H bonds are understood rather than shown.

◀◀ Condensed structures were explored in Section 4.7.

Butane   = $CH_3CH_2CH_2CH_3$
Structural formula   Condensed formula

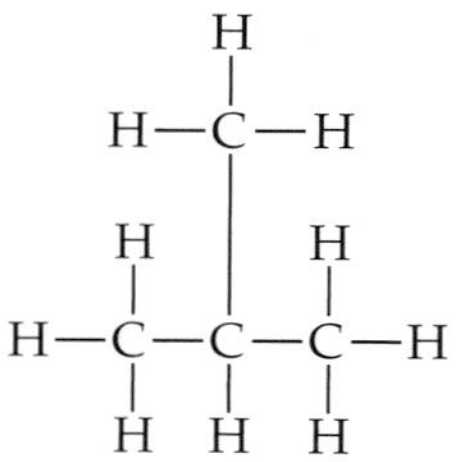

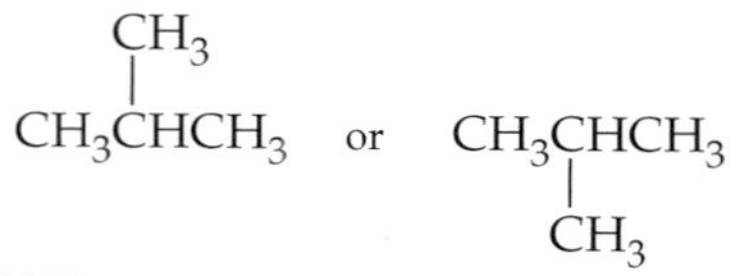

2-Methylpropane   = CH_3CHCH_3 or CH_3CHCH_3
Structural formula   Condensed formula

Note in these condensed structures for butane and 2-methylpropane that the bonds between carbons are not usually shown—the CH_3 and CH_2 units are simply placed next to one another—but that the branch in the 2-methylpropane isomer *is* shown for clarity. It does not matter whether the branch is drawn above or below the main chain.

Occasionally, as a further simplification, not all the CH_2 groups (called **methylenes**) are shown. Instead, CH_2 is shown once in parentheses, with a subscript indicating the number of methylene units strung together. For example, the 6-carbon straight-chain alkane (hexane) can be written as:

Methylene Another name for a CH_2 unit.

$$CH_3CH_2CH_2CH_2CH_2CH_3 \text{ or } CH_3(CH_2)_4CH_3$$

Worked Example 12.4 Molecular Structures: Writing Condensed Structures

Write condensed structures for the isomers from Worked Example 12.3.

ANALYSIS Eliminate all horizontal bonds, substituting reduced formula components (CH_3, CH_2, and so on) for each carbon in the compound. Show bonds in branched isomers for clarity.

SOLUTION

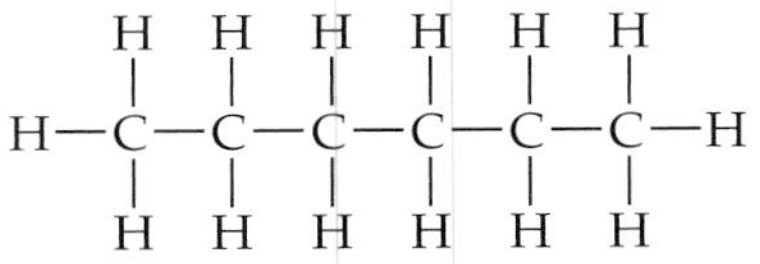 ⟶ $CH_3CH_2CH_2CH_2CH_2CH_3$ or $CH_3(CH_2)_4CH_3$

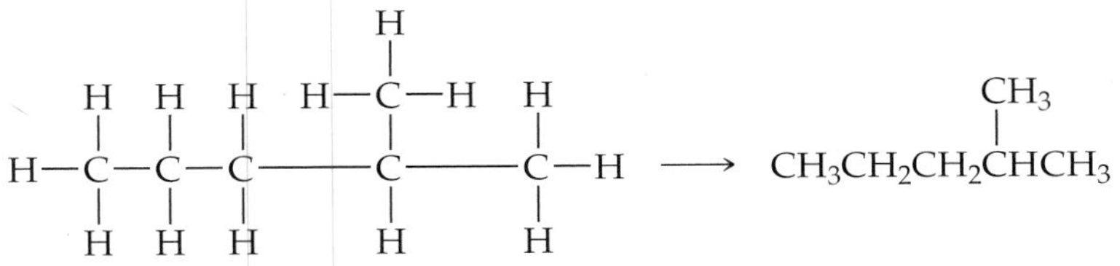

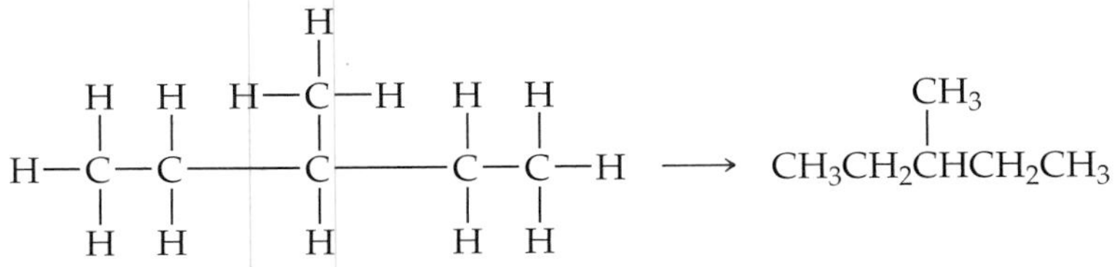

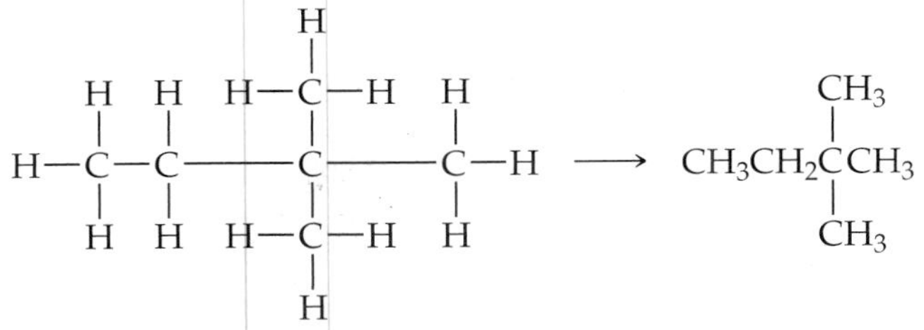

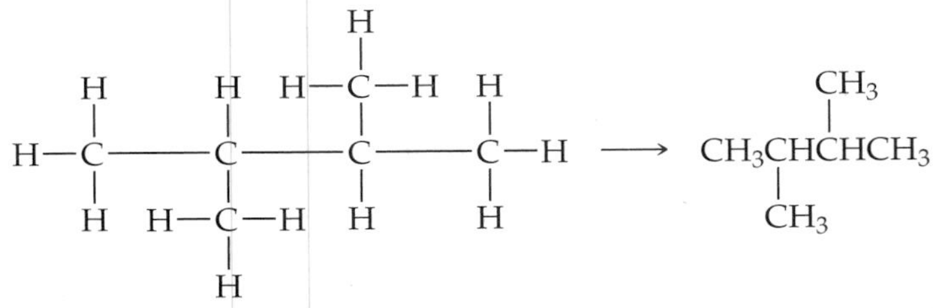

PROBLEM 12.5

Draw the following three isomers of C_5H_{12} as condensed structures:

(a) 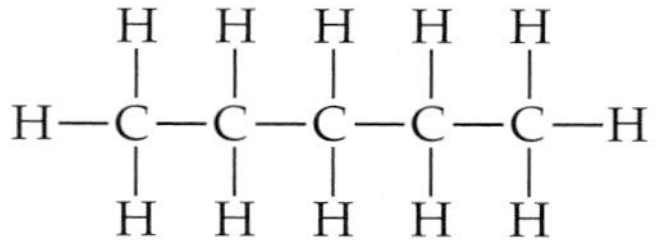
```
    H  H  H  H  H
    |  |  |  |  |
H — C— C— C— C— C— H
    |  |  |  |  |
    H  H  H  H  H
```
Pentane

(b) 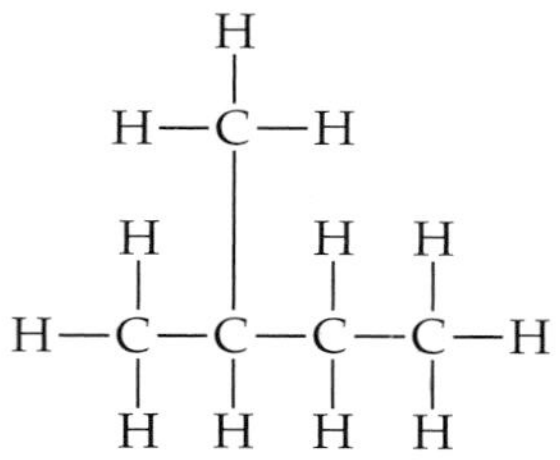
```
          H
          |
      H — C — H
          |
      H   |   H  H
      |   |   |  |
 H — C — C — C — C — H
      |   |   |  |
      H   H   H  H
```
2-Methylbutane

(c) 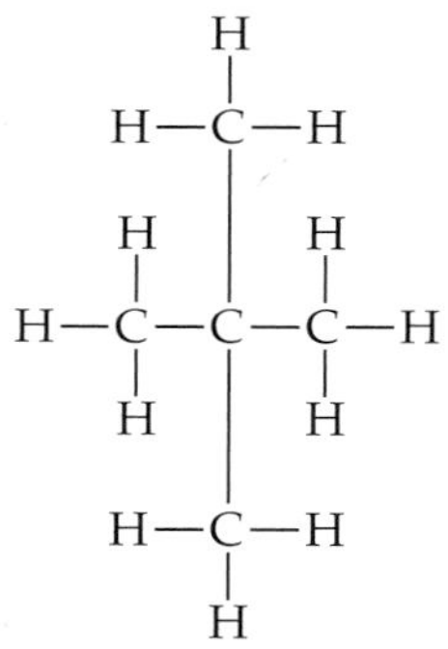
```
          H
          |
      H — C — H
          |
      H   |   H
      |   |   |
 H — C — C — C — H
      |   |   |
      H   |   H
          |
      H — C — H
          |
          H
```
2,2-Dimethylpropane

Line structure Also known as line-angle structure; a shorthand way of drawing structures in which carbon and hydrogen atoms are not explicitly shown. Instead, a carbon atom is understood to be wherever a line begins or ends and at every intersection of two lines, and hydrogens are understood to be wherever they are needed to have each carbon form four bonds.

Another way of representing organic molecules is to use **line (or line-angle) structures,** which are structures in which the symbols C and H do not appear. Instead, a chain of carbon atoms and their associated hydrogens are represented by a zigzag arrangement of short lines, with any branches off the main chain represented by additional lines. The line structure for butane and its branched-chain isomer 2-methylbutane, for instance, is

same as $CH_3CH_2CH_2CH_3$

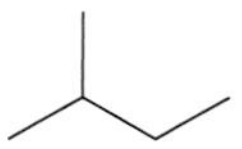

same as
$$
\begin{array}{c}
CH_3 \\
| \\
CH_3CHCH_2CH_3
\end{array}
$$

Line structures are a simple and quick way to represent organic molecules without showing all carbons and hydrogens present. Chemists, biologists, pharmacists, doctors, and nurses all use line structures to conveniently convey to one another very complex organic structures. Another advantage is that a line structure gives a more realistic depiction of the angles seen in a carbon chain.

Drawing a molecule in this way is simple, provided one follows these guidelines:

1. Each carbon–carbon bond is represented by a line.
2. Anywhere a line ends or begins, as well as any vertex where two lines meet, represents a carbon atom.
3. Any atom other than another carbon or a hydrogen attached to a carbon must be shown.
4. Since a neutral carbon atom forms four bonds, all bonds not shown for any carbon are understood to be the number of carbon–hydrogen bonds needed to have

the carbon form four bonds. Only bonds between two carbons (or carbon and an element other than hydrogen) are shown.

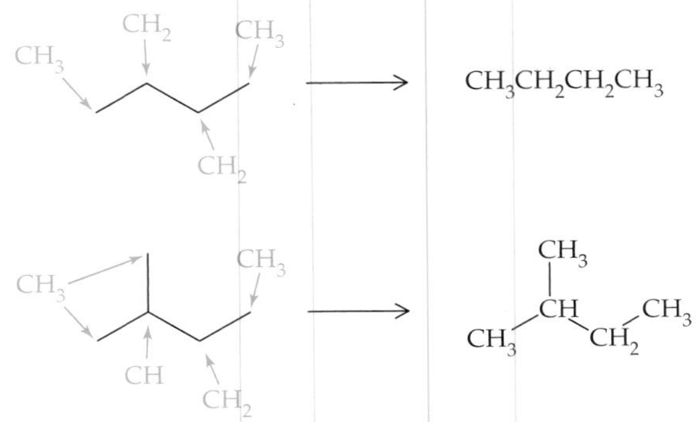

$$CH_3CH_2CH_2CH_3$$

Converting line structures to structural formulas or to condensed structures is simply a matter of correctly interpreting each line ending and each intersection in a line structure. For example, the common pain reliever ibuprofen has the condensed and line structures

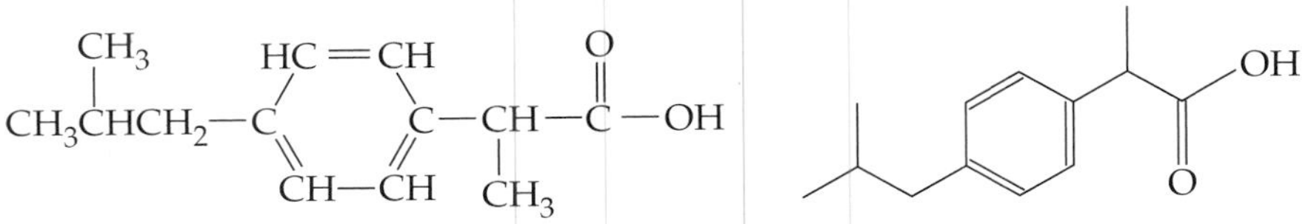

Finally, it is important to note that chemists and biochemists often use a mixture of structural formulas, condensed structures, and line structures to represent the molecules they study. As you progress through this textbook, you will see many complicated molecules represented in this way, so it is a good idea to get used to thinking interchangeably in all three formats.

Worked Example 12.5 Molecular Structures: Converting Condensed Structures to Line Structures

Convert the following condensed structures to line structures:

ANALYSIS Find the longest continuous chain of carbon atoms in the condensed structure. Begin the line structure by drawing a zigzag line in which the number of vertices plus line ends equals the number of carbon atoms in the chain. Show branches coming off the main chain by drawing vertical lines at the vertices as needed. Show all atoms that are not carbons or are not hydrogens attached to carbons.

SOLUTION
(a) Begin by drawing a zigzag line in which the total number of ends + vertices equals the number of carbons in the longest chain (here six, with the carbons numbered for clarity):

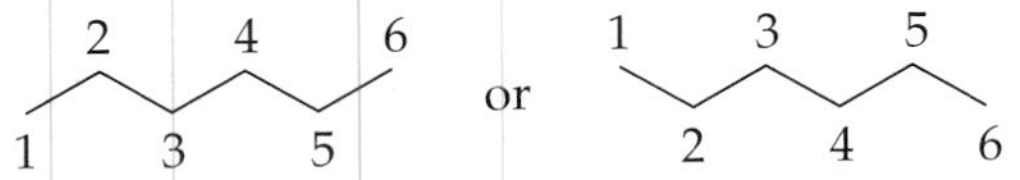

Looking at the condensed structure, you see CH_3 groups on carbons 3 and 4; these two CH_3 groups (methyl groups) are represented by lines coming off those carbons in the line structure:

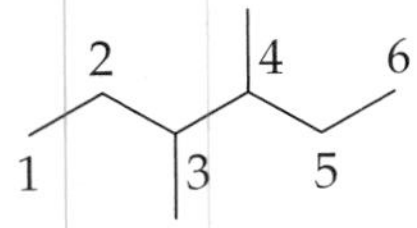

—*continued on next page*

—*continued from previous page*

This is the complete line structure. Notice that the hydrogens are not shown but understood. For example, carbon 4 has three bonds shown: one to carbon 3, one to carbon 5, and one to the branch CH_3 group; the fourth bond this carbon must have is understood to be to a hydrogen.

(b) Proceed as in (a), drawing a zigzag line for the longest chain of carbon atoms, which again contains 6 carbons. Next draw a line coming off each carbon bonded to a CH_3 group (carbons 3 and 4). Both the OH and the Cl groups must be shown to give the final structure:

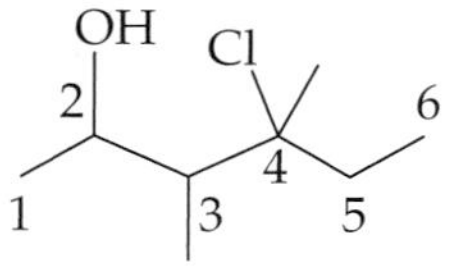

Note from this line structure that it does not matter in such a two-dimensional drawing what direction you show for a group that branches off the main chain, as long as it is attached to the correct carbon. This is true for condensed structures as well. Quite often, the direction that a group is shown coming off a main chain of carbon atoms is chosen simply for aesthetic reasons. The line structure can also be shown this way:

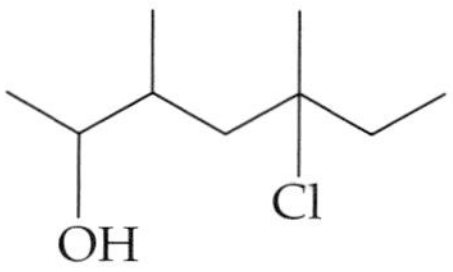

Worked Example 12.6 Molecular Structures: Converting Line Structures to Condensed Structures

Convert the following line structures to condensed structures:

(a)    **(b)**

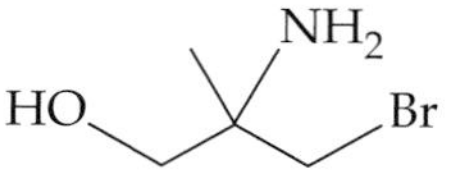

ANALYSIS Convert all vertices and line ends to carbons. Write in any noncarbon atoms and any hydrogens bonded to a noncarbon atom. Add hydrogens as needed so that each carbon has four groups attached. Remove lines connecting carbons except for branches.

SOLUTION

(a) Anywhere a line ends and anywhere two lines meet, write a C:

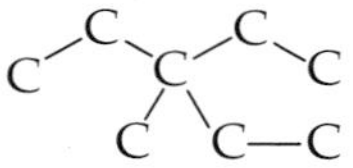

Because there are no atoms other than carbons and hydrogens in this molecule, the next step is to add hydrogens as needed to have four bonds for each carbon:

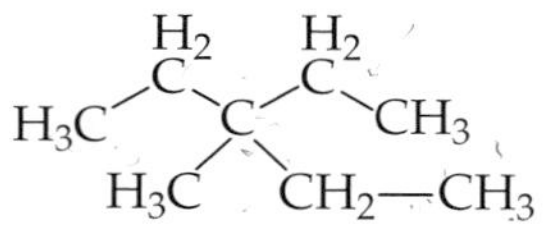

Finally, eliminate all lines except for branches to get the condensed structure:

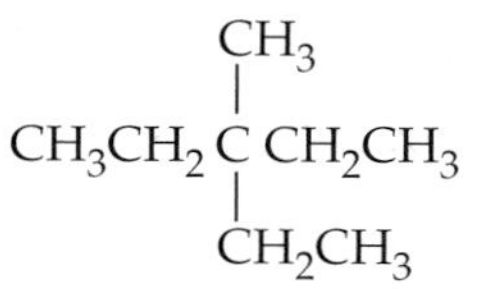

(b) Begin the condensed structure with a drawing showing a carbon at each line end and at each intersection of two lines:

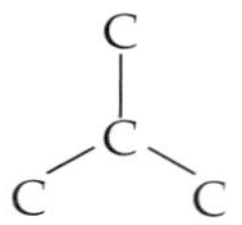

Next, write in all the noncarbon atoms and the hydrogen bonded to the oxygen. Then, add hydrogens so that each carbon forms four bonds:

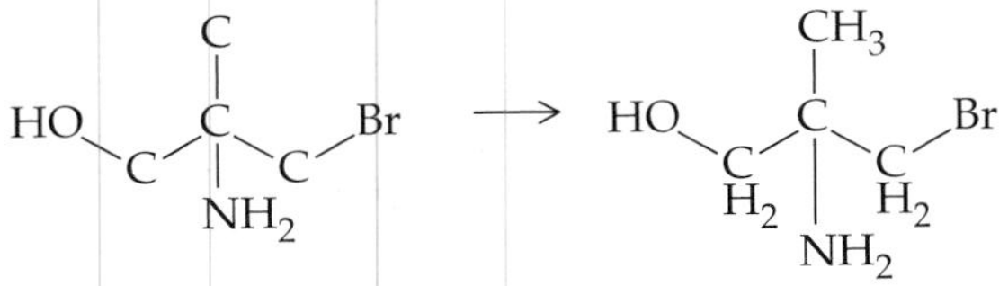

Eliminate all lines except for branches for the completed condensed structure:

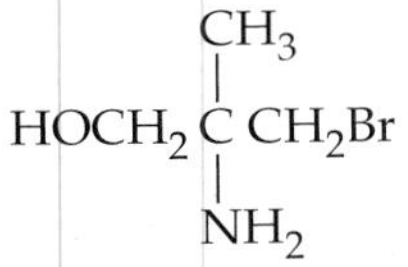

$$\text{HOCH}_2\overset{\overset{\displaystyle CH_3}{|}}{\underset{\underset{\displaystyle NH_2}{|}}{C}}\text{CH}_2\text{Br}$$

PROBLEM 12.6

Convert the following condensed structures to line structures:

(a) 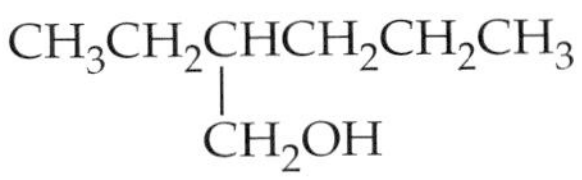 $\text{CH}_3\text{CH}_2\text{CHCH}_2\text{CH}_2\text{CH}_3$
  |
  CH_2OH

(b) 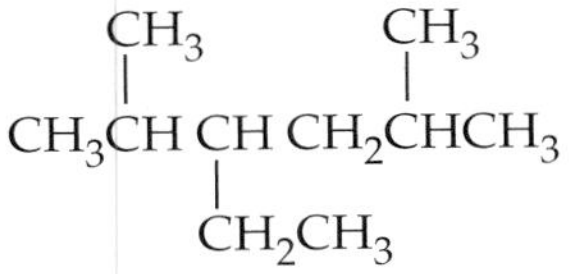 $\text{CH}_3\text{CH}\ \overset{\overset{\displaystyle CH_3}{|}}{CH}\ \text{CH}_2\text{CHCH}_3$
  | |
 CH_3 CH_2CH_3

(c) 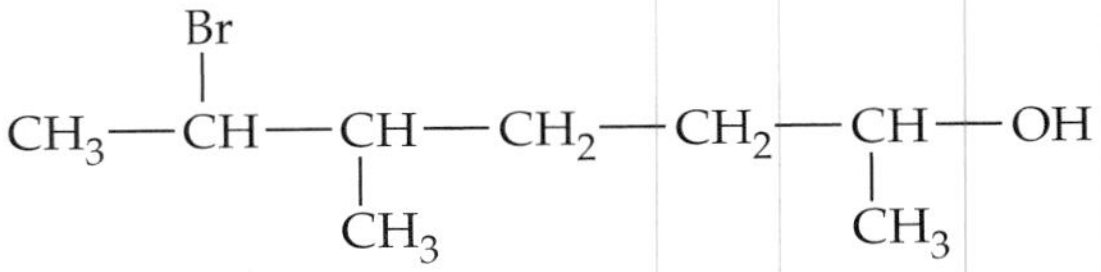
  Br
  |
$\text{CH}_3\!-\!\text{CH}\!-\!\text{CH}\!-\!\text{CH}_2\!-\!\text{CH}_2\!-\!\text{CH}\!-\!\text{OH}$
              | |
             CH_3 CH_3

PROBLEM 12.7

Convert the following line structures to condensed structures:

(a)

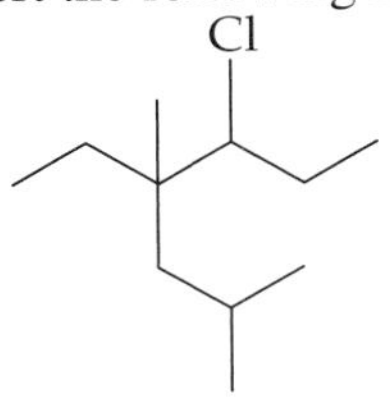

(b)

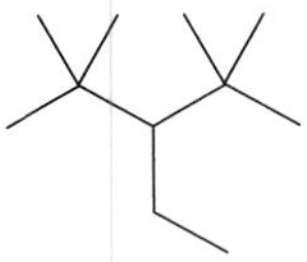

PROBLEM 12.8

Draw both condensed and line structures for the chemicals listed in Problem 12.1.

12.5 The Shapes of Organic Molecules

Learning Objective:

- Determine if two given structures are the different conformers of the same molecule, different structural isomers, or different molecules.

Every carbon atom in an alkane has its four bonds pointing toward the four corners of a tetrahedron, but chemists do not usually worry about three-dimensional shapes when writing condensed structures. Condensed structures do not imply any particular three-dimensional shape; they only indicate the connections between atoms without specifying geometry. Line structures do try to give some limited feeling for the shape of a molecule, but even here, the ability to show three-dimensional shape is limited unless dashed and wedged lines are used for the bonds (Sections 4.8 and 14.10).

Butane, for example, has no one single shape because *rotation* takes place around carbon–carbon single bonds. The two parts of a molecule joined by a carbon–carbon

Conformation The specific three-dimensional arrangement of atoms in a molecule achieved specifically through rotations around carbon–carbon single bonds.

Conformer Molecular structures having identical connections between atoms where the interconversion of C—C bond rotations results only in a different spatial arrangement of atoms.

In Section 14.10, we will see how the three dimensional structure of some organic molecules can lead to enantiomers (isomers that are nonsuperimposable mirror images of one another), an important property of many biologically active molecules.

single bond in a noncyclic structure (like butane) are free to spin around the bond, giving rise to an infinite number of possible three-dimensional geometries, or **conformations.** The various conformations of a molecule such as butane are called **conformers** of one another. Conformers differ from one another as a result of rotation around carbon–carbon single bonds. Although the conformers of a given molecule have different three-dimensional shapes (due to the bond angles in the molecule) and different energies (due to how groups are oriented with respect to one another), the conformers cannot be separated from one another. A given butane molecule might be in its fully extended conformation at one instant but in a more twisted conformation an instant later (Figure 12.2). An actual sample of butane contains a great many molecules that are constantly changing conformation. Some of these conformations have the groups staggered with respect to each other (Figure 12.2a and 12.2b), whereas some have all groups eclipsing one another (Figure 12.2c). Because molecules do have a three-dimensional shape and because atoms do occupy space, a more crowded conformer, where groups larger than H are near one another (Figure 12.2b), will have higher energy than the least crowded conformer, where the large groups are as far apart as possible (Figure 12.2a). Those conformers where groups on adjacent atoms are eclipsed will have the highest energy of all due to what is known as steric crowding. At any given instant, however, most of the molecules have the least crowded, lowest-energy extended conformation shown in Figure 12.2a. The same is true for all other alkanes: At any given instant, most molecules are in the least crowded conformation.

► **Figure 12.2**
Some conformations of butane (there are many others as well). The least crowded, extended conformation in (a) is the lowest-energy one, whereas the eclipsed conformation shown in (c), where the two CH₃ groups are spatially on top of one another, is the highest-energy one. In this drawing, those bonds shown with a wedge are coming out of the plane of the paper toward the reader, whereas those with a dash are going out of the same plane, away from the reader.

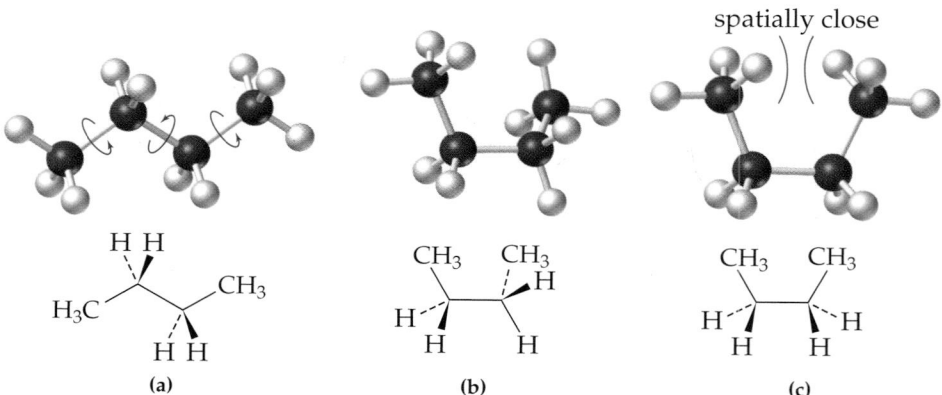

As long as any two structures have identical connections between atoms and are interconvertible either by "flipping" the molecule or by rotating C—C bonds, they are conformers of each other and represent the same compound, no matter how the structures are drawn. It is important to remember that no bonds are broken and reformed when interconverting conformers. Sometimes, you have to mentally rotate structures to see whether they are conformers or actually different molecules. To see that the following two structures represent conformers of the same compound rather than two isomers, picture one of them flipped right to left so that the red CH₃ groups are on the same side.

$$CH_3CHCH_2CH_2CH_3 \qquad CH_3CH_2CH_2CHCH_3$$
$$| \qquad\qquad\qquad\qquad |$$
$$CH_2 \qquad\qquad\qquad\qquad CH_2$$
$$| \qquad\qquad\qquad\qquad |$$
$$OH \qquad\qquad\qquad\qquad OH$$

Another way to determine whether two structures are conformers is to name each one using the International Union of Pure and Applied Chemistry (IUPAC) nomenclature rules (Section 12.6). If two structures have the same name, they are conformers of the same compound.

Worked Example 12.7 Molecular Structures: Identifying Conformers

The following structures all have the formula C_7H_{16}. Which of them represent the same molecule?

$$\begin{array}{c} CH_3 \\ | \end{array}$$
(a) $CH_3CHCH_2CH_2CH_2CH_3$

$$\begin{array}{c} CH_3 \\ | \end{array}$$
(b) $CH_3CH_2CH_2CH_2CHCH_3$

$$\begin{array}{c} CH_3 \\ | \end{array}$$
(c) $CH_3CH_2CH_2CHCH_2CH_3$

ANALYSIS Pay attention to the *connections* between atoms. Do not get confused by the apparent differences caused by writing a structure right to left versus left to right. Begin by identifying the longest chain of carbon atoms in the molecule.

SOLUTION
Molecule (a) has a straight chain of six carbons with a —CH_3 branch on the second carbon from the end. Molecule (b) also has a straight chain of six carbons with a —CH_3 branch on the second carbon from the end and is therefore identical to (a). That is, (a) and (b) are conformers of the same molecule. The only difference between (a) and (b) is that one is written "forward" and one is written "backward." Molecule (c), by contrast, has a straight chain of 6 carbons with a —CH_3 branch on the *third* carbon from the end and is, therefore, an isomer of (a) and (b).

Worked Example 12.8 Molecular Structures: Identifying Conformers and Isomers

Are the following pairs of compounds the same (conformers), isomers, or unrelated?

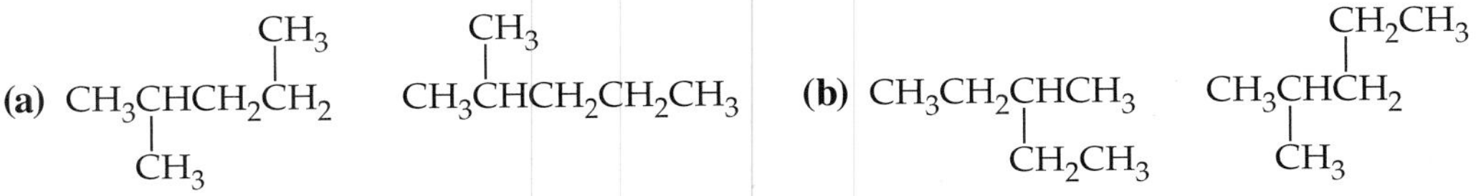

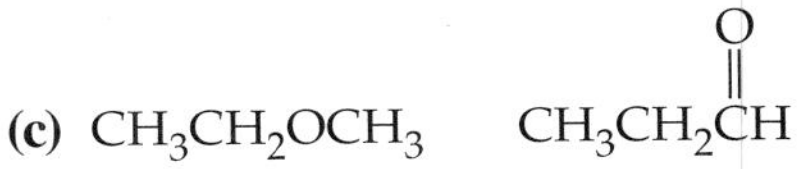

$$\begin{array}{c} CH_3 \\ | \end{array} \qquad \begin{array}{c} CH_3 \\ | \end{array}$$
(a) $CH_3CHCH_2CH_2$ $CH_3CHCH_2CH_2CH_3$
$$\begin{array}{c} | \\ CH_3 \end{array}$$

$$\begin{array}{c} CH_2CH_3 \\ | \end{array}$$
(b) $CH_3CH_2CHCH_3$ CH_3CHCH_2
$$\begin{array}{c} | \\ CH_2CH_3 \end{array} \qquad \begin{array}{c} | \\ CH_3 \end{array}$$

$$\begin{array}{c} O \\ \| \end{array}$$
(c) $CH_3CH_2OCH_3$ CH_3CH_2CH

ANALYSIS First compare molecular formulas to see if the compounds are related, and then look at the structures to see if they are the same compound or isomers. Find the longest continuous carbon chain in each, and then compare the locations of the substituents connected to the longest chain.

SOLUTION
(a) Both compounds have the same molecular formula (C_6H_{14}), so they are related. Since the —CH_3 group is on the second carbon from the end of a 5-carbon chain in both cases, these structures represent the same compound and are conformers of each other.

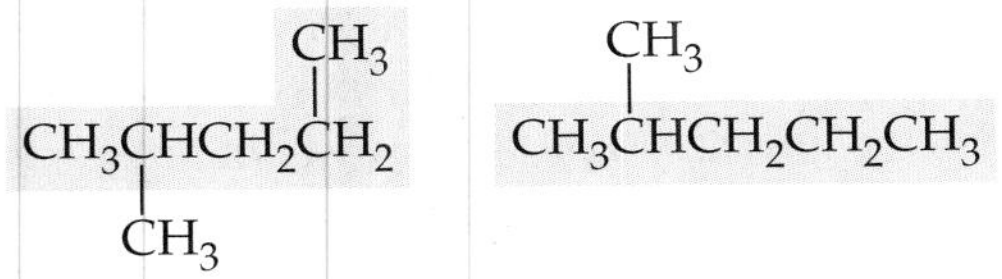

$$\begin{array}{c} CH_3 \\ | \end{array} \qquad \begin{array}{c} CH_3 \\ | \end{array}$$
$CH_3CHCH_2CH_2$ $CH_3CHCH_2CH_2CH_3$
$$\begin{array}{c} | \\ CH_3 \end{array}$$

(b) Both compounds have the same molecular formula (C_6H_{14}), and the longest chain in each is 5 carbon atoms. A comparison shows, however, that the —CH_3 group is on the middle carbon atom in one structure and on the second carbon atom in the other. These compounds are isomers of each other.

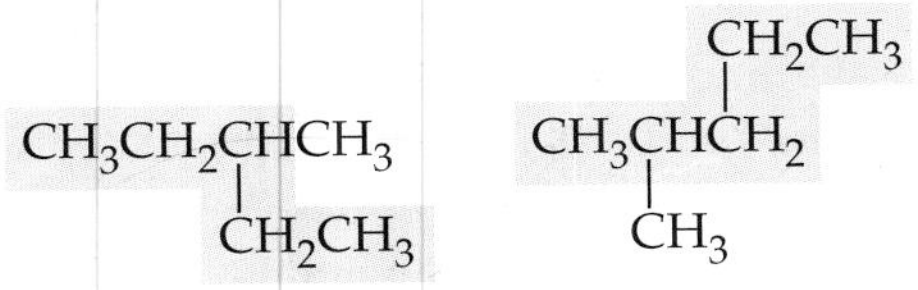

$$\begin{array}{c} CH_2CH_3 \\ | \end{array}$$
$CH_3CH_2CHCH_3$ CH_3CHCH_2
$$\begin{array}{c} | \\ CH_2CH_3 \end{array} \qquad \begin{array}{c} | \\ CH_3 \end{array}$$

(c) These compounds have different formulas $(C_3H_8O$ and $C_3H_6O)$, so they are unrelated; they are neither conformers nor isomers of each other.

PROBLEM 12.9

Which of the following structures represent the same molecule?

$$\text{(a)} \quad \overset{\displaystyle CH_3}{|} \quad \overset{\displaystyle CH_3}{|}$$
$$CH_2CH_2CHCH_2CH_3$$

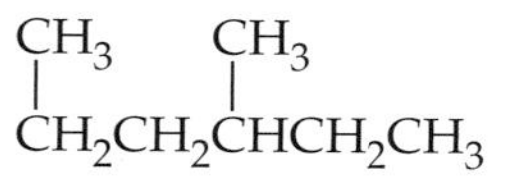

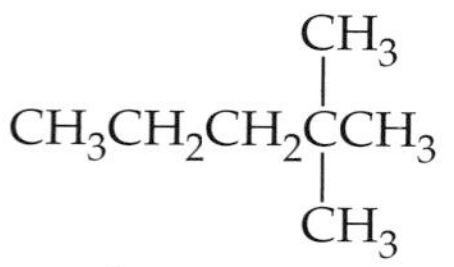

$$\text{(b)} \quad CH_3CH_2CH_2\overset{\displaystyle CH_3}{\underset{\displaystyle CH_3}{|}}CCH_3$$

$$\text{(c)} \quad CH_3CH_2\overset{\displaystyle CH_3}{\overset{|}{C}}HCH_2CH_2CH_3$$

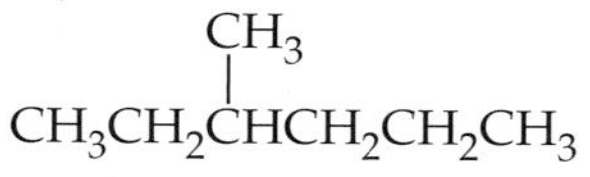

PROBLEM 12.10

Are the pairs of compounds shown below the same molecule, isomers, or different molecules?

(a)

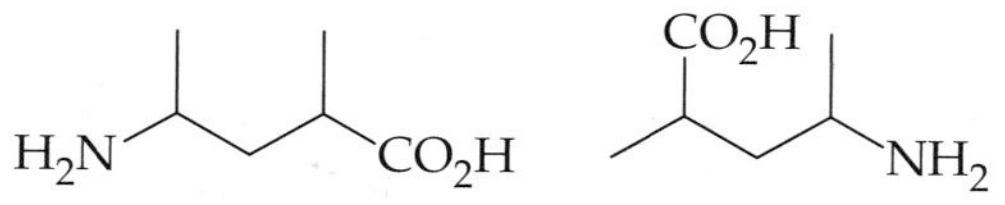

(b)

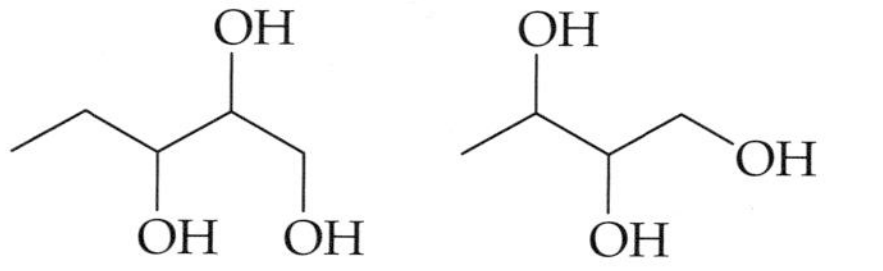

(c)

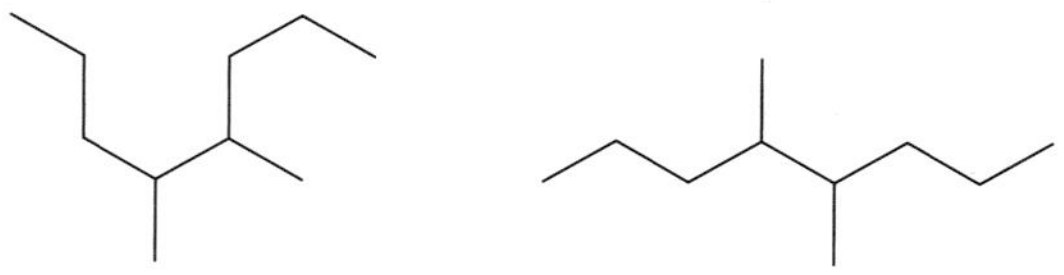

12.6 Naming Alkanes

Learning Objective:

• Name an alkane given its structure and draw an alkane given its name.

When relatively few pure organic chemicals were known, new compounds were named at the whim of their discoverer. Thus, urea is a crystalline substance first isolated from urine, and the barbiturates were named by their discoverer in honor of his friend Barbara. As more and more compounds became known, however, the need for a systematic method of naming compounds became apparent.

The system of naming *(nomenclature)* now used is one devised by IUPAC (pronounced *eye*-you-pack). In the IUPAC system for simple organic compounds, a chemical name has three parts: *prefix, parent,* and *suffix.* The prefix specifies the location of functional groups and other **substituents** in the molecule; the parent tells how many carbon atoms are present in the longest continuous chain; and the suffix identifies what family the molecule belongs to.

> **Substituent** An atom or group of atoms attached to a parent compound.

Prefix — Parent — Suffix

Where are substituents located?　How many carbons?　What family does the molecule belong to?

Straight-chain alkanes are named by counting the number of carbon atoms and adding the family suffix *-ane*. With the exception of the first four compounds—*meth*ane, *eth*ane, *prop*ane, and *but*ane—whose parent names have historical origins, the alkanes are named from Greek numbers according to the number of carbons present (Table 12.2). Thus, *pent*ane is the 5-carbon alkane, *hex*ane is the 6-carbon alkane, and so on. Straight-chain alkanes have no substituents, so prefixes are not needed. The first 10 alkane names are so common that they should be memorized.

> **Alkyl group** The part of an alkane that remains when a hydrogen atom is removed.

Substituents, such as —CH_3 and —CH_2CH_3, that branch off the main chain are called **alkyl groups.** An alkyl group can be thought of as the part of an alkane that

Table 12.2 Names of Straight-Chain Alkanes

Number of Carbons	Structure	Name
1	CH_4	Methane
2	CH_3CH_3	Ethane
3	$CH_3CH_2CH_3$	Propane
4	$CH_3CH_2CH_2CH_3$	Butane
5	$CH_3CH_2CH_2CH_2CH_3$	Pentane
6	$CH_3CH_2CH_2CH_2CH_2CH_3$	Hexane
7	$CH_3CH_2CH_2CH_2CH_2CH_2CH_3$	Heptane
8	$CH_3CH_2CH_2CH_2CH_2CH_2CH_2CH_3$	Octane
9	$CH_3CH_2CH_2CH_2CH_2CH_2CH_2CH_2CH_3$	Nonane
10	$CH_3CH_2CH_2CH_2CH_2CH_2CH_2CH_2CH_2CH_3$	Decane

remains when one hydrogen atom is removed to create an available bonding site. For example, removal of a hydrogen from methane, CH_4, gives the **methyl group,** $—CH_3$, and removal of a hydrogen from ethane, CH_3CH_3, gives the **ethyl group,** $—CH_2CH_3$. Notice that these alkyl groups are named simply by replacing the -*ane* ending of the parent alkane with an -*yl* ending:

Methyl group The $—CH_3$ alkyl group.

Ethyl group The $—CH_2CH_3$ alkyl group.

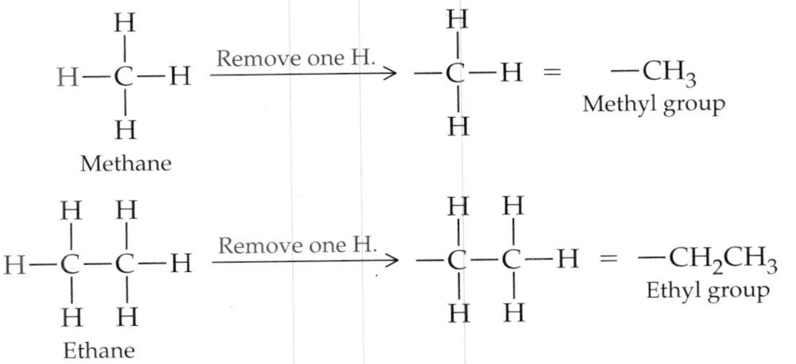

Both methane and ethane have only one "kind" of hydrogen. It does not matter which of the four methane hydrogens is removed, so there is only one possible methyl group. Similarly, it does not matter which of the six equivalent ethane hydrogens is removed, so only one ethyl group is possible.

The situation is more complex for larger alkanes, which contain more than one kind of hydrogen. Propane, for example, has two different kinds of hydrogens. Removal of any one of the 6 hydrogens attached to an end carbon yields a straight-chain alkyl group called **propyl,** whereas removal of either one of the two hydrogens attached to the central carbon yields a branched-chain alkyl group called **isopropyl:**

Propyl group The straight-chain alkyl group $—CH_2CH_2CH_3$.

Isopropyl group The branched-chain alkyl group $—CH(CH_3)_2$.

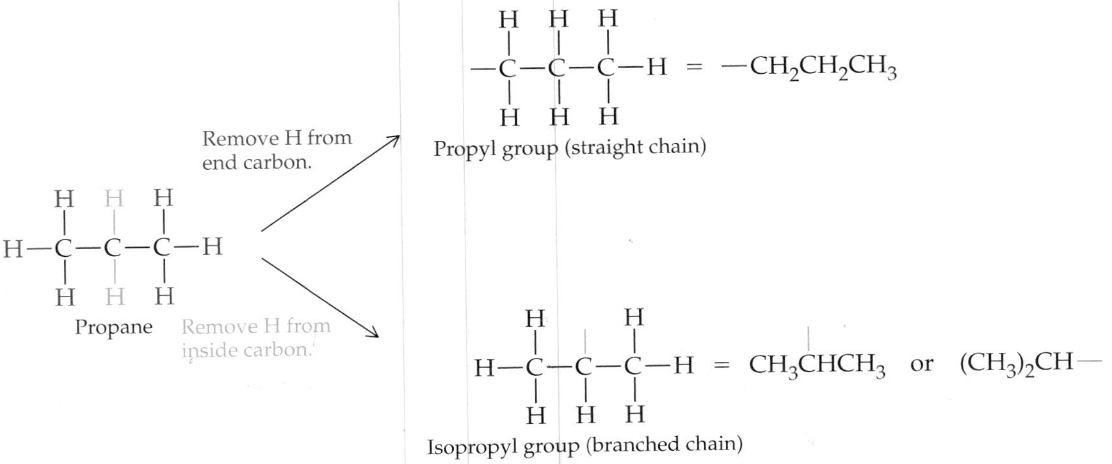

It is important to realize that alkyl groups are not compounds but rather are simply partial structures that help us name compounds. The names of some common alkyl groups are listed in Figure 12.3; you will want to commit them to memory.

Some Common Alkyl Groups (and their abbreviations)*

CH_3—
Methyl (Me)

CH_3CH_2—
Ethyl (Et)

$CH_3CH_2CH_2$—
Propyl

$CH_3\overset{\displaystyle CH_3}{\overset{|}{CH}}$—
Isopropyl (iPr)

$CH_3CH_2CH_2CH_2$—
Butyl

$CH_3\overset{|}{CH}CH_2CH_3$
sec-Butyl

$CH_3\overset{\displaystyle CH_3}{\overset{|}{CH}}CH_2$—
Isobutyl

$CH_3\overset{\displaystyle CH_3}{\overset{|}{\underset{\underset{\displaystyle CH_3}{|}}{C}}}CH_3$
tert-Butyl (tBu)

*The red bond shows the connection to the rest of the molecule.

▲ Figure 12.3
The most common alkyl groups found in organic molecules are shown here; the red bond shows the attachment the group has to the rest of the molecule.*

There are four possible substitution patterns for carbons attached to four atoms and these are designated *primary, secondary, tertiary,* and *quaternary. It is important to note that these designations strictly apply to carbons having only single bonds.* Notice that four butyl (4-carbon) groups are listed in Figure 12.3: butyl, *sec*-butyl, isobutyl, and *tert*-butyl. The prefix iso stands for isomer, and was introduced to distinguish an alkyl group that was attached through a primary carbon, but was branched rather than an unbranched chain. The prefix *sec-* stands for *secondary* (since the attachment point of the alkyl group is via a secondary carbon), and the prefix *tert-* stands for *tertiary,* as the attachment point is a tertiary carbon. A **primary (1°) carbon atom** has one other carbon molecule attached to it (typically indicated as an —R group in the molecular structure), a **secondary (2°) carbon atom** has two other carbons attached, a **tertiary (3°) carbon atom** has three other carbons attached, and a **quaternary (4°) carbon atom** has four other carbons attached:

Primary (1°) carbon atom A carbon atom with one other carbon attached to it.

Secondary (2°) carbon atom A carbon atom with two other carbons attached to it.

Tertiary (3°) carbon atom A carbon atom with three other carbons attached to it.

Quaternary (4°) carbon atom A carbon atom with four other carbons attached to it.

$$R-\overset{\displaystyle H}{\overset{|}{\underset{\underset{\displaystyle H}{|}}{C}}}-H \qquad R-\overset{\displaystyle R}{\overset{|}{\underset{\underset{\displaystyle H}{|}}{C}}}-H \qquad R-\overset{\displaystyle R}{\overset{|}{\underset{\underset{\displaystyle R}{|}}{C}}}-H \qquad R-\overset{\displaystyle R}{\overset{|}{\underset{\underset{\displaystyle R}{|}}{C}}}-R$$

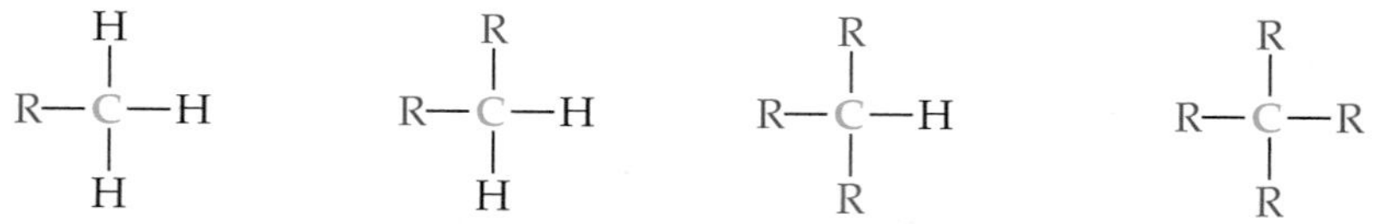

Primary carbon (1°) has one other carbon attached.

Secondary carbon (2°) has two other carbons attached.

Tertiary carbon (3°) has three other carbons attached.

Quaternary carbon (4°) has four other carbons attached.

R represents a linkage to another C.

Organic chemists use the abbreviation R to represent an unspecified group where the direct attachment to the atom under discussion is a carbon; it could be as simple as a CH_3, or as complicated as you could ever imagine! It is used so chemists can focus on a particular group of interest (a functional group, or a specific carbon atom) without the clutter of the rest of the molecule, and allows for more general discussions of reactivity. It is common that when abbreviations are used, some qualifier be placed on them (e.g., $R = CH_3, C_2H_5$).

Table 12.3 contains a list of the most common abbreviations you will see in this text. We will keep the use of these to a minimum; you should only use them yourself if your instructor approves. The use of abbreviations can greatly simplify discussions of reactions; for example, the generalized formula for an alcohol might refer to an

Table 12.3 Common Abbreviations in Organic Chemistry

R	Residue or **R**est of the molecule; used to represent the part of the organic molecule *not* under consideration for the current discussion. Does not contain functional groups that can also react under the conditions being examined. Usually means a carbon group but can generally be anything.
R′, R″, R‴	Prime notation; used when different R groups are needed. Read as "R-prime", "R-double prime", etc.
X	A polar group; usually reserved to represent a halogen. Almost always used to represent a "leaving group": An atom or group that can leave in either its anionic or neutral form.
Y or **Z**	Also a polar group; used when different polar groups are present. Usually used to indicate a group attached via an O or S atom. Infrequently used.
M	A metal or metal ion; used primarily when the exact identity of the metal is not crucial to the discussion. Typically a Na or K.
Ar	An aromatic group ("**Ar**yl"); a more specific **R** group. Typically used when its presence imparts special properties on the C to which it is attached. The most common is a phenyl group (Chapter 13).
Ph	A phenyl group ($-C_6H_5$; Chapter 13); a benzene ring with a single group attached.

alcohol as simple as CH_3OH or CH_3CH_2OH or one as complicated as cholesterol, shown here:

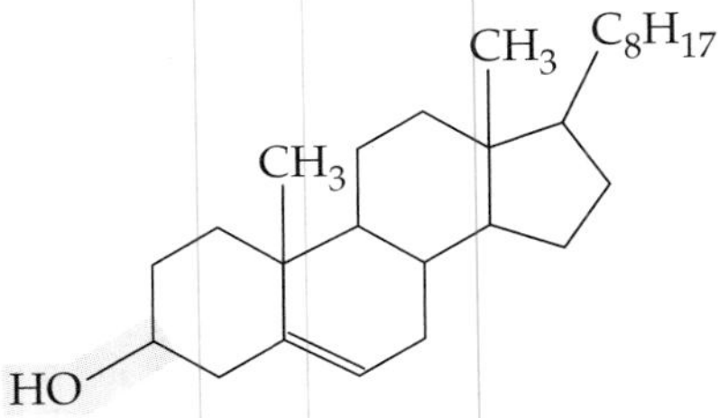

Branched-chain alkanes can be named by following four steps:

STEP 1: Name the main chain. Find the longest continuous chain of carbons, and name the chain according to the number of carbon atoms it contains. The longest chain may not be immediately obvious because it is not always written on one line; you may have to "turn corners" to find it.

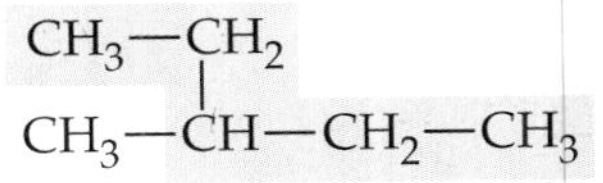

Name as a substituted pentane, not as a substituted butane, because the *longest* chain has five carbons.

STEP 2: Number the carbon atoms in the main chain, beginning at the end nearer the first branch point.

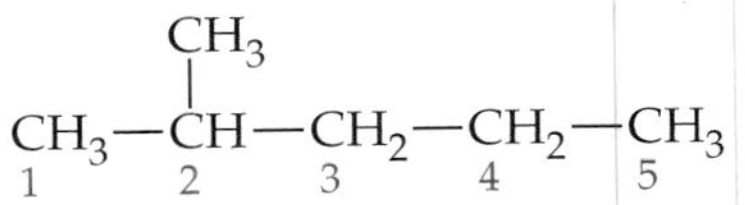

The first (and only) branch occurs at C2 if we start numbering from the left, but would occur at C4 if we started from the right by mistake.

STEP 3: Identify the branching substituents, and number each according to its point of attachment to the main chain.

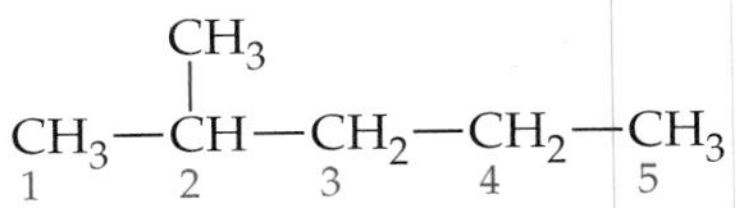

The main chain is a pentane. There is one methyl ($-CH_3$) substituent group connected to C2 of the chain.

If there are two substituents on the same carbon, assign the same number to both. There must always be as many numbers in the name as there are substituents.

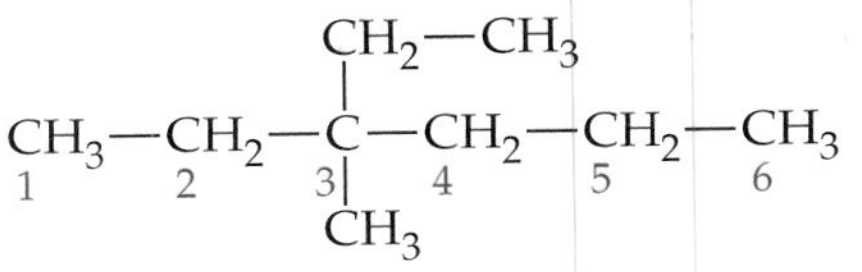

The main chain is a hexane. There are two substituents, a methyl ($-CH_3$) and an ethyl ($-CH_2CH_3$), both connected to C3 of the chain.

STEP 4: **Write the name as a single word,** using hyphens to separate the numbers from the different prefixes and commas to separate numbers, if necessary. If two or more different substituent groups are present, cite them in alphabetical order. If two or more identical substituents are present, use one of the prefixes *di-, tri-, tetra-,* and so forth, but do not use these prefixes for alphabetizing purposes.

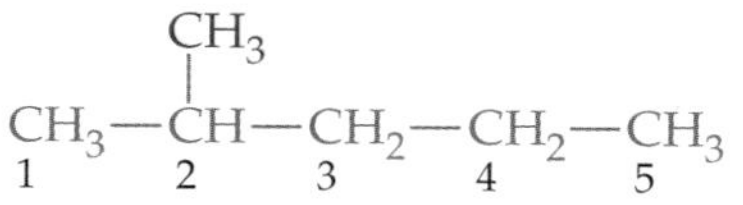

$$CH_3-\underset{1}{C}H_3-\underset{2}{C}H-\underset{3}{C}H_2-\underset{4}{C}H_2-\underset{5}{C}H_3$$
with CH_3 on carbon 2

2-Methylpentane (a 5-carbon main chain with a 2-methyl substituent)

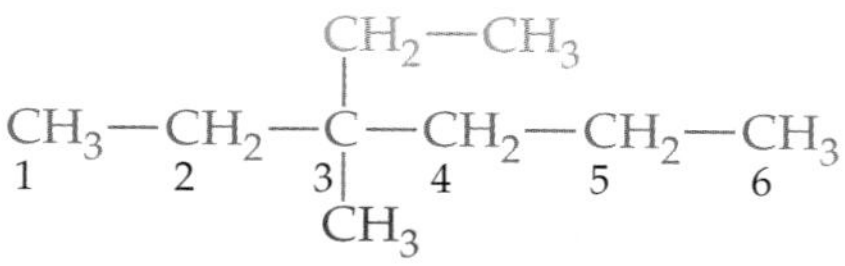

$$CH_3-\underset{1}{C}H_2-\underset{2}{C}H_2-\underset{3}{C}-\underset{4}{C}H_2-\underset{5}{C}H_2-\underset{6}{C}H_3$$
with CH_2-CH_3 above and CH_3 below carbon 3

3-Ethyl-3-methylhexane (a 6-carbon main chain with 3-ethyl and 3-methyl substituents cited alphabetically)

$$CH_3-\underset{3}{C}-\underset{4}{C}H_2-\underset{5}{C}H_2-\underset{6}{C}H_3$$
with $\underset{2}{C}H_2-\underset{1}{C}H_3$ above and CH_3 below carbon 3

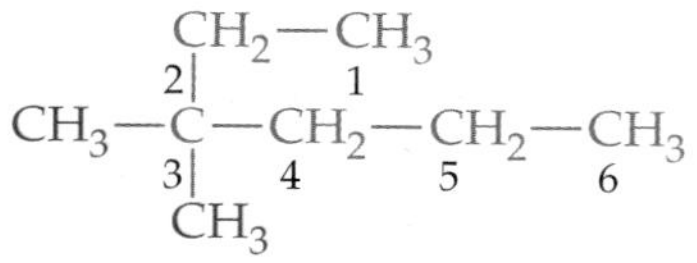

3,3-Dimethylhexane (a 6-carbon main chain with two 3-methyl substituents)

$$CH_3-\underset{3}{C}-\underset{4}{C}H-\underset{5}{C}H_2-\underset{6}{C}H_2-\underset{7}{C}H_3$$
with $\underset{2}{C}H_2CH_3$ above carbon 3, H_3C below carbon 3, and CH_2CH_3 below carbon 4

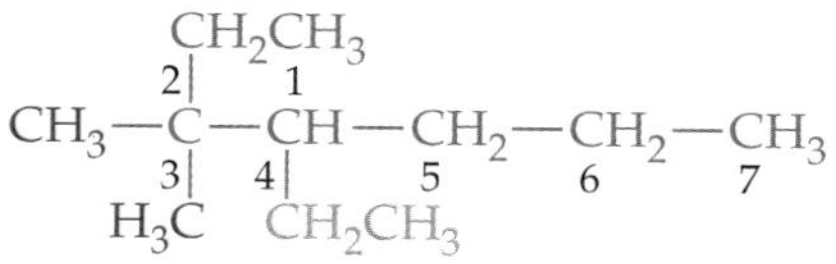

4-Ethyl-3,3-dimethylheptane (a 7-carbon main chain with two 3-methyl substituents and one 4-ethyl substituents, cited alphabetically based on the group, not the prefix (di).

Worked Example 12.9 Naming Organic Compounds: Alkanes

What is the IUPAC name of the following alkanes?

(a) 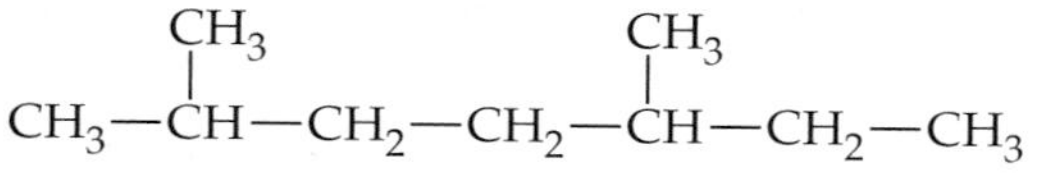 $CH_3-CH-CH_2-CH_2-CH-CH_2-CH_3$ with CH_3 substituents on the 2nd and 5th carbons

(b)

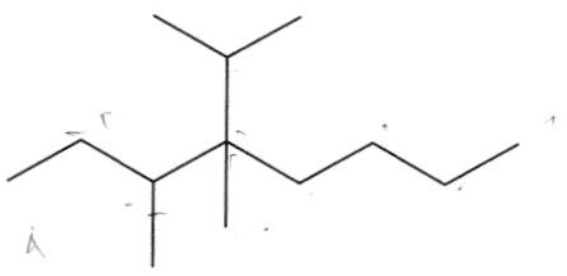

ANALYSIS Follow the four steps outlined in the text.

SOLUTION

(a) STEP 1: The longest continuous chain of carbon atoms is seven, so the main chain is a *hept*ane.

STEP 2: Number the main chain beginning at the end nearer the first branch.

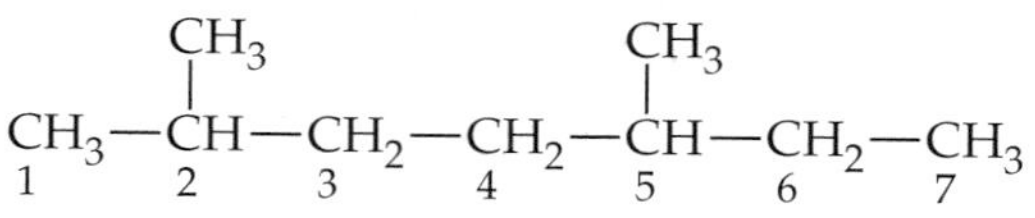

$$CH_3-\underset{1}{C}H_3-\underset{2}{C}H-\underset{3}{C}H_2-\underset{4}{C}H_2-\underset{5}{C}H-\underset{6}{C}H_2-\underset{7}{C}H_3$$
with CH_3 on carbons 2 and 5

STEP 3: Identify and number the substituents (a 2-methyl and a 5-methyl in this case):

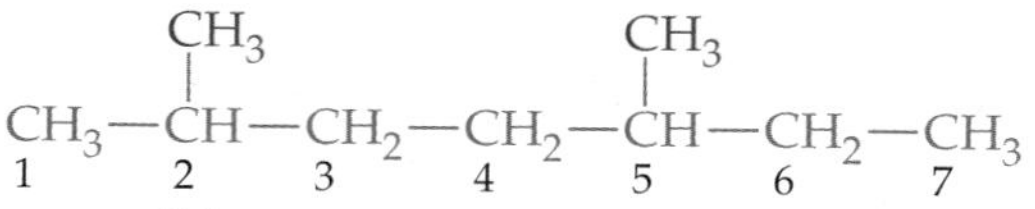

$$CH_3-\underset{1}{C}H_3-\underset{2}{C}H-\underset{3}{C}H_2-\underset{4}{C}H_2-\underset{5}{C}H-\underset{6}{C}H_2-\underset{7}{C}H_3$$
with CH_3 on carbons 2 and 5

Substituents: 2-Methyl and 5-Methyl

STEP 4: Write the name as one word, using the prefix *di-* because there are two methyl groups. Separate the two numbers by a comma, and use a hyphen between the numbers and the word.

Name: 2, 5-Dimethylheptane

(b) STEP 1: The longest continuous chain of carbon atoms is eight, so the main chain is an *oct*ane.

STEP 2: Number the main chain beginning at the end nearer the first branch.

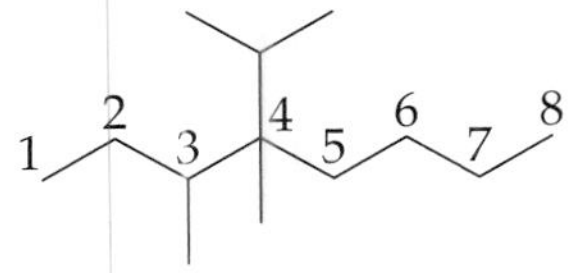

STEP 3: Identify and number the substituents.

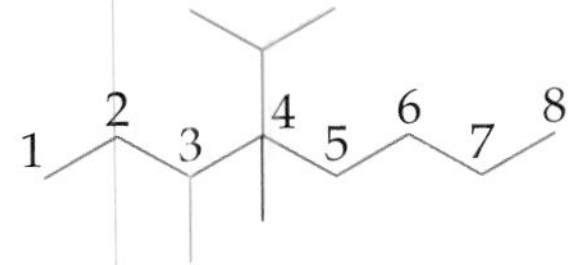

3-Methyl, 4-Methyl, 4-Isopropyl

STEP 4: Write the name as one word, again using the prefix *di-* because there are two methyl groups.

Name: 3, 4-Dimethyl-4-isopropyloctane

Worked Example 12.10 Molecular Structure: Identifying 1°, 2°, 3°, and 4° Carbons

Identify each carbon atom in the following molecule as primary, secondary, tertiary, or quaternary.

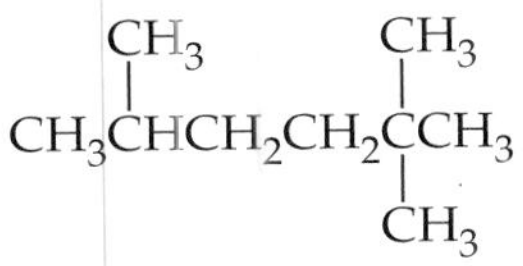

ANALYSIS Look at each carbon atom in the molecule, count the number of other carbon atoms attached, and make the assignment accordingly: primary (1 carbon attached), secondary (2 carbons attached), tertiary (3 carbons attached), and quaternary (4 carbons attached).

SOLUTION

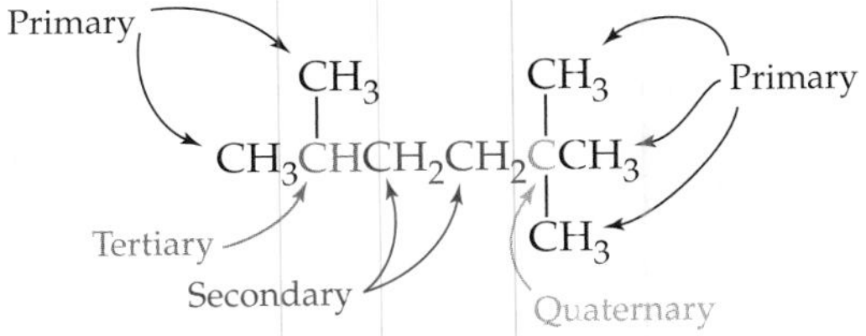

Note: Hydrogens, when attached to a carbon, are given the same primary, secondary, or tertiary designation as the C to which they are attached (and this is why they have been given the same color as their carbons in the figure above).

> ▶ We will see the primary, secondary, and tertiary classification used again when we study alcohols and alkyl halides in Chapter 14, as well as when we study amines in Chapter 16. For alcohols and alkyl halides, the classification will be identical to that used for hydrogens; this will change slightly when we discuss amines.

Worked Example 12.11 Molecular Structures: Drawing Condensed Structures from Names

Draw condensed and line structures corresponding to the following IUPAC names:
(a) 2,3-Dimethylpentane
(b) 3-Ethylheptane
(c) 4-*tert*-Butylheptane

ANALYSIS Starting with the parent chain, add the named alkyl substituent groups to the appropriately numbered carbon atoms.

—continued on next page

—continued from previous page

SOLUTION

(a) The parent chain has 5 carbons (*pent*ane), with two methyl groups (—CH_3) attached to the second and third carbon in the chain.

$$
\begin{array}{c}
CH_3\ CH_3 \\
|\quad | \\
CH_3CH\ CH\ CH_2CH_3 \\
1\quad 2\quad 3\quad 4\quad 5
\end{array}
$$

or

$$
\begin{array}{c}
CH_3 \\
| \\
CH_3CH\ CH\ CH_2CH_3 \\
1\quad 2\quad 3|\quad 4\quad 5 \\
CH_3
\end{array}
$$

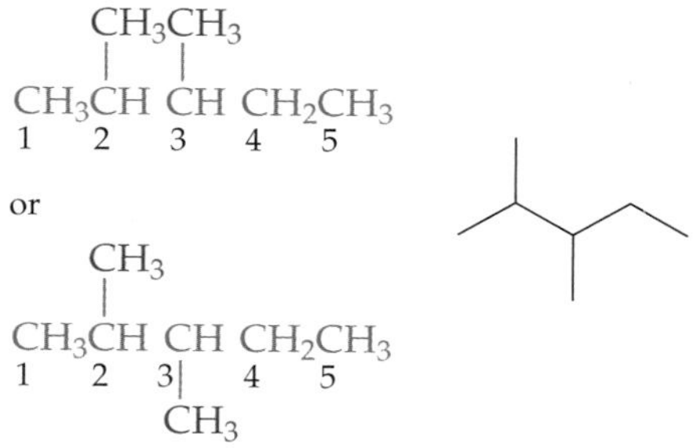

(b) The parent chain has 7 carbons (*hept*ane), with one ethyl group (—CH_2CH_3) attached to the third carbon in the chain.

$$
\begin{array}{c}
CH_2CH_3 \\
| \\
CH_3CH_2CHCH_2CH_2CH_2CH_3 \\
1\quad 2\quad 3\quad 4\quad 5\quad 6\quad 7
\end{array}
$$

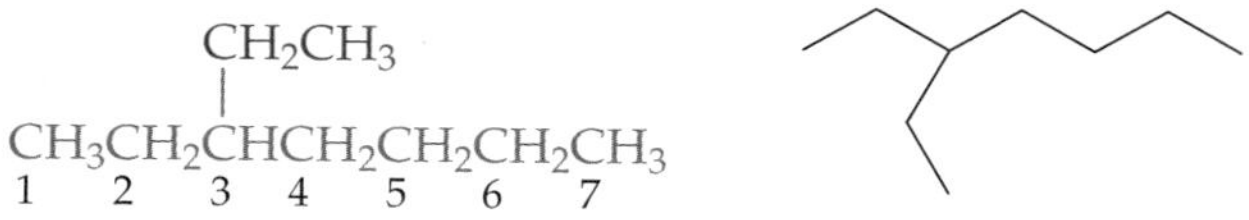

(c) Again, the parent chain has 7 carbons (*hept*ane), with one tert-butyl group (—$C(CH_3)_3$) attached to the fourth carbon in the chain.

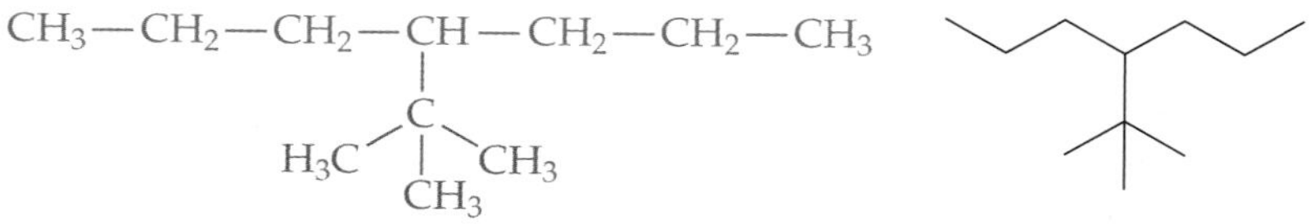

$$
CH_3{-}CH_2{-}CH_2{-}CH{-}CH_2{-}CH_2{-}CH_3
$$
$$
\begin{array}{c}
| \\
C \\
H_3C \quad | \quad CH_3 \\
CH_3
\end{array}
$$

4-(*tert*-butyl)heptane

PROBLEM 12.11

Identify each carbon in the molecule shown in Worked Example 12.9b as primary, secondary, tertiary, or quaternary.

PROBLEM 12.12

What are the IUPAC names of the following alkanes?

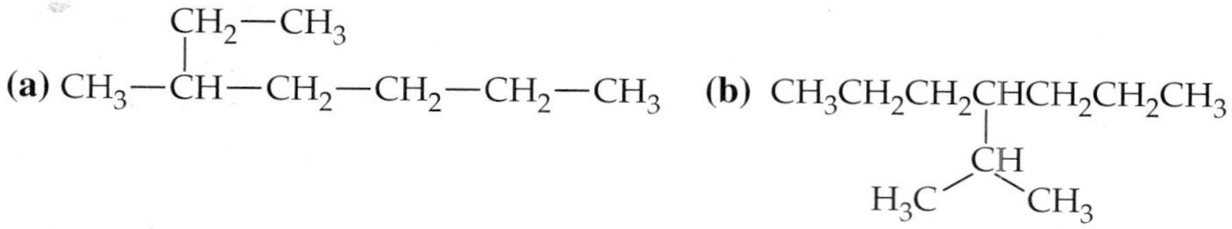

$$
\begin{array}{c}
CH_2{-}CH_3 \\
| \\
\text{(a) } CH_3{-}CH{-}CH_2{-}CH_2{-}CH_2{-}CH_3
\end{array}
$$

(b) $CH_3CH_2CH_2CHCH_2CH_2CH_3$
$$
\begin{array}{c}
| \\
CH \\
H_3C \quad CH_3
\end{array}
$$

PROBLEM 12.13

Draw both condensed and line structures corresponding to the following IUPAC names and label each carbon as primary, secondary, tertiary, or quaternary.
  (a) 3-Methylhexane   **(b)** 3,4-Dimethyloctane   **(c)** 2,2,4-Trimethylpentane

PROBLEM 12.14

Draw and name alkanes that meet the following descriptions:
  (a) A 5-carbon alkane with a tertiary carbon atom
  (b) A 7-carbon alkane that has both a tertiary and a quaternary carbon atom

⊙ KEY CONCEPT PROBLEM 12.15

What are the IUPAC names of the following alkanes?

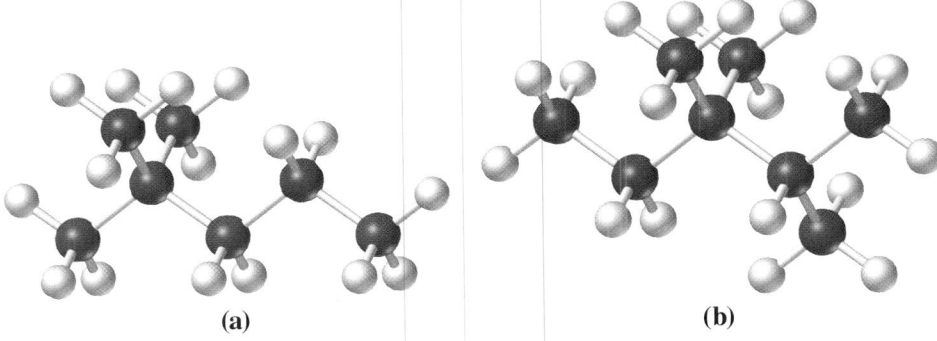

(a)   (b)

CHEMISTRY IN ACTION

☤ How Important Can a Methyl Group Really Be?

How does a living organism make a molecule as complex and beautiful as DNA (Chapter 26) or the neurotransmitters (Chapter 28) from simple starting points? Most complicated biomolecules are synthesized via an anabolic pathway (a biochemical pathway that creates molecules). Anabolic pathways will take a relatively simple starting material (usually obtained from food digestion) and convert it into the desired end product via a series of biochemical steps. Sometimes, however, this is not enough and what is known as a post synthetic modification must be carried out at the cellular level. Universally, one of the most important of these is methylation, the addition of a lowly —CH_3 group to a nitrogen (N-methylation), an oxygen (O-methylation), or a sulfur (S-methylation). Addition of a simple methyl group can greatly change the function of molecules. Biological systems typically need assistance to carry out these molecular conversions, which is accomplished through the use of a class of enzyme known as methyltransferases (Section 19.3), many of which rely on the B vitamins as cofactors (Section 19.2). This highly controlled process is found in every cell in the body and is key to a number of processes, including the regulation of healing, cell energy, and expression of DNA. In fact, the efficiency of the process of biological methylation reduces with time and can cause a number of age-related disorders, including cardiovascular disease and even cancer. Consider homocysteine, a naturally occurring, nonprotein amino acid that is typically found in blood plasma when body chemistry is out of balance. Biologically, it forms from the amino acid methionine (Chapter 18) by loss of the methyl group from sulfur.

Homocysteine is a pro-oxidant and as such is poisonous to cells (cytotoxic). A pro-oxidant is a chemical that interferes with the way cells use or get rid of oxygen and other oxidizing species. One consequence of this is the buildup of the reactive oxygen species (radicals) that cause oxidative damage to the cell

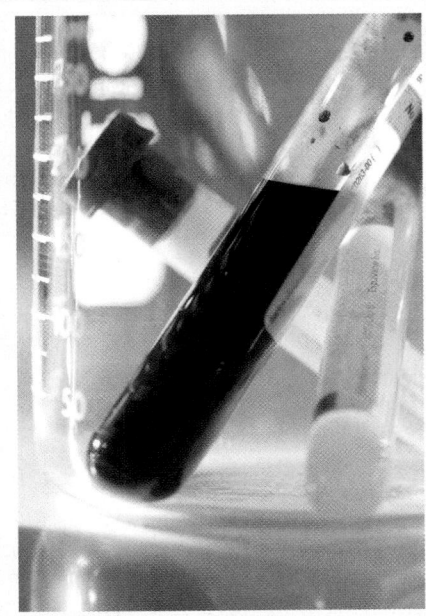

▲ Blood analysis is an invaluable aid in the diagnosis of disease. For example, abnormal levels of homocysteine can indicate an increased risk of atherosclerosis.

(as a note, the over-the-counter pain medication acetaminophen (Tylenol) can also act as a pro-oxidant; overdoses of acetaminophen can fatally damage the liver, where it is metabolized). High levels of homocysteine result in a number of disorders, including DNA strand breakage and an increase in the risk of heart disease. Normally, homocysteine has low circulating levels due to its rapid re-methylation to methionine. Deficiencies in the B vitamins B-12, B-6, and folic acid, the cofactors necessary for the methyltransferases to work, typically lead to high levels of homocysteine. The simple addition of a —CH_3 methyl group to the sulfur of homocysteine can neutralize its cytotoxic behavior.

CIA Problem 12.1 What is an anabolic pathway?

CIA Problem 12.2 What does "cytotoxic" mean?

CIA Problem 12.3 What cofactors are necessary for methyltransferases to work?

HS⌇⌇CO₂H *methyltransferase*→ CH₃—S⌇⌇CO₂H

      NH₂   NH₂

  Homocysteine   Methionine

12.7 Properties of Alkanes

Learning Objective:

• Identify the physical properties of alkanes.

There are three major intermolecular forces that need to be considered when discussing the properties of organic molecules: dipole–dipole forces (attractions between the δ^+ and δ^- ends of adjacent polar molecules; Section 8.2), hydrogen bonding (seen in molecules that contain N—H and O—H groups; Section 8.2), and London dispersion forces (due to instantaneous polarizations of a molecule's electron cloud, these are the only intermolecular forces available to nonpolar molecules; Section 8.2). Intermolecular forces are what cause molecules to aggregate or "stick" to one another; hydrogen bonds are the strongest, dipole–dipole forces follow in strength, and London dispersion forces are the weakest. Alkanes contain only nonpolar C—C and C—H bonds, so the only intermolecular forces influencing them are weak London dispersion forces. London dispersion forces increase both as molecules get bigger (due to an increase in the number of electrons within the molecule) and as their surface area increases. The effect of these forces is shown in the regularity with which the melting and boiling points of straight-chain alkanes increase with molecular size (Figure 12.4). The first four alkanes—methane, ethane, propane, and butane—are gases at room temperature and pressure. Alkanes with 5–15 carbon atoms are liquids; those with 16 or more carbon atoms are generally low-melting, waxy solids. Similar results are seen for branched alkanes; however, due to the ability of these to have more compact, spherical shapes, their melting and boiling points can be quite different from their straight-chain counterparts.

◀◀ Review the effects of London dispersion forces on molecules in Section 8.2.

▶ **Figure 12.4**
The boiling and melting points for the straight-chain alkanes increase with molecular size.

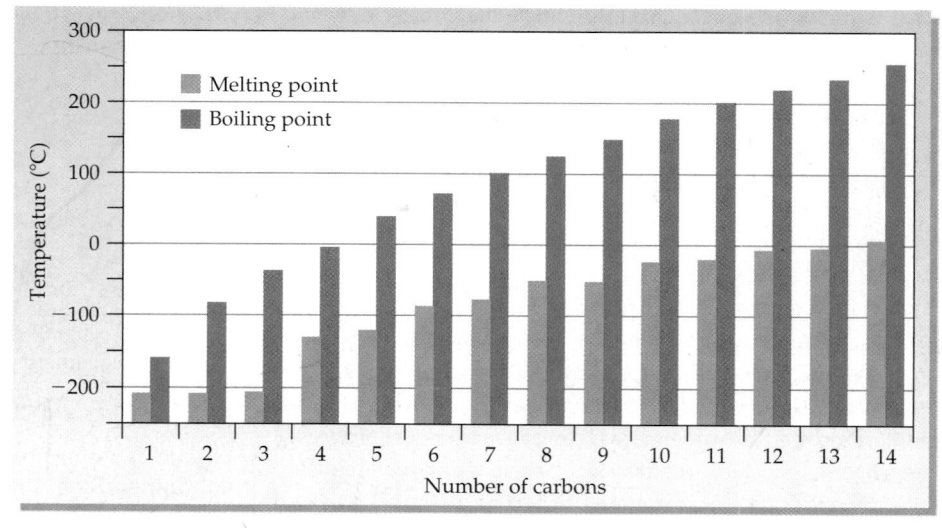

◀◀ Recall from Section 9.2 the rule of thumb when predicting solubility: "like dissolves like."

Since they do not possess significant dipole moments, alkanes are nonpolar and as such are insoluble in polar solvents such as water but soluble in nonpolar organic solvents, such as pentane, hexane, and other alkanes ("like dissolves like"). Because of this aversion to water, alkanes are said to be hydrophobic ("water hating"). Because alkanes are generally less dense than water, they float on its surface. Low-molecular-weight alkanes are volatile and must be handled with care because their vapors are flammable. Mixtures of alkane vapors and air can explode when ignited by a single spark.

The physiological effects of alkanes are limited. Methane, ethane, and propane gases are nontoxic, but the danger of inhaling them lies in potential suffocation due to lack of oxygen. Breathing the vapor of larger alkanes in large concentrations can induce loss of consciousness. There is also a danger in breathing droplets of liquid alkanes because they dissolve nonpolar substances in lung tissue and cause pneumonia-like symptoms.

Mineral oil, petroleum jelly, and paraffin wax are mixtures of higher alkanes. All are harmless to body tissue and are used in numerous food and medical applications. Mineral oil passes through the body unchanged and is sometimes used as a laxative. Petroleum jelly (sold as Vaseline) softens, lubricates, and protects the skin. Paraffin wax is used in candle making, on surfboards, and in home canning. See the Chemistry in Action on page 394 for more surprising uses of alkanes.

Properties of Alkanes:
* Odorless or mild odor; colorless; tasteless; nontoxic
* Nonpolar; insoluble in water but soluble in nonpolar organic solvents; less dense than water
* Flammable; otherwise not very reactive

12.8 Reactions of Alkanes

Learning Objectives:

* Determine the basic reactions of alkanes.
* Draw the isomeric products formed during the halogenation of simple alkanes.

Alkanes do not react with acids, bases, or most other common laboratory *reagents* (a substance that causes a reaction to occur). Their only major reactions are with oxygen (combustion) and with halogens (halogenation). Both of these reaction types have complicated mechanisms and occur through the intermediacy of free radicals (see "Halogenation" later in the chapter).

▶▶ Another important radical reaction is found in the formation of the polymers that make up such things as plastics; this is a radical reaction seen primarily with organic molecules that contain double bonds (Section 13.7).

Combustion

Most of you probably get to school every day using some sort of transportation that uses gasoline, which is a mixture of alkanes, or use a mixture of alkanes when cooking on your gas stove or grilling on your backyard gas barbecue. To power a vehicle or use a gas grill, that mixture of alkanes must be converted into energy. The reaction of an alkane with oxygen is called **combustion,** an oxidation reaction that commonly takes place in a controlled manner in an engine or furnace. Carbon dioxide and water are always the products of complete combustion of any hydrocarbon, and a large amount of heat is released (ΔH is a negative number). Some examples were given in Table 7.1.

Combustion A chemical reaction that produces a flame, usually because of burning with oxygen.

◀◀ Combustion reactions are exothermic, as we learned in Section 7.3.

$$CH_4(g) + 2\,O_2(g) \longrightarrow CO_2(g) + 2\,H_2O(g) \quad \Delta H = -213\,\text{kcal/mol}\,(-891\,\text{kJ/mol})$$

When hydrocarbon combustion is incomplete because of faulty engine or furnace performance, carbon monoxide and carbon-containing soot are among the products. Carbon monoxide is a highly toxic and dangerous substance, especially so because it has no odor and can easily go undetected (see the Chemistry in Action "CO and NO: Pollutants or Miracle Molecules?" in Chapter 4). Breathing air that contains as little as 2% CO for only one hour can cause respiratory and nervous system damage or death. The supply of oxygen to the brain is cut off by carbon monoxide because it binds strongly to blood hemoglobin at the site where oxygen is normally bound. By contrast with CO, CO_2 is nontoxic and causes no harm, except by suffocation when present in high concentration.

MASTERING REACTIONS

Organic Chemistry and the Curved Arrow Formalism

Starting with this chapter and continuing on through the remainder of this text, you will be exploring the world of organic chemistry and its close relative, biochemistry. Both of these areas of chemistry are much more "visual" than those you have been studying; organic chemists, for example, look at how and why reactions occur by examining the flow of electrons. For example, consider the following reaction of 2-iodopropane with sodium cyanide:

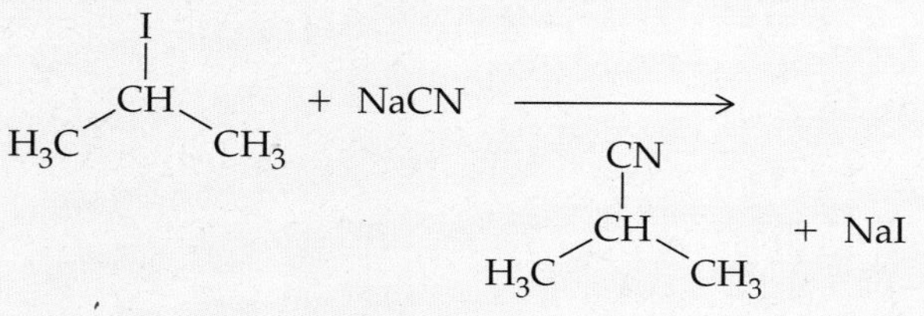

This seemingly simple process (known as a *substitution reaction,* discussed in Chapter 13) is not adequately described by the equation. To help to understand what may really be going on, organic chemists use what is loosely described as "electron pushing" and have adopted what is known as *curved arrow formalism* to represent it. The movement of electrons is depicted using curved arrows, where the number of electrons corresponds to the head of the arrow. Single-headed arrows represent movement of one electron, whereas a double-headed arrow indicates the movement of two.

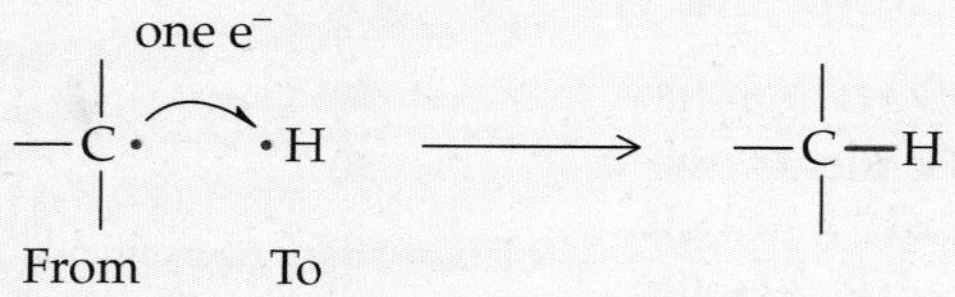

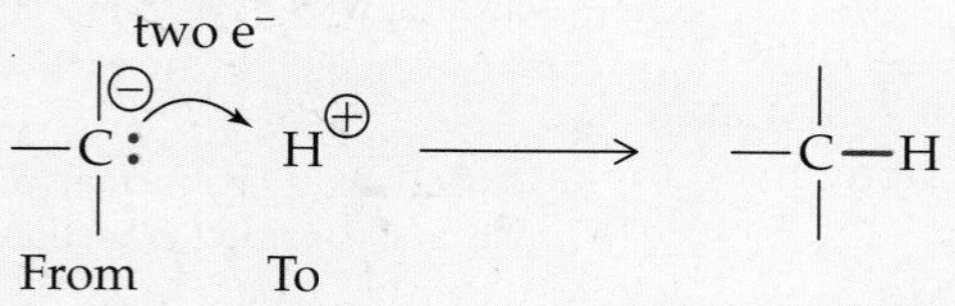

The convention is to show the movement *from* an area of high electron density (the start of the arrow) *to* one of lower electron density (the head of the arrow). Using curved arrow formalism, we can examine the reaction of 2-iodopropane with sodium cyanide in more detail. There are two distinct paths by which this reaction can occur.

Path 1

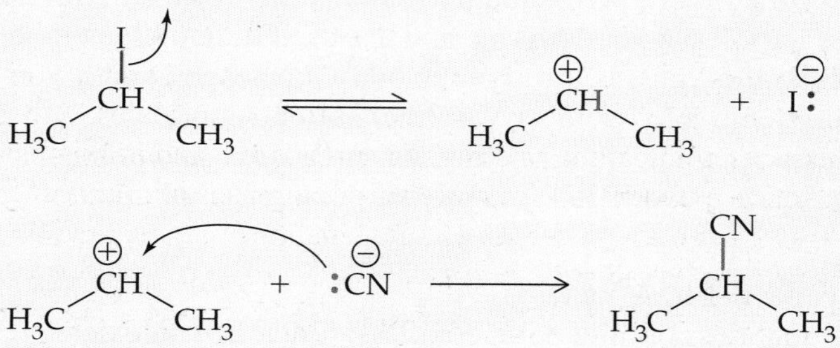

Path 2

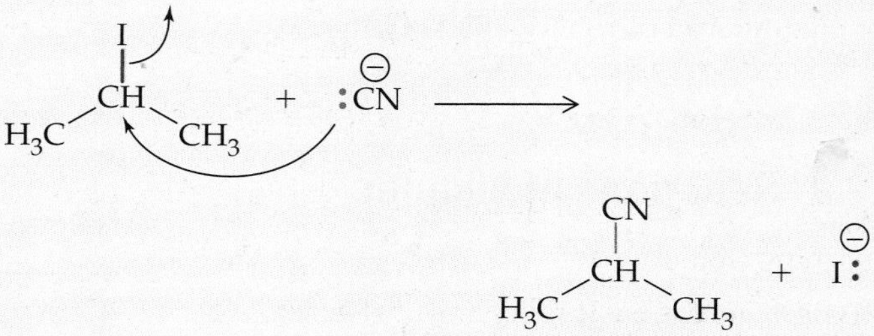

Notice that while both pathways lead ultimately to the same product, the curved arrow formalism shows us that they have significantly different ways of occurring. Although it is not important right now to understand which of the two paths is actually operative (it turns out to be a function of solvent, concentrations, catalysts, temperature, and other conditions), it is important that you get used to thinking of reactions as an "electron flow" of sorts. Throughout the next several chapters, you will see more of these "Mastering Reactions" boxes; they are intended to give you a little more insight into the otherwise seemingly random reactions that organic molecules undergo.

MR Problem 12.1 When ethyl alcohol is treated with acid, the initially formed intermediate is known as an oxonium ion.

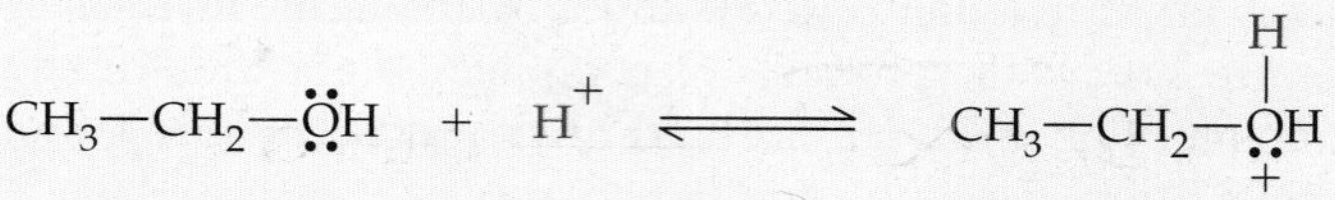

Using the curved arrow formalism, show how this process most likely occurs.

MR Problem 12.2 Consider the following two-step process:

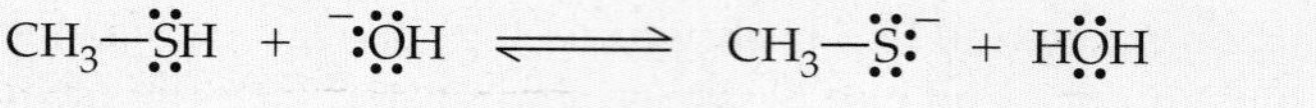

Using the curved arrow formalism, show how each step of this process is most likely to occur.

PROBLEM 12.16

Write a balanced equation for the complete combustion of methane with oxygen (see Worked Example 5.3 for guidance).

Halogenation

The second notable reaction of alkanes is *halogenation,* the replacement of an alkane hydrogen by a chlorine or bromine in a process initiated by heat or light. This process is known as "free radical halogenation" and occurs in a step-wise manner (a "free radical", or a "radical", is a molecule or atom containing a single, unpaired electron; since a radical does not have an octet of electrons around all of its atoms, it is highly reactive). Following is the reaction of methane with chlorine gas; the process is identical for bromine.

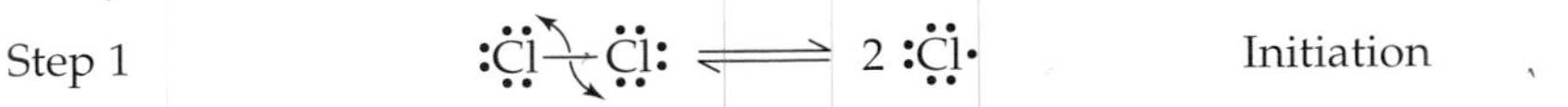

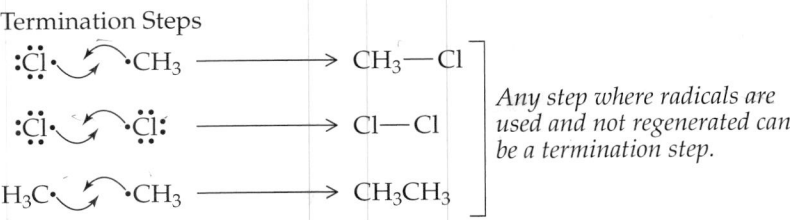

Step 1   :$\ddot{\text{C}}$l$-$$\ddot{\text{C}}$l: $\rightleftharpoons$ 2 :$\ddot{\text{C}}$l·   Initiation

(Note: It is common practice to show only the single electron for radicals with lone pairs—Cl·)

Step 2   :$\ddot{\text{C}}$l·   H$-$CH$_3$ $\rightleftharpoons$ HCl + ·CH$_3$ Propagation-1

Step 3   :$\ddot{\text{C}}$l$-$$\ddot{\text{C}}$l: ·CH$_3$ $\rightleftharpoons$ CH$_3$Cl + :$\ddot{\text{C}}$l·   Propagation-2

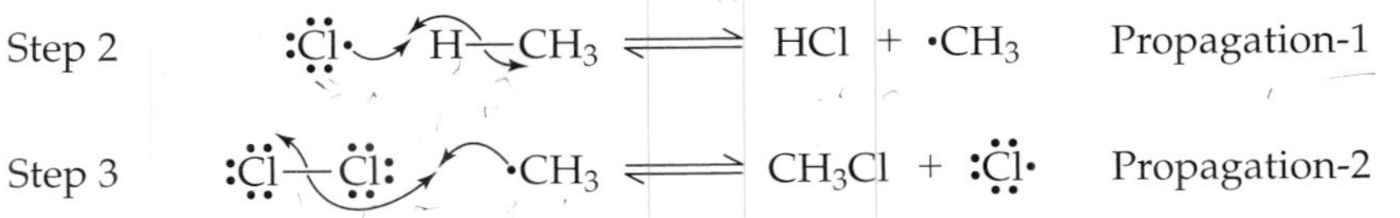

The reaction starts by the formation of chlorine radicals (Cl·); this occurs because the Cl–Cl bond is extremely weak and therefore reactive, in this case being easily broken upon exposure to sunlight or heat. Radicals contain seven electrons (one short of the desired octet) and are extremely reactive, so much so they can remove a hydrogen from a carbon (Step 2). The newly formed carbon radical (here, H$_3$C·) reacts with another Cl$_2$ to give chloromethane and regenerate the chlorine radical (Step 3), which is then free to react with another C–H bond (Step 2). Step 1 is called the initiation step, as a radical is initially formed where none were before. Steps 2 and 3 are called propagation steps, since one radical is used and another generated; this is known as a chain reaction, as the chlorine radical generated in Step 3 reenters the reaction to cause Step 2 to occur again. This process will occur over and over until either (i) the reaction is intentionally stopped, (ii) all C–H bonds have been replaced by Cl, or (iii) a termination step occurs (a step in which two radicals combine, thus eliminating radicals from the reaction).

Termination Steps

:$\ddot{\text{C}}$l·   ·CH$_3$ $\longrightarrow$ CH$_3$$-$Cl

:$\ddot{\text{C}}$l·   ·$\ddot{\text{C}}$l: $\longrightarrow$ Cl$-$Cl

H$_3$C·   ·CH$_3$ $\longrightarrow$ CH$_3$CH$_3$

Any step where radicals are used and not regenerated can be a termination step.

Halogenation is important because it is used to prepare both a number of molecules that are key industrial solvents (such as dichloromethane, chloroform, and carbon tetrachloride) as well as others (such as bromoethane) that are used for the preparation of other larger organic molecules. As shown above, only one H at a time is replaced; however, if allowed to react for a long enough time, all Hs will be replaced with halogens. Complete chlorination of methane, for example, yields carbon tetrachloride:

$$CH_4 + 4\,Cl_2 \xrightarrow{\text{Heat or light}} CCl_4 + 4\,HCl$$

Although the above equation for the reaction of methane with chlorine is balanced, it does not fully represent what actually happens. In fact, this reaction, like many organic reactions, yields a mixture of products.

$$CH_4 + Cl_2 \longrightarrow CH_3Cl + HCl$$
$$\underset{Cl_2}{\big|} \longrightarrow CH_2Cl_2 + HCl$$
$$\underset{Cl_2}{\big|} \longrightarrow CHCl_3 + HCl$$
$$\underset{Cl_2}{\big|} \longrightarrow CCl_4 + HCl$$

CH_3Cl, chloromethane (singly)
CH_2Cl_2, dichloromethane (doubly)
$CHCl_3$, chloroform
CCl_4, carbon tetrachloride

When we write the equation for an organic reaction, our attention is usually focused on converting a particular reactant into a desired product; any minor by-products and inorganic compounds (such as the HCl formed in the chlorination of methane) are often of little interest and are ignored. Thus, it is not always necessary to balance the equation for an organic reaction as long as the reactant, the major product, and any necessary reagents and conditions are shown. A chemist who plans to convert methane into bromomethane might therefore, write the equation as

$$CH_4 \xrightarrow[\text{Light, heat}]{Br_2} CH_3Br$$

Like many equations for organic reactions, this equation is not balanced.

In using this convention, it is customary to put reactants and reagents above the arrow and conditions, solvents, and catalysts below the arrow.

Worked Example 12.12 Drawing Isomers of Singly Chlorinated or Brominated Alkanes

(a) Draw all singly chlorinated isomers obtained upon the reaction of pentane with Cl_2.

$$CH_3CH_2CH_2CH_2CH_3 + Cl_2 \longrightarrow ?$$

ANALYSIS First, identify the parent alkane and then add chlorine systematically to each carbon to create new structures. Compare structures to determine whether they are unique or identical to others you have drawn.

SOLUTION

STEP 1: Begin by drawing the structure of the alkane starting material. Remove all hydrogens to get a skeletal structure; number the carbons.

$$CH_3CH_2CH_2CH_2CH_3 \quad \text{becomes} \quad \underset{1\quad 2\quad 3\quad 4\quad 5}{C-C-C-C-C}$$

STEP 2: One at a time, place a Cl on each carbon that is connected to three or less carbon atoms and draw that skeletal structure.

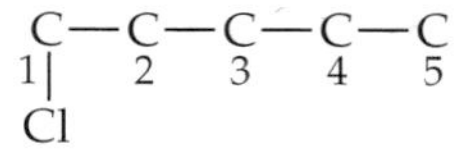

$$\underset{1\;\;\;\;2\;\;\;3\;\;\;4\;\;\;5}{\overset{|}{\underset{Cl}{C}}-C-C-C-C}$$
A

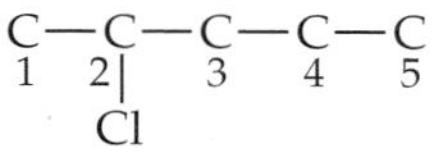

$$\underset{1\;\;\;2\;\;\;3\;\;\;4\;\;\;5}{C-\overset{|}{\underset{Cl}{C}}-C-C-C}$$
B

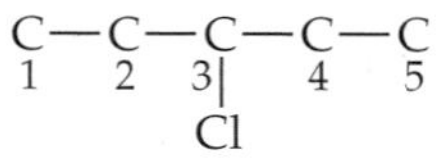

$$\underset{1\;\;\;2\;\;\;3\;\;\;4\;\;\;5}{C-C-\overset{|}{\underset{Cl}{C}}-C-C}$$
C

$$\underset{1\;\;\;2\;\;\;3\;\;\;4\;\;\;5}{C-C-C-\overset{|}{\underset{Cl}{C}}-C}$$
D

$$\underset{1\;\;\;2\;\;\;3\;\;\;4\;\;\;5}{C-C-C-C-\overset{|}{\underset{Cl}{C}}}$$
E

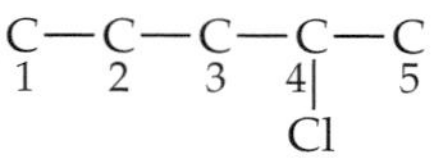

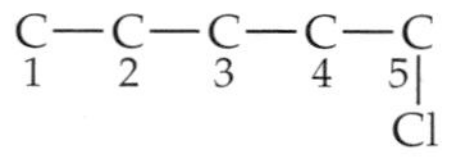

In this example, there are only carbons attached to one or two other carbons.

STEP 3: Now compare the structures you drew in Step 2, eliminating all that are the same. The simplest way to do this is to designate each structure you drew as a "C#" isomer. Be sure to check numbering in both directions.

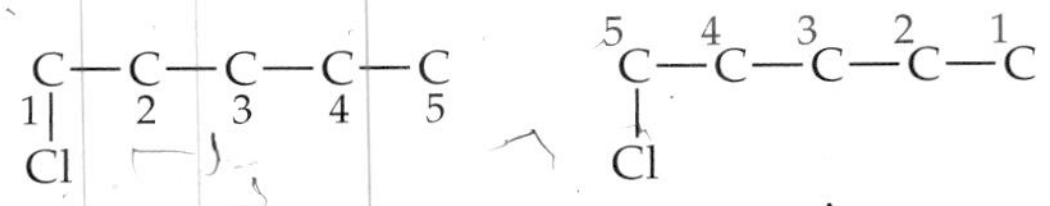

$$C-C-C-C-C \qquad \overset{5}{C}-\overset{4}{C}-\overset{3}{C}-\overset{2}{C}-\overset{1}{C}$$
$$\underset{1}{|} \quad 2 \quad 3 \quad 4 \quad 5 \qquad \underset{}{|}$$
$$Cl \qquad\qquad\qquad\qquad Cl$$

A   **A**
numbered left to right   *numbered right to left*

Structure A is the C1 isomer if numbered from left to right or the C5 isomer if numbered from right to left. Doing this for all structures obtained, we get the following correlations:

Structure **A** = C1 or C5   Structure **B** = C2 or C4   Structure **C** = C3 in either direction

Structure **D** = C4 or C2   Structure **E** = C5 or C1

Based on this, structures A and E are the same, as are B and D. Structure C is unique. Keep all unique structures, as well as one of each identical pair (here, we will keep A and B, since they have the lowest index numbers). From this, we get:

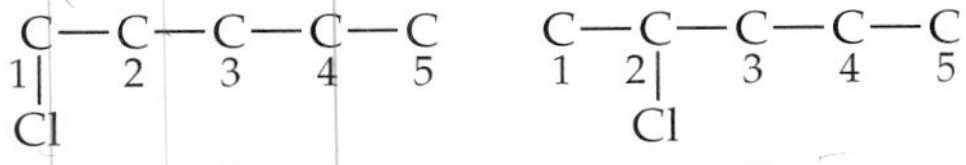

$$C-C-C-C-C \qquad\qquad C-C-C-C-C$$
$$\underset{1}{|} \ \ 2 \ \ 3 \ \ 4 \ \ 5 \qquad\qquad 1 \ \ \underset{2}{|} \ \ 3 \ \ 4 \ \ 5$$
$$Cl \qquad\qquad\qquad\qquad Cl$$
$$\textbf{A} \qquad\qquad\qquad\qquad \textbf{B}$$

$$C-C-C-C-C$$
$$1 \ \ 2 \ \underset{3}{|} \ \ 4 \ \ 5$$
$$Cl$$
$$\textbf{C}$$

STEP 4: Finish by putting in hydrogens so that each C has four bonded atoms.

$$CH_2-CH_2-CH_2-CH_2-CH_3 \qquad\qquad CH_3-CH-CH_2-CH_2-CH_3$$
$$\underset{}{|} \qquad\qquad\qquad\qquad\qquad\qquad\qquad \underset{}{|}$$
$$Cl \qquad\qquad\qquad\qquad\qquad\qquad\qquad\qquad Cl$$

A   **B**
1-Chloropentane   2-Chloropentane

$$CH_3-CH_2-CH-CH_2-CH_3$$
$$\underset{}{|}$$
$$Cl$$
$$\textbf{C}$$
3-Chloropentane

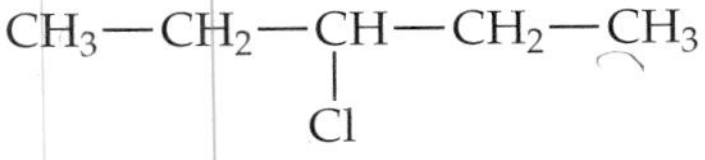

Note: One trick to use if you are not sure if two compounds are the same or different is to name them. Identical compounds will have the same name; if the compounds have different names, they are different compounds.

(b) Repeat for monobromination of the branched alkane 2-methylbutane.

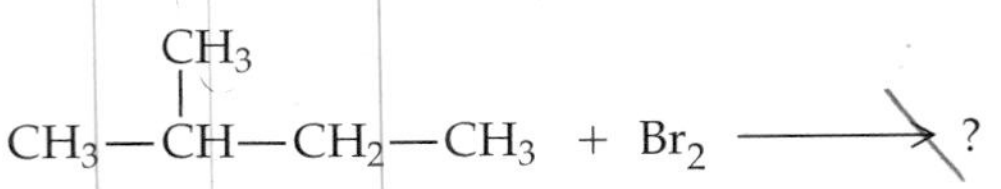

$$CH_3$$
$$\underset{}{|}$$
$$CH_3-CH-CH_2-CH_3 \ + \ Br_2 \ \longrightarrow \ ?$$

SOLUTION

STEP 1: Draw and number the skeletal structure:

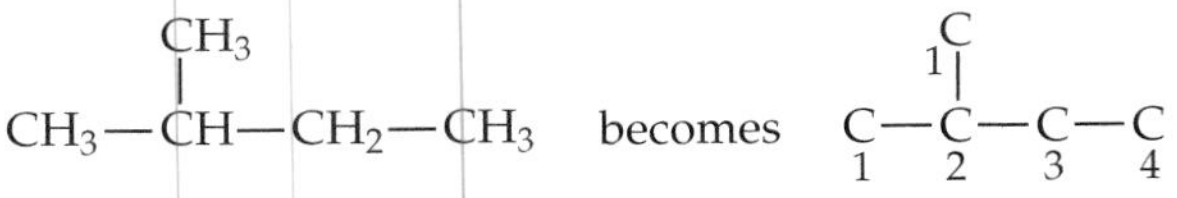

$$CH_3 \qquad\qquad\qquad\qquad\qquad\qquad \overset{C}{\underset{1}{|}}$$
$$\underset{}{|} \qquad\qquad\qquad\qquad\qquad\qquad\qquad$$
$$CH_3-CH-CH_2-CH_3 \quad \text{becomes} \quad C-C-C-C$$
$$\qquad\qquad\qquad\qquad\qquad\qquad\qquad\qquad 1 \ \ 2 \ \ 3 \ \ 4$$

With branched isomers, you need only number in the direction that gives the branch point the lowest number possible. Number in both directions only if you get the same number for the branch point either way.

—continued on next page

—continued from previous page

STEP 2: The possible monobromo isomers are as follows:

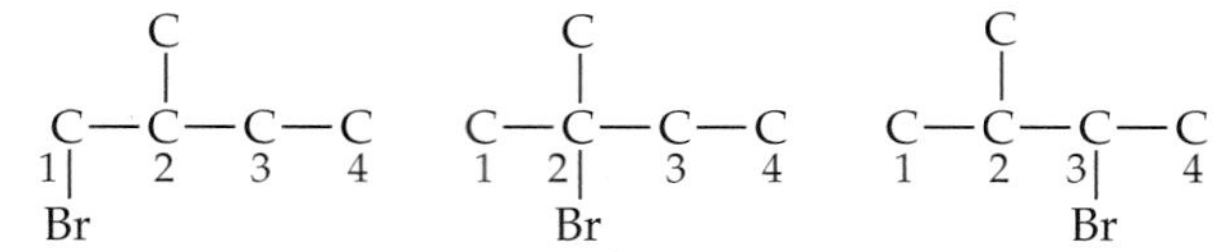

STEP 3: Here, only A and E are identical; all others are unique.

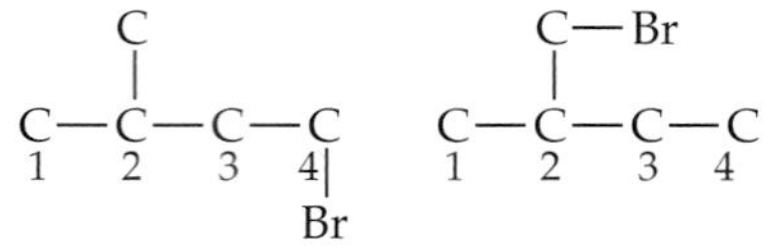

STEP 4: The isomers are, therefore:

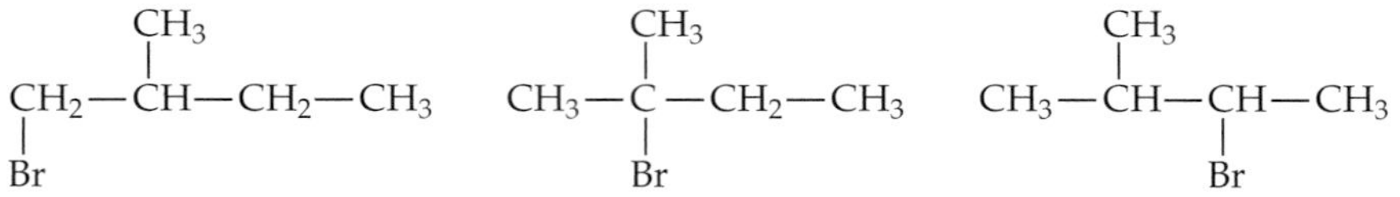

Note: This method can be used to draw isomers of almost any combination of carbons and functional groups (such as —OH, —NH$_2$, etc.)

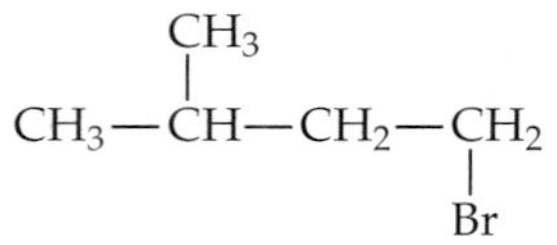

PROBLEM 12.17

Write the structures of all singly chlorinated products that form when 2,4-dimethyl-pentane is reacted with Cl$_2$.

12.9 Cycloalkanes

Learning Objective:

• Identify a cycloalkane from its structure.

The organic compounds described thus far have all been open-chain, or *acyclic,* alkanes. **Cycloalkanes,** which contain rings of carbon atoms, are also well known and are widespread throughout nature, with many of them having unique biological properties:

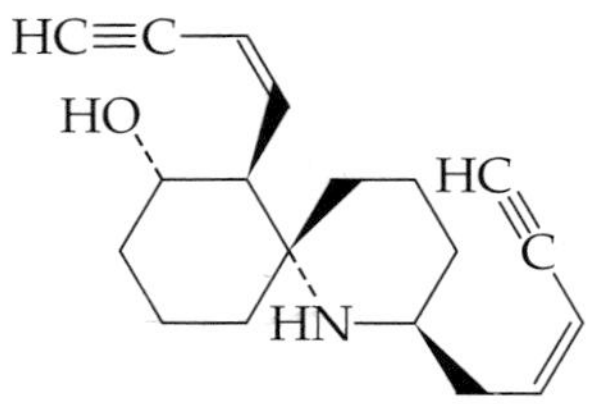

Cycloalkane An alkane that contains a ring of carbon atoms.

Histrionicotoxin 283A
Toxin isolated from poison dart frog

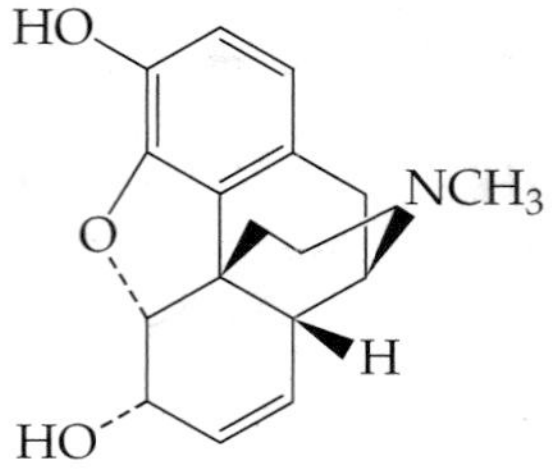

Morphine
Pain killer

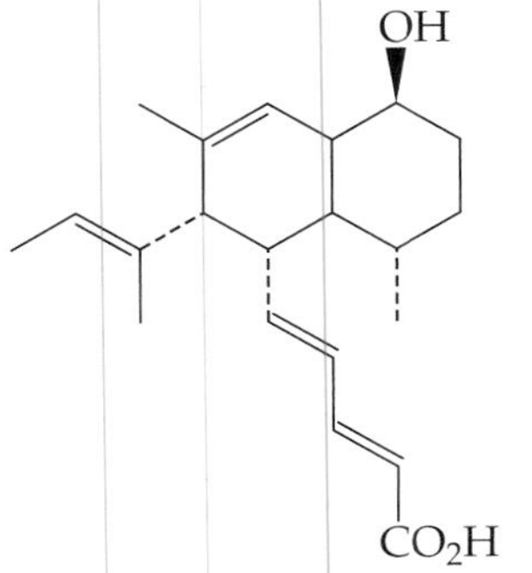

OH

CO₂H

Phomopsidin
Inhibitor of microtubule assembly;
isolated from a marine-derived fungi

To form a closed ring requires an additional C—C bond and the loss of 2 H atoms. Compounds of all ring sizes from 3 through 30 and beyond have been prepared in the laboratory. The two simplest cycloalkanes—cyclopropane and cyclobutane—contain 3 and 4 carbon atoms, respectively.

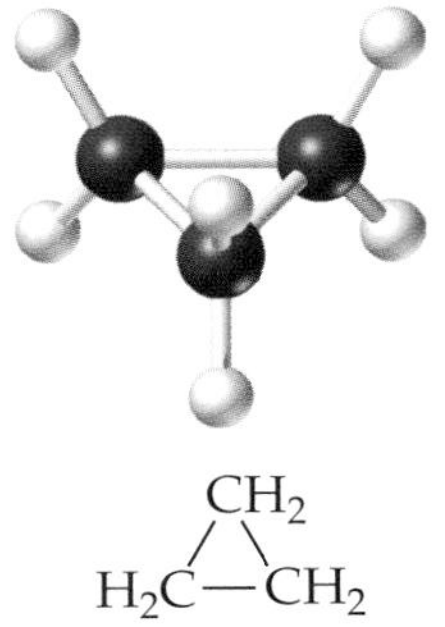

$$CH_2$$
$$H_2C—CH_2$$
Cyclopropane
(mp −128 °C, bp −33 °C)

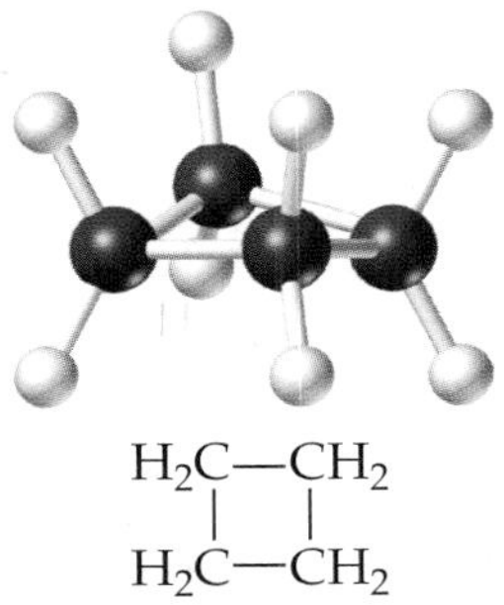

$$H_2C—CH_2$$
$$H_2C—CH_2$$
Cyclobutane
(mp −50 °C, bp −12 °C)

Note that if we flatten the rings in cyclopropane and cyclobutane, the C—C—C bond angles are 60° *and* 90°, respectively—values that are considerably compressed from the normal tetrahedral value of 109.5°. As a result, these compounds are less stable and more reactive than other cycloalkanes. The five-membered (cyclopentane) ring has nearly ideal bond angles, and so does the six-membered (cyclohexane) ring. Both cyclopentane and cyclohexane accomplish this nearly ideal state by adopting a puckered, nonplanar shape, further discussion of which, while important, is beyond the scope of this textbook. Both cyclopentane and cyclohexane rings are therefore stable, and many naturally occurring and biochemically active molecules, such as the steroids (Chapter 28), contain such rings. These rings, and the shape they impart on the molecules that contain them, are an important component of what is known as structure–activity relationships in rational drug design.

Cyclic and acyclic alkanes are similar in many of their properties. Cyclopropane and cyclobutane are gases at room temperature (like propane and butane), whereas larger cycloalkanes, like larger alkanes, are liquids or solids. Like alkanes, cycloalkanes are nonpolar, insoluble in water, and flammable. Because of their cyclic structures, however, cycloalkane molecules are more rigid and less flexible than their open-chain counterparts. Rotation is not possible around the carbon–carbon bonds in cycloalkanes without breaking open the ring. This property is known as **restricted rotation** and can lead to isomer formation (see Group Problem 12.76).

Restricted Rotation The limited ability of a molecule to rotate around a given bond.

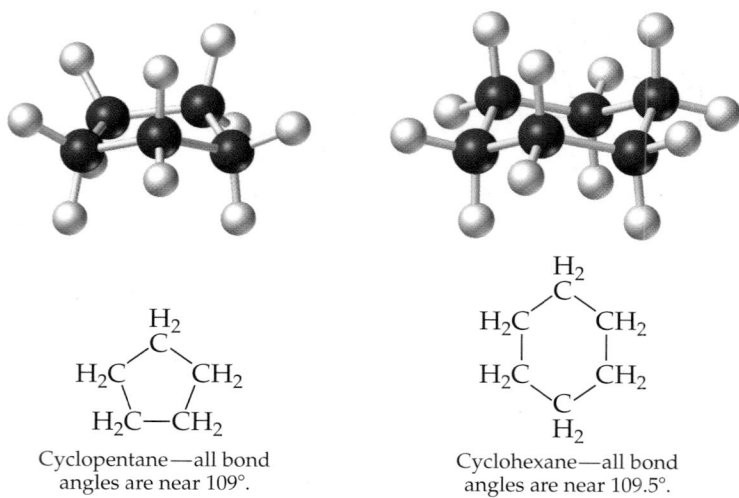

Cyclopentane—all bond angles are near 109°.

Cyclohexane—all bond angles are near 109.5°.

12.10 Drawing and Naming Cycloalkanes

Learning Objective:

• Name a cycloalkane given its structure and draw a cycloalkane given its name.

Even condensed structures become awkward when we work with large molecules that contain rings. Thus, line structures are used almost exclusively in drawing cycloalkanes, with *polygons* used for the cyclic parts of the molecules. A triangle represents cyclopropane, a square represents cyclobutane, a pentagon represents cyclopentane, and so on, where, just like alkanes, a carbon is found at every point two or more lines meet, or wherever a line ends.

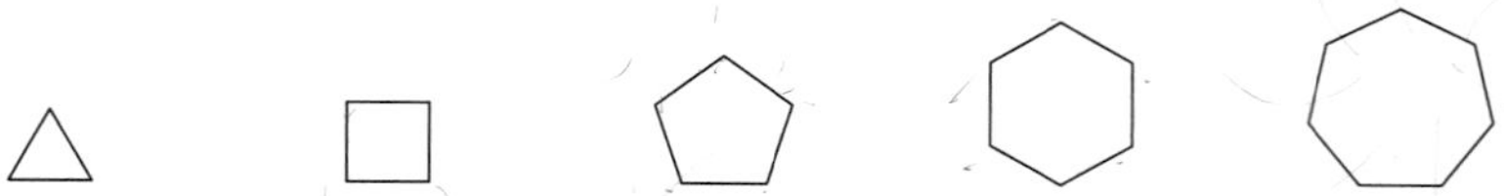

Cyclopropane   Cyclobutane   Cyclopentane   Cyclohexane   Cycloheptane

Methylcyclohexane, for example, looks like this in a line structure.

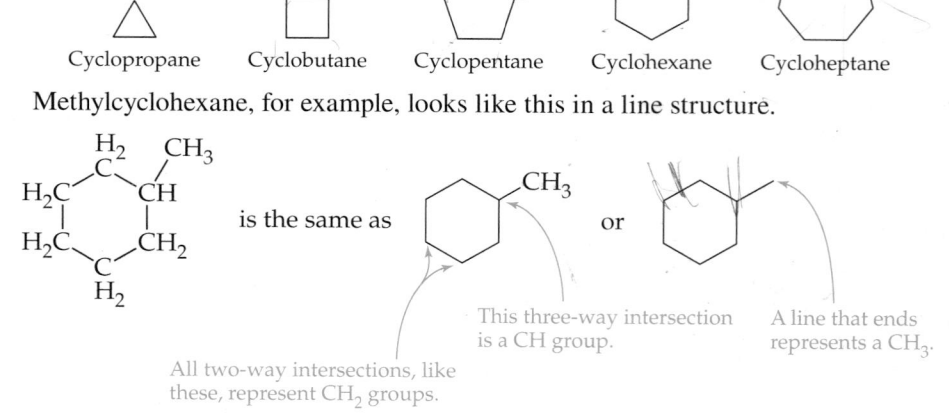

is the same as   or

This three-way intersection is a CH group.

A line that ends represents a CH₃.

All two-way intersections, like these, represent CH₂ groups.

Cycloalkanes are named by a straightforward extension of the rules for naming open-chain alkanes. In most cases, only two steps are needed.

STEP 1: Use the cycloalkane name as the parent. That is, compounds are named as alkyl-substituted cycloalkanes rather than as cycloalkyl-substituted alkanes. If there is only one substituent on the ring, it is not even necessary to assign a number because all ring positions are identical.

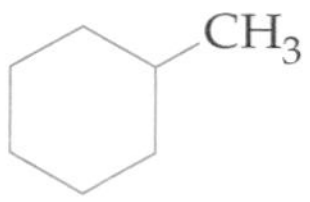

Parent compound: Cyclohexane
Name: Methylcyclohexane
(not cyclohexylmethane)

STEP 2: **Identify and number the substituents.** Start numbering at the group that has alphabetical priority, and proceed around the ring in the direction that gives the second substituent the lowest possible number.

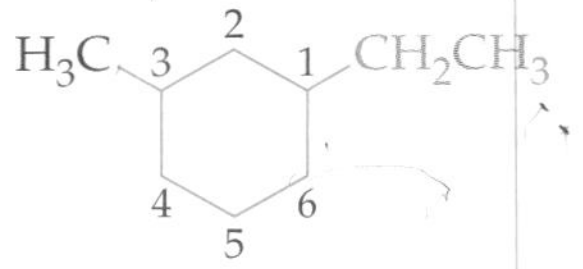

1-Ethyl-3-methylcyclohexane
(not 1-ethyl-5-methylcyclohexane or
1-methyl-3-ethylcyclohexane or
1-methyl-5-ethylcyclohexane)

Worked Example 12.13 Naming Organic Compounds: Cycloalkanes

What is the IUPAC name of the following cycloalkane?

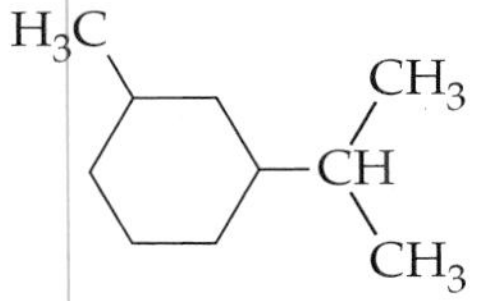

ANALYSIS First, identify the parent cycloalkane and then add the positions and identity of any substituents.

SOLUTION

STEP 1: The parent cycloalkane contains six carbons (*hex*ane), hence, *cyclohexane.*

STEP 2: There are two substituents; a methyl ($-CH_3$) and an isopropyl ($-CH(CH_3)_2$). Alphabetically, the isopropyl group is given priority (number 1); the methyl group is then found on the third carbon in the ring.

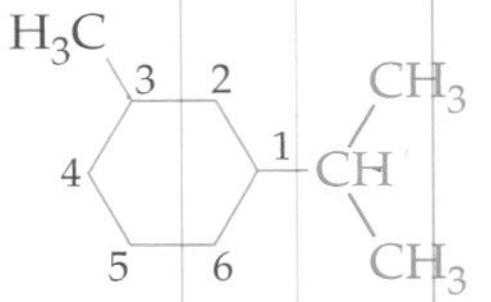

1-Isopropyl-3-methylcyclohexane

Worked Example 12.14 Molecular Structures: Drawing Line Structures for Cycloalkanes

Draw a line structure for 1,3-dimethylcyclohexane.

ANALYSIS This structure consists of a 6-carbon ring (*cyclohex*ane) with two methyl groups (*di*methyl) attached at positions 1 and 3. Draw a hexagon to represent a cyclohexane ring, and attach a $-CH_3$ group at an arbitrary position that becomes the first carbon in the chain, designated as C1. Then count around the ring to the third carbon (C3), and attach another $-CH_3$ group.

SOLUTION

Note that the C3 methyl group could have been written as H_3C- to emphasize that attachment to the ring is through the carbon. This is a common practice for methyl groups that are attached on the left side of a cycloalkane ring. Note also that as long as the methyl groups are 1, 3 to one another, it does not matter how we orient the ring.

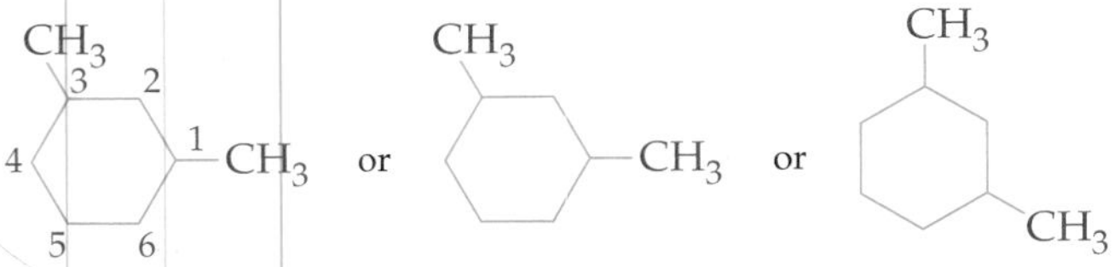

1,3-Dimethylcyclohexane

PROBLEM 12.18

What are the IUPAC names of the following cycloalkanes? Remember to assign priority to the attached groups alphabetically.

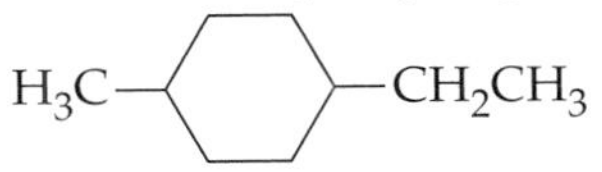

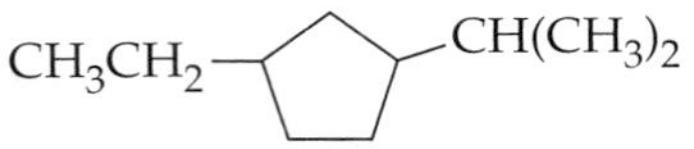

PROBLEM 12.19

Draw line structures that represent the following IUPAC names:

(**a**) 1,1-Diethylcyclohexane   (**b**) 1,3,5-Trimethylcycloheptane

PROBLEM 12.20

What is wrong with the following names? It will be helpful to draw the structures as named before making your decision.

(**a**) 1,4,5-Trimethylcyclohexane   (**b**) Cyclohexylcyclopentane

(**c**) 1-Ethyl-2-methyl-3-ethylcyclopentane

KEY CONCEPT PROBLEM 12.21

Redraw the following cycloalkane in both condensed and line formula format. What is its IUPAC name?

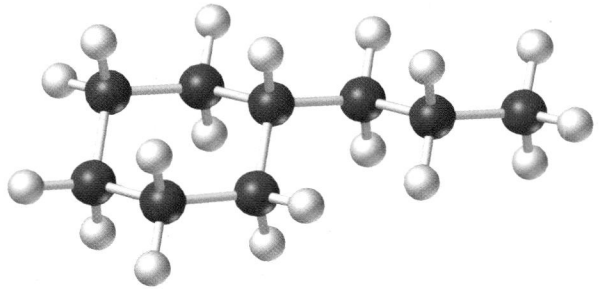

CHEMISTRY IN ACTION

✝ Surprising Uses of Petroleum

Petroleum, arising from the decay of ancient plants and animals, is found deep below the earth's crust; it is a mixture of hydrocarbons of varying sizes. Petroleum's worth as both a portable, energy-dense fuel and as the starting point of many industrial chemicals makes it one of the world's most important commodities. About 90% of vehicular fuel needs worldwide are met by oil. In addition, 40% of total energy consumption in the United States is petroleum-based. In an effort to create a "greener" environment and more sustainable energy, a great fervor has developed to find alternative energy sources, but a question arises: Can we completely eliminate the need for petroleum from our lives, even if we could find an alternative energy for transportation purposes?

Petrochemicals, which we first mentioned in the chapter opener, are chemical products derived specifically from petroleum and generally refer to those products that are not used for fuels. When crude oil is refined and cracked (the process during which complex organic molecules found in oil are converted into simpler molecules by breaking carbon–carbon bonds), a number of fractions having different boiling ranges are obtained. The primary petrochemicals obtained can be broken down into three categories:

1. Alkenes (or olefins; Chapter 13): Primarily ethylene, propylene, and butadiene. Ethylene and propylene are important sources of industrial chemicals and plastics products.

2. Aromatics (Chapter 13): Most important among these are benzene, toluene, and the xylenes. These raw materials are used for making a variety of compounds, from dyes

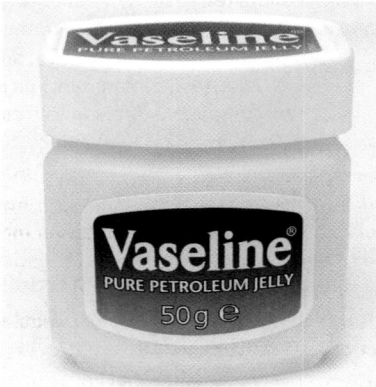

▲ Petroleum jelly, originally an unwanted by-product of drilling, has found many uses in today's average household.

and synthetic detergents, to plastics and synthetic fibers, to pharmaceutical starting materials.

3. Synthesis gas: A mixture of carbon monoxide and hydrogen used to make methanol (which is used as both a solvent and starting point for other products).

What specific types of products are made from these petrochemicals? Let's look at a few:

Lubricants such as light machine oils, motor oils, and greases are products used to keep almost all mechanical devices running smoothly and to prevent them from seizing up under high-use conditions. Wax is another raw petroleum product. Paraffin waxes are used to make candles and polishes as well as food packaging such as milk cartons. The shine you see on the fruit in your local supermarket is also a result of the use of wax.

Most of the rubber soles found on today's shoes are derived from butadiene. Natural rubber becomes sticky when hot and stiff when cold, but man-made rubber stays much more flexible. Car tires are also made from synthetic rubber, which makes them much safer to drive on. Today, the demand for synthetic rubber is four-times greater than for natural rubber.

One very interesting petroleum-derived material was once considered a nuisance by-product of oil drilling. "Black rod wax" is a paraffin-like substance that forms on oil-drilling rigs, causing the drills to malfunction. Workers had to scrape the thick, viscous material off to keep the drills running. However, they found that when applied to cuts and burns it would cause these injuries to heal faster. A young chemist named Robert Chesebrough, after purifying the material, obtained a light-colored gel he named vaseline, or petroleum jelly. Chesebrough demonstrated his miracle product by burning his skin, then spreading the healing ointment on his injuries. Its use in promoting the healing of minor cuts, abrasions, and dry skin and lips soon followed, as we saw in the opening of this chapter. While the use of Vaseline® for burns has fallen out of favor (due to its ability to seal in heat as well as moisture), it is still important as a base for a number of antibacterial ointments. Today, we know that the primary effect that petroleum jelly has on the healing process is that of sealing wounds from moisture loss, allowing the skin to heal from the bottom up more effectively.

As you can see, petroleum has many uses that are key in our everyday lives. Although lessening its use as a fuel for transportation can help to conserve what reserves we have, its complete elimination from our lives is, at this point in time, nearly impossible.

CIA Problem 12.4 (a) Why is the demand for synthetic rubber greater than that of natural rubber? (b) Butadiene is used in the manufacture of synthetic rubber. Why is this more desirable than natural rubber?

CIA Problem 12.5 (a) What common produce items might you see paraffin waxes being used on? (b) What consumer products are manufactured with ethylene and propylene?

SUMMARY REVISITING THE CHAPTER LEARNING OBJECTIVES

- **Identify the general structural characteristics of organic molecules, in particular, the tetravalent nature of carbon and the different ways in which it can be expressed.** Compounds made up primarily of carbon and hydrogen atoms are classified as organic. Each carbon atom in an organic molecule is tetravalent, meaning it can form a total of four bonds. Many organic compounds contain carbon atoms that are joined in chains by a combination of single $(C-C)$, double $(C=C)$, or triple $(C\equiv C)$ bonds. We focused here primarily on *alkanes and cycloalkanes,* hydrocarbon compounds that contain only single bonds between all C atoms *(see Problems 27, 29, 30, 68, 70, and 74).*

- **Define functional group.** Organic compounds can be classified into various families according to the functional groups they contain (Table 12.1). A *functional group* is a part of a larger molecule and is composed of a group of atoms that has characteristic structure and chemical reactivity *(see Problem 28).*

- **Identify the functional groups in organic molecules.** Being able to identify the functional group family to which an organic molecule belongs is important, as a given functional group undergoes nearly the same chemical reactions in every molecule where it occurs *(see Problems 23, 31–35, 64, and 71).*

- **Recognize structural (constitutional) isomers and functional group isomers.** Structural or constitutional isomers are compounds that have the same formula but different structural connections of atoms. When atoms other than carbon and hydrogen are present, the ability to have *functional group isomers* arises; these are molecules that, due to the differences in their connections, have not only different structures but also belong to different families of organic molecules *(see Problems 26, 36–47, 58, 73, and 76).*

- **Draw structural, condensed, and line formulas for simple chemical compounds.** Organic compounds can be represented by *structural formulas* in which all atoms and bonds are shown, by *condensed structures* in which not all bonds are drawn, or by *line structures* in which the carbon skeleton is represented by lines and the locations of C and H atoms are understood *(see Problems 22, 23, 73, and 75).*

- **Convert any given structural, condensed, or line formula into its corresponding alternative.** Chemists and biochemists often use a mixture of structural, condensed, and line formula to represent the complicated molecules they study. Since organic molecules are drawn using all three of these motifs, being able to think interchangeably in all three formats is important in the study of organic and biological molecules *(see Problems 49, 52, and 53).*

- **Determine if two given structures are the different conformers of the same molecule, different structural isomers, or different molecules.** Structural isomers have the same chemical formula but different connections of atoms; different molecules have different chemical formulas; and conformers have the same chemical formula and connections of atoms with different spatial arrangements of those atoms. Free rotation around C—C single bonds allows a given organic compound the ability to adopt a number of different spatial arrangements. These are called *conformations* or *conformers.* Different conformations of a molecule have different energies depending on whether large groups of atoms are close to one another or not *(see Problems 46, 47, 49, 72, and 76).*

- **Name an alkane given its structure and draw an alkane given its name.** A *straight-chain alkane* has all its carbons connected in a row, and a *branched-chain alkane* has a branching connection of atoms somewhere along its chain. Straight-chain alkanes are named by adding the family ending *-ane* to a parent; this tells how many carbon atoms are present. Branched-chain alkanes are named by using the longest continuous chain of carbon atoms for the parent and then identifying the *alkyl groups* present as branches off the main chain. The positions of the substituent groups on the main chain are identified by numbering the carbons in the chain so that the substituents have the lowest index numbers *(see Problems 24, 25, and 50–53).*

- **Identify the physical properties of alkanes.** Alkanes are generally nonpolar, insoluble in water (hydrophobic), and unreactive. They possess low melting and/or boiling points due to their weak intermolecular forces. Alkanes are generally nontoxic and therefore have limited physiological effects *(see Problems 68 and 78).*

- **Determine the basic reactions of alkanes.** Alkanes possess low reactivity; their principal chemical reactions are *combustion,* a reaction with oxygen that gives carbon dioxide and water, and *halogenation,* a reaction in which hydrogen atoms are replaced by chlorine or bromine *(see Problems 60 and 71).*

- **Draw the isomeric products formed during the halogenation of simple alkanes.** Drawing the isomeric products obtained on halogenation of an alkane can be accomplished by systematically and methodically replacing hydrogens one carbon at a time and then comparing each structure obtained with one another to determine if the molecules are the same or different structurally. One way to tell if the compounds are the same or different is to name them; identical compounds have the same name. This procedure for drawing isomeric products can be used to draw isomers of almost any combination of carbons and functional groups [see Problems 62, 63, and 69].

• **Identify a cycloalkane from its structure.** Hydrocarbons that have only single bonds arraigned in a ring of carbon atoms are called *cycloalkanes*. Due to their cyclic nature, they have what is known as restricted rotation, meaning they cannot adopt as wide a range of conformations as the corresponding alkanes can. Cycloalkanes

possess almost identical physical and chemical properties as alkanes [see Problems 25 and 54–56].

• **Name a cycloalkane given its structure and draw a cycloalkane given its name.** Cycloalkanes are named by adding *cyclo-* as a prefix to the name of the alkane corresponding to the number of carbons in the ring. Cycloalkanes-containing groups attached to the main ring are named the same way as branches in an alkane are. The positions of the substituent groups on the ring are identified by numbering the carbons in the chain so that the substituents have the lowest possible set of position numbers [see Problems 25, 41, 53, and 59].

CONCEPT MAP: INTRODUCTION TO ORGANIC CHEMISTRY FAMILIES

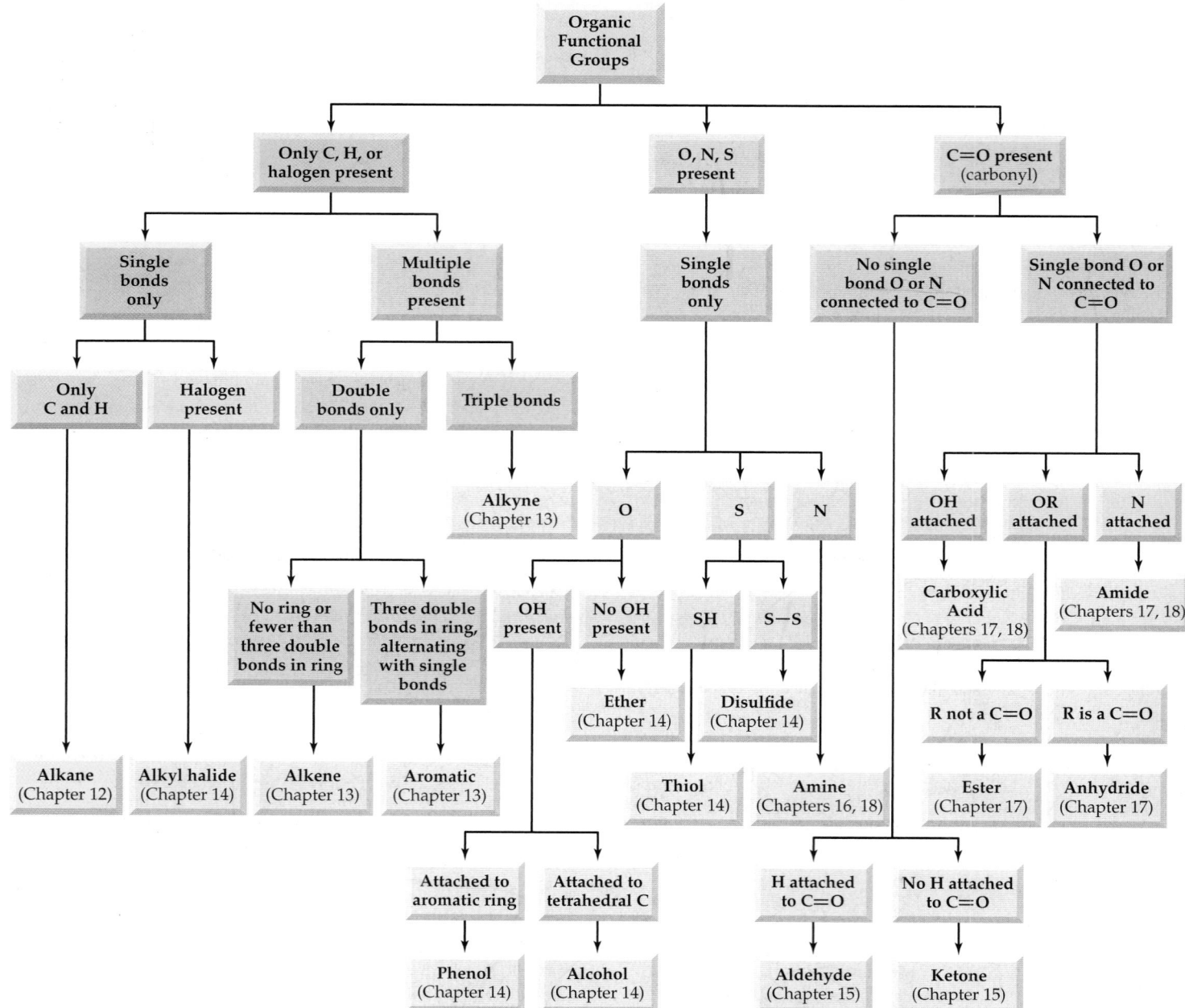

▲ **Figure 12.5 Functional Group Concept Map.** Learning to classify organic molecules by the families they belong to is a crucial skill you need to develop, since the chemistry that both organic and biological molecules undergo is directly related to their functional groups. This concept map will aid you in this classification. First introduced in Section 12.2, it will be a key reference as you proceed through the rest of the chapters in this book. As we discuss each family in later chapters, sections of it will be reproduced and expanded to help also tie in the chemistry that those functional groups undergo. Functional groups will be grayed out until they are discussed; as each functional group is discussed, it will become colorized.

KEY WORDS

Alkane, *p. 365*
Alkyl group, *p. 376*
Branched-chain alkane,
   p. 367
Combustion, *p. 385*
Condensed structure,
   p. 368
Conformation, *p. 374*
Conformer, *p. 374*

Constitutional isomers,
   p. 367
Cycloalkane, *p. 390*
Ethyl group, *p. 377*
Functional group, *p. 360*
Functional group isomer,
   p. 367
Hydrocarbon, *p. 362*
Isomers, *p. 366*

Isopropyl group, *p. 377*
Line structure, *p. 370*
Methyl group, *p. 377*
Methylene group, *p. 369*
Organic chemistry,
   p. 357
Primary (1°) carbon atom,
   p. 378
Propyl group, *p. 377*

Quaternary (4°) carbon
   atom, *p. 378*
Restricted rotation, *p. 391*
Secondary (2°) carbon atom,
   p. 378
Straight-chain alkane, *p. 367*
Substituent, *p. 376*
Tertiary (3°) carbon atom,
   p. 378

SUMMARY OF KEY REACTIONS

Beginning with this chapter, and continuing through Chapter 17, you will find a "Summary of Key Reactions" section located right before the end of chapter problems. In this section, we will summarize all the key reactions discussed in that chapter, along with references to those previously discussed as needed. It is intended as an aid in your study of organic and biochemistry and will be a useful reference guide.

1. **Combustion of an alkane with oxygen to yield carbon dioxide and water (Section 12.8):**

$$CH_4 + 2\,O_2 \longrightarrow CO_2 + 2\,H_2O$$

2. **Halogenation of an alkane to yield an alkyl halide (Section 12.8):**

$$CH_4 + Cl_2 \xrightarrow{light} CH_3Cl + HCl$$

⌗ UNDERSTANDING KEY CONCEPTS

12.22   Convert the following models into line drawings (black = C; white = H; red = O; blue = N):

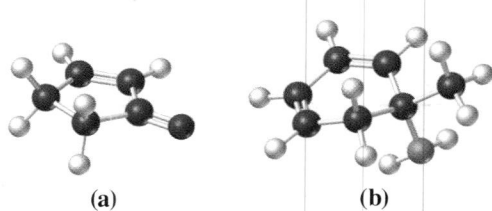

(a)   (b)

12.23   Convert the following models into line drawings and identify the functional groups in each:

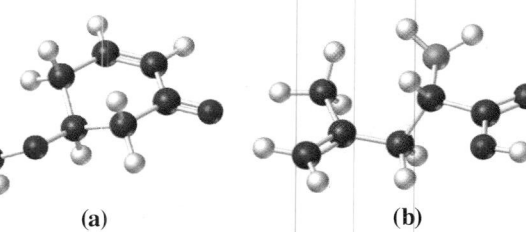

(a)   (b)

12.24   Give the IUPAC names for the following alkanes:

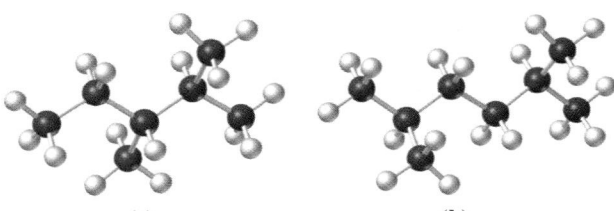

(a)   (b)

12.25   Give the IUPAC names for the following cycloalkanes:

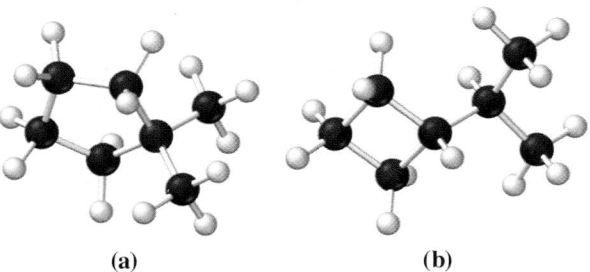

(a)   (b)

12.26   The following two compounds are isomers, even though both can be named 1,3-dimethylcyclopentane. What is the difference between them?

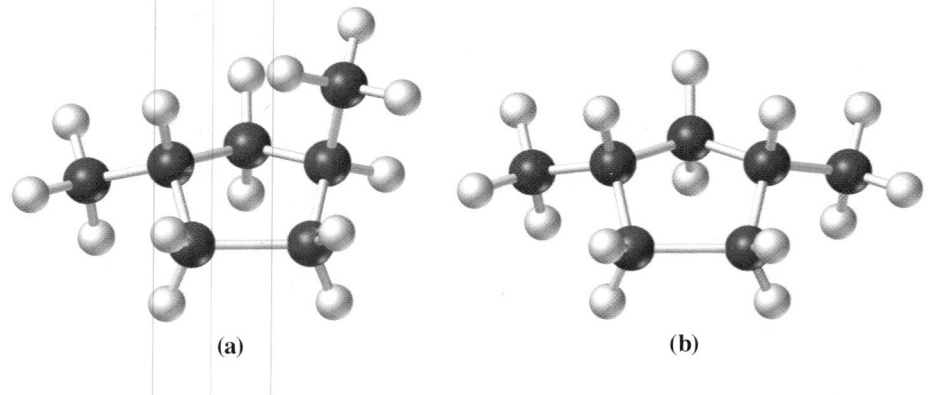

(a)   (b)

ADDITIONAL PROBLEMS

ORGANIC MOLECULES AND FUNCTIONAL GROUPS (SECTIONS 12.1, 12.2)

12.27 What characteristics of carbon make possible the existence of so many different organic compounds?

12.28 What are functional groups, and why are they important?

12.29 Why are most organic compounds nonconducting and insoluble in water?

12.30 What is meant by the term *polar covalent bond*? Give an example of such a bond.

12.31 For each of the following, give an example of a member compound containing 5 carbons total:

(a) Alcohol   (b) Amine

(c) Carboxylic acid   (d) Ether

12.32 Identify the highlighted functional groups in the following molecules:

(a)

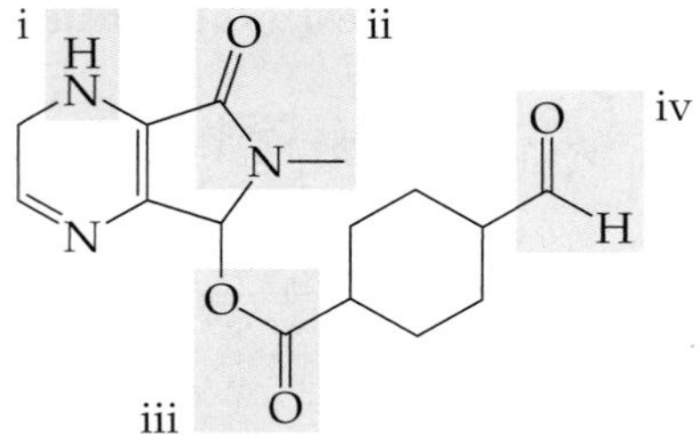

(b)

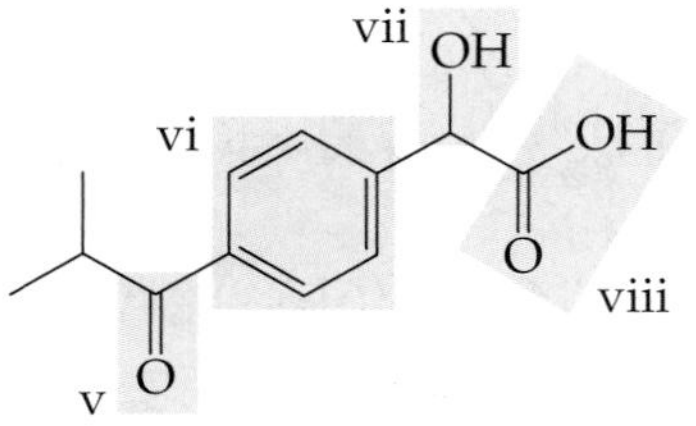

12.33 Identify the functional groups in the following molecules:

(a)

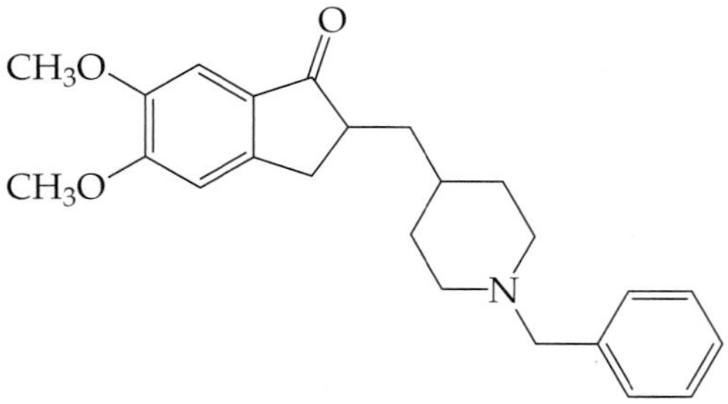

Donepezil
(used in Alzheimers treatment)

(b)

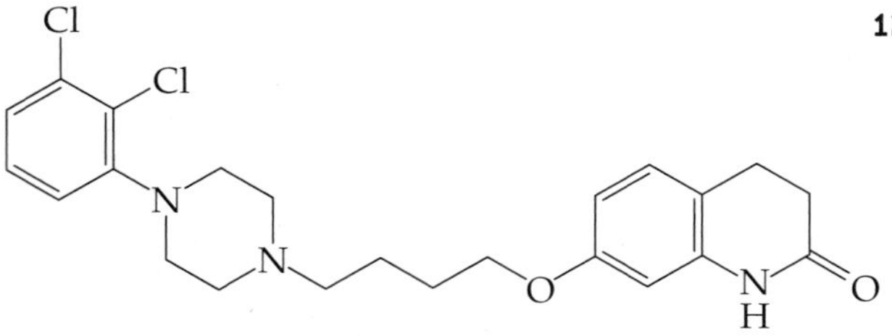

Aripiprazole
(Abilify)

12.34 Propose structures for molecules that fit the following descriptions:

(a) An aldehyde with the formula $C_5H_{10}O$

(b) An ester with the formula $C_6H_{12}O_2$

(c) A compound with the formula C_3H_7NOS that is both an amide and a thiol

12.35 Propose structures for molecules that fit the following descriptions:

(a) An amide with the formula C_4H_9NO

(b) An aldehyde that has a ring of carbons, $C_6H_{10}O$

(c) An aromatic compound that is also an ether, $C_8H_{10}O$

ALKANES AND ISOMERS (SECTIONS 12.3, 12.4, 12.9)

12.36 What requirement must be met for two compounds to be isomers?

12.37 If one compound has the formula C_5H_{10} and another has the formula C_4H_{10}, are the two compounds isomers? Explain.

12.38 (a) What is the difference between a secondary carbon and a tertiary carbon? (b) What about the difference between a primary carbon and a quaternary carbon? (c) How many secondary carbons does the structure shown in Additional Problem 12.33b have? Redraw the structure and highlight them all. (Ignore all double-bonded carbons.)

12.39 Why is it not possible for a compound to have a *quintary* carbon (five groups attached to C)?

12.40 Give examples of compounds that meet the following descriptions:

(a) A six carbon alkane with 2 tertiary carbons

(b) Three different cyclohexanes with having two methyl groups attached.

12.41 Give an example of a compound that meets the following descriptions:

(a) A 5-carbon alkane with only primary and quaternary carbons

(b) A cycloalkane with three substituents

12.42 (a) There are two isomers with the formula C_4H_{10}. Draw both the condensed and line structure for each isomer.

(b) Using the structures you drew in (a) as a starting point, draw both the condensed and line structures for the four isomeric chlorides having the chemical formula C_4H_9Cl.

12.43 Write condensed structures for the following molecular formulas. More than one isomer will be required for each.

(a) Isomers of C_8H_{18} that contain three methyl groups and a longest chain of 5 carbons

(b) Cyclohexanes with a chemical formula of C_8H_{16}

(c) C_2H_4O

(d) Ketones and aldehydes with C_4H_8O

(e) Write the line structures for (b) and (d).

12.44 How many straight-chain isomers can you write that fit the following descriptions? See Worked Example 12.12 for guidance.

(a) Alcohols (—OH) with a longest chain of 6 carbons

(b) Amines ($—NH_2$) with a longest chain of 7 carbons

12.45 How many isomers can you write that fit the following descriptions? See Worked Example 12.12 for guidance.

(a) Monobromides formed from 2-methylpentane

(b) Monochlorides formed from 3-methylpentane

(c) Alcohols (—OH) formed from 2-methylhexane

12.46 Which of the following pairs of structures are identical, which are isomers, and which are unrelated?

(a) 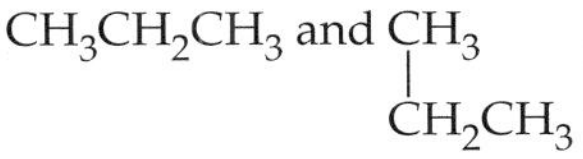

(b) 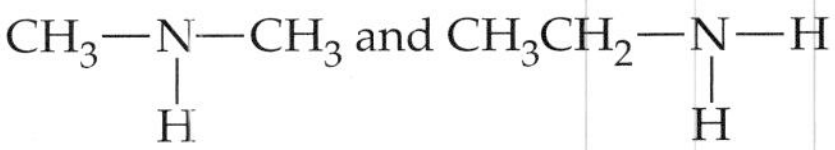

(c) 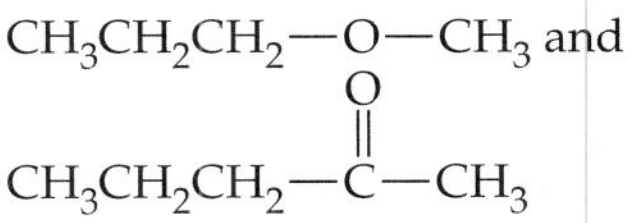

(d) 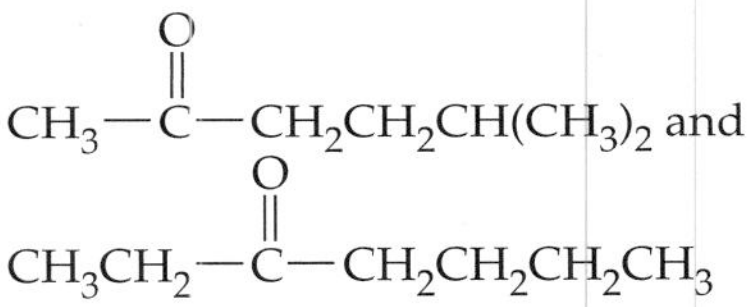

(e) 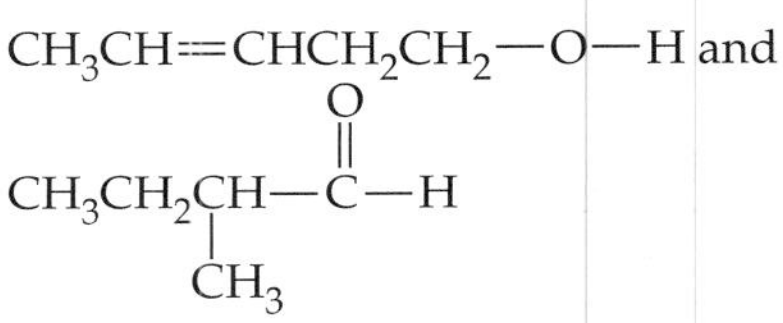

12.47 Which structures in each group represent the same compound and which represent isomers?

(a) 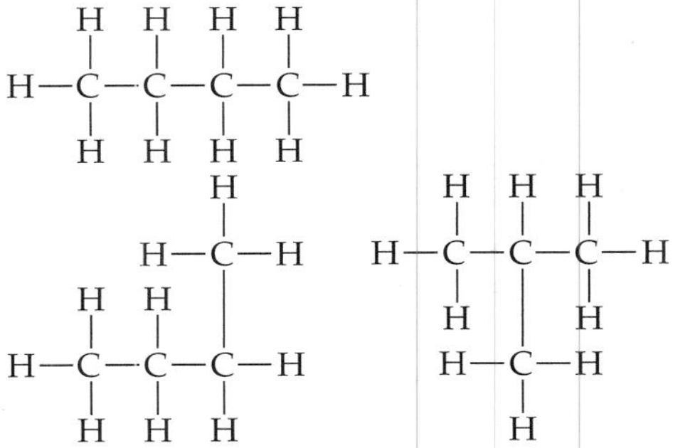

(b) 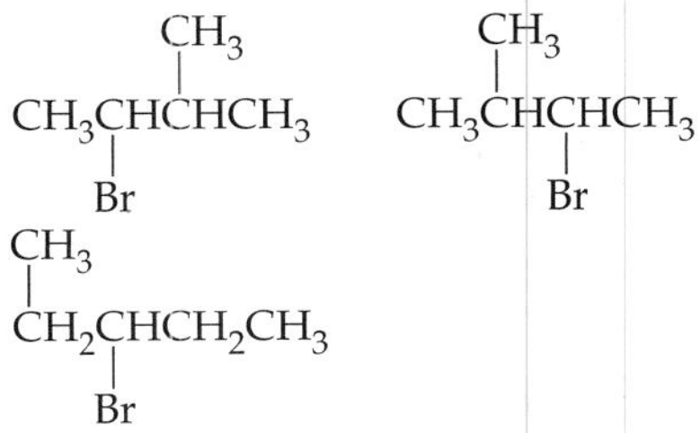

(c) 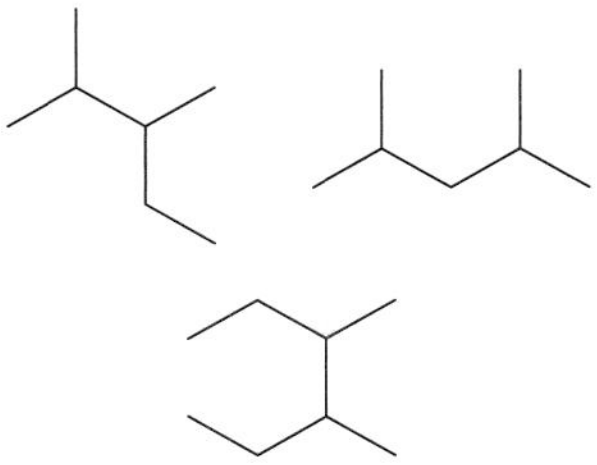

(d) See if you can find some caraway seeds and some mint leaves. Crush each separately and compare their smells. Now look up the structures primarily responsible for the smell of each and carefully compare them. How are they related? These are what are known as *stereoisomers;* this advanced topic is one that will be discussed in Chapter 14.

12.48 What is wrong with the following structures?

(a) $CH_3{=}CHCH_2CH_2OH$

(b) 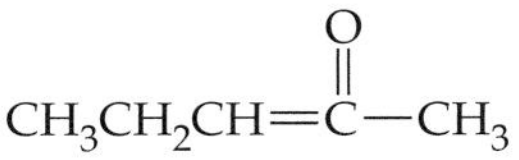

(c) 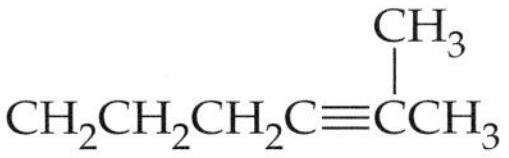

12.49 There are two things wrong with the following structure. What are they?

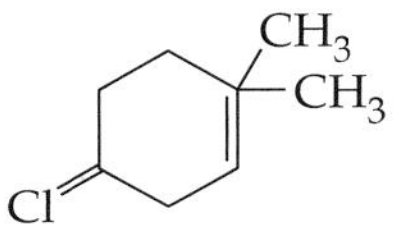

ALKANE NOMENCLATURE (SECTIONS 12.6, 12.10)

12.50 What are the IUPAC names of the following alkanes?

(a) 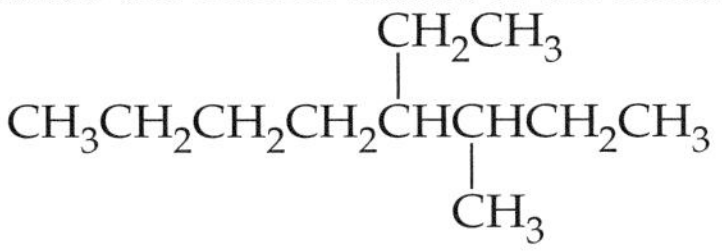

(b) 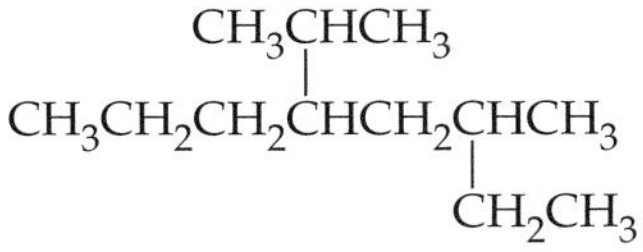

(c) 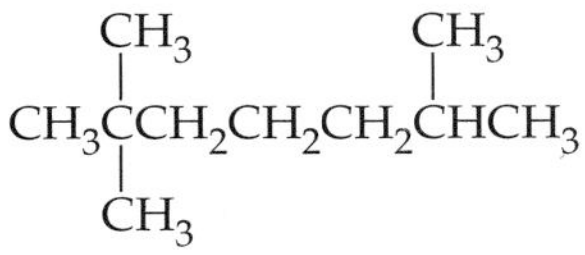

(d) 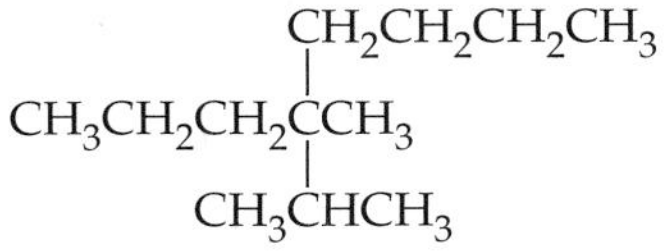

(e) 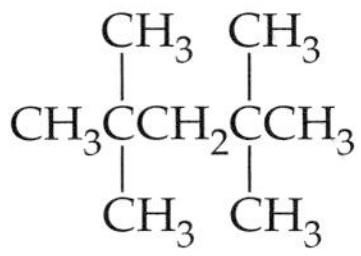

(f) 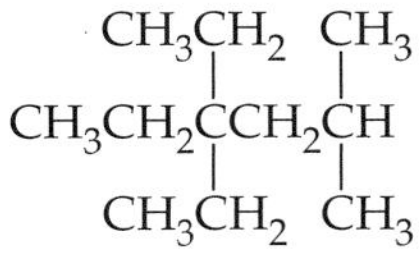

(g) 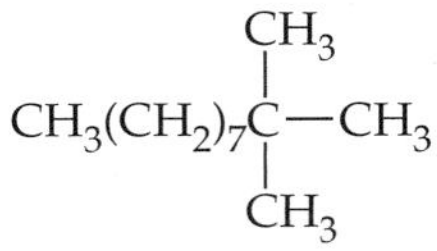

12.51 Give IUPAC names for the five isomers with the formula C_6H_{14}.

12.52 Write condensed structures for the following compounds:

(a) 4-*tert*-Butyl-2-methylheptane

(b) 2,4-Dimethylpentane

(c) 4,4-Diethyl-3-methyloctane

(d) 3-Ethyl-1-isopropyl-5-methylcycloheptane

(e) 1,1,3-Trimethylcyclopentane

12.53 Draw line structures for the following cycloalkanes:

(a) 1,1-Dimethylcyclopropane

(b) 1,3-Dimethylcyclopentane

(c) Ethylcyclohexane

(d) Cycloheptane

(e) 1-Methyl-3-propylcyclohexane

(f) 1-Ethyl-4-isopropylcyclooctane

12.54 Name the following cycloalkanes:

(a) 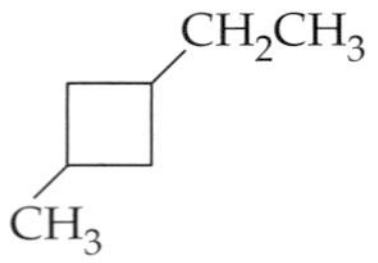
(b) 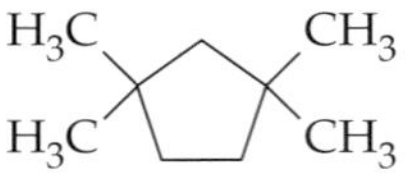
(c) 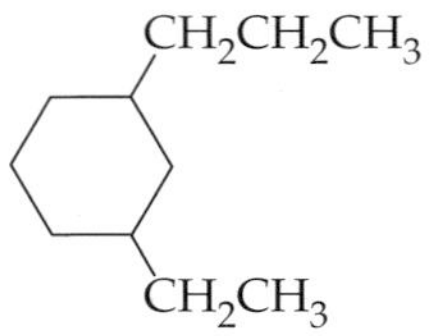
(d)

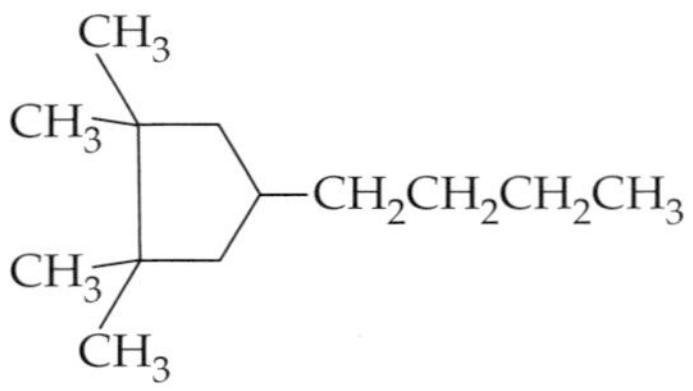

12.55 Name the following cycloalkanes:

(a) 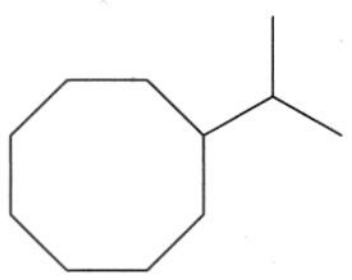
(b) 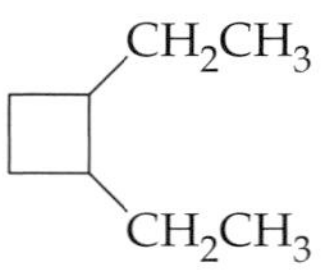
(c) 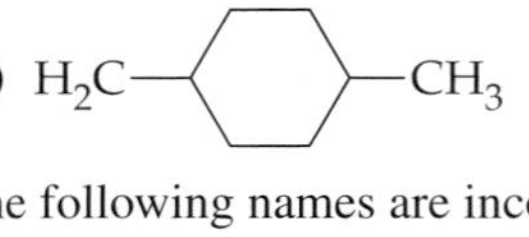 H_2C——CH_3

12.56 The following names are incorrect. Tell what is wrong with each, and provide the correct names.

(a) 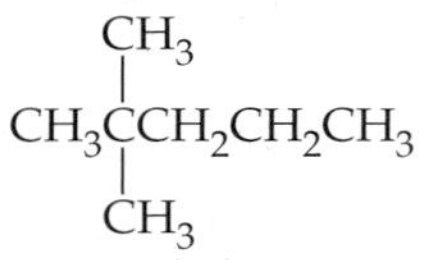 $CH_3CCH_2CH_2CH_3$
2,2-Methylpentane

(b) 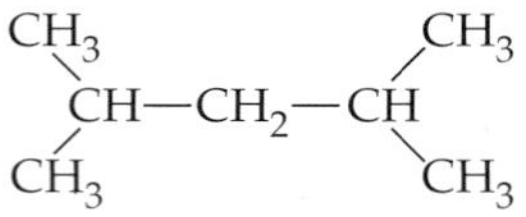 1,1-Diisopropylmethane

(c) 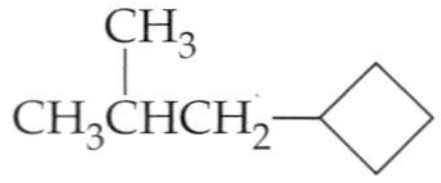 CH_3CHCH_2—
1-Cyclobutyl-2-methylpropane

12.57 The following names are incorrect. Write the structural formula that agrees with the apparent name, and then write the correct name of the compound.

(a) 2-Ethylbutane

(b) 2-Isopropyl-2-methylpentane

(c) 5-Ethyl-1,1-methylcyclopentane

(d) 3-Ethyl-3,5,5-trimethylhexane

(e) 1,2-Dimethyl-4-ethylcyclohexane

(f) 2,4-Diethylpentane

(g) 5,5,6,6-Methyl-7,7-ethyldecane

12.58 Draw structures and give IUPAC names for the nine isomers of C_7H_{16}.

12.59 Draw the structural formulas and name all cyclic isomers with the formula C_5H_{10}.

REACTIONS OF ALKANES (SECTION 12.8)

12.60 Propane, commonly known as liquid petroleum (LP) gas, burns in air to yield CO_2 and H_2O. Write a balanced equation for the reaction.

12.61 Write a balanced equation for the combustion of isooctane, C_8H_{18}, a component of gasoline.

12.62 Write the formulas of the four singly chlorinated isomers formed when 2-methylbutane reacts with Cl_2 in the presence of light.

12.63 Write the formulas of the three doubly brominated isomers formed when 2-methylpropane reacts with Br_2 in the presence of light.

CONCEPTUAL PROBLEMS

12.64 Identify the indicated functional groups in the following molecules:

(a) Testosterone, a male sex hormone

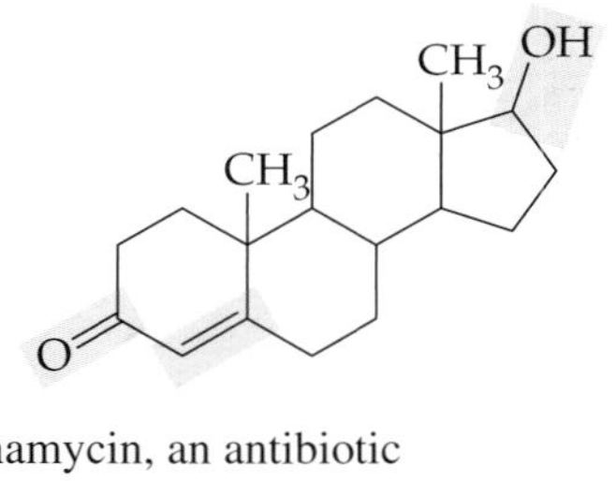

(b) Thienamycin, an antibiotic

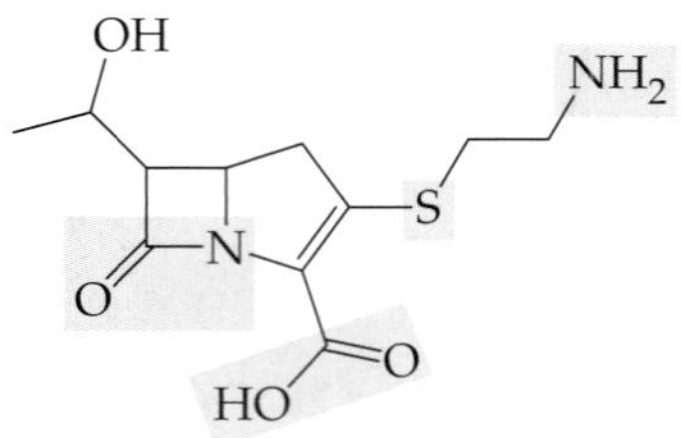

(c) Look up the structure of lisdexamfetamine (Vyvanse), a drug used in the treatment of attention deficit hyperactivity disorder (ADHD). Redraw it and identify all the functional groups present. What is known about its therapeutic properties?

12.65 The line structure for pregabalin (Lyrica) is shown as follows:

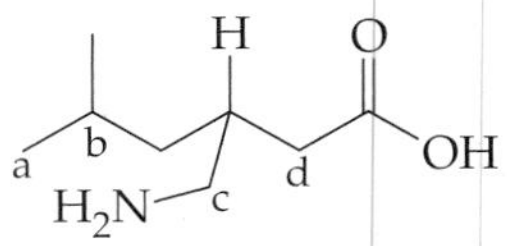

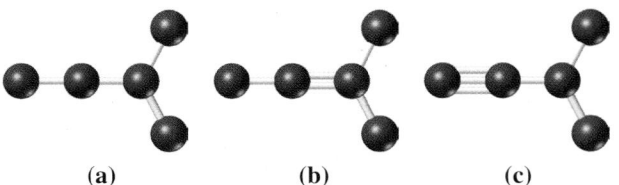

Identify carbons a–d as primary, secondary, tertiary, or quaternary.

12.66 Consider the compound shown in Problem 12.65; how many tertiary carbons does it have?

12.67 If someone reported the preparation of a compound with the formula C_3H_9, most chemists would be skeptical. Why?

12.68 Most lipsticks are about 70% castor oil and wax. Why is lipstick more easily removed with petroleum jelly than with water?

12.69 When pentane is exposed to Br_2 in the presence of light, a halogenation reaction occurs. Write the formulas of:

   (a) All possible products containing only one bromine

   (b) All possible products containing two bromines that are *not* on the same carbon

12.70 Which do you think has a higher boiling point, pentane or neopentane (2,2-dimethylpropane)? Why?

12.71 Propose structures for the following:

   (a) A carboxylic acid, $C_4H_8O_2$

   (b) An iodo-substituted alkene, C_5H_9I

   (c) A cyclopentane having a chemical formula C_7H_{14}

   (d) An alkene containing only two methyl groups and a chemical formula C_4H_8

GROUP PROBLEMS

12.72 Which of the following structures represent the same molecule?

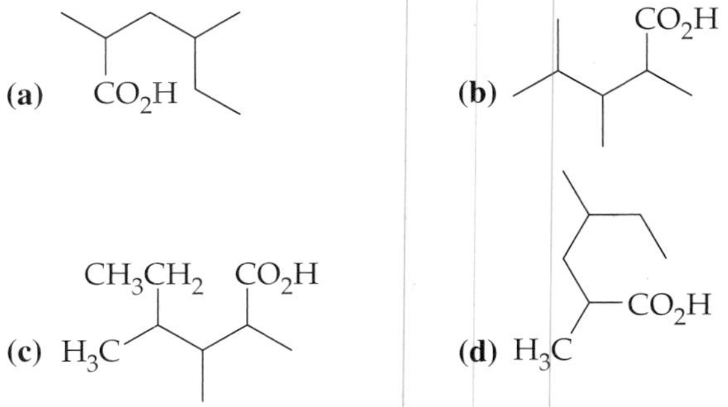

(a) CO_2H

(b) CO_2H

(c) H_3C CH_3CH_2 CO_2H

(d) H_3C CO_2H

12.73 In Problem 12.4, you drew the two branched-chain isomers with the formula C_7H_{16}, where the longest chain in the molecule is 6 carbons long. Now see how many other isomers with this chemical formula you can draw.

12.74 Since its discovery, petroleum jelly has been shown to be a household product with many practical uses. Search the internet and see if you can come up with 10 different uses for this "wonder" product.

12.75 How many hydrogen atoms are needed to complete the hydrocarbon formulas for the following carbon backbones?

   (a)   **(b)**   **(c)**

12.76 Refer to the structures shown in Problem 12.26. Using a model kit or the "gum drops and toothpicks" method presented in Hands-On Chemistry 4.1, build models of both structures (a) and (b). These two isomers demonstrate how restricted rotation comes into play for organic molecules (Section 12.9). Can you convert (a) into (b) without breaking any bonds?

13

Alkenes, Alkynes, and Aromatic Compounds

CONTENTS

◀◀◀ CONCEPTS TO REVIEW

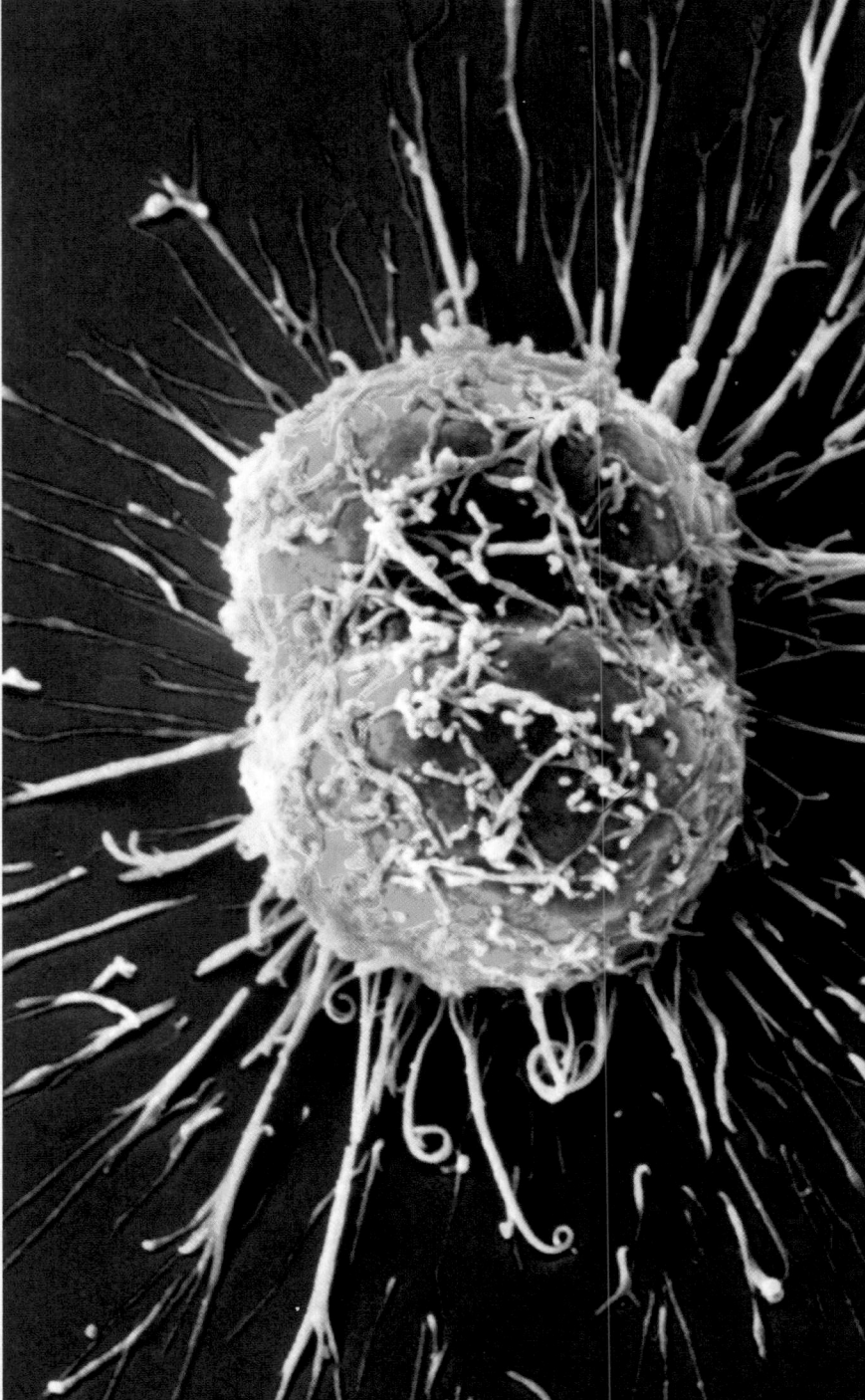

▲ In the war on cancer, potent new drugs containing carbon–carbon triple bonds are providing hope for the treatment of diseases such as cervical cancer.

Functional groups give organic molecules their characteristic physical, chemical, and biological properties. In Chapter 12, we examined the simplest hydrocarbons, alkanes, which provide the scaffolding upon which the complicated molecules responsible for life are built. Now we will look at the chemistry of molecules that contain carbon–carbon multiple bonds, or *unsaturated* hydrocarbons. While alkenes and aromatic systems are found in many naturally occurring biomolecules, alkynes are not as commonly observed. However, when alkynes are found in biological systems, they show surprising physiological activity. Chemists quite often take biologically active molecules that nature provides and use them as starting points in the laboratory to design new drugs to treat disease. Using this strategy, complex alkynes have been isolated from a number of natural sources such as bacterial cultures; these have subsequently shown promise as antitumor agents. Out of this work, the discovery of an extremely interesting class of molecules known as the *enediyne* antibiotics has arisen, a family of naturally occurring compounds that are proving to be among the most potent antitumor agents known. Discussed in more detail in the Chemistry in Action "Enediyne Antibiotics: A Newly Emerging Class of Antitumor Agents" later in the chapter, these toxic molecules, isolated from the bacteria *Micromonospora,* cut deoxyribonucleic acid (DNA) strands, which keeps a cell from reproducing, and could lead to the development of new drugs in the treatment of cancer as well as other diseases.

The last group of unsaturated hydrocarbons we will discuss are known as the aromatic hydrocarbons. *Aromatic compounds* contain a six-membered ring of carbon atoms, have alternating single and double bonds, and possess resonance, which gives aromatic compounds their unique reactivity. If one or more of the carbons in an aromatic ring is replaced by an atom other than C, we obtain what are known as *aromatic heterocyclic* molecules, many of which have unique biological properties. While only alkenes and aromatic compounds are widespread in nature, all of these unsaturated functional groups (including alkynes) are found in many biologically important molecules.

13.1 Alkenes and Alkynes

Learning Objectives:

- Identify the functional groups present in alkenes and alkynes.
- Differentiate between saturated and unsaturated molecules.

Alkanes, introduced in Chapter 12, are **saturated** because each carbon atom has four single bonds. Because this is the maximum number of single bonds a carbon can have, no more atoms can be added to any of the carbons in an alkane—in other words, the molecule is saturated. Alkenes and alkynes, however, are **unsaturated** because they contain carbon–carbon multiple bonds. Atoms can be added to an alkene or alkyne by converting these multiple bonds to single bonds. **Alkenes** are hydrocarbons that contain carbon–carbon double bonds, **cycloalkenes** are hydrocarbons that contain a double bond in a ring system, and **alkynes** are hydrocarbons that contain carbon–carbon triple bonds (cycloalkynes are rare and unknown for rings containing less than eight carbons). As you continue your study of organic and biochemistry, the term *unsaturated* will generically be used to indicate the presence of double bonds; for example, the unsaturated fatty acids (discussed in Chapter 23).

Saturated A molecule in which each carbon atom has the maximum number of single bonds possible (four).

Unsaturated A molecule that contains one or more carbon–carbon multiple bonds.

Alkene A hydrocarbon that contains a carbon–carbon double bond.

Cycloalkene A cyclic hydrocarbon that contains a double bond.

Alkyne A hydrocarbon that contains a carbon–carbon triple bond.

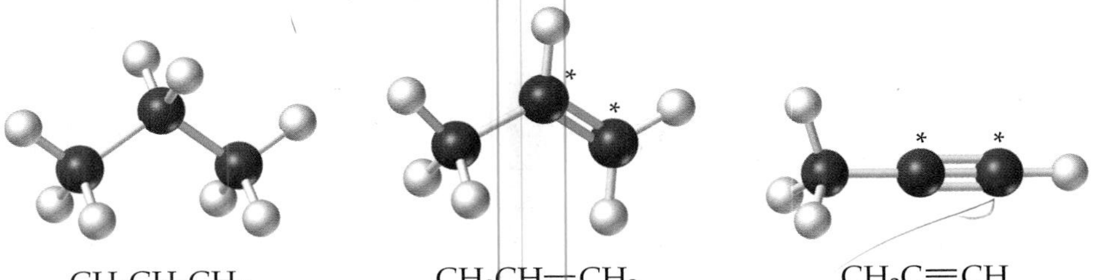

$CH_3CH_2CH_3$
Propane—an alkane
(*saturated*)

$CH_3CH=CH_2$
Propene—an alkene
(*unsaturated*)

$CH_3C\equiv CH$
Propyne—an alkyne
(*unsaturated*)

Unsaturated carbons are marked with an *

Most of the organic chemicals used in making drugs, explosives, paints, plastics, and pesticides are synthesized by routes that begin with alkenes. Ethylene is one of these alkene building blocks that is in tremendous demand, with much of it used for making polyethylene, the most common type of plastic in the world. In fact, ethylene

▲ An elephant weighs five metric tons, while a blue whale weighs 200 metric tons. That means that the amount of ethylene produced worldwide is equal to the weight of 40 million elephants, or 1 million blue whales!

◀◀◀ **CONCEPTS TO REVIEW** Review the IUPAC naming system introduced in Section 12.6.

production worldwide is expected to be at a staggering 175 million tons by the end of 2015 and 200 million metric tons by 2020, demonstrating just how important an industrial starting material it is.

Ethylene is also formed in the leaves, flowers, and roots of plants, where it acts as a hormone to control seedling growth, stimulate root formation, and regulate fruit ripening; it is thought of as the aging hormone in plants. In its role as a hormone, ethylene causes death by signaling the plant to rapidly drop its leaves, effectively shutting down photosynthesis.

13.2 Naming Alkenes and Alkynes

Learning Objectives:

• Name a simple alkene or alkyne given its condensed or line structure.
• Draw the condensed or line structure of an alkene or alkyne given its name.

In the International Union of Pure and Applied Chemistry (IUPAC) system, alkenes and alkynes are named by a series of rules identical to those used for alkanes, with one major addition: the main chain must include all the atoms that are part of the multiple bonds. The parent names indicating the number of carbon atoms in the main chain are the same as those for alkanes, with the *-ene* suffix used in place of *-ane* for alkenes and the *-yne* suffix used for alkynes. The names of alkenes and alkynes also contain a number, called an *index number,* indicating the position of the multiple bond. The main chain in any unsaturated molecule is numbered so that the molecule's name has the lowest index number possible for that multiple bond. This indexing rule for functional groups will be used again and again throughout the remaining chapters of this text.

STEP 1: Name the parent compound. Find the longest chain containing the double or triple bond, and name the parent compound by adding the suffix *-ene* or *-yne* to the name for the main chain. If there is more than one double or triple bond, the number of multiple bonds is indicated using a numerical prefix (*di*ene = two double bonds, *tri*ene = three double bonds, and so forth).

$CH_3CH_2CH_2CH=CH_2$ Name as a *pentene*—a 5-carbon chain containing a double bond.

$CH_3CH_2CH_2C\equiv CCH_3$ Name as a *hexyne*—a 6-carbon chain containing a triple bond.

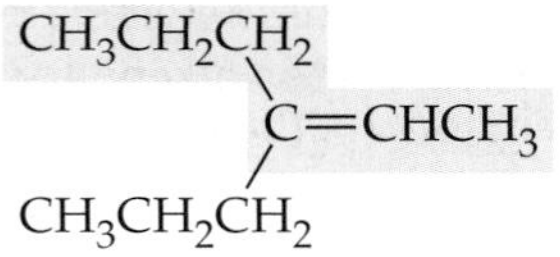

$CH_3CH_2CH_2$
$\qquad\qquad C=CHCH_3$ Name as a *hexene*—a 6-carbon chain containing a double bond . . . 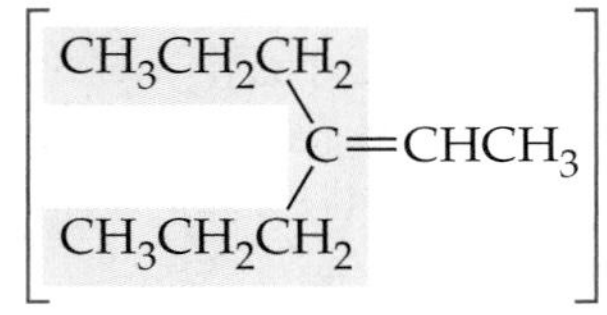
$CH_3CH_2CH_2$

$\left[\begin{array}{c} CH_3CH_2CH_2 \\ \qquad\qquad C=CHCH_3 \\ CH_3CH_2CH_2 \end{array}\right]$ . . . *not* as a heptene, because the double bond must be included in the longest chain.

STEP 2: Number the carbon atoms in the main chain so that those with multiple bonds have the lowest index numbers possible. Thus, begin numbering at the end nearer the multiple bond (Examples 1 and 3). If the multiple bond is an equal distance from both ends, begin numbering at the end nearer the first branch point (Example 2).

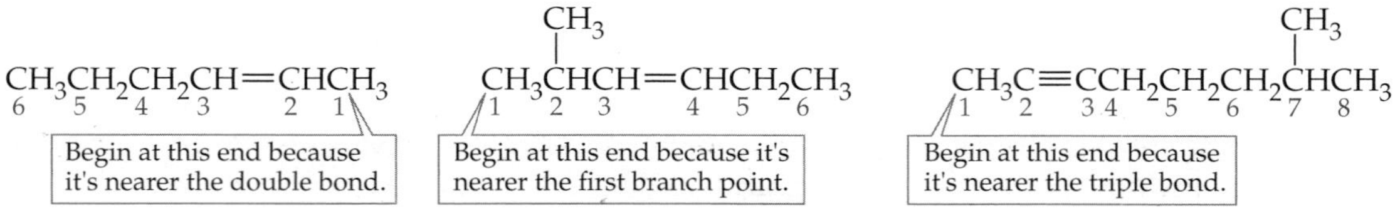

$$\underset{6\quad5\quad4\quad3\quad2\quad1}{CH_3CH_2CH_2CH=CHCH_3}$$

Begin at this end because it's nearer the double bond.

Example 1

$$\overset{CH_3}{\underset{1\quad2\quad3\quad4\quad5\quad6}{CH_3CHCH=CHCH_2CH_3}}$$

Begin at this end because it's nearer the first branch point.

Example 2

$$\overset{CH_3}{\underset{1\quad2\quad3\ 4\quad5\quad6\quad7\ 8}{CH_3C\equiv CCH_2CH_2CH_2CHCH_3}}$$

Begin at this end because it's nearer the triple bond.

Example 3

Cycloalkenes are quite common. The double-bonded carbon atoms in substituted cycloalkenes are assigned index numbers of 1 and 2 so as to give the first substituent the next lowest possible index number.

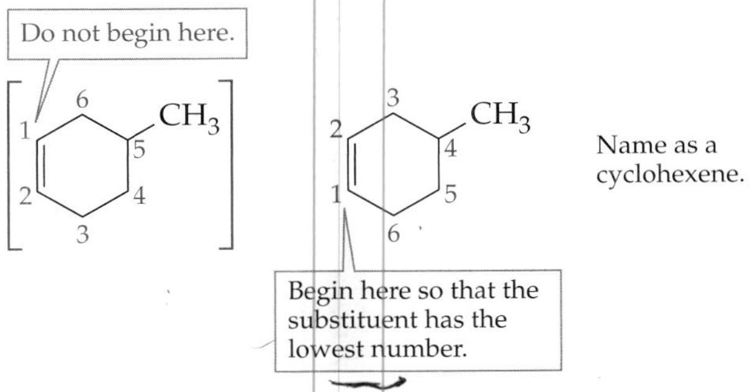

Do not begin here.

Begin here so that the substituent has the lowest number.

Name as a cyclohexene.

(Cyclic alkynes are rare, and even those that are known are far too reactive to be readily available. For these reasons, we will spend no time discussing them.)

STEP 3: Write the full name. Assign numbers to the branching substituents, and list the substituents alphabetically. Use commas to separate numbers and hyphens to separate words from numbers. Indicate the position of the multiple bond in the chain by giving the number of the *first* multiple-bonded carbon. If more than one double bond is present, identify the position of each and use the appropriate name ending (e.g., 1,3-buta*diene* and 1,3,6-hepta*triene*).

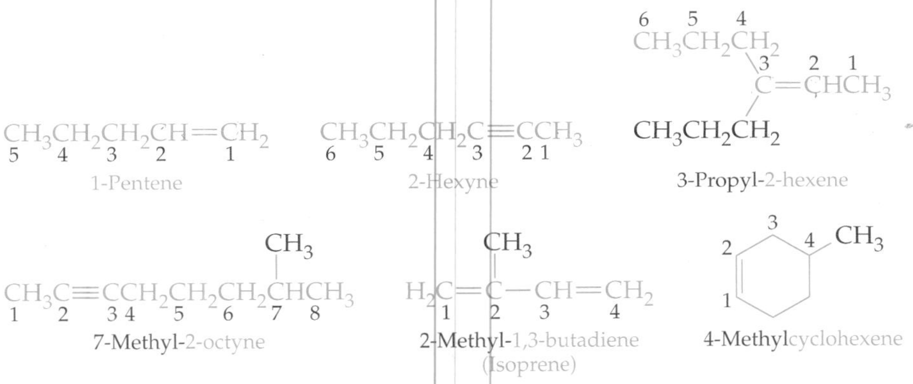

1-Pentene

2-Hexyne

3-Propyl-2-hexene

7-Methyl-2-octyne

2-Methyl-1,3-butadiene (Isoprene)

4-Methylcyclohexene

Common Names. For historical reasons, there are a few alkenes and alkynes whose names do not conform to the IUPAC rules. For instance, the 2-carbon alkene $H_2C{=}CH_2$ should properly be called *ethene*, but the name *ethylene* has been used for so long that it is now accepted by the IUPAC. Similarly, the 3-carbon alkene *propene* ($CH_3CH{=}CH_2$) is commonly called *propylene*, and the 4-carbon diene 2-methyl-1,3-butadiene (see above) is more commonly known as *isoprene*. The simplest alkyne, $HC{\equiv}CH$, should be known as *ethyne* but is almost always called *acetylene*. We will see other examples of common names for molecules that are used to the exclusion of their IUPAC names in this chapter and later as we study other functional group families.

Worked Example 13.1 Naming Organic Compounds: Alkenes

What is the IUPAC name of the following alkene?

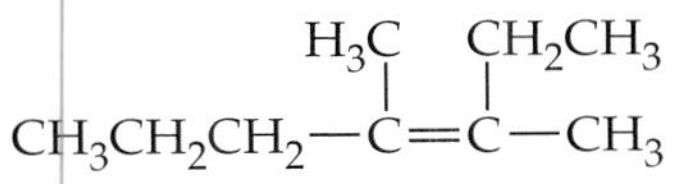

ANALYSIS Identify the parent compound as the longest continuous chain that contains the double bond. The location of the double bond and any substituents are identified by numbering the carbon chain from the end nearer the double bond.

—*continued on next page*

—continued from previous page

SOLUTION

STEP 1: The longest continuous chain containing the double bond has seven carbons—*heptene.* In this case, we have to turn a corner to find the longest chain.

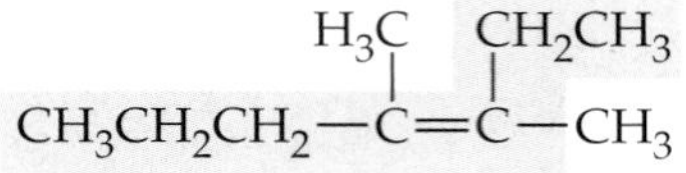

$$H_3C \quad CH_2CH_3$$
$$CH_3CH_2CH_2-C=C-CH_3 \qquad \text{Name as a } \textit{heptene.}$$

STEP 2: Number the chain from the end nearer the double bond. The first double-bond carbon is C4 starting from the left end but C3 starting from the right.

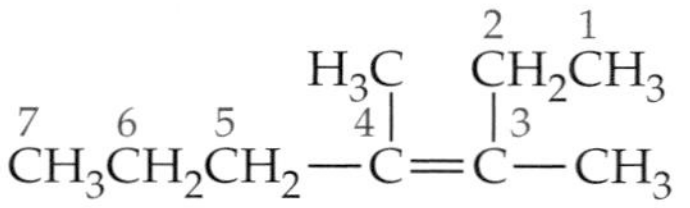

$$\overset{2}{H_3C} \quad \overset{1}{CH_2CH_3}$$
$$\overset{7}{C}H_3\overset{6}{C}H_2\overset{5}{C}H_2-\overset{4}{C}=\overset{3}{C}-CH_3 \qquad \text{Name as a substituted } \textit{3-heptene.}$$

STEP 3: Two methyl groups are attached at C3 and C4.

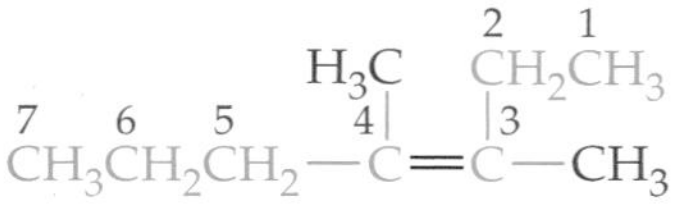

$$\overset{2}{H_3C} \quad \overset{1}{CH_2CH_3}$$
$$\overset{7}{C}H_3\overset{6}{C}H_2\overset{5}{C}H_2-\overset{4}{C}=\overset{3}{C}-CH_3 \qquad \begin{array}{l}\text{Substituents: 3-Methyl, 4-Methyl}\\ \text{Name: 3,4-Dimethyl-3-heptene}\end{array}$$

Worked Example 13.2 Molecular Structures: Alkenes

Draw the structure of 3-ethyl-4-methyl-2-pentene using both condensed and line structure.

ANALYSIS Identify the parent name *(pent)* and the location of the double bond and other substituents by numbering the carbons in the parent chain.

SOLUTION

STEP 1: The parent compound is a five-carbon chain with the double bond between C2 and C3.

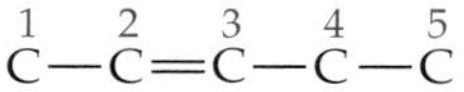

$$\overset{1}{C}-\overset{2}{C}=\overset{3}{C}-\overset{4}{C}-\overset{5}{C} \qquad \text{2-Pentene}$$

STEP 2: Add the ethyl and methyl substituents on C3 and C4, and write in the additional hydrogen atoms so that each carbon atom has four bonds.

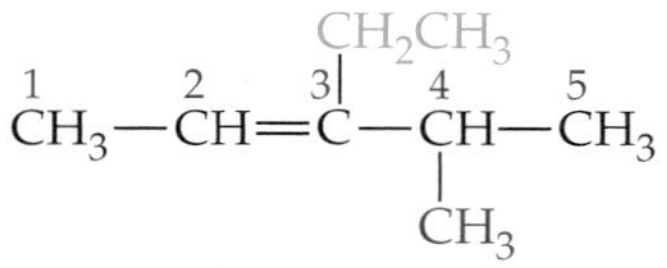

$$\overset{}{CH_2CH_3}$$
$$\overset{1}{C}H_3-\overset{2}{C}H=\overset{3}{C}-\overset{4}{C}H-\overset{5}{C}H_3 \qquad \text{3-Ethyl-4-methyl-2-pentene}$$
$$\qquad\qquad\qquad | $$
$$\qquad\qquad\quad CH_3$$

Using line structures we can draw it in the following ways:

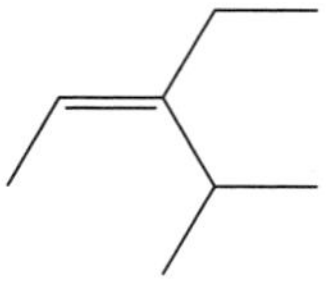

or

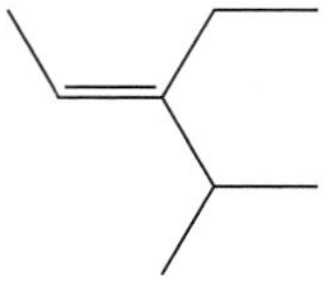

In this particular case either is correct. The two structures differ in the position of the CH_3 with respect to the CH_2CH_3; they are examples of cis–trans isomers (Section 13.3).

PROBLEM 13.1

What are the IUPAC names of the following compounds?

(a) $CH_3CH_2CH_2CH=CHCHCH_3$ with CH_3 substituent above the CHCH_3 carbon

(b) $H_2C=CHCH_2CH_2C=CH_2$ with CH_3 substituent below

(c)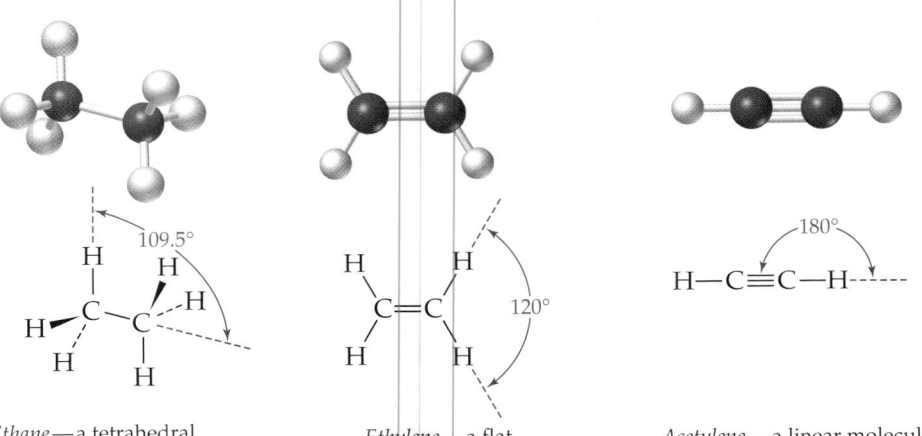

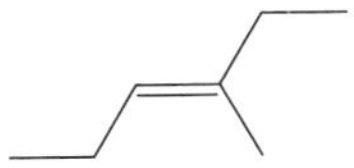

(d) 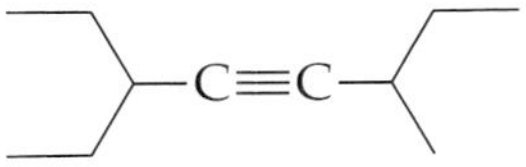 line structure with $-C\equiv C-$

PROBLEM 13.2

Draw both condensed and line structures corresponding to the following IUPAC names:

(a) 3-Methyl-1-heptene   (b) 4,4-Dimethyl-2-pentyne
(c) 2-Methyl-3-hexene   (d) 1,3,3-Trimethylcyclohexene

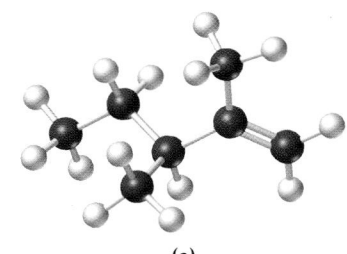

(a)

🔑 **KEY CONCEPT PROBLEM 13.3**

What are the IUPAC names of the two alkenes shown in the margin? Redraw each in line structure format.

13.3 The Structure of Alkenes: Cis–Trans Isomerism

Learning Objective:

• Identify cis–trans isomers of alkenes.

Alkenes and alkynes differ from alkanes in shape because of their multiple bonds. Methane is tetrahedral, but ethylene is flat (planar), and acetylene is linear (straight), as predicted by the valence-shell electron-pair repulsion (VSEPR) model discussed in Section 4.8.

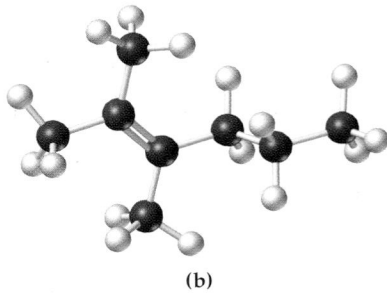

(b)

Ethane—a tetrahedral molecule with bond angles of 109.5°

Ethylene—a flat molecule with bond angles of 120°

Acetylene—a linear molecule with bond angles of 180°

In ethylene, the two carbons and four attached atoms that make up the double-bond functional group lie in a plane. Unlike in alkanes, where free rotation around the C—C single bond occurs, there is no rotation around a double bond, and the molecules are more rigid. However, their restricted freedom of rotation makes a new kind of isomerism possible for alkenes. As a consequence of their rigid nature, alkenes possess *ends* and *sides*.

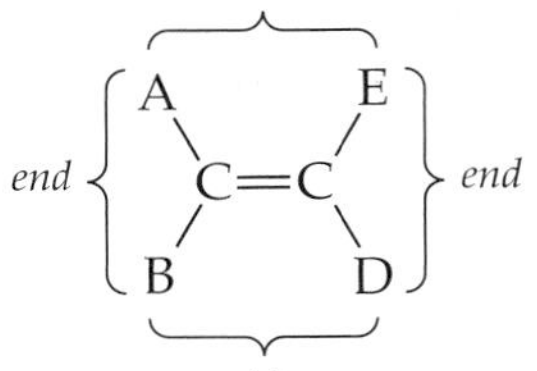

To see this new kind of isomerism, look at the four C_4H_8 compounds shown on the next page. When written as condensed structures, there appears to be only three alkene isomers of formula C_4H_8: 1-butene ($CH_2=CHCH_2CH_3$), 2-butene ($CH_3CH=CHCH_3$), and 2-methylpropene (($CH_3)_2C=CH_2$). The compounds 1-butene and 2-butene are constitutional isomers of each other because their double bonds occur at different positions along the chain, and 2-methylpropene is a constitutional isomer of both 1-butene and 2-butene because it has the same molecular formula but a different connection of carbon atoms (see Section 12.3). In fact, though, there are *four* isomers of C_4H_8. Because rotation cannot occur around carbon–carbon double bonds, *there are two different 2-butenes.* In one isomer, the two —CH_3 groups are on the same side of the double bond; in the other isomer, they are on opposite sides of the double bond.

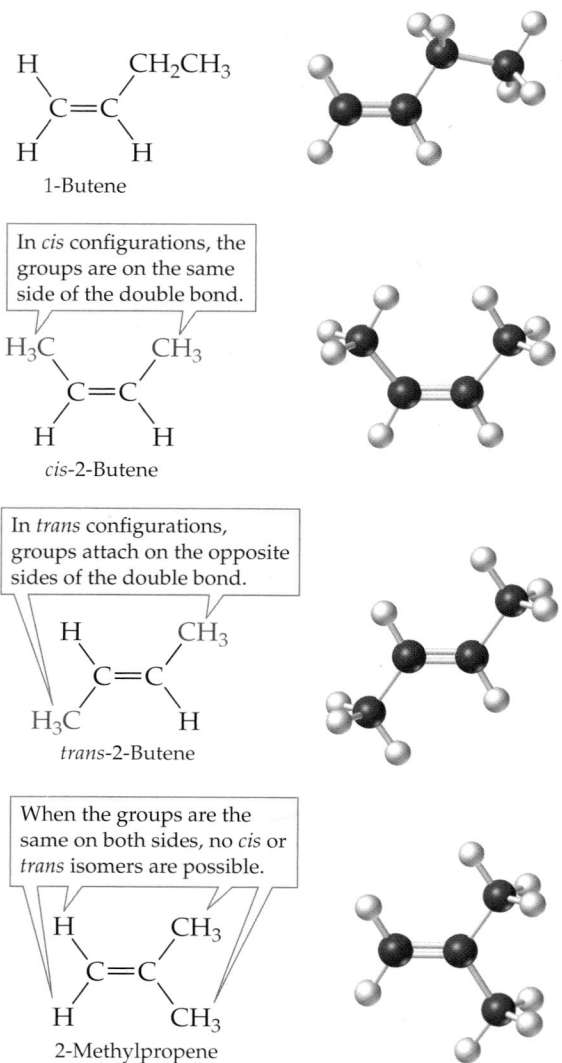

1-Butene

In *cis* configurations, the groups are on the same side of the double bond.

cis-2-Butene

In *trans* configurations, groups attach on the opposite sides of the double bond.

trans-2-Butene

When the groups are the same on both sides, no *cis* or *trans* isomers are possible.

2-Methylpropene

Cis–trans isomer Alkenes that have the same connections between atoms but differ in their three-dimensional structures because of the way those groups attach to different sides of the double bond.

The two 2-butenes are called **cis–trans isomers.** They have the same formula and connections between atoms but have different three-dimensional structures because of the way those groups attach to different sides of the double bond. In this case, the isomer with its methyl groups on the same side of the double bond is named *cis*-2-butene, and the isomer with its methyl groups on opposite sides of the double bond is named *trans*-2-butene.

Cis–trans isomerism is possible whenever an alkene has two *different* substituent groups on each of its ends. (This means that in the earlier drawing illustrating the sides and ends of an alkene molecule, A ≠ B and D ≠ E.) If one of the carbons composing the double bond is attached to two identical groups, cis–trans isomerism cannot exist. In 2-methyl-1-butene, for example, cis–trans isomerism is not possible because C1 is bonded to two identical groups (hydrogen atoms). To convince yourself of this, mentally flip either one of these two structures top to bottom; note that it becomes identical to the other structure.

and

These compounds are identical. Because the carbon left of the double bond has two H atoms attached, cis–trans isomerism is impossible.

2-Methyl-1-butene

In 2-pentene, however, the structures do not become identical when one of them is flipped, so cis–trans isomerism does occur.

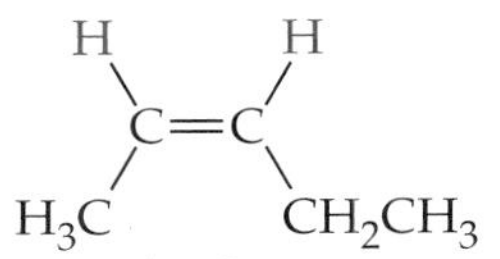

cis-2-Pentene   *trans*-2-Pentene

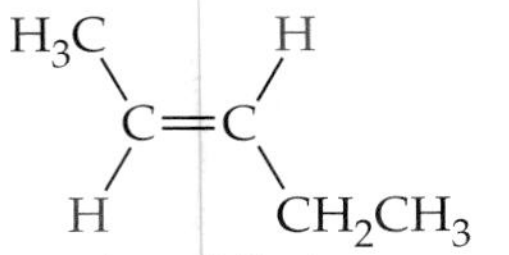

These compounds are not identical. Neither carbon of the double bond has two identical groups attached to it.

It is important to note that the molecule must remain intact when you perform this analysis; you cannot break and reform any bonds when flipping and comparing the two structures.

The two substituents that are on the same side of the double bond in an alkene are said to be cis to each other, and those on opposite sides of the double bond are said to be trans to each other. In our generic molecule on the previous page showing ends and sides, for example, A and E are cis to each other, B and D are cis to each other, B and E are trans to each other, and A and D are trans to each other. Thus, in alkenes, the terms cis and trans are used in two ways: (1) as a *relative* term to indicate how various groups are attached to the double-bond carbons (e.g., "groups A and E are cis") and (2) in nomenclature as a way to indicate how the longest chain in the molecule goes in, through, and out of the double bond (e.g., *cis*-2-butene and *trans*-2-butene). Alkynes, because of their linear structure, cannot have cis–trans isomerism; while the triple bond does have ends, it does not have sides, a necessary requirement of this type of isomer.

◀◀◀ Recall from Section 12.5 that rotation around C—C single bonds allows a molecule to exist in multiple conformations.

Worked Example 13.3 Molecular Structure: Cis and Trans Isomers

Draw structures for both the cis and trans isomers of 2-hexene.

ANALYSIS First, draw a condensed structure of 2-hexene to see which groups are attached to the double-bond carbons.

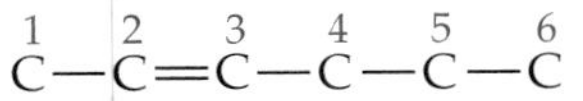

2-Hexene

Next, begin to draw the two isomers. Choose one end of the double bond, and attach its groups in the *same way* to generate two identical partial structures.

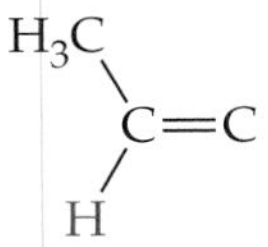

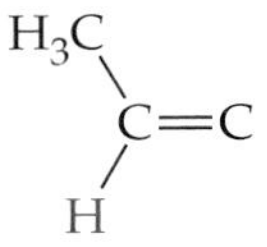

Finally, attach groups to the other end in the two possible *different ways*.

SOLUTION

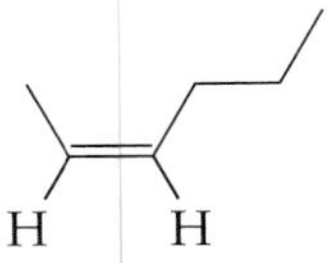

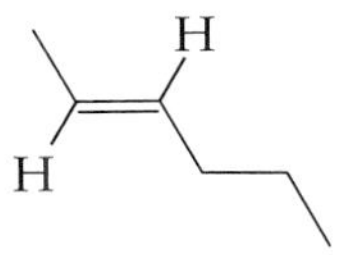

Trace the longest chain in each structure. In the structure on the left, the longest chain comes in on one side of the double bond and exits on the same side; thus, the two hydrogens are on the same side of the double bond and this is the cis isomer. The structure on the left is the trans isomer because the longest chain comes in on one side of the double bond and exits on the opposite side, and the two hydrogens are on opposite sides of the double bond. It is common in line structures to show the hydrogens attached to the double bond, but not necessary.

PROBLEM 13.4

Which of the following substances exist as can cis–trans isomers? Draw both isomers for those that do.
   (a) 2,3-Dimethyl-2-pentene (condensed structures only)
   (b) 2-Methyl-2-hexene (both condensed and line structures)
   (c) 2-Hexene (line structures only)

HANDS-ON CHEMISTRY 13.1

Models are an invaluable tool in organic chemistry when discussing structure. In this exercise, you are going to look at double bonds and how they restrict rotation when present in an organic molecule. You will also look at how they can crucially change the shape of a molecule. To accomplish all of this you are going to use models, *but you do not need a model kit to carry out this exercise.* If you have a model kit, follow the instructions included with it to make the "building blocks" described next. If you do not have access to a model kit, follow the instructions next to make "gumdrop building blocks." You will need a box of toothpicks and a bag of multicolored gumdrops (preferred), gummy bears, or mini marshmallows; it does not matter as long as you can insert a toothpick in it and it will stay in place. Throughout this exercise, remember that carbon is tetravalent (forms four bonds) and that hydrogen and chlorine are monovalent (form one bond).

Building Blocks—for this exercise, you will need the following (use the color coding of atoms listed in Table 4.2 as your guide if possible):

Six tetrahedral carbon units—make these by placing four toothpicks into a gumdrop in a tetrahedral array. Use gumdrops of whatever color you have assigned to being carbon (black or some other dark color). Note: There will be times you will have to remove toothpicks to make connections to other units; when you do, make the new connection in the same location as the toothpick you removed.

Three carbon alkene units—to make these, connect two carbon-colored gumdrops to one another using two toothpicks. Be sure that there is some space between them so that they look like an alkene model.

Six "one group" units—simply stick a toothpick into a gumdrop. The gumdrops should all be the same color, although the color should vary from what you've already used.

Note: You may want to take pictures of each model you make with your phone for review later. Once finished with a question, you can disassemble your models for use in the next question.

a. Start by assembling butane by connecting four of your tetrahedral units (you will have to remove toothpicks as necessary to make connections). Add gumdrops at the end of the toothpicks to represent Hs if you wish. By rotating around the single bonds, write down all the conformations possible. Is any one higher in energy than the others? See Section 12.5 for help.

b. Now, using your alkene units, build models of 2-methylpropene, *cis*-2-butene, and *trans*-2-butene (see Section 13.3). Confirm that these three are all different molecules. Notice that you cannot rotate around the double bond to convert the cis molecule into the trans without breaking the double bond. The cis isomer is slightly higher in energy than the trans; can you come up with a possible reason why?

c. Repeat part b for 2-chloro-1-butene, showing that there is only one possible isomer for this compound.

$$CH_3CH_2CCl{=}CH_2$$

d. Cis double bonds are found in many biological molecules, such as the unsaturated fatty acids (see Section 23.2), despite them being of slightly higher energy than the trans. Build two molecules with the following structure, one where all the double bonds are cis and one where they are all trans. Can you come up with a reasonable explanation as to why the all-*cis* molecule might be more advantageous to have in an aqueous environment over the all-trans molecule?

$$CH_2{=}CH{-}CH{=}CH{-}CH{=}CH_2$$

PROBLEM 13.5

Draw both the condensed and line structures for the cis and trans isomers of 3,4-dimethyl-3-hexene.

 **KEY CONCEPT PROBLEM 13.6** ————————————————————————————

Name the compounds shown below, including the appropriate *cis*- or *trans*- prefix. Redraw each in line structure format.

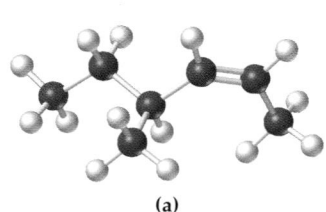

(a)

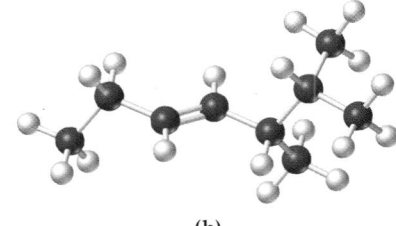

(b)

13.4 Properties of Alkenes and Alkynes

Learning Objective:

• Identify the physical properties of alkenes and alkynes.

The properties of alkenes and alkynes resemble those of alkanes in many respects (Section 12.7). The bonds in alkenes and alkynes are nonpolar, and the physical properties of these compounds are influenced mainly by weak London dispersion forces. Alkenes and alkynes with 1–4 carbon atoms are gases at room temperature, and boiling points increase with the size of the molecules.

◀◀ Intermolecular forces were described in Section 8.2.

Like alkanes, alkenes and alkynes are insoluble in water, soluble in nonpolar solvents, and less dense than water. They are flammable; those that are gases present explosion hazards when mixed with air. Unlike alkanes, alkenes are more reactive because of their double bonds. As we will see in the next section, alkenes undergo addition of various reagents to their double bonds to yield saturated products. Alkynes, as you might expect, are more reactive since they have two double bonds to react.

Properties of Alkenes and Alkynes

• Nonpolar; insoluble in water; soluble in nonpolar organic solvents; less dense than water
• Flammable; nontoxic
• Alkenes display cis–trans isomerism when each double-bond carbon atom has different substituents
• Cis-trans isomers can have different physical and biological properties.
• Multiple bonds are chemically reactive.

13.5 Types of Organic Reactions

Learning Objective:

• Identify the different types of organic reactions.

Before looking at the chemistry of alkenes and alkynes, we should first discuss some general reactivity patterns that make the task of organizing and categorizing organic reactions much simpler. Four particularly important kinds of organic reactions are discussed in this section: *additions, eliminations, substitutions,* and *rearrangements.*

• **Addition Reactions** Additions occur when two reactants add together to form a single product with no atoms "left over." We can generalize the process as

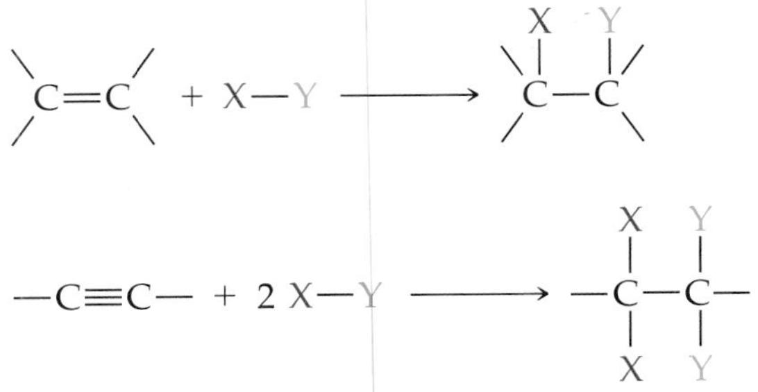

Addition reaction A general reaction type in which a substance X—Y adds to the multiple bond of an unsaturated reactant to yield a saturated product that has only single bonds.

These two reactants add together … $A + B \longrightarrow C$ … to give this single product.

The most common addition reactions encountered in organic chemistry are those in which a reagent adds across a carbon–carbon multiple bond (an unsaturated molecule) to give a product that contains two (for alkenes) or four (for alkynes) new single bonds (a saturated system). This process can be generalized as

$$\begin{array}{c}\diagdown\\ \diagup\end{array}C=C\begin{array}{c}\diagup\\ \diagdown\end{array} + X-Y \longrightarrow \begin{array}{c}X\ \ Y\\ |\ \ |\\ \diagdown|\ \ |\diagup\\ C-C\\ \diagup\ \ \ \diagdown\end{array}$$

$$-C\equiv C- + 2\,X-Y \longrightarrow \begin{array}{c}X\ \ Y\\ |\ \ |\\ -C-C-\\ |\ \ |\\ X\ \ Y\end{array}$$

We'll explore the mechanism of addition reactions further in the Mastering Reactions: How Addition Reactions Occur feature on page 422. An example of an addition reaction is the reaction of an alkene, such as ethylene, with H_2 to yield an alkane.

$$
\underset{\text{Ethylene}}{\overset{\displaystyle H\diagdown \quad \diagup H}{\underset{\displaystyle H \diagup \quad \diagdown H}{C=C}}} + H-H \longrightarrow \underset{\text{Ethane}}{H-\overset{\displaystyle H}{\underset{\displaystyle H}{C}}-\overset{\displaystyle H}{\underset{\displaystyle H}{C}}-H}
$$

Elimination reaction A general reaction type in which a saturated reactant yields an unsaturated product by losing groups from two adjacent atoms.

- **Elimination Reactions** Eliminations are the opposite of addition reactions. Eliminations occur when a single reactant splits into two or more products, a process we can generalize as

$$
\text{This one reactant ...} \quad \overset{X \quad Y}{\underset{A-B}{|\quad|}} \longrightarrow A=B + X + Y \quad \text{... splits apart to give these two products.}
$$

In almost all cases, an elimination reaction converts the starting material to a product that has two fewer single bonds and a carbon–carbon multiple bond in their place.

$$
\overset{X \quad Y}{\underset{\diagup \quad \diagdown}{\diagdown |\;|\diagup}}\!\!C-C \longrightarrow \overset{\diagdown \quad \diagup}{\underset{\diagup \quad \diagdown}{C=C}} + X-Y
$$

As an example of an elimination reaction, we will see in the next chapter that an alcohol, such as ethanol, eliminates to give water and an alkene when treated with an acid catalyst. This specific process is known as a *dehydration reaction* and can be seen in further detail in the Mastering Reactions: How Eliminations Occur feature on page 449.

> Water was *eliminated* from the reactant.

$$
\underset{\text{Ethanol}}{H-\overset{\displaystyle H}{\underset{\displaystyle H}{C}}-\overset{\displaystyle OH}{\underset{\displaystyle H}{C}}-H} \xrightarrow[\text{catalyst}]{H_2SO_4} \underset{\text{Ethylene}}{\overset{\displaystyle H\diagdown \quad \diagup H}{\underset{\displaystyle H \diagup \quad \diagdown H}{C=C}}} + H_2O
$$

Substitution reaction A general reaction type in which an atom or group of atoms in a molecule is replaced by another atom or group of atoms.

- **Substitution Reactions** Substitutions occur when two reactants exchange parts to give two new products, a process we can generalize as

$$
\text{These two reactants exchange parts ...} \quad AB + C \longrightarrow AC + B \quad \text{... to give these two products.}
$$

As an example of a substitution reaction, we saw in Section 12.8 that alkanes, such as methane, react with Cl_2 in the presence of ultraviolet (UV) light to yield alkyl chlorides (the UV light is needed due to the low reactivity of alkanes). Here, a —Cl group substitutes for the —H group of the alkane, and two new products result:

> Cl is *substituted* for H in this reaction.

$$
\underset{\text{Methane}}{H-\overset{\displaystyle H}{\underset{\displaystyle H}{C}}-H} + Cl-Cl \longrightarrow \underset{\text{Chloromethane}}{H-\overset{\displaystyle H}{\underset{\displaystyle H}{C}}-Cl} + H-Cl
$$

A much more common type of substitution reaction is one that involves alkyl halides and Lewis bases, such as the reaction shown here:

$$CH_3CH_2CH_2Cl + CH_3O^- Na^+ \longrightarrow CH_3CH_2CH_2OCH_3 + Na^+Cl^-$$

We previously saw another example of this type of substitution reaction in Chapter 12 in Mastering Reactions: Organic Chemistry and the Curved Arrow Formalism on page 386. We'll learn more about alkyl halides and Lewis bases in Chapters 14 and 16.

- **Rearrangement Reactions** Rearrangement occurs when bonds and atoms in the reactant are reorganized to yield a single product that is an isomer of the reactant. A generalized example of one type of rearrangement seen in organic chemistry is

Rearrangement reaction A general reaction type in which a molecule undergoes bond reorganization to yield an isomer.

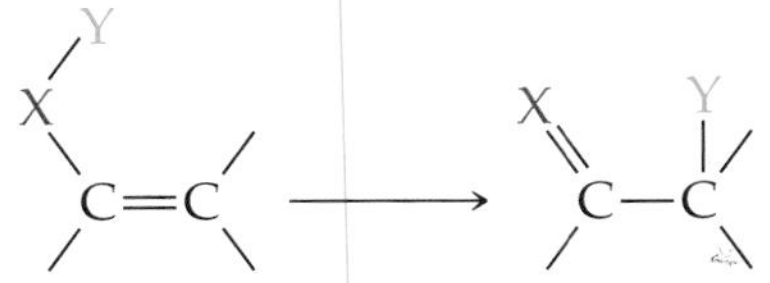

Rearrangement reactions are important in organic chemistry as well as biochemistry. Because of their complex nature, however, we will not discuss them in detail in this book. An example of a rearrangement is the conversion of *cis*-2-butene into its isomer *trans*-2-butene by treatment with an acid catalyst:

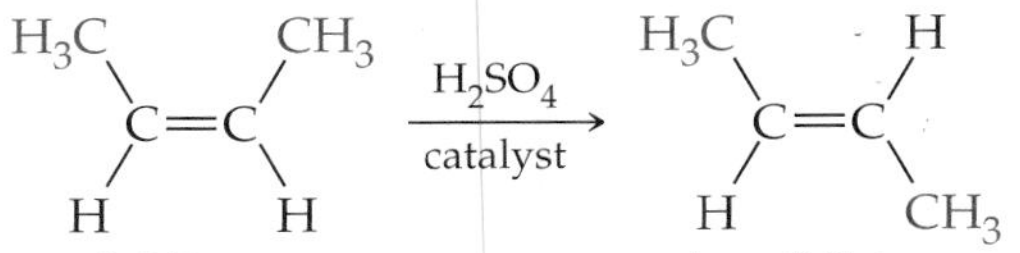

cis-2-Butene   *trans*-2-Butene

This simple-looking interconversion involves the breaking of the C=C bond followed by rotation and reformation of the double bond; this is a key process in vision (see the Chemistry in Action "The Chemistry of Vision and Color" p. 414).

LOOKING AHEAD ➤ The conversion of glucose to fructose (Chapter 22) is an example of tautomerization, converting one carbohydrate into another.

Worked Example 13.4 Identifying Reactions of Alkenes

Classify the following alkene reactions as addition, elimination, or substitution reactions:

(a) $CH_3CH{=}CH_2 + H_2 \longrightarrow CH_3CH_2CH_3$

(b) $CH_3CH_2CH_2OH \xrightarrow[\text{catalyst}]{H_2SO_4} CH_3CH{=}CH_2 + H_2O$

(c) $CH_3CH_2Cl + KOH \longrightarrow CH_3CH_2OH + KCl$

ANALYSIS Determine whether atoms have been added to the starting compound (addition), removed from the starting compound (elimination), or switched with another reactant (substitution).

SOLUTION

(a) Two H atoms have been *added* in place of the double bond, so this is an *addition* reaction.

(b) A water molecule (H_2O) has been formed by *removing* an H atom and an —OH group from adjacent C atoms, forming a double bond in the process, so this is an *elimination* reaction.

(c) The reactants (CH_3CH_2Cl and KOH) have *traded* the —OH and the —Cl substituent groups, so this is a *substitution* reaction.

PROBLEM 13.7

Classify the following reactions as an addition, elimination, or substitution:

(a) $CH_3Br + NaOH \longrightarrow CH_3OH + NaBr$

(b) $H_2C{=}CH_2 + HCl \longrightarrow CH_3CH_2Cl$

(c) $CH_3CH_2Br \longrightarrow H_2C{=}CH_2 + HBr$

CHEMISTRY IN ACTION

✦ The Chemistry of Vision and Color

Our vision, from the vibrant colors we see to the ability of our eyes to adapt to both bright sunlight and pitch darkness, is one of our key sensory systems, but what is the role of chemistry in this system? A critical player in the ability to see is vitamin A, an important biological alkene.

A vitamin is an organic molecule required by the body in trace amounts and usually obtained through diet (Section 19.9). Beta-carotene, a purple-orange alkene, found in carrots and other yellow vegetables provides our main dietary source of vitamin A (also known as *retinol*). The enzymatic conversion of beta-carotene to vitamin A

takes place in the mucosal cells of the small intestine; vitamin A is then stored in the liver, from which it can be transported to the eye. In the eye, vitamin A is oxidized to *retinal,* which undergoes cis–trans isomerization of its C11–C12 double bond to produce 11-*cis*-retinal. Reaction with the protein *opsin* then produces the light-sensitive substance *rhodopsin.*

The human eye has two kinds of light-sensitive cells, *rod cells* and *cone cells.* The 3 million rod cells are primarily responsible for seeing in dim light, whereas the 100 million cone cells are responsible for seeing in bright light and for the perception of bright colors. When light strikes the rod cells, cis–trans isomerization of the C11—C12 double bond occurs

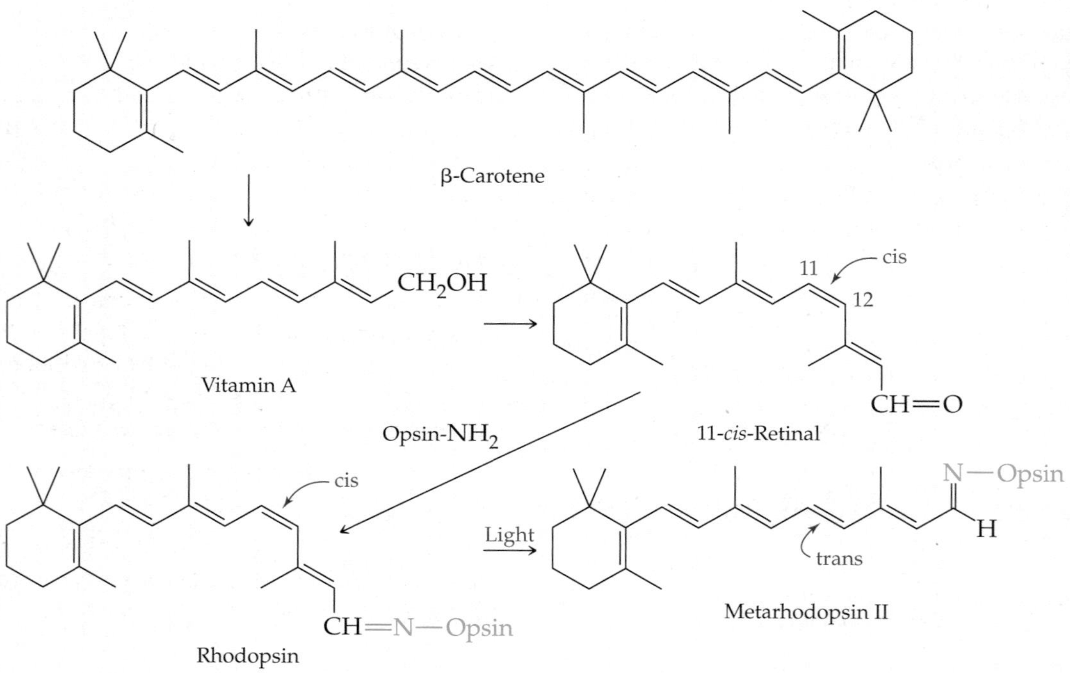

β-Carotene

Vitamin A

11-*cis*-Retinal

Opsin-NH₂

Rhodopsin

Metarhodopsin II

PROBLEM 13.8

Many biological transformations can be simply classified as additions, eliminations, or substitutions. How would you classify the following reactions?

(a) Fumaric acid to malic acid (found in the citric acid cycle, Section 21.8)

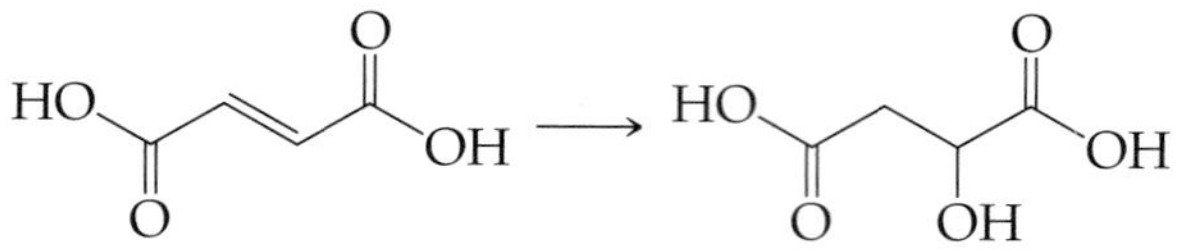

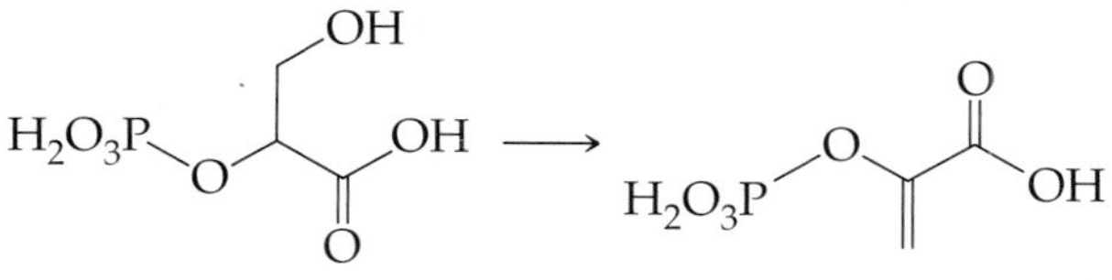

(b) 2-Phosphoglyceric acid to phosphoenolpyruvic acid (found in glycolysis, Section 22.3) via a rearrangement reaction, and 11-*trans*-rhodopsin, also called *meta*rhodopsin II, is produced. This cis–trans isomerization is accompanied by a change in molecular geometry, which in turn causes a nerve impulse to be sent to the brain, where it is perceived as vision. Metarhodopsin II is then changed back to 11-*cis*-retinal for use in another vision cycle.

While this explains how we see, it does not tell us what causes the actual colors themselves. Other organic compounds such as the plant pigment cyanidin are also brightly colored. This is due to the fact that they are extended conjugated systems.

Conjugated systems are molecules that contain arrays of alternating double and single bonds, and the electrons within the double bonds are spread out, or *delocalized,* over the whole molecule. Whenever there is conjugation in a molecule, a delocalized region of electron density is formed that is in turn capable of absorbing light. Compounds with extended stretches of alternating double and single bonds (10 or more) absorb in the visible region. The presence of a charged atom in the conjugated system, such as the oxygen in cyanidin, allows absorption in the visible range to occur with fewer conjugated double bonds.

Cyanidin
(reddish-blue color in flowers
and cranberries)

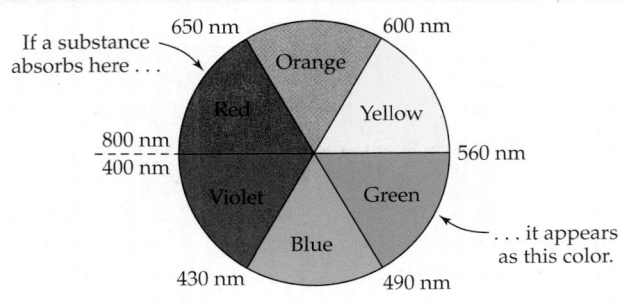

▲ Using an artist's color wheel, it is possible to determine the observed color of a substance by knowing the color of the light absorbed. Observed and absorbed colors are complementary. Thus, if a substance absorbs red light, it has a green color.

The color that we see is complementary to the color that is absorbed; that is, we see what is left of the white light after certain colors have been absorbed. For example, the plant pigment cyanidin absorbs greenish-yellow light and thus appears reddish-blue. It is speculated that this is also the reason that red-colored mulch seems to promote plant growth: the reflected red color is absorbed by the green plant, creating the effect of additional incoming sunlight for photosynthesis.

CIA Problem 13.1 (a) After the reaction of 11-*cis*-retinal with opsin, classify the reaction rhodopsin undergoes in the presence of light to produce 11-*trans*-rhodopsin. (b) How many hydrogens are present in 11-*cis*-retinal? (c) What are the functional groups present in this molecule?

CIA Problem 13.2 What is the difference in the purpose of the rod cells and the cone cells in the eye?

CIA Problem 13.3 Tetrabromofluorescein is a purple dye often used in lipsticks. If the dye is purple, what color does it absorb?

13.6 Addition Reactions of Alkenes

Learning Objectives:

- Predict the addition products obtained when alkenes react with H_2, Cl_2, HCl, or H_2O.
- Identify "unsymmetrically substituted" and "symmetrically substituted" alkenes.
- Utilize Markovnikov's rule when addition reactions to unsymmetrically substituted alkenes occur.

Most of the reactions of alkenes and alkynes are *addition reactions,* where reagent X—Y adds to the multiple bond in the unsaturated reactant to yield a saturated product that has only single bonds.

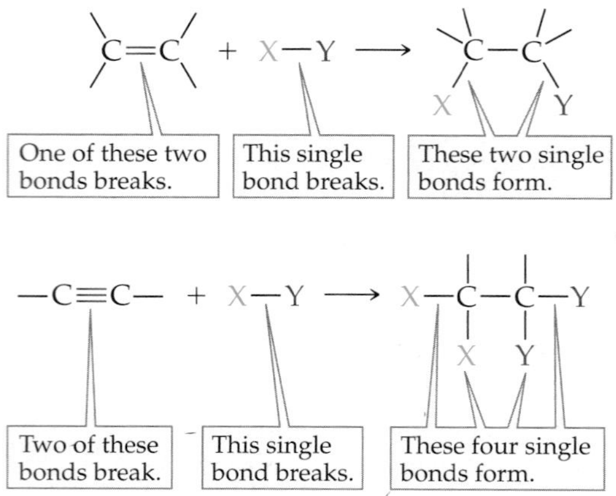

| One of these two bonds breaks. | This single bond breaks. | These two single bonds form. |

Addition reactions

| Two of these bonds break. | This single bond breaks. | These four single bonds form. |

Addition reactions of alkenes are often used to prepare large quantities of industrially important compounds (such as ethyl alcohol). Addition reactions of alkenes and alkynes are similar in many ways. Since alkynes are rarely found in nature, and because addition to an alkyne can generally be thought of as a "double addition" of an alkene, we will limit our discussion in this section to the reactions of alkenes, even though alkynes will do the exact same reactions.

Addition of H₂ to Alkenes: Hydrogenation

Hydrogenation The addition of H_2 to a multiple bond to give a saturated product.

Alkenes and alkynes react with hydrogen, a process called **hydrogenation,** in the presence of a metal catalyst such as palladium to yield the corresponding alkane product.

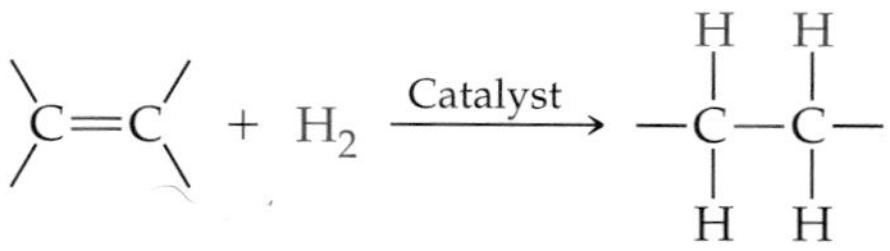

For example,

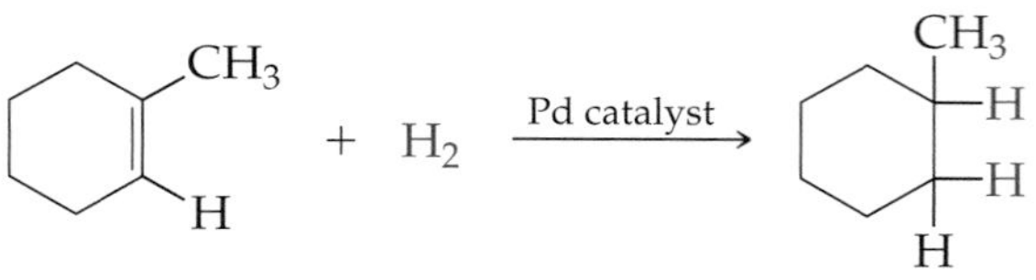

1-Methylcyclohexene   Methylcyclohexane (85% yield)

The addition of hydrogen to an alkene is used commercially to convert unsaturated vegetable oils, which contain numerous double bonds, to the saturated fats used in margarine and cooking fats. This process has come under intense scrutiny in recent years because it also creates *trans*-fatty acids in the product (which, in the diet, has been associated with increased risk of heart disease). We will see the structures of these fats and oils in Chapter 23.

Worked Example 13.5 Organic Reactions: Addition

What product would you obtain from the following reaction? Draw both the condensed structure and the line structure of the product.

$$CH_3CH_2CH_2CH{=}CHCH_3 + H_2 \xrightarrow{\text{Pd}} ?$$

ANALYSIS Rewrite the reactant, showing a single bond and two partial bonds in place of the double bond.

$$CH_3CH_2CH_2CH-CHCH_3$$

Then, add a hydrogen to each carbon atom of the double bond, and rewrite the product in condensed form.

$$CH_3CH_2CH_2CH-CHCH_3 \quad \text{is the same as} \quad CH_3CH_2CH_2CH_2CH_2CH_3$$
$$\qquad\qquad\quad | \quad\quad | \qquad\qquad\qquad\qquad\qquad\qquad\qquad \text{Hexane}$$
$$\qquad\qquad\quad H \quad\quad H$$

SOLUTION
The reaction is

$$CH_3CH_2CH_2CH{=}CHCH_3 + H_2 \xrightarrow{Pd} CH_3CH_2CH_2CH_2CH_2CH_3$$

In line structure format, this reaction would look as follows:

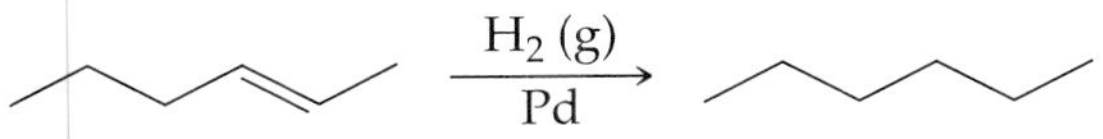

$$\text{(line structure)} \xrightarrow[\text{Pd}]{H_2 \ (g)} \text{(line structure)}$$

PROBLEM 13.9
Write the structures of the products from the following hydrogenation reactions:

(a) 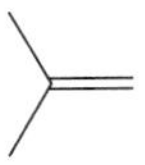 (structure) + H$_2$ $\xrightarrow{Pd}$?

(b) *cis*-2-Butene + H$_2$ $\xrightarrow{Pd}$?

(c) *trans*-3-Heptene + H$_2$ $\xrightarrow{Pd}$?

(d) 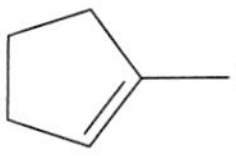 (structure)—CH$_3$ + H$_2$ $\xrightarrow{Pd}$?

Addition of Cl$_2$ and Br$_2$ to Alkenes: Halogenation

Alkenes react with the halogens Br$_2$ and Cl$_2$ to give 1,2-dihaloalkane addition products in a **halogenation (alkene)** reaction.

Halogenation (alkene) The addition of Cl$_2$ or Br$_2$ to a multiple bond to give a dihalide product.

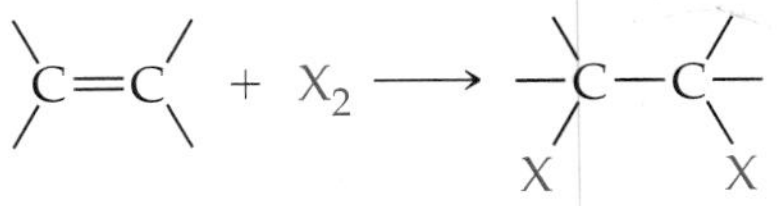

$$\begin{array}{c}\backslash \quad / \\ C{=}C \\ / \quad \backslash \end{array} + X_2 \longrightarrow \begin{array}{c} \backslash \quad / \\ -C-C- \\ / \quad | \quad | \quad \backslash \\ \ \ \ X \quad X \end{array}$$

(A 1,2-dihaloalkane where X = Br or Cl)

For example,

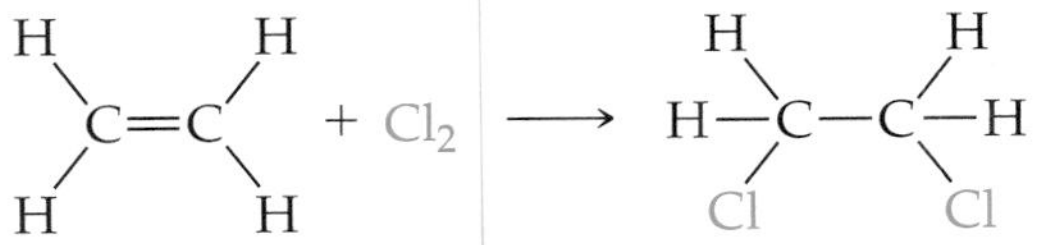

$$\begin{array}{c} H \qquad\quad H \\ \backslash \qquad\quad / \\ C{=}C \\ / \qquad\quad \backslash \\ H \qquad\quad H \end{array} + Cl_2 \longrightarrow \begin{array}{c} H \qquad\quad H \\ | \qquad\quad | \\ H-C-C-H \\ | \qquad\quad | \\ Cl \qquad\quad Cl \end{array}$$

Ethylene   1, 2-Dichloroethane

The addition of Br$_2$ and Cl$_2$ to an alkene occurs in an analogous way to that shown in Worked Example 13.5. This reaction is used to manufacture nearly 8 million tons of 1,2-dichloroethane each year in the United States. It is the first step in making the widely used poly(vinyl chloride) plastics (PVC).

Another halogen, Br$_2$, provides a convenient test for the presence of a carbon–carbon double or triple bond in a molecule (Figure 13.1). A few drops of a reddish-brown solution of Br$_2$ are added to a sample of an unknown compound; the immediate disappearance of the color reveals the presence of a carbon–carbon multiple bond, because the bromine reacts with the compound to form a colorless dibromide. This test can also be used to determine the level of unsaturation of fats (Chapter 23).

(a)

(b)

▲ **Figure 13.1**
Testing for unsaturation with bromine.
(a) No color change results when the bromine solution is added to hexane (C_6H_{14}). (b) Disappearance of the bromine color when it is added to 1-hexene (C_6H_{12}) indicates the presence of a double bond.

Hydrohalogenation The addition of HCl or HBr to a multiple bond to give an alkyl halide product.

PROBLEM 13.10

What products would you expect from the following halogenation reactions?

(a) 2-Methylpropene + Br_2 ⟶?

(b) 1-Pentene + Cl_2 ⟶?

(c) 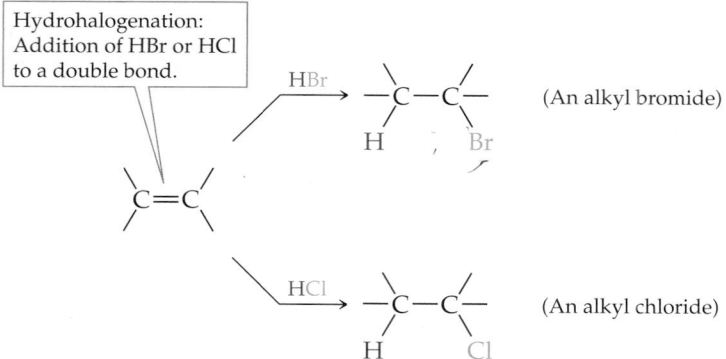 + Cl_2 ⟶?

(d) ⬠⟩ + Br_2 ⟶ ?

Addition of HBr and HCl to Alkenes

Alkenes react with hydrogen bromide (HBr) to yield *alkyl bromides* (R—Br) and with hydrogen chloride (HCl) to yield *alkyl chlorides* (R—Cl), in what are called **hydrohalogenation** reactions.

Hydrohalogenation: Addition of HBr or HCl to a double bond.

C=C $\xrightarrow{\text{HBr}}$ —C—C— (An alkyl bromide)
      (H , Br)

C=C $\xrightarrow{\text{HCl}}$ —C—C— (An alkyl chloride)
      (H , Cl)

The addition of HBr to 2-methylpropene is an example.

H_3C, H_3C C=C H, H + HBr ⟶ $H_3C-\overset{CH_3}{\underset{Br}{C}}-CH_3$

2-Methylpropene   2-Bromo-2-methylpropane

Look carefully at the above example. Only one of the two possible addition products is obtained. 2-Methylpropene *could* add HBr to give 1-bromo-2-methylpropane, but it does not; it gives only 2-bromo-2-methylpropane as the major product.

H_3C, H_3C C=C H, H + HBr ⟶ $H_3C-\overset{CH_3}{\underset{Br \; H}{C}}-CH_2$ $\left[H_3C-\overset{CH_3}{\underset{H \; Br}{C}}-CH_2 \right]$

2-Methylpropene   2-Bromo-2-methylpropane (Major product)   1-Bromo-2-methylpropane (Trace)

This result is typical of what happens when HBr and HCl add to an alkene in which one of the double-bond carbons has more hydrogens than the other (an unsymmetrically substituted alkene). The results of such additions can be predicted using **Markovnikov's rule,** formulated in 1869 by the Russian chemist Vladimir Markovnikov.

Markovnikov's rule In the addition of HX to an alkene, the major product arises from the H attaching to the double-bond carbon that has the larger number of H atoms *directly* attached to it and the X attaching to the carbon that has the smaller number of H atoms attached.

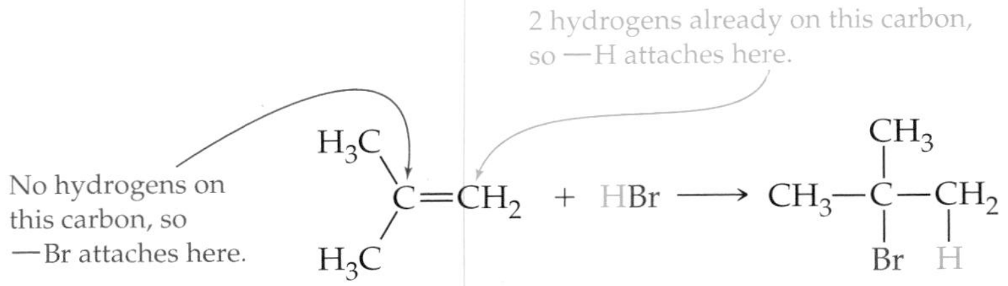

2 hydrogens already on this carbon,
so —H attaches here.

No hydrogens on
this carbon, so
—Br attaches here.

$$H_3C \diagdown C = CH_2 \; + \; HBr \longrightarrow CH_3 - \underset{\underset{Br}{|}}{\overset{\overset{CH_3}{|}}{C}} - \underset{\underset{H}{|}}{CH_2}$$

Note that the terms "unsymmetrically substituted" and "symmetrically substituted" here refer only to the *number* of hydrogens and carbons attached to each carbon engaged in the double bond and not to the *identity* of the carbon groups attached.

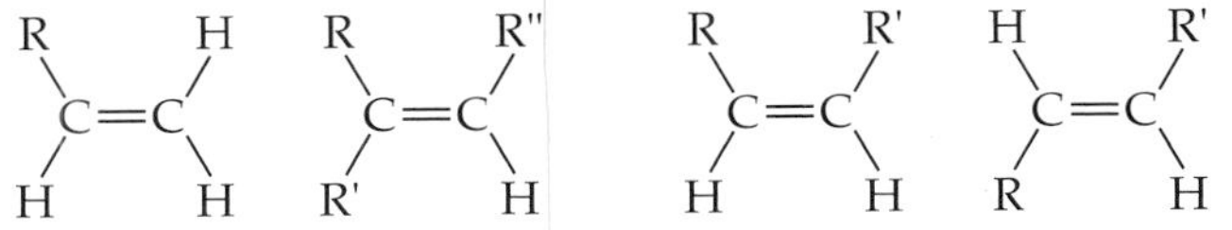

$$\underset{H}{\overset{R}{\diagup}}C = C\underset{H}{\overset{H}{\diagdown}} \qquad \underset{R'}{\overset{R}{\diagup}}C = C\underset{H}{\overset{R''}{\diagdown}} \qquad \underset{H}{\overset{R}{\diagup}}C = C\underset{H}{\overset{R'}{\diagdown}} \qquad \underset{R}{\overset{H}{\diagup}}C = C\underset{H}{\overset{R'}{\diagdown}}$$

"Unsymmetrically substituted"   "Symmetrically substituted"

In the examples above, R, R', and R" can be any group except H and do not have to be different in this context.

The scientific reason behind Markovnikov's rule is a powerful and important principle in organic chemistry. The Mastering Reactions: How Addition Reactions Occur feature on page 422 discusses Markovnikov's rule in further detail, including the stability of intermediates known as *carbocations* that form during the reaction.

Both possible products form in equal amounts if an alkene has equal numbers of H atoms attached to the double-bond carbons (a symmetrically substituted double bond).

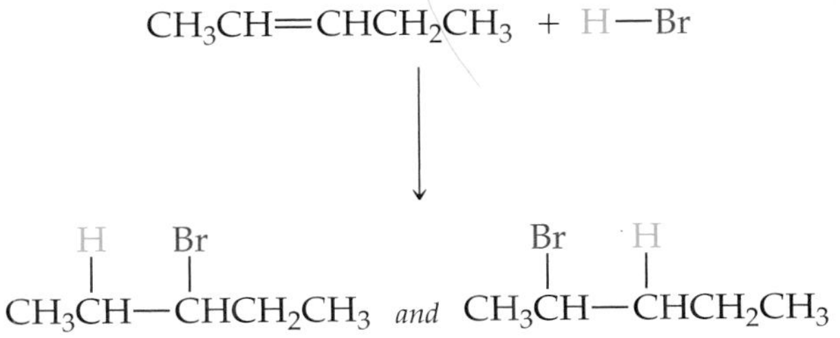

$$CH_3CH = CHCH_2CH_3 \; + \; H-Br$$

$$\underset{\text{3-Bromopentane}}{CH_3\underset{\underset{H}{|}}{CH} - \underset{\underset{Br}{|}}{CH}CH_2CH_3} \quad and \quad \underset{\text{2-Bromopentane}}{CH_3\underset{\underset{Br}{|}}{CH} - \underset{\underset{H}{|}}{CH}CH_2CH_3}$$

(1:1 ratio)

Worked Example 13.6 Organic Reactions: Markovnikov's Rule

What major product do you expect from the following reaction?

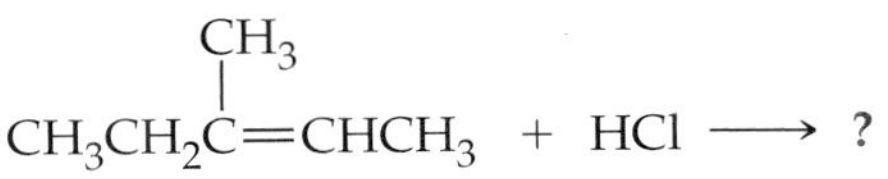

$$CH_3CH_2\underset{\overset{|}{\underset{}{}}}{\overset{\overset{CH_3}{|}}{C}} = CHCH_3 \; + \; HCl \longrightarrow ?$$

ANALYSIS The reaction of an alkene with HCl leads to the formation of an alkyl chloride addition product according to Markovnikov's rule. To make a prediction, look at the starting alkene and count the number of hydrogens attached to each double-bond carbon. Then write the product by attaching H to the carbon with more hydrogens and attaching Cl to the carbon with fewer hydrogens.

SOLUTION

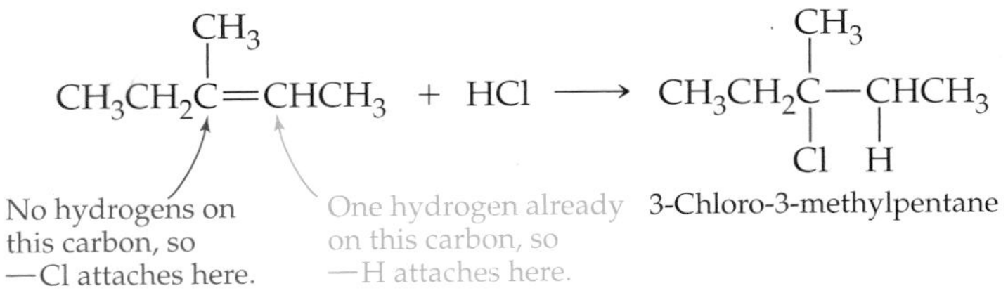

$$CH_3CH_2\overset{\overset{CH_3}{|}}{C} = CHCH_3 \; + \; HCl \longrightarrow CH_3CH_2\underset{\underset{Cl}{|}}{\overset{\overset{CH_3}{|}}{C}} - \underset{\underset{H}{|}}{CH}CH_3$$

No hydrogens on
this carbon, so
—Cl attaches here.

One hydrogen already   3-Chloro-3-methylpentane
on this carbon, so
—H attaches here.

$$\left(\text{same as} \quad CH_3CH_2\underset{\underset{Cl}{|}}{\overset{\overset{CH_3}{|}}{C}}CH_2CH_3 \right)$$

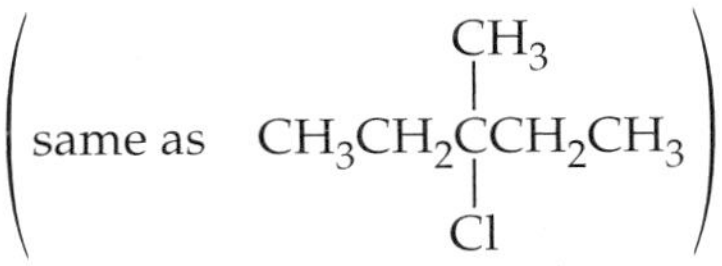

Worked Example 13.7 Organic Reactions: Markovnikov's Rule

From what two different alkenes can 2-chloro-3-methylbutane be made?

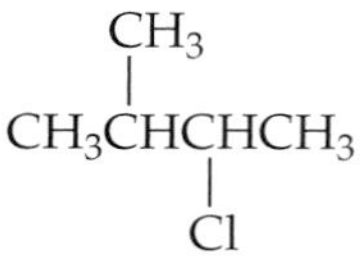

$$CH_3$$
$$|$$
$$CH_3CHCHCH_3$$
$$|$$
$$Cl$$

2-Chloro-3-methylbutane

ANALYSIS 2-Chloro-3-methylbutane is an alkyl chloride that might be made by addition of HCl to an alkene. To generate the possible alkene precursors, remove the —Cl group and an —H atom from adjacent carbons and replace with a double bond.

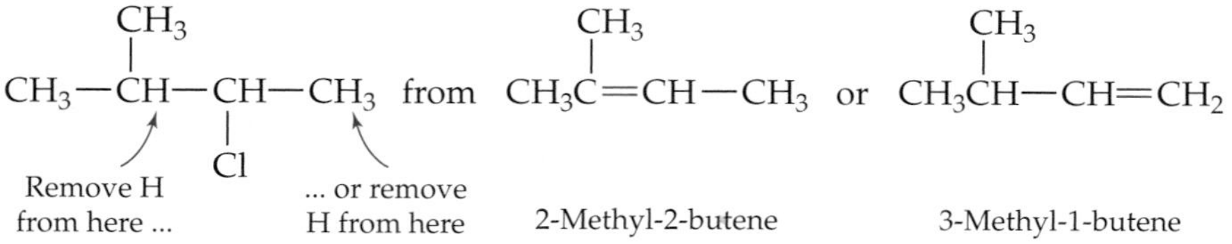

$$CH_3 \qquad\qquad CH_3 \qquad\qquad CH_3$$
$$| \qquad\qquad\qquad | \qquad\qquad\qquad |$$
$$CH_3-CH-CH-CH_3 \text{ from } CH_3C=CH-CH_3 \text{ or } CH_3CH-CH=CH_2$$
$$\qquad\quad \nearrow \quad | \quad \nwarrow$$
$$\qquad\qquad Cl$$
Remove H \qquad ... or remove
from here ... \qquad H from here \qquad 2-Methyl-2-butene \qquad\qquad 3-Methyl-1-butene

Look at the possible alkene addition reactions to see which is compatible with Markovnikov's rule. In this case, addition to 3-methyl-1-butene is compatible. Note that if HCl is added to 2-methyl-2-butene, the major product will have the Cl attached to the wrong carbon (the carbon with the methyl group on it).

SOLUTION

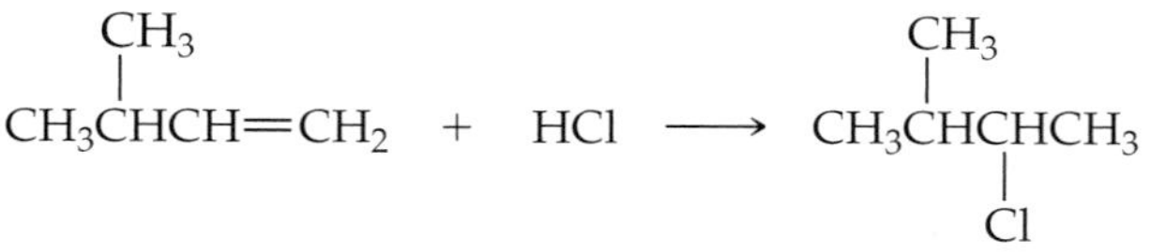

$$CH_3 \qquad\qquad\qquad\qquad CH_3$$
$$| \qquad\qquad\qquad\qquad\qquad |$$
$$CH_3CHCH=CH_2 \ + \ HCl \longrightarrow CH_3CHCHCH_3$$
$$\qquad\qquad\qquad\qquad\qquad\qquad\qquad |$$
$$\qquad\qquad\qquad\qquad\qquad\qquad\qquad Cl$$

3-Methyl-1-butene \qquad\qquad\qquad 2-Chloro-3-methylbutane

PROBLEM 13.11

Draw all possible products formed when 2-methyl-2-butene undergoes addition with HCl. Label them as being either the major or the minor product.

PROBLEM 13.12

What major products do you expect from the following reactions?

(a) 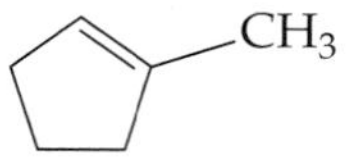 + HCl ⟶ ?   (b)  + HBr ⟶ ?

(c) 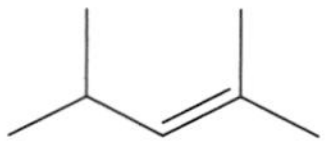 + HCl ⟶ ?

PROBLEM 13.13

In the following addition reactions, are the given alkyl halides obtained as the major products? Give a reason for your answer.

(a) 3-Chloro-3-ethylpentane from addition of HCl to 3-ethyl-2-pentene

(b)

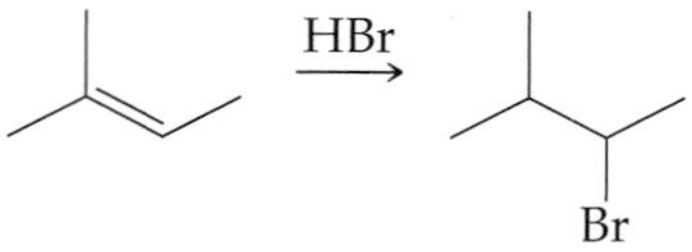

KEY CONCEPT PROBLEM 13.14

What product do you expect from the following reaction? Draw your answer in both condensed and line structure formats.

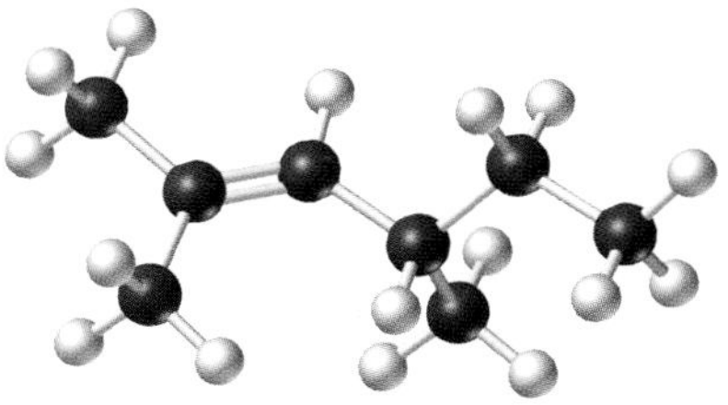

+ HBr ⟶ ?

Addition of Water to Alkenes: Hydration

Although a water molecule (H—OH) could be considered as another type of H—X, an alkene will not react with pure water alone. If, however, a small amount of a strong acid catalyst such as H_2SO_4 is added, an addition reaction takes place to yield an *alcohol* (R—OH); a reaction known as a **hydration** reaction. In fact, the United States produces nearly 100 million gallons of ethyl alcohol (ethanol) each year by this method.

Hydration The addition of water to a multiple bond to give an alcohol product.

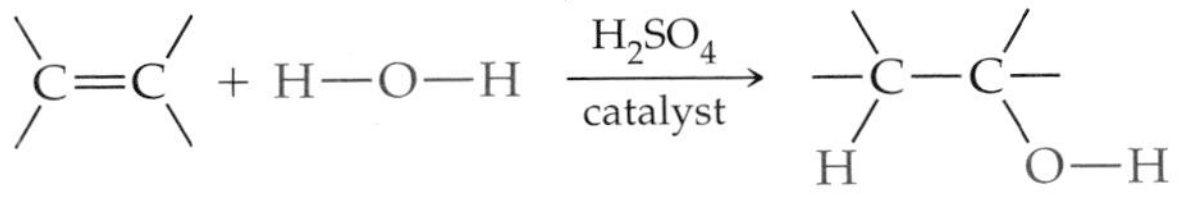

+ H—O—H
H_2SO_4
catalyst

An alcohol

For example,

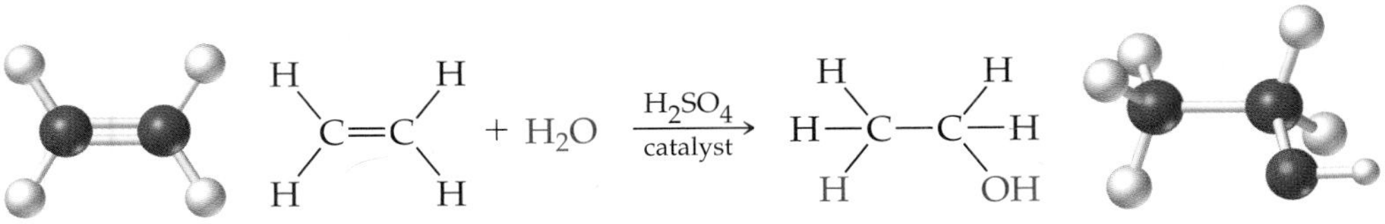

+ H_2O
H_2SO_4
catalyst

Ethylene Ethyl alcohol

As with the addition of HBr and HCl, we can use Markovnikov's rule to predict the product when water adds to an unsymmetrically substituted alkene. Hydration of 2-methylpropene, for example, gives 2-methyl-2-propanol as the major product:

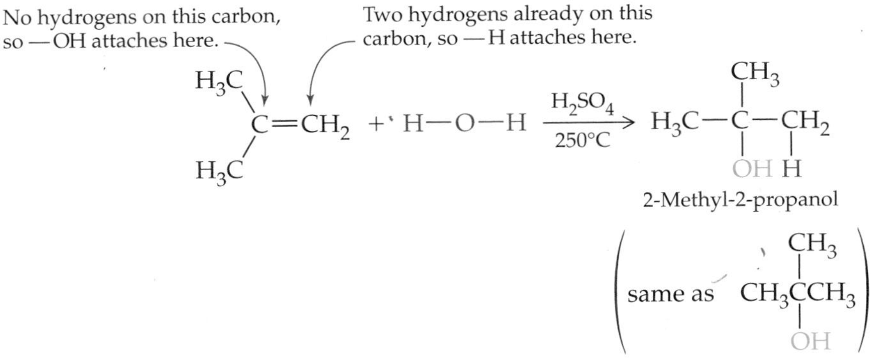

No hydrogens on this carbon, so —OH attaches here.
Two hydrogens already on this carbon, so —H attaches here.
+ H—O—H
H_2SO_4
250°C
2-Methyl-2-propanol
same as

MASTERING REACTIONS

How Addition Reactions Occur

How do alkene addition reactions take place? Do two molecules, say ethylene and HBr, simply collide and immediately form a product molecule of bromoethane, or is the process more complex? In Chapter 12, we presented a useful and convenient way for organic chemists to visualize reactions (see Mastering Reactions: Organic Chemistry and the Curved Arrow Formalism on p. 386). Here, we apply this to the study of addition reactions, specifically those involving H^+. Detailed studies show that alkene addition reactions take place in two distinct steps, as illustrated in the following figure for the addition of HBr to ethylene.

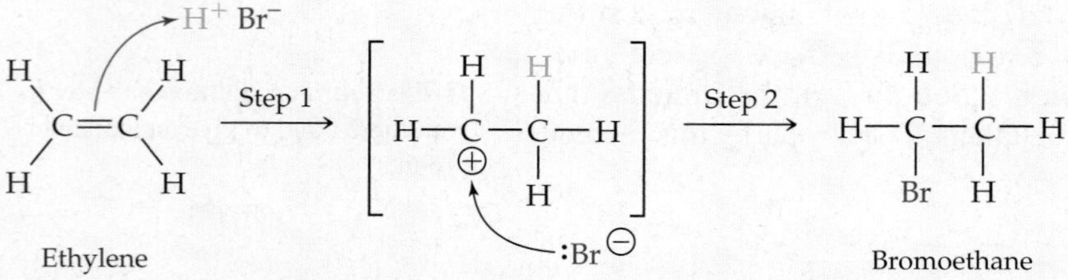

▲ **The mechanism of the addition of HBr to an alkene.** The reaction takes place in two steps and involves a carbocation intermediate. In the first step, two electrons move from the C=C double bond to form a C—H bond. In the second step, Br^- uses two electrons to form a bond to the positively charged carbon.

To begin, recognize that almost all organic reactions can be visualized as occurring between an electron-rich species and an electron-poor species. In the first step, the electron-rich alkene reacts with H^+ from the acid HBr. The carbon–carbon double bond partially breaks, and two electrons move from the double bond to form a new single bond (indicated by the curved red arrow in the figure). The remaining double-bond carbon, having had electrons that were being shared removed from it, now has only six electrons in its outer shell and bears a positive charge. Carbons that possess a positive charge, or *carbocations,* are highly reactive. As soon as this carbocation is formed, it immediately reacts with Br^- to form a neutral product.

For ethylene both carbons have identical substitution. What about the case where the double bond is unsymmetrically substituted, say, with 2-methyl-2-butene? Here, we perform the same analysis as the one we did for ethylene.

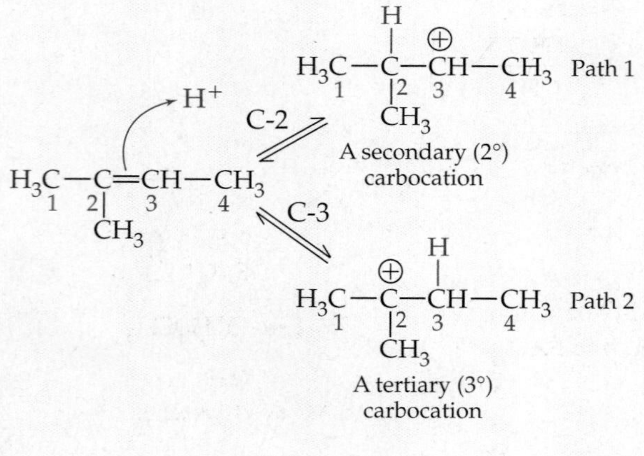

The double bond, being electron rich, attacks the electron-poor H^+ and in doing so, causes a carbocation to form; however, here we have two possibilities. If the H^+ attaches to C2, the carbocation will form on C3 (Path 1); if the H^+ attaches to C3, the carbocation will form on C2 (Path 2). Since this is an equilibrium process (the H^+ can just as easily be removed to regenerate the alkene) we should see both, but is one favored over the other? The answer to that can be arrived at by examining the two carbocations. Carbocations are electron-deficient species, so anything that can help stabilize one over another will cause a preference for that species to be seen. Carbons are known to donate electron density through the single bond; therefore, the more carbons attached to a carbocation, the less electron poor it is the more stable it will be, making it more favorable. The more favorable the carbocation, the more product will arise from it. Studies have shown that tertiary (3°) carbocations are more stable than secondary (2°) carbocations, which are much more stable than primary (1°) carbocations (which are almost never formed).

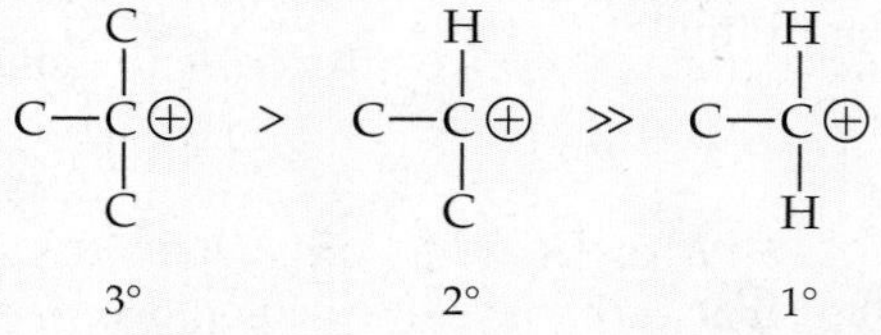

Thus, when the bromide reacts, two possible products are formed, with the major product arising from the more stable carbocation.

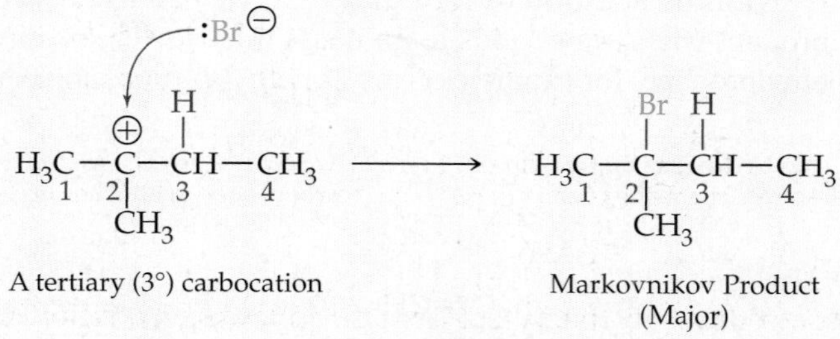

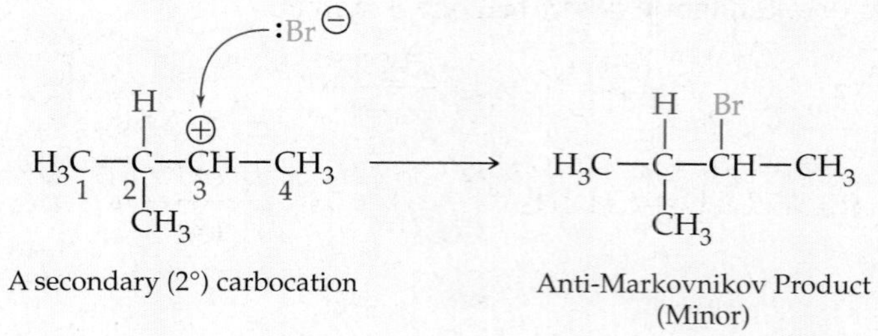

You should notice that the major product is that predicted by Markovnikov's rule. This now shows you the scientific basis for his observations: The major product arises because the intermediate it is derived from is more stable than any other intermediate (here, the 3° carbocation). This concept of the stability of intermediates lies at the very core of organic chemistry and is so powerful that it allows chemists to successfully predict the outcomes of diverse organic reactions.

A description of the individual steps by which old bonds are broken and new bonds are formed in a reaction is called a **reaction mechanism.** Mechanisms allow chemists to classify thousands of seemingly unrelated organic reactions into only a few categories and help us to understand what is occurring during a reaction. Their study is essential to our ever-expanding ability to understand biochemistry and the physiological effects of drugs.

Reaction mechanism A description of the individual steps by which old bonds are broken and new bonds are formed in a reaction.

MR Problem 13.1 Remembering Markovnikov's rule, draw the structure of the carbocation formed during the reaction of 2-methylpropene with HCl.

MR Problem 13.2 Refer to Problem 13.62: Assuming that Markovnikov's rule is followed, predict which of the two structures you drew is formed, and draw the carbocation involved as an intermediate.

MR Problem 13.3 Consider the molecule 1,3-butadiene (shown next). When this is reacted with HBr at 25 °C, the major product obtained is 1-bromo-2-butene. Given that the first step is the formation of a carbocation and assuming that Markovnikov's rule is initially followed, propose an explanation for the formation of the product seen. (Hint: Think about resonance.)

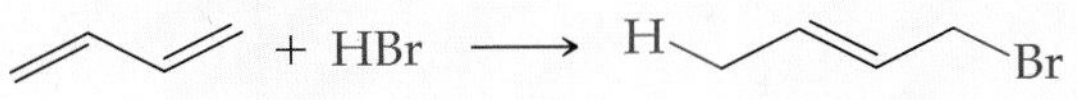

$$ \diagup\!\!\diagdown\!\!\diagup\!\!\diagdown + HBr \longrightarrow H\diagdown\!\!\diagup\!\!\diagdown\!\!\diagup_{Br} $$

 Worked Example 13.8 Reaction of Alkenes: Hydration

What products do you expect from the following hydration reaction?

$$ CH_3CH{=}CHCH_2CH_3 + H_2O \xrightarrow{H_2SO_4} \ ? $$

ANALYSIS Water is added to the double bond, with an H atom added to one carbon and an —OH group added to the other carbon of the double bond.

SOLUTION
Because this is *not* an unsymmetrically substituted alkene, we can add the —OH group to either carbon:

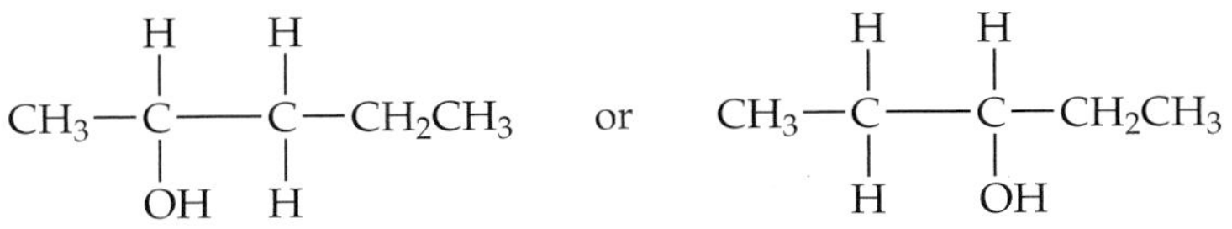

$$ CH_3{-}\underset{\underset{\displaystyle OH}{|}}{\overset{\overset{\displaystyle H}{|}}{C}}{-}\underset{\underset{\displaystyle H}{|}}{\overset{\overset{\displaystyle H}{|}}{C}}{-}CH_2CH_3 \qquad or \qquad CH_3{-}\underset{\underset{\displaystyle H}{|}}{\overset{\overset{\displaystyle H}{|}}{C}}{-}\underset{\underset{\displaystyle OH}{|}}{\overset{\overset{\displaystyle H}{|}}{C}}{-}CH_2CH_3 $$

2-Pentanol   3-Pentanol

PROBLEM 13.15

What products do you expect from the following hydration reactions? Label them as major and minor if more than one is formed.

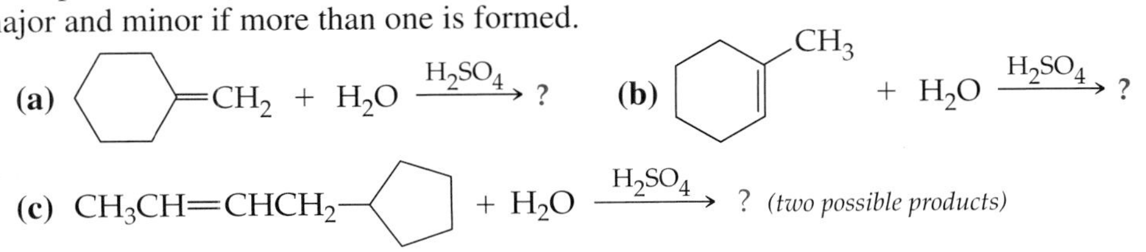

(a) $\bigcirc{=}CH_2 + H_2O \xrightarrow{H_2SO_4} ?$ (b) $\bigcirc^{CH_3} + H_2O \xrightarrow{H_2SO_4} ?$

(c) $CH_3CH{=}CHCH_2{-}\bigcirc + H_2O \xrightarrow{H_2SO_4} ?$ *(two possible products)*

PROBLEM 13.16

Draw the structures of the two different alkenes from which 3-methyl-3-pentanol, shown in the margin, can be made. Draw them in both condensed and line format.

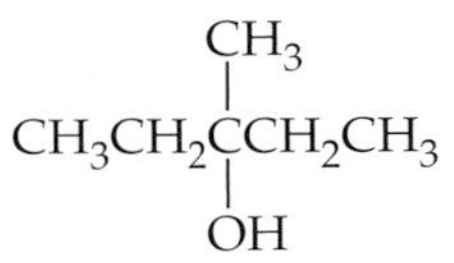

$$ CH_3CH_2\underset{\underset{\displaystyle OH}{|}}{\overset{\overset{\displaystyle CH_3}{|}}{C}}CH_2CH_3 $$

3-Methyl-3-pentanol

13.7 Alkene Polymers

Learning Objective:

• Predict what polymer forms given an alkene monomer.

Polymer A large molecule formed by the repetitive bonding together of many smaller molecules (or monomers).

Monomer A small molecule that is used to prepare a polymer.

A **polymer** is a large molecule formed by the repetitive bonding together of many smaller molecules called **monomers.** As we will see in later chapters, biological polymers such as cellulose, starch, proteins, and DNA occur throughout nature. Although the basic idea is the same, synthetic polymers are much simpler than biopolymers because the starting monomer units are usually small, simple organic molecules.

Many simple alkenes undergo *polymerization* reactions when treated with the proper catalyst. Ethylene yields polyethylene upon polymerization, propylene yields polypropylene, and styrene yields polystyrene. The polymer product might have anywhere from a few hundred to a few thousand monomer units incorporated into a long, repeating chain.

$$H_2C{=}CH_2$$
Ethylene

$$CH_3CH{=}CH_2$$
Propylene

$$CH{=}CH_2$$
Styrene

$$+CH_2{-}CH_2{-}CH_2{-}CH_2+$$
Polyethylene

$$\left(\begin{array}{cc} CH_3 & CH_3 \\ | & | \\ CH{-}CH_2{-}CH{-}CH_2 \end{array}\right)$$
Polypropylene

$$+CH{-}CH_2{-}CH{-}CH_2+$$
Polystyrene

Parentheses are used to indicate the repeating unit in the polymer.

The fundamental reaction in the polymerization of an alkene monomer resembles the addition reactions of a carbon–carbon double bond described in the preceding sections. One of the most common methods used to make polymers involves the use of radicals (see Section 12.8). The reaction begins by addition of a species called an *initiator* to an alkene; this results in the breaking of one of the bonds making up the double bond. A reactive intermediate that contains an unpaired electron (known as a *radical*) is formed in this step, and it is this reactive intermediate that adds to a second alkene molecule. This produces another reactive intermediate, which adds to a third alkene molecule, and so on. Because the result is continuous addition of one monomer after another to the end of the growing polymer chain, polymers formed in this way are *chain-growth polymers.* The basic repeating unit is enclosed in parentheses, and the subscript *n* indicates how many repeating units are in the polymer.

Variations in the substituent group Z attached to the double bond impart different properties to the product, as illustrated by the alkene polymers listed in Table 13.1. Polymer rigidity is controlled by addition of a small amount of a cross-linking agent, typically 1–2% of a dialkene (an alkene containing two double bonds), whose role is to covalently link two chains of monomer units together.

The properties of a polymer depend not only on the monomer but also on the average size of the huge molecules in a particular sample and on how extensively they cross-link and branch. The long molecules in straight-chain polyethylene pack closely together, giving a rigid material called *high-density polyethylene,* which is mainly used in bottles for products such as milk and motor oil. When polyethylene molecules contain many branches (due to the Z groups present), they cannot pack together as tightly and instead form a flexible material called *low-density polyethylene,* which is used mainly in packaging materials.

The use of polymers has changed the nature of activities ranging from plumbing and clothing to items such as skis and snowboards. In the health-care fields, the use of inexpensive, disposable equipment is now common.

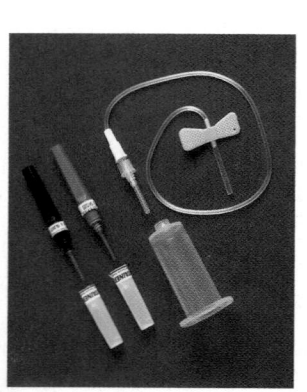

▲ These disposable polypropylene medical supplies are used once and then discarded.

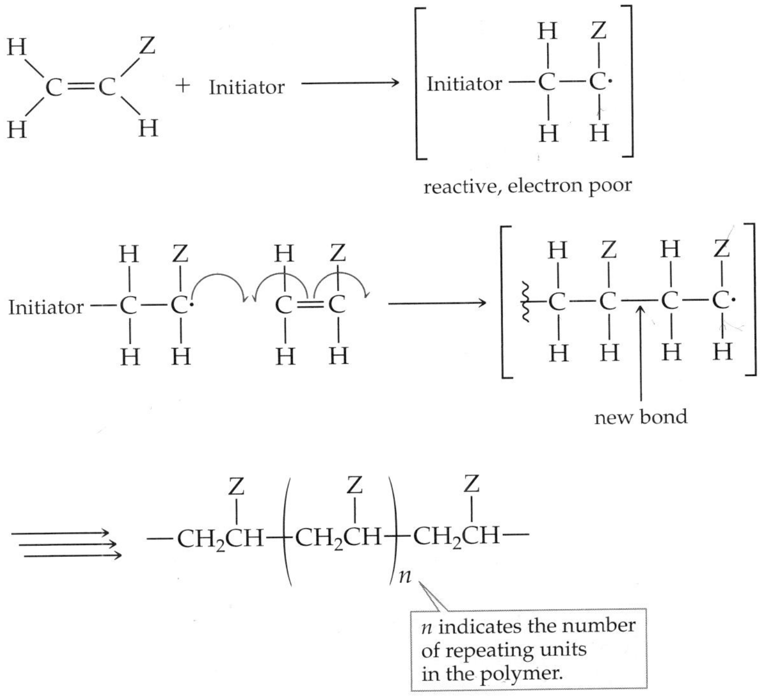

reactive, electron poor

new bond

n indicates the number of repeating units in the polymer.

Table 13.1 Some Alkene Polymers and Their Uses

Monomer Name	Monomer Structure	Polymer Name	Uses
Ethylene	$H_2C{=}CH_2$	Polyethylene	Packaging, bottles
Propylene	$H_2C{=}CH{-}CH_3$	Polypropylene	Bottles, rope, pails, medical tubing
Vinyl chloride	$H_2C{=}CH{-}Cl$	Poly(vinyl chloride)	Insulation, plastic pipe
Styrene	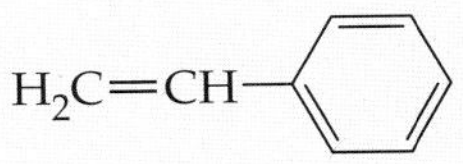 $H_2C{=}CH{-}\bigcirc$	Polystyrene	Foams, molded plastics
Styrene and 1,3-butadiene	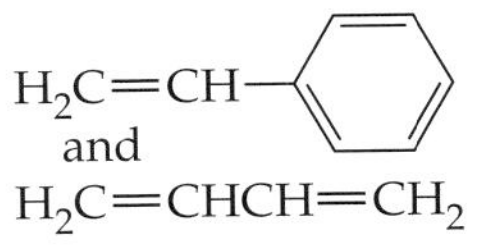 $H_2C{=}CH{-}\bigcirc$ and $H_2C{=}CHCH{=}CH_2$	Styrene-butadiene rubber (SBR)	Synthetic rubber for tires
Acrylonitrile	$H_2C{=}CH{-}C{\equiv}N$	Orlon, Acrilan	Fibers, outdoor carpeting
Methyl methacrylate	$H_2C{=}\underset{\underset{CH_3}{\vert}}{\overset{\overset{O}{\parallel}}{C}}COCH_3$	Plexiglas, Lucite	Windows, contact lenses, fiber optics
Tetrafluoroethylene	$F_2C{=}CF_2$	Teflon	Nonstick coatings, bearings, replacement heart valves and blood vessels

Worked Example 13.9 Reactions of Alkenes: Polymerization

Write the structure of a segment of polystyrene, used in foams and molded plastics. The monomer is

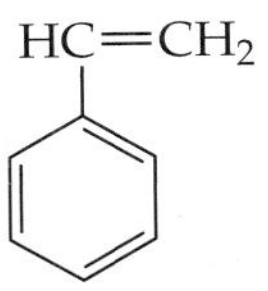

—continued on next page

—continued from previous page

ANALYSIS The polymerization reaction resembles the addition of two monomer units to either end of the double bond.

SOLUTION
Draw three molecules of styrene with the double bonds aligned next to each other; then add the monomer units together with single bonds, eliminating the double bonds in the process.

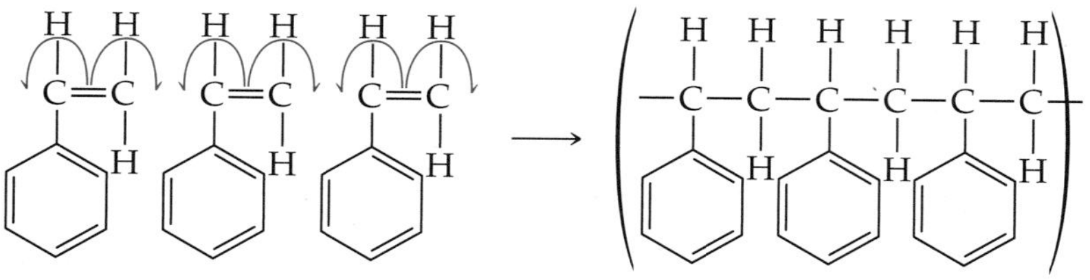

PROBLEM 13.17

The structure of vinyl acetate is shown below (the partial structure $H_2C{=}CH{-}$ is known as a *vinyl group*). When polymerized it produces poly(vinyl acetate), a polymer used for the springy soles in running shoes. Draw the structure of the polymer obtained if three vinyl acetate units underwent polymerization.

$$H_2C{=}CHOCCH_3 \quad \text{Vinyl acetate}$$

PROBLEM 13.18

Polychlorotrifluoroethylene (PCTFE (Kel-F)) is a polymer that has the lowest water vapor transmission rate of any plastic, making it an excellent moisture barrier. It can also be used for injection molding of plastic items, while polytetrafluoroethylene (PTFE (Teflon)) cannot. Given the monomer shown below, draw a representative structure for PCTFE.

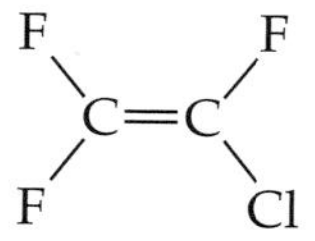

13.8 Aromatic Compounds and the Structure of Benzene

Learning Objectives:

• Identify the structures of aromatic compounds.
• Explain the importance and function of resonance in aromatic compounds.

Chemists initially used the word *aromatic* to describe fragrant substances from fruits, trees, and other natural sources, but they soon realized, however, that many of the substances grouped as aromatic behave differently from most other organic compounds. Today, chemists use the term **aromatic** to refer to the class of compounds that contain benzene-like rings.

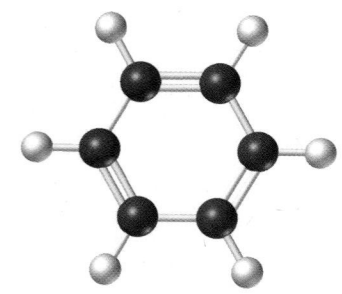

Aromatic The class of compounds containing benzene-like rings.

Benzene, the simplest aromatic compound, is a flat, symmetrical molecule with the molecular formula C_6H_6. It is often represented as cyclohexatriene, a 6-membered carbon ring with three double bonds. Though useful, the problem with this representation is that it gives the wrong impression about benzene's chemical reactivity and bonding. Because benzene appears to have three double bonds, you might expect it to react with H_2, Br_2, HCl, and H_2O to give the same kinds of addition products that alkenes do. But this expectation would be wrong. Benzene and other aromatic compounds are much less reactive than alkenes and do not undergo the usual addition reactions seen in alkenes.

Benzene $\xrightarrow{\begin{array}{c} H_2, Pd \\ Br_2 \\ HCl \\ H_3O^+ \end{array}}$ No reaction

Benzene's relative lack of chemical reactivity is a consequence of its structure. If you were to draw a six-membered ring with alternating single and double bonds, where would you place the double bonds? There are two equivalent possibilities (Figure 13.2b), neither of which is fully correct by itself. Experimental evidence shows that all six carbon–carbon bonds in benzene are identical, so a picture with three double bonds and three single bonds cannot be correct.

The properties of benzene are best explained by assuming that its true structure is an *average* of the two equivalent conventional Lewis structures. Rather than being held between specific pairs of atoms, the double-bond electrons are instead free to move over the entire ring. Each carbon–carbon bond is thus intermediate between a single bond and a double bond. This is known as **resonance,** where the true structure of a molecule is an average among two or more possible conventional structures, and a special double-headed arrow ($\longleftrightarrow$) is used to show the resonance relationship. Resonance allows the electrons in the double bonds to be *delocalized* over the entire molecule, thus lowering the reactivity of the double bonds. It is important to note that *no atoms move between resonance structures, only pairs of electrons* (in this case, double bonds).

Because the real structure of benzene is intermediate between the two forms shown in Figure 13.2b, it is difficult to represent benzene with the standard conventions using lines for covalent bonds. Thus, we sometimes represent the double bonds as a circle inside the six-membered ring, as shown in Figure 13.2c. It is more common, though, to draw the ring with three double bonds, with the understanding that it is an aromatic ring with equivalent bonding all around. We use this convention in this book.

▲ Benzaldehyde, an aromatic compound, gives cherries their odor.

Resonance The phenomenon where the true structure of a molecule is an average among two or more conventional Lewis structures that differ only in the placement of double bonds.

(a)

(b)

Two equivalent structures, which differ in the position of their double-bond electrons. Neither structure is correct by itself.

(c)

▲ **Figure 13.2**
Some representations of benzene.
(a) An electrostatic potential map shows the equivalency of the carbon–carbon bonds. Benzene is usually represented by the two equivalent structures in (b) or by the single structure in (c).

Simple aromatic hydrocarbons like benzene are nonpolar, insoluble in water, volatile, and flammable. Unlike alkanes and alkenes, however, several aromatic hydrocarbons have biological effects. Benzene itself has been implicated as a cause of leukemia, and the dimethyl-substituted benzenes are central nervous system depressants.

Everything we have said about the structure and stability of the benzene ring also applies to the ring when it has substituents, such as in the germicidal agent hexachlorophene and the flavoring ingredient vanillin.

The benzene ring is also present in many biomolecules (including plant dyes and pigments, see the Chemistry in Action on p. 414) and retains its characteristic properties in these compounds as well. In addition, aromaticity is not limited to rings that

Hexachlorophene
(a germicide)

Vanillin
(vanilla flavoring)

contain only carbon. For example, many compounds classified as aromatics have one or more nitrogen atoms in the ring. Pyridine, indole, and adenine are three examples:

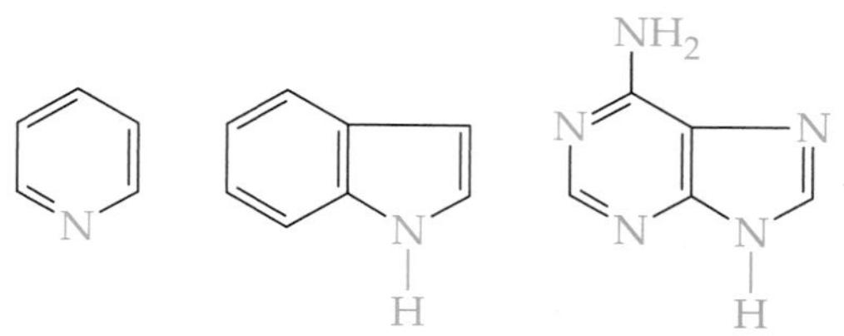

Pyridine   Indole   Adenine

These and all other compounds that contain a substituted benzene ring, or a similarly stable six-membered ring in which double-bond electrons are equally shared around the ring, are classified as aromatic compounds. While the rules regarding exactly what makes a molecule aromatic are not as simple as we discuss here, for the purposes of this text, we say that a 6-membered ring with alternating single and double bonds will be aromatic.

13.9 Naming Aromatic Compounds

Learning Objective:

• Name simple monosubstituted or disubstituted aromatic compounds.

Substituted benzenes are named using -*benzene* as the parent. Thus, C_6H_5Br is bromobenzene, $C_6H_5CH_2CH_3$ is ethylbenzene, and so on. No number is needed for monosubstituted benzenes because all the ring positions are identical.

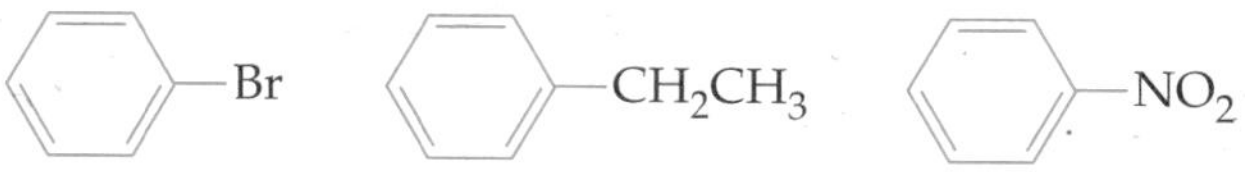

Bromobenzene   Ethylbenzene   Nitrobenzene

When a benzene has more than one substituent present, the positions of those substituents are indicated by numbers, just as in naming cycloalkanes. Disubstituted benzenes (and only disubstituted benzenes) are unique in that the relational descriptors *o-* (ortho), *m-* (meta), and *p-* (para) may be used in place of 1,2-, 1,3-, and 1,4-, respectively. The terms *ortho-, meta-,* or *para-* (or their single-letter equivalents) are then used as prefixes.

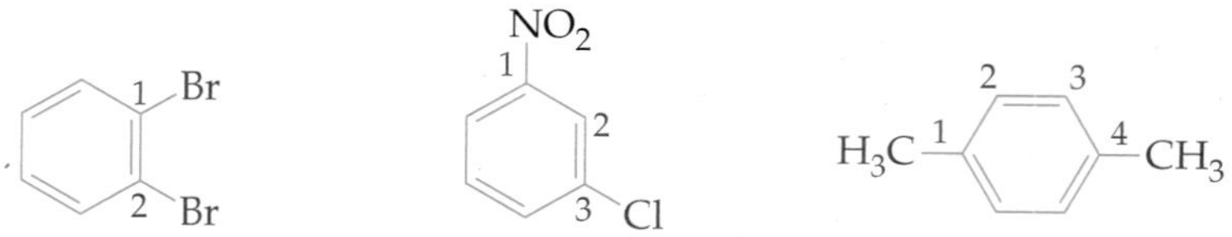

Table 13.2 Common Names of Some Aromatic Compounds

Structure	Name
CH₃	Toluene
OH	Phenol
NH₂	Aniline
H₃C—CH₃	*para*-Xylene (*p*-Xylene)
C—OH	Benzoic acid
C—H	Benzaldehyde

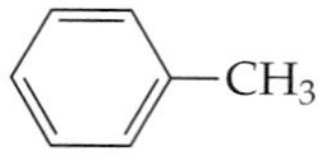

1,2-Dibromobenzene / *ortho*-Dibromobenzene / *o*-Dibromobenzene

3-Chloronitrobenzene / *meta*-Chloronitrobenzene / *m*-Chloronitrobenzene

1,4-Dimethylbenzene / *para*-Dimethylbenzene / *p*-Dimethylbenzene

While any one of these three nomenclature schemes are acceptable, we will almost exclusively use *o-, m-,* and *p-* in naming these disubstituted compounds.

Many substituted aromatic compounds have common names in addition to their systematic names. For example, methylbenzene is familiarly known as *toluene,* hydroxybenzene as *phenol,* aminobenzene as *aniline,* and so on, as shown in Table 13.2. Frequently, these common names are also used together with *o- (ortho), m- (meta),* or *p- (para)* prefixes. For example,

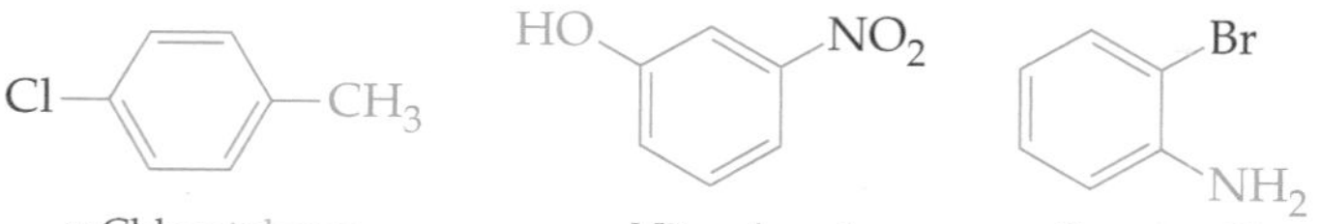

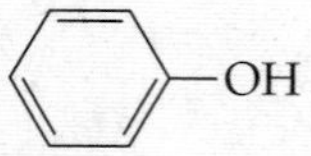

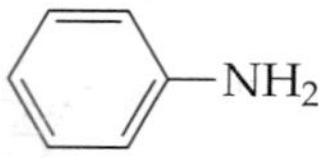

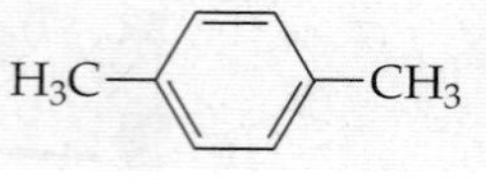

p-Chlorotoluene   *m*-Nitrophenol   *o*-Bromoaniline

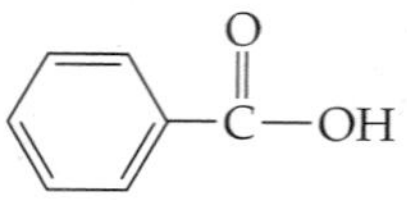

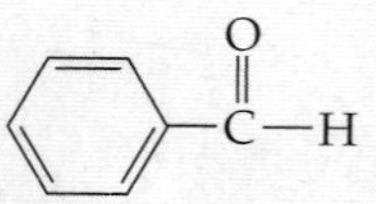

Occasionally, the benzene ring itself may be considered a substituent group attached to another parent compound. When this happens, the name **phenyl** (pronounced *fen*-nil and commonly abbreviated Ph—) is used for the C_6H_5— unit.

Phenyl The C_6H_5— group.

A phenyl group
C_6H_5—

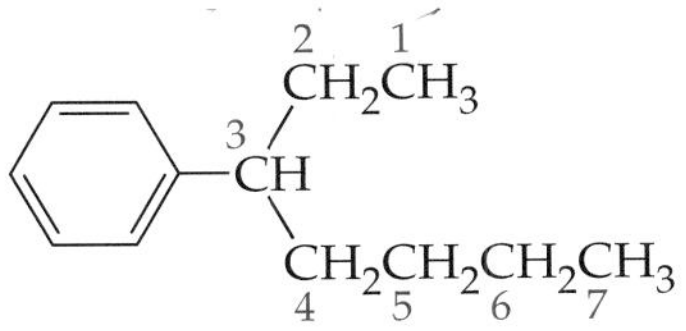

3-Phenylheptane

Worked Example 13.10 Naming Organic Compounds: Aromatic Compounds

Name the following aromatic compound:

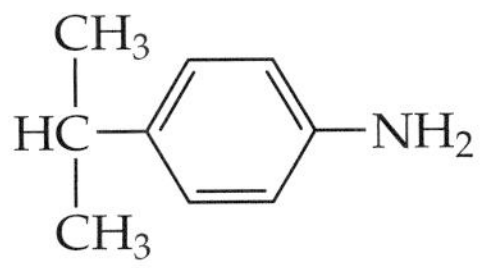

ANALYSIS First, identify the parent organic compound, then identify the location of substituent groups on the benzene ring either by number or by *ortho (o-), meta (m-),* or *para (p-).*

SOLUTION

The parent compound is a benzene ring with an amine group (*aminobenzene,* which is commonly known as *aniline*). The substituent group is attached at the C4, or para, position relative to the amino group. The propyl group is attached to the benzene ring by the middle carbon, so it is *isopropyl.*

The substituent group is at the para position.

The propyl group is attached to the middle carbon, so it is isopropyl.

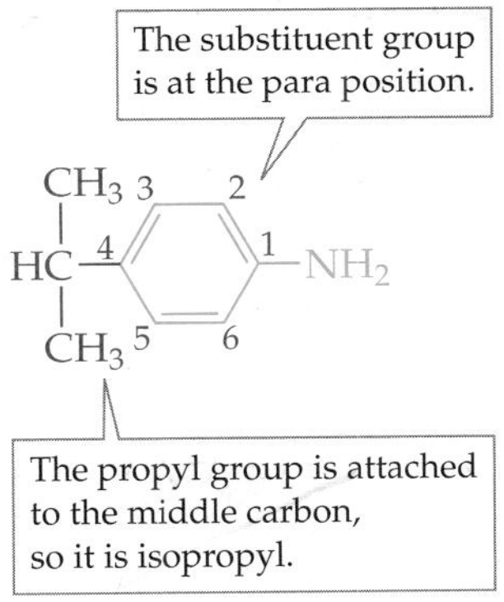

Name: *para*-isopropylaniline, or 4-isopropylaminobenzene

Worked Example 13.11 Molecular Structures: Aromatic Compounds

Draw the structure of *m*-chloroethylbenzene.

ANALYSIS *m*-Chloroethylbenzene has a benzene ring with two substituents, chloro and ethyl, in a meta relationship (i.e., on C1 and C3).

SOLUTION

Since all carbons in the benzene ring are equivalent, draw a benzene ring and attach one of the substituents— for example, chloro—to any position.

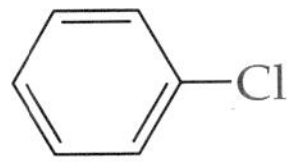

—*continued on next page*

—continued from previous page

Now go to a meta position two carbons away from the chloro-substituted carbon, and attach the second (ethyl) substituent.

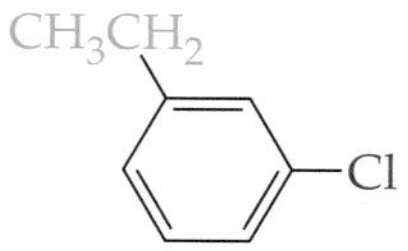

CH₃CH₂

Cl   *m*-Chloroethylbenzene

PROBLEM 13.19

What are the IUPAC names for the following compounds?

(a) HO —⟨benzene⟩— CH₂CH₃

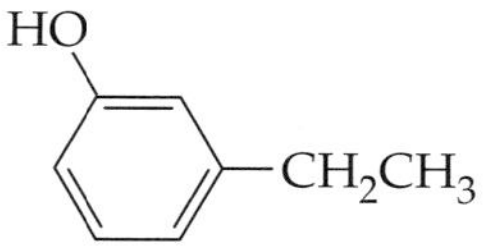

(b) ⟨benzene⟩ with Cl and CH₃

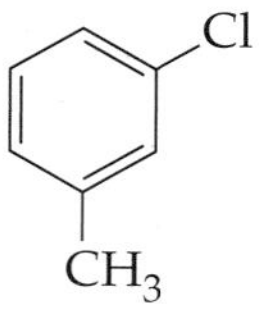

(c) ⟨benzene⟩ with ethyl and isopropyl

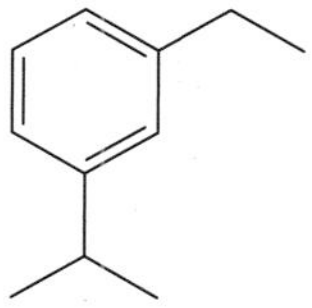

PROBLEM 13.20

Draw structures corresponding to the following names (refer to Table 13.2 if necessary):

    (a) *m*-Chloronitrobenzene   **(b)** *o*-Nitrotoluene
    (c) *p*-Methylaniline   **(d)** *p*-Nitrophenol

⊙ KEY CONCEPT PROBLEM 13.21 ————————————————

Name the following compounds (red = O, blue = N, brown = Br):

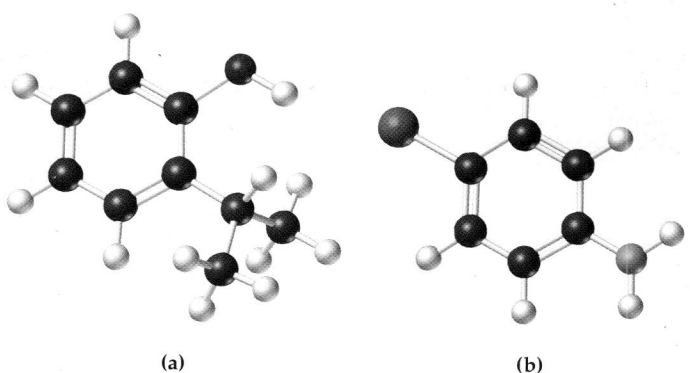

(a)   (b)

13.10 Reactions of Aromatic Compounds

Learning Objective:

• Predict the products obtained when aromatic compounds react with concentrated HNO_3, Cl_2, Br_2, or concentrated H_2SO_4.

Unlike alkenes, which undergo addition reactions, aromatic compounds usually undergo a special type of substitution reaction known as an *electrophilic aromatic substitution* (EAS) reaction. That is, a group Y substitutes for one hydrogen atom on the aromatic ring without changing the ring itself. It does not matter which of the six ring hydrogens in benzene is replaced because all six are equivalent.

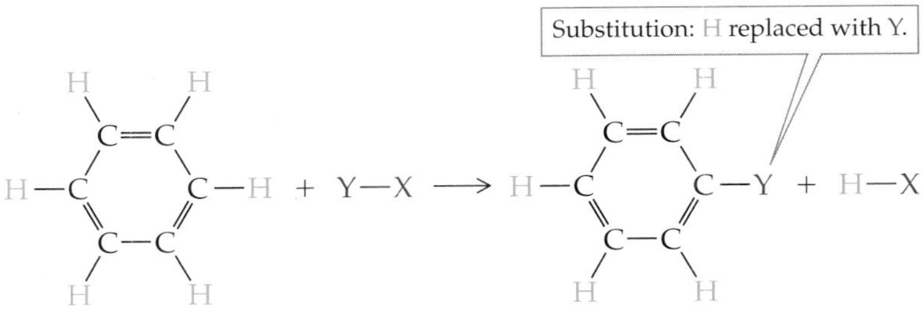

The mechanism responsible for this type of reaction is similar to that seen for alkenes, with the key difference being regeneration of the extremely stable aromatic ring.

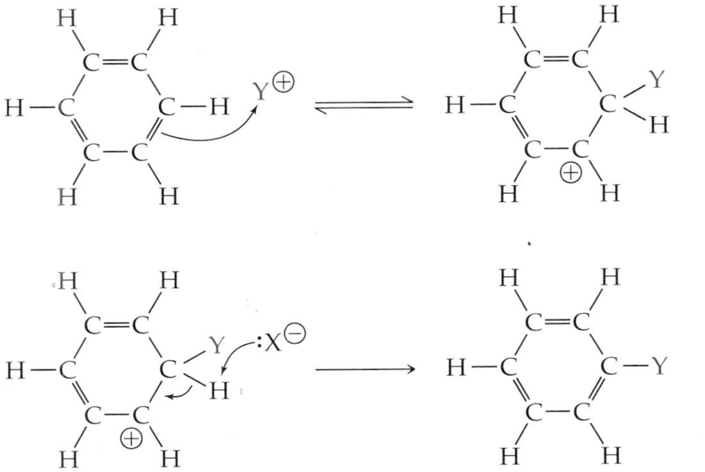

Nitration is the substitution of a *nitro group* (—NO_2) for one of the ring hydrogens. The reaction occurs when benzene reacts with nitric acid in the presence of sulfuric acid as catalyst.

Nitration The substitution of a nitro group (—NO_2) for a hydrogen on an aromatic ring.

Benzene Nitric acid Nitrobenzene

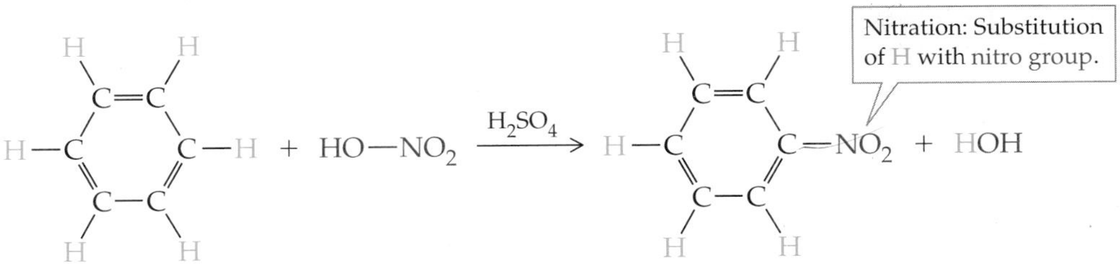

Nitration of aromatic rings is a key step in the synthesis both of explosives like TNT (trinitrotoluene) and of many important pharmaceutical agents, since the —NO_2 group can be readily converted to an —NH_2. Nitrobenzene itself is the industrial starting material for the preparation of aniline, which is used to make many of the brightly colored dyes in clothing.

Halogenation (aromatic) The substitution of a halogen group (—X) for a hydrogen on an aromatic ring.

Halogenation (aromatic) is the substitution of a halogen atom, usually bromine or chlorine, for one of the ring hydrogens. The reaction occurs when benzene reacts with Br_2 or Cl_2 in the presence of $FeBr_3$ or $FeCl_3$ as catalyst.

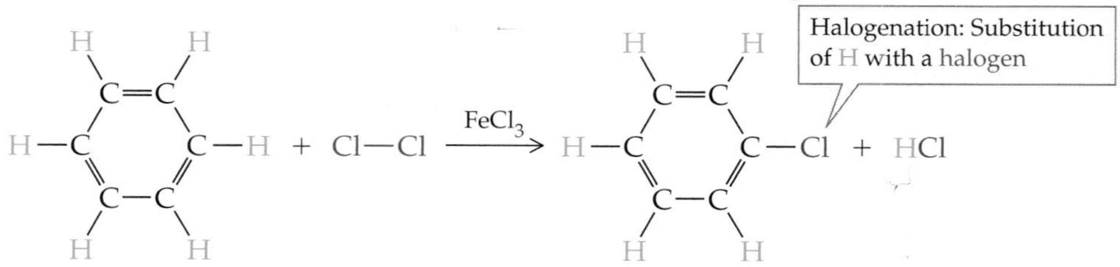

> Halogenation: Substitution of H with a halogen

Benzene   Chlorine   Chlorobenzene

Sulfonation The substitution of a sulfonic acid group (—SO_3H) for a hydrogen on an aromatic ring.

Sulfonation is the substitution of a sulfonic acid group (—SO_3H) for one of the ring hydrogens. The reaction occurs when benzene reacts with concentrated sulfuric acid and SO_3.

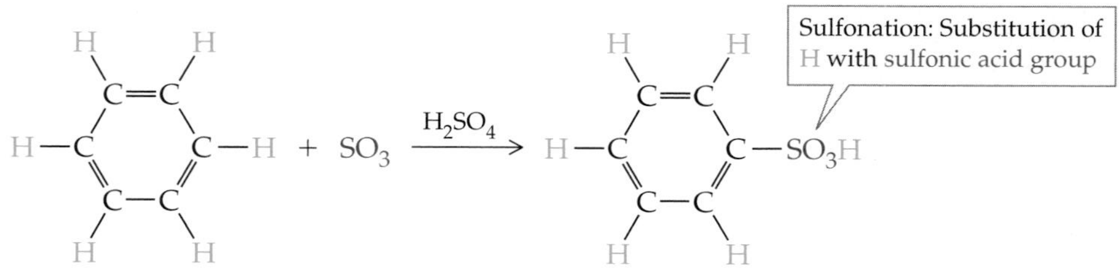

> Sulfonation: Substitution of H with sulfonic acid group

Benzene   Benzenesulfonic acid

CHEMISTRY IN ACTION

⚕ Enediyne Antibiotics: A Newly Emerging Class of Antitumor Agents

While we discuss alkynes only briefly in this chapter and this text as a whole, it is not because alkynes are not important in organic chemistry. Alkynes are not usually found in nature; however, when they are isolated from natural sources, such as plants and bacteria, they have unexpected physiological properties, including toxicity. For example, ichthyothereol, a trialkyne, isolated from the leaves of a small herb found in the Amazon and Central America, inhibits energy production in mitochondria, and while being toxic to fish, mice, and dogs, has no effect on humans. This has caused chemists to investigate what might happen if the alkyne function were introduced into other biologically active molecules, which has led to the discovery of pharmaceuticals such as Rasagiline, a monoamine oxidase inhibitor effective in treating Parkinson's disease. This compound, due to its neuroprotective nature, is also offering a novel approach to Alzheimer's drug therapy. Rasagiline seems to enhance memory and learning, while also improving mood, motivation, and age-related memory decline and provides a great lead for the discovery of new medicines to treat this debilitating disease. Due to successes such as Rasagiline, chemists and biochemists have intensified the hunt for naturally occurring alkynes. This expanding pursuit for new alkyne-containing natural products has led to the discovery of a very unlikely class of antitumor antibiotics known as the enediynes, which we first learned about at the beginning of the

chapter. Initially discovered in a fermentation broth derived from the bacteria *Micromonospora,* they represent a new chemical structure class for antibiotics.

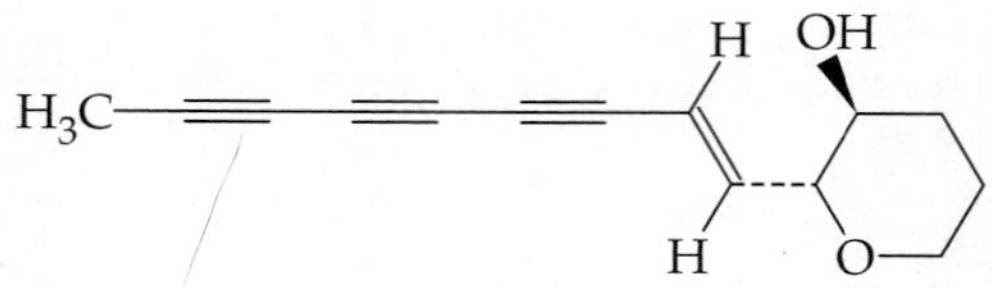

Ichthyotherol

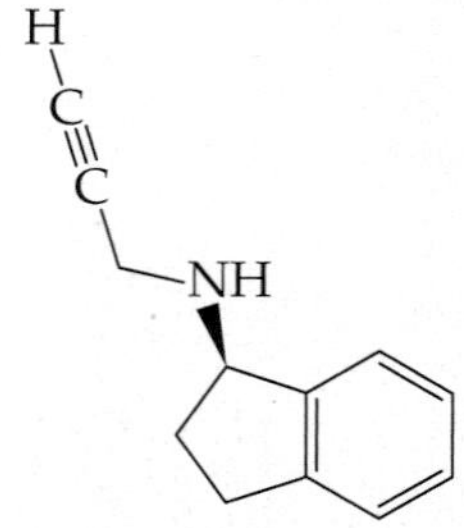

Rasagiline

The enediyne family of compounds represents the most potent antitumor agents known. The toxic nature of these compounds arises from their ability to cause scission of DNA strands in their target. The enediyne antibiotics fall into three basic families: the calicheamicins, the dynemicins (shown next), and the most complex of the group, the chromoproteins. All members have three distinct regions within them: (1) an anthraquinone-like portion; (2) a chemical "warhead" comprised of two triple

Aromatic-ring sulfonation is a key step in the synthesis of such compounds as the sulfa-drug family of antibiotics:

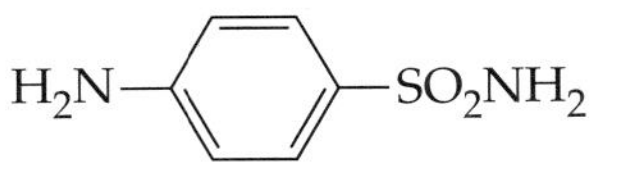

$$H_2N-\!\!\!\bigcirc\!\!\!-SO_2NH_2$$

Sulfanilamide—a sulfa antibiotic

PROBLEM 13.22

What products will be formed when toluene is reacted with the reagents shown here?

(a) Br_2 and $FeBr_3$

(b) HNO_3 and H_2SO_4 catalyst

(c) SO_3 in H_2SO_4

PROBLEM 13.23

Reaction of Br_2 and $FeBr_3$ with phenol can lead to *three* possible substitution products. Show the structure of each and name them.

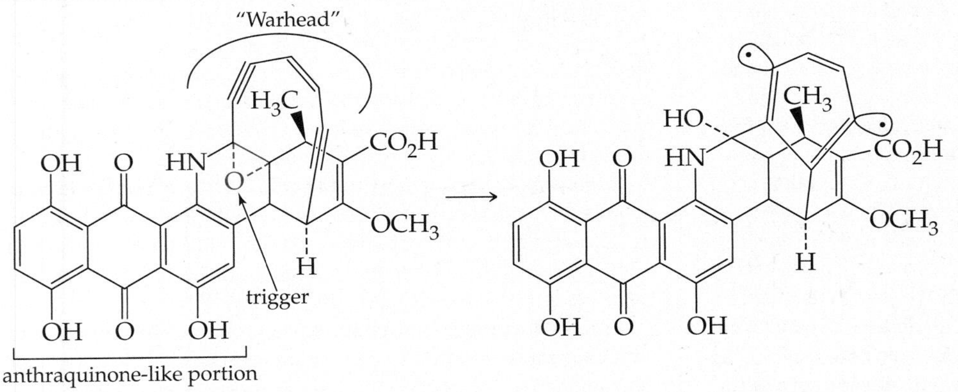

Diynemicin A

bonds, conjugated through a double bond, within a 9–10-membered ring; and (3) a "trigger." In Dynemicin A (shown above), that trigger is the three-membered epoxide ring (highlighted in red). The anthraquinone portion intercalates into the major groove of DNA; the trigger is then activated by some nucleophilic species (such as an oxygen, nitrogen, or sulfur atom) that attacks and then opens the epoxide ring. Once opened, the warhead undergoes a rearrangement reaction, producing an extremely reactive diradical aromatic species, which then induces the breakage of the DNA strands.

All of the enediynes are very toxic, as are all antitumor agents. One way to utilize them in the war on cancer would be to attach them to an antibody specifically prepared to target the tumor cells the doctor wishes to destroy. This method, known as

"immunotargeting," would allow the preparation of a "magic bullet," which would attack only the tumor cells and nothing else. One of the reasons that the enediyne antibiotics are so attractive is that they have activity against drug-resistant tumors. Many cancer cells have natural resistance to a number of the drugs usually used to treat them or will develop resistance over the course of a treatment. This, coupled with a lack of selectivity to antitumor agents (antitumor drugs affect all cells, not just cancer) is one of the major causes of the ineffectiveness of anticancer therapies. Compounds such as Dynemicin A and others discovered through studies of the enediynes could represent a new weapon in our assault on an old and deadly foe: cancer.

The meaning of the wedged and dashed bonds will be clarified in Section 14.10 when we discuss stereochemistry.

CIA Problem 13.4 What beneficial properties of Rasagiline make it useful for the treatment of Alzheimer's disease?

CIA Problem 13.5 Why would attaching an enediyne-containing molecule to an antibody be an attractive way to treat cancer cells?

CIA Problem 13.6 What are the major causes of the ineffectiveness of anticancer therapies?

SUMMARY REVISITING THE CHAPTER LEARNING OBJECTIVES

- **Identify the functional groups present in alkenes and alkynes.** *Alkenes* are hydrocarbons that contain a carbon–carbon double bond, and *alkynes* are hydrocarbons that contain a carbon–carbon triple bond *[see Problems 27, 29–31, 34, 35, and 43]*.

- **Differentiate between saturated and unsaturated molecules.** A *saturated* molecule is one that contains only tetravalent carbon atoms and no double or triple bonds. Compounds are said to be *unsaturated* because they have fewer hydrogens than corresponding alkanes. The term is usually used to indicate the presence of double or triple bonds *[see Problems 30 and 31]*.

- **Name a simple alkene or alkyne given its condensed or line structure.** Alkenes and alkynes are named in a manner almost identical to that used for naming alkanes (Section 12.6), except now the functional group takes priority in numbering the carbon chain. Alkenes are named using the family ending *-ene;* alkynes use the family ending *-yne [see Problems 34–37]*.

- **Draw the condensed or line structure of an alkene or alkyne given its name.** Organic compounds can be represented by *structural formulas* in which all atoms and bonds are shown, by *condensed structures* in which not all bonds are drawn, or by *line structures* in which the carbon skeleton is represented by lines and the locations of C and H atoms are understood *[see Problems 38, 39, 48, 61, and 70]*.

- **Identify cis–trans isomers of alkenes.** Alkenes can be thought of as having sides and ends. Cis–trans isomers are seen in substituted alkenes as a consequence of the lack of rotation around carbon–carbon double bonds. In the cis isomer, the two substituents are on the same side of the double bond; in the trans isomer, they are on opposite sides of the double bond *[see Problems 44–51, 71, 81, 82, and 84]*.

- **Identify the physical properties of alkenes and alkynes.** Alkenes and alkynes are generally nonpolar, insoluble in water (hydrophobic), and unreactive. They possess low melting and/or boiling points due to their weak intermolecular forces. Alkenes are generally nontoxic and therefore have limited physiological effects *[see Problems 72 and 73]*.

- **Identify the different types of organic reactions.** Addition reactions occur when two reactants add together to form a single product with no atoms left over. Elimination reactions occur when a single reactant breaks into two products, forming an alkene or an alkyne in the process. Substitution reactions occur when two reactants exchange atoms or groups to give two new products. Rearrangement reactions occur when a single reactant undergoes a reorganization of bonds and atoms to yield a single isomeric product *[see Problems 52–57]*.

- **Predict the addition products obtained when alkenes react with H_2, Cl_2, HCl, or H_2O.** Alkenes and alkynes undergo addition reactions to their multiple bonds. Addition of hydrogen to an alkene *(hydrogenation)* yields an alkane product, addition of Cl_2 or Br_2 *(halogenation)* yields a 1,2-dihaloalkane product, addition of HBr and HCl *(hydrohalogenation)* yields an alkyl halide product, and addition of water *(hydration)* yields an alcohol product *[see Problems 58–62 and 76–80]*.

- **Identify "symmetrically substituted" and "unsymmetrically substituted" alkenes.** Alkenes can be classified as symmetrically substituted if each carbon of the double bond has the same number of hydrogens directly attached to each carbon and unsymmetrically substituted if the carbons do not *[see Problems 46–48, 50, 70, and 71]*.

- **Utilize Markovnikov's rule when addition reactions to unsymmetrically substituted alkenes occur.** Markovnikov's rule predicts that in the addition of HX or H_2O to a double bond, the H becomes attached to the carbon with more hydrogens and the X or OH becomes attached to the carbon with fewer Hs *[see Problems 58 and 60]*.

- **Predict what polymer forms given an alkene monomer.** Many simple alkenes undergo *polymerization,* a reaction that resembles addition to a carbon–carbon double bond, as described in the preceding sections. An *initiator* adds to an alkene to form a radical; this results in the breaking of one of the bonds making up the double bond. This reactive intermediate adds to a second alkene molecule to produce another reactive intermediate, which adds to a third alkene molecule, and so on. The resulting polymer is the result of the continuous addition of one monomer after another to the end of the growing polymer chain *[see Problems 63, 64, and 83]*.

- **Identify the structures of aromatic compounds.** *Aromatic compounds* contain six-membered, benzene-like rings and are usually written with three double bonds. In fact, however, there is equal bonding between neighboring carbon atoms in benzene rings because the double-bond electrons are symmetrically spread around the entire ring *[see Problems 31–33, 37, and 39]*.

- **Explain the importance and function of resonance in aromatic compounds.** Aromatic compounds exhibit resonance: Lewis structures that are interconvertible by only the movement of pairs of electrons; no atoms can move. Resonance allows for the delocalization of electrons by spreading electron density over the entire molecule. Because of this, delocalized electrons are less reactive than those found in a normal alkene or alkyne *[see Problems 29 and 31]*.

- **Name simple monosubstituted or disubstituted aromatic compounds.** Disubstituted benzenes have the suffix *-benzene* as the parent name, and positions of the substituents are indicated with the prefixes *ortho-* (1,2 substitution), *meta-* (1,3 substitution), or *para-* (1,4 substitution) *[see Problems 26, 33, 37, 39, and 69]*.

- **Predict the products obtained when aromatic compounds react with concentrated HNO_3, Cl_2, Br_2, or concentrated H_2SO_4.** Aromatic compounds are unusually stable but can be made to undergo substitution reactions, in which one of the ring hydrogens is replaced by another group $(C_6H_6 \rightarrow C_6H_5Y)$. Among these substitutions are *nitration* (substitution of $-NO_2$ for $-H$), *halogenation* (substitution of $-Br$ or $-Cl$ for $-H$), and *sulfonation* (substitution of $-SO_3H$ for $-H$) *[see Problems 42 and 65–68]*.

KEY WORDS

Addition reaction, *p. 411*
Alkene, *p. 403*
Alkyne, *p. 403*
Aromatic, *p. 426*
Cis–trans isomer, *p. 408*
Cycloalkene, *p. 403*
Elimination reaction, *p. 412*

Halogenation (alkene), *p. 417*
Halogenation (aromatic), *p. 432*
Hydration, *p. 421*
Hydrogenation, *p. 416*
Hydrohalogenation, *p. 418*

Markovnikov's rule, *p. 418*
Monomer, *p. 424*
Nitration, *p. 431*
Phenyl, *p. 429*
Polymer, *p. 424*
Reaction mechanism, *p. 423*

Rearrangement reaction, *p. 413*
Resonance, *p. 427*
Saturated, *p. 403*
Substitution reaction, *p. 412*
Sulfonation, *p. 432*
Unsaturated, *p. 403*

CONCEPT MAP: ORGANIC CHEMISTRY FAMILIES

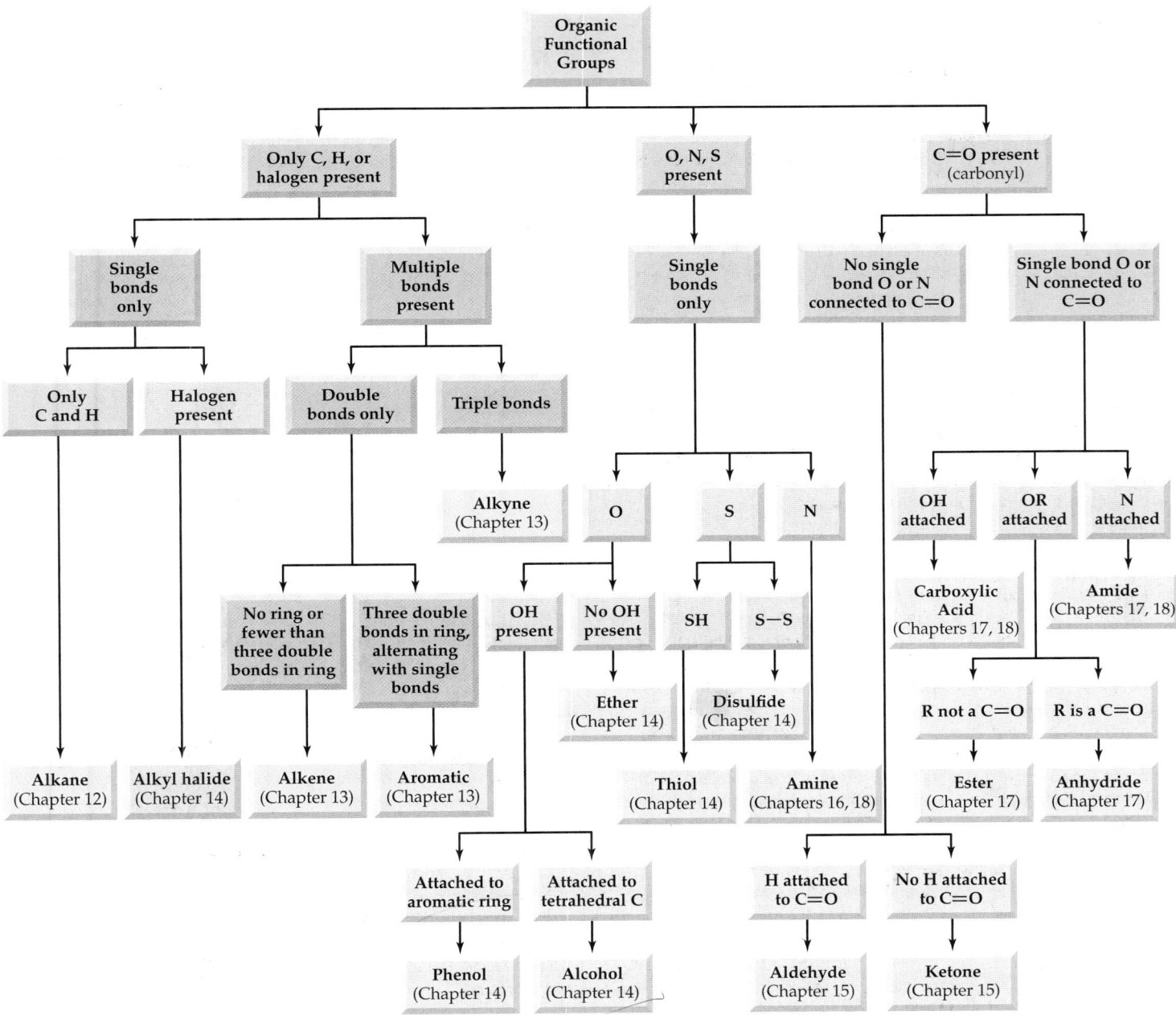

▲ **Figure 13.3 Functional Group Concept Map.** This is the same concept map we saw at the end of Chapter 12, except the functional groups discussed in this chapter, alkenes, alkynes, and aromatic compounds, have now been colorized.

SUMMARY OF REACTIONS

1. Reactions of alkenes and alkynes (Section 13.6):

(a) Addition of H_2 to yield an alkane (hydrogenation):

An alkene:

An alkyne:

(b) Addition of Cl_2 or Br_2 to yield a dihalide (halogenation):

(c) Addition of HCl or HBr to yield an alkyl halide (hydrohalogenation):

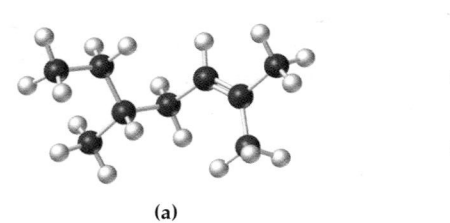

(d) Addition of H_2O to yield an alcohol (hydration):

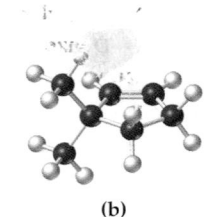

2. Reactions of aromatic compounds (Section 13.10):
   (a) Substitution of an $-NO_2$ group to yield a nitrobenzene (nitration):

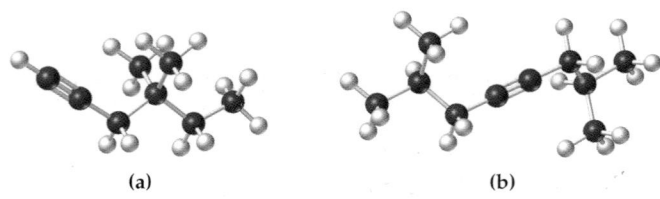

(b) Substitution of a Cl or Br atom to yield a halobenzene (halogenation):

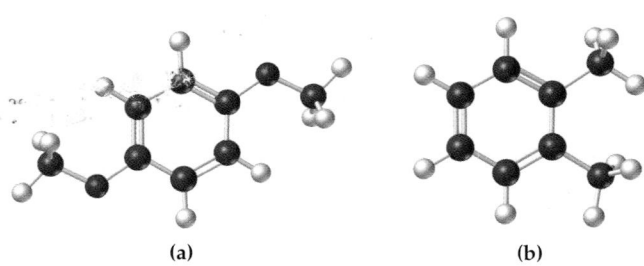

(c) Substitution of an $-SO_3H$ group to yield a benzenesulfonic acid (sulfonation):

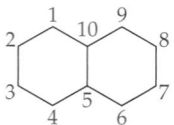

⊙ UNDERSTANDING KEY CONCEPTS

13.24   Name the following alkenes, and predict the products of their reaction with (1) HBr, (2) H_2O, and (3) an acid catalyst.

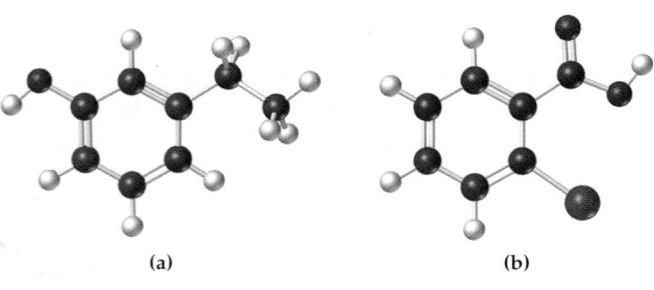

(a)   (b)

13.25   Name the following alkynes:

(a)   (b)

13.26   Give IUPAC names for the following substances (red = O, brown = Br):

(a)   (b)

13.27   Draw the product from reaction of the following substances with (1) Br_2 and $FeBr_3$ and (2) SO_3 and H_2SO_4 catalyst (red = O):

(a)   (b)

13.28   Alkynes undergo hydrogenation to give alkanes, just as alkenes do. Draw and name the products that would result from hydrogenation of the alkynes shown in Problem 13.25.

13.29   We saw in Section 13.8 that benzene can be represented by either of two resonance forms, which differ in the positions of the double bonds in the aromatic ring. Naphthalene, a polycyclic aromatic compound, can be represented by *three* forms with different double-bond positions. Draw all three structures, showing the double bonds in each (the following numbered skeletal structure of naphthalene shows only the connections among atoms).

ADDITIONAL PROBLEMS

NAMING ALKENES, ALKYNES, AND AROMATIC COMPOUNDS (SECTIONS 13.1, 13.2, 13.9)

13.30 **(a)** What do the terms saturated and unsaturated mean?
(b) Draw an example of a saturated four carbon compound and an unsaturated four carbon compound.

13.31 **(a)** What does the term "aromatic" refer to when discussing organic molecules?
(b) What is resonance and why is it important in aromatic compounds?

13.32 What family-name endings are used for alkenes, alkynes, and substituted benzenes?

13.33 What prefixes are used in naming the following?
(a) A 1,3-disubstituted benzene
(b) A 1,4-disubstituted benzene

13.34 Write structural formulas for compounds that meet the following descriptions:
(a) A 6-carbon alkene whose longest chain is 4 carbons in length (three possibilities)
(b) An alkyne with 5 carbons total (three possibilities)
(c) A monosubstituted benzene with a total of 8 carbons (one possibility)
(d) A disubstituted benzene with a total of 8 carbons (three possibilities)

13.35 Write structural formulas for compounds that meet the following descriptions:
(a) An alkene, C_6H_{12}, that cannot have cis–trans isomers and whose longest chain is 5 carbons long
(b) An alkene with a chemical formula of $C_{10}H_{12}$ that has cis–trans isomers and contains a benzene ring.

13.36 What are the IUPAC names of the following compounds?
(a) $CH_3CH=CHCH_2CH$
(b) >─C≡C─<
(c) [line structure]
(d) $H_3C-C=CH-C=CH-CH_3$ with CH_3 and CH_3 substituents
(e)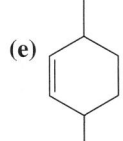
(f) [line structure]

13.37 Give IUPAC names for the following aromatic compounds:
(a) [benzene ring with isopropyl and Cl substituents]
(b) Br─[benzene ring]─NO_2
(c)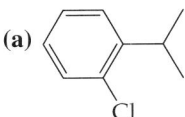

13.38 Draw structures corresponding to the following IUPAC names:
(a) *trans*-2-Pentene
(b) *trans*-3,4-Dimethyl-3-hexene
(c) 2-Methyl-1,3-butadiene
(d) *trans*-3-Heptene
(e) *p*-Nitrotoluene
(f) *o*-Chlorophenol
(g) 1,2-Dimethylcyclobutene
(h) 3,3-Diethyl-6-methyl-4-nonene

13.39 Draw structures corresponding to the following names:
(a) Aniline
(b) Phenol
(c) *o*-Xylene
(d) 2,4,6-Trinitrobenzene
(e) *p*-Chlorobenzoic acid
(f) *m*-Nitroaniline
(g) *o*-Chlorobenzaldehyde
(h) Anisole (methoxybenzene)

13.40 Seven alkynes have the formula C_6H_{10}. Draw them, using line structures.

13.41 Draw and name all phenols with the formula C_7H_8O.

13.42 When ethylbenzene is reacted with nitric acid, three possible benzenes containing both a nitro group and an ethyl group are obtained. Draw and name them.

13.43 There are four different pentenes having the following general structure:

$$CH_3$$
$$C-C-C-C-C$$

The four differ only in the placement of the double bond. Draw and name all four. Ignore cis–trans isomers.

ALKENE CIS–TRANS ISOMERS (SECTION 13.3)

13.44 What requirement(s) must be met for an alkene to show cis–trans isomerism?

13.45 Why do alkynes not show cis–trans isomerism?

13.46 Draw line structures for the following alkenes. Which can exist as cis–trans isomers? For those that can, draw both isomers.
(a) 2-Methyl-2-octene   **(b)** 3-Heptene
(c) 3,4-Dimethyl-3-hexene

13.47 Which compound(s) in Problem 13.43 can exist as cis–trans isomers? Label each as being either a symmetrically or unsymmetrically substituted alkene.

13.48 Draw structures of the following compounds:

(a) *cis*-3-Heptene

(b) *cis*-4-Methyl-2-pentene

(c) *trans*-2,5-Dimethyl-3-hexene

13.49 Each of the following has a cis or trans isomeric form. Draw it.

(a) 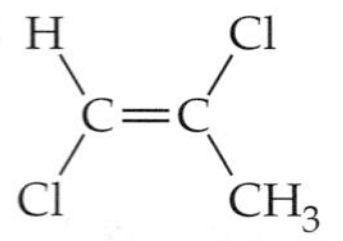 (b)

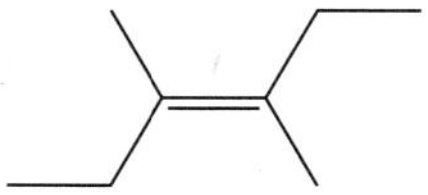

13.50 Which of the following pairs are isomers, and which are identical?

(a)

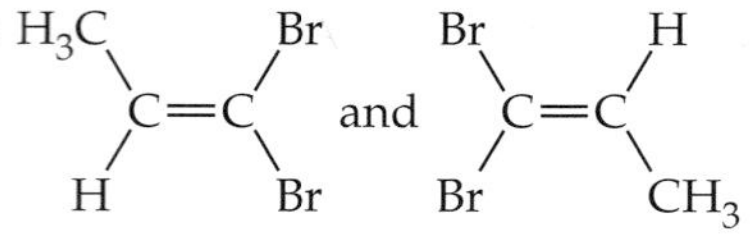

(b)

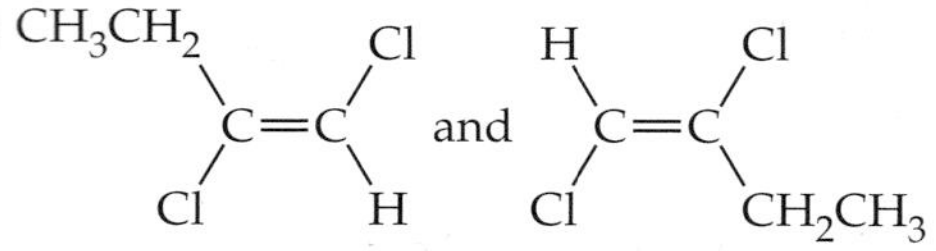

13.51 Draw the other cis–trans isomer for the following molecules:

(a) 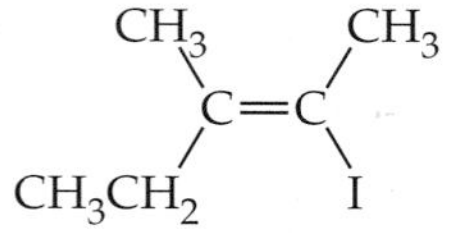 (b)

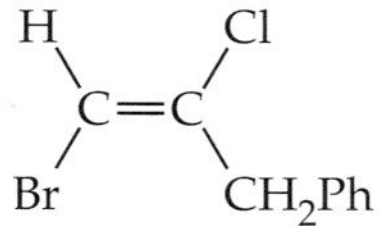

KINDS OF REACTIONS (SECTION 13.5)

13.52 What is the difference between a substitution reaction and an addition reaction?

13.53 Give an example of an addition reaction.

13.54 If 2-methyl-2-pentene were converted into 1-hexene, what kind of reaction would that be?

13.55 If bromocyclohexane were converted into cyclohexene, what kind of reaction would that be?

13.56 Identify the type of reaction for the following:

(a)

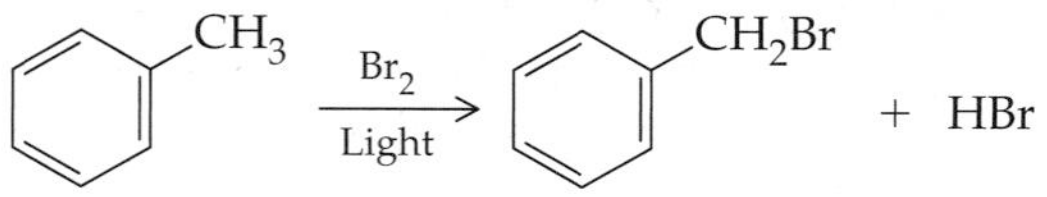

(b)

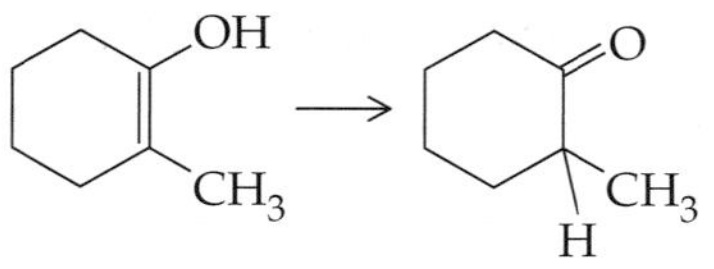

13.57 Identify the type of reaction for the following:

(a)

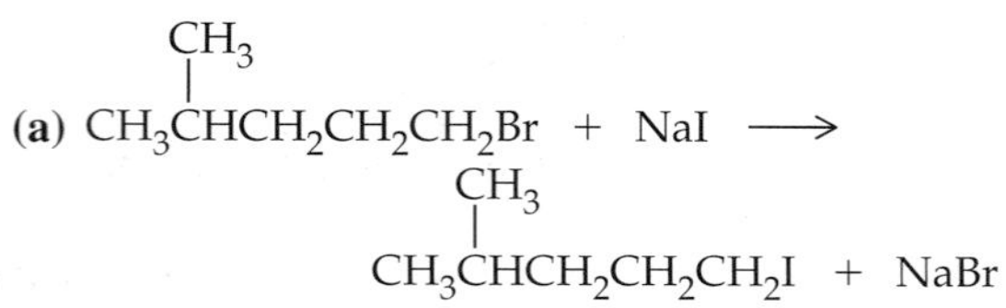

(b)

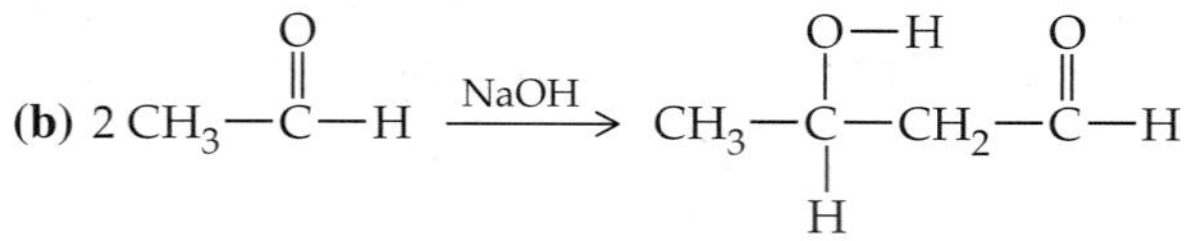

REACTIONS OF ALKENES AND ALKYNES (SECTIONS 13.6–13.7)

13.58 Write equations for the reaction of 2-pentene with the following:

(a) H_2 and Pd catalyst   (b) Br_2

(c) HCl

(d) H_2O and H_2SO_4 catalyst

13.59 Write equations for the reaction of 1-methylcyclohexene with the reagents shown in Problem 13.58.

13.60 What alkene could you use to make the following products? Draw the structure of the alkene, and tell what other reagent is also required for the reaction to occur.

(a) 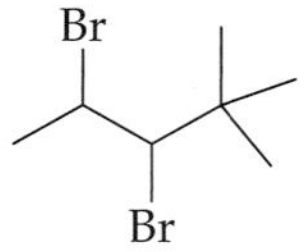   (b) $CH_3CH_2CH_3$

(c)  $CH_3CHCH_2CH_3$ with Br   (d)

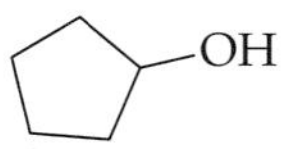

(e)

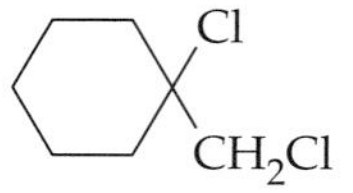

13.61 2,2,3,3-Tetrabromopentane can be prepared by an addition reaction of excess Br_2 with an alkyne. Draw the structure of the alkyne and name it.

13.62 1-Pentyne reacts with HBr in a 1:1 molar ratio to yield two different addition products, both being bromopentenes and having the chemical formula C_5H_9Br. Draw the structures of two possible products.

13.63 Polyvinylpyrrolidone (PVP) is often used in hair sprays to hold hair in place. Draw a few units of the PVP polymer. The vinylpyrrolidone monomer unit has the following structure:

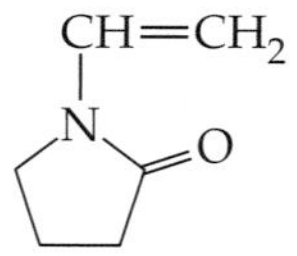

13.64 Saran, used as a plastic wrap for foods, is a polymer with the following structure. What is the monomer unit of Saran?

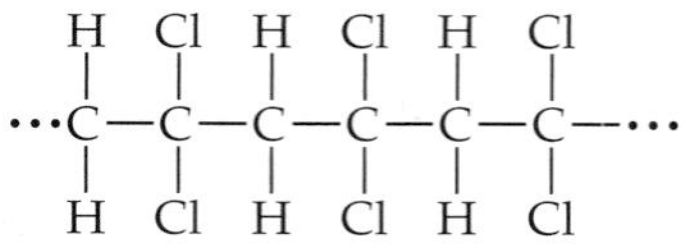

REACTIONS OF AROMATIC COMPOUNDS (SECTION 13.10)

13.65 For each of the following reagents, decide whether chlorobenzene will react with it or not, and, if it does, draw and name the products expected from the reaction.

(a) Br_2 and $FeBr_3$ (b) HBr

(c) HNO_3 and H_2SO_4 catalyst

13.66 Write equations for the reaction of *p*-dichlorobenzene with the following:

(a) Br_2 and $FeBr_3$

(b) HNO_3 and H_2SO_4 catalyst

(c) H_2SO_4 and SO_3 (d) Cl_2 and $FeCl_3$

13.67 Aromatic compounds do not normally react with hydrogen in the presence of a palladium catalyst but will if very high pressures (200 atm) and high temperatures are used. Under these conditions, toluene adds three molecules of H_2 to give an alkane addition product. What is a likely structure for the product?

13.68 The explosive trinitrotoluene (TNT) is made by carrying out three successive nitration reactions on toluene. If these nitrations only occur in the ortho and para positions relative to the methyl group, what is the structure of TNT?

CONCEPTUAL PROBLEMS

13.69 Salicylic acid (*o*-hydroxybenzoic acid) is used as starting material to prepare aspirin. Draw the structure of salicylic acid.

13.70 The following names are incorrect by IUPAC rules. Draw the structures represented by the following names, and write their correct names. Label each as being symmetrically or unsymmetrically substituted.

(a) 2-Methyl-4-hexene

(b) 1,3-Dimethyl-1-hexyne

(c) 2-Isopropyl-1-propene

(d) 1,4,6-Trinitrobenzene

(e) 1,2-Dimethyl-3-cyclohexene

(f) 3-Methyl-2,4-pentadiene

13.71 Which of the compounds in Problem 13.70 are capable of cis–trans isomerism? Draw each isomer.

13.72 Assume that you have two unlabeled bottles, one with cyclohexane and one with cyclohexene. How could you tell them apart by carrying out chemical reactions?

13.73 Assume you have two unlabeled bottles, one with cyclohexene and one with benzene. How could you tell them apart by carrying out chemical reactions?

13.74 The compound *p*-dichlorobenzene has been used as an insecticide. Draw its structure.

13.75 Menthene, a compound found in mint plants, has the formula $C_{10}H_{18}$ and the IUPAC name 1-isopropyl-4-methylcyclohexene. What is the structure of menthene?

13.76 Cinnamaldehyde, the pleasant-smelling substance found in cinnamon oil, has the following structure:

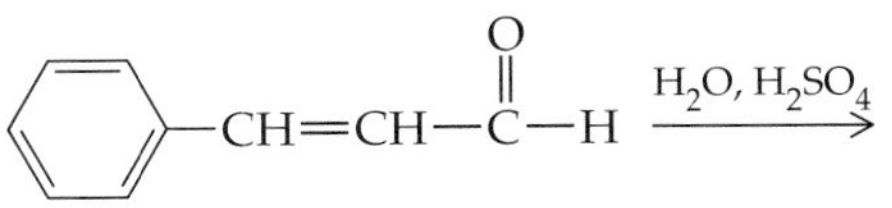

What products would you expect to obtain from reaction of cinnamaldehyde with water and sulfuric acid catalyst?

13.77 Predict the products of the following reactions:

(a) $CH_3CH_2CH=CHCHCH_3$ (with CH_3 substituent) $\xrightarrow{H_2, Pd}$?

(b) 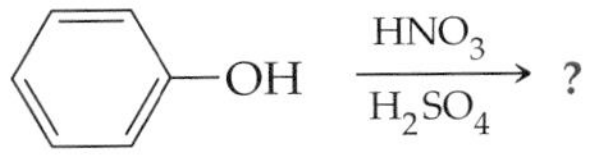 $\xrightarrow{HNO_3}{H_2SO_4}$?
(3 possible disubstituted products)

(c) 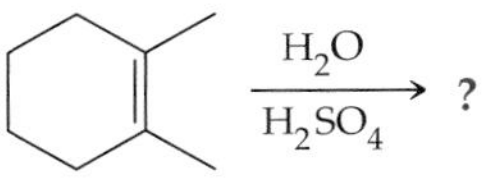 $\xrightarrow{H_2O}{H_2SO_4}$?

(d) 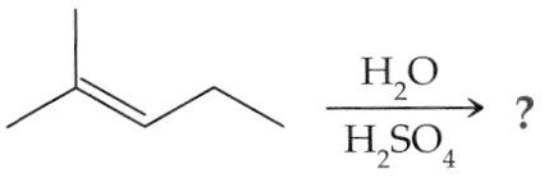 $\xrightarrow{H_2O}{H_2SO_4}$?

(e) $CH_3C\equiv CCH_2CH_3 \xrightarrow{H_2, Pd}$?

13.78 Two products are possible when 2-pentene is treated with HBr. Write the structures of the possible products, and explain why they are made in about equal amounts.

13.79 Ocimene, a compound isolated from the herb basil, has three double bonds and the IUPAC name 3,7-dimethyl-1,3-6-octatriene.

(a) Draw its structure.

(b) Draw the structure of the compound formed if enough HBr is added to react with all the double bonds in ocimene.

13.80 Describe how you could prepare the following compound from an alkene. Draw the formula of the alkene, name it, and list the inorganic reactants or catalysts needed for the conversion.

13.81 Which of the following compounds are capable of cis–trans isomerism?

(a) $CH_3CHCH=CHCH_3$ (with CH_3)   (b) $CH_3CH_2CHCH_3$ (with $CH=CH_2$)

(c) $CH_3CH=CHCHCH_2CH_3$ (with Cl)

GROUP PROBLEMS

13.82 Why do you suppose small-ring cycloalkenes like cyclohexene do not exist as cis–trans isomers, whereas large ring cycloalkenes like cyclodecene *do* show isomerism?

13.83 "Superglue" is an alkene polymer made from the monomer unit.

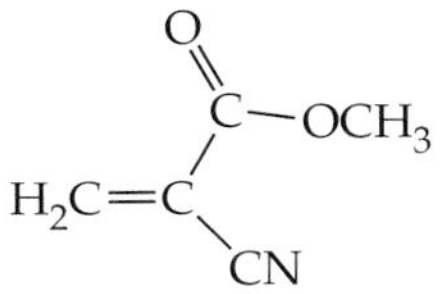

Draw a representative segment of the structure of superglue.

13.84 Draw all possible C_5H_{10} alkene isomers having a longest chain of four carbons and a methyl group. (Hint: Adapt the method described in Worked Example 12.12 to arrive at your answers.)

14

Some Compounds with Oxygen, Sulfur, or a Halogen

CONTENTS

◀◀◀ CONCEPTS TO REVIEW

A. Polar Covalent Bonds
   (Section 4.9)

B. Oxidation and Reduction
   (Section 5.5)

C. Hydrogen Bonds
   (Section 8.2)

D. Acid Dissociation Constants
   (Sections 10.6 and 10.7)

E. Functional Groups
   (Section 12.2)

F. Naming Alkanes
   (Section 12.6)

G. Types of Organic Reactions
   (Section 13.5)

▲ As a mother cuddles her newborn, it is unthinkable that she could harm her child, yet drinking during pregnancy can do just that.

Ethyl alcohol (or ethanol), the substance found in liquor, beer, and other alcoholic beverages, is often the first thing that people think of when the term "alcohol" is mentioned. Ethyl alcohol is also used as an antiseptic, a solvent, and as a fuel. While images of parties and celebrations come to mind, ethyl alcohol can be widely abused and severely toxic if consumed in excess. Ethyl alcohol consumption can have especially dire consequences on the most fragile of all life, a human fetus. Fetal alcohol syndrome (FAS) is one of the leading causes of preventable birth defects in the United States. In fact, in 2015, the Centers for Disease Control and Prevention (CDC) stated that no amount of alcohol is safe to consume at any time during pregnancy. Drinking during pregnancy can lead to a number of neurological problems in newborns, as you will learn in the Chemistry in Action "Fetal Alcohol Syndrome: Ethyl Alcohol as a Toxin" at the end of this chapter.

But do not let the dangers of ethanol consumption fool you; *alcohols* are arguably the most important functional group family in organic chemistry and are present in a large number of organic compounds of biological importance. Alcohols are versatile in organic synthesis; they can be used as a starting material to prepare almost any other functional group family, such as the alkyl halides, ketones, aldehydes, and carboxylic acids. In this chapter, we will concentrate on the functional groups, like alcohols, that contain single bonds to the electronegative atoms oxygen, sulfur, and the halogens.

14.1 Alcohols, Phenols, and Ethers

Learning Objectives:

- Describe the structural differences between alcohols, phenols, and ethers.
- Explain why alcohols have higher boiling points than compounds of similar molecular weight (MW).

An **alcohol** is a compound that has an $-OH$ group (a *hydroxyl group*) bonded to a tetrahedral, carbon atom; a **phenol** has an $-OH$ group bonded directly to an aromatic, benzene-like ring; and an **ether** has two carbon groups (whether alkyl, aromatic or a combination of both) bonded to the same oxygen atom.

◀◀◀ **CONCEPTS TO REVIEW** Recall from Table 12.3 that **R** is used to symbolize an organic substituent; it is the **R**est of the molecule.

Alcohol A compound that has an $-OH$ group bonded to a saturated, carbon atom, R—OH.

Phenol A compound that has an $-OH$ group bonded directly to an aromatic, benzene-like ring, Ar—OH.

Ether A compound that has an oxygen atom bonded to two organic groups, R—O—R.

CH_3CH_2OH	Phenol	$CH_3CH_2OCH_2CH_3$
Ethyl alcohol		Diethyl ether

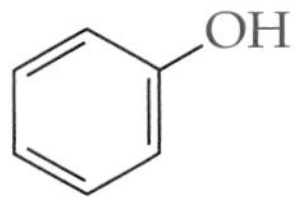

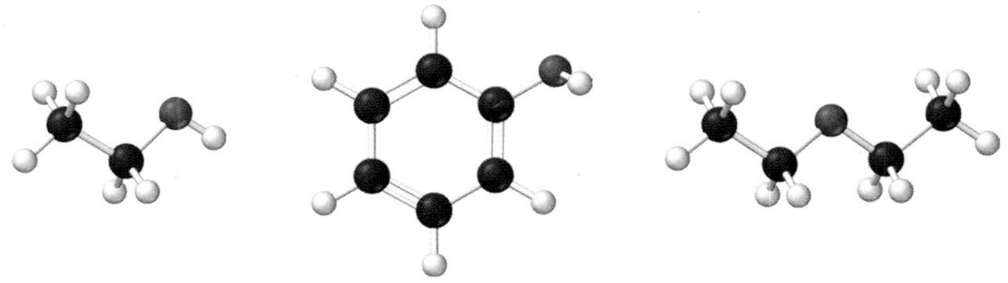

Compounds in all three families can be thought of as organic relatives of water in which one or both of the H_2O hydrogens have been replaced by an organic substituent. The structural similarity between alcohols and water also leads to similarities in many of their physical properties. For example, compare the boiling points of ethyl alcohol, dimethyl ether, propane, and water.

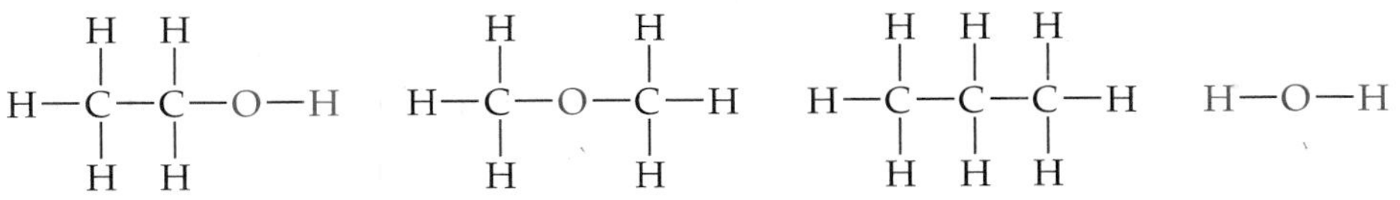

Ethyl alcohol	Dimethyl ether	Propane	Water
(MW 46, bp 78.5 °C)	(MW 46, bp −23 °C)	(MW 44, bp −42 °C)	(MW 18, bp 100 °C)

Ethyl alcohol, dimethyl ether, and propane have similar MWs, yet ethyl alcohol boils more than 100 °C higher than the other two. In fact, the boiling point of ethyl alcohol is close to that of water. Why should this be?

The high boiling point of water is due to hydrogen bonding—the attraction between a lone pair of electrons on the electronegative oxygen in one molecule and the positively polarized $-OH$ hydrogen on another molecule. This attraction holds molecules

◀◀ Review the effect of hydrogen bonding on boiling point in Section 8.2.

together and prevents their easy escape into the vapor phase. In a similar manner, hydrogen bonds form between alcohol (or phenol) molecules (Figure 14.1). Alkanes and ethers do not have hydroxyl groups, however, and cannot form hydrogen bonds. As a result, they have lower boiling points. Ethers, with the exception of their polarity, resemble alkanes in many of their chemical and physical properties.

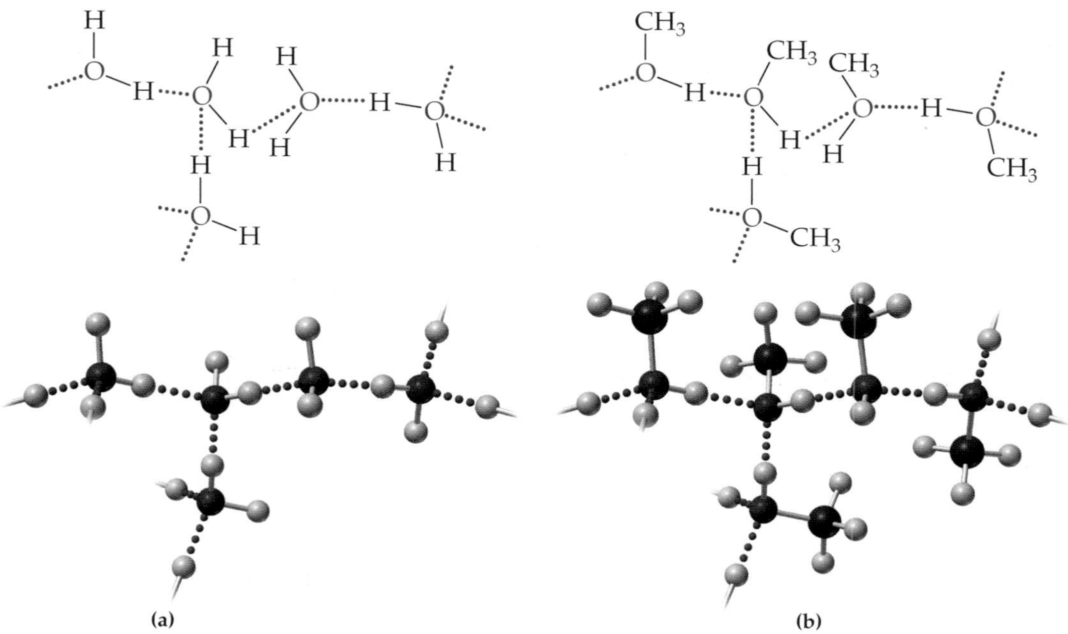

▶ **Figure 14.1**
The formation of hydrogen bonds in water (a) and in alcohols (b).
Because of the hydrogen bonds (shown in red), the easy escape of molecules into the vapor phase is prevented, resulting in high boiling points.

(a)   (b)

PROBLEM 14.1

Identify each of the following compounds as an alcohol, a phenol, or an ether:

(a) $CH_3CH_2CHCH_3$ with OH

(b) 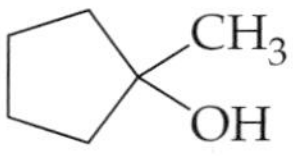 cyclopentane with CH_3 and OH

(c) 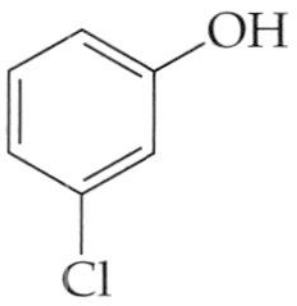 benzene ring with OH and Cl

(d) 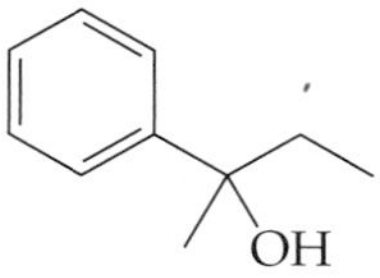 benzene ring with C bearing ethyl and OH

(e) 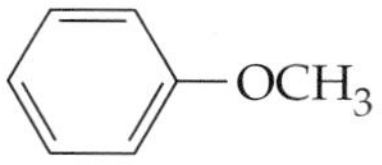 benzene ring with OCH_3

(f) $(CH_3)_2CH-O-CH_2CH_3$

PROBLEM 14.2

Ethers have some slight solubility in water. Explain this using the concept of hydrogen bonding.

14.2 Naming Alcohols

Learning Objectives:

• Write systematic names for simple alcohols.
• Draw the structure of an alcohol given its name, in both condensed and line structure format.
• Classify an alcohol as primary, secondary, or tertiary.
• Define and identify a glycol.

Common names of many alcohols containing one hydroxyl (—OH) group identify the alkyl group and then add the word *alcohol*. Thus, the two-carbon alcohol is ethyl alcohol, the three-carbon alcohol is propyl alcohol, and so on:

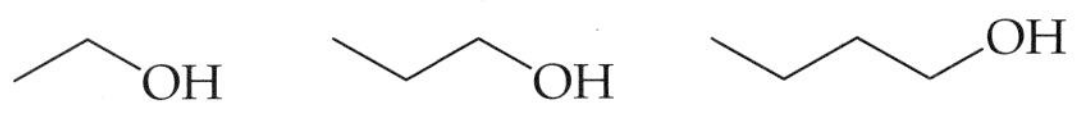

OH   OH   OH

Ethyl alcohol   Propyl alcohol   Butyl alcohol

The International Union of Pure and Applied Chemistry (IUPAC) system names alcohols in a similar manner to that used for alkanes (Section 12.6) but uses index number of the hydroxyl (—OH) group and the *-ol* ending for the parent compound.

STEP 1: Name the parent compound. Find the longest chain that has the hydroxyl substituent attached, and name the chain by replacing the *-e* ending of the corresponding alkane with *-ol:*

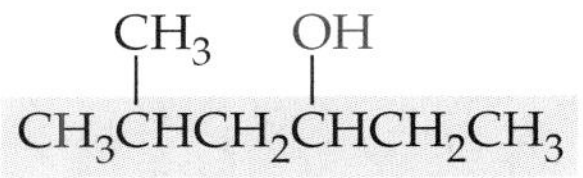

CH_3 OH
$CH_3CHCH_2CHCH_2CH_3$

Name as a *hexanol*— a six-carbon chain containing a hydroxyl group.

If the compound is a cyclic alcohol, add the *-ol* ending to the name of the parent cycloalkane. For example,

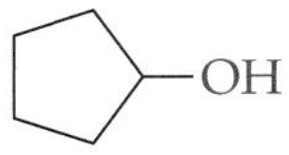

—OH

Cyclopentanol

STEP 2: Number the carbon atoms in the main chain. The carbon bearing the —OH must be assigned the lowest index number possible when numbering the chain. Begin at the end nearer the hydroxyl group, ignoring the location of other substituents for now:

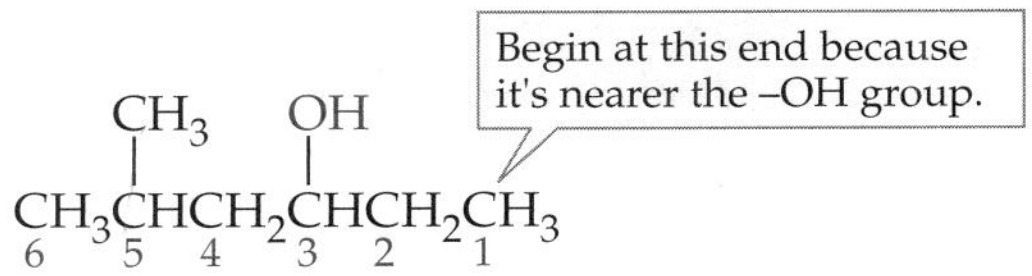

Begin at this end because it's nearer the –OH group.

CH_3 OH
$CH_3CHCH_2CHCH_2CH_3$
 6   5   4   3   2   1

In a cyclic alcohol, begin with the carbon that bears the —OH group and proceed in a direction that gives the other substituents the lowest possible numbers:

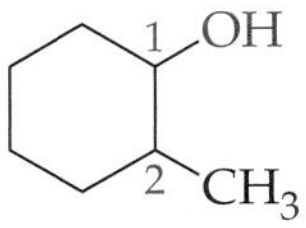

1 OH
2 CH_3

STEP 3: Write the name, placing the number that locates the hydroxyl group immediately before the parent compound name. Number all other substituents according to their positions, and list them alphabetically. Note that in a cyclic alcohol, it is not necessary to use the number 1 to specify the location of the —OH group:

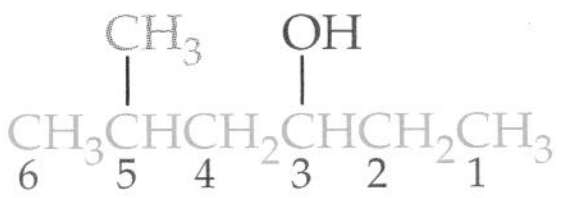

CH_3 OH
$CH_3CHCH_2CHCH_2CH_3$
 6   5   4   3   2   1

5-Methyl-3-hexanol

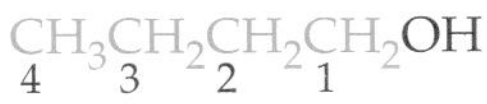

$CH_3CH_2CH_2CH_2OH$
 4   3   2   1

1-Butanol

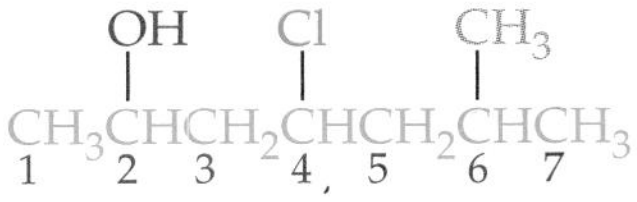

OH Cl CH_3
$CH_3CHCH_2CHCH_2CHCH_3$
 1   2   3   4   5   6   7

4-Chloro-6-methyl-2-heptanol

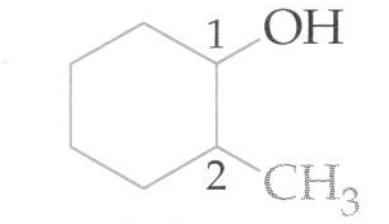

1 OH
2 CH_3

2-Methylcyclohexanol

Diols and Glycols

Dialcohols, or *diols,* are compounds that contain two hydroxy groups in the same molecule. The IUPAC names these alcohols by attaching the ending *diol* to the alkane name. The names will contain two numbers indicating the carbons bonded to the two different — OH groups, with the numbering starting at the end closest to one of the — OH groups:

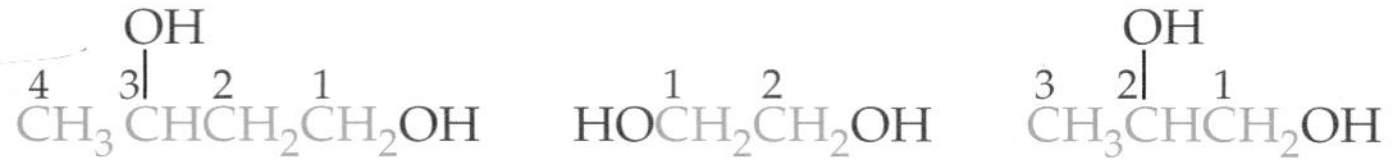

$$\underset{4}{CH_3}\underset{3}{CHCH_2CH_2OH} \qquad \underset{1}{HOCH_2}\underset{2}{CH_2OH} \qquad \underset{3}{CH_3}\underset{2}{CHCH_2OH}$$

1,3-Butanediol   1,2-Ethanediol (Ethylene glycol)   1,2-Propanediol (Propylene glycol)

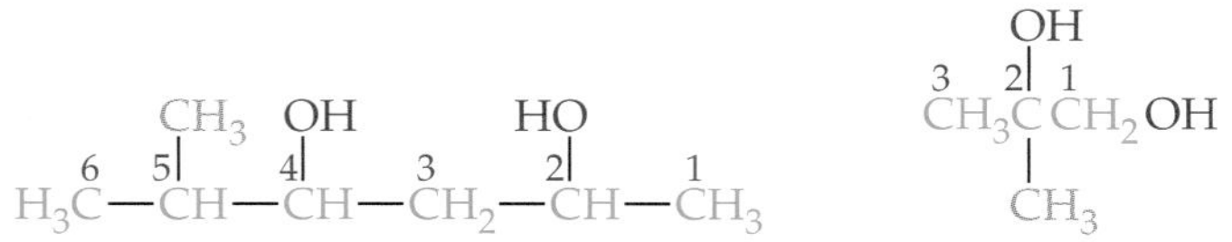

$$H_3C-CH-CH-CH_2-CH-CH_3 \qquad CH_3CCH_2OH$$

5-Methyl-2,4-hexanediol (*not* 2-Methyl-3,5-hexanediol)   2-Methyl-1,2-propanediol (Isobutylene glycol)

Vicinal Referring to groups on adjacent carbons.

Glycol A dialcohol, or diol, having the two — OH groups on adjacent carbons.

When the two — OH groups are on adjacent carbons (commonly called **vicinal** diols), diols are often referred to by the common name **glycols.** Strictly speaking, any diol having the — OH groups on adjacent carbons can be called a glycol, but the term "glycol" is preferably reserved for two compounds, ethylene glycol and propylene glycol. Ethylene glycol is the simplest glycol. Propylene glycol is often used as a solvent for medicines that need to be inhaled or rubbed onto the skin, and, as noted in the previous section, it is also used as a replacement for ethylene glycol in antifreeze. Since glycols are commonly prepared from alkenes, the usual convention for naming simple glycols is to use the name of the alkene from which the diol is made, with the name "glycol" added.

Classification of Alcohols

Alcohols are classified as primary, secondary, or tertiary according to the number of carbon substituents bonded to the hydroxyl-bearing carbon. This classification is useful, as many of the reactions of alcohols are a function of their substitution. Alcohols with one substituent are said to be *primary* (1°), those with two substituents are *secondary* (2°), and those with three substituents are *tertiary* (3°). The substituent groups need not be the same, so we will use the representations R, R′ (read it *R prime*), and R″ (read *R double prime*) to indicate different substituent groups.

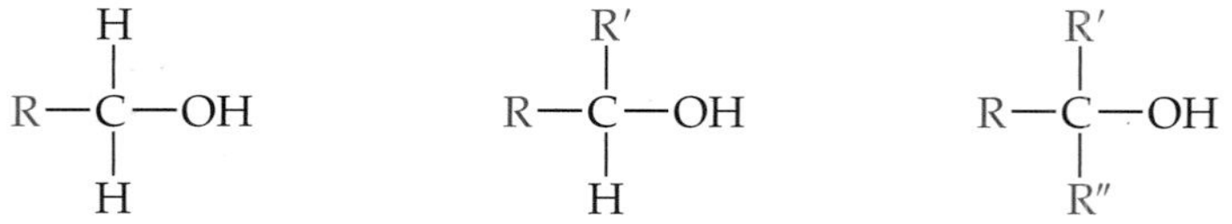

◄◄◄ This same classification is used to describe the carbons in alkanes; see Section 12.6.

A primary alcohol (one R group on OH-bearing carbon)   A secondary alcohol (two R groups on OH-bearing carbon)   A tertiary alcohol (three R groups on OH-bearing carbon)

Worked Example 14.1 Naming Organic Compounds: Alcohols

Give the systematic name of the following alcohol, and classify it as primary, secondary, or tertiary:

$$CH_3CH_2CH_2\overset{CH_3}{\underset{CH_3}{C}}-OH$$

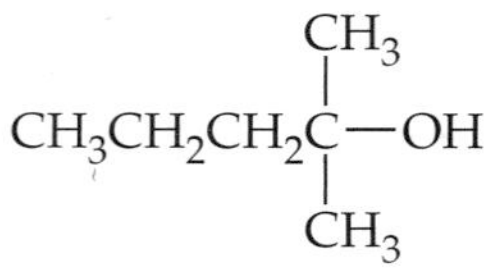

ANALYSIS First, identify the longest carbon chain, and number the carbon atoms beginning at the end nearer the —OH group. The longest chain attached to the —OH has five carbon atoms:

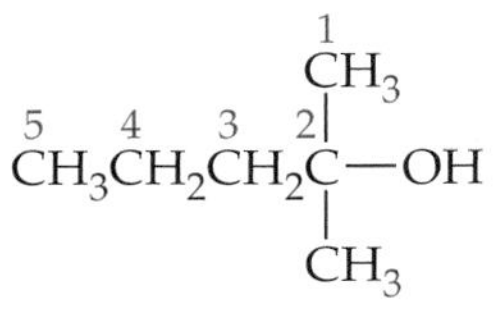

$$\underset{5}{CH_3}\underset{4}{CH_2}\underset{3}{CH_2}\overset{\overset{1}{CH_3}}{\underset{\underset{CH_3}{|}}{\underset{2}{C}}}{-}OH \qquad \text{Name as a pentanol.}$$

Next, identify and number the hydroxyl group and the substituents. Finally, write the name of the compound.

SOLUTION

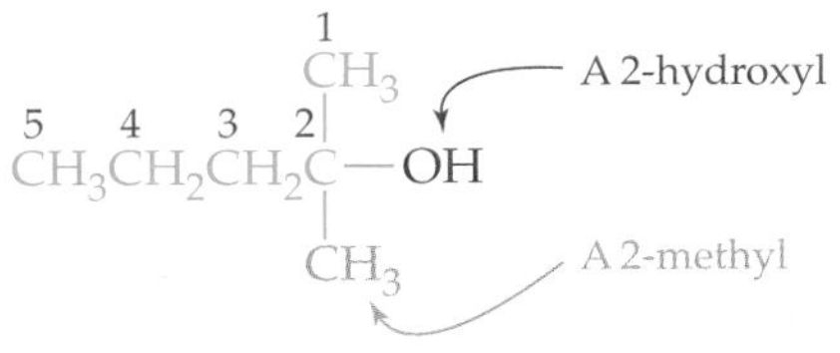

$$\underset{5}{CH_3}\underset{4}{CH_2}\underset{3}{CH_2}\overset{\overset{1}{CH_3}}{\underset{\underset{CH_3}{|}}{\underset{2}{C}}}{-}OH$$

A 2-hydroxyl

A 2-methyl

2-Methyl-2-pentanol

Since the —OH group is bonded to a carbon atom that has three alkyl substituents, this is a tertiary alcohol.

Worked Example 14.2 Drawing Organic Compounds: Alcohols

Draw the structures of (a) 2,3-dimethyl-2-butanol and (b) 3-ethylcyclopentanol. Classify each as primary, secondary, or tertiary.

ANALYSIS For both, begin by determining the longest carbon chain; number the carbon atoms and put groups on appropriate atoms. If no index number is given for the —OH group, it is assumed to be on the first carbon.

SOLUTION

(a) This alcohol is a butanol, so it has a longest chain of four carbons:

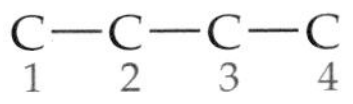

$$\underset{1}{C}-\underset{2}{C}-\underset{3}{C}-\underset{4}{C}$$

Since it is a 2-butanol, the —OH group is bonded to carbon 2; the methyl groups are bonded to carbons 2 and 3:

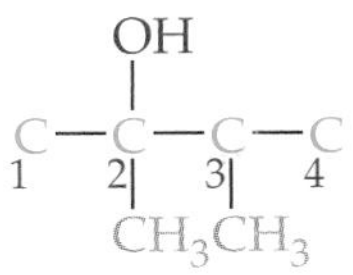

$$\underset{1}{C}-\overset{\overset{OH}{|}}{\underset{\underset{CH_3}{|}}{\underset{2}{C}}}-\overset{}{\underset{\underset{CH_3}{|}}{\underset{3}{C}}}-\underset{4}{C}$$

Filling out the remaining Hs gives us the following (in both condensed and line structure formats):

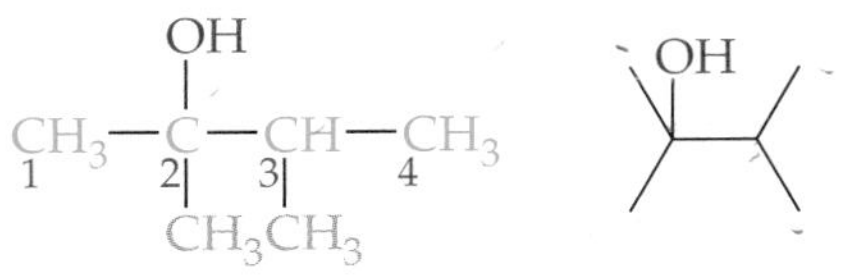

$$\underset{1}{CH_3}-\overset{\overset{OH}{|}}{\underset{\underset{CH_3}{|}}{\underset{2}{C}}}-\overset{}{\underset{\underset{CH_3}{|}}{\underset{3}{CH}}}-\underset{4}{CH_3}$$

2,3-Dimethyl-2-butanol

Since the —OH group is bonded to a carbon atom that has three other carbons bonded to it, this is a tertiary alcohol.

(b) The name tells us that the —OH group is bonded to a cyclopentane ring; since no position number is given, the —OH group is on carbon 1. Putting in the ethyl group on carbon 3 gives us the following:

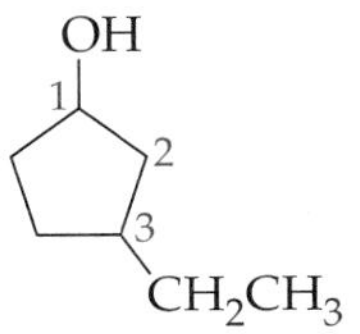

Since the —OH group is bonded to a carbon atom that has two other carbons bonded to it, this is a secondary alcohol.

PROBLEM 14.3

Draw structures corresponding to the following names:

(a) 3-Methyl-1-hexanol

(b) 1-Methyl-3-propylcyclopentanol

(c) 2,2-Dimethyl-3-hexanol

(d) 3-Heptanol

(e) 2,3-Diethylcyclohexanol

PROBLEM 14.4

Give systematic names for the following compounds:

$$
\begin{array}{c}
CH_3 \\
| \\
(a)\ CH_3-C-OH \\
| \\
CH_3
\end{array}
$$

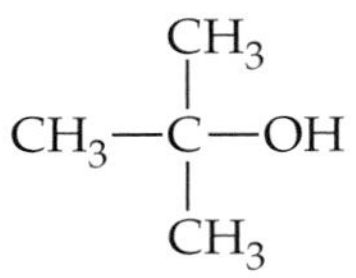

(b)

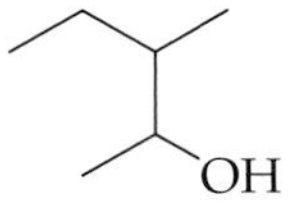

$$
\begin{array}{c}
CH_2OH \\
| \\
(c)\ CH_3CH_2CHCH_2CH_2CHCH_3 \\
| \\
Cl
\end{array}
$$

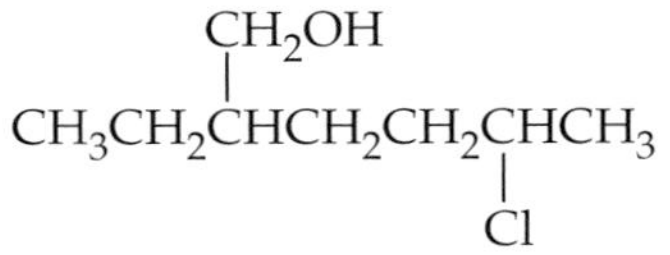

(d)

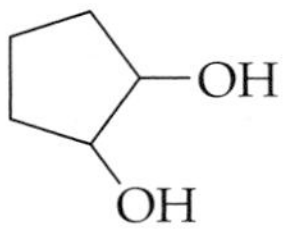

PROBLEM 14.5

Identify each alcohol in Problems 14.3 and 14.4 as primary, secondary, or tertiary.

14.3   Properties of Alcohols

Learning Objectives:

• Describe the properties of alcohols.
• Describe hydrophobic and hydrophilic alcohols.

Alcohols are much more polar than hydrocarbons because of the electronegative oxygen atom that withdraws electrons from the neighboring atoms. As a result, both its polarity and ability to hydrogen bond have a strong influence on alcohol properties.

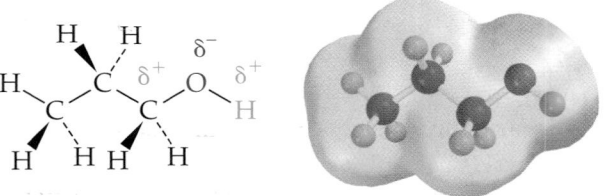

1-Propanol

Straight-chain alcohols with up to 12 carbon atoms are liquids, and each boils at a considerably higher temperature than the related alkane. Alcohols containing one to three carbons, such as methanol, ethanol, and propanol, resemble water in their solubility behavior. Methanol and ethanol are miscible with water, with which they can form hydrogen bonds, and these two alcohols can dissolve small amounts of many ionic compounds. Both are also miscible with many organic solvents because of the presence of the carbon group.

From a water solubility standpoint, all alcohols can be thought of as having two distinct parts: a "water-loving," or *hydrophilic,* part (the —OH) and a "water-fearing," or *hydrophobic,* part (the hydrocarbon chain attached to the alcohol carbon). The larger the hydrocarbon part is, such as in 1-heptanol, the more alkane-like the alcohols are and the less water-soluble they become. 1-Heptanol is nearly insoluble in water and cannot dissolve ionic compounds but does dissolve alkanes. In order for water and another liquid to be miscible, water molecules must be able to entirely surround a molecule of the other liquid; the larger the hydrophobic (or alkane-like) portion of an alcohol molecule is, the harder this is to accomplish.

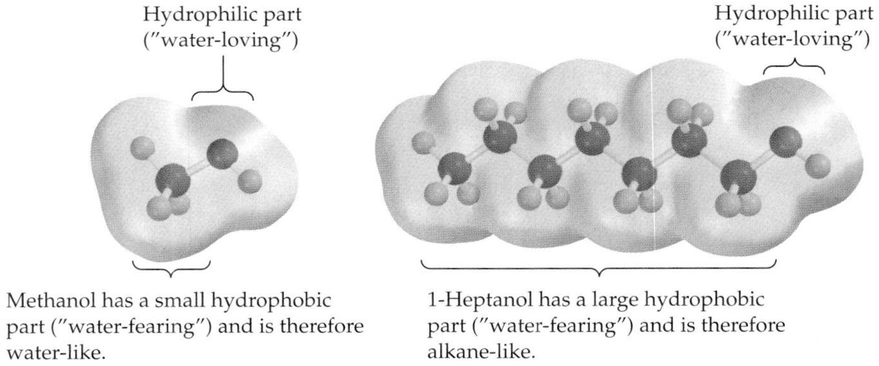

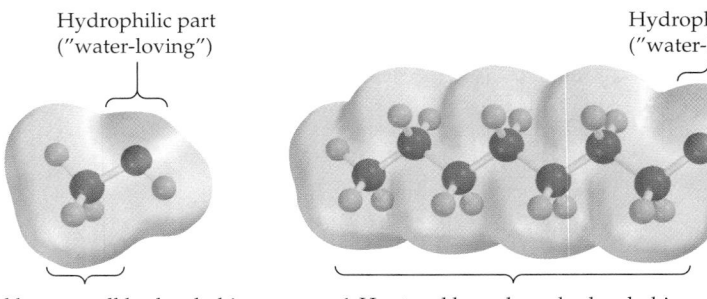

Hydrophilic part ("water-loving")

Hydrophilic part ("water-loving")

Methanol has a small hydrophobic part ("water-fearing") and is therefore water-like.

1-Heptanol has a large hydrophobic part ("water-fearing") and is therefore alkane-like.

$$CH_3-OH \qquad CH_3CH_2CH_2CH_2CH_2CH_2CH_2-OH$$

Alcohols with two or more —OH groups (diols or triols) can form more than one hydrogen bond. Therefore, they are higher boiling and more water-soluble than similar alcohols with only one —OH group. Compare 1-butanol and 1,4-butanediol, for example:

$$CH_3CH_2CH_2CH_2OH$$
1-Butanol
{ bp 117 °C, water solubility of 7 g/100 mL.

$$HOCH_2CH_2CH_2CH_2OH$$
1,4-Butanediol
{ Added –OH raises bp to 230 °C and gives miscibility with water

A general rule of thumb for solubility of uncharged organic molecules containing oxygens is the following: organic molecules having a carbon to oxygen ratio of 1:1 to 3:1 are soluble in water (such as methanol, ethanol, and propanol), while those having ratios of 5:1 and greater are insoluble (molecules with a 4:1 ratio have slight solubility).

Many alcohols have common uses, both commercially and medically. Table 14.1 lists six of them, along with their properties and uses.

LOOKING AHEAD In Chapters 17, 18, and 23, we will revisit this concept of hydrophilic and hydrophobic when we discuss carboxylic acids, proteins, and lipids, respectively.

PROBLEM 14.6

Rank the following according to boiling point, highest to lowest:

(a) $CH_3CH_2CH_2OH$

(b) $CH_3CH_2(OH)CH_2OH$

(c) $CH_3CH_2CH_3$

(d) $CH_2(OH)CH(OH)CH_2OH$

PROBLEM 14.7

For each of the following molecules, (i) redraw using line structure format, (ii) identify its hydrophobic and hydrophilic parts, and (iii) predict its solubility in water.

(a) $CH_3(CH_2)_{10}CH_2OH$

(b) $CH_3CH_2\underset{\underset{OH}{|}}{CH}CH_3$

(c) $CH_3CH_2\underset{\underset{OH}{|}}{CH}CH_2CH_2OH$

14.4 Reactions of Alcohols

Learning Objectives:

- Predict the products obtained upon dehydration of an alcohol.
- Predict the oxidation products of a primary, secondary, and tertiary alcohol.

Alcohols are one of the most important classes of organic molecules because of their versatility in the preparation of other organic molecules. We will examine two of the more important reactions of alcohols here: *dehydration* (an elimination reaction; see Section 13.5) and *oxidation*.

Table 14.1 Some Common Alcohols and Their Uses

Alcohol	Structure	Common Properties and Applications
Methanol (Methyl Alcohol) CH_3OH	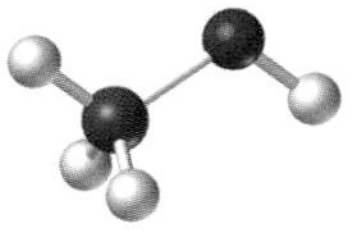	• Commonly known as *wood alcohol* • Made by reaction of carbon monoxide with hydrogen • Used industrially as a solvent; also a starting material for preparing formaldehyde ($H_2C{=}0$) (Chapter 15) • Colorless, miscible with water • Toxic to humans when ingested or inhaled
Ethanol (Ethyl Alcohol) CH_3CH_2OH	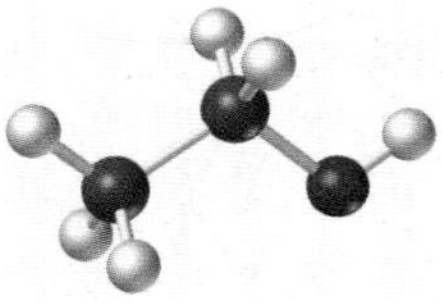	• One of the oldest known organic chemicals • 100% ethyl alcohol is known as *absolute alcohol* • Formed by fermentation of starches or complex sugars • Alcohol present in all alcoholic beverages • A central nervous system (CNS) depressant • Toxic to a developing fetus (see the Chemistry in Action feature "Fetal Alcohol Syndrome: Ethyl Alcohol as a Toxin," p. 467) • Ethanol for nonconsumption is *denatured* by addition of a toxic substance (like methyl alcohol); denatured alcohol is exempt from the tax applied to the sale of consumable alcohol • Industrially made by hydration of ethylene (Chapter 13) • Gasohol (or E85) is a blend of ethyl alcohol and gasoline and is a desirable fuel as it produces fewer air pollutants
Isopropyl Alcohol (Isopropanol; 2-Propanol)  OH	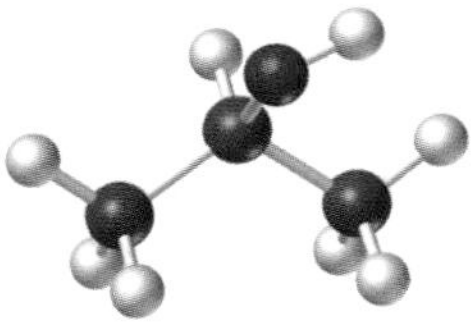	• Also known as *rubbing alcohol* • Used as a 70% mixture with water for rubdowns; cools the skin through evaporation and causes pores to close • Used as a solvent for medicines, as a sterilant for instruments, and as a skin cleanser before drawing blood or giving injections • Not as toxic as methyl alcohol but much more toxic than ethyl alcohol
Ethylene glycol (1,2-Ethandiol)  HO OH	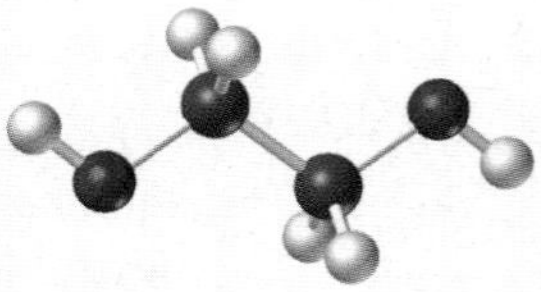	• A *diol* (meaning it has two —OH groups) • A slightly sweet, colorless liquid that is miscible with water and insoluble in nonpolar solvents • Originally used as an engine antifreeze and coolant; now is primarily used to manufacture plastic films and fibers • A CNS depressant • Lethal to humans, dogs, and cats at doses of about 1.5–3 mL/kg of body weight
Propylene Glycol (1,2-Propanediol) 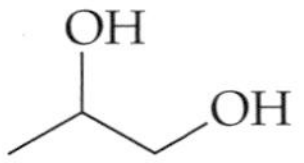 OH OH	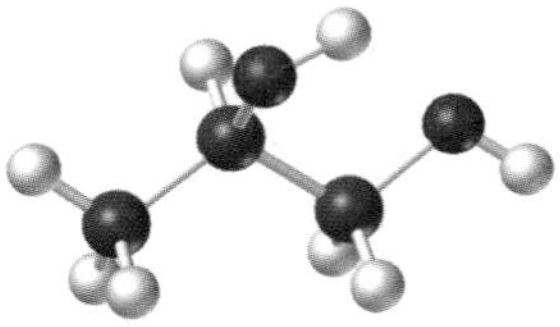	• A diol • Essentially nontoxic; it is used to replace ethylene glycol in automobile antifreezes and coolants • Used as a moisturizer, solvent, and preservative in food products • Used in various edible items such as coffee-based drinks, liquid sweeteners, ice cream, whipped dairy products, and soda. • One of the major "e-liquid" ingredients in electronic cigarettes • Used as a solvent in many pharmaceutical oral, injectable, and topical formulations
Glycerol (1,2,3-Propanetriol) 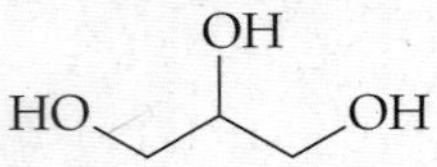 OH HO OH	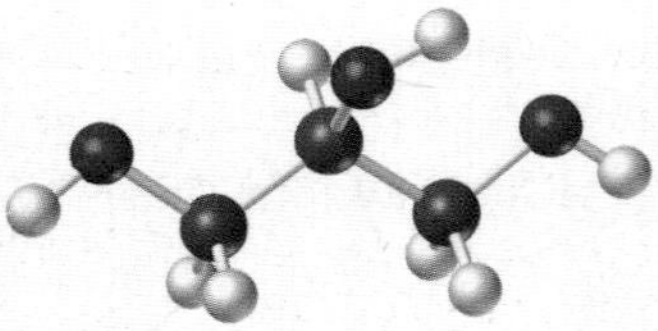	• Also known as *glycerin* • A *triol* (three —OH groups in the molecule). • A sweet tasting, colorless liquid that is miscible with water. • Nontoxic, useful in making candy and prepared foods. • Also used in cosmetics as a moisturizer, in plastics manufacturing, in antifreeze and shock-absorber fluids. • Provides the structural backbone of animal fats and vegetable oils (Chapter 23)

Dehydration

Dehydration The loss of water from an alcohol to yield an alkene.

Alcohols undergo loss of water (**dehydration**) upon treatment with a strong acid catalyst; the reaction is typically driven to completion by heating. The —OH group is lost from one carbon and an —H is lost from an adjacent carbon to yield an alkene product and water.

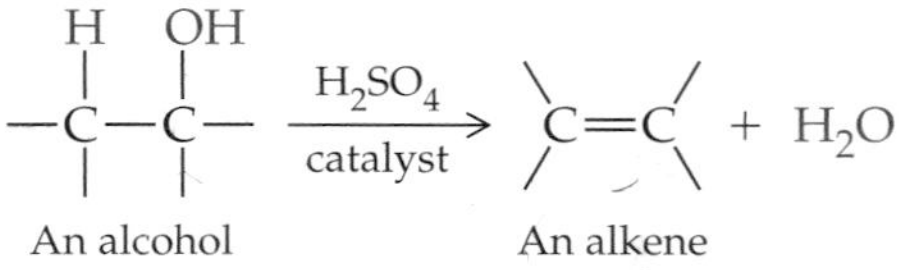

For example,

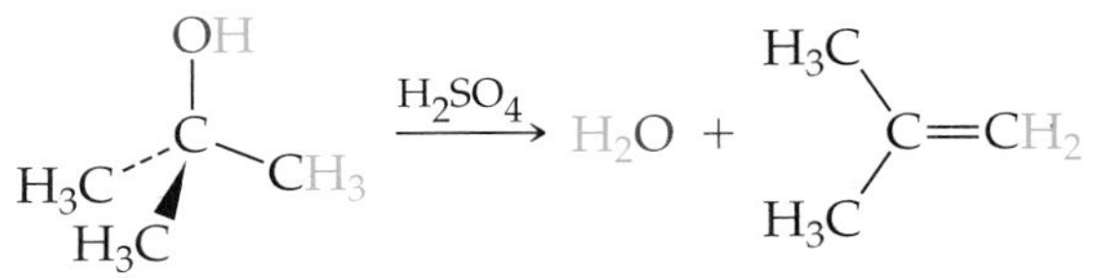

tert-Butyl alcohol   2-Methylpropene

A mixture of products forms when more than one alkene results from dehydration. A good rule of thumb is that the major product is the more substituted alkene, or the alkene that has the greater number of alkyl groups directly attached to the double-bond carbons. For example, when the dehydration of 2-butanol is carried out in the laboratory, a mixture containing 80% 2-butene and only 20% 1-butene is obtained:

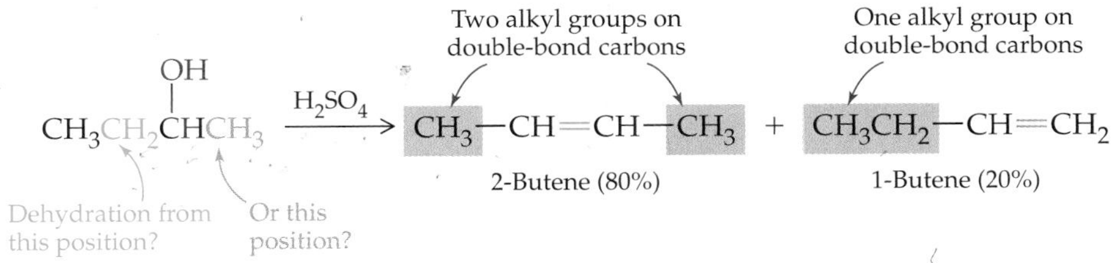

Two alkyl groups on double-bond carbons

One alkyl group on double-bond carbons

$CH_3CH_2CHCH_3$ → CH_3—CH=CH—CH_3 + CH_3CH_2—CH=CH_2

2-Butene (80%)   1-Butene (20%)

Dehydration from this position?   Or this position?

MASTERING REACTIONS

How Eliminations Occur

We have previously discussed the mechanism by which addition reactions occur (p. 422); let us now examine what is essentially the reverse of this reaction, an *elimination*. Eliminations can occur in one of two ways: as a one-step process (known as an *E2 reaction*) or as a two-step process (known as an *E1 reaction*). We will concentrate our efforts here on the latter, the E1 process.

When an alcohol is treated with a strong mineral acid (such as H_2SO_4), the first thing that happens is that the oxygen atom of the alcohol protonates in an equilibrium process:

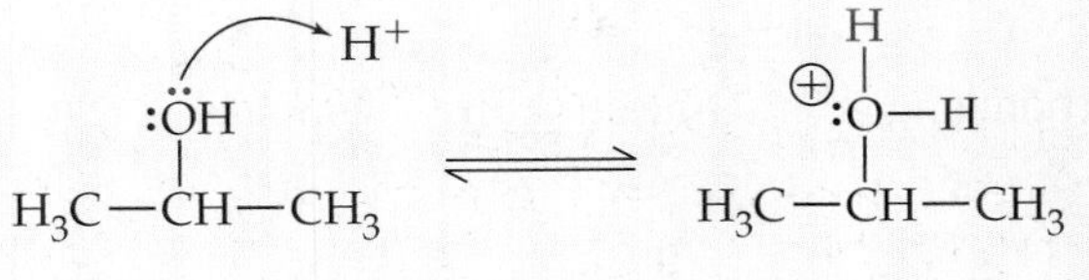

Notice that the —OH has been converted into what is essentially a water molecule. This portion can then leave, and what remains is a carbocation:

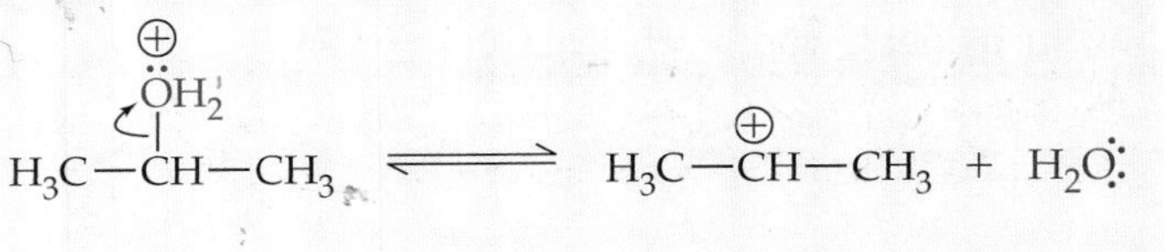

The favorability of this process is a direct function of the stability of the carbocation formed (see Mastering Reactions: How Addition Reactions Occur, p. 422). As a result, 3° alcohols will undergo this process more readily than 2° alcohols, and 1° alcohols undergo the process slowly at best.

The carbocation can then readily undergo loss of H^+ to form the alkene:

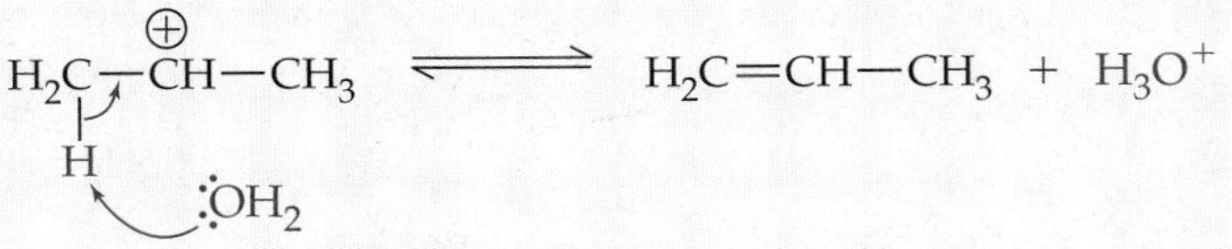

Here, water acting as a Lewis base can remove a hydrogen directly adjacent to the carbocation, forming the alkene. This sets up an equilibrium between the protonated alcohol, the carbocation, and the alkene. Recall that the reaction is typically heated; since the alkene formed has a lower boiling point than the alcohol, it simply escapes from the heated mixture, causing the reaction to proceed to the right (Le Châtelier's principle, Section 7.9).

This back and forth process may occur many times before the alkene is able to escape from the reaction, which helps to explain another observation: If it is possible to form more than one alkene isomer, the one having the more substituted double

(*continued*)

bond will be favored. This observation is known as *Zaitsev's Rule*. Consider the dehydration of 2-butanol; after the initial formation of the carbocation, there are two possible eliminations that can then occur (discussed in the following text).

Each alkene is in equilibrium with the carbocation, but the more substituted alkene (here, 2-butene) is thermodynamically more stable than the less substituted alkene. Once formed, it will be less likely to re-form the carbocation than the less substituted alkene will. Thus, the more substituted alkene accumulates, becoming the major product of the reaction, while the less substituted alkene is the minor product.

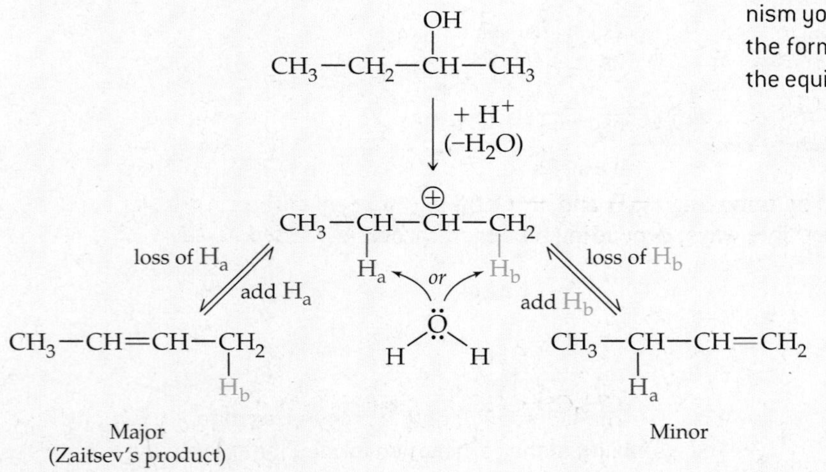

MR Problem 14.1 We discussed in Chapter 13 that H_2SO_4 catalyzes the addition of water to alkenes to form alcohols. In this chapter, however, we saw that H_2SO_4 is also used to dehydrate alcohols to make alkenes. Looking at the two mechanisms, explain with drawings what role sulfuric acid plays in both and why its role in both makes sense.

MR Problem 14.2 Provide the mechanism for the dehydration of 1-methylcyclopentanol.

MR Problem 14.3 When 4-methyl-2-pentanol is heated in H_2SO_4, two alkenes are formed in significant amounts: 4-methyl-2-pentene, the expected product and 2-methyl-2-pentene, the unexpected product. Using just the mechanism you learned here, suggest a reasonable explanation for the formation of this unexpected alkene. (Hint: Think about the equilibria discussed in this feature.)

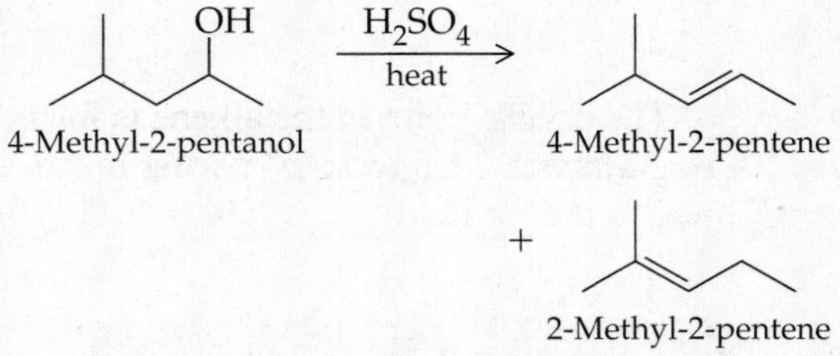

Worked Example 14.3 Organic Reactions: Dehydration

What products would you expect from the following dehydration reaction? Which product will be major and which will be minor?

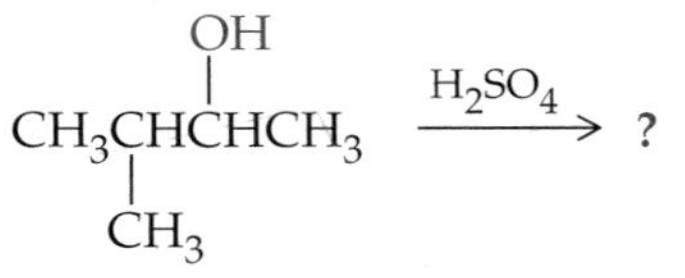

ANALYSIS Find the hydrogens on carbons next to the OH-bearing carbon, and rewrite the structure to emphasize these hydrogens:

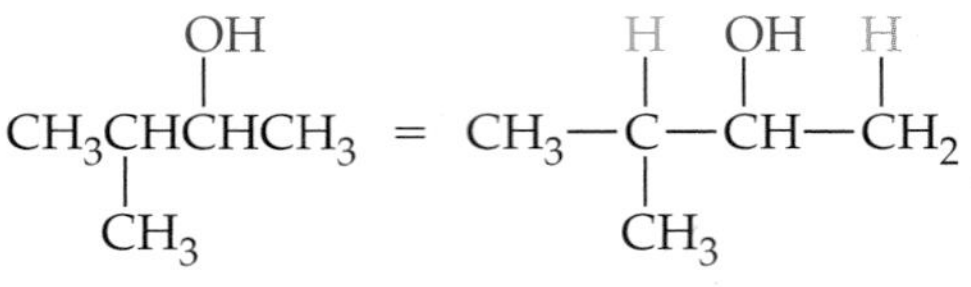

Then, remove the possible combinations of —H and —OH, drawing a double bond each —H and —OH could be removed:

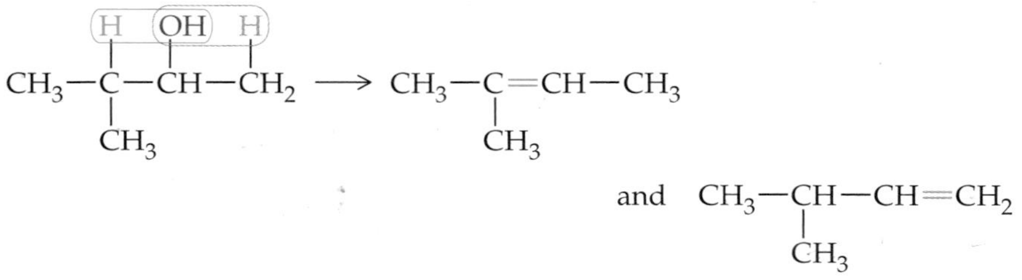

Finally, determine which alkene has the larger number of alkyl substituents on its double-bond carbons and is therefore the major product.

SOLUTION

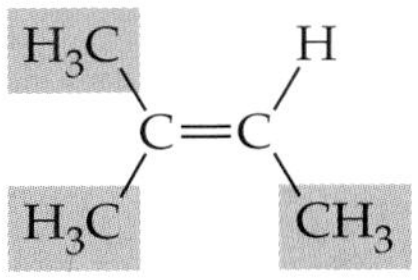

| 2-Methyl-2-butene | and | 3-Methyl-1-butene |
| major product (three alkyl groups) | | minor product (one alkyl group) |

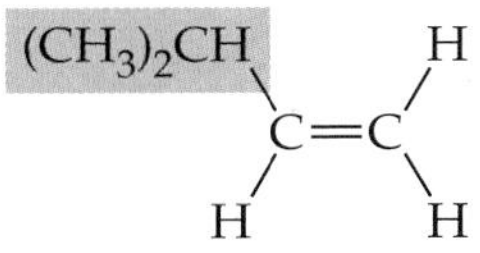

Worked Example 14.4 Organic Reactions: Dehydration

Which alcohol(s) yield 4-methyl-2-hexene on dehydration? Are there any other alkenes that arise from dehydration of these alcohols?

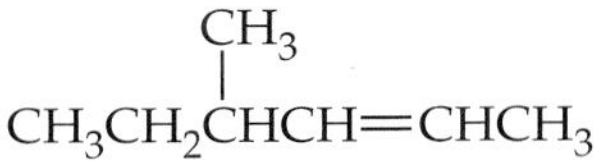

4-Methyl-2-hexene

ANALYSIS The double bond in the alkene is formed by removing —H and —OH from adjacent carbons of the starting alcohol. This removal occurs in two possible ways, depending on which carbon is bonded to the —OH and to the —H.

SOLUTION

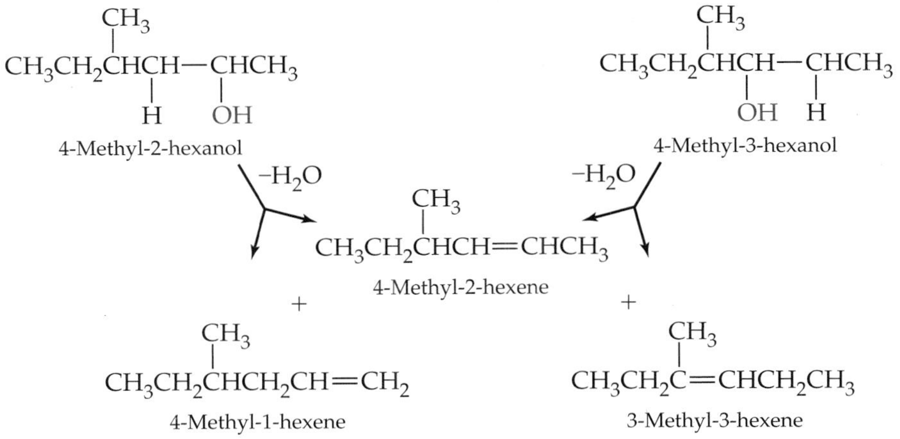

Dehydration of 4-methyl-2-hexanol yields 4-methyl-2-hexene as the major product, along with 4-methyl-1-hexene. Dehydration of 4-methyl-3-hexanol also gives 4-methyl-2-hexene but as the minor product, along with 3-methyl-3-hexene as the major product.

PROBLEM 14.8

What alkenes might be formed by dehydration of the following alcohols? If more than one product is possible in a given case, indicate which is major.

(a) $CH_3CH_2CH_2OH$ **(b)** 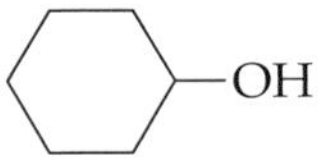 —OH   **(c)** 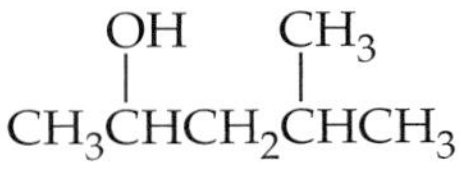 $CH_3\overset{\underset{\displaystyle |}{OH}}{C}HCH_2\overset{\underset{\displaystyle |}{CH_3}}{C}HCH_3$

PROBLEM 14.9

What alcohols yield the following alkenes as the major product on dehydration?

(a) $CH_3-CH=C-CH_3$
           $|$
          CH_3

(b) 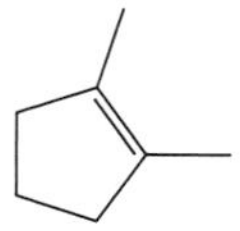 [line structure of dimethylcyclopentene]

(c) 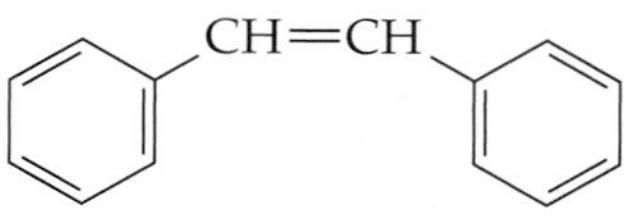 [structure: benzene ring—CH=CH—benzene ring]

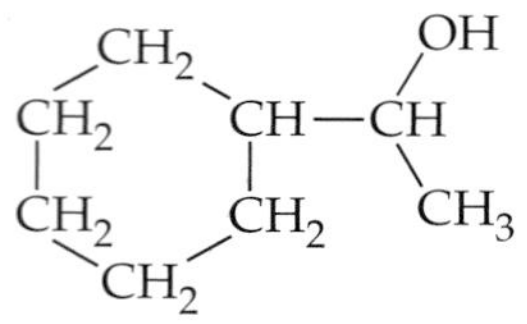

⊙ KEY CONCEPT PROBLEM 14.10

Two different alkenes will be formed by dehydration of the alcohol shown in the margin. Draw their structures using both condensed and line structure format, and label each as being either the major or minor product.

> In Section 21.8, we will see the conversion of citric acid to isocitric acid, a key step in the citric acid cycle. This reaction, which looks simply like an —OH group moving from one carbon to the next, actually occurs via an enzyme-catalyzed dehydration reaction followed by readdition of water to the alkene formed.

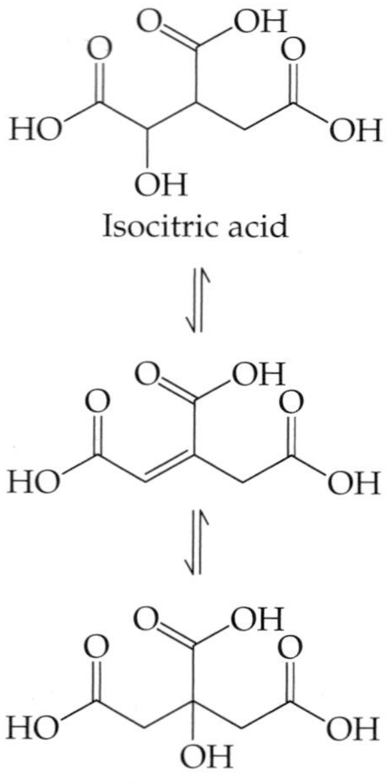

Isocitric acid

Citric acid

Carbonyl group The C=O functional group.

◀ Review redox reactions in Section 5.6.

Oxidation

Primary and secondary alcohols are converted into *carbonyl*-containing compounds on treatment with an oxidizing agent. A **carbonyl group** (pronounced car-bo-*neel*) is a functional group that has a carbon atom joined to an oxygen atom by a double bond, C=O. In a laboratory, many different oxidizing agents can be used—potassium permanganate $(KMnO_4)$, potassium dichromate $(K_2Cr_2O_7)$, or even oxygen gas in some cases—and it often does not matter which specific reagent is chosen. Thus, we will simply use the symbol [O] to indicate a generalized oxidizing agent.

Recall that an *oxidation* is defined in inorganic chemistry as the loss of one or more electrons by an atom, and a *reduction* as the gain of one or more electrons. These terms have the same meaning in organic chemistry, but because of the size and complexity of organic compounds, a more general distinction is made when discussing organic molecules. An *organic oxidation* is one that increases the number of C—O bonds and/or decreases the number of C—H bonds. (Note that in determining whether or not an organic oxidation has taken place, a C=O is counted as *two* C—O bonds. Thus, whenever C—O in a molecule changes to a C=O bond, the number of C—O bonds has increased, and therefore an oxidation has taken place.) Conversely, an *organic reduction* is one that decreases the number of C—O bonds and/ or increases the number of C—H bonds.

In the oxidation of an alcohol, two hydrogen atoms are removed from the alcohol and converted into water during the reaction by the oxidizing agent [O]. One hydrogen comes from the —OH group, and the other hydrogen from the carbon atom bonded to the —OH group. In the process, a new C—O bond is formed and a C—H bond is broken:

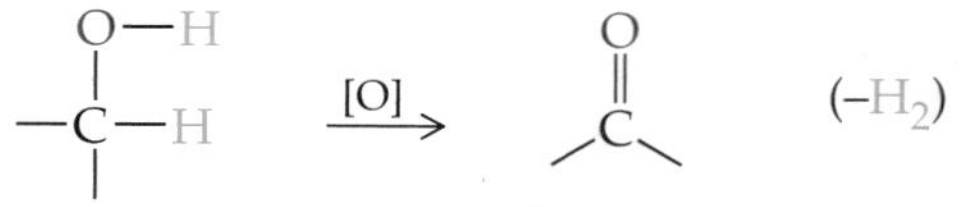

An alcohol   A carbonyl compound

Different kinds of carbonyl-containing products are formed, depending on the structure of the starting alcohol and on the reaction conditions. Primary alcohols (RCH_2OH) are converted first into *aldehydes* $(RCH=O)$ if carefully controlled conditions are used; then, if an excess of oxidant is present, aldehydes are further converted into *carboxylic acids* (pronounced car-box-*ill*-ic) (RCO_2H):

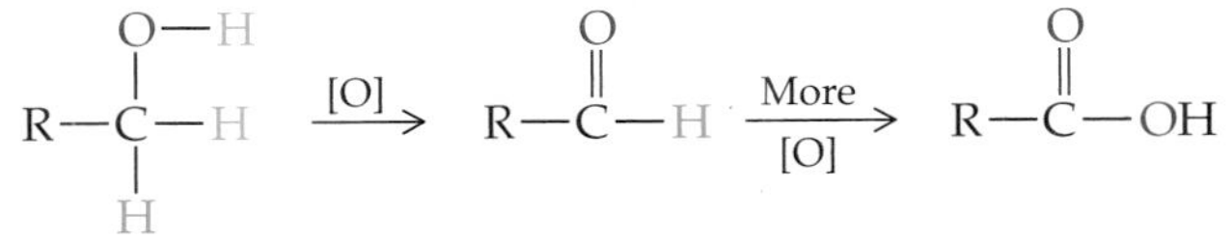

In Section 15.5, we will discuss the oxidation of aldehydes to make carboxylic acids. Carboxylic acids will be discussed in Chapter 17.

A primary alcohol   An aldehyde   A carboxylic acid

For example,

1-Butanol   Butanal   Butanoic acid

Secondary alcohols (R_2CHOH) are converted into *ketones* ($R_2C{=}O$) on treatment with oxidizing agents; further oxidation does not normally occur:

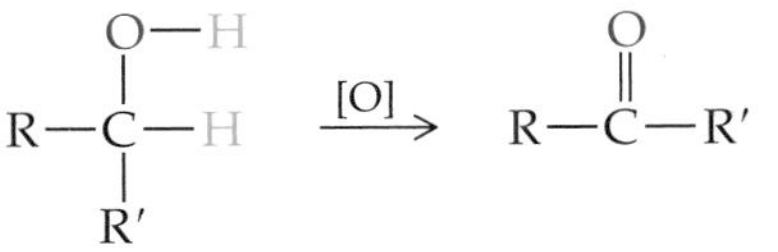

A secondary alcohol   A ketone

For example,

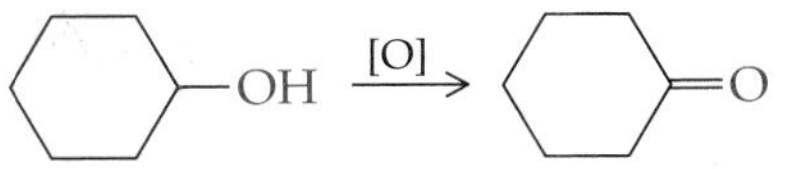

Cyclohexanol   Cyclohexanone

In Chapter 22, we will see that alcohol oxidations are critically important steps in many key biological processes. When lactic acid builds up in tired, overworked muscles, for example, the liver removes it by oxidizing it to pyruvic acid. Our bodies, of course, do not use $K_2Cr_2O_7$ or $KMnO_4$ for the oxidation; instead, they use specialized, highly selective enzymes to carry out this chemistry. Regardless of the details, though, the net chemical transformation is the same whether carried out in a laboratory flask or in a living cell.

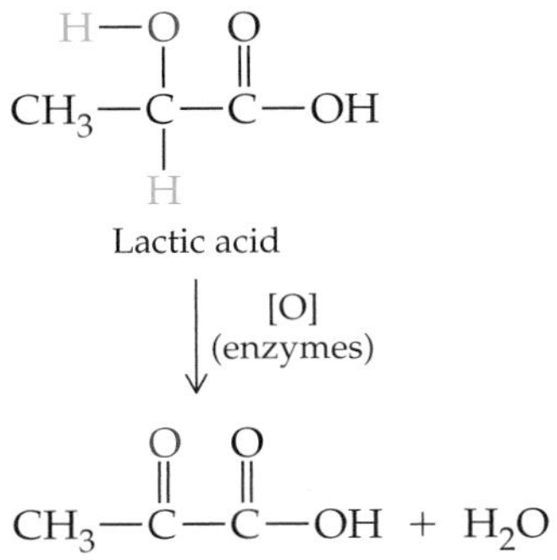

Tertiary alcohols do not normally react with oxidizing agents because they do not have a hydrogen on the carbon atom to which the —OH group is bonded:

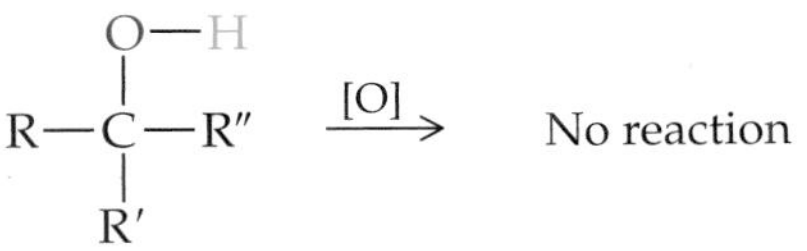

A tertiary alcohol

Lactic acid

Pyruvic acid

▶ Worked Example 14.5 Organic Reactions: Oxidation

What is the product of the following oxidation reaction?

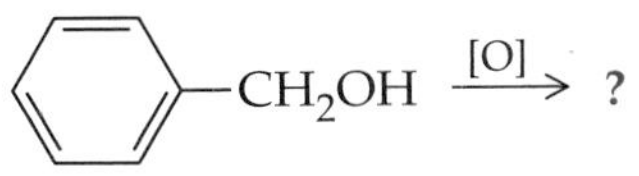

Benzyl alcohol

Recall from Table 12.2 that a commonly used abbreviation for the aromatic group is Ph. Thus benzyl alcohol could also have been written as $PhCH_2OH$.

ANALYSIS The starting material is a primary alcohol, so it will be converted first to an aldehyde and then to a carboxylic acid. To find the structures of these products, first redraw the structure of the starting alcohol to identify the hydrogen atoms on the hydroxyl-bearing carbon:

same as

Next, remove two hydrogens, one from the —OH group and one from the hydroxyl-bearing carbon. In their place, make a C=O double bond. This is the aldehyde product that forms initially. Finally, convert the aldehyde to a carboxylic acid by replacing the hydrogen in the —CH=O group with an —OH group.

—continued on next page

—continued from previous page

SOLUTION

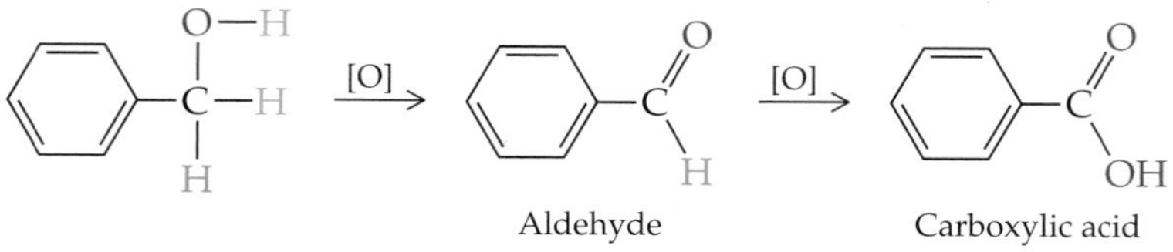

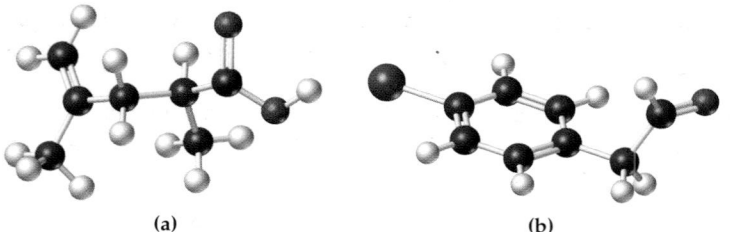

Aldehyde   Carboxylic acid

PROBLEM 14.11

What products would you expect from oxidation of the following alcohols?

(a) CH₃CH₂CH₂OH

(b) CH₃CHCH₂CH₂CH₃
with OH above the CH

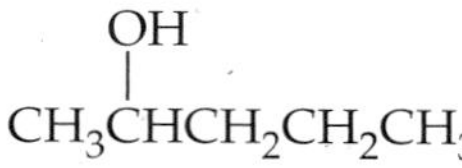

(c) cyclopentyl—CHCH₃ with OH above

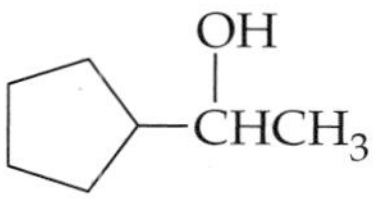

PROBLEM 14.12

From what alcohols might the following carbonyl-containing products have been made?

(a) CH₃CCH₃ (with O double bond)

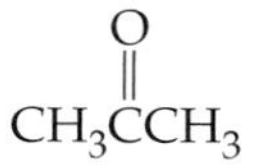

(b) cycloheptanone (=O)

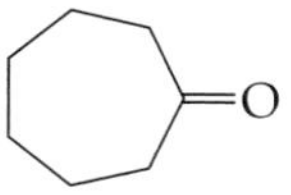

(c) CH₃CHCH₂COH (with CH₃ and O)

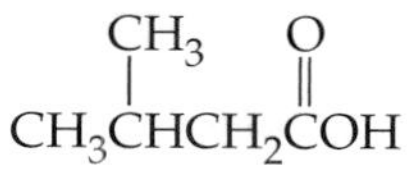

KEY CONCEPT PROBLEM 14.13

From what alcohols might the following carbonyl-containing products have been made (red = O, reddish-brown = Br)?

(a)   (b)

14.5 Phenols

Learning Objective:

• Identify a phenol.

The word *phenol* is the name for both a specific compound (hydroxybenzene, C₆H₅OH) as well as a family of compounds. Phenol itself, formerly called carbolic acid, is a medical antiseptic that was first used by Joseph Lister in 1867. Lister showed that the occurrence of postoperative infection dramatically decreased when phenol was used to cleanse the operating room and the patient's skin. Because phenol numbs the skin, it also became popular in topical drugs for pain and itching and in treating sore throats.

The medical use of phenol is now restricted because it can cause severe skin burns and has been found to be toxic, both by ingestion and by absorption through the skin. Only solutions containing less than 1.5% phenol or lozenges containing a maximum of 50 mg of phenol are now allowed in nonprescription drugs. Many mouthwashes and throat lozenges contain alkyl-substituted phenols such as thymol as active ingredients for pain relief. The presence of an alkyl group lowers the absorption of the compound through skin (among other things), rendering alkyl-substituted phenols less toxic than phenol itself.

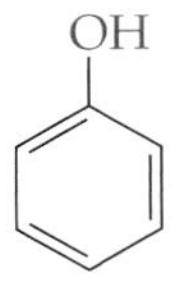

Phenol

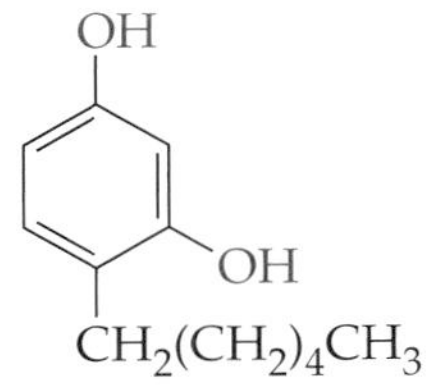

4-Hexylresorcinol
(a topical anesthetic)

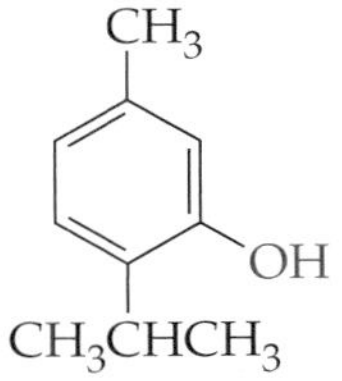

Thymol
(a topical anesthetic; occurs naturally in the herb thyme)

Some other alkyl-substituted phenols such as the cresols (methylphenols) are common as *disinfectants* in hospitals and elsewhere. In contrast to an *antiseptic*, which safely kills microorganisms on living tissue, a disinfectant should be used only on inanimate objects. The germicidal properties of phenols can be partially explained by their ability to disrupt the permeability of cell walls of microorganisms.

Phenols are usually named with the ending -*phenol* rather than -*benzene* even though the —OH group is bonded to a benzene ring. For example,

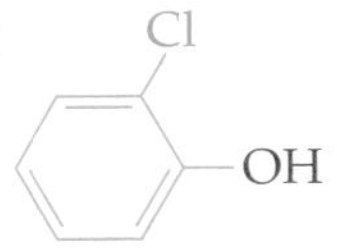

ortho-Chlorophenol
(2-Chlorophenol)

para-Methylphenol
(4-Methylphenol)

The properties of phenols, like those of alcohols, are influenced by the presence of the electronegative oxygen atom and by hydrogen bonding. Most phenols are water-soluble to some degree and have higher melting and boiling points than similarly substituted alkylbenzenes. They are generally less soluble in water than alcohols are, since the benzene ring is very hydrophobic.

Biomolecules that contain a hydroxyl-substituted benzene ring and are considered phenols include the amino acid tyrosine, as well as many other compounds.

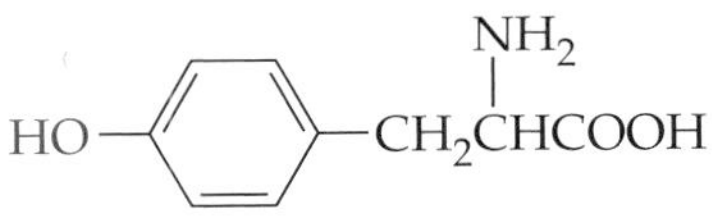

▲ Careful! The urushiol in this poison ivy plant causes severe skin rash.

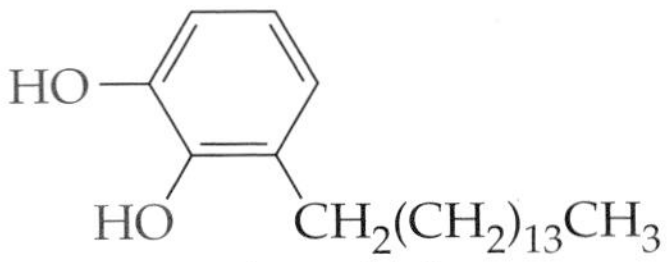

Tyrosine
(an *amino* acid)

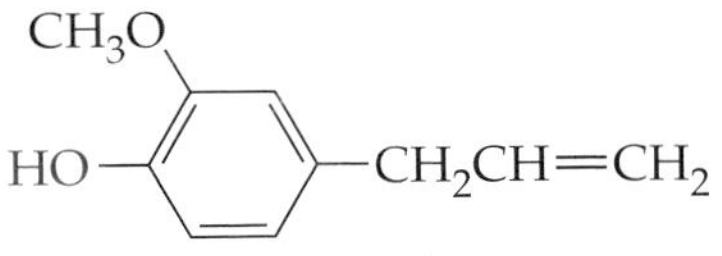

Eugenol
(in cloves, bananas, and other fruits; used for toothache pain)

A urushiol
(skin irritant in poison ivy)

PROBLEM 14.14

Draw structures for the following:
 (a) 2,4-Dinitrophenol

 (b) *m*-Ethylphenol

PROBLEM 14.15

Name the following compounds:

(a)

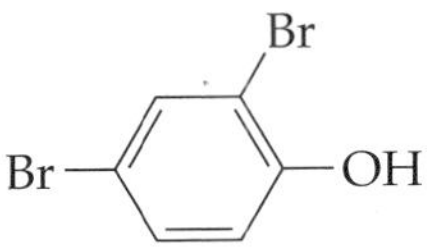

(b)

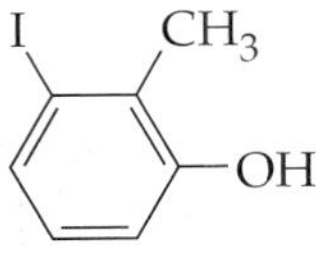

14.6 Acidity of Alcohols and Phenols

Learning Objective:

- Explain why alcohols and phenols are weak acids.

Alcohols and phenols, because of the positively polarized O—H hydrogen, dissociate slightly in aqueous solution and establish an equilibria between their neutral and anionic forms:

$$CH_3CH_2OH \xleftarrow[\text{water}]{\text{Dissolve in}} CH_3CH_2O^- + H_3O^+$$

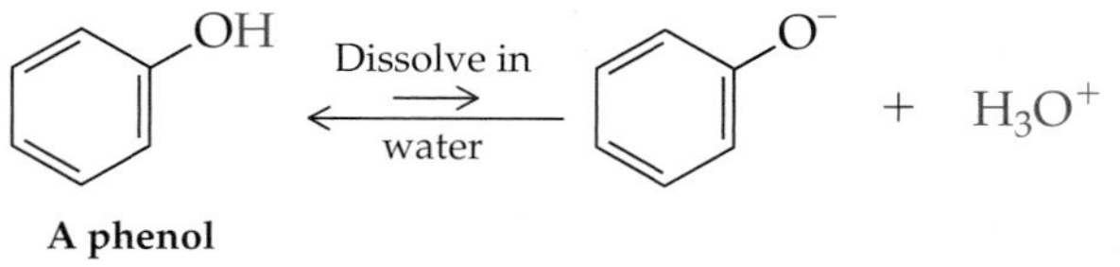

An alcohol

A phenol

Alcohols, such as methanol and ethanol, are about as acidic as water itself (Sections 10.3 and 10.4), with K_a values near 10^{-15}. By comparison, acetic acid has a K_a of 10^{-5}. In fact, both dissociate so little in water that their aqueous solutions are neutral (pH 7). Thus, an **alkoxide ion** (RO^-), or the anion of an alcohol, is as strong a base as a hydroxide ion, OH^-. An alkoxide ion is produced by reaction of an alkali metal with an alcohol, just as a hydroxide ion is produced by reaction of an alkali metal with water. For example,

Alkoxide ion The anion resulting from the removal of the H from an alcohol, RO^-.

$$2H_2O + 2Na \longrightarrow 2\,Na^+\,^-OH + H_2$$
$$\text{Water} \qquad\qquad\qquad \text{Sodium hydroxide}$$

$$2CH_3OH + 2Na \longrightarrow 2\,Na^+\,^-OCH_3 + H_2$$
$$\text{Methanol} \qquad\qquad \text{Sodium methoxide}$$

◀◀◀ Recall from Section 10.7 what K_a refers to and what its magnitude means.

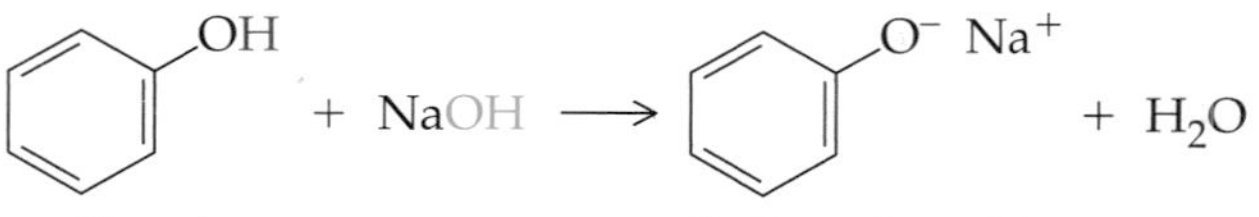

In contrast to alcohols, phenols are about 10,000 times more acidic than water. Phenol itself, for example, has $K_a = 1.0 \times 10^{-10}$. This acidic property means that phenols react with dilute aqueous sodium hydroxide to give a phenoxide ion. (Alcohols do NOT react in this way with sodium hydroxide.)

Phenol   Sodium phenoxide

14.7 Ethers

Learning Objectives:

- Identify an ether.
- Distinguish between an ether and an alcohol.

Simple ethers—compounds with two organic groups bonded to the same oxygen atom $(R-O-R')$—are named by identifying the two organic groups and adding the word *ether*. (The compound frequently referred to simply as "ether" is actually diethyl ether.)

$$CH_3-O-CH_3 \qquad CH_3-O-CH_2CH_3 \qquad CH_3CH_2-O-CH_2CH_3$$

Dimethyl ether   Ethyl methyl ether   Diethyl ether
(bp = −24.5 °C)   (bp = −10.8 °C)   (bp = 34.5 °C)

Compounds that contain the oxygen atom in a ring are classified as cyclic ethers and are often referred to by their common names. You have already seen the presence of a three-membered, oxygen-containing ring (an epoxide) in the structure of the dynemicins (see the Chemistry in Action "Enediyne Antibiotics: A Newly Emerging Class of Antitumor Agents," Chapter 13, p. 432).

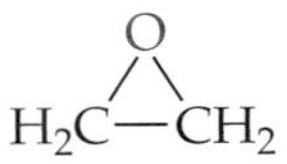

Ethylene oxide
(an epoxide)

Tetrahydrofuran
(a solvent)

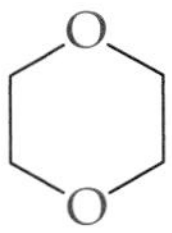

1,4-Dioxane
(a solvent)

An —OR group is referred to as an **alkoxy group;** —OCH$_3$ is a *methoxy* group, —OCH$_2$CH$_3$ is an *ethoxy* group, and so on. These names are used when the ether functional group is present in a compound that also has other functional groups. For example,

Alkoxy group An —OR group.

CH$_3$CH$_2$OCH$_2$CH$_2$OH

2-Ethoxyethanol
(Cellusolve™)

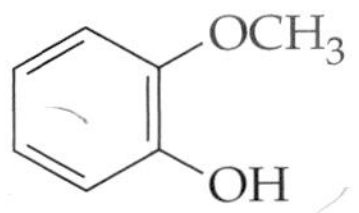

o-Methoxyphenol

CH$_3$OCH$_2$CH$_2$OCH$_3$

Dimethoxyethane
(glyme)

Although they contain polar C—O bonds, ethers lack the —OH group of water and alcohols, and thus do not form hydrogen bonds to one another. Simple ethers therefore boil at higher temperatures than alkanes but lower than alcohols of similar molecular weight. The oxygen atom in ethers can hydrogen bond with water, causing dimethyl ether to be water-soluble and diethyl ether to be partially miscible with water. As with alcohols, ethers with larger organic groups are often insoluble in water. Ethers make very good solvents for organic reactions where a polar solvent is needed but no —OH groups can be present.

Ethers are alkane-like in many of their properties and do not react with most acids, bases, or other reagents. Ethers do, however, react readily with oxygen, and the simple ethers are highly flammable. On standing in air, many ethers form explosive *peroxides,* compounds that contain an O—O bond. Thus, ethers must be handled with care and stored in the absence of oxygen.

Diethyl ether, the best-known ether, is used primarily as a solvent but was for many years a popular anesthetic. Its value as an inhalation anesthetic was discovered in the 1840s, and it was a mainstay of the operating room until the 1940s. Although it acts quickly and is very effective, ether is far from ideal as an anesthetic because it has a long recovery time and it often induces nausea. Moreover, its effectiveness is strongly offset by its hazards. Diethyl ether is a highly volatile, flammable liquid whose vapor forms explosive mixtures with air.

Diethyl ether has been replaced by safer, less flammable anesthetics such as enflurane and isoflurane (see the Chemistry in Action "Inhaled Anesthetics" on p. 458). Both compounds were products of an intensive effort during the 1960s search for improved anesthetics, during which more than 400 halogenated ethers were synthesized.

Ethers are found throughout the plant and animal kingdoms. Some are present in plant oils and are used in perfumes; others have a variety of biological roles. Juvenile hormone, for example, is a cyclic ether that helps govern the growth of the silkworm moth. The three-membered ether ring (an *epoxide* ring) in the juvenile hormone is unusually reactive because of strained 60° bond angles.

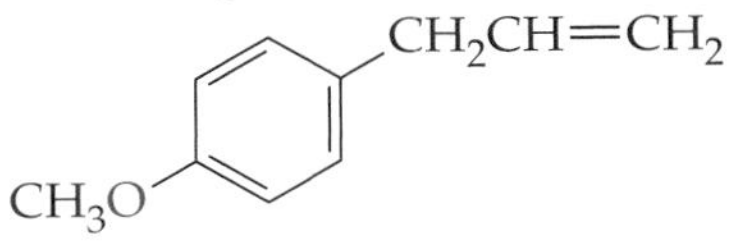

▲ The maturation of this silkworm moth is controlled by a hormone that contains a three-membered ether ring.

Anethole—a flavoring agent
found in anise and fennel

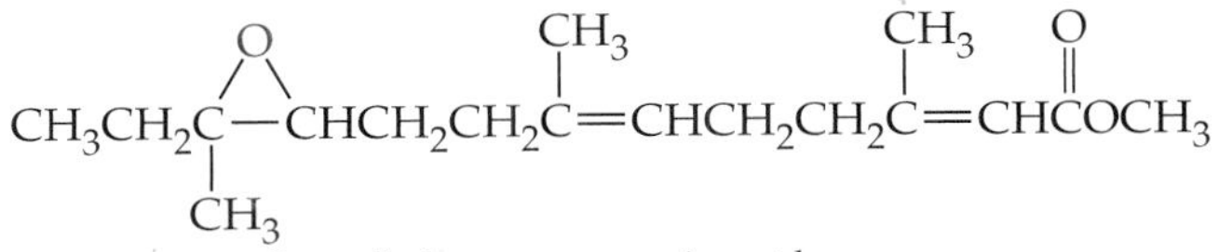

Juvenile hormone—an insect hormone
found in the silkworm moth

CHEMISTRY IN ACTION

☤ Inhaled Anesthetics

William Morton's demonstration in 1846 of ether-induced anesthesia during dental surgery represents one of the most important medical breakthroughs of all time. Before that date, all surgery had been carried out with the patient fully conscious. Use of chloroform ($CHCl_3$) as an anesthetic quickly followed Morton's work, popularized by Queen Victoria of England, who in 1853 gave birth to a child while anesthetized by chloroform.

Hundreds of substances have subsequently been shown to act as inhaled anesthetics. Halothane, enflurane, isoflurane, and methoxyflurane are at present the most commonly used agents in hospital operating rooms. All four are potent at relatively low doses, are nontoxic, and are nonflammable, an important safety feature.

Despite their importance, surprisingly little is known about how inhaled anesthetics work in the body. Remarkably, the potency of different inhaled anesthetics correlates well with their solubility in olive oil, leading many scientists to believe that anesthetics act by dissolving in the fatty membranes surrounding nerve cells. The resultant changes in the fluidity and shape of the membranes apparently decrease the ability of sodium ions to pass into the nerve cells, thereby blocking the firing of nerve impulses.

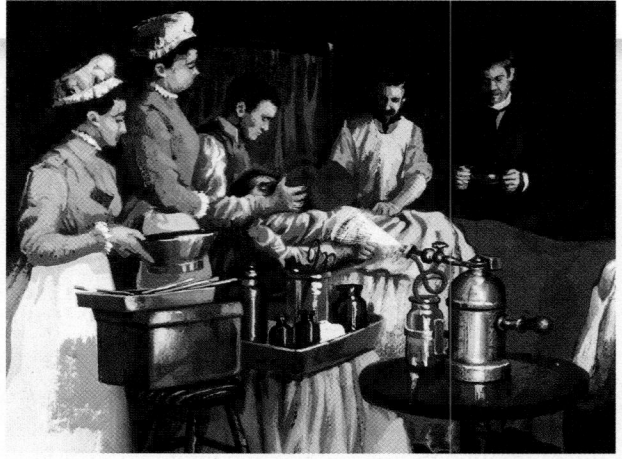

▲ William Morton performed the first public demonstration of ether as an anesthetic on October 16, 1846, at Massachusetts General Hospital.

anesthetic agent in the bloodstream and on its partial pressure in inhaled air. Anesthetic potency is usually expressed as a *minimum alveolar concentration* (MAC), defined as the concentration of anesthetic in inhaled air that results in anesthesia in 50% of patients. As shown in the following table, nitrous oxide, N_2O, is the least potent of the common anesthetics and methoxyflurane is the most potent; a partial pressure of only 1.2 mmHg is sufficient to anesthetize 50% of patients.

Halothane

Enflurane

Isoflurane

Methoxyflurane

Depth of anesthesia is determined by the concentration of anesthetic agent that reaches the brain. Brain concentration, in turn, depends on the solubility and transport of the

Relative Potency of Inhaled Anesthetics

Anesthetic	MAC (%)	MAC (partial pressure, mmHg)
Nitrous oxide	.	>760
Enflurane	1.7	13
Isoflurane	1.4	11
Halothane	0.75	5.7
Methoxyflurane	0.16	1.2

CIA Problem 14.1 What substance was used as the first general anesthetic?

CIA Problem 14.2 The solubility of inhaled anesthetics in what substance correlates to their potency?

CIA Problem 14.3 How is "minimum alveolar concentration" for an anesthetic defined?

Worked Example 14.6 Molecular Structures: Drawing Ethers and Alcohols

Draw the structure for 3-methoxy-2-butanol.

ANALYSIS First, identify the parent compound and then add numbered substituents to appropriate carbons in the parent chain.

SOLUTION

The parent compound is a 4-carbon chain with the —OH attached to C2.

2-Butanol

The 3-methoxy substituent indicates that a methoxy group ($-OCH_3$) is attached to C3.

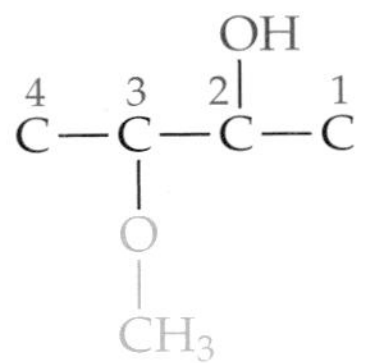

$$\overset{OH}{\underset{\underset{CH_3}{\overset{|}{O}}}{\overset{|}{\underset{2}{C}}}}\ \overset{4}{C}-\overset{3}{C}-\overset{2}{C}-\overset{1}{C}\quad \text{3-Methoxy}$$

Finally, add hydrogens until each carbon atom has a total of four bonds.

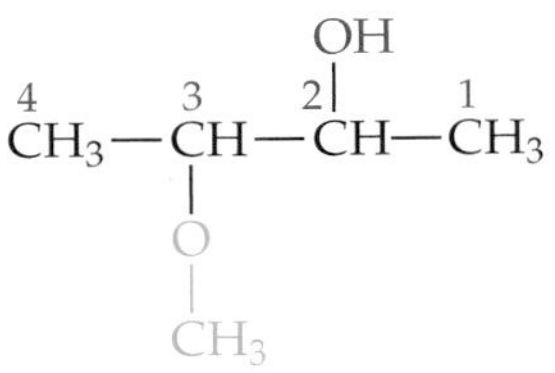

$$\overset{OH}{\underset{\underset{CH_3}{\overset{|}{O}}}{\overset{|}{\underset{2}{C}}}}\ \overset{4}{CH_3}-\overset{3}{CH}-\overset{2}{CH}-\overset{1}{CH_3}\quad \text{3-Methoxy-2-butanol}$$

PROBLEM 14.16

Name the following compounds:

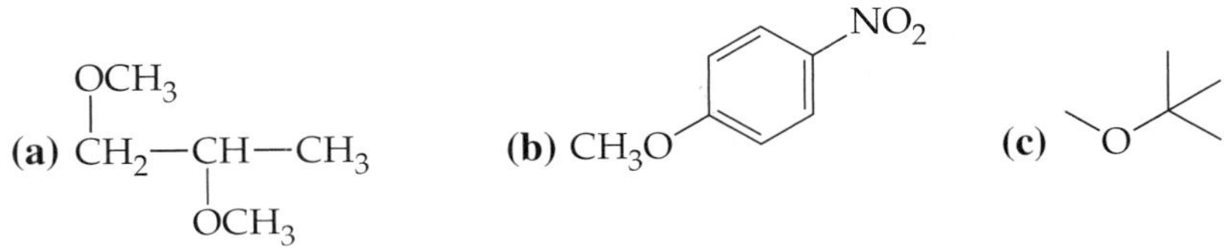

(a) $\overset{OCH_3}{\underset{\underset{OCH_3}{|}}{\overset{|}{CH_2}}}-CH-CH_3$

(b) CH_3O—〈benzene ring〉—NO_2

(c) 〈structure: O attached to tert-butyl group〉

14.8 Thiols and Disulfides

Learning Objectives:

• Identify a thiol.
• Explain how a thiol is converted into a disulfide and vice versa.

Sulfur is just below oxygen in group 6A of the periodic table, and many oxygen-containing compounds have sulfur analogs. For example, **thiols** ($R-SH$), also called *thioalcohols* or *mercaptans,* are sulfur analogs of alcohols (an analog is a molecule that has a structure very similar to that of another one in all but one or two key aspects). The IUPAC name of a thiol is formed by adding *-thiol* to the parent hydrocarbon name. Otherwise, thiols are named in the same way as alcohols.

Thiol A compound that contains an $-SH$ group, $R-SH$.

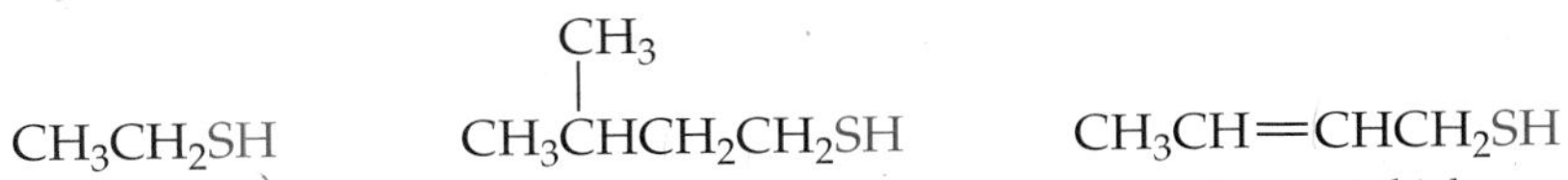

$$CH_3CH_2SH$$
Ethanethiol

$$\overset{CH_3}{\underset{}{\overset{|}{CH_3}CHCH_2CH_2SH}}$$
3-Methyl-1-butanethiol

$$CH_3CH=CHCH_2SH$$
2-Butene-1-thiol

   The most outstanding characteristic of thiols is their terrible odor. The scent of a skunk's spray is caused by two of the simple thiols shown above, 3-methyl-1-butanethiol and 2-butene-1-thiol. Thiols are also responsible for the scent of garlic and onions, or when there is a natural gas leak. Natural gas itself is odorless, but a low concentration of methanethiol (CH_3SH) is added as a safety measure to make leak detection easy.

   Thiols react with mild oxidizing agents, such as Br_2 in water or even O_2, to yield **disulfides,** $RS-SR$. Two thiols join together in this reaction, the hydrogen from each is lost, and a bond forms between the two sulfurs:

Disulfide A compound that contains a sulfur–sulfur bond, $RS-SR$.

$$RSH + HSR \xrightarrow{\text{[O]}} RSSR$$
Two thiol molecules   A disulfide

▲ Skunks repel predators by releasing several thiols with appalling odors.

For example,

$$H_3C-S-H + H-S-CH_3 \xrightarrow{[O]} CH_3-S-S-CH_3 + H_2O$$

Methanethiol   Dimethyl disulfide

The reverse reaction occurs when a disulfide is treated with a reducing agent, represented by [H]:

$$RSSR \xrightarrow{[H]} RSH + RSH$$

Thiols are important biologically because they occur as a functional group in the amino acid cysteine, which is part of many proteins:

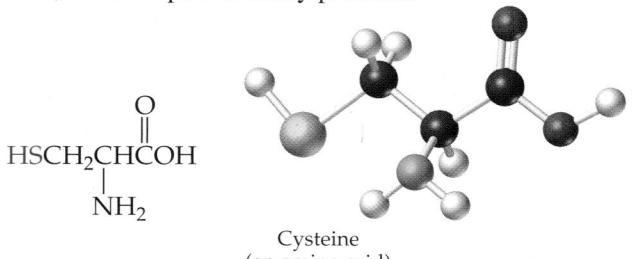

$$HSCH_2\overset{\displaystyle O}{\overset{\displaystyle \|}{C}}HCOH$$
$$\underset{NH_2}{|}$$

Cysteine
(an amino acid)

The easy formation of S — S bonds between two cysteines helps pull large protein molecules into the shapes they need to function. The proteins in hair, for example, are unusually rich in — S — S — and — SH groups. When hair is "permed," some disulfide bonds are broken and others are then formed. As a result, the hair proteins are held in a different shape (Figure 14.2). The hair straightening procedure known as "rebonding" works in a similar way. The importance of the disulfide linkage will be discussed further in Section 18.8.

▶ Figure 14.2
Chemistry can curl your hair. A permanent wave results when disulfide bridges are formed between — SH groups in hair protein molecules.

PROBLEM 14.17

What disulfides would you obtain from oxidation of the following thiols?

(a) $CH_3CH_2CH_2SH$ (b) 3-Methyl-1-butanethiol (skunk scent)

14.9 Halogen-Containing Compounds

Learning Objective:

• Identify an alkyl or aryl halide.

Alkyl halide A compound that has an alkyl group bonded to a halogen atom, R—X.

Aryl halide A compound that has an aromatic group bonded to a halogen atom, Ar—X.

The simplest halogen-containing compounds are the **alkyl halides,** RX, where R is an alkyl group and X is a halogen and the **aryl halides,** ArX, where Ar represents an aromatic ring. Many alkyl halides have common names that consist of the name of the alkyl group followed by the halogen name with an -ide ending. The compound CH_3Br, for example, is commonly called *methyl bromide.*

In Section 12.6, we discussed the naming of alkanes. The systematic names (IUPAC) of alkyl halides treat the halogen atom as a substituent on a parent alkane in the same way that alkyl groups are treated. The parent alkane is named in the usual way by selecting the longest continuous chain and numbering from the end nearer the first substituent, either alkyl or halogen. The *halo-* substituent name is then given as a prefix, just as if it were an alkyl group. A few common halogenated compounds are also known by nonsystematic names, such as chloroform ($CHCl_3$). The naming of aryl halides was discussed in Section 13.9.

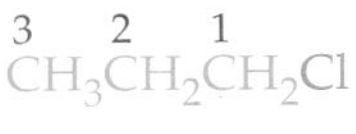

$$
\underset{\substack{3 \quad 2 \quad 1}}{CH_3CH_2CH_2Cl} \qquad \underset{\substack{6 \quad 5 \quad 4 \quad 3 \quad 2 \quad 1}}{CH_3CHCH_2CH_2CHCH_3} \qquad CHCl_3
$$

1-Chloropropane 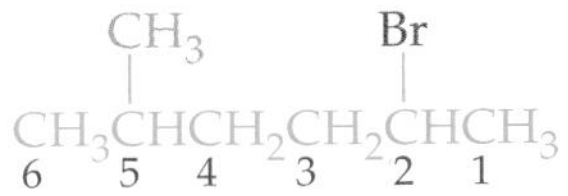   2-Bromo-5-methylhexane   Trichloromethane
(Chloroform)

Halogenated organic compounds have a variety of medical and industrial uses. Ethyl chloride is used as a topical anesthetic because it cools the skin through rapid evaporation; halothane is an important anesthetic. Chloroform was once employed as an anesthetic and as a solvent for cough syrups and other medicines but is now considered too toxic for such uses. Bromotrifluoromethane, CF_3Br, is useful for extinguishing fires in aircraft and electronic equipment because it is nonflammable and nontoxic, and it evaporates without a trace.

Although a large number of halogen-containing organic compounds are found in nature, especially in marine organisms, few are significant in human biochemistry. One exception is thyroxine, an iodine-containing hormone secreted by the thyroid gland. A deficiency of iodine in the human diet leads to a low thyroxine level, which causes a swelling of the thyroid gland called a *goiter*. To ensure adequate iodine in the diet of people who live far from an ocean, potassium iodide is sometimes added to table salt (to create the product we know as *iodized salt*).

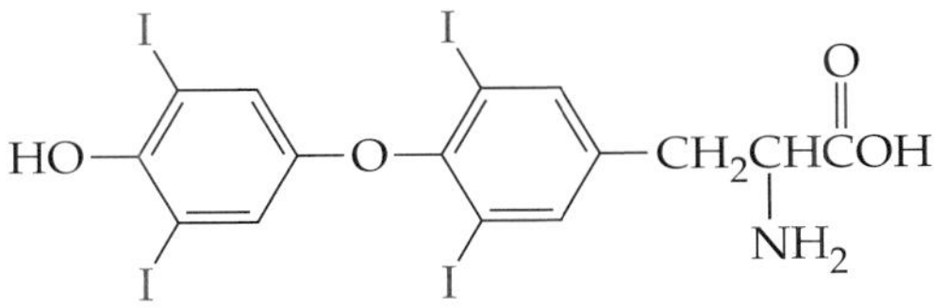

Thyroid gland hormone; deficiency causes goiter

Thyroxine

Halogenated compounds are also used widely in industry and agriculture. Dichloromethane (CH_2Cl_2, methylene chloride), trichloromethane ($CHCl_3$, chloroform), and trichloroethylene ($Cl_2C{=}CHCl$) are used as solvents and degreasing agents, although their use is diminishing as less-polluting alternatives become available. Because these substances are excellent solvents for the oils in skin, continued exposure often causes dermatitis.

The use of halogenated herbicides such as 2,4-D and fungicides such as Captan has resulted in vastly increased crop yields in recent decades, and the widespread application of chlorinated insecticides such as dichlorodiphenyltrichloroethane (DDT) is largely responsible for the progress made toward worldwide control of malaria and typhus. Despite their enormous benefits, however, chlorinated pesticides present problems because they persist in the environment and are not broken down rapidly. They remain in the fatty tissues of organisms and accumulate up the food chain as larger organisms consume smaller ones. Eventually, the concentration in some animals becomes high enough to cause harm. In an effort to maintain a balance between the value of halogenated pesticides and the harm they can do, the use of many has been restricted, and others have been banned altogether.

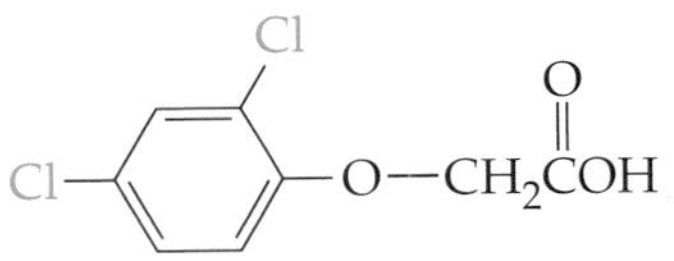

2,4-D 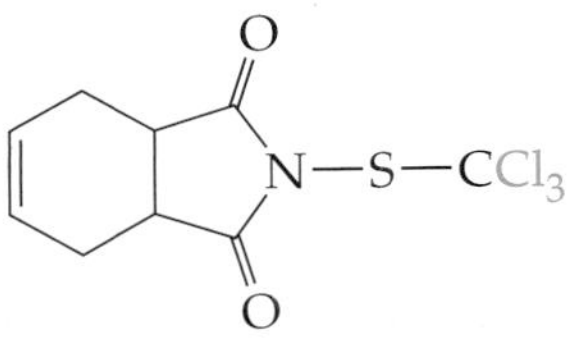   Captan 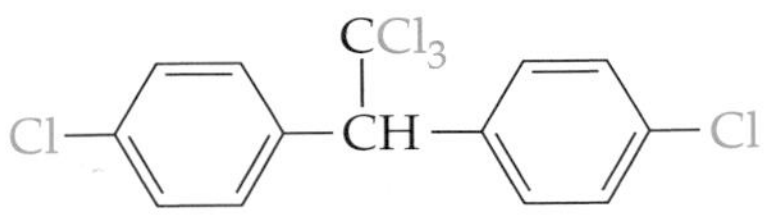   DDT

PROBLEM 14.18

Give systematic names for the following alkyl halides:

(a)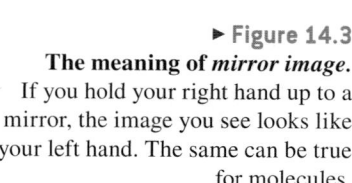

(b) $CH_3CH_2CHCH_2CHCH_2CH_3$ with substituents CH_3 and Br

14.10 Stereochemistry and Chirality

Learning Objective:

• Identify a chiral carbon.

In Chapters 12 and 13, you saw wedges and dashes used in drawing certain molecules, where the solid wedge indicated a bond coming out of the plane of the paper toward you and the dashed wedge indicated a bond going out of the paper away from you. This concept was first introduced in Chapter 8 when the idea of three-dimensional structure was first discussed. **Stereochemistry** is the study of molecules that have the same overall connectivity of atoms but differ in how those atoms are arraigned in three-dimensional space. In Section 12.5, we discussed the concept of conformational isomers, while in Section 13.3, we learned about cis–trans isomers; in both cases the compounds differed only in how the atoms were orientated in space. Isomers that have the same formula and whose atoms have the same connections but different spatial arrangements are known as **stereoisomers.**

Conformational isomers of a molecule can be interconverted by simple rotations around carbon–carbon single bonds; but what if two isomers *cannot,* such as cis–trans isomers? We say that these stereoisomers have different **configurations.** Let us examine why this is important in organic and biological chemistry.

Do you write with your left or your right hand? If you are right handed, have you ever tried to write with your left hand? Your "handedness" affects almost everything you do, from writing, to hitting a golf ball, to using a fork. Just like you, molecules can also possess handedness, and it can dramatically affect their biochemical activity. To get a feel for this idea, hold your right hand up to a mirror. The image you see looks like your left hand as shown in Figure 14.3. This happens because your hands are not identical. Rather, they are mirror images.

Stereochemistry The study of the relative three-dimensional spatial arrangement of the atoms in a molecule.

Stereoisomers Isomers that have the same molecular and structural formulas but different spatial arrangements of their atoms.

Configurations Stereoisomers that *cannot* be converted into one another by rotation around a single bond.

▶ **Figure 14.3**
The meaning of *mirror image*.
If you hold your right hand up to a mirror, the image you see looks like your left hand. The same can be true for molecules.

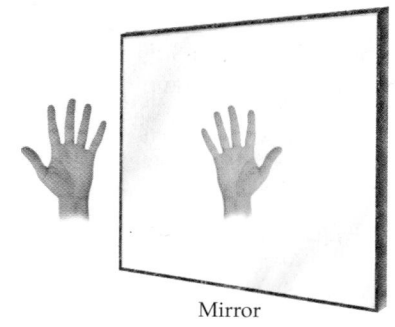
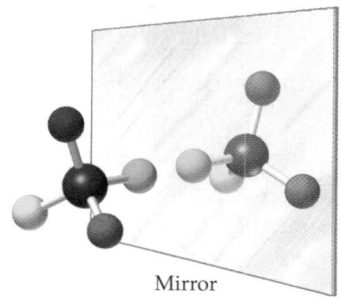

Mirror

Mirror

Additionally, note that the mirror images of your hand cannot be superimposed on each other; one does not completely fit on top of the other. Objects that have handedness in this manner are said to be **chiral** (pronounced *ky*-ral, from the Greek *cheir,* meaning "hand").

Not all objects are chiral. Consider both the chair and its mirror image as well as the molecule and its mirror image shown in Figure 14.4. When a chair is reflected in a mirror, its image is identical to chair itself. Objects that lack handedness are said to be nonchiral, or **achiral.** The molecule in this figure is also achiral. Convince yourself of this by studying the chair and the molecule in Figure 14.4. Each of these has mirror images that are superimposable because they possess a plane of symmetry. Any item that,

Chiral Having right- or left-handedness with two *different* mirror-image forms.

Achiral The opposite of chiral, having superimposable mirror images and thus no right- or left-handedness.

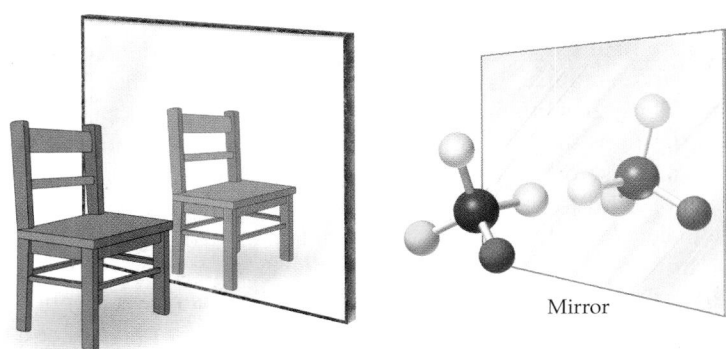

◄ **Figure 14.4**
The meaning of *superimposable*.
It is easy to visualize the chair on top of its mirror image. The molecular model shown is also superimposable but not as easy to visualize.

Mirror

when bisected with an imaginary mirror plane, has two halves that are mirror images of one another will be achiral. All that is required for a molecule to be achiral is one plane of symmetry. Figure 14.5 illustrates this concept.

A plane of symmetry
(one half reflects the other)

Not a plane of symmetry
(one half does not reflect the other)

◄ **Figure 14.5**
The meaning of *plane of symmetry*.
The items from Figure 14.3 are shown here with their plane of symmetry illustrated. Note that the imaginary mirror splits both (a) the chair and (b) the molecular model into two identical pieces. Notice that the molecular model shown in (c) has no such plane of symmetry and is therefore chiral.

(a)   (b)   (c)

Can we predict whether a molecule will be chiral from structural formulas? Recall that carbon forms four bonds oriented to the four corners of an imaginary tetrahedron. The formulas for 2-butanol and butane are shown below in a manner that emphasizes the four groups bonded to the central carbon atom. In 2-butanol, this carbon is connected to *four different groups:* a —CH_3 group, an ⪰H atom, an —OH group, and a —CH_2CH_3 group:

▶▶ Don't be concerned if you struggle with the concept of chirality; you will become more comfortable with it the more you use it.

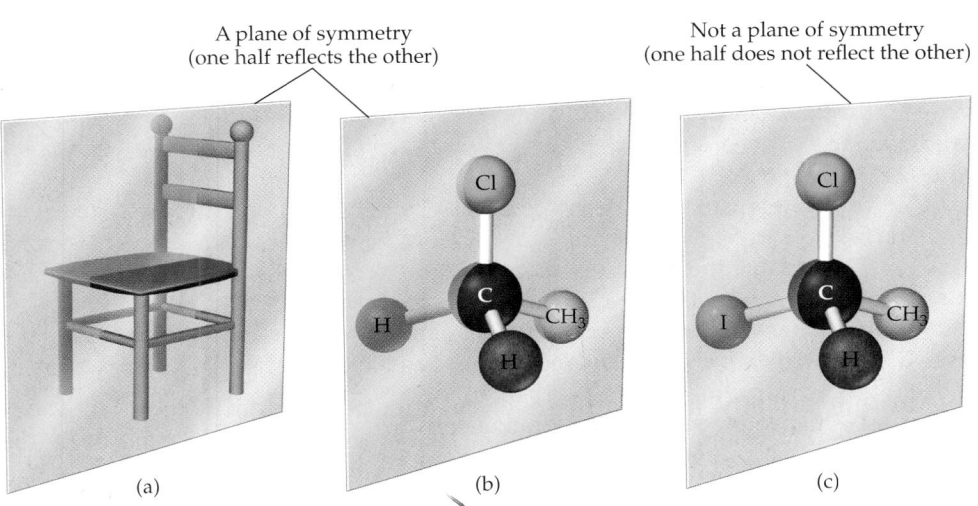

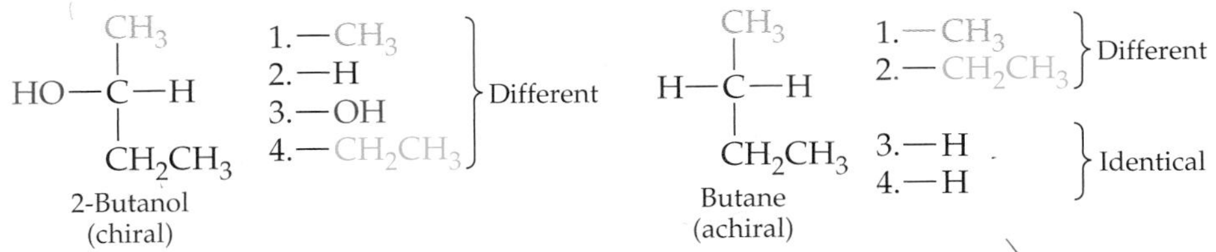

$$HO-\underset{\underset{CH_2CH_3}{|}}{\overset{\overset{CH_3}{|}}{C}}-H$$

1. —CH_3
2. —H
3. —OH
4. —CH_2CH_3
⎫ Different

2-Butanol
(chiral)

$$H-\underset{\underset{CH_2CH_3}{|}}{\overset{\overset{CH_3}{|}}{C}}-H$$

1. —CH_3
2. —CH_2CH_3
⎫ Different
3. —H
4. —H
⎫ Identical

Butane
(achiral)

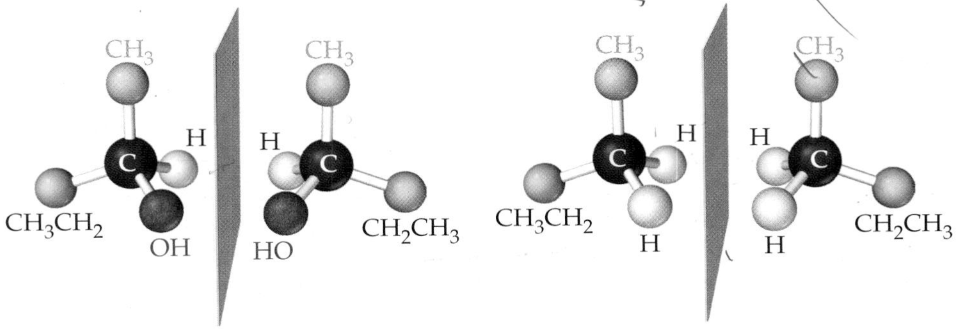

Chiral carbon atom A carbon atom bonded to four different groups. Also referred to as a chiral center or stereocenter.

➤➤ We will see the use rotation of polarized light to distinguish enantiomers used again in Section 20.2.

Enantiomers (optical isomers) The two mirror-image forms of a chiral molecule.

A carbon atom that is BOTH tetrahedral AND has four different groups attached is referred to as a **chiral carbon atom,** or a chiral center (or stereocenter). The presence of one chiral carbon atom always produces a chiral molecule that exists in two mirror-image forms. Thus, 2-butanol is chiral. In butane, the central carbon atom shown is bonded to two groups that are different (the —CH_3 and the —CH_2CH_3 groups) and one pair of identical groups, the two hydrogen atoms. Possessing no chiral center, butane is therefore achiral. Molecules can have more than one chiral carbon atom, but whether the molecule itself is chiral will depend on overall shape.

The two mirror-image forms of a chiral molecule like 2-butanol are called either **enantiomers** (pronounced en-*an*-ti-o-mers) or **optical isomers** ("optical" because of their effect on polarized light). The chemical and physical properties of a given pair of enantiomers (such as 2-butanol and its mirror image) are usually identical in all aspects *except* for how they are affected by polarized light. Both enantiomers of 2-butanol, for example, have the same boiling point, the same solubility in water, the same isoelectric point, and the same density; yet when polarized light is transmitted through a solution containing one enantiomer, it rotates that light to the right (and is called the *d* or (+) enantiomer) while a solution containing the other enantiomer rotates light to the left (and is called the *l* or (−) enantiomer). Enantiomers often differ in their biological activity, odors, and tastes. For example, the very different natural flavors of spearmint and caraway seeds are attributed to these two enantiomers.

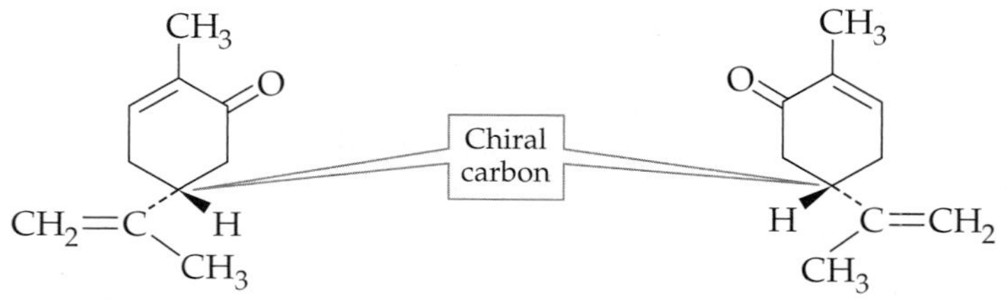

l–carvone
(in spearmint)

d–carvone
(in caraway)

➤➤ In Chapter 18, you will be introduced to the α-amino acids, all except one of which are chiral. Chirality is also an important property of another major class of biomolecules, the carbohydrates (Chapter 20).

Most importantly, however, pairs of enantiomers often differ in their activity as drugs. For example, *l*-ethambutol is used to treat tuberculosis and is on the World Health Organization's List of Essential Medicines; however, its enantiomer, *d*-ethambutol, causes blindness:

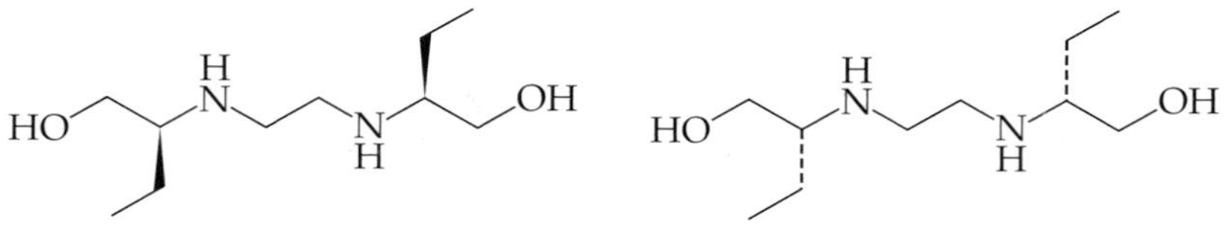

l–Ethambutol
(used to treat tuberculosis)

d–Ethambutol
(causes blindness)

HANDS-ON CHEMISTRY 14.1

Being able to grasp the idea of superimposable molecules, plane of symmetry, and chirality is important when you study biochemistry, where the three-dimensional shape of the molecules is crucial to its biological activity. In this exercise, you are going to look at molecules that have zero, one, or two chiral centers and see if you can get a grasp on the concept of chirality. To accomplish all of this, you are going to use models, *but you do not need a model kit to carry out this exercise.* If you have a model kit, follow the instructions included with it to make the "building blocks" described here. If you do not have access to a model kit, follow the instructions to

make "gumdrop building blocks." You will need a box of toothpicks and a bag of multicolored gumdrops (preferred), gummy bears, or mini-marshmallows; it does not matter as long as you can insert a toothpick in it and it will stay in place. Throughout this exercise, remember that (1) carbon is tetravalent (forms four bonds), (2) hydrogen and halogen (Cl, Br, and I) are monovalent (forms one bond), (3) you will want to be sure that your units have real angles and represent tetrahedrons as closely as possible, and (4) once you build a model you can rotate around single bonds but you CANNOT remove any atoms and swap them when making comparisons.

Building Blocks—for this exercise, you will need the following (use the color coding of atoms listed in Table 4.2 as your guide if possible):

Eight tetrahedral carbon units—make these by placing four toothpicks into a gumdrop in a tetrahedral array. Use gumdrops of whatever color you have assigned to being carbon (black or some other dark color). Note: There will be times you will have to remove toothpicks to make connections to other units; when you do, make the new connection in the same location as the toothpick you removed.

Six to eight "one group" unit pairs—simply stick a toothpick into a gumdrop. Make two of each color so that you have 12–16 total. The gumdrops should all be the same color.

Once you have these assembled, you can begin. Be prepared to use more toothpicks and/or gumdrops as necessary. If possible, you may want to take pictures of each model you make for review later.

a. Start by assembling CH_2BrCl. Use different colors for each atom. Now, put your model in front of a mirror (or use a small piece of reflective material, like aluminum foil) and build the mirror image of what you just built. Can you superimpose them on top of one another? For this to be true, you must be able to do the following:

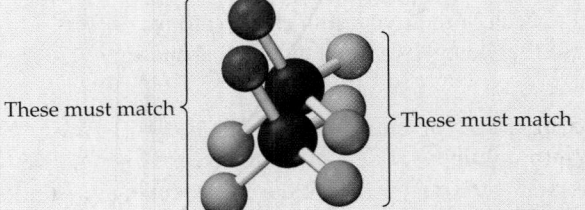

These must match ⟩ ⟨ These must match

If they do superimpose, can you find a plane of symmetry in your model?

b. Repeat part a by making CHIBrCl. Can you superimpose them on top of one another? Can you find a plane of symmetry?

c. Now build the following molecules, using your tetrahedral units:

$$\begin{array}{c} CH_3 \\ H \blacktriangleright C \blacktriangleleft Br \\ H \blacktriangleright C \blacktriangleleft Br \\ CH_3 \end{array} \text{ + Its mirror image}$$

Set 1

$$\begin{array}{c} CH_3 \\ H \blacktriangleright C \blacktriangleleft Br \\ Br \blacktriangleright C \blacktriangleleft H \\ CH_3 \end{array} \text{ + Its mirror image}$$

Set 2

(Rather than building a CH_3, simply use a different colored ball or gumdrop to represent the entire methyl group, but use the same color for all the CH_3's in both molecules). Start by looking at Set 1. How many chiral centers does each model have? Can you superimpose one on top of the other? Try doing rotations around the C—C bond. Is there a plane of symmetry in the molecule? Repeat this for Set 2. What you should find is that the models you made for Set 1 are superimposable, whereas those for Set 2 are not.

d. (Optional) Take the first molecule of Set 1 and compare it to the first molecule of Set 2. Are they mirror images of one another? Try to superimpose these on top of one another, doing rotations around the central C—C bond if necessary. You should find that these two are neither mirror images of one another, nor are they superimposable. These are examples of *diastereomers*: Stereoisomers that have the same gross connections of atoms but differ in their spatial orientation and are NOT related to one another as mirror images. The simplest example of diastereomers is cis–trans isomers (Chapter 13). For a molecule containing only tetrahedral carbons to exist as diastereomers, it must have two or more chiral centers; this is one of the things that can happen when a molecule has more than one chiral center. You will come across this again when you study carbohydrates (Chapter 20).

Worked Example 14.7 Determining Whether a Carbon Is Chiral

(a) Glyceraldehyde-3-phosphate is a key intermediate in the metabolism of glucose (both glycolysis and gluconeogenesis). Determine which (if any) of the carbons in this molecule are chiral (The carbons have been numbered for clarity).

$$\underset{HO}{\overset{O}{\underset{OH}{\overset{\|}{P}}}}-O-\underset{3}{CH_2}-\underset{2}{\overset{OH}{\underset{|}{CH}}}-\underset{1}{\overset{O}{\overset{\|}{C}}}-H$$

ANALYSIS Identify the tetrahedral carbons in the molecule; a carbon will be chiral if it is tetrahedral AND is bonded to four different groups.

SOLUTION
We can ignore C1, as it is not tetrahedral (carbons that are part of a double bond are trigonal planar). List the groups attached to each of the remaining carbon atoms.

Groups on Carbon 2	Groups on Carbon 3
1. —CHO	1. —CH(OH)CHO
2. —OH	2. —H
3. —H	3. —H
4. —$CH_2OPO_3H_2$	4. —$CH_2OPO_3H_2$

—*continued on next page*

—continued from previous page

Looking at the lists we see that only carbon 2 has four different groups attached. Therefore, only C2 is chiral.

(b) 2-Deoxyribose is a carbohydrate that makes up the backbone of the biomolecule ribonucleic acid (RNA). Determine which (if any) of the carbons in this molecule are chiral (The carbons have been numbered for clarity).

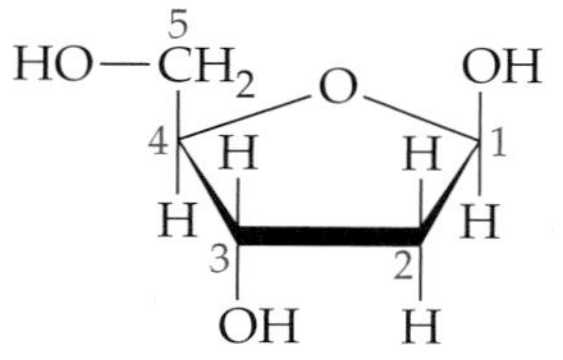

ANALYSIS As in part (a), begin by identifying the tetrahedral carbons in the molecule and then list what is attached; use R, R′, and R″ to represent different carbon chains when the groups are complex and not as easy to list.

SOLUTION

When dealing with molecules in line structure format, it is sometimes easier to actually put the carbons in to avoid confusion:

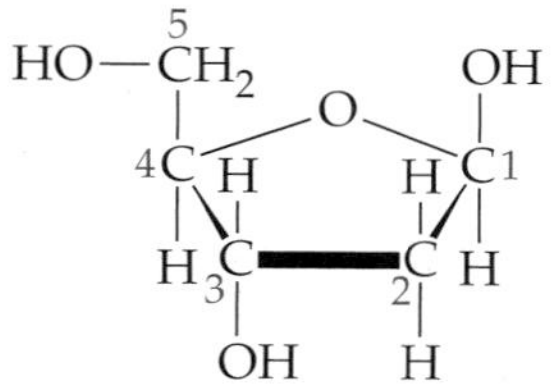

All carbons in this molecule are tetrahedral. List the groups attached to each of the remaining carbon atoms; indicate *different* complex carbon chains beyond the carbon adjacent to that being examined by using R and R′. Analyze each of the carbons one at a time to determine chirality:

Groups on C1	Groups on C2	Groups on C3	Groups on C4	Groups on C5
1. —OR	1. —CH(OH)R	1. —CH₂R′	1. —CH(OH)R	1. —OH
2. —OH	2. —H	2. —OH	2. —CH₂OH	2. —H
3. —H	3. —H	3. —H	3. —H	3. —H
4. —CH₂R′	4. —CH(OH)R′	4. —CH(CH₂OH)OR	4. —OR′	4. —CH(R)(R′)

Comparing the groups on each carbon, we see that C2 and C5 are both achiral; note that both have only three different groups attached (also note that on C2 the —CH(OH)R and —CH(OH)R′ are different, noted by the use of R and R′). The other carbons have four different groups attached. Therefore, C1, C3, and C4 are chiral.

PROBLEM 14.19

2-Aminopropane is an achiral molecule, but 2-aminobutane is chiral. Explain.

PROBLEM 14.20

Which of the following molecules are chiral? (Hint: Draw each molecule and analyze it as illustrated in Worked Example 14.2.)

(a) 3-Chloropentane

(b) 2-Chloropentane

(c) CH₃CHCH₂CHCH₂CH₃
      | |
     CH₃   CH₃

CHEMISTRY IN ACTION

✝ Fetal Alcohol Syndrome: Ethyl Alcohol as a Toxin

As we learned in the beginning of the chapter, ethyl alcohol is classified for medical purposes as a CNS depressant. The passage of ethyl alcohol through the body begins with its absorption in the stomach and small intestine, followed by rapid distribution to all body fluids and organs. Its direct effects (being "drunk") resemble the response to anesthetics, with the amount in the bloodstream easily measurable and reported as blood alcohol concentration (BAC, expressed as a percentage of ethanol in the blood in units of grams of alcohol per deciliter of blood). At a BAC of 0.06–0.20%, motor coordination and pain perception are affected, accompanied by loss of balance, slurred speech, and amnesia; at a BAC of 0.20–0.40%, there may be nausea and loss of consciousness. At BAC levels above 0.50%, spontaneous respiration and cardiovascular regulation are affected, ultimately resulting in death. All of these effects point to alcohol as being a toxin, but one that in small enough amounts the human body can tolerate.

But what happens when the organism affected has almost no body mass nor the complete biochemistry to deal with alcohol in the blood? What happens when a fetus is exposed to alcohol? Alcohol crosses the placenta, rapidly reaching the fetus. Studies have demonstrated that BAC levels are the same in both the mother and the fetus, suggesting an unimpeded movement of alcohol across the placenta. Since the activity of alcohol dehydrogenase (ADH) in the fetal liver is less than 10% of that of an adult, a fetus depends on the mothers' liver to detoxify the alcohol. Even more chilling, amniotic fluid seems to act as a reservoir for alcohol, prolonging fetal exposure. Prenatal exposure to alcohol is associated with a wide variety of effects, the most severe of which is known as FAS. A syndrome is a specific set of medical indications and symptoms that are often linked to one another and to a specific disease. For FAS, the signs and symptoms are birth defects that result from a woman's use of alcohol during her pregnancy. Children with FAS may grow less quickly than other children, have facial abnormalities, and can have CNS problems that can include delayed development of motor skills such as rolling over, sitting up, crawling and walking, hyperactivity, attention-deficit disorder, conduct disorder, and, at the severe end of the spectrum, mental retardation.

The mechanism for the adverse effects of alcohol on virtually all organ systems of the developing fetus is unknown. Ethyl alcohol metabolism in the liver is a two-step process: oxidation of the alcohol to acetaldehyde, followed by oxidation of the aldehyde to acetic acid. These oxidations are mediated by the liver enzyme ADH. When continuously present

▲ Danger can come in pretty packages, especially for a pregnant woman.

in the bodies of chronic alcoholics, alcohol and acetaldehyde are toxic, leading to devastating physical and metabolic deterioration. Since a fetus lacks the body mass of an adult, these effects are undoubtedly magnified to perilous proportions.

$$CH_3CH_2OH \xrightarrow[\substack{\text{Alcohol} \\ \text{dehydrogenase} \\ \text{enzyme}}]{NAD^+} CH_3\overset{\displaystyle O}{\overset{\|}{C}}H \xrightarrow[\substack{\text{Aldehyde} \\ \text{dehydrogenase} \\ \text{enzyme}}]{NAD^+} CH_3\overset{\displaystyle O}{\overset{\|}{C}}OH$$

So, is alcohol consumption safe at any level for a pregnant woman? In 2015, the CDC issued the following statement: "There is no known safe amount of alcohol use during pregnancy or while trying to get pregnant. There is also no safe time during pregnancy to drink. All types of alcohol are equally harmful, including all wines and beer. When a pregnant woman drinks alcohol, so does her baby."[1] While this overall topic generates a great deal of controversy, there is one thing to say for sure, exposure of a fetus to alcohol is not recommended. There is always the possibility that some harm to a baby might result from light or moderate drinking during pregnancy. Given this possibility, even if remote, the very safest choice for an expectant mother's fetus would be to abstain. Why take the chance?

CIA Problem 14.4 Is ethanol a stimulant or a depressant?

CIA Problem 14.5 At what BAC does speech begin to be slurred? What is the approximate lethal concentration of ethyl alcohol in the blood?

CIA Problem 14.6 What is a syndrome?

CIA Problem 14.7 What are some of the CNS disorders possible in children with FAS?

[1] *From the article "Alcohol Use in Pregnancy," Centers for Disease Control and Prevention (2014 April 17). www.cdc.gov/ncbddd/fasd /alcohol-use.html*

SUMMARY REVISITING THE CHAPTER LEARNING OBJECTIVES

- **Describe the structural differences between alcohols, phenols, and ethers.** An *alcohol* has an —OH group (a *hydroxyl* group) bonded to a saturated, carbon atom; a *phenol* has an —OH group bonded directly to an aromatic ring; and an *ether* has an oxygen atom bonded to two organic groups *(see Problems 26, 27, 30, and 31)*.

- **Explain why alcohols have higher boiling points than compounds of similar molecular weight (MW).** Alcohols, like water, can undergo hydrogen bonding. This leads to alcohols having higher boiling points than expected based on molecular mass. Alcohols with two or more —OH groups can form more than one hydrogen bond and will have even higher boiling points *(see Problems 28 and 38)*.

- **Write systematic names for simple alcohols.** Alcohols are named using the *-ol* ending, and phenols are named using the *-phenol* ending *(see Problems 32, 33, 60, 68, 69, and 73)*.

- **Draw the structure of an alcohol given its name, in both condensed and line structure format.** The structure of an alcohol is drawn in a similar fashion to that for an alkane; the numbering system uses index number of the hydroxyl (—OH) group as the basis for the location of all other groups in the molecule *(see Problems 34, 35, 67, and 73)*.

- **Classify an alcohol as primary, secondary, or tertiary.** A primary alcohol has one carbon attached to the carbon containing the —OH group, a secondary alcohol has two carbons attached to the carbon containing the —OH group, and a tertiary alcohol has three carbons attached to the carbon containing the —OH group *(see Problems 36 and 37)*.

- **Define and identify a glycol.** A diol is an alcohol containing two —OH groups. When the groups are on adjacent carbons, the diol is given the special name glycol *(see Problems 32, 34, and 39)*.

- **Describe the properties of alcohols.** Alcohols are much more polar than hydrocarbons, and the presence of the —OH group provides the ability to hydrogen bond to other alcohols and to water. Due to the presence of the carbon group, alcohols are also miscible with many organic solvents *(see Problems 28, 29, 54, 55, and 62)*.

- **Describe hydrophobic and hydrophilic alcohols.** Alcohols R—OH have both a hydrophilic (—OH) and hydrophobic (R—) part. *Hydrophilic* means "water-loving," and *hydrophobic* means "water-fearing." The larger the hydrophobic organic part is, the more alkane-like and less water-like alcohols become *(see Problems 36, 39, and 62)*.

- **Predict the products obtained upon dehydration of an alcohol.** Alcohols undergo loss of water *(dehydration)* to yield alkenes when treated with a strong acid. When mixtures of alkenes are possible, the major product expected is the one with the most carbons directly attached to the carbon–carbon double bond *(see Problems 46, 47, 69, 74, and 75)*.

- **Predict the oxidation products of a primary, secondary, and tertiary alcohol.** Alcohols undergo *oxidation* to yield compounds that contain a *carbonyl group* ($C=O$). Primary alcohols (RCH_2OH) are oxidized to yield either aldehydes ($RCHO$) or carboxylic acids (RCO_2H), secondary alcohols (R_2CHOH) are oxidized to yield ketones ($R_2C=O$), and tertiary alcohols are not oxidized *(see Problems 48, 49, 69, 70, and 72)*.

- **Identify a phenol.** A *phenol* has an —OH group bonded directly to an aromatic ring. Phenols are notable for their use as disinfectants and antiseptics *(see Problems 33, 35, 44, and 64)*.

- **Explain why alcohols and phenols are weak acids.** Like water, alcohols and phenols are weak acids that can donate H^+ from their —OH group to a strong base. Alcohols are similar to water in acidity; phenols are more acidic than water and will react with aqueous NaOH *(see Problems 29 and 64)*.

- **Identify an ether.** An *ether* has an oxygen atom bonded to two organic groups. The groups can be alkyl, aromatic, or a mixture of both. Simple ethers are named by identifying the two organic groups attached to oxygen, followed by the word *ether*. Ethers are used primarily as solvents *(see Problems 30, 33, and 35)*.

- **Distinguish between an ether and an alcohol.** Both alcohols and phenols are like water in their ability to form hydrogen bonds. As the size of the carbon part of the molecule increases, alcohols become less soluble in water. Ethers do not hydrogen bond and are more alkane-like in their properties *(see Problems 32–35)*.

- **Identify a thiol.** *Thiols* are sulfur analogs of alcohols, containing an —SH in place of an —OH. Thiols use the name ending *-thiol* *(see Problems 50 and 51)*.

- **Explain how a thiol is converted into a disulfide and vice versa.** Thiols react with mild oxidizing agents to yield *disulfides* (RSSR), a reaction of importance in protein chemistry. Reducing agents will convert disulfides back to thiols *(see Problems 52 and 53)*.

- **Identify an alkyl or aryl halide.** *Alkyl halides* contain a halogen atom bonded to an alkyl group, R—X, while *aryl halides* have a halogen attached to an aromatic ring, Ar—X. Halogenated compounds are rare in human biochemistry but are widely used in industry as solvents and in agriculture as herbicides, fungicides, and insecticides *(see Problems 68 and 69)*.

- **Identify a chiral carbon.** A chiral carbon is a carbon atom that is bonded to four different groups. Also referred to as a chiral center or stereocenter. The presence of a chiral carbon atom can lead to stereoisomers: Isomers that have the same bonded connections of atoms but differ in how those atoms are oriented in space *(see Problems 56–59, 65, and 67)*.

KEY WORDS

Achiral, *p. 462*
Alcohol, *p. 441*
Alkoxide ion, *p. 456*
Alkoxy group, *p. 457*
Alkyl halide, *p. 460*
Aryl halide, *p. 460*

Carbonyl group, *p. 452*
Chiral carbon atom, *p. 464*
Chiral, *p. 462*
Configurations, *p. 462*
Dehydration, *p. 448*

Disulfide, *p. 459*
Enantiomers (optical isomers), *p. 464*
Ether, *p. 441*
Glycol, *p. 444*
Phenol, *p. 441*

Stereochemistry, *p. 462*
Stereoisomers, *p. 462*
Thiol, *p. 459*
Vicinal, *p. 444*

CONCEPT MAP: ORGANIC CHEMISTRY FAMILIES

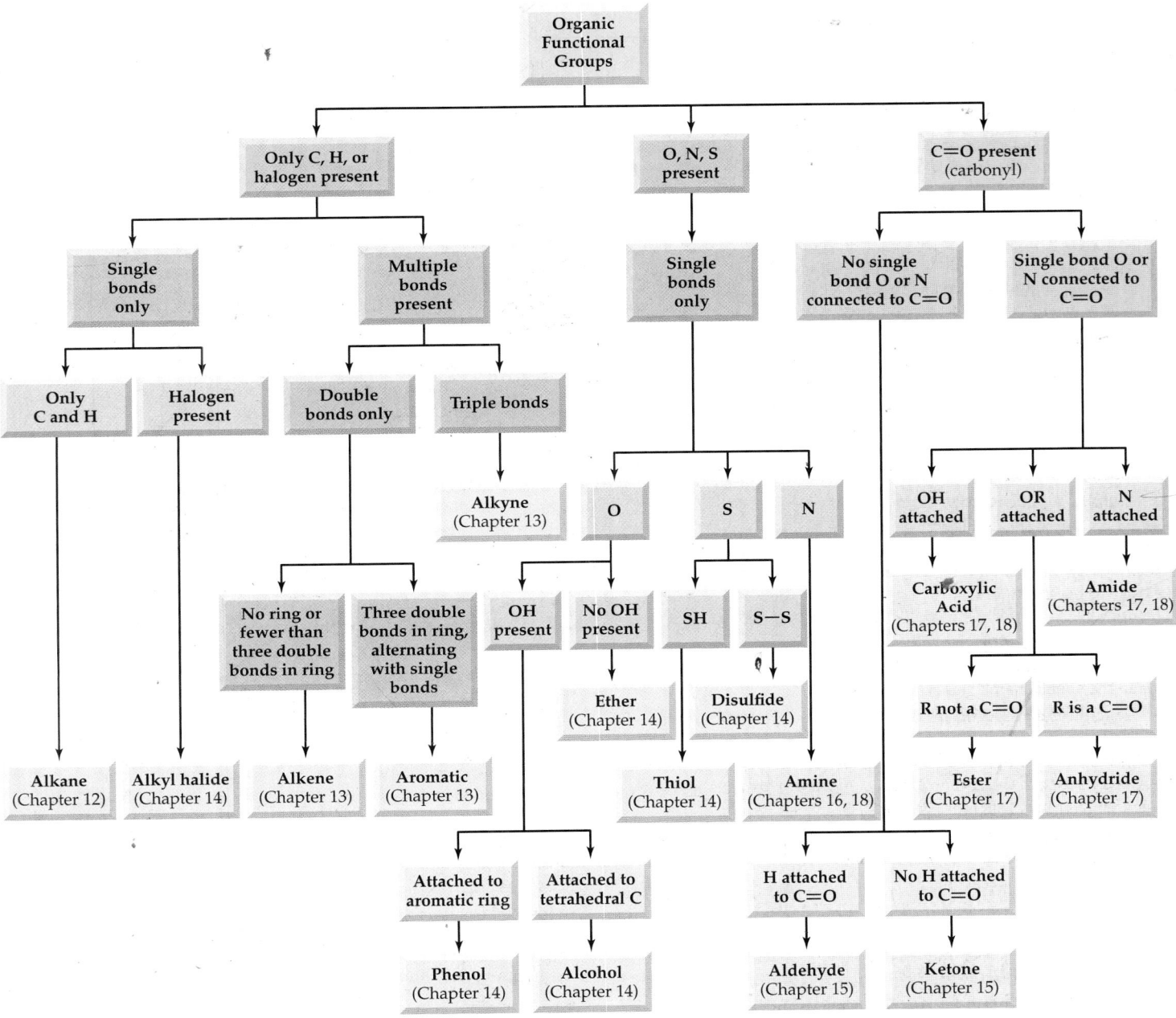

▲ **Figure 14.6 Concept Map.** This is the same concept map we saw at the end of Chapters 12 and 13, except the functional groups discussed in this chapter, alcohols, ethers, thiols, and disulfides have now been colored.

SUMMARY OF REACTIONS

1. **Reactions of alcohols** (Section 14.6)
   (a) Loss of H_2O to yield an alkene (dehydration):
   (b) Oxidation to yield a carbonyl compound:

2. Reactions of thiols (Section 14.10); oxidation to yield a
disulfide:

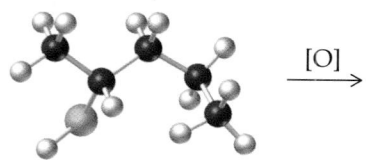

$$RSH + HSR \xrightarrow{[O]} RSSR$$

Two thiol molecules　　　A disulfide

🔑 UNDERSTANDING KEY CONCEPTS

14.21　Give IUPAC names for the following compounds
(black = C, red = O, white = H).

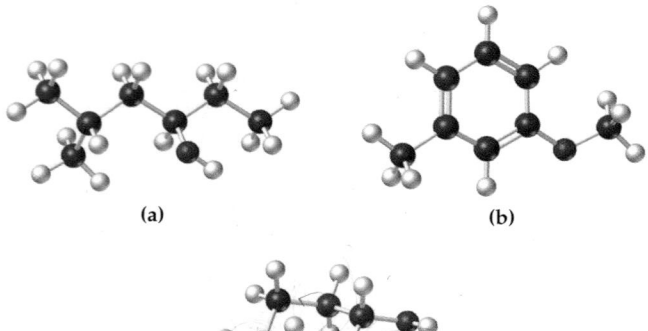

(a)　　　　　　　　　　　　　　(b)

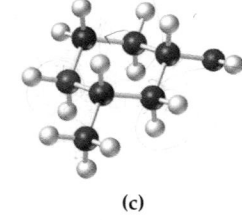

(c)

14.22　Predict the product of the following reaction:

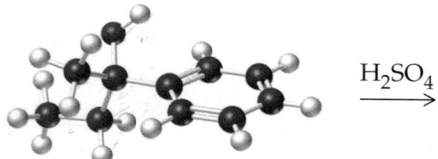

$$\xrightarrow{H_2SO_4}$$

14.23　Predict the products of the following reaction:

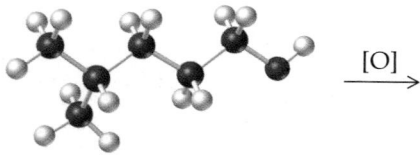

$$\xrightarrow{[O]}$$

14.24　The compound pictured here is a thiol. (a) Draw its line
structure, and (b) draw the structure of the disulfide formed when
it is treated with an oxidizing agent (yellow = S).

$$\xrightarrow{[O]}$$

14.25　From what alcohols might the following carbonyl compounds have been made (reddish-browm = Br)?

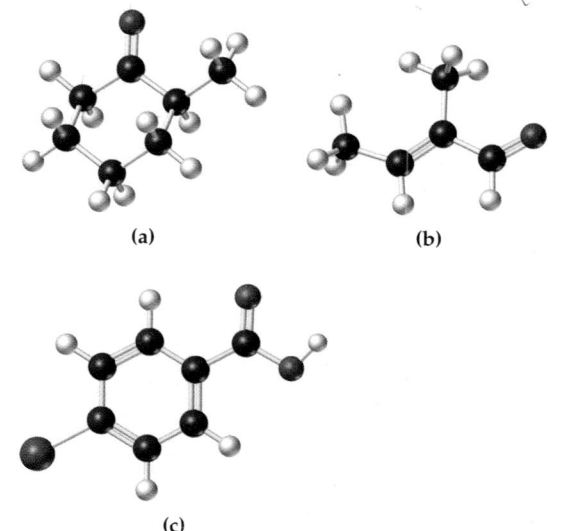

(a)　　　　　　　　　　(b)

(c)

ADDITIONAL PROBLEMS

ALCOHOLS, ETHERS, AND PHENOLS
(SECTIONS 14.1–14.2 AND 14.5–14.7)

14.26　How do alcohols, ethers, and phenols differ structurally?

14.27　What is the structural difference between primary, secondary, and tertiary alcohols?

14.28　Why do alcohols have higher boiling points than ethers of
the same MW?

14.29　Which is the stronger acid, ethanol or phenol?

14.30　The Taxane nucleus is shown here; it is the basis of a
number of new drugs used to treat cancers. Identify the
functional groups present in this molecule.

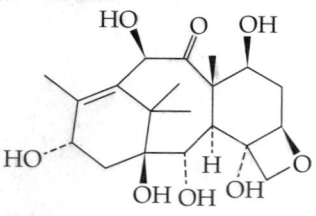

Taxane nucleus

14.31　Vitamin E has the structure shown. Identify the functional
group to which each oxygen belongs.

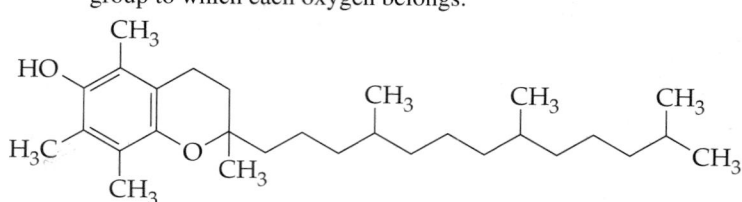

Vitamin E (a naturally occurring antioxidant)

14.32　Give systematic names for the following alcohols:

(a) 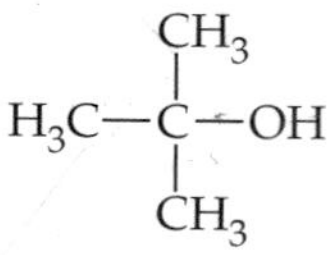 $H_3C-\overset{\overset{\displaystyle CH_3}{|}}{\underset{\underset{\displaystyle CH_3}{|}}{C}}-OH$

(b) $(CH_3)_2CHCH_2OH$

(c) 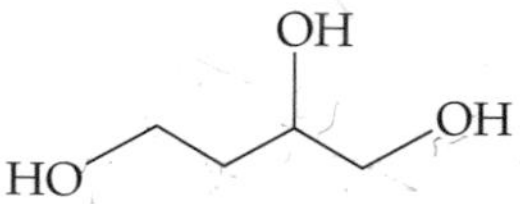 (diol structure: HO ... OH)

(d) 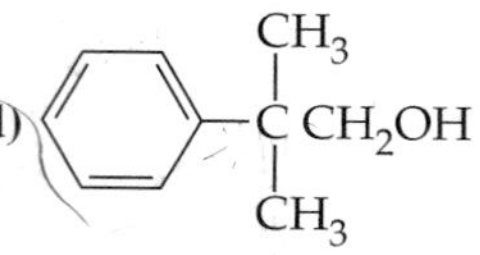 (benzene ring)$-\overset{\overset{\displaystyle CH_3}{|}}{\underset{\underset{\displaystyle CH_3}{|}}{C}}CH_2OH$

(e) [cyclohexane structure with OH and CH₃]

(f) $CH_3CH_2CH_2\overset{\overset{\displaystyle CH_2CH_3}{|}}{\underset{\underset{\displaystyle CH_3}{|}}{\underset{CHOH}{C}}}CH_3$

14.33 Give systematic names for the following compounds:

(a) [benzene ring with three H₃C groups and OH]

(b) $CH_3-\overset{\overset{\displaystyle CH_3}{|}}{CH}-O-CH_2CH_3$

(c) [benzene ring with NO₂, O₂N, OH, NO₂ substituents]

(Also known as picric acid)

(d) [cyclobutyl–O–cyclopentyl ether structure]

(e) [benzene ring with OH and CH₂CH₂CH₂CH₃]

(f) $CH_3CH_2CH_2OCH_2CH_2CH_3$

14.34 Draw structures corresponding to the following names:
(a) 2,4-Dimethyl-2-heptanol
(b) 2,2-Diethylcyclohexanol
(c) 5-Ethyl-5-methyl-1-heptanol
(d) 4-Ethyl-2-hexanol
(e) 3-Methoxycyclooctanol
(f) 3,3-Dimethyl-1,6-heptanediol

14.35 Draw structures corresponding to the following names:
(a) Isopropyl methyl ether
(b) *o*-Dihydroxybenzene (catechol)
(c) Phenyl *tert*-butyl ether
(d) *m*-Iodophenol
(e) 2,4-Dimethoxy-3-methylpentane
(f) 3-Methoxy-4-methyl-1-pentene

14.36 (a) Identify each alcohol named in Problem 14.32 as primary, secondary, or tertiary.
(b) Classify each alcohol in Problem 14.32 as water-soluble or water insoluble. Identify the hydrophobic and hydrophilic areas of each alcohol.

14.37 Locate the alcohol functional groups in the taxane nucleus (Problem 14.30), and identify each as primary, secondary, or tertiary.

14.38 Arrange the following 6-carbon compounds in order of their expected boiling points, and explain your ranking:
(a) Hexane   (b) 1-Hexanol
(c) Dipropyl ether $(CH_3CH_2CH_2-O-CH_2CH_2CH_3)$

14.39 Glucose is much more soluble in water than 1-hexanol, even though both contain 6 carbons. Explain.

$HOCH_2\overset{\overset{\displaystyle OH}{|}}{CH}CH\overset{}{CH}CH\overset{\overset{\displaystyle O}{||}}{CH}$ Glucose
with HO OH OH below

REACTIONS OF ALCOHOLS (SECTION 14.4)

14.40 What functional group is formed on oxidation of a secondary alcohol? Demonstrate your answer using isopropyl alcohol.

14.41 What structural feature is necessary for an alcohol to undergo oxidation reactions?

14.42 What product can form on oxidation of a primary alcohol with an excess of oxidizing agent?

14.43 What type of product is formed on reaction of an alcohol with Na metal?

14.44 Assume that you have samples of the following two compounds, both with formula C_7H_8O. Both compounds dissolve in ether, but only one of the two dissolves in aqueous NaOH. How could you use this information to distinguish between them?

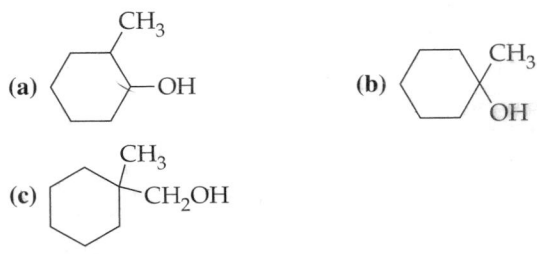

H_3C—[benzene]—OH   and   [benzene]—CH_2OH

14.45 Which of the following alcohols can undergo oxidation? Draw the line structure of the product expected for those that can. Assume an excess of oxidizing agent is present.

(a) [cyclohexane with CH₃ and OH]
(b) [cyclohexane with CH₃ and OH]
(c) [cyclohexane with CH₃ and CH₂OH]

14.46 The following alkenes can be prepared by dehydration of an appropriate alcohol. Show the structure of the alcohol in each case that would provide the alkene shown as the major product.

(a) [cyclopentene with CH₂CH₃ and CH₂CH₃]
(b) [alkene structure]   Two possible alcohols
(c) 2-Phenyl-2-hexene
(d) [cyclohexane with C=CH₂ and CH₃]
(e) 1,4-Pentadiene

14.47 What alkenes might be formed by dehydration of the following alcohols? If more than one product is possible, indicate which you expect to be major.

(a) 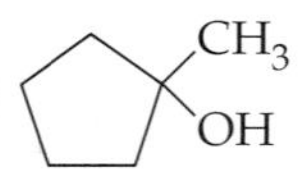 [structure: cyclopentane with CH₃ and OH]

(b) 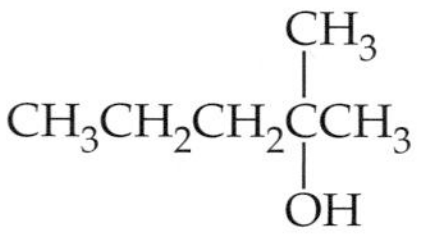 CH₃CH₂CH₂CCH₃ with CH₃ and OH

(c) 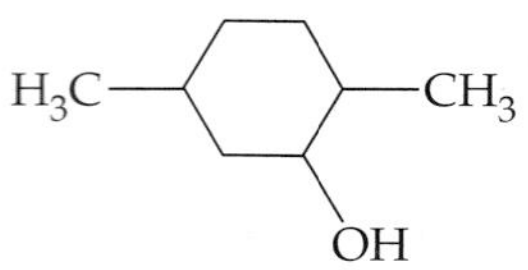 H₃C—[cyclohexane ring]—CH₃ with OH

(d) 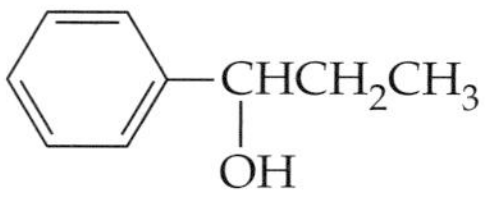 [benzene]—CHCH₂CH₃ with OH

(e) 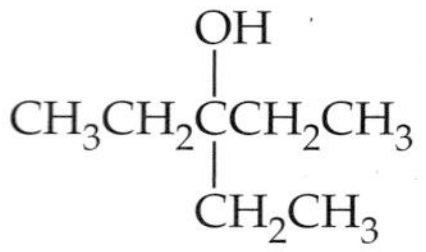 CH₃CH₂CCH₂CH₃ with OH above and CH₂CH₃ below

14.48 What carbonyl-containing products would you obtain from the oxidation of the following alcohols? If no reaction occurs, write "NR."

(a) 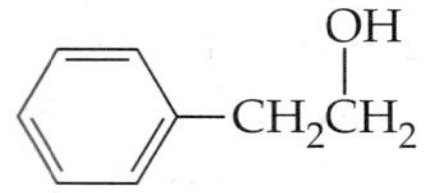 [benzene]—CH₂CH₂ with OH

(b) 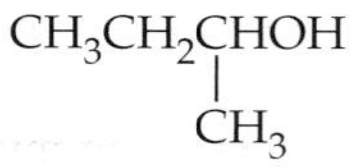 CH₃CH₂CHOH with CH₃

(c) 2,3-Pentanediol

(d) 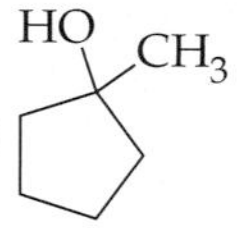 [cyclopentane with HO and CH₃]

(e) 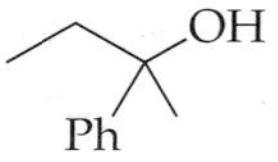 [structure with OH and Ph]

(f) 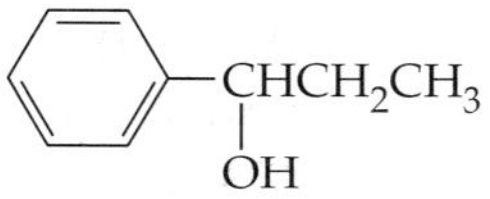 [benzene]—CHCH₂CH₃ with OH

14.49 What alcohols would you oxidize to obtain the following carbonyl compounds?

(a) 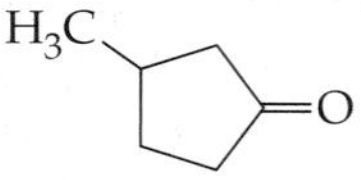 H₃C—[cyclopentanone]=O

(b) 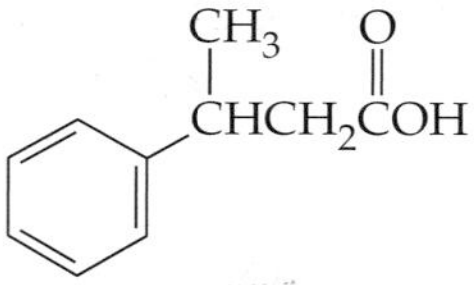 [benzene]—CHCH₂COH with CH₃ and O

(c) 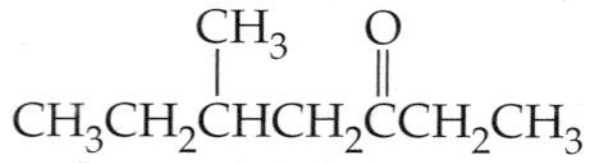 CH₃CH₂CHCH₂CCH₂CH₃ with CH₃ and O

THIOLS AND DISULFIDES (SECTION 14.8)

14.50 What is the most noticeable characteristic of thiols?

14.51 What is the structural relationship between a thiol and an alcohol?

14.52 The amino acid cysteine forms a disulfide when oxidized. What is the structure of the disulfide?

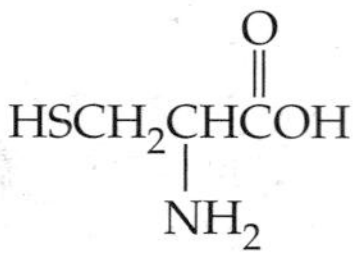

HSCH₂CHCOH with O and NH₂   Cysteine

14.53 Oxidation of a dithiol such as 2,5-hexanedithiol forms a six-membered ring containing a disulfide group as part of

the ring. Draw the structure of this cyclic disulfide (Hint: Draw the starting compound in line structure format first).

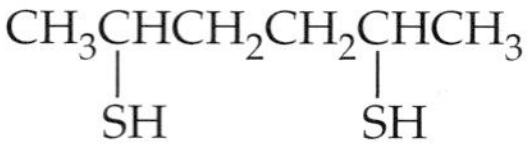

CH₃CHCH₂CH₂CHCH₃ with SH and SH

2,5-Hexanedithiol

14.54 The boiling point of propanol is 97 °C, much higher than that of either ethanethiol (37 °C) or chloroethane (13 °C), even though all three compounds have similar MWs. Explain.

14.55 Propanol is very soluble in water, but ethanethiol and chloroethane are only slightly soluble. Explain.

STEREOCHEMISTRY AND CHIRALITY (SECTION 14.10)

14.56 Define the following terms:

(a) Chiral   (b) Achiral

(c) Chiral carbon   (d) Enantiomer

14.57 Are the following items chiral or achiral? Give a justification for your answers.

(a) A fork   (b) This textbook

(c) Your right hand

(d) A blank 3 × 5 index card

14.58 Identify the chiral center(s) in each of the following molecules:

(a) 2-Methyl-3-pentanol   (b) 3-Chloro-1-butanol

(c) 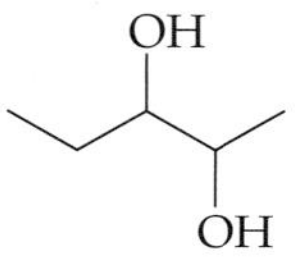 [structure with OH and OH]
two chiral centers

(d) [cyclohexane with OH and I]
two chiral centers

14.59 Are the following molecules chiral or achiral? If they are chiral, identify the chiral carbon atom(s).

(a) 3-Pentanol   (b) 2-Bromobutane

(c) 2-Methylcyclohexanol

(d)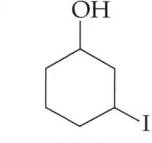

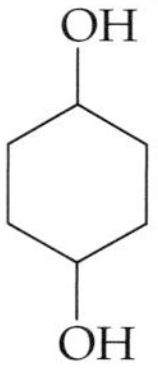

CONCEPTUAL PROBLEMS

14.60 Name all unbranched ether and alcohol isomers with formula $C_5H_{12}O$, and write their structural formulas.

14.61 Thyroxine (Section 14.9) is synthesized in the body by reaction of thyronine with iodine. Write the reaction, and tell what kind of process is occurring (Hint: See Section 13.5).

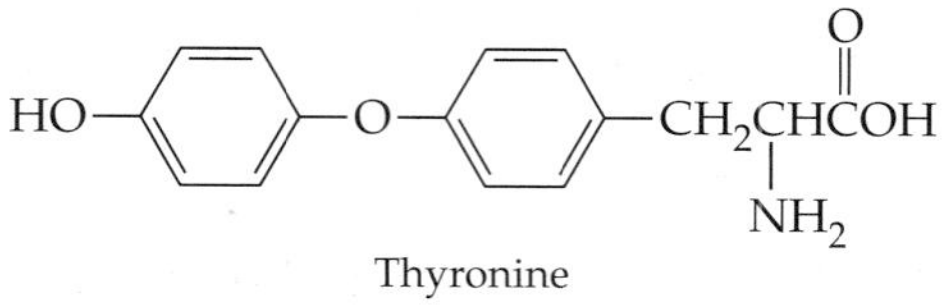

HO—[benzene]—O—[benzene]—CH₂CHCOH with O and NH₂

Thyronine

14.62 1-Propanol is freely soluble in water, 1-butanol is marginally soluble, and 1-hexanol is essentially insoluble. Explain.

14.63 Phenols undergo the same kind of substitution reactions that other aromatic compounds do (Section 13.11). Formulate the reaction of *p*-methylphenol with Br_2 to give a mixture of two substitution products.

14.64 What is the difference between an antiseptic and a disinfectant?

14.65 Which of the alcohols pictured in Problem 14.47 are achiral?

14.66 Which of the alcohols pictured in Problem 14.48 are chiral? Indicate the chiral carbons for those that are chiral.

14.67 Write the formulas and IUPAC names for the following common alcohols (Hint: See Table 14.1).

   (a) Rubbing alcohol   **(b)** Wood alcohol

   (c) Grain alcohol

   (d) Diol used as antifreeze (two answers)

14.68 Name the following compounds:

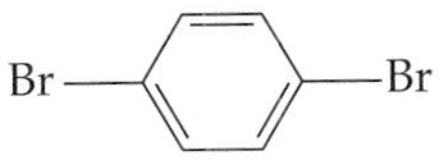

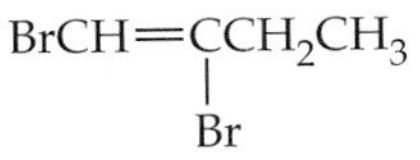

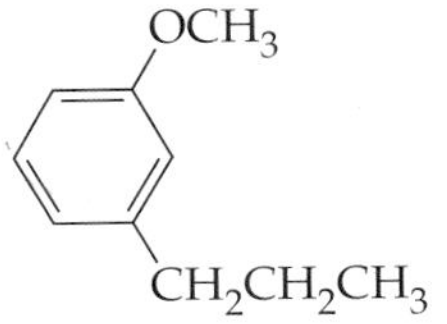

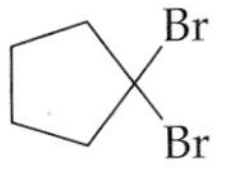

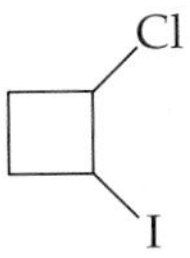

14.69 Complete the following reactions:

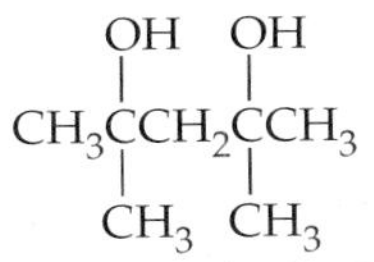

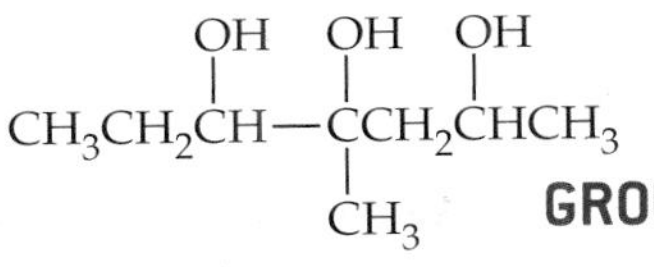

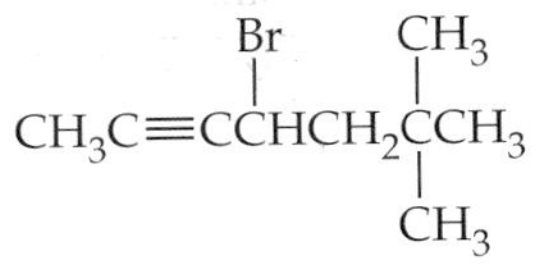

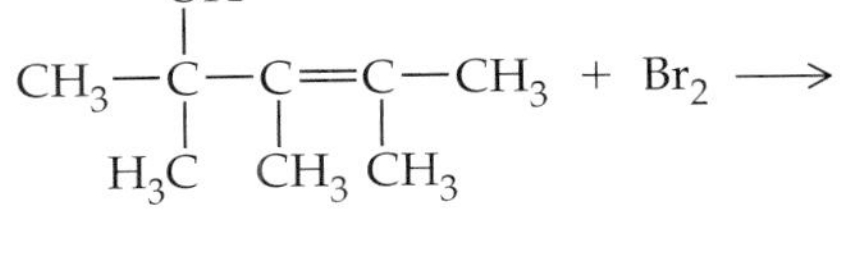

(e) $2(CH_3)_3C\!-\!SH \xrightarrow{[O]}$

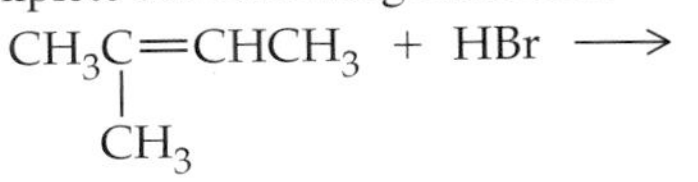

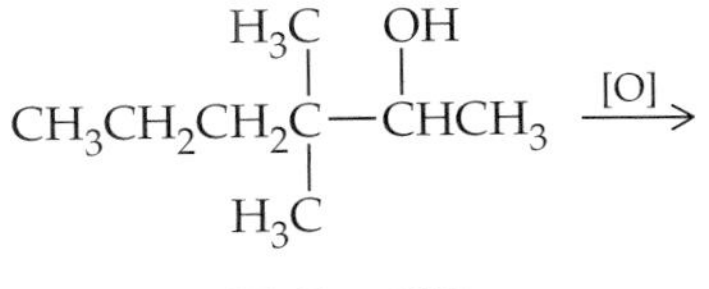

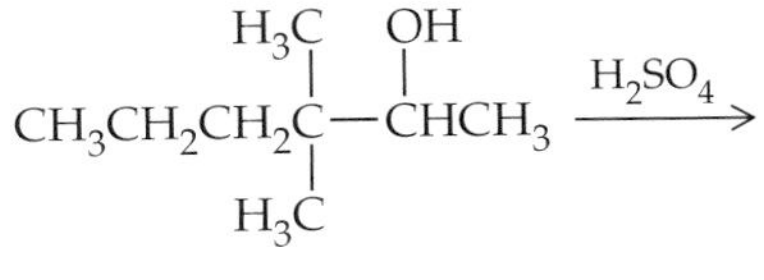

(f)

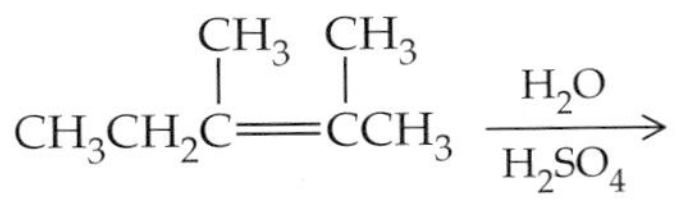

(g)

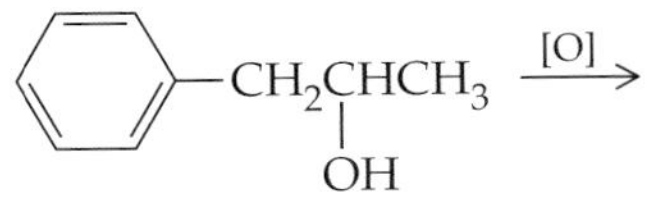

14.70 The aroma of roses is due to geraniol.

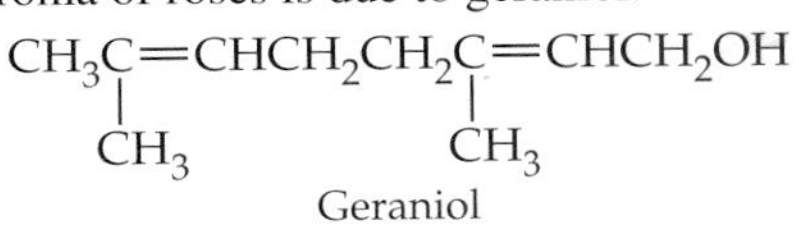

Geraniol

   (a) What is the systematic name of geraniol?

   (b) When geraniol is oxidized, the aldehyde citral, one of the compounds responsible for lemon scent, is formed. Write the structure of citral.

14.71 "Designer vinegars" have become very popular over the past decade. Vinegars made from champagne, merlot, and other wines are but a few of these. All wines contain ethanol, and these vinegars are simply wines containing microorganisms that have caused oxidation of the ethanol present. If vinegar is simply ethanol that has been oxidized, what is the structure of the acid formed?

14.72 "Flaming" desserts, such as cherries jubilee, use the ethanol in brandy or other distilled spirits as the flame carrier. Write the equation for the combustion of ethanol.

GROUP PROBLEMS

14.73 **(a)** Draw all possible cyclic $C_7H_{14}O$ alcohol isomers having a cyclohexane ring and a methyl group. (Hint: Adapt the method described in Worked Example 12.12 to arrive at your answers.)

   (b) Identify all chiral centers in the isomers that you drew for part (a).

14.74 Using the alcohol shown, draw all the possible alkenes that might be formed on its dehydration. Which do you think will be the major product(s)? Which do you think will be the minor product(s)? It is alright to have more than one major and minor product.

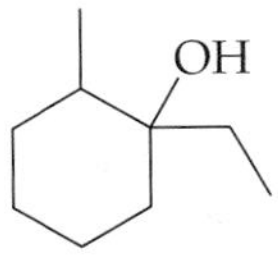

14.75 Using the alcohol shown, draw all the possible alkenes that might be formed on its dehydration. Which alkenes can exist as cis–trans isomers? Draw them, in both condensed and line structure, and identify each as cis or trans. Explain your choices.

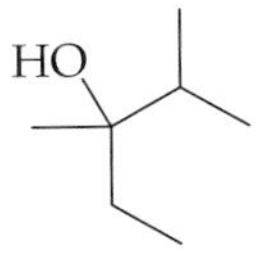

15

Aldehydes and Ketones

CONTENTS

◀◀◀ CONCEPTS TO REVIEW

▲ Isolated from the bark of the Pacific Yew is the carbonyl-containing compound paclitaxel, which may lead to the new medicines in cancer chemotherapy.

Many intricate biological processes, such as the reproduction of a cell, are regulated by increasing complex molecules that contain many different functional groups, ketones and aldehydes included. As an outcome of this, the medicines needed to treat diseases have become more and more complicated. Nowhere is this more evident than in the drugs needed to treat cancer. A well-known adage in medicine is "the dose makes the poison," and these drugs embody this better than any others. Chemotherapy relies on the use of molecules that are not only complicated but toxic as well, blurring the line between a drug and a toxin. While there are five general categories of chemotherapeutic agents, the newest of these, the mitotic inhibitors, seem to be among the most promising as they primarily affect rapidly dividing cells. These compounds prevent mitosis, the part of the cell cycle during which chromosomes are duplicated and separated into two identical sets of chromosomes, each in its own nucleus. Two members of this class of compounds contain the ketone functional group. One of these, paclitaxel, was originally isolated from the bark of the Pacific Yew tree and has shown much promise in the treatment of a number of solid tumor cancers. We will discuss the difference between a drug and a toxin, as well as chemotherapy, in the Chemistry in Action "When Is Toxicity Beneficial?" found at the end of this chapter.

Paclitaxel contains the carbonyl group $(C{=}O)$; this functional group is found in many important and biologically significant molecules, including the carbohydrates (Chapter 20). In this chapter and Chapter 17, we will study the families of compounds that contain this functional group, beginning with the two simplest families of carbonyl compounds, the *aldehydes* and *ketones*.

15.1 The Carbonyl Group

Learning Objective:

• Identify a carbonyl group and describe its polarity and shape.

The presence of a **carbonyl group** $(C{=}O)$ distinguishes **carbonyl compounds** from other organic compounds; carbonyl compounds are then classified according to what is bonded to the carbonyl carbon, as illustrated in Table 15.1.

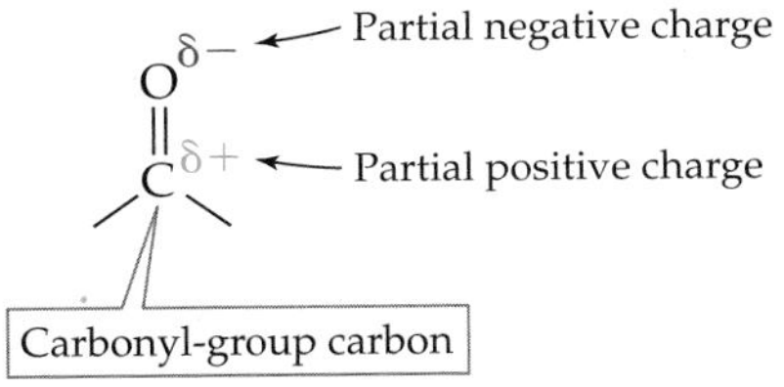

Table 15.1 General Classes of Carbonyl Compounds

Family Name	Structure	Example	
Aldehyde	$R{-}\overset{\overset{\displaystyle O}{\|\|}}{C}{-}H$	$H_3C{-}\overset{\overset{\displaystyle O}{\|\|}}{C}{-}H$	Acetaldehyde
Ketone	$R{-}\overset{\overset{\displaystyle O}{\|\|}}{C}{-}R'$	$H_3C{-}\overset{\overset{\displaystyle O}{\|\|}}{C}{-}CH_3$	Acetone
Carboxylic acid	$R{-}\overset{\overset{\displaystyle O}{\|\|}}{C}{-}O{-}H$	$H_3C{-}\overset{\overset{\displaystyle O}{\|\|}}{C}{-}O{-}H$	Acetic acid
Ester	$R{-}\overset{\overset{\displaystyle O}{\|\|}}{C}{-}O{-}R'$	$H_3C{-}\overset{\overset{\displaystyle O}{\|\|}}{C}{-}O{-}CH_3$	Methyl acetate
Amide	$R{-}\overset{\overset{\displaystyle O}{\|\|}}{C}{-}N{\diagup}$	$H_3C{-}\overset{\overset{\displaystyle O}{\|\|}}{C}{-}NH_2$	Acetamide

Carbonyl group A functional group that has a carbon atom joined to an oxygen atom by a double bond.

Carbonyl compound Any compound that contains a carbonyl group $(C{=}O)$.

Partial negative charge
Partial positive charge
Carbonyl-group carbon

◀◀◀ **CONCEPTS TO REVIEW** Remember that electronegativity is the ability of an atom to attract electrons to itself (see Figure 4.6).

Aldehyde A compound that has a carbonyl group bonded to at least one hydrogen, RCHO.

Ketone A compound that has a carbonyl group bonded to two carbons in organic groups that can be the same or different, $R_2C{=}O$, RCOR′.

Carbonyl-group carbon

Aldehyde
RCHO

Ketone
RCOR′

Since oxygen is more electronegative than carbon, carbonyl groups are strongly polarized, with a partial positive charge on the carbon atom and a partial negative charge on the oxygen atom. The polarity of the carbonyl group contributes to its reactivity.

Chemists find it useful to divide carbonyl compounds into two major groups based on their chemical properties. In one group are the **aldehydes** and **ketones,** which have similar properties because their carbonyl groups are bonded to atoms that do not attract electrons strongly—carbon and hydrogen. In the second group are *carboxylic acids, esters,* and *amides* (the *carboxyl* family). The carbonyl-group carbon in these compounds is bonded to an atom (other than carbon or hydrogen) that *does* attract electrons strongly, typically an oxygen or nitrogen atom. This second group of carbonyl-containing compounds is discussed in Chapter 17.

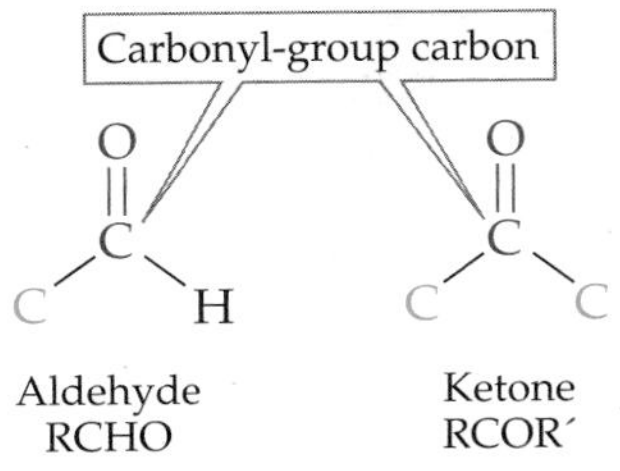

There are various ways of representing carbonyl compound structures on paper. All carbonyl groups are planar (or flat). The bond angles between the three substituents on the carbonyl carbon atom are 120° or close to it. Because of this trigonal planar arrangement of atoms around the carbonyl group, the bonds of the carbonyl carbon are often drawn at 120° angles to remind us that such angles are present in the molecules. Structures like those in Table 15.1, on the other hand, which emphasize the location of the double bond, do not fit well on a single line of type, so the simplified formulas shown next are often used for aldehydes and ketones.

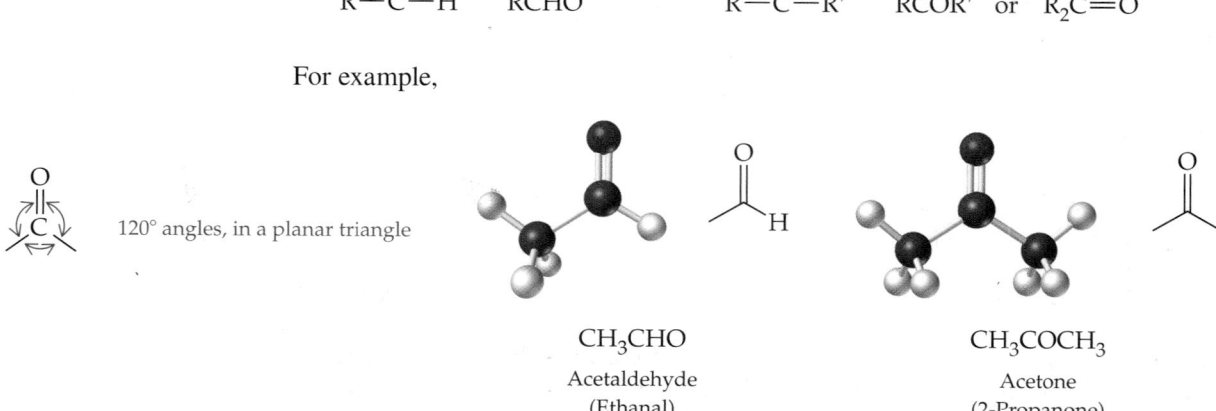

Aldehydes

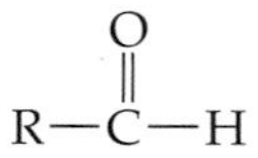

$$R-\overset{\overset{\displaystyle O}{\|}}{C}-H \qquad RCHO$$

Ketones

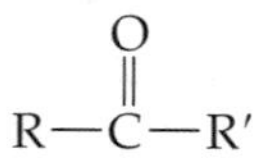

$$R-\overset{\overset{\displaystyle O}{\|}}{C}-R' \qquad RCOR' \ \text{ or } \ R_2C{=}O$$

For example,

120° angles, in a planar triangle

CH_3CHO
Acetaldehyde
(Ethanal)

CH_3COCH_3
Acetone
(2-Propanone)

The aldehyde group, you will notice, can only be connected to one carbon atom and therefore is always at the end of a carbon chain (—CHO is the common abbreviation for the aldehyde functional group; be careful not to confuse it with an alcohol, which you may see written as —COH). In line structure format, the aldehyde H must be explicitly shown. The ketone group, by contrast, must be connected to two carbon groups, and thus always occurs within a carbon chain.

PROBLEM 15.1

Which of the following molecules contain aldehyde or ketone functional groups? You may want to refer to Table 15.1, Table 12.1, and Figure 15.3 to help in your identification. Copy the formulas and circle these functional groups.

(a)

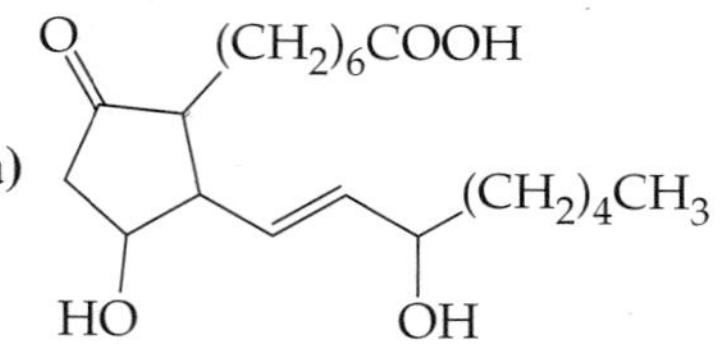

$(CH_2)_6COOH$

$(CH_2)_4CH_3$

HO   OH
Prostaglandin E₁

(b)

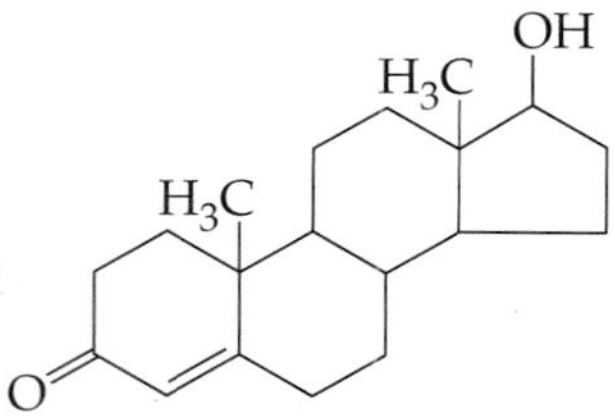

OH
H_3C
H_3C
O
Testosterone
(a male hormone)

(c) CH_3O HO—⟨ ⟩—CHO
Vanillin
(a flavoring agent)

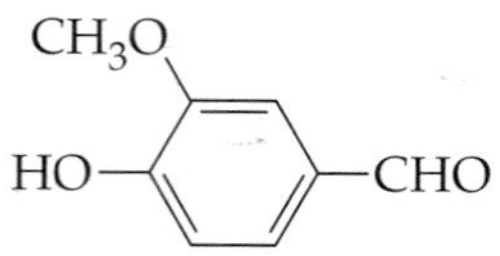

(d) $C_4H_9COCH_3$

(e) C_4H_9CHO

LOOKING AHEAD ▸▸ Aldehyde or ketone groups are present in biomolecules with a wide range of functions, from the steroid hormones that regulate sexual function (Section 28.5), to the carbohydrate backbones that are essential to nucleic acids and the genetic code (Section 26.2). Most distinctively, the structure and reactions of aldehydes and ketones are fundamental to the chemistry of carbohydrates, those in our diet and those that provide energy and structure to our bodies (Chapters 20, 21, and 22).

PROBLEM 15.2

Draw the structures of compounds (d) and (e) in Problem 15.1 to show all individual atoms and all covalent bonds. Assume that all carbons are connected in a continuous chain. Redraw each in line structure format.

15.2 Naming Simple Aldehydes and Ketones

Learning Objective:

• Name and draw simple aldehydes and ketones given a structure or a name.

The aldehyde and ketone functional groups are typically found in molecules that contain more than one functional group. As a result, we will limit our discussion of nomenclature to only the simplest of aldehydes and ketones, focusing on the common names wherever possible.

The simplest aldehydes have common names, which end in *aldehyde;* for example, formaldehyde, acetaldehyde, and benzaldehyde. To name aldehydes systematically in the International Union of Pure and Applied Chemistry (IUPAC) system, the final *-e* of the name of the parent alkane is replaced by *-al*. The three-carbon aldehyde derived from propane is named systematically as propanal, the four-carbon aldehyde as butanal, and so on. When substituents are present, the chain is numbered beginning with 1 for the carbonyl carbon, as illustrated next for 3-methylbutanal.

Aldehydes

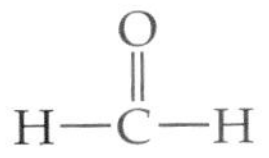

Formaldehyde 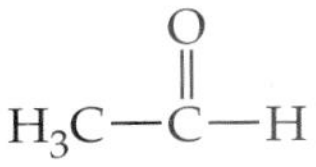   Acetaldehyde 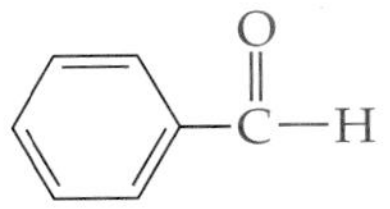   Benzaldehyde 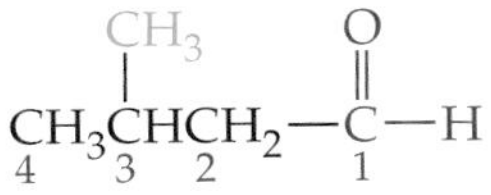   3-Methylbutanal

Most simple ketones are best known by common names that use the names of the two alkyl groups bonded to the carbonyl carbon followed by the word *ketone*—for example, methyl ethyl ketone, shown next. An exception to this common-name scheme is seen for the simplest ketone, acetone. Ketones are named systematically by replacing the final *-e* of the corresponding alkane name with *-one* (pronounced *own*). The numbering of the alkane chain begins at the end nearest the carbonyl group. As shown here for 2-butanone and 2-pentanone, the location of the carbonyl group is indicated by placing the number of the carbonyl carbon in front of the name. Using this nomenclature scheme, acetone would be named 2-propanone.

Ketones

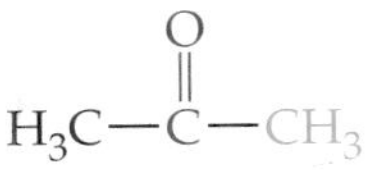

Acetone   Methyl ethyl ketone   Methyl propyl ketone   Cyclohexanone
(2-Propanone)   (2-Butanone)   (2-Pentanone)

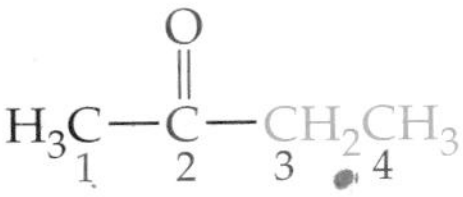

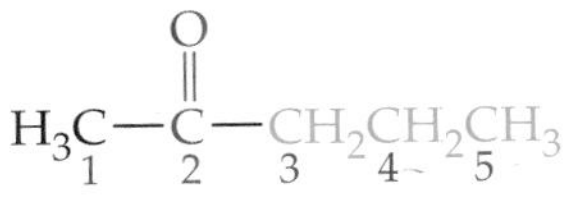

Worked Example 15.1 Naming a Ketone Given Its Structure

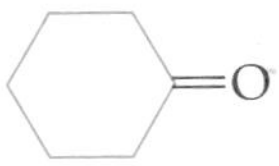

Give both the systematic (IUPAC) name and the common name for the following compound:

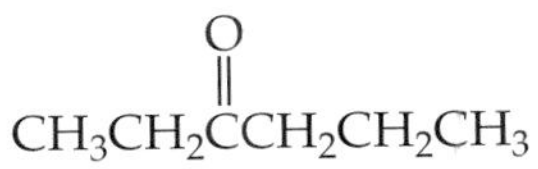

$$\underset{\text{CH}_3\text{CH}_2\overset{\displaystyle \text{O}}{\overset{\|}{\text{C}}}\text{CH}_2\text{CH}_2\text{CH}_3}{}$$

ANALYSIS The compound is a ketone, as shown by the single carbonyl group bonded to two alkyl groups: an ethyl group on the left (CH_3CH_2—) and a propyl group on the right (—$CH_2CH_2CH_3$). The IUPAC system identifies and numbers carbon chains to indicate where the carbonyl group is located, counting in the direction that gives the carbonyl carbon the lowest number possible.

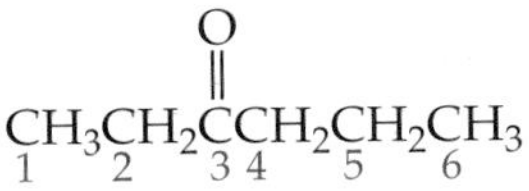

The common name uses the names of the two alkyl groups.

$$\underset{1 \quad 2 \quad 3\,4 \quad 5 \quad 6}{\text{CH}_3\text{CH}_2\overset{\displaystyle \text{O}}{\overset{\|}{\text{C}}}\text{CH}_2\text{CH}_2\text{CH}_3}$$

SOLUTION
The IUPAC name is 3-hexanone. The common name is ethyl propyl ketone.

PROBLEM 15.3

Draw structures corresponding to the following names:

(a) Octanal

(b) Methyl phenyl ketone

(c) 4-Methylhexanal

(d) Methyl *tert*-butyl ketone

CHEMISTRY IN ACTION

Chemical Warfare among the Insects

Life in the insect world is a jungle. Predators abound, just waiting to make a meal of any insect that happens along. To survive, insects have evolved extraordinarily effective means of chemical protection. Take the humble millipede *Apheloria corrugata*, for example. When attacked by ants, the millipede protects itself by discharging benzaldehyde cyanohydrin.

In the laboratory, cyanohydrins $[RCH(OH)C≡N]$ are formed by addition of the toxic gas HCN (hydrogen cyanide) to ketones or aldehydes, not unlike the addition of HCl or H_2O to alkenes (Section 13.6 and Mastering Reactions: Carbonyl Additions on p. 493). The reaction with HCN to yield a cyanohydrin is reversible, just like the reaction of a ketone or aldehyde with an alcohol to yield a hemiacetal, as we'll see in Section 15.7. Thus, the benzaldehyde cyanohydrin secreted by the millipede decomposes to yield benzaldehyde and HCN. This action protects the millipede because while the cyanohydrin itself is safe, the decomposition reaction releases deadly hydrogen cyanide gas, a remarkably clever and very effective kind of chemical warfare.

▲ The beautifully colored millipede *Apheloria corrugata* can produce as much as 0.6 mg of HCN to defend itself against attacks.

CIA Problem 15.1 Draw the structures of the cyanohydrins expected to be formed when HCN is added to compounds (a) and (b) in Problem 15.4.

CIA Problem 15.2 HCN is quite toxic. How do you suppose the millipede uses this weapon without killing itself?

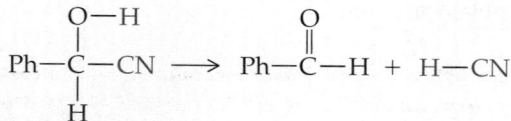

PROBLEM 15.4

Give systematic, IUPAC names for the following compounds. Redraw each in line structure format.

(a) CH₃CH₂CH₂CH₂CH (with O double bonded)

(b) CH₃CH₂CCH₂CH₃ (with O double bonded)

(c) CH₃CH₂CHCH₂CH₂CH (with CH₃ branch and O double bonded)

(d) Dipropyl ketone

PROBLEM 15.5

Draw the line structures and provide common names for the following ketones:

(a) 1-Phenylpropanone

(b) 2-Methyl-3-pentanone

(c) 1-Cyclohexyl-3,3-dimethyl-2-butanone

⊙➡ KEY CONCEPT PROBLEM 15.6 ——————————————————

Which of these two molecules is a ketone and which is an aldehyde? Write the condensed and line structure formulas for both of them.

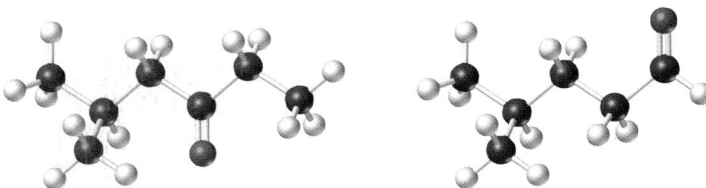

15.3 Properties of Aldehydes and Ketones

Learning Objective:

• Describe the polarity, hydrogen bonding, and water solubility of aldehydes and ketones.

The polarity of the carbonyl group makes aldehydes and ketones moderately polar compounds (Section 15.1). As a result, they boil at a higher temperature than alkanes with similar molecular weights. Since they have no hydrogen atoms bonded to oxygen or nitrogen, individual molecules do not hydrogen bond with each other, which makes aldehydes and ketones lower boiling than alcohols. In a series of compounds with similar molecular weights, the alkane is lowest boiling, the alcohol is highest boiling, and the aldehyde and ketone fall in between.

$CH_3CH_2CH_2CH_3$

Butane
(bp 0 °C)

$$CH_3CH_2\overset{\displaystyle O}{\overset{\displaystyle \|}{C}}H$$

Propanal
(bp 50 °C)

$$CH_3\overset{\displaystyle O}{\overset{\displaystyle \|}{C}}CH_3$$

Acetone
(bp 56 °C)

$CH_3CH_2CH_2OH$

Propanol
(bp 97 °C)

Formaldehyde (HCHO), the simplest aldehyde, is a gas; acetaldehyde (CH_3CHO) boils close to room temperature. The other simple aldehydes and ketones are liquids and those with more than 12 carbon atoms are solids. The lower-boiling aldehydes and ketones are flammable and can form explosive mixtures with air.

Aldehydes and ketones are soluble in common organic solvents, and those with fewer than four carbon atoms show significant solubility in water because they are able to accept hydrogen bonds from water molecules (Figure 15.1). Once again, as in the case of alcohols, as the number of carbons compared to oxygens increases, the solubility decreases (Section 14.3). This is even more dramatic with ketones and aldehydes; while alcohols have the ability to both accept and donate hydrogen bonds with water, ketones and aldehydes can only accept them.

◀◀◀ Since solubility in a solvent requires the molecule to be completely surrounded by that solvent, as the hydrophobic portion of the molecule becomes larger, the ability of water to solvate it decreases (Section 14.3).

◀ **Figure 15.1**
Hydrogen bonding with water (highlighted in blue) of an aldehyde (CH_3CHO) and a ketone (CH_3COCH_3). The dotted red lines indicate the hydrogen bond formed between the carbonyl group oxygen and the hydrogen of water.

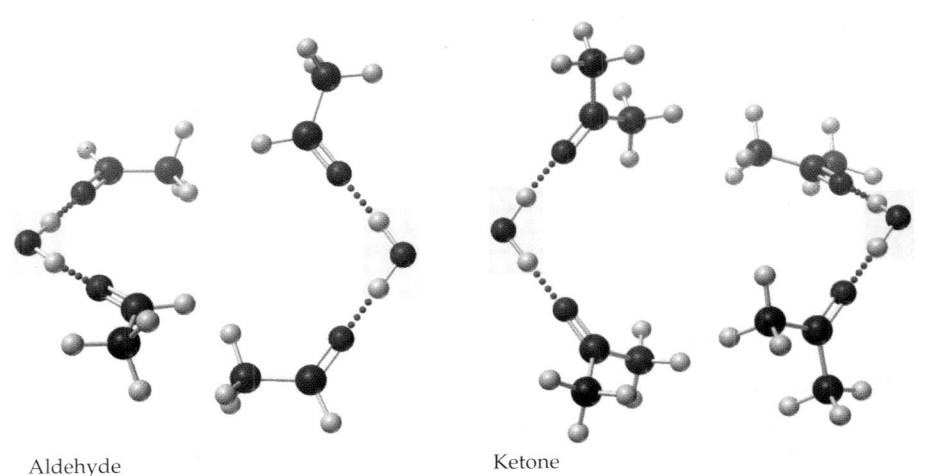

Aldehyde   Ketone

➤➤ In the biochemistry chapters that lie ahead, you will find that all of the simplest sugars—the monosaccharides (Section 20.4)—contain either an aldehyde group or a ketone group. Glucose, the 6-carbon sugar shown below, plays a major role in metabolism as the primary fuel molecule for energy generation (Section 22.2).

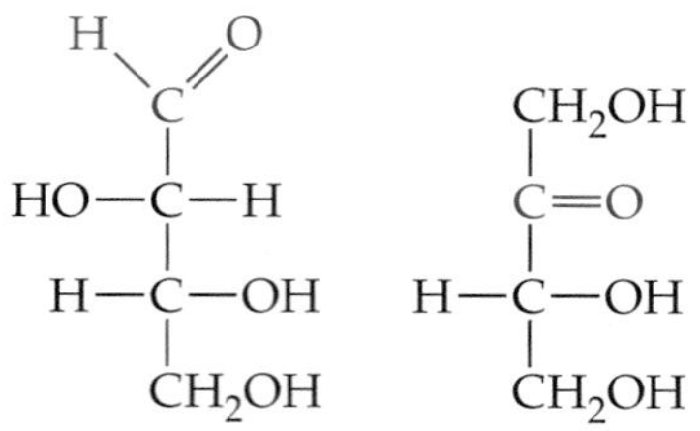

Aldehyde and ketone
4-carbon sugars

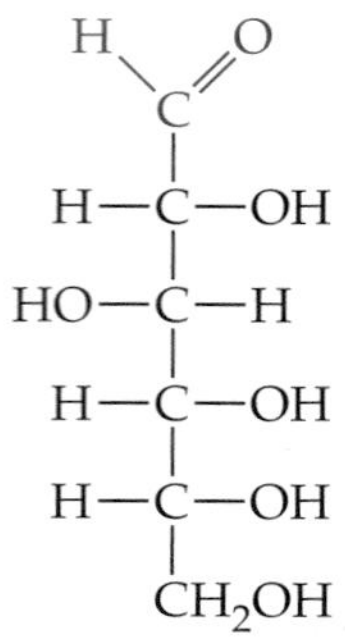

Glucose

$$CH_3C{=}CHCH_2CH_2CHCH_2CHO$$

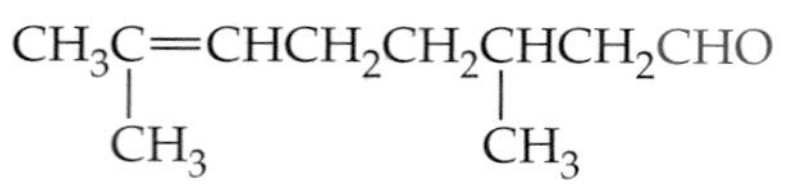

Citronellal
(insect repellant, also used
in perfumes; from citronella
and lemon grass oils)

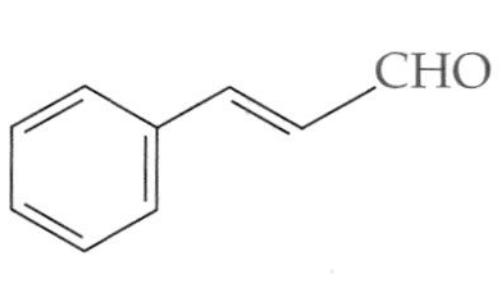

Simple ketones are excellent solvents because they dissolve both polar and nonpolar compounds. With increasing numbers of carbon atoms, aldehydes and ketones become more alkane-like and less water-soluble.

Properties of Aldehydes and Ketones

*   Aldehyde and ketone molecules are polar due to the presence of the carbonyl group.
*   Since aldehydes and ketones cannot hydrogen bond with one another, they have lower boiling points than alcohols but higher boiling points than alkanes because of dipole–dipole interactions (Section 8.2).
*   Common aldehydes and ketones are typically liquids.
*   Simple aldehydes and ketones are water-soluble due to hydrogen bonding with water molecules, and ketones are good solvents for many polar and nonpolar solutes.
*   Many aldehydes and ketones have distinctive odors.
*   Simple ketones are less toxic than simple aldehydes.

🔑 KEY CONCEPT PROBLEM 15.7

For each compound shown next (a–d), indicate whether the compound is polar or nonpolar, and whether it is soluble or insoluble in water.

(a) $CH_3\overset{O}{\overset{\|}{C}}CH_2CH_3$

(b) $CH_3CH_2{-}\overset{O}{\overset{\|}{C}}{-}H$

(c) $CH_3CH_2CH_2CH_2CH_3$

(d)

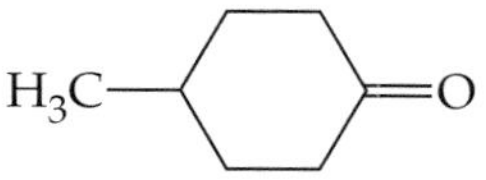

🔑 KEY CONCEPT PROBLEM 15.8

Why do aldehydes and ketones have lower boiling points than alcohols with similar molecular weights? Why are their boiling points higher than those of alkanes with similar molecular weights?

15.4 Some Common Aldehydes and Ketones

Learning Objective:

*   Identify common aldehydes and ketones and their uses.

Many aromas and flavors derive largely from naturally occurring aldehydes and ketones. Some examples are carvenone (dill oil), fenchone (fennel oil), junionone (juniper berry oil), piperitone (eucalyptus oil), citronellal (lemon oil), vanillin (vanilla), and cinnamaldehyde (cinnamon). The structures of a few naturally occurring aldehydes and ketones with distinctive odors are shown next; all are used in soaps, cosmetics, and perfumes.

Cinnamaldehyde
(cinnamon flavor in
foods, drugs; from
cinnamon bark)

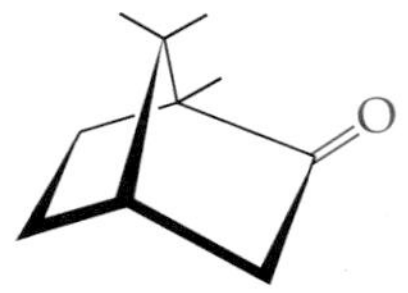

Camphor
(moth repellant from
camphor tree)

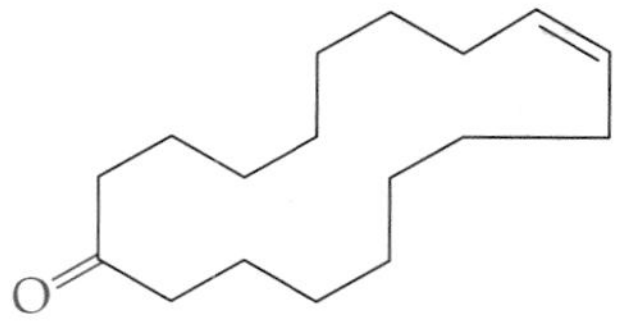

Civetone
(musky odor in perfumes;
from the scent gland of
the civet cat)

Chemically, the aldehyde and ketone functional groups are used as starting points for the synthesis of many complex organic molecules and pharmaceuticals, such as the anticancer drugs discussed in the Chemistry in Action "When Is Toxicity Beneficial?" at the end of the chapter. Four of the most common aldehydes and ketones used industrially are formaldehyde, acetaldehyde, acetone, and benzaldehyde; Table 15.2 shows their properties and uses.

Table 15.2 Common Aldehydes and Ketones and Their Uses.

Name	Structure	Properties and Uses
Formaldehyde (HCHO)	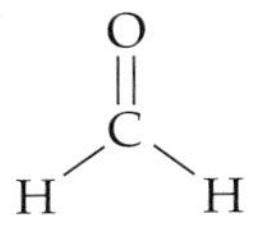	• Colorless gas with a pungent, suffocating odor; commonly sold as an aqueous solution under the name *formalin*. • Low concentrations in the air can cause eye, throat, and bronchial irritation, and higher concentrations can trigger asthma attacks. Skin contact can produce dermatitis. • Formed during incomplete combustion of hydrocarbon fuels; partly responsible for the irritation caused by smog. • Formaldehyde is very toxic by ingestion; can cause kidney damage and death. • Formed when methanol is broken biochemically; one reason methanol is so toxic. • Once commonly used as a preservative for biological specimens. • Major industrial use of formaldehyde is in the production of polymers used as adhesives for binding plywood, foam insulation for buildings, textile finishes, and hard and durable manufactured objects. • Because of concern over the toxicity and possible carcinogenicity of formaldehyde from polymeric materials, their use in most household applications is limited.
Acetaldehyde (CH_3CHO)	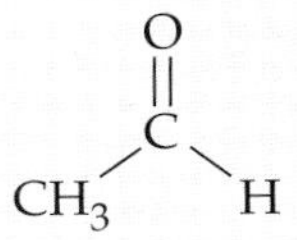	• Sweet-smelling, flammable liquid. • Present in ripe apples and other fruits; formed by the oxidation of ethanol. • Less toxic than formaldehyde; large doses can cause respiratory failure. • Chronic exposure produces symptoms like those of alcoholism. • Small amounts are produced in the normal breakdown of carbohydrates (Chapter 20). • Used historically in the production of acetic acid and acetic anhydride (Chapter 17). • Used industrially for the preparation of polymeric resins and as a reagent used in the silvering of mirrors.
Acetone (CH_3COCH_3)	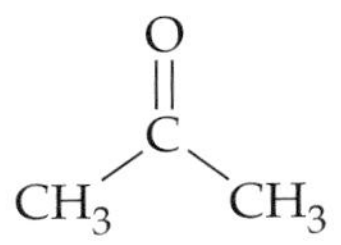	• Highly volatile liquid; a serious fire and explosion hazard when allowed to evaporate in closed spaces. • One of the most widely used of all organic solvents. • Dissolves most organic compounds and is miscible with water. • No chronic health risk associated with casual acetone exposure. • Sold for general-purpose cleanup work in home improvement stores. • Used as a solvent in many varnishes, lacquers, and nail polish removers. Produced in the liver when the biochemical breakdown of fats and carbohydrates is out of balance (ketosis; Section 24.7).
Benzaldehyde (PhCHO)	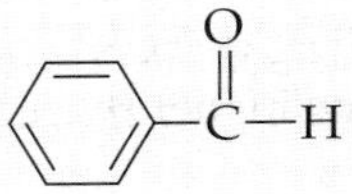	• Simplest aromatic aldehyde. • Colorless liquid; pleasant almond or cherry-like odor; first extracted from bitter almonds. • Used as a flavoring and fragrance in food, cosmetics, pharmaceuticals, and soap and is "generally regarded as safe" by the Food and Drug Administration (FDA). • Used industrially as a forerunner to other organic compounds, ranging from pharmaceuticals to plastic additives.

KEY CONCEPT PROBLEM 15.9

Identify the functional groups in the following compounds:

(a)

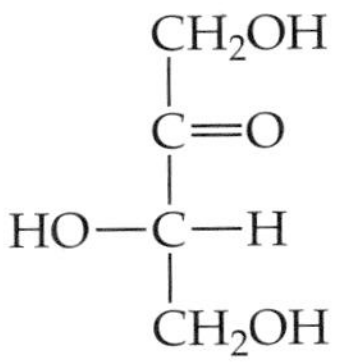

(b)

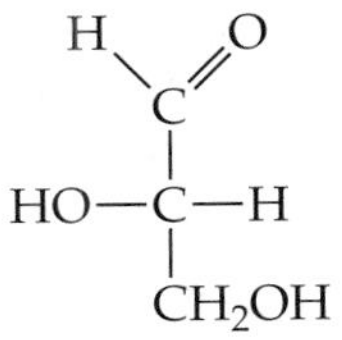

(c)

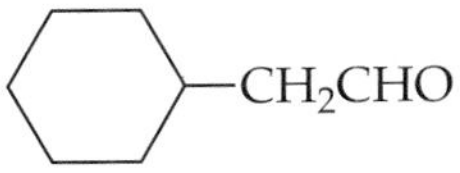

(d) $H_2NCH_2CH_2COCH_3$

15.5 Oxidation of Aldehydes

Learning Objective:

• Identify the products formed from the oxidation of aldehydes (and see that ketones do not oxidize in the same way).

Alcohols can be oxidized to aldehydes or ketones (Section 14.6), and aldehydes can be further oxidized to carboxylic acids. In aldehyde oxidation, the hydrogen bonded to the carbonyl carbon (shown in gold) is replaced by an —OH group. Ketones, because they do not have this hydrogen, do not react cleanly with oxidizing agents (except with those strong enough to destroy the molecule).

Oxidation of aldehydes and ketones

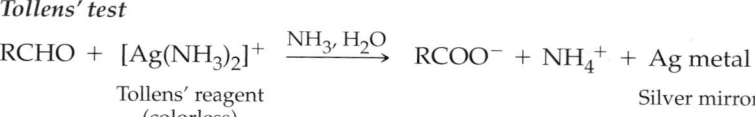

Of the mild oxidizing agents that convert aldehydes to carboxylic acids, oxygen in the air is the simplest. Aldehydes typically have a musty odor due to their partial oxidation to carboxylic acids, which generally have a strong, unpleasant odor. To prevent air oxidation, aldehydes are often stored under a layer of nitrogen gas, limiting contact with oxygen in the air.

Because ketones cannot be oxidized, treatment with a mild oxidizing agent is used as a test to distinguish between aldehydes and ketones. *Tollens' reagent,* which consists of a solution containing silver ion in aqueous ammonia, is the most visually appealing oxidizing agent for aldehydes. Treatment of an aldehyde with this reagent, in which the Ag^+ ion (present as $[Ag(NH_3)_2]^+$) is the oxidizing agent, rapidly yields the carboxylic acid anion and metallic silver. If the reaction is done in a clean glass container, metallic silver deposits on the inner walls, producing a beautiful shiny mirror (Figure 15.2a). Before modern instrumental methods were available, chemists had to rely on such visible chemical changes to identify chemical compounds.

Tollens' test

$$RCHO + [Ag(NH_3)_2]^+ \xrightarrow{NH_3, H_2O} RCOO^- + NH_4^+ + Ag \text{ metal}$$

Tollens' reagent (colorless)   Silver mirror

A test with another mild oxidizing agent, known as *Benedict's reagent,* also relies on reduction of a metal ion to produce visible evidence of the presence of aldehydes. The reagent solution contains blue copper(II) ion, which is reduced to give a precipitate of red copper(I) oxide in the reaction with an aldehyde (Figure 15.2b). Unlike the Tollens' test, however, Benedict's reagent does not unequivocally distinguish between ketones and aldehydes, as it will also produce a positive result in the presence of ketones that have an —OH on the carbon next to the carbonyl (*alpha* hydroxy ketones), a common grouping of atoms found in sugars. As with aldehydes, a red copper(I) precipitate is evidence of the presence of these ketones. As a result, a negative Tollens' test and a positive Benedict's test will allow one to distinguish between these two biologically important functional groups.

At one time, Benedict's reagent was extensively used as a test for sugars in the urine, which are primarily aldehydes and *alpha* hydroxy ketones. Today, more specific and more sensitive enzyme-based tests are preferred (see the Chemistry in Action "Diagnosis and Monitoring of Diabetes" on p. 708 in Chapter 22).

Benedict's test

$$RCHO + Cu^{2+} \xrightarrow{Buffer} RCOO^- + Cu_2O$$

Blue in solution   Brick-red solid

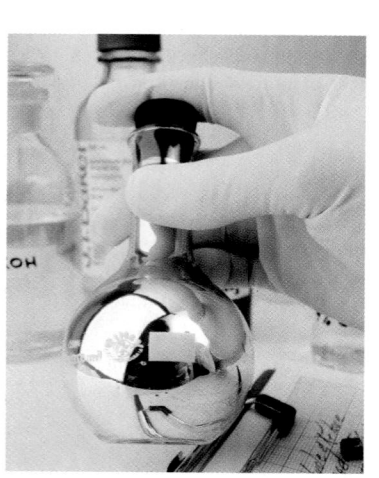

(a)

(b)

▲ **Figure 15.2**

The Tollens' and Benedict's tests for aldehydes.

(a) In the Tollens' test, colorless silver ion (Ag^+) is reduced to metallic silver. (b) In the Benedict's test for aldehyde-containing sugars, the blue copper(II) ion $(Cu^{2+}$ tube on left) is reduced to copper(I) to give brick-red copper(I) oxide $(Cu_2O$, tube on right). Glucose was used to produce the brick-red precipitate on the right. In both tests, an aldehyde is oxidized to the carboxylic acid anion.

PROBLEM 15.10

Indicate whether the following compounds will give a positive or negative result when treated with (i) Tollens' reagent or (ii) Benedict's reagent.

(a)

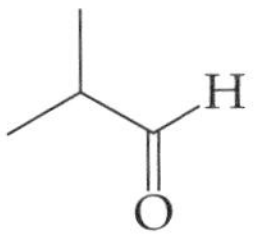

(b) Cyclohexanone   (c)

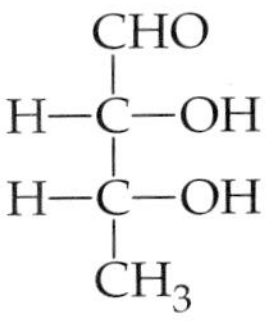

$$
\begin{array}{c}
\text{CHO} \\
\mid \\
\text{H}-\text{C}-\text{OH} \\
\mid \\
\text{H}-\text{C}-\text{OH} \\
\mid \\
\text{CH}_3
\end{array}
$$

(d)

$$
\begin{array}{c}
\text{CH}_2\text{OH} \\
\mid \\
\text{C}=\text{O} \\
\mid \\
\text{HO}-\text{C}-\text{H} \\
\mid \\
\text{CH}_2\text{OH}
\end{array}
$$

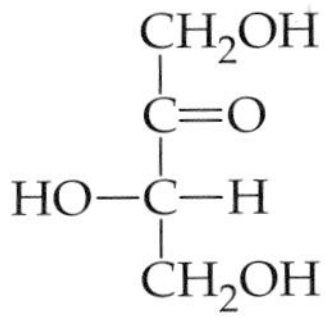

15.6   Reduction of Aldehydes and Ketones

Learning Objective:

• Identify the products of the reduction of aldehydes and ketones.

The reduction of a carbonyl group occurs with the addition of hydrogen across the double bond to produce an —OH group, a reaction that is the reverse of the oxidation of an alcohol.

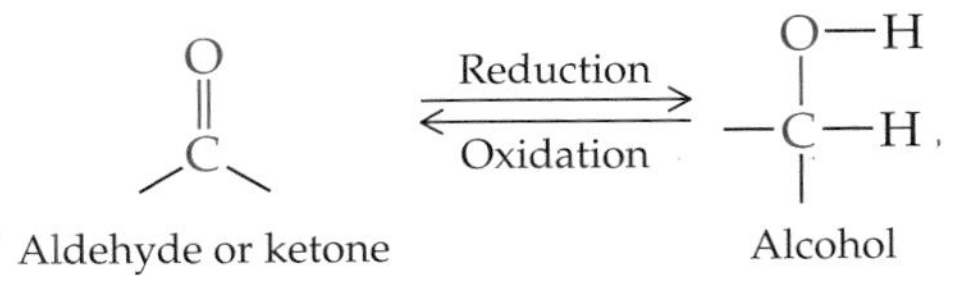

Aldehyde or ketone   Alcohol

Aldehydes are reduced to primary alcohols, and ketones are reduced to secondary alcohols.

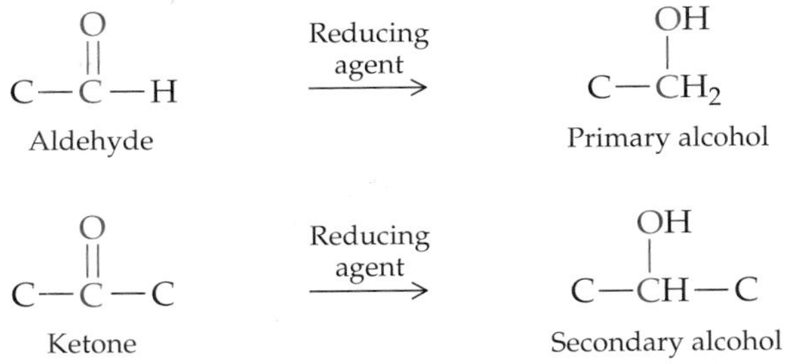

Aldehyde   Primary alcohol

Ketone   Secondary alcohol

These reductions occur by formation of a bond to the carbonyl carbon atom by a hydride ion $(:\text{H}^-)$ accompanied by bonding of a hydrogen ion (H^+) to the carbonyl oxygen atom. The reductions make good sense when you think about the polarity of the carbonyl group. The carbonyl-group carbon has a partial positive charge because electrons are drawn away by the electronegative oxygen atom, so the negatively charged hydride ion is drawn to this carbon atom. Because the oxygen atom has a partial negative charge, the positively charged hydrogen atom is attracted there.

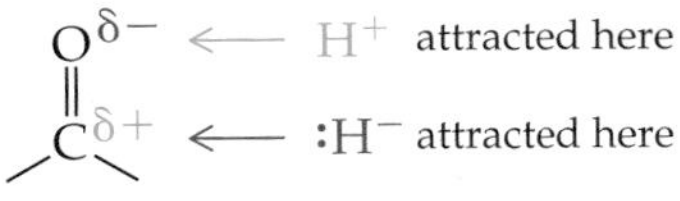

Note that a hydride ion $(:\text{H}^-)$ has a lone pair of valence electrons. Both electrons are used to form a covalent bond to the carbonyl carbon. This change leaves a negative charge on the carbonyl oxygen. Aqueous acid is then added, H^+ bonds to the oxygen, and a neutral alcohol results. Thus, the two new hydrogen atoms in the alcohol product come from different sources.

$\text{O}^{\delta-}$ ← H^+ attracted here
$\text{C}^{\delta+}$ ← $:\text{H}^-$ attracted here

Reduction of an aldehyde

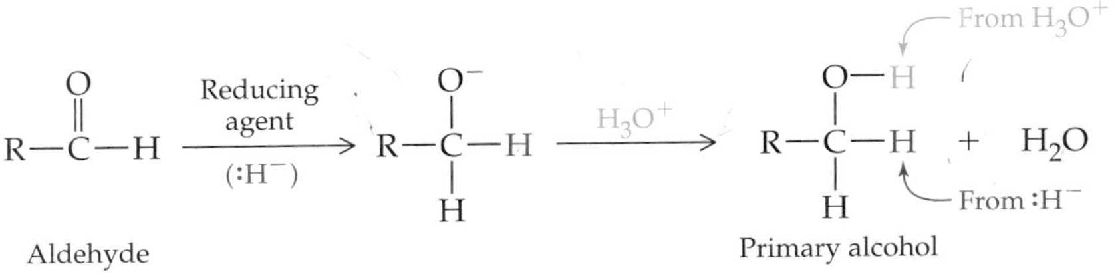

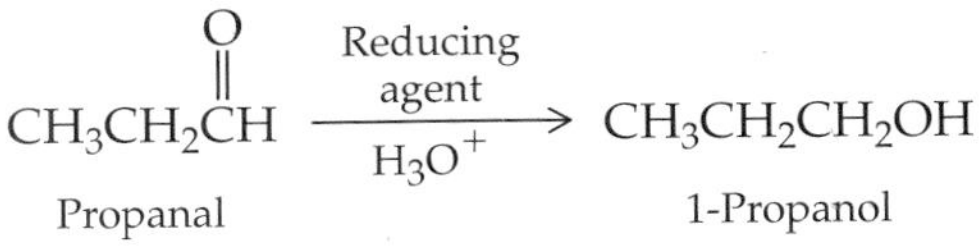

Aldehyde   Primary alcohol

$$
\begin{array}{c}
\text{O} \\
\parallel \\
\text{CH}_3\text{CH}_2\text{CH}
\end{array}
\xrightarrow[\text{H}_3\text{O}^+]{\text{Reducing agent}}
\text{CH}_3\text{CH}_2\text{CH}_2\text{OH}
$$

Propanal   1-Propanol

Reduction of a ketone

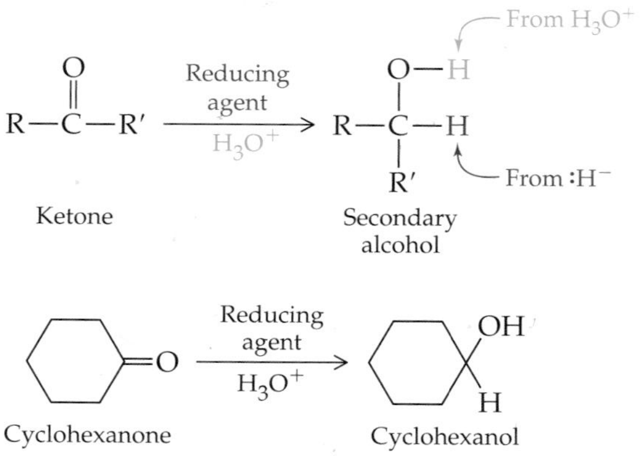

Ketone → Secondary alcohol

Cyclohexanone → Cyclohexanol

In biological systems, the reducing agent for a carbonyl group is often the coenzyme nicotinamide adenine dinucleotide (abbreviated as NAD), which cycles between reacting as a reducing agent (NADH) and an oxidizing agent (NAD^+) by the loss and gain of a hydride ion ($:H^-$). The biochemical reduction of pyruvic acid, a ketone-containing acid that plays a pivotal role in energy production, utilizes NADH. The reaction occurs in active skeletal muscles. Vigorous exercise causes a buildup of the reduction product, lactic acid, which can irritate muscles and cause discomfort and soreness.

▶▶ The reduction of aldehydes and ketones to alcohols is an important reaction in living cells, and NADH is the common source of the hydride ion. It donates H^- to an aldehyde or ketone to yield an anion, which then picks up H^+ from surrounding aqueous fluids. The major role of NADH as a biochemical reducing agent is introduced in Section 21.7 and the transformation of pyruvate to lactate will be discussed in Section 22.5.

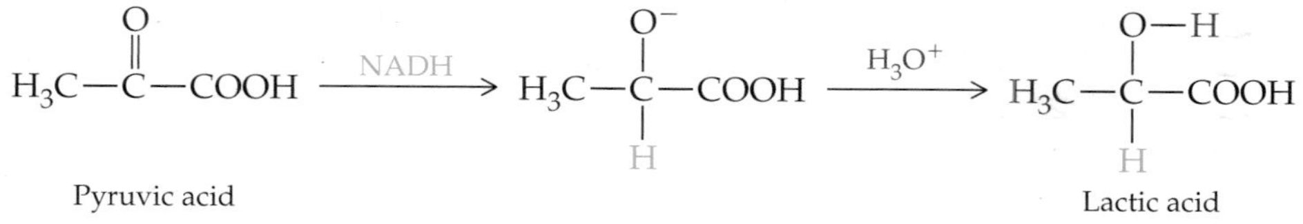

Pyruvic acid → Lactic acid

Worked Example 15.2 Writing the Products of a Carbonyl Reduction

What product would you obtain by reduction of benzaldehyde?

ANALYSIS First, draw the structure of the starting material, showing the double bond in the carbonyl group. Then rewrite the structure showing only a single bond between C and O, along with partial bonds to both C and O.

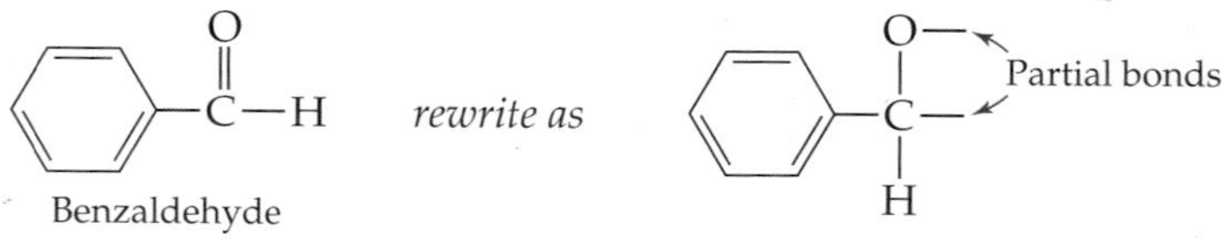

Benzaldehyde *rewrite as* Partial bonds

Finally, attach hydrogen atoms to the two partial bonds and rewrite the product.

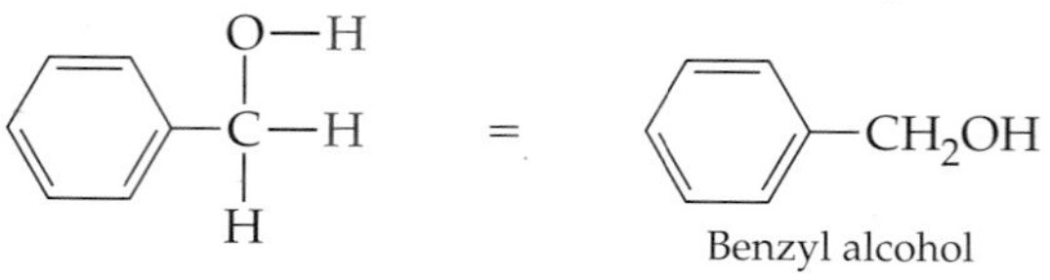

Benzyl alcohol

SOLUTION
The product obtained is benzyl alcohol.

PROBLEM 15.11

Draw line structures of the following compounds and the product you would obtain from the reduction of each.

(a) Isopropyl methyl ketone   (b) *p*-Hydroxybenzaldehyde

(c) 2-Methylcyclopentanone

PROBLEM 15.12

What ketones or aldehydes might be reduced to yield the following alcohols?

(a) 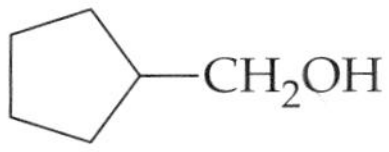 [structure: cyclopentane ring]—CH_2OH (b) 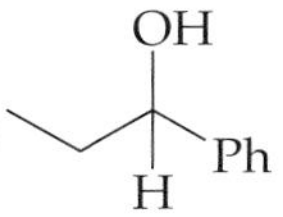 [structure with OH, H, Ph]   (c) $HOCH_2$—CH_2—CH_2OH

15.7   Addition of Alcohols: Hemiacetals and Acetals

Learning Objectives:

• Identify the differences between hemiacetals, hemiketals, acetals, and ketals.
• Predict the products of hemiacetal, hemiketal, acetal, and ketal formation and their hydrolysis.

Hemiacetal and Hemiketal Formation

In Section 13.6, we discussed the addition of water to a carbon–carbon double bond to form alcohols. Similarly, aldehydes and ketones also undergo **addition reactions** in which an alcohol combines with the carbonyl carbon and oxygen. When this occurs with an aldehyde, the initial addition products are known as *hemiacetals*. **Hemiacetals** have both an alcohol-like —OH group and an ether-like —OR group bonded to what was once the carbonyl carbon atom of the aldehyde, forming a new chiral carbon. The H from the alcohol bonds to the carbonyl-group oxygen, and the OR from the alcohol bonds to the carbonyl-group carbon. When this reaction occurs with ketones, the initial addition products are known as **hemiketals.**

Addition reaction, aldehydes and ketones Addition of an alcohol or other compound to the carbon double bond to give a carbon–oxygen single bond.

Hemiacetal A compound with both an alcohol-like —OH group and an ether-like —OR group bonded to the carbon atom that was at one time the aldehyde carbonyl carbon.

Hemiketal A compound with both an alcohol-like —OH group and an ether-like —OR group bonded to the carbon atom that was at one time the ketone carbonyl carbon.

◀ Recall the concept of a chiral carbon was discussed in Section 14.10.

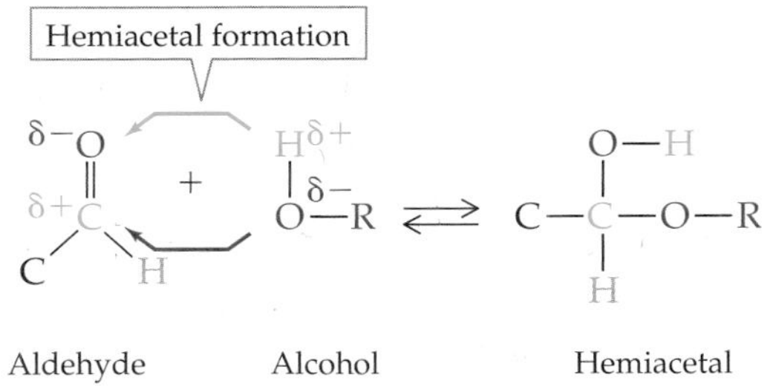

Hemiacetal formation

Aldehyde   Alcohol   Hemiacetal

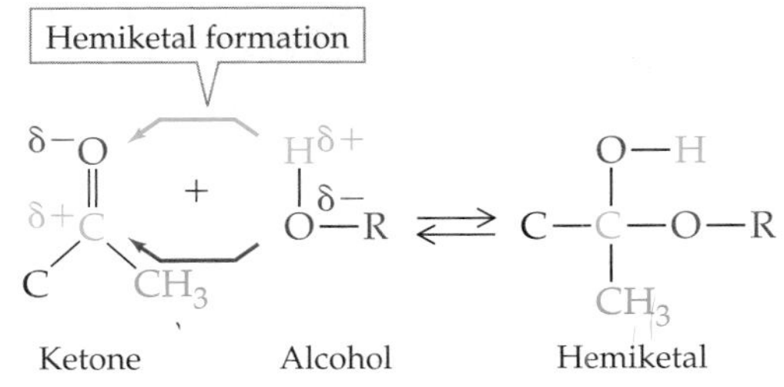

Hemiketal formation

Ketone   Alcohol   Hemiketal

- *The negatively polarized alcohol oxygen atom adds to the positively polarized carbonyl carbon* (similar to what happens in reduction of the carbonyl group). Almost all carbonyl-group reactions follow this same polarity pattern.
- *The reaction is reversible.* Hemiacetals and hemiketals rapidly revert back to aldehydes or ketones by loss of alcohol and establish an equilibrium with the aldehyde or ketone.

Ethanol (CH_3CH_2OH) forms a hemiacetal with acetaldehyde and a hemiketal with acetone as follows:

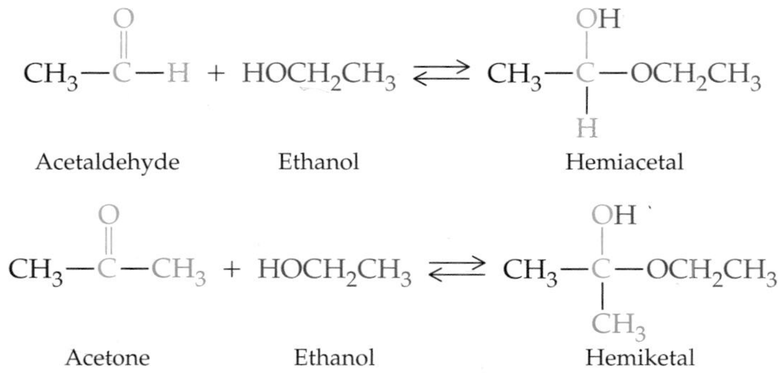

$$CH_3-\overset{\overset{\textstyle O}{\|}}{C}-H \;+\; HOCH_2CH_3 \;\rightleftarrows\; CH_3-\overset{\overset{\textstyle OH}{|}}{\underset{\underset{\textstyle H}{|}}{C}}-OCH_2CH_3$$

| Acetaldehyde | Ethanol | Hemiacetal |

$$CH_3-\overset{\overset{\textstyle O}{\|}}{C}-CH_3 \;+\; HOCH_2CH_3 \;\rightleftarrows\; CH_3-\overset{\overset{\textstyle OH}{|}}{\underset{\underset{\textstyle CH_3}{|}}{C}}-OCH_2CH_3$$

| Acetone | Ethanol | Hemiketal |

(For a more detailed look at how hemiacetals and acetals are formed, see Mastering Reactions: Carbonyl Additions on p. 493.)

In practice, hemiacetals and hemiketals are often too unstable to be isolated. When equilibrium is reached, very little of the hemi-species is present. A major exception occurs when the alcohol —OH and carbonyl —C=O functional groups that react are part of the *same* molecule. For thermodynamic reasons, the resulting *cyclic* hemiacetals or hemiketals are more stable than the noncyclic hemi-species. Because of their greater stability, most simple sugars exist mainly in the cyclic hemiacetal or hemiketal form, as shown next for glucose, rather than in the open-chain form shown below. This occurs when the carbohydrate "folds up" on itself, allowing the internal hemiacetal of hemiketal to form, again shown next for glucose.

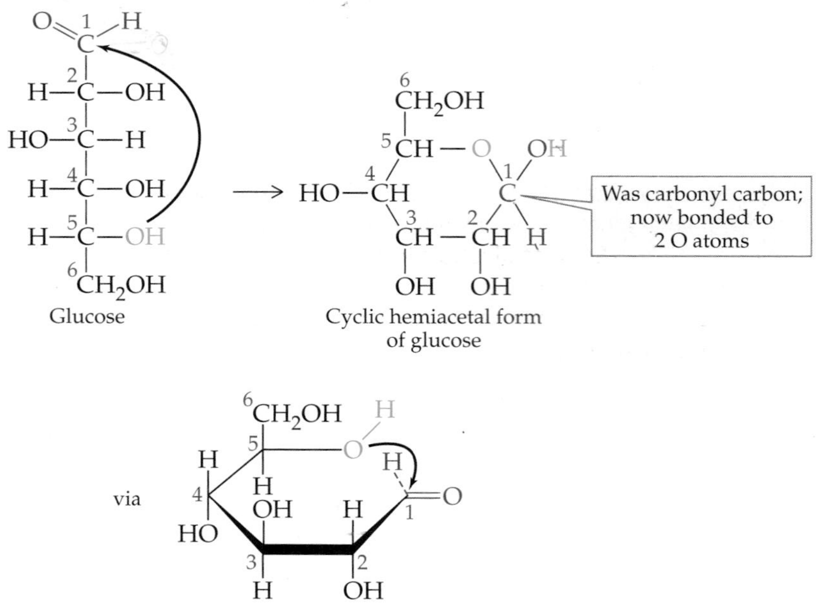

Glucose → Cyclic hemiacetal form of glucose

Was carbonyl carbon; now bonded to 2 O atoms

via

The cyclic form of glucose is customarily written as

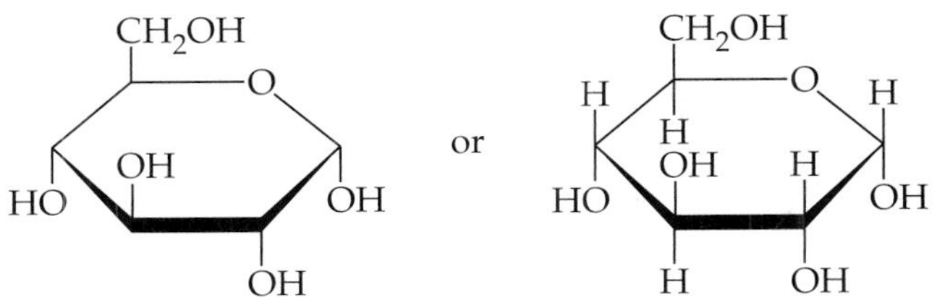

In Section 20.4, we will see the concept of anomers: cyclic isomers of a carbohydrate that differ in the spatial orientation of the —OH on what was originally the carbon of the C=O. This carbon will be called the anomeric carbon (see Problem 15.8).

Acetal and Ketal Formation

If a small amount of acid catalyst is added to the reaction of an alcohol with an aldehyde or ketone, the hemi-species initially formed is converted into an *acetal* or a *ketal* in a substitution reaction. An **acetal** is a compound that has *two* ether-like —OR groups bonded to what was the carbonyl carbon atom of an aldehyde (the two —OR groups can be different). A **ketal** is a compound that has *two* ether-like —OR groups bonded to what was the carbonyl carbon atom of a ketone.

Acetal A compound that has two ether-like —OR groups bonded to the same carbon atom of what was once an aldehyde.

Ketal A compound that has two ether-like —OR groups bonded to the same carbon atom of what was once a ketone.

Aldehyde or ketone → Hemiacetal or hemiketal → Acetal or ketal

For example,

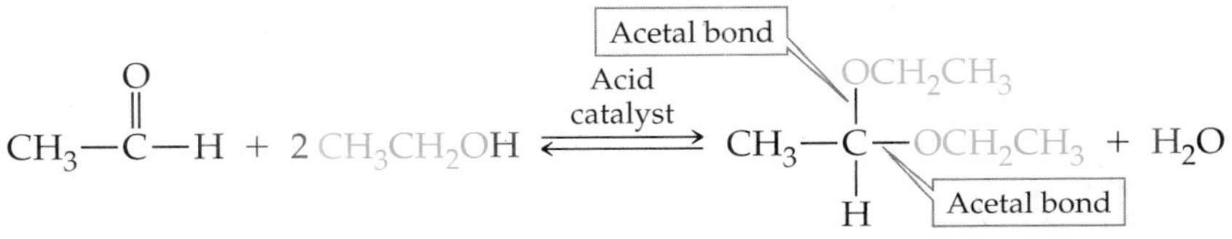

Acetaldehyde + Ethanol → Acetal + H_2O

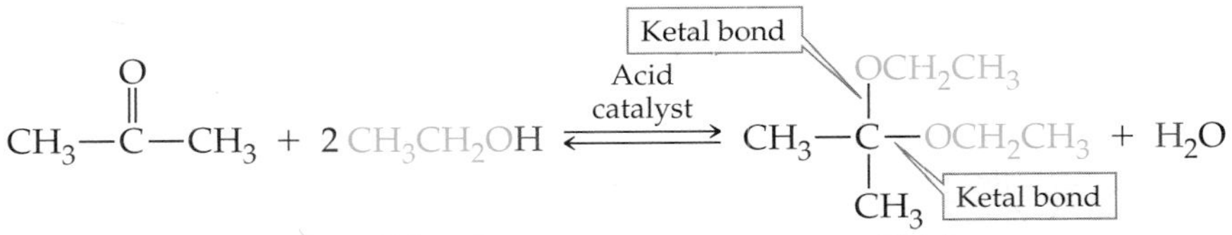

Acetone + Ethanol → Ketal + H_2O

It is important to note that the current set of IUPAC guidelines discourages the use of the hemiketal and ketal labels and instead favors the use of hemiacetal and acetal for the products formed upon addition of alcohols to *both* aldehydes and ketones, thereby recognizing them more as functional groups than as specific addition products. While we will make a distinction in this chapter between the products obtained when alcohols add to an aldehyde versus a ketone, keep in mind that the reaction is identical in both cases.

 Worked Example 15.3 Predicting the Products of Hemiacetal and Acetal Formation

Write the structure of the intermediate hemiacetal and the acetal final product formed in the following reaction:

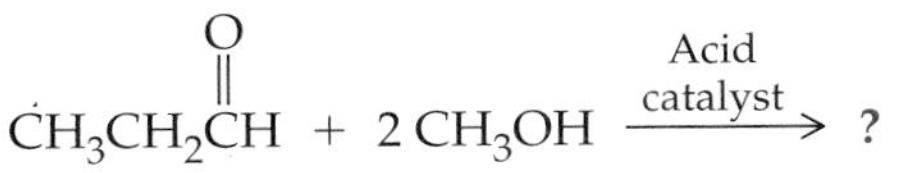

$$CH_3CH_2CH(O) + 2\ CH_3OH \xrightarrow{\text{Acid catalyst}}\ ?$$

—*continued on next page*

—continued from previous page

ANALYSIS First, rewrite the structure showing only a single bond between C and O, along with partial bonds to both C and O.

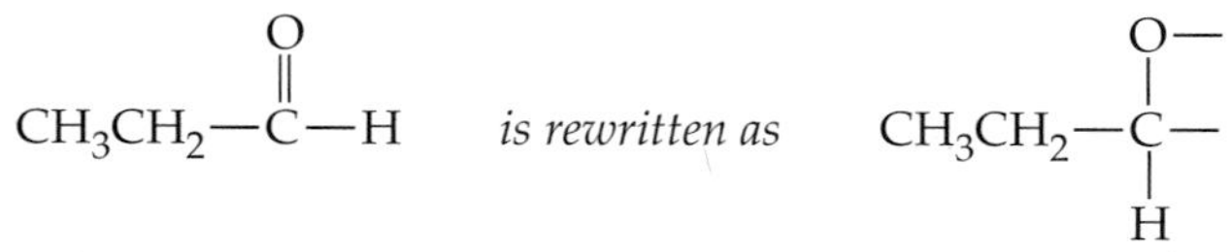

$$
\underset{\text{O}}{\overset{\overset{\text{O}}{\|}}{CH_3CH_2-C-H}} \quad \textit{is rewritten as} \quad CH_3CH_2-\overset{\overset{\displaystyle O-}{|}}{\underset{\underset{\displaystyle H}{|}}{C}}-
$$

Next, add 1 molecule of the alcohol (CH_3OH in this case) by attaching —H to the oxygen partial bond and —OCH_3 to the carbon partial bond. This yields the hemiacetal intermediate.

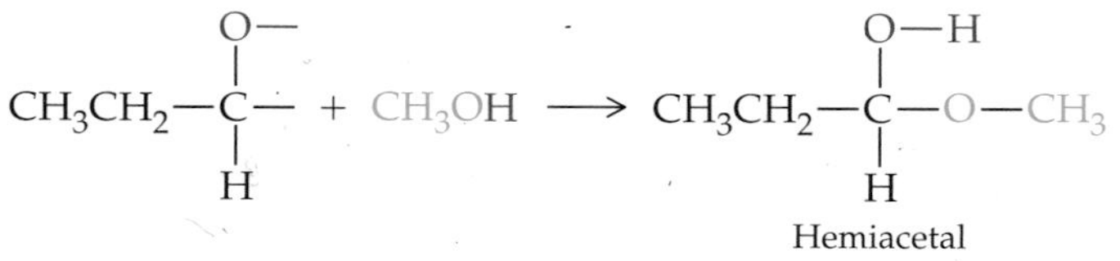

$$
CH_3CH_2-\overset{\overset{\displaystyle O-}{|}}{\underset{\underset{\displaystyle H}{|}}{C}}- \; + \; CH_3OH \longrightarrow CH_3CH_2-\overset{\overset{\displaystyle O-H}{|}}{\underset{\underset{\displaystyle H}{|}}{C}}-O-CH_3
$$

Hemiacetal

Finally, replace the —OH group of the hemiacetal with an —OCH_3 from a second molecule of alcohol.

SOLUTION
The reaction produces acetal and water.

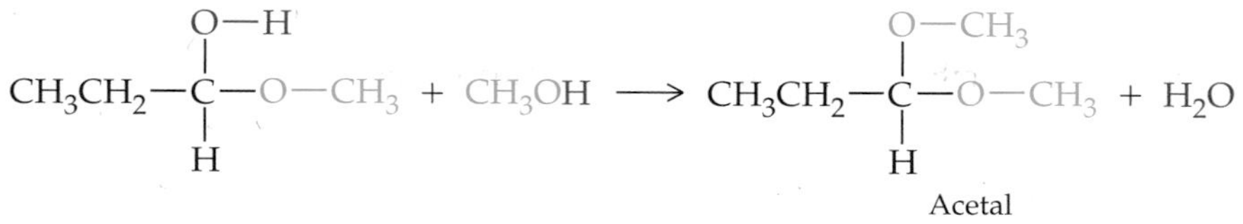

$$
CH_3CH_2-\overset{\overset{\displaystyle O-H}{|}}{\underset{\underset{\displaystyle H}{|}}{C}}-O-CH_3 \; + \; CH_3OH \longrightarrow CH_3CH_2-\overset{\overset{\displaystyle O-CH_3}{|}}{\underset{\underset{\displaystyle H}{|}}{C}}-O-CH_3 \; + \; H_2O
$$

Acetal

Worked Example 15.4 Identification of Hemiacetals and Hemiketals

Which of the following compounds are hemiacetals and which are hemiketals?

(a)

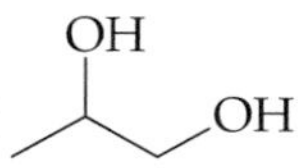

(b)

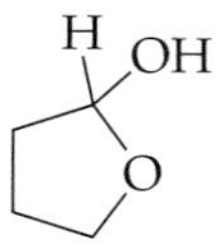

(c) 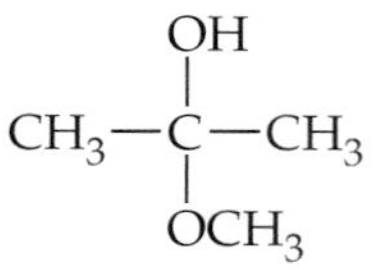 $CH_3-\overset{\overset{\displaystyle OH}{|}}{\underset{\underset{\displaystyle OCH_3}{|}}{C}}-CH_3$

ANALYSIS To identify a hemiacetal or a hemiketal, look for a carbon atom with single bonds to two oxygen atoms, with one being an —OH group and one an —OR group. Note that the O of the —OR group can be part of a ring. If the two remaining groups are carbons, it is a hemiketal; if one is a carbon and the other a hydrogen, it is a hemiacetal.

SOLUTION
Compound (a) contains two O atoms, but they are bonded to *different* C atoms; it is not a hemiacetal; rather it is a diol. Compound (b) has one ring C atom bonded to two oxygen atoms, one in the substituent —OH group and one bonded to the rest of the ring, which is the R group; the other two groups bonded to that carbon are a H and another C; it is a cyclic hemiacetal. Compound (c) also contains a C atom bonded to one —OH group and one —OR group, but here the other two bonded groups are carbons, so (c) is a hemiketal.

Worked Example 15.5 Identification of Acetals and Ketals

Which of the following compounds are acetals and ketals?

(a) 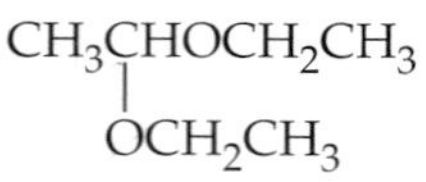 $CH_3\underset{\underset{\displaystyle OCH_2CH_3}{|}}{CH}OCH_2CH_3$

(b) 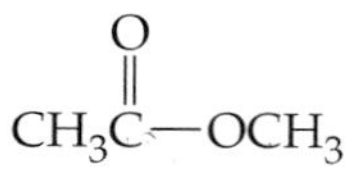 $CH_3\overset{\overset{\displaystyle O}{\|}}{C}-OCH_3$

(c)

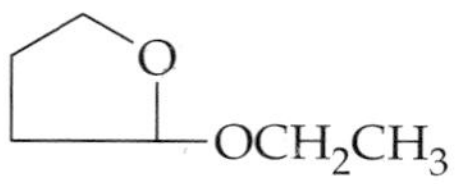

(d)

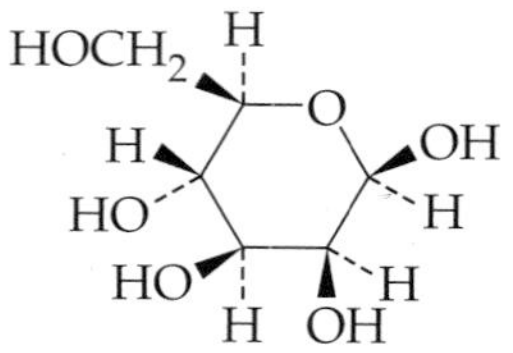

Mannose
(a sugar found attached to proteins in humans)

ANALYSIS As in identifying hemiacetals and hemiketals, look for a carbon atom that has single bonds to two oxygen atoms, but in this case both of them will be —OR groups. Note that the O of the —OR group can be part of a ring. If the two remaining bonded groups are carbons, it is a ketal; if one is a carbon and the other a hydrogen, it is an acetal.

SOLUTION
In (a), the central carbon atom is bonded to one —CH₃, one —H, and *two* —OCH₂CH₃ groups, so the compound is an acetal. Compound (b) does have a carbon atom bonded to two oxygen atoms, but one of the bonds is a double bond rather than a single bond, so this is not an acetal (it is, in fact, an ester; Chapter 17). Compound (c) has an oxygen atom in a ring, making it also part of an —OR group, where R is the ring. Since one of the carbons connected to the O in the ring is also connected to an —OCH₂CH₃ group, compound (c) is an acetal. Compound (d) is a sugar known as mannose; it too has an oxygen atom in a ring, making it part of an —OR group, where R is the ring. Since one of the carbons connected to the O in the ring is also connected to a H and an OH, compound (d) is a hemiacetal.

It should be noted that cyclic systems of these types are the most difficult to recognize, yet they will be the ones you will see most often as you progress through biochemistry, so the more practice you get at recognizing these, the better! Anytime you see an oxygen in a ring, always look at the carbons attached to either side of it to see if one of them has another oxygen attached. If one of them does, you have a cyclic hemiacetal, hemiketal, acetal, or ketal.

PROBLEM 15.13

For each compound shown next, determine whether it is a hemiacetal, a hemiketal, or neither.

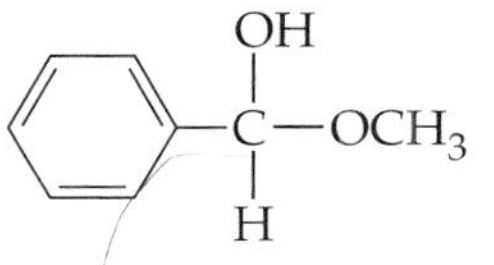

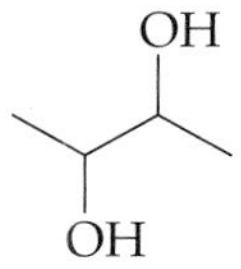

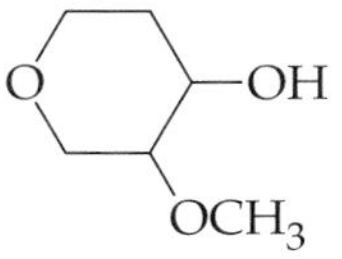

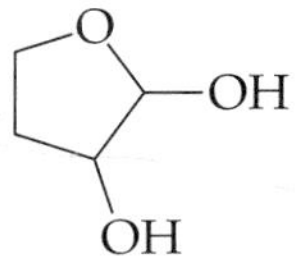

PROBLEM 15.14

Determine whether the following compounds are acetals or ketals. Draw the structure of the aldehyde or ketone it came from.

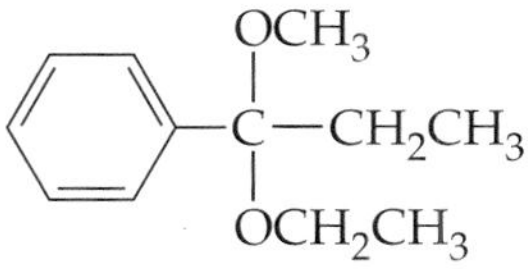

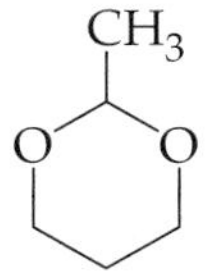

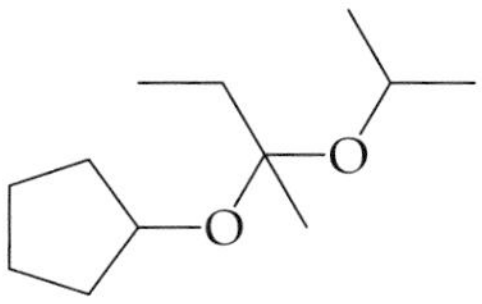

PROBLEM 15.15

Draw the structures of the hemiacetals or hemiketals formed in these reactions:

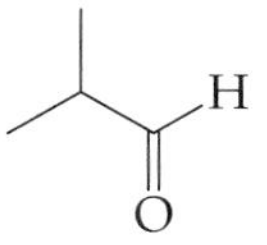

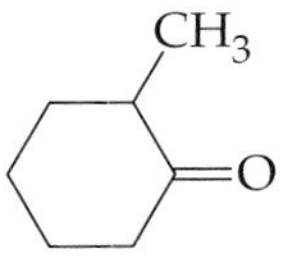

PROBLEM 15.16

Draw the structure of each acetal or ketal final product formed in the reactions shown in Problem 15.15 if an excess of alcohol was used.

PROBLEM 15.17

For each compound shown next, determine whether it is a hemiacetal, a hemiketal, an acetal, or a ketal.

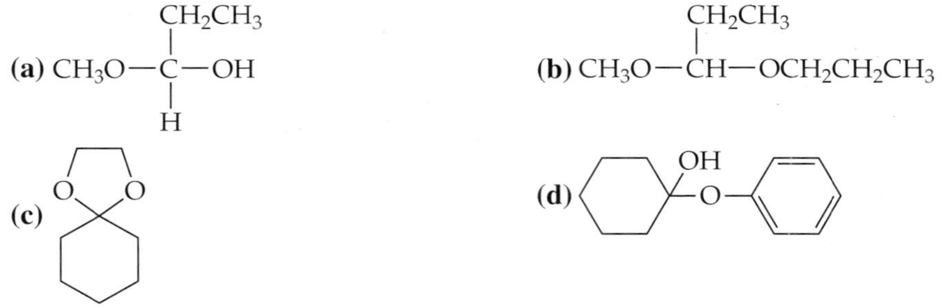

(a) $CH_3O—\underset{\underset{H}{\mid}}{\overset{\overset{CH_2CH_3}{\mid}}{C}}—OH$

(b) $CH_3O—\underset{\underset{}{}}{\overset{\overset{CH_2CH_3}{\mid}}{CH}}—OCH_2CH_2CH_3$

(c)

(d)

PROBLEM 15.18

Sugars (or carbohydrates, Chapter 20) form cyclic hemiacetals and hemiketals very readily; the carbon that is part of the hemiacetal or hemiketal linkage (and originally came from the $C{=}O$) is known as the *anomeric carbon* (Section 20.4). For each of the following, determine whether it is a hemiacetal or a hemiketal, and put a star on the anomeric carbon for each.

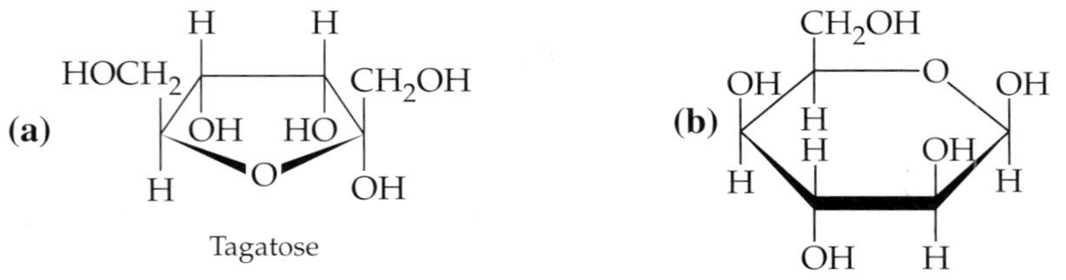

(a)

Tagatose

(b)

Idose

Acetal and Ketal Hydrolysis

Because acetal and ketal formation are equilibrium reactions, the extent to which the reaction proceeds in either direction can be controlled by changing the reaction conditions. Remember that water is one of the products formed during their formation; therefore, the aldehyde or ketone from which an acetal or ketal is formed can be regenerated by reversing the reaction. As a result, reversal simply requires an acid catalyst and a large quantity of water to drive the reaction back toward the aldehyde or ketone (Le Châtelier's principle, Section 7.9).

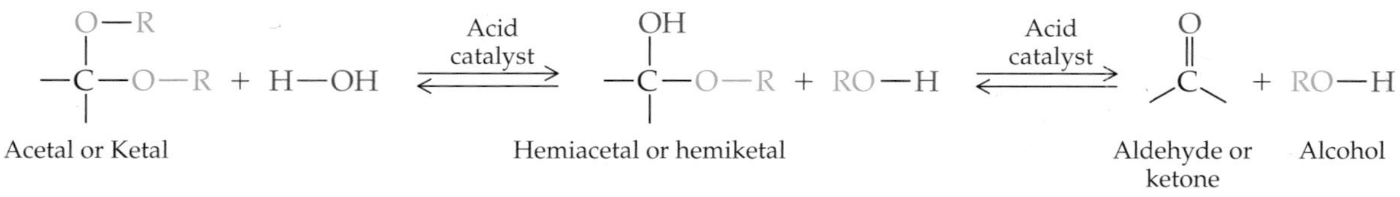

| Acetal or Ketal | Hemiacetal or hemiketal | Aldehyde or ketone | Alcohol |

For example,

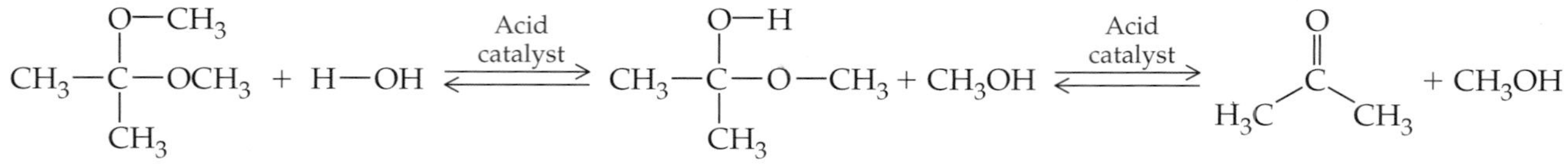

The reaction shown earlier is an example of **hydrolysis** (*Latin*: "to split with water"), a reaction in which a bond or bonds are broken and the —H and —OH of water add to the atoms of the broken bond or bonds. With either an acetal or ketal, the first step is formation of the hemi-species as the water breaks one of the C—OR bonds and a C—OH bond is formed in its place. The carbonyl group is then formed as the bond to the H of the C—OH and the hemi-species C—OR bond is broken. The result is the ketone or aldehyde from which the acetal or ketal was made plus two molecules of the alcohol RO—H. A simple way for you to show the steps of this reaction is presented in Worked Example 15.6.

It should be noted that although acetals, ketals, hemiketals, and hemiacetals react with water in the presence of acid, they are unreactive under basic conditions $(pH > 7)$, which is important since physiological pH is slightly greater than seven.

Hydrolysis A reaction in which a bond or bonds are broken and the H— and —OH of water add to the atoms of the broken bond or bonds.

▶▶ Consider for a moment that biochemical reactions take place in an environment where water molecules are always available, along with enzyme catalysts precisely suited to the necessary reactions. In this environment, it is not surprising that hydrolysis reactions play an important role. During digestion, hydrolysis breaks bonds in carbohydrates (Section 22.1), triacylglycerols (Section 24.1), and proteins (Section 25.1).

Worked Example 15.6 Writing the Products Obtained from Acetal Hydrolysis

Write the structure of the aldehyde or ketone that forms by hydrolysis of the following acetal:

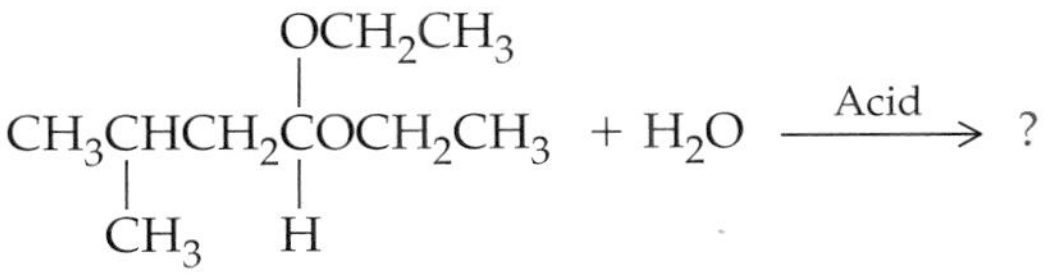

ANALYSIS The products are the aldehyde or ketone plus two molecules of the alcohol from which the acetal could have been formed. First, identify the two C—O acetal bonds, redrawing the structure if necessary.

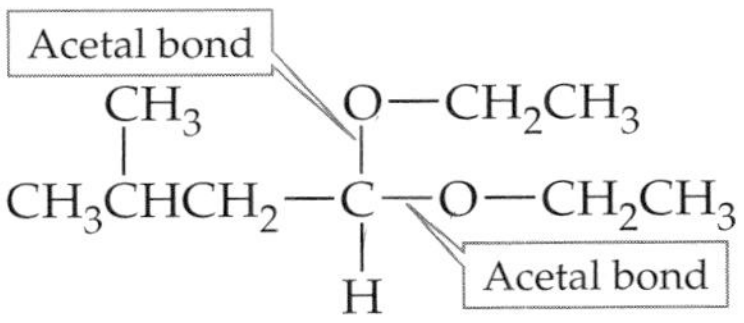

Next, break the H—OH bond and one of the acetal C—OR bonds (in this case, it does not matter which one); move the water OH to the acetal carbon to form the hemiacetal and the water H to the OR to form one molecule of HOR.

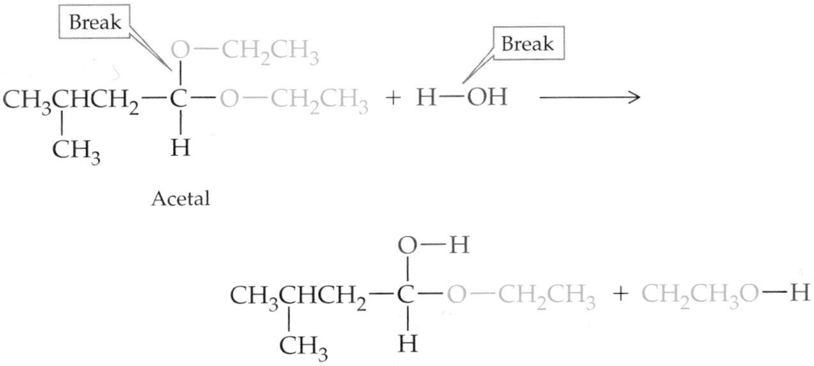

Acetal

Hemiacetal

Remove the H and OR groups from the hemiacetal, and change the C—O single bond to a C=O double bond to give carbon the four bonds it must have. Combine the H and OR you removed from the second alcohol molecule.

—*continued on next page*

—continued from previous page

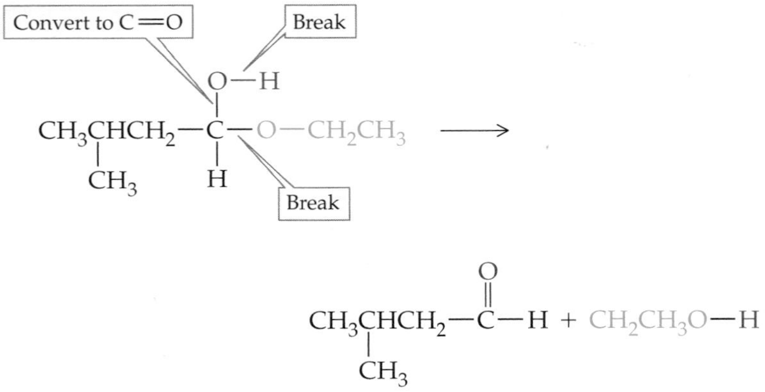

| Convert to C=O | | Break |

$$CH_3CHCH_2-\overset{\overset{\displaystyle O-H}{|}}{\underset{\underset{\displaystyle CH_3}{|}}{C}}-O-CH_2CH_3 \longrightarrow$$

| Break |

$$CH_3CHCH_2-\overset{\overset{\displaystyle O}{\|}}{C}-H + CH_2CH_3O-H$$
$$\underset{CH_3}{|}$$

3-Methylbutanal

SOLUTION

In this example, the product is an aldehyde. The procedure is identical if you start with a ketal rather than an acetal.

PROBLEM 15.19

What aldehydes or ketones result from the following hydrolysis reactions? What alcohol is formed in each case? It may help to redraw these in line structure format.

(a) 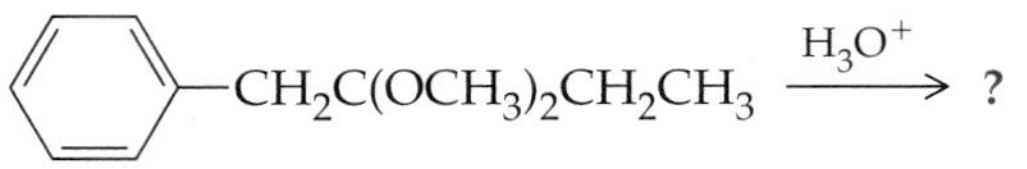 [benzene ring]$-CH_2C(OCH_3)_2CH_2CH_3 \xrightarrow{H_3O^+}$?

(b) $CH_3CH_2CH_2OCHOCH_2CH_2CH_3 \xrightarrow{H_3O^+}$?
    $\qquad\qquad\quad \underset{CH_2CH_3}{|}$

(c) $CH_3CH_2CH_2OCH_2OCH_2CH_2CH_3 \xrightarrow{H_3O^+}$?

HANDS-ON CHEMISTRY 15.1

One of the more complex groups of molecules you will have to recognize and deal with are the carbohydrates (Chapter 20), which exist almost exclusively in their hemiacetal and hemiketal form. In this exercise, you are going to get a feel for them by building models of glucose, galactose, and fructose (the heavy ring bonds are meant to look like they are coming out toward you).

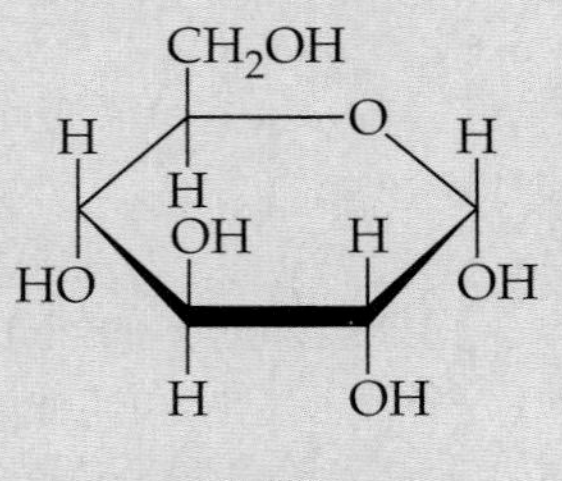

alpha-Glucose
(α-Glucose)

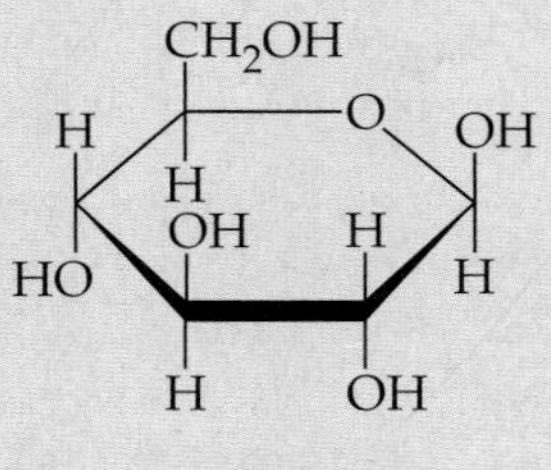

beta-Glucose
(β-Glucose)

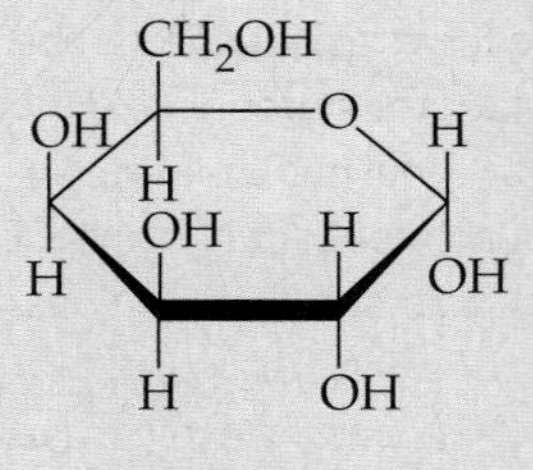

alpha-Galactose
(α-Galactose)

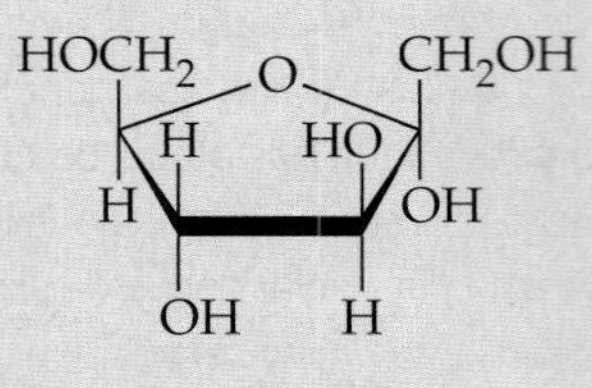

alpha-Fructose
(α-Fructose)

You will be using the methods and techniques outlined in Hands-On Chemistry 13.1 (p. 410). For this exercise, you will be building what are known as *Haworth representations* of the molecules; that is to say that you will build the molecules as if the ring were flat (this is perfectly fine for the comparisons we will be doing here). Throughout this exercise, remember that carbon is tetravalent (four bonds); you will approximate the OH groups using a single gumdrop.

Building Blocks Needed for This Exercise—for this exercise, you will need the following (this will build four structures):

One box of toothpicks—round is best but any will do.

Nineteen carbon gumdrops—use either black or some other dark color, as long as they are different colors than those needed for other structures.

Four ring oxygen gumdrops—use red or orange. These will be used only when an oxygen is in a ring.

Fifteen "OH" gumdrops—use blue or green. You will use these to represent the OH groups that are attached to the ring.

Sixteen hydrogen gumdrops—use white or clear. You will use these to represent a H when it is attached to a ring carbon.

Five "CH_2OH" gumdrops—rather than building each CH_2OH unit needed, you will represent these using a single gumdrop. Use any color other than the ones you used earlier. We will use these to represent the OH groups.

Make the ring flat and all groups coming off of a ring carbon perpendicular to the ring. Based on this, your model of *alpha*-glucose should look like the following:

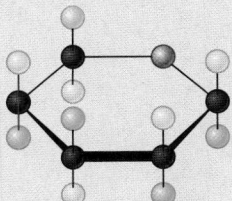

Once you have these assembled, you can begin. Be prepared to use more toothpicks and/or gumdrops if needed. You may want to take pictures of each model you make with your phone for review later.

a. Start by assembling *alpha*-glucose. How many chiral carbons does it have? (Review Section 14.10 if necessary.) Identify the hemiacetal carbon in this molecule.

b. Now, assemble *beta*-glucose. How many chiral carbons does it have? (Review Section 14.10 if necessary.) Identify the hemiacetal carbon in this molecule.

c. Now, compare *alpha*-glucose to *beta*-glucose. Are they mirror images? Use a small hand mirror to check if you are not sure. You should find that they are NOT mirror images; what carbon(s) have different configurations (orientation in space) in the two molecules? Two molecules with more than one chiral carbon that have the same configuration on all carbons EXCEPT the hemiacetal or hemiketal carbon one are known as *anomers,* and the hemiacetal or hemiketal carbon is said to be the *anomeric carbon*. Notice the spatial location of the OH on the anomeric carbon when compared to the CH_2OH attached to the ring. In carbohydrate chemistry, when these groups are on the same side of the ring they are said to be *beta;* when on opposite sides, they are said to be *alpha*.

d. Now, build *alpha*-galactose; how many chiral carbons does it have? Compare it to *alpha*-glucose; which carbon(s) have different configurations? Are these two molecules anomers? Two molecules with more than one chiral carbon that have the same configuration on all non-hemiacetal or hemiketal carbons EXCEPT one are known as *epimers*. An anomer is a special type of epimer.

e. (Optional) Build the model of *alpha*-fructose. How many chiral carbons does it have? Can you identify the anomeric carbon? See if you can deduce what the structure of *beta*-fructose might look like.

MASTERING REACTIONS

Carbonyl Additions

In Chapter 13, we learned how additions to carbon—carbon ($C=C$) double bonds occur (see Mastering Reactions: How Addition Reactions Occur on p. 422). We were able to predict the products by examining the initially formed intermediate (the carbocation) and evaluating its stability. This was necessary because there is no inherent preference for attack at one carbon over the other in an alkene. Now consider the carbon—oxygen double bond ($C=O$) of a carbonyl. A carbonyl has a natural polarity, and because it is also a double bond, its reactions should be similar to those of a $C=C$. Let's look closer at these additions.

A carbonyl is a polarized double bond (Section 15.1), such that the carbon carries a partial positive charge δ^+ and the oxygen carries a partial negative charge δ^-. As a result, there will always be a preference for how a similarly polarized reagent will add.

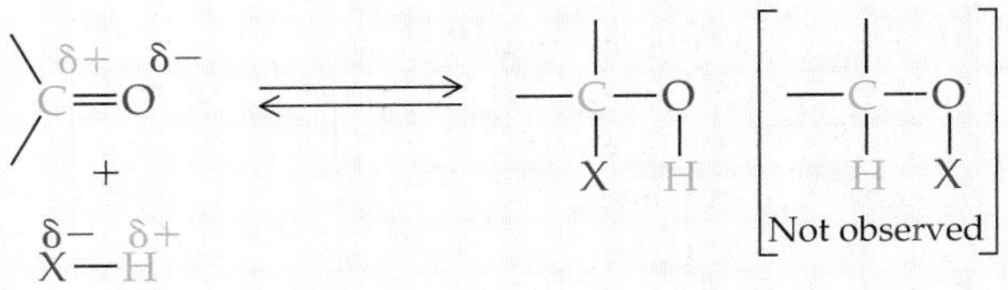

Thus, the electron-poor end (δ^+) of the reagent will *always* attach to the O of the carbonyl and the electron-rich end (δ^-) to the C. This process is also a true equilibrium and is governed by Le Châtelier's principle. So, in the presence of water one might expect the following to occur:

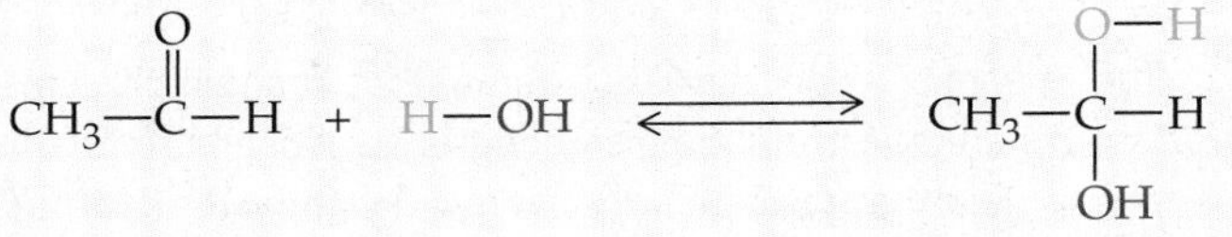

Carbonyl hydrate

The carbonyl hydrate formed is similar to the alcohol obtained when water adds across a $C=C$; unlike an alcohol, however, most carbonyl hydrates are impossible to isolate. The reason for this stems from Le Châtelier's principle: One must remove water to isolate the carbonyl hydrate, but the very act of doing so pushes the equilibrium back to the starting material side, the $C=O$. This points out an important difference in the two reactions: unlike alkenes, only a few addition products of carbonyls are stable enough to be isolated. Here, we will focus on the two most important reactions: addition of HCN and addition of alcohols (here, we concern ourselves exclusively with ketones and aldehydes; in Chapter 17, we will examine what happens if the $C=O$ is part of a carboxyl group).

The mechanism for addition of methanol to propionaldehyde is shown next; it begins in the same manner as for a $C=C$. A trace

(*continued*)

catalytic amount of acid protonates the carbonyl (Step 1), which is then activated toward addition; this is necessary as the carbonyl, while more reactive than a C=C, is still not quite reactive enough for the addition to occur to any great extent on its own.

Step 1

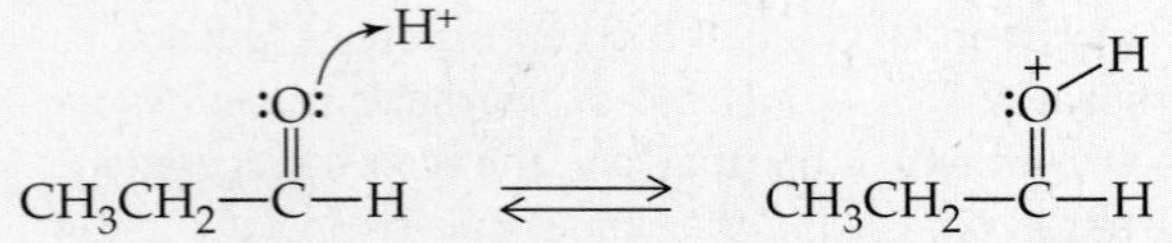

Step 2

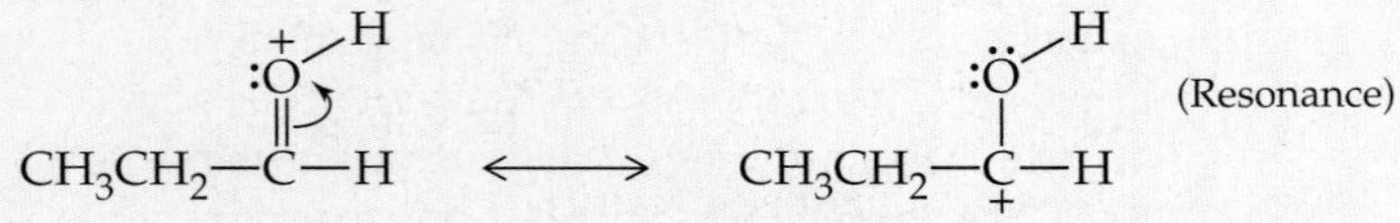

(Resonance)

Step 3

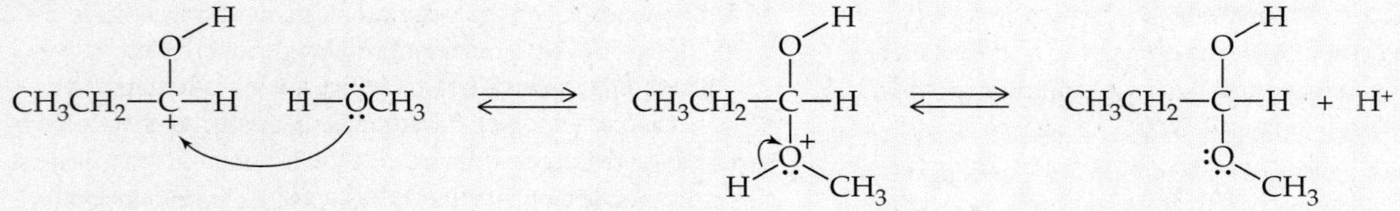

Hemiacetal

Acetal Formation

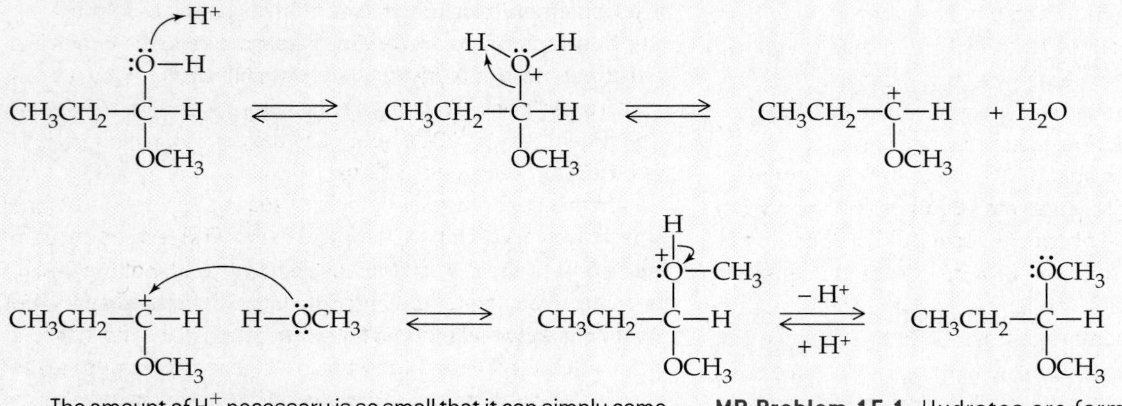

The amount of H⁺ necessary is so small that it can simply come from anywhere. The protonated carbonyl is in resonance with the species in which the positive charge has migrated from the O to the C (Step 2), thus providing an ideal intermediate to which the alcohol can add. Addition of methanol followed by loss of H⁺ provides the hemiacetal (Step 3). As long as there is an excess of alcohol, the equilibrium should favor the formation of the hemiacetal.

Although only a trace of acid (if any) is needed for formation of the hemiacetal, the presence of H⁺ is absolutely necessary for further conversion to the acetal. Protonation of the —OH of the hemiacetal, followed by loss of water and subsequent attack by another alcohol molecule will provide, after loss of H⁺, the acetal.

Notice here that water is one of the products formed; as long as the amount of water is much less than the amount of alcohol present, the equilibrium will favor the acetal. In fact, if the acid is neutralized at the end of the reaction (by addition of base), the acetal can be easily isolated, as both acid and water are necessary for the equilibrium to reverse direction.

The mechanism of the hydrolysis of an acetal is simply the reverse of the processes shown earlier; by addition of both H⁺ and H_2O the equilibrium can be made to proceed in the direction that favors the ketone or aldehyde and alcohol-starting materials.

MR Problem 15.1 Hydrates are formed when water, rather than an alcohol, adds across the carbonyl carbon. Chloral hydrate, a potent sedative and component in "knockout" drops, is formed by reacting trichloroacetaldehyde with water in a reaction analogous to hemiacetal formation. Draw the formula of chloral hydrate.

MR Problem 15.2 Provide the mechanism for the hydrolysis of the acetal shown next. (Hint: Apply all the steps given in the mechanism for the formation of the acetal in reverse.)

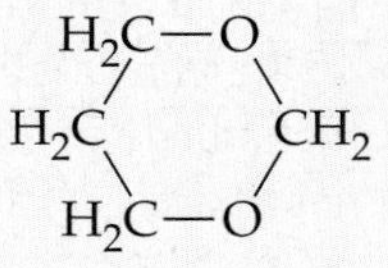

MR Problem 15.3 Cyclic hemiacetals form easily and have enhanced stability due to their compactness. Provide the mechanism for the following reaction:

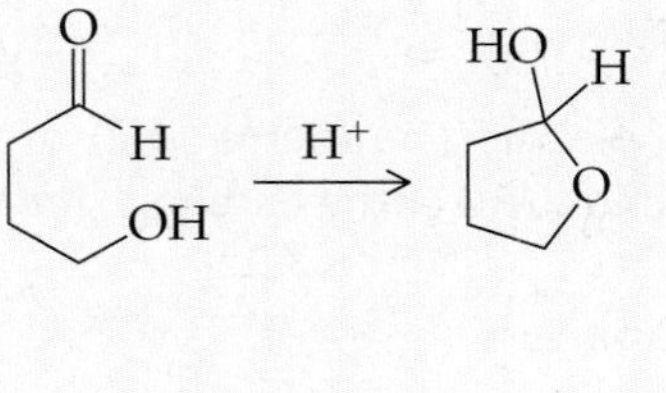

CHEMISTRY IN ACTION

☤ When Is Toxicity Beneficial?

We rely on medicines throughout our life, but almost all medicines have side effects, toxicity being one of them. Are there any times that toxicity is a good thing?

In its broadest meaning, the term *drug* refers to any chemical agent, other than food, that affects living organisms and is usually reserved for substances that prevent or treat disease. By contrast, a *poison* or *toxic substance* is any chemical agent that harms living organisms. As a result, the categories "drugs" and "toxin" are not mutually exclusive. Often a substance that cures disease or alleviates symptoms in low concentrations will cause injury or death when taken in larger amounts. Perhaps the most significant class of medicines that have to be toxic to carry out their designed purpose are the drugs used to treat cancer.

The treatment of cancers with chemical agents (chemotherapy or chemo) has long been both a frustrating and rewarding experience in medicine. Since most drugs used to treat cancer affect only cells that are actively reproducing, and since cancer cells grow and multiply much more rapidly than most normal cells in the body, these rogue cells will usually be much more strongly affected by these drugs than "normal" cells. However, the fact remains that chemo drugs will also kill normal cells just as readily as cancer cells.

Drugs used in chemotherapy can be classified into five general categories: 1) *alkylating agents* (chemicals that directly damage deoxyribonucleic acid (DNA), preventing its reproduction), 2) *antimetabolites* (agents that substitute for the normal building blocks of DNA and ribonucleic acid (RNA)), 3) *antitumor antibiotics* (drugs that alter the DNA inside cancer cells), 4) *topoisomerase inhibitors* (compounds that interfere with enzymes called topoisomerases, which help separate the strands of DNA for replication), and 5) *mitotic inhibitors,* the newest class of chemo drugs that prevent cell division by interfering with the protein called tubulin, which is used to form microtubules. Microtubules are very long, cable-like proteins that are assembled when needed to move organelles in a cell around; they are necessary to move and separate chromosomes and other components when a cell undergoes division (mitosis). Because cancer cells grow and spread by nonstop mitotic division, they are more sensitive to inhibition of mitosis than normal cells. If cell growth can be stopped, then one of two things can happen: the cell will eventually die or undergo internal repair. In either case, the cancer cell is stopped dead in its tracks.

▲ The beautiful autumn crocus; one of the most endangered plants in the world and the most lethal, it contains colchicine, a toxin for which there is no antidote.

Almost all known mitotic inhibitors are intricate organic molecules that contain a wide variety of functional groups, with some containing the ketone function. Originally isolated from plants, these compounds inhibit mitosis. One example is colchicine. Originally isolated from the autumn crocus, colchicine is known to interfere with mitosis; however, it was dropped from further study due to its extremely toxic nature. Scientists studying tubulin discovered a colchicine-binding site and reasoned that synthetic analogs with lower overall toxicity might be possible; however, out of this work, two colchicine-binding site inhibitors (CBSIs) were discovered (Phenstatin and BCN-105P) and are currently being investigated for the treatment of solid tumors.

Another promising mitotic inhibitor that also contains a ketone is paclitaxel (also known as Taxol), which we first learned about at the beginning of the chapter. Isolated from the bark of the Pacific Yew tree, this complex, highly oxygenated molecule has shown great promise in the treatment of a number of solid tumor cancers including ovarian, breast, lung, bladder, and melanoma, as well as Kaposi's sarcoma, the cancer most often associated with patients suffering from acquired immunodeficiency syndrome (AIDS). While paclitaxel has drawbacks associated with it (including hair loss, lowering of white blood cell count, gastrointestinal problems, high blood pressure, depression, muscle cramps, and headache), it is considered so important that it has been placed on the World Health Organization's List of Essential Medicines, a list of the most important medications needed in for good, basic health.

CIA Problem 15.3 What are the five classes of chemotherapy drugs?

CIA Problem 15.4 (a) What are mirotubules? (b) Why would drugs that target microtubules make good chemo medicines?

CIA Problem 15.5 Tetrodotoxin, found in the puffer fish, has been investigated for use in treatment of moderate to severe cancer pain. This extremely toxic compound is lethal to humans when injected in doses of 8 µg or more per kilogram of body weight. If an average adult male weighs 200 lb, how much tetrodotoxin is needed to kill him?

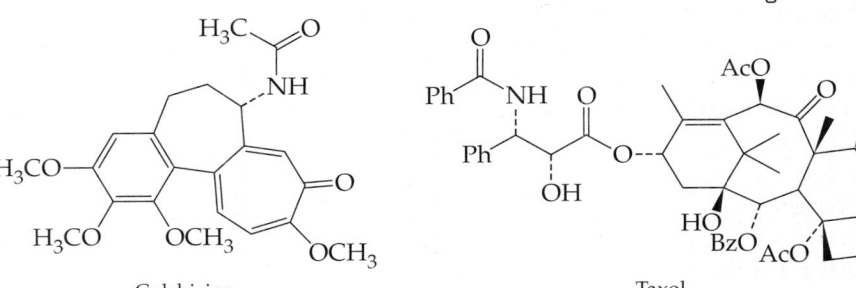

Colchicine   Taxol

SUMMARY REVISITING THE CHAPTER LEARNING OBJECTIVES

- **Identify the carbonyl group and describe its polarity and shape.** The *carbonyl group* is a carbon atom connected by a double bond to an oxygen atom, $C=O$. Because of the electronegativity difference between carbon and oxygen, the $C=O$ group is polar, with a partial negative charge on oxygen and a partial positive charge on carbon. The oxygen and the two substituents on the carbonyl-group carbon atom form a planar triangle *[see Problems 20, 27–29, 48, 49, and 66]*.

- **Name and draw simple aldehydes and ketones given a structure or a name.** The simplest *aldehydes* and *ketones* are known by common names (formaldehyde, acetaldehyde, benzaldehyde, and acetone). Aldehydes are named systematically by replacing the final *-e* in an alkane name with *-al* and when necessary numbering the chain starting with 1 at the —CHO group. Ketones are named systematically by replacing the final *-e* in an alkane name with *-one* and numbering starting with 1 at the end nearer the $C=O$ group. In ketones, the location of the carbonyl group is indicated by placing the number of its carbon before the name. Some common names of ketones identify each alkyl group separately *[see Problems 26, 27, 29–35, 50, 54–57, and 63]*.

- **Describe the polarity, hydrogen bonding, and water solubility of aldehydes and ketones.** Aldehyde and ketone molecules are moderately polar, do not hydrogen bond with each other, but can accept hydrogen bonds from water molecules. Those with less than four to five carbons are water-soluble, and the ketones are excellent solvents. In general, aldehydes and ketones are higher boiling than alkanes but lower boiling than alcohols of similar molar mass. Many aldehydes and ketones have distinctive, sometimes pleasant odors *[see Problems 20, 22, 52, 53, 61, and 62]*.

- **Identify common aldehydes and ketones and their uses.** Aldehydes and ketones are present in many plants, where they contribute to their aromas; many are used as food flavorings. Such natural aldehydes and ketones are widely used in perfumes and flavorings. Formaldehyde (an irritating and toxic substance) is used in polymers, is present in smog-laden air, and is produced biochemically from ingested methanol. Acetone is a widely used solvent and is a by-product of food breakdown during uncontrolled diabetes and starvation. Many sugars (*carbohydrates*) are aldehydes or ketones *[see Problems 45, 49, 52, and 53]*.

- **Identify the products formed from the oxidation of aldehydes (and see that ketones do not oxidize in the same way).** Mild oxidizing agents convert aldehydes to carboxylic acids but have no effect on simple ketones. Tollens' reagent is used to indicate the presence of an aldehyde, while Benedict's reagent will give a positive test result for both aldehydes and *alpha* hydroxy ketones *[see Problems 21, 38, 40, 41, 52, 58, and 60]*.

- **Identify the products of the reduction of aldehydes and ketones.** Reducing agents, such as the hydride ion (H^-), add to the C of the $C=O$ group in an aldehyde or ketone, while the accompanying hydrogen ion (H^+) adds to the O. Aldehydes produce primary alcohols, whereas ketones produce secondary alcohols. In biological systems, the reducing agent for a carbonyl group is often the coenzyme NAD, which cycles between reacting as a reducing agent (NADH) and an oxidizing agent (NAD^+) by the loss and gain of a hydride ion ($:H^-$) *[see Problems 20, 39, and 58]*.

- **Identify the differences between hemiacetals, hemiketals, acetals, and ketals.** Aldehydes establish equilibria with alcohols to form hemiacetals or acetals, whereas ketones do the same to form hemiketals and ketals. *Hemiacetals* and *hemiketals* have an —OH and an —OR on a tetravalent carbon; in a hemiacetal the other two groups attached are a C and a H, whereas in a hemiketal the other two groups are both C *[see Problems 23, 25, 36, 42–44, and 47]*.

- **Predict the products of hemiacetal, hemiketal, acetal, and ketal formation and their hydrolysis.** The relatively unstable *hemiacetals and hemiketals*, which have an —OH and an —OR on what was the carbonyl carbon, result from addition of one alcohol molecule (which provides the —OR group) to the $C=O$ bond. The more stable *acetals and ketals*, which have two —OR groups on what was the carbonyl carbon, form by the addition of a second alcohol molecule to a hemiacetal or hemiketal. The aldehyde or ketone $C=O$ bond can be regenerated from an acetal or ketal by treatment with an acid catalyst and a large quantity of water, with the —OR groups being converted back into the alcohols they came from (RO-H). This is an example of a *hydrolysis* reaction *[see Problems 23, 24, 36, 37, 42–47, 59, 64, and 65]*.

KEY WORDS

Acetal, *p. 487*	**Aldehyde**, *p. 475*	**Hemiacetal**, *p. 485*	**Ketal**, *p. 487*
Addition reaction, aldehydes and ketones, *p. 485*	**Carbonyl compound**, *p. 475*	**Hemiketal**, *p. 485*	**Ketone**, *p. 475*
	Carbonyl group, *p. 475*	**Hydrolysis**, *p. 491*	

CONCEPT MAP: ORGANIC CHEMISTRY FAMILIES

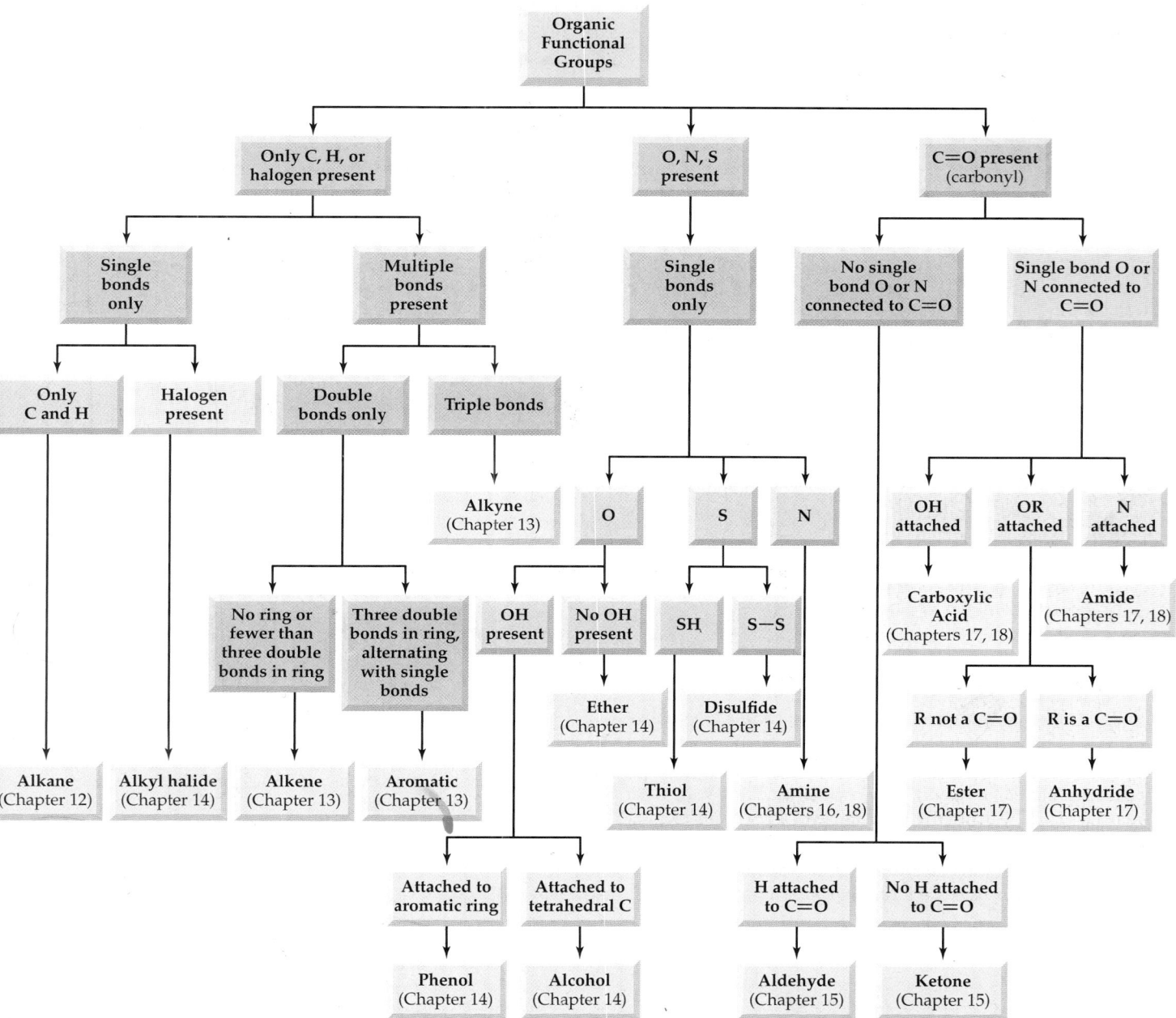

▲ **Figure 15.3 Functional Group Concept Map.** This is the same concept map we saw at the end of Chapters 12–14, except the functional groups discussed in this chapter, aldehydes and ketones, have now been colorized.

SUMMARY OF REACTIONS

1. **Reactions of aldehydes**
   (a) Oxidation to yield a carboxylic acid (Section 15.5).

$$CH_3CH_2\overset{\displaystyle O}{\overset{\|}{C}}H \xrightarrow{[O]} CH_3CH_2\overset{\displaystyle O}{\overset{\|}{C}}OH$$

   (b) Reduction to yield a primary alcohol (Section 15.6).

$$CH_3CH_2\overset{\displaystyle O}{\overset{\|}{C}}H \xrightarrow{[H]} CH_3CH_2CH_2OH$$

   (c) Addition of alcohol to yield a hemiacetal or acetal (Section 15.7).

$$CH_3\overset{\displaystyle O}{\overset{\|}{C}}H + CH_3CH_2OH \longrightarrow CH_3\underset{\underset{\displaystyle OH}{|}}{C}OCH_2CH_3$$

$$CH_3\underset{\underset{\displaystyle OH}{|}}{\overset{\overset{\displaystyle H}{|}}{C}}OCH_2CH_3 + CH_3CH_2OH \longrightarrow CH_3\underset{\underset{\displaystyle OCH_2CH_3}{|}}{\overset{\overset{\displaystyle H}{|}}{C}}OCH_2CH_3 + H_2O$$

2. Reactions of ketones

(a) Reduction to yield a secondary alcohol (Section 15.6).

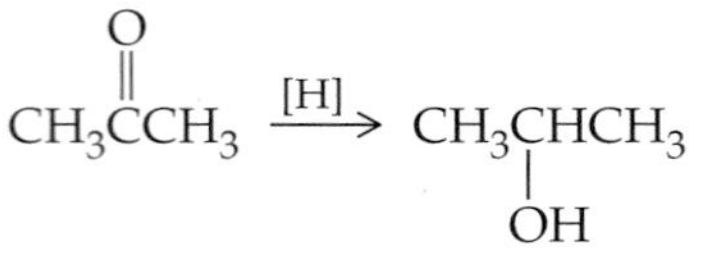

$$CH_3\overset{\displaystyle O}{\overset{\|}{C}}CH_3 \xrightarrow{[H]} CH_3\underset{\underset{\displaystyle OH}{|}}{CH}CH_3$$

(b) Addition of an alcohol to yield a hemiketal or ketal (Section 15.7).

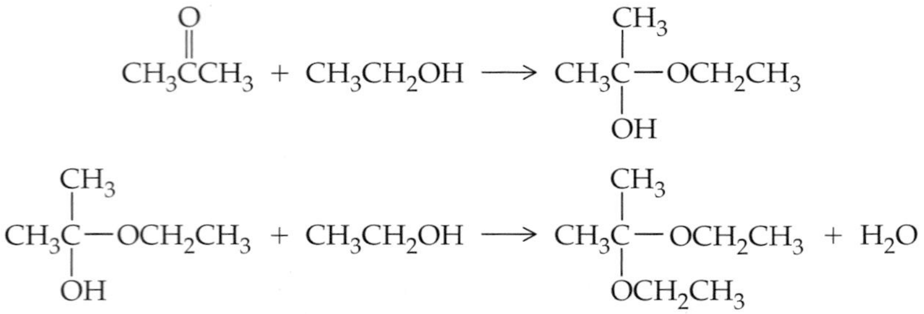

$$CH_3\overset{\displaystyle O}{\overset{\|}{C}}CH_3 + CH_3CH_2OH \longrightarrow CH_3\underset{\underset{\displaystyle OH}{|}}{\overset{\overset{\displaystyle CH_3}{|}}{C}}-OCH_2CH_3$$

$$CH_3\underset{\underset{\displaystyle OH}{|}}{\overset{\overset{\displaystyle CH_3}{|}}{C}}-OCH_2CH_3 + CH_3CH_2OH \longrightarrow CH_3\underset{\underset{\displaystyle OCH_2CH_3}{|}}{\overset{\overset{\displaystyle CH_3}{|}}{C}}-OCH_2CH_3 + H_2O$$

3. Reaction of acetals and ketals

Hydrolysis to regenerate an aldehyde or ketone (Section 15.7).

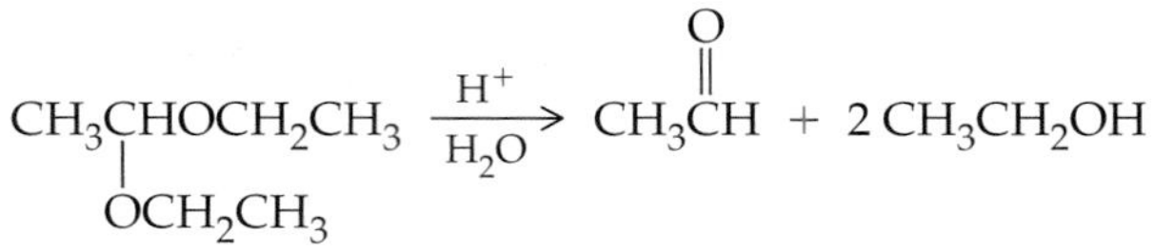

$$CH_3\underset{\underset{\displaystyle OCH_2CH_3}{|}}{CH}OCH_2CH_3 \xrightarrow[H_2O]{H^+} CH_3\overset{\displaystyle O}{\overset{\|}{C}}H + 2\,CH_3CH_2OH$$

UNDERSTANDING KEY CONCEPTS

15.20   The carbonyl group can be reduced by addition of a hydride ion (H^-) and a proton (H^+). Removal of H^- and H^+ from an alcohol results in a carbonyl group.

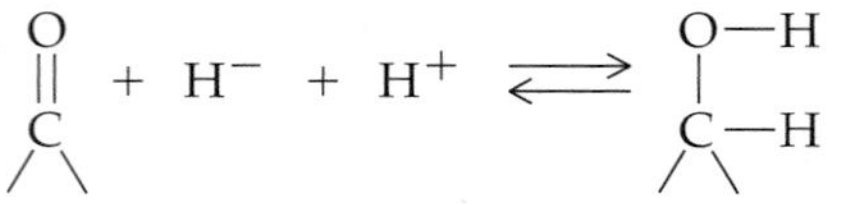

$$\overset{\displaystyle O}{\overset{\|}{C}} + H^- + H^+ \rightleftharpoons \overset{\displaystyle O-H}{\overset{|}{C}}-H$$

(a) To which atom of the carbonyl is the hydride ion added and why?

(b) In the reaction, indicate which direction represents reduction and which represents oxidation.

15.21   A fundamental difference between aldehydes and ketones is that one can be oxidized to carboxylic acids but the other cannot. Which is which? Give an example of a test to differentiate aldehydes from ketones.

15.22   In the following diagram, indicate with dashed lines where hydrogen bonds would form. Explain why you chose these atoms to hydrogen bond.

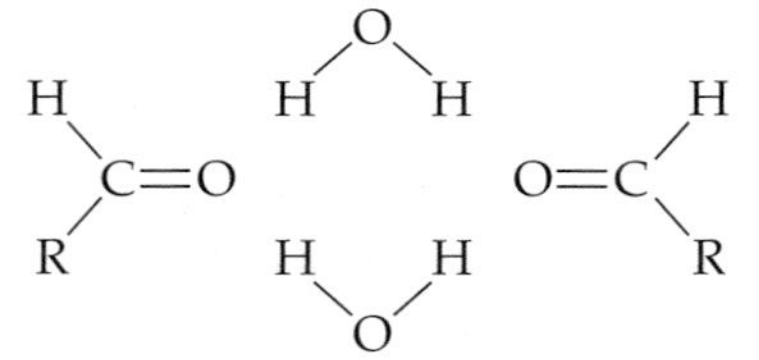

15.23   (a) Describe what happens in the reaction of an aldehyde with an alcohol.

(b) Copy the following structures and use lines to show where new bonds are formed. Cross out bonds that no longer exist as the aldehyde and alcohol react to form a hemiacetal.

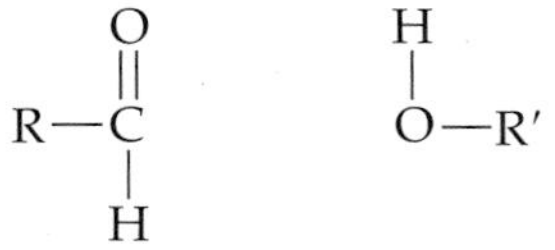

15.24   Glucose is the major sugar in mammalian blood. We often see it represented as either the "free aldehyde" or the cyclic hemiacetal forms shown here. Of the two forms of glucose, the cyclic hemiacetal is the preferred form found in blood. Can you suggest two reasons why?

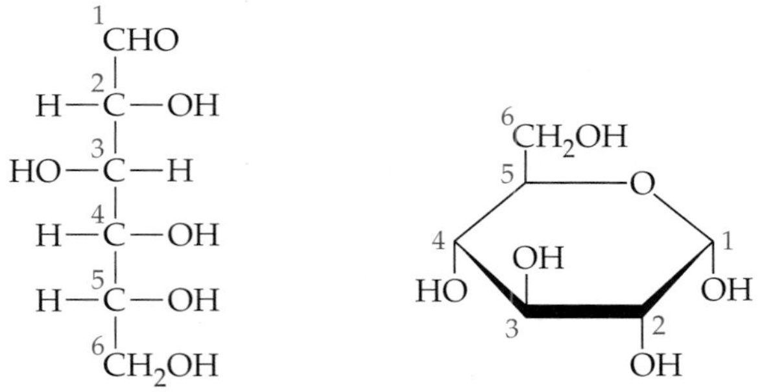

"Free aldehyde"   Cyclic hemiacetal

15.25   Describe the structural difference between a ketal and an acetal. Draw one of each to demonstrate your point.

ADDITIONAL PROBLEMS

(Note: For the following, the term "alpha" (α) refers to the carbon directly attached to the carbonyl group and "beta" (β) to the carbon two away from the carbonyl group.)

ALDEHYDES AND KETONES (SECTIONS 15.1 AND 15.2)

15.26   Draw a structure for a compound that meets each of the following descriptions:

(a) A 6-carbon cyclic ketone with a methyl group on the beta carbon

(b) An aldehyde with four carbons

(c) An *alpha*-bromoaldehyde, C_4H_7BrO

(d) A *beta*-hydroxyketone, $C_4H_8O_2$

15.27 Draw a structure for a compound that meets each of the following descriptions:

(a) A 5-carbon cyclic ketone. What is the approximate C—O bond angle in this ketone?

(b) An 8-carbon ketone with six carbons as its longest chain

(c) A *beta*-ketoaldehyde, $C_6H_{10}O_2$

(d) A cyclic *alpha*-hydroxyketone, $C_5H_8O_2$

15.28 Indicate which compounds contain aldehyde or ketone carbonyl groups.

(a) $CH_3CH_2\overset{\displaystyle O}{\overset{\|}{C}}CH_3$

(b) 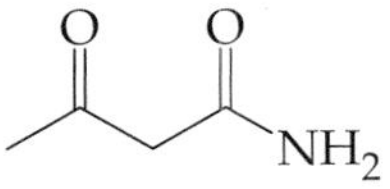 (structure with two C=O groups and NH₂)

(c) $CH_3CH_2-O-CH_2-CHO$

(d) $CH_3CH_2\overset{\displaystyle CH_2OH}{\underset{\displaystyle OCH_3}{CH}}$

(e) 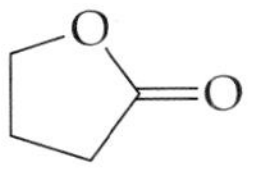 (lactone structure)

(f) $H_3C\overset{\displaystyle O}{\overset{\|}{C}}CH_2CH_2OH$

15.29 Redraw each of the following in line structure format. Indicate which compounds have an aldehyde carbonyl group, a ketone carbonyl group, or neither.

(a) CH_3CH_2CHO

(b) $(CH_3)_2C(OH)CH_2CH_2CH_3$

(c) 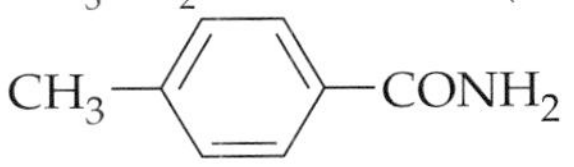 CH_3-⬡$-CONH_2$

(d) $CH_3\underset{\displaystyle OH}{CH}CH_2\underset{\displaystyle OCH_3}{CH}CH_3$

(e) $CH_3CH_2COCH_2CH_3$

15.30 Draw structures corresponding to the following aldehyde and ketone names:

(a) 3-Methylpentanal

(b) 4-Chloro-2-hydroxybutanal

(c) *p*-Methylbenzaldehyde

(d) 2-Ethylcycloheptanone

(e) Cyclopropyl methyl ketone

(f) Methyl phenyl ketone (also known as acetophenone)

15.31 Draw structures corresponding to the following aldehyde and ketone names:

(a) 4-Hydroxy-2,2,4-trimethylheptanal

(b) 4-Ethyl-2-isopropylhexanal

(c) *p*-Bromobenzaldehyde

(d) 2,4-Dihydroxycyclohexanone

(e) 1,1,1-Trichloro-3-pentanone

(f) 2-Methyl-3-hexanone

15.32 Give systematic names for the following aldehydes and ketones:

(a) $CH_3CH_2\underset{\displaystyle CH_3}{\overset{\displaystyle CH_3}{C}}CHO$

(b) $CH_3CH_2CH_2\underset{\displaystyle OH}{\overset{\displaystyle CHO}{C}}CH_3$

(c)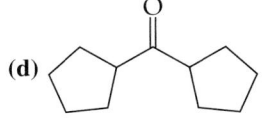

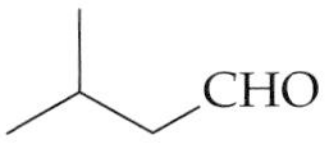

(d)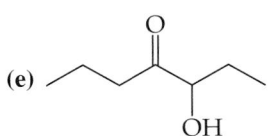

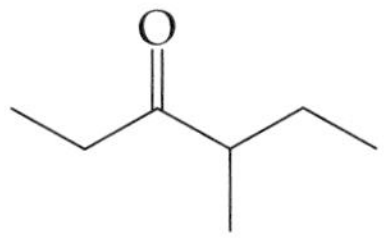

(e) 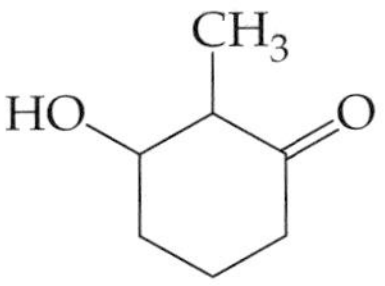 HO—(cyclohexanone with CH₃ and =O)

15.33 Give IUPAC names for the following aldehydes and ketones:

(a) 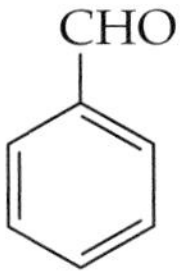 ⬡—CHO

(b) $CH_3CH_2\overset{\displaystyle O}{\overset{\|}{C}}CH(CH_3)_2$

(c) $CH_3-\underset{\displaystyle CH_3}{\overset{\displaystyle CH_3CH_2}{CH}}-CH-CH_2-\overset{\displaystyle O}{\overset{\|}{C}}-H$

(d) (dicyclopentyl ketone)

(e) (ketone with OH structure)

15.34 The following names are incorrect. What is wrong with each?

(a) 1-Pentanone

(b) 4-Methyl-3-pentanone

(c) 3-Butanone

15.35 The following names are incorrect. What is wrong with each?

(a) Cyclohexanal

(b) 2-Butanal

(c) 1-Methyl-1-pentanone

REACTIONS OF ALDEHYDES AND KETONES (SECTIONS 15.5–15.7)

15.36 Draw the structure of the compound obtained when one mole of methanol reacts with one mole of butanal in the presence of an acid catalyst.

15.37 Draw the structure of the compound obtained when two moles of methanol reacts with one mole of methyl ethyl ketone in the presence of an acid catalyst.

15.38 Which of the following compounds will react with Tollens' reagent? With Benedict's reagent?

(a) Cyclopentanone

(b) Hexanal

(c) $CH_3-\underset{\displaystyle H}{\overset{\displaystyle OH}{C}}-\underset{\displaystyle H}{\overset{\displaystyle OH}{C}}-\overset{\displaystyle O}{\overset{\|}{C}}-H$

15.39 Draw the structures of the products formed when the following compounds react with a reducing agent.

(a)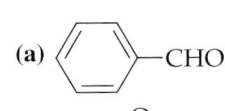

(b) $CH_3CH_2\overset{\displaystyle O}{\overset{\|}{C}}CH_3$

(c)

15.40 Draw the structures of the aldehydes that might be oxidized to yield the following carboxylic acids:

(a) 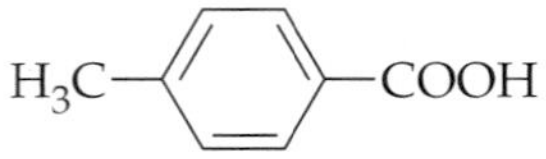

(b) 

(c) $CH_3CH{=}CHCOOH$

15.41 Draw the structures of the aldehydes that might be oxidized to yield the following carboxylic acids:

(a) 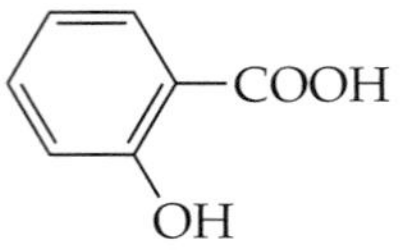

(b) 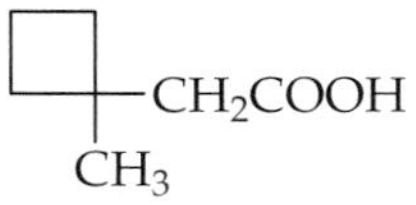

(c) $CH_3CH{=}CHCH_2COOH$

15.42 Write the structures of the hemiacetal or hemiketal that result from reactions (a) and (b). Label each product as a hemiacetal or hemiketal. Write the structures of the complete hydrolysis products of the acetal or ketal in (c) and (d).

(a) 2-Butanone + 1-Propanol ⟶ ?

(b) Butanal + Isopropyl alcohol ⟶ ?

(c) 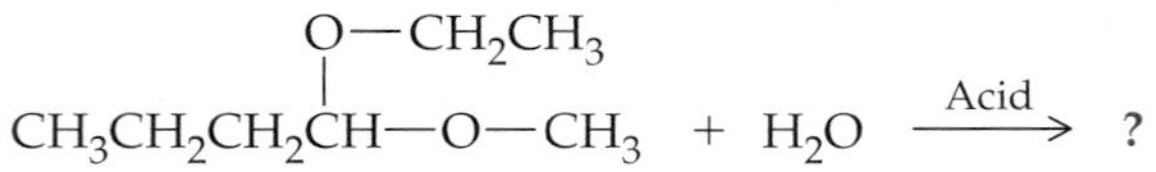

(d) 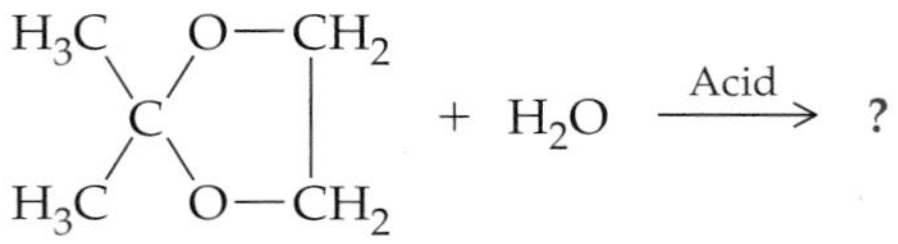

15.43 Write the structures of the hemiacetal or hemiketal that result from reactions (a) and (b). Write the structures of the complete hydrolysis products of the acetal or ketal in (c) and (d).

(a) Acetone + Ethanol ⟶ ?

(b) Hexanal + 2-Butanol ⟶ ?

(c) 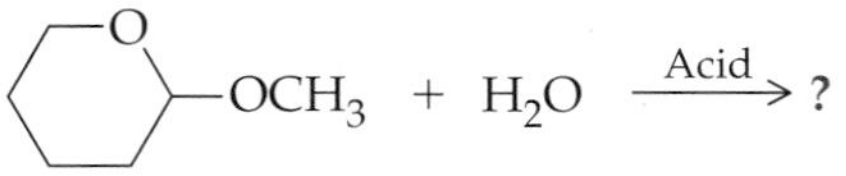

(d) 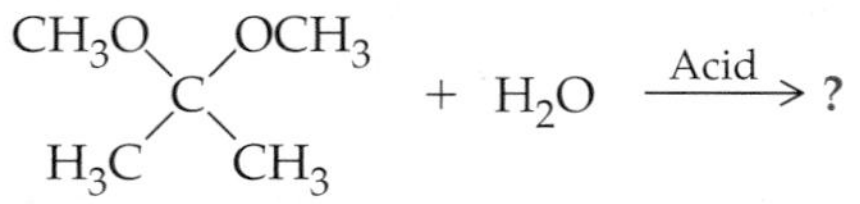

15.44 Cyclic hemiacetals commonly form if a molecule has both an alcohol group and a carbonyl group elsewhere in the same molecule, especially if they are four or five carbons apart. What is the structure of the hydroxy aldehyde from which this hemiacetal might form?

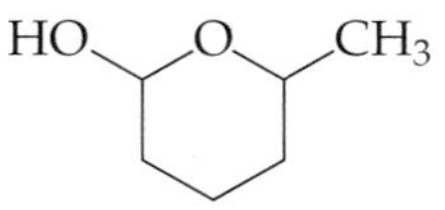

Cyclic hemiacetal

15.45 Glucosamine is found in the shells of lobsters; it exists largely in the cyclic hemiacetal form shown here. Draw the structure of glucosamine in its open-chain hydroxy aldehyde form (the hemiacetal carbon is labeled 1).

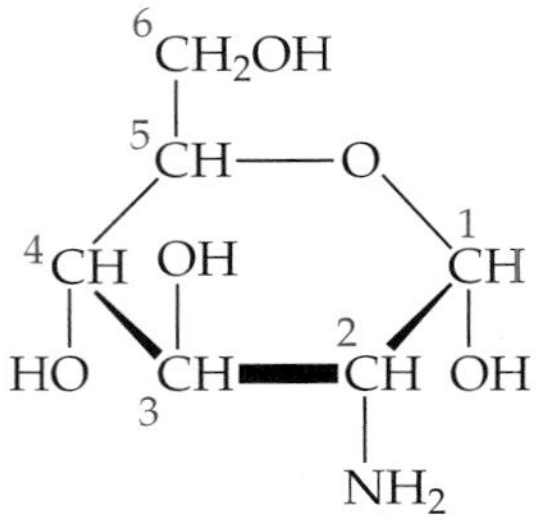

15.46 What two products result from the complete hydrolysis of this cyclic acetal?

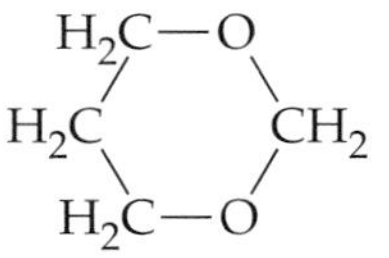

15.47 Acetals and ketals are usually made by reaction of an aldehyde or ketone with two molecules of a monoalcohol. If an aldehyde or ketone reacts with one molecule of a dialcohol, however, a cyclic acetal or ketal results.

(a) Draw the structure of the hemiketal formed when the —OH labeled in red reacts with cyclopentanone;

(b) Draw the cyclic ketal formed when the hemiketal from part (a) reacts with the —OH labeled in blue.

15.48 Aldosterone is a key steroid involved in controlling the sodium–potassium balance in the body. Identify the functional groups in aldosterone.

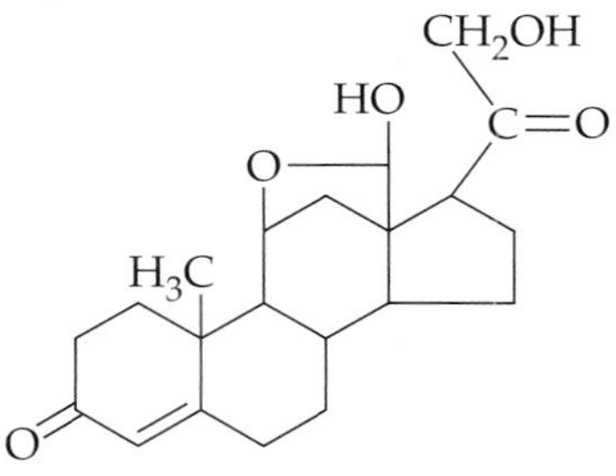

15.49 The compound carvone is responsible for the odor of spearmint. Identify the functional groups in carvone.

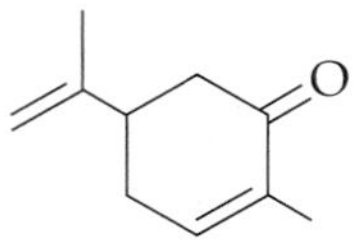

Carvone

CONCEPTUAL PROBLEMS

15.50 Name the following compound, which is used in the fragrance industry.

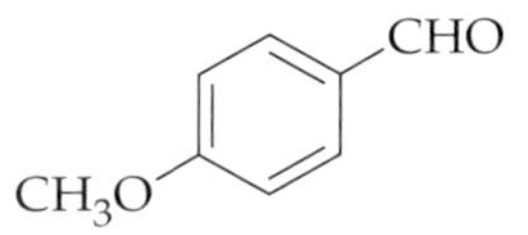

15.51 Can the alcohol $(CH_3)_3COH$ be formed by the reduction of an aldehyde or ketone? Why or why not?

15.52 Many flavorings and perfumes are partially based on fragrant ketones, with far fewer being based on fragrant aldehydes. Why do you think ketones are used more frequently than aldehydes? See Section 15.5 for a clue.

15.53 One problem with burning some plastics is the release of formaldehyde. What are some of the physiological effects of exposure to formaldehyde?

15.54 Name the following compounds using IUPAC nomenclature:

(a) $CH_3CH_2\overset{\overset{\displaystyle O}{\|}}{C}CH(CH_3)_2$

(b) $CH_3CH_2CH_2CH{=}CH_2$

(c)

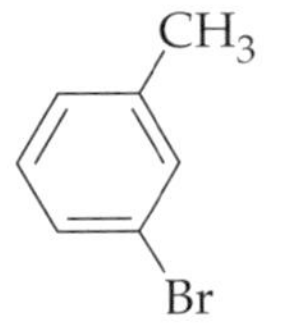

(d) $(CH_3)_3CCH_2\overset{\overset{\displaystyle O}{\|}}{C}CH_2CH_3$

15.55 Name the following compounds:

(a)

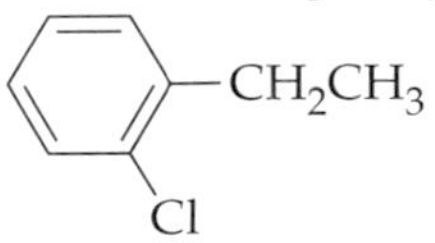

(b)

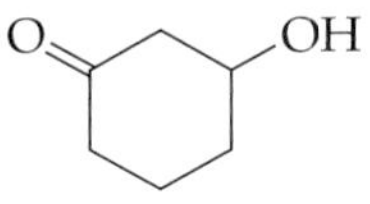

(c)

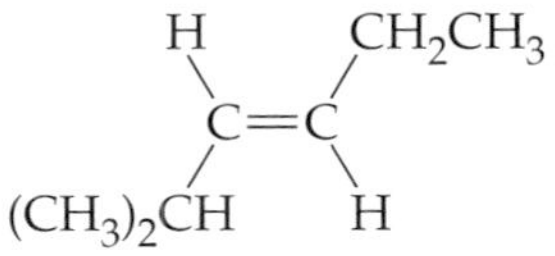

(be sure to include *cis* or *trans* in the name)

(d) $(CH_3)_2CH{-}\overset{\overset{\displaystyle O}{\|}}{C}{-}H$

15.56 Draw the structural formulas of the following compounds:

(a) 2,4-Dinitroacetophenone

(b) 2,4-Dihydroxycyclopentanone

(c) 2-Methoxy-2-methylpropane

(d) 2,3,4-Trimethyl-3-pentanol

15.57 Draw the structural formulas of the following compounds:

(a) 2,3-Dimethylpentanal

(b) 1,3-Dibromopropanone

(c) 4-hydroxy-4-methyl-2-hexanone

15.58 Complete the following equations (refer to "Summary of Reactions" in Chapters 13 and 14 if necessary):

(a) 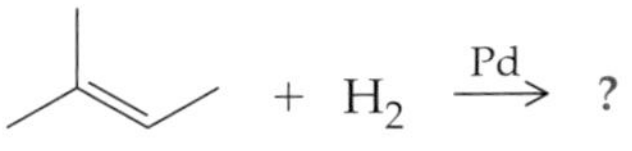 $+\ H_2\ \xrightarrow{\ Pd\ }\ ?$

(b) $CH_3\overset{\overset{\displaystyle OH}{|}}{CH}\underset{\underset{\displaystyle CH_3}{|}}{CH}CH_3\ \xrightarrow{[O]}\ ?$

(c) $\overset{\overset{\displaystyle O}{\|}}{HC}CH_2CH_2CH_3\ \xrightarrow[\ H_3O^+\ ]{\text{Reducing agent}}\ ?$

(d) 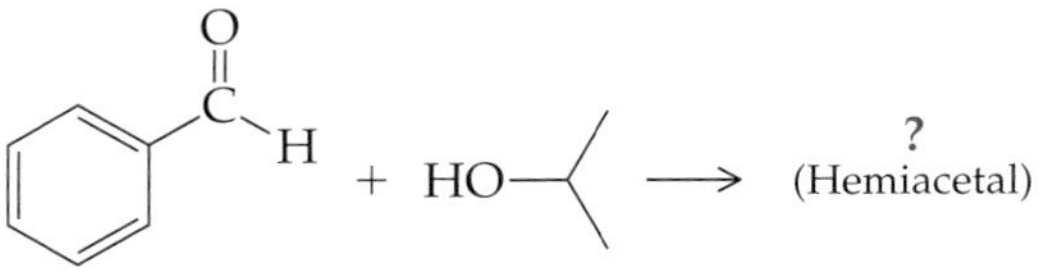 $+\ HO{-}\!\!<\ \longrightarrow\ \overset{?}{\text{(Hemiacetal)}}$

15.59 Complete the following equations:

(a) 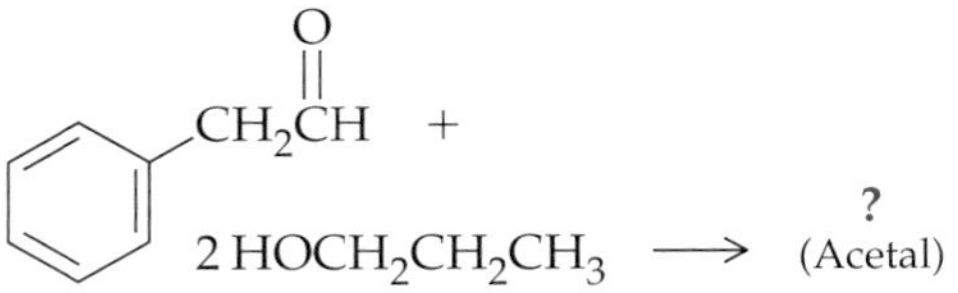 $+$

$2\,HOCH_2CH_2CH_3\ \longrightarrow\ \overset{?}{\text{(Acetal)}}$

(b) $CH_3CH{=}\underset{\underset{\displaystyle CH_3}{|}}{\overset{\overset{\displaystyle CH_2CH_3}{|}}{C}}CH_2CH_2CH_3\ +\ HCl\ \longrightarrow\ ?$

(c)  $CH_3{-}\!\!\!\bigcirc\!\!\!{-}CH_2CH_2OH\ \xrightarrow{H_2SO_4}\ ?$

15.60 How could you differentiate between 3-hexanol and hexanal using a simple chemical test?

15.61 The liquids 1-butanol and butanal have similar molar masses. Which is expected to have the higher boiling point? Explain your choices.

15.62 2-Butanone has a solubility of 26 g/100 mL of H_2O, but 2-heptanone, which is found in clove and cinnamon bark oils, is only very slightly soluble in water. Explain the difference in solubility of these two ketones.

GROUP PROBLEMS

15.63 Draw all the ketones you can with a chemical formula of $C_8H_{16}O$, whose longest chain is eight carbons. Name each using both its IUPAC and common name.

15.64 In Problem 15.24, you were given the structure of the free aldehyde form of glucose. Try to draw the two cyclic hemiacetal forms of glucose you would get if (a) the OH on C4 formed the ring and (b) the OH on C3 formed the ring.

15.65 Using the ketone structural form of fructose (Section 20.1), draw the hemiketal you would get if (a) the OH on C4 formed the ring and (b) if the OH on C6 formed the ring.

15.66 In the Chemistry in Action "Enediyne Antibiotics: A Newly Emerging Class of Antitumor Agents" in Chapter 13, you were given the structure of Diynemicin A. Identify all of the functional groups present in this molecule.

16

Amines

CONTENTS

◀◀◀ CONCEPTS TO REVIEW

▲ Sometimes the stress of our day-to-day life can be overwhelming. When anxiety becomes uncontrollable, medications can help.

The brain is the organ we know the least about, yet it controls essentially every aspect of who and what we are. Packed away and isolated from the rest of your body, it has an extraordinary set of defenses in place to keep it protected (see the Chemistry in Action "The Blood–Brain Barrier" in Chapter 29). But things can go wrong: seizures, strokes, anxiety, and depression to name but a few. Anxiety is something that all of us face at multiple times during our life; most of the time we can combat it through exercise, meditation, and other natural remedies such as chamomile tea or lemon balm. For an extreme case of anxiety, therapy may be indicated; but what if our anxiety is so great that these methods do not work? When this is the case, medical intervention is called for. Luckily, medications exist for just such a condition. These drugs, which are molecules that effect how signals are transmitted in the brain, can have both good and bad properties of their own. Benzodiazepines can provide immediate relief but carry the possibility of addiction; Serotonin reuptake inhibitors do not carry the problem of being addictive but are not usually able to provide immediate relief. What do all of these drugs have in common? They are all amines. We will examine these closer in the Chemistry in Action "Calming a Stormy Mind: Amines as Anti-Anxiety Medications" at the end of this chapter.

From a biochemical standpoint, many of the molecules that carry chemical messages (such as the neurotransmitters, Chapter 28) are relatively simple amines with extraordinary powers. Histamine, the compound that initiates hay fever and other allergic reactions, is an amine; you have experienced its power first-hand if you have ever had an insect bite. In addition, many of the drugs that have been developed to mimic or to control the activity of histamine—the antihistamines present in cold and allergy medications—are amines. The amino group ($-NH_2$) is important in the formation and stability of proteins, and heterocyclic amines play a crucial part in the function of DNA and RNA. These are but a few examples of the roles played by amines.

16.1 Classifying Amines

Learning Objective:

• Identify and classify an amine as primary, secondary, or tertiary.

Amines contain one or more organic groups bonded to nitrogen; they have the general formulas RNH_2, R_2NH, and R_3N. In the same way that alcohols and ethers can be thought of as organic derivatives of water, amines are organic derivatives of ammonia (NH_3). In general, they are classified as *primary* (1°), *secondary* (2°), or *tertiary* (3°), according to how many organic groups are individually bound *directly* to the nitrogen atom. The organic groups (represented below by colored rectangles) may be large or small, they may be the same or different, or they may be connected to one another through a ring.

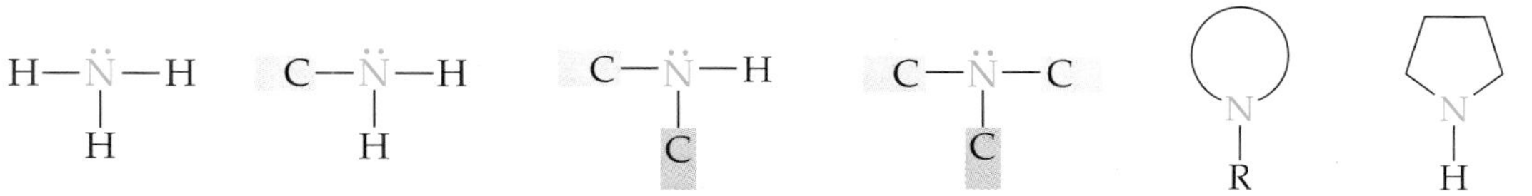

Ammonia	A primary amine (RNH₂)	A secondary amine (R₂NH)	A tertiary amine (R₃N)	A cyclic amine	Pyrrolidine

NH_3 $CH_3CH_2NH_2$ $(CH_3CH_2)_2NH$ $(CH_3CH_2)_3N$

Note that each amine nitrogen atom has a lone pair of electrons. The lone pair, although not always shown, is always there for a nitrogen that has three groups bonded to it and is responsible in large part for the chemistry of amines. When a fourth group bonds to the nitrogen, it does so through this lone pair; the product is a **quaternary ammonium ion** (Section 16.6), which has a permanent positive charge and forms ionic compounds with anions [for example, $(CH_3CH_2)_4N^+Cl^-$]:

LOOKING AHEAD ➤ We will explore the function of amines in proteins and DNA in Chapters 18 and 25, respectively.

Amine A compound that has one or more organic groups bonded to nitrogen: primary, RNH_2; secondary, R_2NH; or tertiary, R_3N.

Quaternary ammonium ion A positive ion with four organic groups bonded to the nitrogen atom (R_4N^+).

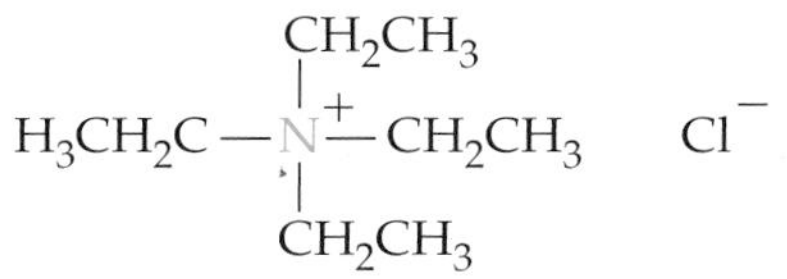

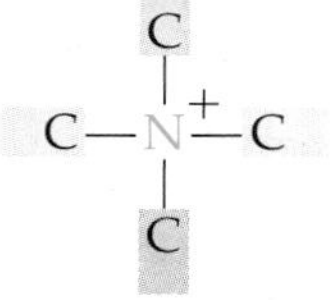

A quaternary ammonium ion (R_4N^+)

503

The groups bonded to the amine nitrogen atom may be alkyl or aryl (aromatic) groups and may or may not contain other functional groups. For example:

CH_3NH_2

Methylamine
(a primary alkyl amine)

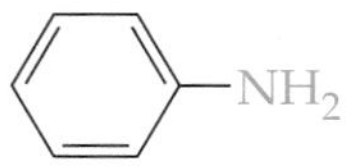

$-NH_2$

Aniline
(a primary
aromatic amine)

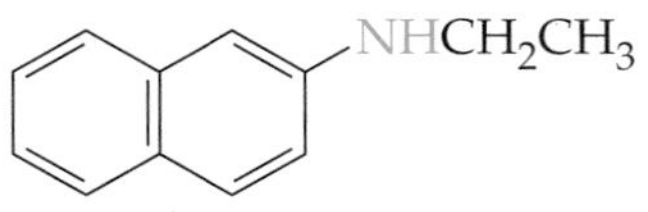

$-NHCH_2CH_3$

N-Ethylnaphthylamine
(a secondary aromatic amine)

$CH_3 \overset{+}{N} \hspace{-1mm}\begin{smallmatrix}CH_3\\|\\\\|\\CH_3\end{smallmatrix}\hspace{-1mm}-CH_2CH_2O\overset{O}{\overset{||}{C}}CH_3$

Acetylcholine, a neurotransmitter
(a quaternary ammonium ion)

16.2 Naming and Drawing Amines

Learning Objective:

• Name a simple amine given its structure or draw an amine given its name.

Primary alkyl amines (RNH_2) are named by identifying the alkyl group attached to nitrogen and adding the suffix -*amine* to the alkyl group name.

Some examples of naming primary amines

$CH_3CH_2-NH_2$ $CH_3\overset{CH_3}{\overset{|}{CH}}-NH_2$ $\hexagon-NH_2$

Ethylamine   Isopropylamine   Cyclohexylamine

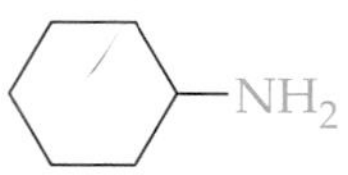

Simple, nonheterocyclic secondary (R_2NH) and tertiary (R_3N) amines (those possessing two or three identical groups on the nitrogen, respectively) are named by adding the appropriate prefix, *di-* or *tri-*, to the alkyl group name along with the suffix -*amine*.

Some examples of naming simple 2° and 3° amines

$CH_3CH_2CH_2-\overset{}{\underset{H}{N}}-CH_2CH_2CH_3$ $CH_3CH_2-\overset{}{\underset{CH_2CH_3}{N}}-CH_2CH_3$

Dipropylamine   Triethylamine

When the R groups in secondary or tertiary amines are different, the compounds are named as *N*-substituted derivatives of a primary amine. The parent compound chosen as the primary amine based on the R group containing the longest carbon chain; all other groups are considered to be *N*-substituents (*N* because they are attached directly to nitrogen). The following compounds, for example, are named as propylamines because the propyl group in each is the largest alkyl group:

Some examples of naming more complex 2° and 3° amines

$CH_3CH_2-\overset{}{\underset{H}{N}}-CH_2CH_2CH_3$ $CH_3-\overset{}{\underset{CH_3}{N}}-CH_2CH_2CH_3$

N-Ethylpropylamine   N,N-Dimethylpropylamine

Heteroyclic amines (Section 16.3) are an important family of amines in which the nitrogen is part of the ring structure; the nomenclature of these compounds is too complicated to discuss here and will be addressed as needed.

Proteins are polymers of α-amino acids, in which the —NH₂ group of one amino acid is linked through the carboxyl of a second via an amide bond. All amino acids contain both the amino functional group, —NH₂, and the carboxylic acid functional group, —COOH (in addition to whatever functional groups are part of the side chain). The chemistry of carboxylic acids, esters, and amides is discussed in Chapter 17. The amino acids and their combination to form proteins are covered in Chapter 18.

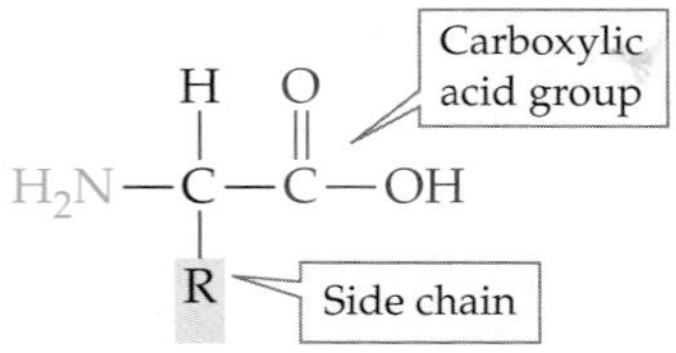

$H_2N-\overset{\overset{H}{|}}{\underset{\underset{R}{|}}{C}}-\overset{\overset{O}{||}}{C}-OH$

Carboxylic
acid group

Side chain

An amino acid

The —NH_2 functional group is an **amino group,** and when this group is a substituent, *amino-* is used as a prefix in the name of the compound (for example, when the compound has a C=O present, Chapters 15 and 17). Aromatic amines are an exception to this rule and are primarily known by their historical, or common, names. The simplest aromatic amine is known by its common name aniline, and derivatives of it are named as anilines:

$H_2NCH_2CH_2COOH$

3-Aminopropanoic acid

$CH_3—CH—CH=CH_2$ (with NH_2 above the CH)

3-Amino-1-butene

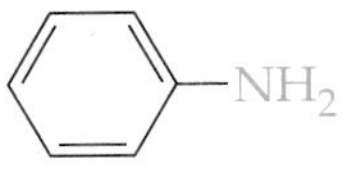

Aniline (ring with $—NH_2$)

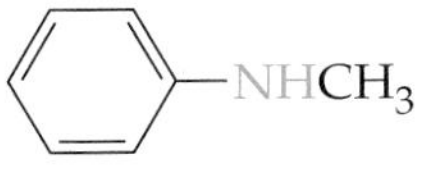

N-Methylaniline (ring with $—NHCH_3$)

Amino group The —NH_2 functional group.

Worked Example 16.1 Drawing and Classifying Amines from Their Names

Write the structure of *N,N*-diethylbutylamine and identify it as a primary, secondary, or tertiary amine.

ANALYSIS Look for terms within the name that provide clues about the parent compound and its substituents. For example, the word "butyl" immediately preceding the *-amine* suffix indicates that butylamine, the 4-carbon alkyl amine, is the parent compound. The *N,N* indicates that two other groups are bonded to the amino nitrogen, and the *diethyl* indicates they are both ethyl groups.

SOLUTION
The structure shows that three alkyl groups are bonded to the N atom, so this must be a tertiary amine.

$$CH_3CH_2CH_2CH_2N \begin{matrix} CH_2CH_3 \\ CH_2CH_3 \end{matrix}$$

Worked Example 16.2 Naming and Classifying an Amine from Its Structure

Name the following compound. Is it a primary, secondary, or tertiary amine?

(cyclohexyl)—NH—CH_3

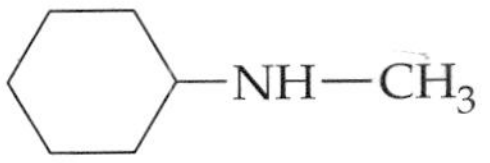

ANALYSIS Determine how many organic groups are attached to the nitrogen. We can see that two carbon groups are bonded to the nitrogen. Since the cyclohexyl group is the largest alkyl group bonded to N, the compound is named as a cyclohexylamine. One methyl group is bonded to the nitrogen; we indicate this with the prefix *N*.

SOLUTION
The name is *N*-methylcyclohexylamine. Because the compound has two groups bonded to N, it is a secondary amine.

Worked Example 16.3 Classifying a Cyclic Amine from Its Structure

The following heterocyclic amine is named octahydroindolizine. Is it a primary, secondary, or tertiary amine?

(bicyclic ring with N)

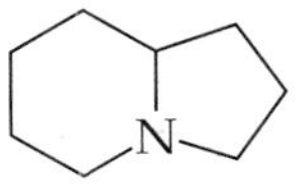

ANALYSIS Start by looking at the nitrogen; we can see that it is attached to three different carbons (as indicated by red, blue, and black bond lines). Even when the nitrogen is part of a ring, an amine will be classified by the number of organic groups that are bonded to it.

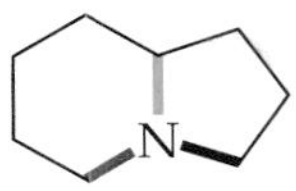

(bicyclic ring with N)

SOLUTION
In this molecule, three individual carbon groups are bound to N; it therefore is a tertiary amine.

PROBLEM 16.1

Identify the following compounds as primary, secondary, or tertiary amines.

(a) $CH_3(CH_2)_4CH_2NH_2$

(b) $CH_3CH_2CH_2NHCH(CH_3)_2$

(c)

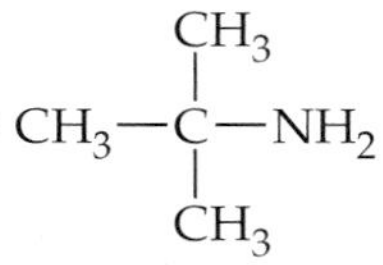

$$CH_3-\underset{\underset{CH_3}{|}}{\overset{\overset{CH_3}{|}}{C}}-NH_2$$

(d)

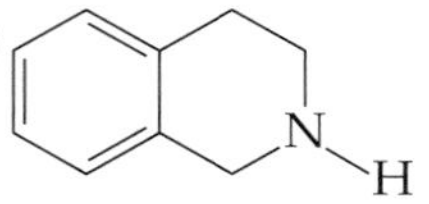

(e)

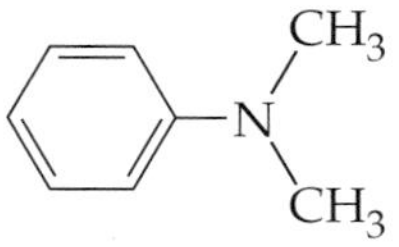

PROBLEM 16.2

What are the names of these amines?

(a) $(CH_3CH_2CH_2)_2NH$

(b)

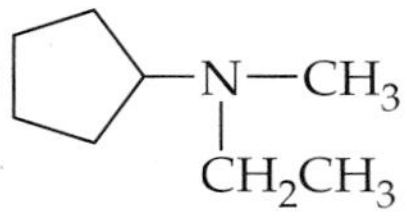

(c)

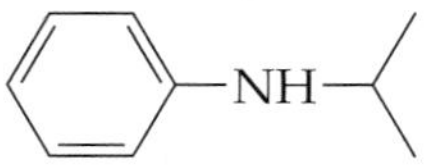

PROBLEM 16.3

Draw structures corresponding to the following names:

(a) Octylamine

(b) N-Methylpentylamine

(c) N-Ethylaniline

(d) 4-Amino-2-butanol

PROBLEM 16.4

Classify the amines in Problem 16.3 (a)–(c) as primary, secondary, or tertiary.

KEY CONCEPT PROBLEM 16.5

Draw the structure of the tetramethylammonium ion. Why does this species have a permanent positive charge? (See Sections 16.1 and 16.6.)

KEY CONCEPT PROBLEM 16.6

Draw the condensed and line formula of the molecule in the margin. Is it a primary, secondary, or tertiary amine? Why?

16.3 Properties of Amines

Learning Objective:

• Describe amine properties such as hydrogen bonding, solubility, boiling point, and basicity.

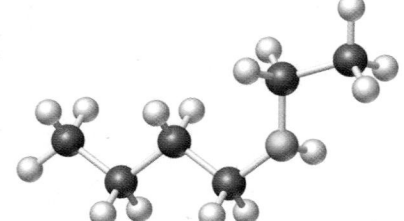

Lewis base A compound containing an unshared pair of electrons (an amine, for example).

The lone electron pair on the nitrogen in amines, like the lone electron pair in ammonia, causes amines to act as either weak Brønsted–Lowry bases or as **Lewis bases,** by forming a bond with an H^+ ion from an acid or water (see Sections 10.1 and 16.5).

The lone pair on the nitrogen makes it a Lewis base.

$$\underset{\substack{| \\ H}}{\overset{\substack{H \\ |}}{H-N:}}(aq) + H_2O(l) \rightleftharpoons \underset{\substack{| \\ H}}{\overset{\substack{H \\ |}}{H-N^+}}-H(aq) + OH^-(aq)$$

$$\underset{\substack{| \\ H}}{\overset{\substack{H \\ |}}{CH_3-N:}}(aq) + HCl(aq) \rightleftharpoons \underset{\substack{| \\ H}}{\overset{\substack{H \\ |}}{CH_3-N^+}}-H(aq) + Cl^-(aq)$$

In primary and secondary amines, hydrogen bonds can form between the lone pair on the very electronegative nitrogen atom and the slightly positive hydrogen atom on another primary or secondary amine. All amines (primary, secondary, and tertiary) can form hydrogen bonds with water (Figure 16.1).

(a)

2° amine–H$_2$O hydrogen bonds

(b)

2° amine–2° amine hydrogen bonds

▲ **Figure 16.1**
Hydrogen bonding of a secondary amine.
Hydrogen bonding (shown by red dots) between (a) a secondary amine and water; and (b) two secondary amines.

Because of their ability to engage in hydrogen bonding, primary and secondary amines have higher boiling points than alkanes of similar size. Amines are, in general, lower boiling than alcohols of similar size due to the fact that hydrogen bonds amines form with one another are weaker than those found in alcohols. Primary and secondary amines can hydrogen bond with each other and as a result have higher boiling points than expected; however, tertiary amine molecules have no hydrogen atoms attached to nitrogen and therefore cannot hydrogen-bond with each other. As a result, they are much lower boiling than alcohols or primary or secondary amines of similar molecular weight. All amines, however, can hydrogen-bond to water molecules through the lone electron pair on their nitrogen atoms, so amines with up to about six carbon atoms have appreciable solubility in water.

◄ **CONCEPTS TO REVIEW** Remember that, in the absence of hydrogen bonding, boiling points of molecules increase with increasing molecular mass; see Figure 12.4.

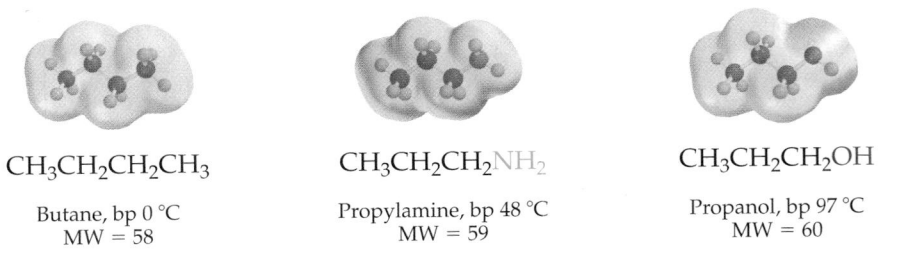

$CH_3CH_2CH_2CH_3$

Butane, bp 0 °C
MW = 58

$CH_3CH_2CH_2NH_2$

Propylamine, bp 48 °C
MW = 59

$CH_3CH_2CH_2OH$

Propanol, bp 97 °C
MW = 60

Many volatile amines have strong odors. Some smell like ammonia and others like stale fish or decaying meat. The protein in flesh contains amine groups, and the smaller, volatile amines produced during decay and protein breakdown are responsible for the odor of rotten meat. One such amine, 1,5-diaminopentane, is commonly known as cadaverine.

Many amines cause physiological responses. The simpler amines (such as methyl amine, diethyl amine, or triethylamine) are irritating to the skin, eyes, and mucous membranes and are toxic by ingestion. Some of the more complex amines from plants (such as the alkaloids) can be very poisonous, while others exhibit powerful analgesic (pain relieving) properties (see Section 16.6). All living organisms contain a wide variety of amines, and many useful drugs are amines (see the Chemistry in Action "Calming a Stormy Mind: Amines as Anti-Anxiety Medications" and Hands-On Chemistry 16.1).

Summary: Properties of Amines

- Primary and secondary amines can hydrogen-bond with each other and thus are higher boiling than alkanes but lower boiling than alcohols, due to weaker hydrogen bonds.
- Tertiary amines are lower boiling than secondary or primary amines because hydrogen bonding between tertiary amines is not possible.
- Methylamine, ethylamine, dimethylamine, and trimethylamine are gases; all other simple amines are liquids.
- Volatile amines usually have unpleasant odors.
- Simple amines (those with less than four carbons) are water-soluble due to their ability to hydrogen bonding with water.
- Amines are weak Brønsted–Lowry/Lewis bases (Section 16.5).
- Many amines are physiologically active, and many are toxic.

PROBLEM 16.7

Arrange the following compounds in order of increasing boiling point. Explain why you placed them in that order.

$$\underset{\textbf{(a)}}{} CH_3 \overset{\overset{\displaystyle CH_3}{|}}{-N} - CH_2CH_3 \qquad \textbf{(b)}\ CH_3CH_2CH_2CH_2OH \qquad \textbf{(c)}\ CH_3CH_2CH_2CH_2NH_2$$

PROBLEM 16.8

Draw the structures of (a) ethylamine and (b) trimethylamine. Use dashed lines to show how they would form hydrogen bonds to water molecules.

HANDS-ON CHEMISTRY 16.1

The amine functional group is part of a great many compounds you come in contact with on a daily basis. To see how prevalent the amine functional group is in medicine, let's take a look at some of the top 200 drugs of 2015, many of which you have probably heard about, and see what functional groups are present. You will need to have an internet connection to fully carry out this activity.

a. Let's begin by looking at some antibiotics you may be familiar with. Look up the structures of the following four antibiotics: Amoxicillin, Doxycycline, Ciprofloxacin, and Metronidazole. What is each typically prescribed for? Draw their line structure and identify as many functional groups as you can in them (use Table 12.1 to help you). Which of these have the amino functional group present? Classify each amine nitrogen you find as primary, secondary, or tertiary.

b. As of September 2014, the top 10 selling prescription drugs by trade name were as follows:

   1. Crestor 2. Synthroid 3. Nexium 4. Ventolin 5. Advair
   6. Lantus 7. Vyvanse 8. Lyrica 9. Spiriva 10. Diovan

   Look up the structures of each and answer the following questions for each:

   1. What is its generic name?
   2. What medical condition is it used to treat?
   3. Does it contain an amine? If so, classify it.
   4. What other functional groups are present in each? (Refer to Table 12.1 if needed.)

c. After completing parts a and b, what can you say about the importance of the amino function in medications that are used everyday?

16.4 Heterocyclic Nitrogen Compounds

Learning Objective:

• Identify a heterocyclic amine.

In many nitrogen-containing compounds, the nitrogen atom is in a ring with carbon atoms. Compounds that contain atoms other than carbon in the ring are known as **heterocycles.** Heterocyclic nitrogen compounds may be nonaromatic or aromatic. Piperidine, for example, is a saturated heterocyclic amine with a six-membered ring, and pyridine is an aromatic heterocyclic amine that, like other aromatic compounds, is often represented on paper as a ring with alternating double and single bonds.

Table 16.1 gives the names and structures of several heterocyclic nitrogen compounds. Because the names of these compounds are historical in origin, they are seemingly random at first sight (for example, the word "purine" was devised by the German chemist Emil Fischer, being a shortened form of "pure urine," alluding to how it was first synthesized). You need not memorize these names and structures, but you should take note that such rings are very common in many natural compounds found in plants and animals. For example, nicotine, from tobacco leaves, contains one pyridine ring and one pyrrolidine ring; quinine, an antimalarial drug isolated from the bark of the South American *Cinchona* tree, contains a quinoline ring system plus a nitrogen ring with a 2-carbon bridge across it. The amino acid tryptophan contains an indole ring system in addition to its amino group.

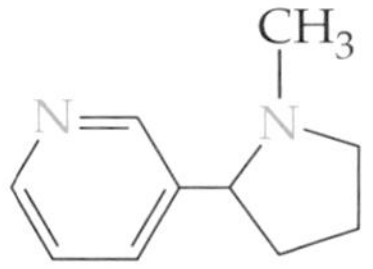

Heterocycle A ring that contains nitrogen or some other atom in addition to carbon.

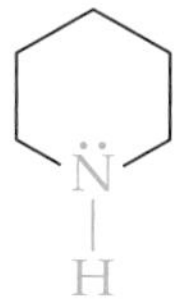

Piperidine
(a saturated cyclic amine)

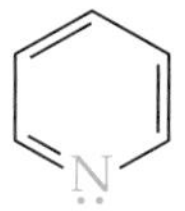

Pyridine
(an aromatic amine)

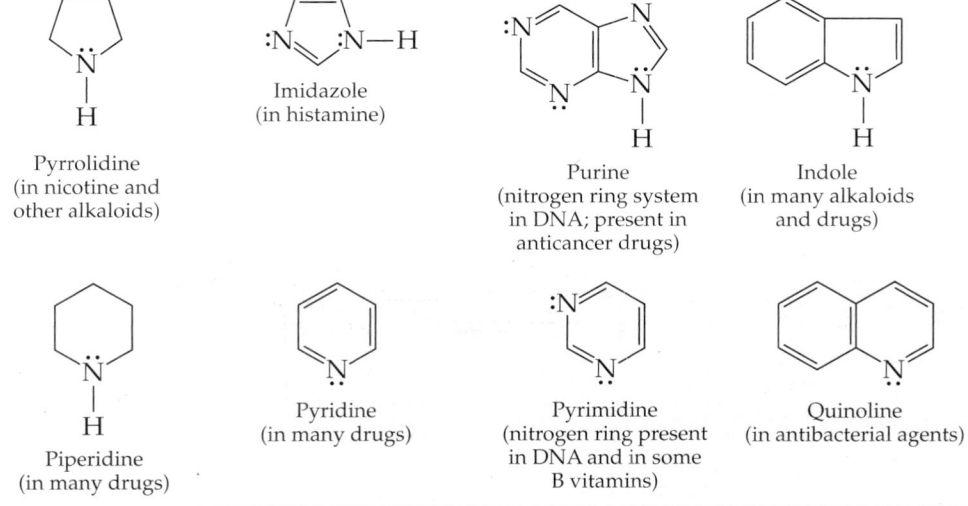

Nicotine
from tobacco
(an insecticide; an
active ingredient
in cigarette smoke)

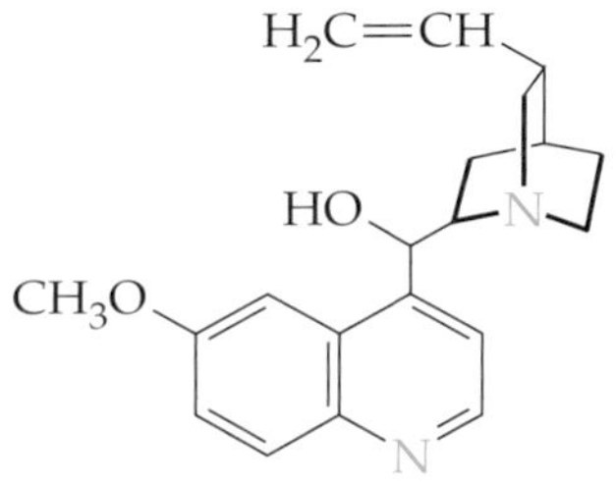

Quinine
from the *Cinchona* tree
(an antimalarial drug)

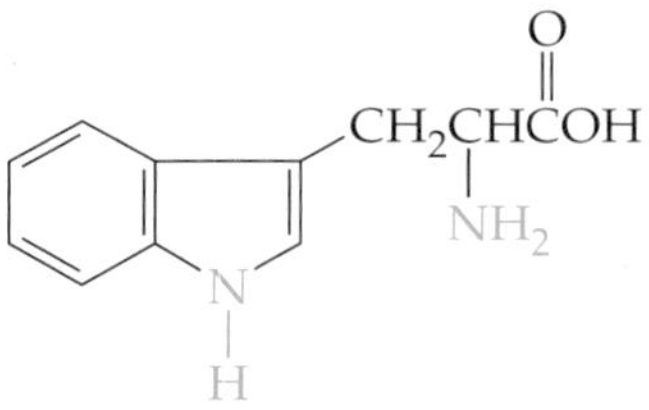

Tryptophan
(an amino acid)

Table 16.1 Some Heterocyclic Nitrogen Compounds

Pyrrolidine
(in nicotine and
other alkaloids)

Imidazole
(in histamine)

Purine
(nitrogen ring system
in DNA; present in
anticancer drugs)

Indole
(in many alkaloids
and drugs)

Piperidine
(in many drugs)

Pyridine
(in many drugs)

Pyrimidine
(nitrogen ring present
in DNA and in some
B vitamins)

Quinoline
(in antibacterial agents)

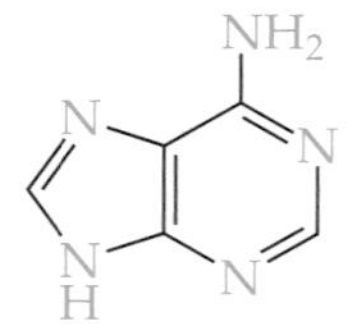

Adenine

➤➤ Hydrogen bonding that occurs between hydrogen atoms on nitrogens and oxygens and the oxygen or nitrogen atoms of other groups within a molecule helps to determine the shape of many biomolecules. Such attractions contribute to the complex shapes into which large protein molecules are folded (Section 18.8). Hydrogen bonding of amine groups also plays a crucial role in the helical structure of the molecule that carries hereditary information—deoxyribonucleic acid, DNA (Section 26.4).

Ammonium ion A positive ion formed by addition of hydrogen to ammonia or an amine (may be primary, secondary, or tertiary).

◀◀ The concepts of equilibrium, and its reversibility, were discussed in Chapters 7 and 10.

Adenine, a nitrogen-containing cyclic compound, is one of the four amines that compose the "bases" in DNA that code for genetic traits, as well as being present in ATP (Section 21.5).

PROBLEM 16.9

Provide compounds that fit the following descriptions:

(a) Two amines that are gases at room temperature

(b) A heterocyclic amine

(c) A compound with an amine group on an aromatic ring

PROBLEM 16.10

Consult Table 16.1 and write the molecular formulas for pyrimidine and purine.

PROBLEM 16.11

Which of the following compounds are heterocyclic nitrogen compounds?

(a) 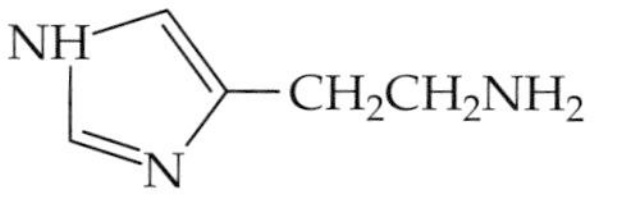 [structure] $-CH_2CH_2NH_2$

(b) 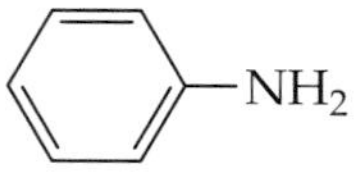 [structure] $-NH_2$

(c) 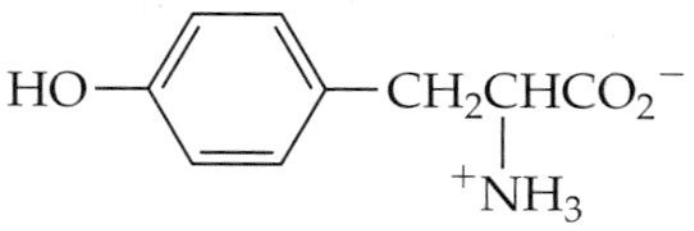 $HO-$[structure]$-CH_2CHCO_2^-$ with $^+NH_3$

(d) 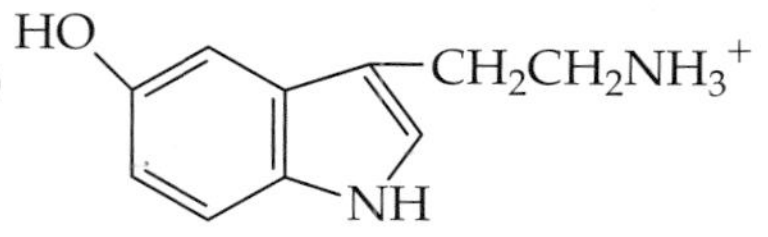 [structure] $-CH_2CH_2NH_3^+$

16.5 Basicity of Amines

Learning Objective:

• Identify and draw the products formed when an amine reacts with acid.

Just like ammonia, aqueous solutions of amines are weakly basic because of the formation of OH^- and R_3NH^+ ions in water. Consider the following equilibria of the neutral amines and their **ammonium ions:**

$$CH_3CH_2NH_2 + H_2O \rightleftharpoons CH_3CH_2NH_3^+ + OH^-$$
$$(CH_3CH_2)_2NH + H_2O \rightleftharpoons (CH_3CH_2)_2NH_2^+ + OH^-$$
$$(CH_3CH_2)_3N + H_2O \rightleftharpoons (CH_3CH_2)_3NH^+ + OH^-$$

Notice that these are reversible reactions; ammonium ions can react as acids in the presence of bases to regenerate the amines. This equilibrium is found to exist in solutions with pH values as high as 8.

Ammonium ions are also formed when amines react with the hydronium ion in acidic solutions:

$$CH_3CH_2NH_2 + H_3O^+ \rightleftharpoons CH_3CH_2NH_3^+ + H_2O$$
$$(CH_3CH_2)_2NH + H_3O^+ \rightleftharpoons (CH_3CH_2)_2NH_2^+ + H_2O$$
$$(CH_3CH_2)_3N + H_3O^+ \rightleftharpoons (CH_3CH_2)_3NH^+ + H_2O$$

The positive ions formed by addition of H^+ to alkylamines are named by replacing the ending -*amine* with -*ammonium*. To name the ions of heterocyclic amines, the amine name is modified by replacing the -*e* with -*ium*. For example:

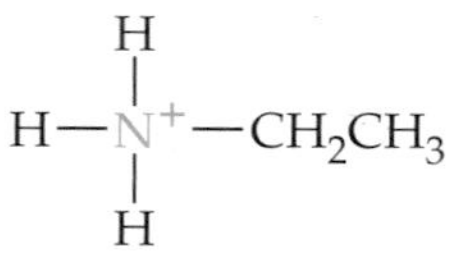

$$H-\overset{\overset{H}{|}}{\underset{\underset{H}{|}}{N^+}}-CH_2CH_3 \qquad CH_3CH_2CH_2-\overset{\overset{H}{|}}{\underset{\underset{H}{|}}{N^+}}-CH_2CH_2CH_3$$

[pyridinium structure]

Ethylammonium ion
(from ethylamine)

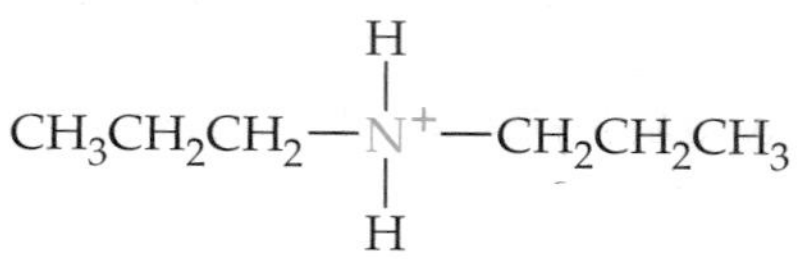

Dipropylammonium ion
(from dipropylamine)

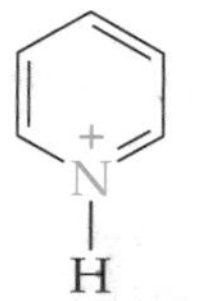

Pyridinium ion
(from pyridine)

As long as at least one group attached to the nitrogen is a hydrogen, ammonium ions are weakly acidic and will react with bases, such as hydroxide, to regenerate the amine:

$$CH_3CH_2NH_3^+ + OH^- \rightleftharpoons CH_3CH_2NH_2 + H_2O$$
$$(CH_3CH_2)_2NH_2^+ + OH^- \rightleftharpoons (CH_3CH_2)_2NH + H_2O$$
$$(CH_3CH_2)_3NH^+ + OH^- \rightleftharpoons (CH_3CH_2)_3N + H_2O$$

As a result of the aqueous equilibria shown, amines exist as ammonium ions in the water environment of blood and other body fluids, which have a typical pH value of 7.4; for this reason, they are written as ions in the context of biochemistry. For example, histamine and serotonin (both neurotransmitters, Section 28.7) are represented as follows:

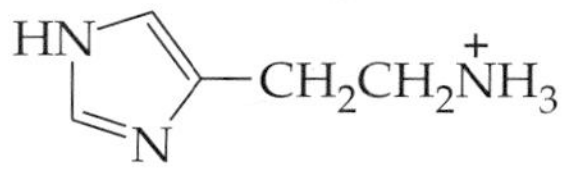

Histamine
(causes allergic reaction)

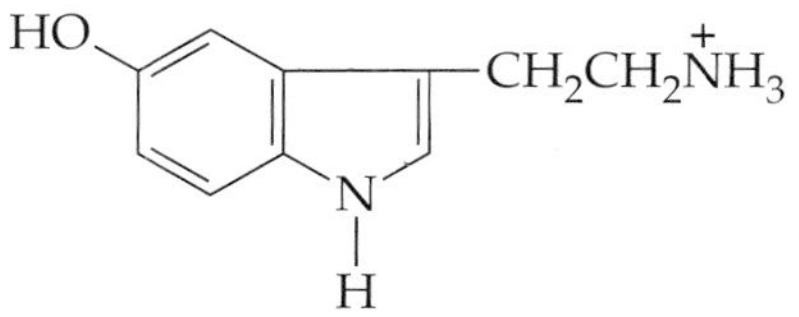

Serotonin
(a neurotransmitter active in the brain)

In general, nonaromatic amines (such as $CH_3CH_2NH_2$ or piperidine, Table 16.2) are slightly stronger bases than ammonia, and aromatic amines (such as aniline or pyridine, Table 16.2) are weaker bases than ammonia:

Basicity: Nonaromatic amines > Ammonia > Aromatic amines

▶ Worked Example 16.4 Amines as Bases in Water

Write balanced equations for the reaction of ammonia with water and for the reaction of ethylamine with water. Label each species in your equations as either an acid or a base.

ANALYSIS Determine which species is the base and which is the acid. Remember that the base will accept a hydrogen ion from the acid. Review the definitions for a Brønsted–Lowry base (Section 10.1) and a Lewis base (Section 16.3).

SOLUTION
Like ammonia, amines have a lone pair of electrons on the nitrogen atom. Because ammonia is a base that reacts with water to accept a hydrogen ion (which bonds to the lone pair), it is reasonable to expect that amines are bases that react in a similar manner.

$$NH_3 + H_2O \rightleftharpoons NH_4^+ + OH^-$$

Base   Acid   Acid   Base

$$CH_3CH_2NH_2 + H_2O \rightleftharpoons CH_3CH_2NH_3^+ + OH^-$$

Base   Acid   Acid   Base

Notice that in both cases, water acts as an acid because it donates a hydrogen ion to the nitrogen.

PROBLEM 16.12

Write an equation for the acid-base equilibrium of:

(a) Pyrrolidine and water   (b) Pyridine and water

Label each species in the equilibrium as either an acid or a base.

Worked Example 16.5 Ammonium Ions as Acids in Water

Histamine will react with acids (such as acetic acid) to form ammonium salts, which themselves are weak acids. When treated with KOH, the free amine is regenerated. Write a balanced equation for the reaction of histamine acetate with potassium hydroxide:

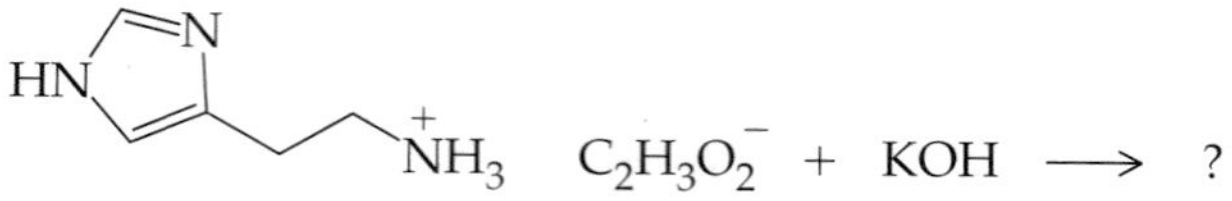

Histamine acetate

ANALYSIS The ammonium ion is a weak acid and will react with a base to give the amine, water, and the salt of the anion that was originally paired with the ammonium ion. It is also important to remember that a nitrogen with both a positive charge and at least one hydrogen can be written as follows:

Since the H on the positively charged nitrogen is acidic, the KOH will react as follows:

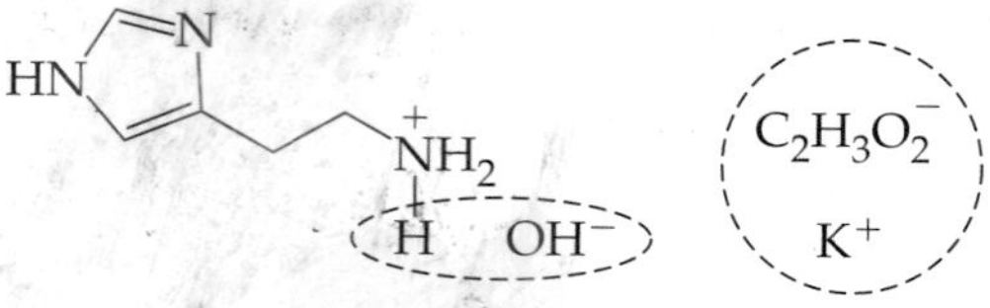

SOLUTION
The balanced overall reaction can be written as such:

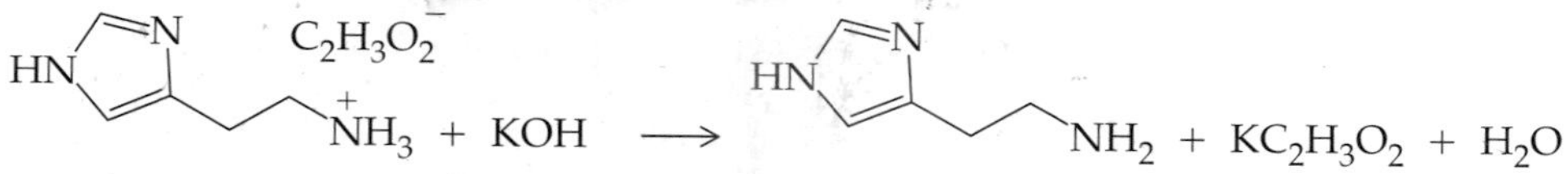

| Histamine acetate | + | Potassium hydroxide | $\longrightarrow$ | Histamine | + | Potassium acetate | + | Water |

PROBLEM 16.13
Complete the following equations:

(a) 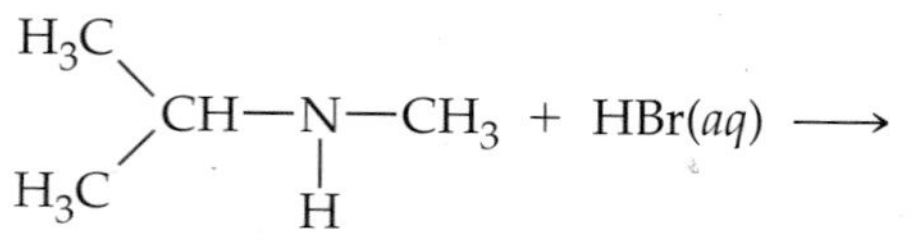 $(CH_3)_2CH-N(H)-CH_3$ + HBr(*aq*) $\longrightarrow$?

(b) $C_6H_5-NH_2$ + HCl(*aq*) $\longrightarrow$?

(c) (piperidine) + HCl(*aq*) $\longrightarrow$?

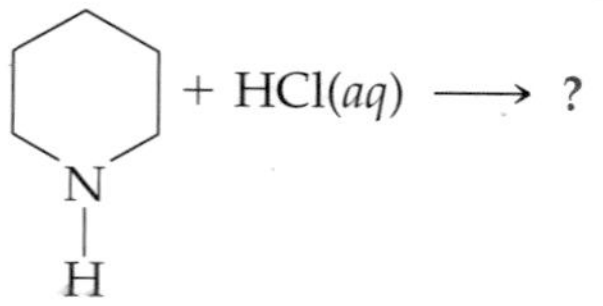

(d)  $R-\overset{+}{N}H_3$ + NaOH(*aq*) $\longrightarrow$?

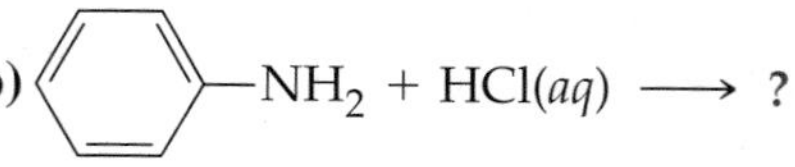

PROBLEM 16.14
Name the organic ions produced in reactions (a)–(c) in Problem 16.13.

PROBLEM 16.15

Which is the stronger base in each pair?

(a) Ammonia or ethylamine   (b) Triethylamine or pyridine

PROBLEM 16.16

When each of the following biologically active amines is placed into the body, they immediately pick up an H^+ to form an ammonium ion. Draw the structures of the ammonium ions formed by the following amines:

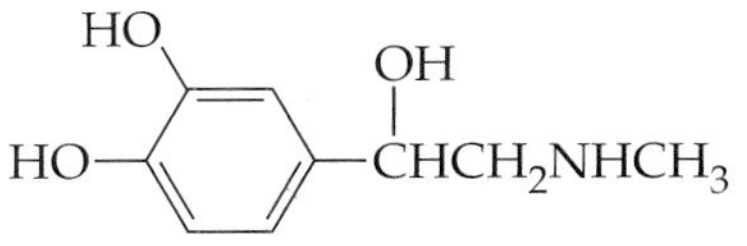

Epinephrine
(a biochemical messenger)

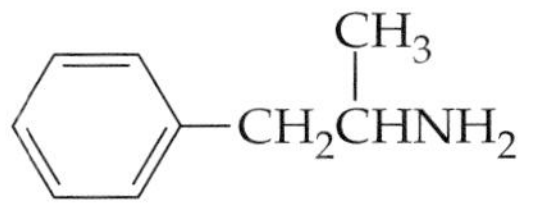

Amphetamine
(a CNS stimulant and drug of abuse)

16.6 Amine Salts

Learning Objective:

• Identify a quaternary ammonium ion and describe its properties.

An **ammonium salt** (also known as an *amine salt*) is composed of a cation and an anion and is named by combining the ion names. For example, in methylammonium chloride $(CH_3NH_3^+Cl^-)$, the methylammonium ion, $CH_3NH_3^+$, is the cation and the chloride ion is the anion.

Ammonium salt An ionic compound composed of an ammonium cation and an anion; an amine salt.

Ammonium salts are generally odorless, white, crystalline solids that are much more water-soluble than neutral amines because they are ionic (see the Chemistry in Action "Medications, Body Fluids, and the 'Solubility Switch'" on p. 546). For example:

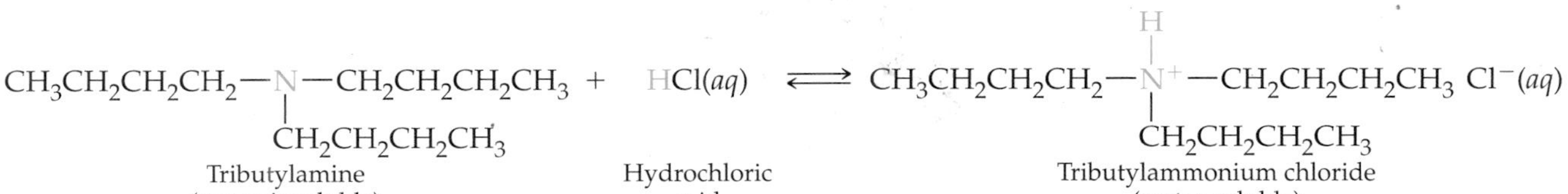

Tributylamine
(water-insoluble)

Hydrochloric
acid

Tributylammonium chloride
(water-soluble)

In medicinal chemistry, amine salt formulas are quite often written and named by combining the structures and names of the amine and the acid used to form its salt. By this system, methylammonium chloride is written $CH_3NH_2 \cdot HCl$ and named methylamine hydrochloride (this will be a convention you will see more as you study the biochemistry sections of this book). This system is often used with drugs that are amine salts. For example, diphenhydramine is one of a family of antihistamines available in over-the-counter medications. Antihistamines of this type are oily liquids and difficult to formulate as such, so they are converted to amine salts for formulation into medications (see the Chemistry in Action "Medications, Body Fluids, and the 'Solubility Switch,'" Chapter 17).

$$(CH_6H_5)_2CHOCH_2CH_2N(CH_3)_2 \cdot HCl$$

or

$$(C_6H_5)_2CHOCH_2CH_2CH_2NH(CH_3)_2{}^+Cl^-$$

Diphenhydramine hydrochloride
(Benadryl), an antihistamine

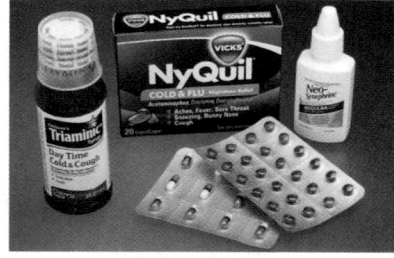

▲ Over-the-counter ammonium salts. The active ingredient in each of these over-the-counter medications is an ammonium salt.

Quaternary ammonium salt An ionic compound composed of a quaternary ammonium ion and an anion.

If a free amine is needed, it is easily regenerated from an amine salt by treatment with a base:

$$CH_3NH_3{}^+Cl^-(aq) + NaOH(aq) \longrightarrow CH_3NH_2(aq) + NaCl(aq) + H_2O(l)$$

Quaternary ammonium ions have four organic groups bonded to the nitrogen atom, and this bonding gives the nitrogen a permanent positive charge. With no H atom that can be removed by a base and no lone pair on the nitrogen that can bond to H^+, ammonium ions are neither acidic nor basic, and their structures in solution are unaffected by changes in pH. Their salts are known as **quaternary ammonium salts.** One commonly encountered quaternary ammonium salt has the following structure, where R represents a range of C_8 to C_{18} alkyl groups:

$$\text{Benzalkonium chloride} \qquad R = -C_8H_{17} \text{ to } -C_{18}H_{37}$$

Benzalkonium chloride
(an antiseptic and disinfectant)

These benzalkonium chlorides have both antimicrobial and detergent properties. As dilute solutions, they are used in surgical scrubs and for sterile storage of instruments; concentrated solutions, however, are harmful to body tissues.

PROBLEM 16.17

Write the structures of the following compounds:

(a) Butyldiethylammonium bromide   (b) Tetrabutylammonium hydroxide

(c) Propylammonium iodide   (d) Isopropylmethylammonium chloride

PROBLEM 16.18

Identify each compound in Problem 16.17 as the salt of a primary, secondary, tertiary, or quaternary amine.

PROBLEM 16.19

Write an equation for the formation of the free amine from butylammonium chloride by reaction with aqueous OH^-.

PROBLEM 16.20

The general structure of an antihistamine is shown in the margin. Does Benadryl (p. 513) have that general structure? Explain your comparison of the two structures.

PROBLEM 16.21

Write the structure of benzylamine hydrochloride in two different ways, and name the hydrochloride as an ammonium salt.

PROBLEM 16.22

Provide the products expected from the following reactions:

(a) $(CH_3CH_2)_3\overset{+}{N}H \ Br^- + LiOH \longrightarrow ?$

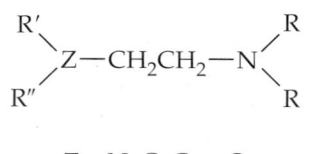

$$Z = N, C, C-O$$

Benzylamine

(b)

$C_2H_3O_2{}^- + NaOH \longrightarrow ?$

(c) $+ 2\ KOH \longrightarrow ?$

16.7 Amines in Plants: Alkaloids

Learning Objective:

• Describe the sources of alkaloids, name some examples, and tell how their properties are typical of amines.

The roots, leaves, and fruits of flowering plants are a rich source of nitrogen compounds. These compounds, once called "vegetable alkali" because their water solutions are basic, are now referred to as **alkaloids.**

The molecular structures of many thousands of alkaloids have been determined, with many having important medical uses. Most are bitter-tasting, physiologically active, structurally complex, and toxic to human beings and other animals in sufficiently high doses. One hypothesis is that the bitterness and poisonous nature of alkaloids probably evolved to protect plants from being devoured by animals. Not all alkaloids are known for their poisonous nature, however; most people are familiar with the physiological activity of two alkaloids—caffeine and nicotine (p. 509), which are stimulants. Quinine (p. 509) was for a long time the only drug available for treating malaria (caused by a parasitic protozoan); it is still used as a standard for bitterness: even a micromolar solution (μM; 1×10^{-6} mol/L) tastes bitter. Other alkaloids are notable as pain relievers *(analgesics)*, as sleep inducers, and for the euphoric states they can create. The opiates (named because they are naturally occurring alkaloids found in the opium poppy *[Papaver somniferum]*) have been known since ancient times. About 20 alkaloids are present in the poppy, including morphine and codeine. The alkaloids themselves are oily liquids, and not very soluble in water; in contrast, their ammonium salts tend to be crystalline solids that are freely soluble in water.

Table 16.2 lists some of the more historically common alkaloids along with their properties and uses.

Alkaloid A naturally occurring, nitrogen-containing compound isolated from a plant; usually basic, bitter, and often poisonous.

Table 16.2 Some Alkaloids and Their Properties

Name	Structure	Properties and Uses
Coniine	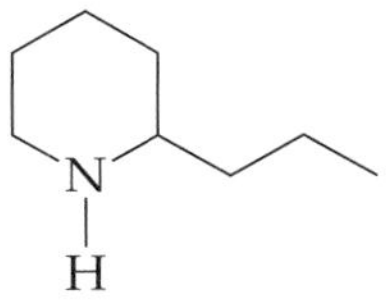	• Extracted from poison hemlock *(Conium maculatum)*. • Toxic to humans and all classes of livestock. • Fatal at levels below 0.1 g; death is caused by respiratory paralysis • Used to carry out death sentences in ancient Greece (most famously Socrates).
Atropine	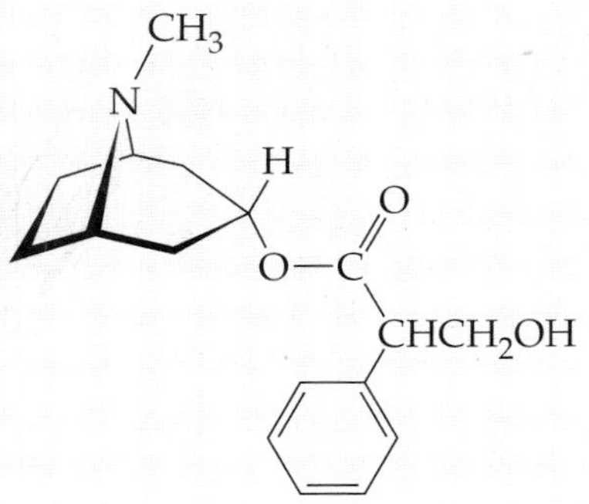	• Toxic substance in the herb known as *deadly nightshade* or *belladonna (Atropa belladonna)*. • Acts on the central nervous system. • In appropriately low dosage, used medically to reduce cramping of the digestive tract and in the treatment of slow heart rate (bradycardia). • Used as a treatment against nerve gases, such as Sarin.
Solanine	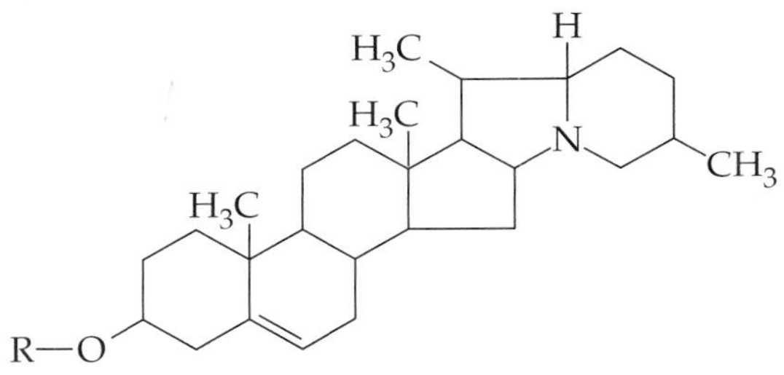 R = three sugar molecules	• More potent poison than atropine. • Found in tiny amounts in potatoes just under the skin and contributes to their characteristic flavor. • Amounts increase in potatoes upon exposure to light and is the reason you must peel green potatoes deeply (the green is due to chlorophyll, which is not toxic, and acts as a warning). • Has fungicidal and pesticidal properties. • Possesses sedative and anticonvulsant properties, and has been used as a treatment for asthma, with questionable effectiveness.

(Continued)

Table 16.2 (*Continued*)

Name	Structure	Properties and Uses
Reserpine	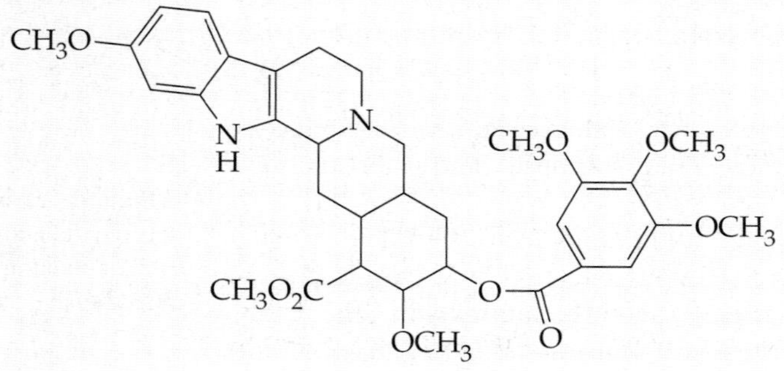	• An indole alkaloid isolated from the dried root of *Rauwolfia serpentina* (Indian snakeroot). • Used for centuries in India for the treatment of insanity, as well as fever and snakebites. • Historically used medically for the control of high blood pressure, it revolutionized treatment of a previously untreatable and life-threatening condition. • Rarely used today in humans due to the development of better drugs for hypertension. • Used as a long-acting tranquilizer to subdue excitable or difficult horses.
Morphine	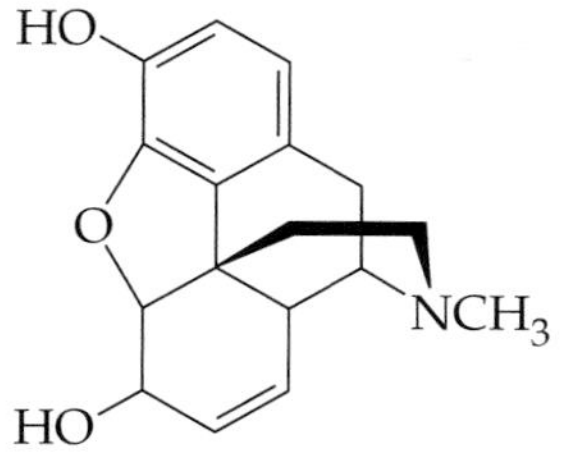	• The most abundant opiate found in opium; is believed to be historically the first active ingredient, natural plant alkaloid ever isolated. • Originally named after the Greek god of dreams, Morpheus, due to its tendency to cause sleep. • Acts directly on the central nervous system (CNS) to relieve pain; medically used to treat both acute and chronic pain. • Has a high potential for addiction due to rapid development of both tolerance to its analgesic effects and psychological dependence.
Codeine (3-methyl-morphine)	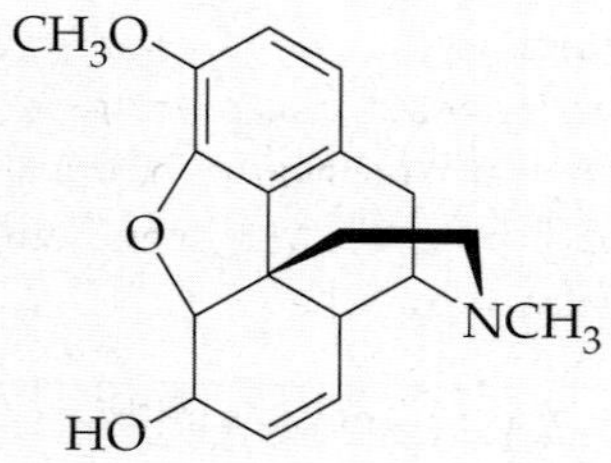	• The second-most abundant alkaloid in opium, it is a naturally occurring methylated morphine. • Used to treat mild to moderate pain and to relieve coughing; also used to suppress premature labor contractions. • Often used in combination with other pain relievers such as acetaminophen, aspirin, or ibuprofen, providing greater pain relief than either compound alone.
Heroin (diacetyl-morphine)	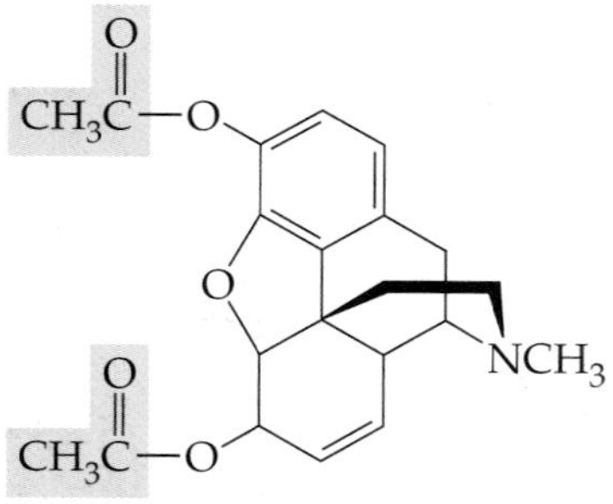	• A synthetic opiate, it is prepared by acetylation of the —OH groups of morphine (highlighted in orange). • Developed chiefly as a nonaddictive morphine substitute for cough suppressants; since proven to be false. • When injected, it is two to four times more potent than morphine with a faster onset of action. • The higher potency and speed of action are due to its ability to very rapidly cross the blood–brain barrier (the acetyl groups render it much more fat soluble than morphine itself) where it is deacetylated ultimately to morphine. • Used as a legal, medically prescribed drug for pain, as a cough suppressant and as an antidiarrhea drug. • Highly addictive, making its illegal, recreational use a real problem in society.

CHEMISTRY IN ACTION

✚ Calming a Stormy Mind: Amines as Anti-Anxiety Medications

Anxiety. We all experience it at one time or another in our daily life, whether getting to an appointment on time, taking a test, a job interview, or just meeting your date for the first time. For most of us, it is a fleeting condition: we deal with it and move on with our lives. When stress in our life is more persistent, like applying to nursing or graduate school, or raising a family, many people find ways to lessen the effects of anxiety through exercise, meditation, or other methods to relieve stress. But what if you cannot find a way to deal with your anxiety? In 2015, the United States alone has approximately 40 million people with anxiety disorders, many of whom feel their anxiety is so severe they cannot eat, sleep, work, or function normally. Prolonged anxiety can lead to depression, so its treatment is a real medical concern.

Medications to treat anxiety (anxiolytics) include alprazolam (Xanax), clomipramine (Anafanil), fluoxetine (Prozac), and sertraline (Zoloft), which are but a few anxiolytics regularly prescribed for the treatment of obsessive-compulsive disorder (OCD), social anxiety disorder, and panic attacks. What all of these drugs have in common is that they are heterocyclic amines that also contain aromatic rings with halogens present on them.

Alprazolam

Clomipramine

Fluóxetine

Sertraline

The mode of action of these anti-anxiety drugs depends on what brain receptors they target. For example, alprazolam and clomipramine target gamma-aminobutyric acid (GABA) receptors in the brain, increasing feelings of relaxation. These two molecules belong to a class known as the benzodiazapines (BZDs), a name that reflects the core structure found in all BZDs.

Benzodiazapines are regarded as the most effective class of medications for reducing anxiety, as they can in many cases be used on an "as needed" basis; the most famous member of this class being diazepam (Valium). For short-term use, they are considered the drug of choice, but their effectiveness comes with a high risk of both tolerance (higher and higher doses needed over time to achieve a desired effect) and addiction. Long-term regular use also has an associated risk of the development of dementia and permanent memory impairment. To overcome these side effects, new classes of anxiolytics were needed.

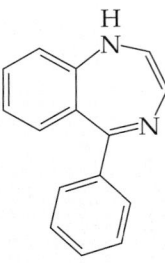

Benzodiazepine core structure

A second group of anti-anxiety medications belong to what are known as the selective serotonin reuptake inhibitors, or SSRIs. Fluoxetine and sertraline are examples of this class of anxiolytic.

SSRIs are believed to increase levels of the neurotransmitter serotonin by inhibiting its reuptake, making more of this important neurotransmitter available. Serotonin in the brain plays an important role in many behaviors, including sleep, appetite, and mood. Serotonin is believed to be a contributor to feelings of well-being and happiness, so when levels drop, it is thought that mood swings follow; the SSRIs can alleviate these. Unlike the BZDs, however, they cannot be used as needed but rather require a breaking in period to reach effective levels, sometimes taking two to eight weeks for the full, positive effects of the medication to be seen. Since they have not been shown to be addictive, and tolerance has a slower onset, they are more effective as a long-term option. In addition, the SSRIs have been found to be safe to take with almost all other medicines, another important aspect of a long-term drug. But even the SSRIs are not the answer for all; they can be poorly tolerated in many patients, as well as producing significant unwanted side effects such as weight gain, sleepiness or insomnia, and headaches. Still, the benefits of these amazing amines in almost all cases outweigh the drawbacks. Current research into this area is still going at full speed; as we get better at understanding what biochemical mechanisms are at work in anxiety and depression, new, safer, and more effective medications to treat these conditions will undoubtedly become available.

Serotonin

CIA Problem 16.1 A medication used to treat anxiety disorders is generally called what?

CIA Problem 16.2 What are the benefits of the benzodiazapines? What are the side effects?

CIA Problem 16.3 What are the benefits of the SSRIs as compared to the benzodiazapines? Their side effects?

CONCEPT MAP: ORGANIC CHEMISTRY FAMILIES

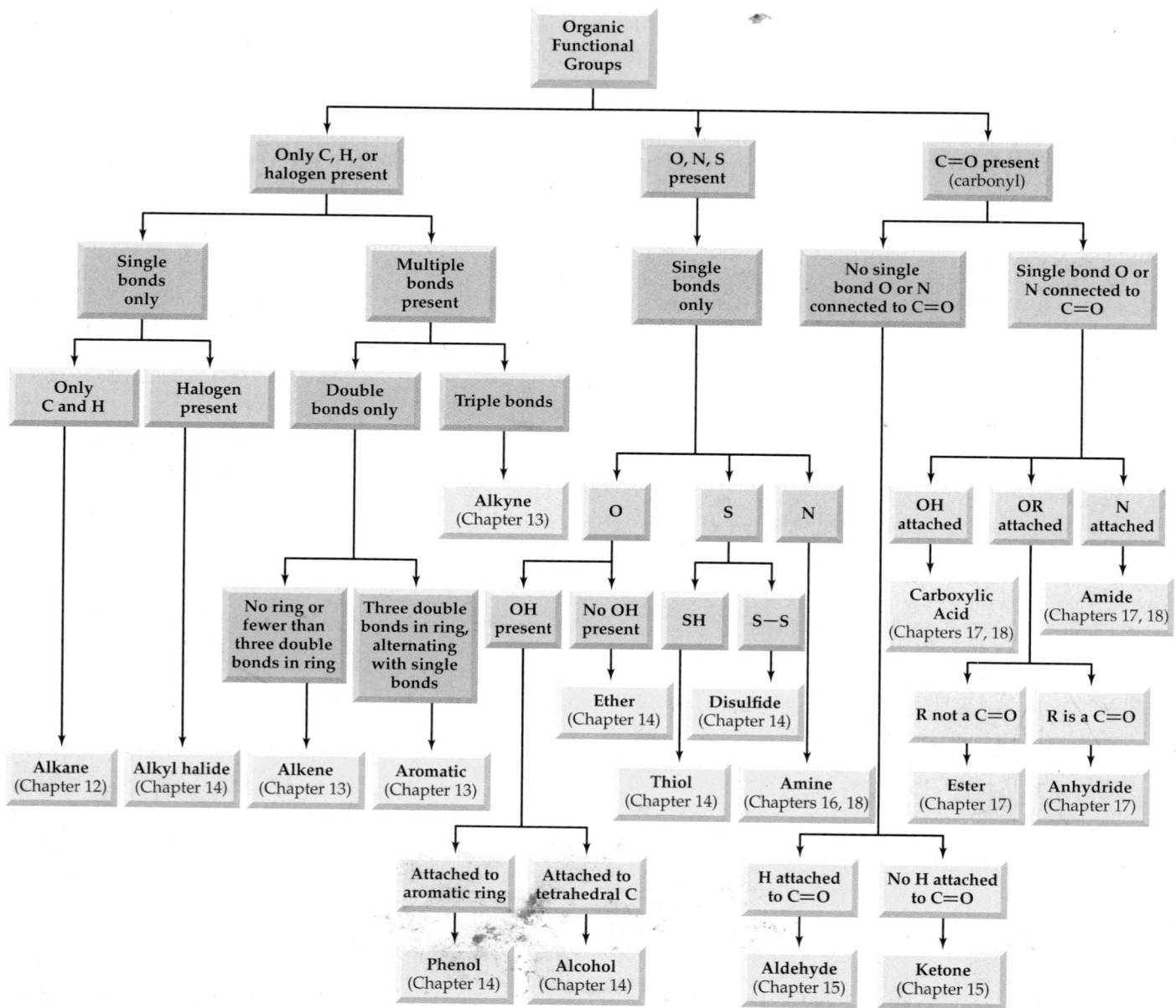

▲ **Figure 16.2 Functional Group Concept Map.** This is the same concept map we saw at the end of Chapters 12–15, except the functional groups discussed in this chapter, aldehydes and ketones, have now been colorized.

SUMMARY REVISITING THE LEARNING OBJECTIVES

- **Identify and classify an amine as primary, secondary, or tertiary.** *Amines* are classified as *primary, secondary,* or *tertiary*, depending on whether they have one, two, or three organic groups individually bonded to nitrogen. These amines can all accept hydrogen ion (H⁺) to form *ammonium ions*, which have four bonds to the nitrogen, which bears a single positive charge. Ions with four organic groups bonded to nitrogen are known as *quaternary ammonium ions (see Problems 23, 31, 32, 35, and 36).*

- **Name a simple amine given its structure or draw an amine given its name.** Primary amine names have *-amine* added to the alkyl group name, and secondary and tertiary amines with identical R groups have *di-* and *tri-* prefixes. When the R groups are different, amines are named as *N-substituted derivatives* of the amine with the largest R group. Ions derived from amines are named by replacing *-amine* in the name with *-ammonium*. The structure of a simple amine is drawn

by starting with the nitrogen and placing alkyl groups on as called for. The $-NH_2$ group when found as a substituent in a molecule is called an *amino group (see Problems 29–32, 35, 36, 45, 46, 52, and 58).*

- **Describe amine properties such as hydrogen bonding, solubility, boiling point, and basicity.** Amines have an unshared electron pair on nitrogen that is available to allow it to behave as a base (and accept a proton) or to be used for hydrogen bonding. Primary and secondary amine molecules hydrogen-bond to each other, but tertiary amine molecules cannot do so. Thus, the general order of boiling points for molecules of comparable size is

Hydrocarbons < Tertiary amines < Primary and secondary amines
< Alcohols

All amines can, however, hydrogen-bond to other molecules containing OH and NH groups, and for this reason small amine molecules are water-soluble. Many amines are physiologically active. Volatile amines have strong, unpleasant odors *(see Problems 23–25, 27, 33, 34, 49, 50, 54, and 57).*

- **Identify a heterocyclic amine.** In *heterocyclic amines*, the nitrogen of the amine group is bonded to two carbon atoms that are part of a ring. The ring can be aromatic or nonaromatic. Nonaromatic, heterocyclic amines are about as basic as regular amines. If the nitrogen is part of an aromatic ring, its lone pair of electrons becomes part of the aromatic system, making it less basic than a nonaromatic amine. Heterocyclic amines tend to have names that are historical in origin *(see Problems 48 and 55–57).*

- **Identify and draw the products formed when an amine reacts with acid.** Amines are weak bases and establish equilibria with water by accepting H^+ to form ammonium ions (RNH_3^+, $R_2NH_2^+$, R_3NH^+) and hydroxide ions (OH^-). They react directly with acids to form ammonium ions, which are water soluble. Ammonium ions react as acids (proton donors) in the presence of a base; when that base is hydroxide, water

is formed and the uncharged amine is regenerated *(see Problems 28, 39–42, 44, and 53).*

- **Identify a quaternary ammonium ion and describe its properties.** *Quaternary ammonium ions* (R_4N^+) are ions that form when all four bonds to the nitrogen are to carbons. Quaternary ammonium ions have a permanent positive charge since they have no lone electron pair; because of this, they are not bases, nor can they form hydrogen bonds. They are not acids, because all bonds to nitrogen are to carbons and not hydrogens. Due to their fixed positive charge, they are water soluble *(see Problems 28, 35, 36, 39, 40, 43–45, and 49).*

- **Describe the sources of alkaloids, name some examples, and tell how their properties are typical of amines.** *Alkaloids* are naturally occurring nitrogen compounds found in plants. Quinine, morphine, and atropine are three examples of alkaloids. All alkaloids are amines and, therefore, basic. Most possess a bitter taste. Like other amines, many are physiologically active, notably as poisons or analgesics *(see Problems 38, 48, 51, and 55).*

KEY WORDS

Alkaloid, *p. 515*
Amine (primary, secondary, tertiary), *p. 503*
Amino group, *p. 505*

Ammonium ion, *p. 510*
Ammonium salt, *p. 513*

Heterocycle, *p. 509*
Lewis base, *p. 506*
Quaternary ammonium ion, *p. 503*

Quaternary ammonium salt, *p. 514*

SUMMARY OF REACTIONS

1. **Reactions of amines (Section 16.4)**
   (a) Acid-base reaction with water:

   $$CH_3CH_2NH_2 + H_2O \rightleftharpoons CH_3CH_2NH_3^+ + OH^-$$

   (b) Acid-base reaction with a strong acid to yield an ammonium ion:

   $$CH_3CH_2NH_2 + H_3O^+ \longrightarrow CH_3CH_2NH_3^+ + H_2O$$

2. **Reaction of ammonium ion (Section 16.4) or amine salt (Section 16.5)** Acid-base reaction of primary, secondary, or tertiary amine salt (or ion) with a base to regenerate the amine:

   $$CH_3CH_2NH_3^+Cl^- + NaOH \longrightarrow CH_3CH_2NH_2 + NaCl + H_2O$$

⬤ UNDERSTANDING KEY CONCEPTS

16.23

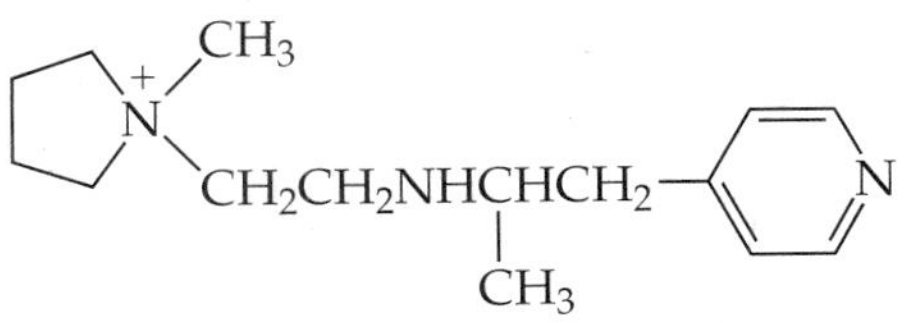

(a) For the compound above, identify each nitrogen as either a primary, secondary, tertiary, quaternary, or aromatic amine.

(b) Which amine group(s) would be able to provide a hydrogen bond? Which could accept a hydrogen bond?

16.24 The structure of the amino acid lysine (in its uncharged form) is shown below.

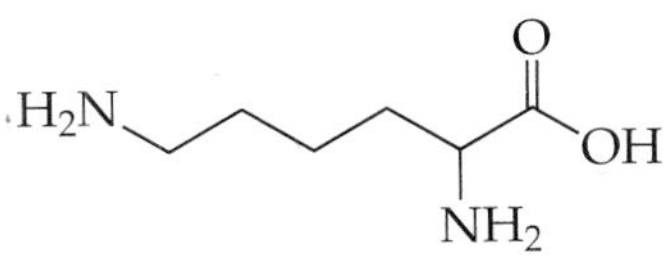

(a) Which amine groups would be able to participate in hydrogen bonding?

(b) Is lysine likely to be water-soluble? Explain.

16.25 Draw structures to illustrate hydrogen bonding (similar to those on p. 507) between the following compounds.

(a) Four 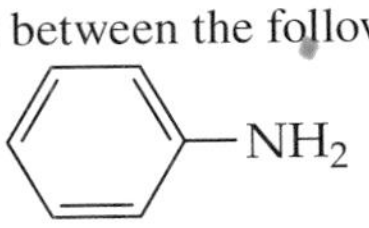 molecules

(b) Two 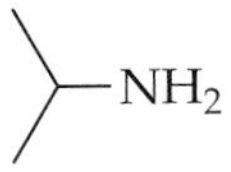 and two H_2O

(c) Two CH_3NH_2 and two

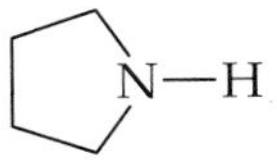

16.26 Explain what bonds must be made or broken and where the electrons go when the hydrogen-bonded water between the two amines shown on page 507 reacts to form an amine, ammonium ion, and OH^-.

16.27 Which of these amines is the strongest base? The weakest? (See Section 16.4.)

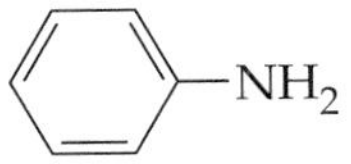

16.28 Complete the following equations:

(a)

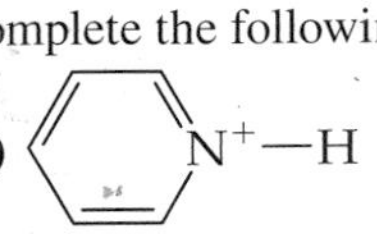

(b)

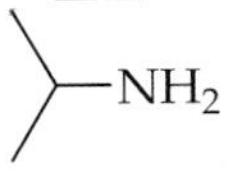

(c) $(CH_3CH_2)_3N + HBr \longrightarrow$

(d)

ADDITIONAL PROBLEMS

AMINES AND AMMONIUM SALTS (SECTIONS 16.1–16.3)

16.29   Draw the structures corresponding to the following names:

(a) *N*-Methylcyclohexylamine

(b) Dipropylamine   (c) Pentylamine

16.30   Draw the structures corresponding to the following names:

(a) *N*-Methylpentylamine

(b) *N*-Ethylcyclobutylamine   (c) *p*-Propylaniline

16.31   Name the following amines, and classify them as primary, secondary, or tertiary:

(a) 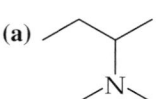   (b) 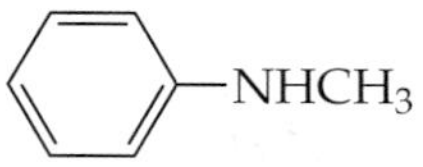 ⬡—NHCH₃

16.32   Name the following amines, and identify them as primary, secondary, or tertiary:

(a) 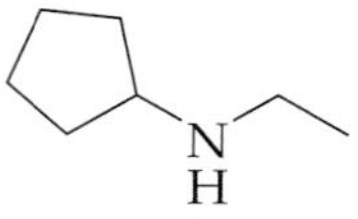 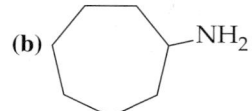   (b) (cycloheptyl)—NH₂

16.33   Is water a weaker or stronger base than ammonia?

16.34   Which is a stronger base, diethyl ether or diethylamine?

16.35   Give names or structures for the following ammonium salts. Indicate whether each is the ammonium salt of a primary, secondary, or tertiary amine.

(a) 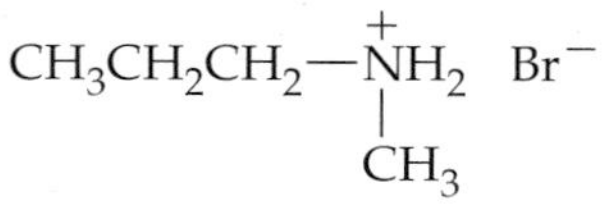 $CH_3CH_2CH_2 \overset{+}{\underset{\underset{CH_3}{|}}{N}H_2}$ Br⁻

(b) 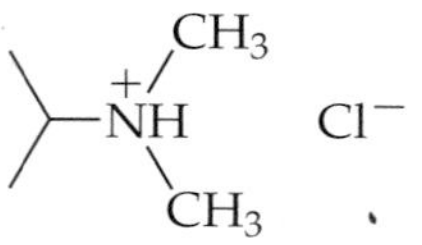 $\overset{CH_3}{\underset{CH_3}{\underset{|}{\overset{+}{N}H}}}$ Cl⁻

(c) *N*-Propylbutylammonium bromide

(d) Cyclobutylammonium bromide

16.36   Give names or structures for the following ammonium salts. Indicate whether each is the ammonium salt of a primary, secondary, or tertiary amine.

(a) 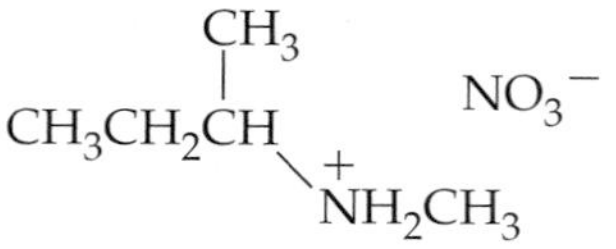 $CH_3CH_2\overset{\overset{\displaystyle CH_3}{|}}{CH}\overset{+}{\underset{NH_2CH_3}{}}$ NO_3^-

(b) Pyridinium chloride

(c) *N*-Butyl-*N*-isopropylhexylammonium chloride

16.37   The compound lidocaine is used medically as a local anesthetic. Identify the functional groups present in lidocaine (refer to Section 12.2).

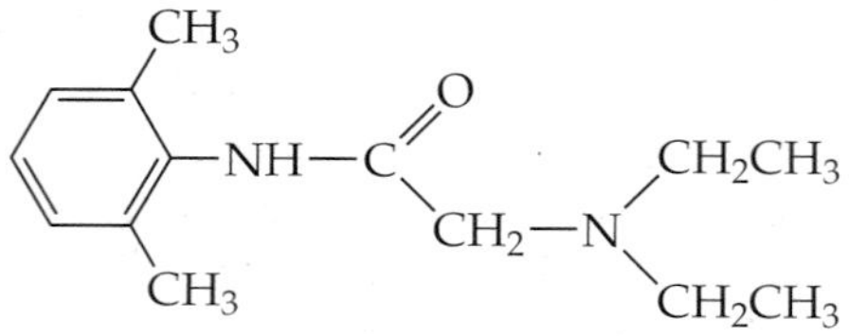

Lidocaine

16.38   Identify the functional groups in cocaine (refer to Section 12.2).

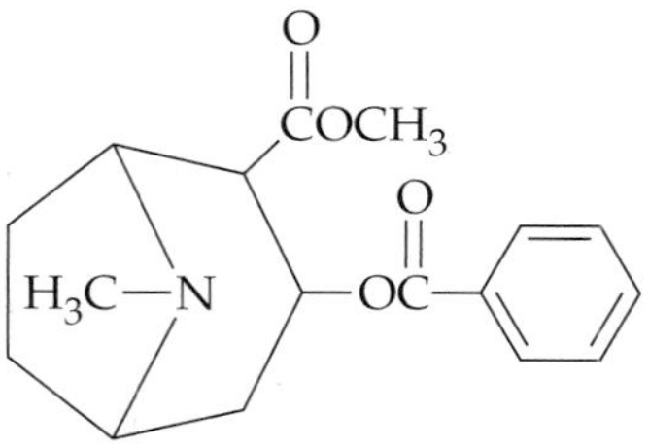

Cocaine

16.39   Draw the structures of the ammonium ions formed when the amines in Problem 16.29 are treated with acid.

16.40   Draw the structures of the ammonium ions formed when the amines in Problem 16.30 are treated with acid.

REACTIONS OF AMINES (SECTIONS 16.3, 16.5, 16.6)

16.41   Complete the following equations (hint: remember that a nitrogen with three groups bound to it has a lone pair and one with four does not; see Worked Examples 16.4 and 16.5 for help):

(a) 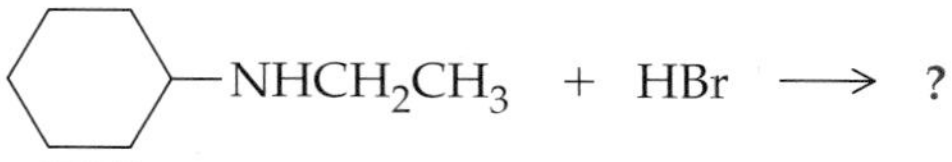 ⬡—NHCH₂CH₃ + HBr ⟶ ?

(b) 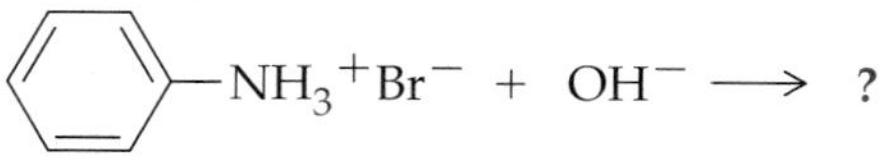 ⬡—NH₃⁺Br⁻ + OH⁻ ⟶ ?

(c) 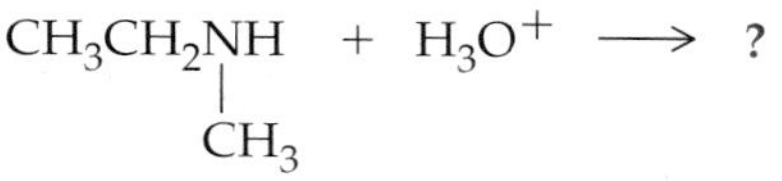 $CH_3CH_2\underset{\underset{CH_3}{|}}{N}H + H_3O^+ ⟶$?

16.42   Complete the following equations. (Hint: Remember that a nitrogen with three groups bound to it has a lone pair and one with four does not; see Worked Examples 16.4 and 16.5 for help.)

(a) 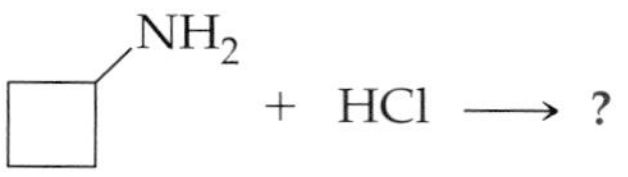 (cyclobutyl)—NH₂ + HCl ⟶ ?

(b) 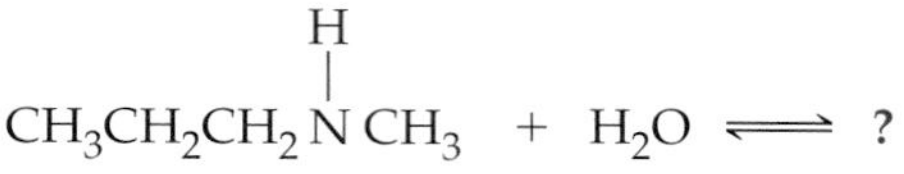 $CH_3CH_2CH_2\overset{\overset{\displaystyle H}{|}}{N}CH_3 + H_2O ⇌$?

(c) 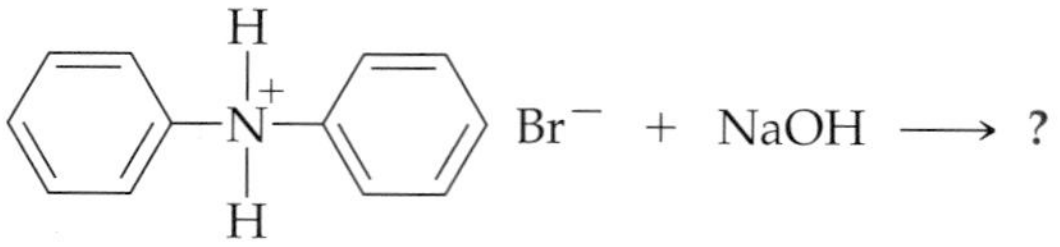 ⬡—$\overset{+}{\underset{\underset{H}{|}}{N}}$—⬡ Br⁻ + NaOH ⟶ ?

16.43   Many hair conditioners contain an ammonium salt such as the following to help prevent "fly-away" hair. These ions will react with neither acid nor base. Provide a reason why.

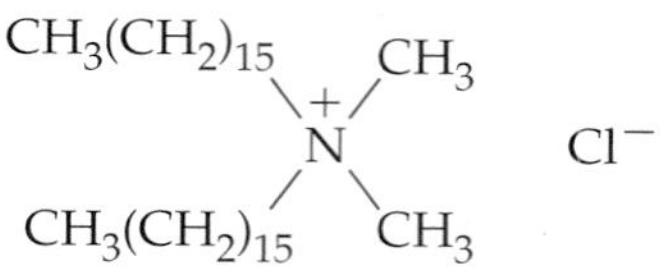

$CH_3(CH_2)_{15} \underset{CH_3(CH_2)_{15}}{\overset{CH_3}{\underset{}{\overset{+}{N}}}} CH_3$ Cl⁻

16.44   Choline has the following structure. Do you think that this substance reacts with aqueous hydrochloric acid? If so, what is the product? If not, why not?

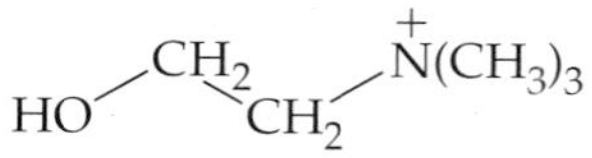

$HO\overset{CH_2}{\underset{CH_2}{\diagdown\diagup}}\overset{+}{N}(CH_3)_3$

CONCEPTUAL PROBLEMS

16.45 Propose structures for amines that fit these descriptions:

(a) A secondary amine with formula $C_5H_{13}N$

(b) A tertiary amine with formula $C_6H_{13}N$

(c) A cyclic quaternary amine that has the formula $C_6H_{14}N^+$

16.46 *para*-Aminobenzoic acid (PABA) is a common ingredient in sunscreens. Draw the structure of PABA (refer to Table 13.2).

16.47 PABA (Problem 16.46) is used by certain bacteria as a starting material from which folic acid (a necessary vitamin, Table 19.3) is made. Sulfa drugs such as sodium sulfanilamide work because they resemble PABA. The bacteria try to metabolize the sulfa drug, fail to do so, and die due to lack of folic acid.

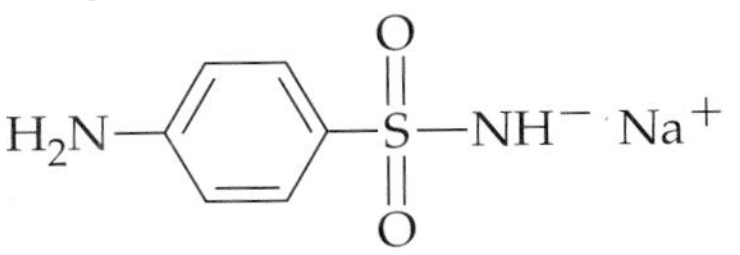

Sodium sulfanilamide

(a) Describe how this structure is similar to that of PABA.

(b) Why do you think the sodium salt, rather than the neutral compound, is used as the drug?

16.48 Acyclovir is an antiviral drug used to treat herpes infections. It has the following structure:

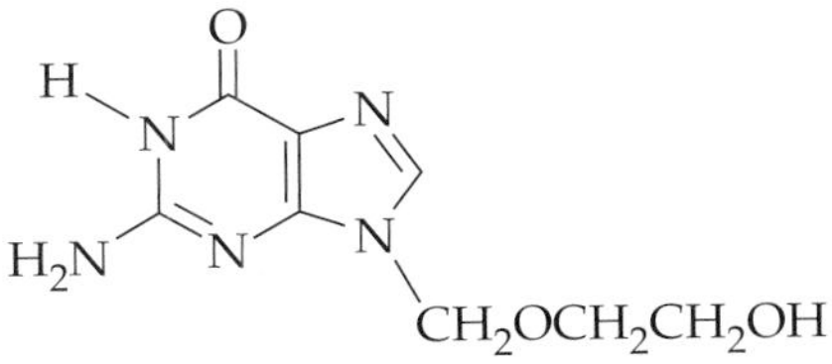

Acyclovir

(a) What heterocyclic base (Table 16.1) is the parent of this compound?

(b) Label the other functional groups present.

16.49 Which is the stronger base, trimethylamine or ammonia? In which direction will the following reaction proceed?

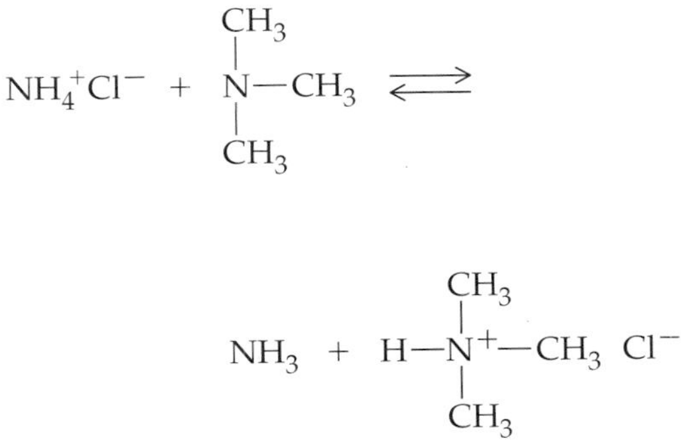

16.50 How do amines differ from analogous alcohols in (a) odor, (b) basicity, and (c) boiling point?

16.51 Name at least two undesirable characteristics are often associated with alkaloids.

16.52 Name the following compounds:

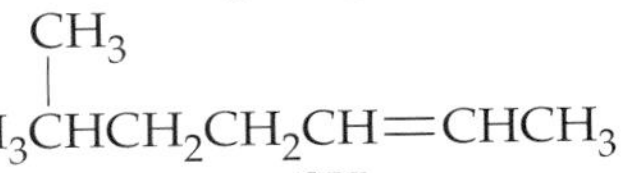

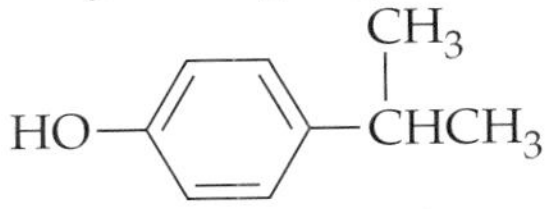

(c) $(CH_3CH_2CH_2CH_2)_2NH$

16.53 Complete the following equations (Hint: Answers may include concepts learned from previous organic chapters):

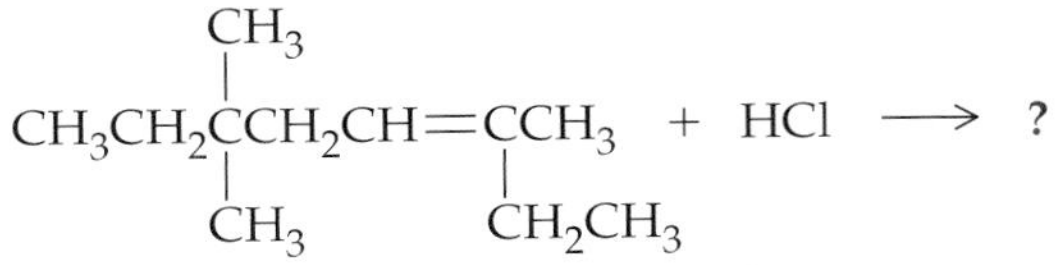

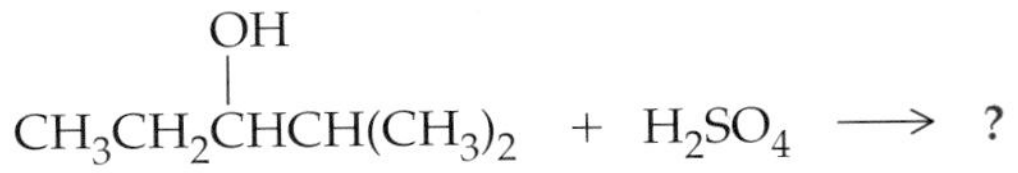

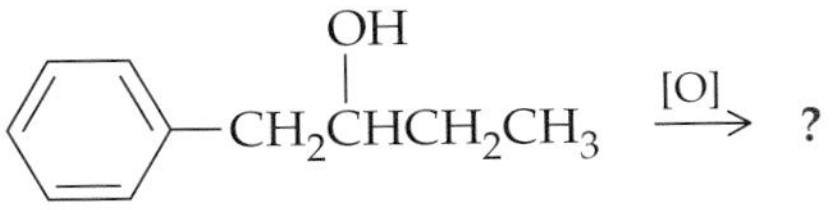

(e) $(CH_3)_3N + H_2O \rightleftharpoons$?

(f) $(CH_3)_3N + HCl \longrightarrow$?

(g) $(CH_3)_3NH^+ + OH^- \longrightarrow$?

16.54 Hexylamine and triethylamine have the same molar mass. The boiling point of hexylamine is 129 °C, whereas that of triethylamine is only 89 °C. Explain these observations.

16.55 Baeocystin is a hallucinogenic compound that is isolated from the mushroom *Psilocybe baeocystis* and has the structure shown below. What heterocyclic base (Table 16.1) is the parent of this compound?

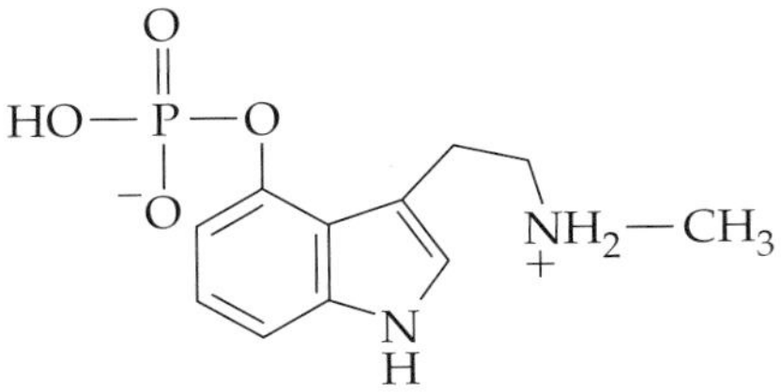

Baeocystin

16.56 Why is cyclohexylamine not considered to be a heterocyclic nitrogen compound?

16.57 Benzene and pyridine are both single-ring, aromatic compounds. Benzene is a neutral compound that is insoluble in water. Pyridine, with a similar molar mass, is basic and completely miscible with water. Explain these phenomena.

16.58 Name the organic reactants in Problem 16.41.

GROUP PROBLEMS

16.59 1-Propylamine, 1-propanol, acetic acid, and butane have about the same molar masses. Which would you expect to have the (a) highest boiling point, (b) lowest boiling point, (c) least solubility in water, and (d) least chemical reactivity? Have each member of your group chose a part to answer, and then discuss with each other why those answers were chosen.

16.60 Which of the two amines, decylamine or ethylamine, would you expect to be more soluble in water and why?

16.61 Lemon juice, which contains citric acid, is traditionally recommended for removing the odor associated with cleaning fish. What functional group is responsible for a "fishy" odor, and why does lemon juice work to remove the odor? If possible, test this at home using a piece of fish.

17

Carboxylic Acids and Their Derivatives

CONTENTS

◀◀◀ CONCEPTS TO REVIEW

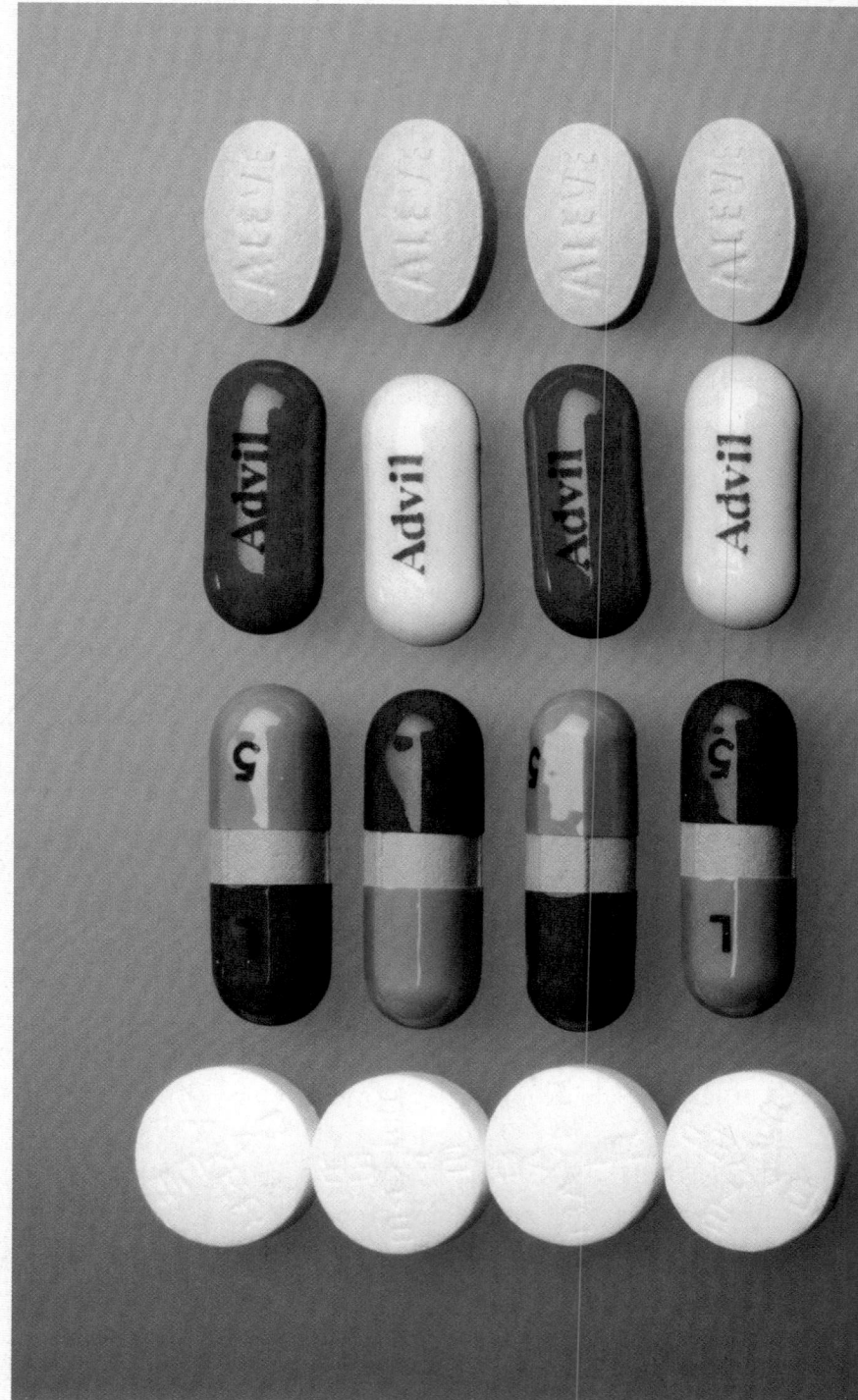

▲ Many pain relievers utilize the carboxylic acid functional group as a solubility switch, aiding in their ability to be effective analgesiscs.

We humans are composed of about 60–65% water, so it is safe to say that biochemically we live and function in an aqueous environment. Yet, the vast majority of the organic molecules you have seen to date have little to no solubility in water. So how are molecules that are not soluble in water used in an aqueous environment? This is a particularly important question when those organic molecules are medicines. To accomplish this, nature has ingeniously used the idea of incorporating a "solubility switch" into many of the biomolecules found. A solubility switch is simply a group present in a molecule that can turn it from being insoluble to soluble and back again as needed. The two most common functional groups that allow this to be achieved are amines (Chapter 16) and carboxylic acids, which we will discuss in this chapter. In a basic environment a carboxylic acid will be converted into a carboxylate ion, making it soluble. This strategy has been used by chemists to make medicines soluble in bodily fluids, allowing them to be transported from their entry point in the body to their site of action. Common carboxylic acid-containing drugs such as naproxen (Aleve) utilize this strategy. We will examine the idea of the solubility switch in the Chemistry in Action "Medications, Body Fluids, and the 'Solubility Switch'" found at the end of this chapter.

The last group of carbonyl compounds to be discussed are the *carboxylic acids* and their *derivatives*—the *esters* and *amides*. Esters of phosphoric acid are introduced here as well because of their major role in biochemistry and their chemical similarity to carboxylic acids and esters.

17.1 Carboxylic Acids and Their Derivatives: Properties and Names

Learning Objectives:

- Compare and contrast the structures, reactions, hydrogen bonding, water solubility, boiling points, and acidity or basicity of carboxylic acids, esters, and amides.
- Name simple carboxylic acids, esters, and amides given a structure and write a structure given a name.

Carboxylic acids have an —OH group bonded to the carbonyl carbon atom. In their derivatives, the —OH group is replaced by other groups. **Esters** have an —OR′ group bonded to the carbonyl carbon atom. **Amides** have an —NH$_2$, —NHR′, or —NR′$_2$ group bonded to the carbonyl carbon atom. Finally, there are the esters of phosphoric acid; these are important in the chemistry of a number of biomolecules, especially deoxyribonucleic acid (DNA) (Chapter 28).

Carboxylic acid A compound that has a carbonyl group bonded to an —OH group, RCOOH.

Ester A compound that has a carbonyl group bonded to an —OR′ group, RCOOR′.

Amide A compound that has a carbonyl group bonded to a nitrogen-atom group, RCONR′$_2$, where the R′ groups may be alkyl groups or hydrogen atoms.

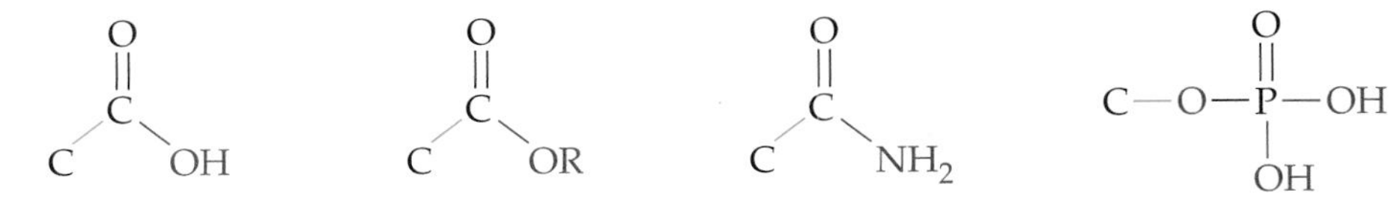

Carboxylic acid   Ester   Amide   Phosphoric acid ester

Since carboxylic acids, esters, and amides all contain a carbonyl carbon atom (C=O) bonded either to an oxygen or to a nitrogen, they are all polar. Their structural similarities also account for many similarities in the properties of these compounds. As a result, they all boil at a higher temperature than comparable alkanes. Carboxylic acids and amides that have a H on the nitrogen can also take part in hydrogen bonding, which plays a prominent role in their chemical, physical, and biochemical properties.

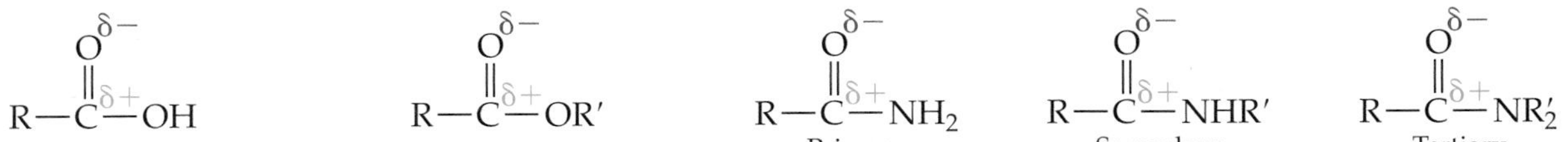

Carboxylic acid (RCOOH or RCO$_2$H)   Ester (RCOOR′ or RCO$_2$R′)   Amides (RCONH$_2$, RCONHR′, RCONR′$_2$)

Carboxylic acids occur throughout the plant and animal kingdoms; two of the most common you will regularly come across are acetic acid and citric acid. Acetic acid is the primary organic component of vinegar, which is simply a solution of 4–8% acetic

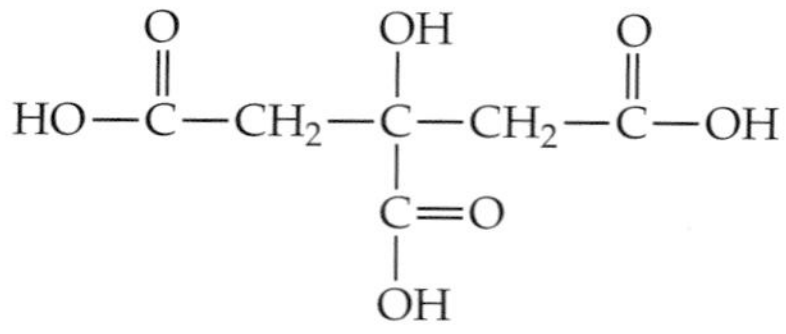

$$HO-\overset{O}{\overset{\|}{C}}-CH_2-\overset{\overset{\displaystyle OH}{|}}{\underset{\underset{\displaystyle OH}{|}}{\underset{\displaystyle C=O}{C}}}-CH_2-\overset{O}{\overset{\|}{C}}-OH$$

Citric acid

LOOKING AHEAD ▶ Citric acid lends its name to the *citric acid cycle*, part of the major biochemical pathway that leads directly to the generation of energy. Citric acid is the product of the first reaction of an eight-reaction cycle, which is presented in Section 21.8.

Carbonyl-group substitution reaction A reaction in which a new group replaces (substitutes for) a group attached to a carbonyl-group carbon.

acid in water (with various flavoring agents). Arising from the fermentation of fruit in the presence of excess oxygen, the production of "boutique" vinegars from various wine varietals has become big business. Citrus fruits owe their tartness to citric acid; for example, lemon juice contains 4–8% and orange juice about 1% citric acid. Citric acid is what is known as a tricarboxylic acid, since it has three carboxylic acid groups in it. Produced by almost all plants and animals during metabolism, its normal concentration in human blood is about 2 mg/100 mL. Citrates (a term used to describe mixtures of citric acid and its salts) are commonly used to add tartness to candies and soft drinks and react with bicarbonate ion to produce the fizz in Alka-Seltzer; they are also used extensively in pharmaceuticals and cosmetics.

Because these compounds all contain a carbonyl group attached to an electronegative atom, they all are able to undertake substitution reactions at the carbonyl carbon, unlike ketones and aldehydes. Carboxylic acids and their derivatives commonly undergo **carbonyl-group substitution reactions,** in which a group we represent as —Z replaces (substitutes for) the group bonded to the carbonyl carbon atom:

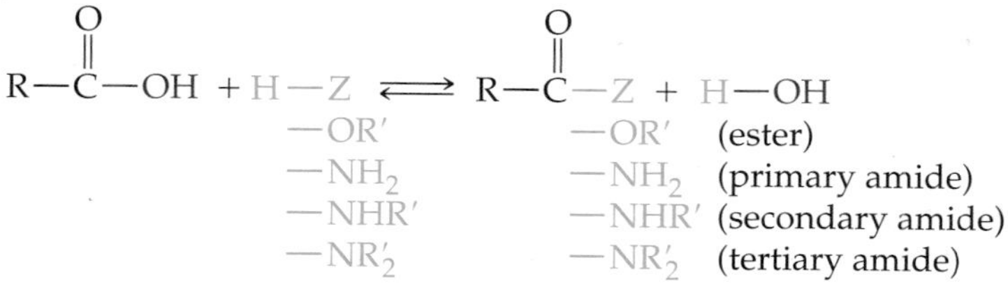

$$R-\overset{O}{\overset{\|}{C}}-OH + H-Z \rightleftharpoons R-\overset{O}{\overset{\|}{C}}-Z + H-OH$$

—OR′	—OR′ (ester)
—NH₂	—NH₂ (primary amide)
—NHR′	—NHR′ (secondary amide)
—NR′₂	—NR′₂ (tertiary amide)

For example, esters are routinely made by such reactions.

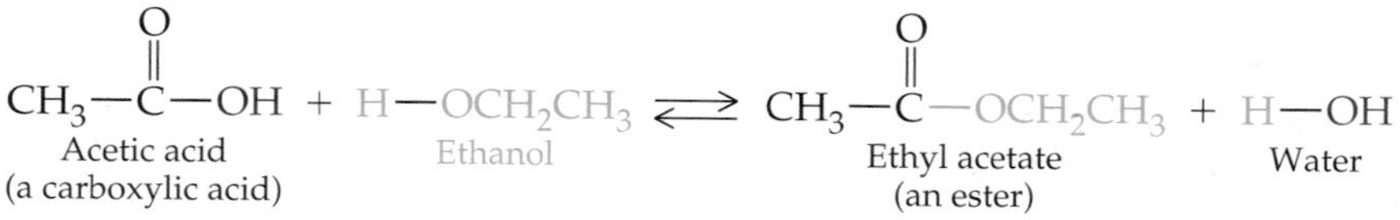

$$CH_3-\overset{O}{\overset{\|}{C}}-OH + H-OCH_2CH_3 \rightleftharpoons CH_3-\overset{O}{\overset{\|}{C}}-OCH_2CH_3 + H-OH$$

Acetic acid (a carboxylic acid)   Ethanol   Ethyl acetate (an ester)   Water

And esters can be converted back to carboxylic acids by reversing the reaction (this is known as hydrolysis).

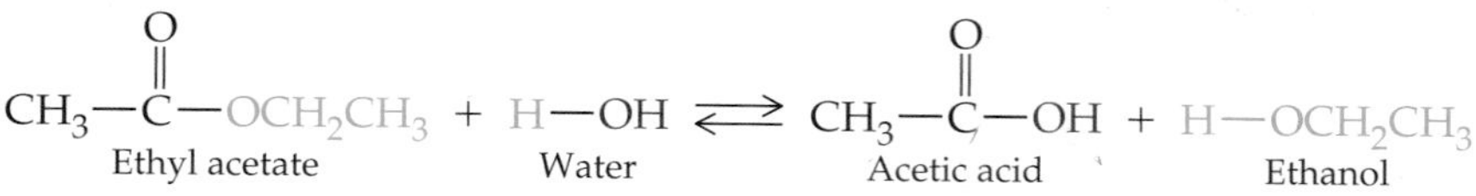

$$CH_3-\overset{O}{\overset{\|}{C}}-OCH_2CH_3 + H-OH \rightleftharpoons CH_3-\overset{O}{\overset{\|}{C}}-OH + H-OCH_2CH_3$$

Ethyl acetate   Water   Acetic acid   Ethanol

Acyl group An RC=O group.

Acyl groups

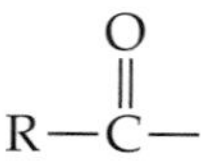

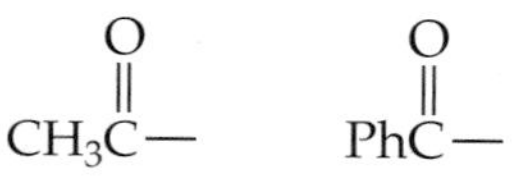

$$R-\overset{O}{\overset{\|}{C}}-$$

$$CH_3\overset{O}{\overset{\|}{C}}-$$ $$Ph\overset{O}{\overset{\|}{C}}-$$

Acetyl (Ac)   Benzoyl (Bz)

The portion of the carboxylic acid that does not change during a carbonyl-group substitution reaction is known as an **acyl group.**

In biochemistry, carbonyl-group substitution reactions are called *acyl transfer reactions* and play an important role in the metabolism of a variety of biomolecules.

PROBLEM 17.1

Identify the following molecules as a carboxylic acid, an amide, an ester, or none of these.

(a) $CH_3\overset{O}{\overset{\|}{C}}NH_2$

(b) CH_3OCH_3

(c) CH_3COOH

(d) $CH_3COOCH_2CH_3$

(e) CH_3COCH_3

(f) $CH_3CH_2CONHCH_3$

(g) $CH_3CH_2NH_2$

(h) $CH_3CH_2\overset{O}{\overset{\|}{C}}NH_2$

Carboxylic Acids

The most significant property of carboxylic acids is their behavior as weak acids. They surrender the hydrogen of the **carboxyl group,** —COOH, to bases and establish an acid-base equilibria in aqueous solution (a property further discussed in Section 17.3). The common carboxylic acids share the concentration-dependent corrosive properties of all acids but are not generally hazardous to human health.

Like alcohols, carboxylic acids form hydrogen bonds with each other so that even formic acid (HCOOH), the simplest carboxylic acid, is a liquid at room temperature with a boiling point of 101 °C.

Carboxylic acids pair up by hydrogen bonding, as illustrated for formic acid.

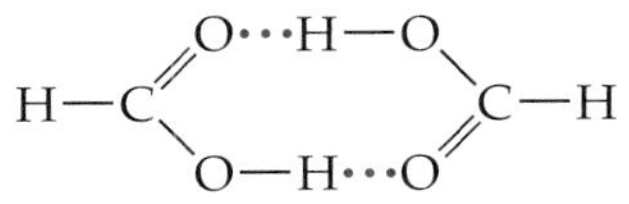

$$H-C\overset{O\cdots H-O}{\underset{O-H\cdots O}{}}C-H$$

Acids with saturated, straight-chain R groups of up to nine carbon atoms are volatile liquids with strong, pungent, and usually unpleasant odors; those with up to four carbons are water-soluble. Acids with R groups larger than nine carbons are waxy, odorless solids. In general, as the carbon chain length gets longer, the melting and boiling points increase; this is especially true for boiling points, where each carbon that is added increases the boiling temperature by 20–25 °C. Their water solubility decreases as the size of the hydrophobic, alkane-like R group increases relative to the size of the water-soluble —COOH portion.

Nomenclature

Since we have now introduced all of the main functional groups found in organic chemistry, we need to learn how to name compounds that contain more than one functional group. Within the International Union of Pure and Applied Chemistry (IUPAC) nomenclature scheme, a hierarchy exists when more than one functional group is present; that is, the priority of the functional group determines how the compound is named. That priority, from most important to least, is as follows:

Carboxylic Acids>Esters>Amides>Aldehydes>Ketones>Alcohols>Thiols>Amines>Ethers>Alkenes>Alkynes>Alkyl Halides>Alkanes.

So, a molecule that contains both an alcohol and a carboxylic acid is named as a carboxylic acid, and a molecule that contains an amine and an alcohol would be named as an amine, and so on. Numbering starts with the carbon that is either attached to or part of the functional group. While you will need to know how to name only simple multifunctional compounds, it is important that you are aware of this hierarchy, as it will come up later in biochemistry and will help you to understand why these molecules are named or classified as they are.

Carboxylic acids are named in the IUPAC system by replacing the final -e of the corresponding alkane name with -oic acid. The 3-carbon acid is propanoic acid; the straight-chain, 4-carbon acid is butanoic acid; and so on. If alkyl substituents are present, the chain is numbered beginning at the —COOH end, as in 3-methylbutanoic acid; the same goes if a second, lower priority functional group is present as in 2-hydroxypropanoic acid (better known as lactic acid, the acid present in sour milk).

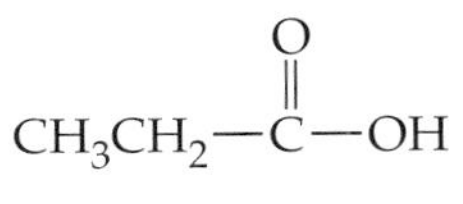

Carboxyl group The —COOH functional group.

◄◄◄ **CONCEPTS TO REVIEW** Recall that acid–base equilibria were discussed in Sections 10.1–10.3.

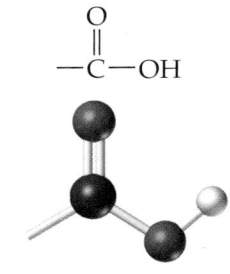

$$\overset{O}{\underset{\|}{-C-OH}}$$

Carboxyl group

◄◄◄ Recall that the relationship between the size of the hydrophobic portion of an organic molecule and its solubility was discussed in Section 14.3.

$$\underset{\text{Propanoic acid}}{CH_3CH_2-\overset{\overset{O}{\|}}{C}-OH}$$

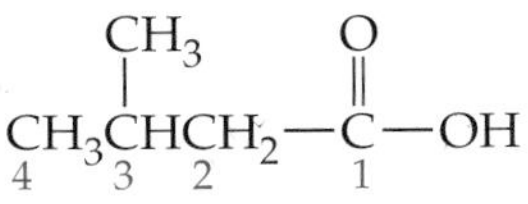

$$\underset{\text{3-Methylbutanoic acid}}{\overset{CH_3}{\underset{4\ \ 3\ \ 2}{CH_3\overset{|}{C}HCH_2}}-\overset{\overset{O}{\|}}{\underset{1}{C}}-OH}$$

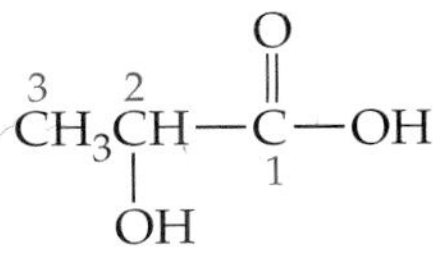

$$\underset{\substack{\text{Lactic acid}\\ \text{(2-hydroxypropanoic acid)}}}{\overset{3\ \ 2}{CH_3\overset{}{C}H}-\underset{\underset{OH}{|}}{\overset{\overset{O}{\|}}{\underset{1}{C}}}-OH}$$

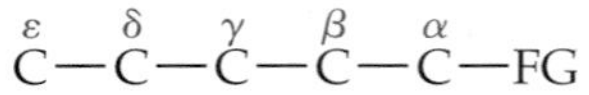

$$\overset{\varepsilon}{C}-\overset{\delta}{C}-\overset{\gamma}{C}-\overset{\beta}{C}-\overset{\alpha}{C}-FG$$

Greek indexing system used in common nomenclature. The α carbon is the first C attached to the functional group (FG)

Table 17.1 Some Common Carboxylic Acids

Structure	Common Name
Carboxylic Acids	
HCOOH	Formic
CH_3COOH	Acetic
CH_3CH_2COOH	Propionic
$CH_3CH_2CH_2COOH$	Butyric
$CH_3CH_2CH_2CH_2COOH$	Valeric
$CH_3(CH_2)_{16}COOH$	Stearic
Dicarboxylic Acids	
HOOCCOOH	Oxalic
$HOOCCH_2COOH$	Malonic
$HOOCCH_2CH_2COOH$	Succinic
$HOOCCH_2CH_2CH_2COOH$	Glutaric
Unsaturated Acids	
$H_2C=CHCOOH$	Acrylic
$CH_3CH=CHCOOH$	Crotonic
Aromatic Acids	
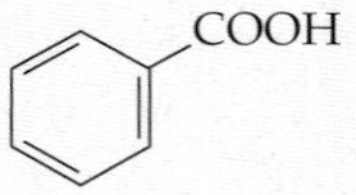 (benzene ring with COOH)	Benzoic
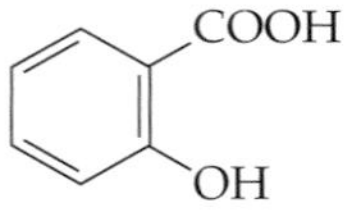 (benzene ring with COOH and OH)	Salicylic

Acetyl group (Ac) A $CH_3-\overset{O}{\overset{\|}{C}}-$ group.

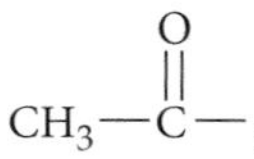

>> Biochemistry is dependent on the continual breakdown of food molecules. Frequently, this process requires transfer of acetyl groups from one molecule to another. Acetyl-group transfer occurs, for example, at the beginning of the citric acid cycle, which is central to the production of life-sustaining energy (Section 21.8).

Unfortunately, the common names of many of the carboxylic acids are used far more often than their IUPAC names, primarily because carboxylic acids were among the first organic compounds to be isolated and purified. Formic acid (from the Latin *formica*, "ant"), acetic acid (from the Latin *acetum*, "sour"), and lactic acid (from *lactis*, "milk") are but three examples. Recognizing the common acid names given in Table 17.1 is important, as they provide the basis for many of the derivatives of these acids. When using common names, the carbon atoms attached to the —COOH group are identified by Greek letters α, β, γ, and so on, rather than numbers. For example, using the common system to name the structure on the left below, the 3-carbon acid is *propionic acid,* and the second C=O group (a *keto* group in common nomenclature) next to the —COOH group is an α-keto group and the compound called an α-keto acid.

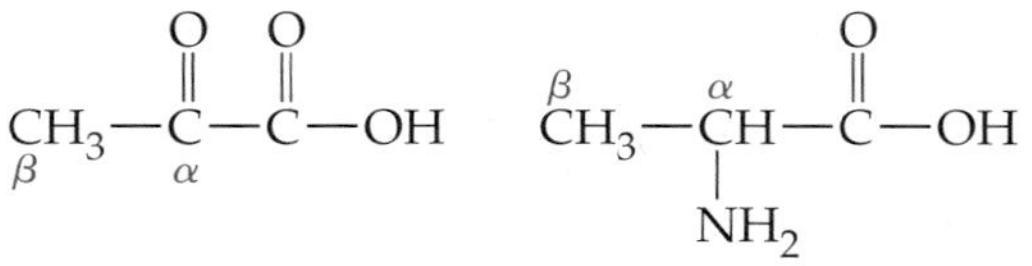

$$\underset{\beta}{CH_3}-\overset{O}{\overset{\|}{\underset{\alpha}{C}}}-\overset{O}{\overset{\|}{C}}-OH \qquad \underset{\beta}{CH_3}-\underset{\underset{NH_2}{|}}{\overset{\alpha}{CH}}-\overset{O}{\overset{\|}{C}}-OH$$

α-Ketopropionic acid (an α-keto acid, Pyruvic acid, a key biochemical intermediate)

α-Aminopropionic acid (alanine)

In alanine, as in all common amino acids, the $–NH_2$ group is on the α carbon atom (the C next to –COOH).

When discussing the acyl group that remains after a carboxylic acid loses its —OH, we replace the *-ic acid* at the end of the acid name with *-oyl.* One very important exception is the acyl group from acetic acid, which is traditionally called an **acetyl group** and is abbreviated Ac.

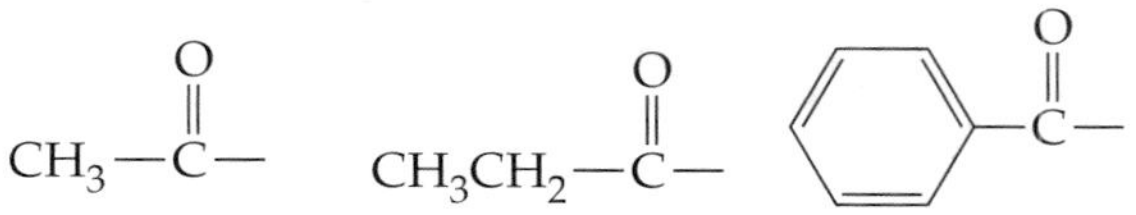

$$CH_3-\overset{O}{\overset{\|}{C}}- \qquad CH_3CH_2-\overset{O}{\overset{\|}{C}}- \qquad (\text{benzene ring})-\overset{O}{\overset{\|}{C}}-$$

Acetyl group   Propanoyl group   Benzoyl group

Dicarboxylic acids, which contain two —COOH groups, are named systematically by adding the ending *-dioic acid* to the alkane name (the *-e* is retained). Again, the simple dicarboxylic acids are usually referred to by their common names. Oxalic acid (IUPAC name: ethanedioic acid) is found in plants of the genus *Oxalis,* which includes rhubarb and spinach. You will encounter succinic acid, glutaric acid, and several other dicarboxylic acids when we come to the generation of biochemical energy and the citric acid cycle (Section 21.8).

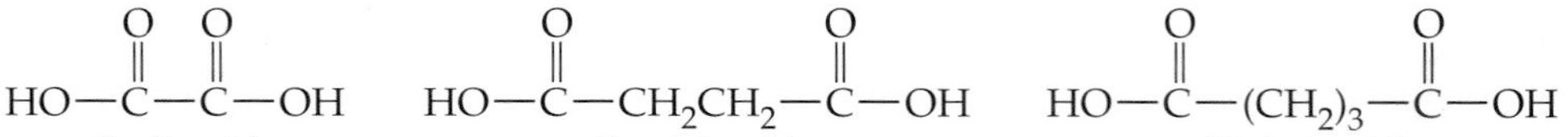

$$HO-\overset{O}{\overset{\|}{C}}-\overset{O}{\overset{\|}{C}}-OH \qquad HO-\overset{O}{\overset{\|}{C}}-CH_2CH_2-\overset{O}{\overset{\|}{C}}-OH \qquad HO-\overset{O}{\overset{\|}{C}}-(CH_2)_3-\overset{O}{\overset{\|}{C}}-OH$$

Oxalic acid (ethanedioic acid)

Succinic acid (butanedioic acid)

Glutaric acid (pentanedioic acid)

Unsaturated acids (carboxylic acids that contain one or more carbon–carbon double bonds) are named systematically in the IUPAC system with the ending *-enoic.* For example, the simplest unsaturated acid, $H_2C=CHCOOH$, is named propenoic acid. It is, however, best known as acrylic acid, which is a raw material for acrylic polymers.

▶ **Worked Example 17.1** Naming a Carboxylic Acid

(a) Give the systematic and common names for this compound:

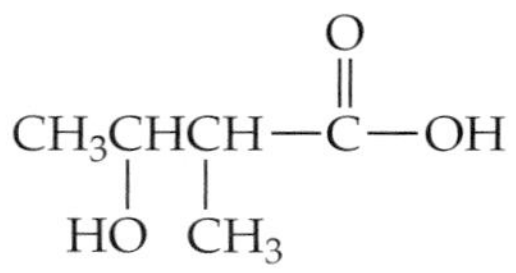

$$\underset{\underset{HO\ \ \ CH_3}{|\ \ \ \ \ \ |}}{CH_3CHCH}-\overset{O}{\overset{\|}{C}}-OH$$

ANALYSIS Because this molecule contains both an alcohol and a carboxylic acid, and the carboxylic acid has the higher priority, it will be named as a carboxylic acid. First identify the longest chain containing the —COOH group and number it starting with the carboxyl-group carbon.

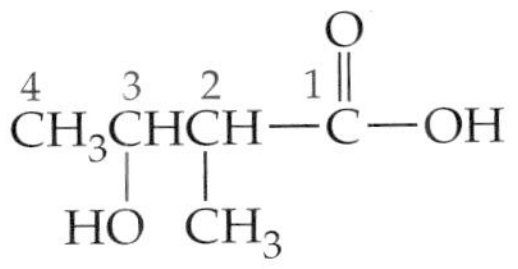

$$
\begin{array}{ccccc}
4 & 3 & 2 & 1 & \overset{O}{\overset{\|}{} } \\
CH_3 & CHCH & — & C & —OH \\
 & | & | & & \\
 & HO & CH_3 & &
\end{array}
$$

The parent compound is the 4-carbon acid, butanoic acid. It has a methyl group on carbon 2 and a hydroxyl group on carbon 3. From Table 17.1 we see that the common name for the 4-carbon acid is butyric acid. In the common nomenclature scheme, substituents are located by Greek letters rather than numbers.

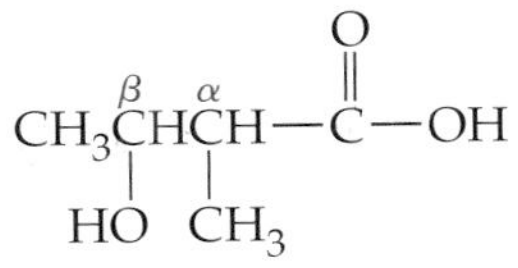

$$
\begin{array}{ccccc}
 & \beta & \alpha & & \overset{O}{\overset{\|}{}} \\
CH_3 & CHCH & — & C & —OH \\
 & | & | & & \\
 & HO & CH_3 & &
\end{array}
$$

SOLUTION
The IUPAC name of this molecule is 3-hydroxy-2-methylbutanoic acid; the common name of this acid is β-hydroxy-α-methylbutyric acid.

(b) Give the systematic and common names for this compound:

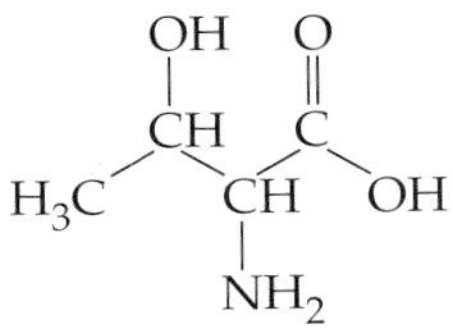

$$
\begin{array}{ccc}
OH & & O \\
| & & \| \\
CH & & C \\
H_3C & CH & OH \\
 & | & \\
 & NH_2 &
\end{array}
$$

ANALYSIS Because this molecule contains an alcohol, an amine, and a carboxylic acid, and the carboxylic acid has the higher priority, it will be named as a carboxylic acid. Again, identify the longest chain containing the —COOH group and number it starting with the carboxyl-group carbon.

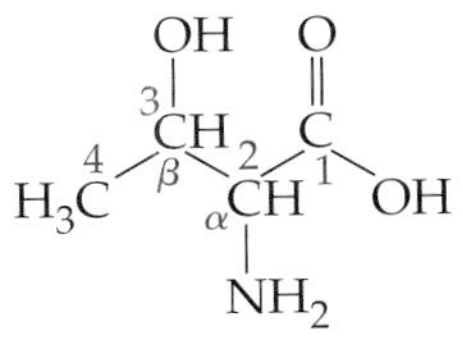

$$
\begin{array}{ccc}
OH & & O \\
3| & & \| \\
CH & 2 & C \\
4 & \beta & \\
H_3C & CH & 1 OH \\
 & \alpha | & \\
 & NH_2 &
\end{array}
$$

The parent compound is the 4-carbon acid, butanoic acid. It has an —NH_2 group (amino) on carbon 2 and a hydroxyl group on carbon 3. The common name for the 4-carbon acid is butyric acid.

SOLUTION
The IUPAC name of this molecule is 3-hydroxy-2-aminobutanoic acid; the common name of this acid is β-hydroxy-α-aminobutyric acid. It is an amino acid that is commonly known as threonine (Chapter 18).

PROBLEM 17.2
Draw the structures of the following acids:

(a) 2-Ethyl-3-hydroxyhexanoic acid   (b) *m*-Nitrobenzoic acid

PROBLEM 17.3
Write both the complete structural formula of succinic acid (refer to Table 17.1), showing all bonds, and the line-angle structural formula.

PROBLEM 17.4
Draw and name the acid that is formed by addition of Br_2 to the double bond in acrylic acid (refer to Table 17.1 and Section 13.6).

$$\begin{array}{c} \text{O} \\ \parallel \\ -\text{C}-\text{O}-\text{CH}_3 \end{array}$$

Ester

Esters

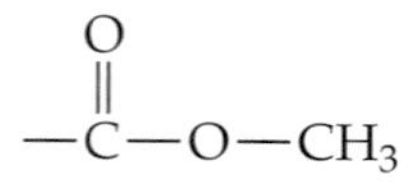

When the —OH of the carboxyl group is converted to the —OR′ of an ester group (—COOR′), the ability of the molecules to hydrogen-bond with each other is lost (although esters can still accept hydrogen bonds from water). Simple esters therefore have lower boiling than the acids from which they are derived.

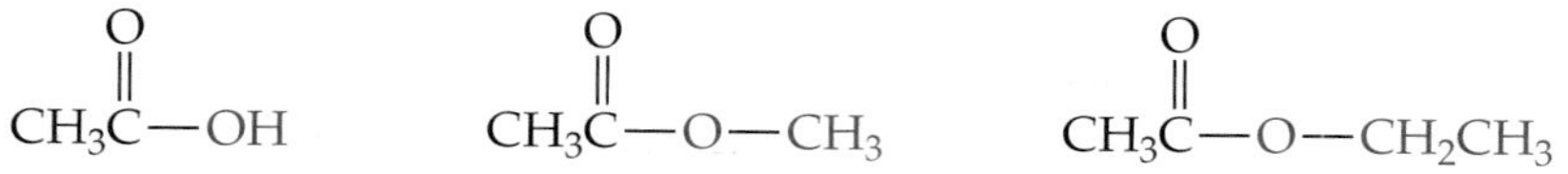

$$\begin{array}{ccc} \text{O} & \text{O} & \text{O} \\ \parallel & \parallel & \parallel \\ \text{CH}_3\text{C}-\text{OH} & \text{CH}_3\text{C}-\text{O}-\text{CH}_3 & \text{CH}_3\text{C}-\text{O}-\text{CH}_2\text{CH}_3 \end{array}$$

Acetic acid (bp 118 °C) Methyl ester (bp 57 °C) Ethyl ester (bp 77 °C)

The simple esters are colorless, volatile liquids with pleasant odors, and many of them contribute to the natural fragrance of flowers and ripe fruits. The lower-molecular-weight esters are somewhat soluble in water and are quite flammable. Esters are neither acids nor bases in aqueous solution.

Nomenclature

Ester names consist of two words. The first is the name of the alkyl group R′ in the ester group —COOR′. The second is the name of the parent acid, with the family-name ending -ic acid replaced by -ate. Note that the order of the two parts of the name is the reverse of the order in which ester condensed formulas are usually written.

Naming an ester

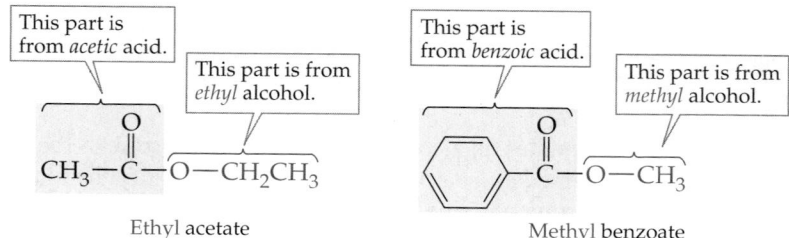

Ethyl acetate   Methyl benzoate

Both common and systematic names are derived in this manner. For example, an ester of a straight-chain, 4-carbon carboxylic acid is named systematically as a butanoate (from butanoic acid) or by its common name as a butyrate (from butyric acid).

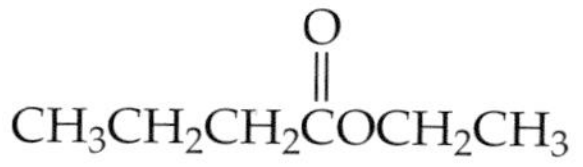

$$\begin{array}{c} \text{O} \\ \parallel \\ \text{CH}_3\text{CH}_2\text{CH}_2\text{COCH}_2\text{CH}_3 \end{array}$$

Ethyl butyrate (ethyl butanoate)

This ester is used as a food flavoring to give the taste and smell of pineapples.

Worked Example 17.2 Writing the Structure of an Ester from Its Name

What is the structure of butyl acetate?

ANALYSIS The two-word name consisting of an alkyl group name followed by an acid name with an -ate ending shows that the compound is an ester. The name "acetate" shows that the RCO— part of the molecule is from acetic acid (CH_3COOH). The "butyl" part of the name indicates that a butyl group has replaced H in the carboxyl group.

SOLUTION
The structure of butyl acetate is

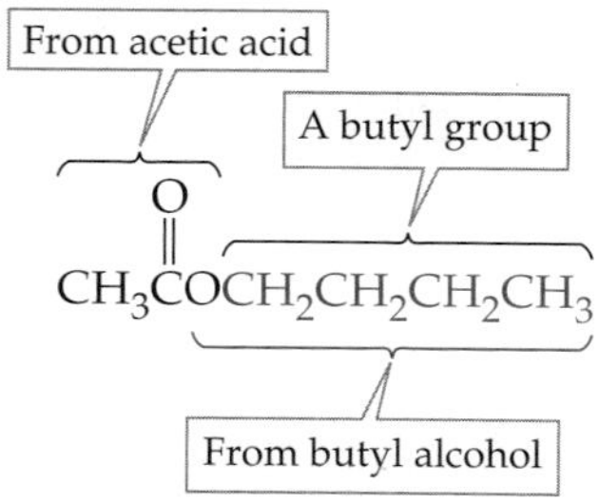

From acetic acid A butyl group

$$\begin{array}{c} \text{O} \\ \parallel \\ \text{CH}_3\text{COCH}_2\text{CH}_2\text{CH}_2\text{CH}_3 \end{array}$$

From butyl alcohol

Worked Example 17.3 Naming an Ester from Its Structure

What is the name of this compound?

$$CH_3(CH_2)_{16}\overset{\displaystyle O}{\overset{\displaystyle \|}{C}}OCH_2CH_2CH_3$$

ANALYSIS The compound has the general formula RCOOR′, so it is an ester. The acyl part of the molecule (RCO—) is from stearic acid (see Table 17.1). The R′ group has three carbon atoms and is therefore a propyl group.

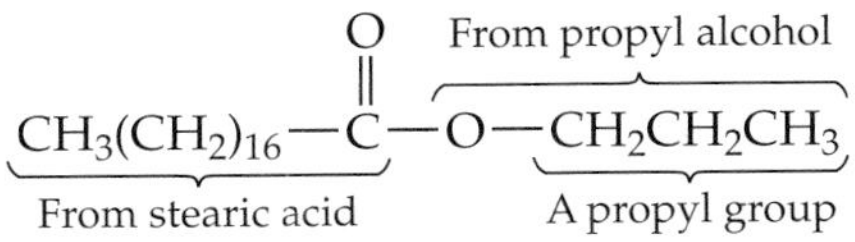

$$\underbrace{CH_3(CH_2)_{16}}_{\text{From stearic acid}}-\overset{\displaystyle O}{\overset{\displaystyle \|}{C}}-O-\overbrace{\underbrace{CH_2CH_2CH_3}_{\text{A propyl group}}}^{\text{From propyl alcohol}}$$

SOLUTION
The compound is propyl stearate.

PROBLEM 17.5

Draw the structures of the following compounds:

(a) Hexyl benzoate   (b) Methyl formate

(c) Ethyl acrylate (See Table 17.1)

PROBLEM 17.6

Which of the following compounds would you expect to have the highest boiling point and which the lowest boiling point? Explain your answer.

(a) CH_3OCH_3 (b) CH_3COOH (c) $CH_3CH_2CH_3$

PROBLEM 17.7

In the following pairs of compounds, which would you expect to be more soluble in water? Why?

(a) $C_8H_{17}COOH$ or $CH_3CH_2CH_2COOH$ (b) $CH_3\underset{\underset{\displaystyle CH_3}{|}}{C}HCOOH$ or $CH_3CH_2COO\underset{\underset{\displaystyle CH_3}{|}}{C}HCH_3$

Amides

Compounds with a nitrogen directly attached to the carbonyl carbon atom are *amides*. The nitrogen of an amide may be an —NH$_2$ group or may have one or two R′ groups bonded to it. *Unsubstituted (or primary) amides* (RCONH$_2$) can form multiple hydrogen bonds to other amide molecules and thus have higher melting points and higher boiling points than the acids from which they are derived.

$$-\overset{\displaystyle O}{\overset{\displaystyle \|}{C}}-NH_2$$

Amide

Hydrogen bonding in $R\overset{\displaystyle O}{\overset{\displaystyle \|}{C}}NH_2$

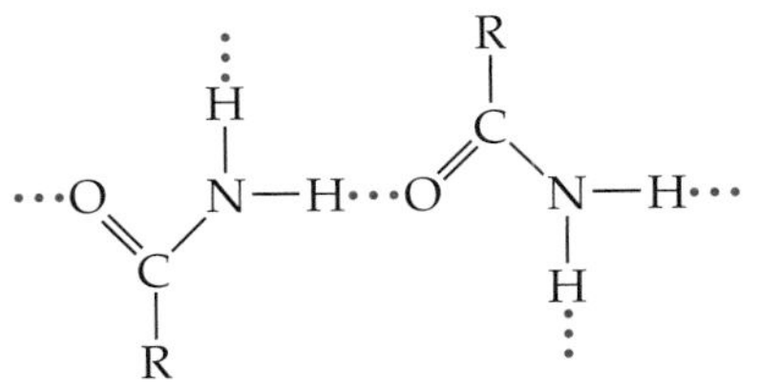

(Red dotted line indicates hydrogen bonds.)

Low-molecular-weight unsubstituted amides are solids (except for the simplest amide [formamide, $HCONH_2$, a liquid]) that are soluble in both water (with which they form hydrogen bonds) and organic solvents. *Monosubstituted (or secondary) amides* (RCONHR′) can also form hydrogen bonds to each other, but *disubstituted (or tertiary) amides* (RCONR′$_2$) cannot do so and, therefore, have lower boiling points.

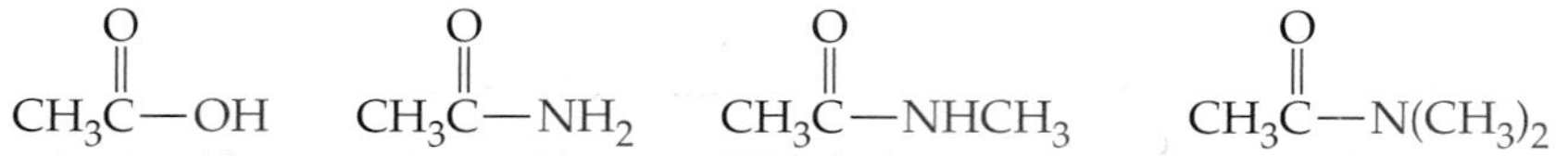

$$CH_3\overset{\overset{\displaystyle O}{\|}}{C}-OH$$
Acetic acid
(bp 118 °C)

$$CH_3\overset{\overset{\displaystyle O}{\|}}{C}-NH_2$$
Acetamide
(bp 222 °C)
Primary amide

$$CH_3\overset{\overset{\displaystyle O}{\|}}{C}-NHCH_3$$
N-Methylacetamide
(bp 206 °C)
Secondary amide

$$CH_3\overset{\overset{\displaystyle O}{\|}}{C}-N(CH_3)_2$$
N,N-Dimethylacetamide
(bp 165 °C)
Tertiary amide

It is important to note the distinction between amines (Chapter 16) and amides. The nitrogen atom is bonded to a carbonyl-group carbon in an amide but *not* in an amine.

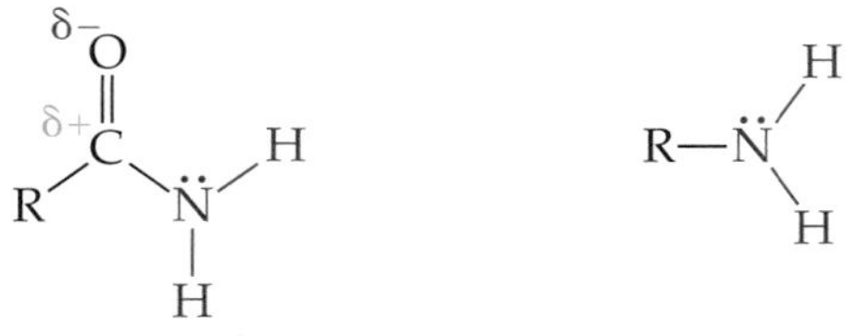

An amide
(RCONH$_2$)

An amine
(RNH$_2$)

The positive end of the carbonyl group attracts the unshared pair of electrons on nitrogen strongly enough to prevent it from acting as a base by accepting a hydrogen atom. As a result, while amines are basic *amides are NOT*.

Nomenclature

Primary amides (those with an unsubstituted —NH$_2$ group) are named by replacing the *-ic acid* or *-oic acid* of the corresponding carboxylic acid name with *-amide*. For example, the amide derived from acetic acid is called acetamide. If the nitrogen atom of the amide has alkyl substituents on it, the compound is named by first specifying the alkyl group and then identifying the amide name. The alkyl substituents are preceded by the italicized letter *N* to identify them as being attached directly to nitrogen.

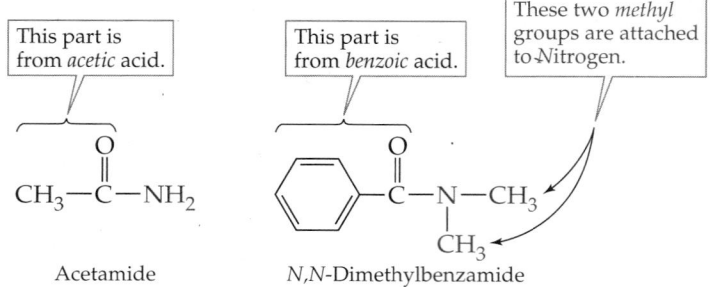

This part is from *acetic* acid.

$$CH_3-\overset{\overset{\displaystyle O}{\|}}{C}-NH_2$$

Acetamide

This part is from *benzoic* acid.

These two *methyl* groups are attached to Nitrogen.

N,N-Dimethylbenzamide

SUMMARY: To review, some derivatives of acetic acid are shown here.

Carbonyl derivatives of acetic acid

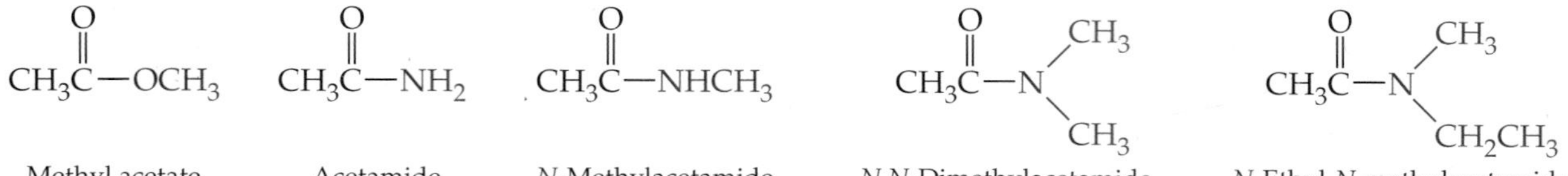

$$CH_3\overset{\overset{\displaystyle O}{\|}}{C}-OCH_3$$
Methyl acetate
(ester)

$$CH_3\overset{\overset{\displaystyle O}{\|}}{C}-NH_2$$
Acetamide
(primary amide)

$$CH_3\overset{\overset{\displaystyle O}{\|}}{C}-NHCH_3$$
N-Methylacetamide
(secondary amide)

$$CH_3\overset{\overset{\displaystyle O}{\|}}{C}-N\overset{\displaystyle CH_3}{\underset{\displaystyle CH_3}{}}$$
N,N-Dimethylacetamide

$$CH_3\overset{\overset{\displaystyle O}{\|}}{C}-N\overset{\displaystyle CH_3}{\underset{\displaystyle CH_2CH_3}{}}$$
N-Ethyl-N-methylacetamide
(tertiary amides)

Properties of Carboxylic Acids, Esters, and Amides

- All undergo carbonyl-group substitution reactions.
- Esters and amides are made from carboxylic acids.
- Esters and amides can be converted back to carboxylic acids.
- Carboxylic acids, primary amides, and secondary amides exhibit strong hydrogen bonding to one another; esters and tertiary amides do not hydrogen bond to one another. All carboxylic acids and their derivatives, however, can still hydrogen bond to water molecules.
- Simple acids and esters are liquids; all primary amides (except formamide) are solids.
- Carboxylic acids are weak acids and produce acidic aqueous solutions.
- Esters and amides are neither acids nor bases (pH neutral).
- Small (low-molecular-weight) amides are water-soluble, while small esters are slightly water-soluble.
- Volatile acids have strong, sharp odors while volatile esters have pleasant, fruity odors. Amides generally are odorless.

In later chapters, you will see that the fundamental bonding connections in proteins are amide bonds (Section 18.2) and those in oils and fats are ester bonds (Section 24.2).

HANDS-ON CHEMISTRY 17.1

Carboxylic acids and their derivatives are important parts of many of the medicines used daily by many people. Similarly to what we did in Hands-On Chemistry 16.1, let's take a look at some of the top 200 drugs of 2015, many of which you have probably heard about and see what functional groups are present. You will need to have an internet connection to fully carry out this activity.

a. Let's begin by looking at an antibiotic you have surely heard of—penicillin. What you may not know is that there are two commonly used forms: penicillin G and penicillin V. Look up the structures of these, draw their line structure, and identify all the carboxylic acid derived functional groups present. How do the two penicillins differ from one another? How are they the same? From a treatment standpoint, what is each used for?

b. As of September 2014, the top 10 selling prescription drugs by trade name were as follows:

1. Crestor 2. Synthroid 3. Nexium 4. Ventolin 5. Advair
6. Lantus 7. Vyvanse 8. Lyrica 9. Spiriva 10. Diovan

Look up the structures of each and answer the following questions for each:

1. Does it contain a carboxylic acid?
2. Does it contain an amide?
3. If it contains an amide, classify it as primary, secondary, or tertiary.

c. Finally, look up the structure of paclitaxel (see the Chemistry in Action "When Is Toxicity Beneficial?" in Chapter 15). Identify all of the ester functional groups present.

PROBLEM 17.8

Write both condensed and line structures for (a) the ester formed when butyric acid reacts with cyclopentanol, (b) the amide formed when isopropyl amine is reacted with butyric acid, and (c) the amide formed when diethylamine is reacted with butyric acid. (d) Name the derivatives you created in parts (a)–(c).

PROBLEM 17.9

What are the names of the following compounds?

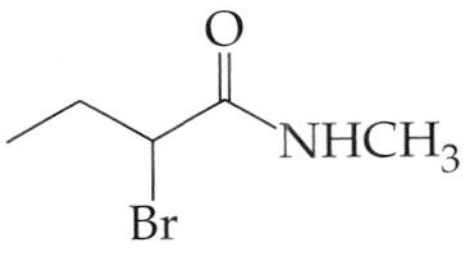

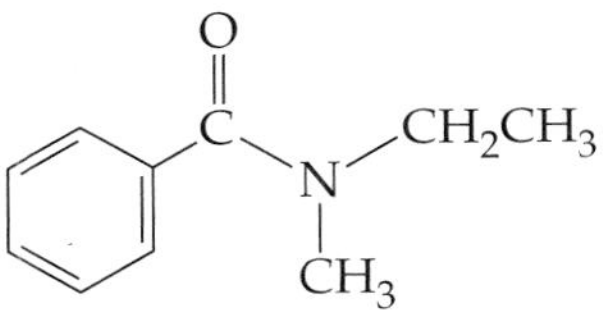

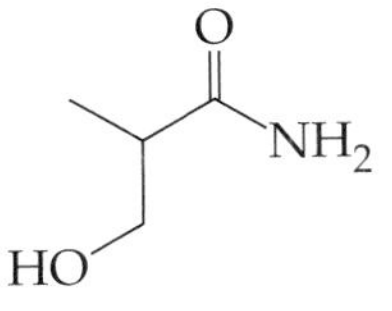

PROBLEM 17.10

Draw structures corresponding to these names:

(a) 4-Methylpentanamide

(b) *N*-Ethyl-*N*-methylpropanamide

PROBLEM 17.11

Many important biomolecules are multifunctional; given the molecule shown here, identify the following classes of compounds: (i) α-amino group, (ii) monosubstituted amide, (iii) methyl ester, (iv) carboxylic acid, and (v) disubstituted amide.

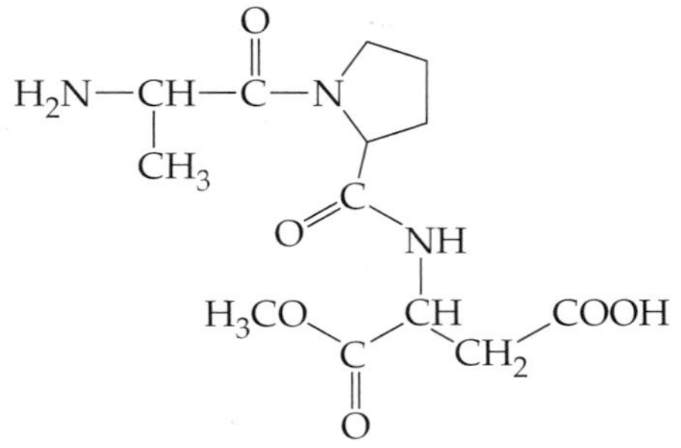

PROBLEM 17.12

Classify each compound (a)–(f) as one of the following: (i) amide, (ii) ester, or (iii) carboxylic acid.

(a) CH_3COOCH_3

(b) RCONHR

(c) C_6H_5COOH

(d) $CH_3CH_2\overset{\overset{\displaystyle O}{\|}}{C}-N(CH_3)_2$

(e) $CH_3CH_2CH_2CONH_2$

(f) $HOOCCH_2-CH-CH_3$ with CH_3 below the CH

KEY CONCEPT PROBLEM 17.13 ————————————————

Identify the following molecules as an ester, a carboxylic acid, or an amide, and write both the condensed and line-structural formula for each.

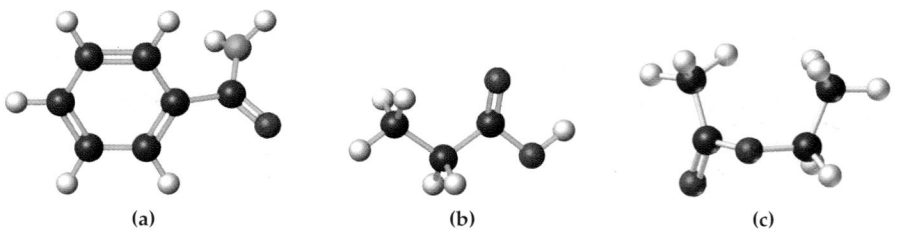

(a)   (b)   (c)

17.2 Acidity of Carboxylic Acids

Learning Objective:

- Describe the acidity of different carboxylic acids and predict the products obtained when they react with strong bases.

Carboxylic acids are weak acids that establish equilibria in aqueous solution with **carboxylate anions,** $RCOO^-$. The carboxylate anions are named by replacing the *-ic* ending in the carboxylic acid name with *-ate* (giving the same names and endings used in naming esters). At pH 7.4 in body fluids, carboxylic acids exist mainly as their carboxylate anions.

Carboxylate anion The anion that results from ionization of a carboxylic acid, $RCOO^-$.

$$CH_3\overset{\overset{\displaystyle O}{\|}}{C}-OH + H_2O \rightleftharpoons CH_3\overset{\overset{\displaystyle O}{\|}}{C}-O^- + H_3O^+$$

Acetic acid   Acetate ion

$$CH_3\overset{\overset{\displaystyle O}{\|}}{C}-\overset{\overset{\displaystyle O}{\|}}{C}-OH + H_2O \rightleftharpoons CH_3\overset{\overset{\displaystyle O}{\|}}{C}-\overset{\overset{\displaystyle O}{\|}}{C}-O^- + H_3O^+$$

Pyruvic acid   Pyruvate ion

The comparative strength of an acid is measured by its acid dissociation constant (K_a); the smaller the value of K_a, the weaker the acid (Section 10.3). Most organic and biochemists prefer to use pK_a when discussing the acidity of organic and biomolecules; pK_a is defined as minus the log of the K_a ($pK_a = -\log K_a$). With pK_a the *larger and more positive* the number, the *weaker* the acid is; in addition, there is a 10-fold difference in acidity for every 1 pK_a unit.

One of the advantages to using pK_a values is that it makes comparing acidities much quicker, since there is no scientific notation involved. Many carboxylic acids have about the same acid strength as acetic acid, as shown by the values in Table 17.2. There are some exceptions, though. Trichloroacetic acid, used to prepare microscope slides, for chemical skin peeling, and to precipitate proteins from body fluids, is a strong acid that must be handled with the same respect as sulfuric acid. Dicarboxylic acids, such as oxalic and glutaric acid, will have two K_a or pK_a values: the first for removal of the first acidic H (K_{a1} and pK_{a1}) and the second for formation of the dianion (K_{a2} and pK_{a2}). Because removal of the second H is 10 to 1000 times harder to accomplish after the first one has been removed, only K_{a1} and pK_{a1} are of any real importance.

Recall that this is the same relationship seen for pH values (Section 10.5).

Table 17.2 Carboxylic Acid Dissociation Constants and pK_as*

Name	Structure	K_a	pK_a
Trichloroacetic acid	Cl_3CCOOH	2.3×10^{-1}	0.64
Chloroacetic acid	$ClCH_2COOH$	1.4×10^{-3}	2.85
Formic acid	$HCOOH$	1.8×10^{-4}	3.74
Acetic acid	CH_3COOH	1.8×10^{-5}	4.74
Propanoic acid	CH_3CH_2COOH	1.3×10^{-5}	4.89
Hexanoic acid	$CH_3(CH_2)_4COOH$	1.3×10^{-5}	4.89
Benzoic acid	C_6H_5COOH	6.5×10^{-5}	4.19
Acrylic acid	$H_2C=CHCOOH$	5.6×10^{-5}	4.25
Oxalic acid	$HOOCCOOH$	5.4×10^{-2}	1.27
	$^-OOCCOOH$	5.2×10^{-5}	4.28
Glutaric acid	$HOOC(CH_2)_3COOH$	4.5×10^{-5}	4.35
	$^-OOC(CH_2)_3COOH$	3.8×10^{-6}	5.42

*The acid dissociation constant K_a is the equilibrium constant for the ionization of an acid; the smaller its value, the weaker the acid.

$$RCOOH + H_2O \rightleftharpoons RCOO^- + H_3O^+ \qquad K_a = \frac{[RCOO^-][H_3O^+]}{[RCOOH]}$$

For pK_a, the larger the value, the weaker the acid.

Carboxylic acids undergo neutralization reactions with bases in the same manner as other acids. With strong bases, such as sodium hydroxide, a carboxylic acid reacts to give water and a **carboxylic acid salt,** as shown here for the formation of sodium acetate. Like all other such aqueous acid–strong base reactions, this reaction proceeds much more favorably in the forward direction than in the reverse direction and is thus written with a single arrow. As for all salts, a carboxylic acid salt is named with cation and anion names. In biological systems, however, where the identity of the cation is unclear or unknown, the ionized form of a carboxylic acid will simply be referred to using only its anion name; for example, the ionized form of citric acid would simply be known as citrate (this is a common practice that you will see used when you study metabolism in Chapters 21, 22, and 25).

Carboxylic acid salt An ionic compound containing a cation and a carboxylate acid anion.

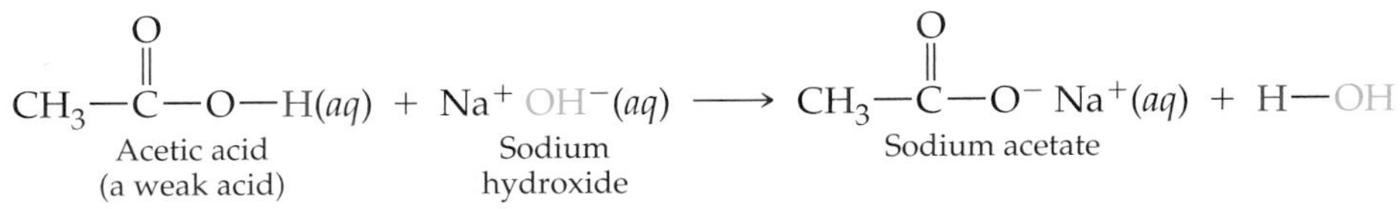

$$CH_3-\overset{O}{\overset{\|}{C}}-O-H(aq) + Na^+OH^-(aq) \longrightarrow CH_3-\overset{O}{\overset{\|}{C}}-O^-Na^+(aq) + H-OH$$

Acetic acid (a weak acid)   Sodium hydroxide   Sodium acetate

CHEMISTRY IN ACTION

Medicinally Important Carboxylic Acids and Derivatives

Carboxylic acids, esters, and amides have many uses in medicine and living systems. Almost everyone is familiar with aspirin, but you may be surprised to learn that many over-the-counter medications contain one or more carboxyl-containing compounds. The following table lists a few of the most familiar over-the-counter medications that are carboxylic acids or derivatives.

Some Medicinally Important Carboxylic Acids and Derivatives

Name	Structure	Origins and Uses
Salicylic acid	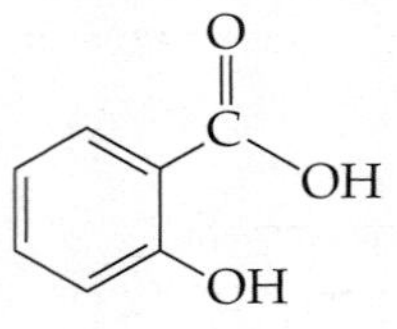	• Found in the bark of the willow tree *(Salix alba)*. • Biosynthesized from the amino acid phenylalanine (Chapter 19). • Found in plants; it has roles in plant development, photosynthesis, and ion transport. • Cherokees used an infusion of willow bark for fever, pain, and other medicinal purposes. • Too insoluble in water and irritating to the stomach to be of widespread use.
Aspirin	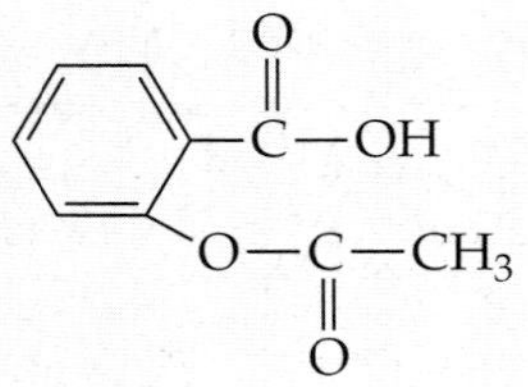	• Member of the group of drugs known as salicylates, it was discovered through chemical modifications of salicylic acid. • Undergoes ester hydrolysis in the stomach to give salicylic acid. • Best known for providing pain relief (an *analgesic*), reducing fever (an *antipyretic*), and reducing inflammation (an *anti-inflammatory*). • In recent years, aspirin has been found to inhibit the clumping of blood platelets, protecting against heart attacks caused by blood clots. Small regular doses of aspirin are often recommended for some individuals at risk for heart attack. See Section 23.9 for the chemical action of aspirin. • Undesirable side effects are gastric bleeding and gastrointestinal distress; it also inhibits the action of an enzyme necessary for coagulation of blood cells, causing the time it takes for bleeding to stop to double for several days. • On the WHO Model List of Essential Medicines*.
Methyl salicylate (oil of wintergreen)	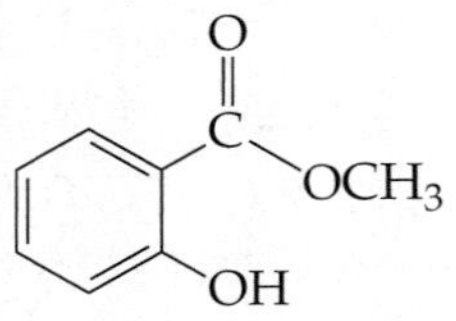	• Too poisonous to be of any value as an oral medication. • In low concentration it is used as a fragrance in foods and beverages. • Used as an antiseptic in some mouthwashes. • Therapeutically useful as a *counterirritant*, a substance that relieves internal pain by stimulating nerve endings in the skin. • One of the active ingredients in liniments such as Bengay and Heet.
Acetaminophen	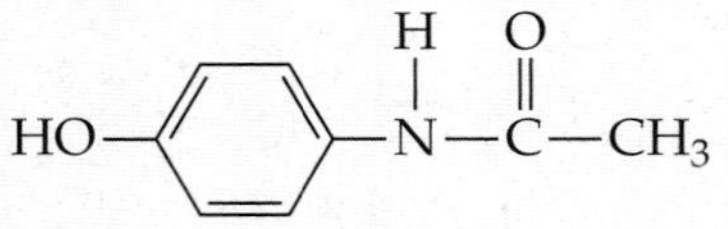	• An alternative to aspirin for pain relief. • Best known by the trade name Tylenol. • Reduces fever but is not an anti-inflammatory agent. • Recommended for use in children over aspirin. • Major advantage is that it does not cause internal bleeding; the pain reliever of choice for individuals prone to bleeding or recovering from surgery or wounds. • Overdoses can cause kidney and liver damage. • On the WHO Model List of Essential Medicines*.

The sodium and potassium salts of carboxylic acids are ionic solids that are usually far more soluble in water than the carboxylic acids themselves; for example, sodium benzoate is about 150 times more soluble in water than benzoic acid. The formation of carboxylic acid salts, as well as the formation of amine salts, is useful in creating water-soluble derivatives of drugs. See the Chemistry in Action "Medications, Body Fluids, and the 'Solubility Switch'" on p. 546.

Name	Structure	Origins and Uses
Ibuprofen		• A nonsteroidal anti-inflammatory drug (NSAID).
		• Most notably sold as Advil and Motrin.
		• It is used for relief of symptoms of arthritis, abdominal cramps, fever, and as an analgesic, especially where there is inflammation.
		• Known to have an effect on blood-clotting times, though this effect is relatively mild and short lived compared with aspirin.
		• At doses commonly prescribed, it seems to have the lowest incidence of adverse gastrointestinal side effects of all general NSAIDs. On the WHO Model List of Essential Medicines*.
Naproxen		• An NSAID of the same class as ibuprofen.
		• Known by various trade names, including Aleve and Anaprox.
		• Commonly used for relief of a wide variety of pain, fever, swelling, and stiffness.
		• The preferred NSAID for long-term use in people with a high risk of heart attack or stroke due to its relatively low risk of causing such complications.
		• Current research suggests it may have antiviral activity against influenza.
Benzocaine	H_2N — benzene ring — $C(=O)$ — O — CH_2CH_3	• A local anesthetic used in many over-the-counter *topical* preparations (those applied to the skin surface).
		• Used for pain relief associated with cold sores, poison ivy, sore throats, and hemorrhoids.
		• Works by blocking the transmission of impulses by sensory nerves.
Lidocaine		• Structurally related to benzocaine.
		• More soluble than benzocaine, so it can be used in injections.
	— $NHCCH_2N(CH_2CH_3)_2$	• Local anesthetic most commonly administered by injection to prevent pain during dental work.

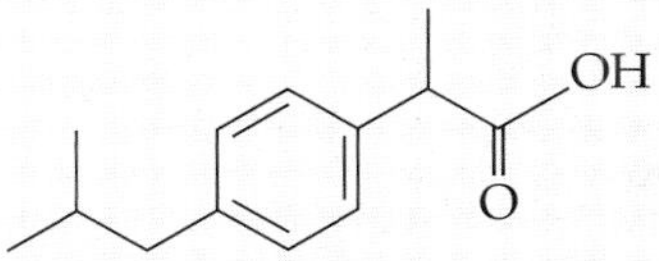

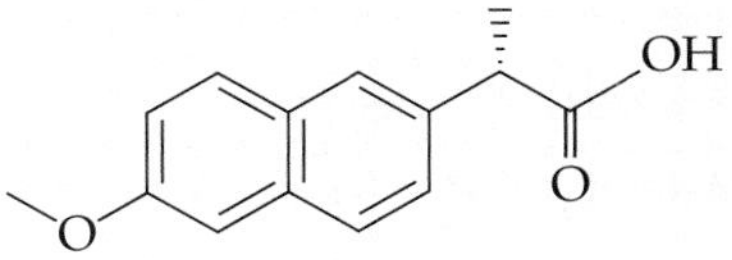

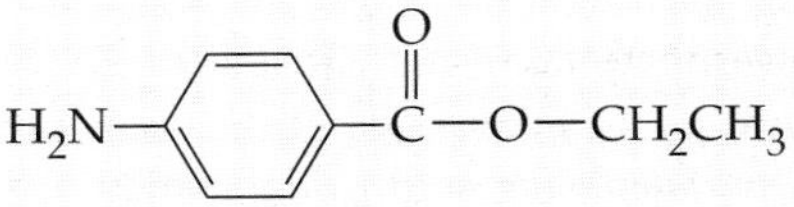

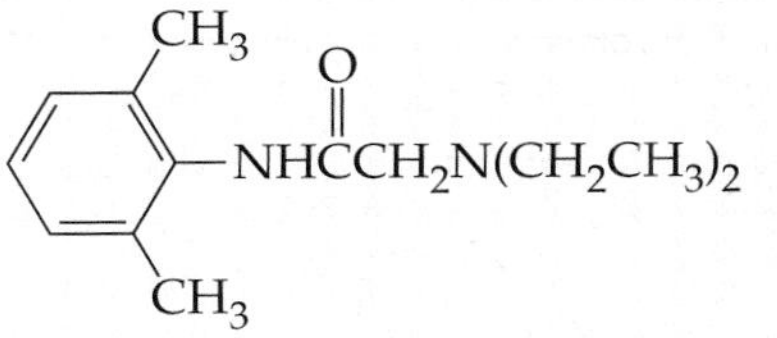

*The World Health Organization (WHO) Model List of Essential Medicines is a list of the most effective, safest, and cost-efficient medicines needed for a basic health-care system. From the April 2015 updated list.

CIA Problem 17.1 *Salsalate*, which is an ester formed by the reaction of two molecules of salicylic acid, is another salicylate used as an aspirin alternative for those who are hypersensitive to aspirin. Draw the structures of salicylic acid and salsalate.

CIA Problem 17.2 What does NSAID stand for?

CIA Problem 17.3 Examine the structures of aspirin, acetaminophen, benzocaine, and lidocaine, and, for each compound, indicate whether it is acidic, basic, or neither.

Worked Example 17.4 Effect of Structure on Carboxylic Acid Strength

Write the structural formulas of trichloroacetic acid and acetic acid and explain why trichloroacetic acid is the much stronger acid of the two.

ANALYSIS

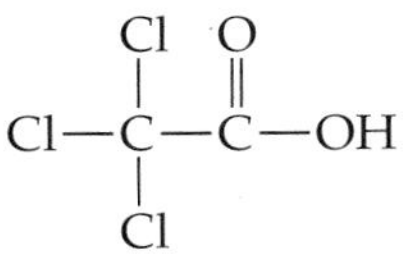

Trichloroacetic acid 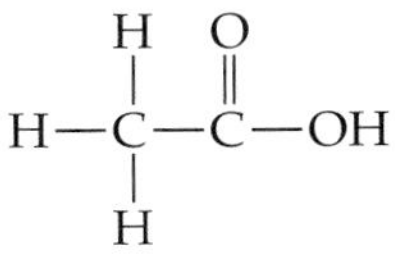   Acetic acid

The structural difference is the replacement of three hydrogen atoms on the alpha carbon by three chlorine atoms. The chlorines are much more electronegative than the hydrogen and therefore draw electrons away from the rest of the molecule in trichloroacetic acid (indicated next by the arrows). The result is that the hydrogen atom of the —COOH group in trichloroacetic acid is held less strongly and is much more easily removed than the corresponding hydrogen atom in acetic acid.

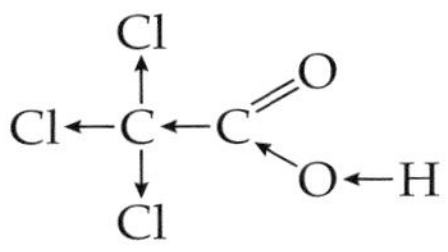

SOLUTION

Since the —COOH hydrogen atom in trichloroacetic acid is held less strongly, it is the stronger acid.

PROBLEM 17.14

Write the products of the following reactions:

(a) $CH_3CH_2CH(CH_3)COOH + NaOH \longrightarrow$?

(b) 2,2-Dimethylpentanoic acid $+ KOH \longrightarrow$?

PROBLEM 17.15

Write the formulas of potassium salicylate and disodium oxalate (refer to Table 17.1).

PROBLEM 17.16

Suppose that potassium acetate and disodium glutarate are dissolved in water. Write the formulas of each organic ion present in the solution (refer to Table 17.1).

17.3 Reactions of Carboxylic Acids: Ester and Amide Formation

Learning Objective:

• Describe how esters and amides are formed from carboxylic acids

The reactions of alcohols and amines with carboxylic acids follow the same pattern—both result in substitution of other groups for the —OH of the acid and formation of water as a by-product. With alcohols, the —OH of the acid is replaced by the —OR′ of the alcohol. With amines, the —OH of the acid is replaced by the —NH$_2$, —NHR′, or —NR′$_2$ of the amine.

Ester formation

This –OH group is replaced by this –OR′ group.

$$\underset{\substack{\text{A carboxylic} \\ \text{acid}}}{R-\overset{\overset{\displaystyle O}{\|}}{C}-OH} + \underset{\text{An alcohol}}{H-OR'} \underset{}{\overset{H^+ \text{ catalyst}}{\rightleftharpoons}} \underset{\text{An ester}}{R-\overset{\overset{\displaystyle O}{\|}}{C}-OR'} + H_2O$$

Amide formation

This –OH group is replaced by this –NR′$_2$ group.

$$\underset{\substack{\text{A carboxylic} \\ \text{acid}}}{R-\overset{\overset{\displaystyle O}{\|}}{C}-OH} + \underset{\text{Amine}}{H-NR'_2} \overset{\text{heat}}{\longrightarrow} \underset{\text{Amide}}{R-\overset{\overset{\displaystyle O}{\|}}{C}-NR'_2} + H_2O$$

▲ The unique flavors and aromas of various beers are due in part to esters formed during fermentation.

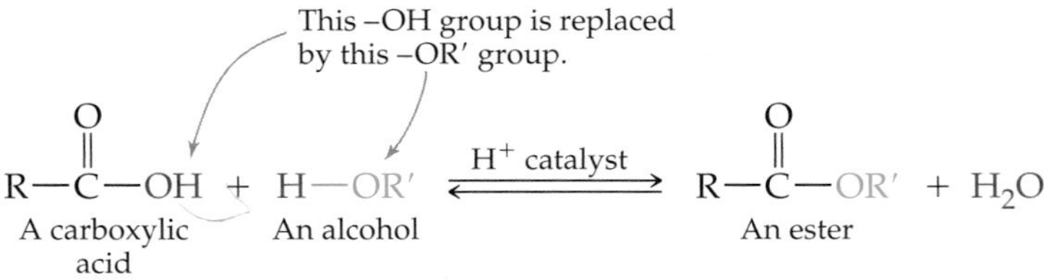

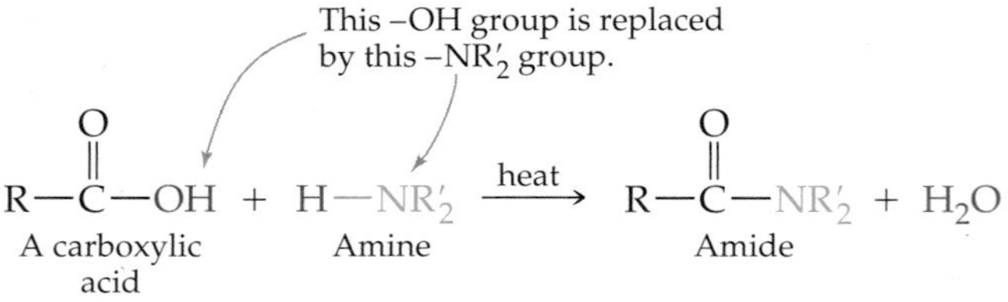

Esterification The reaction between an alcohol and a carboxylic acid to yield an ester plus water.

Esterification

In the laboratory, ester formation, known as **esterification,** is carried out by warming a carboxylic acid with an alcohol in the presence of a strong acid catalyst such as sulfuric acid. For example,

$$\underset{\text{Butanoic acid}}{CH_3CH_2CH_2-\overset{\overset{\displaystyle O}{\|}}{C}-OH} + \underset{\text{Ethanol}}{H-OCH_2CH_3} \overset{H^+ \text{ catalyst}}{\rightleftharpoons}$$

$$\underset{\substack{\text{Ethyl butanoate} \\ \text{(in pineapple oil)}}}{CH_3CH_2CH_2-\overset{\overset{\displaystyle O}{\|}}{C}-OCH_2CH_3} + H_2O$$

Esterification reactions are reversible and often reach equilibrium with approximately equal amounts of both reactants and products present. Ester formation is favored either by using a large excess of the alcohol or by continuously removing one of the products (e.g., by distilling off a low-boiling ester or removing water in a similar fashion). Both techniques are applications of Le Châtelier's principle (Section 7.9).

Worked Example 17.5 Writing the Products of an Esterification Reaction

The flavor ingredient in oil of wintergreen is an ester that is made by reaction of *o*-hydroxybenzoic acid (salicylic acid) with methanol. What is its structure?

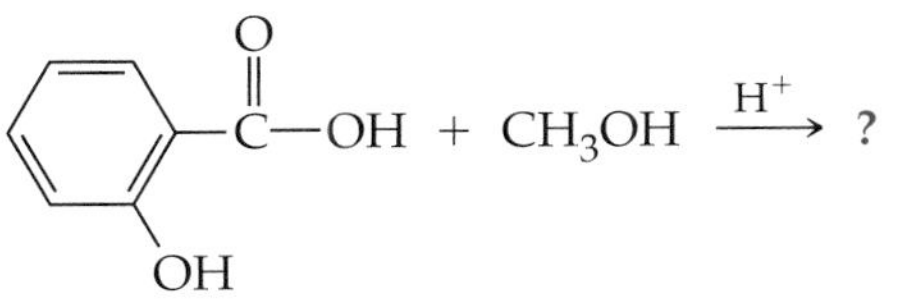

ANALYSIS First, write the two reaction partners so that the —COOH group of the acid and the —OH group of the alcohol face each other.

o-Hydroxybenzoic acid

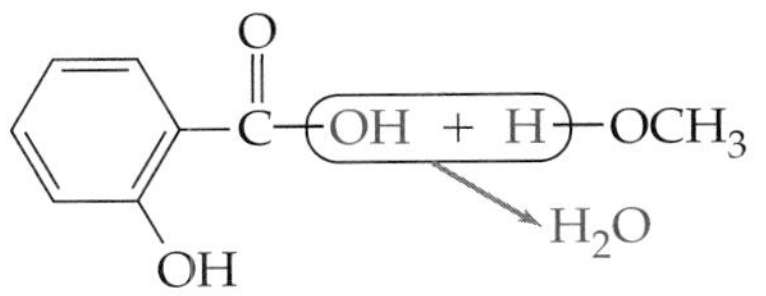

Methanol

Next, remove —OH from the acid and —H from the alcohol to form water and then join the two resulting organic fragments with a single bond.

SOLUTION

The product is the ester.

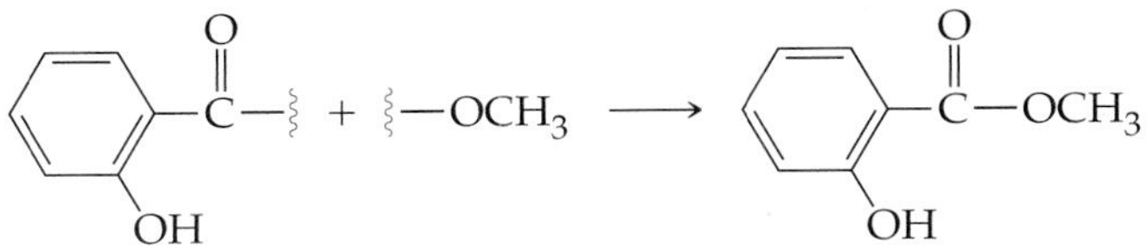

Methyl *o*-hydroxybenzoate
(methyl salicylate)

PROBLEM 17.17

One of the compounds that gives orange oil its unique odor is an ester formed when acetic acid reacts with 1-octanol. Draw the structure of this ester and name it.

PROBLEM 17.18

Raspberry oil contains an ester that is made by reaction of formic acid with 2-methyl-1-propanol. What is its structure?

$$HCOOH + (CH_3)_2CHCH_2OH \longrightarrow ?$$

PROBLEM 17.19

Which carboxylic acid and alcohol are needed to make the following esters?

(a) $Ph-CH_2-CH_2-\overset{\overset{\displaystyle O}{\|}}{C}-O-CH_2CH_2CH_3$

(b) 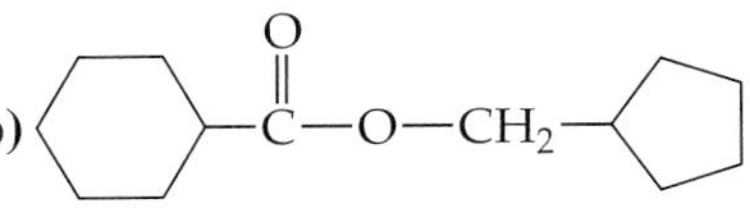

Amide Formation

Primary amides are formed by the reaction of carboxylic acids with ammonia (NH_3).

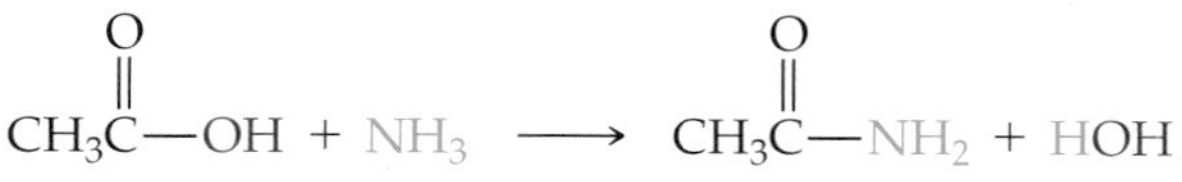

$$CH_3\overset{\overset{\textstyle O}{\|}}{C}-OH + NH_3 \longrightarrow CH_3\overset{\overset{\textstyle O}{\|}}{C}-NH_2 + HOH$$

Acetic acid   Acetamide
(a primary amide)

Secondary and tertiary amides are produced in reactions between primary or secondary amines and carboxylic acids, respectively.

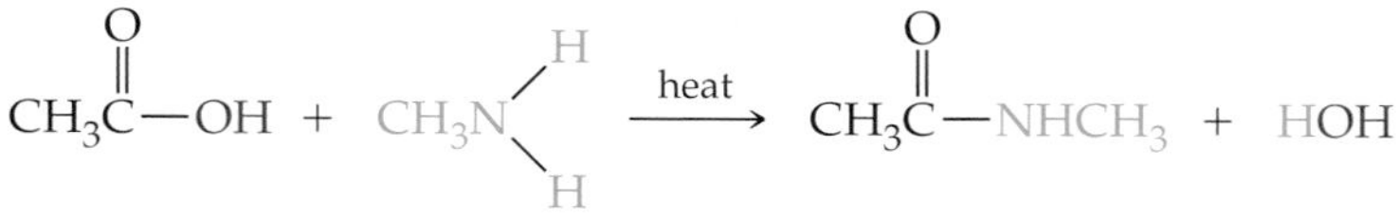

$$CH_3\overset{\overset{\textstyle O}{\|}}{C}-OH + CH_3N\overset{\nearrow H}{\underset{\searrow H}{}} \xrightarrow{\text{heat}} CH_3\overset{\overset{\textstyle O}{\|}}{C}-NHCH_3 + HOH$$

Acetic acid   Methylamine   N-Methylacetamide
(a 1° amine)   (a secondary amide)

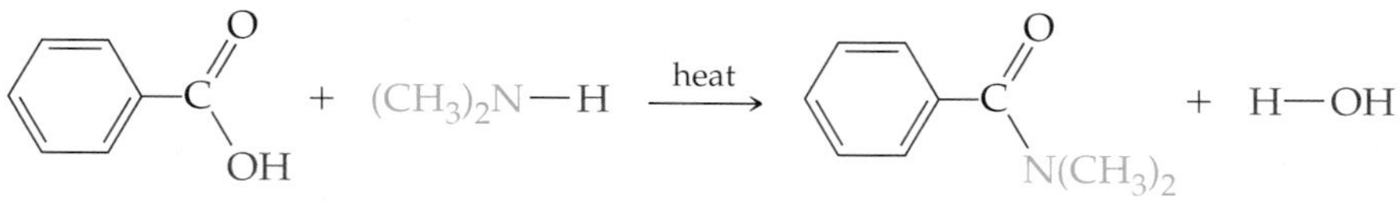

Benzoic acid   Dimethylamine   N,N-Dimethylbenzamide
(a 2° amine)   (a tertiary amide)

▶▶ Proteins are constructed of long chains of amino acids held together by amide bonds. The biochemical synthesis of proteins, described in Section 26.10, is a strictly controlled process in which amino acids with different R groups must be assembled in an exact order that is determined by an organism's DNA sequence.

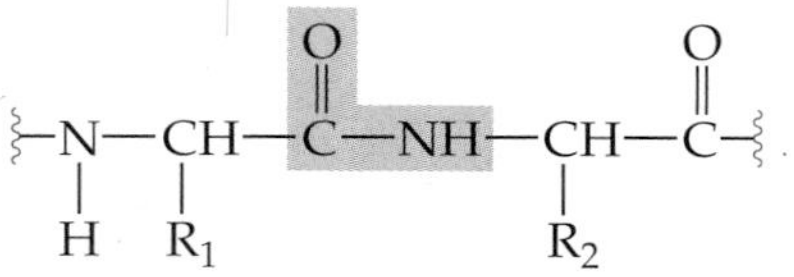

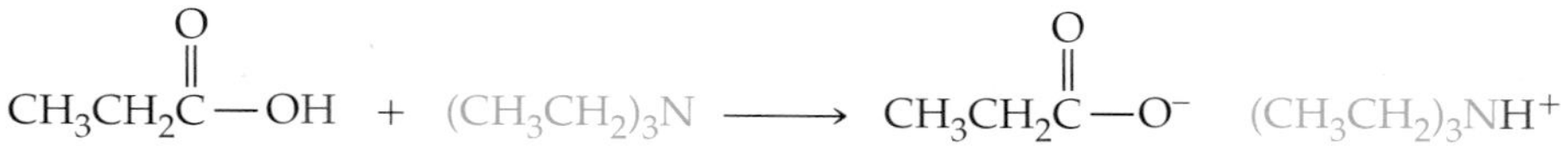

In all cases, the first step of the reaction is actually formation of the ammonium salt; the amide formation reactions must be heated to proceed as shown. In each case, the overall reaction is formation of an amide accompanied by formation of water by the —OH group of the acid and an —H atom from ammonia or an amine. Chemists have developed what are known as coupling reagents, making this reaction easier to do in the laboratory; biological systems use what are known as acyl transfer agents (Chapter 21). Tertiary amines (such as triethylamine) do not have a hydrogen on the amine nitrogen and therefore do not form amides, generating only the ammonium salt.

$$CH_3CH_2\overset{\overset{\textstyle O}{\|}}{C}-OH + (CH_3CH_2)_3N \longrightarrow CH_3CH_2\overset{\overset{\textstyle O}{\|}}{C}-O^- \;(CH_3CH_2)_3NH^+$$

Propanoic acid   Triethylamine   Triethylammonium propanoate

Worked Example 17.6 Writing the Products of Amide Formation

The mosquito and tick repellent DEET (diethyltoluamide) is prepared by reaction of diethylamine with *m*-methylbenzoic acid (*m*-toluic acid). What is the structure of DEET?

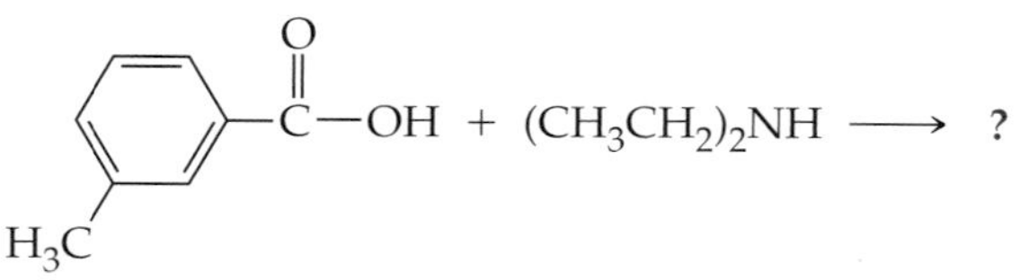

$$\text{(m-toluic acid)}-C-OH + (CH_3CH_2)_2NH \longrightarrow ?$$

ANALYSIS First, rewrite the equation so that the —OH of the acid and the —H of the amine face each other.

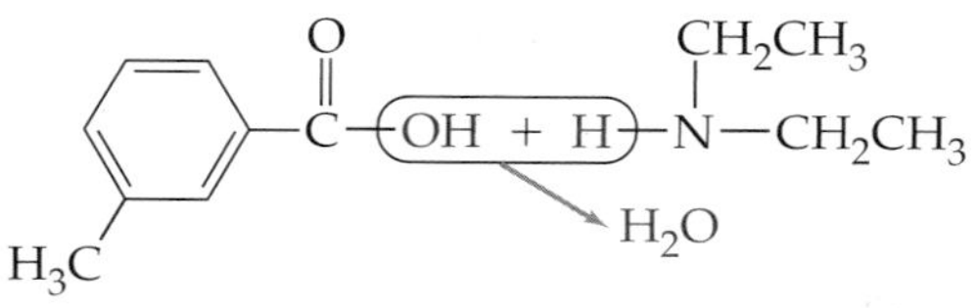

Next, remove the —OH from the acid and the —H from the nitrogen atom of the amine to form water and then join the two resulting fragments together to form the amide product.

SOLUTION

The structure of DEET is

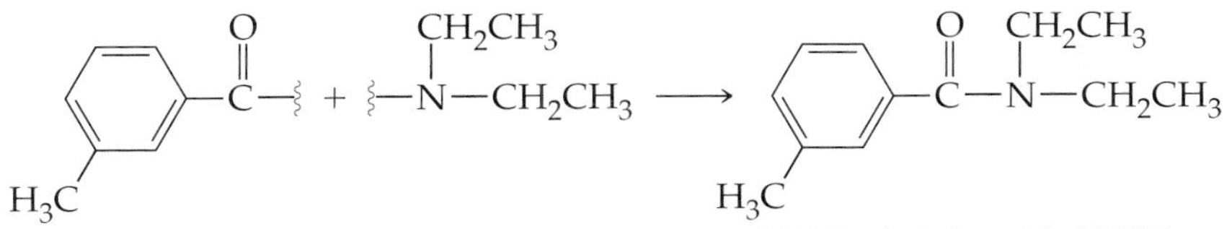

N,N-Diethyltoluamide (DEET)

PROBLEM 17.20

Draw structures of the amides that can be made from the following reactants:

(a) $CH_3NH_2 + (CH_3)_2CHCOOH \longrightarrow$? **(b)**

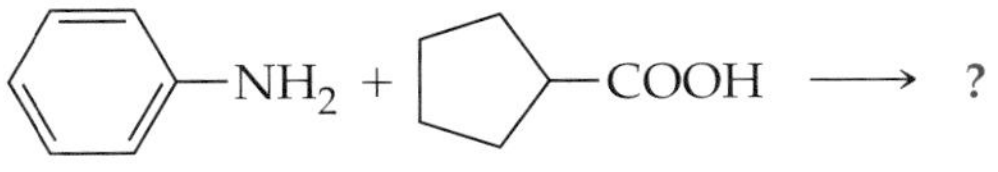

PROBLEM 17.21

Phenacetin (shown in the margin) was once used in headache remedies but is now banned because of its potential for causing kidney damage. (a) Identify all the functional groups present in phenacetin. (b) Draw the structures of the carboxylic acid and amine needed to prepare phenacetin.

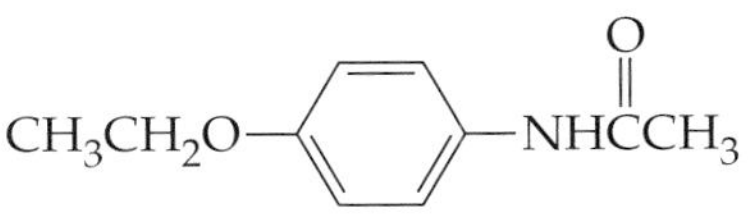

Phenacetin

17.4 Hydrolysis of Esters and Amides

Learning Objective:

- Predict the hydrolysis products of esters and amides.

Recall that in hydrolysis a bond or bonds are broken and the —H and —OH of water add to the atoms that were part of the broken bond. Esters and amides undergo hydrolysis to give back carboxylic acids plus alcohols or amines in reactions that follow the carbonyl-group substitution pattern (see Section 17.4).

For esters, the net effect of hydrolysis is substitution of —OH for OR′.

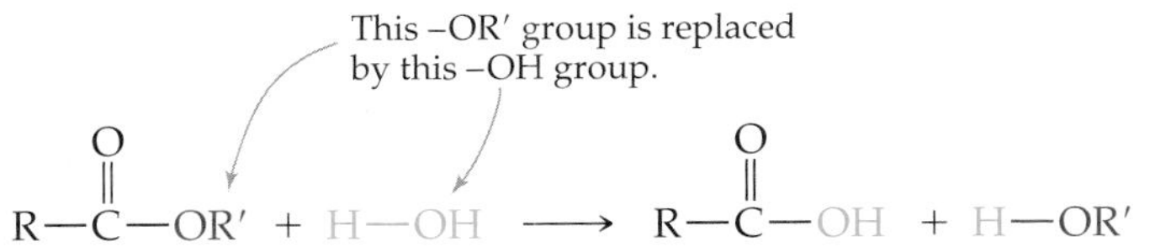

An ester   Carboxylic acid   Alcohol

For amides, the net effect of hydrolysis is substitution of —OH for —NH_2, —NHR, or —NR_2.

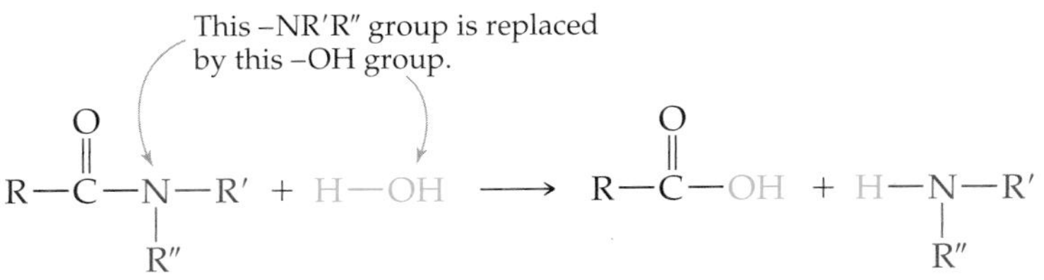

An amide   Carboxylic acid   Amine

Ester Hydrolysis

Both acids and bases can cause ester hydrolysis. Acid-catalyzed hydrolysis is simply the reverse of the esterification. An ester is treated with water in the presence of a strong acid catalyst such as sulfuric acid, and hydrolysis takes place.

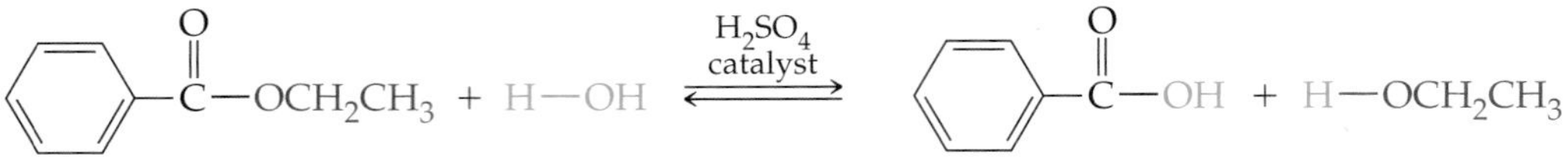

Ethyl benzoate · Benzoic acid · Ethanol

An excess of water pushes the equilibrium to the right.

Ester hydrolysis using a base such as NaOH or KOH is known as **saponification** (after the Latin word *sapo,* soap). The product of saponification is a carboxylate anion rather than a free carboxylic acid; the initially formed carboxylic acid reacts with base to accomplish this. The use of saponification in making soap is discussed in Section 23.4.

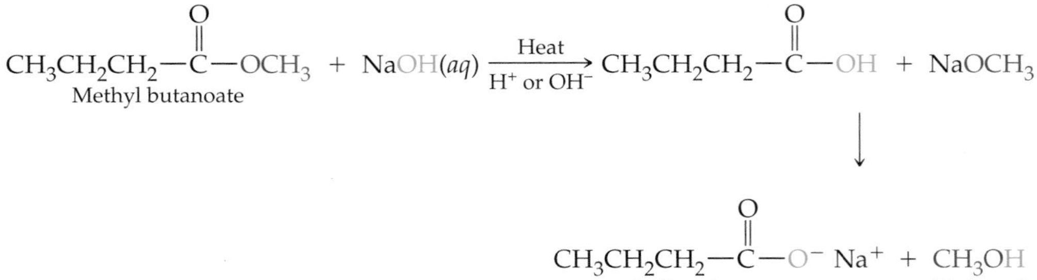

Saponification The reaction of an ester with aqueous hydroxide ion to yield an alcohol and the metal salt (usually sodium or potassium) of a carboxylic acid.

Methyl butanoate

Sodium butanoate · Methanol

Worked Example 17.7 Writing the Products of an Ester Hydrolysis

What product would you obtain from acid-catalyzed hydrolysis of ethyl formate, a flavor constituent of rum?

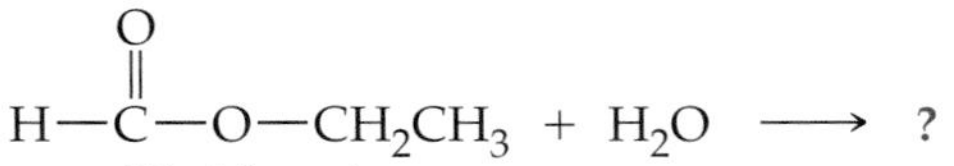

Ethyl formate

ANALYSIS The name of an ester gives a good indication of the names of the two products. Thus, ethyl formate yields ethyl alcohol and formic acid. To find the product structures in a more systematic way, write the structure of the ester and locate the bond between the carbonyl-group carbon and the —OR′ group.

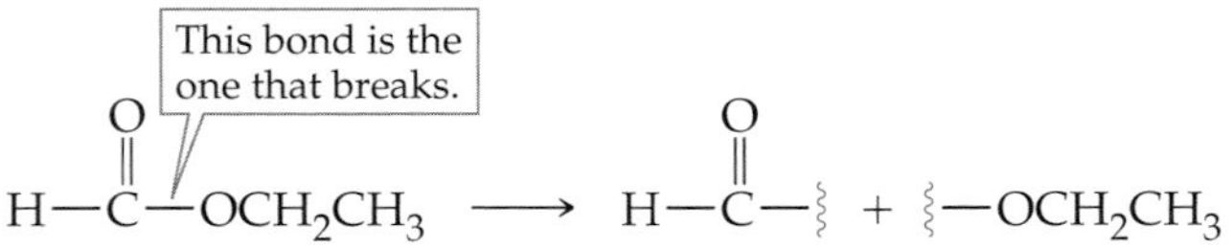

SOLUTION
Carry out a hydrolysis reaction on paper. First form the carboxylic acid product by connecting an —OH to the carbonyl-group carbon. Then add an —H to the —OCH₂CH₃ group to form the alcohol product.

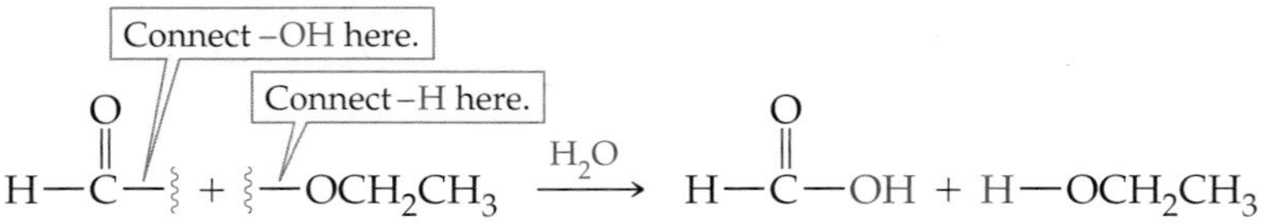

Formic acid · Ethyl alcohol

PROBLEM 17.22

If a bottle of aspirin tablets has the aroma of vinegar, it is time to discard those tablets. Explain why, and include a chemical equation in the explanation.

PROBLEM 17.23

Draw the products you would obtain from acid-catalyzed hydrolysis of the following esters.

(a) Isopropyl benzoate

(b)

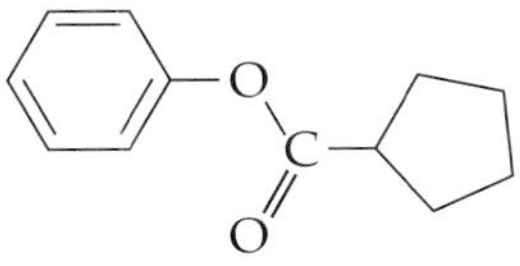

(c) $CH_3-CH_2-\overset{\overset{\displaystyle O}{\|}}{C}-O\,CH_2CH_3$

Amide Hydrolysis

Amides are extremely stable in water but do undergo hydrolysis with prolonged heating in the presence of acids or bases. The products are the carboxylic acid and amine from which the amide was synthesized.

$$\overset{\overset{\displaystyle O}{\|}}{RC}-NHR + H-OH \longrightarrow \overset{\overset{\displaystyle O}{\|}}{RC}-OH + HN\overset{R}{\underset{H}{\diagdown}}$$

In practice, the products obtained depend on whether the hydrolysis is done using acid or base. Under acidic conditions, the carboxylic acid and amine salt are obtained. Doing this reaction using base produces the neutral amine and carboxylate anion. For example, in the hydrolysis of N-methylacetamide.

Hydrolysis products of **N-Methylacetamide**

$$CH_3\overset{\overset{\displaystyle O}{\|}}{C}-NHCH_3 + H_3O^+ \longrightarrow CH_3\overset{\overset{\displaystyle O}{\|}}{C}-OH + CH_3NH_3^+ \quad \text{Acid hydrolysis}$$

$$CH_3\overset{\overset{\displaystyle O}{\|}}{C}-NHCH_3 + OH^- \longrightarrow CH_3\overset{\overset{\displaystyle O}{\|}}{C}-O^- + CH_3NH_2 \quad \text{Base hydrolysis}$$

▶ In Chapter 25, you will see that the cleavage of amide bonds by hydrolysis is the key process that occurs in the stomach during digestion of proteins.

Worked Example 17.8 Writing the Products of an Amide Hydrolysis

What carboxylic acid and amine are produced by the hydrolysis of N-ethylbutanamide?

$$CH_3CH_2CH_2\overset{\overset{\displaystyle O}{\|}}{C}-NHCH_2CH_3 + H_2O \longrightarrow ?$$

N-Ethylbutanamide

ANALYSIS First, look at the name of the starting amide. Often, the amide's name incorporates the names of the two products. Thus, N-ethylbutanamide yields ethylamine and butanoic acid. To find the product structures systematically, write the amide and locate the bond between the carbonyl-group carbon and the nitrogen. Then break this amide bond and write the two fragments.

This amide bond is the one that breaks.

$$CH_3CH_2CH_2\overset{\overset{\displaystyle O}{\|}}{C}-NHCH_2CH_3 \longrightarrow CH_3CH_2CH_2\overset{\overset{\displaystyle O}{\|}}{C}- + -NHCH_2CH_3$$

—*continued on next page*

—continued from previous page

SOLUTION

Carry out a hydrolysis reaction on paper and form the products by connecting an —OH to the carbonyl-group carbon and an —H to the nitrogen.

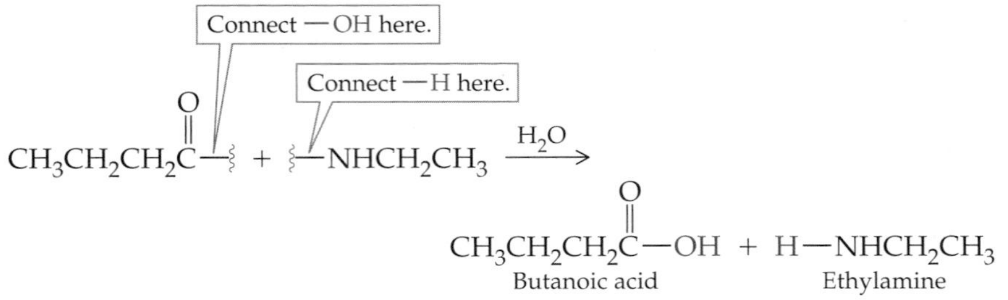

Connect —OH here.

Connect —H here.

$$CH_3CH_2CH_2C\overset{O}{\underset{|}{\|}} + \underset{}{-NHCH_2CH_3} \xrightarrow{H_2O}$$

$$CH_3CH_2CH_2\overset{O}{\underset{\|}{C}}-OH + H-NHCH_2CH_3$$
Butanoic acid   Ethylamine

PROBLEM 17.24

What carboxylic acids and amines result from hydrolysis of the following amides?

(a) $CH_3CH=CH\overset{O}{\overset{\|}{C}}-NHCH_3$ (b) *N,N*-Dimethyl-*p*-nitrobenzamide

17.5 Polyamides and Polyesters

Learning Objective:

• Describe the formation and uses of polyesters and polyamides.

Imagine what would happen if a molecule with *two* carboxylic acid groups reacted with a molecule having *two* amino groups. Amide formation could join the two molecules together, but further reactions could then link more and more molecules together until a giant chain resulted. This is exactly what happens when certain kinds of synthetic polymers are made.

Nylons are *polyamides* produced by reaction of diamines with diacids. One such nylon, nylon 6,6 (pronounced "six-six"), is so named because of the structures of the two compounds that are used to produce it. Nylon 6,6 is made by heating adipic acid (hexanedioic acid, a 6-carbon dicarboxylic acid) with hexamethylenediamine (1,6-hexanediamine, a 6-carbon diamine) at 280 °C.

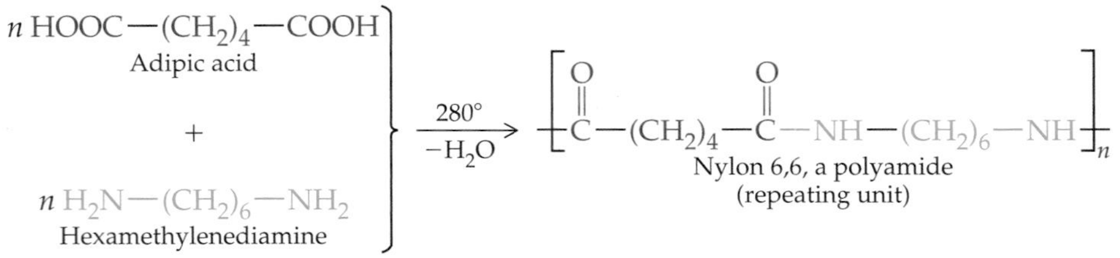

$$\left.\begin{array}{c} n \text{ HOOC}-(CH_2)_4-\text{COOH} \\ \text{Adipic acid} \\ + \\ n \text{ H}_2\text{N}-(CH_2)_6-NH_2 \\ \text{Hexamethylenediamine} \end{array}\right\} \xrightarrow[-H_2O]{280°} \left[\overset{O}{\overset{\|}{C}}-(CH_2)_4-\overset{O}{\overset{\|}{C}}-NH-(CH_2)_6-NH\right]_n$$
Nylon 6,6, a polyamide
(repeating unit)

The polymer molecules are composed of thousands of the repeating units, shown here enclosed in square brackets. In the next chapter, you will see that proteins are also polyamides; unlike nylon, however, proteins do not normally have identical repeating units.

The properties of nylon make it suitable for a wide range of applications. High-impact strength, abrasion resistance, and a naturally slippery surface make nylon an excellent material for bearings and gears. It can be formed into very strong fibers, making it valuable for a range of applications from nylon stockings, to clothing, to mountaineering ropes and carpets. Sutures and replacement arteries are also fabricated from nylon, which is resistant to deterioration in body fluids.

Just as diacids and diamines react to yield polyamides, diacids and dialcohols react to yield *polyesters*. The most widely used polyester is made by the reaction of terephthalic acid (1,4-benzenedicarboxylic acid) with ethylene glycol.

▲ Nylon being pulled from the interface between adipic acid and hexamethylenediamine.

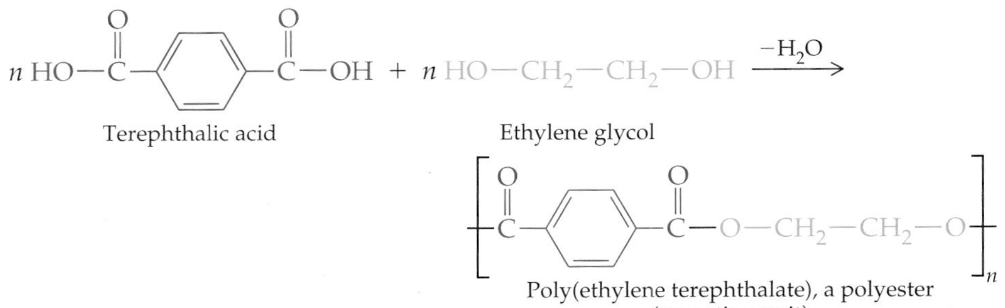

Terephthalic acid   Ethylene glycol

Poly(ethylene terephthalate), a polyester
(repeating unit)

We know this polyester best in clothing fiber, where it has the trade name Dacron. Under the name Mylar it is used in plastic film and recording tape. Its chemical name, poly(ethylene terephthalate) or PET, is usually applied when it is used in clear, flexible soft-drink bottles.

PROBLEM 17.25

One of the first polyamides discovered was Nomex; it has excellent thermal, chemical, and radiation resistance. Provide the structure of the repeating unit in Nomex, given that it is made from the following compounds:

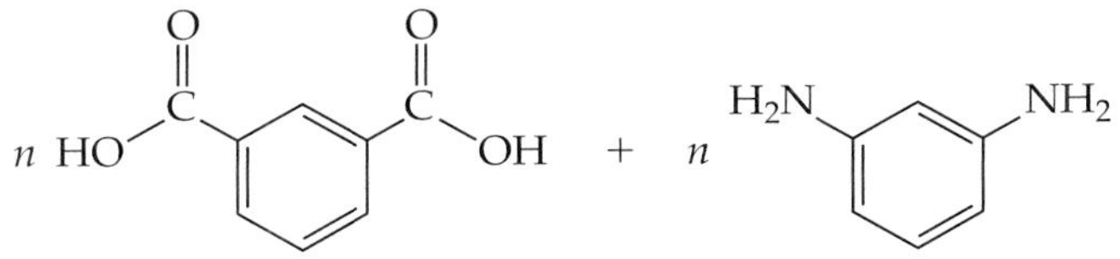

KEY CONCEPT PROBLEM 17.26

Give the structure of the repeating units in the polymers that are formed in the reactions of the following compounds.

(a) 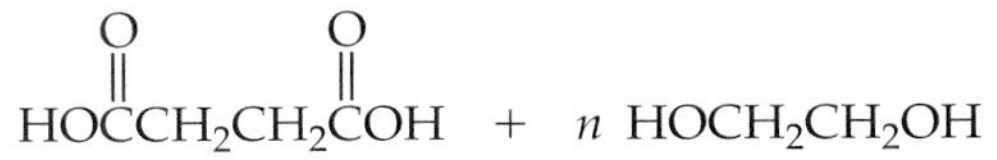 n HOCCH$_2$CH$_2$COH   + n HOCH$_2$CH$_2$OH

(b) 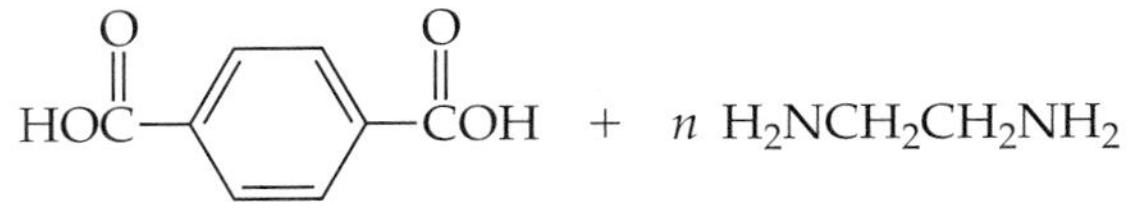 n HOC—⬡—COH   + n H$_2$NCH$_2$CH$_2$NH$_2$

17.6 Phosphoric Acid Derivatives

Learning Objective:

• Recognize and draw the structures of phosphate esters and their ionized forms.

Phosphoric acid is an inorganic acid with a striking resemblance to a carboxylic acid; it has three acidic hydrogen atoms (red), allowing it to form three different anions.

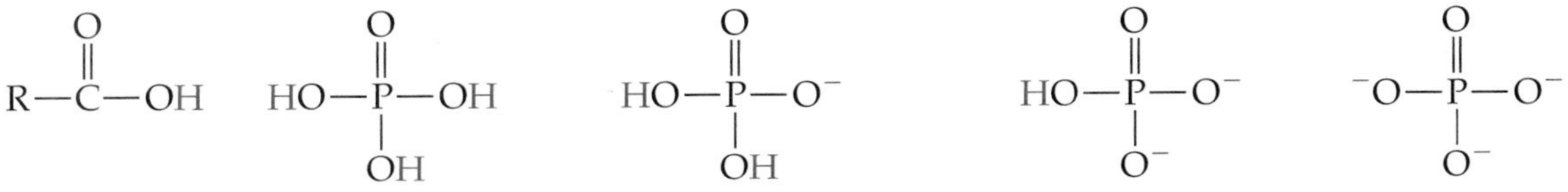

Carboxylic acid   Phosphoric acid (H_3PO_4)   Dihydrogen phosphate ion ($H_2PO_4^-$)   Hydrogen phosphate ion (HPO_4^{2-})   Phosphate ion (PO_4^{3-})

Phosphate ester A compound formed by reaction of an alcohol with phosphoric acid; may be a monoester, $ROPO_3H_2$; a diester, $(RO)_2PO_3H$; or a triester, $(RO)_3PO$; also may be a di- or triphosphate.

Just like a carboxylic acid, phosphoric acid reacts with alcohols to form **phosphate esters.** It may be esterified at one, two, or all three of its —OH groups by reaction with an alcohol. Reaction with one molecule of methanol gives the monoester.

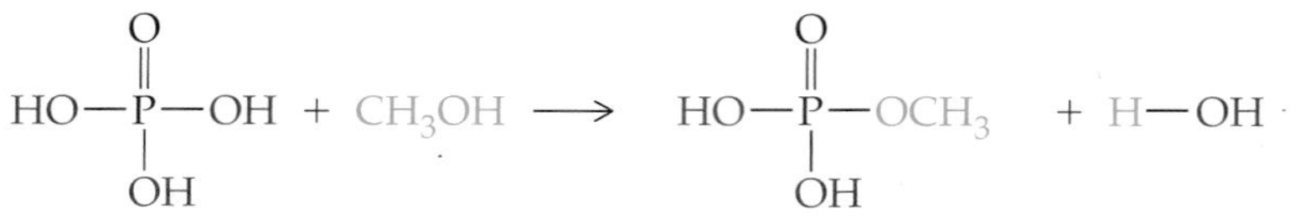

Methyl phosphate
(a phosphate monoester)

The corresponding diester and triester are also possible.

Phosphate monoesters and diesters are acidic because they still contain acidic hydrogen atoms and in most body fluids they are present as ions. Because of this, chemists usually write the phosphate groups in their ionized forms. For example, you will most often see the formula for glyceraldehyde monophosphate, a key intermediate in the metabolism of glucose (Section 22.2), written as an ion in one of these following two ways:

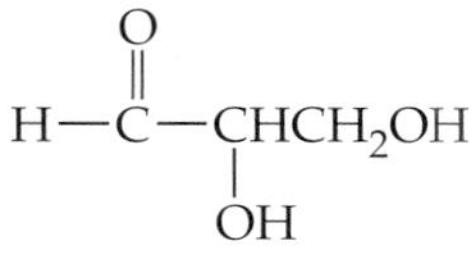

Glyceraldehyde 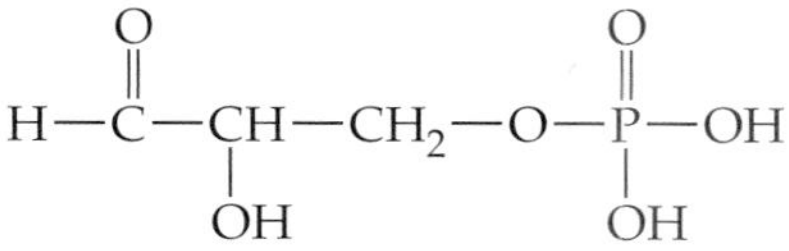   Glyceraldehyde monophosphate

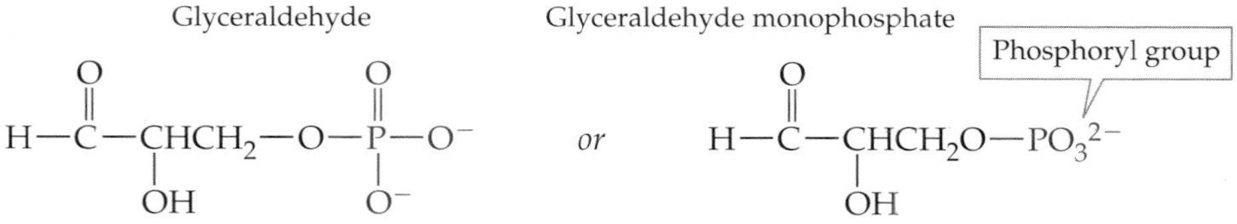

Ionized glyceraldehyde monophosphate

Phosphoryl group The $-PO_3^{2-}$ group in organic phosphates.

The $-PO_3^{2-}$ group as part of a larger molecule is referred to as a **phosphoryl group** (pronounced fos-for-*eel*).

One group of carboxylic acid derivatives we did not discuss are the acid anhydrides, formed when two carboxylic acids join together by eliminating a molecule of water.

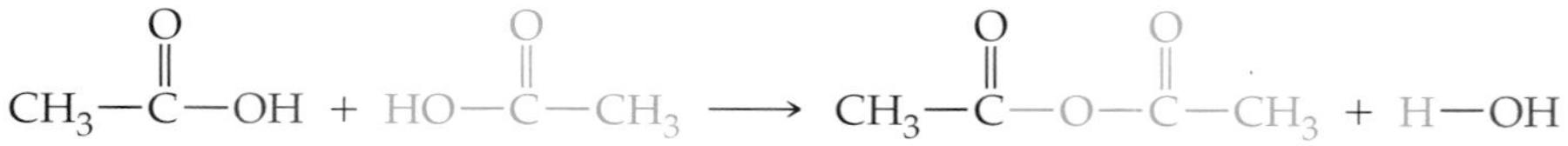

Acetic anhydride

Carboxylic acid anhydrides, although important in an organic chemistry lab, are of little importance in biochemistry, but the anhydrides of phosphoric acid *do* play a key role in biochemistry. If two molecules of phosphoric acid combine to lose water, they form a phosphoric acid anhydride. The resulting acid (*pyrophosphoric acid* or *diphosphoric acid*) reacts with yet another phosphoric acid molecule to give *triphosphoric acid.*

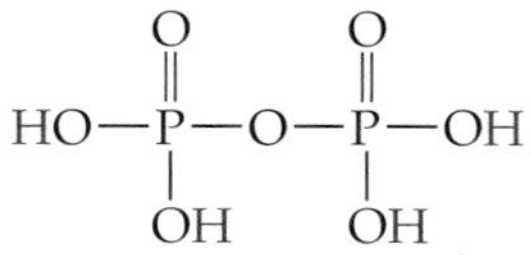

Pyrophosphoric acid 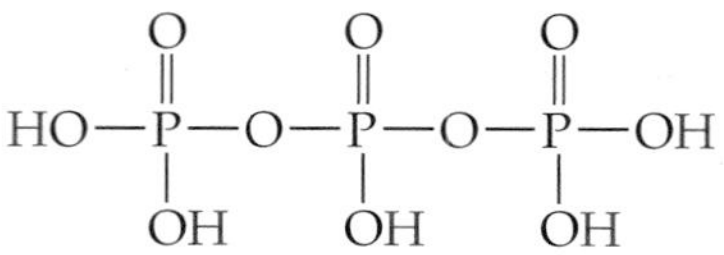   Triphosphoric acid

These anhydride-containing acids can also form esters, which are known as diphosphates and triphosphates.

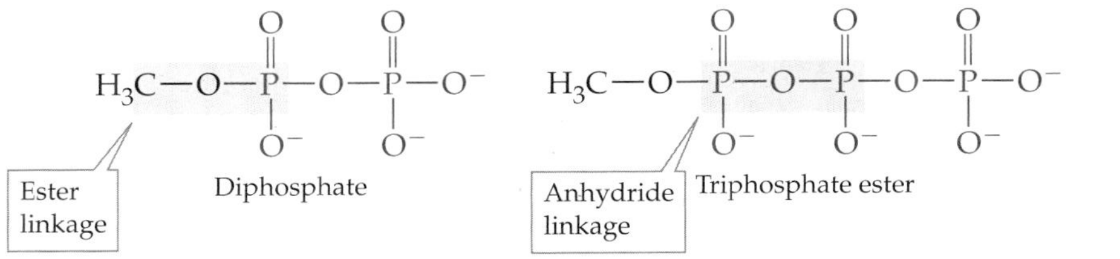

Transfer of a phosphoryl group from one molecule to another is known as **phosphorylation.** In biochemical reactions, the phosphoryl groups are often provided by a triphosphate (adenosine triphosphate, ATP), which is converted to a diphosphate (adenosine diphosphate, ADP) in a reaction accompanied by the release of energy. The addition and removal of phosphoryl groups is a common mechanism for regulating the activity of biomolecules (Section 19.8).

Phosphorylation Transfer of a phosphoryl group, $-PO_3^{2-}$, between organic molecules.

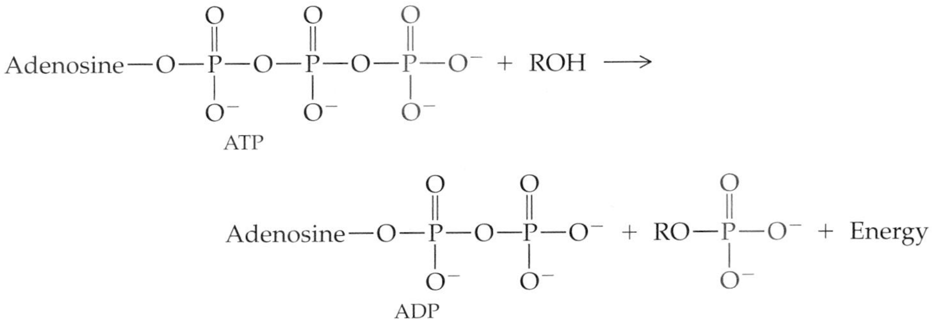

Organic Phosphates:

- Organic phosphates contain $-C-O-P-$ linkages; those with one, two, or three R groups have the general formulas $ROPO_3H_2$, $(RO)_2PO_2H$, and $(RO)_3PO$.
- Organic phosphates with one or two R groups (monoesters, $ROPO_3^{2-}$, or diesters, $(RO)_2PO_2^-$) are acids and exist in ionized form in body fluids.
- The diphosphate and triphosphate groups, which are important in biomolecules, contain one or two $P-O-P$ anhydride linkages, respectively.
- Phosphorylation is the transfer of a phosphoryl group $(-PO_3^{2-})$ from one molecule to another.

PROBLEM 17.27

Write the formula for the phosphate monoester formed from isopropyl alcohol and phosphoric acid.

PROBLEM 17.28

Identify the functional group in the following compounds and give the structures of the products of hydrolysis for these compounds.

$$\text{(a) } CH_3\overset{\overset{\displaystyle O}{\|}}{C}NH_2 \qquad \text{(b) } CH_3CH_2OPO_3^{2-} \qquad \text{(c) } CH_3CH_2\overset{\overset{\displaystyle O}{\|}}{C}OCH_3$$

CHEMISTRY IN ACTION

Medications, Body Fluids, and the "Solubility Switch"

The chemical reactions that keep us alive occur in the aqueous solutions known as *body fluids*—blood, digestive juices, and the fluid inside cells, whereas waste products from these metabolic reactions are excreted in urine (Chapter 29). Additionally, the medicines we rely on to keep us well, which are often large, complex organic molecules, must also be able to function in this aqueous environment. For organic compounds of all classes, water solubility decreases as the hydrophobic portions of the molecules become larger and molecular weight increases, so how can a drug that is primarily hydrophobic work in an aqueous environment?

Luckily, many biologically active molecules contain acidic and basic functional groups. At the pH of body fluids (e.g., approximately 7.4 for blood), many of these groups are ionized and thus water-soluble, providing what is often called a *solubility switch*. The most frequently seen ionized functional groups present in biomolecules are carboxylate (pronounced car-*box-ill*-late) groups (from carboxylic acids, —COOH, discussed in Section 17.3), phosphate groups (as well as diphosphates and triphosphates, discussed in Section 17.6), and ammonium groups. These same groups are also present in many of the medicines we use.

Ionic solubility switches

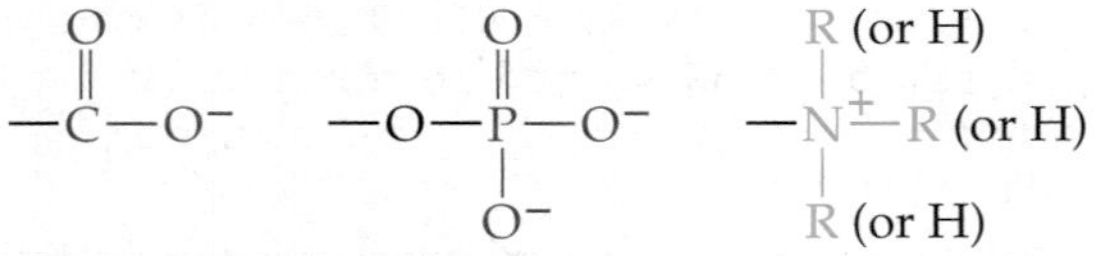

Carboxylate
(—COO⁻)

Phosphate
(—OPO₃²⁻)

Ammonium
(—NR₃⁺)

For a drug to be able to be absorbed in the stomach or intestine, or be injected, it must first be soluble in water. Medications must be soluble in body fluids in order to be transported from their entry point in the body to their site of action. Many drugs are weak acids or bases and therefore are present as their ions in body fluids. Examples include aspirin and naproxen (both carboxylic acids; see the Chemistry in Action "Medicinally Important Carboxylic Acids and Derivatives," p. 534) and morphine and codeine (both weak bases; see Table 16.2).

The extent of ionization of a drug helps determine how it is distributed in the body. Weak acids, such as aspirin and naproxen, are essentially un-ionized in the acidic environment in the stomach and are therefore readily absorbed there. On the other hand, weak bases, such as the decongestant phenylephrine and the anoxlytics discussed in the Chemistry in Action "Calming a Stormy Mind: Amines as Anti-Anxiety

Medications" in Chapter 16, are completely ionized in the stomach, and therefore no significant absorption occurs there. It is not until they reach the more basic environment of the small intestine that these weak bases revert to their neutral form and are absorbed. For mostly formulation reasons, many oral pharmaceutical agents must be delivered to the body in their more water-soluble, salt forms. Amines are typically converted to their ammonium salts and carboxylic acids to their carboxylate salt form. For example, phenylephrine is converted to its ammonium hydrochloride, while naproxen is converted to its sodium salt.

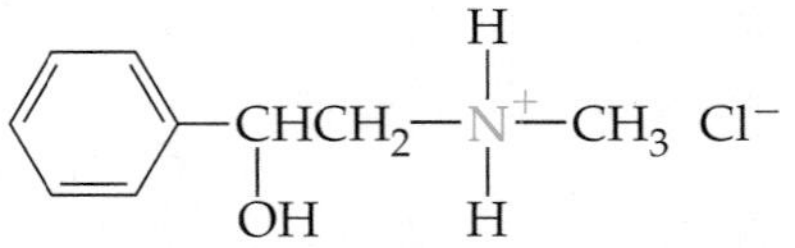

Phenylephrine hydrochloride
(a decongestant)

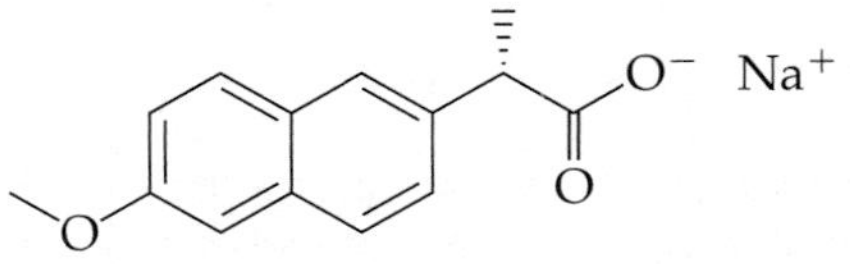

naproxen sodium
(an NSAID)

It is crucial that injectable medications, such as morphine, be delivered to the body in their more water-soluble form; thus converting morphine to its sulfate salt is a common strategy to increase its solubility to the point where delivery in solution is possible. Some drugs, however, such as Taxol (see the Chemistry in Action feature "When Is Toxicity Beneficial?", Chapter 15), a promising candidate in the war on cancer, suffers from poor solubility due to lack of these switches. Strategies such as those outlined earlier may one day soon allow modified versions of this important medicine to be synthesized so that it can be used as a chemotherapeutic agent.

CIA Problem 17.4 Promazine, a potent antipsychotic tranquilizer, is administered as the hydrochloride salt. Write the formula of the salt (there is only one HCl in the salt).

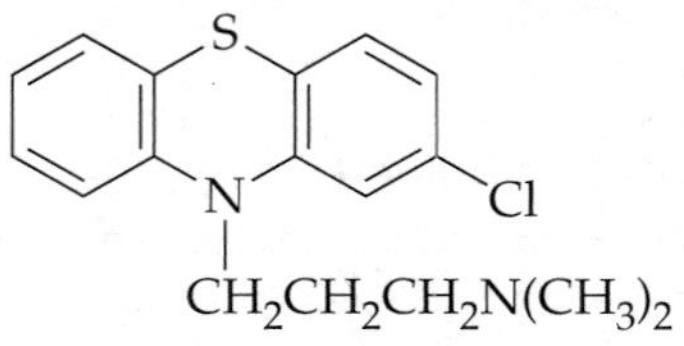

Promazine

CIA Problem 17.5 Why is naproxen converted to its sodium salt before being administered?

PROBLEM 17.29

In the structure of acetyl coenzyme A drawn here, identify a phosphate monoester group, a phosphorus anhydride linkage, two amide groups, and the acetyl group.

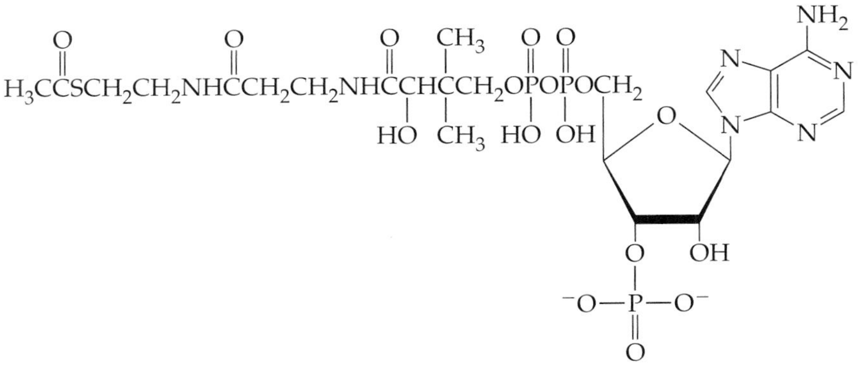

Acetyl coenzyme A
(AcCoA)

SUMMARY REVISITING THE CHAPTER LEARNING OBJECTIVES

- **Compare and contrast the structures, reactions, hydrogen bonding, water solubility, boiling points, and acidity or basicity of carboxylic acids, esters, and amides.** *Carboxylic acids, amides,* and *esters* have the following general structures:

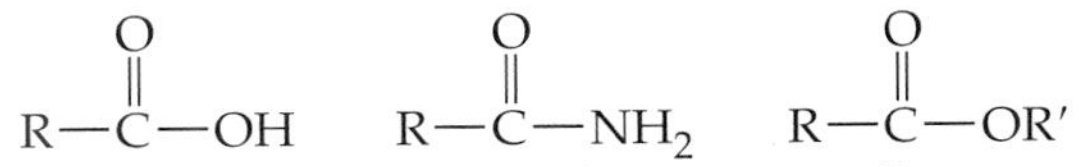

They undergo *carbonyl-group substitution reactions.* Most carboxylic acids are weak acids (a few are strong acids), but esters and amides are neither acids nor bases, being pH neutral. Acids and unsubstituted (primary) or monosubstituted (secondary) amides hydrogen bond with each other, but esters and disubstituted (tertiary) amide molecules do not. Simple acids and esters are liquids; all amides (except formamide) are solids. The simpler compounds of all three classes are water-soluble or partially water-soluble *(see Problems 30, 32, 35, 62, 63, 66, 67, 76, 78, and 79).*

- **Name simple carboxylic acids, esters, and amides given a structure and write a structure given a name.** Many carboxylic acids are best known by their common names (Table 17.1), and these names are the basis for the common names of esters and amides. Esters are named with two words: The first is the name of the alkyl group from the alcohol that has replaced the —H in —COOH, and the second is the name of the parent acid with *-ic acid* replaced by *-ate* (e.g., methyl acetate). For amides, the ending *-amide* is used, and when there are organic groups on the N, these are named first, preceded by *N* (as in *N*-methylacetamide) *(see Problems 33, 35, 37, 40–55, 58, 77, 81, and 83).*

- **Describe the acidity of different carboxylic acids and predict the products obtained when they react with strong bases.** Carboxylic acids are weak acids, with acid dissociation constants typically in the 10^{-4} to 10^{-5} range (or pK_a 4–5). They undergo neutralization reactions with sodium and potassium hydroxide to form the sodium

or potassium carboxylate salts ($RCOO^-Na^+$ or $RCOO^-K^+$). These salts are far more soluble than the carboxylic acids themselves; this property can be used to create water-soluble derivatives of medicines *(see Problems 31, 33, 38, 39, 50, 51, and 79).*

- **Describe how esters and amides are formed from carboxylic acids.** In ester formation, the —OH of a carboxylic acid group is replaced by the —OR' group of an alcohol. In amide formation, the —OH group of a carboxylic acid is replaced by NH_2 from ammonia to give primary amides or by —NHR' or —NR'$_2$ from an amine to give secondary and tertiary amides, respectively *(see Problems 32, 34, 56, 57, 60, 62, and 63).*

- **Predict the hydrolysis products of esters and amides.** Hydrolysis of esters with acids or bases breaks the C(=O)—OR' bond and adds an —H to the —OR' group and —OH to the C=O group to restore the carboxylic acid and the alcohol. Hydrolysis of amides with acids or bases adds an —H to the —N group and —OH to the C=O group to restore the carboxylic acid and ammonia or the amine used to form the amide *(see Problems 31, 36, and 61–67).*

- **Describe the formation and uses of polyesters and polyamides.** Polyesters and polyamides are formed when a dicarboxylic acid is allowed to react with either a dialcohol or a diamine, respectively. Dacron is an example of a polyester, while Nylon is an example of a polyamide. These polymers are used to make plastic bottles, recording tape, fabric, ropes, sutures, and even replacement arteries *(see Problems 34, 68, and 69).*

- **Recognize and draw the structures of phosphate esters and their ionized forms.** Phosphoric acid forms mono-, di-, and triesters: $ROPO_3H_2$, $(RO)_2PO_2H$, and $(RO)_3PO$. There are also esters that contain the diphosphate and triphosphate groups from pyrophosphoric acid and triphosphoric acid (p. 544). Esters that retain hydrogen atoms are ionized in body fluids—for example, $ROPO_3^{2-}$ and $(RO)_2PO^{2-}$. *Phosphorylation* is the transfer of a *phosphoryl group,* —PO_3^{2-}, from one molecule to another. In biochemical reactions, the phosphoryl group is often donated by a triphosphate (such as ATP) with release of energy *(see Problems 70–75).*

CONCEPT MAP: ORGANIC CHEMISTRY FAMILIES

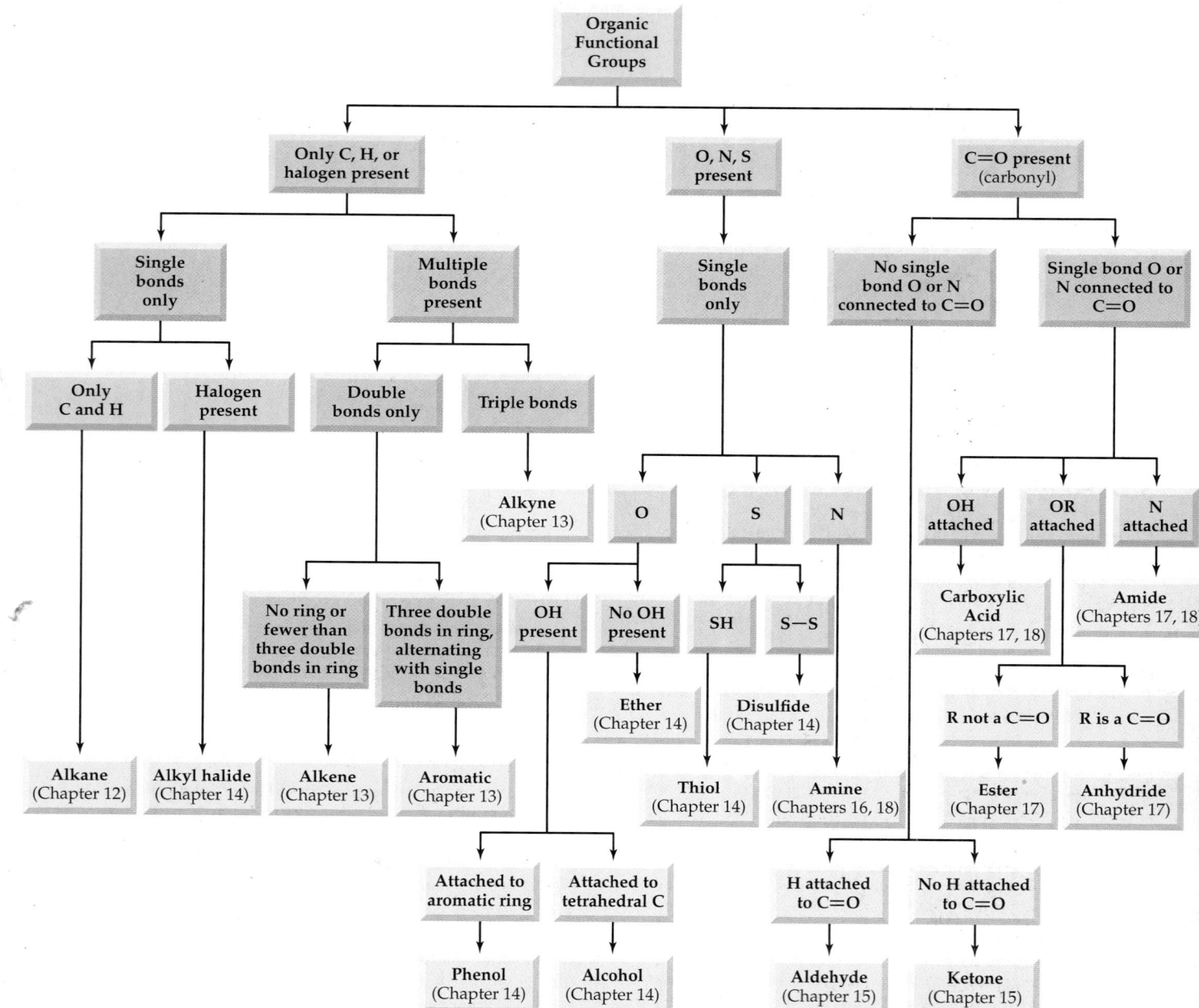

▲ **Figure 17.1 Functional Group Concept Map.** This is the same concept map we saw at the end of Chapters 12 through 16, except the functional groups discussed in this chapter, carboxylic acids, esters, and amides have now been colorized.

KEY WORDS

Acetyl group (Ac), p. 526
Acyl group, p. 524
Amide, p. 523
Carbonyl-group substitution reaction, p. 524

Carboxyl group, p. 525
Carboxylate anion, p. 532
Carboxylic acid, p. 523
Carboxylic acid salt, p. 533

Ester, p. 523
Esterification, p. 536
Phosphate ester, p. 544
Phosphoryl group, p. 544

Phosphorylation, p. 545
Saponification, p. 540

SUMMARY OF REACTIONS

1. Reactions of carboxylic acids
   (a) Acid-base reaction with water (Section 17.2).

$$CH_3\overset{\displaystyle O}{\overset{\displaystyle \|}{C}}OH + H_2O \rightleftharpoons CH_3\overset{\displaystyle O}{\overset{\displaystyle \|}{C}}O^- + H_3O^+$$

   (b) Acid-base reaction with a strong base to yield a carboxylic acid salt (Section 17.3).

$$CH_3\overset{\displaystyle O}{\overset{\displaystyle \|}{C}}OH(aq) + NaOH(aq) \longrightarrow CH_3\overset{\displaystyle O}{\overset{\displaystyle \|}{C}}O^-\,Na^+(aq) + H_2O$$

   (c) Substitution with an alcohol to yield an ester (Section 17.4).

$$CH_3\overset{\displaystyle O}{\overset{\displaystyle \|}{C}}OH + CH_3OH \xrightarrow{H^+} CH_3\overset{\displaystyle O}{\overset{\displaystyle \|}{C}}OCH_3 + H_2O$$

   (d) Substitution with an amine to yield an amide (Section 17.4).

$$CH_3\overset{\displaystyle O}{\overset{\displaystyle \|}{C}}OH + CH_3NH_2 \xrightarrow{heat} CH_3\overset{\displaystyle O}{\overset{\displaystyle \|}{C}}NHCH_3 + H_2O$$

2. Reactions of esters (Section 17.4)
   (a) Hydrolysis to yield an acid and an alcohol.

$$CH_3\overset{\displaystyle O}{\overset{\displaystyle \|}{C}}OCH_3 \xrightarrow[H_2O]{H^+} CH_3\overset{\displaystyle O}{\overset{\displaystyle \|}{C}}OH + CH_3OH$$

   (b) Hydrolysis with a strong base to yield a carboxylate anion and an alcohol (saponification).

$$CH_3CH_2CH_2CH_2CH_2\overset{\displaystyle O}{\overset{\displaystyle \|}{C}}OCH_3 + NaOH(aq) \xrightarrow{H_2O}$$

$$CH_3CH_2CH_2CH_2CH_2\overset{\displaystyle O}{\overset{\displaystyle \|}{C}}O^-\,Na^+ + CH_3OH$$

3. Reactions of amides (Section 17.4)
   (a) Hydrolysis to yield an acid and an amine.

$$CH_3\overset{\displaystyle O}{\overset{\displaystyle \|}{C}}NHCH_3 \xrightarrow[H_2O]{H^+\ or\ OH^-} CH_3\overset{\displaystyle O}{\overset{\displaystyle \|}{C}}OH + CH_3NH_2$$

4. Phosphate reactions (Section 17.6)
   (a) Phosphate ester formation

$$HO-\overset{\displaystyle O}{\overset{\displaystyle \|}{\underset{\displaystyle OH}{P}}}-OH + CH_3OH \longrightarrow HO-\overset{\displaystyle O}{\overset{\displaystyle \|}{\underset{\displaystyle OH}{P}}}-OCH_3 + H_2O$$

   (b) Phosphorylation

$$Adenosine-O-\overset{\displaystyle O}{\overset{\displaystyle \|}{\underset{\displaystyle O^-}{P}}}-O-\overset{\displaystyle O}{\overset{\displaystyle \|}{\underset{\displaystyle O^-}{P}}}-O-\overset{\displaystyle O}{\overset{\displaystyle \|}{\underset{\displaystyle O^-}{P}}}-O^- + ROH \longrightarrow$$

$$Adenosine-O-\overset{\displaystyle O}{\overset{\displaystyle \|}{\underset{\displaystyle O^-}{P}}}-O-\overset{\displaystyle O}{\overset{\displaystyle \|}{\underset{\displaystyle O^-}{P}}}-O^- + RO-\overset{\displaystyle O}{\overset{\displaystyle \|}{\underset{\displaystyle O^-}{P}}}-O^- + Energy$$

UNDERSTANDING KEY CONCEPTS

17.30 Muscle cells deficient in oxygen reduce pyruvate (an intermediate in metabolism) to lactate at a cellular pH of approximately 7.4.

$$CH_3-\overset{\displaystyle O}{\overset{\displaystyle \|}{C}}-COO^- \xrightarrow{[H]} CH_3-\overset{\displaystyle OH}{\overset{\displaystyle |}{C}H}-COO^-$$
$$\text{Pyruvate} \qquad\qquad \text{Lactate}$$

   (a) Why do we say pyruvate and lactate, rather than pyruvic acid and lactic acid?

   (b) Alter the above structures to create pyruvic acid and lactic acid.

   (c) Show hydrogen bonding of water to both pyruvate and lactate. Would you expect a difference in water solubility of lactate and pyruvate? Explain.

17.31 *N*-Acetylglucosamine (also known as NAG) is an important component on the surfaces of cells.

   (a) Under what chemical conditions might the acetyl group be removed, changing the nature of the cell-surface components?

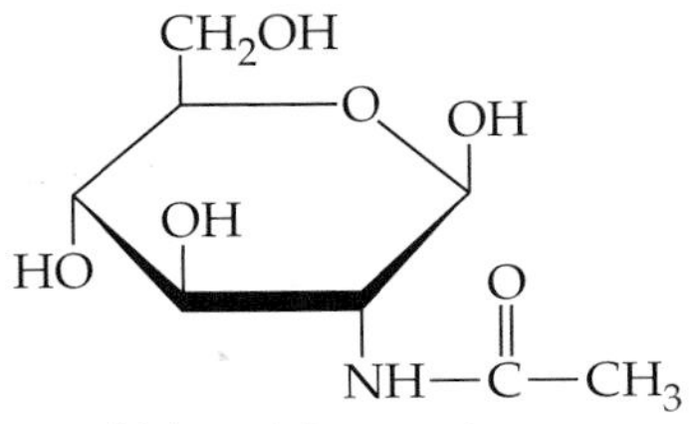

N-Acetylglucosamine

   (b) Draw the structures of the products of acid hydrolysis.

17.32 One phosphorylated form of glycerate is 3-phosphoglycerate (a metabolic intermediate found in the glycolytic cycle, Section 22.3).

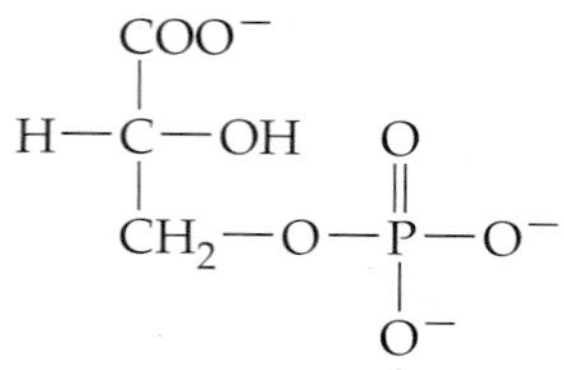

$$
\begin{array}{c}
\text{COO}^- \\
| \\
\text{H}-\text{C}-\text{OH} \quad\quad \text{O} \\
| \quad\quad\quad\quad\quad || \\
\text{CH}_2-\text{O}-\text{P}-\text{O}^- \\
| \\
\text{O}^-
\end{array}
$$

(a) Identify the type of linkage between glycerate and phosphate.

(b) 1,3-Bisphosphoglycerate (two phosphates on glycerate) has an anhydride linkage between the carbonyl at C1 of glycerate and phosphate. Draw the structure of 1,3-bisphosphoglycerate (another metabolic intermediate).

17.33 The names of the first nine dicarboxylic acids can be remembered by using the first letter of each word of the saying "*Oh My, Such Good Apple Pie! Sweet As Sugar!*" to remind us of *o*xalate, *m*alonate, *s*uccinate, *g*lutarate, *a*dipate, *p*imelate, *s*uberate, *a*zelate, and *s*ebacate (the dianionic form in which these acids occur at physiological pH). Write the structures of the first six dicarboxylate anions.

17.34 Consider the following unnatural amino acid:

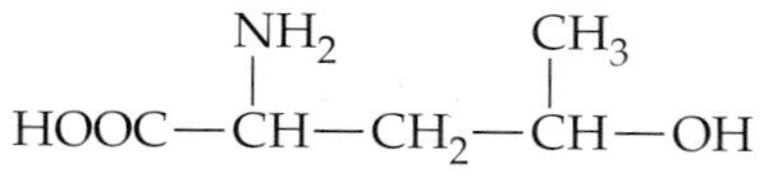

$$
\begin{array}{c}
\quad\quad \text{NH}_2 \quad\quad\quad \text{CH}_3 \\
\quad\quad | \quad\quad\quad\quad\quad | \\
\text{HOOC}-\text{CH}-\text{CH}_2-\text{CH}-\text{OH}
\end{array}
$$

(a) If two molecules react to form an ester, what is the structure of the ester product?

(b) If two molecules react to form an amide, what is the structure of the amide product?

(c) Draw the cyclic ester resulting from the intramolecular reaction of the hydroxyl group of this amino acid with its carboxyl group (cyclic esters are called *lactones*).

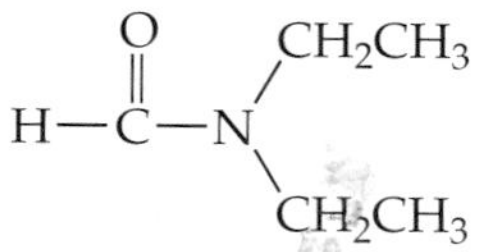

ADDITIONAL PROBLEMS

CARBOXYLIC ACIDS (SECTIONS 17.1–17.2)

17.38 Write the equation for the ionization of hexanoic acid in water at pH 7.4. (Hint: See Section 17.2.)

17.39 Suppose you have a sample of benzoic acid dissolved in water.

(a) Draw the structure of benzoic acid.

(b) Now assume that aqueous NaOH is added to the benzoic acid solution until pH 12 is reached. Draw the structure of the major organic species present.

(c) Finally, assume that aqueous HCl is added to the solution from (b) until pH 2 is reached. Draw the structure of the major organic species present.

17.35 **(a)** Draw the structures of the following compounds and use dashed lines to indicate where they form hydrogen bonds to other molecules of the same kind: (i) formic acid, (ii) methyl formate, and (iii) formamide.

(b) Arrange these compounds in order of increasing boiling points and explain your rationale for the order.

17.36 Volicitin, in the "spit" from beet armyworms, causes corn plants to produce volatile compounds that act as signaling compounds for parasitoid wasps. Draw the three hydrolysis products that form from volicitin that match the common names given here.

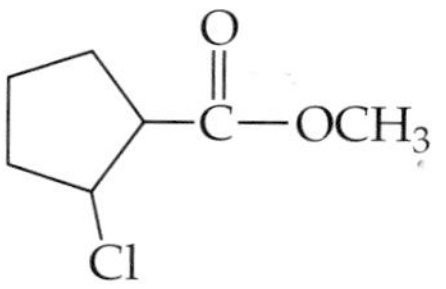

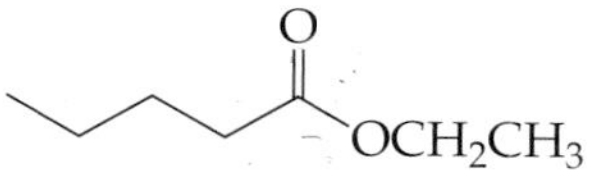

(a) Glutamic acid (α-aminoglutaric acid)

(b) Ammonia

(c) 17-Hydroxylinolenic acid

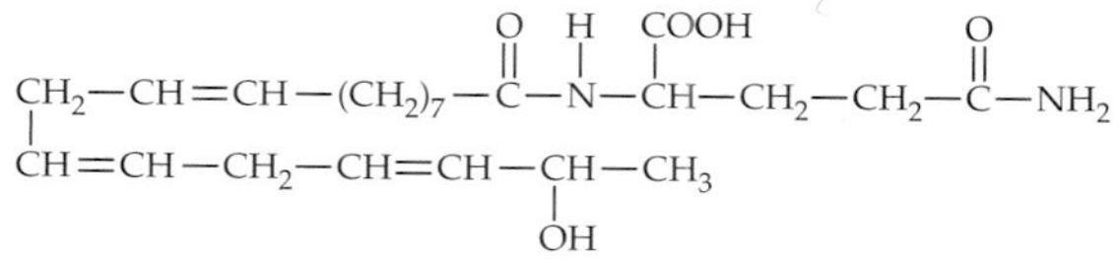

$$
\begin{array}{c}
\quad\quad\quad\quad\quad\quad\quad\quad \text{O} \quad \text{H} \quad \text{COOH} \quad\quad\quad\quad \text{O} \\
\quad\quad\quad\quad\quad\quad\quad\quad || \quad | \quad\quad | \quad\quad\quad\quad\quad\quad || \\
\text{CH}_2-\text{CH}=\text{CH}-(\text{CH}_2)_7-\text{C}-\text{N}-\text{CH}-\text{CH}_2-\text{CH}_2-\text{C}-\text{NH}_2 \\
| \\
\text{CH}=\text{CH}-\text{CH}_2-\text{CH}=\text{CH}-\text{CH}-\text{CH}_3 \\
\quad\quad\quad\quad\quad\quad\quad\quad\quad | \\
\quad\quad\quad\quad\quad\quad\quad\quad\quad \text{OH}
\end{array}
$$

Volicitin

17.37 For the following compounds, give the systematic name.

(a)
$$
\begin{array}{c}
\text{O} \\
|| \\
\text{C} \quad\quad \text{CH}_2\text{CH}_3 \\
\quad\quad\text{N} \\
\quad\quad | \\
\quad\quad \text{H}
\end{array}
$$

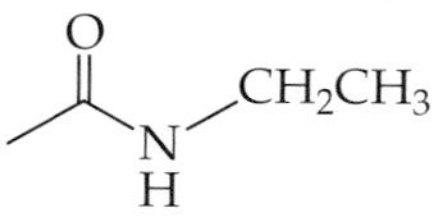

(b) (cyclopentane ring with)
$$
\begin{array}{c}
\text{O} \\
|| \\
\text{C}-\text{OCH}_3
\end{array}
$$
with Cl substituent

(c)
$$
\begin{array}{c}
\text{O} \\
|| \\
\text{C} \\
\quad \text{OCH}_2\text{CH}_3
\end{array}
$$

(d)
$$
\begin{array}{c}
\text{O} \quad\quad \text{CH}_2\text{CH}_3 \\
|| \quad\quad\quad / \\
\text{H}-\text{C}-\text{N} \\
\quad\quad\quad\quad \backslash \\
\quad\quad\quad\quad \text{CH}_2\text{CH}_3
\end{array}
$$

17.40 There are two different carboxylic acids with the formula $C_4H_8O_2$. Draw and name them.

17.41 There are two different butanoic acids with the formula $C_5H_{10}O_2$. Draw and name them.

17.42 Give systematic names for the following carboxylic acids:

(a) 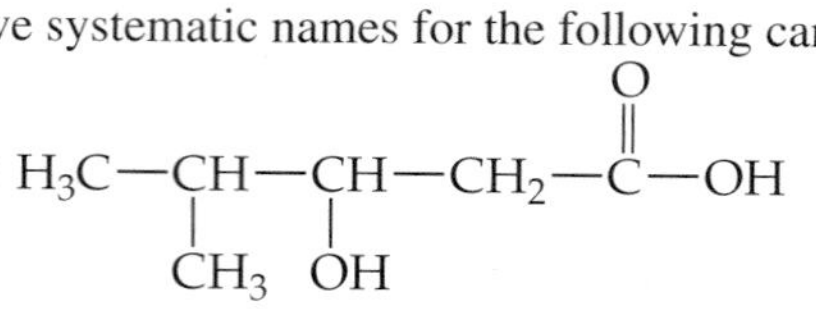
$$
\begin{array}{c}
\quad\quad\quad\quad\quad\quad\quad\quad\quad\quad \text{O} \\
\quad\quad\quad\quad\quad\quad\quad\quad\quad\quad || \\
\text{H}_3\text{C}-\text{CH}-\text{CH}-\text{CH}_2-\text{C}-\text{OH} \\
\quad\quad\quad | \quad\quad | \\
\quad\quad\quad \text{CH}_3 \quad \text{OH}
\end{array}
$$

(b) $CH_3-(CH_2)_7-COOH$

(c) 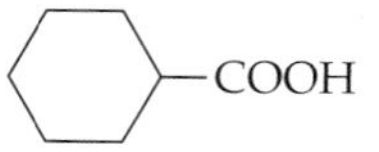 (cyclohexane)—COOH

(d) 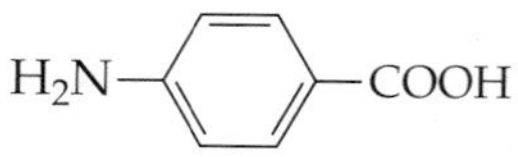 H_2N—(benzene ring)—COOH

17.43 Give systematic names for the following carboxylic acids:

(a) 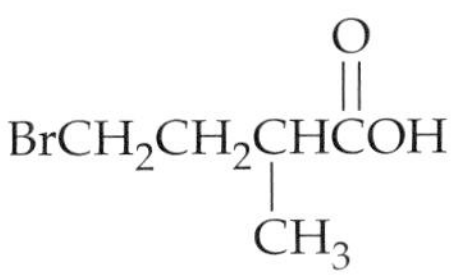 BrCH$_2$CH$_2$CHCOH with CH$_3$ substituent and =O

(b) 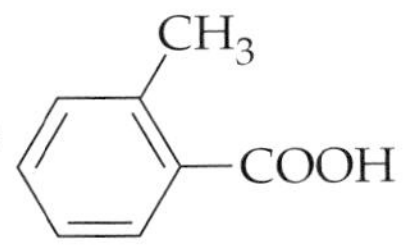 benzene ring with CH$_3$ and —COOH

(c) (CH$_3$CH$_2$)$_3$CCOOH

(d) CH$_3$(CH$_2$)$_5$COOH

17.44 Give systematic names for the following carboxylic acid salts:

(a) 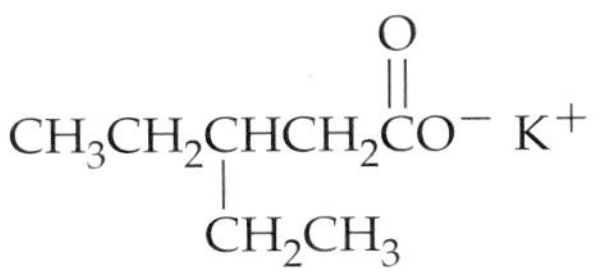 CH$_3$CH$_2$CHCH$_2$CO$^-$ K$^+$ with CH$_2$CH$_3$ substituent and =O

(b) 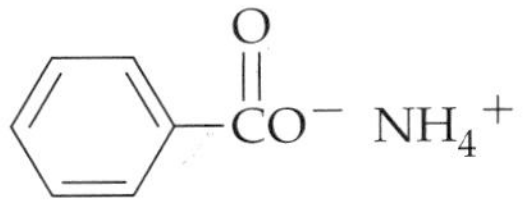 benzene ring with —CO$^-$ NH$_4$$^+$ and =O

(c) [CH$_3$CH$_2$CO$^-$]$_2$ Ca^{2+}

17.45 Give systematic names and common names for the following carboxylic acid salts:

(a) CH$_3$C—O$^-$ NH$_4$$^+$ with =O

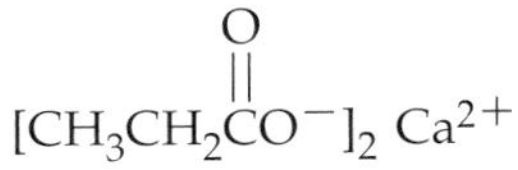

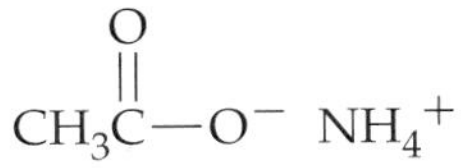

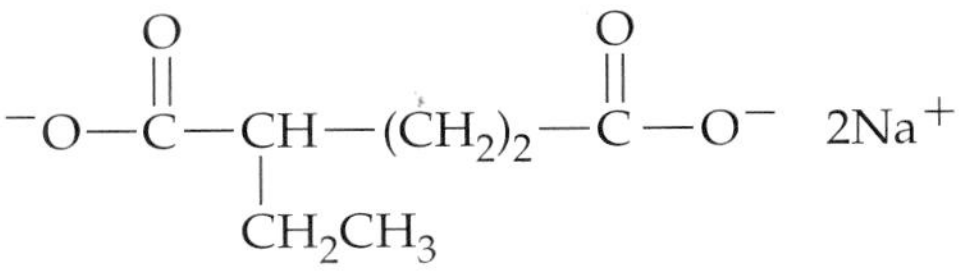

(b) $^-$O—C—CH—(CH$_2$)$_2$—C—O$^-$ 2Na$^+$ with CH$_2$CH$_3$ substituent and =O groups

(c) C—O$^-$ / C—O$^-$ Ca^{2+} with =O groups

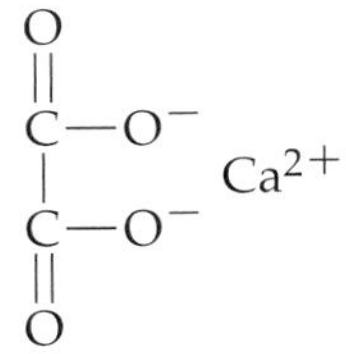

17.46 Draw structures corresponding to the following names:

(a) 3,4-Dimethylhexanoic acid

(b) Phenylacetic acid

(c) 3,4-Dinitrobenzoic acid

(d) Triethylammonium butanoate

17.47 Draw structures corresponding to the following names:

(a) 2,2,3-Trifluorobutanoic acid

(b) 3-Hydroxybutanoic acid

(c) 3,3-Dimethyl-4-phenylpentanoic acid

17.48 Malic acid, a dicarboxylic acid found in apples, has the systematic name hydroxybutanedioic acid. Draw its structure.

17.49 Fumaric acid is a metabolic intermediate that has the systematic name *trans*-2-butenedioic acid. Draw its structure.

17.50 What is the formula for the diammonium salt of fumaric acid? (See Problem 17.49)

17.51 Aluminum acetate is used as an antiseptic ingredient in some skin-rash ointments. Draw its structure.

ESTERS AND AMIDES (SECTIONS 17.3–17.4)

17.52 Draw and name compounds that meet these descriptions:

(a) Three different amides with the formula C$_5$H$_{11}$NO

(b) Three different esters with the formula C$_6$H$_{12}$O$_2$

17.53 Draw and name compounds that meet these descriptions:

(a) Three different amides with the formula C$_6$H$_{13}$NO

(b) Three different esters with the formula C$_5$H$_{10}$O$_2$

17.54 Give systematic names for the following structures and structures for the names:

(a)  CH$_3$COCH$_2$CH$_2$CHCH$_3$ with CH$_3$ substituent and =O

(b)  CH$_3$CHCH$_2$CH$_2$COCH$_3$ with CH$_3$ substituent and =O

(c) Cyclohexyl acetate

(d) Phenyl-*o*-hydroxybenzoate

17.55 Give systematic names for the following structures and structures for the names:

(a) 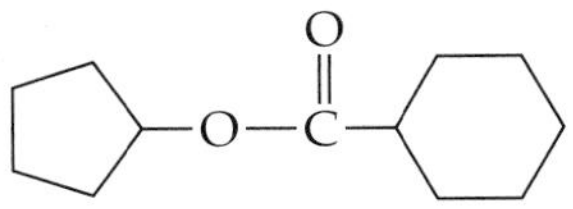 cyclopentyl—O—C—cyclohexyl with =O

(b) Ethyl 2-hydroxypropanoate

(c) 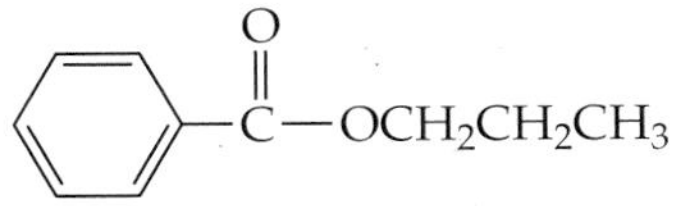 benzene ring—C—OCH$_2$CH$_2$CH$_3$ with =O

(d) Butyl 3,3-dimethylhexanoate

(e)  (CH$_3$)$_2$CHCOC(CH$_3$)$_3$ with =O

17.56 Draw structures of the carboxylic acids and alcohols you would use to prepare each ester in Problem 17.54.

17.57 Draw structures of the carboxylic acids and alcohols you would use to prepare each ester in Problem 17.55.

17.58 Give systematic names for the following structures and structures for the names:

(a) 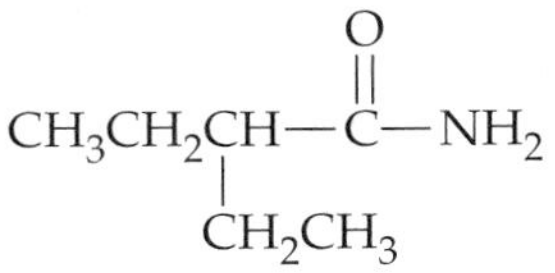 CH$_3$CH$_2$CH—C—NH$_2$ with CH$_2$CH$_3$ substituent and =O

(b) 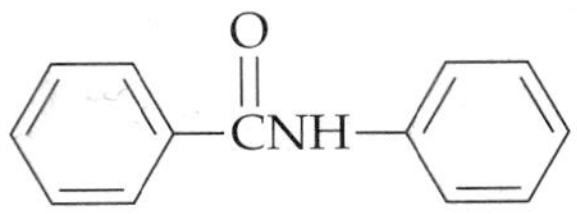 benzene ring—CNH—benzene ring with =O

(c) *N*-Ethyl-*N*-methylbenzamide

(d) 2,3-Dibromohexanamide

17.59 Give systematic names for the following structures and structures for the names:

(a) 3-Methylpentanamide   (b) *N*-Phenylacetamide

(c) HCN(CH$_3$)$_2$ with =O

(d) CH$_3$CH$_2$CNHCHCH$_3$ with =O and CH$_3$ substituent

17.60 Show how you would prepare each amide in Problem 17.58 from the appropriate carboxylic acid and amine.

17.61 What compounds are produced from hydrolysis of each amide in Problem 17.59?

REACTIONS OF CARBOXYLIC ACIDS AND THEIR DERIVATIVES (SECTIONS 17.3–17.4)

17.62 Procaine, a local anesthetic whose hydrochloride is Novocain, has the following structure. Identify the functional groups present, and show the structures of the alcohol and carboxylic acids you would use to prepare procaine.

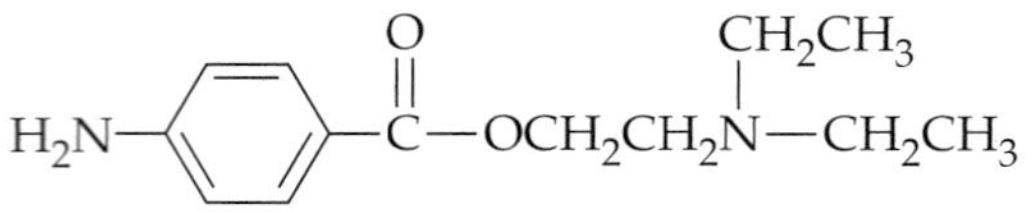

Procaine

17.63 Lidocaine (Xylocaine) is a local anesthetic closely related to procaine. Identify the functional groups present in lidocaine, and show how you might prepare it from a carboxylic acid and an amine.

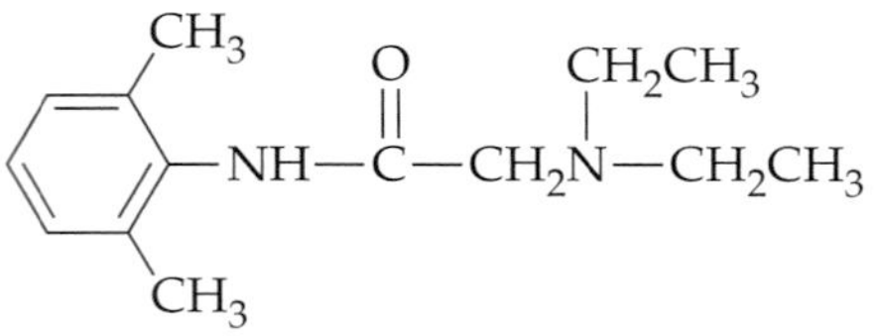

Lidocaine

17.64 Lactones are cyclic esters in which the carboxylic acid part and the alcohol part are connected to form a ring. One of the most notorious lactones is gamma-butyrolactone (GBL), whose hydrolysis product is the "date-rape" drug GHB. Draw the structure of GHB.

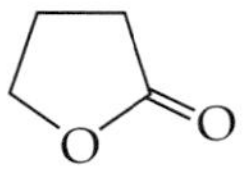

GBL

17.65 When both the carboxylic acid and the amine are in the same molecule, amide formation produces lactams. A *lactam* is a cyclic amide, where the amide group is part of the ring. Draw the structure of the product(s) obtained from acid hydrolysis of these lactams.

(a) epsilon-lactam

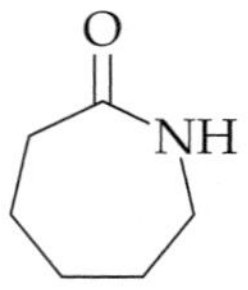

(b) beta-lactam

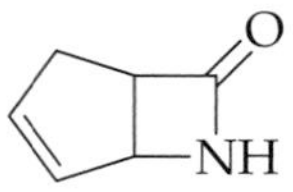

17.66 LSD (lysergic acid diethylamide), a semisynthetic psychedelic drug of the ergoline family, has the structure shown here. Identify the functional groups present, and give the structures of the products you would obtain from hydrolysis of LSD.

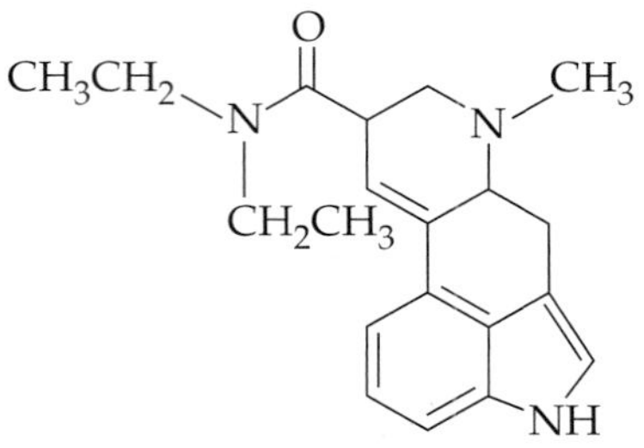

LSD

17.67 Household soap is a mixture of the sodium or potassium salts of long-chain carboxylic acids that arise from saponification of animal fat.

(a) Identify the functional groups present in the fat molecule shown in the reaction next.

(b) Draw the structures of the soap molecules produced in the following reaction:

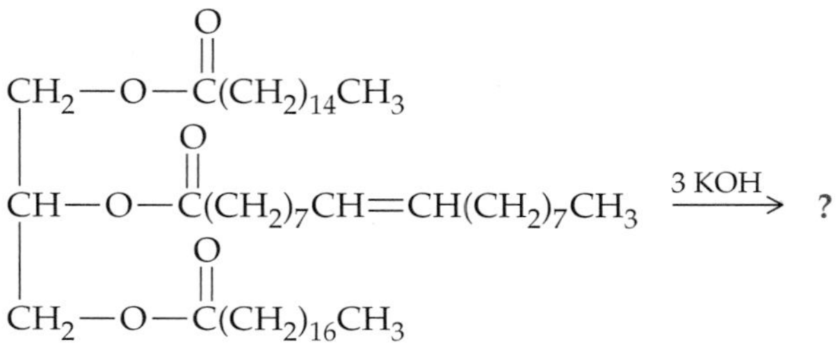

A fat

POLYESTERS AND POLYAMIDES (SECTION 17.5)

17.68 Baked-on paints used for automobiles and many appliances are often based on *alkyds,* such as can be made from terephthalic acid and glycerol. Sketch a section of the resultant polyester polymer that would be obtained if two glycerols reacted with two terephthalic acids, using the –OH on the first and third carbon of glycerol. Note that the glycerol can actually be esterified at any of the three alcohol groups, providing *cross-linking* to form a very strong surface.

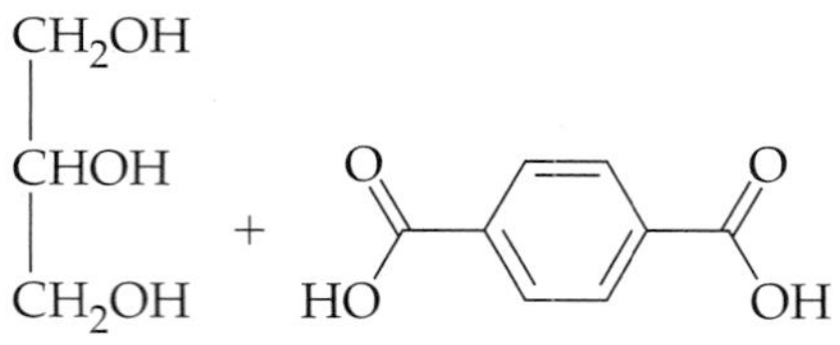

Glycerol   Terephthalic acid

17.69 A simple polyamide can be made from ethylenediamine and oxalic acid (Table 17.1). Draw the polymer formed when three units of ethylenediamine reacts with two units of oxalic acid.

$$H_2N—CH_2—CH_2—NH_2$$
Ethylenediamine

PHOSPHATE ESTERS AND ANHYDRIDES (SECTION 17.6)

17.70 The following phosphate ester is an important intermediate in carbohydrate metabolism. What two products result from hydrolysis of this phosphate ester?

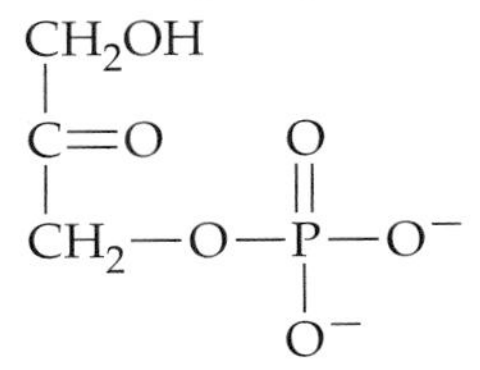

$$\begin{array}{c} CH_2OH \\ | \\ C{=}O \quad\quad O \\ | \quad\quad\quad || \\ CH_2—O—P—O^- \\ | \\ O^- \end{array}$$

17.71 In the following compound

$$\begin{array}{c} O \quad\quad O \\ || \quad\quad || \\ HO—P—O—P—O—CH_2{-}\bigcirc \\ | \quad\quad | \\ OH \quad\quad OH \end{array}$$

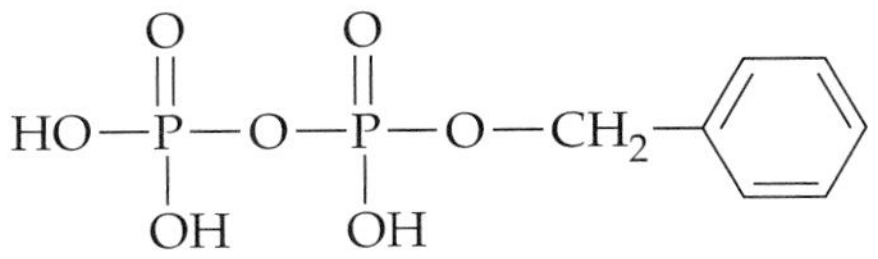

   (a) Identify the phosphate ester linkage.

   (b) Identify the phosphate anhydride linkage.

   (c) When this molecule is treated with acid and water, three products are obtained. Draw them. (Hint: Two of the products formed are the same.)

17.72 The metabolic intermediate *acetyl phosphate* is an anhydride formed from acetic acid and phosphoric acid. What is the structure of acetyl phosphate?

17.73 Acetyl phosphate (see Problem 17.74) has what is called "high phosphoryl-group transfer potential." Write a reaction in which there is phosphoryl-group transfer from acetyl phosphate to ethanol to make a phosphate ester.

17.74 Cyclic ribose nucleotide phosphates, such as cyclic AMP (cAMP), are important signaling agents in living cells; all have the general structure shown here. What kind of linkage holds the phosphate to the ribose (see arrows; ribose is highlighted in blue)?

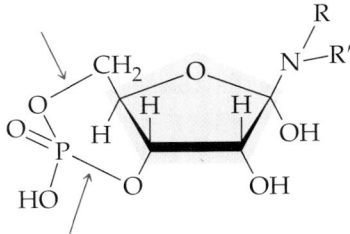

Cyclic Ribose Phosphate

17.75 What is the difference between a phosphate diester and an ester of a diphosphate? Give an example of each.

CONCEPTUAL PROBLEMS

17.76 Three amide isomers, *N,N*-dimethylformamide, *N*-methylacetamide, and propanamide, have respective boiling points of 153 °C, 202 °C, and 213 °C. Explain these boiling points in light of their structural formulas.

17.77 Salol, the phenyl ester of salicylic acid, is used as an intestinal antiseptic. Draw the structure of phenyl salicylate.

17.78 Propanamide and methyl acetate have about the same molar mass, both are quite soluble in water, and yet the boiling point of propanamide is 213 °C, whereas that of methyl acetate is 57 °C. Explain.

17.79 Mention at least two simple chemical tests by which you can distinguish between benzaldehyde and benzoic acid.

17.80 Write the formula of the triester formed from glycerol and stearic acid (Table 17.1).

17.81 Name the following compounds.

(a) 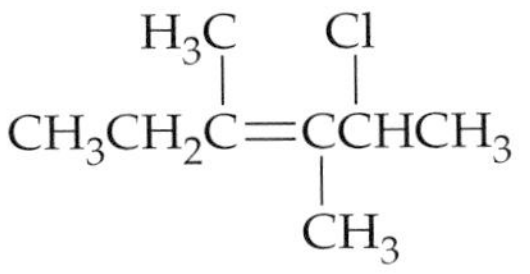 $\begin{array}{c} H_3C \quad\quad Cl \\ | \quad\quad\quad | \\ CH_3CH_2C{=}CCHCH_3 \\ | \\ CH_3 \end{array}$

(b) $CH_3CH_2\overset{\displaystyle O}{\overset{||}{C}}NCH_3$ (with phenyl ring attached to N)

(c) $(CH_3CH_2)_3C\overset{\displaystyle O}{\overset{||}{C}}O{-}\bigcirc$

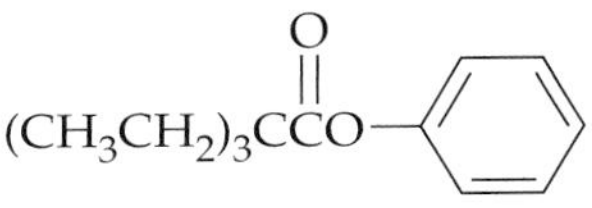

(d) 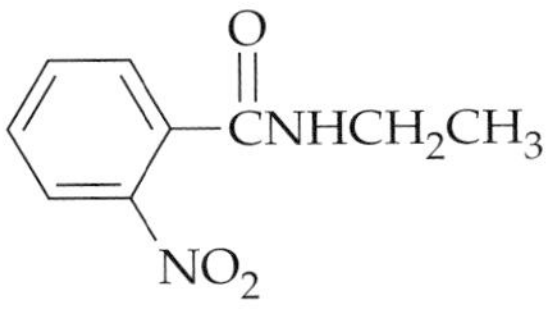 a benzene ring with NO_2 substituent attached to $\overset{\displaystyle O}{\overset{||}{C}}NHCH_2CH_3$

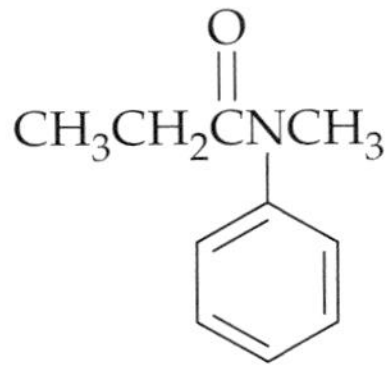

GROUP PROBLEMS

17.82 Each of the following materials has an ester that is responsible for its smell and/or flavor. Search the internet and determine what that ester is, draw its structure, and what carboxylic acid and alcohol are used to form it.

   (a) Juicy Fruit gum flavoring

   (b) Peach odor

   (c) Apple odor

   (d) Rum odor

17.83 Draw all possible carboxylic acids with the formula $C_5H_{10}O_2$.

17.84 Some of the most well-known antibiotics belong to a class of carboxylic acid derivatives known as beta-lactams. Search the internet and find at least four antibiotics that belong to this class. Draw their structures and identify the functional groups present. Other than the presence of the beta-lactam, what other common structural features and/or functional groups do they have in common?

18

Amino Acids and Proteins

CONTENTS

◄◄◄ CONCEPTS TO REVIEW

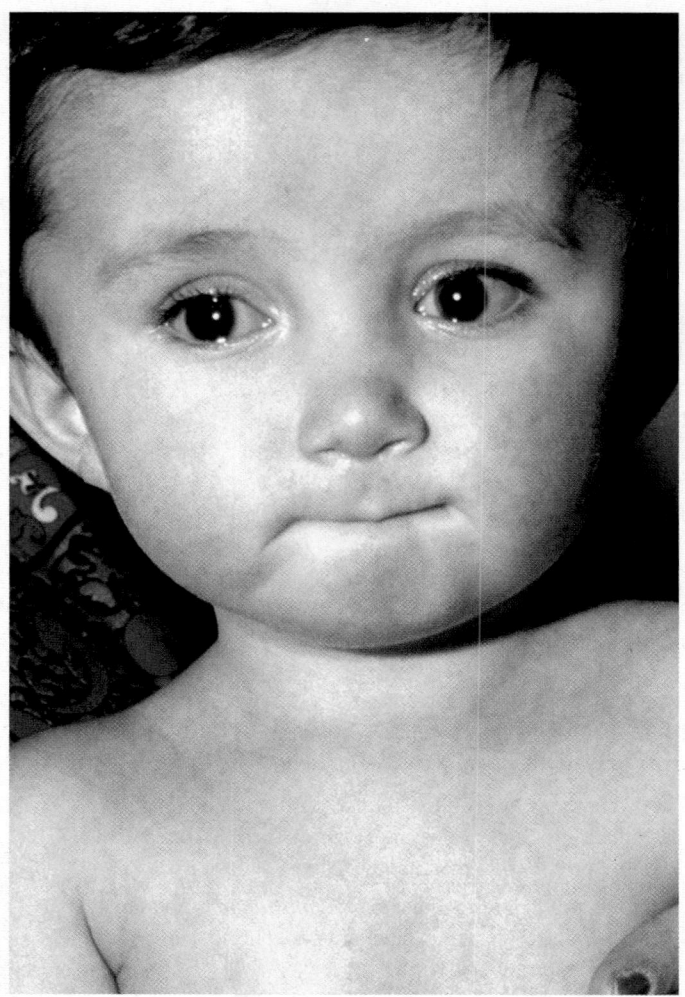

▲ Child with osteogenesis imperfecta, a genetic disease. One characteristic of osteogenesis imperfecta is the blue color of the sclera (whites) of the eyes.

Imagine being introduced to a newborn with startlingly blue eyes—not blue irises as we see typically but with the part of the eye known as the "white" or sclera completely blue instead, as in the picture above. This coloration of the sclera is an indication of a genetic disease called *osteogenesis imperfecta*, or brittle bone disease. Osteogenesis imperfecta is a result of the synthesis of imperfect collagen, the most abundant protein in the human body. Genetic mutations result in amino acid substitutions in collagen, creating imperfect collagen. Collagen is the scaffold for bone and is present in cartilage, connective tissue, and the sclera of the eye. You will learn more about collagen throughout this chapter, including how amino acids are bonded to form collagen as well as other proteins. Also, some functions of proteins will be discussed that help health professionals understand diseases such as osteogenesis imperfecta. The study of proteins and how they lead to diseases like osteogenesis imperfecta is just one example of a topic that falls under the discipline of biochemistry. Osteogenesis imperfecta is discussed further in the Chemistry in Action on page 583.

18.1 An Introduction to Biochemistry

Biochemistry, the study of molecules and their reactions in living organisms, is built upon the inorganic and organic chemical principles outlined in the first 17 chapters of this book. Now we are ready to investigate the chemical basis of life. Physicians are faced with biochemistry every day because all diseases are associated with abnormalities in biochemistry. Nutritionists evaluate our dietary needs based on our biochemistry. And the pharmaceutical industry designs molecules that mimic or alter the action of biomolecules. The ultimate goal of biochemistry is to understand the structures of biomolecules and the relationships between their structures and functions.

Biochemistry is the common ground for the life sciences. Microbiology, botany, zoology, immunology, pathology, physiology, toxicology, neuroscience, cell biology—in all these fields, answers to fundamental questions are found at the molecular level.

The principal classes of biomolecules are *proteins, carbohydrates, lipids,* and *nucleic acids.* Some biomolecules are small and have only a few functional groups. Others are huge and their biochemistry is governed by the interactions of large numbers of functional groups. Proteins, the subject of this chapter; nucleic acids (Chapter 26); and large carbohydrates (Section 20.7) are all polymers, some containing hundreds, thousands, or even millions of repeating units.

Biochemical reactions must continuously break down food molecules, generate and store energy, build up new biomolecules, and eliminate waste. Each biomolecule has its own role to play in these processes, but despite the huge size of some biomolecules and the complexity of their interactions, their functional groups and chemical reactions are no different from those of simpler organic molecules. *All the principles of chemistry introduced thus far apply to biochemistry.* Of the functional groups introduced in previous chapters, those listed in Table 18.1 are of greatest importance in biomolecules.

LOOKING AHEAD ▶▶ The focus in the rest of this book is on human biochemistry and the essential structure–function relationships of biomolecules. In this and the next chapter, we examine the structure of proteins and the roles of proteins and other molecules in controlling biochemical reactions. Next, we discuss the structure and function of carbohydrates (Chapter 20). Then, we present an overview of metabolism and the production of energy (Chapters 21 and 22). Then, we discuss the structure and function of lipids (Chapters 23 and 24), the role of nucleic acids in protein synthesis and heredity (Chapters 26 and 27), the metabolism of proteins (Chapter 25), the role of small molecules in neurochemistry (Chapter 28), and the chemistry of body fluids (Chapter 29).

18.2 Proteins and Their Functions: An Overview

Learning Objective:

• Describe the different functions of proteins and give an example for each function.

The word *protein* is a familiar one. Taken from the Greek *proteios,* meaning "primary," "protein" is an apt description for the biological molecules that are of primary importance to all living organisms. Approximately 50% of your body's dry weight is protein.

What roles do proteins play in living things? No doubt you are aware that a hamburger is produced from animal muscle protein and that we depend on our own muscle proteins for every move we make. But this is only one of many essential roles of proteins. They provide *structure* (keratin) and *support* (actin filaments) to tissues and organs throughout our bodies. As *hormones* (oxytocin) and *enzymes* (catalase), they control all aspects of metabolism. In body fluids, water-soluble proteins pick up other molecules for *storage* (casein) or *transport* (transferrin, Fe^{3+}). And the proteins of the immune system provide *protection* (Immunoglobulin G) against invaders such as bacteria and viruses. To accomplish their biological functions, which are summarized in Table 18.2, some proteins must be tough and fibrous, whereas others must be globular and soluble in body fluids. The overall shape of a protein molecule, as you will see often in the following chapters, is essential to the role of that protein in our metabolism.

PROBLEM 18.1

Alcohol dehydrogenase, found in liver cells, converts ethanol into acetaldehyde. What type of protein is alcohol dehydrogenase?

PROBLEM 18.2

Cortisol levels rise under stressful conditions. Oxytocin can induce relaxation and romantic feelings. What type of protein are cortisol and oxytocin?

Table 18.1 Functional Groups of Importance in Biochemical Molecules

Functional Group	Structure	Type of Biomolecule
Ammonium ion, amino group	$-NH_3^+$, $-NH_2$	Amino acids and proteins (Sections 18.3 and 18.4)
Hydroxyl group	$-OH$	Monosaccharides (carbohydrates) and glycerol: a component of triacylglycerols (lipids) (Sections 20.3 and 23.2)
Carbonyl group	$-\overset{\overset{O}{\|\|}}{C}-$	Monosaccharides (carbohydrates); in acetyl group (CH_3CO) used to transfer carbon atoms during catabolism (Sections 21.4 and 21.8)
Carboxyl group, carboxylate anion	$-\overset{\overset{O}{\|\|}}{C}-OH$, $-\overset{\overset{O}{\|\|}}{C}-O^-$	Amino acids, proteins, and fatty acids (lipids) (Sections 18.3, 18.4, and 23.2)
Amide group	$-\overset{\overset{O}{\|\|}}{C}-\overset{\underset{\|}{}}{N}-$	Links amino acids in proteins; formed by reaction of amino group and carboxyl group (Section 18.4)
Carboxylic acid ester	$-\overset{\overset{O}{\|\|}}{C}-O-R$	Triacylglycerols (and other lipids); formed by reaction of carboxyl group and hydroxyl group (Section 23.2)
Phosphates, mono-, di-, tri-	$-\overset{\underset{\|}{}}{C}-O-\overset{\overset{O}{\|\|}}{\underset{\underset{O^-}{\|}}{P}}-O^-$ $-\overset{\underset{\|}{}}{C}-O-\overset{\overset{O}{\|\|}}{\underset{\underset{O^-}{\|}}{P}}-O-\overset{\overset{O}{\|\|}}{\underset{\underset{O^-}{\|}}{P}}-O^-$ $-\overset{\underset{\|}{}}{C}-O-\overset{\overset{O}{\|\|}}{\underset{\underset{O^-}{\|}}{P}}-O-\overset{\overset{O}{\|\|}}{\underset{\underset{O^-}{\|}}{P}}-O-\overset{\overset{O}{\|\|}}{\underset{\underset{O^-}{\|}}{P}}-O^-$	Adenosine triphosphate (ATP) and many metabolism intermediates (Sections 17.6, 21.4, and throughout metabolism sections)
Hemiacetal group	$-\overset{\underset{\underset{OR}{\|}}{\|}}{C}-OH$	Cyclic forms of monosaccharides; formed by a reaction of carbonyl group with hydroxyl group (Sections 15.7 and 20.4)
Acetal group	$-\overset{\underset{\underset{OR}{\|}}{\|}}{C}-OR$	Connects monosaccharides in disaccharides and larger carbohydrates; formed by reaction of carbonyl group with hydroxyl group (Sections 15.7, 20.6, and 20.7)
Thiols Sulfides Disulfides	$-SH$ $-S-$ $-S-S-$ $\Big\}$	Found in amino acids cysteine, methionine; structural components of proteins (Sections 14.8, 18.3, 18.8, and 18.10)

In Table 18.1, both the amino group and the carboxyl group are shown having two different structures. This is explained in Section 18.4.

Table 18.2 Classification of Proteins by Function

Type	Function	Example
Enzymes	Catalyze biochemical reactions	*Amylase*—begins digestion of carbohydrates by hydrolysis
Hormones	Regulate body functions by carrying messages to receptors	*Insulin*—facilitates use of glucose for energy generation
Storage proteins	Make essential substances available when needed	*Myoglobin*—stores oxygen in muscles
Transport proteins	Carry substances through body fluids	*Serum albumin*—carries fatty acids in blood
Structural proteins	Provide mechanical shape and support	*Collagen*—provides structure to tendons and cartilage
Protective proteins	Defend the body against foreign matter	*Immunoglobulin*—aids in destruction of invading bacteria
Contractile proteins	Do mechanical work	*Myosin* and *actin*—govern muscle movement

18.3 Amino Acids

Learning Objectives:

- Describe and recognize the 20 alpha amino acid structures and their side chains.
- Categorize amino acids by the polarity or neutrality of the side chain and predict which are hydrophilic and which are hydrophobic.
- Explain chirality and identify which amino acids are chiral.

Amino acids are the building blocks for the polymers called **proteins.** Every amino acid contains an amino functional group ($-NH_2$), a carboxyl functional group ($-COOH$), and an R group called a **side chain,** all bonded to the same carbon atom. This central carbon is known as the alpha (α)-carbon, named so because it is the carbon atom directly adjacent to a carboxyl functional group. Thus, the amino acids in proteins are **alpha-amino (α-amino) acids** because the amino group in each is connected to the alpha-carbon atom. Each α-amino acid has a different R group, and that is what distinguishes amino acids from one another. The R groups may be only hydrocarbons, or they may also contain a functional group.

An α-amino acid

> The alpha carbon is the central carbon in an amino acid to which the amine, carboxyl, and side-chain R groups attach.

$$H_2N-\overset{\overset{\displaystyle H}{|}}{\underset{\underset{\displaystyle R}{|}}{C}}\overset{\alpha}{}-\overset{\overset{\displaystyle O}{||}}{C}-OH$$

Side-chain R group, different for each amino acid

All of the diverse proteins in living organisms are built from just 20 common α-amino acids, listed in Table 18.3. Each amino acid has a three-letter shorthand code that is included in the table; for example, Ala for alanine, Gly for glycine, and Pro for proline. Biochemists use a one-letter code; for example, A for alanine, G for glycine, and P for proline. The one-letter codes are also in Table 18.3. All of these amino acids (with the exception of glycine and proline) have the same structure except for the side chain (R group) attached to the α-carbon. The different R groups of each amino acid give each its unique identity and determines its function. For example, alanine has a methyl (CH_3) group bonded to the alpha carbon, but cysteine has a thiol (SH) group. Glycine, the simplest amino acid, has an H atom instead of an alkyl side chain, whereas proline's amino nitrogen atom is bonded to the α-carbon atom forming a five-membered ring. Not included in this table are several rare amino acids found primarily in microbes. Table 18.3 identifies the different R groups of each amino acid in green.

Amino acid A molecule that contains both an amino functional group and a carboxyl functional group.

Protein A large biological molecule made of many amino acids linked together through amide bonds.

Side chain (amino acid) The variable group bonded to the central carbon atom in an amino acid; different in each amino acid.

Alpha- (α-) amino acid An amino acid in which the amino group is bonded to the carbon atom next to the $-COOH$ group.

PROBLEM 18.3

Consult Table 18.3 and draw alanine. Label the functional groups and give the three-letter abbreviation and the one-letter abbreviation. What group does the side chain fall into?

💬 KEY CONCEPT PROBLEM 18.4 ───────────────

Examine the ball-and-stick model of valine in the margin. Identify the carboxyl group, the amino group, and the R group.

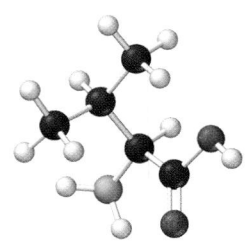

Table 18.3 The 20 α-Amino Acids Found in Proteins, with Their Abbreviations, One-Letter Codes, and Isoelectric Points. The structures are written here in their fully ionized forms. These ions and the isoelectric points given in parentheses are explained in Section 18.4.

Nonpolar, Neutral Side Chains

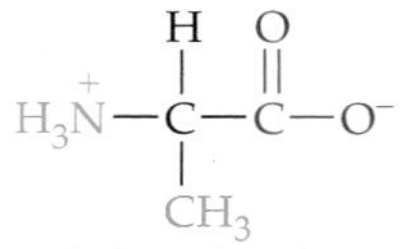

Alanine, Ala, A (6.0)

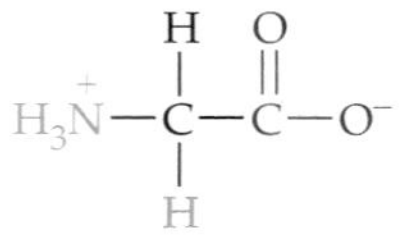

Glycine, Gly, G (6.0)

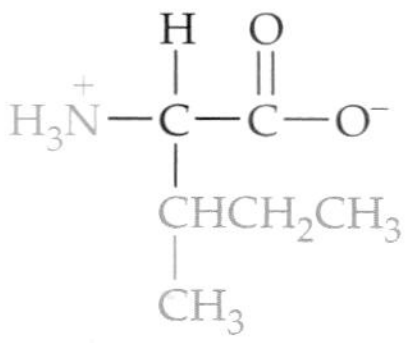

Isoleucine, Ile, I (6.0)

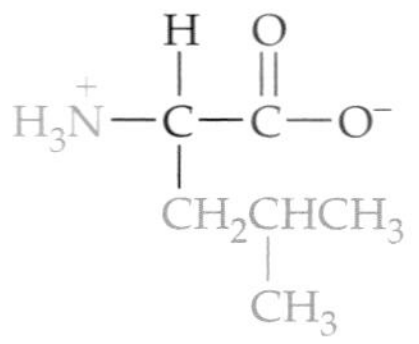

Leucine, Leu, L (6.0)

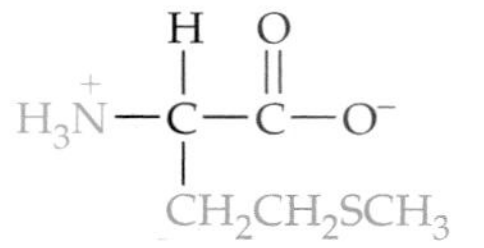

Methionine, Met, M (5.7)

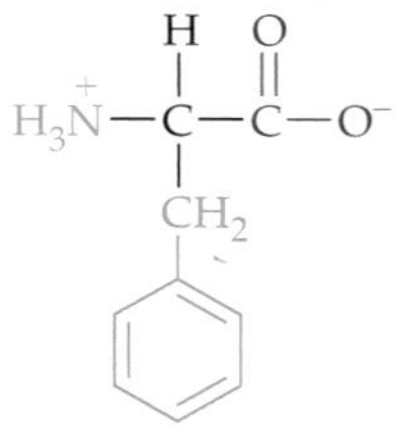

Phenylalanine, Phe, F (5.5)

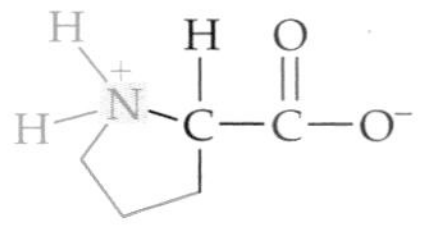

Proline, Pro, P (6.3)

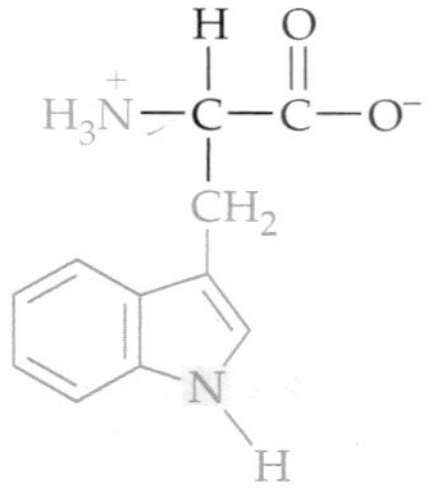

Tryptophan, Trp, W (5.9)

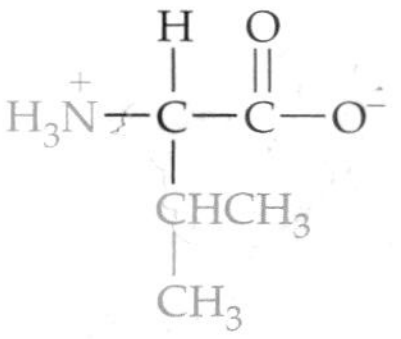

Valine, Val, V (6.0)

Polar, Neutral Side Chains

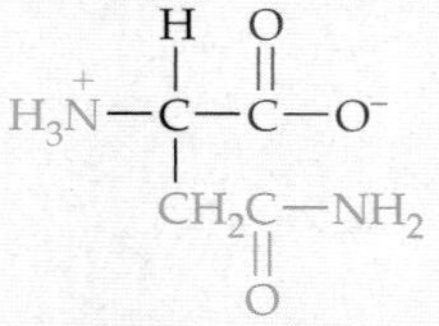

Asparagine, Asn, N (5.4)

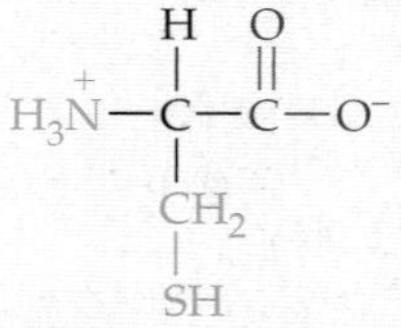

Cysteine, Cys, C (5.0)

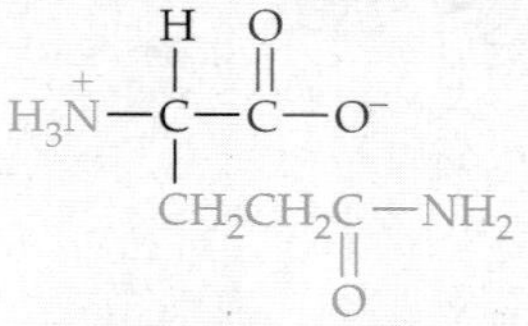

Glutamine, Gln, Q (5.7)

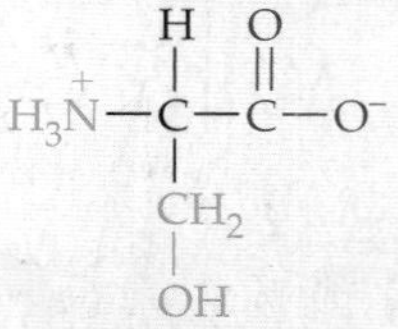

Serine, Ser, S (5.7)

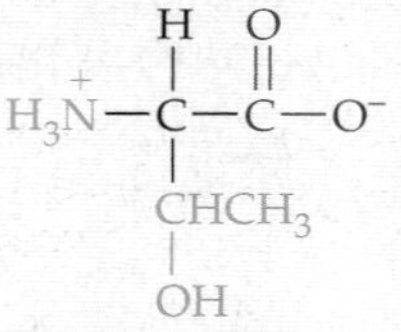

Threonine, Thr, T (5.6)

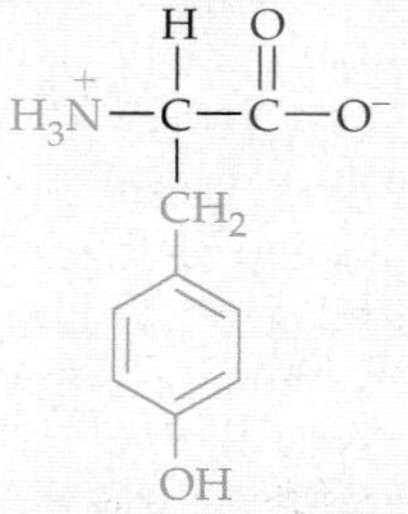

Tyrosine, Tyr, Y (5.7)

Acidic Side Chains

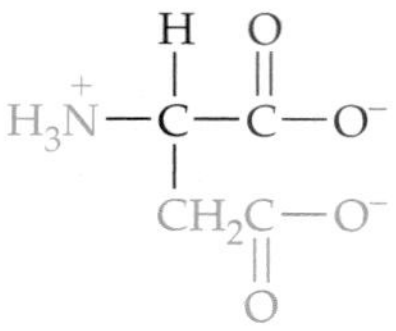

Aspartic acid, Asp, D (3.0)
(Aspartate)

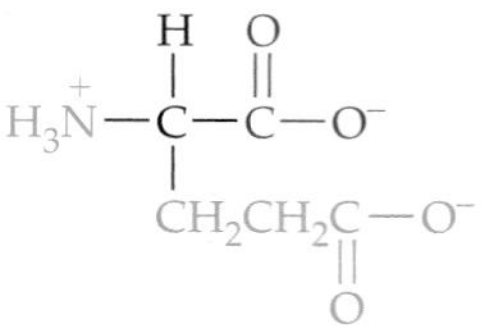

Glutamic acid, Glu, E (3.2)
(Glutamate)

Basic Side Chains

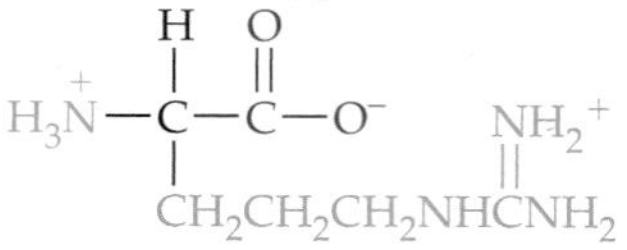

Arginine, Arg, R (10.8)

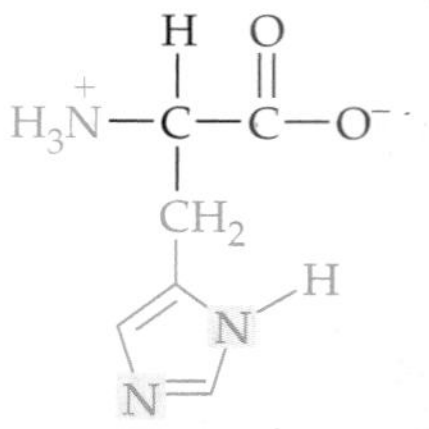

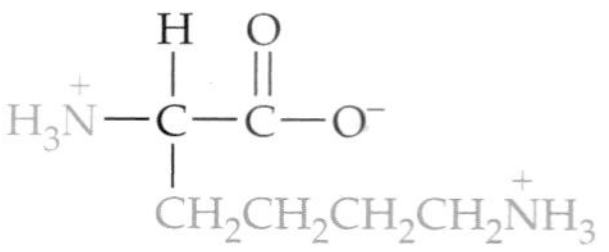

Lysine, Lys, K (9.7)

Histidine, His, H (7.6)

PROBLEM 18.5

Indicate whether each of the following molecules is an α-amino acid or not, and explain why.

(a) 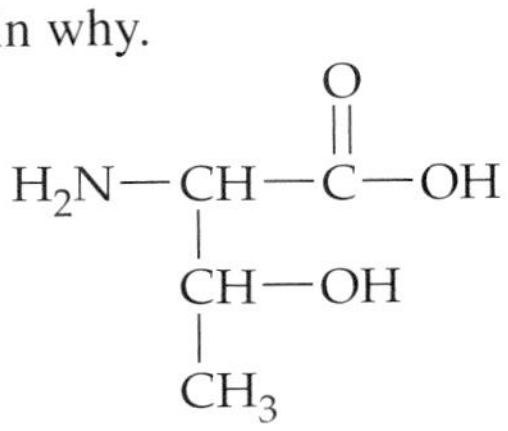 $H_2N-CH-C(=O)-OH$, with $CH-OH$ and CH_3 below

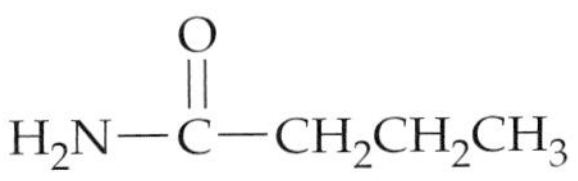

(b) $H_2N-C(=O)-CH_2CH_2CH_3$

(c) $CH_3CH_2CH-CH_2-NH_2$, with OH below

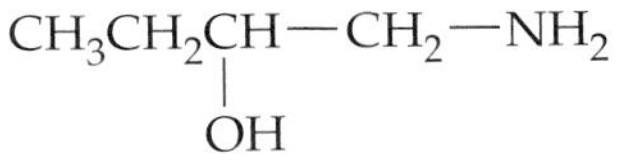

(d) 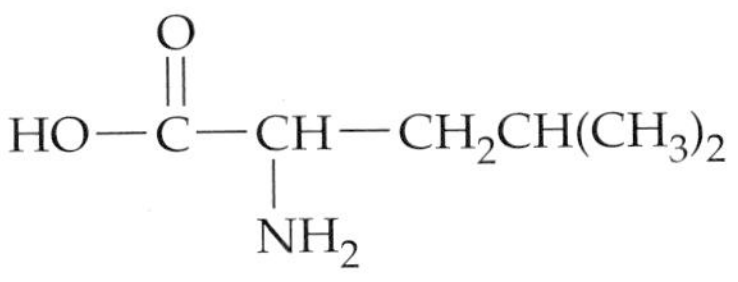 $HO-C(=O)-CH-CH_2CH(CH_3)_2$, with NH_2 below

PROBLEM 18.6

Using Table 18.3, name the α-amino acids that (a) contain an aromatic ring, (b) contain sulfur, (c) are alcohols, and (d) have alkyl-group side chains.

Side-Chain Polarity and Water Interactions

The 20 α-amino acids that make up proteins are classified as neutral, acidic, or basic, depending on the nature of their side chains. The 15 neutral amino acids are further divided into groups with nonpolar or polar side chains, which can be seen in Table 18.3. The neutral side chains contain alkyl groups that do not ionize to carry a positive or negative charge. Those with nonpolar side chains, such as leucine, contain only alkyl side chains. Several amino acids have polar side chains that do not ionize and are classed as neutral, polar. Serine is an example of this group; serine's side chain contains a hydroxyl group, which is polar. Two amino acids have side chains that contain the carboxylic acid functional group and can lose H^+, functioning as an acid; these are referred to as acidic amino acids. Three amino acids have an amine functional group in the side chain; the amine group can gain H^+ atoms, acting as a base. These are referred to as basic amino acids. As we explore the structure and function of proteins, you will see that it is the sequence of amino acids in a protein and the chemical nature of their side chains that enable proteins to perform their varied functions.

Intermolecular forces are of central importance in determining interactions between amino acids. In the context of biochemistry, it is more meaningful to refer to all interactions other than covalent bonding as **noncovalent forces.** The intermolecular forces present between amino acids or between protein chains are hydrogen bonding, Van der Waals forces, ionic bonding, and disulfide bonds.

The nonpolar side chains are **hydrophobic** ("water-fearing")—they are *not* attracted to water molecules and are not soluble in water. The polar, acidic, and basic side chains are **hydrophilic** ("water-loving"), polar side chains that *are* attracted to polar water molecules and are soluble in water.

◄◄◄ **CONCEPTS TO REVIEW** The various types of intermolecular forces were introduced in Section 8.2. Review water interactions with other molecules in Section 9.2.

Noncovalent forces Forces of attraction other than covalent bonds that can act between molecules or within molecules.

Hydrophobic "Water-fearing;" a hydrophobic substance does not dissolve in water.

Hydrophilic "Water-loving;" a hydrophilic substance dissolves in water.

Worked Example 18.1 Determining Side-Chain Hydrophobicity/Hydrophilicity

Consider the structures of phenylalanine and serine in Table 18.3. Which of these two amino acids has a hydrophobic side chain and which has a hydrophilic side chain?

ANALYSIS Identify the side chains. The side chain in phenylalanine is an alkane. The side chain in serine contains a hydroxyl group.

SOLUTION
The hydrocarbon side chain in phenylalanine is an alkane, which is nonpolar and hydrophobic. Therefore phenylalanine is hydrophobic. The hydroxyl group in the side chain of serine is polar and is hydrophilic. Thus, serine is hydrophilic.

⊙ KEY CONCEPT PROBLEM 18.7 _____

Valine is an amino acid with a nonpolar side chain and serine is one with a polar side chain. Draw the two amino acids.

(a) Why is the side chain for valine nonpolar, whereas the side chain for serine is polar?

(b) Which amino acid has a hydrophilic side chain and which has a hydrophobic side chain?

PROBLEM 18.8

Which amino acid is hydrophilic (dissolves in aqueous solutions)? Why?

(a) isoleucine   (b) phenylalanine   (c) aspartic acid

PROBLEM 18.9

Which amino acid is hydrophobic (does not dissolve in aqueous solutions)? Why?

(a) glutamic acid   (b) tryptophan   (c) arginine

Chirality of Amino Acids

◀◀ Review chirality in Section 14.10.

Of the 20 common amino acids, 19 are chiral. Only glycine is achiral. Even though the 19 chiral α-amino acids can exist either as D- or L-enantiomers, nature selectively uses only L-amino acids for making proteins. As shown next, alanine and glycine provide a visual comparison between chiral and achiral amino acids.

Alanine, a chiral molecule   *Glycine, an achiral molecule*

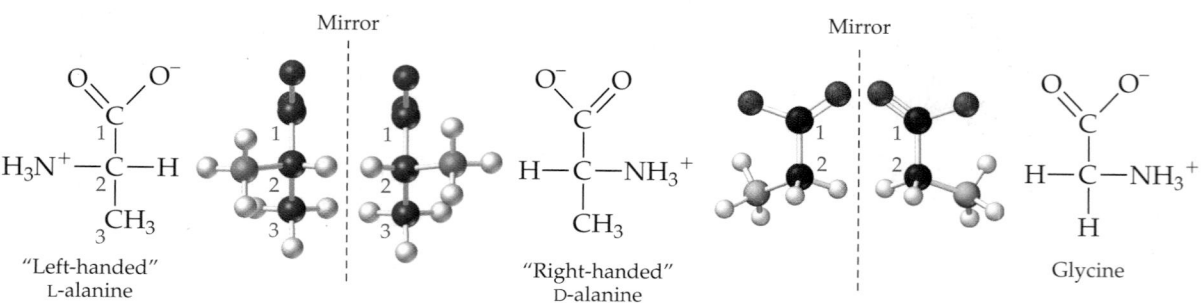

"Left-handed"   "Right-handed"   Glycine
L-alanine   D-alanine

▶▶ Amino acids, as you have seen, are chiral. Chirality is an important property of another major class of biomolecules. The individual sugar units in all carbohydrates are chiral, a topic addressed in Section 20.2.

Because alanine is a chiral molecule, its mirror images cannot be superimposed. As a result, alanine exists in two forms that are mirror images of each other: a "right-handed" form known as D-alanine and a "left-handed" form known as L-alanine. Glycine, by contrast, is an achiral molecule. The molecule and its mirror image are identical, and it has no left- and right-handed isomers. A molecule needs only one chiral carbon atom to be chiral.

PROBLEM 18.10

Is serine chiral? Draw serine and identify the chiral atom. Explain why serine is chiral.

PROBLEM 18.11

Draw the mirror images of serine. Identify the D-form and the L-form.

PROBLEM 18.12

Two of the 20 common amino acids have two chiral carbon atoms in their structures. Identify these amino acids and their chiral carbon atoms.

18.4 Acid-Base Properties of Amino Acids

Learning Objective:

- Draw all ionic structures for an amino acid under acidic and basic conditions, and identify the zwitterion.

Amino acids contain both an acidic group, $-COOH$ (carboxyl group), and a basic group, $-NH_2$ (amino group). As you might expect, these two groups can undergo an intramolecular acid-base reaction, a reaction within the amino acid itself. The result is a loss of the hydrogen ion from the $-COOH$ group (leaving the carboxylate anion, $-COO^-$) and a gain of a hydrogen ion to the $-NH_2$ group (forming $-NH_3{}^+$, the ammonium ion). This H^+ transfer within the amino acid forms a *dipolar* ion, an ion that has one positive charge and one negative charge and is thus electrically neutral because the sum of the charges on the molecule is zero. Dipolar ions are known as **zwitterions** (from the German *zwitter*, "hybrid"). The zwitterion form of threonine is shown here; however, the α-amino acids in Table 18.3 are shown in their fully ionized forms. If the R group contains either an acidic or basic group, that group is shown as ionized in Table 18.3 and that amino acid is not in the zwitterion form. Amino acids with neutral R groups are in the zwitterion form.

Because they are zwitterions, amino acids have many of the physical properties we associate with salts. Pure amino acids can form crystals, have high melting points, and are soluble in water but not in hydrocarbon solvents.

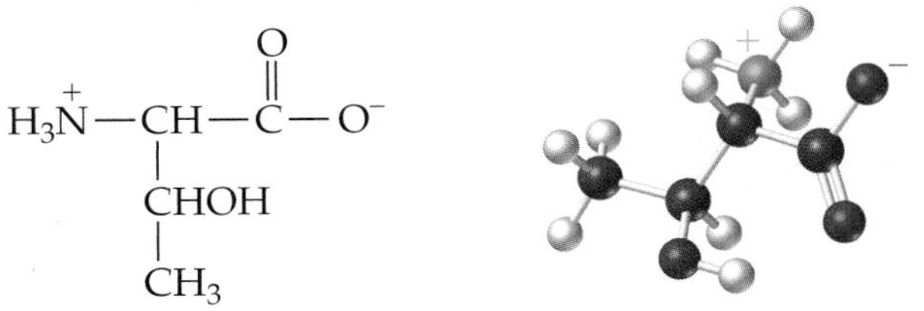

In an acidic solution (low pH), amino acids accept protons on their basic $-COO^-$ groups, to leave only the positively charged $-NH_3{}^+$ groups. In basic solution (high pH), amino acids *lose* protons from their acidic $-NH_3{}^+$ groups, to leave only the negatively charged $-COO^-$ groups.

Zwitterion A neutral dipolar ion that has one positive charge and one negative charge.

$$H_3\overset{+}{N}-CH-\overset{\displaystyle O}{\overset{\|}{C}}-O^-$$
$$|$$
$$CHOH$$
$$|$$
$$CH_3$$

Threonine—zwitterion

◀◀ Review the properties of ionic compounds introduced in Section 3.10. Review properties of acids and bases introduced in Chapter 10.

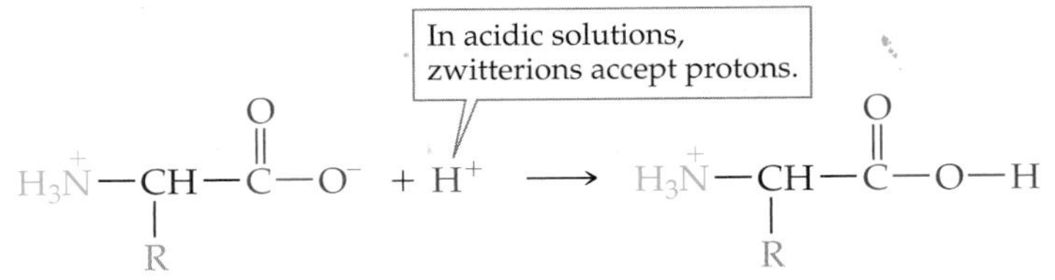

In acidic solutions, zwitterions accept protons.

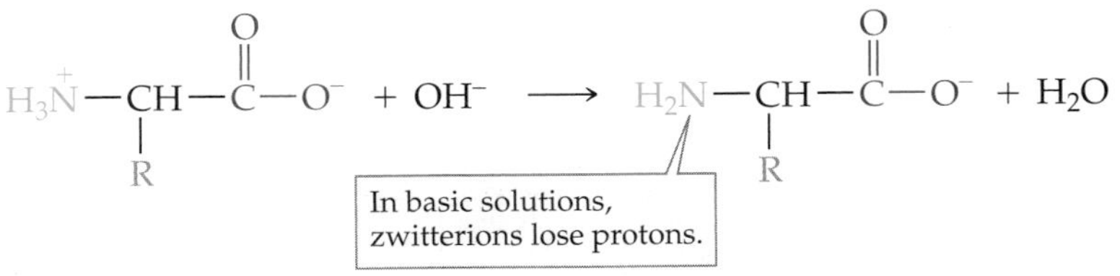

$$H_3\overset{+}{N}-CH-\overset{\displaystyle O}{\overset{\|}{C}}-O^- \ + \ H^+ \ \longrightarrow \ H_3\overset{+}{N}-CH-\overset{\displaystyle O}{\overset{\|}{C}}-O-H$$
$$\qquad\quad | \qquad\qquad\qquad\qquad\qquad\qquad\quad |$$
$$\qquad\quad R \qquad\qquad\qquad\qquad\qquad\qquad\quad R$$

$$H_3\overset{+}{N}-CH-\overset{\displaystyle O}{\overset{\|}{C}}-O^- \ + \ OH^- \ \longrightarrow \ H_2N-CH-\overset{\displaystyle O}{\overset{\|}{C}}-O^- \ + \ H_2O$$
$$\qquad\quad | \qquad\qquad\qquad\qquad\qquad\qquad\qquad |$$
$$\qquad\quad R \qquad\qquad\qquad\qquad\qquad\qquad\qquad R$$

In basic solutions, zwitterions lose protons.

Amino acids are present in the ionized form in both the solid state and in aqueous solution. The charge of an amino acid molecule at any given moment depends on the particular amino acid and the pH of the solution. The pH at which the net positive and negative charges are evenly balanced to form an electrically neutral molecule is the **isoelectric point (pI)** for that particular amino acid. At this point, the net charge of all the molecules of that amino acid in a pure sample is zero. The pI for each amino acid is different, due to the influence of the side-chain functional groups and can be found in parentheses next to the amino acid in Table 18.3. This electrically neutral molecule is the zwitterion form.

A few amino acids have isoelectric points that are not near neutrality (pH 7). For example, the two amino acids with acidic side chains, aspartic acid and glutamic acid, have isoelectric points at more acidic (lower) pH values than those with neutral side

Isoelectric point (pI) The pH at which a sample of an amino acid has equal numbers of positive and negative charges.

chains. Since the side-chain —COOH groups of these compounds are substantially ionized at physiological pH of 7.4, these amino acids are usually referred to as *aspartate* and *glutamate*, the names of the anions formed when the —COOH groups in the side chains are ionized. (Recall that the same convention is used, for example, for sulfate ion from sulfuric acid or nitrate ion from nitric acid; see Table 3.3.)

Side-chain interactions are important in stabilizing protein structure; thus, it is important to be aware of their charges at physiological pH (pH 7.4). Furthermore, pI influences protein solubility and determines which amino acids in an enzyme participate directly in enzymatic reactions. The acidic and basic side chains are particularly important because at physiological pH these groups are fully charged and can participate not only in ionic bonds within a protein chain but can also transfer H^+ from one molecule to another during reactions, as we will see in Chapter 19.

CHEMISTRY IN ACTION

⚕ Protein Analysis by Electrophoresis

Protein molecules in solution can be separated from each other by taking advantage of their net charges. In the electric field between two electrodes, a positively charged particle moves toward the negative electrode and a negatively charged particle moves toward the positive electrode. This movement, known as *electrophoresis*, varies with the strength of the electric field, the charge of the particle, the size and shape of the particle, and the buffer/polymer gel combination through which the protein is moving.

The net charge on a protein is determined by how many of the acidic or basic side-chain functional groups in the protein are ionized, and this, like the charge of an amino acid, depends on the pH. Thus, the mobility of a protein during electrophoresis depends on the pH of the buffer. If the buffer is at a pH equal to the isoelectric point of the protein, the protein does not move.

By varying the pH of the buffer between the electrodes and other conditions, proteins can be separated in a variety of ways, including by their molecular weight. Once the separation is complete, the various proteins are made visible by the addition of a dye.

Electrophoresis is routinely used in the clinical laboratory for determining which proteins are present, and in what amounts, in a blood sample. One commonly used test is for the diagnosis of sickle-cell anemia (p. 568). Normal adult hemoglobin (HbA) and hemoglobin showing the inherited sickle-cell trait (HbS) differ in their net charges. Therefore, HbA and HbS move different distances during electrophoresis. The accompanying diagram compares the results of electrophoresis of the hemoglobin extracted from red blood cells for a normal individual, one with sickle-cell anemia (two inherited sickle-cell genes) and one with sickle-cell trait (one normal and one inherited sickle-cell gene). With sickle-cell trait, an individual is likely to suffer symptoms of the disease only under conditions of severe oxygen deprivation.

CIA Problem 18.1 The proteins collagen, bovine insulin, and human hemoglobin have isoelectric points of 6.6, 5.4, and 7.1, respectively. Suppose a sample containing

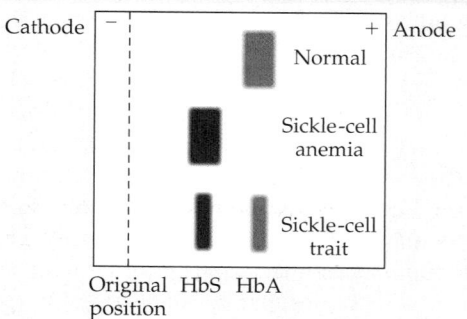

▲ **Gel electrophoresis of hemoglobin.** Hemoglobin in samples placed at the original position in a porous polymer gel immersed in a constant pH buffer has moved left to right during electrophoresis. The normal individual has only HbA. The individual with sickle-cell anemia has no HbA, and the individual with sickle-cell trait has roughly equal amounts of HbA and HbS. HbA and HbS have negative charges of different magnitudes because HbS has two fewer Glu residues than HbA.

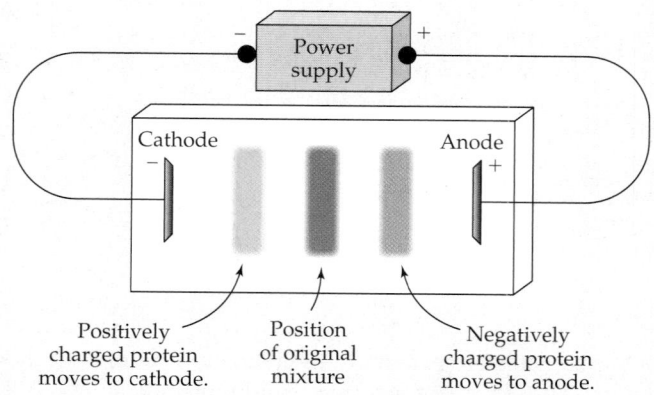

▲ Movement of charged molecules in electrophoresis.

these proteins is subjected to electrophoresis in a buffer at pH 6.6. Describe the motion of each with respect to the positive and negative electrodes in the electrophoresis apparatus.

CIA Problem 18.2 Three dipeptides are separated by electrophoresis at pH 5.8. If the dipeptides are Arg-Trp, Asp-Thr, and Val-Met, describe the motion of each with respect to the positive and negative electrodes in the electrophoresis apparatus.

Worked Example 18.2 Drawing Zwitterion Forms

Look up the zwitterion form of valine in Table 18.3. Draw valine as it would be found (a) at low pH (acidic conditions) and (b) at high pH (basic conditions).

ANALYSIS At low pH, which is acidic, basic groups may gain H$^+$. At high pH, which is basic, acidic groups may lose H$^+$. In the zwitterion form of an amino acid, the —COO$^-$ group is basic and the —NH$_3$$^+$ is acidic.

SOLUTION
Valine has an alkyl-group side chain that is unaffected by pH. At low pH, valine adds a hydrogen ion to its carboxyl group to give the structure on the left. At high pH, valine loses a hydrogen ion from its acidic —NH$_3$$^+$ group to give the structure on the right.

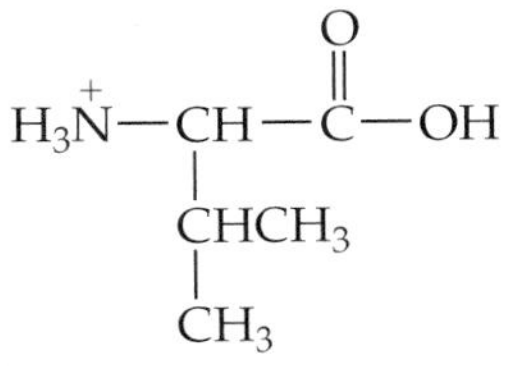

Low (acidic) pH 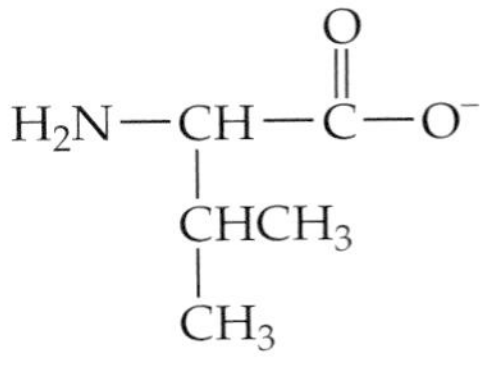   High (basic) pH

PROBLEM 18.13

Draw the structure of glutamic acid at low pH, at high pH, and at the two forms that exist between low pH and high pH. Which of these structures represents the zwitterion?

PROBLEM 18.14

Use the definitions of acids and bases as proton donors and proton acceptors to explain which functional group in the zwitterion form of an amino acid is an acid and which is a base (see Section 10.3).

18.5 Peptides

Learning Objectives:

- Identify a peptide bond, and explain how it is formed.
- Draw and name a simple protein structure given its amino acid sequence.
- Identify the amino-terminal end and the carboxyl-terminal end of a simple protein (peptide) structure given its amino acid sequence.

Two or more amino acids can link together by forming amide bonds, which are known as **peptide bonds** when they occur in proteins. A *dipeptide* results from the formation of a peptide bond between the —NH$_2$ group of one amino acid and the —COOH group of a second amino acid. When this link is formed, an H$^+$ is released from the amino group of one amino acid and an —OH$^-$ group is released from the other amino acid. The H$^+$ and —OH$^-$ combine to form HOH, water. For example, valine and cysteine are connected in a dipeptide as follows:

Peptide bond An amide bond that links two amino acids together.

◀◀ Review amide bonds in Section 17.3.

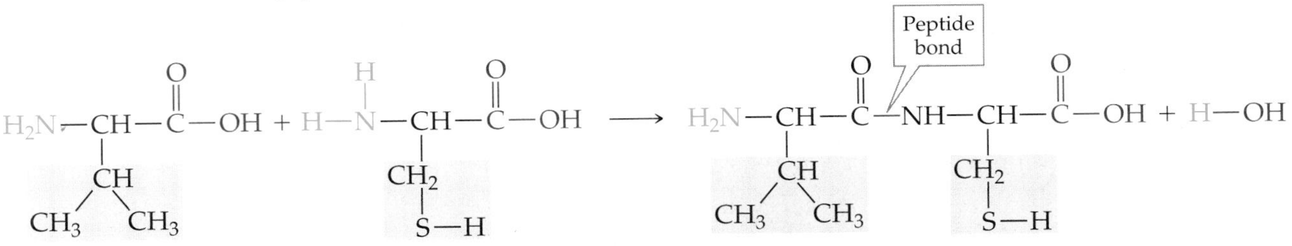

Valine   Cysteine   A dipeptide

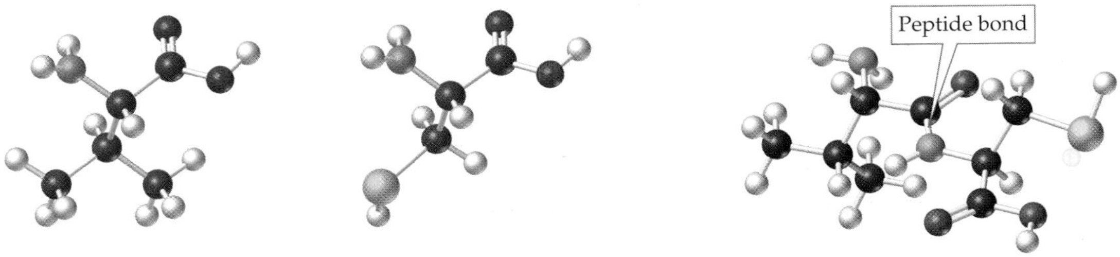

Peptide bond

A *tripeptide* results from the linkage of three amino acids via two peptide bonds. Any number of amino acids can link together to form a linear chainlike polymer—a *polypeptide.* Very large peptides (oligopeptides) contain hundreds of amino acids and are referred to as proteins. Proteins have four levels of structure, each of which is explored later in this chapter.

The exact sequence of amino acids in a peptide or protein chain is important; variation in the sequence indicates a different molecule. A pair of amino acids—for example, alanine and serine—can be combined to form two different dipeptides. The —COOH in alanine can react with the $—NH_2$ in serine as follows:

Alanine (Ala, A) Serine (Ser, S) Alanylserine (Ala-Ser, AS)

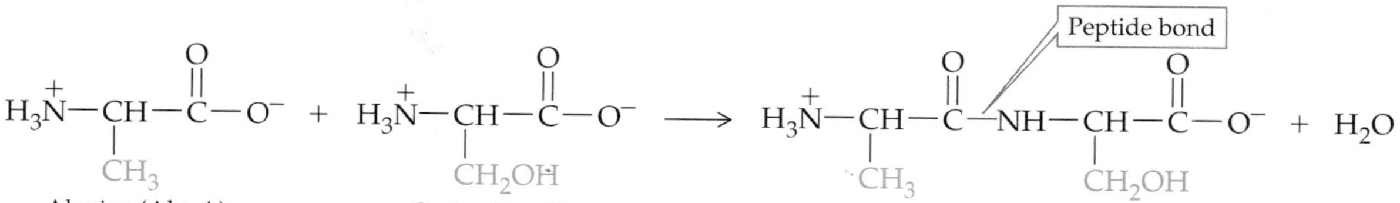

Or the —COOH in serine can react with $—NH_2$ in alanine as follows:

Serine (Ser, S) Alanine (Ala, A) Serylalanine (Ser-Ala, SA)

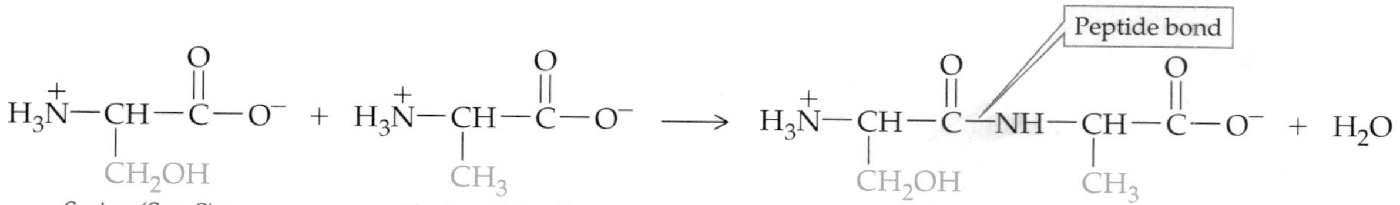

Amino-terminal (N-terminal) amino acid The amino acid with the free $—NH_3^+$ group at the end of a protein.

Carboxyl-terminal (C-terminal) amino acid The amino acid with the free $—COO^-$ group at the end of a protein.

Residue An amino acid unit in a polypeptide.

By convention, peptides and proteins are always written with the **amino-terminal amino acid** (also called N-terminal amino acid, the one with the free $—NH_3^+$) on the left and the **carboxyl-terminal amino acid** (also called the C-terminal amino acid, the one with the free $—COO^-$ group) on the right. The individual amino acids joined in the chain are referred to as **residues.**

A peptide is named by citing the amino acid residues in order, starting at the N-terminal amino acid and ending with the C-terminal amino acid. All residue names except the C-terminal one have the *-yl* ending instead of *-ine,* as in alanylserine (abbreviated Ala-Ser) or serylalanine (Ser-Ala). The one-letter name would be AS.

Worked Example 18.3 Drawing Dipeptides

Draw the structure of the dipeptide Ala-Gly.

ANALYSIS You need the names and structures of the two amino acids. Since alanine is named first, it is the N-terminal amino acid and glycine is the C-terminal amino acid. Ala-Gly must have a peptide bond between the $—COO^-$ on alanine and the $—NH_3^-$ on glycine.

SOLUTION

The structures of alanine and glycine, and the structure of the Ala-Gly dipeptide are as follows:

Alanine (Ala, A) Glycine (Gly, G) Ala-Gly (AG)

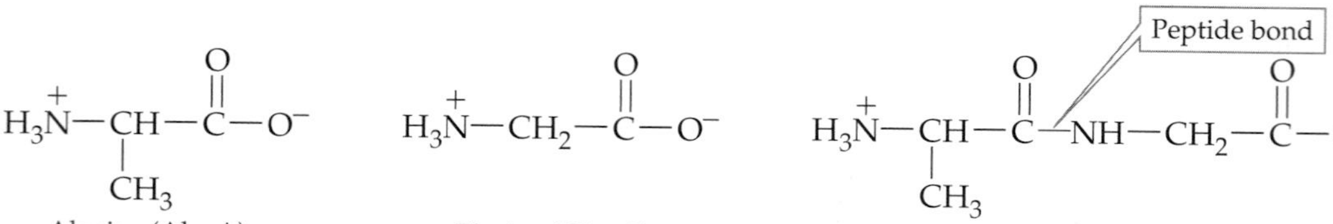

HANDS-ON CHEMISTRY 18.1

Models of Amino Acids

Use either a molecular model kit or buy a package of small marshmallows and some toothpicks. Build alanine, glycine, and alanylglycine. Identify the chiral carbon atoms, the carboxyl groups, the amino groups, and the peptide bonds. What atoms were eliminated to form the peptide bond? What molecule do these atoms form?

PROBLEM 18.15

Valine is an amino acid with a nonpolar side chain, and serine is an amino acid with a polar side chain. Draw the two dipeptides that can be formed by these two amino acids. Identify the peptide bond.

PROBLEM 18.16

Tripeptides are composed of three amino acids linked by peptide bonds. Given a set of amino acids, you can make several different tripeptides.

(a) Use the three-letter shorthand notations to name all the tripeptides that can be made from serine, tyrosine, and glycine. Each amino acid will be used once in each tripeptide.
(b) Draw the complete structure of the tripeptides that have glycine as the N-terminal amino acid.

PROBLEM 18.17

Using three-letter abbreviations, show the six tripeptides that contain isoleucine, arginine, and valine.

◘ KEY CONCEPT PROBLEM 18.18 ────────────────────

Identify the amino acids in the following dipeptide and tripeptide, and write the abbreviated forms of the peptide names. Copy the dipeptides, draw a box around the peptide bonds, and use an arrow to identify the α-carbon atoms. Draw a circle around the R groups, and indicate if the R groups are neutral, polar, acidic, or basic.

(a) 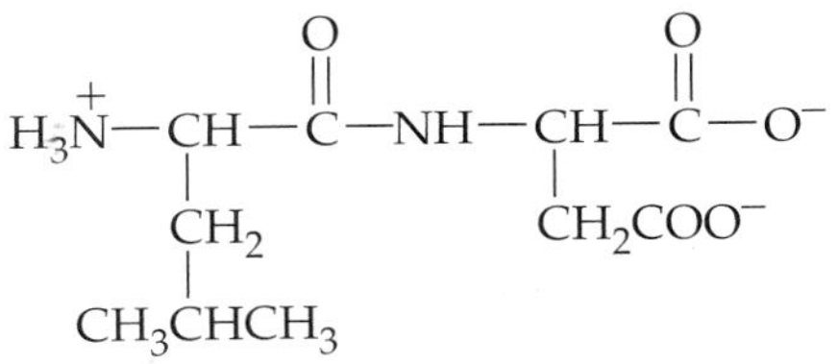 $H_3\overset{+}{N}-CH-\overset{O}{\overset{\|}{C}}-NH-CH-\overset{O}{\overset{\|}{C}}-O^-$
      with CH_2 / CH_3CHCH_3 below first CH, and CH_2COO^- below second CH

(b) 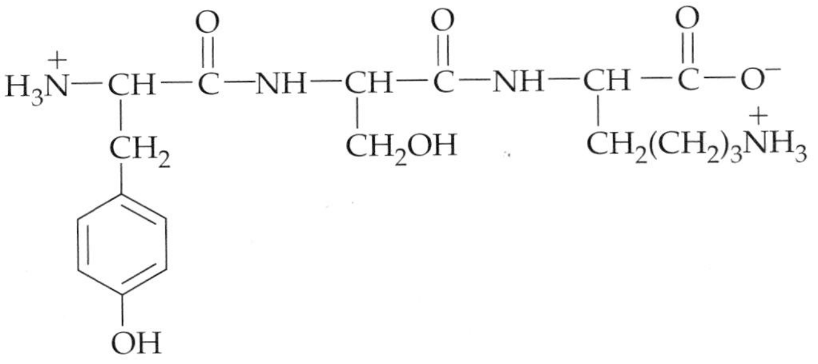 $H_3\overset{+}{N}-CH-\overset{O}{\overset{\|}{C}}-NH-CH-\overset{O}{\overset{\|}{C}}-NH-CH-\overset{O}{\overset{\|}{C}}-O^-$
      with CH_2 / benzene ring with OH below first CH, CH_2OH below second CH, $CH_2(CH_2)_3\overset{+}{N}H_3$ below third CH

PROBLEM 18.19

There are eight amino acids in vasopressin. How many peptide bonds are in this small protein?

CHEMISTRY IN ACTION

Proteins in the Diet

Proteins are a necessary part of the daily diet because our bodies do not store proteins like they do carbohydrates and fats. Children need large amounts of protein for proper growth, and adults need protein to replace what is lost each day by normal biochemical reactions. Furthermore, 9 of the 20 amino acids cannot be synthesized by adult humans and must be obtained in the diet. These are known as the *essential amino acids* (histidine, isoleucine, leucine, lysine, methionine, phenylalanine, threonine, tryptophan, and valine).

▲ This traditional Mexican meal contains a complementary protein food combination: beans and rice.

The total recommended daily amount of protein for an adult, which is the *minimum* required for good health, is 0.8 g per kilogram of body weight. The average protein intake in the United States is about 110 g/day, well above what most of us need.

Not all foods are equally good sources of protein. A *complete* protein source provides each of the nine essential amino acids in sufficient amounts to meet our minimum daily needs. Most meat and dairy products meet this requirement, but many vegetable sources such as wheat and corn do not.

Vegetarians must be careful to adopt a diet that includes all of the essential amino acids, which means consuming a variety of foods. In some regions of the world, food combinations that automatically provide *complementary* proteins (proteins that together supply all of the essential amino acids) are traditional, such as rice and lentils in India, corn tortillas and beans in Mexico, and rice and black-eyed peas in the southern United States. Grains are low in lysine and threonine but contain methionine and tryptophan. In contrast, legumes (lentils, beans, and peas) supply lysine and threonine but are low in methionine and tryptophan. Thus, the two sources of protein complement each other.

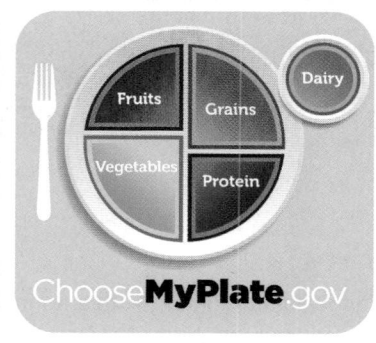

When protein intake is inadequate, during starvation, a number of pathologic conditions including malignancies, malabsorption syndromes (such as celiac disease, an autoimmune disease caused by the protein gluten), and kidney disease occur. Health and nutrition professionals group all disorders caused by inadequate protein intake as *protein-energy malnutrition* (PEM). Children, because of their higher protein needs, suffer most from this kind of malnutrition. The problem is rampant where meat and milk are in short supply and where the dietary staples are vegetables or grains. An individual is malnourished to some degree if *any* of the essential amino acids is deficient in their diet. Protein deficiency alone is rare, however, and its symptoms are usually accompanied by those of vitamin deficiencies, infectious diseases, and starvation.

As a guide to a healthy diet, the U.S. Department of Agriculture has released a guide to healthy eating called MyPlate. As shown in the figure, half of the plate is filled with vegetables and fruits, while the other half is allotted for protein and carbohydrates. Additionally, a small side portion is allowed for dairy. The goal is to aid the public in understanding the role of each nutrient in the diet. Additional online resources exist to augment the visual information in MyPlate and can be found at http://www.choosemyplate.gov.

CIA Problem 18.3 Why is it more important to have a daily source of protein than a daily source of fat or carbohydrates?

CIA Problem 18.4 What is an incomplete protein?

CIA Problem 18.5 Two of the most complete (balanced) proteins (i.e., proteins that have the best ratio of the amino acids for humans) are cow's milk protein (casein) and egg-white protein. Explain why (not surprisingly) these are very balanced proteins for human growth and development.

18.6 Protein Structure: An Overview and Primary Protein Structure (1°)

Learning Objectives:

- Define primary protein structure and explain how primary structures are represented.
- Describe the planar sections of the primary sequence, their influence on the shape of the protein backbone, and identify these sections given a drawing of the primary sequence.
- Give an example of how the change in primary sequence can change the function of a protein.

The **primary protein structure** (1°) of a protein is the sequence in which its amino acids are lined up and connected by peptide bonds. Along the *backbone* of the protein is a chain of alternating peptide bonds and α-carbon atoms. The amino acid side chains (R_1, R_2) are substituents along the backbone, where they are bonded to the α-carbon atoms. Note the positions of the hydrogen atoms bonded to the amino nitrogen atom, the R groups, and the carbonyl oxygen atom. These specific orientations contribute to secondary structure, which is discussed in the next section of this chapter.

Primary protein structure The sequence in which amino acids are linked by peptide bonds in a protein.

The carbon and nitrogen atoms along the backbone lie in a zigzag arrangement, with tetrahedral bonding around the α-carbon atoms. The electrons of each carbonyl-group double bond are shared with the adjacent C—N bond. This electron sharing is called delocalization, which you saw in the benzene molecule in Section 13.8. Sharing electrons from C=O makes the C—N bond similar to a double bond in that there is no rotation around it. The result is that the carbonyl group, the —NH group bonded to it, and the two adjacent α-carbons form a rigid, planar unit, as shown in the margin. The side-chain groups on the two α-carbons extend out to opposite sides of the plane. A long polymer chain forms a connected series of these planar peptide units, and the backbone NCC repeat is a zigzag form.

◀◀ Review the properties of carbon—oxygen double bonds in Section 13.4.

Planar units along a protein chain

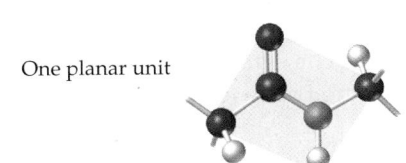

One planar unit

The primary structure of a protein consists of the amino acids being lined up one by one to form peptide bonds in precisely the correct order for a specific protein. The number of arrangements for a set of amino acids can be calculated. If you have n amino acids, where n is an integer, then the number of arrangements are n factorial, represented as n! mathematically. For example, if n = 3, then n! = 3! and 3! = 3 × 2 × 1 = 6. Therefore, there are six ways in which three different amino acids can be joined, more than 40,000 ways in which eight amino acids can be joined, and more than 360,000 ways in which 10 amino acids can be joined. However, the equation predicts the total number of combinations only if each amino acid is represented once. Despite the rapid increase in possible combinations as the number of amino acid residues present increases, the function of a protein depends on the precise order of amino acids, and only the correct peptide can do the job. For example, human *angiotensin II* must have its eight amino acids arranged in exactly the correct order.

Asp (D)   Arg (R)   Val (V)   Tyr (Y)   Ile (I)   His (H)   Pro (P)   Phe (F)

CHEMISTRY IN ACTION

✝ What Is Sickle-Cell Anemia?

Sickle-cell anemia is a hereditary disease caused by a genetic difference that replaces one amino acid (glutamate, Glu) with another (valine, Val) in each of two polypeptide chains of the hemoglobin molecule resulting in a modified hemoglobin molecule. Affected red blood cells distort into a curved, sickle-like shape giving the disease its name. The change replaces a hydrophilic, carboxylic acid–containing side chain (Glu) in normal hemoglobin with a hydrophobic, neutral hydrocarbon side chain (Val) altering the shape of the hemoglobin molecule. (The effect of this change on the charge of hemoglobin is illustrated in the Chemistry in Action "Protein Analysis by Electrophoresis," p. 562.) Instead of hemoglobin retaining the normal soluble (globular) form both while carrying and after releasing oxygen, it forms fibrous chains after releasing oxygen due to the ability of modified hemoglobin molecules to associate in a "hooked" fashion as a result of the amino acid change in the primary structure. These associations of hemoglobin molecules in stiff, fibrous chains deform the red blood cells, causing the disease symptoms.

Sickled red blood cells are fragile and inflexible, blocking capillaries, causing inflammation and pain, and possibly restricting blood flow in a manner that damages major organs. Also, they have a shorter lifespan than normal red blood cells, causing afflicted individuals to become severely anemic.

Sickle-cell anemia arises by inheriting two defective copies of the hemoglobin gene, one from each parent. If a person has one functional gene and one defective gene, he or she is said to carry the sickle-cell trait but does not have sickle-cell anemia. The percentage of individuals carrying the genetic trait for sickle-cell anemia is highest among ethnic groups

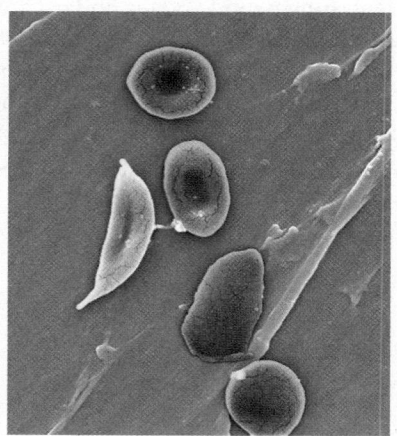

▲ Four normal (convex) red blood cells and one sickled red blood cell. Because of their shape, sickled cells tend to clog blood vessels.

originating in tropical regions where malaria is prevalent. The ancestors of these individuals survived because malaria infections were not fatal. Malaria-causing parasites enter red blood cells and reproduce there. In a person with the sickle-cell trait, the cells respond by sickling and the parasites cannot multiply. As a result, the genetic trait for sickle-cell anemia is carried forward in the surviving population. Those who carry sickle-cell trait are generally healthy and lead normal lives; those who have sickle-cell anemia have multiple health problems.

CIA Problem 18.6 Describe the symptoms of sickle-cell anemia.

CIA Problem 18.7 Explain the difference between sickle-cell anemia and sickle-cell trait.

▶▶ More than any other kind of biomolecule, proteins are in control of our biochemistry. Are you wondering how each of our thousands of proteins is produced with all their amino acids lined up in the correct order? The information necessary to do this is stored in deoxyribonucleic acid (DNA), and the remarkable machinery that does the job resides in the nuclei of our cells. Chapter 26 provides the details of how protein synthesis is accomplished. In order to synthesize proteins, our cells need a constant supply of amino acid building blocks from the diet because human cells can synthesize only some of the 20 amino acids used to make proteins. Read more about diet and protein requirements in the Chemistry in Action "Proteins in the Diet," page 566.

If its amino acids are not arranged properly, this hormone will not participate as it should in regulating blood pressure.

Sometimes one or two changes in the amino acids of a peptide change the function of the peptide. For example, two hormones secreted by the pituitary gland differ in only two amino acids, as seen in the following figure, and as a result have entirely different functions in the body. Oxytocin acts on uterine smooth muscle causing contractions during labor and on mammary gland tissue to encourage milk release. With two amino acid changes, the peptide becomes vasopressin and participates in blood pressure control by regulating both water reabsorption in the kidney and blood vessel constriction.

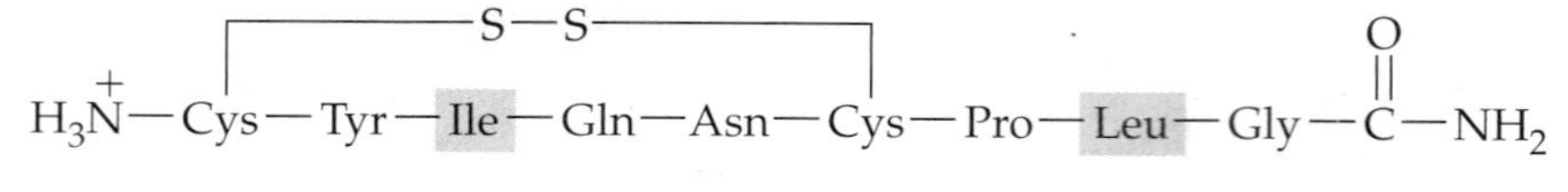

$$H_3\overset{+}{N}—Cys—Tyr—Ile—Gln—Asn—Cys—Pro—Leu—Gly—\overset{\displaystyle O}{\overset{\|}{C}}—NH_2$$

Oxytocin

$$H_3\overset{+}{N}—Cys—Tyr—Phe—Gln—Asn—Cys—Pro—Arg—Gly—\overset{\displaystyle O}{\overset{\|}{C}}—NH_2$$

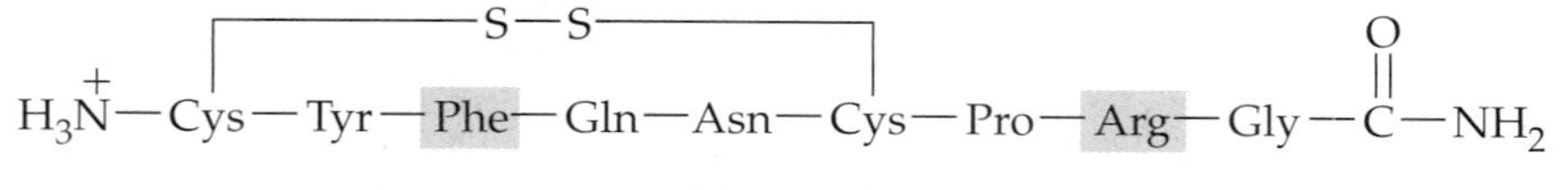

Vasopressin

So crucial is the primary structure to function—no matter how big the protein—that the change of only one amino acid can sometimes drastically alter a protein's biological properties. Sickle-cell anemia is the result of a single amino acid substitution and is discussed further in the Chemistry in Action on page 568.

PROBLEM 18.20

(a) What atoms are present in a planar unit in a protein chain?
(b) How many amino acid units do these atoms come from? Why are these units planar?

PROBLEM 18.21

How many ways can four different amino acids be arranged in a peptide so that each peptide is unique?

PROBLEM 18.22

Why is the exact order of amino acids (primary structure) in a protein important?

18.7 Secondary Protein Structure (2°)

Learning Objectives:

- Identify the α-helix and β-sheet structures and give an example of a protein that contains primarily helix and one that contains primarily sheet secondary structure.
- Describe the specific hydrogen bonding responsible for secondary structures.
- Distinguish between fibrous and globular proteins.

Without interactions between atoms in amino acid side chains or along the backbone, protein chains would twist about randomly in body fluids like spaghetti strands in boiling water. The essential structure–function relationship for each protein depends on the polypeptide chain being held in its necessary shape by various interactions. As we look at the secondary, tertiary, and quaternary structures of proteins, it will be helpful to understand the kinds of interactions that determine the shapes of protein molecules for each level of structure.

The spatial arrangement of the polypeptide backbones of proteins determines **secondary protein structure** (2°). The secondary structure includes two kinds of repeating patterns known as the *alpha-helix (α-helix)* and the *beta-sheet (β-sheet)*. In both, hydrogen bonding between *backbone* atoms holds the polypeptide chain in place and connects the carbonyl oxygen atom of one peptide unit with the amide hydrogen atom of another peptide unit ($-C=O \cdots H-N-$).

Secondary protein structure Regular and repeating structural patterns (e.g., α-helix and β-sheet) created by hydrogen bonding between backbone atoms in neighboring segments of protein chains.

Hydrogen Bonds along the Backbone

Hydrogen bonds form when a hydrogen atom bonded to a highly electronegative atom is attracted to another highly electronegative atom that has an unshared electron pair. The hydrogen atoms in the $-NH-$ (amide) groups and the oxygen atoms in the $-C=O$ (carbonyl) groups along protein backbones meet these conditions.

This type of hydrogen bonding creates both pleated sheet and helical secondary structures. Individual hydrogen bonds are weak forces, but the sum of many weak forces, as in the helical and sheet structures, is large enough to stabilize the structure.

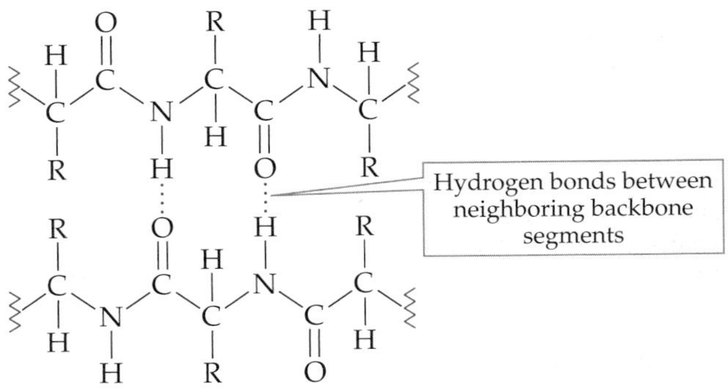

Hydrogen bonds between neighboring backbone segments

α-Helix

A single protein chain coiled in a spiral with a right-handed (clockwise) twist is known as an **alpha-helix (α-helix)** (Figure 18.1a). The helix, which resembles a coiled spring, is stabilized by hydrogen bonds between each backbone carbonyl oxygen atom and

Alpha-helix (α-helix) Secondary protein structure in which a protein chain forms a right-handed coil stabilized by hydrogen bonds between peptide groups along its backbone.

an amide hydrogen atom four amino acid residues farther along the backbone. The hydrogen bonds lie vertically along the helix, and the amino acid R groups extend to the outside of the coil. Although the strength of each individual hydrogen bond is small, the large number of bonds in the helix results in an extremely stable secondary structure. A view of the helix from the top (Figure 18.1b) clearly shows the side chains on the amino acids oriented to the exterior of the helix.

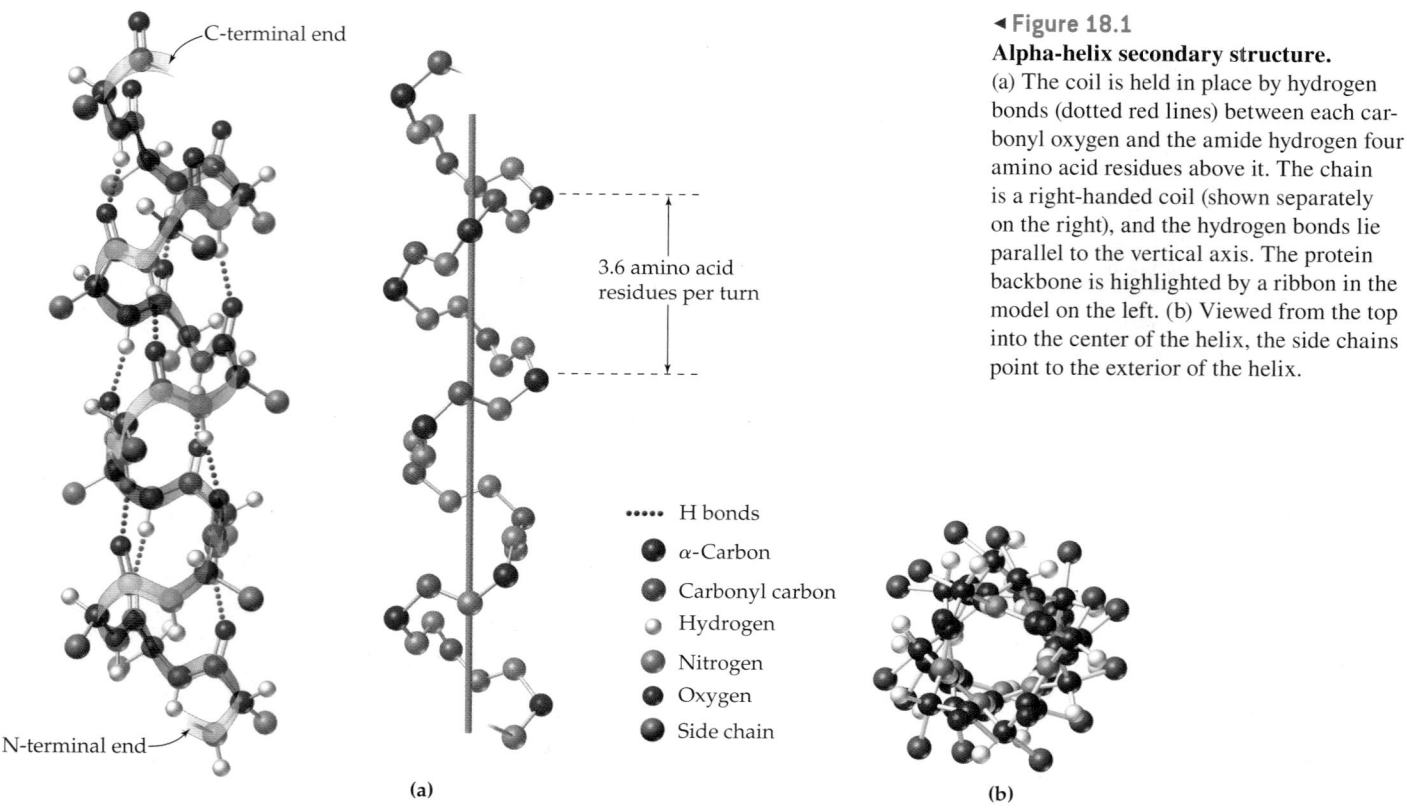

◄ **Figure 18.1**
Alpha-helix secondary structure.
(a) The coil is held in place by hydrogen bonds (dotted red lines) between each carbonyl oxygen and the amide hydrogen four amino acid residues above it. The chain is a right-handed coil (shown separately on the right), and the hydrogen bonds lie parallel to the vertical axis. The protein backbone is highlighted by a ribbon in the model on the left. (b) Viewed from the top into the center of the helix, the side chains point to the exterior of the helix.

3.6 amino acid residues per turn

⦙⦙⦙⦙ H bonds
● α-Carbon
● Carbonyl carbon
○ Hydrogen
● Nitrogen
● Oxygen
● Side chain

(a)   (b)

β-Sheet

Beta-sheet (β-sheet) Secondary protein structure in which adjacent protein chains either in the same molecule or in different molecules are held together by hydrogen bonds along the backbones, forming a flat sheet-like structure.

In the **beta-sheet (β-sheet)** structure, the polypeptide chains are held in place by hydrogen bonds between pairs of peptide units along neighboring backbone segments. The protein chains, which are extended to their full length, bend at each α-carbon so that the sheet has a pleated contour, with the R groups extending above and below the sheet (Figure 18.2).

PROBLEM 18.23

Examine the α-helix in Figure 18.1 and determine how many backbone C and N atoms are included in the loop between an amide hydrogen atom and the carbonyl oxygen to which it is hydrogen bonded.

PROBLEM 18.24

Consult the β-sheet in Figure 18.2 and (a) name the bonding responsible for the sheet formation and (b) identify the specific atoms responsible for this bonding.

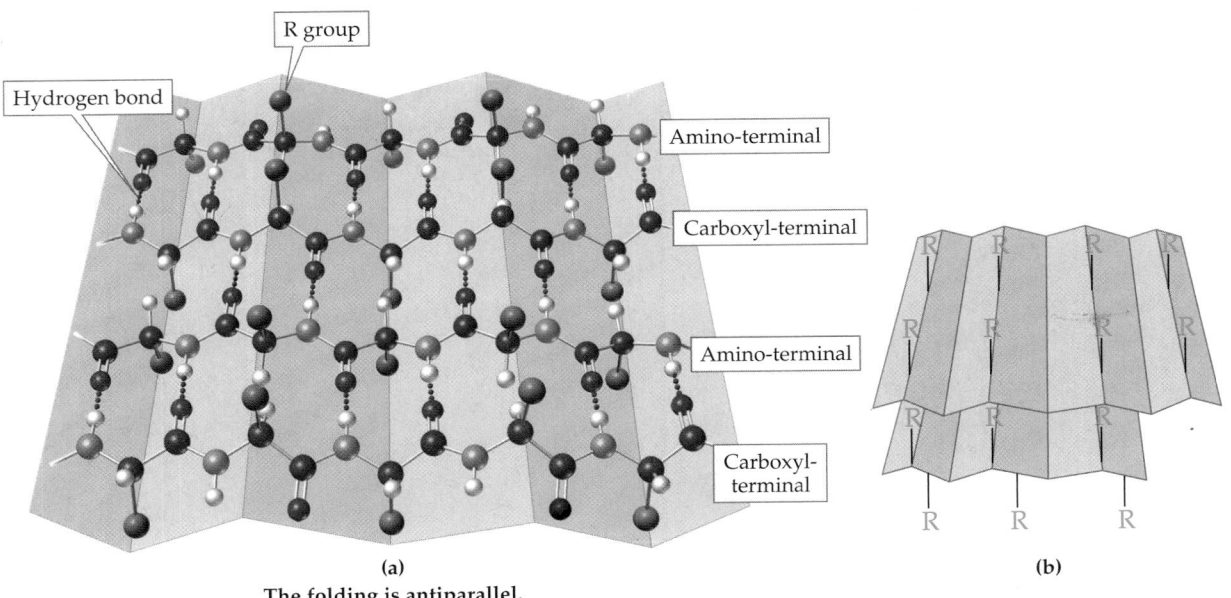

R group

Hydrogen bond

Amino-terminal

Carboxyl-terminal

Amino-terminal

Carboxyl-terminal

(a)

(b)

The folding is antiparallel.

▲ **Figure 18.2**
Beta-sheet secondary structure.
(a) The hydrogen bonds between neighboring protein chains. The protein chains usually lie side-by-side so that alternating chains run from the N-terminal end to the C-terminal end and from the C-terminal end to the N-terminal end (known as the *antiparallel* arrangement). (b) A pair of stacked pleated sheets illustrating how the R groups point above and below the sheets.

Secondary Structure in Fibrous and Globular Proteins

Proteins are classified in several ways, one of which is to identify them as either *fibrous proteins* or *globular proteins*. In an example of the integration of molecular structure and function that is central to biochemistry, fibrous and globular proteins each have functions made possible by their distinctive structures.

Secondary structure is primarily responsible for the function of **fibrous proteins**—tough, insoluble proteins in which the chains form long fibers. Wool, hair, and fingernails are made of fibrous proteins known as α-keratins, which are composed almost completely of α-helices. In α-keratins, pairs of α-helices are twisted together into small fibrils that are in turn twisted into larger and larger bundles. The hardness, flexibility, and stretchiness of the material vary with the number of disulfide bonds present. In fingernails, for example, large numbers of disulfide bonds hold the bundles in place.

Natural silk and spider webs are made of *fibroin,* another fibrous protein almost entirely composed of stacks of β-sheet. For such close stacking, the R groups must be relatively small (see Figure 18.6b). Fibroin contains regions of alternating glycine (—H on the α carbon) and alanine (—CH₃ on the α carbon). The sheets stack so that sides with the smaller glycine hydrogen atoms face each other and sides with the larger alanine methyl groups face each other.

Unlike fibrous proteins, **globular proteins** are water-soluble proteins whose chains are folded into compact, globe-like shapes. Their structures, which vary widely with their functions, are not repeating structures like those of fibrous proteins. Where the protein chain folds back on itself, sections of α-helix and β-sheet are usually present, as illustrated in Figure 18.3. The presence of hydrophilic amino acid side chains on the outer surfaces of globular proteins accounts for their water solubility, allowing them to be soluble in both intercellular and extracellular body fluids in order to perform their disparate functions. Furthermore, many globular proteins are enzymes that are dissolved in the intercellular fluids inside cells. The overall shapes

Fibrous protein A tough, insoluble protein whose protein chains form fibers or sheets.

Globular protein A water-soluble protein whose chain is folded in a compact shape with hydrophilic groups on the outside.

▲ A spider web is made from fibrous protein. The proteins found in eggs, milk, and cheese are examples of globular proteins.

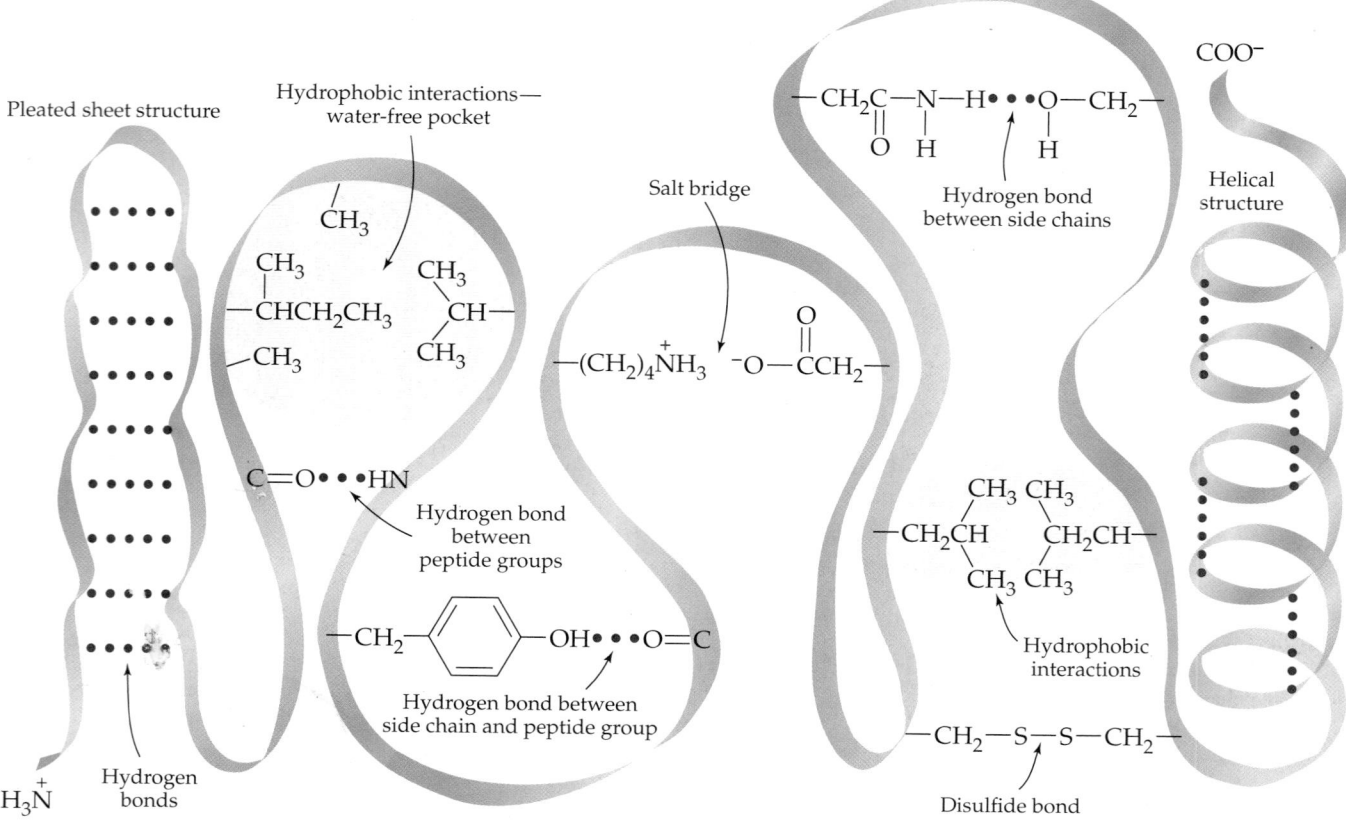

▲ **Figure 18.3**

Interactions that determine protein shape.

The regular pleated sheet *(left)* and helical structure *(right)* are created by hydrogen bonding between neighboring back-bone atoms; the other interactions involve side-chain groups that can be nearby or quite far apart in the protein chain.

of globular proteins represent another level of structure, tertiary structure, discussed in the next section.

Table 18.4 compares the occurrences and functions of some fibrous and globular proteins.

Table 18.4 Some Common Fibrous and Globular Proteins

Name	Occurrence and Function
Fibrous proteins (insoluble)	
Keratins	Found in skin, wool, feathers, hooves, silk, and fingernails
Collagens	Found in animal hide (skin), tendons, bone, eye cornea, and other connective tissue
Elastins	Found in blood vessels and ligaments, where ability of the tissue to stretch is important
Myosins	Found in muscle tissue
Fibrin	Found in blood clots
Globular proteins (soluble)	
Insulin	Regulatory hormone for controlling glucose metabolism
Ribonuclease	Enzyme that catalyzes ribonucleic acid (RNA) hydrolysis
Immunoglobulins	Proteins involved in immune response
Hemoglobin	Protein involved in oxygen transport
Albumins	Proteins that perform many transport functions in blood; protein in egg white

PROBLEM 18.25

Complete the following two sentences with either globular or fibrous:

(a) Proteins with secondary structure composed primarily of alpha-helix are
_____ proteins.

(b) Proteins with secondary structure composed primarily of beta-sheets are
_____ proteins.

◉ KEY CONCEPT PROBLEM 18.26 ————————————————————————

Why does your skin not dissolve when you go swimming or are caught in the rain?

18.8 Tertiary Protein Structure (3°)

Learning Objectives:

• Identify the four specific forces responsible for tertiary structure.
• Identify what forces or bonds exist between amino acid side chains.
• Distinguish between simple and conjugated protein.

The overall three-dimensional shape that results from the folding of a single protein chain is the protein's **tertiary protein structure** (3°). In contrast to secondary structure, which depends mainly on attraction between backbone amide peptide bonds ($C=O$ to HN), resulting in hydrogen bonding, tertiary structure depends mainly on interactions of amino acid side chains (R groups) that are far apart along the entire backbone.

Although the bends and twists of the protein chain within a globular protein may appear irregular and the three-dimensional structure may appear random, this is not the case. Each protein molecule folds in a distinctive manner that is determined by its primary and secondary structure, with the forces described next holding the tertiary structure in place. The result is maximum stability for the native protein configuration. A **native protein** has the shape that allows it to function in living systems.

Tertiary protein structure The way in which an entire protein chain is coiled and folded into its specific three-dimensional shape.

Native protein A protein with the shape (primary, secondary, tertiary, and quaternary structure) in which it exists naturally in living organisms.

Hydrogen Bonds of R Groups with Each Other or with Backbone Atoms

Some amino acid side chains contain atoms that can form hydrogen bonds. Side-chain hydrogen bonds can connect different parts of a protein molecule, whether they are in close proximity or far apart along the polypeptide chain. In the protein in Figure 18.3, hydrogen bonds between side chains have created folds in two places. Often, hydrogen-bonding side chains are present on the surface of a folded protein, where they can form hydrogen bonds with surrounding water molecules. Recall that hydrogen bonds are noncovalent bonds.

An example of R group hydrogen bonding between the hydrogen atom of a polar group such as hydroxyl and the oxygen or nitrogen atom of another polar group in a different amino acid is shown in the margin.

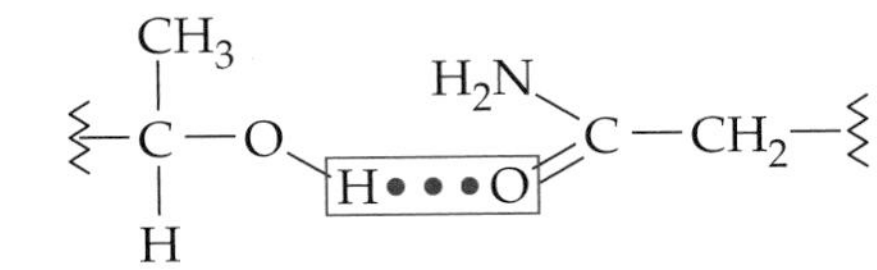

Thr (T)   Asn (N)

Ionic Attractions between R Groups (Salt Bridges)

Where there are ionized acidic and basic side chains, the attraction between their positive and negative charges creates *salt bridges*. A salt bridge is a noncovalent bond; it is an ionic bond (an attraction). For example, a basic lysine side chain and an acidic aspartate side chain have formed a salt bridge in the middle of the protein shown in Figure 18.3.

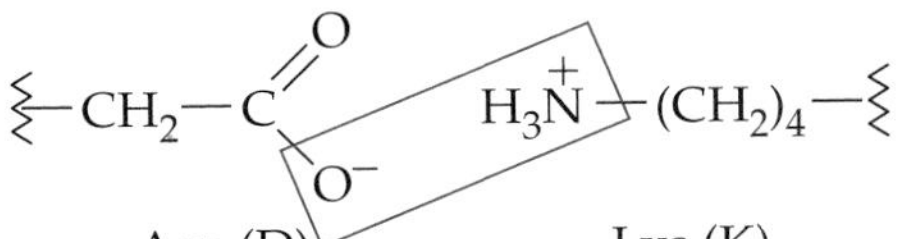

Asp (D)   Lys (K)

Hydrophilic Interactions between R Groups and Water

Amino acids with charged R groups will interact with water through hydrogen bonding. The figure in the margin shows the interaction between aspartic acid and water. These interactions are attractions not covalent bonds.

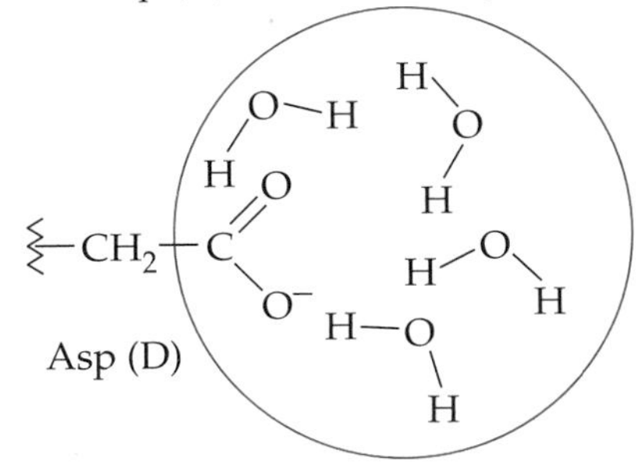

Asp (D)

◀◀ Review dispersion forces in Section 8.2 and Van der Waals forces in Section 9.2.

Hydrophobic Interactions between R Groups

Hydrocarbon side chains are attracted to each other by the dispersion forces (primarily Van der Waals forces) caused by a momentary uneven distribution of electrons. Although this attraction is noncovalent in nature, the result is that these groups cluster together in the same way that oil molecules cluster on the surface of water, so that these interactions are often referred to as *hydrophobic*. By clustering in this manner, the hydrophobic groups shown in Figure 18.3 and more explicitly in the margin create a water-free pocket in the protein chain. Although the individual attractions are weak, their large number in proteins plays a major role in stabilizing the folded structures.

Phe (F)   Leu (L)

Covalent Sulfur–Sulfur Bonds: The Disulfide Bridge

◀◀ Disulfide bond formation was explored in Section 14.8.

In addition to the noncovalent interactions described above, one type of covalent bond plays a role in determining protein shape. Cysteine amino acid residues have side chains containing thiol functional groups ($-SH$) that can react to form sulfur–sulfur bonds ($-S-S-$).

Cysteine (Cys, C)   Cysteine (Cys, C)

Disulfide bond A S—S bond formed between two cysteine side chains; can join two separate peptide chains together or cause a loop in a single peptide chain.

If the two cysteine residues are in different protein chains, the two separate chains become covalently linked together by the disulfide bond. If the two cysteine residues are in the same chain, a loop is formed in the chain. Insulin provides a good example. It consists of two polypeptide chains connected by **disulfide bonds** in two different places connecting the A and B chains with two interchain bonds. Additionally, the A chain has an intrachain loop caused by a third disulfide bond.

Structure of insulin

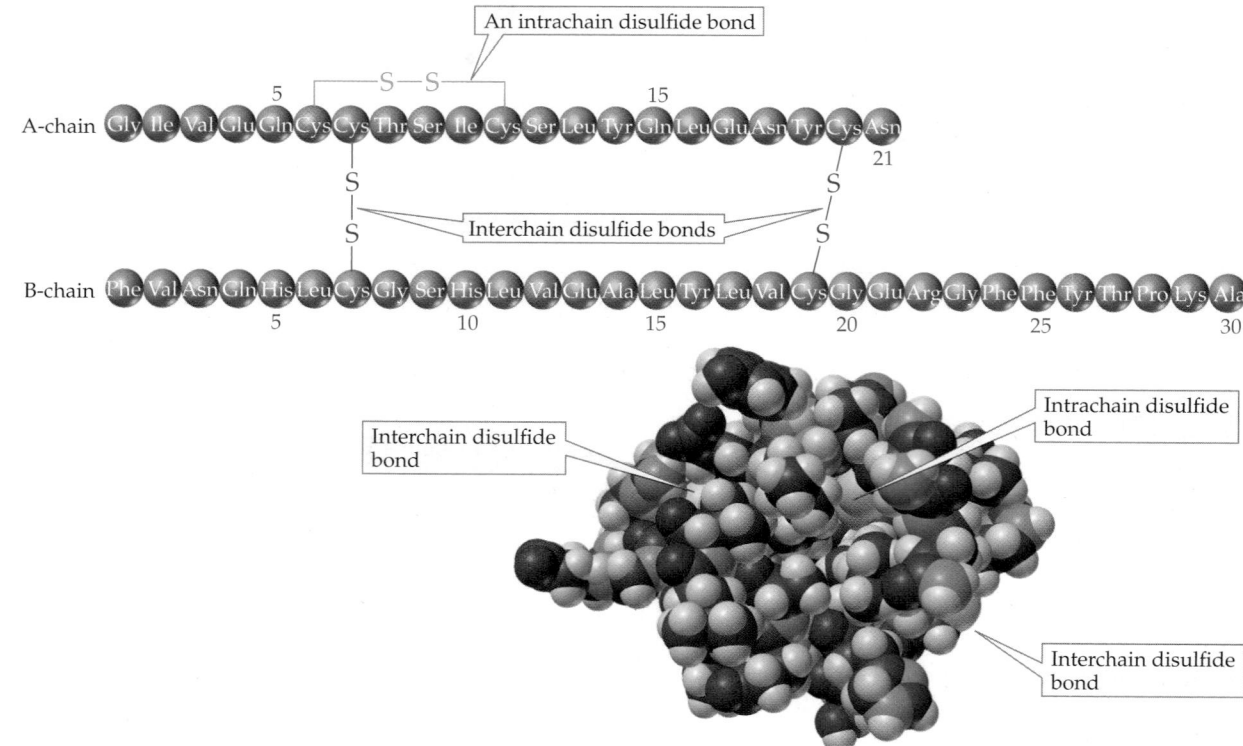

Insulin is representative of a class of small polypeptides (proteins) that function as hormones, which are released when a chemical message must be carried from one place to another (angiotensin II on p. 567 is another example of a polypeptide hormone). The structure and function of insulin are of intense interest because of its role in glucose metabolism and the need for supplementary insulin by individuals with diabetes. Insulin signals cells to take in glucose when blood glucose levels rise; many diabetics need supplemental insulin because their bodies either do not produce insulin or have lost the ability to respond to their own insulin. Diabetes and the role of insulin in glucose metabolism are discussed further in Section 22.7. Undoubtedly because of this need, studies of insulin have led the way in developing our ability to determine the structure of a biomolecule and prepare it synthetically.

We will learn more about polypeptide hormones in Chapter 28 and diabetes in Section 22.7.

In a historically important accomplishment, the amino acid sequence of insulin was determined in 1951—it was the *first* protein for which this was done. It took 15 years before the cross-linking and complete molecular structure determined and a successful laboratory synthesis was carried out. With the advent of biotechnology in the 1980s, once again insulin was first. Until then, individuals with diabetes relied on insulin extracted from the pancreases of cows, and because of differences in three amino acids between bovine and human insulin, allergic reactions occasionally resulted. In 1982, human insulin became the first commercial product of genetic engineering to be licensed by the U.S. government for clinical use.

The four noncovalent interactions and disulfide covalent bonds described above govern tertiary structure. The enzyme *ribonuclease,* shown here as an example in its ribbon structure, is drawn in a style that shows the combination of α-helix and β-sheet regions, the loops connecting them, and four disulfide bonds.

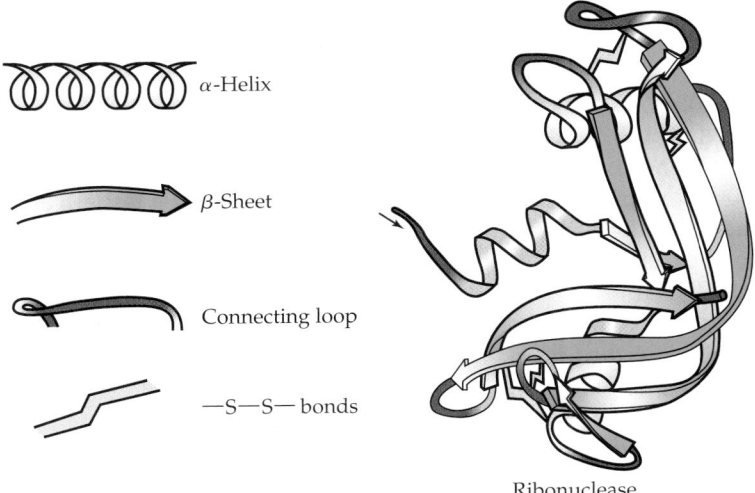

α-Helix

β-Sheet

Connecting loop

—S—S— bonds

Ribonuclease

The structure of ribonuclease is representative of the tertiary structure of globular, water-soluble proteins. The hydrophobic, nonpolar side chains congregate in a hydrocarbon-like interior, and the hydrophilic side chains, which provide water solubility, congregate on the outside. Ribonuclease is classified as a **simple protein** because it is composed only of amino acid residues (124 of them). The drawing shows ribonuclease in a style that clearly represents the combination of primary and secondary structures in the overall tertiary structure of a globular protein. The symbols in the left side of the figure above are standard representations for these components of protein structure.

Simple protein A protein composed of only amino acid residues.

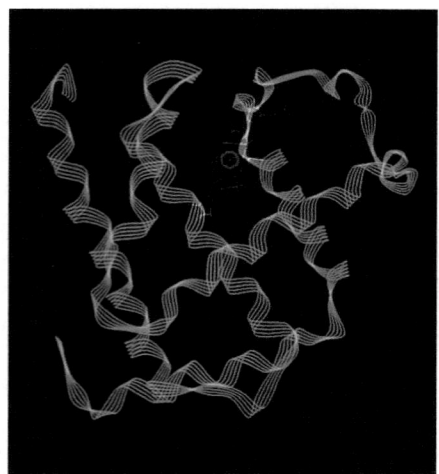

(a)

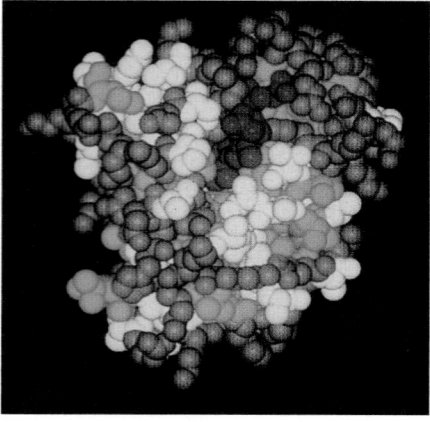

(b)

▲ **Figure 18.4**
Myoglobin, drawn in two styles.
In each panel, the red structure embedded in
the protein is a molecule of heme, to which
O_2 binds. (a) A protein *ribbon model* shows
the helical portions as a ribbon. This type
of representation clearly shows protein secondary structure. (b) A computer-generated
space-filling model of myoglobin shows the
hydrophobic residues in blue and the hydrophilic residues in purple. This type of representation better conveys the overall shape and
dimensions of the protein.

Conjugated protein A protein that
incorporates one or more non–amino
acid units in its structure.

Myoglobin is an example of a small globular protein, consisting of a single
amino acid chain. A relative of hemoglobin, myoglobin stores oxygen in skeletal
muscles for use when there is an immediate need for energy. Structurally, the
153 amino acid residues of myoglobin are arranged in eight α-helical segments
connected by short segments looped so that hydrophilic amino acid residues are
on the exterior of the compact, spherical tertiary structure. Like many proteins,
myoglobin is not a simple protein but is a **conjugated protein**—a protein that is
aided in its function by an associated non–amino acid unit. The oxygen-carrying
portion of myoglobin has a heme group embedded within the polypeptide chain.
In Figure 18.4, the myoglobin molecule is shown in two different ways; both types
of molecular representation are routinely used to illustrate the shapes of protein
molecules. Some examples of other kinds of conjugated proteins are listed in
Table 18.5.

Table 18.5 Some Examples of Conjugated Proteins

Class of Protein	Nonprotein Part	Examples
Glycoproteins	Carbohydrates	Glycoproteins in cell membranes (Section 20.7)
Lipoproteins	Lipids	High- and low-density lipoproteins that transport cholesterol and other lipids through the body (Section 24.2)
Metalloproteins	Metal ions	The enzyme cytochrome oxidase, necessary for biological energy production, and many other enzymes
Phosphoproteins	Phosphate groups	Milk casein, which provides essential nutrients to infants
Hemoproteins	Heme	Hemoglobin (transports oxygen) and myoglobin (stores oxygen)
Nucleoproteins	RNA	Found in cell ribosomes, where they take part in protein synthesis

How do proteins "know" the correct three-dimensional structure to fold up
into? As a protein is synthesized, adding amino acids one at a time, from the
N-terminal end to the C-terminal end of the protein, it is anchored to a structure called a ribosome (see Chapter 26). The lengthening protein chain folds in
a manner that allows hydrophilic residues to interact with the aqueous cellular
environment and sequesters the hydrophobic residues in the interior of the final
structure. This folding is encouraged by amino acid side chains that interact either
with each other or with the aqueous environment, resulting in the lowest energy
state possible for the folded protein, stabilizing the structure. Many proteins spontaneously fold into the native structure during synthesis. However, some do not.
Proteins referred to as "chaperones" guide their folding, especially if the final
structure of the protein being synthesized is unstable. The folding step for each
protein must result in a functional protein. Misfolded proteins typically are non-
functional and often toxic.

 Worked Example 18.4 Drawing Side-Chain Interactions

What type of noncovalent interaction occurs between the glutamine and threonine side chains? Draw the
structures of these amino acids to show the interaction.

ANALYSIS The side chains of glutamine and threonine contain an amide group and a hydroxyl group,
respectively. Since the hydroxyl group does not ionize, this pair will not form salt bridges. They are polar and
therefore not hydrophobic. This pair of amino acids can form a hydrogen bond between the oxygen of the
amide carbonyl group and the hydrogen of the hydroxyl group.

SOLUTION

The noncovalent, hydrogen bond interaction between threonine and glutamine is as follows:

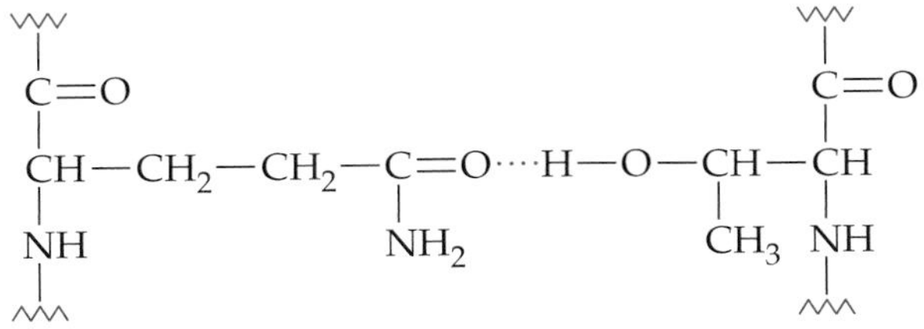

Worked Example 18.5 Identifying Groups Involved in Hydrogen Bonding

Hydrogen bonds are important in stabilizing both the secondary and tertiary structures of proteins. How do the groups that form hydrogen bonds in the secondary and tertiary structures differ?

ANALYSIS Examine the hydrogen bonding in secondary structure. See Figures 18.1 and 18.2. Note the regularity along the backbone of the hydrogen bonding. Only hydrogen atoms on backbone nitrogen atoms and oxygen atoms on nearby carbonyl carbon atoms are involved in this bonding. In tertiary structure hydrogen bonding occurs primarily between polar R groups and these groups are not necessarily nearby.

SOLUTION

Secondary structure is the product of regular, repetitive bonding between hydrogen atoms on backbone nitrogen atoms and oxygen atoms on nearby carbonyl carbon atoms. The regular, repetitive bonding leads to alpha-helix and beta-pleated sheet structures.

Tertiary structure depends on several different types of bonding and not totally on hydrogen bonding. The hydrogen bonding is primarily between R group atoms and is spread irregularly throughout the molecule.

PROBLEM 18.27

Which of the following pairs of amino acids can form hydrogen bonds between their side-chain groups? Draw the pairs that can hydrogen bond through their side chains and indicate the hydrogen bonds.

(a) Phe, Thr   (b) Asn, Ser   (c) Thr, Tyr   (d) Gly, Trp

◑▤ KEY CONCEPT PROBLEM 18.28 ────────────────────

Look at Table 18.3 and identify the type of noncovalent interaction expected between the side chains of the following pairs of amino acids:

(a) Glutamine and serine   (b) Isoleucine and proline
(c) Aspartate and lysine   (d) Alanine and phenylalanine

PROBLEM 18.29

In Figure 18.3, identify the amino acids that have formed (a) hydrogen bonds from their side chains and (b) hydrophobic side-chain interactions.

PROBLEM 18.30

For each of the conjugated proteins described, identify to which class of conjugated protein it belongs.

(a) Cholesterol is attached to this protein in order to move through the blood system.
(b) Ionized zinc is attached to this protein so the protein can function.
(c) Phosphate groups are attached to this protein.
(d) Complex sugars are attached to this membrane protein.
(e) A large multi-ring, conjugated hydrocarbon containing a ferric ion enables this protein to function.
(f) RNA attached to this protein facilitates protein synthesis.

18.9 Quaternary Protein Structure ($4°$)

Learning Objectives:

- Define quaternary structure.
- Identify the forces responsible for quaternary structure.
- Give examples of proteins with quaternary structure.

Quaternary protein structure The way in which two or more protein chains aggregate to form large, ordered structures.

Cellular protein A protein found inside cells.

Mobile protein A protein found in body fluids such as blood.

➤➤ We will learn more about oxygen transport in Chapter 29.

The fourth and final level of protein structure, and the most complex, is **quaternary protein structure** ($4°$)—the way in which two or more polypeptide subunits associate to form a single three-dimensional protein unit. The individual polypeptides are held together by the same noncovalent forces responsible for tertiary structure. In some cases, there are also covalent bonds (disulfide bonds) and the protein may incorporate a non–amino acid portion. *Hemoglobin* and *collagen* are both well-understood examples of proteins with quaternary structure essential to their function.

Hemoglobin

Hemoglobin (Figure 18.5a) is a conjugated quaternary protein composed of four polypeptide chains (two each of two different polypeptides called the α-chain and the β-chain) held together primarily by the interaction of hydrophobic groups and four heme groups, one per chain. Each polypeptide is similar in composition and tertiary structure to myoglobin (Figure 18.4). The α-chains have 141 amino acids, and the β-chains have 146 amino acids.

The heme unit (Figure 18.5) contains an iron atom that is essential to its function. One heme unit is found in each of the four polypeptides that make up a hemoglobin molecule. The association of the four polypeptide chains with their heme units is the quaternary structure of hemoglobin, the oxygen carrier in red blood cells. In the lungs, O_2 binds to Fe^{2+}, so that each hemoglobin molecule can carry a maximum of four O_2 molecules. In tissues in need of oxygen, O_2 is released, and CO_2 (the product of respiration) is picked up and carried back to the lungs. Although hemoglobin is a soluble protein, it is a **cellular protein** normally found only inside cells and carried throughout the body inside red blood cells. Serum albumin, also a soluble protein is referred to as a **mobile protein** because it is dissolved in an extracellular (outside the cell) fluid, carries CO_2 to the lungs for disposal.

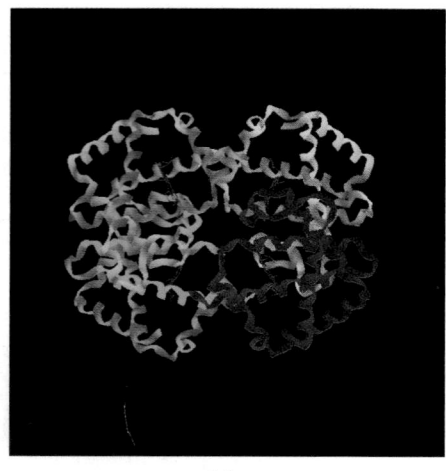

(a)

(b)

▲ **Figure 18.5**

Heme and hemoglobin, a protein with quaternary structure.

(a) The polypeptides are shown in purple, green, blue, and yellow, with their heme units in red. Each polypeptide resembles myoglobin in structure. (b) A heme unit is present in each of the four polypeptides in hemoglobin.

Collagen

Collagen is the most abundant of all proteins in mammals, making up 30% or more of the total. A fibrous protein, collagen is the major constituent of skin, tendons, bones, blood vessels, and other connective tissues. The basic structural unit of collagen *(tropocollagen)* consists of three intertwined chains of about 1000 amino acids each. Each chain is loosely coiled in a left-handed (counter-clockwise) direction (Figure 18.6a). Three of these coiled chains wrap around one another (in a clockwise direction) to form a stiff, rod-like tropocollagen triple helix (Figure 18.6b) in which the chains are held together by hydrogen bonds.

There are several different types of collagen found throughout the body that vary slightly in their primary sequence of amino acids. However, all the various kinds of collagen have in common a glycine residue at every third position. Only glycine residues (with —H as the side chain on the α-carbon) can fit in the center of the tightly coiled tropocollagen triple helix. The larger side chains face the exterior of the helix. After the collagen protein is synthesized, hydroxyl (—OH) groups are added to some of its proline residues in a reaction that requires vitamin C. This hydroxylation of proline residues is important for strong collagen fiber formation. Herein lies the explanation for the symptoms of scurvy, the disease that results from vitamin C deficiency. When vitamin C is in short supply, collagen is deficient in hydroxylated proline residues and, as a result, forms fibers poorly. This results in

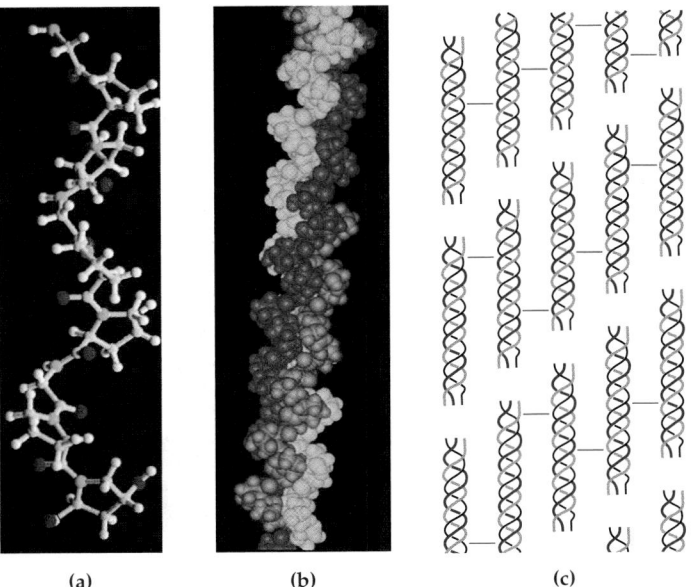

(a)   (b)   (c)

◀ **Figure 18.6**
Collagen.
(a) A single collagen helix (carbon, green; hydrogen, light blue; nitrogen, dark blue; oxygen, red). (b) The triple helix of tropocollagen. (c) The quaternary structure of a cross-linked collagen, showing the assemblage of tropocollagen molecules.

the skin lesions and fragile blood vessels that accompany scurvy, an uncommon disease in modern times.

The tropocollagen triple helices are assembled into collagen in a quaternary structure formed by a great many strands overlapping lengthwise (Figure 18.6). Depending on the exact purpose collagen serves in the body, further structural modifications occur. In connective tissue like tendons, covalent bonds between strands give collagen fibers a rigid, cross-linked structure. In teeth and bones, calcium hydroxyapatite $[Ca_5(PO_4)_3OH]$ deposits in the gaps between chains to further harden the overall assembly.

▶▶ For more on the role of vitamin C in collagen synthesis, see Section 19.9.

Protein Structure Summary

- **Primary structure**—the sequence of amino acids connected by peptide bonds in the polypeptide chain; for example, Asp-Arg-Val-Tyr.
- **Secondary structure**—the arrangement in space of the polypeptide chain, which includes the regular patterns of the α-helix and the β-sheet formations (held together by hydrogen bonds between backbone carbonyl oxygen atoms and backbone amino hydrogen atoms in amino acid residues) plus the loops that connect these segments.
- **Tertiary structure**—the folding of a single protein chain into a specific three-dimensional shape held together by noncovalent interactions (salt bridges, hydrogen bonding, hydrophobic interactions) primarily between amino acid side chains, in some cases, by disulfide bonds between side-chain thiol groups.
- **Quaternary structure**—two or more protein chains assembled in a larger three-dimensional structure held together by noncovalent interactions.

Classes of Proteins Summary

- *Fibrous proteins* are tough, insoluble, and composed of fibers and sheets.
- *Globular proteins* are water-soluble and have chains folded into compact shapes.
- *Simple proteins* contain only amino acid residues.
- *Conjugated proteins* include one or more non–amino acid units.
- *Native proteins* are functional, nondenatured proteins.
- *Mobile proteins* are soluble and move through the body in extracellular fluid such as blood. An example is serum albumin.
- *Cellular proteins* are soluble and remain inside a cell. An example is hemoglobin.

Note that a protein may belong to more than one class listed above. For example, functioning hemoglobin is a native protein, which is globular, conjugated, and cellular.

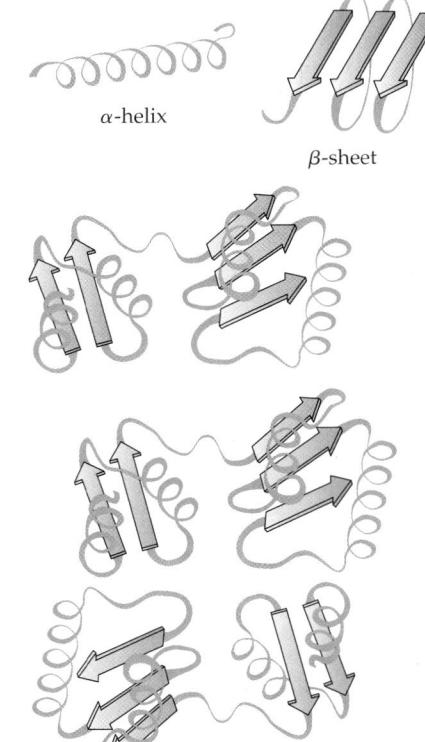

α-helix

β-sheet

Worked Example 18.6 Identifying Levels of Protein Structure

Identify the following statements as descriptive of the secondary, tertiary, or quaternary structure of a protein. What types of interactions stabilize each type of structure?

(a) The polypeptide chain has a number of bends and twists, resulting in a compact structure.

(b) The polypeptide backbone forms a right-handed coil.

(c) The four polypeptide chains are arranged in a spherical shape.

ANALYSIS Consider what you know about secondary, tertiary, and quaternary structure. Quaternary structure occurs when more than one polypeptide chain is present. A right-hand coil is characteristic of one type of secondary structure. Many bends and twists as well as a compact structure are characteristic of some kinds of tertiary structure.

SOLUTION

(a) Tertiary structure—stabilized by hydrophilic and hydrophobic interactions, salt bridges, hydrogen bonds, and disulfide bonds

(b) Secondary structure—stabilized by hydrogen bonds between backbone carbonyl oxygen atoms and backbone amino hydrogen atoms

(c) Quaternary structure—the same interactions that stabilize tertiary structure

PROBLEM 18.31

Both α-keratin and tropocollagen have helical secondary structure. How do these molecules differ in (a) amino acid composition and (b) three-dimensional structure?

18.10 Chemical Properties of Proteins

Learning Objectives:

• Describe both chemical and enzymatic protein hydrolysis.
• Define denaturation and give some examples of agents that cause denaturation.

Protein Hydrolysis

► Review amide bond hydrolysis in Section 17.4.

Just as a simple amide can be hydrolyzed to yield an amine and a carboxylic acid, a protein can also be hydrolyzed. In protein hydrolysis, the reverse of protein formation, peptide bonds are hydrolyzed to yield amino acids. In fact, digestion of proteins in the diet involves nothing more than hydrolyzing peptide bonds. For example,

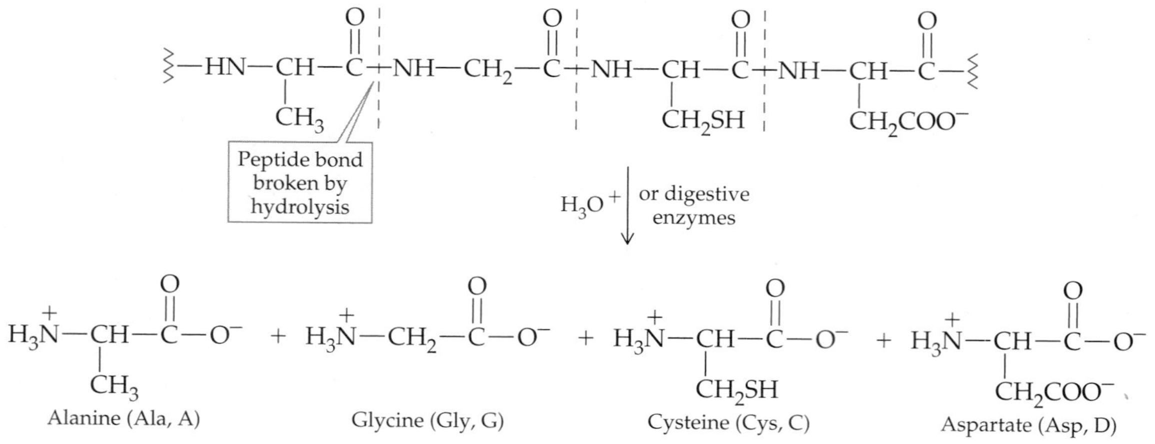

A chemist in the laboratory would preferentially choose to hydrolyze a protein by heating it in a solution of hydrochloric acid rather than in sodium hydroxide, because the basic solution destroys some of the amino acids. Digestion of proteins in the body takes place in the stomach and small intestine, where the process is catalyzed by enzymes. Endoproteases are enzymes that hydrolyze the peptide bonds in proteins at specific points within their sequences. Chymotrypsin is an endoprotease that hydrolyzes a peptide bond on the carboxyl-terminal side of aromatic amino acids. A second endoprotease is trypsin that hydrolyzes peptide bonds on the carboxyl side of lysine and arginine. Once individual amino acids are hydrolyzed from proteins, they are absorbed through the wall of the intestine and transported in the bloodstream to wherever they are needed.

▶▶ Digestion is discussed further in Section 22.1.

Worked Example 18.7   Identifying Protein Hydrolysis Fragments

In Table 18.3, identify the amino acids that have aromatic side chains. Now determine the number of fragments that result when chymotrypsin reacts with vasopressin, which has the structure

Asp-Tyr-Phe-Glu-Asn-Cys-Pro-Lys-Gly,

and then write out the sequences of these fragments using the standard three-letter designator for each amino acid.

ANALYSIS Identify the three aromatic amino acids in vasopressin. Recall that hydrolysis is the addition of water to a bond resulting in breaking that bond, in this case the peptide bond between a pair of amino acids. The enzyme chymotrypsin will hydrolyze vasopressin on the C-terminal side of aromatic amino acids.

SOLUTION
The aromatic amino acids present are tyrosine and phenylalanine. The "cuts" in a chain will produce three fragments. These fragments are as follows:

Asp-Tyr Phe Glu-Asn-Cys-Pro-Lys-Gly

PROBLEM 18.32

Another endoprotease is trypsin. Trypsin hydrolyzes peptide bonds on the carboxyl side of lysine and arginine. If the following peptide sequence is hydrolyzed by trypsin, how many fragments will there be? Use the three-letter amino acid abbreviations to write the fragments out.

Ala-Phe-Lys-Cys-Gly-Asp-Arg-Leu-Leu-Phe-Gly-Ala

PROBLEM 18.33

If the same peptide found in Problem 18.32 is subjected to acid hydrolysis, how many fragments will result? Why?

Protein Denaturation

Since the overall shape of a protein is determined by a delicate balance of noncovalent forces as we saw in previous sections, it is not surprising that a change in protein shape often results when that balance is disturbed. A disruption in shape that does not affect the protein's primary structure (the order of the amino acids within the protein chain) is known as **denaturation.** When denaturation of a globular protein occurs, for example, the structure unfolds from a well-defined globular shape to a randomly looped chain, but the order of amino acids within the chain does not change.

Denaturation The loss of secondary, tertiary, or quaternary protein structure due to disruption of noncovalent interactions and/or disulfide bonds that leaves peptide bonds and primary structure intact.

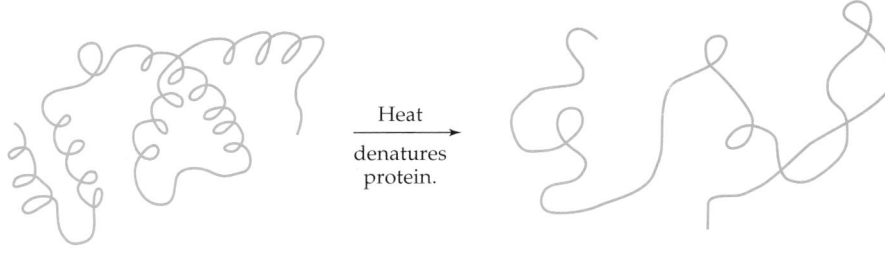

Heat
denatures
protein.

▲ Protein denaturation in action: The egg white denatures as the egg fries.

Denaturation is accompanied by changes in physical, chemical, and biological properties. Solubility is often decreased by denaturation, as occurs when egg whites are cooked and the albumins coagulate into an insoluble white mass. Enzymes lose their catalytic activity, and other proteins are no longer able to carry out their biological functions when their shapes are altered by denaturation.

Agents that cause denaturation include heat, mechanical agitation, detergents, organic solvents, extremely acidic or basic pH, and inorganic salts.

- **Heat** The weak side-chain attractions in globular proteins are easily disrupted by heating, in many cases only to temperatures above 50 °C. Cooking meat converts some of the insoluble collagen into soluble gelatin, which can be used in glue and for thickening sauces.
- **Mechanical agitation** The most familiar example of denaturation by agitation is the foam produced by beating egg whites. Denaturation of proteins at the surface of the air bubbles stiffens the protein and causes the bubbles to be held in place.
- **Detergents** Even very low concentrations of detergents can cause denaturation by disrupting the association of hydrophobic side chains.
- **Organic compounds** Polar solvents such as acetone and ethanol interfere with hydrogen bonding by competing for bonding sites. The disinfectant action of ethanol, for example, results from its ability to denature bacterial protein.
- **pH change** Excess H^+ or OH^- ions react with the basic or acidic side chains in amino acid residues and disrupt salt bridges. One familiar example of denaturation by pH change is the protein coagulation that occurs when milk turns sour because it has become acidic as milk bacteria convert lactose to lactic acid.
- **Inorganic salts** Sufficiently high concentrations of ions can disturb salt bridges.

Most denaturation is irreversible: Hard-boiled eggs do not soften when their temperature is lowered. Many cases are known, however, in which unfolded proteins spontaneously undergo *renaturation*—a return to their native state when placed in a nondenaturing solution. Renaturation is accompanied by recovery of biological activity, indicating that the protein has completely refolded to its stable secondary and tertiary structure. By spontaneously refolding into their native shapes, proteins demonstrate that all the information needed to determine these shapes is present in the primary structure.

Misfolding of proteins, either during synthesis or later on, leads to abnormal secondary and tertiary structures that compromise the original function of the protein. Technically, misfolded proteins are denatured since they cannot function properly. These misfolded proteins often form aggregates in the cell that the cell may not be able to degrade. One disease where aggregates of protein (called plaques) are seen is Alzheimer's disease, a neurological disease resulting in degeneration of brain functions. Other, unrelated diseases that involve misfolded proteins are prion diseases such as Creutzfeldt–Jacob disease, scrapie in sheep, kuru in some New Guinea natives, and "mad cow disease" (bovine spongiform encephalopathy). These diseases are the result of prions duplicating themselves in brain tissue, causing either tangles of protein or open spaces in brain tissue.

HANDS-ON CHEMISTRY 18.2

Demonstrate for yourself that the denaturing methods listed above are effective.

1. Heat an egg in a frying pan and observe the changes in the egg white.
2. Gently mix an egg white in a household acid such as vinegar or pickle juice.
3. Gently mix an egg white in a solution of dish detergent and water.
4. Make a lemon meringue pie. What did you do to the egg whites to produce the meringue?

Note: The suggested protein to use is egg whites. All activities are done with a raw egg, minus the shell. If the egg whites stiffen into any shape, including "strings," the albumins within have denatured.

CHEMISTRY IN ACTION

✛ Imperfect Collagen—An Unfortunate Event

Remember the infant in the chapter-opening photo with the strikingly blue eyes? This same six-month-old girl also suffered a broken arm, but what could have happened to the infant to cause her broken arm? The two most obvious assumptions are accident or child abuse; however, there is a third possibility. This child's osteogenesis imperfecta, known as brittle bone disease, an incurable, inherited genetic disease also caused the broken bone.

Osteogenesis imperfecta is a collagen disease. The genetic defect is dominant, meaning that it will occur even when inherited from only one parent. The primary symptoms of the most common form of this disease are spontaneous broken bones, thin skin, abnormal teeth, weak tendons, and a blue tint to the sclera of the eyes. In severe forms of osteogenesis imperfecta, children may have numerous, frequent fractures, even before birth, small stature, and respiratory problems. Treatment is supportive, aimed at preventing fractures and strengthening muscles. There is no cure for osteogenesis imperfecta, although current research is directed at understanding the underlying biochemical defect in hopes of designing better treatment.

So how is collagen responsible? Collagen forms the scaffold for bone. Collagen fibers are the bone matrix, which is filled in with calcium-containing crystals of hydroxyapatite ($Ca_5[PO_4]_3OH$). The combination of collagen and hydroxyapatite makes strong bone tissue. In osteogenesis imperfecta, incorrectly synthesized collagen leads to weaker bone structures. Mutations in collagen genes lead to substitution of amino acids with bulky side chains for glycine in collagen. Normal collagen has a repeating sequence of glycine—proline—hydroxyproline. Glycine allows for the tight triple helix and strong fibrils of collagen. Bulky side chains on substituted amino acids prevent the tight triple helix from forming, weakening the fibrils and dependent structures such as skin, bone, and ligaments.

It can be difficult to distinguish osteogenesis imperfecta from child abuse. However, the types of spontaneous bone fractures seen in osteogenesis imperfecta are not the typical fractures seen in child abuse cases. A definitive diagnosis of osteogenesis imperfecta requires genetic testing of tissue from the child. Only a small amount of skin tissue is needed. (See Chapter 27, "Genomics," for DNA testing.) The child in the chapter opener tested positive for osteogenesis imperfecta.

CIA Problem 18.8 Describe the biochemical defect that results in osteogenesis imperfecta.

CIA Problem 18.9 Why is it important for collagen to be strong?

SUMMARY REVISITING THE LEARNING OBJECTIVES

- **Describe the different functions of proteins and give an example for each function.** Proteins can be grouped by function such as structural, transport, etc. See Table 18.2 *(see Problems 40 and 41)*.
- **Describe and recognize the 20 alpha amino acid structures and their side chains.** Amino acids in body fluids have an ionized carboxylic acid group ($-COO^-$), an ionized amino group ($-NH_3^+$), and a side-chain R group bonded to a central carbon atom (the α-carbon). Twenty different amino acids occur in *proteins* (Table 18.3) *(see Problems 38 and 42–45)*.
- **Categorize amino acids by the polarity or neutrality of the side chain and predict which are hydrophilic and which are hydrophobic.** Amino acid side chains have acidic or basic functional groups or neutral groups that are either polar or nonpolar. Side chains that form hydrogen bonds with water are hydrophilic; nonpolar side chains that do not form hydrogen bonds with water are hydrophobic *(see Problems 50–51, 110, and 111)*.
- **Explain chirality and identify which amino acids are chiral.** All α-amino acids except glycine are chiral *(see Problems 39 and 42–51)*.
- **Draw all ionic structures for an amino acid under acidic and basic conditions, and identify the zwitterion.** The dipolar ion in which an amino group and a carboxylic acid group are both ionized is known as a *zwitterion* and the electrical charge on the molecule is zero. For each amino acid, there is a distinctive *isoelectric point*—the pH at which the numbers of positive and negative charges in a solution are equal. At a more acidic pH, all carboxylic acid groups are protonated; at a more basic pH, all amino groups are protonated *(see Problems 34 and 52–59)*.

- **Identify a peptide bond, and explain how it is formed.** The amide bond formed between the carboxyl group of one amino acid with the amino group of a second amino acid is called a peptide bond *(see Problems 36 and 60–65)*.
- **Draw and name a simple protein structure given its amino acid sequence.** Peptides are named by combining the names of the amino acids. Amino acid sequences are often represented by using the three-letter or one-letter abbreviations for the amino acids in a left to right order *(see Problems 36 and 60–65)*.
- **Identify the amino-terminal end and the carboxyl-terminal end of a simple protein (peptide) structure given its amino acid sequence.** Amino acid sequences are written with the amino group of the end amino acid on the left and the carboxyl group of the amino acid on the other end of the chain on the right *(see Problems 36 and 60–65)*.
- **Define primary protein structure and explain how primary structures are represented.** Protein *primary structure* is the sequence in which the amino acids are connected by peptide bonds. Using formulas or amino acid abbreviations, the primary structures are written with the amino-terminal end on the left and the carboxyl-terminal end on the right *(see Problems 66–69)*.

- **Describe the planar sections of the primary sequence, their influence on the shape of the protein backbone, and identify these sections given a drawing of the primary sequence.** Due to electron dispersion between the carbonyl oxygen atom and the nitrogen atom in the peptide bond, a planar structure develops between those atoms and the two alpha carbon atoms involved. Thus, there exists a series of planes along the backbone resulting in a zigzag formation for the backbone *[see Problems 66–69].*

- **Give an example of how the change in primary sequence can change the function of a protein.** Sickle-cell anemia results from a single amino acid change in the primary sequence of hemoglobin *[see Problems 66–69].*

- **Describe the α-helix and β-sheet structures and give an example of a protein that contains primarily helix and one that contains primarily sheet secondary structure.** Secondary structures include regular, repeating three-dimensional structures held in place by hydrogen bonding between backbone atoms within a chain or in adjacent chains *[see Problems 37, 70–75, and 103].*

- **Describe the specific hydrogen bonding responsible for secondary structures.** The α-helix is a coil with hydrogen bonding between carbonyl oxygen atoms and amide hydrogen atoms four amino acid residues farther along the same chain. The β-sheet is a pleated sheet with adjacent protein-chain segments connected by hydrogen bonding between peptide groups by the same atoms as in the alpha helix *[see Problems 37, 70–73, and 103].*

- **Distinguish between fibrous and globular proteins.** Secondary structure determines the properties of *fibrous proteins,* which are tough and insoluble. Fibrous proteins are insoluble and globular proteins are soluble in aqueous solutions *[see Problems 37, 74, and 75].*

- **Identify the four specific forces responsible for tertiary structure.** Tertiary structure is the overall three-dimensional shape of a folded protein chain. Protein chains are drawn into their native shapes by attractions between atoms along their backbones and between atoms in side-chain groups *[see Problems 76, 77, 82–87, 98, and 99].*

- **Identify what forces or bonds exist between amino acid side chains.** Note that *hydrogen bonding* can also occur between R group atoms or R groups and backbone atoms. *Noncovalent interactions* between side chains include ionic bonding and *hydrophobic interactions* among nonpolar groups. Covalent *disulfide bonds* form bridges between side chains containing cysteine *[see Problems 76–83].*

- **Distinguish between simple and conjugated proteins.** Simple proteins are composed only of amino acids while conjugated proteins, such as hemoglobin, contain a nonprotein group *[see Problems 76–83, 90, and 91].*

- **Define quaternary structure.** Proteins that incorporate more than one peptide chain have *quaternary structure [see Problems 84, 85, and 88].*

- **Identify the forces responsible for quaternary structure.** In a quaternary structure, two or more folded protein subunits are united in a single structure by noncovalent interactions *[see Problems 86 and 87].*

- **Give examples of proteins with quaternary structure.** Hemoglobin, for example, consists of two pairs of subunits, with a nonprotein heme molecule in each of the four subunits. Collagen is a fibrous protein composed of protein chains twisted together in triple helixes *[see Problem 89].*

- **Describe both chemical and enzymatic protein hydrolysis.** Peptide bonds are broken by *hydrolysis,* which may occur in acidic solution or during enzyme-catalyzed digestion of proteins in food. Hydrolysis yields the individual amino acids comprising the protein *[see Problems 92–97 and 106].*

- **Define denaturation and give some examples of agents that cause denaturation.** *Denaturation* is the loss of overall structure by a protein while retaining its primary structure. Among the agents that cause denaturation are heat, mechanical agitation, pH change, and exposure to a variety of chemical agents, including detergents *[see Problems 92–97 and 106].*

KEY WORDS

Alpha- (α-) amino acid, p. 557	Cellular protein, p. 578	Mobile protein, p. 578	Secondary protein structure, p. 569
Alpha-helix (α-helix), p. 569	Conjugated protein, p. 576	Native protein, p. 573	Side chain (amino acid), p. 557
Amino acid, p. 557	Denaturation, p. 581	Noncovalent forces, p. 559	
Amino-terminal (N-terminal) amino acid, p. 564	Disulfide bond (in protein), p. 574	Peptide bond, p. 563	Simple protein, p. 575
	Fibrous protein, p. 571	Primary protein structure, p. 567	Tertiary protein structure, p. 573
Beta-sheet (β-sheet), p. 570	Globular protein, p. 571	Protein, p. 557	Zwitterion, p. 561
Carboxyl-terminal (C-terminal) amino acid, p. 564	Hydrophilic, p. 559	Quaternary protein structure, p. 578	
	Hydrophobic, p. 559	Residue (amino acid), p. 564	
	Isoelectric point (pI), p. 561		

CONCEPT MAP: AMINO ACIDS AND PROTEINS

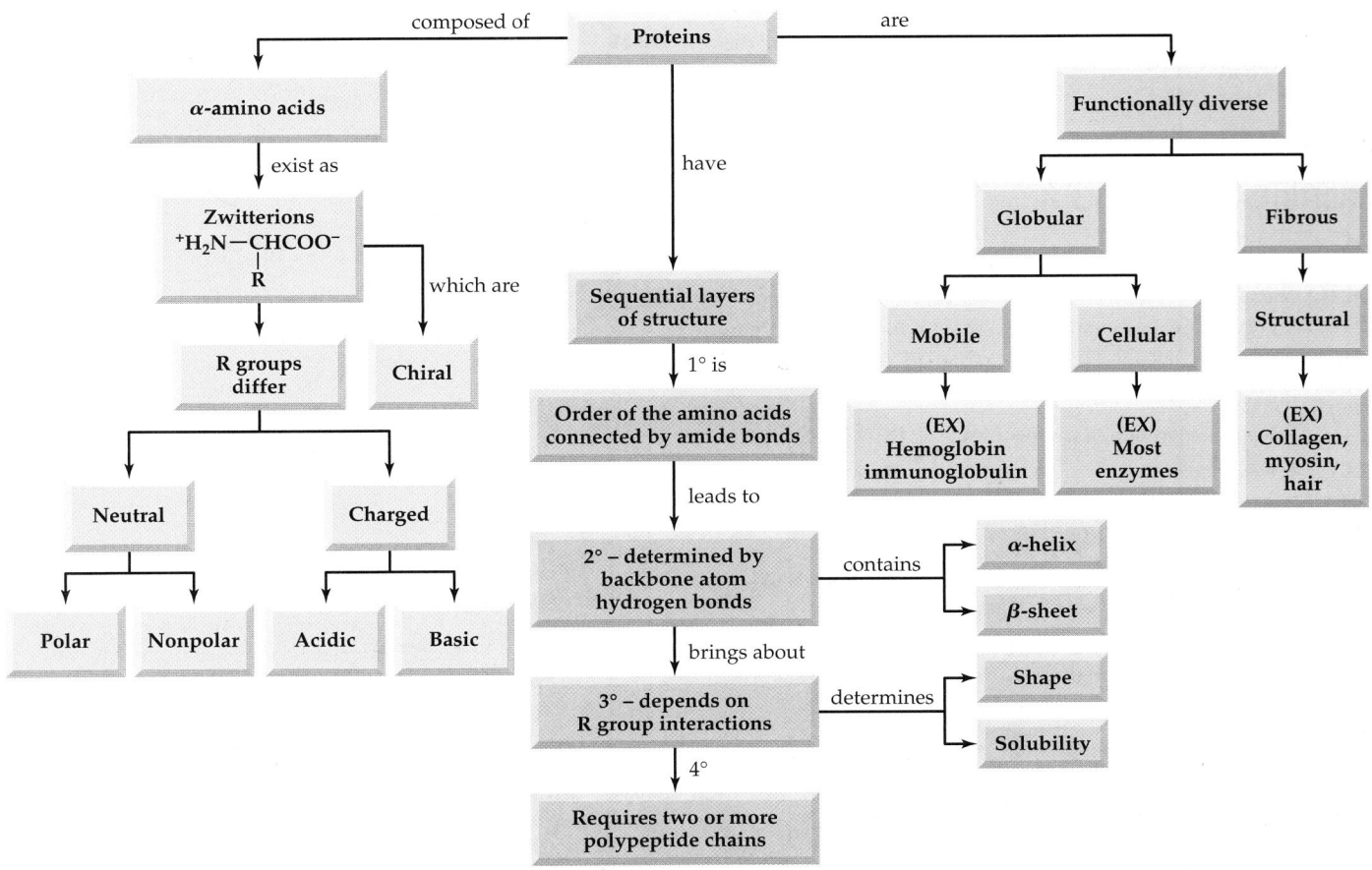

▲ **Figure 18.7 Concept Map.** Although the wide variety of structures that various proteins assume can seem complex, examination of this concept map illustrates the connection between proteins, their building blocks (amino acids), and the fundamental principles underlying protein structure. The levels of structure are organized from simplest to most complex, and interrelated concepts are shown. The functional groups can be found in the Functional Group Concept Map (Figure 12.5) if you need to review those. Earlier concept maps (Figures 4.8 and 8.25) will aid in review of molecular interactions and bonding. All of these concepts are integrated in biological molecules.

UNDERSTANDING KEY CONCEPTS

18.34 Draw the structure of the following amino acids, dipeptides, and tripeptides at low pH (pH 1) and high pH (pH 14). At each pH, assume that all functional groups that might do so are ionized. (Hint: See Worked Example 18.2.)

(a) Val

(b) Arg

(c) Tyr-Ser

(d) Glu-Asp

(e) Gln-Ala-Asn

(f) Met-Trp-Cys

18.35 Interactions of amino acids on the interior of proteins are key to the shapes of proteins. In group (a), which pairs of amino acids form hydrophobic interactions? In group (b), which pairs form ionic interactions? Which pairs in group (c) form hydrogen bonds?

(a) 1 Pro . . . Phe

2 Lys . . . Ser

3 Thr . . . Leu

4 Ala . . . Gly

(b) 1 Val . . . Leu

2 Glu . . . Lys

3 Met . . . Cys

4 Asp . . . His

(c) 1 Cys . . . Cys

2 Asp . . . Ser

3 Val . . . Gly

4 Met . . . Cys

18.36 Draw the hexapeptide Asp-Gly-Phe-Leu-Glu-Ala in linear form showing all of the atoms, and show (using dotted lines) the hydrogen bonding that stabilizes this structure if it is part of an α-helix.

18.37 Compare and contrast the characteristics of fibrous and globular proteins. Consider biological function, water solubility, amino acid composition, secondary structure, and tertiary structure. Give examples of three fibrous and three globular proteins. (Hint: Make a table.)

18.38 Cell membranes are studded with proteins. Some of these proteins, involved in the transport of molecules across the membrane into the cell, span the entire membrane and are called transmembrane proteins. The interior of the cell membrane is hydrophobic and nonpolar, whereas both the extracellular and intracellular fluids are water-based.

(a) List three amino acids you would expect to find in the part of a transmembrane protein that lies within the cell membrane.

(b) List three amino acids you would expect to find in the part of a transmembrane protein that lies outside the cell.

(c) List three amino acids you would expect to find in the part of a transmembrane protein that lies inside the cell.

18.39   Threonine has two chiral centers. Draw L-threonine and indicate which carbon atoms are chiral. Which carbon atom is responsible for D and L configuration?

ADDITIONAL PROBLEMS

PROTEINS AND THEIR FUNCTIONS: AN OVERVIEW (SECTION 18.2)

18.40   Name four biological functions of proteins in the human body, and give an example of a protein for each function.

18.41   What kind of biological function would each of the following proteins perform?

(a) Human growth hormone   **(b)** Myosin

(c) Protease   **(d)** Myoglobin

AMINO ACIDS (SECTION 18.3)

18.42   What amino acids do the following abbreviations stand for? Draw the structure of each.
(a) Val   **(b)** Ser   **(c)** Glu

18.43   What amino acids do the following abbreviations stand for? Draw the structure of each.

(a) Ile   **(b)** Thr   **(c)** Gln

18.44   Name and draw the structures of the amino acids that fit the following descriptions:

(a) Contains a thiol group   **(b)** Contains a phenol group

18.45   Name and draw the structures of the amino acids that fit the following descriptions:

(a) Contains an isopropyl group

(b) Contains a secondary alcohol group

18.46   What does the term *chiral* mean? Give two examples.

18.47   What does the term *achiral* mean? Give two examples.

18.48   Draw leucine and identify any chiral carbon atoms with arrows.

18.49   Draw isoleucine and identify any chiral carbon atoms with arrows.

18.50   Is phenylalanine hydrophilic or hydrophobic? Explain why.

18.51   Is histidine hydrophilic or hydrophobic? Explain why.

ACID–BASE PROPERTIES OF AMINO ACIDS (SECTION 18.4)

18.52   At neutral pH, which of the following amino acids has a net positive charge, which has a net negative charge, and which is neutral? (Hint: Draw the various charged forms of each amino acid before deciding.)

(a) Asparagine   **(b)** Lysine   **(c)** Proline

18.53   At neutral pH, which of the following amino acids has a net positive charge, which has a net negative charge, and which is neutral? (Hint: Draw the various charged forms of each amino acid before deciding.)

(a) Aspartic acid   **(b)** Histidine   **(c)** Valine

18.54   Which of the following forms of aspartic acid would you expect to predominate at low pH, neutral pH, and high pH?

(a) $\overset{\displaystyle O}{\overset{\|}{HOC}}-CH_2\underset{\underset{\textstyle {}^+NH_3}{|}}{CH}-\overset{\displaystyle O}{\overset{\|}{CO^-}}$

(b) $\overset{\displaystyle O}{\overset{\|}{{}^-OC}}-CH_2\underset{\underset{\textstyle NH_2}{|}}{CH}-\overset{\displaystyle O}{\overset{\|}{CO^-}}$

(c) $\overset{\displaystyle O}{\overset{\|}{HOC}}-CH_2\underset{\underset{\textstyle {}^+NH_3}{|}}{CH}-\overset{\displaystyle O}{\overset{\|}{COH}}$

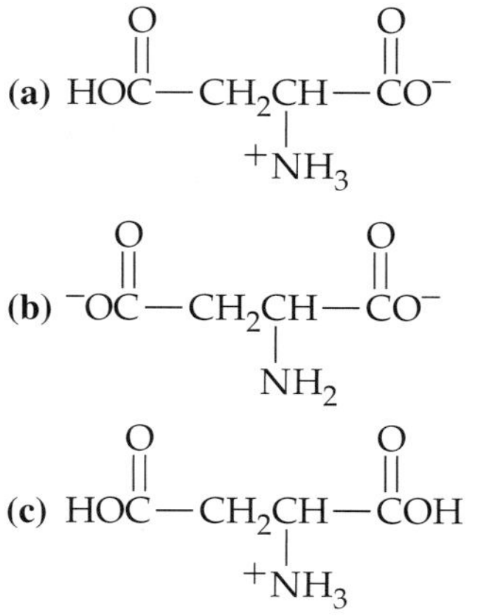

18.55   Which form of aspartic acid in Problem 18.54 is the zwitterion? What is the pI for the zwitterion?

18.56   Which of the following forms of lysine would you expect to predominate at low pH, neutral pH, and high pH?

(a) $\overset{+}{N}H_3-\underset{\underset{\textstyle (CH_2)_4}{\overset{\overset{\textstyle H}{|}}{C}}}{}-\overset{\overset{\displaystyle O}{\|}}{C}-O^-$ with $NH_3{}^+$ below

(b) $\overset{+}{N}H_3-\underset{\underset{\textstyle (CH_2)_4}{\overset{\overset{\textstyle H}{|}}{C}}}{}-\overset{\overset{\displaystyle O}{\|}}{C}-OH$ with $NH_3{}^+$ below

(c) $\overset{+}{N}H_3-\underset{\underset{\textstyle (CH_2)_4}{\overset{\overset{\textstyle H}{|}}{C}}}{}-\overset{\overset{\displaystyle O}{\|}}{C}-O^-$ with NH_2 below

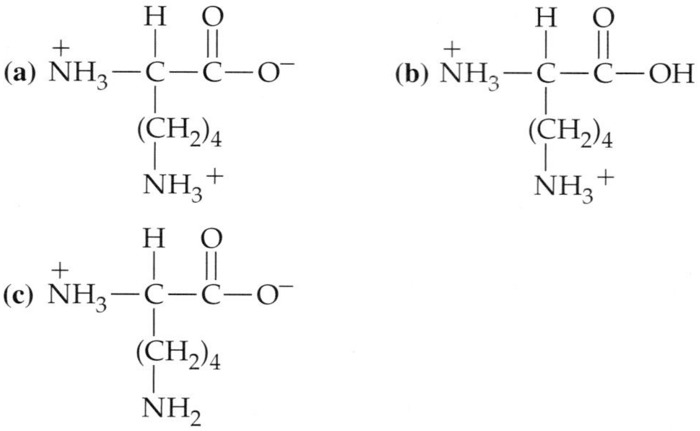

18.57   Which form of lysine in Problem 18.56 is the zwitterion? What is the pI for the zwitterion?

18.58   Proteins are usually least soluble in water at their isoelectric points. Explain.

18.59   How could you make the zwitterion of aspartic acid more soluble in water?

PEPTIDES (SECTION 18.5)

18.60   Use the three-letter abbreviations to name all tripeptides that contain valine, methionine, and leucine.

18.61   Write structural formulas for the two dipeptides that contain leucine and aspartate.

18.62 The *endorphins* are a group of naturally occurring neurotransmitters that act in a manner similar to morphine to control pain. Research has shown that the biologically active parts of the endorphin molecules are simple pentapeptides called *enkephalins*. Draw the structure of the methionine enkephalin with the sequence Tyr-Gly-Gly-Phe-Met. Identify the N-terminal and C-terminal amino acids.

18.63 Refer to Problem 18.62. Draw the structure of the leucine enkephalin with the sequence Tyr-Gly-Gly-Phe-Leu. Identify the N-terminal and C-terminal amino acids.

18.64 (a) Identify the amino acids present in the peptide shown and name the peptide using the three-letter abbreviations.

(b) Identify the N-terminal and C-terminal amino acids of the peptide.

$$H_3\overset{+}{N}-CH-\overset{O}{\overset{\|}{C}}-\overset{H}{\underset{}{N}}-CH-\overset{O}{\overset{\|}{C}}-\overset{H}{\underset{}{N}}-CH-\overset{O}{\overset{\|}{C}}-\overset{H}{\underset{}{N}}-CH-\overset{O}{\overset{\|}{C}}-\overset{H}{\underset{}{N}}-CHCO^-$$

side chains: CH_3CHCH_3, H, CH_2OH, CH_3, CH_2COO^-

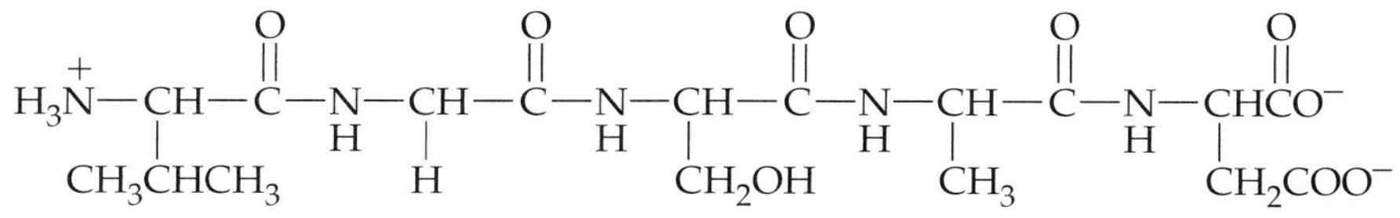

18.65 (a) Identify the amino acids present in the peptide shown and name the peptide using the three-letter abbreviations.

(b) Identify the N-terminal and C-terminal amino acids of the peptide.

$$H_3\overset{+}{N}-CH-\overset{O}{\overset{\|}{C}}-\overset{H}{\underset{}{N}}-CH-\overset{O}{\overset{\|}{C}}-\overset{H}{\underset{}{N}}-CH-\overset{O}{\overset{\|}{C}}-N-CH-COO^-$$

side chains: CH_2–SH; $(CH_2)_4$–$\overset{+}{N}H_3$; $(CH_2)_2$–$C(=O)-O^-$; CH_2/CH_2–CH_2

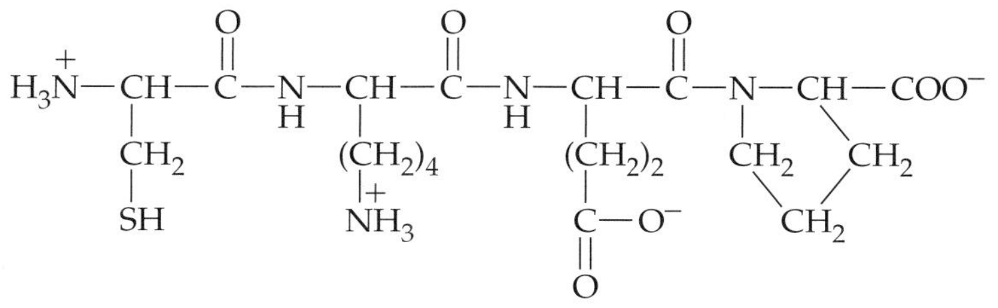

PROTEIN STRUCTURE: AN OVERVIEW AND PRIMARY PROTEIN STRUCTURE (1°) (SECTION 18.6)

18.66 What is the primary structure of a protein?

18.67 What is the sequence of atoms along the "backbone" of a protein?

18.68 Bradykinin, a peptide that helps to regulate blood pressure, has the primary structure Arg-Pro-Pro-Gly-Phe-Ser-Pro-Phe-Arg.

(a) Draw the complete structural formula of bradykinin.

(b) Bradykinin has a very kinked secondary structure. Why?

18.69 What effect on the overall structure of hemoglobin in the presence and absence of oxygen did the substitution of valine for glutamic acid in the primary structure of hemoglobin?

SECONDARY PROTEIN STRUCTURE (2°) (SECTION 18.7)

18.70 Describe the specific bonding responsible for secondary structure in proteins, including which atoms are involved.

18.71 Is hydrogen bonding covalent or noncovalent?

18.72 How does the alpha-helix result from hydrogen bonding?

18.73 How does the beta-pleated sheet result from hydrogen bonding?

18.74 Give an example of a protein containing primarily alpha-helices. Is this a fibrous or globular protein?

18.75 Give an example of a protein containing primarily beta-pleated sheets. Is this a fibrous or globular protein?

TERTIARY PROTEIN STRUCTURE (3°) (SECTION 18.8)

18.76 What kind of bond would you expect between the side chains of the following amino acids?

(a) Cysteine and cysteine

(b) Alanine and leucine

(c) Aspartic acid and asparagine

(d) Serine and lysine

18.77 Is the bond formed between each pair in Problem 18.76 covalent or noncovalent?

18.78 What drives spontaneous folding into the correct tertiary structure for a newly synthesized protein?

18.79 What is the function of proteins that are called chaperone proteins?

18.80 What is the difference between a simple protein and a conjugated protein?

18.81 What kinds of molecules are found in the following classes of conjugated proteins in addition to the protein part?

(a) Metalloproteins   (b) Hemoproteins

(c) Lipoproteins   (d) Nucleoproteins

18.82 Why is cysteine such an important amino acid for defining the tertiary structure of some proteins?

18.83 What conditions are required for disulfide bonds to form between cysteine residues in a protein?

QUATERNARY PROTEIN STRUCTURE (4°) (SECTION 18.9)

18.84 What is meant by the following terms as they apply to protein structure, and what bonds or molecular interactions stabilize that level of structure?

(a) Primary structure   (b) Secondary structure

(c) Tertiary structure   (d) Quaternary structure

18.85 What level of protein structure is determined by the following:

(a) Peptide bonds between amino acids?

(b) Hydrogen bonds between backbone carbonyl oxygen atoms and hydrogen atoms attached to backbone nitrogen atoms?

(c) R group interactions that may involve Van der Waals forces, ionic interactions, or hydrogen bonds?

18.86 How do the following noncovalent interactions help to stabilize the tertiary and quaternary structure of a protein? Give an example of a pair of amino acids that could give rise to each interaction.

(a) Hydrophobic interactions

(b) Salt bridges (ionic interactions)

18.87 How do the following interactions help to stabilize the tertiary and quaternary structure of a protein? Give an example of a pair of amino acids that could give rise to each interaction.

(a) Side-chain hydrogen bonding

(b) Disulfide bonds

18.88 What is the minimum number of polypeptide chains necessary for quaternary structure to exist?

18.89 Give an example of a protein that has quaternary structure. How many polypeptide chains are present in this protein?

18.90 What is a conjugated protein? Give an example.

18.91 What kinds of molecules provide the nonprotein part of a conjugated protein? Give an example.

CHEMICAL PROPERTIES OF PROTEINS SECTION (18.10)

18.92 What kinds of changes take place in a protein when it is denatured?

18.93 Explain how a protein is denatured by the following:

(a) Heat

(b) Strong acids

(c) Organic solvents

18.94 What is the difference between protein digestion and protein denaturation? Both occur after a meal.

18.95 Why is hydrolysis of a protein not considered to be denaturation?

18.96 Fresh pineapple cannot be used in gelatin desserts because it contains an enzyme that hydrolyzes the proteins in gelatin, destroying the gelling action. Canned pineapple can be added to gelatin with no problem. Why?

18.97 As a chef, you prepare a wide variety of foods daily. The following dishes all contain protein. What method (if any) has been used to denature the protein present in each food?

(a) Charcoal-grilled steak

(b) Pickled pigs' feet

(c) Meringue

(d) Steak tartare (raw, chopped beef)

(e) Salt pork

CONCEPTUAL PROBLEMS

18.98 For each amino acid listed, tell whether its influence on tertiary structure is largely through hydrophobic interactions, hydrogen bonding, formation of salt bridges, covalent bonding, or some combination of these effects.

(a) Tyrosine   (b) Cysteine

(c) Asparagine   (d) Lysine

(e) Tryptophan   (f) Alanine

(g) Leucine   (h) Methionine

18.99 Oxytocin is a small peptide that is used to induce labor by causing contractions in uterine walls. It has the primary structure Cys-Tyr-Ile-Gln-Asn-Cys-Pro-Leu-Gln. This peptide is held in a cyclic configuration by a disulfide bridge. Draw a diagram of oxytocin, showing the disulfide bridge.

18.100 Methionine has a sulfur atom in its formula. Explain why methionine does not form disulfide bridges.

18.101 Four of the most abundant amino acids in proteins are leucine, alanine, glycine, and valine. What do these amino acids have in common? Would you expect these amino acids to be found on the interior or on the exterior of the protein?

18.102 Globular proteins are water-soluble, whereas fibrous proteins are insoluble in water. Indicate whether you expect the following amino acids to be on the surface of a globular protein or on the surface of a fibrous protein.

(a) Ala   (b) Glu

(c) Leu   (d) Phe

(e) Ser   (f) Val

18.103 Figure 18.4 shows sharp directional changes in the path of the peptide chain. This can be seen in both the ribbon model and the space-filling rendering. These sharp directional changes connecting adjacent regions of secondary structure are often referred to either as "reverse turns" or as "bends." The two most common amino acids in reverse turns are glycine and proline. Use your knowledge of the structures of these two amino acids to speculate on why they might be found in reverse turns.

18.104 During sickle-cell anemia research to determine the modification involved in sickling, sequencing of the affected person's hemoglobin β-subunit reveals that the sixth amino acid is valine rather than glutamate; thus, the replacement of glutamate by valine severely alters the three-dimensional structure of hemoglobin. Which amino acid, if it replaced the Glu, would cause the least disruption in hemoglobin structure? Why?

18.105 A family visits a pediatrician with their sick child. The four-month-old baby is pale, has obvious episodes of pain, and is not thriving. The doctor orders a series of blood tests, including a test for hemoglobin types. The results show that the infant is not only anemic but that the anemia is due to sickle-cell anemia. The family wants to know if their other two children have sickle-cell anemia, sickle-cell trait, or no sickle-cell gene at all.

(a) What test will be used?

(b) Sketch the expected results if samples for each child are tested at the same time.

(c) What is the difference between sickle-cell anemia and sickle-cell trait?

18.106 Why do you suppose individuals with diabetes must receive insulin subcutaneously by injection rather than orally?

18.107 Individuals with phenylketonuria (PKU) are sensitive to phenylalanine in their diet. Why is a warning on foods containing aspartame (L-aspartyl-L-phenylalanine methyl ester) of concern to individuals with PKU?

18.108 What could you prepare for dinner for a strict vegan that provides all of the essential amino acids in appropriate amounts? (Remember, strict vegans do not eat meat, eggs, milk, or products that contain those animal products.)

GROUP PROBLEMS

18.109 Which would you expect to be more soluble in water, a peptide containing mostly alanine and leucine or a peptide containing mostly lysine and aspartic acid? Explain. (Hint: Consider side-chain interactions with water.)

18.110 Which of the following amino acids is most likely to be found on the outside of a soluble protein, and which of them is more likely to be found on the inside? Explain each answer. (Hint: Consider the effect of the amino acid side chain in each case and that the protein is folded up into its globular form.)

(a) Valine   (b) Aspartate

(c) Histidine   (d) Alanine

18.111 Which of the following amino acids is most likely to be found on the outside of a soluble protein? Which is more likely to be found on the inside? Explain each answer. (Hint: Consider the effect of the amino acid side chain in each case and that the protein is folded up into its globular form.)

(a) Leucine   (b) Glutamate

(c) Phenylalanine   (d) Glutamine

18.112 List the amino acids with side chains that are capable of hydrogen bonding. Draw an example of two of these amino acids hydrogen bonding to one another. For each one, draw a hydrogen bond to water in a separate sketch. Refer to Section 8.2 for help with drawing hydrogen bonds.

19

Enzymes and Vitamins

CONTENTS

◀◀◀ CONCEPTS TO REVIEW

A. Coordinate covalent bonds
(Section 4.4)

B. Reaction rates
(Section 7.5)

C. pH
(Section 10.5)

D. Effects of conditions on reaction rates
(Section 7.6)

E. Tertiary protein structure
(Section 18.8)

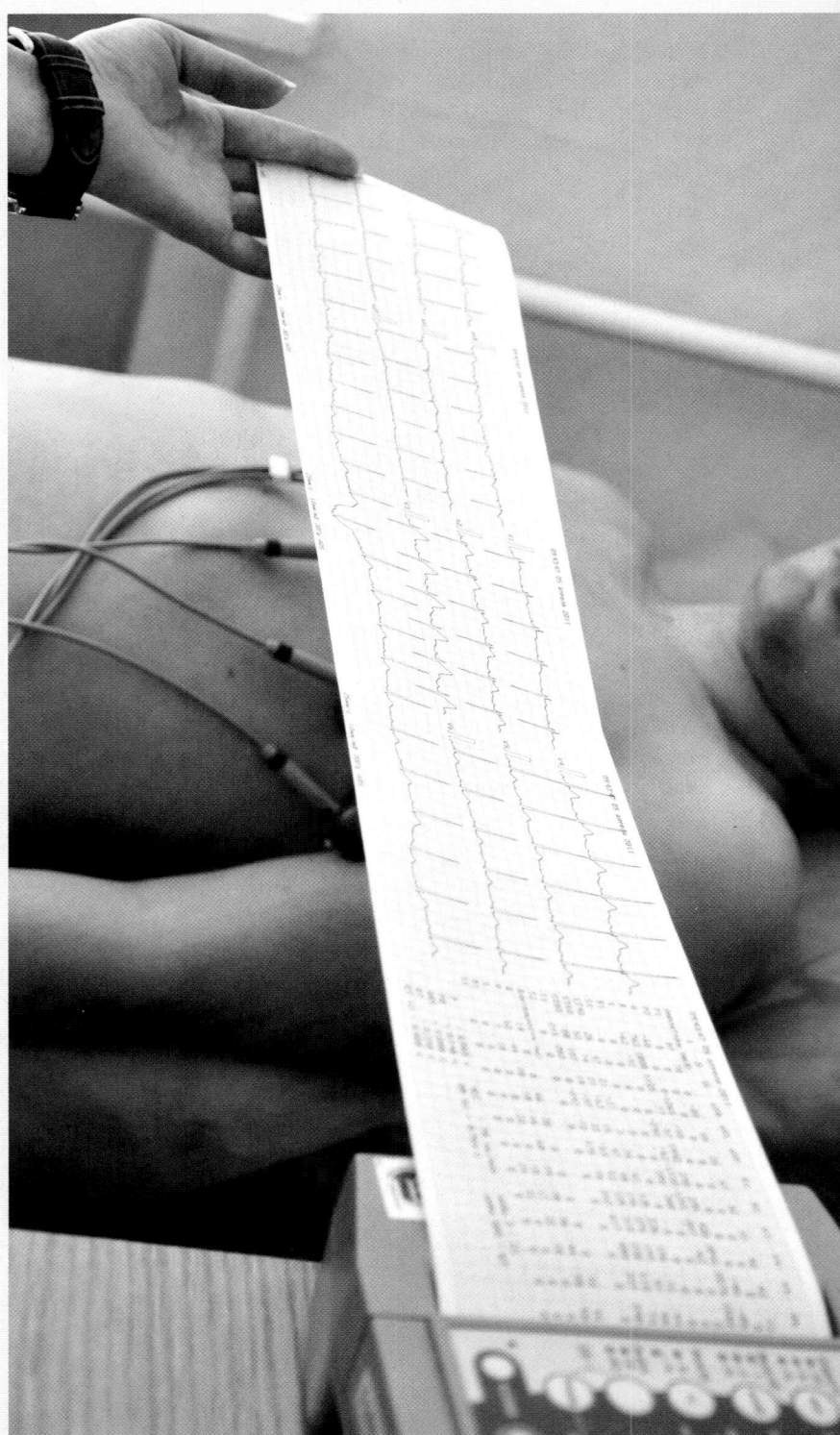

▲ The electrocardiogram (ECG) seen here is a recording of the electrical signals generated by the patient's beating heart. This recording helps the physician team determine what may be wrong with the patient's heart.

Ann, an emergency room (ER) nurse, is challenged with a variety of patients every shift. One night two patients required immediate, rapid care. The first, 52-year-old John Smith, arrived with central chest pain radiating to his left arm and difficulty breathing. These symptoms suggest heart attack as one diagnosis. A few minutes later, 75-year-old Brenda Givens arrived. She had difficulty speaking and walking and one side of her face was droopy. Ann recognized these as signs of a stroke—brain damage usually caused by a blood clot in the brain. The ER doctor ordered continuous electrocardiogram (EKG) monitoring and several blood tests for both patients. Both Mr. Smith and Ms. Givens had their blood tested for enzymes and selected proteins that normally are found only inside intact cells. These tests helped in diagnosis by ruling out other possible problems and confirming the other symptoms. For a heart attack, Mr. Smith's damaged heart cells released several enzymes specific to the heart and a large quantity of troponins, small proteins intimately involved with muscle cell contraction. Blood lipid levels were also checked for both patients. Ms. Givens was treated intravenously with tissue plasminogen activator (tPA) to activate plasminogen, which acts on fibrin, the major protein in blood clots. This treatment dissolved the blood clot and restored blood flow to the affected part of the brain. Enzymes, the subject of this chapter, are used for both diagnosis and treatment of many medical conditions.

Animals and plants are composed of millions of cells organized into different functional types. Among the many thousands of protein molecules in each cell, there are more than 2000 different specialized proteins, called enzymes, each one used in a different reaction. Although enzymes—powerful and highly selective biological catalysts—carry out the chemical reactions in cells, how do cells organize so many different reactions so that all occur to the proper extent? The answer is that all enzyme reactions in living organisms are under tight regulation by a variety of mechanisms. An important difference between chemistry in a laboratory and chemistry in a living organism is control. In a laboratory, the speed of a reaction is controlled by adjusting experimental conditions such as temperature, solvent, and pH. In an organism, these conditions cannot be adjusted. The human body maintains a temperature near 37 °C (99 °F), the solvent must be water, and the pH must be close to 7.4 in most body fluids.

In this chapter, the focus will be on enzymes and the regulation of enzymatic reactions. We will also look at *vitamins* and *minerals,* because they are essential to the function of certain enzymes. Chapter 28 is devoted to the role of *hormones* and *neurotransmitters* in keeping our biochemistry under control, which they do primarily by regulating the activity of enzymes.

19.1 Catalysis by Enzymes

Learning Objective:

• Describe the function of enzymes in biochemical reactions.

Enzymes are catalysts that accelerate the rates of biochemical reactions but at the end of the reaction remain unchanged themselves. However, as catalysts, enzymes do change the molecules acted on by breaking existing bonds and forming new ones in the reaction products. Like all catalysts, an enzyme does not affect the equilibrium point of a reaction and cannot bring about a reaction that is energetically unfavorable. Rather, an enzyme decreases the time it takes for the reaction to reach equilibrium by lowering its activation energy.

Enzyme A protein or other molecule that acts as a catalyst for a biological reaction.

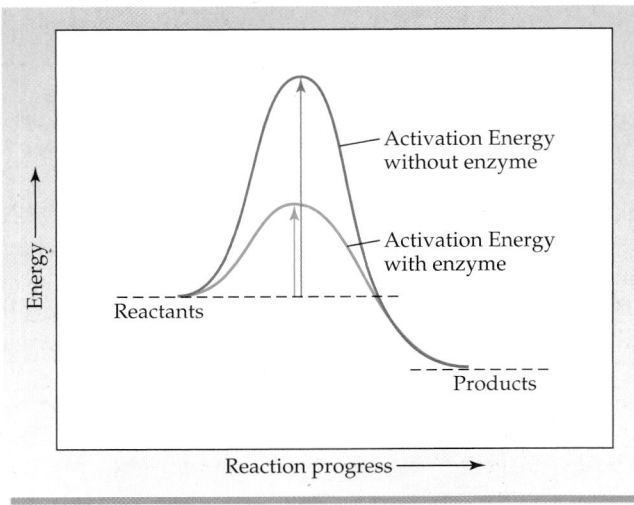

◄◄ **CONCEPTS TO REVIEW** See Figure 7.4 for a visual representation of the effect of a catalyst on a reaction's activation energy.

Active site A pocket in an enzyme with the specific shape and chemical makeup necessary to bind a substrate.

Substrate A reactant in an enzyme-catalyzed reaction.

Specificity (enzyme) The limitation of the activity of an enzyme to a specific substrate, specific reaction, or specific type of reaction.

Enzymes, with few exceptions, are water-soluble globular proteins (Section 18.9). As proteins, they are far larger and more complex molecules than simple inorganic catalysts. Because of their size and complexity, enzymes have more ways available in which to connect with reactants, speed up reactions, and be controlled by other molecules.

Within the folds of an enzyme's protein chain is the **active site**—the region where the reaction takes place. The active site has the specific shape and chemical reactivity needed to catalyze the reaction. One or more **substrates** (the substance the enzyme binds to and the reactants in an enzyme-catalyzed reaction) are held in place by intermolecular forces to groups that line the active site.

The extent to which an enzyme's activity is limited to a certain substrate and a certain type of reaction is referred to as the **specificity** of the enzyme. Enzymes differ greatly in their specificity. *Catalase,* for example, catalyzes one reaction: the decomposition of hydrogen peroxide (Figure 19.1). Catalase destroys hydrogen peroxide before it oxidizes essential biomolecules, damaging them.

$$\text{Reactant} \quad \overset{\text{Enzyme}}{\underset{\text{Catalase}}{}} \quad \text{Products}$$

$$2\,H_2O_2 \; \underset{\text{Reversible reaction}}{\rightleftharpoons} \; 2\,H_2O + O_2\,(g)$$

HANDS-ON CHEMISTRY 19.1

Do food items contain active catalase? You can test this at home with samples of raw meat and vegetables. You will need clear (not colored), transparent glasses, 3% hydrogen peroxide (from a drugstore or grocery store), and a few 1 cm cubes of raw meat such as chicken liver or a bit of hamburger. Also cube some raw potato. Drop some of the raw meat in a glass with an inch or two of hydrogen peroxide in it. Using a different glass of hydrogen peroxide, do the same thing with potato cubes. What happened with the meat? With the potato? Does the amount

of meat or potato used matter? Repeat your experiment with cooked meat and cooked potato. What happened?

Evolution of bubbles means catalase present in the sample was converting hydrogen peroxide to water and oxygen; the enzyme was active, in its native state and not denatured. If no significant amount of bubbles appeared, catalase was either absent or inactive. Based on the results of the trials with raw and cooked samples, was catalase present, absent, or inactive? If inactive, why?

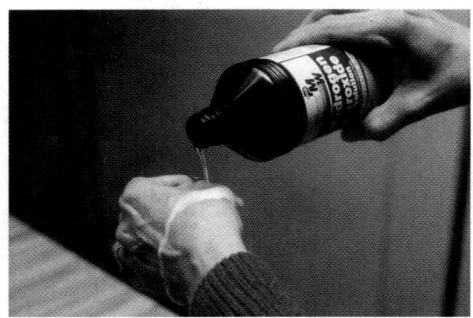

▲ **Figure 19.1**
Dilute hydrogen peroxide is frequently used to treat minor wounds. The bubbles produced are oxygen due to the action of the enzyme catalase released from injured tissue and bacteria.

Thrombin is specific for catalyzing hydrolysis of a peptide bond following the amino acid arginine and primarily acts on fibrinogen, a protein essential to blood clotting. When this bond breaks, the product (fibrin) proceeds to polymerize into a blood clot (Section 29.5). *Carboxypeptidase A* is less specific—it removes many different C-terminal amino acid residues from protein chains during digestion. And the enzyme *papain* from papaya fruit catalyzes the hydrolysis of peptide bonds in many locations. It is this ability to break down proteins that accounts for the use of papain in meat tenderizers, in contact-lens cleaners, and in cleansing dead or infected tissue from wounds (*debridement*).

Since the amino acids in enzymes are all L-amino acids, it should come as no surprise that enzymes are also specific with respect to stereochemistry. If a substrate is chiral, an enzyme usually catalyzes the reaction of only one of the pair of enantiomers because only one fits the active site in such a way that the reaction can occur. The enzyme lactate dehydrogenase (LDH), for example, catalyzes the removal of hydrogen from L-lactate but not from D-lactate.

$$\underset{\text{L-Lactate}}{\overset{\displaystyle\overset{\displaystyle O}{\underset{\displaystyle |}{\overset{\displaystyle \|}{C}}}\!\!\overset{\displaystyle O^-}{}}{\underset{\displaystyle CH_3}{\overset{\displaystyle |}{\underset{\displaystyle |}{HO-C-H}}}} + NAD^+ \underset{\text{dehydrogenase}}{\overset{\text{Lactate}}{\rightleftharpoons}} \underset{\text{Pyruvate}}{\overset{\displaystyle\overset{\displaystyle O}{\underset{\displaystyle |}{\overset{\displaystyle \|}{C}}}\!\!\overset{\displaystyle O^-}{}}{\underset{\displaystyle CH_3}{\overset{\displaystyle |}{\underset{\displaystyle |}{C=O}}}} + NADH + H^+$$

Substrate   Oxidized coenzyme   Product   Reduced coenzyme

This is another example of the importance of molecular shape in biochemistry. The specificity of an enzyme for one of two enantiomers is a matter of fit. A left-handed enzyme cannot fit with a right-handed substrate any more than a left-handed glove fits on a right hand (Figure 19.2).

The catalytic activity of an enzyme is measured by its **turnover number,** the maximum number of substrate molecules acted upon by one molecule of enzyme per unit time (Table 19.1). Most enzymes turn over 10–1000 molecules per second, but some are much faster. Catalase, with its essential role in protecting against molecular damage, is one of the fastest—it can turn over 10 million molecules per second. This is the fastest reaction rate attainable in the body because it is the rate at which molecules collide.

Turnover number The maximum number of substrate molecules acted upon by one molecule of enzyme per unit time.

Table 19.1 Turnover Numbers for Some Enzymes (Maximum Number of Catalytic Events Per Second)

Enzyme	Reaction Catalyzed	Turnover Number
Papain	Hydrolysis of peptide bonds	10
Ribonuclease	Hydrolysis of phosphate ester link in ribonucleic acid (RNA)	10^2
Kinase	Transfer of phosphoryl group between substrates	10^3
Acetylcholinesterase	Deactivation of the neurotransmitter acetylcholine	10^4
Carbonic anhydrase	Converts CO_2 to HCO_3^-	10^6
Catalase	Decomposition of H_2O_2 to $H_2O + O_2$	10^7

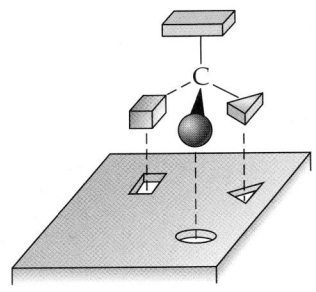

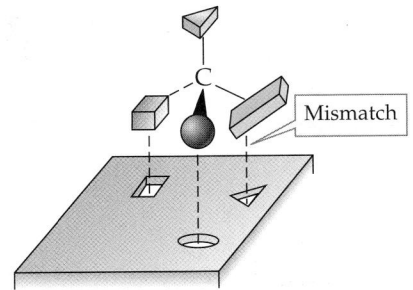

▲ **Figure 19.2**
A chiral reactant and a chiral reaction site.
The enantiomer at the top fits the reaction site like a hand in a glove, but the enantiomer at the bottom does not fit and therefore cannot be a substrate for this enzyme.

PROBLEM 19.1

Which of the enzymes listed in Table 19.1 catalyzes a maximum of 1000 reactions per second?

PROBLEM 19.2

The enzyme LDH converts lactate to pyruvate. In mammals, this enzyme accepts only L-lactate as substrate, but the correct substrate in invertebrates such as oysters is D-lactate. Explain why LDH has two different forms, each accepting one of the enantiomers of the substrate, lactate, but not the other.

19.2 Enzyme Cofactors

Learning Objective:

• Explain the role of cofactors in some enzymatic reactions.

Many enzymes are conjugated proteins that require nonprotein **cofactors** as part of their structure to function. Some cofactors are metal ions, while others are nonprotein organic molecules called **coenzymes.** To be active, an enzyme may require a metal ion, a coenzyme, or both. Some enzyme cofactors are tightly held by noncovalent intermolecular forces or are covalently bound to their enzymes; others are more loosely bound, entering and leaving the active site as needed.

Cofactor A nonprotein part of an enzyme that is essential to the enzyme's catalytic activity; a metal ion or a coenzyme.

Coenzyme An organic molecule that acts as an enzyme cofactor.

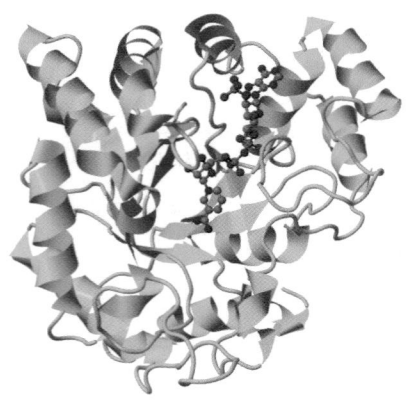

▲ The ribbon structure for aldose reductase, an oxidoreductase enzyme that reduces a C=O group in a sugar molecule to a —C—OH group with the aid of the coenzyme NADH. The sugar glucose (orange) and NADH (gray) are shown in the active site of the enzyme. Note the alpha helices in this enzyme.

Why are cofactors necessary? The functional groups in enzymes are limited to those of the amino acid side chains in the protein. By combining with cofactors, enzymes acquire chemically reactive groups not available in side chains. For example, as illustrated in the ribbon structure for aldose reductase, the nicotinamide adenine dinucleotide (NADH) molecule bound by intermolecular forces to aldose reductase (an enzyme) is a coenzyme and is the reducing agent that makes the reaction possible. (Vitamins that function as cofactors are discussed in Section 19.9.) Because many enzymes require metal ion cofactors, we need trace minerals in our diet. Table 19.2 shows the many different metal ions that function as enzyme cofactors.

Table 19.2 Inorganic Ion Cofactors

Ions	Enzyme Examples
$Cu^{2+}*$	Cytochrome oxidase
Fe^{2+} or $Fe^{3+}*$	Catalase, peroxidase
K^{+}	Pyruvate kinase
Mg^{2+}	Hexokinase, glucose-6-phosphatase
$Mn^{2+}*$	Arginase
Mo	Dinitrogenase
Ni^{2+}	Urease
Se*	Glutathione peroxidase
$Zn^{2+}*$	Alcohol dehydrogenase

*Trace minerals

◀◀◀ Recall from Section 4.4 that a coordinate covalent bond is one that is formed when both electrons are donated by the same atom.

◀◀◀ Review Lewis acids and bases from Sections 4.6 and 4.7

Metal ions are able to form coordinate covalent bonds and function as Lewis acids by accepting lone-pair electrons present on nitrogen or oxygen atoms in enzymes or substrates. This bonding may anchor a substrate in the active site and may also allow the metal ion to participate in the catalyzed reaction. For example, every molecule of the digestive enzyme carboxypeptidase A contains one Zn^{2+} ion that is essential for its catalytic action. We say that the zinc ion is "coordinated" to a nitrogen atom in each of two histidine side chains and one oxygen atom in a glutamate side chain in the active site. In this way, the ion is held in place in the active site of the enzyme.

Metal ion in enzyme active site

Coordinate covalent bond

Zn^{2+}

HN N: :N NH

His 69   Ö⁻   His 196

C=O

Glu 72

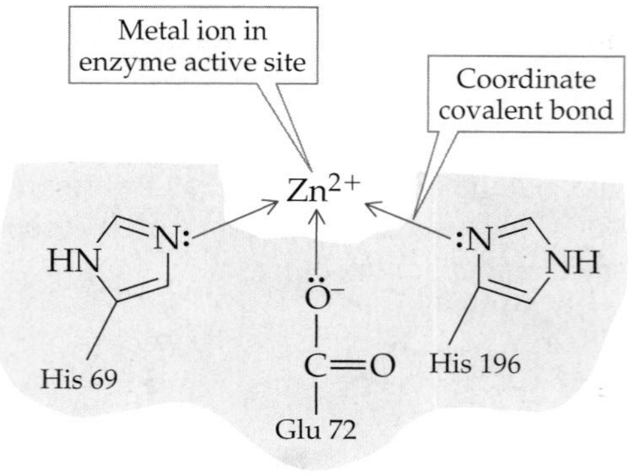

Like the trace minerals that are our source of metal ion cofactors, certain vitamins are also a dietary necessity for humans because we cannot synthesize them in the body, yet they are critical building blocks for coenzymes. See Table 19.3 for examples.

Table 19.3 Some Important Coenzymes

Coenzyme	Type of Chemical Group Moved	Dietary Molecule
Coenzyme A	Acyl groups	Pantothenic acid
Coenzyme B_{12}	H atoms and alkyl groups	Vitamin B_{12}
Flavin adenine dinucleotide (FAD)	Electrons	Riboflavin (vitamin B_{12})
Nicotinamide adenine dinucleotide (NAD^+)	Hydride ion ($:H^-$)	Nicotinic acid (niacin)
Pyridoxyl phosphate	Amino groups	Pyridoxine (vitamin B_6)

HANDS-ON CHEMISTRY 19.2

Check the label on a bottle of multivitamin/multimineral tablets and identify any metal ion cofactors listed in Table 19.2 that are included in the supplement. Identify the dietary molecules listed in Table 19.3 as well.

KEY CONCEPT PROBLEM 19.3

The cofactors NAD^+, Cu^{2+}, Zn^{2+}, coenzyme A, FAD, and Ni^{2+} are all needed by your body for enzymatic reactions.

(a) Which cofactors are coenzymes?

(b) What is the primary difference between coenzymes and cofactors?

19.3 Enzyme Classification

Learning Objectives:

- Give an enzyme the appropriate name given the substrate.
- Assign an enzyme to the correct class based on its reaction.

MASTERING REACTIONS

How to Read Biochemical Reactions

At first glance, biochemical reactions appear complicated. However, biochemical reactions are simply organic chemistry reactions inside living organisms. Let us look at the following reaction and dissect it for understanding.

Firstly, this is a one-way, two-step reaction catalyzed by the same enzyme for both steps where no helper molecules are needed. Like the reactions you have seen throughout the text, this reaction also occurs from left to right, with citrate as the first substrate and aconitate as the first product. Then aconitate becomes the second substrate and isocitrate forms the second (and final) product. We also see that H_2O is removed in the first step and added back in the second step. If you compare the initial substrate (citrate) to the final product (isocitrate), notice that they both have exactly the same number of C atoms, O atoms, and H atoms. Therefore, the atoms have been rearranged, but the number of atoms in product and substrate are exactly the same and of the same kind. Aconitate, however, has the same number of C atoms but one less O atom and two fewer H atoms than either citrate or isocitrate. Aconitase, then, must be an isomerase because citrate, the first substrate, and isocitrate, the final product, are isomers. Remember, only an isomerase can convert one molecule into its isomer, generally through an intermediate form as seen in this reaction.

You can use the same step-by-step process to read any biochemical reaction and identify the substrates and enzymes within the reaction.

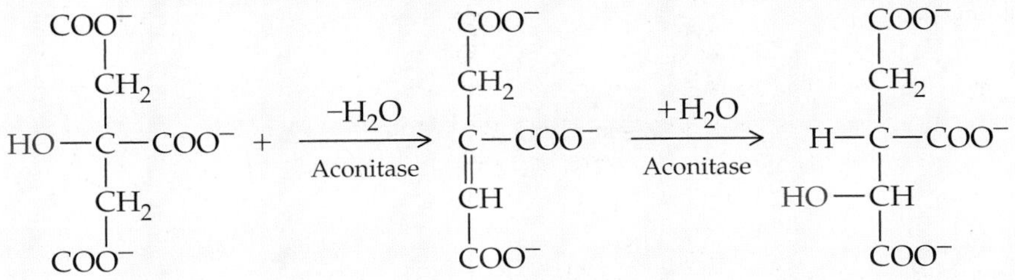

Nomenclature of Enzymes

Most enzymes have the family-name ending *-ase*. Exceptions to this rule occur for enzymes such as papain and trypsin, which are still referred to by older common names. The more informative systematic names typically have two parts: the first identifies the substrate (reactant) on which the enzyme operates, and the second part is an enzyme class name that describes the reaction. For example, *pyruvate carboxylase* is a ligase that acts on the substrate *pyruvate* to add a *carboxyl group*. Some enzymes are named by dropping the terminal syllable and adding *-ase* to the substrate name. Fumarase, an enzyme that converts fumarate to succinate in the citric acid cycle, is one. The enzymes that act on a few other long-studied substrates such as urea and sucrose are named in the same way, that is, urease and sucrase. Note also that some enzymes are capable of catalyzing both forward and reverse reactions, and where both directions are of significance, the equations are written with double arrows.

Enzyme Classification

Thousands of enzymes keep our bodies running. Not every enzyme is found in every cell in the body; enzymes are specialists that are found only where needed. Enzymes are divided into six main classes according to the kind of reaction catalyzed, and each main class is further subdivided based on substrate specificity. Table 19.4 lists the main classes and subclasses with examples.

Table 19.4 Classification of Enzymes

	Examples
Main Class: **Oxidoreductases** catalyze oxidation–reduction reactions. **Subclasses:** *Oxidases* catalyze oxidation by addition of O_2 to a substrate. *Reductases* catalyze reduction of a substrate. *Dehydrogenases* catalyze the removal or addition of 2 H atoms and require a coenzyme.	Alcohol dehydrogenase, an *oxidoreductase*, is found in liver cells, and it oxidizes naturally occurring alcohols found in foods to aldehydes and ketones. In yeast, this enzyme provides the first step in metabolizing ethanol, a component of beer, wine, and distilled spirits. $\text{A(Reduced)} + \text{B(Oxidized)} \longrightarrow \text{A}'\text{(Oxidized)} + \text{B}'\text{(Reduced)}$ $\underset{\text{Reduced substrate}}{CH_3{-}CH_2{-}OH} + \underset{\text{Oxidized coenzyme}}{NAD^+} \xrightleftharpoons{\text{Alcohol dehydrogenase}} \underset{\text{Oxidized product}}{CH_3{-}\overset{O}{\overset{\Vert}{C}}{-}H} + \underset{\text{Reduced coenzyme}}{NADH} + H^+$
Main Class: **Transferases** catalyze the transfer of a functional group between two different compounds. **Subclasses:** *Transaminases* catalyze the transfer of an amino group from one substrate to another using energy supplied by adenosine triphosphate (ATP). *Kinases* catalyze the transfer of phosphate groups from one substrate to another.	Phosphofructokinase, a *transferase*, transfers a phosphate group from ATP to fructose-6-phosphate to complete the energy priming process in the catabolism (degradation) of glucose. Glucose catabolism is an important energy source for our bodies and is examined in depth in Chapter 22. Glycolysis occurs in brain and muscle tissue. $\text{A} + \text{B{-}C} \rightleftharpoons \text{A{-}B} + \text{C}$ Fructose 6-phosphate; Fructose 1,6-*bis*phosphate

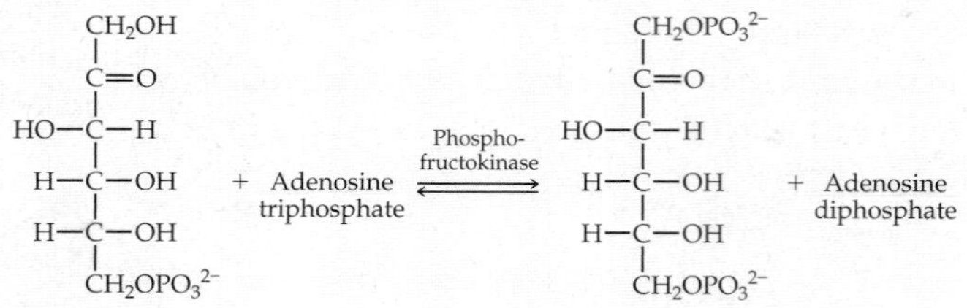

Main Class:

Hydrolases catalyze bond breaking with the addition of water as H and OH to the fragments.

  Subclasses:

  Lipases break glycerides (fats) into glycerol and fatty acids.

  Proteases break proteins into peptides and amino acids.

  Amylases break starch into sugars.

  Nucleases break deoxyribonucleic acid (DNA) and RNA into nucleic acids.

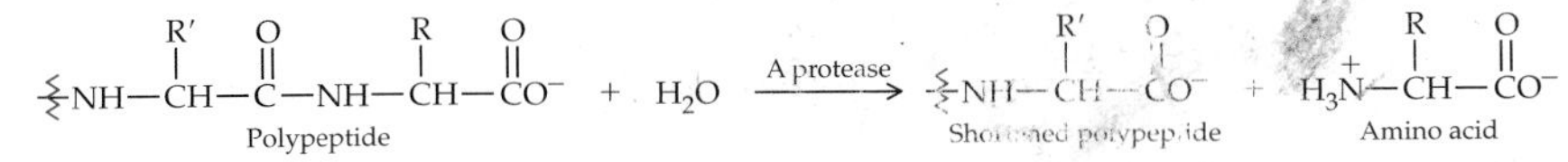

Main Class:

Isomerases catalyze the rearrangement of atoms in a substrate.

  No Subclasses

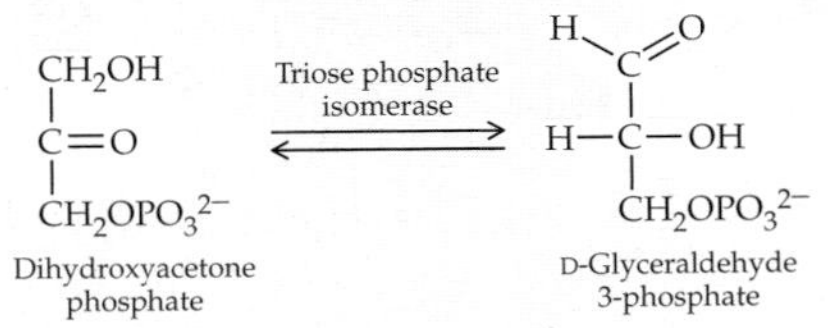

Main Class:

Lyases catalyze the addition or elimination of a functional group from a substrate without hydrolysis.

  Subclasses:

  Decarboxylases catalyze the removal of CO_2.

  Deaminases catalyze the removal of NH_3.

  Dehydratases catalyze the removal of H_2O.

  Hydratases catalyze the addition of H_2O.

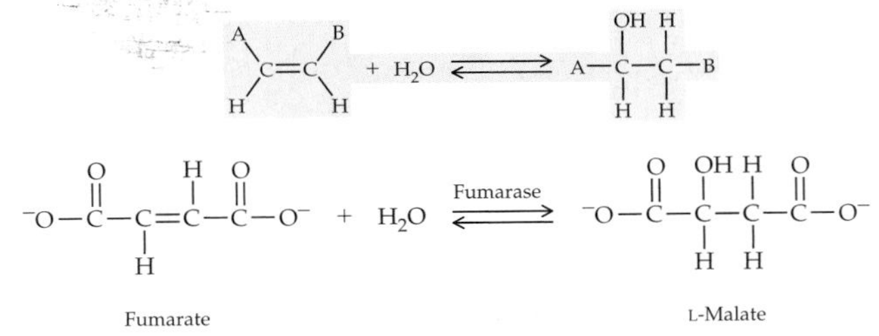

Main Class:

Ligases catalyze the bonding of two substrate molecules.

  Subclasses:

  Synthetases catalyze the formation between two substrates using ATP energy.

  Carboxylases catalyze the formation of a bond between CO_2 and a substrate using ATP energy.

Hydrolases are particularly important during digestion. Proteins are hydrolyzed into amino acids by various proteases, and carbohydrates such as starch, lactose, and sucrose are hydrolyzed to glucose, fructose, and galactose by specific enzymes. Hydrolases are essential to provide amino acids for protein synthesis and glucose for use in energy generating pathways.

During glycolysis (the breakdown of glucose to produce energy) the enzyme triose phosphate isomerase ensures that both of the products of an intermediate step can be further used. It does so by converting dihydroxyacetone phosphate, which otherwise cannot be further metabolized, to D-glyceraldehyde 3-phosphate, the substrate for the next enzyme in the glycolysis reaction sequence. Because of *isomerases,* maximum energy can be obtained from glucose metabolism. Glycolysis occurs in all cells but primarily in red blood cells, kidney, brain, and muscle tissue.

Fumarase, an enzyme found in the citric acid cycle, is a *lyase.* The citric acid cycle occurs in the mitochondria of cells. Plant lyases are responsible for fruit softening and ripening by degrading pectin, a structural component of plant cell walls.

Ligases are involved in synthesis of biological polymers such as proteins and DNA. DNA ligase both repairs DNA in response to environmental damage such as ultraviolet (UV) rays from the sun or exposure to chemical carcinogens and links nucleic acids during DNA replication, which occurs in cell division during development and tissue regeneration. Protein and DNA ligases are found in nearly all cells.

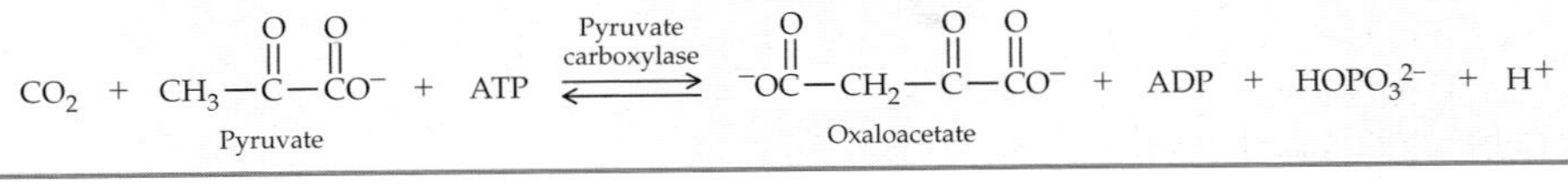

Worked Example 19.1 Classifying Enzymes

To what class does the enzyme that catalyzes the following reaction belong?

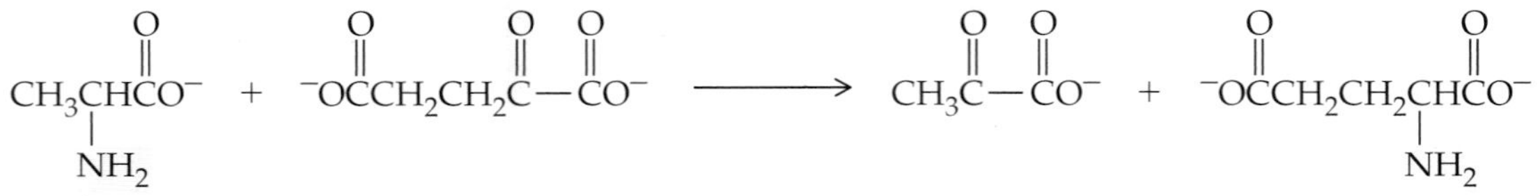

$$CH_3\underset{NH_2}{\overset{O}{\overset{\|}{CHCO^-}}} + {}^-\overset{O}{\overset{\|}{OCCH_2CH_2\overset{O}{\overset{\|}{C}}}}-\overset{O}{\overset{\|}{CO^-}} \longrightarrow CH_3\overset{O}{\overset{\|}{C}}-\overset{O}{\overset{\|}{CO^-}} + {}^-\overset{O}{\overset{\|}{OCCH_2CH_2}}\underset{NH_2}{\overset{O}{\overset{\|}{CHCO^-}}}$$

ANALYSIS First, identify the type of reaction that has occurred by "reading" the chemical reaction to find what has changed. An amino group and a carbonyl keto oxygen atom have been exchanged between the two molecules, forming two different molecules. Then, determine what class of enzyme catalyzes a functional group exchange.

SOLUTION
Because the amino group and carbonyl keto oxygen atom (highlighted in yellow) have changed places, the reaction is a transfer of an amino functional group; therefore, the enzyme is a transferase.

PROBLEM 19.4

Describe the reactions that you would expect these enzymes to catalyze.

(a) Alcohol dehydrogenase   (b) Aspartate transaminase

(c) Tyrosine-tRNA synthetase   (d) Phosphohexose isomerase

PROBLEM 19.5

Name the enzyme whose substrate is

(a) Urea   (b) Cellulose

PROBLEM 19.6

To what class of enzymes does hexokinase belong? Describe in general the reaction it catalyzes.

PROBLEM 19.7

Identify and describe the chemical change in the lyase-catalyzed reaction in Table 19.4 that involves fumarate and malate. Identify the substrate(s) and product(s).

PROBLEM 19.8

Which of the following reactions can be catalyzed by a decarboxylase?

(a)

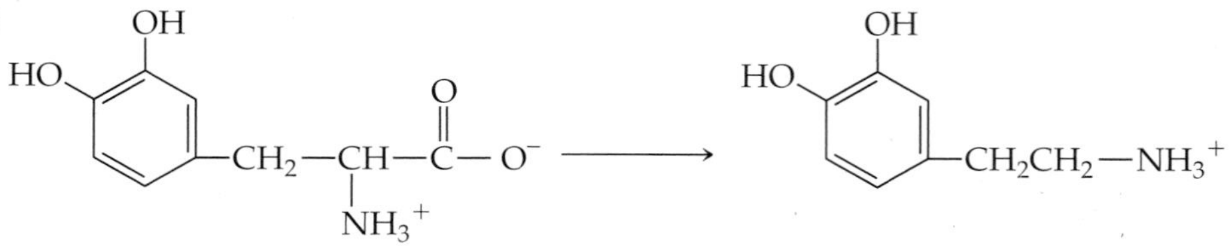

(b)

$${}^+H_3NCH_2CH_2CH_2-\overset{O}{\overset{\|}{C}}-O^- \longrightarrow H-\overset{O}{\overset{\|}{C}}-CH_2CH_2\overset{O}{\overset{\|}{C}}-O^-$$

19.4 How Enzymes Work

Learning Objectives:

- Explain the two models of enzyme catalysis.
- Describe how an enzyme and substrate combine to facilitate a reaction.

Enzyme *specificity* is determined by the active site, which provides the exact right environment for the reaction to take place. There, amino acid side-chain groups from the enzyme attract and hold the substrate or substrates in position through noncovalent, intermolecular forces and sometimes by temporary covalent bonding. The active site also may contain acidic or basic side chains needed for catalysis of the reaction.

Descriptions of catalysis reactions are often written in general symbols: E (enzyme), S (substrate), P (product), [P] (concentration of product), ES (enzyme–substrate complex), and EP (enzyme–product complex). A reaction is written as

$$E + S \rightarrow ES \rightarrow EP \rightarrow E + P$$

Instead of

$$Enzyme + Substrate \rightarrow Enzyme–substrate\ complex \rightarrow Enzyme–product\ complex \rightarrow Enzyme + Product$$

Two Models of Enzyme–Substrate Interaction

Two models explain the interaction between substrates and enzymes. Historically, the **lock-and-key model** came first; it was proposed when the need for a spatial fit between substrates and enzymes was first recognized. The substrate is described as fitting into the active site as a key fits into a lock; the fit is rigid and unchanging, and only one substrate fits one specific enzyme, just like a key for a lock.

Lock-and-key model A model of enzyme action in which the enzyme is a rigid lock that exactly fits the substrate, the key for the reaction.

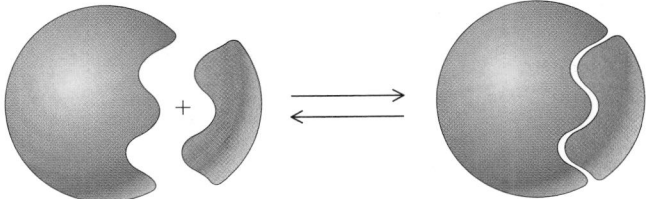

Enzyme + substrate   Enzyme–substrate complex

When it became possible to study enzyme–substrate interaction more closely, experimental results suggested the *lock-and-key model* was incorrect. Modern understanding of molecular structure makes it clear that enzyme molecules are not totally rigid, like locks. The **induced-fit model** accounts for changes in the shape of the enzyme active site that accommodates the substrate (and other, similar substrates) and facilitates the reaction. As an enzyme and substrate come together, their interaction induces exactly the right fit for catalysis of the reaction.

Induced-fit model A model of enzyme action in which the enzyme has a flexible active site that changes shape to best fit the substrate and catalyze the reaction.

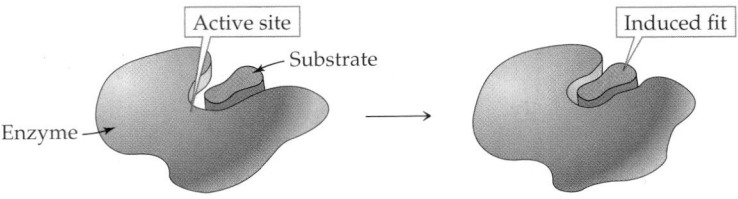

Figure 19.3 illustrates a well-studied example of induced fit, the interaction between glucose (a hexose) and hexokinase. The transferase reaction is a phosphorylation—the addition of a phosphoryl group to a —OH group—catalyzed by a kinase. The reaction is the first step in glucose metabolism (Section 22.3). Notice in Figure 19.3 on the following page how the enzyme closes in once the glucose molecule has entered the active site—this is the induced fit.

▶ **Figure 19.3**

A space-filling model showing the induced fit of hexokinase (blue) and its substrate, glucose (red).
(a) The active site is a groove in the hexokinase molecule. (b) When glucose enters the active site, the enzyme changes shape, wrapping itself more closely around the substrate.

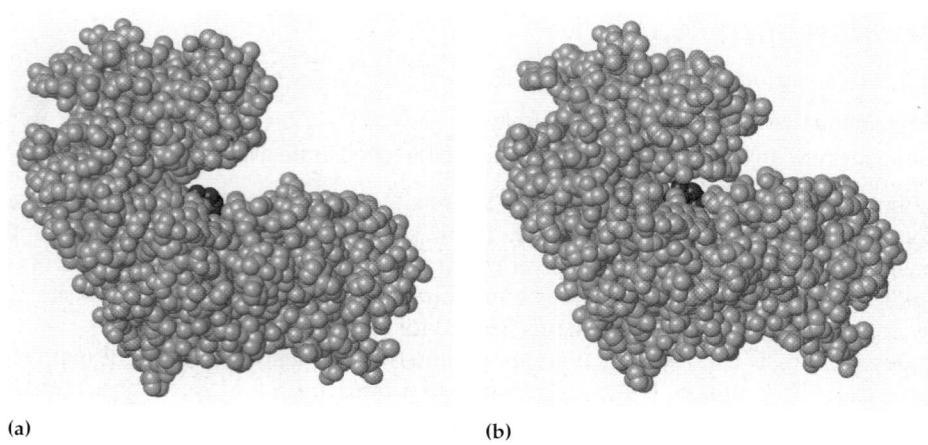

(a) (b)

Enzyme-catalyzed reactions begin with migration of the substrate (S) or substrates into the active site of the enzyme (E) to form an *enzyme–substrate complex* (ES). The substrate is first drawn into position by the same kinds of noncovalent forces that govern the shapes of protein molecules (see Figure 19.4).

Before forming an enzyme–substrate complex, the substrate molecule is in its most stable, lowest-energy shape. Within the enzyme–substrate complex, the substrate is forced into a less stable shape, and bonding electrons may be drawn away from some bonds in preparation for breaking them and forming new bonds. The result is that the *activation energy barrier between substrate and product is lowered* without the need for a large energy input. This is shown in the energy diagram on page 591 comparing the energy input needed for a purely chemical reaction with the same reaction catalyzed by an enzyme.

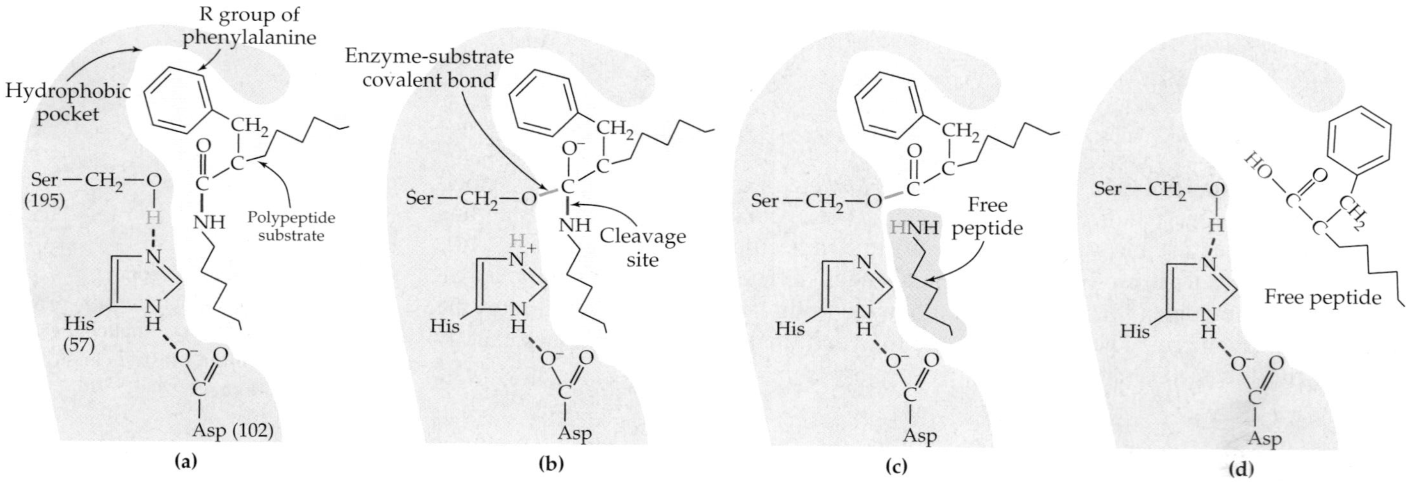

(a) (b) (c) (d)

▲ **Figure 19.4**

Hydrolysis of a peptide bond by chymotrypsin.

(a) The polypeptide enters the enzyme active site with its hydrophobic side chain (the aromatic ring) in the hydrophobic pocket and the peptide bond to be broken (red) opposite serine and histidine residues. (b) H^+ transfer from serine to histidine allows formation of a strained intermediate in which the serine side chain bonds to the peptide bond carbon (green). (c) The peptide bond is broken and the segment with the new terminal —NH_2 group leaves the active site. (d) In subsequent steps, a water molecule enters the active site; its H atom restores the serine side chain and its —OH bonds to the other piece of the substrate protein to give a new terminal —COOH group so that this piece can also leave the active site.

Within the enzyme–substrate complex, atoms that will form new bonds must connect with each other. The new bonds might be with a second substrate or temporary bonds with atoms in the enzyme. Also, groups needed for catalysis must be close to the correct locations in the substrate. Many organic reactions, for example, require acidic, basic, or metal ion catalysts. An enzyme's active site can provide acidic and basic groups without disrupting the constant-pH environment in body fluids, while the necessary metal ions are present as cofactors. Once the chemical reaction is completed, enzyme and product molecules separate from each other and the enzyme, restored to its original condition, becomes available for another substrate molecule.

The hydrolysis of a peptide bond by chymotrypsin, shown in Figure 19.4, illustrates how an enzyme functions. Chymotrypsin is one of several enzymes active in the digestion of proteins by breaking them down to smaller molecules. It cleaves polypeptide chains by breaking the peptide bond on the carbonyl side of amino acid residues that include an aromatic ring.

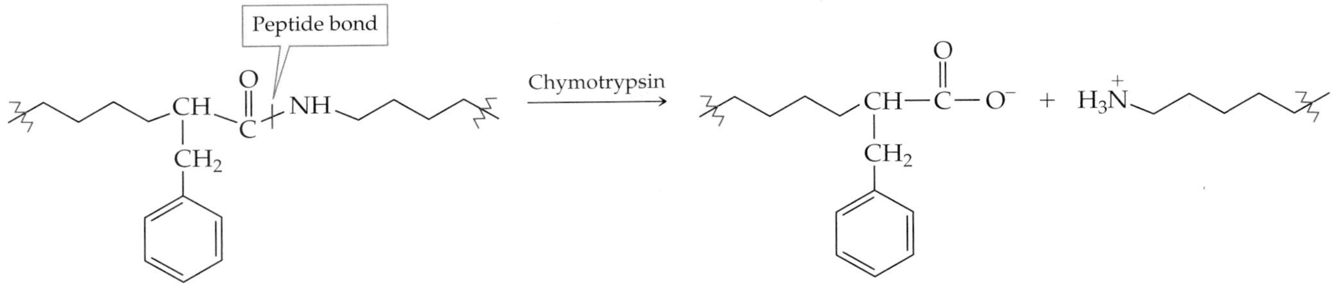

The enzyme–substrate complex forms (Figure 19.4a and b) due to stabilization of a substrate hydrophobic side chain (here, the aromatic ring) in a hydrophobic pocket in the enzyme active site by intermolecular forces and the subsequent formation of a covalent bond (green) to the substrate. The result is to position the substrate with the peptide bond to be broken (red) next to the amino acid side chains that function as catalysts. The enzyme has not only bound to the substrate (the *proximity effect*) but has done so in such a way as to bring the groups that must connect close to each other (the *orientation effect*). Aspartate, histidine, and serine provide functional groups needed for catalysis within the active site (the *catalytic effect*). As an illustration of the critical nature of protein folding, note that in the 241-amino-acid primary structure of chymotrypsin, aspartate is number 102, histidine is number 57, and serine is number 195. These amino acids are distant from each other along the linear backbone but are brought close together by backbone folding so that their side chains are in exactly the positions needed in the active site.

With the peptide bond carbon atom temporarily bonded to serine in the active site, it is easier for the peptide bond to break because the activation energy barrier has been lowered (the *energy effect*). As the bond breaks, nitrogen picks up a hydrogen atom (blue) from histidine to form the new terminal amino group and this portion of the substrate is set free (Figure 19.4c). Reaction with a water molecule restores the hydrogen to serine and supplies an OH group to form the new terminal carboxyl group of the shortened peptide. This part of the substrate is set free and the enzyme is restored to its original state (Figure 19.4d).

In summary, enzymes act as catalysts because of their following abilities to:

- Bring substrates and catalytic sites together (*proximity effect*)
- Hold substrates at the exact distance and in the exact orientation necessary for reaction (*orientation effect*)
- Provide acidic, basic, or other types of groups required for catalysis (*catalytic effect*)
- Lower the energy barrier by inducing strain in bonds in the substrate molecule (*energy effect*)

Worked Example 19.2 Identifying active site side-chain functions

Look at the hydrolysis of a peptide bond by chymotrypsin in Figure 19.4.

(a) Which amino acids have side chains that could provide stabilization to the aromatic ring shown in the substrate?

(b) What does the serine side chain do in the reaction and why can it do this?

(c) What does the histidine side chain do in the reaction and why can it do this?

ANALYSIS Look critically at the diagrams of the reaction in Figure 19.4 to follow the movement of atoms. Consider each part of the question separately, using the diagrams as an aid.

(a) Note that the aromatic ring of phenylalanine fits into a "hydrophobic pocket." Therefore, the side chains of the amino acids surrounding this pocket in chymotrypsin must be nonpolar.

(b) In the second diagram, note that serine has donated a hydrogen ion to histidine. Remember that acids are proton donors.

(c) Also in the second diagram, note that histidine has accepted a proton from serine. Remember that bases are proton acceptors.

SOLUTION

(a) Any of the following nonpolar amino acids could be part of the hydrophobic pocket in chymotrypsin: alanine, leucine, isoleucine, methionine, proline, valine, phenylalanine, or tryptophan (see Table 18.3).

(b) Serine is a polar amino acid and can donate a proton from the —OH group on the side chain, functioning as an acid. The RO⁻ remaining can interact with the substrate, initiating cleavage of the substrate.

(c) Histidine is a basic amino acid and can accept a proton until needed to complete the cleavage reaction.

In this example, nonpolar amino acids held the substrate in place via weak intermolecular forces while amino acids that could act as acids or bases carried out the reaction.

KEY CONCEPT PROBLEM 19.9

The active sites of enzymes usually contain amino acids with acidic, basic, and polar side chains. Some enzymes also have amino acids with nonpolar side chains in their active sites. Which types of side chains would you expect to participate in holding the substrate in the active site? Which types would you expect to be involved in the catalytic activity of the enzyme?

19.5 Factors Affecting Enzyme Activity

Learning Objective:

• Describe the changes in enzyme activity that result when substrate concentration, enzyme concentration, temperature, or pH change.

For a reaction to occur, the enzyme and substrate molecules must come together and form the enzyme–substrate complex. There are several factors that affect enzyme activity and cause a variation in the reaction rate. Substrate concentration, enzyme concentration, temperature, and pH all affect reaction rates. Enzymes have been finely tuned through evolution so that their maximum catalytic activity is dependent on these four factors. As you might expect, optimum conditions vary for each enzyme.

Substrate Concentration

Frequently, in cells, the substrate concentration varies while the enzyme concentration remains unchanged. If the substrate concentration is low relative to that of the enzyme, not all the enzyme molecules are in use. The reaction rate will increase as the concentration of substrate increases because more of the enzyme molecules are put to work. In this situation, shown at the far left of the curve in Figure 19.5, the rate increases as the available substrate increases. Initially, this is a directly proportional relationship, so if the substrate concentration doubles, the reaction rate doubles. However, as the substrate concentration continues to increase, the increase in the rate begins to level off as more of the active sites are occupied. (Think of people waiting in line to take their seats in a theater. The line moves more slowly as more seats fill and it becomes more difficult to find an empty one.) Eventually, the substrate concentration reaches a point at which none of the available active sites are free; the enzyme is saturated with substrate. The reaction rate is now determined by how fast the enzyme–substrate complex is converted to product. Since the maximum number of enzyme molecules are converting substrate to product at the same time, the rate of conversion from substrate to product occurs at the maximum rate for that reaction.

Once the enzyme is saturated, increasing substrate concentration has no effect on the rate. In the absence of a change in the concentration of the enzyme, the rate when the enzyme is saturated is determined by the efficiency of the enzyme, the pH, and the temperature.

Under most conditions, an enzyme is not likely to be saturated. Therefore, at a given pH and temperature, the reaction rate is controlled by the amount of substrate and the overall efficiency of the enzyme. If the enzyme–substrate complex is rapidly converted to product, the rate at which enzyme and substrate combine to form the complex becomes the limiting factor. Calculations show an upper limit to this rate: enzyme and substrate molecules moving at random in solution can collide with each other no faster than 10^8 collisions per mole per liter per second. Remarkably, a few enzymes actually operate close to this efficiency—every one of the collisions results in the formation of product! We saw an example of such an efficient enzyme earlier in catalase, the enzyme that breaks down hydrogen peroxide at the rate of 10^7 catalytic events per second (see Table 19.1).

Enzyme Concentration

It is possible for the concentration of an active enzyme to vary according to our metabolic needs. So long as the concentration of substrate does not become a limitation, the reaction rate varies directly with the enzyme concentration (Figure 19.6). If the enzyme concentration doubles, the rate doubles; if the enzyme concentration triples, the rate triples; and so on.

Effect of Temperature on Enzyme Activity

An increase in temperature increases the rate of most chemical reactions, and enzyme-catalyzed reactions are no exception. Unlike many simple reactions, however, the rates of enzyme-catalyzed reactions do not increase continuously with rising temperature. Instead, the rates reach a maximum and then begin to decrease, as shown in Figure 19.7a on the following page. This falloff in rate occurs because enzymes begin to denature when heated too strongly. The noncovalent attractions between protein side chains are disrupted, the delicately maintained three-dimensional shape of the enzyme begins to come apart, and as a result, the active site needed for catalytic activity is destroyed.

Most enzymes denature and lose their catalytic activity above 50–60 °C, a fact that explains why medical instruments and laboratory glassware are sterilized by heating with steam in an autoclave. The high temperature of the steam permanently denatures the enzymes of any bacteria present, killing them.

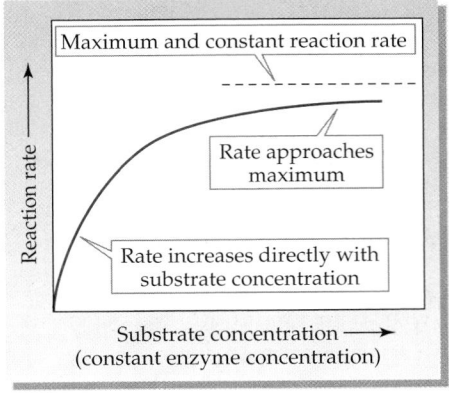

▲ **Figure 19.5**
Change of reaction rate with substrate concentration when enzyme concentration is constant.
At low substrate concentration, the reaction rate is directly proportional to the substrate concentration (at constant pH and temperature). With increasing substrate concentration, the increase in rate slows as more of the active sites are occupied. Eventually, with all active sites occupied, the rate reaches a maximum and constant rate.

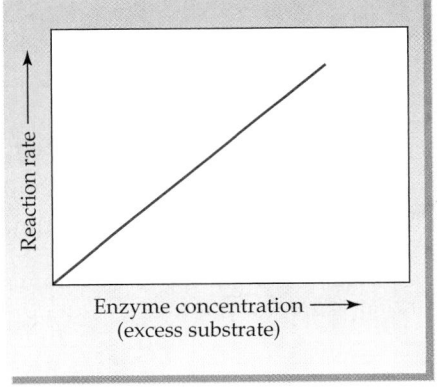

▲ Figure 19.6
Change of reaction rate with enzyme concentration in the presence of excess substrate.

◄◄◄ Review the chemical properties of proteins in Section 18.12.

▶ **Figure 19.7**

Effect of temperature (a) and pH (b) on reaction rate.

(a) The reaction rate increases with increasing temperature until a temperature is reached at which the enzyme begins to denature; then the rate decreases rapidly. (b) The optimum activity for an enzyme occurs at the pH where it acts, as illustrated for two protein hydrolysis enzymes—pepsin, which acts in the highly acidic environment of the stomach, and trypsin, which acts in the small intestine, an alkaline environment.

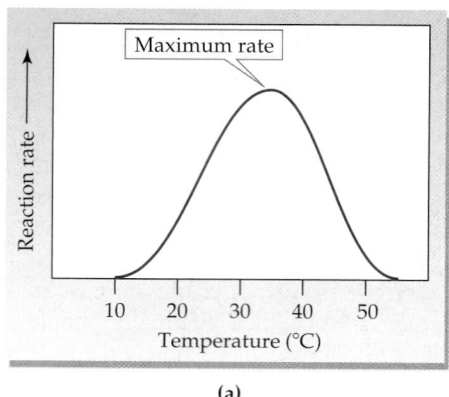

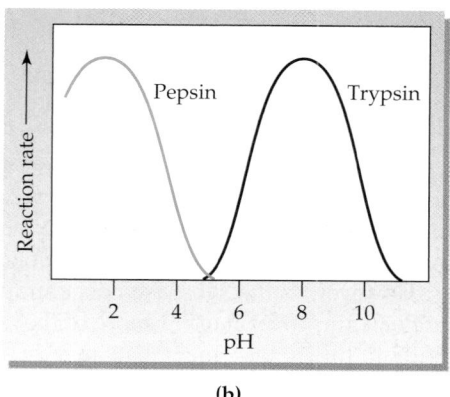

(a)

(b)

A severe drop in body temperature creates the potentially fatal condition of hypothermia, which is accompanied by a slowdown in metabolic reactions. This effect is used to advantage by cooling the body during cardiac surgery. Upon gentle warming, enzymatic reaction rates return to normal because cooling does not denature proteins.

Effect of pH on Enzyme Activity

The catalytic activity of many enzymes depends on pH and usually has a well-defined optimum point at the normal, buffered pH of the enzyme's environment. For example, pepsin, which initiates protein digestion in the highly acidic environment of the stomach, has its optimum activity at pH 2 (Figure 19.7b). By contrast, trypsin—like chymotrypsin, an enzyme that aids digestion of proteins in the small intestine—has optimum activity at pH 8. Most enzymes have their maximum activity between the pH values of 5–9. Eventually, both extremes of pH will denature a protein. The "typical" body pH is the pH of the blood, pH 7.4. pH extremes that change the pH of the blood significantly are highly damaging to body tissues; that is why swallowing concentrated HCl (pH 1 or less) or drain cleaner (mostly NaOH, pH 14 or more) is often fatal.

Worked Example 19.3 Enzymatic Activity: Determining Optimum Temperature

Consider the following temperature activity curve. Enzymatic activity is shown for muscle LDH from 0 °C to 60 °C. Suppose you wish to test a sample for LDH activity; what is the best temperature for the test?

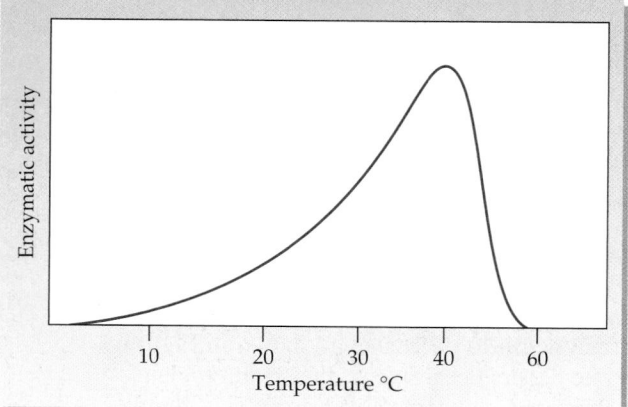

ANALYSIS An enzyme shows its highest catalytic activity at a certain temperature, with less activity at temperatures below and above the optimum temperature. Look at the curve of activity versus temperature and find the highest point on the curve—that point represents the optimum activity.

SOLUTION

From the highest point on the curve of activity versus temperature, drop a vertical line down to the x-axis (the one that reads "Temperature") to find the optimum temperature. The temperature optimum for LDH is 40 °C.

Worked Example 19.4 Enzymatic Activity: Determining Optimum pH

Enzymatic activity is shown for three different enzymes as a function of pH in the following graph. What is the optimum pH for pepsin (curve A), for urease (curve B), and for alanine dehydrogenase (curve C)?

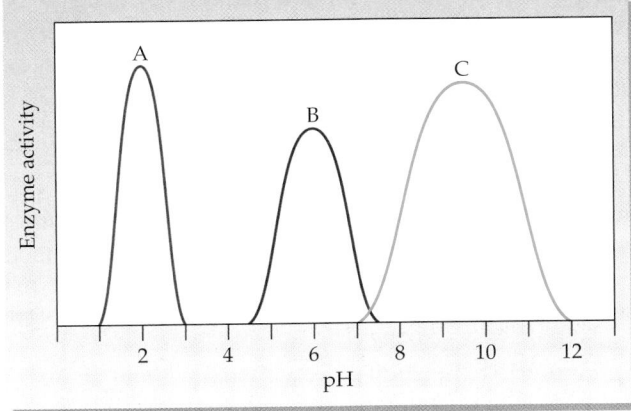

ANALYSIS Recall that the optimum pH is the pH at which the enzyme shows the highest activity; therefore, the highest point on the curve, representing maximum activity, is the optimum pH for the enzyme.

SOLUTION
Find the correct curve for each enzyme and the peak of each activity curve. Drop a vertical line to the pH axis and read the optimum pH directly from the axis scale. The optimum pH for pepsin is approximately 2.0, that for urease approximately 6.0, and that for alanine dehydrogenase approximately 9.5.

◖▶ KEY CONCEPT PROBLEM 19.10 —————————————————————

What do we mean when we say an enzyme is saturated with substrate? When an enzyme is saturated with substrate, how does adding more (a) substrate and (b) enzyme affect the rate of the reaction?

PROBLEM 19.11

Will the reaction catalyzed by the enzyme represented in Figure 19.7a have a higher rate of reaction at 25 °C or at 35 °C? Will it have a higher rate of reaction at 35 °C or at 45 °C?

PROBLEM 19.12

How will the rates of the reaction catalyzed by pepsin (Figure 19.7b) compare at pH 2 and pH 4?

19.6 Enzyme Regulation: Inhibition

Learning Objectives:
• Define and identify reversible and irreversible inhibition.
• Define and identify uncompetitive and competitive inhibition.

In the body, the concentrations of thousands of different compounds must vary continuously to meet changing conditions as we eat, sleep, exercise, or fall ill. Enzymes do more than just speed up reactions; at a moment's notice, they turn some reactions off, slow some down, or quickly accelerate others to their maximum possible rate. Clearly, then, the enzymes themselves must be regulated. How is this regulation achieved?

A variety of strategies adjust the rates of enzyme-catalyzed reactions. Any process that starts or increases the action of an enzyme is **activation.** Conversely, any process that slows or stops the action of an enzyme is **inhibition.** Although we will describe the strategies of enzyme control one by one, keep in mind that several strategies usually operate together. Considering that a cell contains thousands of proteins—many molecules of some proteins and only a few molecules of other proteins—and hundreds of

Activation (of an enzyme) Any process that initiates or increases the action of an enzyme.

Inhibition (of an enzyme) Any process that slows or stops the action of an enzyme.

other kinds of biomolecules, all in concentrations required to maintain constant conditions, the achievement of enzyme control by the body is awe-inspiring.

The inhibition of an enzyme can be *reversible* or *irreversible*. In reversible inhibition, the inhibitor can leave, restoring the enzyme to its uninhibited level of activity. In irreversible inhibition, the inhibitor remains permanently bound and the enzyme is permanently inhibited. The inhibition can also be *competitive, uncompetitive,* or *mixed,* depending on whether the inhibitor binds to the active site, the substrate, or some combination of enzyme and substrate.

Reversible Uncompetitive Inhibition

In **uncompetitive inhibition,** the inhibitor does not compete with the substrate for the active site and cannot bind to enzyme alone. An uncompetitive inhibitor exerts control by binding to the enzyme–substrate complex so that the reaction occurs less efficiently or not at all. This type of inhibition is reversible and often occurs in reactions where two substrates are involved.

In Figure 19.8, reaction rates with and without an uncompetitive inhibitor are compared in the bottom and top curves. With the inhibitor, the reaction rate increases with increasing substrate concentration more gradually than when no inhibitor is present. The maximum rate is lowered, and once that rate is reached, no amount of substrate can increase it further. As long as the inhibitor is present at constant concentration, this upper limit does not change.

Uncompetitive (enzyme) inhibition Enzyme regulation in which an inhibitor binds reversibly to the enzyme–substrate complex, blocking the binding of the second substrate to the active site.

Uncompetitive inhibition

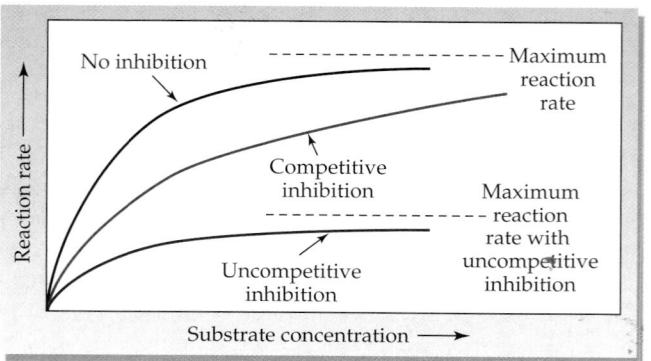

▶ **Figure 19.8**
Enzyme inhibition. The top curve and dashed line show the reaction rate and maximum rate with no inhibitor. With a competitive inhibitor (middle curve), the maximum rate is unchanged, but a higher substrate concentration is required to reach it. With an uncompetitive inhibitor (bottom curve), the maximum rate (bottom dashed line) is lowered.

Reversible Competitive Inhibition

What happens if an enzyme encounters a molecule very much like its normal substrate in shape, size, and functional groups? The impostor molecule enters the enzyme's active site, binds to it, and thereby prevents the usual substrate molecule from binding to the same site. Consequently, the enzyme is tied up, making it unavailable as a catalyst. This situation is called **competitive inhibition**—the inhibitor *competes* with substrate for binding to the active site. A competitive inhibitor binds reversibly to an active site through noncovalent interactions but undergoes no reaction. While it is there, it prevents the substrate from entering the active site.

Competitive (enzyme) inhibition Enzyme regulation in which an inhibitor competes with a substrate for binding to the enzyme active site.

Substrate + Enzyme ⇌ Substrate–enzyme complex
Inhibitor + Enzyme ⇌ Inhibitor–enzyme complex

Whether the substrate or the inhibitor occupies the active site depends on their relative concentrations. A substrate in relatively high concentration occupies more of the active sites, so the reaction is less inhibited. An inhibitor in relatively high concentration occupies more of the active sites, so the reaction is more inhibited.

The middle curve in Figure 19.8 shows that in the presence of a competitive inhibitor at constant concentration, the reaction rate increases more gradually with increasing substrate concentration than when there is no inhibitor present. Unlike uncompetitive inhibition, however, the maximum reaction rate is unchanged. Eventually, all of an enzyme's active sites can be occupied by substrate, but a higher substrate concentration is required to reach that condition.

Competitive inhibition

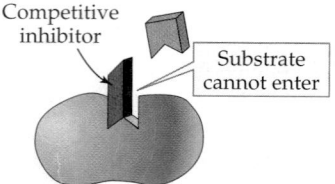

The product of a reaction may be a competitive inhibitor for the enzyme that catalyzes that reaction. For example, glucose 6-phosphate is a competitive inhibitor for hexokinase, which catalyzes formation of this phosphorylated form of glucose. Thus, when supplies of glucose 6-phosphate are ample, glucose is available for other reactions.

A competitive inhibitor is sometimes used in treating an unhealthy condition because the inhibitor mimics the structure of the substrate and fits into the enzyme's active site. For example, competitive inhibition is used to good advantage in the treatment of methanol poisoning. Although not harmful itself, methanol (wood alcohol) is oxidized in the body to formaldehyde, which is highly toxic $(CH_3OH \longrightarrow H_2C{=}O)$. Because of its molecular similarity to methanol, ethanol acts as a competitive inhibitor of alcohol dehydrogenase. With the oxidation of methanol blocked by ethanol, methanol is excreted without causing harm. Thus, the medical treatment of methanol poisoning includes administering ethanol, to avoid blindness or death of the patient.

Another example of reversible inhibition involves lead poisoning. Lead can poison animals, including humans, in two ways. One way is by displacing an essential metal cofactor from the active site of an enzyme. When lead displaces zinc in an enzyme essential to the synthesis of heme, the oxygen-carrying part of hemoglobin, the enzyme becomes inactive and anemia can result. Physicians treat this sort of lead poisoning with chelation therapy. Ethylenediaminetetraacetic acid (EDTA) forms coordinate covalent bonds preferentially with lead in the body, and lead is then excreted in the urine as a chelated compound.

The second way lead can poison involves the process known as irreversible inhibition, the topic we look at next.

Irreversible Inhibition

If an inhibitor forms a bond that is not easily broken with a group in an active site, the result is **irreversible inhibition.** The enzyme's reaction cannot occur because the substrate cannot connect appropriately with the active site. Many irreversible inhibitors are poisons as a result of their ability to completely shut down the active site. Heavy metal ions, such as mercury (Hg^{2+}) and lead (Pb^{2+}), are irreversible inhibitors that form covalent bonds to the sulfur atoms in the $-SH$ groups of cysteine residues.

Often, heavy metal ions like lead and mercury affect enzymes that function in the nervous system. At low levels, lead can cause decreased attention span and mental difficulties. These symptoms are noticed in children who eat flakes of lead-containing paint, which have a sweet taste. Primarily, for this reason, lead-containing paint has not been used since the 1950s, but it is often still present in older homes. Small amounts of mercury in the diet cause similar problems. For this reason, children and pregnant women are advised to severely limit their intake of fish, particularly large deep-sea fish such as tuna. Tuna accumulate mercury in their tissues; the mercury is absorbed from our digestive system and remains in our bodies.

Organophosphorus insecticides, such as parathion and malathion, and nerve gases, such as Sarin, are irreversible inhibitors of the enzyme acetylcholinesterase, which breaks down a chemical messenger *(acetylcholine)* that transmits nerve impulses (Section 28.7). The acetylcholinesterase inhibitors bond covalently to a serine residue in the enzyme's active site.

Irreversible (enzyme) inhibition Enzyme deactivation in which an inhibitor forms covalent bonds to the active site, permanently blocking it.

Serine residue at active site of acetylcholinesterase

Sarin

Covalent bond that irreversibly binds the inhibitor to the enzyme

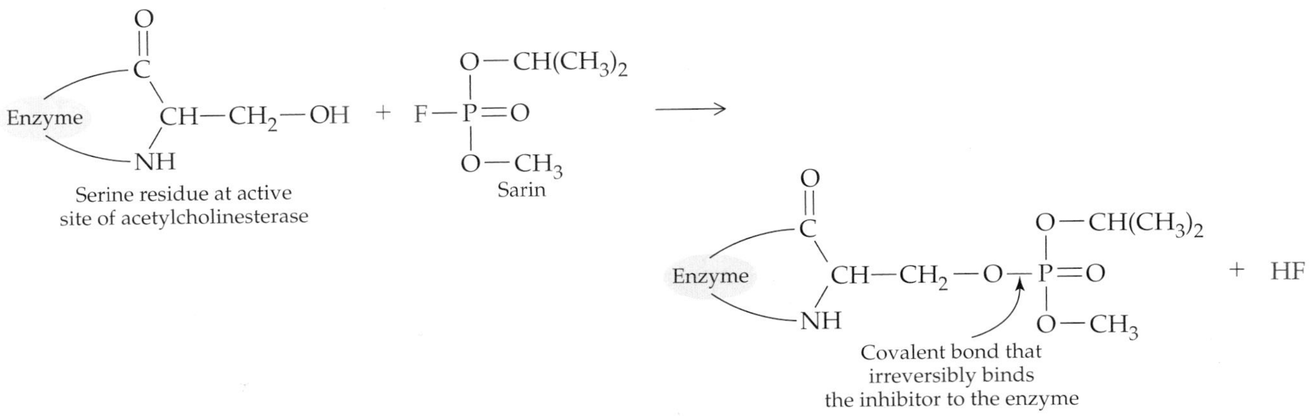

Normally, acetylcholinesterase breaks down acetylcholine immediately after that molecule transmits a nerve impulse. Removal of acetylcholine "resets" the receiving cells, getting them ready to receive further signals. Without acetylcholinesterase activity, accumulating acetylcholine blocks transmission of further nerve impulses, resulting in paralysis of muscle fibers and death from respiratory failure. Sarin, one of the most toxic nerve agents, is now classified by the United Nations as a weapon of mass destruction, as exposure can be fatal. There is no effective treatment to counteract this irreversible inhibitor of acetylcholinesterase.

PROBLEM 19.13

Could either of the following molecules be a competitive inhibitor for the enzyme that has *p*-aminobenzoate as its substrate? If so, why?

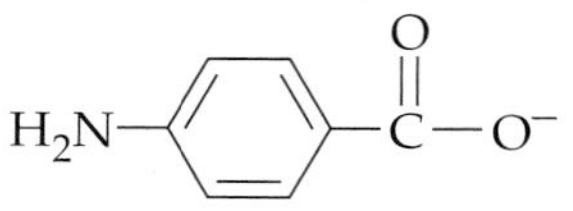

p-Aminobenzoate, the substrate

(a) $H_2NCH_2CH_3$ **(b)**

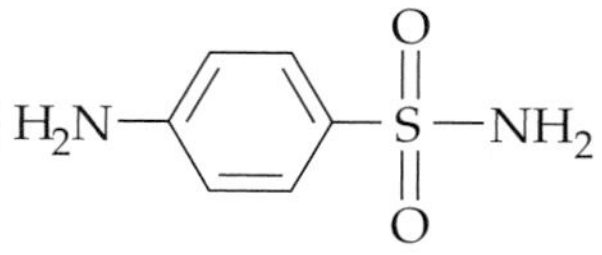

PROBLEM 19.14

What kind of reaction product might be a competitive inhibitor for the enzyme that catalyzes its formation?

19.7 Enzyme Regulation: Allosteric Control and Feedback Inhibition

Learning Objectives:

• Define and identify allosteric control.
• Define feedback control and explain how it regulates enzyme catalysis.

In Section 19.6, we explored enzyme regulation by inhibition of activity, both reversible and irreversible, which required specific kinds of binding of substrate and inhibitor to the enzyme. Now, we look at two other common methods of enzyme regulation: allosteric control and feedback control. Both of these enzyme regulation methods also require the regulators to bind to the enzyme, but differently from inhibition regulation.

Allosteric Control

Allosteric control An interaction in which the binding of a regulator at one site on a protein affects the protein's ability to bind another molecule at a different site.

Allosteric enzyme An enzyme whose activity is controlled by the binding of an activator or inhibitor at a location other than the active site.

Many enzymes are regulated by *allosteric* control (from the Greek *allos,* meaning "other" and *steros,* meaning "space"). In **allosteric control,** the binding of a molecule (an *allosteric regulator* or *effector*) at one site on a protein affects the binding of another molecule at a different site. Most **allosteric enzymes** have more than one protein chain and two kinds of binding sites—those for substrates and those for regulators (Figure 19.9). Binding of a regulator, usually by noncovalent intermolecular forces, changes the shape of the enzyme. This change alters the shape of the active site, affecting the ability of the enzyme to bind its substrate and catalyze its reaction. One advantage of allosteric enzyme control is that the regulators need not be structurally similar to the substrate because they do not bind to the active site.

Allosteric control of an enzyme by regulator molecules can be either positive or negative but always involves subtle shape changes in the enzyme. Binding a positive regulator changes an unavailable active site so that the substrate can fit into the active site and the reaction occurs. The presence of positive allosteric regulator molecules increases the reaction rate. Conversely, binding a negative regulator changes the active site so that the enzyme can no longer bind substrate to the active site, slowing the

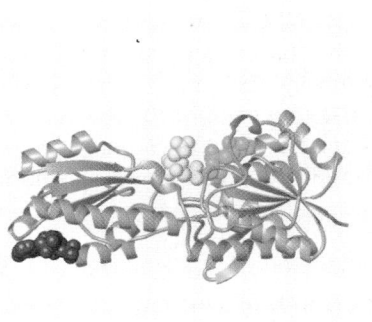

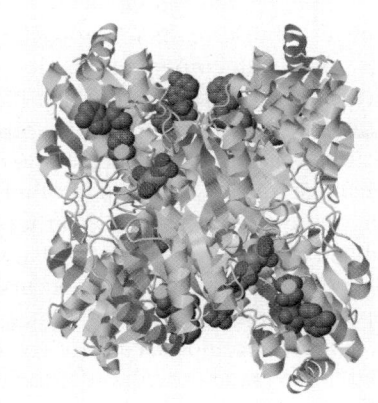

(a)   (b)

▲ **Figure 19.9**
An allosteric enzyme
(a) One of the four identical subunits in phosphofructokinase, an enzyme that catalyzes transfer of a phosphoryl group from ATP to fructose 6-phosphate (see transferase reaction in Section 19.3). The subunit is shown after the reaction has occurred and contains the reaction product fructose-1, 6-bisphosphate; a molecule formed in the third step of glycolysis. The diphosphate portion of the phosphorylated substrate (yellow) and adenosine diphosphate (ADP) (green) are in the active site and the allosteric activator (red, also ADP) in the regulatory site. (b) The four subunits of the complete enzyme are shown in blue. ADP (green), the cofactor, is shown in the active site and ADP (red) that acts as the allosteric activator is shown in the regulatory site. Note that there is one cofactor and one regulator molecule per protein chain.

reaction. Because allosteric enzymes can have several substrate binding sites and several regulator-binding sites and because there may be interaction among them, very fine control is achieved.

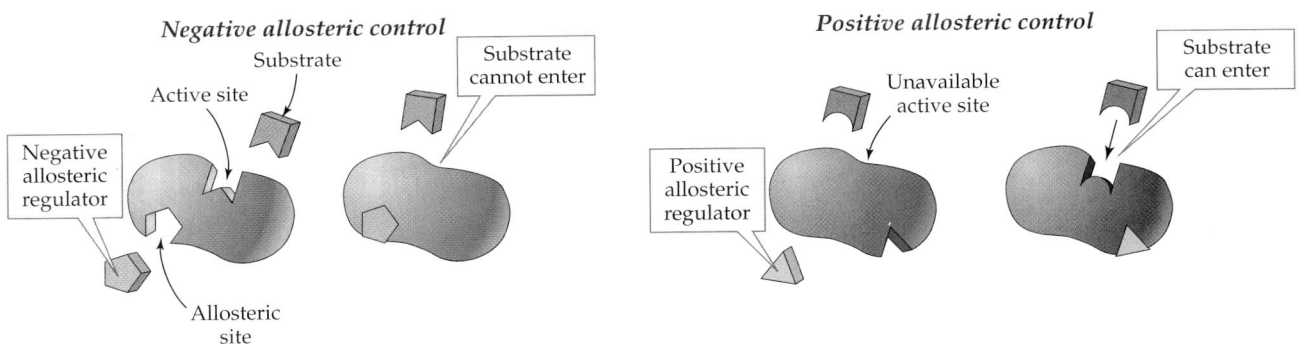

Feedback Control

As you will see in subsequent chapters, biochemical reaction pathways are dependent on a series of consecutive reactions in which the product of one reaction is the reactant for the next. Such pathways are subject to *feedback control,* which occurs when the result of a process feeds information back to affect the beginning of the process. Any device that maintains a constant temperature, such as an oven, is regulated by feedback control. Ovens have sensors that detect temperature and feed back that information to turn heating elements on or off.

Consider a biochemical pathway in which A is converted to B, then B is converted to C, and so on, with each reaction catalyzed by its own enzyme:

$$A \xrightarrow{\text{Enzyme 1}} B \xrightarrow{\text{Enzyme 2}} C \xrightarrow{\text{Enzyme 3}} D$$

Feedback control Regulation of an enzyme's activity by the product of a reaction later in a pathway.

What happens if product D inhibits enzyme 1? This inhibition causes the amount of A converted to B to decrease, so the synthesis of B and C decrease in turn. The effect of this **feedback control** mechanism is to control the concentration of D. When more D is present than is needed for other biochemical pathways, enzyme 1 is inhibited and its reaction is slowed or stopped. By inhibiting the first enzyme in the pathway, no energy is wasted making the unneeded intermediates B and C. When the amount of available D decreases as it is used up in other reactions, any D bound to enzyme 1 dissociates. Soon, there is no D available for feedback control. As a result, enzyme 1 is no longer inhibited and the production of D accelerates.

Feedback control typically occurs at points in a pathway where control is critical. In the pathway above, this point is the conversion of A to B by enzyme 1. The intermediates B and C are not used in other metabolic pathways (the pathway is unbranched); B and C are made only in order to convert A to D, so it is not important for the cell to continue to synthesize either of the intermediates. Thus, from an energetic standpoint, it makes the most sense for product D to regulate the first step in the pathway. Pyruvate dehydrogenase and citrate synthase, enzymes involved in sugar metabolism, and aspartate transcarboxylase, the first enzyme in the pyrimidine synthesis pathway, are examples of enzymes regulated by feedback control.

Worked Example 19.5 Determining Feedback Control Points

Look at the three-step pathway (reaction route) for the conversion of 3-phosphoglycerate to serine:

$$\text{3-phosphoglycerate} \xrightarrow{1} \text{3-phosphohydroxypyruvate} \xrightarrow{2} \text{3-phosphoserine} \xrightarrow{3} \text{serine}$$

When the cell has plenty of serine available, which enzyme in the pathway, 1, 2, or 3, is most likely to be inhibited?

ANALYSIS This is a simple, linear pathway. The pathway is most likely controlled by feedback control of the final product.

SOLUTION
Assuming that feedback control is the simplest control mechanism for this linear pathway, serine, the product of the pathway, will inhibit the first enzyme in the pathway when sufficient serine is available in the cell.

PROBLEM 19.15

(a) L-Threonine is converted to L-isoleucine in a linear pathway involving five separate enzymes. Which of the enzymes in the following pathway is most likely inhibited by the product of the pathway, L-isoleucine?

$$\text{L-threonine} \xrightarrow{E1} A \xrightarrow{E2} B \xrightarrow{E3} C \xrightarrow{E4} D \xrightarrow{E5} \text{L-isoleucine}$$

(b) If product A inhibited the first enzyme in the pathway (E1), could this be called feedback control? Explain.

19.8 Enzyme Regulation: Covalent Modification and Genetic Control

Learning Objectives:

• Define and identify inhibition by covalent modification.
• Define and identify inhibition by genetic control of enzymes.

Covalent Modification

There are two modes of enzyme regulation by covalent modification—removal of a covalently bonded portion of an enzyme or addition of a group. Some enzymes are synthesized in inactive forms that differ from the active forms in composition. Activation of such enzymes, known as **zymogens** or *proenzymes,* requires a chemical reaction that splits off part of the molecule. Blood clotting, for example, is initiated by activation of zymogens.

Other examples of zymogens include *trypsinogen, chymotrypsinogen,* and *proelastase,* precursors of enzymes that digest proteins in the small intestine. Produced in the pancreas, these enzymes must be inactive when they are synthesized so that they do not immediately digest the pancreas. Each zymogen has a polypeptide segment at one end that is not present in the active enzymes. The extra segments are snipped off to produce trypsin, chymotrypsin, and elastase, the active enzymes, when the zymogens reach the small intestine, where protein digestion occurs.

Zymogen A compound that becomes an active enzyme after undergoing a chemical change.

Chymotrypsinogen (inactive)

— S–S —   — S–S —

| Trypsin   Dipeptides

Chymotrypsin (active)

— S–S —   — S–S —

▲ Chymotrypsinogen (a zymogen) at top, and the active enzyme chymotrypsin at bottom.

One danger of traumatic injury to the pancreas or the duct that leads to the small intestine is premature activation of these zymogens inside pancreatic cells, resulting in acute pancreatitis, a painful and potentially fatal condition in which the activated enzymes attack the pancreas.

Another mode of covalent modification is the reversible addition of phosphoryl groups ($-PO_3^{2-}$) to a serine, tyrosine, or threonine residue. *Kinase* enzymes catalyze the addition of a phosphoryl group supplied by ATP *(phosphorylation). Phosphatase enzymes* catalyze the removal of the phosphoryl group *(dephosphorylation).* This control strategy swings into action, for example, when glycogen stored in muscles must be hydrolyzed to glucose that is needed for quick energy, a process known as glycogenolysis. Two serine residues in glycogen phosphorylase, the enzyme that initiates glycogen breakdown, are phosphorylated. Only with these phosphoryl groups in place is glycogen phosphorylase active. The groups are removed, changing both the shape and charge on the enzyme, once the need to break down glycogen for quick energy has passed.

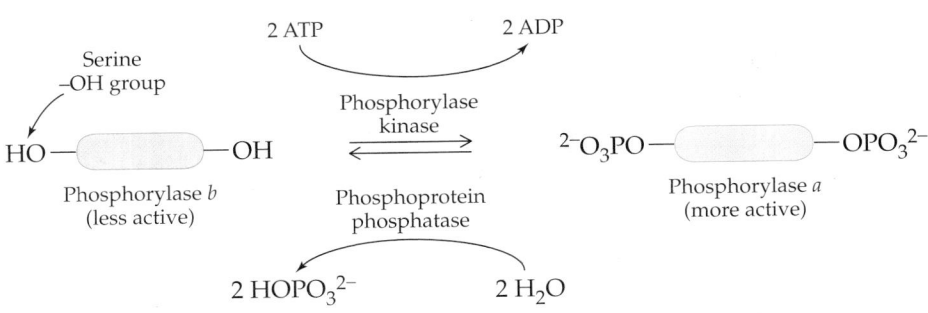

The curved arrows shown above are used frequently in biochemical equations in later chapters. While the focus of the main reaction arrow is on changes in the major biomolecule reactant, the participation of other reactants needed to accomplish the chemical change is shown by the curved arrows adjacent to the main reaction arrow. Coenzymes and energy-providing molecules like ATP are often included in this manner. Here, the top curved arrow shows that the reaction in the forward direction requires ATP to supply the phosphoryl groups and produces ADP. The bottom curved arrow shows that water is needed for the reverse reaction, the hydrolysis that removes the phosphoryl groups as hydrogen phosphate anions.

CHEMISTRY IN ACTION

✝ Enzyme Inhibitors as Drugs

Consider the medical possibilities when the chemical structures of a substrate and the active site to which it binds are known. A drug designer can create a molecule similar in structure to the substrate so that it binds to the active site and acts as an inhibitor. Inhibiting a particular enzyme can help treat a variety of medical conditions.

The family of drugs known as angiotensin-converting enzyme (ACE) inhibitors is a good example of enzyme inhibitors that help treat a medical condition. Angiotensin II, the octapeptide illustrated next, is a potent *pressor*—it elevates blood pressure, in part by causing contraction of blood vessels. Angiotensin I, is an inactive precursor of angiotensin II. To become active, two amino acid residues—His and Leu—must be cut off the end of angiotensin I, a reaction catalyzed by ACE. This reaction is part of a normal pathway for blood pressure control and is accelerated when blood pressure drops because of bleeding or dehydration. Inhibition of ACE activity lowers high blood pressure to more normal levels.

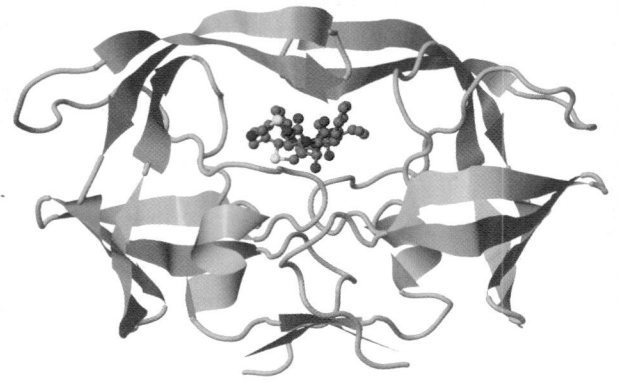

▲ Ritonavir, an enzyme inhibitor, in the active site of HIV protease.

$$\text{Asp-Arg-Val-Tyr-Ile-His-Pro-Phe-His-Leu} \xrightarrow[\text{(ACE)}]{\substack{\text{Angiotensin-}\\\text{converting}\\\text{enzyme}}}$$

Angiotensin I

$$\text{Asp-Arg-Val-Tyr-Ile-His-Pro-Phe} + \text{His-Leu}$$

Angiotensin II

The first ACE inhibitor on the market, *captopril,* was developed by experimenting with modifications of the proline-like structure. Success was achieved by introducing an —SH group that binds to the zinc ion in the active site.

Captopril
(an ACE inhibitor)

Several other ACE inhibitors have subsequently been developed, and they are now common medications for patients with high blood pressure.

The development of enzyme inhibitors also plays a continuing, major role in the battle against *acquired immunodeficiency syndrome* (AIDS). The battle is far from won, but two important AIDS-fighting drugs are enzyme inhibitors. The first, known as AZT *(azidothymidine, also called zidovudine),* resembles in structure a molecule essential to reproduction of the AIDS-causing *human immunodeficiency virus (HIV).* Because

AZT is accepted by an HIV enzyme as a substrate, it prevents the virus from producing duplicate copies of itself.

The most successful AIDS drug thus far inhibits a *protease,* an enzyme that cuts a long protein chain into smaller pieces needed by the HIV. *Protease inhibitors,* such as ritonavir, cause dramatic decreases in the virus population and AIDS symptoms. The success is only achieved, however, by taking a "cocktail" of several drugs, including AZT. The cocktail is expensive and requires precise adherence to a schedule of taking 20 pills a day. These conditions make it unavailable or too difficult for many individuals to use.

Many drugs are enzyme inhibitors. For example, topiramate, a carbonic anhydrase inhibitor, is prescribed to treat seizure disorders and also to prevent migraines. Sildenafil (Viagra) inhibits a specific phophodiesterase responsible for some forms of erectile dysfunction. And most antibiotics inhibit enzymes involved in microbial growth and reproduction.

CIA Problem 19.1 The primary structure of angiotensin II has Pro-Phe at the C-terminal end of the octapeptide. An ACE inhibitor from the South American pit viper is a pentapeptide with a C-terminal proline and is a mild ACE inhibitor. Captopril has a modified proline structure and is also a mild ACE inhibitor.

(a) Why do you suppose that a mild ACE inhibitor is more valuable for the treatment of high blood pressure than a very potent ACE inhibitor? (Hint: How much should blood pressure change at once?)

(b) What structural modifications to the pit viper peptide might make it a more powerful ACE inhibitor? (Hint: Compare protein structures at C-terminal end.)

CIA Problem 19.2 AZT (zidovudine) inhibits the synthesis of the HIV virus RNA because AZT resembles substrate molecules. Which kind of inhibition is most likely taking place in this reaction?

CIA Problem 19.3 Ritonavir inhibits the action of HIV protease. What kind of inhibition is imposed on HIV protease by ritonavir?

Genetic Control

The synthesis of all proteins, including enzymes, is regulated by genes (Chapter 27) and is a strategy that controls enzyme availability. **Genetic control** is especially useful for enzymes needed only at certain stages of development. Mechanisms controlled by hormones (Section 28.2) can accelerate or decelerate enzyme synthesis. For example, lactase, needed to digest lactose is not synthesized in most adults because adults have a more varied diet than infants and do not need to digest milk sugar. Conversely, fetuses and infants do not metabolize ethanol because alcohol dehydrogenase, the necessary enzyme, is under genetic control and does not appear until later in life.

> **Genetic (enzyme) control** Regulation of enzyme activity by control of the synthesis of enzymes.

In summary, we have described the most important strategies that control the activity of enzymes. In any given biochemical pathway in a healthy individual, several of these strategies are likely occurring simultaneously at any given moment.

Summary: Mechanisms of Enzyme Control

- *Inhibition,* which is either *reversible* or *irreversible. Reversible inhibition* that occurs away from the active site is termed uncompetitive inhibition, while reversible inhibition that occurs at the active site and often involves molecules that mimic substrate structure is termed competitive inhibition. *Irreversible inhibition* occurs due to covalent bonding of the inhibitor to the enzyme. Competitive inhibition is a strategy often utilized in medications, and irreversible inhibition is a mode of action of many poisons.
- *Feedback control* is exerted on an earlier reactant by a later product in a reaction pathway and is made possible by *allosteric control.* The feedback molecule binds to a specific enzyme early in the pathway in a way that alters the shape and therefore the efficiency of the enzyme.
- *Production of inactive enzymes (zymogens),* which must be activated by cleaving a portion of the molecule.
- *Covalent modification of an enzyme by addition and removal of a phosphoryl group,* with the phosphoryl group supplied by ATP.
- *Genetic control,* whereby the amount of enzyme available is regulated by limiting its synthesis.

PROBLEM 19.16

Which type of enzyme regulation is best for the following situations?

  (a) An enzyme that becomes overactive during a disease
  (b) An enzyme needed only when there is low blood glucose
  (c) An enzyme that springs into action when a traumatic injury occurs
  (d) An enzyme needed only during adolescence

19.9 Vitamins, Antioxidants, and Minerals

Learning Objectives:

- Describe the two classes of vitamins, the reasons vitamins are necessary in the diet, and the results of vitamin excesses or deficiencies.
- Identify antioxidants and explain their function.
- Identify essential minerals, explain why minerals are necessary in the diet, and explain the results of mineral deficiencies.

> ◀◀◀ The role of vitamin C in collagen synthesis was examined in Section 18.11.

Long before the reasons were understood, people knew that lime and other citrus juices cure scurvy, meat and milk cure pellagra, and cod-liver oil prevents rickets. Eventually, researchers discovered that these diseases are caused by deficiencies of **vitamins**—organic molecules required in only trace amounts that must be obtained through the diet. Vitamins are a dietary necessity for humans because our bodies do not have the ability to synthesize them.

> **Vitamin** An organic molecule, essential in trace amounts that must be obtained in the diet because it is not synthesized in the body.

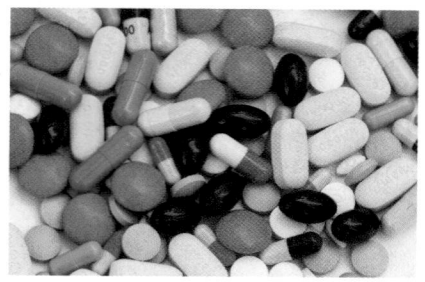

▲ A myriad of vitamin pills in capsule and tablet form.

Water-Soluble Vitamins

Vitamins are grouped by solubility into two classes: water-soluble and fat-soluble. The water-soluble vitamins, listed in Table 19.5, are found in the aqueous environment inside cells, where most of them are needed as components of coenzymes. Over time, an assortment of names, letters, and numbers for designating vitamins have accumulated. Structurally, the water-soluble vitamins have —OH, —COOH, or other polar groups that make them water soluble, but otherwise they range from simple molecules like vitamin C to large, complex structures like vitamin B_{12}.

Most vitamins are components of coenzymes, but some function as coenzymes themselves. *Vitamin C* is biologically active without any change in structure from the molecules present in foods. Similarly, *biotin* is connected to enzymes by an amide bond at its carboxyl group but otherwise undergoes no structural change from dietary biotin.

Vitamin C
(Ascorbic acid)

Biotin

Other water-soluble vitamins are incorporated into coenzymes. The vitamin-derived portions of two of the most important coenzymes, NAD^+ and coenzyme A, are illustrated in Figure 19.10. Table 19.5 includes the functions, deficiency symptoms, and major dietary sources of water-soluble vitamins.

Niacin
(Nicotinic acid)

Nicotinamide

Nicotinamide adenine dinucleotide (NAD^+), a coenzyme

Pantothenic acid

Coenzyme A

▲ **Figure 19.10**
The vitamin-derived portions of NAD^+ and coenzyme A.

Table 19.5 The Water-Soluble Vitamins*

Vitamin	Significance	Sources	Reference Daily Intake (RID)**	Effects of Deficiency	Effects of Excess
Thiamine (B_1)	In coenzyme for decarboxylation reactions	Milk, meat, bread, legumes	1.2 mg	Muscle weakness, and cardiovascular problems including heart disease, causes beriberi	Low blood pressure
Riboflavin (B_2)	In coenzymes flavin mononucleotide (FMN) and FAD	Milk, meat	1.3 mg	Skin and mucous membrane deterioration	Itching, tingling sensations
Niacin (nicotinic acid, nicotinamide,B_3)	In coenzyme NAD^+	Meat, bread, potatoes	16 mg	Nervous system, gastrointestinal, skin, and mucous membrane deterioration, causes pellagra	Itching, burning sensations, blood vessel dilation, death after large dose
B_6 (pyridoxine)	In coenzyme for amino acid and lipid metabolism	Meat, legumes	1.3 mg	Retarded growth, anemia, convulsions, epithelial changes	Central nervous system alterations, perhaps fatal
Folic acid	In coenzyme for amino acid and nucleic acid metabolism	Vegetables, cereal, bread	0.4 mg	Retarded growth, anemia, gastrointestinal disorders, neural tube defects	Few noted except at massive doses
B_{12} (cobalamin)	In coenzyme for nucleic acid metabolism	Milk, meat	2.4 μg	Pernicious anemia	Excess red blood cells
Biotin	Coenzyme for carboxylation reactions	Eggs, meat, vegetables	0.3 mg	Fatigue, muscular pain, nausea, dermatitis	None reported
Pantothenic acid (B_5)	In coenzyme A	Milk, meat	5 mg	Retarded growth, central nervous system disturbances	None reported
C (ascorbic acid)	Coenzyme; delivers hydride ions; antioxidant	Citrus fruits, broccoli, greens	90 mg	Epithelial and mucosal deterioration, causing scurvy	Kidney stones

*Adapted in part from Frederic H. Martini, Fundamentals of Anatomy and Physiology, 4th edition (Prentice Hall, 1998).

**RDI values are the basis for information on the Nutrition Facts Label included on most packaged foods. The values are based on the Recommended Dietary Intake Reports (2006–2011). See www.nap.edu.

Worked Example 19.6 Identifying Coenzymes

Identify the substrate, product, and coenzyme in the reaction shown. The reaction is catalyzed by the enzyme alcohol dehydrogenase.

$$\text{Ethanol} + NAD^+ \longrightarrow \text{Acetaldehyde} + NADH + H^+$$

ANALYSIS Identify which molecules have been changed and how, starting from the left side of the arrow (the beginning of the reaction) to the right side of the arrow (the end of the reaction). In this case, ethanol is oxidized to acetaldehyde and NAD^+ is reduced to $NADH/H^+$. Recognize that nicotinamide adenine dinucleotide (NAD^+) is a coenzyme involved in oxidation/reduction reactions.

SOLUTION
Since NAD^+ is a coenzyme involved in oxidation/reduction reactions, ethanol (the other molecule on the left side of the equation) is the substrate and acetaldehyde (on the right side of the arrow) is the product of the reaction. $NADH + H^+$ is the reduced form of NAD^+ and is considered to be reduced coenzyme only—not a product of the reaction.

PROBLEM 19.17 Does the enzyme described in each of the following statements require a cofactor to be active?

(a) Ni^{2+} is present in the active site.

(b) Addition of FAD allows the reaction to occur.

(c) The presence of K^+ does not affect the reaction.

PROBLEM 19.18 Which vitamin provides us with each of the following?

(a) NAD^+ (b) Coenzyme A

▲ Deeply pigmented vegetables and fruits contain vitamins.

Fat-Soluble Vitamins

Fat-soluble vitamins A, D, E, and K are stored in the body's fat deposits. Although the clinical effects of deficiencies of these vitamins are well documented, the molecular mechanisms by which they act are not nearly as well understood as those of the water-soluble vitamins. None have been identified as a coenzyme. Table 19.6 summarizes the functions, sources, and deficiency symptoms of fat-soluble vitamins. The hazards of overdosing on fat-soluble vitamins are greater than the hazards of overdosing on water-soluble vitamins because the fat-soluble vitamins accumulate in body fats. Excesses of the water-soluble vitamins are more likely to be excreted in the urine.

PROBLEM 19.19

Compare the structures of vitamin A and vitamin C. Which one is water-soluble and which is fat-soluble? What structural features does each have that make one water-soluble and the other fat-soluble?

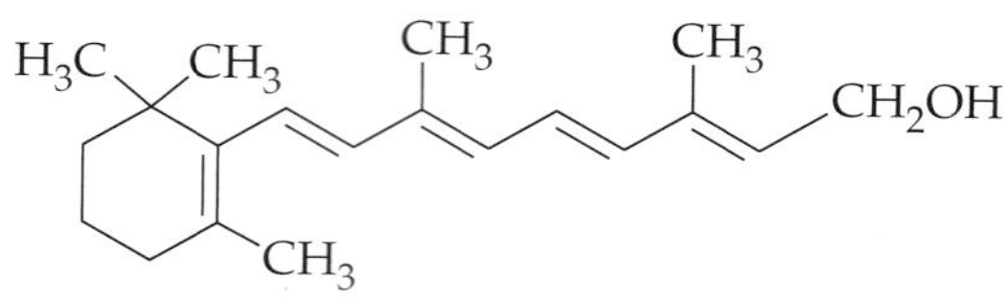

Vitamin A
(Retinol)

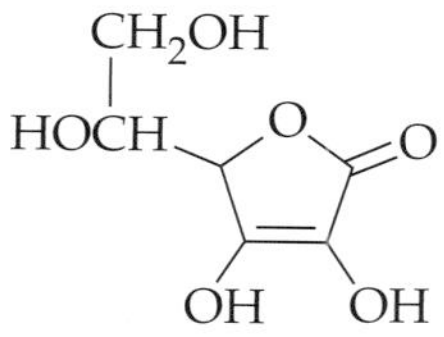

Vitamin C
(Ascorbic acid)

Table 19.6 The Fat-Soluble Vitamins*

Vitamin	Significance	Sources	Reference Daily Intake**	Effects of Deficiency	Effects of Excess
A	Essential for night vision, healthy eyes, and normal development of epithelial tissue; antioxidant	Leafy green and yellow vegetables	900 μg	Retarded growth, night blindness, deterioration of epithelial membranes	Liver damage, skin peeling, central nervous system effects (nausea, anorexia)
D	Required for normal bone growth, calcium and phosphorus absorption at gut, and retention in kidneys	Synthesized in skin exposed to sunlight	15 μg	Rickets, skeletal deterioration	Calcium deposits in many tissues, disrupting functions
E	Prevents breakdown of vitamin A and fatty acids; antioxidant	Meat, milk, vegetables	15 mg	Anemia, other problems suspected	None reported
K	Essential for liver synthesis of prothrombin and other clotting factors	Vegetables; production by intestinal bacteria	120 μg	Bleeding disorders	Liver dysfunction, jaundice

*Adapted in part from Frederic H. Martini, Fundamentals of Anatomy and Physiology, 4th edition (Prentice Hall, 1998).

**RDI values are the basis for information on the Nutrition Facts Label included on most packaged foods. The values are based on the Recommended Dietary Intake Reports (2006–2011). See www.nap.edu. RDIs for fat-soluble vitamins are often reported in International Units (IU), which are defined differently for each vitamin. The values given here are approximate equivalents in mass units.

PROBLEM 19.20

Based on the structure shown for retinol (vitamin A) and the names of the two related forms of vitamin A, retinal and retinoic acid, what do you expect to be the structural differences among these three compounds?

Antioxidants

Antioxidant A substance that prevents oxidation by reacting with an oxidizing agent.

[radical] An atom or molecule [with an unp]aired electron.

An **antioxidant** is a substance that prevents oxidation. The food industry uses antioxidants to combat oxidation of unsaturated fats by air, which causes deterioration of baked goods. In the body, we need similar protection against active oxidizing agents that are byproducts of normal metabolism.

Our principal dietary antioxidants are vitamin C, vitamin E, β-carotene, and the mineral selenium. They work together to defuse the potentially harmful action of **free radicals,** highly reactive molecular fragments with unpaired electrons (e.g., superoxide ion, $\cdot O_2^-$). Free radicals quickly gain stability by picking up electrons from nearby molecules, which are left damaged.

Vitamin E is unique in having antioxidant activity as its principal biochemical role. It acts by giving up the hydrogen from its —OH group to oxygen-containing free radicals. The hydrogen is then restored by reaction with vitamin C. Selenium joins the list of important antioxidants because it is a cofactor in an enzyme that converts hydrogen peroxide (H_2O_2) to water before the peroxide can go on to produce free radicals.

LOOKING AHEAD ➤➤ The role of vitamins as antioxidants is explored further in the discussion of elimination of cellular damaging reactive oxygen species in the Chemistry in Action "Harmful Oxygen Species and Antioxidant Vitamins," page 669.

🔑 KEY CONCEPT PROBLEM 19.21

Vitamins are a diverse group of compounds that must be present in the diet. List four functions of vitamins in the body.

PROBLEM 19.22

See the Chemistry in Action "Vitamins, Minerals, and Food Labels" below. Which vitamin listed on the label functions as an antioxidant in the body? Why is this important?

CHEMISTRY IN ACTION

Vitamins, Minerals, and Food Labels

It is not uncommon to encounter incomplete or incorrect information about vitamins and minerals. We have been frightened by the possibility that aluminum causes Alzheimer's disease and tantalized by the possibility that vitamin C defeats the common cold. Sorting out fact from fiction or distinguishing preliminary research results from scientifically proven relationships is especially difficult in this area of nutrition.

One consistent source of information on nutrition is the Food and Nutrition Board of the National Academy of Sciences-National Research Council. They periodically survey the latest nutritional information and publish Recommended Dietary Allowances (RDAs) that are "designed for the maintenance of good nutrition of the majority of healthy persons in the United States." Another source is the U.S. Food and Drug Administration (FDA), which sets the guidelines for food labeling.

Since 1994, as mandated by the FDA, most packaged food products carry standardized *Nutrition Facts* labels. The nutritional value of a food serving of a specified size is reported as *% Daily Value*. For vitamins and minerals, these percentages are calculated from RDI values published in 1968. RDIs are averages for adults and children over 4 years of age. The values for vitamins are included in Tables 19.3 and 19.4. For minerals, they are listed in the accompanying table.

All vitamins and minerals are important and essential, but in choosing which vitamins and minerals *must* be listed on the new labels, the government has focused on those currently of greatest importance in maintaining good health. The choices reflect a new emphasis on preventing disease rather than preventing deficiencies. The *mandatory* listings are for vitamin A, vitamin C, calcium, and iron. These recommendations are based on evidence for the benefits of high dietary levels of the antioxidants vitamin A (or the related compound, β-carotene) and vitamin C. Calcium deficiencies are related to osteoporosis, and iron deficiencies are a special concern for women because of their menstrual blood loss.

Reference Daily Intake Values* for Minerals			
Mineral	RDI	Mineral	RDI
Calcium	1.0 g	Selenium	70 µg
Iron	18 mg	Manganese	2 mg
Phosphorus	1.0 g	Fluoride	2.5 mg
Iodine	150 µg	Chromium	120 µg
Magnesium	400 mg	Molybdenum	75 µg
Zinc	15 mg	Chloride	3.4 g
Copper	2 mg		

*On Nutrition Facts labels, calcium and iron must be listed; phosphorus, iodine, magnesium, zinc, and copper listings are optional; by law, the others cannot be listed.

Nutrition Facts
Serving Size 55 pieces (30g/1.1oz)
Servings Per Container About 6

Amount Per Serving
Calories 140   Calories from Fat 45

	% Daily Value*
Total Fat 5g	**8%**
Saturated Fat 1g	**5%**
Trans Fat 0g	
Polyunsaturated Fat 1.5g	
Monounsaturated Fat 2.5g	
Cholesterol Less than 5mg	**1%**
Sodium 250mg	**10%**
Total Carbohydrate 19g	**6%**
Dietary Fiber 2g	**7%**
Sugars Less than 1g	
Protein 4g	

Vitamin A	0%	•	Vitamin C	0%
Calcium	4%	•	Iron	6%

*Percent Daily Values are based on a 2,000 calorie diet. Your daily values may be higher or lower depending on your caloric needs:

	Calories:	2,000	2,500
Total Fat	Less than	65g	80g
Sat. Fat	Less than	20g	25g
Cholesterol	Less than	300mg	300mg
Sodium	Less than	2,400mg	2,400mg
Total Carbohydrate		300g	375g
Dietary Fiber		25g	30g

CIA Problem 19.4 Which vitamins and minerals are listed on the food label and in what amount? Is this a good nutritional choice for consuming these vitamins and minerals?

CIA Problem 19.5 Read the labels on foods that you eat for a day, or look up the foods in a nutrition table and determine what percent of your daily dosage of vitamins and minerals you get from each. Are you getting the recommended amounts from the food you eat, or should you be taking a vitamin or mineral supplement?

CIA Problem 19.6 For what reasons are listings for vitamin A, vitamin C, iron, and calcium mandatory on food labels?

CIA Problem 19.7 In addition to the four nutrients named in CIA Problem 19.6, what other nutrients may be listed on food labels? (Hint: Look at all the ingredients that have amounts listed on the label shown.)

Minerals

The other important group of micronutrients is minerals, some of which are transition group elements. Table 19.7 lists the essential minerals, their sources and functions. A balanced diet supplies sufficient amounts of each of these micronutrients. Many of the transition elements are necessary for proper functioning of enzymes, since these elements are used as cofactors. Other minerals are used as building blocks for the body and some exist as ions, called electrolytes, in our body fluids. The RDI for most of these minerals is listed in the Chemistry in Action "Vitamins, Minerals, and Food Labels."

Dietary minerals are divided into macrominerals, those with required daily amounts greater than 100 mg per day, and microminerals, those needed in lesser quantities. The macrominerals listed in Table 19.7 do not include sulfur because it is an integral part of the amino acids cysteine and methionine, which are taken in sufficient amounts in the diet. Adequate, regular intake of calcium and phosphorus is necessary for formation and maintenance of bone. Magnesium is also necessary for bone metabolism and is stored in bone tissue; it is also a cofactor in many different enzymes ranging from glucose and lipid metabolism to protein synthesis.

We generally do not think of the other three macrominerals as essential, since deficiencies are rare. Rather, we often consume too much sodium, chloride, and potassium by eating processed food. These macronutrients function as electrolytes, maintaining

Table 19.7 Macro and Trace Minerals

Mineral	Significance	Sources	Effects of Deficiency	Effects of Excess
Macrominerals				
Calcium	Bone formation, muscle contraction	Dairy, eggs, beans	Osteoporosis, muscle cramps	Kidney stones, heart arrhythmias
Phosphorus	Bone formation, component of DNA and energy molecules	Any protein	Muscle weakness	Impaired calcium metabolism
Potassium	Osmotic balance inside cells	Fruit, vegetables, meat	Loss of appetite, muscle cramps	Inhibited heart function
Chloride	Primary negative ion in extracellular fluid	All foods, especially processed	Convulsions (rare)	Hypertension
Sodium	Nerve impulse conduction, electrolyte (osmotic balance)	All foods, especially processed	Muscle cramps, nausea	Hypertension
Magnesium	Protein synthesis, glucose metabolism	Dairy, whole grains, plants	Muscle weakness	Nausea
Microminerals				
Iron	Hemoglobin and cytochrome component	Meat, whole grains, legumes	Fatigue, anemia	Hemochromatosis
Fluoride	Part of vitamin B_{12}	Milk, eggs, seafood	Dental cavities	Discolored teeth
Zinc	Enzyme cofactor, smell and taste functions	Meat, dairy, whole grains	Poor immune function, slow wound healing	Poor immune system, increased low-density lipoprotein (LDL) cholesterol
Copper	Enzymes for oxidations and connective tissue formation	Meat, nuts, eggs, bran cereal	Anemia	Nausea
Selenium	Cofactor for glutathione peroxidase	Meat, whole grains	Cardiac muscle damage	Nausea, hair loss
Manganese	Coenzyme for many enzymes in energy metabolism	Whole grains, legumes	Poor growth	Weakness, mental confusion
Iodine	Production of thyroid hormones	Iodized salt, seafood	Goiter	Depressed thyroid activity
Molybdenum	Coenzyme	Meat, whole grains, legumes	Not found	Not found
Chromium	Enhances insulin function	Meat, whole grains	Glucose intolerance	Rare from diet

CHEMISTRY IN ACTION

✚ Enzymes in Medical Diagnosis

In a healthy person, certain enzymes, such as those responsible for forming and dissolving blood clots, are normally present in high concentrations in blood serum. Enzymes that function within cells are found normally in low concentrations in blood serum due to normal degeneration of healthy cells. However, when tissue is injured, large quantities of cellular enzymes are released into the blood from dying cells, with the distribution of enzymes and other proteins dependent on the identity of the injured cells. Measurement of blood levels of specific molecules is therefore a valuable diagnostic tool. For example, higher-than-normal activities of the enzymes included in a routine blood analysis indicate the following conditions:

Enzyme	Diagnosis
Aspartate transaminase (AST)	Damage to heart or liver
Alanine transaminase (ALT)	Damage to heart or liver
Lactate dehydrogenase (LDH)	Damage to heart, liver, or red blood cells
Alkaline phosphatase (ALP)	Damage to bone and liver cells
γ-Glutamyl transferase (GGT)	Damage to liver cells; alcoholism
Creatine phosphokinase (CPK-2)	Damage to heart
Acid phosphatase	Prostate cancer

Enzyme analysis measures the activity of an enzyme rather than its concentration. Because activity is influenced by pH, temperature, and substrate concentration, it is measured in IU at standard conditions. One IU is defined as the amount of an enzyme that converts 1 μmol of its substrate to product per minute under defined standard conditions of pH, temperature, and substrate concentration. The analytical results are reported in units per liter (U/L).

Enzyme assays are done to diagnose heart attacks *(myocardial infarctions, MI)*, like in Mr. Smith's case at the beginning of the chapter, and differentiate them from other conditions like liver disease. CPK has three isomeric forms: CPK-1 is found in brain tissue, CPK-2 is found in heart tissue, and CPK-3 is found in skeletal muscle. After an MI, CPK-2 values rise rapidly within 6 hours and peak around 12 hours after the event, then decrease. AST and ALT blood levels are also measured to help in diagnosis but are also indicators of liver disease. LDH, which has five isomeric forms, one of which is found only in heart muscle, formerly was used as an MI indicator. Currently

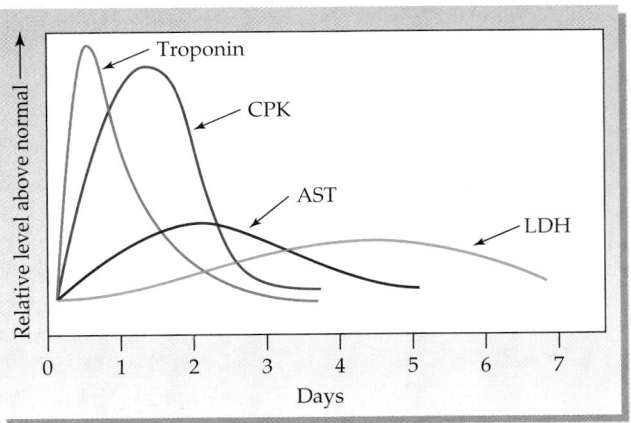

▲ Blood levels of troponins, CPK-2, AST, and LDH in the days following a heart attack.

the levels of troponin proteins are measured in blood samples over 18 hours. There are several troponin isomers; cardiac troponin is specific to heart muscle cells and is associated with actin and myosin in cells; troponins are not enzymes but are a reliable marker for an MI. Troponin levels rise rapidly immediately and dramatically after an MI, decreasing over several days post event rise.

What happened to Mr. Smith and Ms. Givens from the beginning of the chapter? Physicians determined from elevated CPK and AST levels (both enzymes), the characteristic rise in troponin levels (determined in an assay involving enzymes), and other tests that Mr. Smith had a heart attack. His blood lipids were also elevated, and he was placed on a heart-healthy diet along with appropriate medications. Ms. Givens, indeed, had suffered an ischemic stroke, blocking blood circulation in part of her brain. She was promptly treated with an intravenous infusion of tPA, an enzyme obtained from recombinant DNA technology. Early treatment with tPA results in clot dissolution and better recovery from a stroke. Ms. Givens was also given diet recommendations and medications before discharge from the hospital.

CIA Problem 19.8 Enzyme levels in blood are often elevated in various disease states. Which enzyme or other blood marker gives the earliest indication of a heart attack? Which test is used to confirm a heart attack, after several tests over several days?

CIA Problem 19.9 Why must enzyme activity be monitored under standard conditions?

osmotic balance in both intracellular and extracellular spaces. They also help in the production of electrical signals throughout the nervous system; potassium ions are important in regulating heartbeat.

Magnesium and selenium, along with the transition elements chromium, copper, manganese, molybdenum, and zinc, are classed as micronutrients. Our bodies need only tiny amounts of these elements to supply enough cations to function as cofactors for enzymes. Some of these elements, such as copper and selenium, are highly toxic if ingested in high amounts. Each of these transition elements exists as a cation that can form covalent-coordinated bonds with specific, charged residues in the protein structure of their respective enzymes. Because these are transition element cations, with variable oxidation states, they can also serve as transient holders of electrons during enzymatic reactions.

Vitamins and micronutrient minerals serve complementary functions. Both serve as cofactors for enzymatic reactions. Minerals serve directly, whereas vitamins may be modified into other organic molecules in order to participate in a reaction. The other essential minerals are used as building material or to maintain electrolyte balance.

PROBLEM 19.23
Which micronutrient mineral do you think is the most toxic in excess? Why is it necessary if it is toxic?

SUMMARY REVISITING THE CHAPTER LEARNING OBJECTIVES

- **Describe the function of enzymes in biochemical reactions.** *Enzymes* are the catalysts for biochemical reactions, acting by lowering the activation energy needed for the reaction. They are mostly water-soluble, globular proteins *(see Problems 84 and 85)*.
- **Explain the role of cofactors in some enzymatic reactions.** Some enzymes require *cofactors,* which are either metal ions or the nonprotein organic molecules known as *coenzymes,* for activity. These cofactors facilitate electron transfer and chemical group movement during the reaction *(see Problems 25, 27, and 32–35)*.
- **Give an enzyme the appropriate name given the substrate.** Enzymes are named for the substrate (first part of the name) and type of reaction involved (second part of the name) with the suffix *-ase* attached. Some enzymes retain classical names and do not follow these rules *(see Problems 25, 36, and 37)*.
- **Assign an enzyme to the correct class based on its reaction.** There are six major classes of reactions that are catalyzed by enzymes. Each major class encompasses subclasses of similar reactions (Table 19.2) *(see Problems 25, 36, 37, and 41–46)*.
- **Explain the two models of enzyme catalysis.** In the *lock-and-key model* of catalysis, the substrate fits the active site of the enzyme like a key fits a lock. It is a rigid model. In the *induced-fit model,* substrate is drawn into the active site by noncovalent interactions. As the substrate enters the active site, the enzyme shape adjusts to best accommodate the substrate and catalyze the reaction *(see Problems 40, 41, 48, and 49)*.
- **Describe how an enzyme and substrate combine to facilitate a reaction.** Within the *enzyme–substrate complex,* the substrate is held in the best orientation for reaction and in a strained condition that allows the activation energy to be lowered. When the reaction is complete, the product is released and the enzyme returns to its original condition. The *specificity* of each enzyme is determined by the presence within the active site of catalytically active groups, hydrophobic pockets, and ionic or polar groups that exactly fit the chemical makeup of the substrate *(see Problems 24, 30, 50–53, 81, and 82)*.

- **Describe the changes in enzyme activity that result when substrate concentration, enzyme concentration, temperature, or pH change.** With fixed enzyme concentration, reaction rate first increases with increasing substrate concentration and then approaches a fixed maximum at which all active sites are occupied. In the presence of excess substrate, reaction rate is directly proportional to enzyme concentration. With increasing temperature, reaction rate increases to a maximum and then decreases as the enzyme protein denatures. Reaction rate is maximal at a pH that reflects the pH of the enzyme's site of action in the body *(see Problems 54–57 and 82)*.
- **Define and identify reversible and irreversible inhibition.** The effectiveness of enzymes is controlled by a variety of *activation* and *inhibition* strategies. *Competitive inhibitors* are *reversible inhibitors* that typically resemble the substrate and reversibly block the active site; they slow the reaction rate but do not change the maximum rate. *Irreversible inhibitors* form covalent bonds to an enzyme that permanently inactivate it; most are poisons *(see Problems 30, 62, 64, and 65)*.
- **Define and identify uncompetitive and competitive inhibition.** *Uncompetitive inhibitors* act on the enzyme–substrate complex, blocking a second substrate from entering the active site; they lower the maximum reaction rate. *Competitive inhibitors* are molecules similar to the substrate that fit the active site and slow the reaction rate *(see Problems 28 and 58–61)*.
- **Define and identify allosteric control.** Allosteric control is achieved by an enzyme regulator molecule that can exercise control over an enzyme by binding to a site different from the active site. Binding a regulator induces a change of shape in the active site, increasing or decreasing the efficiency of the enzyme. The regulator molecule does not need to resemble the reaction substrate *(see Problems 29, 30, 66, and 67)*.
- **Define feedback control and explain how it regulates enzyme catalysis.** Feedback control acts through *allosteric control* of enzymes that have regulatory sites separate from their active sites. When enough product of a series of reactions is present, the excess inhibits

the activity of the first enzyme in the reaction series preventing more product from accumulating *(see Problems 29, 30, 68, and 69)*.

- **Define and identify inhibition by covalent modification.** Enzyme activity is also regulated by *reversible* phosphorylation and dephosphorylation and by synthesis of inactive *zymogens* that are later activated by removal of part of the molecule *(see Problems 29, 71, and 73)*.
- **Define and identify inhibition by genetic control of enzymes.** *Genetic control* is exercised by regulation of the synthesis of enzymes specific to the stage of life and need of the organism *(see Problems 29, 30, 70, and 72)*.
- **Describe the two classes of vitamins, the reasons vitamins are necessary in the diet, and the results of vitamin excesses or deficiencies.** *Vitamins* are organic molecules required in small amounts in the body that must be obtained from the diet. The water-soluble vitamins (Table 19.5) are coenzymes or parts of coenzymes. The

fat-soluble vitamins (Table 19.6) have diverse and less well-understood functions. In general, excesses of water-soluble vitamins are excreted and excesses of fat-soluble vitamins are stored in body fat, making excesses of the fat-soluble vitamins potentially more harmful *(see Problems 80, 81, and 88)*.

- **Identify antioxidants and explain their function.** Vitamin C, β-carotene (a precursor of vitamin A), vitamin E, and selenium work together as *antioxidants* to protect biomolecules from damage by free radicals.
- **Identify essential minerals, explain why minerals are necessary in the diet, and explain the results of mineral deficiencies.** Minerals are chemical elements needed in small amounts in the diet. Minerals function as macronutrients (calcium and phosphorus for bone), electrolytes, and micronutrients used primarily as enzyme cofactors.

CONCEPT MAP: ENZYMES

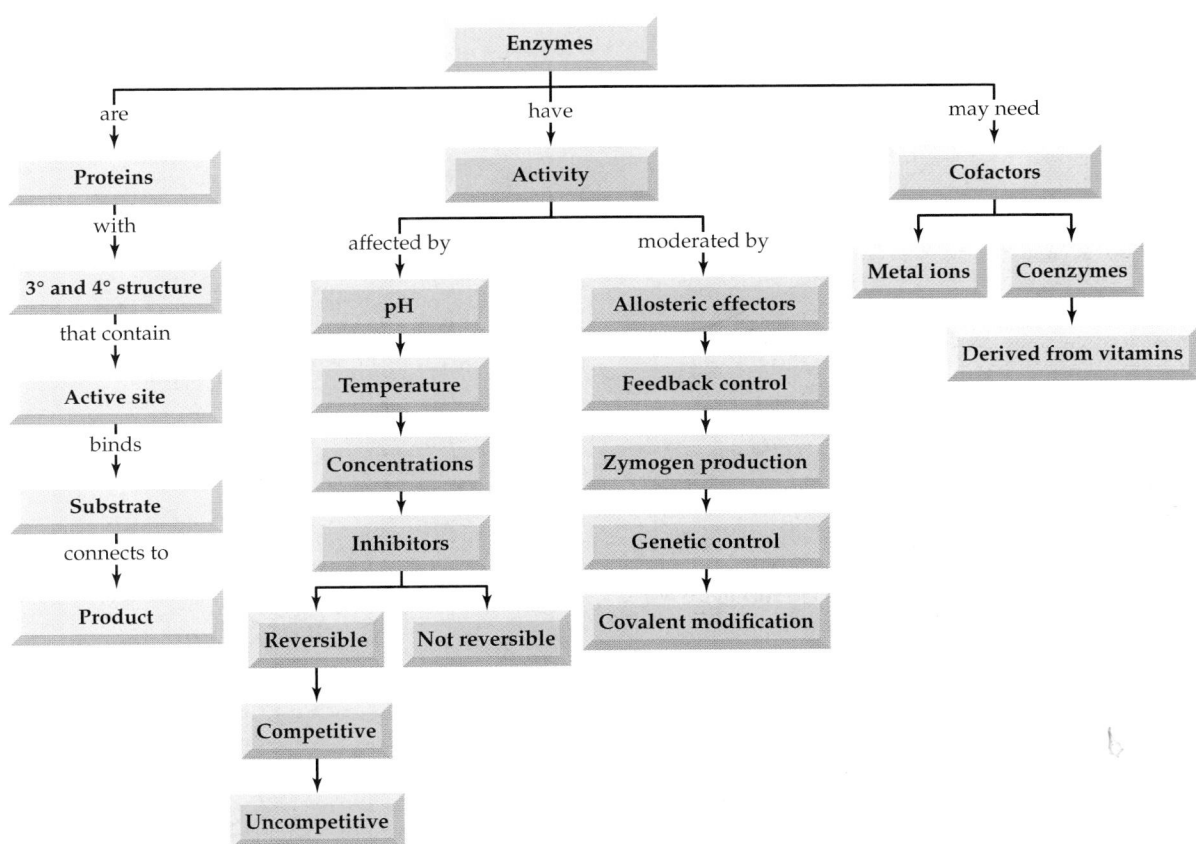

▲ Figure 19.11 **Concept Map.** Protein tertiary and quaternary structures provide active sites where biochemical reactions occur in enzymes. Activity is affected by several physical factors and can be affected by inhibitory molecules. Several different forms of control, depending on the enzyme, control activity. Some enzymes require cofactors, either metal ions or coenzymes, for activity.

KEY WORDS

Activation (of an enzyme), *p. 605*
Active site, *p. 592*
Allosteric control, *p. 608*
Allosteric enzyme, *p. 608*
Antioxidant, *p. 616*
Coenzyme, *p. 593*
Cofactor, *p. 593*

Competitive (enzyme) inhibition, *p. 606*
Enzyme, *p. 591*
Feedback control, *p. 610*
Free radical, *p. 616*
Genetic (enzyme) control, *p. 613*
Induced-fit model, *p. 599*

Inhibition (of an enzyme), *p. 605*
Irreversible (enzyme) inhibition, *p. 607*
Lock-and-key model, *p. 599*
Specificity (enzyme), *p. 592*

Substrate, *p. 592*
Turnover number, *p. 593*
Uncompetitive (enzyme) inhibition, *p. 606*
Vitamin, *p. 613*
Zymogen, *p. 611*

UNDERSTANDING KEY CONCEPTS

19.24 On the following diagram, indicate with dotted lines the bonding between the enzyme (a dipeptidase; several amino acid residues in black) and the substrate (in blue) that might occur to form the enzyme–substrate complex. What are the two types of bonding likely to occur?

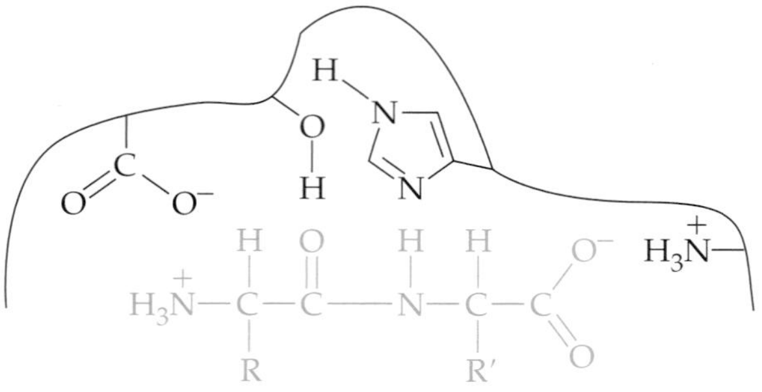

19.25 Answer questions (a)–(e) concerning the following reaction:

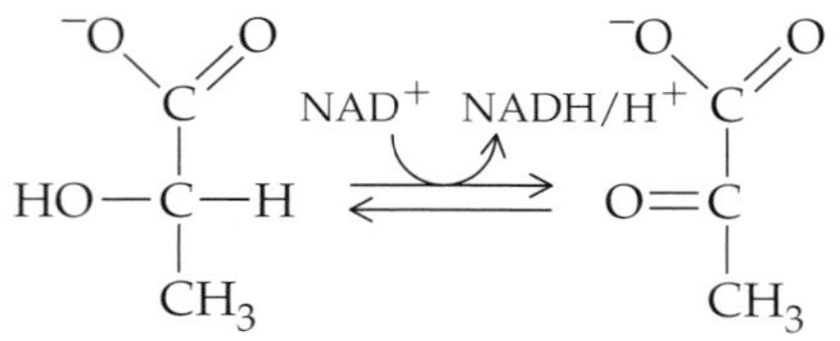

(a) The enzyme involved in this reaction belongs to what class of enzymes?

(b) Since hydrogens are removed, the enzyme belongs to what subclass of the enzyme class from part (a)?

(c) What is the substrate for the reaction as written?

(d) What is the product for the reaction as written?

(e) The enzyme name is derived from the substrate name and the subclass of the enzyme and ends in the family-name ending for an enzyme. Name the enzyme.

19.26 In the reaction shown in Problem 19.25, will the enzyme likely also use D-lactate as a substrate? Explain your answer. If D-lactate binds to the enzyme, how is it likely to affect the enzyme?

19.27 In the reaction shown in Problem 19.25, identify the coenzyme required for catalytic activity. Is the coenzyme an oxidizing agent or a reducing agent? What vitamin is a part of the coenzyme for this reaction?

19.28 Explain how the following changes affect the rate of an enzyme-catalyzed reaction in the presence of an uncompetitive inhibitor: (a) increasing the substrate concentration at a constant inhibitor concentration, (b) decreasing the inhibitor concentration at a constant substrate concentration.

19.29 Explain how the following mechanisms regulate enzyme activity.

(a) Covalent modification   (b) Genetic control

(c) Allosteric regulation   (d) Feedback inhibition

19.30 What type of enzyme regulation occurs in the following situations?

(a) Buildup of the product of the pathway that converts glucose to pyruvate stops at the first enzyme in the multistep process.

(b) Sarin, a nerve gas, covalently binds to acetylcholinesterase, stopping nerve signal transmission.

(c) Lactase is not produced in the adult.

(d) Conversion of isocitrate to α-ketoglutarate is inhibited by high levels of ATP. (Hint: ATP is neither a product nor a substrate in this reaction.)

19.31 Acidic and basic groups are often found in the active sites of enzymes. Identify the acidic and basic amino acids in the active site in the following diagram. (Hint: Consult Table 18.3 and Chapter 10 for the definition of acids and bases.)

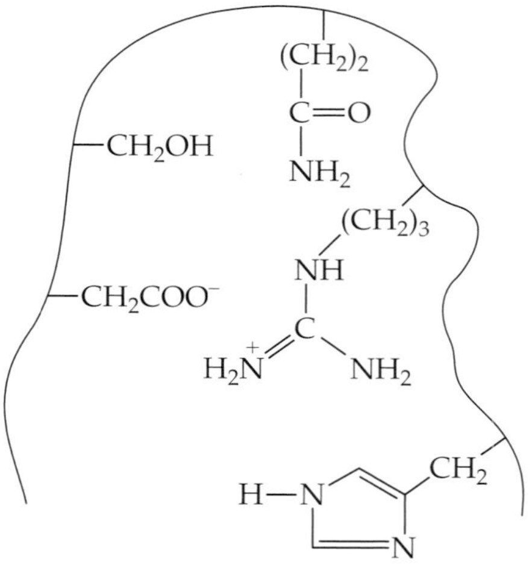

ADDITIONAL PROBLEMS

ENZYME COFACTORS (SECTION 19.2)

19.32 Name the vitamin to which each of these coenzymes is related.

(a) FAD   (b) Coenzyme A

(c) NAD^+

19.33 Which of the following is a cofactor and which is a coenzyme?

(a) Cu^{2+} (b) Tetrahydrofolate

(c) NAD^+ (d) Mg^{2+}

19.34 Which of these vitamins can serve as a cofactor?

(a) Vitamin A   (b) Vitamin C

(c) Vitamin D

19.35 Which of the following is a cofactor and which is a coenzyme?

(a) Fe^{2+} (b) Pyridoxyl phosphate

(c) FAD   (d) Ni^{2+}

STRUCTURE AND CLASSIFICATION OF ENZYMES (SECTION 19.3)

19.36 What general kinds of reactions do the following types of enzymes catalyze?

(a) Dehydrogenases   (b) Decarboxylases

(c) Lipases

19.37 What general kinds of reactions do the following types of enzymes catalyze?

(a) Kinases   (b) Isomerases

(c) Synthetases

19.38 Name an enzyme that acts on each molecule.

(a) Amylose   (b) Peroxide   (c) DNA

19.39 Name an enzyme that acts on each molecule.

(a) Lactose   (b) Protein   (c) RNA

19.40 What features of enzymes make them so specific in their action?

19.41 Describe in general terms how enzymes act as catalysts.

19.42 What classes of enzymes would you expect to catalyze the following reactions?

(a) H₂NCHCNHCHCOH + H₂O ⟶
  (R, R')
  H₂NCHCOH + H₂NCHCOH
  (R)   (R')

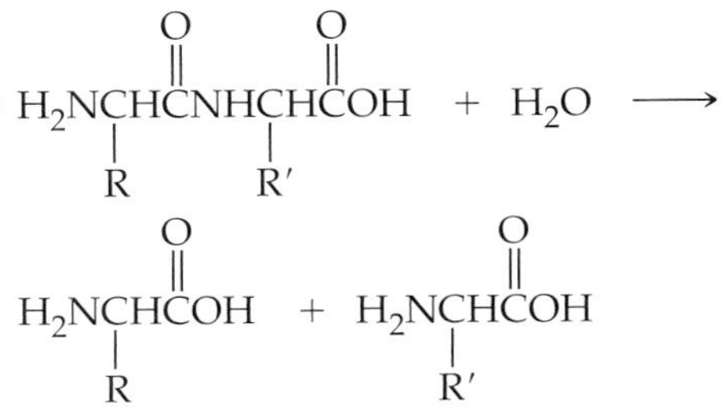

(b) HOOC—CH₂—C—COOH ⟶
  CH₃—C—COOH + CO₂

(c) HOCCH₂CH₂COH ⟶ HOCCH=CHCOH

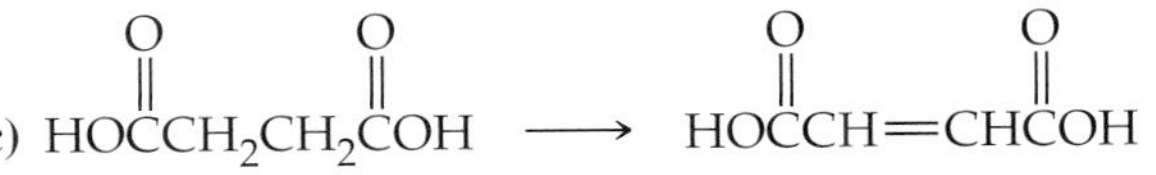

19.43 What classes of enzymes would you expect to catalyze the following reactions?

(a)
Pyruvate + H₃NCH (L-Aspartate) ⇌ (Vitamin B₆) H₃NCH (L-Alanine) + Oxaloacetate

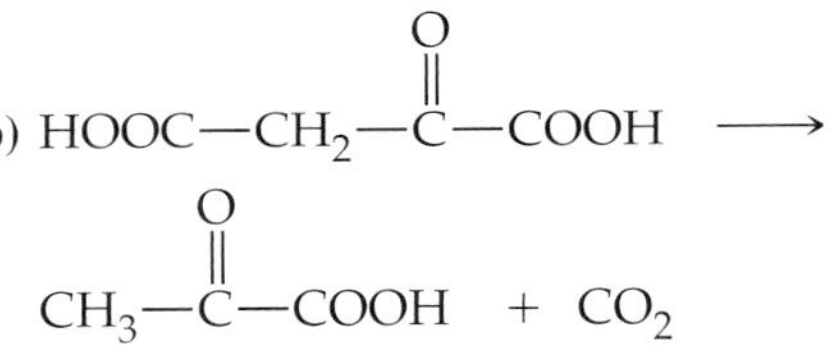

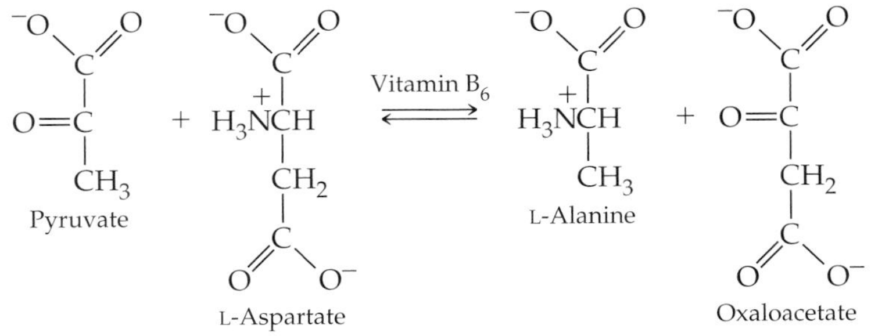

(b) 3-Phosphoglyceraldehyde ⇌ Dihydroxyacetone phosphate

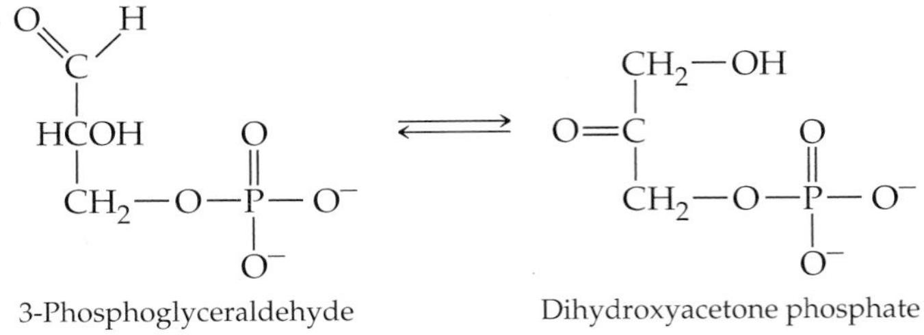

(c) Pyruvate + CO₂ ⟶ (ATP → ADP) Oxaloacetate

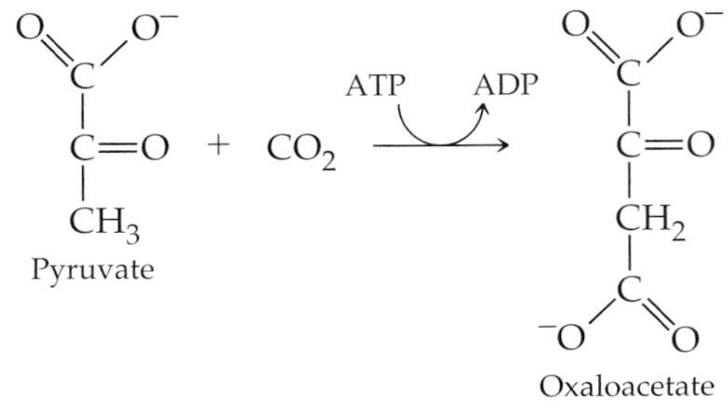

19.44 What kind of reaction does each of these enzymes catalyze?

(a) A ligase

(b) A transmethylase

(c) A reductase

19.45 What kind of reaction does each of these enzymes catalyze?

(a) A dehydrase

(b) A carboxylase

(c) A protease

19.46 The following reaction is catalyzed by the enzyme urease. To what class of enzymes does urease belong?

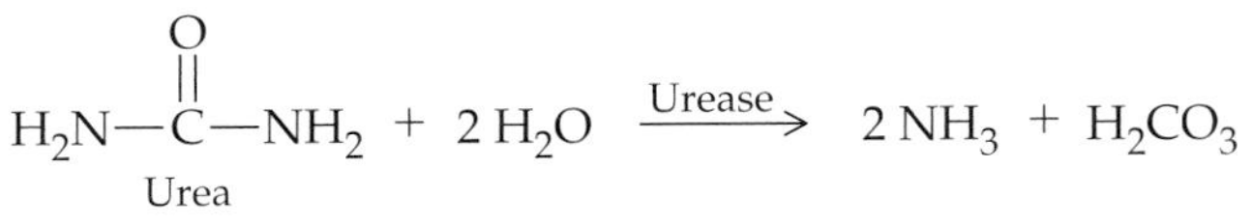

H₂N—C—NH₂ (Urea) + 2 H₂O ⟶(Urease) 2 NH₃ + H₂CO₃

19.47 Alcohol dehydrogenase (ADH) catalyzes the following reaction. To what class of enzymes does ADH belong?

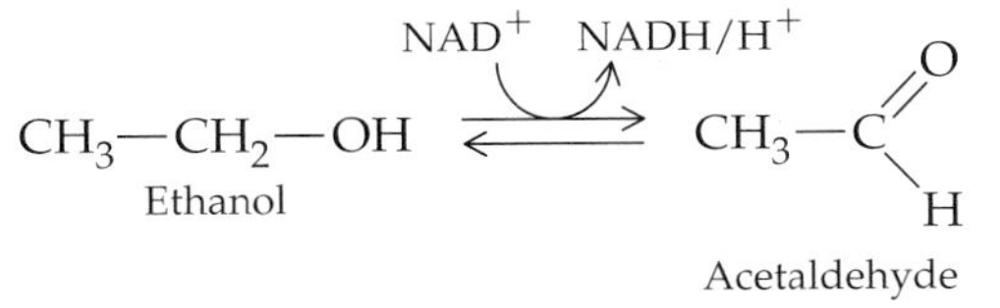

CH₃—CH₂—OH (Ethanol) ⇌ (NAD⁺ → NADH/H⁺) CH₃—C (Acetaldehyde)

HOW ENZYMES WORK (SECTION 19.4)

19.48 What is the difference between the lock-and-key model of enzyme action and the induced-fit model?

19.49 Why is the induced-fit model a more likely model than the lock-and-key model?

19.50 Must the amino acid residues in the active site be near each other along the polypeptide chain? Explain.

19.51 The active site of an enzyme is a small portion of the enzyme molecule. What is the function of the rest of the huge molecule?

19.52 How do you explain the observation that pepsin, a digestive enzyme found in the stomach, has a high catalytic activity at pH 1.5, while trypsin, an enzyme of the small intestine, has no activity at pH 1.5?

19.53 Amino acid side chains in the active sites of enzymes can act as acids or bases during catalysis. List the amino acid side chains that can accept H^+ and those that can donate H^+ during enzyme-catalyzed reactions.

FACTORS AFFECTING ENZYME ACTIVITY (SECTION 19.5)

19.54 If the rate of an enzymatic reaction doubles when the amount of enzyme is doubled, what do you expect the rate of reaction to be if the amount of enzyme is tripled? Why?

19.55 What happens to the rate of an enzymatic reaction if the amount of substrate is doubled? Why?

19.56 What general effects would you expect the following changes to have on the rate of an enzyme-catalyzed reaction for an enzyme that has its maximum activity at body temperature (about 37 °C)?

   (a) Raising the temperature from 37 °C to 70 °C

   (b) Lowering the pH from 7 to 3

   (c) Adding an organic solvent, such as methanol

19.57 What general effects would you expect the following changes to have on the rate of an enzyme-catalyzed reaction for an enzyme that has its maximum activity at body temperature (about 37 °C)?

   (a) Lowering the reaction temperature from 40 °C to 10 °C

   (b) Adding a drop of a dilute $HgCl_2$ solution

   (c) Adding an oxidizing agent, such as hydrogen peroxide

ENZYME REGULATION: INHIBITION (SECTION 19.6)

19.58 The text discusses three forms of enzyme inhibition: uncompetitive inhibition, competitive inhibition, and irreversible inhibition.

   (a) Describe how an enzyme inhibitor of each type works.

   (b) What kinds of bonds are formed between an enzyme and each of these three kinds of inhibitors?

19.59 What kind of inhibition (uncompetitive, competitive, or irreversible) is present in each of the following:

   (a) Penicillin is used to treat certain bacterial infections. Penicillin is effective because it binds to the enzyme glycopeptide transpeptidase and does not dissociate.

   (b) Accidental methanol consumption is fairly common. The treatment includes the ingestion of ethanol. Both molecules can be converted to aldehydes by alcohol dehydrogenase. Ethanol is the true substrate.

   (c) The antibiotic deoxycycline inhibits the bacterial enzyme collagenase, slowing bacterial growth. Deoxycycline does not fit into the active site of collagenase and binds elsewhere on the enzyme.

19.60 EcoRI, an enzyme that hydrolyzes DNA strands, requires Mg^{2+} as a cofactor for activity. EDTA chelates divalent metal ions in solution. In the graphs shown here, the arrow indicates the point at which EDTA is added to a reaction mediated by EcoRI. Which graph represents the activity curve you would expect to see? (Activity is shown as total product from the reaction as time increases.)

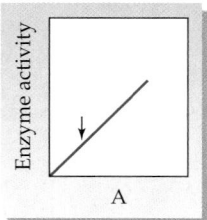 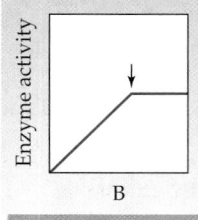 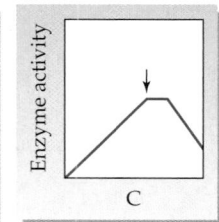

19.61 The enzyme lactate dehydrogenase converts lactic acid to pyruvate with the aid of the coenzyme NAD^+. In the graphs of Problem 19.60, the arrow indicates the point at which EDTA is added to a reaction mixture of lactic dehydrogenase and lactic acid. Which graph represents the activity curve you would expect to see? (Activity is shown as total product from the reaction as time increases.)

19.62 Lead exerts its poisonous effect on enzymes by two mechanisms. Which mechanism is irreversible and why?

19.63 One mechanism by which lead exerts its poisonous effect on enzymes can be stopped by chelation therapy with EDTA. Describe this type of lead poisoning and explain why it is reversible.

19.64 The meat tenderizer used in cooking is primarily papain, a protease enzyme isolated from the fruit of the papaya tree. Why do you suppose papain is so effective at tenderizing meat?

19.65 Bumblebee venom contains several related heptadecapeptides from the bomditin family. Papain can be used to help relieve the pain of bee stings. Why do you suppose it works?

ENZYME REGULATION: ALLOSTERIC CONTROL AND FEEDBACK (SECTION 19.7)

19.66 Why do allosteric enzymes have two types of binding sites?

19.67 Discuss the purpose of positive and negative regulation.

19.68 What is feedback inhibition?

19.69 What are the cellular advantages to feedback inhibition?

ENZYME REGULATION: COVALENT MODIFICATION AND GENETIC CONTROL (SECTION 19.8)

19.70 What is a zymogen? Why must some enzymes be secreted as zymogens?

19.71 Activation of a zymogen is by covalent modification. How might phosphorylation or dephosphorylation (also covalent modification) modify an enzyme to make it more active (or more inactive)?

19.72 Why are the protein-digesting enzymes trypsin and chymotrypsin secreted as the zymogen chymotrypsinogen?

19.73 Infants do not have the ability to metabolize ethanol and are assumed to lack the enzyme alcohol dehydrogenase? What kind of regulation is this?

VITAMINS, ANTIOXIDANTS, AND MINERALS (SECTION 19.9)

19.74 What criteria make a compound a vitamin?

19.75 What is the relationship between vitamins and enzymes?

19.76 Why is daily ingestion of vitamin C more critical than daily ingestion of vitamin A?

19.77 List the four fat-soluble vitamins. Why is excess consumption of three of these vitamins of concern?

19.78 Why is it important that the macronutrients calcium and phosphorus be ingested in approximately equal amounts?

19.79 Most of the micronutrients are transition elements. What property of the transition elements makes them especially suitable for their roles in the body?

CONCEPTUAL PROBLEMS

19.80 Look up the structures of vitamin C and vitamin E on the Web, and identify the functional groups in these vitamins.

19.81 What is the relationship between vitamin A and β-carotene? (Hint: Look up the structures on the Web.)

19.82 Many vegetables are "blanched" (dropped into boiling water) for a few minutes before being frozen. Why is blanching necessary?

19.83 How can you distinguish between a competitive inhibitor and an uncompetitive inhibitor experimentally?

19.84 What is the activation energy for a reaction? Why is activation energy necessary?

19.85 Does an enzyme-mediated reaction need the same, more, or less activation energy than the same reaction occurring without the presence of the enzyme? Explain why.

19.86 How will changing the conditions in an enzymatic reaction affect the rate of that reaction? Explain why in each case.

   (a) Lowering the temperature from 37 °C to 15 °C

   (b) Raising the temperature from 37 °C to 60 °C

   (c) Lowering the pH from 7.4 to 3.0

   (d) Raising the pH from 7.4 to 10

   (e) Doubling the amount of substrate

   (f) Decreasing the amount of substrate by half

19.87 Why are irreversible enzyme inhibitors referred to as poisons?

GROUP PROBLEMS

19.88 The adult RDA of riboflavin is 1.3 mg. If one glass (100 mL) of apple juice contains 0.014 mg of riboflavin, how much apple juice would an adult have to consume to obtain the RDA?

19.89 The ability to change a selected amino acid residue to another amino acid is referred to as "point mutation" by biochemists. Referring to the reaction for peptide bond hydrolysis in Figure 19.4, speculate on the effects that the following point mutations might have on the chymotrypsin mechanism shown in Figure 19.4: serine to valine; aspartate to glutamate.

19.90 Trypsin is an enzyme that cleaves on the C-terminal side (i.e., to the right of) all basic amino acids in a protein or peptide. (Consult Table 18.3 to identify basic amino acids.) Consider the following peptide. Predict the fragments that would be formed by treatment of this peptide with trypsin.

   N-terminal end-Leu-Gly-Arg-Ile-Met-His-Tyr-Trp-Ala-C-terminal end

19.91 Apple slices and peeled potatoes rapidly brown in open air due to the presence of phenolases. Phenolases cause the oxidation of phenolic molecules like tyrosine to quinones, colored molecules responsible for the brown colors seen. An experiment comparing the time it took for a change to occur in the color of apple slices versus potato slices was done to test for phenolase activity. Then, a second experiment was done with new apple and potato slices with H_2O_2 measuring time until bubbles appeared.

Enzyme	Apple	Potato
Phenolase	130 sec.	180 sec.
Catalase	20 sec.	10 sec.

   (a) Which sample contains more phenolase? Why?

   (b) Which sample contains more catalase? Why?

   (c) What variables in the experiment would affect your answers to (a) and (b)?

   (d) Which enzyme has the higher turnover rate?

20

Carbohydrates

CONTENTS

◀◀◀ CONCEPTS TO REVIEW

▲ Carbohydrates are found in many of the foods available at this picnic as well as in the table, plates, and clothing.

Imagine for a moment, Sarah and Jacob, two college students, discussing diets over lunch. Sarah makes a healthy choice to order vegetable soup and a salad while Jacob orders a juicy bacon cheeseburger with fries and lots of ketchup. They finish their meal with a stop for ice cream. Sarah claims the vegetables in her soup and her salad had fewer carbohydrates than Jacob's lunch, but Jacob disagrees, arguing that the only food he ate that had carbohydrates was the hamburger bun. Who is right? And how can they find out? There are many resources available to find the carbohydrate, fiber, and sugar values for all food items, which will be discussed in more detail in the Chemistry in Action "Carbohydrates and Fiber in the Diet" later in chapter. Knowing these values in the foods you eat is important for maintaining a healthy lifestyle. This chapter explains carbohydrates, which are present in many of the foods you eat every day so that you can decide their place in your diet.

The word *carbohydrate* originally described glucose, the simplest and most readily available sugar. Because glucose has the formula $C_6H_{12}O_6$, it was once thought to be a "hydrate of carbon," $C_6(H_2O)_6$. Although this view has been abandoned, the name "carbohydrate" persisted, and we now use it to refer to a large class of biomolecules with similar structures. Carbohydrates have in common many hydroxyl groups on adjacent carbons together with either an aldehyde or ketone group. Glucose, for example, has five hydroxyl ($-OH$) groups and one aldehyde ($-CHO$) group:

$$
\begin{array}{c}
\quad\;\; H \quad H \quad H \quad OH \quad H \quad\; O \\
\quad\;\; | \quad\;\; | \quad\;\; | \quad\;\; | \quad\;\;\; | \quad\;\;\; \| \\
HO-C-C-C-C-C-C-H \\
\quad\;\; | \quad\;\; | \quad\;\; | \quad\;\; | \quad\;\;\; | \\
\quad\;\; H \quad OH \; OH \; H \quad OH
\end{array}
$$
Glucose

Carbohydrates are synthesized by plants and stored as starch, a polymer of glucose. When starch is eaten and digested, the freed glucose becomes a major source of the energy required by living organisms. Thus, carbohydrates are intermediaries by which energy from the sun is made available to animals.

20.1 An Introduction to Carbohydrates

Learning Objective:

- Classify carbohydrates by functional group and number of carbon atoms and label them accordingly.

Carbohydrates are a large class of naturally occurring polyhydroxy aldehydes and ketones. **Monosaccharides,** sometimes known as **simple sugars,** are the simplest carbohydrates. They have from three to seven carbon atoms, and each contains one aldehyde or one ketone functional group. If the sugar has an aldehyde group, it is classified as an **aldose.** If it has a ketone group, the sugar is classified as a **ketose.** The aldehyde group is always at the end of the carbon chain, and the ketone group is always on the second carbon of the chain. In either case, there is a $-CH_2OH$ group at the other end of the chain.

Carbohydrate A member of a large class of naturally occurring polyhydroxy aldehydes and ketones.

Monosaccharide (simple sugar) A carbohydrate with three to seven carbon atoms.

Aldose A monosaccharide that contains an aldehyde carbonyl group.

Ketose A monosaccharide that contains a ketone carbonyl group.

Monosaccharides

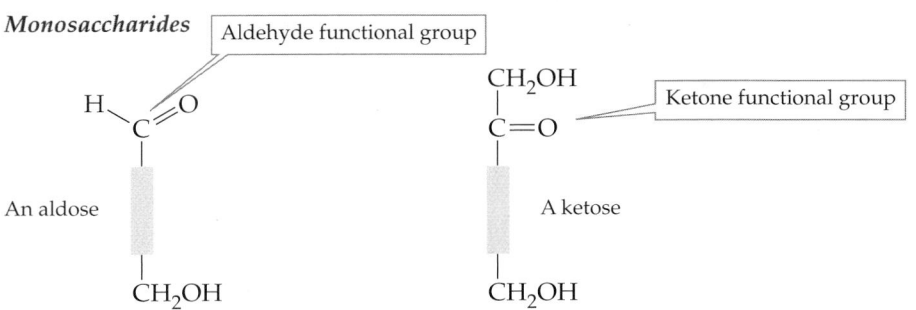

There are hydroxyl groups on all the carbon atoms between the carbonyl carbon atom and the —CH$_2$OH at the other end and also on the end carbon next to a ketone group, as illustrated in the following three structures. The family-name ending *-ose* indicates a carbohydrate, and simple sugars are known by common names like *glucose, ribose,* and *fructose* rather than systematic names.

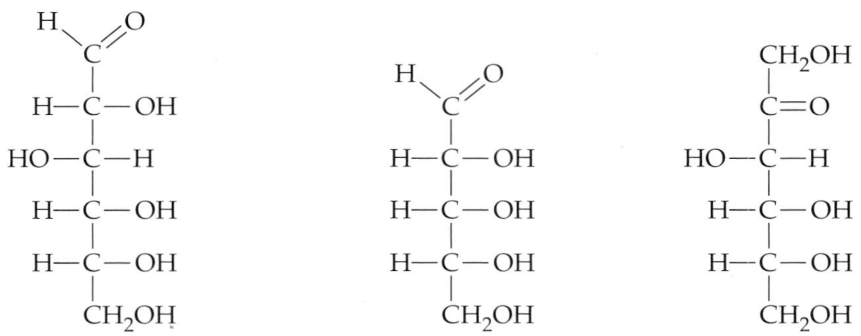

Glucose, an aldohexose
(monomer for starch and cellulose;
major source of energy)

Ribose, an aldopentose
(a component of ATP,
coenzymes, and RNA)

Fructose, a ketohexose
(present in corn syrup
and fruit)

The number of carbon atoms in an aldose or ketose is specified by the prefixes *tri-, tetr-, pent-, hex-,* or *hept-*. Thus, glucose is an aldo*hex*ose (*aldo* = aldehyde; *-hex* = six carbons; *-ose* = sugar); fructose is a keto*hex*ose (a 6-carbon ketone sugar); and ribose is an aldo*pent*ose (a five-carbon aldehyde sugar). Most naturally occurring simple sugars are aldehydes with either five or six carbon atoms.

Because of their many functional groups, monosaccharides undergo a variety of structural changes and chemical reactions. They react with each other to form **disaccharides** and **polysaccharides** (also known as **complex carbohydrates**), which are polymers of monosaccharides. Their functional groups are involved in reactions with alcohols, lipids, or proteins to form biomolecules with specialized functions. These and other carbohydrates are introduced in later sections of this chapter. First, we are going to discuss two important aspects of carbohydrate structure:

Disaccharide A carbohydrate composed of two monosaccharides.

Polysaccharide (complex carbohydrate) A carbohydrate that is a polymer of monosaccharides.

- Monosaccharides are chiral molecules (Section 20.2).
- Monosaccharides exist mainly in cyclic forms rather than the straight-chain forms shown earlier (Section 20.3).

Worked Example 20.1 Classifying Monosaccharides

Classify the monosaccharide shown as an aldose or a ketose, and label it according to its number of carbon atoms.

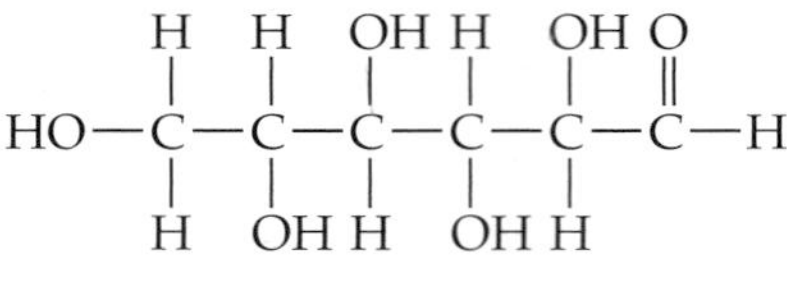

$$HO-\overset{\overset{\displaystyle H}{|}}{\underset{\underset{\displaystyle H}{|}}{C}}-\overset{\overset{\displaystyle H}{|}}{\underset{\underset{\displaystyle OH}{|}}{C}}-\overset{\overset{\displaystyle OH}{|}}{\underset{\underset{\displaystyle H}{|}}{C}}-\overset{\overset{\displaystyle H}{|}}{\underset{\underset{\displaystyle OH}{|}}{C}}-\overset{\overset{\displaystyle OH}{|}}{\underset{\underset{\displaystyle H}{|}}{C}}-\overset{\overset{\displaystyle O}{||}}{C}-H$$

ANALYSIS First, determine if the monosaccharide is an aldose or a ketose. Then determine the number of carbon atoms present. This monosaccharide is an aldose because an aldehyde group is present. It contains 6 carbon atoms.

SOLUTION
The monosaccharide is a 6-carbon aldose, so we refer to it as an aldohexose.

PROBLEM 20.1

Classify the following monosaccharides as an aldose or a ketose, and label each according its number of carbon atoms.

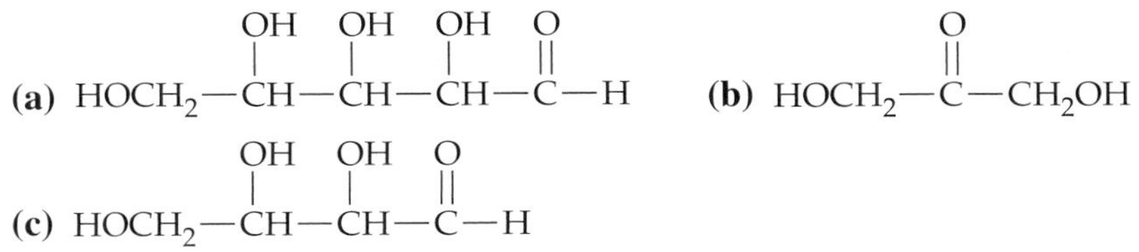

(a) $HOCH_2-\overset{\underset{|}{OH}}{CH}-\overset{\underset{|}{OH}}{CH}-\overset{\underset{|}{OH}}{CH}-\overset{\overset{O}{||}}{C}-H$ (b) $HOCH_2-\overset{\overset{O}{||}}{C}-CH_2OH$

(c) $HOCH_2-\overset{\underset{|}{OH}}{CH}-\overset{\underset{|}{OH}}{CH}-\overset{\overset{O}{||}}{C}-H$

PROBLEM 20.2

Draw the structures of an aldopentose and a ketohexose.

20.2 Handedness of Carbohydrates and Fischer Projections

Learning Objectives:

- Identify D and L enantiomers and any diastereomers of a monosaccharide from the Fischer projection.
- Draw the Fischer projection for a monosaccharide.

You learned that amino acids are chiral because they contain carbon atoms bonded to four different groups. Glyceraldehyde, an aldotriose and the simplest naturally occurring carbohydrate, has the structure shown next. Because four different groups are bonded to the number 2 carbon atom ($-CHO$, $-H$, $-OH$, and $-CH_2OH$), glyceraldehyde is also chiral.

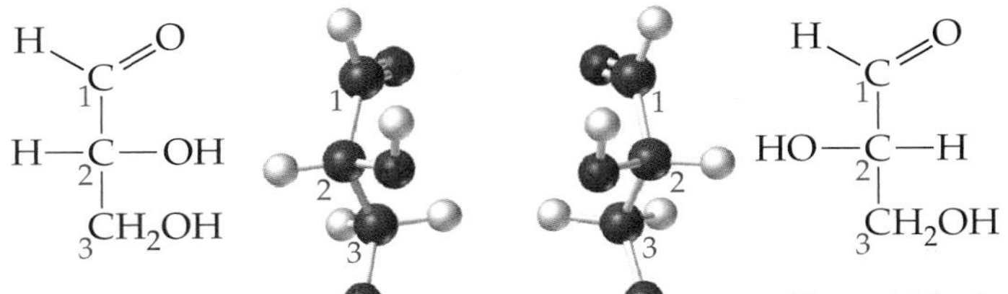

CONCEPTS TO REVIEW Chiral molecules are not superimposable on their mirror images (see Section 14.10).

D-Glyceraldehyde
Right-handed

L-Glyceraldehyde
Left-handed

Chiral compounds lack a plane of symmetry and exist as a pair of enantiomers in either a "right-handed" D form or a "left-handed" L form. Like all enantiomers, the two forms of glyceraldehyde have the same physical properties except for the way in which they affect polarized light. When polarized light is passed separately through a pair of enantiomers, each one rotates the light by the same amount, but the directions of rotation are *opposite*. If one enantiomer rotates the plane of the light to the left, the other rotates it to the right. But *the direction of rotation cannot be predicted*. There are D isomers that rotate polarized light to the left and L isomers that rotate it to the right. Recall from Section 14.10 that lower case d and l are used to indicate right and left light rotation but are unrelated to D and L absolute conformation (structure).

Compounds like glyceraldehyde that have *one* chiral carbon atom can exist as two enantiomers. But what about compounds with more than one chiral carbon atom? How many isomers are there for compounds that have two, three, four, or more chiral carbons? Aldotetroses, for example, have two chiral carbon atoms and can exist in the four isomeric forms shown in Figure 20.1. These four aldotetrose stereoisomers consist of two mirror-image pairs of enantiomers, one pair named *erythrose* and one pair named *threose*. Because erythrose and threose are stereoisomers but not mirror images of each other, they are described as **diastereomers.**

Diastereomers Stereoisomers that are not mirror images of each other.

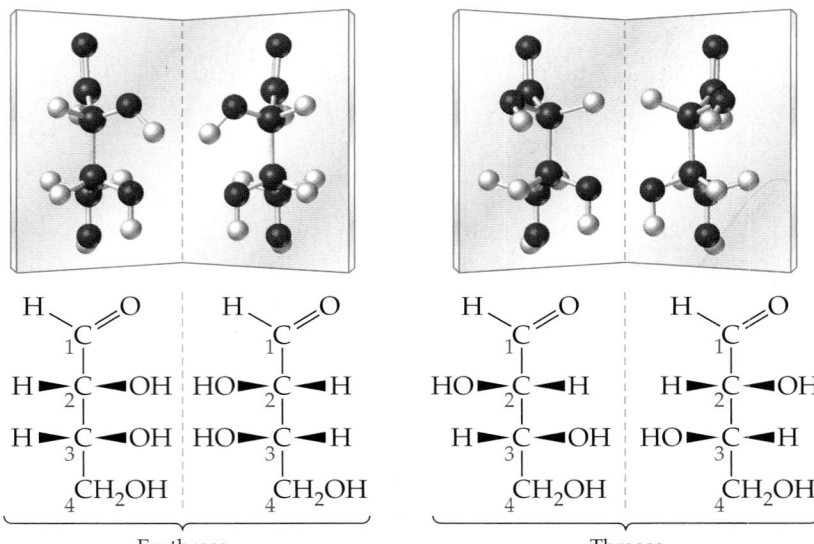

▶ **Figure 20.1**
Two pairs of enantiomers:
The four isomeric aldotetroses
(2,3,4-trihydroxybutanals).
Carbon atoms 2 and 3 are chiral. Their
—H atoms and —OH groups are
written here to show their mirror-
image relationship. Erythrose and
threose exist as enantiomeric pairs.

By convention, the carbonyl group and the terminal CH$_2$OH are drawn pointing to the right. It is understood that the bonds between those carbon atoms and the other carbon atoms freely rotate and do not affect the symmetry of the molecule.

PROBLEM 20.3

Notice in the following structures (a)–(d) that the bottom carbon and its substituents are written as CH$_2$OH in every case. How does the C in this group differ in each case from the C atoms above it? Why must the locations of the H atoms and —OH groups attached to the carbons between this one and the carbonyl group be shown?

PROBLEM 20.4

From monosaccharides (a)–(d) in Problem 20.3, choose the one that is the enantiomer of the unlabeled monosaccharide shown.

PROBLEM 20.5

Aldoheptoses have five chiral carbon atoms. What is the maximum possible number of aldoheptose stereoisomers? Draw all of the aldoheptose stereoisomers.

Drawing Sugar Molecules: Fischer Projections

A standard method of representation called a **Fischer projection** has been adopted for drawing stereoisomers on a flat page so that we can tell one from another. A chiral carbon atom is represented in a Fischer projection as the intersection of two crossed lines, and this carbon atom is considered to be on the printed page. Bonds that point towards you are shown as horizontal lines, and bonds that point away from you are shown as vertical lines. Until now, we have used solid wedges and dashed lines to represent bonds above and behind the printed page, respectively, with ordinary solid lines for bonds in the plane of the page. The relationship between such a structure and a Fischer projection is as follows:

Fischer projection Structure that represents chiral carbon atoms as the intersections of two lines, with the horizontal lines representing bonds pointing out of the page and the vertical lines representing bonds pointing behind the page. For sugars, the aldehyde or ketone is at the top.

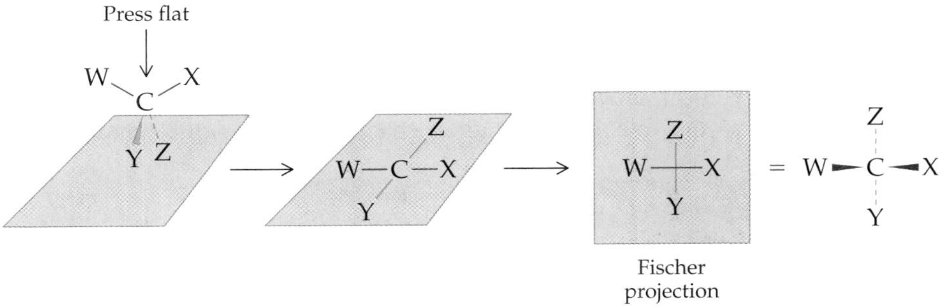

In a Fischer projection, the aldehyde or ketone carbonyl group of a monosaccharide is always placed at the top. The result is that —H and —OH groups projecting above the page are on the left and right of the chiral carbons, and groups projecting behind the page are above and below the chiral carbons. The Fischer projection of one of the enantiomers of glyceraldehyde is therefore interpreted as follows:

Fischer projection of a glyceraldehyde enantiomer

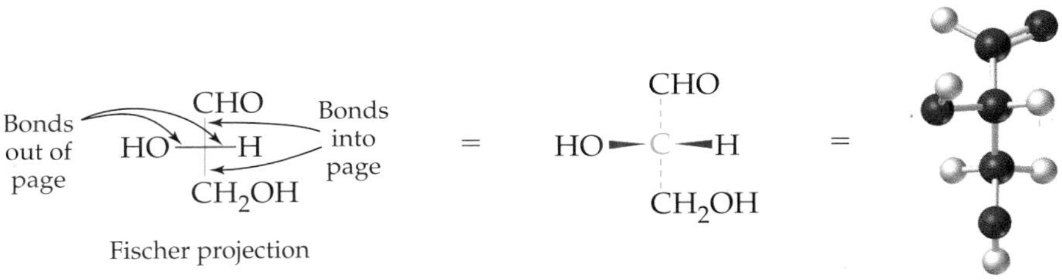

For comparison, the same glyceraldehyde enantiomer is represented next in the conventional manner, showing the tetrahedral arrangement of bonds to the chiral carbon.

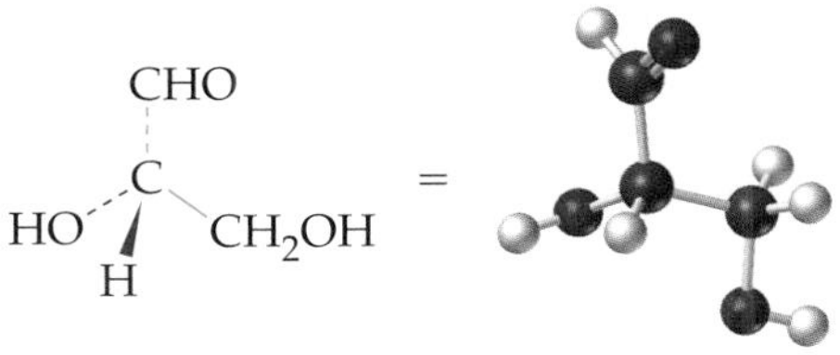

Monosaccharides are divided into two families—the **D sugars** and the **L sugars**—based on their structural relationships to glyceraldehyde. Consistently writing monosaccharide formulas as Fischer projections allows us to identify the D and L forms at a glance. Look again at the structural formulas of the D and L forms of glyceraldehyde.

D Sugar Monosaccharide with the —OH group on the chiral carbon atom farthest from the carbonyl group pointing to the right in a Fischer projection.

L Sugar Monosaccharide with the —OH group on the chiral carbon atom farthest from the carbonyl group pointing to the left in a Fischer projection.

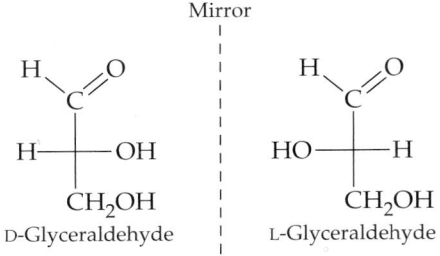

▲ Nature's preference. Snail shells have a preferred handedness, as do many molecules.

In the D form, the —OH group on carbon 2 comes out of the plane of the paper and points to the *right;* in the L form, the —OH group at carbon 2 comes out of the plane of the paper and points to the *left.* If you mentally place a mirror plane between these Fischer projections, you can see that they are mirror images.

Nature has a strong preference for one type of handedness in carbohydrates, just as it does in amino acids and in snail shells. It happens, however, that carbohydrates and amino acids have opposite handedness. Most naturally occurring α-amino acids belong to the L family, but most carbohydrates belong to the D family.

Fischer projections of molecules with more than one chiral carbon atom are written with the chiral carbons one above the other in a vertical line. To simplify visualizing the structures, we often include the C's for the chiral carbons in the plane of the page. Otherwise, the structures are interpreted like Fischer projections. Two pairs of aldohexose enantiomers are represented next in this manner. Given the Fischer projection of one enantiomer, you can draw the other by reversing the substituents on the left and right of each chiral atom. Note that each pair of enantiomers has a different name.

Two pairs of aldohexose enantiomers

H—C—OH	HO—C—H	H—C—OH	HO—C—H
H—C—OH	HO—C—H	HO—C—H	H—C—OH
H—C—OH	HO—C—H	H—C—OH	HO—C—H
H—C—OH	HO—C—H	H—C—OH	HO—C—H
CH₂OH	CH₂OH	CH₂OH	CH₂OH
D-Allose	L-Allose	D-Glucose	L-Glucose

Chiral C atom farthest from C=O

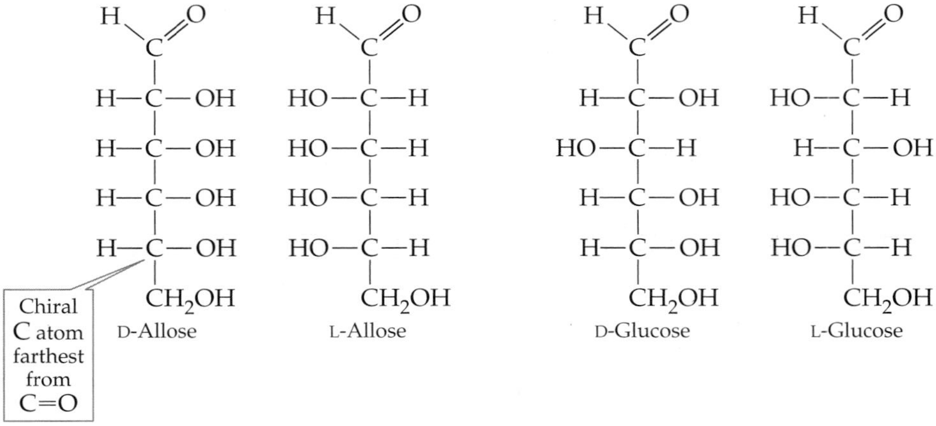

Worked Example 20.2 Identifying D and L Isomers

Identify the following monosaccharides as (a) D-ribose or L-ribose and (b) D-mannose or L-mannose.

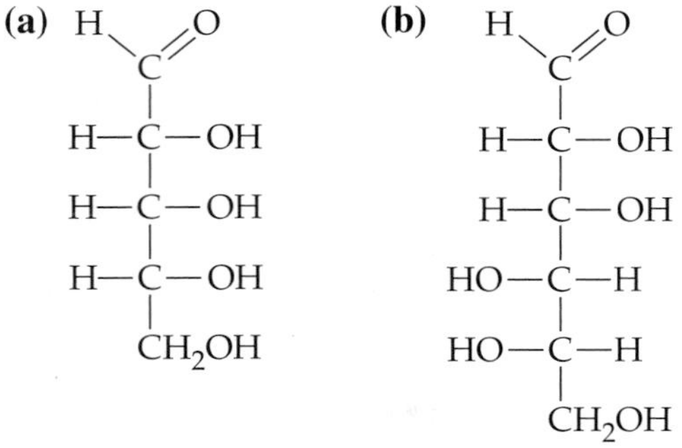

(a)

H—C—OH
H—C—OH
H—C—OH
CH₂OH

(b)

H—C—OH
H—C—OH
HO—C—H
HO—C—H
CH₂OH

ANALYSIS To identify D or L isomers, you must check the location of the —OH group on the chiral carbon atom farthest from the carbonyl group. In a Fischer projection, this is the carbon atom above the bottom one. The —OH group points left in an L enantiomer and right in a D enantiomer.

SOLUTION

In (a), the —OH group on the chiral carbon above the bottom of the structure points to the right, so this is D-ribose. In (b), this —OH group points to the left, so this is L-mannose.

PROBLEM 20.6

Draw the enantiomer of the following monosaccharides, and in each pair identify the
D sugar and the L sugar.

(a)

H   O
 \\ //
   C
   |
HO—C—H
   |
 H—C—OH
   |
 H—C—OH
   |
  CH₂OH

(b)

  CH₂OH
   |
   C=O
   |
 H—C—OH
   |
HO—C—H
   |
HO—C—H
   |
  CH₂OH

20.3 Structure of Glucose and Other Monosaccharides

Learning Objectives:

- Convert five- and six-carbon monosaccharides from the Fischer projection to the
  Haworth projection.
- Identify the anomeric carbon and the alpha (α) or beta (β) form of the monosaccharide
  and describe the role of mutarotation in cyclic structure.

D-Glucose, also called *dextrose* or *blood sugar,* is the most abundant of all monosaccharides and has the most important function. In nearly all organisms, D-glucose serves
as a source of energy to fuel biochemical reactions. It is stored as starch in plants and
glycogen in animals (Section 20.7). The structure of D-glucose illustrates a major point
about the structure of monosaccharides: Although they can be written with the carbon
atoms in a straight chain, monosaccharides with five or six carbon atoms exist primarily in their cyclic forms when in solution, as they are found in living organisms. These
cyclic structures, represented by *Haworth projections,* formed by internal reactions to
give hemiacetals or hemiketals, are shown in Figure 20.2.

◄◄◄ Recall from Section 15.7 that the
key to recognizing the hemiacetal is a
carbon atom bonded to both an —OH
group and an —OR group.

◄ **Figure 20.2**
The structure of D-glucose.
D-Glucose can exist as an open-chain
polyhydroxy aldehyde or as a pair of
cyclic hemiacetals. The cyclic forms
differ only at C1, where the —OH
group is either on the opposite side
of the six-membered ring from the
CH₂OH (α) or on the same side (β).
(Hs on carbons 2–5 are omitted here
for clarity.)

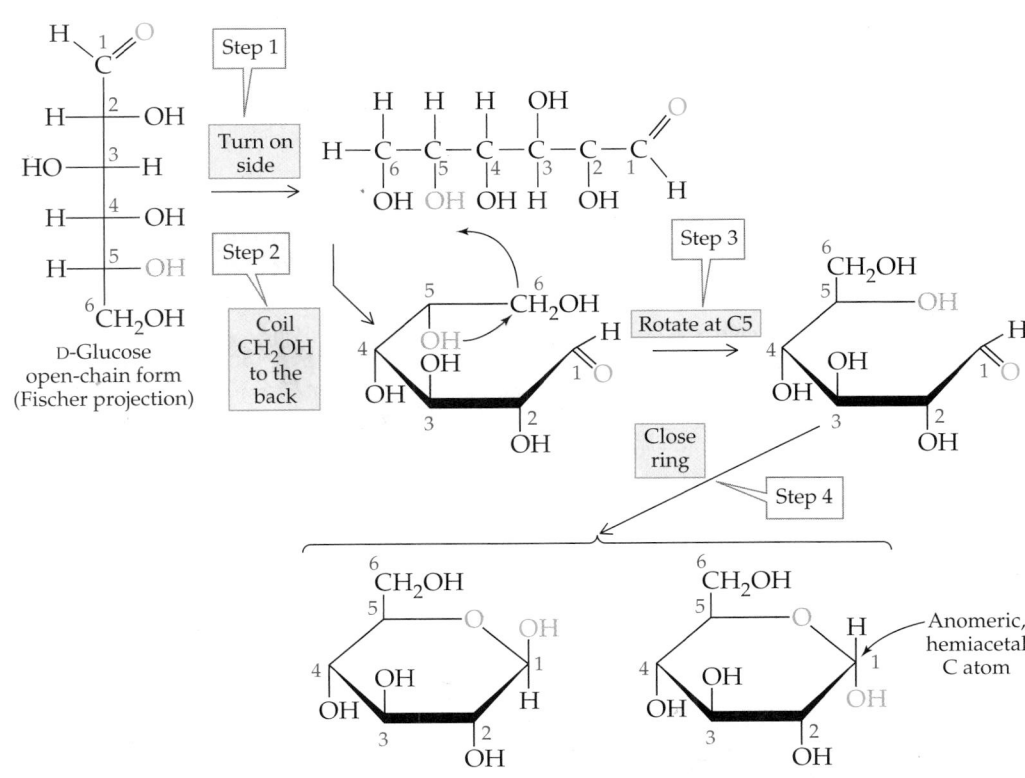

β-D-Glucose   α-D-Glucose

Look at the Fischer projection of D-glucose at the top left-hand corner of Figure 20.2, and notice the locations of the aldehyde group and the hydroxyl groups. You learned that aldehydes and ketones react reversibly with alcohols to yield hemiacetals and hemiketals, respectively.

Since glucose has alcohol hydroxyl groups and an aldehyde carbonyl group in the same molecule, *internal* hemiacetal formation is possible. The aldehyde carbonyl group at carbon 1 (C1) and the hydroxyl group at carbon 5 (C5) in glucose react to form a six-membered ring that is a hemiacetal. Ketones undergo internal hemiketal formation as well; in ketones, the reacting carbonyl group is on C2. Monosaccharides with five or six carbon atoms form rings in this manner.

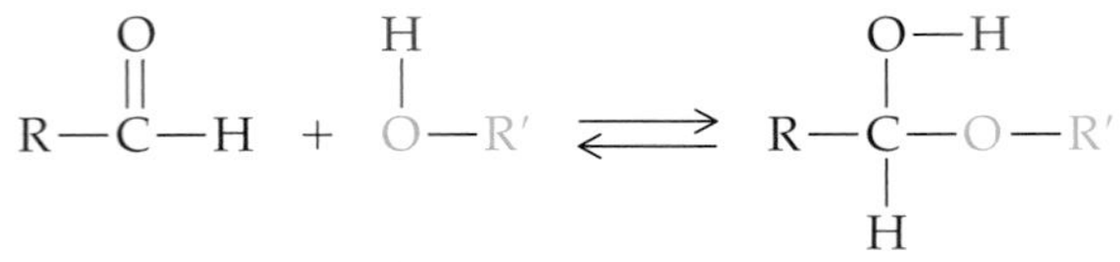

$$
\underset{\text{An aldehyde}}{R-\overset{\overset{\textstyle O}{\|}}{C}-H} \; + \; \underset{\text{An alcohol}}{\overset{\overset{\textstyle H}{|}}{O}-R'} \;\; \rightleftharpoons \;\; \underset{\text{A hemiacetal}}{R-\overset{\overset{\textstyle O-H}{|}}{\underset{\underset{\textstyle H}{|}}{C}}-O-R'}
$$

The four structures at the top in Figure 20.2 show how to picture the C5-hydroxyl and the C1-aldehyde group approaching each other for hemiacetal formation. When visualized in this manner, Fischer projections are converted to cyclic structures that (like the Fischer projections) can be interpreted consistently because the same relative arrangements of the groups on the chiral carbon atoms are maintained.

In the cyclic structures at the bottom of Figure 20.2, note how the —OH group on carbon 3, which is on the left in the Fischer projection, points *up* in the cyclic structure, and —OH groups that are on the right on carbons 2 and 4 point *down*. When Haworth projections are drawn as shown in Figure 20.2, such relationships are always maintained. Note also that the —CH₂OH group in D sugars is always *above* the plane of the ring.

The hemiacetal carbon atom (C1) in the cyclic structures, like that in other hemiacetals, is bonded to two oxygen atoms (one in —OH and one in the ring). This carbon is chiral. As a result, there are two cyclic forms of glucose, known as the α and β forms. To see the difference, compare the locations of the hemiacetal —OH groups on C1 in the two bottom structures in Figure 20.2. In the β form, the hydroxyl at C1 points *up* and is on the same side of the ring as the —CH₂OH group at C5. In the α form, the hydroxyl at C1 points *down* and is on the opposite side of the ring from the —CH₂OH group.

Cyclic monosaccharides that differ only in the positions of substituents at carbon 1 are known as **anomers,** and carbon 1 is said to be an **anomeric carbon atom.** It is the carbonyl carbon atom (C1 in an aldose and C2 in a ketose) that is now bonded to two O atoms. Note that the α and β anomers of a given sugar are not optical isomers because they are not mirror images.

Although the structural difference between anomers appears small, it has enormous biological consequences. For example, this one small change in structure accounts for the vast difference between the digestibility of starch, which we can digest, and that of cellulose, which we cannot digest (Section 20.7).

Ordinary crystalline glucose is entirely in the cyclic α form. Once dissolved in water, however, equilibrium is established among the open-chain form and the two anomers. A solution of β-D-glucose or a mixture of the α and β forms undergoes a gradual change in rotation, known as **mutarotation,** until the ring opening and closing reactions come to the following equilibrium:

Anomers Cyclic sugars that differ only in positions of substituents at the hemiacetal carbon (the anomeric carbon); the α form has the —OH on the opposite side from the —CH₂OH; the β form has the —OH on the same side as the —CH₂OH.

Anomeric carbon atom The hemiacetal C atom in a cyclic sugar; the C atom bonded to an —OH group and an O in the ring.

Mutarotation Change in rotation of plane-polarized light resulting from the equilibrium between cyclic anomers and the open-chain form of a sugar.

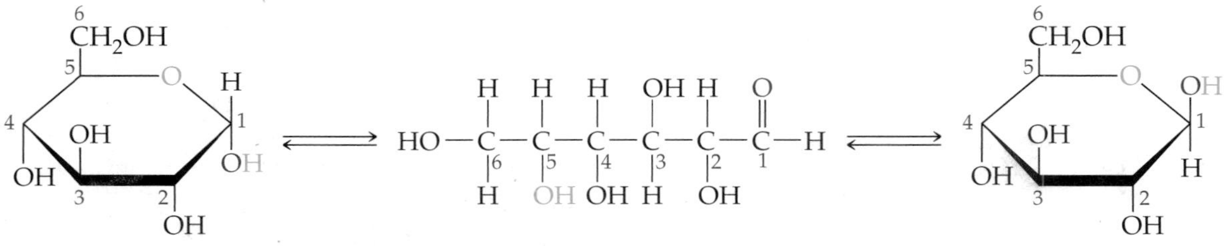

α-D-Glucose
(36%)
⇌
Open-chain D-Glucose
(0.02%)
⇌
β-D-Glucose
(64%)

All monosaccharides with five or six carbon atoms establish similar equilibria but with different percentages of the different forms present.

Enantiomers

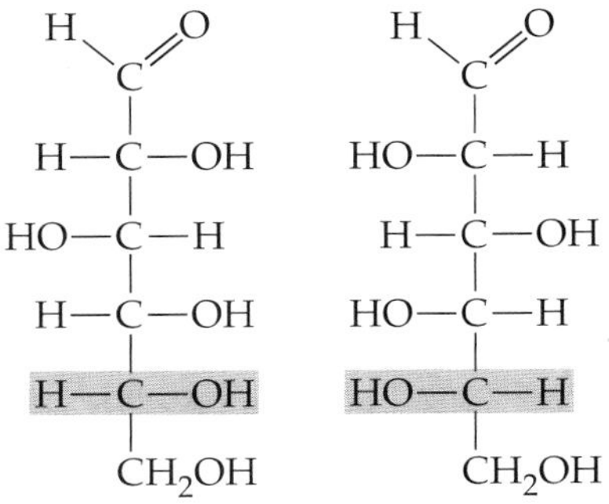

Anomers

D-Glucose

L-Glucose

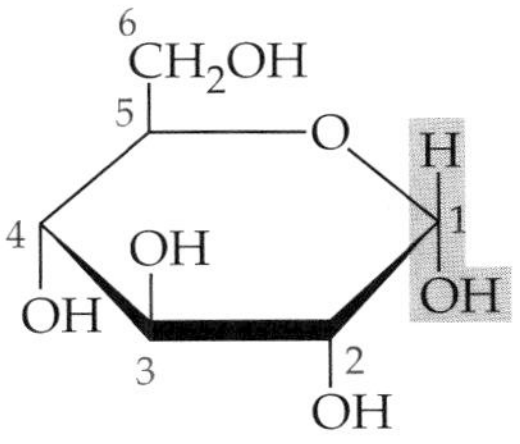

α-D-Glucose

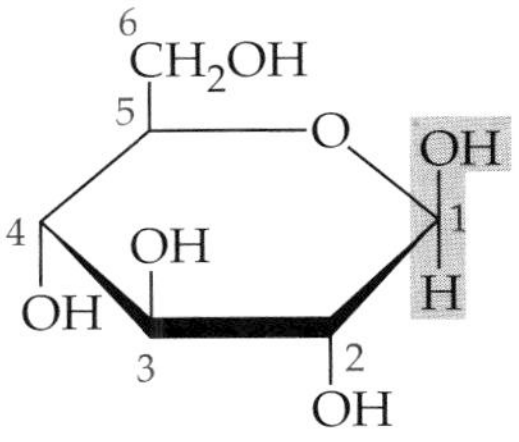

β-D-Glucose

HANDS-ON CHEMISTRY 20.1

Although monosaccharides can be written with the carbon atoms in an open-chain form (Fischer projection), monosaccharides with five or six carbon atoms exist primarily in their cyclic forms (Haworth projection) when in solution, as they are found in living organisms. Writing this conversion out on paper or doing it mentally can be confusing, but building a model and converting the model from one form to another helps to visualize the conversion.

You will use the same methods and techniques outlined in Hands-On Chemistry 13.1 (p. 410) and Hands-On Chemistry 15.1 (p. 492). For this exercise, you will build the straight chain Fischer model of glucose and then convert it to the Haworth model.

Building Blocks—for this exercise, you will need the following:

1 box of toothpicks—round are best but any will do.

12 carbon gumdrops—use either black or some other dark color, as long as they are different colors than those needed next.

4 ring oxygen gumdrops—use red or orange. Use these for the O atom on carbon numbers 1 and 5.

8 other oxygen gumdrops—use blue or green. You will use these to represent the OH groups that are attached to the ring and to carbon number 6

24 hydrogen gumdrops—use white or clear. You will use these to represent an H when it is attached to a ring carbon.

Build D-glucose in the open-chain, Fischer projection form as shown in Figure 20.2. Be certain that C2–C6 have tetrahedral angles. C1 and C5 should have red or orange O atoms. The OH on C5 must have an H attached to the O. The other H atoms may be omitted from OH groups. C1 is in the aldose form and the bonds angles are 120 degrees. Note that glucose is neither straight nor flat.

Follow the illustrations in Figure 20.2 while going through these steps.

Step 1: Converting the open-chain form to the cyclic form requires rotating the molecule so that it is horizontal with C6 on the left and C1 on the right.

Step 2: Keeping C1 in position, form an "almost" hexagon by coiling C6 to the back of the model.

Step 3: Rotate C6 around C5 so that it is above the plane of C1–C5.

Step 4: Form a hemiacetal bond between the O part of the — OH on C5 and C1. The H from the C5 — OH bonds with the O on C1 to form an OH. Depending on the orientation of the resulting C1 — OH group, you have either α-D-glucose or β-D-glucose.

Step 5: Build a second Fischer model of D-glucose and convert it to the cyclic form (Haworth) with the opposite orientation of the C1 — OH group.

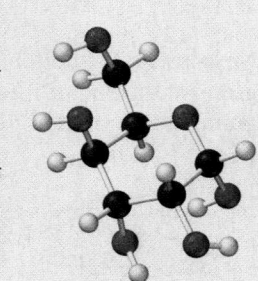

Questions:

1. How many chiral carbon atoms are in glucose in the open-chain form?

2. How many chiral carbon atoms are in glucose in the cyclic form?

3. Are any of these different? Why?

4. What is the relationship between α-D-glucose or β-D-glucose? Are they mirror images?

5. What is an anomer? Are these two models anomers? Explain.

Monosaccharide Structures—Summary

- Monosaccharides are polyhydroxy aldehydes or ketones.
- Monosaccharides have three to seven carbon atoms.
- D and L enantiomers differ in the orientation of the —OH group on the chiral carbon atom farthest from the carbonyl. In Fischer projections, D sugars have this —OH on the right and L sugars have this —OH on the left.
- D-Glucose, and other 6-carbon aldoses, form cyclic hemiacetals conventionally represented (as in Figure 20.2) so that —OH groups on chiral carbons on the left in Fischer projections point up and those on the right in Fischer projections point down.
- In glucose, the hemiacetal carbon (*the anomeric carbon*) is chiral, and α and β anomers differ in the orientation of the —OH groups on this carbon. The α anomer has the —OH on the opposite side of the ring from the —CH₂OH, and the β anomer has the —OH on the same side of the ring as the —CH₂OH.

Worked Example 20.3 Converting Fischer Projections to Haworth Projections

The open-chain form of D-altrose, an aldohexose isomer of glucose, has the following structure. Draw D-altrose in its cyclic hemiacetal form.

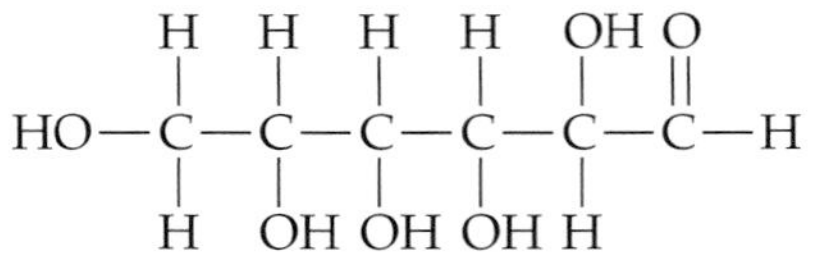

D-Altrose

SOLUTION

First, coil D-altrose into a circular shape by mentally grasping the end farthest from the carbonyl group and bending it backward into the plane of the paper.

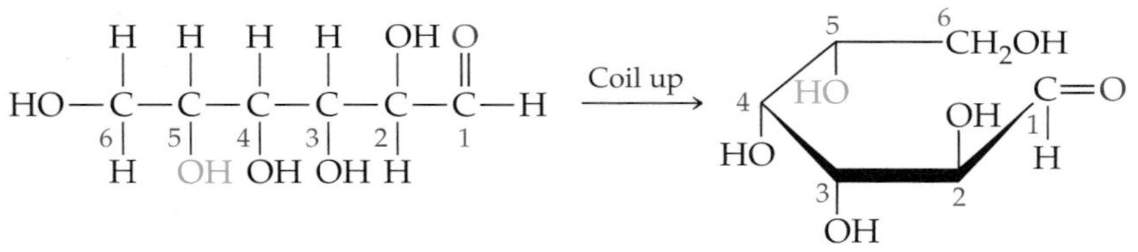

Next, rotate the bottom of the structure around the single bond between C4 and C5 so that the —CH₂OH group at the end of the chain points up and the —OH group on C5 points toward the aldehyde carbonyl group on the right.

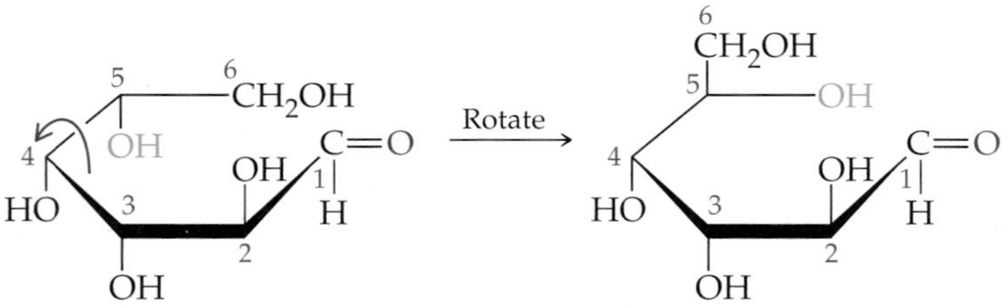

Finally, add the —OH group at C5 to the carbonyl C=O to form a hemiacetal ring. The new —OH group formed on C1 can be either up (β) or down (α).

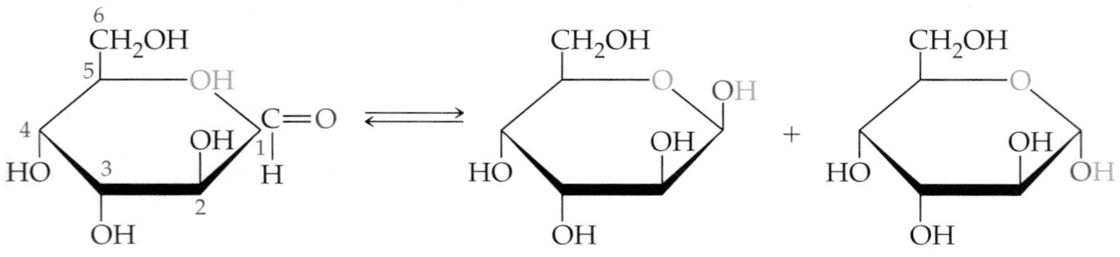

PROBLEM 20.7

D-Talose, a constituent of certain antibiotics, has the open-chain structure shown next. Draw D-talose in its cyclic hemiacetal form.

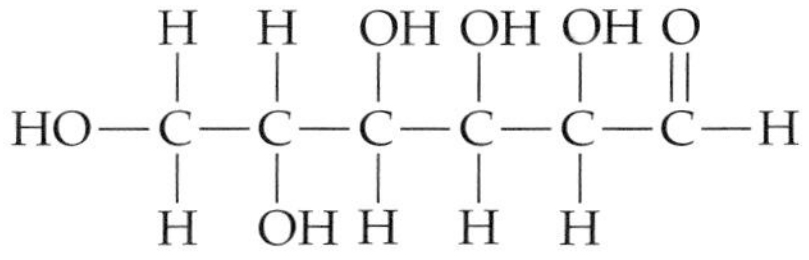

D-Talose

PROBLEM 20.8

The cyclic structure of D-idose, an aldohexose, is shown in the margin. Convert this to the straight-chain Fischer projection structure.

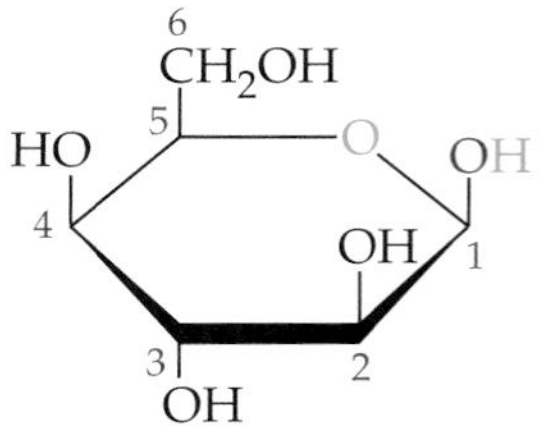

PROBLEM 20.9

Draw the structure that completes the mutarotation reaction between the two cyclic forms of (a) galactose and (b) fructose.

D-Idose

(a)

α-D-Galactose   β-D-Galactose

(b)

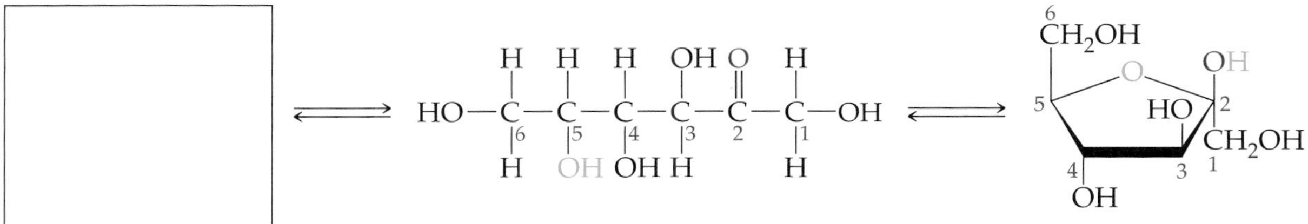

Open-chain D-Fructose   β-D-Fructose

20.4 Some Important Monosaccharides

Learning Objective:

• Identify by name and structure the common monosaccharides, their sources and uses.

Monosaccharides can form multiple hydrogen bonds through their hydroxyl groups and are generally high-melting, white, crystalline solids that are soluble in water and insoluble in nonpolar solvents. Most monosaccharides and disaccharides are sweet-tasting (Table 20.2), digestible, and nontoxic (Figure 20.3). Except for glyceraldehyde (an aldotriose) and fructose (a ketohexose), the carbohydrates of interest in human biochemistry are all aldohexoses or aldopentoses. Most are in the D family. Of the five described in Table 20.1, glucose is the most important simple carbohydrate in human metabolism. It is the final product of complex carbohydrate digestion and provides acetyl groups for entry into the citric acid cycle as acetyl-CoA to be converted to energy.

LOOKING AHEAD ▶ In Chapter 22, we will describe the metabolic pathway (glycolysis) by which glucose is converted to pyruvate and then to acetyl-CoA for entry into the citric acid cycle. The role of insulin in controlling blood glucose concentrations and the way in which those concentrations are affected by diabetes mellitus are also examined there.

Table 20.1 Common Monosaccharides

Monosaccharide Structure	Common Name and Class	Alternate Names	Source, Function, and Uses
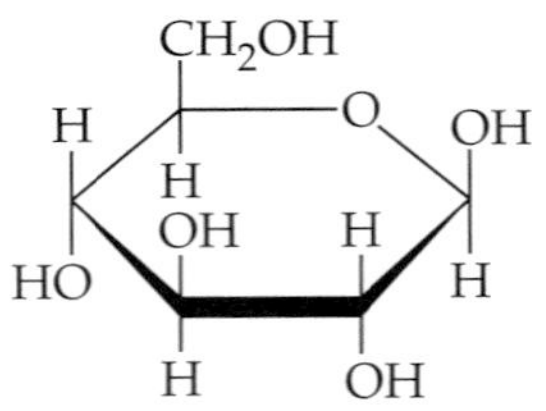	D-glucose aldohexose	Dextrose, Blood sugar	• Product of photosynthesis, made by plants and stored as starch • Found in fruits, vegetables, corn syrup, and honey • A building block for some disaccharides and polysaccharides • Source of acetyl groups for citric acid cycle to provide metabolic energy for mammals, especially for red blood cells, muscle tissue, kidney tissue, and brain tissue • Stored as glycogen in muscle for use as energy source • Glucose level in blood regulated by the hormones insulin and glucagon • Medical use to maintain blood glucose levels and supply energy source via intravenous drip
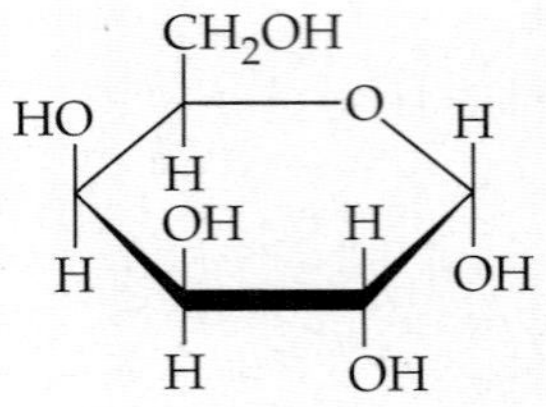	D-galactose aldohexose	none	• Found in plant gums and pectins • Found in milk as half of the disaccharide lactose • Component of brain and nervous system tissues • Metabolized to glucose for energy-yielding pathways • Galactosemia results from an inherited deficiency of any of the enzymes needed to convert glucose to galactose, which may cause liver failure, mental retardation, and cataracts. Galactosemia is treated by a galactose-free diet
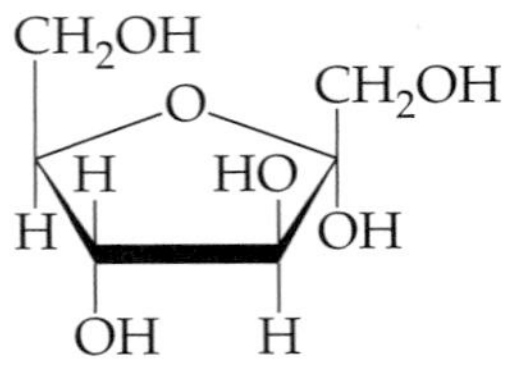	D-fructose ketohexose	Levulose, Fruit sugar	• Found in fruits and honey • Produced by the hydrolysis of corn starch to make high-fructose corn syrup • One of the two units bonded to make sucrose • Phosphorylated fructose is an intermediate in glucose metabolism • Sweeter than sucrose, used to sweeten many beverages and prepared foods
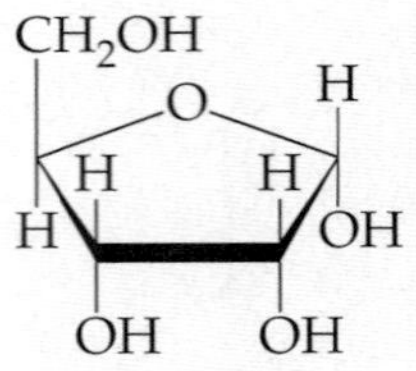	Ribose aldopentose	none	• Found as parts of larger molecules in organisms • Part of ribonucleic acid, involved in protein synthesis (Chapter 26) • Part of coenzyme A • Part of the second messenger cyclic AMP (Chapter 28)
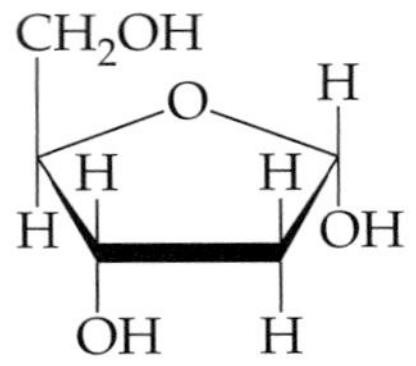	2-Deoxyribose	none	• Part of DNA, the genetic material of the cell (Chapter 26)

Worked Example 20.4 Identifying Sugars and Sugar Derivatives in Antibiotics

Framycetin, a topical antibiotic, is a four-ring molecule consisting of several aminoglycosides—sugars that have some of the —OH groups on the sugars replaced by —NH₂ groups—and another ring, with oxygen links between the rings. What sugar or other molecule is each ring derived from?

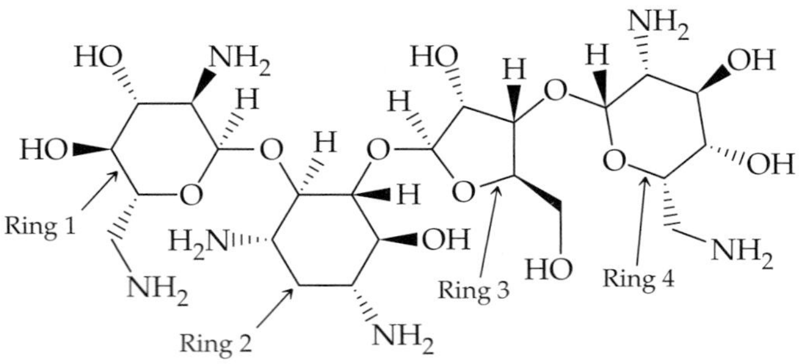

ANALYSIS Look at each ring carefully. Ring 2 does not include an O. It cannot be a sugar. Rings 1, 3, and 4 all contain O as a ring member. Imagine the rings as underivatized sugars, that is with —OH groups instead of —NH$_2$ groups; count the number of carbon atoms in each sugar and draw the sugar form to help identify the sugar.

SOLUTION
Ring 2 has six carbon atoms and no oxygen atoms as part of the ring; it is not a sugar, but is a cyclohexane derivative. Rings 1 and 4 are derived from the aldohexose, glucose, while ring 3 is derived from the aldopentose, ribose.

KEY CONCEPT PROBLEM 20.10

Neomycin is an antibiotic used in topical applications to inhibit the growth of bacteria. It is an aminoglycoside, that is, some of the —OH groups on the sugars have been replaced by —NH$_2$ or R groups. The four rings that constitute neomycin are joined by glycosidic bonds and two of the rings are amino sugars. In the structure shown, identify (a) the amino sugar rings by number, (b) the unmodified sugar ring structure, and (c) the non–sugar ring structure. List how many carbon atoms are in each ring.

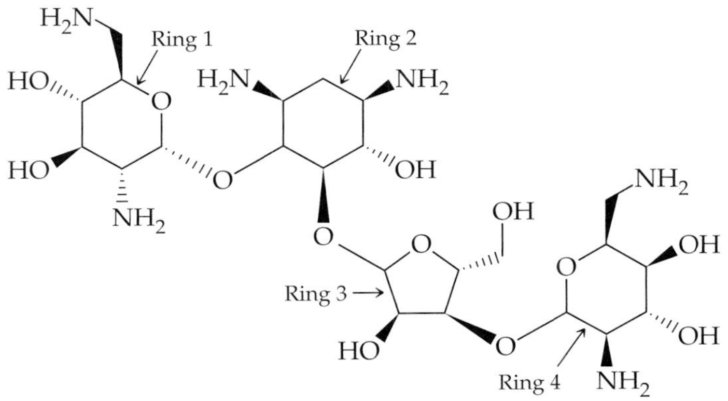

PROBLEM 20.11
In the monosaccharide hemiacetal shown in the margin, number all the carbon atoms, identify the anomeric carbon atom, and identify it as the α or β anomer.

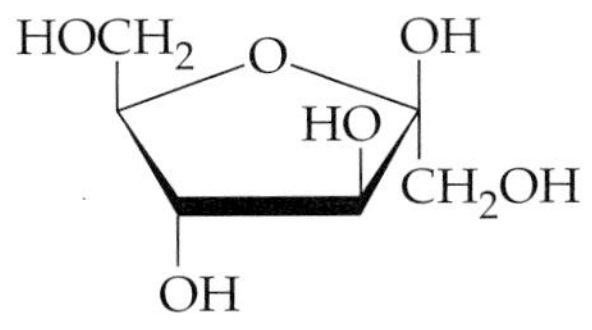

PROBLEM 20.12
Identify the chiral carbons in α-D-fructose, α-D-ribose, and β-D-2-deoxyribose.

PROBLEM 20.13
L-Fucose is one of the naturally occurring L monosaccharides. It is present in the short chains of monosaccharides by which blood groups are classified (see the Chemistry in Action "Cell-Surface Carbohydrates and Blood Type" on p. 640). Compare the structure of L-fucose shown in the margin with the structures of α- and β-D-galactose and answer the following questions.

(a) Is L-fucose an α or β anomer?
(b) Compared with galactose, on which carbon is L-fucose missing an oxygen?
(c) How do the positions of the —OH groups above and below the plane of the ring on carbons 2, 3, and 4 compare in D-galactose and L-fucose?
(d) "Fucose" is a common name. Is 6-deoxy-L-galactose a correct name for fucose? Why or why not?

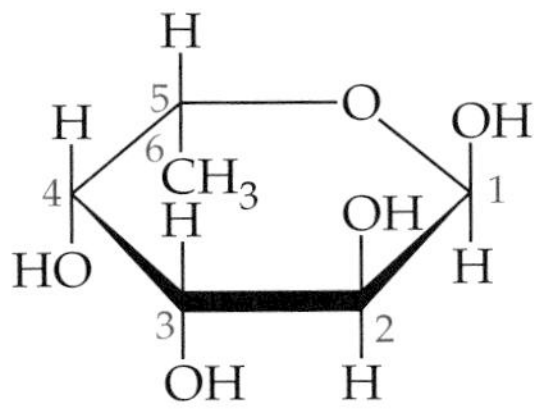

L-Fucose

CHEMISTRY IN ACTION

✚ Cell-Surface Carbohydrates and Blood Type

A century ago, scientists discovered that human blood can be classified into four blood group types, called A, B, AB, and O. This classification indirectly results from the presence on red blood cell surfaces of three different oligosaccharides (sugar chains), designated A, B, and O (see the diagram). Individuals with type AB blood have both A and B oligosaccharides displayed on the same cells.

Selecting a matching blood type is vitally important in choosing blood for transfusions because a major component of the body's immune system (Chapter 29) is a collection of proteins called *antibodies* that recognize and attack foreign substances, such as viruses, bacteria, potentially harmful macromolecules, and foreign blood cells. Among the targets of these antibodies are cell-surface molecules that are not present on the individual's own cells and are thus "foreign blood cells." For example, if you have type A blood, your plasma (the liquid portion of the blood) contains antibodies to the type B oligosaccharide. Thus, if type B blood enters your body, its red blood cells will be recognized as foreign and your immune system will launch an attack on them. The result is clumping of the cells (agglutination), blockage of capillaries, and possibly death.

Because of the danger of such interactions, both the blood types that individuals can receive and the blood types of recipients to whom they can donate blood are limited, as indicated in the accompanying table. A few features of the table deserve special mention.

- People with blood types A, B, and AB all lack antibodies to type O cells. Individuals with type O blood are therefore known as "universal donors"—in an emergency, their blood can safely be given to individuals of all blood types.

- Type AB individuals are known as "universal recipients." Because people with type AB blood have both A and B molecules on their red cells, their blood contains no antibodies to A, B, or O, and they can, if necessary, receive blood cells of all types.

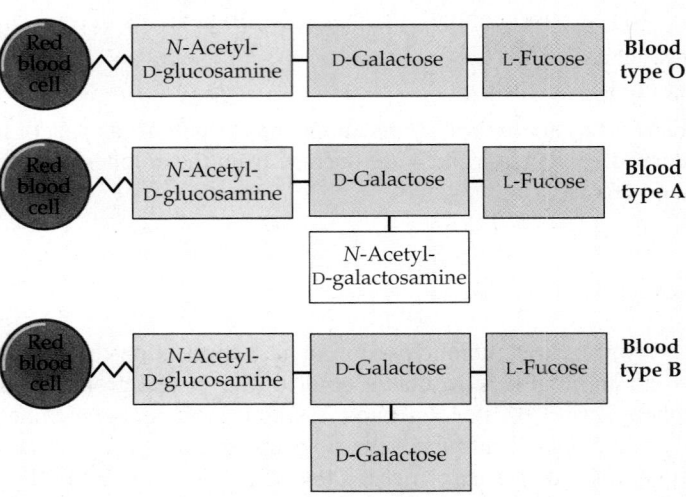

Individuals with blood type...	...have antibodies to type...	...can receive from type...	...and can donate to type
O	A and B	O	O, A, and B*
A	B	O and A	A and AB
B	A	O and B	B and AB
AB	None	O, A, and B*	AB

*Red blood cells only

CIA Problem 20.1 Look at the structures of the blood group determinants. What makes the blood types different?

CIA Problem 20.2 People with type O blood can donate blood to anyone, but they cannot receive blood from everyone. From whom can they not receive blood? People with type AB blood can receive blood from anyone, but they cannot give blood to everyone. To whom can they give blood? Why?

CIA Problem 20.3 All cells in your body contain glycoproteins (proteins with short oligosaccharide chains attached, Chapter 18) as part of the cell membrane. The carbohydrate part of a glycoprotein extends out of the membrane into the intercellular fluid and is the signaling part of the molecule. Red blood cells have specific glycoproteins that we use to specify the different blood types. Which sugars and sugar derivatives are found in all blood types? (Hint: Look closely at the sugar chains attached to each red blood cell in the diagram.)

20.5 Reactions of Monosaccharides

Learning Objectives:

- Predict the products of oxidation and reduction reactions on monosaccharides.
- Predict the products of reactions between monosaccharides and alcohols.
- Recognize and predict the products of hydrolysis reactions of polysaccharides and phosphorylation reactions of monosaccharides.

Reaction with Oxidizing Agents: Reducing Sugars

Aldehydes can be oxidized to carboxylic acids ($RCHO \longrightarrow RCOOH$) a reaction that applies only to the open-chain form of aldose monosaccharides (Section 15.5). As the open-chain aldehyde is oxidized, its equilibrium with the cyclic form is displaced, and, in accordance with Le Châtelier's principle, the open-chain form continues to be produced. As a result, the aldehyde group of the monosaccharide is ultimately oxidized to a carboxylic acid group. For glucose, the reaction is

◀◀◀ Le Châtelier's principle states that when a stress is applied to a system at equilibrium, the equilibrium shifts to relieve the stress (Section 7.9).

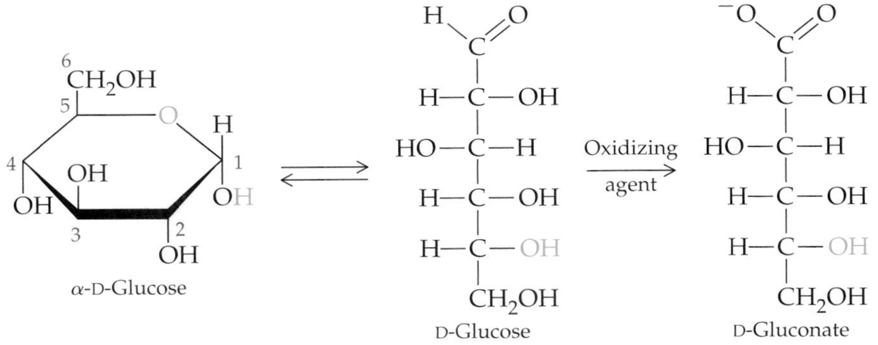

Carbohydrates that react with mild oxidizing agents are classified as **reducing sugars** (they reduce the oxidizing agent). The Benedict's test is a common test for the presence of reducing sugars. Benedict's test relies on the ability of Cu^{2+} in alkaline solution to be reduced by aldose and some ketose monosaccharides. The appearance of a green, brown, orange, or red precipitate upon heating the sample in Benedict's solution is a positive test for the presence of reducing sugar.

Recall from Section 15.5 that ketones do not generally undergo oxidation, because they lack the hydrogen attached to the carbonyl carbon that aldehydes have. In basic solution some ketoses are reducing sugars because in a ketone that has an H atom on the carbon adjacent to the carbonyl carbon undergoes a rearrangement. This H atom moves over to the carbonyl oxygen. The product is an *enediol*, "ene" for the double bond and "diol" for the two hydroxyl groups. The enediol rearranges to give an aldose, which is susceptible to oxidation.

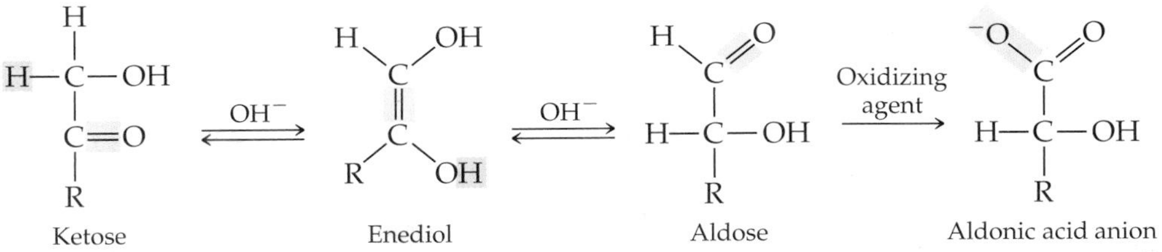

Reducing sugar A carbohydrate that reacts in basic solution with a mild oxidizing agent.

Here, also, oxidation of the aldehyde to an acid drives the equilibria toward the right, and complete oxidation of the ketose occurs. Thus, *in basic solution, all monosaccharides, whether aldoses or ketoses, are reducing sugars*. This ability to act as reducing agents is the basis for most laboratory tests for the presence of monosaccharides.

Reaction with Reducing Agents: Sugar Alcohols

Monosaccharides are easily converted to sugar alcohols, called alditols, by the reduction of the carbonyl group to an alcohol group. This is accomplished industrially by exposing the sugar to H_2 in the presence of the catalyst Pt. The sugar alcohols are named as derivatives of the sugars, with the suffix -*ose* replaced with -*itol*. Thus, D-glucose becomes D-glucitol, also known as D-sorbitol, D-xylose becomes D-xylitol, and D-mannose becomes D-mannitol. These three sugar alcohols are used as sweeteners in diet drinks and sugarless gums as well as in many diet foods designed for those who are on restricted sugar intake for health reasons. However, caution must be taken in the amount of sugar alcohols ingested at any time because too much may cause gas and diarrhea.

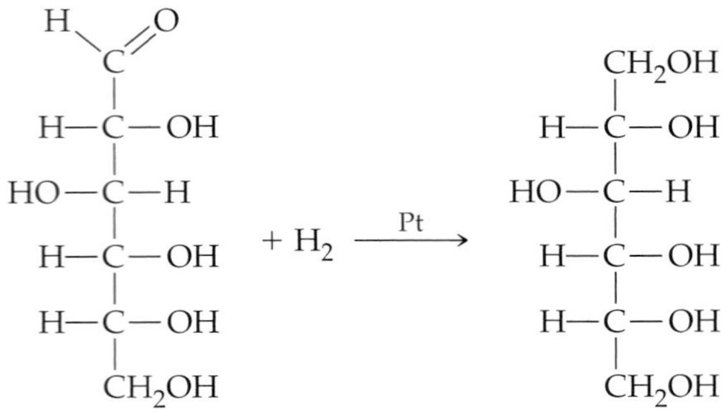

D-Glucose   D-Glucitol
                   (aka D-Sorbitol)

Reaction with Alcohols: Glycoside and Disaccharide Formation

Hemiacetals react with alcohols with the loss of water to yield acetals, compounds with two —OR groups bonded to the same carbon (Section 15.7).

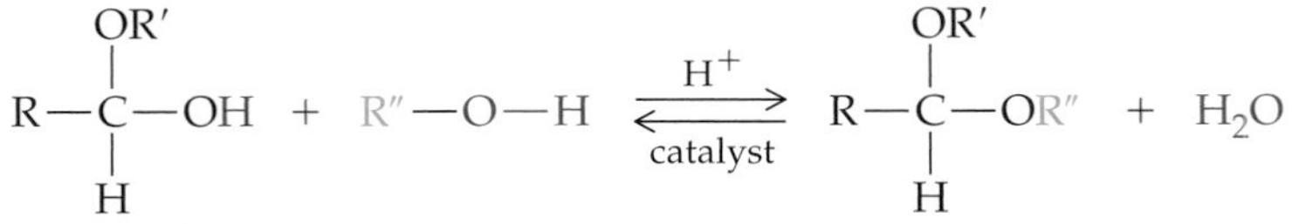

A hemiacetal   An alcohol   An acetal

Glycoside A cyclic acetal formed by reaction of a monosaccharide with an alcohol, accompanied by loss of H_2O.

Because glucose and other monosaccharides are cyclic hemiacetals, they also react with alcohols to form acetals, which are called **glycosides**. In a glycoside, the —OH group on the anomeric carbon atom is replaced by an —OR group. For example, glucose reacts with methanol to produce methyl glucoside. Note that a *gluc*oside is a cyclic acetal formed by glucose. A cyclic acetal derived from *any* sugar is a *gly*coside.

Formation of a glycoside

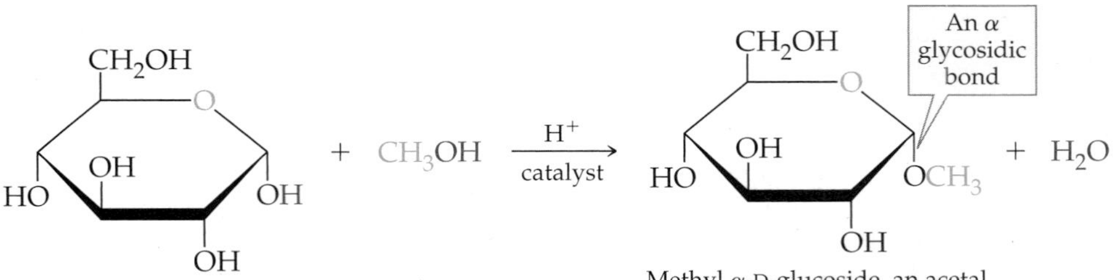

α-D-Glucose   Methyl α-D-glucoside, an acetal

Glycosidic bond Bond between the anomeric carbon atom of a monosaccharide and an —OR group.

The bond between the anomeric carbon atom of the monosaccharide and the oxygen atom of the —OR group is called a **glycosidic bond.** Since glycosides like the one shown earlier do not contain hemiacetal groups that establish equilibria with open-chain forms, they are *not* reducing sugars.

In larger molecules, including disaccharides and polysaccharides, monosaccharides are connected to each other by glycosidic bonds. For example, a disaccharide forms by reaction of the anomeric carbon of one monosaccharide with an —OH group of a second monosaccharide.

Formation of a glycosidic bond between two monosaccharides

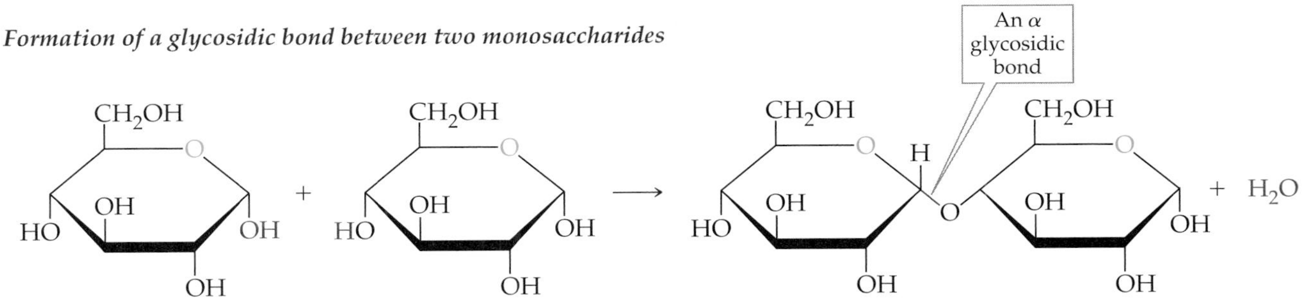

The reverse of this reaction is a *hydrolysis* and is the reaction that takes place during digestion of all carbohydrates.

Hydrolysis of a disaccharide

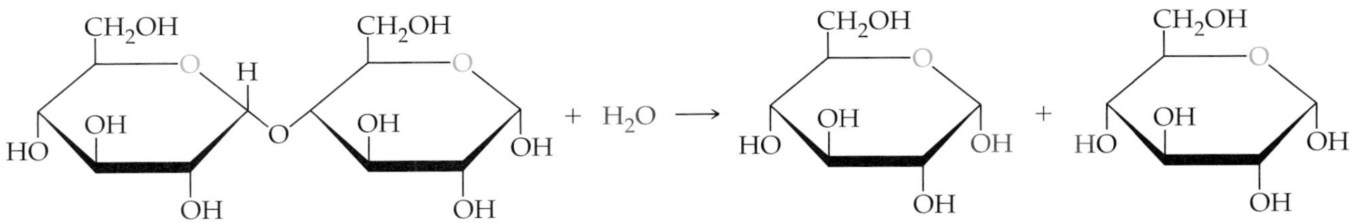

PROBLEM 20.14

Draw the structure of the α and β anomers that result from the reaction of methanol and ribose. Are these compounds acetals or hemiacetals?

Formation of Phosphate Esters of Alcohols

Phosphate esters of alcohols contain a $-PO_3^{2-}$ group bonded to the oxygen atom of an $-OH$ group. The $-OH$ groups of sugars can add $-PO_3^{2-}$ groups to form phosphate esters in the same manner. The resulting phosphate esters of monosaccharides appear as reactants and products throughout the metabolism of carbohydrates. Glucose phosphate is the first to be formed and sets the stage for subsequent reactions. It is produced by the transfer of a $-PO_3^{2-}$ group from ATP to glucose in the first step of glycolysis, the multistep metabolic pathway followed by glucose and other sugars, which is described in Chapter 22. Glycolysis converts glucose to the acetyl groups that are carried into the citric acid cycle.

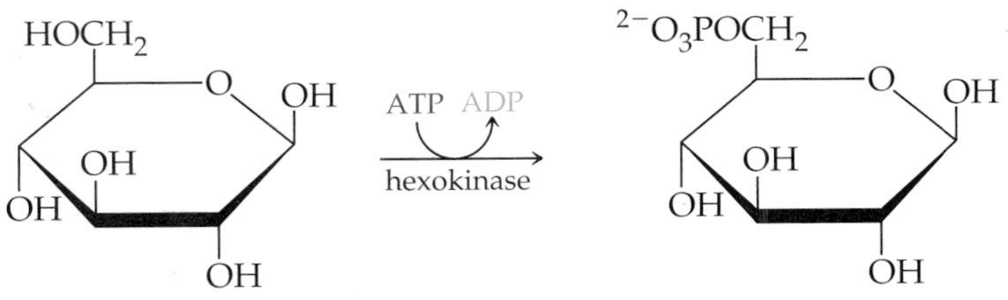

20.6 Common Disaccharides

Learning Objective:

- Identify by name and structure the common disaccharides, the subunits and the bond between them, their sources and uses.

Every day, you eat a disaccharide—sucrose, common table sugar. Sucrose is made of two monosaccharides, one glucose and one fructose, covalently bonded to each other. Sucrose is present in modest amounts, along with other monosaccharides and disaccharides, in

(a)

(b)

(c)

▲ Figure 20.3
Common sugars.
(a) The disaccharide sucrose
(glucose + fructose) is found in sugar
cane and sugar beets. (b) Jam contains
the monosaccharide galactose in the
pectin that stiffens it. (c) Honey is high
in the monosaccharide fructose.

1,4 Link A glycosidic link between
the hemiacetal hydroxyl group at C1 of
one sugar and the hydroxyl group at C4
of another sugar.

most fresh fruits and many fresh vegetables. But most sucrose in our diets has been added
to something. Perhaps you add it to your coffee or tea. Or it is there in a ready-to-eat
food product that you buy—maybe breakfast cereal, ice cream, or a "super-sized" soda,
or even bread. Excessive consumption of high-sucrose foods has been blamed for everything from criminal behavior to heart disease to hyperactivity in children, but without any
widely accepted scientific proof. A proven connection with heart disease does exist, of
course, but by way of the contribution of excess sugar calories to obesity.

Sweetness of sugars and substitutes is determined on a relative scale with sucrose
assigned a value of 100. Sweetness is assessed by taste panels and the results of many
tests have been averaged to produce the relative values found in Table 20.2. Sugar alcohols and synthetic·sweeteners are used in many foods advertised for those who for
medical or personal reasons choose to reduce the amount of natural sugars in their diet.
The sugar alcohols, found in products such as candy and desserts marketed to diabetics,
are non-digestible and therefore do not influence blood sugar levels. However, the sugar
alcohols can cause diarrhea if ingested in large amounts.

Table 20.2 Relative Sweetness of Some Sugars and Sugar Substitutes

Name/Type	Sweetness (relative to sucrose = 100)	Common Source
Monosaccharide		
Fructose	175	fruit
Galactose	30	fruit pectin
Glucose	75	sugar, starch
Disaccharide		
Lactose	16	milk
Maltose	33	germinating grain
Sucrose	100	sugar cane, sugar beets
Sugar Alcohol		
Maltitol	80	diet foods*
Sorbitol	60	diet foods*
Xylitol	100	diet foods*
Synthetic Sweetener		
Aspartame	18,000	sugar substitute
Cyclamate	3000	sugar substitute
Saccharin	45,000	sugar substitute
Sucralose	60,000	sugar substitute

*Diet foods, especially for diabetics

Disaccharide Structure

The two monosaccharides in a disaccharide are connected by a glycosidic bond. The bond
may be α or β, as in cyclic monosaccharides: α points below the ring and β points above the
ring (see Figure 20.2). The structures include glycosidic bonds that create a **1,4 link,** that is, a
link between C1 of one monosaccharide and C4 of the second monosaccharide.

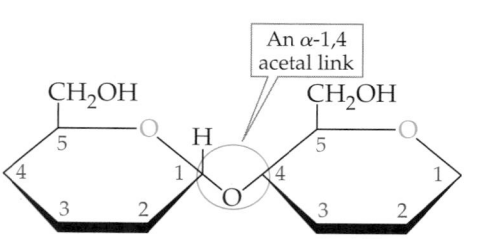

An α-1,4 disaccharide

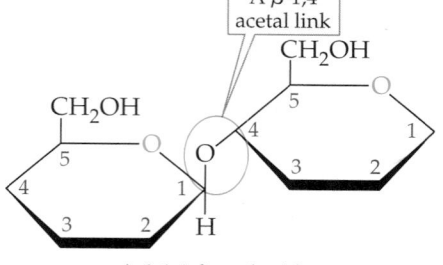

A β-1,4 disaccharide

Table 20.3 outlines the three naturally occurring and most common disaccharides. These disaccharides illustrate the three different ways monosaccharides are linked: by a glycosidic bond in the α orientation (maltose), a glycosidic bond in the β orientation (lactose), or a bond that connects two anomeric carbon atoms (sucrose).

Table 20.3   Common Disaccharides

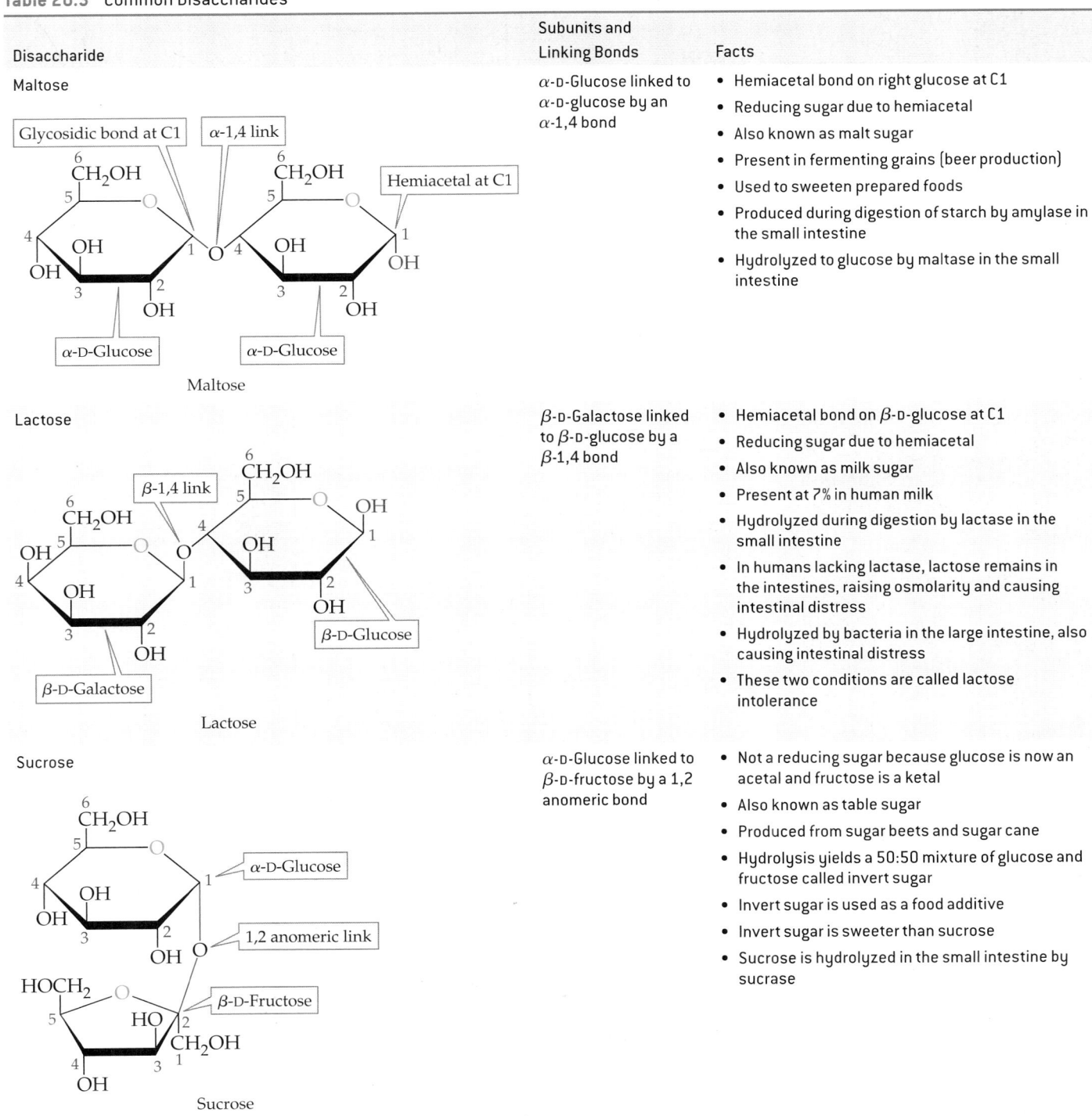

Disaccharide	Subunits and Linking Bonds	Facts
Maltose	α-D-Glucose linked to α-D-glucose by an α-1,4 bond	• Hemiacetal bond on right glucose at C1 • Reducing sugar due to hemiacetal • Also known as malt sugar • Present in fermenting grains (beer production) • Used to sweeten prepared foods • Produced during digestion of starch by amylase in the small intestine • Hydrolyzed to glucose by maltase in the small intestine
Lactose	β-D-Galactose linked to β-D-glucose by a β-1,4 bond	• Hemiacetal bond on β-D-glucose at C1 • Reducing sugar due to hemiacetal • Also known as milk sugar • Present at 7% in human milk • Hydrolyzed during digestion by lactase in the small intestine • In humans lacking lactase, lactose remains in the intestines, raising osmolarity and causing intestinal distress • Hydrolyzed by bacteria in the large intestine, also causing intestinal distress • These two conditions are called lactose intolerance
Sucrose	α-D-Glucose linked to β-D-fructose by a 1,2 anomeric bond	• Not a reducing sugar because glucose is now an acetal and fructose is a ketal • Also known as table sugar • Produced from sugar beets and sugar cane • Hydrolysis yields a 50:50 mixture of glucose and fructose called invert sugar • Invert sugar is used as a food additive • Invert sugar is sweeter than sucrose • Sucrose is hydrolyzed in the small intestine by sucrase

Worked Example 20.5 Identifying Reducing Sugars

The disaccharide cellobiose can be obtained by enzyme-catalyzed hydrolysis of cellulose. Do you expect cellobiose to be a reducing or a nonreducing sugar?

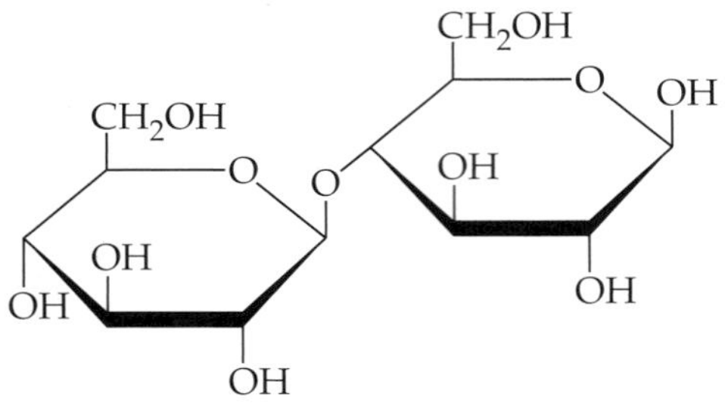

$$
\text{Cellobiose}
$$

ANALYSIS To be a reducing sugar, a disaccharide must contain a hemiacetal group, that is, a carbon bonded to one —OH group and one —OR group. The ring at the right in the structure above has such a group.

SOLUTION
Cellobiose is a reducing sugar.

▲ Milk for lactose-intolerant individuals. The lactose content of the milk has been decreased by treating it with lactase.

PROBLEM 20.15

Refer to the cellobiose structure in Worked Example 20.5. How would you classify the link between the monosaccharides in cellobiose?

PROBLEM 20.16

Refer to the cellobiose structure in Worked Example 20.5. Show the structures of the two monosaccharides that are formed on hydrolysis of cellobiose. What are their names?

⊙━ KEY CONCEPT PROBLEM 20.17 ———————————

Identify the following disaccharides. Give a natural source for each of these disaccharides. (a) The disaccharide that contains two glucose units joined by an α-glycosidic linkage. (b) The disaccharide that contains fructose and glucose. (c) The disaccharide that contains galactose and glucose.

20.7 Some Important Polysaccharides Based on Glucose

Learning Objectives:

• Recognize common polysaccharides and identify where each polysaccharide is found in nature and its function.
• Identify the monomers and type of bond present in each polysaccharide.
• Identify the modified monosaccharides found in naturally occurring polysaccharides and identify the functions of these polysaccharides.

Polysaccharides are polymers of tens, hundreds, or even many thousands of monosaccharides linked together through glycosidic bonds of the same type as in maltose and lactose. Three of the most important polysaccharides are *cellulose, starch,* and *glycogen.* Compare the repeating units of cellulose and starch shown in Table 20.4. A slight change in the glycosidic bond has an enormous effect on the structure and function of a glucose polymer.

Table 20.4 Common Polysaccharides Containing Glucose

Molecule/Repeating Unit	Bond	Facts
Cellulose 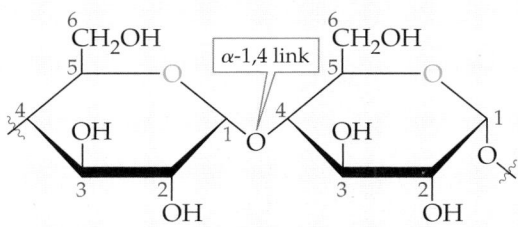 Cellulose repeating unit	β-1,4 link	• Most abundant polysaccharide on earth • Fibrous polysaccharide found in plants • Forms part of cell walls • Provides rigid structure in plants • Each cellulose molecule consists of thousands of glucose units in an unbranched chain • β-1,4 Linkage confers a rigid, puckered conformation on the cellulose molecule • Microorganisms in the gut of some animals (cows and other grazing animals) and some insects (termites and moths) produce cellulase, which hydrolyzes cellulose to glucose • Humans do not digest cellulose • Provides "roughage" (fiber) in our diet • Cellulose is used to build houses, make cardboard, and other paper products • cellulose derivatives are cellophane, rayon, and guncotton
Amylose (starch) 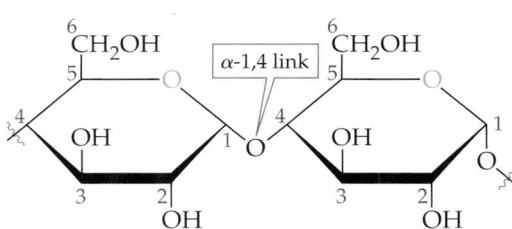 Starch and glycogen repeating unit	α-1,4 link	• Found in plants, especially in the seeds • Common sources are beans, grains like wheat and rice, and tubers like potatoes • Accounts for about 20% of starch • Chains are several hundred to 1000 units long • α-1,4 linkage between units results in a flexible chain that coils into helices • Soluble in hot water • Hydrolyzed to glucose in animals by α-amylase in saliva and in small intestine to supply glucose for use in metabolism or for energy storage • Figure 20.4 shows the helical structure
Amylopectin (starch) 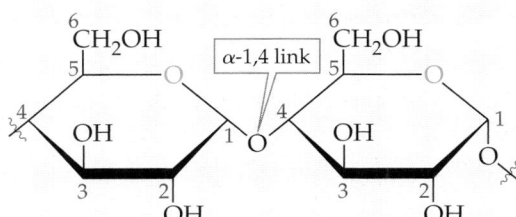 Starch and glycogen repeating unit	α-1,4 link with α-1,6 link branch points*	• Found in plants, especially in the seeds • Common sources are beans, grains like wheat and rice, and tubers like potatoes • Accounts for about 80% of starch • Chains are several hundred to 1000 units long • α-1,4 Linkage between units results in a flexible chain • α-1,6 Linkage between units results in branching from a chain • Multiple branches occur in amylopectin • Insoluble in hot water • Molecular weight of amylopectin molecules is up to 200 million • Ideal glucose storage molecule; large, insoluble, and compact due to branching • Supplies energy for seed germination and early growth • Hydrolyzed to glucose in animals by amylase in small intestine to supply glucose for use in metabolism or for energy storage • Only α-1,4 bonds are hydrolyzed by α-amylase; α-1,6 bonds are not hydrolyzed by α-amylase
Glycogen Starch and glycogen repeating unit	α-1,4 link with α-1,6 link branch points*	• Found in animals • Often referred to as animal starch • Used as glucose storage in liver and muscle cells • Stored in aggregates referred to as granules • Liver glycogen supplies glucose to maintain blood sugar levels and needs of other cell types • Muscle glycogen supplies glucose to muscle cells for conversion to ATP when these cells need energy during exercise (work) • α-1,4 Linkage between units results in a flexible chain • α-1,6 Linkage between units results in branching from a chain • Multiple branches occur in glycogen, but it is more highly branched than amylopectin • Glycogen has up to one million glucose units per molecule and is much larger than amylopectin

*The chain branching with α-1,6 linkages is shown in the drawings on page 649.

CHEMISTRY IN ACTION

⚕ Bacterial Cell Walls: Rigid Defense Systems

All cells are defined by the presence of a plasma membrane, which confines the cell's contents inside a lipid bilayer studded with proteins (Section 21.3). Bacteria and higher plants surround the plasma membrane with a rigid cell wall, while cells of other organisms do not have walls, only a plasma membrane. Cell walls differ markedly in composition but not in function among organisms. The functions of a cell wall are to make the cell rigid, prevent the cell from bursting due to osmotic pressure, give shape to the cell, and protect it from pathogens.

Bacterial cell walls provide strength, shape, and a rigid platform for the attachment of flagella and pilli. The composition of the cell wall also provides attachment sites for bacteriophages (viruses that infect bacteria). Cell-wall composition varies among bacterial species and is an important factor in distinguishing between some groups of bacteria. A majority of bacterial cell walls are composed of a polymer of *peptidoglycan,* an alternating sequence of the modified sugars N-acetylglucosamine (NAG) and N-acetylmuraminic acid (NAMA). Peptidoglycan strands are cross-linked to one another by short peptide bridges; these bridges are unique in that both D-alanine and L-alanine are present. The interlocked strands form a porous, multilayered grid over the bacterial plasma membrane.

Fortunately, animals have developed natural defenses that can control many bacteria. For example, lysozyme—an enzyme found naturally in tears, saliva, and egg white—hydrolyzes the peptidoglycan cell wall of pathogenic bacteria, thereby killing them. In the middle of the twentieth century the antibiotic penicillin was developed. The penicillin family members all contain a beta-lactam ring that allows these compounds to act as "suicide inhibitors" of the enzymes that synthesize the peptidoglycan cross-linking peptide chain. Penicillin and its relatives target only reproducing bacteria. Mammals do not contain the enzyme pathway that synthesizes peptidoglycans, and this is what allows us to kill the bacteria without harming ourselves.

Today, we take the availability and effectiveness of antibiotics for granted. When penicillin was discovered, it was hailed as a "magic bullet" because it could cure bacterial infections that were often fatal. Unfortunately, many bacteria have developed resistance to penicillin and its relatives; resistant bacteria have developed enzymes that destroy the beta-lactam ring, thereby destroying the effectiveness of penicillin. Other antibiotics have since been developed, but the spread of antibiotic-resistant bacterial strains is a public health concern due to the "bullet-proof vest" nature of the bacterial cell wall in resistant strains.

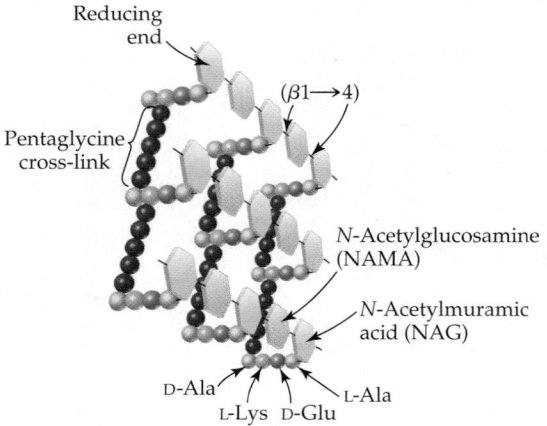

▲ Peptidoglycan structure: Strands of alternating NAG and NAMA connected by peptides form a mesh covering the bacterial cell membrane.

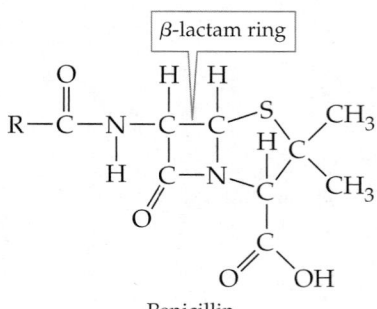

Penicillin

CIA Problem 20.4 List three functions of all cell walls.

CIA Problem 20.5 Name the individual units and the cross-link for the polymer that makes up most of a bacterial cell wall.

CIA Problem 20.6 How does penicillin inhibit the growth of certain bacteria?

CIA Problem 20.7 When you take the antibiotic penicillin when you are ill, why does the penicillin kill a bacterial cell but not your liver cells?

The following structures allow comparison of the structures of amylose, amylopectin, and cellulose. The small drawings compare the density of branch points in amylose versus glycogen.

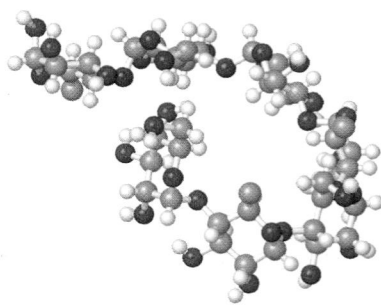

▲ Figure 20.4
Helical structure of amylose.

Amylose

α-1,4 link

Branch point in amylopectin (also glycogen)

α-1,6 link

α-1,4 link

cellulose (1,4-β-D-polyglucose)

Comparison of branching in amylopectin and glycogen

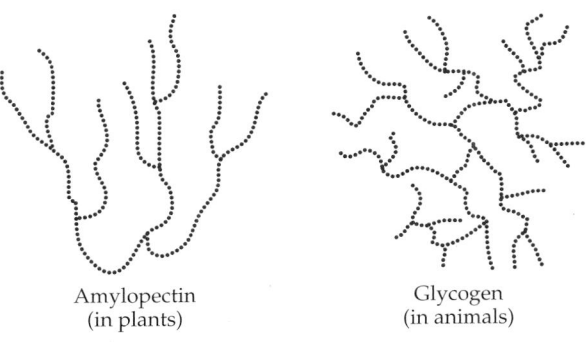

Amylopectin
(in plants)

Glycogen
(in animals)

Some Polysaccharides Based on Modified Glucose

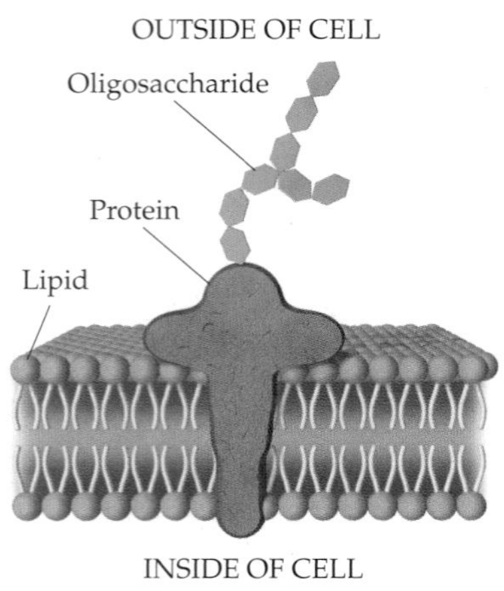

Monosaccharides with modified functional groups are components of a wide variety of biomolecules. Some of the modified monosaccharides form polymers with distinct functions. Additionally, short chains of monosaccharides bind to proteins forming glycoproteins and to lipids forming glycolipids; the addition of short chains of mono-saccharides to some proteins and lipids enhance their functions. There are three common polymers of interest. Hyaluronate formed from β-D-glucuronate and N-acetyl-β-D-glucosamine linked as a repeating pair and is found in synovial fluid in joints and in the vitreous humor of the eye. Chondroiton-6-sulfate is a polymer of β-D-glucuronate and N-acetyl-β-D-glucosamine-6-sulfate; it is found in tendons and cartilage. Heparin is a polymer of β-D-glucuronate-2-sulfate and acetylsulfate -β-D-glucosamine-6-sulfate. Medically heparin is used as an anticoagulant (an agent that prevents blood clotting). The structures of the three modified glucose molecules found in these three polymers are shown next.

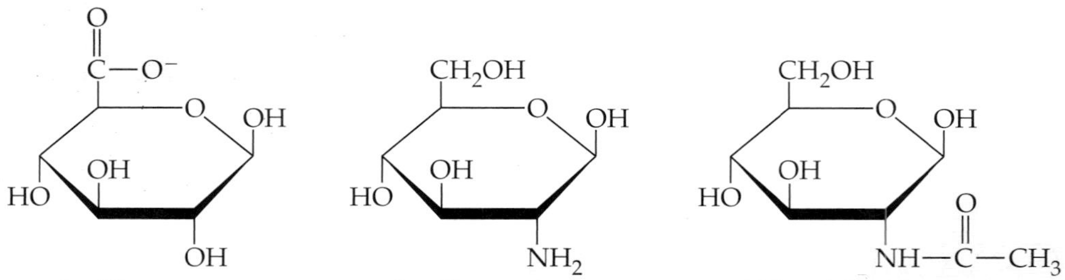

OUTSIDE OF CELL

Oligosaccharide

Protein

Lipid

INSIDE OF CELL

β-D-Glucuronate

β-D-Glucosamine

N-Acetyl-β-D-Glucosamine

The basic components of cell membranes are lipid molecules. The wonderfully complex structure and function of the membrane are explored in Sections 23.5 and 23.6. Glycolipids—carbohydrates bonded to lipids—are, like glycoproteins, essential in cell membranes.

PROBLEM 20.18

What is the structural difference between glucose and (a) β-D-glucuronate, (b) β-D-glucosamine, (c) N-acetyl-β-D-glucosamine?

PROBLEM 20.19

In N-linked glycoproteins, the sugar is usually attached to the protein by a bond to the N atom in a side-chain amide. Which amino acids can form such a bond?

HANDS-ON CHEMISTRY 20.2

Have you ever wondered what is in the packaged foods you buy in the grocery store? Do the food labels appear to be in a foreign language? You have learned enough chemistry to identify the sugars and complex carbohydrates among the ingredients listed on the food label.

For example, a box of multigrain crackers lists the following ingredients: enriched flour (wheat flour, niacin, folic acid), sunflower and/or canola oil (contains ascorbic acid), sugar, oats, inulin, rye flour, multigrain flour blend (wheat, rye, triticale, barley, corn, millet, soybean, sunflower seeds, rice, flax, durum, oats), wheat germ, modified corn starch, invert syrup, and some inorganic compounds used in baking. Any item in this list labeled flour is starch, a mixture of amylose and amylopectin; note the large number of starch sources used in this product. Sugars are represented by sugar, which in this context always means sucrose, and invert sugar.

a. There are three vitamins in this list. What are they?

b. Use the internet to look up the following: triticale, millet, flax, durum, inulin, and modified corn starch. What is each of these and why can each be used in food products?

c. List the ingredients on the label of your breakfast cereal, a granola bar, or some other food item in your home or local grocery store. Identify the sugars and complex carbohydrates present.

CHEMISTRY IN ACTION

⚕ Carbohydrates and Fiber in the Diet

As we learned from the chapter opener, carbohydrates are a large part of our diet and the major monosaccharides in our diets are fructose and glucose from fruits and honey. The major disaccharides are sucrose (table sugar) refined from both sugar cane and sugar beets and lactose from milk. In addition, our diets contain large amounts of the digestible polysaccharide starch, present in grains (wheat and rice), root vegetables (potatoes), and legumes (beans and peas). Nutritionists refer to these polysaccharides as *complex carbohydrates.* Some polysaccharides, such as cellulose, are not digested by humans. Cellulose and all other indigestible carbohydrates are collectively known as *dietary fiber.*

How easily and rapidly complex carbohydrates are digested and absorbed affects blood sugar levels. Consumption of rapidly digested carbohydrates, found in potatoes and refined foods (white bread and white rice), results in rapid elevation of blood glucose levels followed by lower-than-desired levels a few hours later. Carbohydrates that are digested and absorbed more slowly, such as those found in pasta, whole grain cereals and breads, and beans are associated with healthier blood sugar responses.

The body's major use of digestible carbohydrates is to provide energy, 4 kcal (16.7 kJ) per gram of carbohydrate. A small amount of any excess carbohydrate is converted to glycogen for storage in the liver and muscles, but most dietary carbohydrate in excess of our immediate needs for energy is converted into fat.

The MyPlate meal-planning tool (p. 566) reflects the emphasis on decreasing the amounts of meat and increasing the amounts of other foods in our diet, especially complex carbohydrates and fiber through the consumption of whole grains, vegetables, and fruit.

In terms of *total* carbohydrate, which includes both digestible carbohydrates and fiber, the *Nutrition Facts* labels on packaged foods (p. 617) give percentages based on a recommended 300 g per day of total carbohydrate and 25 g per day of dietary fiber. This quantity of total carbohydrate represents 60% of the calories in a 2000 Cal/day (8400 kJ/day) diet. The *Nutrition Facts* label also gives the total grams of sugars in the food without a percentage because there is no recommended daily quantity of sugars. For purposes of the label, "sugars" are defined as all monosaccharides and disaccharides, whether naturally present or added.

As an option, the label may also include grams of *soluble fiber* and *insoluble fiber.* Taken together, these are the types of polysaccharides that are neither hydrolyzed to monosaccharides nor absorbed into the bloodstream. These polysaccharides include cellulose and all other indigestible polysaccharides in vegetables, both soluble and insoluble.

▲ Part of a healthy diet includes a variety of complex carbohydrates that can be supplied by whole grains, beans, and peas.

Foods high in insoluble fiber include wheat, bran cereals, and brown rice. Beans, peas, and other legumes contain both soluble and insoluble fiber. Fiber functions in the body to soften and add bulk to solid waste. Studies have shown that increased fiber in the diet may reduce the risk of colon and rectal cancer, hemorrhoids, diverticulosis, and cardiovascular disease. A reduction in the risk of developing colon and rectal cancer may also occur because potentially carcinogenic substances are absorbed on fiber surfaces and eliminated before doing any harm. Pectin, the soluble portion of dietary fiber, may also absorb and carry away bile acids, causing an increase in their synthesis from cholesterol in the liver and a resulting decrease in blood cholesterol levels.

The U.S. Food and Drug Administration is responsible for reviewing the scientific basis for health claims for foods. Two allowed claims relate to carbohydrates. The first states that a diet high in fiber may lower the risk of cancer and heart disease if the diet is also low in saturated fats and cholesterol. The second states that foods high in the soluble fiber from whole oats (oat bran) may also reduce the risk of heart disease, again when the diet is also low in saturated fats and cholesterol.

CIA Problem 20.8 Give an example of a complex carbohydrate in the diet and a simple carbohydrate in the diet. Are soluble fiber and insoluble fiber complex or simple carbohydrates?

CIA Problem 20.9 Our bodies do not have the enzymes required to digest cellulose, yet it is a necessary addition to a healthy diet. Why?

CIA Problem 20.10 Name two types of soluble fiber and their sources.

SUMMARY REVISITING THE CHAPTER LEARNING OBJECTIVES

- **Classify carbohydrates by functional group and number of carbon atoms, and label them accordingly.** *Monosaccharides* are compounds with three to seven carbons, an aldehyde group on carbon 1 (an *aldose*) or a ketone group on carbon 2 (a *ketose*), and hydroxyl groups on all other carbons. *Disaccharides* consist of two monosaccharides; *polysaccharides* are polymers composed of up to thousands of monosaccharides *[see Problems 28–31 and 83]*.

- **Identify D and L enantiomers and any diastereomers of a monosaccharide from the Fischer projection.** Monosaccharides can contain several chiral carbon atoms, each bonded to one —H, one —OH and two other carbon atoms in the carbon chain. A monosaccharide with n chiral carbon atoms may have 2^n stereoisomers and half that number of pairs of enantiomers. The members of different enantiomeric pairs are *diastereomers*—they are *not* mirror images of each other *[see Problems 21, 23, 32, 33, and 38–43]*.

- **Draw the Fischer projection for a monosaccharide.** *Fischer projection formulas* represent the open-chain structures of monosaccharides. They have D and L enantiomers in a pair identified by having the —OH group on the chiral carbon farthest from the carbonyl group on the right (the D isomer) or the left (the L isomer). *[see Problems 34, 35, 74, 75, 78, and 79]*.

- **Convert five and six carbon monosaccharides from the Fischer projection to the Haworth projection.** The open-chain form of the monosaccharide (Fischer projection drawing) is coiled into the cyclic form of the monosaccharide (Haworth projection form) with the formation of the glycosidic bond closing the cyclic form *[see Problems 50, 51, 76, and 77]*.

- **Identify the anomeric carbon and the alpha (α) or beta (β) form of the monosaccharide and describe the role of mutarotation in cyclic structure.** In the cyclic form, the glycosidic bond contains the hemiacetal carbon (bonded to two O atoms), which is referred to as the *anomeric carbon*, and this carbon is chiral. Two isomers of the cyclic form of a D or L monosaccharide, known as *anomers*, are possible because the —OH on the anomeric carbon may lie above or below the plane of the ring *[see Problems 22, 46–49, 67, and 69]*.

- **Identify by name and structure the common monosaccharides, their sources and uses.** The five common monosaccharides are described in Table 20.2 *[see Problems 36, 37, and 84]*.

- **Predict the products of oxidation and reduction reactions on monosaccharides.** Oxidation of a monosaccharide can result in a carboxyl group on the first carbon atom (C1 in the Fischer projection). Ketoses, as well as aldoses, are *reducing sugars* because the ketose is in equilibrium with an aldose form that can be oxidized *[see Problems 24, 27, 44, 45, and 52–55]*.

- **Predict the products of reactions between monosaccharides and alcohols.** Reaction of a hemiacetal with an alcohol produces an acetal. For a cyclic monosaccharide, reaction with an alcohol converts the —OH group on the anomeric carbon to an —OH group. The bond to the —OR group, known as a *glycosidic bond*, is α or β to the ring as was the —OH group. Disaccharides result from glycosidic bond formation between two monosaccharides *[see Problems 56–59]*.

- **Recognize and predict the products of hydrolysis reactions of polysaccharides and phosphorylation reactions of monosaccharides.** Hydrolysis reactions of polysaccharides produce the monomeric units that formed the polysaccharide. For example, hydrolysis of starch yields glucose. Phosphorylated monosaccharides become reactants in the metabolism of carbohydrates *[see Problems 20, 66, and 68]*.

- **Identify by name and structure the common disaccharides, the subunits and the bond between them, their sources and uses.** *Maltose* (D-glucose and D-glucose), *lactose* (D-galactose and D-glucose), and *sucrose* (D-fructose and D-glucose) are described in Table 20.3. Unlike maltose and lactose, sucrose is not a *reducing sugar* because it has no hemiacetal that can establish equilibrium with an aldehyde *[see Problems 25, 60, 61, 65, 81, 82, and 84–86]*.

- **Recognize common polysaccharides and identify where each polysaccharide is found in nature and its function.** *Cellulose* provides structure in plants. Starch is a storage form of glucose for plants and is digestible by humans. *Glycogen* is a storage form of glucose for animals *[see Problems 62–64 and 84]*.

- **Identify the monomers and type of bond present in each polysaccharide.** *Cellulose* is a straight-chain polymer of β-D-glucose with β-1,4 links. *Starch* is a polymer of α-D-glucose connected by α-1,4 links in straight-chain (*amylose*) and branched-chain (*amylopectin*) forms. Glycogen is also a polymer of α-D-glucose connected by α-1,4 links in straight-chain *[see Problems 26 and 70]*.

- **Identify the modified monosaccharides found in naturally occurring polysaccharides and identify the functions of these polysaccharides.** Hyaluronate, chondroitin-6-sulfate, heparin, and glycoproteins have different modified glucose subunits paired (dimers) as repeating units in the polymer chains. Joints and intracellular spaces are lubricated by polysaccharides like *hyaluronate* and *chondroitin 6-sulfate*. *Heparin* binds to a clotting factor in the blood and thus acts as an anticoagulant. *Glycoproteins* function as receptors at cell surfaces *[see Problems 33, 72, and 73]*.

CONCEPT MAP: CARBOHYDRATES

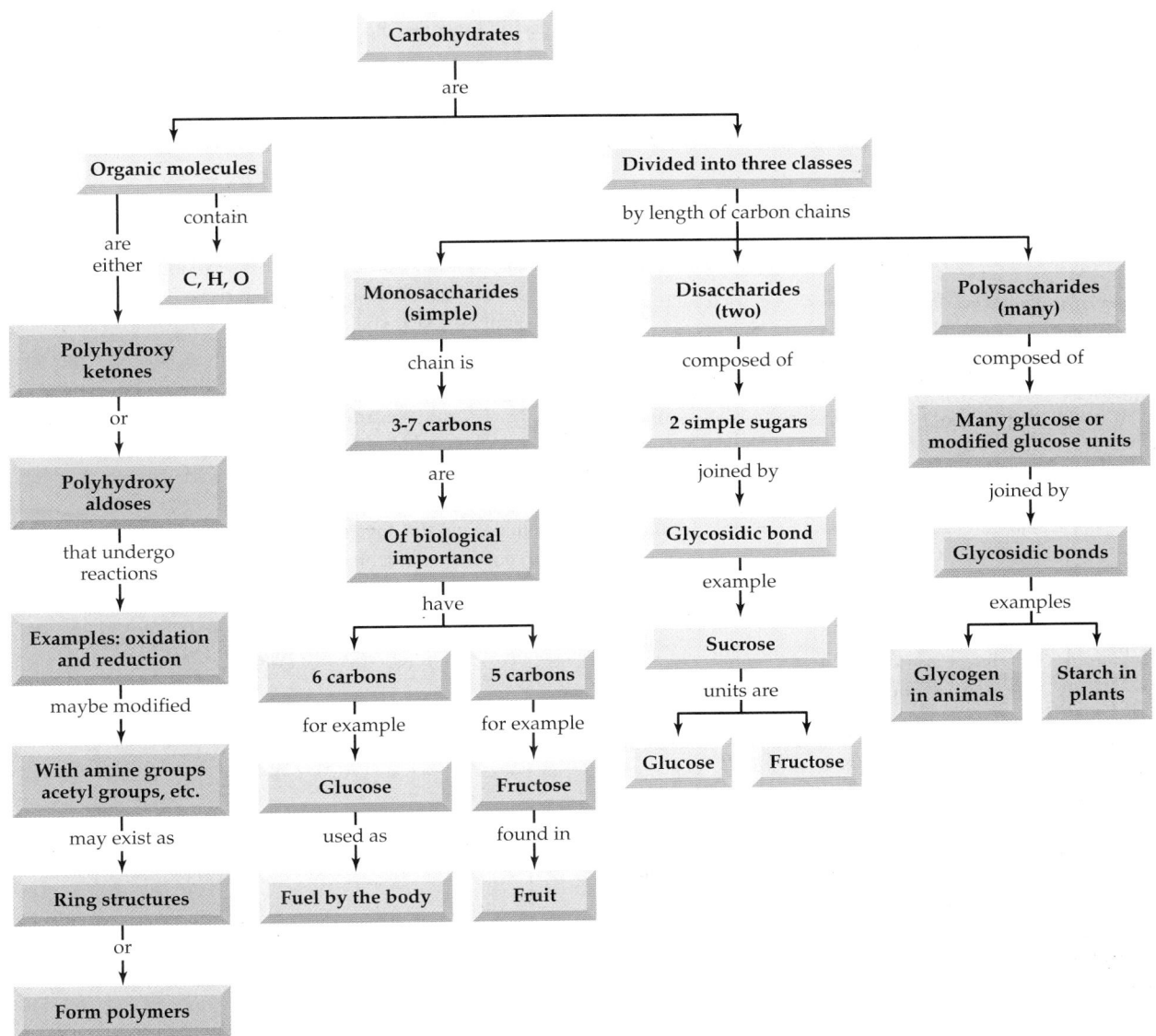

▲ **Figure 20.5 Concept Map.** Carbohydrates are a diverse group of biologically important organic molecules unified by a common monomeric structural pattern. Monosaccharides are used for energy generation and are obtained primarily from dietary disaccharides and polysaccharides. Some energy reserves are maintained by the storage of glycogen by animals or starch by plants. This concept map shows the relationships and commonalities of these molecules.

KEY WORDS

1,4 Link, *p. 644*
Aldose, *p. 627*
Anomeric carbon atom,
p. 634
Anomers, *p. 634*
Carbohydrate, *p. 627*

D Sugar, *p. 631*
Diastereomers, *p. 629*
Disaccharide, *p. 628*
Fischer projection,
p. 631
Glycoside, *p. 642*

Glycosidic bond,
p. 642
Ketose, *p. 627*
L Sugar, *p. 631*
Monosaccharide
(simple sugar), *p. 627*

Mutarotation, *p. 634*
Polysaccharide
(complex carbohydrate),
p. 628
Reducing sugar, *p. 641*

⊙ UNDERSTANDING KEY CONCEPTS

20.20 During the digestion of starch from potatoes, the enzyme α-amylase catalyzes the hydrolysis of starch into maltose. Subsequently, the enzyme maltase catalyzes the hydrolysis of maltose into two glucose units. Write an equation (in words) for the enzymatic conversion of starch to glucose. Classify each of the carbohydrates in the equation as a disaccharide, monosaccharide, or polysaccharide.

20.21 Identify the following as diastereomers, enantiomers, and/or anomers. (a) α-D-fructose and β-D-fructose (b) D-galactose and L-galactose (c) L-allose and D-glucose (both aldohexoses)

20.22 Consider the trisaccharide A, B, C shown in Problem 20.23.
(a) Identify the hemiacetal and acetal linkages.
(b) Identify the anomeric carbon atoms, and indicate whether each is α or β.
(c) State the numbers of the carbon atoms that form glycosidic linkages between monosaccharide A and monosaccharide B.
(d) State the numbers of the carbon atoms that form glycosidic linkages between monosaccharide B and monosaccharide C.

20.23 Hydrolysis of both glycosidic bonds in the following trisaccharide A, B, C yields three monosaccharides.
(a) Are any two of these monosaccharides the same?
(b) Are any two of these monosaccharides enantiomers?
(c) Draw the Fischer projections for the three monosaccharides.
(d) Assign a name to each monosaccharide.

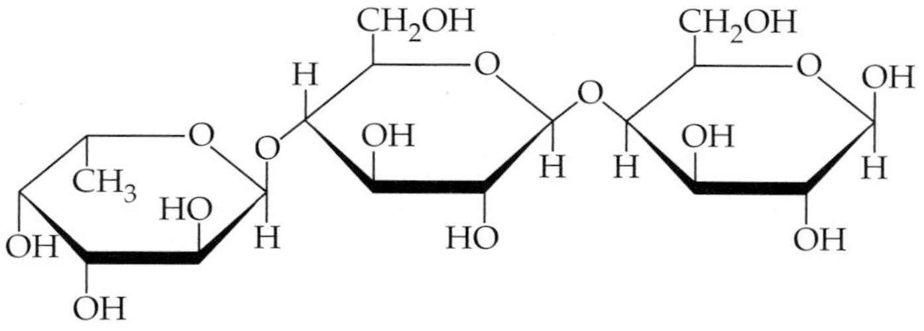

20.24 The trisaccharide shown with Problem 20.23 has a specific sequence of monosaccharides. To determine this sequence, we could react the trisaccharide with an oxidizing agent. Since one of the monosaccharides in the trisaccharide is a reducing sugar, it would be oxidized from an aldehyde to a carboxylate. Which of the monosaccharides (A, B, or C) is oxidized? Write the structure of the oxidized monosaccharide that results after hydrolysis of the trisaccharide. How does this reaction assist in identifying the sequence of the trisaccharide?

20.25 Are one or more of the disaccharides maltose, lactose, cellobiose, and sucrose part of the trisaccharide in Problem 20.23? If so, identify which disaccharide and its location. (Hint: Look for an α-1,4 link, β-1,4 link, or 1,2 link, and then determine if the correct monosaccharides are present.)

20.26 Cellulose, amylose, amylopectin, and glycogen are the polysaccharides of glucose that we examined in this chapter. The major criteria that distinguish these four polysaccharides include α-glycosidic links or β-glycosidic links, 1,4 links or both 1,4 and 1,6 links, and the degree of branching. Create a table evaluating each polysaccharide using these five criteria.

20.27 In solution, glucose exists predominantly in the cyclic hemiacetal form, which does not contain an aldehyde group. How is it possible for mild oxidizing agents to oxidize glucose?

ADDITIONAL PROBLEMS

CLASSIFICATION AND STRUCTURE OF CARBOHYDRATES (SECTION 20.1)

20.28 What is a carbohydrate?

20.29 What is the family-name ending for a sugar?

20.30 What is the structural difference between an aldose and a ketose?

20.31 Classify the four carbohydrates (a)–(d) by indicating the nature of the carbonyl group and the number of carbon atoms present. For example, glucose is an aldohexose.

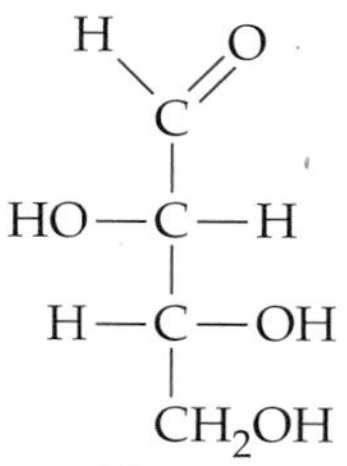

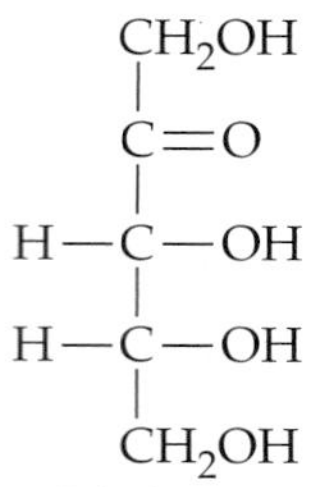

(c)

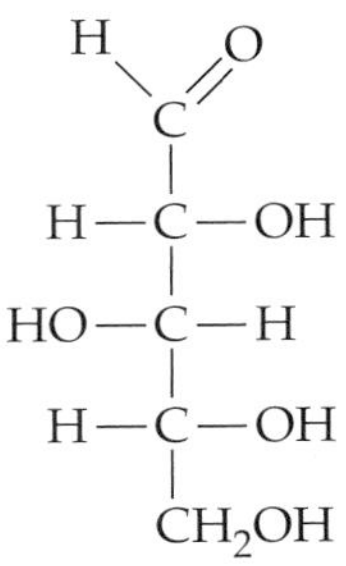

Xylose

(d)

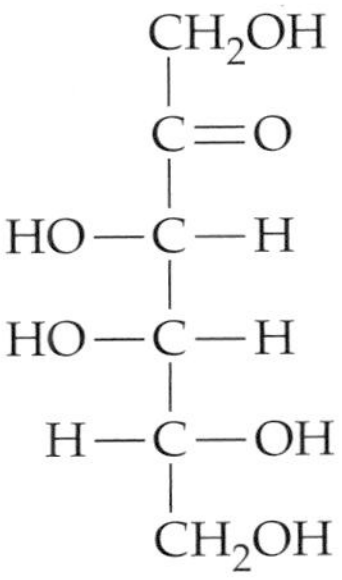

Tagatose

20.32 How many chiral carbon atoms are present in each of the molecules shown in Problem 20.31?

20.33 How many chiral carbon atoms are there in each of the two parts of the repeating unit in heparin (p. 650)? What is the total number of chiral carbon atoms in the repeating unit?

20.34 Draw the open-chain structure of a ketoheptose.

20.35 Draw the open-chain structure of a 4-carbon deoxy sugar.

20.36 Name four important monosaccharides and tell where each occurs in nature.

20.37 Name a common use for each monosaccharide listed in Problem 20.36.

HANDEDNESS IN CARBOHYDRATES (SECTION 20.2)

20.38 How are enantiomers related to each other?

20.39 What is the structural relationship between L-glucose and D-glucose?

20.40 Only three stereoisomers are possible for 2,3-dibromo-2, 3-dichlorobutane. Draw them, indicating which pair are enantiomers (optical isomers). Why does the other isomer not have an enantiomer?

20.41 In Section 15.6, you saw that aldehydes react with reducing agents to yield primary alcohols $(RCH{=}O \longrightarrow RCH_2OH)$ The structures of two D-aldotetroses are shown. One of them can be reduced to yield a chiral product, but the other yields an achiral product. Explain.

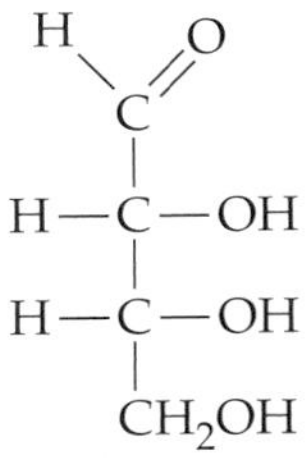

D-Erythrose 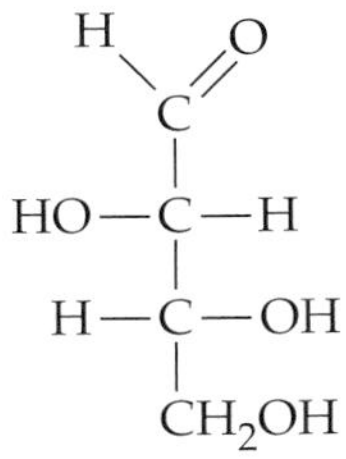   D-Threose

20.42 Sucrose and D-glucose rotate plane-polarized light to the right; D-fructose rotates light to the left. When sucrose is hydrolyzed, the glucose–fructose mixture rotates light to the left.

(a) What does this indicate about the relative degrees of rotation of light of glucose and fructose?

(b) Why do you think the mixture is called "invert sugar"?

20.43 What generalization can you make about the direction and degree of rotation of light by enantiomers?

REACTIONS OF CARBOHYDRATES (SECTIONS 20.3, 20.4, AND 20.5)

20.44 What does the term *reducing sugar* mean?

20.45 What structural property makes a sugar a reducing sugar?

20.46 What is mutarotation? Do all chiral molecules do this?

20.47 What are anomers, and how do the anomers of a given sugar differ from each other?

20.48 What is the structural difference between the α hemiacetal form of a carbohydrate and the β form?

20.49 D-Gulose, an aldohexose isomer of glucose, has the cyclic structure shown here. Which is shown, the α form or the β form?

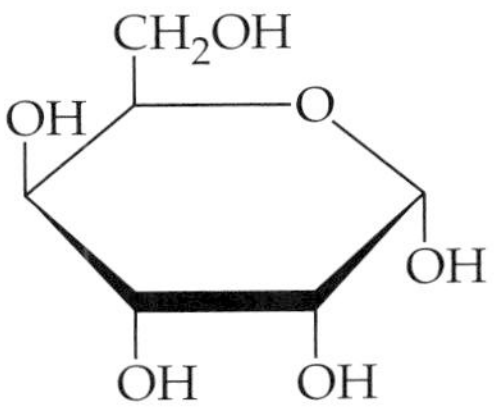

D-Gulose

20.50 In its open-chain form, D-mannose, an aldohexose found in orange peels, has the structure shown here. Coil mannose around and draw it in the cyclic hemiacetal α and β forms.

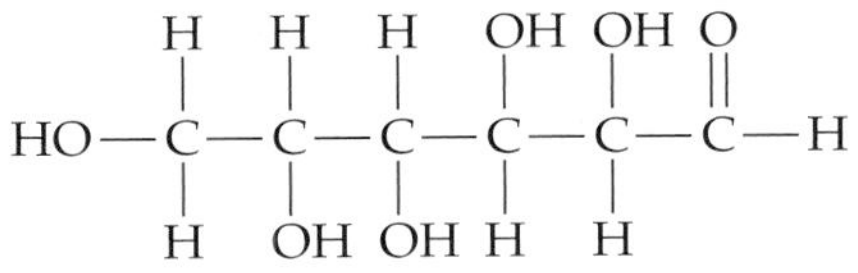

D-Mannose

20.51 In its open-chain form, D-altrose has the structure shown here. Coil altrose around and draw it in the cyclic hemiacetal α and β forms.

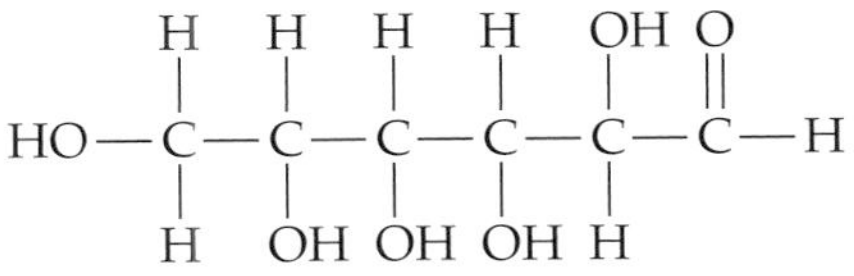

D-Altrose

20.52 Treatment of D-glucose with a reducing agent yields sorbitol, a substance used as a sugar substitute by people with diabetes. Draw the structure of sorbitol.

20.53 Reduction of D-fructose with a reducing agent yields a mixture of D-sorbitol along with a second, isomeric product. What is the structure of the second product?

20.54 Treatment of an aldose with an oxidizing agent such as Tollens' reagent (Section 15.5) yields a carboxylic acid. Gluconic acid, the product of glucose oxidation, is used as its magnesium salt for the treatment of magnesium deficiency. Draw the structure of gluconic acid.

20.55 Oxidation of the aldehyde group of ribose yields a carboxylic acid. Draw the structure of ribonic acid.

20.56 What is the structural difference between a hemiacetal and an acetal?

20.57 What are glycosides, and how can they be formed?

20.58 Look at the open-chain form of D-mannose (Problem 20.50) and draw the two glycosidic products that you expect to obtain by reacting D-mannose with methanol.

20.59 Draw a disaccharide of two cyclic mannose molecules attached by an α-1,4 glycosidic linkage. Explain why the glycosidic products in Problem 20.58 are *not* reducing sugars, but the product in this problem *is* a reducing sugar.

DISACCHARIDES AND POLYSACCHARIDES (SECTIONS 20.6 AND 20.7)

20.60 Give the names of three important disaccharides. Tell where each occurs in nature. From which two monosaccharides is each made?

20.61 Lactose and maltose are reducing disaccharides, but sucrose is a nonreducing disaccharide. Explain.

20.62 Amylose (a form of starch) and cellulose are both polymers of glucose. What is the main structural difference between them? What roles do these two polymers have in nature?

20.63 How are amylose and amylopectin similar to each other, and how are they different from each other?

20.64 Which of the following is not a use for cellulose?

(a) lumber for building
(b) fodder for cattle
(c) raw material for computer chips
(d) fabric for t-shirts

20.65 Which of the following foods can someone who has lactose intolerance eat?

(a) ice cream
(b) french fries
(c) a chocolate milkshake

20.66 *Gentiobiose,* a rare disaccharide found in saffron, has the following structure. What simple sugars do you obtain on hydrolysis of gentiobiose?

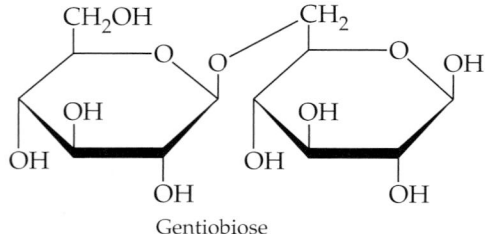

Gentiobiose

20.67 Does gentiobiose (Problem 20.66) have an acetal grouping? A hemiacetal grouping? Do you expect gentiobiose to be a reducing or nonreducing sugar? How would you classify the linkage (α or β and carbon numbers) between the two monosaccharides?

20.68 *Trehalose,* a disaccharide found in the blood of insects, has the following structure. What simple sugars would you obtain on hydrolysis of trehalose? (Hint: Rotate one of the rings in your head or redraw it rotated.)

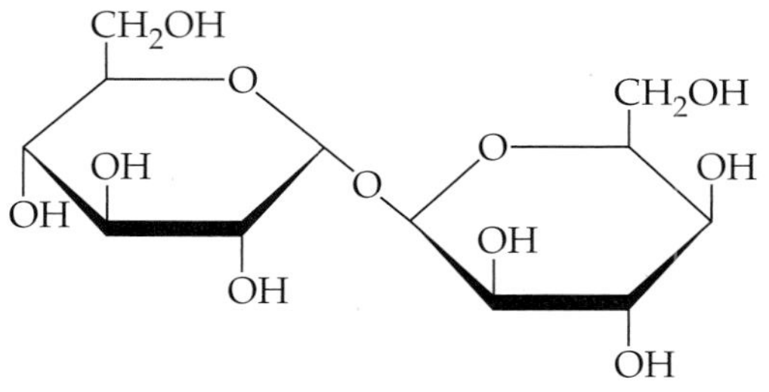

Trehalose

20.69 Does trehalose (Problem 20.68) have an acetal grouping? A hemiacetal grouping? Do you expect trehalose to be a reducing or nonreducing sugar? Classify the linkage between the two monosaccharides.

20.70 Amylopectin (a form of starch) and glycogen are both α-linked polymers of glucose. What is the structural difference between them?

20.71 What is the physiological purpose of starch in a seed or other plant tissue? What is the physiological purpose of glycogen in a mammal?

20.72 What modified sugars makeup heparin, hyaluronate, and chondroitin-6-sulfate?

20.73 What is the function of heparin, hyaluronate, and chondroitin-6-sulfate?

CONCEPTUAL PROBLEMS

20.74 Are the α and β forms of monosaccharides enantiomers of each other? Why or why not?

20.75 Are the α and β forms of the disaccharide lactose enantiomers of each other? Why or why not?

20.76 D-Fructose can form a six-membered cyclic hemiacetal as well as the more prevalent five-membered cyclic form. Draw the α isomer of D-fructose in the six-membered ring.

20.77 *Raffinose,* found in sugar beets, is the most prevalent trisaccharide. It is formed by an α-1,6 linkage of D-galactose to the glucose portion of sucrose. Draw the structure of raffinose.

20.78 Write the open-chain structure of the only ketotriose. Name this compound and explain why it has no optical isomers.

20.79 Write the open-chain structure of the only ketotetrose. Name this compound. Does it have an optical isomer?

20.80 What is lactose intolerance, and what are its symptoms?

20.81 What is the group of disorders that result when the body lacks an enzyme necessary to digest galactose? What are the symptoms?

20.82 When a person cannot digest galactose, its reduced form, called dulcitol, often accumulates in the blood and tissues. Write the structure of the open-chain form of dulcitol. Does dulcitol have an enantiomer? Why or why not?

20.83 Describe the differences between mono-, di-, and polysaccharides.

20.84 Name a naturally occurring carbohydrate and its source for each type of carbohydrate listed in Problem 20.83.

20.85 Compare and contrast lactose intolerance with galactosemia. (Hint: Make a table.)

GROUP PROBLEMS

20.86 Many people who are lactose intolerant can eat yogurt, which is prepared from milk curdled by bacteria, without any digestive problems. Give a reason why this is possible. (Hint: Read the label on each of several yogurt containers. Do the ingredients make a difference?)

20.87 Carbohydrates provide 4 kcal per gram. If a person eats 200 g per day of digestible carbohydrates, what percentage of a 2000 kcal daily diet would be digestible carbohydrate?

20.88 A 12 oz can of cherry-flavored cola contains 42 grams of sugar. If sugar provides 4 kcal per gram (16.7 kJ/g), how many kilocalories are in one can of cola? How many kilojoules?

20.89 Explain why cotton fibers, which are nearly pure cellulose, are insoluble in water, while glycogen, another polymer of glucose, will dissolve in water.

21

The Generation of Biochemical Energy

CONTENTS

◀◀◀ CONCEPTS TO REVIEW

▲ Exercise routines like this require the constant generation of large amounts of biological energy, the topic of this chapter.

Jasmine, 22, was enthusiastic about bodybuilding and how it improved her self-confidence. After a year of training and following advice on dietary supplements from older bodybuilders, Jasmine prepared for competition by sculpting. Sculpting involves losing fat to emphasize muscles and requires dieting. After several weeks of dieting, Jasmine turned to diet pills recommended by others at the training gym to try to speed up her results. Unsatisfied with her slow fat loss, Jasmine doubled the daily dose of the diet pills.

Several hours later she collapsed and was unresponsive. When she arrived at the emergency room (ER), Jasmine's body temperature was 106 °F (41 °C) and rising. In her possession were diet pills containing dinitrophenol, a known toxic substance with dangerous side effects. We'll learn more about dinitrophenol (or DNP) later in the chapter in the Chemistry in Action "Metabolic Poisons" on page 683.

All organisms obtain energy from their surroundings to stay alive. In animals, the energy comes from food and is released through the exquisitely interconnected reaction pathways of metabolism. We are powered by the oxidation of biomolecules made mainly of carbon, hydrogen, and oxygen. The end products are carbon dioxide, water, and energy.

$$\text{C, H, O (food molecules)} + O_2 \longrightarrow CO_2 + H_2O + \text{Energy}$$

The principal food molecules—lipids, proteins, and carbohydrates—differ in structure and are broken down by individual pathways that are examined in later chapters. The product of these individual pathways, usually acetyl coenzyme A, enters the central final pathways that yield usable energy. In this chapter, we are going to concentrate on these final common pathways that release energy from all types of food molecules.

21.1 Energy, Life, and Biochemical Reactions

Learning Objectives:

- Identify energy sources and our specific requirements for energy regulation.
- Explain the significance of exergonic and endergonic reactions in metabolism.

Living things must do mechanical work—microorganisms engulf food, plants bend toward the sun, and humans walk about. Organisms must do the chemical work of synthesizing the biomolecules needed for energy storage, growth, repair, and replacement. In addition, cells need energy for the work of moving molecules and ions across cell membranes. In humans, it is the energy released from food that allows this work to be done.

Energy can be converted from one form to another but can be neither created nor destroyed (see Section 7.2). Ultimately, the energy used by all but a few living things comes from the sun (Figure 21.1). Plants convert sunlight to potential energy stored mainly in the chemical bonds of carbohydrates.

Plant-eating animals utilize this energy, some of it for immediate needs and the rest to be stored for future needs, mainly in the chemical bonds of fats. Other animals, including humans, are able to eat plants or animals and use the chemical energy these organisms have stored.

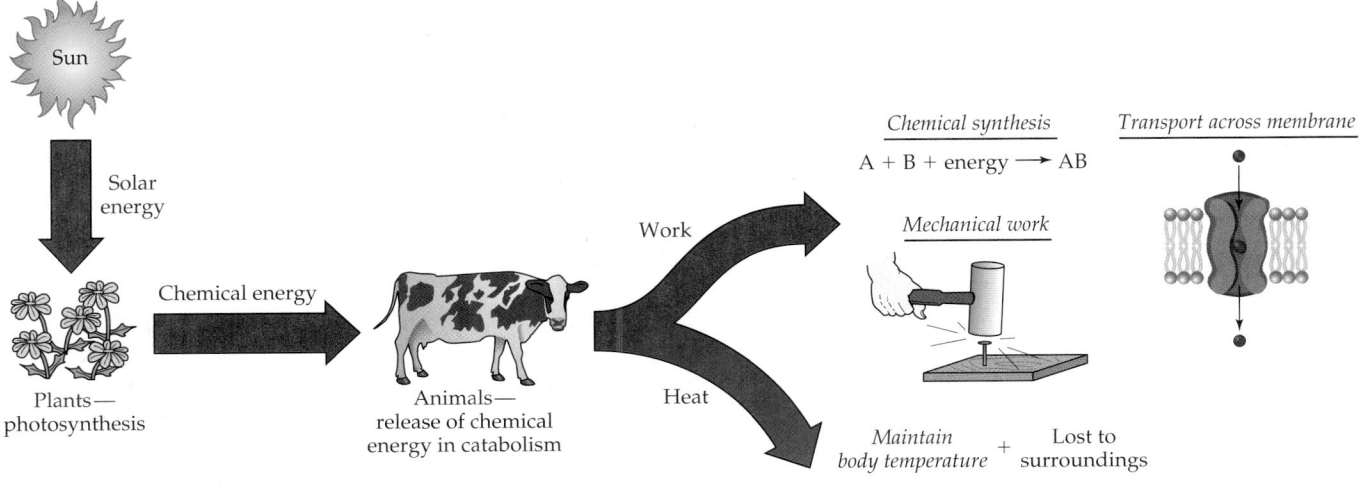

▲ Figure 21.1
The flow of energy through the biosphere.
Energy from the sun is ultimately stored in chemical bonds, used for cellular or mechanical work, used to maintain body temperature, or lost as heat.

Our bodies do not produce energy by burning up a meal all at once because the release of a large quantity of energy (primarily as heat) would be harmful to us. Furthermore, it is difficult to capture energy for storage once it has been converted to heat. We need energy that can be stored and then released in the right amounts when and where it is needed, whether we are jogging, studying, or sleeping. We, therefore, have some specific requirements for energy.

- Energy must be released from food gradually.
- Energy must be stored in readily accessible forms as glycogen and fat (triacylglycerides).
- Release of energy from storage must be finely controlled so that it is available exactly when and where it is needed.
- Just enough energy must be released as heat to maintain constant body temperature.
- Energy in a form other than heat must be available to drive chemical reactions that are not favorable at body temperatures.

This chapter looks at some of the ways these requirements for energy regulation are met. We begin by reviewing basic concepts about energy and then learn about *metabolism*. Next, we look at the *citric acid cycle* and *oxidative phosphorylation*, which together form the common pathway for the production of energy.

Biochemical Reactions

◀◀◀ **CONCEPTS TO REVIEW** Review entropy, enthalpy, endergonic, exergonic, and free-energy change in Sections 7.2–7.4.

Chemical reactions either release or absorb energy. Whether a reaction is favorable or not depends on either the release or absorption of energy as heat (the change in enthalpy, ΔH), together with the increase or decrease in disorder (ΔS, the entropy change) caused by the reaction. The net effect of these changes is given by the free-energy change of a reaction: $\Delta G = \Delta H - T\Delta S$.

Reactions in living organisms are no different from reactions in a chemistry laboratory. Both follow the same laws, and both have the same energy requirements. Spontaneous reactions—that is, those that are *favorable* in the forward direction—release free energy, and the energy released is available to do work. Such reactions, described as *exergonic*, are the source of our biochemical energy.

As shown by the energy diagram in Figure 7.3 the products of a favorable, exergonic reaction are farther *downhill* on the energy scale than the reactants. That is, the products are more stable than the reactants, and as a result the free-energy change (ΔG) has a negative value. Oxidation reactions, for example, are usually downhill reactions that release energy. Oxidation of glucose, the principal source of energy for animals, produces 686 kcal (2870 kJ) of free energy per mole of glucose.

$$C_6H_{12}O_6 + 6\,O_2 \longrightarrow 6\,CO_2 + 6\,H_2O \qquad \Delta G = -686\,\text{kcal/mol}\,(-2870\,\text{kJ/mol})$$

The greater the amount of free energy released, the farther a reaction proceeds toward product formation before reaching equilibrium.

Reactions in which the products are higher in energy than the reactants can also take place, but such *unfavorable* reactions cannot occur without the input of energy from an external source; such reactions are *endergonic*.

The free-energy change switches sign for the reverse of a reaction, but the value does not change. Photosynthesis, the process whereby plants convert CO_2 and H_2O to glucose and O_2, is the reverse of the oxidation of glucose. Its ΔG is therefore positive and equal to the value for the oxidation of glucose (see the Chemistry in Action "Plants and Photosynthesis" on p. 662). The sun provides the necessary external energy for photosynthesis (686 kcal/mol [2870 kJ/mol] of glucose formed).

$$\text{Photosynthesis} \quad \Delta G = +686 \text{ kcal/mol} (+2870 \text{ kJ/mol}) \text{ (endergonic, energy required)}$$

$$6CO_2 + 6H_2O \quad \rightleftharpoons \quad C_6H_{12}O_6 + 6O_2$$

$$\text{Oxidation} \quad \Delta G = -686 \text{ kcal/mol} (-2870 \text{ kJ/mol}) \text{ (exergonic, energy released)}$$

Living systems make constant use of this principle in the series of chemical reactions we know as the biochemical **pathways.** Energy is stored in the products of an overall endergonic reaction pathway. This stored energy is released as needed in an overall exergonic reaction pathway that regenerates the original reactants. It is not necessary that every reaction in the pathways between the reactants and products be the same, so long as the pathways connect the same reactants and products.

Pathway A series of enzyme-catalyzed chemical reactions that are connected by their intermediates, that is, the product of the first reaction is the reactant for the second reaction, and so on.

 Worked Example 21.1 Determining Reaction Energy

Are the following reactions exergonic or endergonic?

(a) Glucose 6-phosphate $\rightarrow$ Fructose 6-phosphate

$$\Delta G = +0.5 \text{ kcal/mol} (+2.09 \text{ kJ/mol})$$

(b) Fructose 6-phosphate $+$ ATP $\rightarrow$ Fructose 1,6-bisphosphate $+$ ADP

$$\Delta G = -3.4 \text{ kcal/mol} (-14.2 \text{ kJ/mol})$$

ANALYSIS Exergonic reactions release free energy, and ΔG is negative. Endergonic reactions gain free energy, and so ΔG is positive.

SOLUTION
Reaction (a), the conversion of glucose 6-phosphate to fructose 6-phosphate has a positive ΔG; therefore, it is endergonic. Reaction (b), the conversion of fructose 6-phosphate to fructose 1,6-bisphosphate has a negative ΔG; therefore it is exergonic.

KEY CONCEPT PROBLEM 21.1

In a cell, glucose can be oxidized via metabolic pathways. Alternatively, you could burn glucose in the laboratory. Which of these methods consumes or produces more energy? (Hint: All of the energy comes from converting the energy stored in the reduced bonds in glucose into the most oxidized form, carbon dioxide.)

KEY CONCEPT PROBLEM 21.2

The overall equation in this section,

$$6CO_2 + 6H_2O \underset{\text{oxidation}}{\overset{\text{photosynthesis}}{\rightleftharpoons}} C_6H_{12}O_6 + 6O_2,$$

shows the cycle between photosynthesis and oxidation. Pathways operating in opposite directions cannot be exergonic in both directions.
(a) Which of the two pathways in this cycle is exergonic and which is endergonic?
(b) Where does the energy for the endergonic pathway come from?

CHEMISTRY IN ACTION

Plants and Photosynthesis

The principal biochemical difference between humans and plants is that plants derive energy directly from sunlight and we cannot. In the process of *photosynthesis,* plants use solar energy to synthesize oxygen and energy-rich carbohydrates from energy-poor reactants: CO_2 and water. Our metabolism breaks down energy-rich reactants to extract the useful energy and produce energy-poor products: CO_2 and water. Is it surprising to discover that despite this difference in the direction of their reactions, plants rely on biochemical pathways very much like our own?

The energy-capturing phase of photosynthesis takes place mainly in green leaves. Plant cells contain *chloroplasts,* which, though larger and more complex in structure, resemble mitochondria. Embedded in membranes within the chloroplasts are large groups of *chlorophyll* molecules and the enzymes of an electron-transport chain. Chlorophyll is similar in structure to heme but contains magnesium ions (Mg^{2+}) instead of iron ions (Fe^{2+}).

As solar energy is absorbed, chlorophyll molecules pass it along to specialized reaction centers, where it is used to boost the energy of electrons. The excited electrons then give up their extra energy as they pass down a pair of electron-transport chains.

Some of this energy is used to oxidize water, splitting it into oxygen, hydrogen ions, and electrons (which replace those entering the electron-transport chain). At the end of the chain, the hydrogen ions, together with the electrons, are used to reduce $NADP^+$ to NADPH. Along the way, part of the energy of the electrons is used to pump hydrogen ions across a membrane to create a concentration gradient. As in mitochondria, the hydrogen ions can only return across the membrane at enzyme complexes that convert ADP to ATP. Water needed for these *light-dependent reactions* enters the plant through the roots and leaves, and the oxygen that is formed is released through openings in the leaves.

The energy-carrying ATP and NADPH enter the fluid interior of the chloroplasts. Here their energy is used to drive the synthesis of carbohydrate molecules. So long as ATP and NADH are available, this part of photosynthesis is *light-independent*—it can proceed in the absence of sunlight.

Plants have mitochondria as well as chloroplasts, so they can also carry out the release of energy from stored carbohydrates. Because the breakdown of carbohydrates continues in many harvested fruits and vegetables, the goal in storage is to slow it down. Refrigeration is one measure that is taken, since (like most chemical reactions) the rate of respiration decreases at lower temperatures. Another is replacement of air over stored fruits and vegetables with carbon dioxide or nitrogen.

▲ These flowers are converting the potential energy of the sun into chemical potential energy stored in the bonds of carbohydrates.

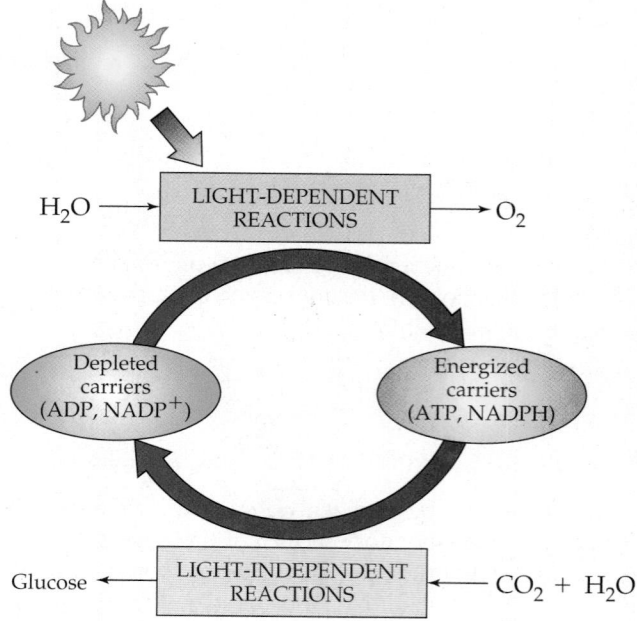

▲ The coupled reactions of photosynthesis.

CIA Problem 21.1 Chlorophyll is similar in structure to heme in red blood cells but does not have an iron atom. What metal ion is present in chlorophyll?

CIA Problem 21.2 Photosynthesis consists of both light-dependent and light-independent reactions. What is the purpose of each type of reaction?

CIA Problem 21.3 One step of the cycle that incorporates CO_2 into glyceraldehyde in plants is the production of two 3-phosphoglycerates. $\Delta G = -0.84$ kcal/mol $(-3.5$ kJ/mol$)$ for this reaction. Is this process endergonic or exergonic?

CIA Problem 21.4 What general process does refrigeration of harvested fruits and vegetables slow? What cellular processes are slowed by refrigeration?

21.2 Cells and Their Structure

Learning Objective:

• Describe the eukaryotic cell and explain the function of each structure.

Before learning about metabolism, it is important to see where the energy-generating reactions take place within the cells of living organisms. There are two main categories of cells: *prokaryotic cells,* found in single-celled organisms (e.g., bacteria and blue-green algae), and *eukaryotic cells,* found in some single-celled organisms, such as yeast, and all plants and animals.

Eukaryotic cells are about 1000 times larger than bacterial cells, have a membrane-enclosed nucleus that contains their deoxyribonucleic acid (DNA), and include several other kinds of internal structures known as *organelles*—small, functional units that perform specialized tasks. A generalized eukaryotic cell is shown in Figure 21.2 with short descriptions of the functions of some of its major parts. Everything between the cell membrane and the nuclear membrane in a eukaryotic cell, including the various organelles, is the **cytoplasm.** The organelles are surrounded by the fluid part of the cytoplasm, the **cytosol,** which contains electrolytes, nutrients, and many enzymes, all in aqueous solution.

Cytoplasm The region between the cell membrane and the nuclear membrane in a eukaryotic cell.

Cytosol The fluid part of the cytoplasm surrounding the organelles within a cell, contains dissolved proteins and nutrients.

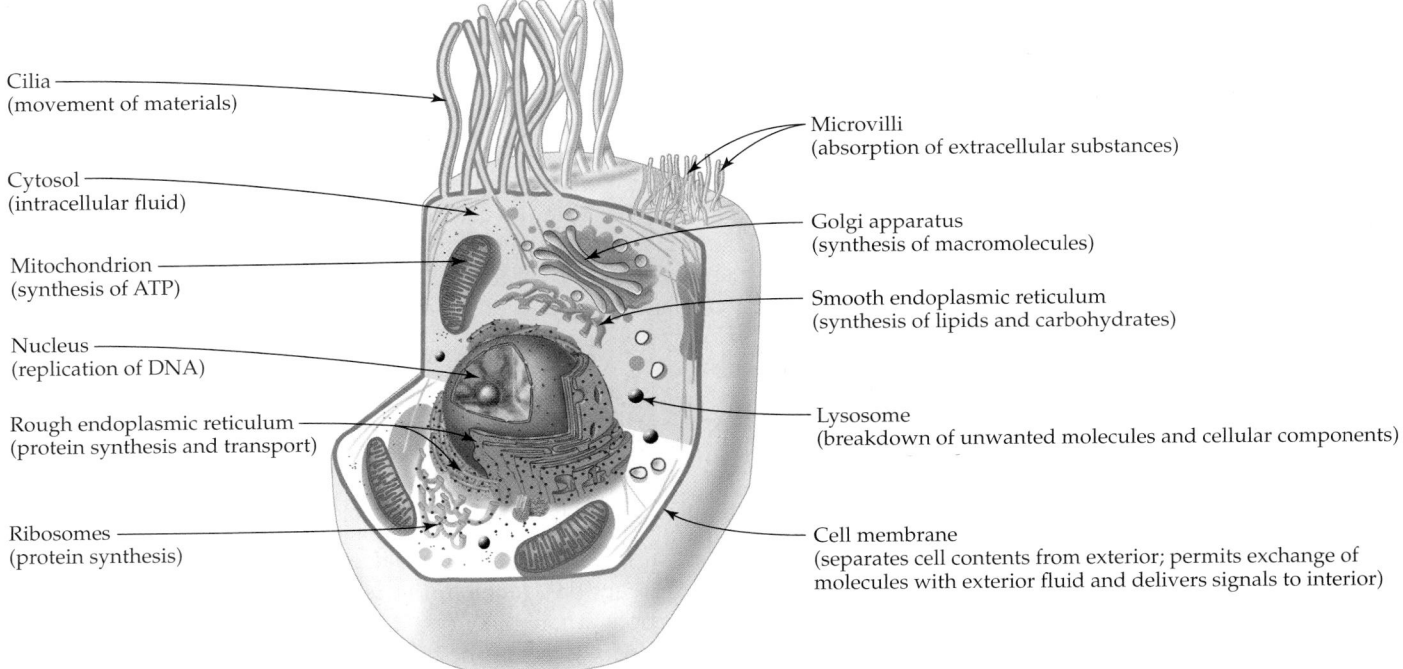

Cilia
(movement of materials)

Cytosol
(intracellular fluid)

Mitochondrion
(synthesis of ATP)

Nucleus
(replication of DNA)

Rough endoplasmic reticulum
(protein synthesis and transport)

Ribosomes
(protein synthesis)

Microvilli
(absorption of extracellular substances)

Golgi apparatus
(synthesis of macromolecules)

Smooth endoplasmic reticulum
(synthesis of lipids and carbohydrates)

Lysosome
(breakdown of unwanted molecules and cellular components)

Cell membrane
(separates cell contents from exterior; permits exchange of molecules with exterior fluid and delivers signals to interior)

▲ Figure 21.2
A generalized eukaryotic cell.
Major cell components are labeled with a description of their primary function.

The **mitochondria** (singular, **mitochondrion**), often called the cell's "power plants," are the most important of the organelles for energy production and produce about 90% of the body's energy-carrying molecule, ATP.

A mitochondrion is a roughly egg-shaped structure composed of a smooth outer membrane and a folded inner membrane (Figure 21.3). The space enclosed by the inner membrane is the **mitochondrial matrix.** Within the matrix, the citric acid cycle (Section 21.7) and production of most of the body's **adenosine triphosphate (ATP)** take place. The coenzymes and proteins that manage the transfer of energy to the chemical bonds of ATP (Section 21.8) are embedded in the inner membrane of the mitochondrion.

Mitochondrion (plural, mitochondria) An egg-shaped organelle where small molecules are broken down to provide the energy for an organism.

Mitochondrial matrix The space surrounded by the inner membrane of a mitochondrion.

Adenosine triphosphate (ATP) The principal energy-carrying molecule, removal of a phosphoryl group to give ADP releases free energy.

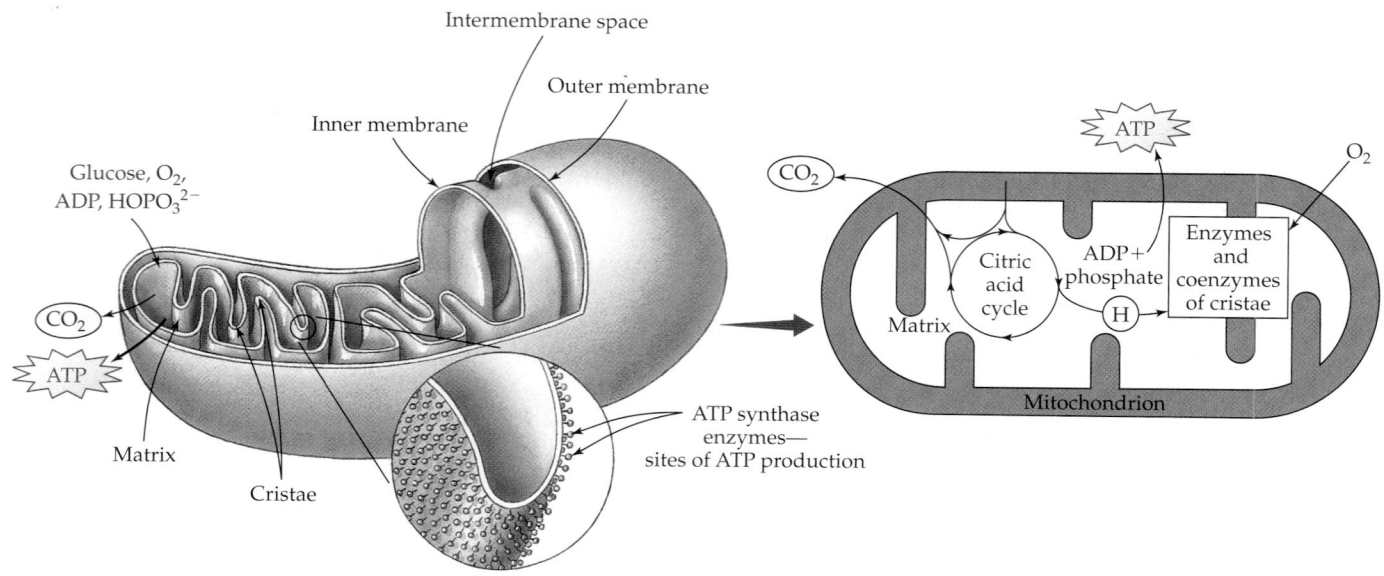

▲ **Figure 21.3**
The mitochondrion.
Cells have many mitochondria. The citric acid cycle takes place in the matrix. Electron transport and ATP production, the final stage in biochemical energy generation (described in Section 21.8), take place at the inner surface of the inner membrane. The numerous folds in the inner membrane—known as *cristae*—increase the surface area over which these pathways can take place.

Mitochondria contain their own DNA, synthesize some of their own proteins, and multiply using chemicals moved from the cell cytosol into the mitochondrial matrix. The number of mitochondria is greatest in eye, brain, heart, and muscle cells, where the need for energy is greatest. The ability of mitochondria to reproduce is seen in athletes who put heavy energy demands on their bodies—they develop an increased number of mitochondria to aid in energy production.

21.3 An Overview of Metabolism and Energy Production

Learning Objective:

• List the stages in catabolism of food and describe the role of each stage.

Metabolism The sum of all of the chemical reactions that take place in an organism.

Together, all of the chemical reactions that take place in an organism constitute its **metabolism.** Most of these reactions occur in the reaction sequences of *metabolic pathways,* a sequence of reactions where the product of one reaction serves as the starting material for the next. Such pathways may be linear (a series of reactions that convert a reactant into a specific product through a series of intermediate molecules and reactions), cyclic (a series of reactions that regenerates one of the first reactants), or spiral (the same set of enzymes progressively builds up or breaks down a molecule).

A linear sequence $A \xrightarrow{\text{Enzyme 1}} B \xrightarrow{\text{Enzyme 2}} C \xrightarrow{\text{Enzyme 3}} \ldots$

A cyclic sequence

Enzyme 4 — A — Enzyme 1
D — B
Enzyme 3 — C — Enzyme 2

A spiral sequence

A — Enzymes 1 ⟶ 4
B — Enzymes 1 ⟶ 4
C — Enzymes 1 ⟶ 4
— Final product

Catabolism Metabolic reaction pathways that break down food molecules and release biochemical energy.

As we study metabolism we will encounter each of these types of pathways. Those pathways that break molecules apart are known collectively as **catabolism,** whereas those that put building blocks back together to assemble larger molecules are known collectively as **anabolism.** The purpose of catabolism is to release energy from food, and the purpose of anabolism is to synthesize new biomolecules, including those that store energy.

Anabolism Metabolic reactions that build larger biological molecules from smaller pieces.

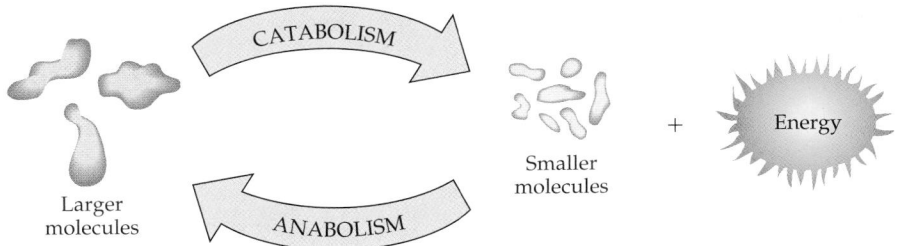

The overall picture of digestion, catabolism, and energy production is simple: eating provides fuel, breathing provides oxygen, and our bodies oxidize the fuel to extract energy. The process can be roughly divided into the four stages described here and shown in Figure 21.4.

STAGE 1: Digestion Enzymes in saliva, the stomach, and the small intestine convert the large molecules of carbohydrates, proteins, and lipids to smaller molecules. Carbohydrates are broken down to glucose and other sugars; proteins are broken down to amino acids; and triacylglycerols, the lipids commonly known as fats and oils, are broken down to glycerol plus long-chain carboxylic acids, termed fatty acids. These smaller molecules are transferred into the blood for transport to cells throughout the body.

STAGE 2: Acetyl-coenzyme A production The small molecules from digestion follow separate pathways that separate their carbon atoms into two-carbon acetyl groups. The acetyl groups are attached to coenzyme A by a high-energy bond between the sulfur atom of the thiol (—SH) group at the end of the coenzyme A molecule and the carbonyl carbon atom of the acetyl group.

◄◄ See the chemical structure of coenzyme A in Figure 19.10.

Acetyl-coenzyme A (acetyl-CoA) Acetyl-substituted coenzyme A—the common intermediate that carries acetyl groups into the citric acid cycle.

Attachment of acetyl group to coenzyme A

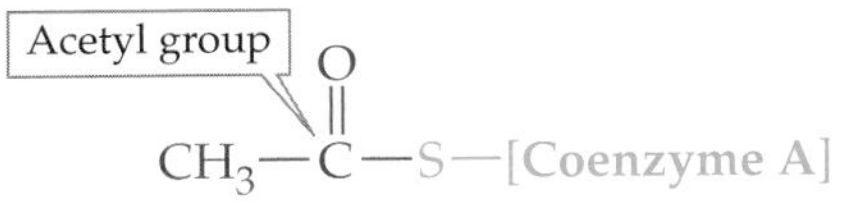

Acetyl group

$$CH_3 - \overset{\overset{\displaystyle O}{\|}}{C} - S - [\text{Coenzyme A}]$$

The resultant compound, **acetyl-coenzyme A,** which is abbreviated **acetyl-CoA,** is an intermediate in the breakdown of *all* classes of food molecules. It carries the acetyl groups into the common pathways of catabolism—Stage 3, the citric acid cycle and Stage 4, electron transport and ATP production.

STAGE 3: Citric acid cycle Within mitochondria, the acetyl-group carbon atoms are oxidized to the carbon dioxide that we exhale. Most of the energy released in the oxidation leaves the citric acid cycle in the chemical bonds of reduced coenzymes (NADH, FADH$_2$). Some energy also leaves the cycle stored in the chemical bonds of ATP or a related triphosphate.

STAGE 4: ATP production Electrons from the reduced coenzymes are passed from molecule to molecule down an electron-transport chain. Along the way, their energy is harnessed to produce more ATP. At the end of the process, these electrons—along with hydrogen ions from the reduced coenzymes—combine with oxygen we breathe in to produce water. Thus, the reduced coenzymes are in effect oxidized by atmospheric oxygen, and the energy that they carried is stored in the chemical bonds of ATP molecules.

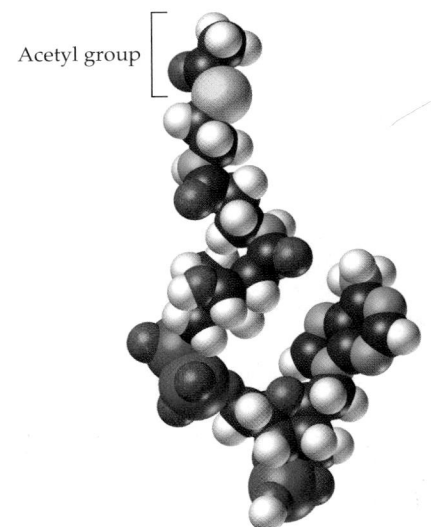

Acetyl group

Acetyl-coenzyme A

LOOKING AHEAD ▶▶ Digestion and conversion of food molecules to acetyl-CoA, Stages 1 and 2 in Figure 21.4, occur by different metabolic pathways for carbohydrates, lipids, and proteins. Each of these pathways is discussed separately in later chapters: carbohydrate metabolism in Chapter 22, lipid metabolism in Chapter 24, and protein metabolism in Chapter 25.

► Figure 21.4
Pathways for the digestion of food and the production of biochemical energy. This diagram summarizes pathways covered in this chapter (the citric acid cycle and electron transport) and also the pathways discussed in Chapter 22 for carbohydrate metabolism, in Chapter 24 for lipid metabolism, and in Chapter 25 for protein metabolism.

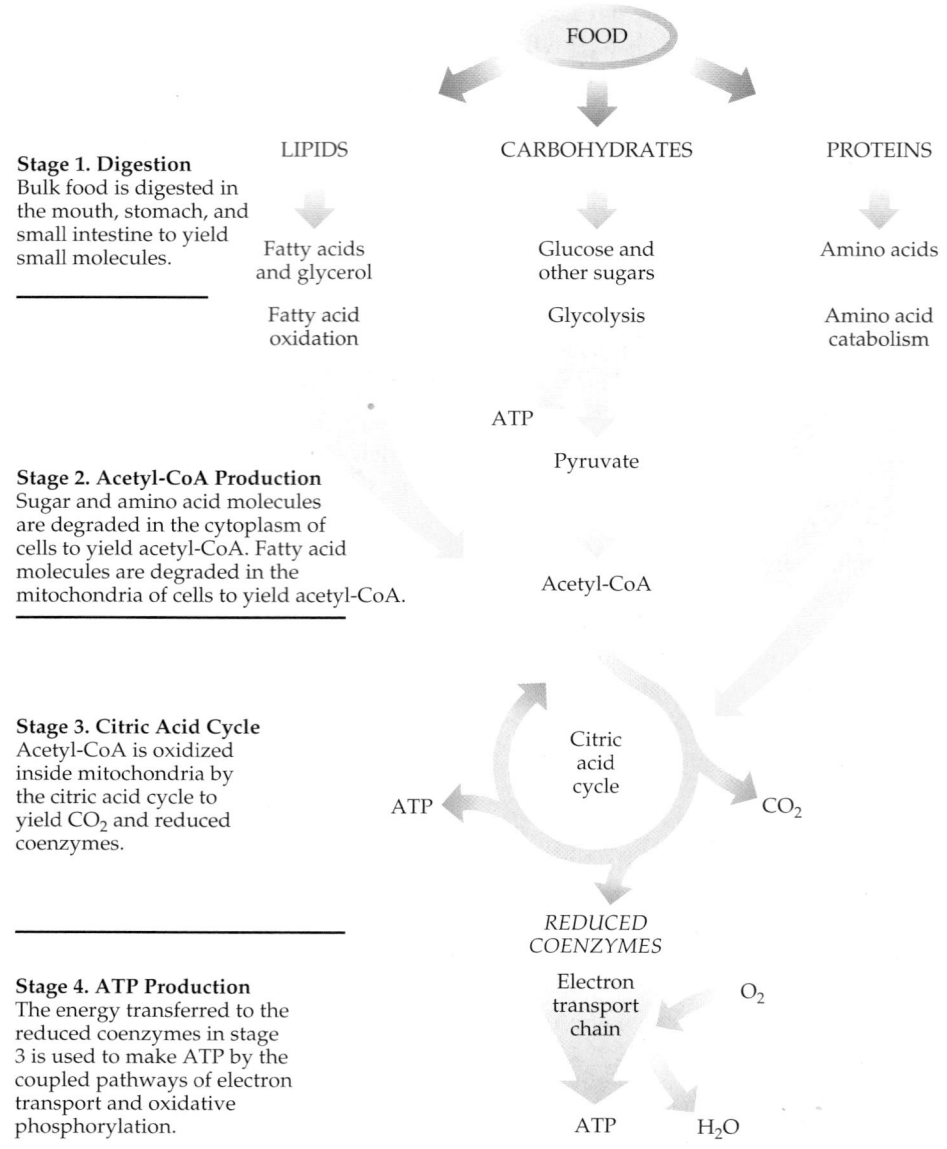

Stage 1. Digestion
Bulk food is digested in the mouth, stomach, and small intestine to yield small molecules.

Stage 2. Acetyl-CoA Production
Sugar and amino acid molecules are degraded in the cytoplasm of cells to yield acetyl-CoA. Fatty acid molecules are degraded in the mitochondria of cells to yield acetyl-CoA.

Stage 3. Citric Acid Cycle
Acetyl-CoA is oxidized inside mitochondria by the citric acid cycle to yield CO_2 and reduced coenzymes.

Stage 4. ATP Production
The energy transferred to the reduced coenzymes in stage 3 is used to make ATP by the coupled pathways of electron transport and oxidative phosphorylation.

Worked Example 21.2 Identifying Metabolic Pathways That Convert Basic Molecules to Energy

(a) In Figure 21.4, identify the stages in the catabolic pathway in which lipids ultimately yield ATP.

(b) In Figure 21.4, identify the place at which the products of lipid catabolism can join the common metabolism pathway.

ANALYSIS Look at Figure 21.4 and find the pathway for lipids. Follow the arrows to trace the flow of energy. Note that Stage 3 is the point at which the products of lipid, carbohydrate, and protein catabolism all feed into a central, common metabolic pathway, the citric acid cycle. The lipid molecules that feed into Stage 3 do so via acetyl-CoA (Stage 2). Note also that most products of Stage 3 catabolism feed into Stage 4 catabolism to produce ATP.

SOLUTION
The lipids in food are broken down in Stage 1 (digestion) to fatty acids and glycerol. Stage 2 (acetyl-CoA production) results in fatty acid oxidation to acetyl-CoA. In Stage 3 (citric acid cycle), acetyl-CoA enters the citric acid cycle (the common metabolism pathway), which produces ATP, reduced coenzymes, and CO_2. In Stage 4 (ATP production), the energy stored in the reduced coenzymes (from the citric acid cycle) is converted to ATP energy.

PROBLEM 21.3

(a) In Figure 21.4, identify the stages in the pathway for the conversion of the energy from carbohydrates to energy stored in ATP molecules.

(b) In Figure 21.4, identify the three places at which the products of amino acid catabolism can join the central metabolism pathway.

21.4 Strategies of Metabolism: ATP and Energy Transfer

Learning Objective:

• Describe the role of ATP in energy transfer.

ATP is the body's energy-transporting molecule. What exactly does that mean? Consider that the molecule has three $-PO_3^-$ groups.

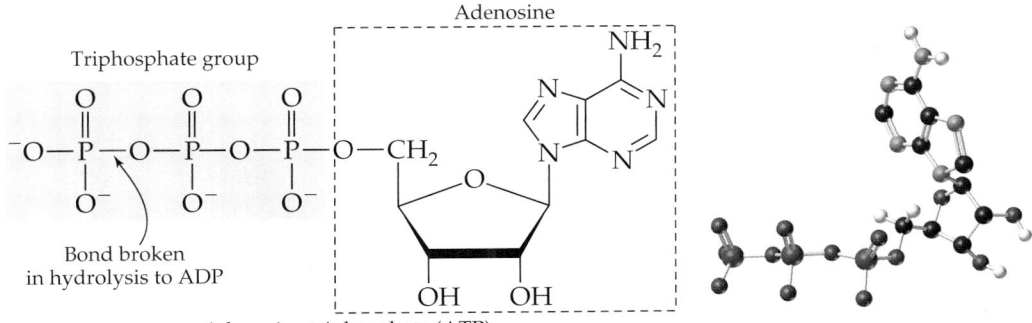

Adenosine triphosphate (ATP)

Removal of the terminal $-PO_3^{-2}$ group from ATP by hydrolysis gives adenosine diphosphate (ADP). The ATP → ADP reaction is exergonic; it releases chemical energy that was held in the bond to the $-PO_3^{2-}$ group.

$$ATP + H_2O \longrightarrow ADP + HOPO_3^{2-} + H^+ \quad \Delta G = -7.3 \text{ kcal/mol} \ (-30.5 \text{ kJ/mol})$$

The reverse of ATP hydrolysis—a phosphorylation reaction—is endergonic.

$$ADP + HOPO_3^{2-} + H^+ \longrightarrow ATP + H_2O \quad \Delta G = +7.3 \text{ kcal/mol} \ (+30.5 \text{ kJ/mol})$$

(In equations for biochemical reactions, we represent ATP and other energy-carrying molecules in red and their lower-energy equivalent molecules in blue.)

ATP is an energy transporter because its production from ADP requires an input of energy that is released when the reverse reaction occurs. Biochemical energy is gathered from exergonic reactions and stored in the bonds of the ATP molecule. ATP hydrolysis releases energy for energy-requiring work. *Biochemical energy production, transport, and use, all depend upon the ATP ⇌ ADP interconversion.*

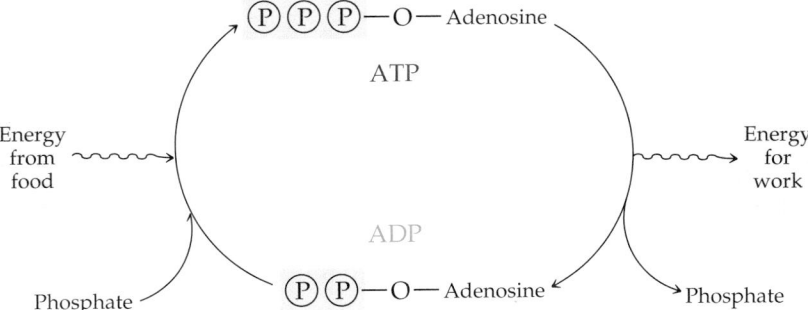

The hydrolysis of ATP to give ADP and its reverse, the phosphorylation of ADP, are reactions perfectly suited to their role in metabolism for two major reasons. Firstly, ATP hydrolysis occurs slowly in the absence of a catalyst, so the stored energy is released only in the presence of the appropriate enzymes.

Secondly, the free energy of hydrolysis of ATP is an intermediate value for energy carriers (Table 21.1). Since the primary metabolic function of ATP is to transport energy, it is often referred to as a "high-energy" molecule or as containing "high-energy" phosphorus–oxygen bonds. These terms are misleading because they promote the idea that ATP is somehow different from other compounds. The terms mean only that ATP is reactive and that a useful amount of energy is released when a phosphoryl group is removed from it by hydrolysis.

Table 21.1 Free Energies of Hydrolysis of Some Phosphates

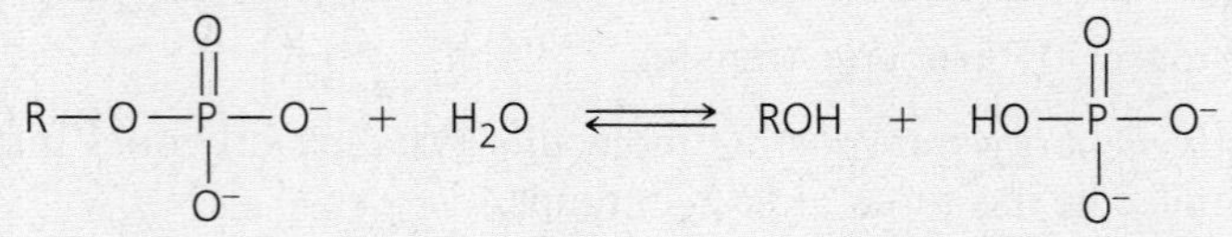

$$R-O-\overset{\overset{\displaystyle O}{\|}}{\underset{\underset{\displaystyle O^-}{|}}{P}}-O^- \ + \ H_2O \ \rightleftharpoons \ ROH \ + \ HO-\overset{\overset{\displaystyle O}{\|}}{\underset{\underset{\displaystyle O^-}{|}}{P}}-O^-$$

Compound Name	Function	ΔG (kcal/mol)	ΔG (kJ/mol)
Phosphoenol pyruvate	Final intermediate in conversion of glucose to pyruvate (glycolysis)—Stage 2, Figure 21.5	−14.8	−61.9
1, 3-Bisphosphoglycerate	Another intermediate in glycolysis	−11.8	−49.4
Creatine phosphate	Energy storage in muscle cells	−10.3	−43.1
ATP ($\longrightarrow$ ADP)	Principal energy carrier	−7.3	−30.5
Glucose 1-phosphate	First intermediate in breakdown of carbohydrates stored as starch or glycogen	−5.0	−20.9
Glucose 6-phosphate	First intermediate in glycolysis	−3.3	−13.8
Fructose 6-phosphate	Second intermediate in glycolysis	−3.3	−13.8

In fact, if removal of a phosphoryl group from ATP released *unusually* large amounts of energy, other reactions would not be able to provide enough energy to convert ADP back to ATP. ATP is a convenient energy carrier in metabolism because its free energy of hydrolysis has an *intermediate value* among high energy carriers. For this reason, the phosphorylation of ADP can be driven by coupling this reaction with a more exergonic reaction.

PROBLEM 21.4

Acetyl phosphate, whose structure is given here, is another compound with a relatively high free energy of hydrolysis.

$$CH_3-\overset{\overset{\displaystyle O}{\|}}{C}-O-\overset{\overset{\displaystyle O}{\|}}{\underset{\underset{\displaystyle O^-}{|}}{P}}-O^-$$

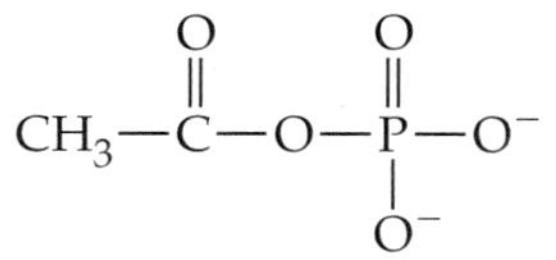

Using structural formulas, write the equation for the hydrolysis of this phosphate.

PROBLEM 21.5

A common metabolic strategy is the lack of reactivity—that is, the slowness to react—of compounds whose breakdown is exergonic. For example, hydrolysis of ATP to ADP or adenosine monophosphate (AMP) is exergonic but does not take place without an appropriate enzyme present. Why would the cell use this metabolic strategy?

CHEMISTRY IN ACTION

⚕ Harmful Oxygen Species and Antioxidant Vitamins

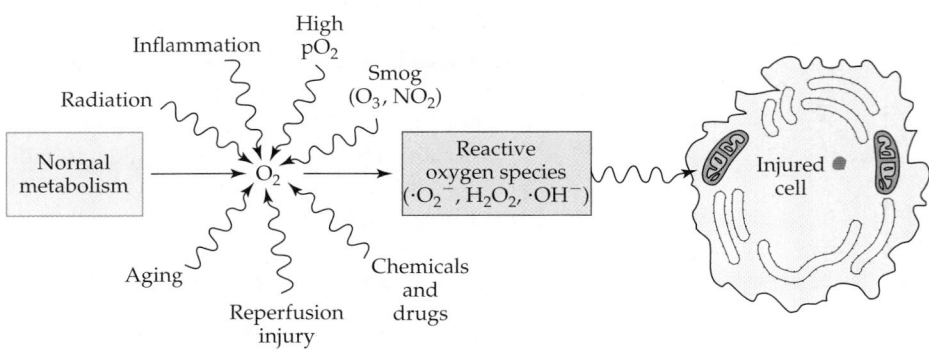

More than 90% of the oxygen we breathe is used in electron-transport–ATP synthesis reactions. In these and other O_2 consuming reactions, the product can be water or one of these oxygen-containing free radicals: the superoxide ion ($\cdot O_2^-$), the hydroxyl free radical ($\cdot OH^-$), and hydrogen peroxide, H_2O_2, a relatively strong oxidizer. These three species are dangerous to cells; the superoxide ion is beneficial in destroying infectious microorganisms. In what is known as a "respiratory burst," *phagocytes* (cells that engulf bacteria) produce superoxide ions that react destructively with bacteria.

$$2\,O_2 + NADPH \longrightarrow 2\cdot O_2^- + NADP^+ + H^+$$

Reactive oxygen species (ROS) are dangerous to our own cells, especially since most ROS are produced in mitochondria where they can disrupt energy production. ROS can break covalent bonds in enzymes and other proteins, DNA, and the lipids in cell membranes causing cell injury or death. Among the possible outcomes of such destruction are cancer, liver damage, rheumatoid arthritis, heart disease, immune system damage, and possibly the changes regarded as normal aging. Internal processes such as inflammation and drug ingestion and external influences like radiation and smog, including second-hand cigarette smoke, all produce these ROS in our bodies.

Our protection against ROS is provided by superoxide dismutase (converts the superoxide ion to hydrogen peroxide) and catalase (converts hydrogen peroxide to water), which are among the fastest-acting enzymes (see Section 19.1). Other enzymes in cells also provide some protection; however, certain vitamins, such as vitamins E, C, and A (or its precursor β-carotene), function as antioxidants as well. These molecules disarm free radicals by bonding with them (see Section 19.9). Vitamin E is fat-soluble, and its major function is to protect cell membranes from potential damage initiated when a cell membrane lipid (RH) is converted to an oxygen-containing free radical ROO $\cdot$. Because Vitamin C is water-soluble, it is a free-radical scavenger in the blood. There are also many other natural antioxidants among the chemical compounds distributed in fruits and vegetables.

CIA Problem 21.5 Which of the following are ROS?
 (a) H_2O **(b)** H_2O_2 **(c)** ROO $\cdot$ **(d)** $\cdot OH^-$

CIA Problem 21.6 How does a cell disarm each of the ROS in CIA Problem 21.5? What enzymes and vitamins are involved?

21.5 Strategies of Metabolism: Metabolic Pathways and Coupled Reactions

Learning Objective:

• Explain why some reactions are coupled and give an example of a coupled reaction.

How is stored chemical energy gradually released and how is it used to drive endergonic (uphill) reactions? Remember that your body cannot burn up the energy obtained from consuming a meal all at once. As shown in Figure 7.3, however, the energy difference between a reactant (the meal) and the ultimate products of its catabolism (mainly carbon dioxide and water) is a fixed quantity. The same amount of energy is released no matter what pathway is taken between reactants and products. The metabolic pathways of catabolism take advantage of this fact by releasing energy bit by bit in a series of reactions, somewhat like the stepwise release of potential energy as water flows down an elaborate waterfall.

The overall reaction and the overall free-energy change for any series of reactions can be found by summing up the equations and the free-energy changes for the individual steps. For example, glucose is converted to pyruvate via the 10 reactions of the glycolysis pathway (part of Stage 2, Figure 21.4, and Section 22.3). The overall free-energy change for glycolysis is about −8 kcal/mol (−33.5 kJ/mol), showing that the

▲ This waterfall illustrates a stepwise release of potential energy. No matter what the pathway from the top to the bottom, the amount of potential energy released as the water falls from the top to the very bottom is the same.

pathway is exergonic—that is, downhill and favorable. The reactions of all metabolic pathways *sum* to favorable processes with negative free-energy changes.

Unlike the waterfall, however, not every individual step in every metabolic pathway is downhill. The metabolic strategy for dealing with what would be an energetically unfavorable reaction is to *couple* it with an energetically favorable reaction so that the overall energy change for the two reactions is favorable. For example, consider the reaction of glucose with hydrogen phosphate ion ($HOPO_3^{2-}$) to yield glucose 6-phosphate plus water, for which $\Delta G = +3.3\,\text{kcal/mol}\ (+13.8\,\text{kJ/mol})$. This reaction is unfavorable because the two products are 3.3 kcal/mol (13.8 kJ/mol) higher in energy than the starting materials. This phosphorylation of glucose is, however, the essential first step toward all metabolic use of glucose. To accomplish this reaction, it is coupled with the exergonic hydrolysis of ATP to give ADP.

(*Unfavorable*)	Glucose + $HOPO_3^{2-}$ ⟶ Glucose 6-phosphate + H_2O	$\Delta G = +3.3\,\text{kcal/mol}\ (+13.8\,\text{kJ/mol})$
(*Favorable*)	ATP + H_2O ⟶ ADP + $HOPO_3^{2-}$ + H^+	$\Delta G = -7.3\,\text{kcal/mol}\ (-30.5\,\text{kJ/mol})$
(*Favorable*)	Glucose + ATP ⟶ Glucose 6-phosphate + ADP	$\Delta G = -4.0\,\text{kcal/mol}\ (-16.7\,\text{kJ/mol})$

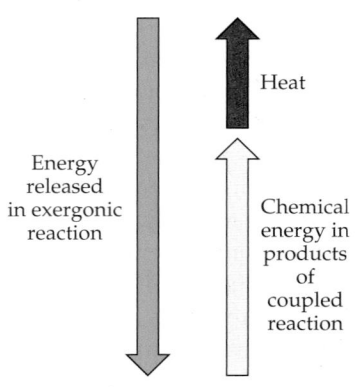

▲ **Figure 21.5**

Energy exchange in coupled reactions.

The energy provided by an exergonic reaction is either released as heat or stored as chemical potential energy in the bonds of products of the coupled endergonic reaction.

The net energy change for this pair of coupled reactions is favorable: 4.0 kcal (16.7 kJ) of free energy is released for each mole of glucose that is phosphorylated. Only by such coupling can the energy stored in one chemical compound be transferred to other compounds. Any excess energy is released as heat and contributes to maintaining body temperature (Figure 21.5).

Although these reactions are written separately to show how their energies combine, coupled reactions do not take place separately. The net change occurs all at once as represented by the overall equation. The phosphoryl group is transferred directly from ATP to glucose without the intermediate formation of $HOPO_3^{2-}$.

The same principle of coupling is used for the endergonic synthesis of ATP from ADP, $\Delta G = +7.3\,\text{kcal/mol}\ (+30.5\,\text{kJ/mol})$. For this endergonic reaction to occur, it must be coupled with a reaction that releases *more* than 7.3 kcal/mol (30.5 kJ/mol). In a different step of glycolysis, for example, the formation of ATP is coupled with the hydrolysis of phosphoenolpyruvate, a phosphate of higher energy than ATP (Table 21.1). Here, the overall reaction is transfer of a phosphoryl group from phosphoenolpyruvate to ADP.

$$
\begin{array}{l}
\underset{\text{Phosphoenolpyruvate}}{\overset{\displaystyle O-PO_3^{2-}}{H_2C=\overset{|}{C}-COO^-}} + H_2O \longrightarrow \underset{\text{Pyruvate}}{CH_3-\overset{\displaystyle O}{\overset{||}{C}}-COO^-} + HOPO_3^{2-}
\end{array}
\qquad
\begin{array}{l}
\Delta G = -14.8\,\text{kcal/mol} \\
\Delta G = (-61.9\,\text{kJ/mol})
\end{array}
$$

$$
ADP + HOPO_3^{2-} + H^+ \longrightarrow ATP + H_2O
\qquad
\begin{array}{l}
\Delta G = +7.3\,\text{kcal/mol} \\
\Delta G = (+30.5\,\text{kJ/mol})
\end{array}
$$

$$
\underset{}{\overset{\displaystyle O-PO_3^{2-}}{H_2C=\overset{|}{C}-COO^-}} + ADP \longrightarrow CH_3\overset{\displaystyle O}{\overset{||}{C}}-COO^- + ATP
\qquad
\begin{array}{l}
\Delta G = -7.5\,\text{kcal/mol} \\
\Delta G = (-31.4\,\text{kJ/mol})
\end{array}
$$

Remember that in equations representing coupled reactions, a *curved arrow* often connects the reactants and products in one of the two chemical changes. For example, the reaction of phosphoenolpyruvate illustrated earlier can be written as

$$
\underset{}{\overset{\displaystyle O-PO_3^{2-}}{H_2C=\overset{|}{C}-COO^-}} \xrightarrow[]{\quad ADP \quad ATP \quad} CH_3-\overset{\displaystyle O}{\overset{||}{C}}-COO^-
$$

PROBLEM 21.6

One of the steps in lipid metabolism is the reaction of glycerol (1,2,3-propanetriol, $HOCH_2CH(OH)CH_2OH$), with ATP to yield glycerol 1-phosphate. Write the equation for this reaction using the curved arrow symbolism.

PROBLEM 21.7

Why must a metabolic pathway that synthesizes a given molecule occur by a different series of reactions than a pathway that breaks down the same molecule?

CHEMISTRY IN ACTION

✚ Basal Metabolism

The minimum amount of energy expenditure required per unit of time to stay alive—to breathe, maintain body temperature, circulate blood, and keep all body systems functioning—is referred to as the *basal metabolic rate*. Ideally, it is measured in a person who is awake, is lying down at a comfortable temperature, has fasted and avoided strenuous exercise for 12 hours, and is not under the influence of any medications. The basal metabolic rate is measured by monitoring respiration and finding the rate of oxygen consumption, which is proportional to the energy used.

An *average* basal metabolic rate is 70 kcal/hr (293 kJ/hr) or about 1700 kcal/day (7100 kJ/day). The rate varies with many factors, including sex, age, weight, and physical condition. A rule of thumb used by nutritionists to estimate basal energy needs per day is the requirement for 1 kcal/hr (4.2 kJ/hr) per kilogram of body weight by a male and 0.95 kcal/hr (4 kJ/hr) per kilogram of body weight by a female. For example, a 50 kg (110 lb) female has an estimated basal metabolic rate of (50 kg)(0.95 kcal/kg hr) = (48 kcal/hr) giving a daily requirement of approximately 1200 kcal. Calculated in joules this would be (50 kg)(4 kJ/kg hr) = 200 kJ/hr, resulting in a daily requirement of 4800 kJ.

The total calories a person needs each day is determined by his or her basal requirements plus the energy used in additional physical activities. The caloric consumption rates associated with some activities are listed in the accompanying table. A relatively inactive person requires about 30% above basal requirements per day, a lightly active person requires about 50% above basal, and a very active person such as an athlete or construction worker can use 100% above basal requirements in a day. Each day that you consume food with more calories than you use, the excess calories are stored as potential energy in the chemical bonds of fats in your body and your weight rises. Each day that you consume food with fewer calories than you burn, some chemical energy in your body is taken out of storage to make up the deficit. Fat is metabolized to CO_2 and H_2O, which the body gets rid of, and your weight drops.

▲ The cola drink contains 160 Cal (kcal) (680 kJ) and the hamburger contains 500 Cal (2100 kJ). How long would you have to jog at 5 mph to burn off these calories?

Calories Used in Various Activities

Activity	Kilocalories (Nutrition Calories) or Kilojoules Used per Minute
Sleeping	1.2 (5 kJ)
Reading	1.3 (5.4 kJ)
Listening to lecture	1.7 (7.1 kJ)
Weeding garden	5.6 (23 kJ)
Walking, 3.5 mph	5.6 (23 kJ)
Pick-and-shovel work	6.7 (25 kJ)
Recreational tennis	7.0 (29 kJ)
Soccer, basketball	9.0 (38 kJ)
Walking up stairs	10.0–18.0 (42–75 kJ)
Running, 12 min/mi (5 mph)	10.0 (42 kJ)
Running, 5 min/mi (12 mph)	25.0 (105 kJ)

CIA Problem 21.7 How is basal metabolic rate defined?

CIA Problem 21.8 An average 12 oz. can of soda pop contains 160 Calories and a typical hamburger contains 500 Calories. Using the table, calculate how long would you need to jog at 5 miles per hour to burn off these calories.

CIA Problem 21.9 Calculate the total calories needed in a day for an 80 kg lightly active male. Use the "Kilocalories used per minutes" values given in the table in the application.

CIA Problem 21.10 Why do activities such as walking raise a body's needs above the basal metabolic rate?

HANDS-ON CHEMISTRY 21.1

How many calories do you need in a day to maintain your current weight? The best way is to estimate calories by using this formula:

Basal calories + activity calories = total calories

Calculate your basal metabolism caloric need as described in the Chemistry in Action "Basal Metabolism"(p. 671). To convert pounds to kilograms, divide your weight in pounds by 2.2 pounds/kilogram.

Next, estimate your other energy needs based on your activities. Are you inactive, lightly active, or highly active? Use that as a guide and add the appropriate number of calories to the basal calories. Is this an accurate estimate?

As a check, list your daily activities and search the Web for a chart of activities and calories expended. Estimate time spent on these activities, especially if you exercise regularly, have a strenuous job or similar activity, and add these calories to your basal metabolism caloric requirement. Is there a difference from your first estimate? If so, why do you suppose there is a difference?

Worked Example 21.3 Determining If a Coupled Reaction Is Favorable

The hydrolysis of succinyl-CoA is coupled with the production of GTP (guanosine triphosphate—closely related to ATP). The equations for the reactions are given below. Combine the equations appropriately and determine if the coupled reaction is favorable.

$$\text{Succinyl-CoA} \longrightarrow \text{Succinate} + \text{CoA} \qquad \Delta G = -9.4 \text{ kcal/mol} \, (-39.3 \text{ kJ/mol})$$
$$\text{GDP} + \text{HOPO}_3^{2-} + \text{H}^+ \longrightarrow \text{GTP} + \text{H}_2\text{O} \qquad \Delta G = +7.3 \text{ kcal/mol} \, (+30.5 \text{ kJ/mol})$$

ANALYSIS Add the two equations together to produce the equation for the coupled reaction. Also add the ΔG values together, paying close attention to the signs. If the ΔG is positive, the reaction is not favorable and will not occur; if the ΔG is negative, the reaction is favorable and will occur.

SOLUTION

$$\text{Succinyl-CoA} + \text{GDP} + \text{HOPO}_3^{2-} + \text{H}^+ \longrightarrow \text{Succinate} + \text{GTP} + \text{H}_2\text{O} + \text{CoA}$$
$$\Delta G = -2.1 \text{ kcal/mol} \, (-8.8 \text{ kJ/mol})$$

Since ΔG is negative, the coupled reaction will occur as written.

PROBLEM 21.8

The hydrolysis of acetyl phosphate to give acetate and hydrogen phosphate ion has $\Delta G = -10.3 \text{ kcal/mol} \, (-43.1 \text{ kJ/mol})$. Combine the equations and ΔG values to determine whether coupling of this reaction with phosphorylation of ADP to produce ATP is favorable. (You need give only compound names or abbreviations in the equations.)

21.6 Strategies of Metabolism: Oxidized and Reduced Coenzymes

Learning Objective:

• Give an example of a coenzyme changing from oxidized to reduced form in a reaction and explain the purpose of the change.

The net result of catabolism is the oxidation of food molecules to release energy. Many metabolic reactions are therefore oxidation–reduction reactions, which means that a steady supply of oxidizing and reducing agents must be available. To meet this requirement, a few coenzymes cycle continuously between their oxidized and reduced forms, just as adenosine cycles continuously between its triphosphate and diphosphate forms.

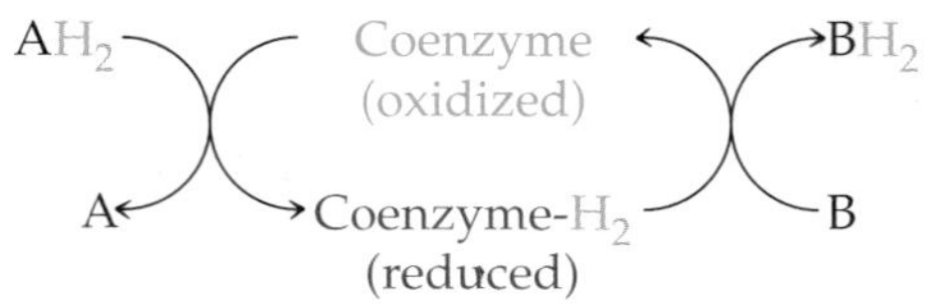

Table 21.2 lists some important cycling coenzymes in their oxidized and reduced forms. The oxidized form acts as an oxidizing agent for a reaction while the reduced form acts as a reducing agent for the reverse reaction. For example, lactate is oxidized by lactate dehydrogenase in the presence of NAD^+ (oxidizing agent) to pyruvate; in the reverse reaction pyruvate is reduced in the presence of NADH (reducing agent) to lactate.

Table 21.2 Oxidized and Reduced Forms of Important Coenzymes

Coenzyme	Oxidized Form	Reduced Form
Nicotinamide adenine dinucleotide	NAD^+	$NADH/H^+$
Nicotinamide adenine dinucleotide phosphate	$NADP^+$	$NADPH/H^+$
Flavin adenine dinucleotide	FAD	$FADH_2$
Flavin mononucleotide	FMN	$FMNH_2$

To review briefly, keep in mind these important points about oxidation and reduction:

- Oxidation can be loss of electrons, loss of hydrogen, or addition of oxygen.
- Reduction can be gain of electrons, gain of hydrogen, or loss of oxygen.
- Oxidation and reduction always occur together.

Each increase in the number of carbon–oxygen bonds is an oxidation, and each increase in the number of carbon–hydrogen bonds is a reduction, as shown in Figure 21.6. Oxidation of carbon increases by increased bonding to oxygen.

The coenzymes nicotinamide adenine dinucleotide (NAD^+/NADH) and nicotinamide adenine dinucleotide phosphate ($NADP^+$/NADPH) are ubiquitous in cells and organelles, where they participate in oxidation/reduction reactions in conjunction with oxidoreductases. As oxidizing agents, NAD^+ and $NADP^+$ remove hydrogen from a substrate, and as reducing agents, NADH and NADPH provide hydrogen that adds to a substrate. Some enzymes, such as lactate dehydrogenase, require the cofactor NAD^+/NADH, while enzymes involved in fatty acid synthesis require $NADP^+$/NADPH as the cofactor. The complete structure of NAD^+ is shown with the change that converts it to NADH. The only difference between the structures of NAD^+/NADH and $NADP^+$/NADPH is that the color-shaded —OH group in NAD^+/NADH is instead a —OPO_3^{2-} group in $NADP^+$ and NADPH.

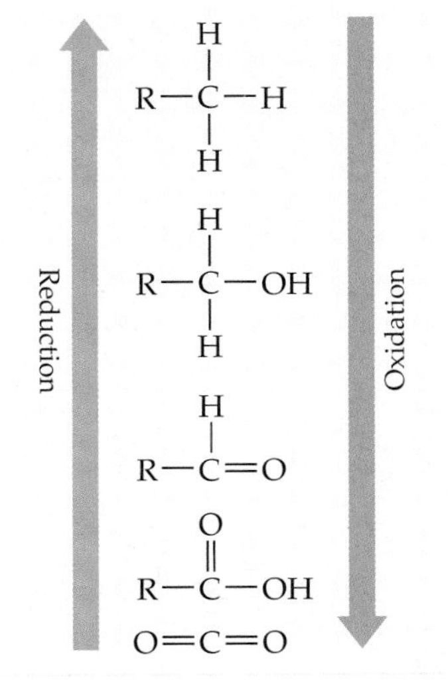

▲ **Figure 21.6**
Oxidation of carbon by increased bonding to oxygen

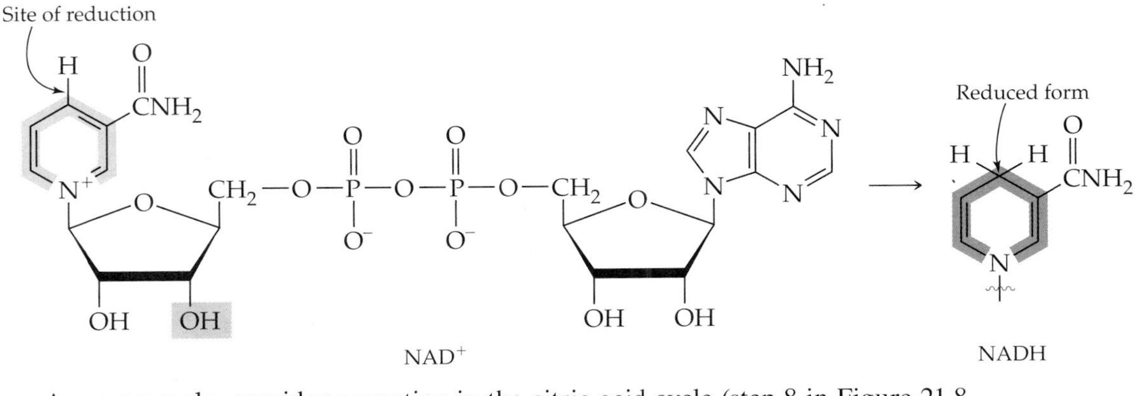

As an example, consider a reaction in the citric acid cycle (step 8 in Figure 21.8, Section 21.7) from the oxidation–reduction, or redox, point of view.

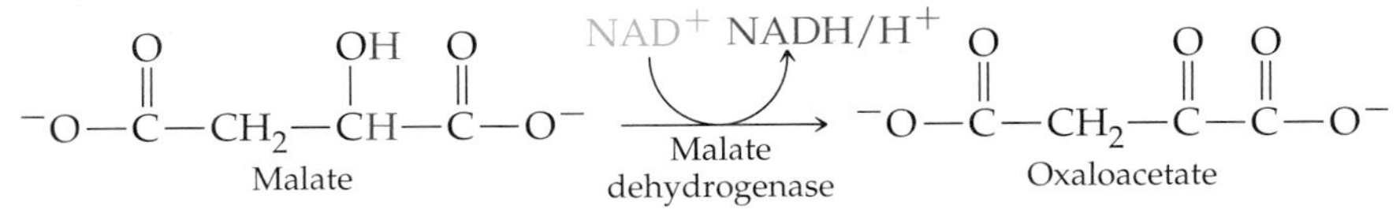

Oxidation of malate to oxaloacetate requires the removal of two hydrogen atoms to convert a secondary alcohol to a ketone. The oxidizing agent, which will be reduced

◀◀ Recall from Section 15.1 that a ketone is $R_2C{=}O$.

during the reaction, is NAD^+, functioning as a *coenzyme* for the enzyme malate dehydrogenase. Sometimes NAD^+ is written as a reactant or product to emphasize its role in a reaction. Keep in mind that although it is free to enter and leave the active site, it always functions as a coenzyme with the appropriate enzyme for the reaction.

When considering enzyme-catalyzed redox reactions, it is important to recognize that a hydrogen atom is equivalent to a hydrogen *ion*, H^+, plus an electron, e^-. Thus, for the two hydrogen atoms removed in the oxidation of malate,

$$2H \text{ atoms} = 2H^+ + 2e^-$$

When NAD^+ is reduced, both electrons accompany one of the hydrogen atoms to give a hydride ion,

$$H^+ + 2e^- = :H^-$$

The reduction of NAD^+ occurs by addition of H^- to the ring in the nicotinamide part of the structure, where the two electrons of H^- form a covalent bond.

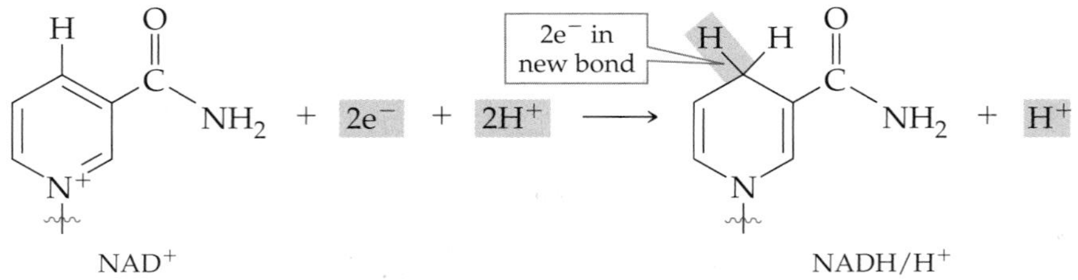

NAD$^+$ NADH/H$^+$

The second hydrogen removed from the oxidized substrate enters the surrounding aqueous solution as a hydrogen ion, H^+. The product of NAD^+ reduction is therefore often represented as $NADH/H^+$ to show that two hydrogen atoms have been removed from the reactant, one of which has bonded to NAD^+ and the other of which is a hydrogen ion in solution. ($NADP^+$ is reduced in the same way to form $NADPH/H^+$.)

Flavin adenine dinucleotide (FAD), another common oxidizing agent in catabolic reactions, is reduced by the formation of covalent bonds to two hydrogen atoms to give $FADH_2$. It participates in several reactions of the citric acid cycle, which is described in the next section.

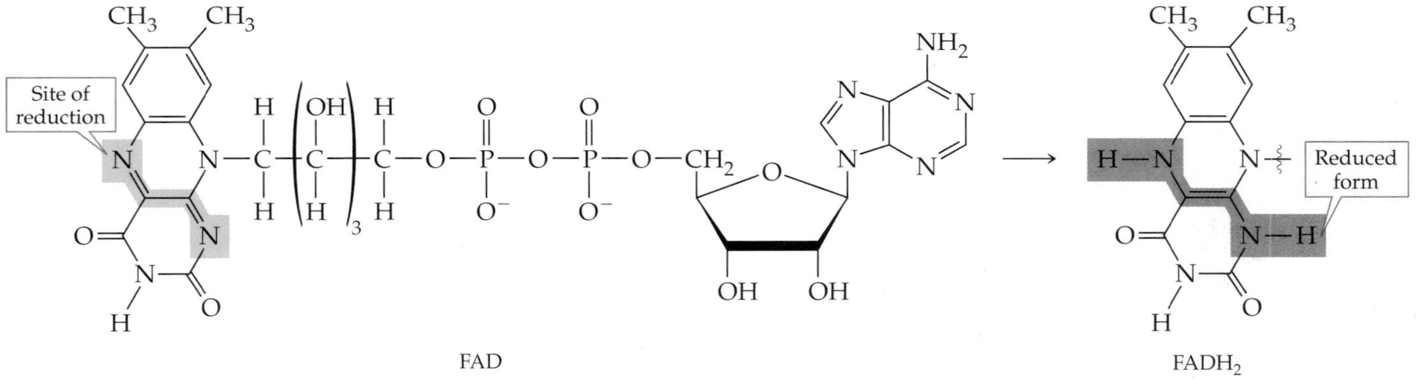

FAD   FADH$_2$

Because the reduced coenzymes, NADH and $FADH_2$, have picked up electrons (in their bonds to hydrogen) that are passed along in subsequent reactions, they are often referred to as *electron carriers*. As these coenzymes cycle through their oxidized and reduced forms, they also carry energy along from reaction to reaction. Ultimately, this energy is passed on to the bonds in ATP, as described in Section 21.8.

PROBLEM 21.9

Which of the following is found in the coenzyme FAD?
(a) Two heterocyclic rings   (b) ADP
(c) A substituted benzene ring   (d) A phosphate anhydride bond

PROBLEM 21.10

Look ahead to Figure 21.8 for the citric acid cycle. (a) Draw the structures of the reactants in steps 3, 6, and 8, and indicate which hydrogen atoms are removed in these reactions. (b) What class of enzymes carry out these reactions?

21.7 The Citric Acid Cycle

Learning Objective:

• Describe the reactions in the citric acid cycle and explain its role in energy production.

The carbon atoms from the first two stages of catabolism are carried into the third stage as acetyl groups bonded to coenzyme A. Like the phosphoryl groups in ATP molecules, the acetyl groups in acetyl-SCoA molecules are readily removed in an energy-releasing hydrolysis reaction.

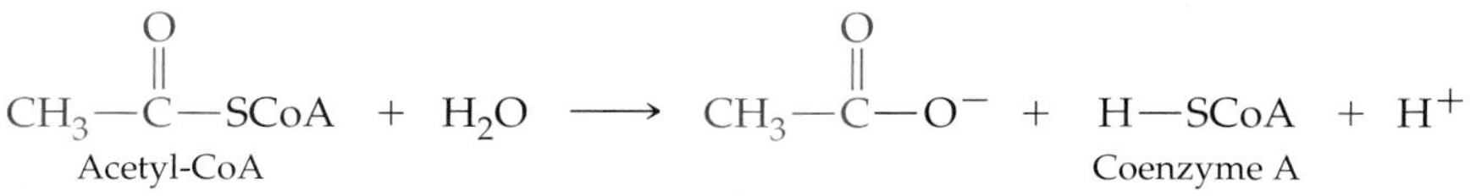

$$CH_3 \overset{\overset{O}{\|}}{-C} -SCoA \; + \; H_2O \; \longrightarrow \; CH_3 \overset{\overset{O}{\|}}{-C} -O^- \; + \; H-SCoA \; + \; H^+ \qquad \begin{array}{l} \Delta G = -7.5 \text{ kcal/mol} \\ (\Delta G = -31.4 \text{ kJ/mol}) \end{array}$$

Acetyl-CoA   Coenzyme A

Oxidation of two carbons to give two CO_2 and transfer of energy to reduced coenzymes occur in the **citric acid cycle,** also known as the *tricarboxylic acid cycle (TCA)* or *Krebs cycle* (after Sir Hans Krebs, who unraveled its complexities in 1937). As its name implies, the citric acid *cycle* is a closed loop of reactions in which the product of the final step, oxaloacetate, a 4-carbon molecule, is the reactant in the first step. The pathway of carbon atoms through the cycle and the significant products formed are summarized in Figure 21.7 and shown in greater detail in Figure 21.8. The two carbon atoms of the acetyl group add to the four carbon atoms of oxaloacetate in step 1, and two carbon atoms are set free as carbon dioxide in steps 3 and 4. The cycle continues as 4-carbon intermediates progress toward regeneration of oxaloacetate and production of additional reduced coenzymes.

A brief description of the eight steps of the citric acid cycle is given in Figure 21.8. The enzymes involved in each step are listed in the accompanying table. The cycle takes place in mitochondria, where seven of the enzymes are dissolved in the matrix and one (for step 6) is embedded in the inner mitochondrial membrane. The citric acid cycle is not reversible in an organism, although some enzymes of the cycle can carry out the reverse reaction in a test tube.

The cycle operates as long as acetyl groups are available from acetyl-CoA and the oxidizing agent coenzymes NAD^+ and FAD are available. Since these compounds are not stored, the reduced coenzymes NADH and $FADH_2$ must be reoxidized via the electron-transport chain in Stage 4 of catabolism (described in Section 21.8). Because Stage 4 relies on oxygen as the final electron acceptor, the cycle is also dependent upon the availability of oxygen. The steps of the citric acid cycle are summarized next.

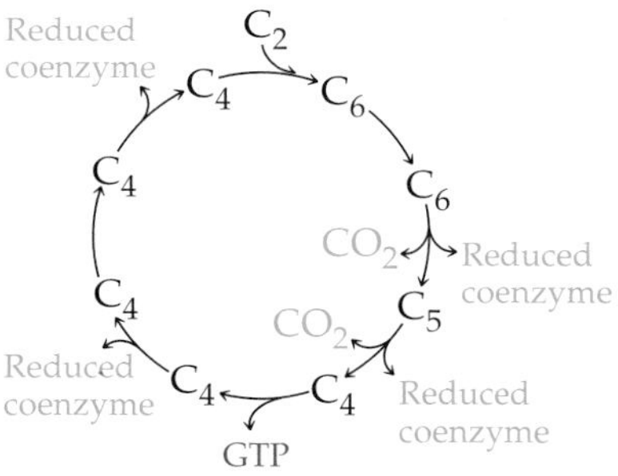

STEP 1: Addition of acetate from acetyl-CoA by citrate synthase to 4-carbon oxaloacetate yields citrate, a 6-carbon intermediate in the cycle. Citrate is a tertiary alcohol and cannot be oxidized. $\Delta G = -7.7 \text{ kcal/mol}\ (-32.2\text{ kJ/mol})$.

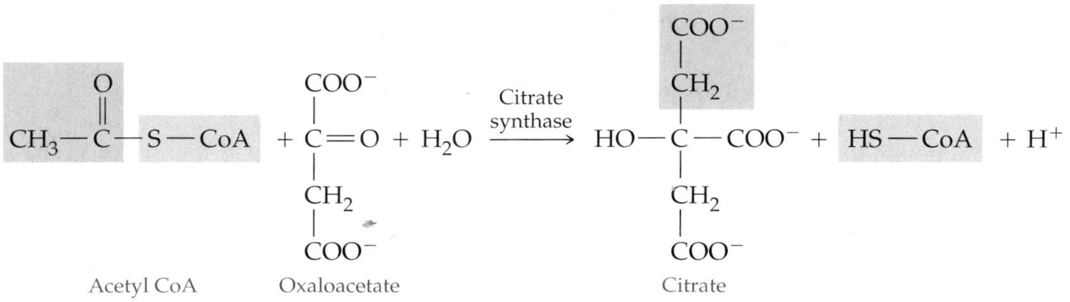

Citric acid cycle The series of biochemical reactions that breaks down acetyl groups to produce energy carried by reduced coenzymes and carbon dioxide.

▲ **Figure 21.7**
Significant outcomes of the citric acid cycle.
For every acetyl-CoA the eight steps of the cycle produce two molecules of carbon dioxide, four molecules of reduced coenzymes, and one energy-rich phosphate (GTP). The final step regenerates the reactant for step 1 of the next turn of the cycle. (step 1 occurs where C_2 enters the cycle to form C_6 by adding to C_4.)

Acetyl CoA   Oxaloacetate   Citrate

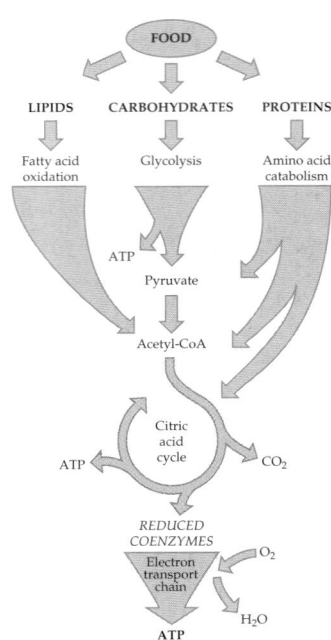

STEP 2: Conversion of citrate to its isomer isocitrate, a secondary alcohol that can be oxidized, is done in a two-step reaction with both steps catalyzed by aconitase. Water is removed, creating a temporary double bond, and then added back to the intermediate, which remains in the active site, so that the −OH is on a different carbon atom. $\Delta G = +3.2$ kcal/mol ($+13.3$ kJ/mol)

Citrate $\xrightarrow[\text{Aconitase}]{-\,H_2O}$ Aconitate $\xrightarrow[\text{Aconitase}]{+\,H_2O}$ Isocitrate

STEP 3: Isocitrate is oxidized to α-ketoglutarate by isocitrate dehydrogenase with the simultaneous reduction of NAD^+ to NADH and the release of CO_2. α-Ketoglutarate is a 5-carbon molecule with a ketone group. $\Delta G = -2.0$ kcal/mol (-8.4 kJ/mol)

Isocitrate $+$ NAD^+ $\xrightarrow{\text{Isocitrate dehydrogenase}}$ α-Ketoglutarate $+$ CO_2 $+$ $NADH + H^+$

STEP 4: α-Ketoglutarate dehydrogenase converts α-ketoglutarate to succinate in a reaction requiring CoA and NAD^+. The products of the reaction are succinyl-CoA, $NADH/H^+$, and CO_2. Succinyl-CoA carries four carbon atoms along to the next step. $\Delta G \doteq -8.0$ kcal/mol (-33.5 kJ/mol)

α-Ketoglutarate $+$ NAD^+ $+$ $HS-CoA$ $\xrightarrow{\text{$\alpha$-Ketoglutarate dehydrogenase}}$ Succinyl CoA $+$ CO_2 $+$ $NADH + H^+$

Guanosine diphosphate (GDP)
An energy-carrying molecule that can gain or lose a phosphoryl group to transfer energy.

Guanosine triphosphate (GTP)
An energy-carrying molecule similar to ATP; removal of a phosphoryl group to give GDP releases free energy.

STEP 5: This step begins rebuilding oxaloacetate for the next turn of the cycle. Conversion of succinyl-CoA to succinate by succinyl-CoA synthetase is coupled with phosphorylation of **guanosine diphosphate (GDP)** to give **guanosine triphosphate (GTP).** GTP is immediately converted to ATP by coupling the GTP to GDP reaction with the ADP to ATP reaction. This is the only step in the cycle that generates an energy-rich triphosphate. $\Delta G = -0.7$ kcal/mol (-2.9 kJ/mol)

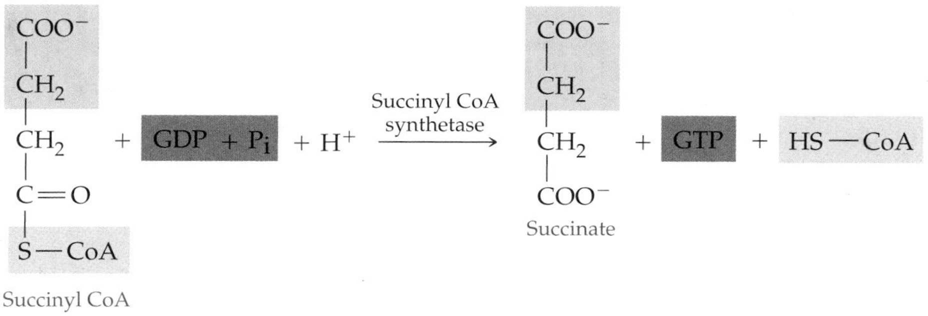

STEP 6: Succinate is oxidized by succinate dehydrogenase to yield fumarate, a 4-carbon molecule containing a carbon–carbon double bond. FAD is reduced to $FADH_2$ in this reaction. FAD is covalently bonded to succinate dehydrogenase, which is embedded in the inner mitochondrial membrane. Succinate dehydrogenase and FAD participate in Stage 4 of catabolism by passing electrons directly into electron transport. $\Delta G = 0$ kcal/mol (0 kJ/mol)

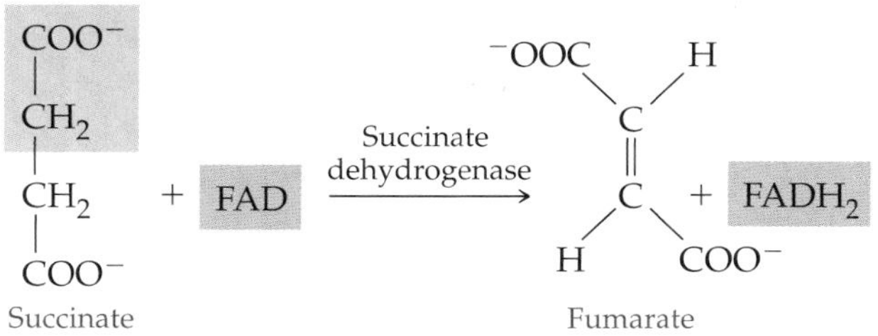

STEP 7: Fumarase adds water across the double bond of fumarate to give malate, which contains a secondary alcohol group. $\Delta G = -0.9$ kcal/mol (-3.8 kJ/mol)

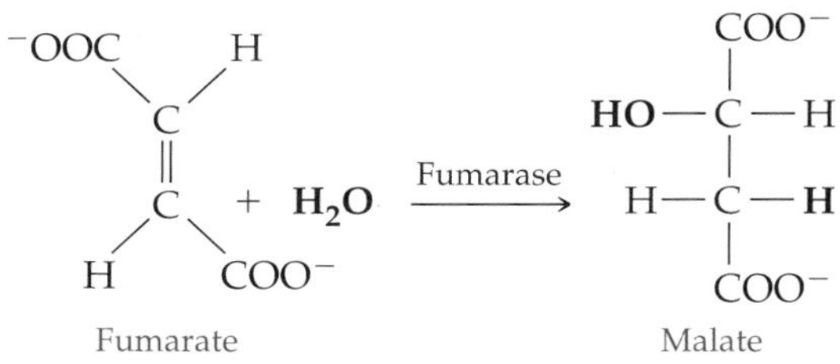

STEP 8: Malate dehydrogenase oxidizes malate to oxaloacetate, changing the secondary alcohol to a ketone group. At the same time NAD^+ is reduced to $NADH/H^+$. Oxaloacetate has been regenerated for the next turn of the cycle. $\Delta G = +7.1$ kcal/mol ($+29.7$ kJ/mol)

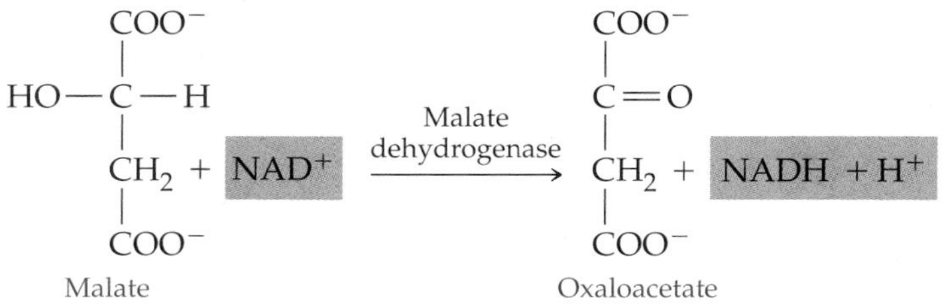

Net result of citric acid cycle

Acetyl-CoA + 3NAD$^+$ + FAD + GDP + HOPO$_3^{2-}$ + H$_2$O $\longrightarrow$ HSCoA + 3NADH + 3H$^+$
$+ FADH_2 + GTP + 2CO_2$

- Production of four reduced coenzyme molecules (3NADH, 1FADH$_2$)
- Conversion of an acetyl group to two CO$_2$ molecules
- Production of one energy-rich molecule (GTP, *converted immediately to ATP*)

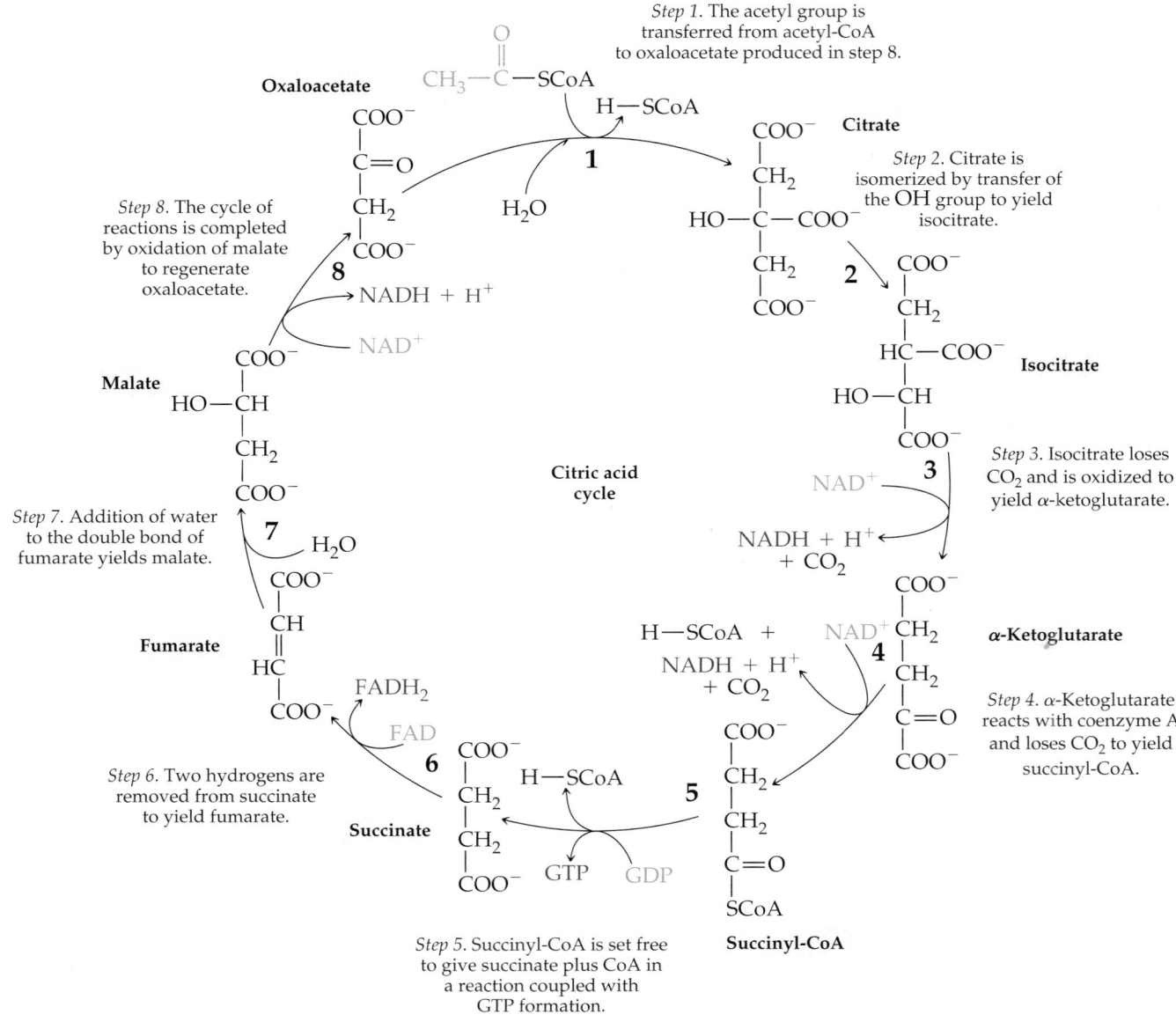

Step 1. The acetyl group is transferred from acetyl-CoA to oxaloacetate produced in step 8.

Step 2. Citrate is isomerized by transfer of the OH group to yield isocitrate.

Step 3. Isocitrate loses CO_2 and is oxidized to yield α-ketoglutarate.

Step 4. α-Ketoglutarate reacts with coenzyme A and loses CO_2 to yield succinyl-CoA.

Step 5. Succinyl-CoA is set free to give succinate plus CoA in a reaction coupled with GTP formation.

Step 6. Two hydrogens are removed from succinate to yield fumarate.

Step 7. Addition of water to the double bond of fumarate yields malate.

Step 8. The cycle of reactions is completed by oxidation of malate to regenerate oxaloacetate.

Enzymes of the Citric Acid Cycle

Step	Enzyme Name	Enzyme Class/Subclass	Reaction Product
1	Citrate synthase	Lyase/synthase	Citrate
2	Aconitase	Lyase/dehydrase	Isocitrate
3	Isocitrate dehydrogenase complex	Oxidoreductase/oxidase	α-Ketoglutarate
4	α-Ketoglutarate dehydrogenase complex	Oxidoreductase/oxidase	Succinyl-CoA
5	Succinyl-CoA synthetase	Ligase/synthetase	Succinate
6	Succinate dehydrogenase	Oxidoreductase/oxidase	Fumarate
7	Fumarase	Lyase/dehydrase	Malate
8	Malate dehydrogenase	Oxidoreductase/oxidase	Oxaloacetate

▲ **Figure 21.8**
The citric acid cycle.
The net effect of this eight-step cycle of reactions is the metabolic breakdown of acetyl groups (from acetyl-CoA) into two molecules of carbon dioxide and energy carried by reduced coenzymes. Here and throughout this and the following chapters, energy-rich reactants or products (ATP, reduced coenzymes) are shown in red and their lower-energy counterparts (ADP, oxidized coenzymes) are shown in blue.

The rate of the citric acid cycle is controlled by the body's cellular need for ATP and reduced coenzymes and for the energy derived from them. For example, when energy is being used at a high rate, ADP accumulates and acts as an allosteric activator (positive regulator, see Section 19.7) for isocitrate dehydrogenase, the enzyme for step 3 and for α-ketoglutarate dehydrogenase, the enzyme for step 4. When the body's supply of energy is abundant, ATP and NADH are present in excess and act as inhibitors of both of those enzymes. By such feedback mechanisms, as well as by variations in the concentrations of necessary reactants, the cycle is activated when energy is needed and inhibited when energy is in good supply.

Worked Example 21.4 Identifying Reactants and Products in the Citric Acid Cycle

What substance(s) are the substrate(s) for the citric acid cycle? What are the products of the citric acid cycle?

ANALYSIS Study Figure 21.8. Note that acetyl-CoA feeds into the cycle but does not come out anywhere. Can you see that all of the other reaction substrates are integral to the cycle and are always present, being continuously synthesized and degraded? Note also that the coenzymes NAD^+ and FAD are reduced and the reduced versions are considered energy-carrying products of the cycle. Also, CO_2 is produced at two different steps in the cycle. Finally, GDP is converted to GTP in step 5 of the cycle.

SOLUTION
Acetyl-CoA is the substrate for the cycle. Along with GDP and CoA, the oxidized coenzymes NAD^+ and FAD might also be considered substrates, despite their status as coenzymes, because these substances cycle between the reduced and oxidized states. The products of the cycle are CO_2 and the energy-rich reduced coenzymes $NADH/H^+$ and $FADH_2$ as well as GTP.

PROBLEM 21.11

Which substances in the citric acid cycle are tricarboxylic acids (thus giving the cycle its alternative name)?

PROBLEM 21.12

In Figure 21.11, identify the steps at which reduced coenzymes are produced.

PROBLEM 21.13

Why, do you suppose, the coenzyme for the reaction in the citric acid cycle that is catalyzed by succinate dehydrogenase is FAD and not NAD^+?

PROBLEM 21.14

Identify the participants in the citric acid cycle that contain alcohol groups. Identify these groups as primary, secondary, or tertiary alcohols.

PROBLEM 21.15

Which of the reactants in the citric acid cycle have two chiral carbon atoms?

▣ KEY CONCEPT PROBLEM 21.16 ─────────

The citric acid cycle can be divided into two stages. In one stage, carbon atoms are added and removed, and in the second stage, oxaloacetate is regenerated. Which steps of the citric acid cycle correspond to each stage?

21.8 The Electron-Transport Chain and ATP Production

Learning Objective:

• Describe the electron-transport chain, oxidative phosphorylation, and how the two processes are coupled.

Keep in mind that in some ways catabolism is just like burning fuel oil. In both cases, the goal is to produce useful energy and the reaction products are water and carbon

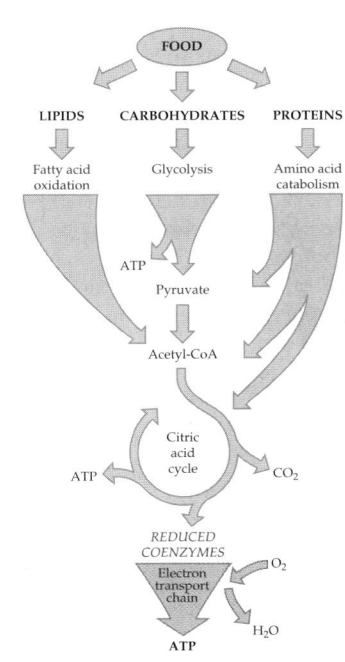

dioxide. The difference is that in catabolism the products are not released all at once and not all of the energy is released as heat.

For each turn of the citric acid cycle, the reduced coenzymes formed during the turn donate their energy to making additional ATP. The energy is released in a series of oxidation–reduction reactions that move electrons from one electron carrier to the next as each carrier is reduced (gains an electron from the preceding carrier) and then oxidized (loses an electron by passing it along to the next carrier). Each reaction in the series is favorable; that is, it is exergonic. You can think of each reaction as a step along the way down a waterfall. The sequence of reactions that move the electrons along is known as the **electron-transport chain or system (ETS)** and is also called the *respiratory chain*. The enzymes and coenzymes of the chain and ATP synthesis are embedded in the inner membrane of the mitochondrion (Figure 21.9).

In the last step of the chain, the electrons combine with the oxygen that we breathe and with hydrogen ions from their surroundings to produce water.

$$O_2 + 4e^+ + 4H^+ \longrightarrow 2H_2O$$

This reaction is fundamentally the combination of hydrogen and oxygen gases. Carried out all at once with the gases themselves, the reaction is explosive. What happens to all that energy during electron transport?

As electrons move down the electron-transport pathway, the energy released is used to move hydrogen ions out of the mitochondrial matrix by crossing the inner membrane and into the intermembrane space. Because the inner membrane is otherwise impermeable to the H^+ ion, the result is a higher H^+ concentration in the intermembrane space than in the mitochondrial matrix. Moving ions from a region of lower concentration to one of higher concentration opposes the natural tendency for random motion to equalize concentrations throughout a mixture and therefore requires energy to make it happen. This energy is recaptured for use in ATP synthesis.

Electron Transport

Electron transport proceeds via four enzyme complexes held in fixed positions within the inner membrane of mitochondria, along with two electron carriers that move through the membrane from one complex to another. The complexes and mobile electron carriers are organized in the sequence of their ability to pick up electrons, as illustrated in Figure 21.9. The four fixed complexes are very large assemblages of polypeptides and electron acceptors. The most important electron acceptors are of three types: (1) various cytochromes that are proteins that contain heme groups (Figure 21.9a) in which the

Electron-transport chain The series of biochemical reactions that passes electrons from reduced coenzymes to oxygen and is coupled to ATP formation. Also called the respiratory chain.

▶ **Figure 21.9**
A heme group and a cytochrome.
(a) Heme groups, in which the substituents at the bonds marked in red vary, are iron-containing coenzymes in the cytochromes of the electron-transport chain. They are also the oxygen carriers in hemoglobin in red blood cells.
(b) In the cytochrome shown here, the coiled blue ribbon is the amino acid chain and the heme group is in red.

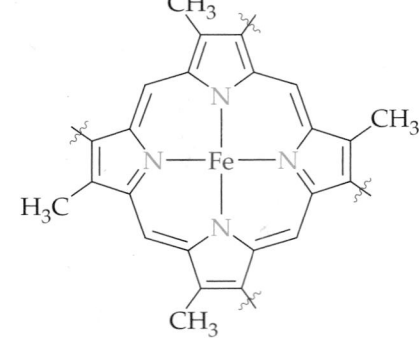

(a) A heme group

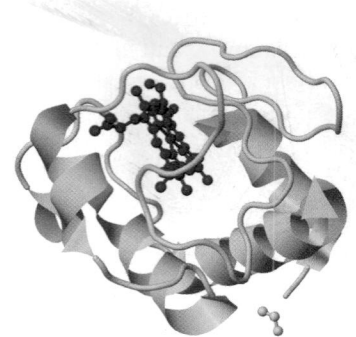

(b) A representative cytochrome protein

iron cycles between Fe^{2+} and Fe^{3+}; (2) proteins containing iron–sulfur groups in which the iron also cycles between Fe^{2+} and Fe^{3+}; and (3) coenzyme Q (CoQ), often known as *ubiquinone* because of its ubiquitous (widespread) occurrence and because its ring structure with the two ketone groups is a *quinone*.

The details of the reactions that move electrons in the electron-transport chain are not important here. Focus only on the following essential features of the pathway (Figure 21.10; refer also to Figure 21.11).

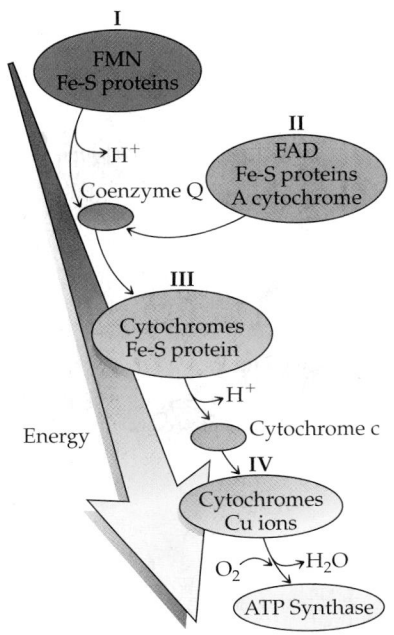

◄ **Figure 21.10**
Pathway of electrons in electron transport.
Each of the enzyme complexes I–IV contains several electron carriers. FMN in complex I is similar in structure to FAD. Hydrogen ions and electrons move through the components of the electron-transport pathway in the direction of the arrow. Energy is transferred, with some loss, at each complex; each succeeding complex is at a lower energy level than the preceding, as indicated by the color change.

- Hydrogen ions and electrons from NADH and $FADH_2$ enter the electron-transport chain at enzyme complexes I and II, respectively. These complexes function independently and not necessarily in numerical order. The enzyme for step 6 of the citric acid cycle is part of complex II, where $FADH_2$ is produced when that step of the cycle occurs. $FADH_2$ does not leave complex II. It is immediately oxidized there by reaction with mobile coenzyme Q, forming QH_2. After formation of reduced mobile coenzyme QH_2, hydrogen ions no longer participate directly in the reductions of electron carriers. Instead, electrons are transferred directly, one by one from carrier to carrier.
- Electrons are passed from weaker to increasingly stronger oxidizing agents, with energy released at each transfer. Much of this energy is conserved during the transfer; however, some energy is used to pump protons across the inner mitochondrial membrane, and some is lost as heat at each electron transfer.
- Hydrogen ions are released for transport through the inner mitochondrial membrane to the intermembrane space at complexes I, III, and IV, creating an H^+ gradient, with the intermembrane space becoming acidic and the matrix alkaline due to changes in H^+ concentration. Some of these ions come from the reduced coenzymes and some from the matrix—exactly how the hydrogen ions are transported to the intermembrane space is not yet fully understood, although the process appears to be via an energy-requiring pump.
- The H^+ concentration difference creates a potential energy difference across the two sides of the inner membrane (like the energy difference between water at the top and bottom of a waterfall). The maintenance of this concentration gradient across the membrane is *crucial*—it is the mechanism by which energy for ATP formation is made available.

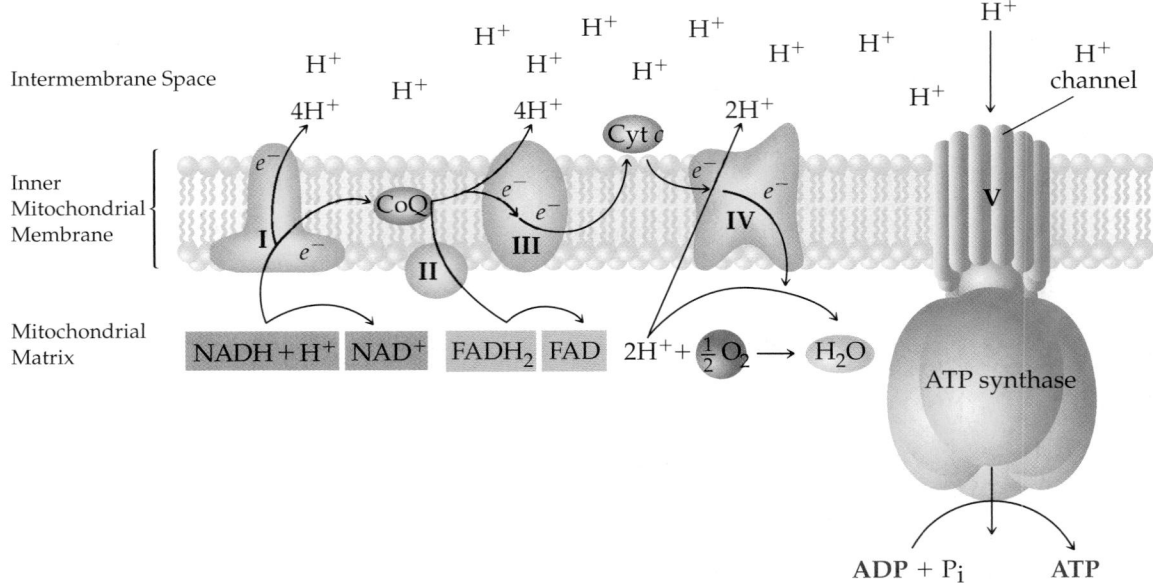

▲ **Figure 21.11**
The mitochondrial electron-transport chain and ATP synthase.
The arrows show the path of electrons and the hydrogen ions. The movement of hydrogen ions across the inner membrane at complexes I, III, and IV creates a higher concentration of hydrogen ions on the intermembrane side of the inner membrane than on the matrix side. The energy released by hydrogen ions returning to the matrix through ATP synthase provides the energy needed for ATP synthesis.

Plant cells, like animal cells, contain mitochondria and carry out oxidative phosphorylation. In addition, plant cells also contain chloroplasts, organelles that are similar to mitochondria but instead carry out photosynthesis, a series of reactions that also involve electron and hydrogen ion transfer through a series of enzyme complexes arranged in an electron transport chain. See the Chemistry in Action "Plants and Photosynthesis" on page 662 for more information.

ATP Synthesis

Oxidative phosphorylation The synthesis of ATP from ADP using energy released in the electron-transport chain.

ATP synthase The enzyme complex in the inner mitochondrial membrane where hydrogen ions cross the membrane and ATP is synthesized from ADP.

The reactions of the electron-transport chain are tightly coupled to **oxidative phosphorylation,** the conversion of ADP to ATP, by a reaction that is both an oxidation and a phosphorylation. Hydrogen ions can return to the matrix only by passing through a channel that is part of the **ATP synthase** enzyme complex. In doing so, they release the potential energy gained as they were moved against the concentration gradient at the enzyme complexes of the electron-transport chain. This energy release drives the phosphorylation of ADP by reaction with hydrogen phosphate ion $\left(HOPO_3^{2-}\right)$.

$$ADP + HOPO_3^{2-} \longrightarrow ATP + H_2O$$

ATP synthase has knob-tipped stalks that protrude into the matrix and are clearly visible in electron micrographs. ADP and $\left(HOPO_3^{2-}\right)$ are attracted into the knob portion. As hydrogen ions flow through the complex, ATP is produced and released back into the matrix. The reaction is facilitated by changes in the shape of the enzyme complex that are induced by the flow of hydrogen ions.

How much ATP energy is produced from a molecule of NADH or a molecule of $FADH_2$ by oxidative phosphorylation? The electrons from molecules of NADH enter the electron-transport chain at complex I, while those from $FADH_2$ enter at complex II. These different entry points into the electron-transport chain result in different yields of ATP molecules. In this book, we use the yields of three ATP molecules generated for every NADH molecule and two ATP molecules generated from every $FADH_2$ molecule during oxidative phosphorylation.

PROBLEM 21.17

Within the mitochondrion, is the pH higher in the intermembrane space or in the mitochondrial matrix? Why?

PROBLEM 21.18

Plants carry out both photosynthesis and oxidative phosphorylation (see the Chemistry in Action "Plants and Photosynthesis" on p. 662). Photosynthesis occurs in chloroplasts, while oxidative phosphorylation occurs in mitochondria. Name some similarities and some differences between photosynthesis and oxidative phosphorylation.

KEY CONCEPT PROBLEM 21.19

The reduced coenzymes NADH and $FADH_2$ are oxidized in the ETS. What is the final electron acceptor of the ETS? What is the function of the H^+ ion in ATP synthesis?

CHEMISTRY IN ACTION

✚ Metabolic Poisons

Cyanide and barbiturates such as sodium amytal have long been known to be so dangerous—even fatal—that mystery writers often use these substances in their books as murder weapons. What makes them so dangerous? They are among a group of substances that block respiration (oxidative phosphorylation) at one of the electron transfer stages, resulting in blockage of electron flow through the ETS and cessation of ATP production. Blockers interfere with electron transfer in several ways. Barbiturates act as reversible inhibitors while inorganic ions like CN^- (cyanide) and HS^- bind tightly to Fe^{2+} and Cu^{2+} in cytochromes acting as irreversible inhibitors and preventing electron transfer. CO and CN^- bind to the heme groups present in cytochromes preventing electron transfer in mitochondria. Blocking of electron transport is an emergency for the organism. Because ATP is not stored, continuous production of ATP at tightly regulated levels is crucial to an organism's survival. ATP is the energy link between the oxidation of fuels and energy-requiring processes. Without continuous ATP production, the organism will die.

A second category of molecules act as uncouplers of electron transport. These molecules allow electron transport to occur but prevent the conversion of ADP to ATP by ATP synthase. If this happens, the rate of oxygen use increases as the proton gradient between the mitochondrial matrix and the intermembrane space dissipates, with the simultaneous formation of water but no ATP.

When ATP production is severed from energy use, we say ATP production is *uncoupled* from the energy of the proton gradient. One chemical that has this effect, once used as a weight-reducing drug is 2,4-dinitrophenol (DNP). Occupational exposure in a munitions factory during World War I led to the first deaths from DNP.

However, during the 1930's DNP, available as an over-the-counter drug, was used as a weight-loss aid. Yes, indeed, taking DNP resulted in rapid weight loss without dieting. It seemed to be the ideal weight-loss aid. But, DNP ingestion also results in an increase in body temperature to fever levels, sweating, shortness of breath, and rapid heart rate. Some users of DNP develop cataracts or skin lesions and animal studies suggest DNP is a carcinogen. Aside from these side effects, a major difficulty with DNP is that the toxic dose is very close to the therapeutic dose. Ingesting a toxic dose often results in death.

As a supplement and not a drug, DNP is not regulated by any government agency and is available for use. DNP is particularly popular with bodybuilders and athletes with a recent increase in use and accidental abuse. Jasmine, the bodybuilder discussed at the beginning of the chapter, was sculpting her body for competition, using diet pills containing DNP in addition to exercise. When she increased the dosage for faster results, she ingested a lethal dose and the ER staff was unable to save her life.

CIA Problem 21.11 Why is DNP no longer recommended as a weight-loss aid?

CIA Problem 21.12 How does a blocker of respiration work?

CIA Problem 21.13 How does an uncoupler of respiration work?

SUMMARY REVISITING THE LEARNING OBJECTIVES

- **Identify energy sources and our specific requirements for energy regulation.** We derive energy by oxidation of food molecules that contain energy captured by plants from sunlight. The energy is released gradually in exergonic reactions and is available to do work, to drive endergonic reactions, to provide heat, or to be stored until needed. Energy generation in eukaryotic cells takes place in mitochondria *(see Problems 20, 27–32, and 76).*

- **Explain the significance of exergonic and endergonic reactions in metabolism.** *Exergonic* reactions are favorable, proceed spontaneously, and release free energy. *Endergonic* reactions are unfavorable and require an external source of free energy to occur *(see Problems 20 and 27–29).*

- **Describe the eukaryotic cell and explain the function of each structure.** The eukaryotic cell is a membrane-bound entity containing a number of specialized organelles in a nutrient- and protein-rich fluid called the cytosol. See Figure 21.2 *(see Problems 33–38).*

- **List the stages in catabolism of food and describe the role of each stage.** Food molecules undergo *catabolism* (are broken down) to provide energy in four stages (Figure 21.4): (1) digestion to form smaller molecules that can be absorbed into cells; (2) decomposition (by separate pathways for lipids, carbohydrates, and proteins) into two-carbon acetyl groups that are bonded to coenzyme A in *acetyl coenzyme A*; (3) reaction of the acetyl groups via the *citric acid cycle* to generate energy-rich reduced coenzymes and liberate carbon dioxide; and (4) *electron transport* and transfer of the energy of the reduced coenzymes from the citric acid cycle to our principal energy transporter, ATP *(see Problems 21 and 39–42).*

- **Describe the role of ATP in energy transfer.** Using the energy from exergonic reactions, ADP is *phosphorylated* to give ATP. Where energy must be expended, it is released by removal of a phosphoryl group from ATP to give back ADP *(see Problems 22, 43, and 44).*

- **Explain why some reactions are coupled and give an example of a coupled reaction.** An otherwise "uphill" reaction in a metabolic pathway is driven by coupling with an exergonic, "downhill" reaction that provides enough energy that their combined outcome is exergonic and favorable *(see Problems 45–48).*

- **Give an example of a coenzyme changing from oxidized to reduced form in a reaction and explain the purpose.** The oxidizing and reducing agents needed by the many redox reactions of metabolism are coenzymes that constantly cycle between their oxidized and reduced forms *(see Problems 23, 49, 50, 79, and 81).*

- **Describe the reactions in the citric acid cycle and explain its role in energy production.** The *citric acid cycle* (Figure 21.8) is a cyclic pathway of eight reactions, in which the product of the final reaction is the substrate for the first reaction. The reactions of the citric acid cycle (1) set the stage for oxidation of the acetyl group (steps 1 and 2); (2) remove two carboxyl groups as CO_2 molecules (oxidative decarboxylation) from the tricarboxylic acid isocitrate (steps 3 and 4); and (3) oxidize the 4-carbon dicarboxylic acid succinate and regenerate oxaloacetate so that the cycle can start again (steps 5–8). Along the way, four reduced coenzyme molecules and one molecule of GTP (converted immediately to ATP) are produced for each acetyl group oxidized. The reduced coenzymes carry energy for the subsequent production of additional ATP. The cycle is activated when energy is in short supply and inhibited when energy is in good supply *(see Problems 24, 25, 51–58, 77, and 78).*

- **Describe the electron-transport chain, oxidative phosphorylation, and how the two processes are coupled.** ATP generation is accomplished by a series of enzyme complexes in the inner membranes of mitochondria (Figure 21.9). Electrons and hydrogen ions enter the first two complexes of the electron-transport chain from succinate (in the citric acid cycle), NADH, and $FADH_2$, where they are transferred to *coenzyme Q*. Then, the electrons and hydrogen ions proceed independently; the electrons gradually give up their energy to the transport of hydrogen ions across the inner mitochondrial membrane to maintain different concentrations on opposite sides of the membrane. The hydrogen ions return to the matrix by passing through *ATP synthase*, where the energy they release is used to convert ADP to ATP *(see Problems 26, 59–75, and 80).*

KEY WORDS

Acetyl-coenzyme A (acetyl-CoA), *p. 665*
Adenosine triphosphate (ATP), *p. 663*
Anabolism, *p. 665*
ATP synthase, *p. 682*
Catabolism, *p. 664*
Citric acid cycle, *p. 675*
Cytoplasm, *p. 663*
Cytosol, *p. 663*
Electron-transport chain, *p. 680*
Guanosine diphosphate (GDP), *p. 676*
Guanosine triphosphate (GTP), *p. 676*
Metabolism, *p. 664*
Mitochondrial matrix, *p. 663*
Mitochondrion, *p. 663*
Oxidative phosphorylation, *p. 682*
Pathway, *p. 661*

CONCEPT MAP: THE GENERATION OF BIOCHEMICAL ENERGY

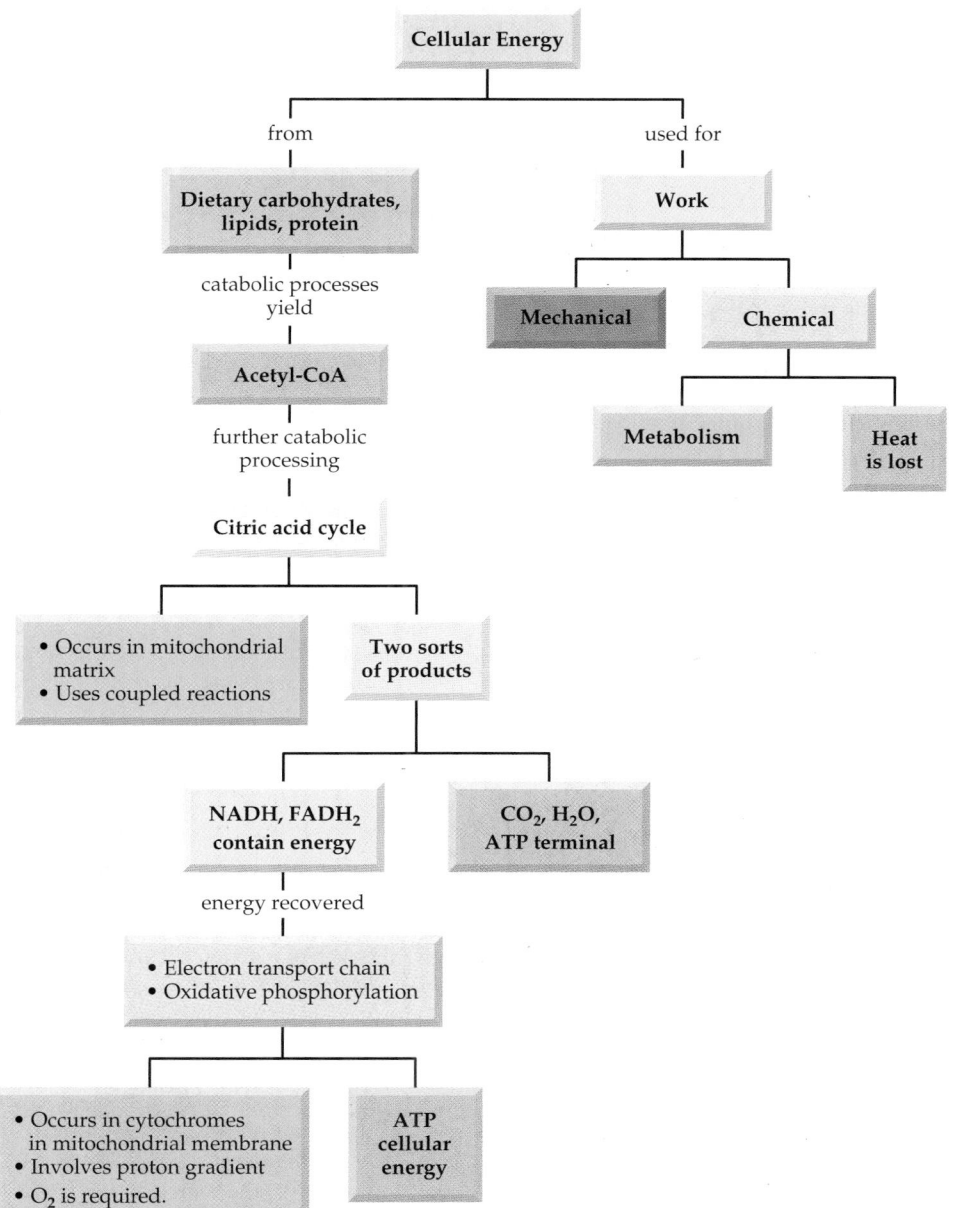

▲ **Figure 21.12 Concept Map.** This concept map shows both the uses and the sources of cellular energy by focusing on the generation of ATP from the total oxidation of acetyl-CoA through the citric acid cycle and recovery of the energy stored in the NADH and $FADH_2$ produced in the cycle. This energy is recovered by the ETS coupled with oxidative phosphorylation to yield ATP. All of these processes follow the principles of thermodynamics, which are connected to these concepts. The concept map above summarizes the ideas in this chapter and shows their connection to Figure 7.7 through thermodynamics.

UNDERSTANDING KEY CONCEPTS

21.20 The following coupled reaction is the result of an exergonic reaction and an endergonic reaction:

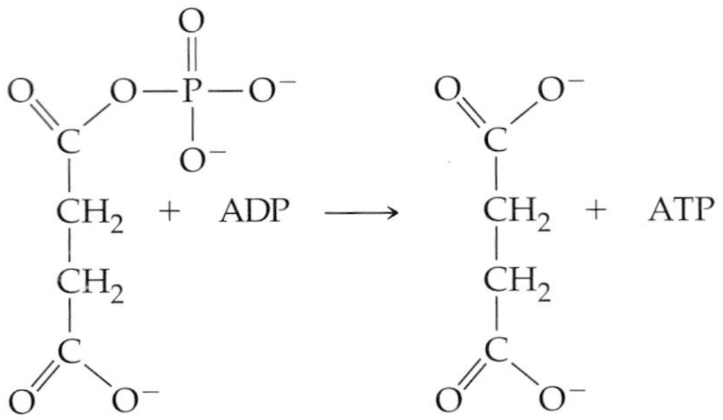

Succinyl phosphate   Succinate

   (a) Write the exergonic portion of the reaction.

   (b) Write the endergonic portion of the reaction.

21.21 Each of these reactions is involved in one of the four stages of metabolism shown in Figure 21.4. Identify the stage in which each reaction occurs.

   (a) Hydrolysis of starch to produce glucose

   (b) Oxidation of NADH coupled with synthesis of ATP

   (c) Conversion of glucose to acetyl-CoA

   (d) Oxidation of acetyl-CoA in a series of reactions where NAD^+ is reduced and CO_2 is produced

21.22 For the first step in fatty acid catabolism, we say that ATP is used to "drive" the reaction that links the fatty acid with coenzyme-A. Without ATP hydrolysis, would you predict that the linking of fatty acid to coenzyme-A would be exergonic or endergonic? In fatty acid CoA synthesis, the hydrolysis of the ATP portion is based on what major strategy of metabolism?

21.23 Since no molecular oxygen participates in the citric acid cycle, the steps in which acetyl groups are oxidized to CO_2 involve removal of hydride ions and hydrogen ions. What is the acceptor of hydride ions? What is the acceptor of hydrogen ions?

21.24 The reaction that follows is catalyzed by isocitrate dehydrogenase and occurs in two steps, the first of which

ADDITIONAL PROBLEMS

FREE ENERGY AND BIOCHEMICAL REACTIONS (SECTION 21.1)

21.27 What energy requirements must be met in order for a reaction to be favorable?

21.28 What is the difference between an endergonic process and an exergonic process?

21.29 Why is ΔG a useful quantity for predicting the favorability of biochemical reactions?

21.30 Many biochemical reactions are catalyzed by enzymes. Do enzymes have an influence on the magnitude or sign of ΔG? Why or why not?

(step A) is formation of an unstable intermediate (shown in brackets).

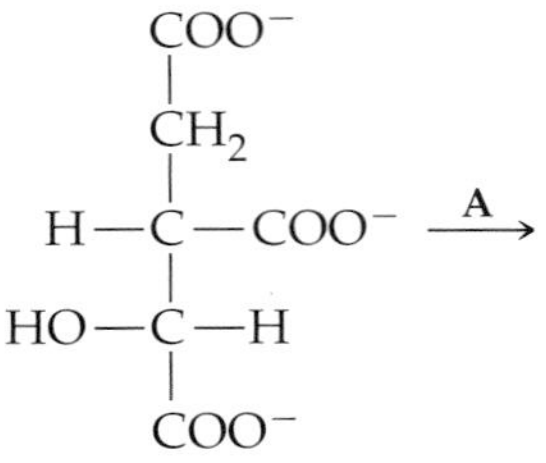

Isocitrate

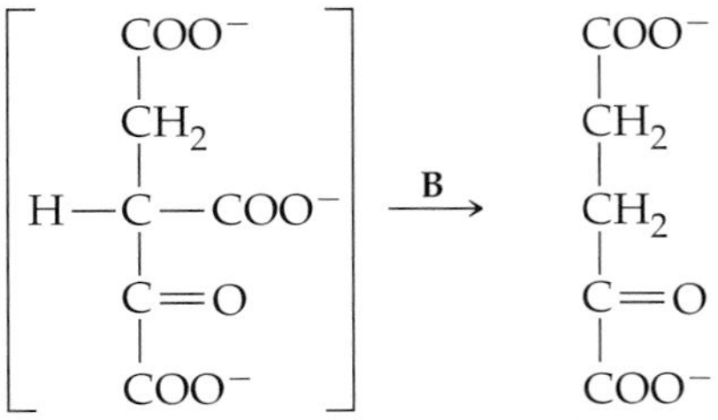

α-Ketoglutarate

   (a) In which step is a coenzyme needed? Identify the coenzyme.

   (b) In which step is CO_2 evolved and a hydrogen ion added?

   (c) Which of the structures shown can be described as a β-keto acid?

   (d) To what class of enzymes does isocitrate dehydrogenase, the enzyme that catalyzes this reaction, belong?

21.25 For each of the eight reactions in the citric acid cycle, give the type of reaction occurring, name the enzyme involved, and indicate which of the six classes of enzymes it belongs to. Some may have more than one kind of enzyme activity.

21.26 The electron-transport chain uses several different metal ions, especially iron, copper, zinc, and manganese. Why are metals used frequently in these two pathways? What can metals do better than organic biomolecules?

21.31 The following reactions occur during the catabolism of acetyl-CoA. Which are exergonic? Which is endergonic? Which reaction produces a phosphate that later yields energy by giving up a phosphate group?

   (a) Succinyl-CoA + GDP + Phosphate (P_i) →
   $$\text{Succinate} + \text{CoA-SH} + \text{GTP} + H_2O$$
   $\Delta G = -0.4 \, \text{kcal/mol} \, (-1.67 \, \text{kJ/mol})$

   (b) Acetyl-CoA + Oxaloacetate → Citrate + CoA-SH
   $\Delta G = -8 \, \text{kcal/mol} \, (-33.5 \, \text{kJ/mol})$

   (c) L-Malate + NAD^+ → Oxaloacetate + NADH + H^+
   $\Delta G = +17 \, \text{kcal/mol} \, (+129.3 \, \text{kJ/mol})$

21.32 The following reactions occur during the catabolism of glucose. Which are exergonic? Which is endergonic? Which proceeds farthest toward products at equilibrium?

   (a) 1,3-Biphosphoglycerate $+$ $H_2O \rightarrow$
$$3\text{-Phosphoglycerate} + P_i$$
$$\Delta G = -11.8 \text{ kcal/mol} (-49.4 \text{ kJ/mol})$$

   (b) Phosphoenol pyruvate $+$ $H_2O \rightarrow$
$$\text{Pyruvate} + \text{Phosphate} (P_i)$$
$$\Delta G = -14.8 \text{ kcal/mol} (-61.9 \text{ kJ/mol})$$

   (c) Glucose $+$ $P_i \rightarrow$ Glucose 6-phosphate $+$ H_2O
$$\Delta G = +3.3 \text{ kcal/mol} (+13.8 \text{ kJ/mol})$$

CELLS AND THEIR STRUCTURE (SECTION 21.2)

21.33 Which of the following organisms are prokaryotes, and which are eukaryotes?

   (a) Humans

   (b) The bacteria responsible for "strep throat"

   (c) Carrots

   (d) Brewer's yeast

21.34 Label each of the following as a characteristic of a prokaryote or a eukaryote.

   (a) DNA is surrounded by a membrane

   (b) Has a cell wall as well as a cell membrane

   (c) Contains chloroplasts

   (d) Lives in specialized groups termed organs

   (e) Single-celled organisms

21.35 What is the difference between the cytoplasm and the cytosol?

21.36 What is an organelle?

21.37 Describe in general terms the structural makeup of a mitochondrion.

21.38 What is the function of cristae in the mitochondrion?

METABOLISM (SECTION 21.3)

21.39 What is the difference between catabolism and anabolism?

21.40 What is the difference between digestion and metabolism?

21.41 Arrange the following events in the order in which they occur in a catabolic process: electron transport, digestion, oxidative phosphorylation, citric acid cycle.

21.42 What key metabolic intermediate is formed from the catabolism of all three major classes of foods: carbohydrates, lipids, and proteins?

METABOLISM (SECTIONS 21.4–21.6)

21.43 Why is ATP sometimes called a high-energy molecule?

21.44 What general kind of chemical reaction does ATP participate in?

21.45 What does it mean when we say that two reactions are coupled?

21.46 Show why coupling the reaction for the hydrolysis of 1,3-bisphosphoglycerate to the phosphorylation of ADP is energetically favorable. Combine the equations and calculate ΔG for the coupled process. You need only give names or abbreviations in your equations not chemical structures.

21.47 Write the reaction for the hydrolysis of 1,3-bisphosphoglycerate coupled to the phosphorylation of ADP using the curved-arrow symbolism.

21.48 Is the hydrolysis of fructose 6-phosphate favorable for phosphorylating ADP? Why or why not? Refer to Table 21.1. If not, what would make this reaction favorable?

21.49 FAD is a coenzyme for dehydrogenation.

   (a) When a molecule is dehydrogenated, is FAD oxidized or reduced?

   (b) Is FAD an oxidizing agent or a reducing agent?

   (c) What type of substrate is FAD associated with, and what is the type of product molecule after dehydrogenation?

   (d) What is the form of FAD after dehydrogenation?

   (e) Use the curved-arrow symbolism to write a general equation for a reaction involving FAD.

21.50 NAD^+ is a coenzyme for dehydrogenation.

   (a) When a molecule is dehydrogenated, is NAD^+ oxidized or reduced?

   (b) Is NAD^+ an oxidizing agent or a reducing agent?

   (c) What type of substrate is NAD^+ associated with, and what type of product molecule is formed after dehydrogenation?

   (d) What is the form of NAD^+ after dehydrogenation?

   (e) Use the curved-arrow symbolism to write a general equation for a reaction involving NAD^+.

THE CITRIC ACID CYCLE (SECTION 21.7)

21.51 What is the purpose of the citric acid cycle?

21.52 Where in the cell does the citric acid cycle take place?

21.53 What substance acts as the starting point of the citric acid cycle, reacting with acetyl-CoA in the first step and being regenerated in the last step? Draw its structure.

21.54 What is the final fate of the carbons in acetyl-CoA after several turns of the citric acid cycle?

21.55 Look at the eight steps of the citric acid cycle (Figure 21.8) and answer the following questions:

   (a) Which steps involve oxidation reactions?

   (b) Which steps involve decarboxylation (loss of CO_2)?

   (c) Which step or steps involve a hydration reaction?

21.56 How many NADH and how many $FADH_2$ molecules are formed in the citric acid cycle?

21.57 Which reactions of the citric acid cycle transfer energy as $FADH_2$?

21.58 Which reactions of the citric acid cycle transfer energy as NADH?

THE ELECTRON-TRANSPORT CHAIN; OXIDATIVE PHOSPHORYLATION (SECTION 21.8)

21.59 What are the two primary functions of the electron-transport chain?

21.60 How are the processes of the citric acid cycle and the electron-transport chain interrelated?

21.61 What two coenzymes are involved with initial events of the electron-transport chain?

21.62 What are the ultimate products of the electron-transport chain?

21.63 Where are the following found in the cell?

(a) FAD

(b) CoQ

(c) NADH/H$^+$

(d) Cytochrome c

21.64 What do the following abbreviations stand for?

(a) FAD

(b) CoQ

(c) NADH/H$^+$

(d) Cytochrome c

21.65 What atom in the cytochromes undergoes oxidation and reduction in the electron-transport chain? What atoms in coenzyme Q undergo oxidation and reduction in the electron-transport chain?

21.66 Put the following substances in the correct order of their action in the electron-transport chain: cytochrome *c*, coenzyme Q, and NADH.

21.67 Fill in the missing substances in these coupled reactions:

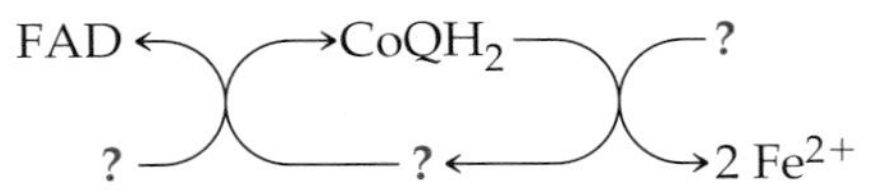

$$FAD \longleftarrow \quad \longrightarrow CoQH_2 \longrightarrow \quad ?$$
$$? \longrightarrow \quad ? \longleftarrow \quad \longrightarrow 2\ Fe^{2+}$$

21.68 What would happen to the citric acid cycle if NADH and FADH$_2$ were not reoxidized?

21.69 What does the term "oxidative phosphorylation" mean? What is substrate-level phosphorylation? Are these processes the same? Explain.

21.70 In oxidative phosphorylation, what is oxidized and what is phosphorylated?

21.71 Oxidative phosphorylation has three reaction products.

(a) What is the energy-carrying product?

(b) What are the other two products?

21.72 What supplies the energy to drive oxidative phosphorylation?

21.73 The antibiotic piericidin, a nonpolar molecule, is structurally similar to ubiquinone (coenzyme Q) and can cross the mitochondrial membrane. What effect might the presence of piericidin have on oxidative phosphorylation?

21.74 When oxidative phosphorylation is uncoupled, does oxygen consumption decrease, increase, or stay the same? Explain.

21.75 Which animal would you expect to have more brown fat (provides heat by uncoupling ATP production), a seal or a domestic cat? Explain.

CONCEPTUAL PROBLEMS

21.76 Why must the breakdown of molecules for energy in the body occur in several steps, rather than in one step?

21.77 The first step in the citric acid cycle involves the reaction of acetyl-CoA and oxaloacetate. Show the product of this reaction before hydrolysis to yield citrate.

21.78 Fumarate produced in step 6 of the citric acid cycle must have a *trans* double bond to continue on in the cycle. Suggest a reason why the corresponding *cis* double-bond isomer cannot continue in the cycle.

21.79 With what class of enzymes are the coenzymes NAD$^+$ and FAD associated?

21.80 We talk of burning food in a combustion process, producing CO$_2$ and H$_2$O from food and O$_2$. Explain how O$_2$ is involved in the process although no O$_2$ is directly involved in the citric acid cycle.

21.81 One of the steps that occurs when lipids are metabolized is shown here. Does this process require FAD or NAD$^+$ as the coenzyme? What is the general class of enzyme that catalyzes this process?

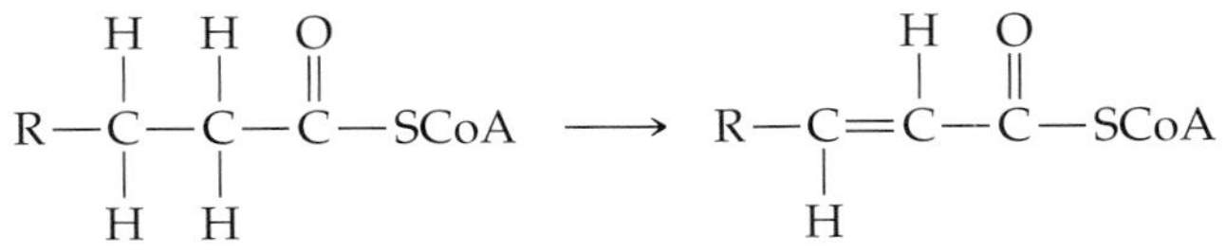

21.82 If you use a flame to burn a pile of glucose completely to give carbon dioxide and water, the overall reaction is identical to the metabolic oxidation of glucose. Explain the differences in the fate of the energy released in each case.

21.83 The mitochondrion pumps H$^+$ from the matrix into the intermembrane space. Which region is more acidic, the matrix or the intermembrane space? Why?

21.84 Does any step of the citric acid cycle directly produce ATP? Explain.

21.85 The citric acid cycle contains four 4-carbon dicarboxylic acids.

(a) Name them.

(b) Arrange them in order from least oxidized to most oxidized.

21.86 Sometimes, ATP is referred to as the "energy-storage molecule." The cell does not actually store energy as a lot of extra ATP but as glycogen or triacylglycerides. Why do you suppose this is the case?

GROUP PROBLEMS

21.87 Sodium fluoroacetate $(FH_2CCOO^- Na^+)$ is highly toxic. Patients with fluoroacetate poisoning accumulate citrate and fluorocitrate in their cells. Which enzyme is inhibited by fluoroacetate for this to occur? Explain.

21.88 After running a mile, you stop and breathe heavily for a short period due to oxygen debt. Why do you need to breathe so heavily? (Hint: Look up "oxygen debt" on the Web. Which metabolic pathway requires oxygen?)

21.89 Put in order, from lowest to highest number of mitochondria per cell, the following tissues: adipose tissue (regular), brain, heart muscle, skin, skeletal muscle. Explain your reasoning. You may need to consult the Web.

22

Carbohydrate Metabolism

CONTENTS

◄◄◄ CONCEPTS TO REVIEW

▲ The simple and complex carbohydrates in this meal provide fuel for metabolism.

Maria, age 40 years, has a doctor's appointment because she has been feeling somewhat ill for several months. In addition, she sometimes feels confused, is often thirsty despite adequate fluid intake, and urinates more frequently. One day, while grocery shopping, she realizes her vision is so blurry she cannot read the package labels. Her doctor does a typical exam, noting that Maria is overweight for her height (body mass index [BMI] = 30) and has elevated blood pressure. There is a history of heart disease and diabetes in her family. Her doctor orders a typical blood panel that includes measuring glucose, cholesterol, and triacylglycerides, as well as enzymes that reflect liver and kidney function. He also orders a glucose tolerance test, an A1C test, which measures the amount of glycated hemoglobin (an indicator of blood glucose levels over several months), and schedules a return visit. He suspects Type II diabetes because of her age and symptoms but must have the test results to confirm this guess. Type II diabetes more commonly develops in middle age.

Diabetes is a common consequence of faulty glucose metabolism regulation. During carbohydrate metabolism, glucose is converted to acetyl-coenzyme A (acetyl-CoA) for entrance into the citric acid cycle, it's stored as glycogen and released for use, and synthesized when glucose is in short supply. Because of the importance of glucose, the body has several strategies for regulating the glucose concentration in blood and providing glucose to cells that depend on it. This chapter discusses those strategies and carbohydrate metabolism as a whole.

22.1 Digestion of Carbohydrates

Learning Objective:

- Describe carbohydrate digestion, where it takes place in the body, the enzymes involved, and name the major products of the process.

The first stage in catabolism is **digestion,** the breakdown of food into small molecules. Digestion entails the physical grinding, softening, and mixing of food, as well as enzyme-catalyzed hydrolysis of carbohydrates, proteins, and fats. Digestion begins in the mouth, continues in the stomach, and concludes in the small intestine.

The products of digestion are mostly small molecules that are absorbed from the intestinal tract. Nutrients are absorbed through millions of tiny projections (the *villi*) in the intestinal lining and transferred into the bloodstream. The bloodstream transports these small molecules into target cells, where they may be broken down completely to release energy as their carbon atoms are converted to carbon dioxide. Others are excreted, and some are used as building blocks to synthesize new biomolecules.

The digestion of carbohydrates is summarized in Figure 22.1. Salivary α-amylase catalyzes the hydrolysis of α glycosidic bonds in amylose and amylopectin—plant starches. Starches from plants and glycogen from meat are hydrolyzed to give smaller polysaccharides and the disaccharide maltose. Plant cellulose, with its β glycosidic bonds linking glucose molecules together, is not digested by humans. Salivary α-amylase continues to act upon dietary polysaccharides in the stomach until the enzyme is inactivated by stomach acid. No further carbohydrate digestion takes place in the stomach.

α-Amylase is also secreted by the pancreas and enters the small intestine, where conversion of polysaccharides to maltose continues. Maltase, sucrase, and lactase are secreted from the mucous lining of the small intestine and hydrolyze maltose, sucrose, and lactose to the monosaccharides glucose, fructose, and galactose, which are transported across the intestinal wall into the bloodstream. The focus in this chapter is on the metabolism of glucose; both fructose and galactose can be converted to intermediates that enter the same metabolic pathway followed by glucose.

22.2 Glucose Metabolism: An Overview

Learning Objective:

- Identify the pathways by which glucose is first synthesized and then broken down, and describe their interrelationships.

Glucose is the major fuel for your body. It is the preferred fuel for the brain, working muscle cells, and red blood cells. Through a series of metabolic oxidations, the energy stored in glucose is converted to ATP energy and used to power other reactions within the cell. The initial metabolic fate of glucose is conversion into pyruvate and then usually to acetyl-CoA, the common intermediate in the catabolism of all foods. Acetyl-CoA delivers

Digestion A general term for the breakdown of food into small molecules.

◀◀ **CONCEPTS TO REVIEW** Recall from Section 20.7 that the plant starches amylose and amylopectin, plant cellulose, and glycogen (animal starch) are all large polymers of glucose. Plant starches and glycogen are digestible, whereas cellulose is not.

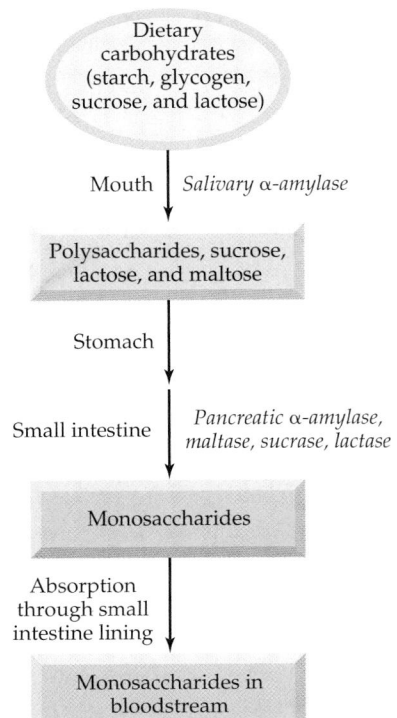

▲ **Figure 22.1**
The digestion of carbohydrates.

691

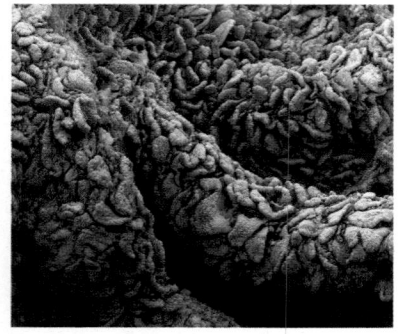

▲ A micrograph showing *villi*, the projections that line the small intestine. Each villus is covered with microvilli, where the digested food molecules are absorbed into the bloodstream.

acetyl groups to the citric acid cycle for oxidation, with the energy captured transferred through the electron transport system, resulting ultimately in the formation of ATP. We discussed the citric acid cycle and the electron transport chain in Chapter 21.

Glycolysis is the first of two sequential, catabolic pathways leading to ATP synthesis as a result of electron transfer. When glucose enters a cell from the bloodstream, it is immediately converted to glucose 6-phosphate. Once phosphorylated, glucose is trapped within the cell because phosphorylated molecules cannot cross the cell membrane unaided by a transporter. Like the first step in many metabolic pathways, the formation of glucose 6-phosphate is highly exergonic and not reversible in the glycolytic pathway, thereby committing the initial substrate to the subsequent reactions.

Several pathways are available to glucose 6-phosphate.

- When energy is needed, glucose 6-phosphate moves down the central catabolic pathway shown in light brown in Figure 22.2, proceeding via the reactions of *glycolysis* to pyruvate and then to acetyl-CoA, which enters the citric acid cycle (discussed in Section 21.7).

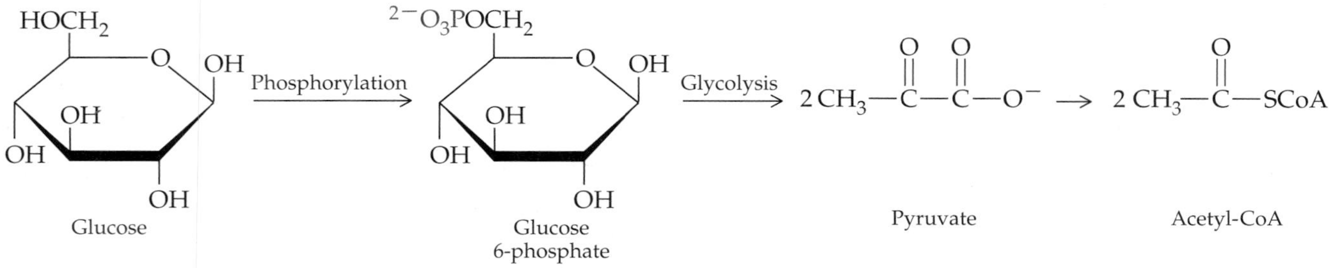

Glucose —Phosphorylation→ Glucose 6-phosphate —Glycolysis→ $2\ CH_3-C(=O)-C(=O)-O^- \rightarrow 2\ CH_3-C(=O)-SCoA$

Glucose | Glucose 6-phosphate | Pyruvate | Acetyl-CoA

- When cells are well supplied with glucose, excess glucose is converted to other forms for storage: into glycogen, the glucose storage polymer, by the *glycogenesis* pathway, or into fatty acids by entrance of acetyl-CoA into the pathways of lipid metabolism (Chapter 24) rather than the citric acid cycle.

Pentose phosphate pathway The biochemical pathway that produces ribose (a pentose), NADPH, and other sugar phosphates from glucose; an alternative to glycolysis.

- Glucose 6-phosphate can also enter the **pentose phosphate pathway.** This multistep pathway yields two products important to our metabolism. One is a supply of the coenzyme nicotinamide adenine dinucleotide phosphate (NADPH), a reducing agent that is essential for many biochemical reactions. The other is ribose 5-phosphate, which is the precursor for the synthesis of nucleic acids (deoxyribonucleic acid [DNA] and ribonucleic acid [RNA]). Glucose 6-phosphate enters the pentose phosphate pathway when a cell's need for NADPH or ribose 5-phosphate exceeds its need for ATP.

PROBLEM 22.1

Name the following pathways:

(a) Pathway for synthesis of glycogen

(b) Pathway for release of glucose from glycogen

(c) Pathway for synthesis of glucose from lactate

PROBLEM 22.2

Name the synthetic pathways that have glucose 6-phosphate as their first reactant.

22.3   Glycolysis

Learning Objective:

- Describe the glycolysis pathway and its products.

Glycolysis The biochemical pathway that breaks down a molecule of glucose into two molecules of pyruvate plus energy.

Glycolysis is a series of 10 enzyme-catalyzed reactions that converts a glucose molecule into two pyruvate molecules and in the process yields two ATP molecules and two NADH molecules. The steps of glycolysis are summarized in Figure 22.3, where the reactions and structures of intermediates should be noted as you read the following paragraphs. Almost all organisms carry out glycolysis; in humans it occurs in the cytosol of all cells.

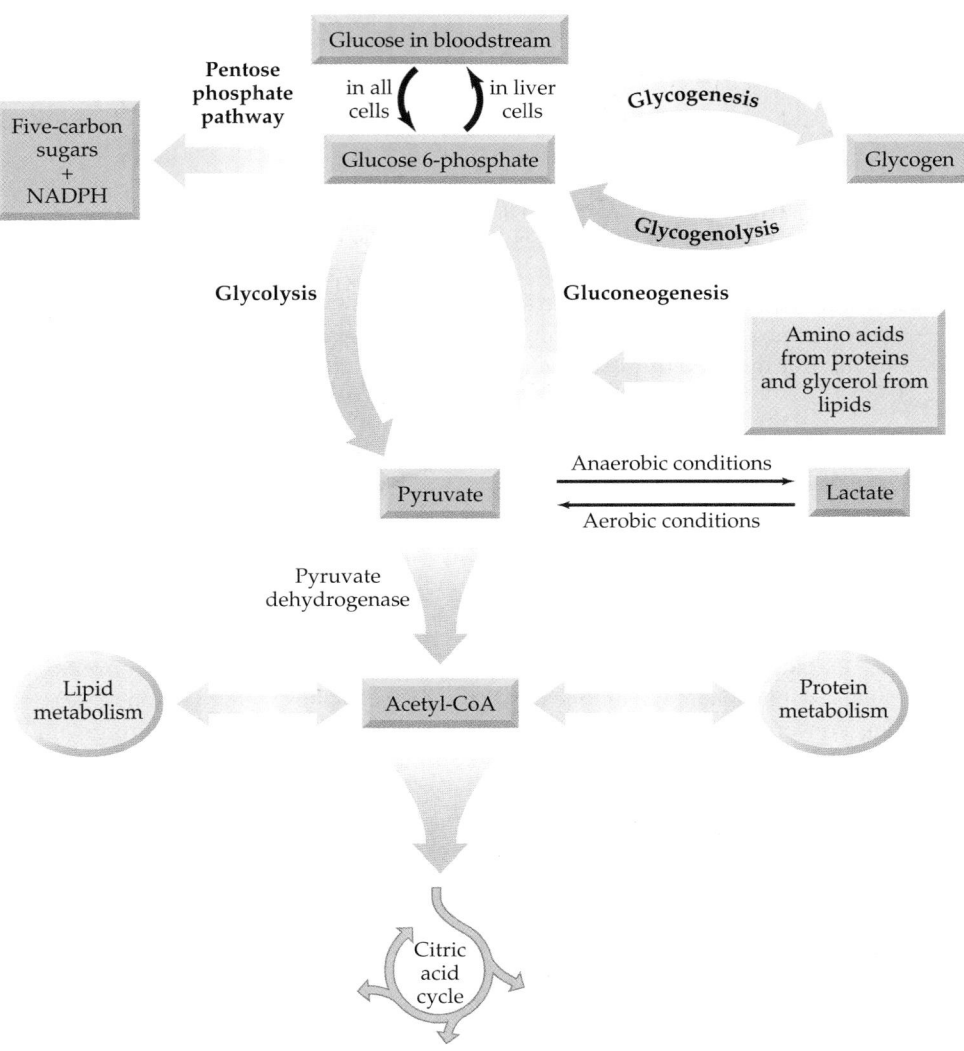

◄ Figure 22.2
Glucose metabolism.
Synthetic pathways (anabolism) are shown in blue, pathways that break down biomolecules (catabolism) are shown in light brown, and connections to lipid and protein metabolism are shown in green.

Metabolic Pathways of Glucose

Name	Derivation of Name	Function
Glycolysis (Section 22.3)	*glyco-*, glucose (from Greek, meaning "sweet") *-lysis*, decomposition	Conversion of glucose to pyruvate
Gluconeogenesis (Section 22.9)	*gluco-*, glucose *-neo-*, new *-genesis*, creation	Synthesis of glucose from amino acids, pyruvate, and other noncarbohydrates
Glycogenesis (Section 22.8)	*glyco(gen)-*, glycogen *-genesis*, creation	Synthesis of glycogen from glucose
Glycogenolysis (Section 22.8)	*glycogen-*, glycogen *-lysis*, decomposition	Breakdown of glycogen to glucose
Pentose phosphate pathway (Section 22.2)	*pentose-*, a five-carbon sugar	Conversion of glucose to five-carbon sugar phosphates

Steps 1–5 are referred to as the *energy investment* part of glycolysis. So far, two ATP molecules have been invested and no income earned, but the stage is now set for a small energy profit. Note that since one glucose molecule yields two glyceraldehyde 3-phosphate molecules that pass separately down the rest of the pathway, steps 6–10 of glycolysis each take place twice for every glucose molecule that enters at step 1. *Energy generation,* the second half of glycolysis (steps 6–10) is devoted to generating molecules with phosphate groups that can be transferred to ATP.

◄◄ Phosphorylation is the transfer of a phosphoryl group ($-PO_3^{2-}$) from one molecule to another (see Section 17.6).

◄◄ Review enzyme regulation by allosteric control in Section 19.7.

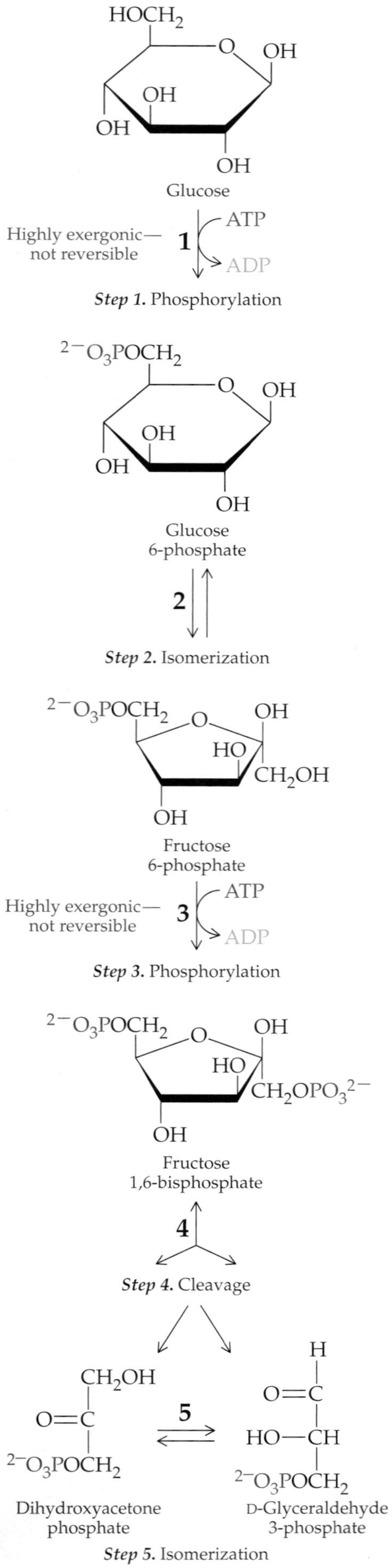

Glucose

Highly exergonic— not reversible **1** ATP → ADP

Step 1. Phosphorylation

Glucose
6-phosphate

2

Step 2. Isomerization

Fructose
6-phosphate

Highly exergonic— not reversible **3** ATP → ADP

Step 3. Phosphorylation

Fructose
1,6-bisphosphate

4

Step 4. Cleavage

$2^-O_3POCH_2$

$O=C$

CH_2OH $O=C$ **5** H $O=C$ $HO-CH$ $2^-O_3POCH_2$

Dihydroxyacetone
phosphate

D-Glyceraldehyde
3-phosphate

Step 5. Isomerization

Energy Investment Steps in Glycolysis

STEP 1: Phosphorylation Glucose is carried in the bloodstream to cells, where it is transported across the cell membrane into the cytosol. As soon as glucose enters the cell, it is phosphorylated in step 1 of glycolysis, which requires energy investment from ATP. This is the first highly exergonic, irreversible step in glycolysis. The product of step 1, glucose 6-phosphate, is an allosteric inhibitor for the enzyme for this step (*hexokinase*). This is the first control point for glycolysis.

STEP 2: Isomerization The enzyme *glucose 6-phosphate isomerase* converts glucose 6-phosphate (an aldohexose) to fructose 6-phosphate (a ketohexose). This conversion of a six-membered glucose ring to a five-membered ring with a —CH$_2$OH group prepares the molecule for addition of another phosphoryl group in the next step.

STEP 3: Phosphorylation A second energy invest-ment is made as *phosphofructokinase* converts fructose 6-phosphate to fructose 1,6-bisphosphate by reaction with ATP in an exergonic reaction. This irreversible reaction is another major control point for glycolysis. When the cell is short of en-ergy, adenosine diphosphate (ADP) and adenosine monophosphate (AMP) concentrations build up and activate the step 3 enzyme, *phosphofructo-kinase*. When energy is in good supply, ATP and citrate build up and allosterically inhibit this enzyme. The outcome of steps 1–3 is the forma-tion of a molecule ready to be split into the two 3-carbon intermediates that will ultimately become two molecules of pyruvate.

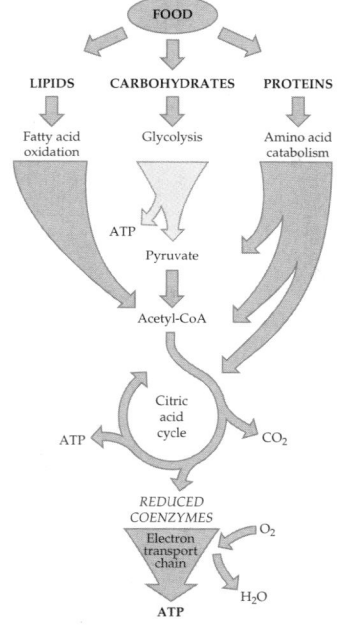

STEP 4: Cleavage *Aldolase* catalyzes cleavage of the bond between carbons 3 and 4 in fructose 1,6-bisphosphate. The products of this reversible reaction are dihy-droxyacetone phosphate and glyceraldehyde 3-phosphate. Only glyceraldehyde 3-phosphate can be used to generate energy, but these two 3-carbon sugar phos-phates are interconvertible in an aldose–ketose equilibrium.

STEP 5: Isomerization *Triose phosphate isomerase* catalyzes the conversion of dihydroxyacetone phosphate to glyceraldehyde 3-phosphate. As glyceraldehyde 3-phosphate reacts in step 6, the equilibrium of step 5 shifts to the right. The overall result of steps 4 and 5 is therefore the production of *two* molecules of glyceraldehyde 3-phosphate.

Energy Generation Steps in Glycolysis

STEP 6: Oxidation Glyceraldehyde 3-phosphate from both steps 4 and 5 is oxidized to 1,3-bisphosphoglycerate by *glyceraldehyde 3-phosphate dehydrogenase*. The enzyme cofactor NAD^+ is the oxidizing agent for this reaction. Some of the energy from the exergonic oxidation is captured in NADH, and some is used in forming the phosphate. This is the first energy-generating step of glycolysis.

$$6 \quad \begin{array}{c} NAD^+ + HOPO_3{}^{2-} \\ NADH/H^+ \end{array}$$

$$\begin{array}{c} OH \quad O \\ | \quad \quad \| \\ {}^{2-}O_3POCH_2-CH-C-OPO_3{}^{2-} \end{array}$$

1,3-Bisphosphoglycerate
Step 6. Oxidation and Phosphorylation

STEP 7: Phosphorylation *Phosphoglycerate kinase* transfers a phosphate group from 1,3-bisphosphoglycerate to ADP. The products of the reaction are 3-phosphoglycerate and ATP, the first ATP generated by glycolysis. Because this step occurs twice for each glucose molecule, the ATP-energy balance sheet in glycolysis is even after step 7. Two ATP molecules were spent in steps 1–5, and now they have been replaced.

$$7 \quad \begin{array}{c} ADP \\ ATP \end{array}$$

$$\begin{array}{c} OH \quad O \\ | \quad \quad \| \\ {}^{2-}O_3POCH_2-CH-C-O^- \end{array}$$

3-Phosphoglycerate
Step 7. Phosphate Transfer

STEP 8: Isomerization *Phosphoglycerate mutase* catalyzes the isomerization of 3-phosphoglycerate to 2-phosphoglycerate. This rearrangement is necessary for the next step.

$$8$$

$$\begin{array}{c} {}^{2-}O_3PO \quad \quad O \\ | \quad \quad \quad \| \\ HO-CH_2-CH-C-O^- \end{array}$$

2-Phosphoglycerate
Step 8. Isomerization

STEP 9: Dehydration *Enolase* catalyzes the dehydration of 2-phosphoglycerate to phosphoenolpyruvate, the second energy-providing phosphate of glycolysis. Water is the other product of this reaction.

$$9 \quad H_2O$$

$$\begin{array}{c} {}^{2-}O_3PO \quad \quad O \\ | \quad \quad \quad \| \\ H_2C=C-C-O^- \end{array}$$

Phosphoenolpyruvate
Step 9. Dehydration

STEP 10: Phosphate Transfer *Pyruvate kinase* transfers a phosphate group from phosphoenolpyruvate to ADP forming pyruvate and ATP in a highly exergonic, irreversible reaction. The production of ATP by transfer of a phosphate group to ADP from another molecule is called *substrate-level phosphorylation*.

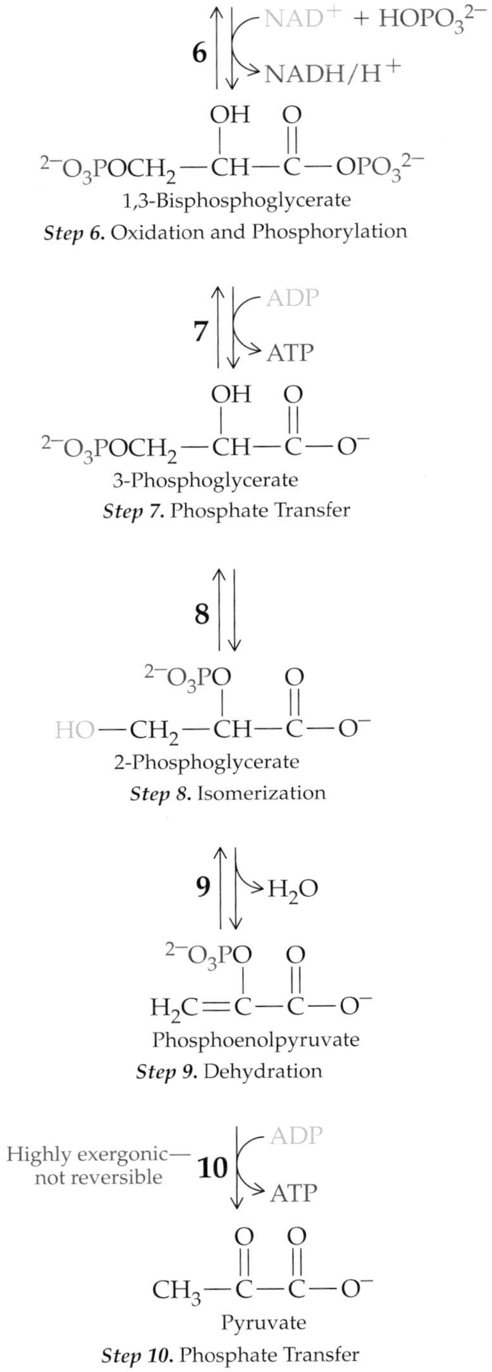

Highly exergonic— not reversible $$10 \quad \begin{array}{c} ADP \\ ATP \end{array}$$

$$\begin{array}{c} O \quad O \\ \| \quad \| \\ CH_3-C-C-O^- \end{array}$$

Pyruvate
Step 10. Phosphate Transfer

▲ **Figure 22.3**
The glycolysis pathway for converting glucose to pyruvate.

The two ATP molecules formed by the reactions in step 10 are pure profit, and the overall results of glycolysis are as follows:

Net result of glycolysis

$$C_6H_{12}O_6 + 2NAD^+ + 2HOPO_3{}^{2-} + 2ADP \longrightarrow 2CH_3-\overset{\overset{\textstyle O}{\|}}{C}-\overset{\overset{\textstyle O}{\|}}{C}-O^- + 2NADH + 2ATP + 2H_2O + 2H^+$$

Glucose   Pyruvate

- Conversion of glucose to two pyruvate molecules
- Net production of two ATP molecules
- Production of two molecules of reduced coenzyme NADH from NAD^+

Worked Example 22.1 Relating Enzyme Names with Reaction Steps of Glycolysis

How do the names of the enzymes involved in the first two steps of glycolysis relate to the reactions involved?

ANALYSIS Look at the names of the enzymes and the reactions. Also recall the enzyme classification scheme from Chapter 19 (Table 19.4).

SOLUTION

In the first reaction, a phosphoryl group is added to glucose. The enzyme name is hexokinase; *kinase* because kinases transfer phosphoryl groups and *hexo-* for a hexose sugar as the substrate. In the second reaction, glucose 6-phosphate is rearranged to fructose 6-phosphate by phosphoglucose isomerase. This enzyme belongs to the enzyme class of isomerases, enzymes that rearrange molecules to an isomer of the original molecule. The phosphoglucose part of the name tells us that a phosphorylated glucose molecule will be rearranged; inspection of the reaction shows that this is true.

PROBLEM 22.3

There are two sets of reactions in glycolysis in which phosphate intermediates are synthesized in the first reaction and their energy harvested as ATP in the second reaction. Identify the two sets of reactions.

PROBLEM 22.4

Identify each step in glycolysis that is an isomerization.

PROBLEM 22.5

Verify the isomerization that occurs in step 2 of glycolysis by drawing the open-chain forms of glucose 6-phosphate and fructose 6-phosphate.

KEY CONCEPT PROBLEM 22.6

In Figure 22.3, compare the starting compound (glucose) and the final product (pyruvate).

(a) Which is oxidized to a greater extent?

(b) Are there any steps in the glycolytic pathway in which an oxidation or reduction occurs? Identify the oxidizing or reducing agents that are involved in these steps.

22.4 Entry of Other Sugars into Glycolysis

Learning Objective:

• Identify where the major monosaccharides enter glycolysis.

Glucose is not the only monosaccharide that our bodies metabolize. The other major monosaccharides from digestion—fructose, galactose, and mannose—eventually join the glycolysis pathway. Like glucose, these sugars are also metabolized by the bacteria that populate our mouths and digestive systems. The effect of dietary sugars on dental health is explored in the Chemistry in Action "Tooth Decay."

Fructose, from fruits or hydrolysis of the disaccharide sucrose, is converted to glycolysis intermediates in two ways: in muscle cells, it is phosphorylated to fructose 6-phosphate by hexosekinase, and in liver cells, it is converted to glyceraldehyde 3-phosphate. Fructose 6-phosphate is the substrate for step 3 of glycolysis; glyceraldehyde 3-phosphate is the substrate for step 6.

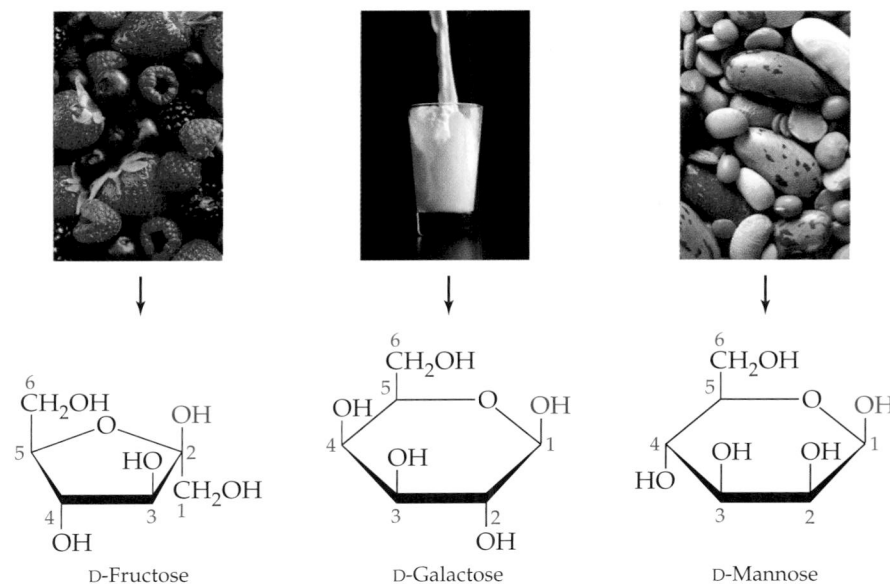

▲ Major dietary monosaccharides other than glucose.

Galactose from hydrolysis of the disaccharide lactose is converted to glucose 6-phosphate, the substrate for step 2 of glycolysis, by a five-step pathway that begins with galactokinase. A hereditary defect affecting any enzyme in this pathway can cause galactosemia (see Table 20.1).

CHEMISTRY IN ACTION

⚕ Tooth Decay

Tooth decay is a complex interaction between food, bacteria, and your body. The clinical term for tooth decay is *dental caries.* Dentists recognize it as an infectious microbial disease that results in the destruction of the calcified structures of the teeth.

The mouth is home to many different species of bacteria. Two permanent bacterial residents of the oral cavity, *Streptococcus sanguis* and *Streptococcus mutans,* compete for the same habitat on the biting surfaces of the teeth. *Dental plaque,* bacterial aggregations on the teeth that cannot be removed by a strong water spray, begin to form again immediately after plaque has been removed. First, a coating of organic material composed of glycoproteins from the saliva begins to form; then bacteria quickly colonize this film and secrete a sticky matrix of an insoluble polysaccharide known as *dextran.* The mass of bacteria, their sticky matrix, and the glycoprotein film together comprise dental plaque. Plaque is, therefore, not simply adherent food debris but rather a community of microorganisms (known as a *biofilm*) that forms through an orderly sequence of events.

The bacteria resident in plaque release products consisting of proteins and carbohydrates. Some polysaccharides form intracellular granules that serve as energy storage depots for periods of low nutrient availability (between meals). Other products are toxic to the gums and can promote periodontal disease.

What our dentists and parents told us—that eating candy would create cavities—is true! A diet high in sucrose favors

the growth of *S. mutans* over that of *S. sanguis.* Although both bacteria can cause tooth decay, *S. mutans* attacks teeth much more vigorously. It has an enzyme (a glucosyltransferase) that transfers glucose units from sucrose to the dextran polymer. The mature plaque community then metabolizes fructose from the sucrose to lactate, and this acid causes the local pH in the area of the tooth to drop dramatically. If the pH stays low enough for a long enough time, the minerals in the teeth are dissolved away and the tooth begins to decay. The disruption of plaque via oral hygiene and a diet low in sucrose favors the growth of *S. sanguis* over *S. mutans.* To control the decay process, it is necessary to limit both the amount of sucrose in the diet and the frequency with which it is ingested.

CIA Problem 22.1 What is the function of the insoluble polysaccharide known as dextran in the formation of dental plaque?

CIA Problem 22.2 Name four of the major components of dental plaque.

CIA Problem 22.3 How is dental plaque associated with periodontal disease?

CIA Problem 22.4 Explain the chemical process that leads to cavities after dental plaque has formed.

CIA Problem 22.5 Why is table sugar bad for your teeth? Would using honey instead be a better choice for tooth health?

Mannose is a product of the hydrolysis of plant polysaccharides other than starch. It is converted (by hexokinase) to mannose 6-phosphate, which then undergoes a multistep, enzyme-catalyzed rearrangement to fructose 6-phosphate in order to enter glycolysis as the substrate for step 3.

PROBLEM 22.7

Use curved arrows (like those in Figure 22.3) to write an equation for the conversion of fructose to fructose 6-phosphate by ATP. At what step does fructose 6-phosphate enter glycolysis?

PROBLEM 22.8

Compare glucose and galactose (see Table 20.1), and explain how their structures differ.

22.5 The Fate of Pyruvate

Learning Objective:

• Describe the pathways involving pyruvate and their respective outcomes.

Aerobic In the presence of oxygen.

Anaerobic In the absence of oxygen.

The conversion of glucose to pyruvate is a central metabolic pathway in most living systems. The further reactions of pyruvate, however, depend on metabolic conditions and the organism. Under normal oxygen-rich (**aerobic**) conditions, pyruvate is converted to acetyl-CoA in mammals. This pathway, however, is short-circuited in some tissues, especially when there is not enough oxygen present (**anaerobic** conditions). Under anaerobic conditions, pyruvate is instead reduced to lactate. When sufficient oxygen again becomes available, lactate is recycled back to pyruvate in muscle cells or to glucose via the Cori cycle in liver cells. A third pathway for pyruvate is conversion back to glucose by *gluconeogenesis*, which also occurs only in liver cells (we will discuss gluconeogenesis and the Cori cycle in Section 22.9). This pathway is essential when the body is starved for glucose. The pyruvate necessary for gluconeogenesis may come not only from glycolysis but also from amino acids or glycerol from lipids. Use of protein and lipid for glucose synthesis occurs when calories needed exceed calorie intake as in starvation, certain diseases, and some carbohydrate-restricted diets.

Yeast is an organism with a different pathway for pyruvate; it converts pyruvate to ethanol under anaerobic conditions. Humans exploit this property of yeast in leavening bread and brewing beer. We use certain strains of the bacteria *Lactobacillus* and other bacteria, which convert pyruvate to lactate to produce yogurt, kimchee, and sauerkraut. In these and similar products, the lactate produced by these bacteria provide the familiar acidic tang and help preserve the food.

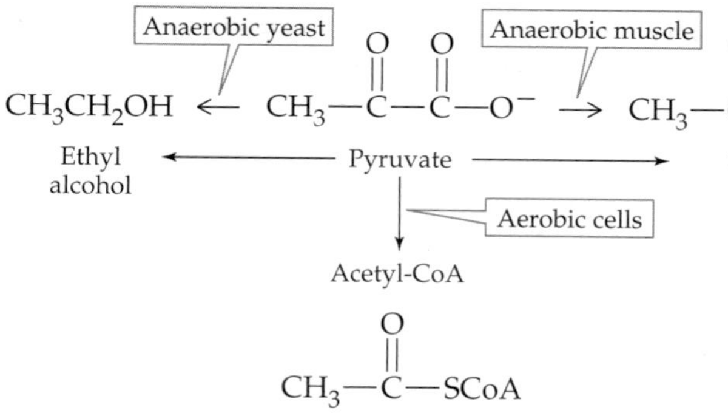

▲ The biochemical transformations of pyruvate.

Aerobic Oxidation of Pyruvate to Acetyl-CoA

For aerobic oxidation to proceed, pyruvate first moves across the outer mitochondrial membrane from the cytosol where it was produced. Next, a transporter protein carries pyruvate across the otherwise impenetrable inner mitochondrial membrane. Once within the mitochondrial matrix, pyruvate encounters the *pyruvate dehydrogenase complex,* a large multienzyme complex that catalyzes the conversion of pyruvate to acetyl-CoA, the substrate for the citric acid cycle. The other product of the reaction, CO_2 is exhaled.

$$CH_3-\overset{\overset{\displaystyle O}{\|}}{C}-\overset{\overset{\displaystyle O}{\|}}{C}-O^- \ + \ HS-CoA \ \xrightarrow[\substack{\text{Pyruvate} \\ \text{dehydrogenase} \\ \text{complex}}]{NAD^+ \ NADH/H^+} \ CH_3\overset{\overset{\displaystyle O}{\|}}{C}-SCoA \ + \ CO_2$$

Pyruvate   Acetyl-CoA

Anaerobic Reduction to Lactate

In certain tissues, like muscle, under anaerobic conditions pyruvate is reduced to lactate instead of oxidized to acetyl-CoA. Since glycolysis is anaerobic, why should oxygen be necessary? It does not appear as part of the reaction. Note that for glycolysis to proceed, NAD^+ is necessary for step 6 (Figure 22.3). Under aerobic conditions, NADH is continually reoxidized to NAD^+ during electron transport (see Section 21.8); under anaerobic conditions, electron transport slows and so does the production of NAD^+. The oxidation of pyruvate to lactate results in the reduction of NADH to NAD^+, allowing glycolysis to continue. Lactate is oxidized to pyruvate by another pathway when oxygen is available.

$$CH_3-\overset{\overset{\displaystyle O}{\|}}{C}-\overset{\overset{\displaystyle O}{\|}}{C}-O^- \ \underset{\substack{\text{Aerobic} \\ \text{conditions}}}{\overset{\substack{NADH/H^+ \ NAD^+ \\ \text{Anaerobic} \\ \text{conditions}}}{\rightleftarrows}} \ CH_3-\overset{\overset{\displaystyle OH}{|}}{CH}-\overset{\overset{\displaystyle O}{\|}}{C}-O^-$$

Pyruvate   Lactate

Tissues where oxygen is in short supply also rely on the anaerobic production of ATP by glycolysis. Red blood cells have no mitochondria and thus must always form lactate as the end product of glycolysis. Other examples are the cornea of the eye, where there is little blood circulation, and muscles during intense activity. The resulting buildup of lactate in working muscles causes fatigue and discomfort (see the Chemistry in Action "The Biochemistry of Running" on p. 704).

Alcoholic Fermentation

Microorganisms often must survive in the absence of oxygen and thus have evolved numerous anaerobic strategies for energy production, generally known as **fermentation.** When pyruvate undergoes fermentation by yeast, it is converted into ethanol plus carbon dioxide. This process, known as **alcoholic fermentation,** is used to produce beer, wine, and other alcoholic beverages and also to make bread. The carbon dioxide causes the bread to rise, and the alcohol evaporates during baking.

Fermentation The production of energy under anaerobic conditions.
Alcoholic fermentation The anaerobic breakdown of glucose to ethanol plus carbon dioxide by the action of yeast enzymes.

 Worked Example 22.2 Identifying Catabolic Stages

Complete oxidation of glucose produces six molecules of carbon dioxide. Describe the stage of catabolism at which each one is formed.

ANALYSIS Look at each stage of catabolism for the complete oxidation of glucose to carbon dioxide. Notice how many molecules of carbon dioxide are produced and by which step. Pathways to consider (in order) are glycolysis, conversion of pyruvate to acetyl-CoA, and the citric acid cycle. There is no need to consider oxidative phosphorylation because glucose is completely oxidized at the end of the citric acid cycle.

—continued on next page

—continued from previous page

SOLUTION

No molecules of carbon dioxide are produced during glycolysis. Conversion of one molecule of pyruvate to one molecule of acetyl-CoA yields one molecule of carbon dioxide. In the citric acid cycle, two molecules of carbon dioxide are released for each molecule of acetyl-CoA oxidized. One is released in step 3 when isocitrate is converted to α-ketoglutarate and the other when α-ketoglutarate is converted to succinyl-CoA in Step 4. Since each glucose molecule produces two pyruvate molecules, the total is three molecules twice, or six molecules of carbon dioxide.

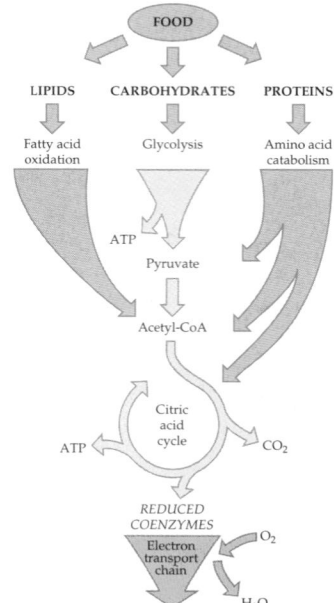

⊙▬ KEY CONCEPT PROBLEM 22.9

In alcoholic fermentation, each mole of pyruvate is converted to one mole of carbon dioxide and one mole of ethanol. In the process, about 50 kcal/mol (209 kJ/mol) of energy is produced. Under the most favorable conditions, more than one-half of this energy is stored as ATP.

(a) What happens to the remaining energy produced in alcoholic fermentation?

(b) Give two reasons why it would be nearly impossible to reverse the reaction that converts pyruvate to ethanol and carbon dioxide.

PROBLEM 22.10

Name three ways humans have exploited the ability of microorganisms to ferment carbohydrates.

PROBLEM 22.11

Pyruvate has three different fates. What are the three different molecules pyruvate is converted into? What conditions exist for the formation of each product?

HANDS-ON CHEMISTRY 22.1

Let's try a fermentation experiment. Look in a cookbook or on the web for a basic yeast bread recipe or buy a frozen, unbaked loaf. Obtain the ingredients and bake a loaf of bread. Observe how it rises—what makes that happen? Dissolve some yeast in water (cold and warm, separately) and observe what happens. What do you smell while the bread rises? While it bakes? If you let it raise too long, you may smell alcohol. Why did this happen?

If you do not have access to an oven, go to a bakery and see if you can find a really fresh bread sample. Or, try to make yogurt from milk and a bit of yogurt containing active cultures. Remember to be very clean with this procedure. Instructions can be found on the web.

22.6   Energy Output in Complete Glucose Catabolism

Learning Objective:

• Calculate the energy produced by partial or total oxidation of glucose.

The total energy output from oxidation of glucose is the combined result of (a) glycolysis, (b) conversion of pyruvate to acetyl-CoA, (c) conversion of two acetyl groups to four molecules of CO_2 in the citric acid cycle, and, finally, (d) the passage of reduced coenzymes from each of these pathways through electron transport and the production of ATP by oxidative phosphorylation.

To determine the total number of ATP molecules generated from one glucose molecule, we first sum the net equations for each pathway that precedes oxidative phosphorylation. Since each glucose yields two pyruvate molecules and two acetyl-CoA molecules, the net equations for pyruvate oxidation and the citric acid cycle are multiplied by 2.

Net result of catabolism of one glucose molecule

Glycolysis (Section 22.3)

Glucose + 2NAD$^+$ + 2HOPO$_3^{2-}$ + 2ADP $\longrightarrow$ 2Pyruvate + 2NADH + 2ATP + 2H$_2$O + 2H$^+$

Pyruvate oxidation (Section 22.5)

2Pyruvate + 2NAD$^+$ + 2HSCoA $\longrightarrow$ 2Acetyl-CoA + 2CO$_2$ + 2NADH + 2H$^+$

Citric acid cycle (Section 20.8)

2Acetyl-CoA + 6NAD$^+$ + 2FAD + 2ADP + 2HOPO$_3^{2-}$ + 4H$_2$O $\longrightarrow$

2HSCoA + 6NADH + 6H$^+$ + 2FADH$_2$ + 2ATP + 4CO$_2$

Glucose + 10NAD$^+$ + 2FAD + 2H$_2$O + 4ADP + 4HOPO$_3^{2-}$ $\longrightarrow$

10NADH + 10H$^+$ + 2FADH$_2$ + 4ATP + 6CO$_2$

The summation shows a total of 4 ATP molecules produced per glucose molecule. The remainder of our ATP is generated via electron transport and oxidative phosphorylation. Thus, the total number of ATP molecules produced per glucose molecule is the 4 ATP molecules from glucose catabolism plus the number of ATP molecules produced for each reduced coenzyme that enters electron transport.

Based on an energy-yield assumption of 3 ATP molecules per NADH and 2 ATP molecules per FADH$_2$ the maximum yield for the complete catabolism of one molecule of glucose is 38 ATP molecules, as calculated here:

$$10NADH\left(\frac{3ATP}{NADH}\right) + 2FADH_2\left(\frac{2ATP}{FADH_2}\right) + 4ATP = 38ATP$$

PROBLEM 22.12

Glycolysis of one molecule of glucose produces 8 ATP molecules. How many ATP molecules are produced from glycolysis of 10 glucose molecules?

PROBLEM 22.13

Complete catabolism of one glucose molecule yields 38 ATP molecules. How many moles of ATP are produced by the complete catabolism of one mole of glucose?

22.7 Regulation of Glucose Metabolism and Metabolism during Stress

Learning Objective:

• Identify the hormones that influence glucose metabolism and describe the changes in metabolism during stress conditions.

A stable blood glucose concentration is vital for proper functioning of the body. Wide fluctuations in glucose levels lead to unwanted side effects. The body uses the hormones insulin and glucagon to control blood glucose levels along with mechanisms to store and release glucose as needed. Glucose is the preferred fuel for brain, muscle during activity, and red blood cells.

Normal blood glucose concentration a few hours after a meal ranges roughly from 65 to 100 mg/dL. When departures from normal occur, specific physiological responses begin to occur (Figure 22.4). Low blood glucose (**hypoglycemia**) causes weakness, sweating, and rapid heartbeat; very low glucose levels in brain cells causes mental

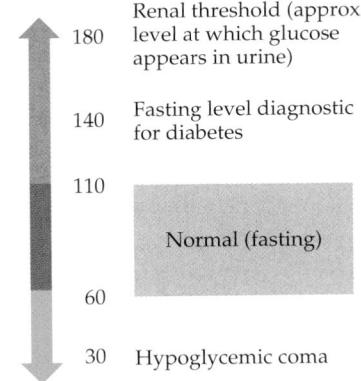

▲ **Figure 22.4**
Blood glucose.
The ranges for low blood glucose (in green; hypoglycemia), normal blood glucose (in purple), and high blood glucose (in orange; hyperglycemia) are indicated.

Hypoglycemia Lower than normal blood glucose concentration.

Hyperglycemia Higher than normal blood glucose concentration.

confusion, convulsions, coma, and eventually death. Glucose is the primary energy source for the brain; alternate fuels are not normally available for brain cells. At a blood glucose level of 30 mg/dL, consciousness is impaired or lost, and prolonged hypoglycemia can cause permanent dementia. High blood glucose (**hyperglycemia**) causes increased urine flow as the normal osmolarity balance of fluids within the kidney is disturbed. Prolonged hyperglycemia can cause low blood pressure, coma, and death.

Two hormones from the pancreas regulate blood glucose levels. The first, insulin, is released when blood glucose concentration rises (Figure 22.5). Its role is to decrease blood glucose concentrations by signaling cells to take in glucose, where it is used for energy production, and by stimulating synthesis of glycogen, proteins, and lipids.

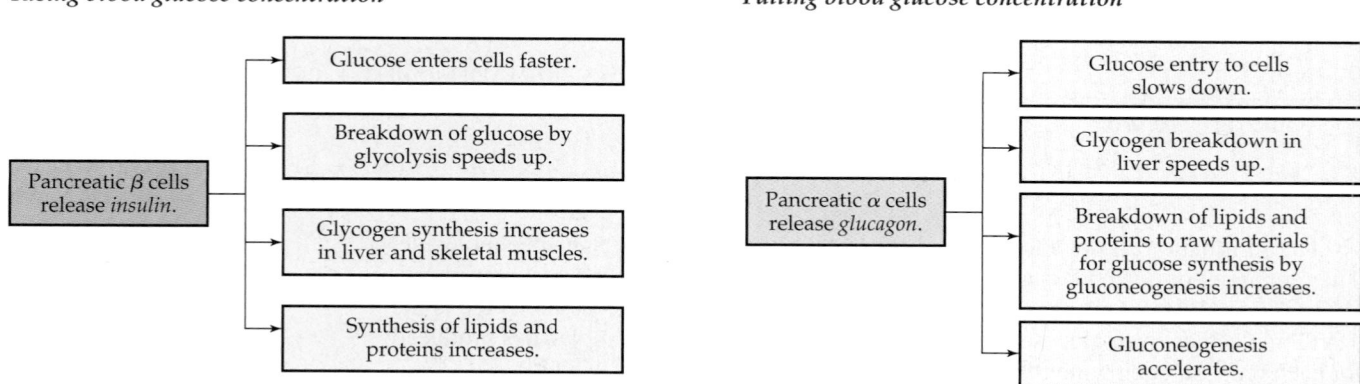

Rising blood glucose concentration

Pancreatic β cells release *insulin*.
- Glucose enters cells faster.
- Breakdown of glucose by glycolysis speeds up.
- Glycogen synthesis increases in liver and skeletal muscles.
- Synthesis of lipids and proteins increases.

Falling blood glucose concentration

Pancreatic α cells release *glucagon*.
- Glucose entry to cells slows down.
- Glycogen breakdown in liver speeds up.
- Breakdown of lipids and proteins to raw materials for glucose synthesis by gluconeogenesis increases.
- Gluconeogenesis accelerates.

▲ **Figure 22.5**
Regulation of glucose concentration by insulin and glucagon from the pancreas.

The second hormone, glucagon, is released when blood glucose concentration drops. In a reversal of insulin's effects, glucagon stimulates the breakdown of glycogen in the liver and release of glucose. Proteins and lipids are also broken down so that amino acids from proteins and glycerol from lipids can be converted to glucose in the liver by the gluconeogenesis pathways (see Section 22.9). Epinephrine (the "fight-or-flight" hormone) also accelerates the breakdown of glycogen, but primarily in muscle tissue, where glucose is used to generate energy needed for quick action (discussed in Section 28.3).

Stress: Dieting, Fasting, and Starvation

Dieting, fasting, and starvation all induce the same metabolic response to an inadequate or nonexistent intake of carbohydrates. Glycogen stored in liver and muscle cells provides glucose for less than 24 hours during fasting conditions, longer while dieting. The primary storage sites for glycogen are liver cells (about 90 g in a 70 kg man) and muscle cells (about 350 g in a 70 kg man). Circulating free glucose and stored glycogen represent less than 1% of our energy reserves and are used up in 15–20 hours of normal activity. Once glycogen stores are exhausted, the liver synthesizes glucose via gluconeogenesis (Section 22.9). This new glucose is delivered preferentially to the brain. The metabolic changes in the absence of food begin with a gradual decline in blood glucose concentration accompanied by an increased release of glucose from glycogen (Figure 22.6 and glycogenolysis, Section 22.8).

Fats are our largest energy reserve, but adjusting to dependence on fat for energy takes several days because there is no direct pathway for generating glucose from the fatty acids in fats (as shown in Figure 22.2). Catabolism of fatty acids to acetyl-CoA, oxidation of acetyl-CoA via the citric acid cycle, and production of ATP energy from electron transport is the path for generating energy from fat. Protein is also broken down into amino acids that can be used to generate energy. Amino acids can enter the citric acid cycle for oxidation to energy or can be used to synthesize glucose in liver cells via the gluconeogenesis pathway (Section 22.9).

The relationship of changes in amounts of blood glucose, liver glycogen, fatty acids, ketone bodies, insulin, and glucagon present is seen in Figure 22.6.

A body deprived of glucose sources gradually adjusts to producing most of the necessary energy from fat catabolism and begins to conserve protein. As part of the catabolism of fat, acetyl-CoA molecules derived from breakdown of lipids accumulate. Eventually, the citric acid cycle is overloaded and cannot degrade acetyl-CoA as rapidly as it is produced. Acetyl-CoA therefore builds up inside cells and begins to be removed by a new series of metabolic reactions that transform it into a group of compounds collectively known as *ketone bodies*. These ketone bodies enter the bloodstream and the brain and other tissues are able to switch over to producing up to 50% of their ATP from catabolism of ketone bodies instead of glucose. Acetone is so volatile that much of it is excreted through the lungs, giving the breath a fruity odor—an indicator of ketoacidosis in a diabetic.

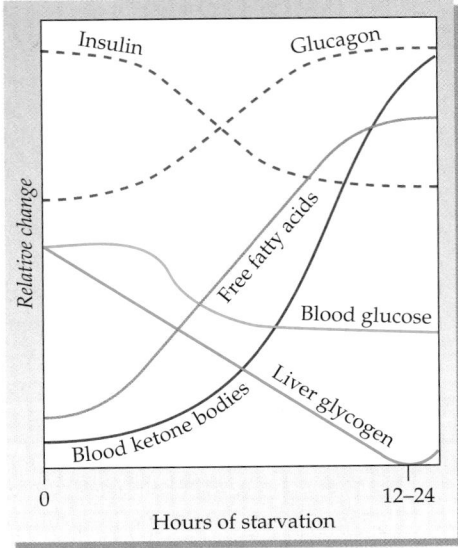

▲ **Figure 22.6**
Relative changes during early stages of starvation.

Ketone bodies

$$\underset{\underset{\displaystyle OH}{|}}{CH_3CHCH_2}\overset{\displaystyle O}{\overset{\|}{C}}-O^- \qquad CH_3-\overset{\displaystyle O}{\overset{\|}{C}}-CH_2\overset{\displaystyle O}{\overset{\|}{C}}-O^- \qquad CH_3-\overset{\displaystyle O}{\overset{\|}{C}}-CH_3$$

3-Hydroxybutyrate   Acetoacetate   Acetone

PROBLEM 22.14

Refer to Figure 22.6 and summarize the changes in liver glycogen and blood glucose during the starvation period represented in the figure.

PROBLEM 22.15

In a diabetic some glucose is converted to sorbitol, an alcohol that accumulates in the eye and can cause cataracts. Draw the open-chain structure of sorbitol, which is identical to that of D-glucose except that the aldehyde group has been reduced to an alcohol group. Can sorbitol form a five- or six-membered cyclic hemiacetal? Explain why or why not. (Hint: The open-chain structure of glucose is found in Section 20.1.)

LOOKING AHEAD ➤ The breakdown of triacylglycerols from fatty tissue produces not only ketone bodies but also glycerol, one of the compounds that can be converted to glucose by gluconeogenesis. The production of glycerol and ketone bodies from triacylglycerols is described in Chapter 24, which is devoted to lipid metabolism.

⬡ KEY CONCEPT PROBLEM 22.16

Ketoacidosis is relieved by rapid breathing, which converts bicarbonate ions and hydrogen ions in the blood to gaseous carbon dioxide and water, as shown in this equation.

$$H^+ + HCO_3^- \longrightarrow H_2CO_3 \longrightarrow H_2O + CO_2 \text{ (Exhaled)}$$

(a) Assuming that these reactions can go in either direction, how does a state of acidosis help to increase the generation of carbon dioxide?

(b) What principle describes the effect of added reactants and products on an equilibrium?

HANDS-ON CHEMISTRY 22.2

Go for a run. If you do not run, go for a very fast walk. Monitor your breathing and how your leg muscles feel. If you have exercised long enough and hard enough, you may be in oxygen debt and will breathe heavily for several minutes after coming to a stop. If your leg muscles hurt, it is due to the accumulation of lactic acid generated during exercise. Resting allows lactic acid to be converted into pyruvate by the Cori cycle, and your leg muscles will no longer ache.

CHEMISTRY IN ACTION

The Biochemistry of Running

A runner is poised, tense, and expectant, waiting for the sound of the starting gun. Running requires a constant, rapid source of energy and stresses the entire energy production scheme in the body. Long hours of training have prepared heart, lungs, and red blood cells to deliver the maximum amount of oxygen to the muscles, which have been conditioned to use it as efficiently as possible. In the moments before the race, mounting levels of epinephrine have readied the body for action. Now, everything depends on biochemistry: Chemical reactions in muscle cells will provide the energy to see the race through. How will that energy be produced?

The first source is the supply of immediately available ATP, but this is used up very quickly—probably within a matter of seconds. Additional ATP is then provided by the reaction of ADP with creatine phosphate, an amino acid phosphate in muscle cells that maintains the following equilibrium:

$$ADP + Creatine\ phosphate \rightleftharpoons ATP + Creatine$$

After about 30 seconds to a minute, stores of creatine phosphate are depleted, and glucose from glycogenolysis becomes the chief energy source. During maximum muscle exertion, oxygen cannot enter muscle cells fast enough to keep the citric acid cycle and oxidative phosphorylation going. Under these anaerobic conditions, the pyruvate from glycolysis is converted to lactate rather than entering the citric acid cycle.

In a 100 m sprint, all the energy comes from available ATP, creatine phosphate (CP in the figure), and glycolysis of glucose from muscle glycogen. Anaerobic glycolysis suffices for only a minute or two of maximum exertion, because a buildup of lactate causes muscle fatigue.

Beyond this, other pathways must come into action. As breathing and heart rate speed up and oxygen-carrying blood flows more quickly to muscles, the aerobic pathway is activated and ATP is once again generated by oxidative

▲ The energy used by these runners is fueled by glycogen stores. The stored glucose is converted to energy through glycolysis, the citric acid cycle, and the electron transport system.

phosphorylation. The trick to avoiding muscle exhaustion in a long race is to run at a speed just under the "anaerobic threshold"—the rate of exertion at which oxygen is in short supply, ATP is supplied only by glycolysis, and lactate is produced.

Now the question is, which fuel will metabolism rely on during a long race—carbohydrate or fat? Burning fatty acids from fats is more efficient. Burning a gram of fat yields more than twice as many calories than burning a gram of carbohydrate. When we are sitting quietly, in fact, our muscle cells are burning mostly fat, and the fat in storage could support the exertion of marathon running for several days. By contrast, glycogen alone can provide enough glucose to fuel only 2–3 hours of such running under aerobic conditions.

The difficulty is that fatty acids cannot be delivered to muscle cells fast enough to maintain the ATP level needed for running, so metabolism compromises and the glycogen stored in muscles remains the limiting factor for the marathon runner. Once glycogen is gone, extreme exhaustion and mental confusion set in—the condition known as "hitting the wall." Running speed becomes limited to that sustainable by fats only. To delay this point as long as possible, a runner encourages glycogen synthesis by a diet high in carbohydrates prior to and during a race. In the hours just before the race, however, carbohydrates are avoided. Their effect of triggering insulin release is undesirable at this point because the resulting faster use of glucose will hasten depletion of glycogen.

CIA Problem 22.6 Why is it not possible for a person to sprint for miles?

CIA Problem 22.7 Order the following sources of energy (from first used to last used) when muscles are called upon to do extensive work:

(a) Fatty acids from triacylglycerols
(b) ATP
(c) Glycogen
(d) Creatine phosphate
(e) Glucose

CIA Problem 22.8 Why is creatine phosphate a better source of quick energy for a runner than either glucose or glycogen?

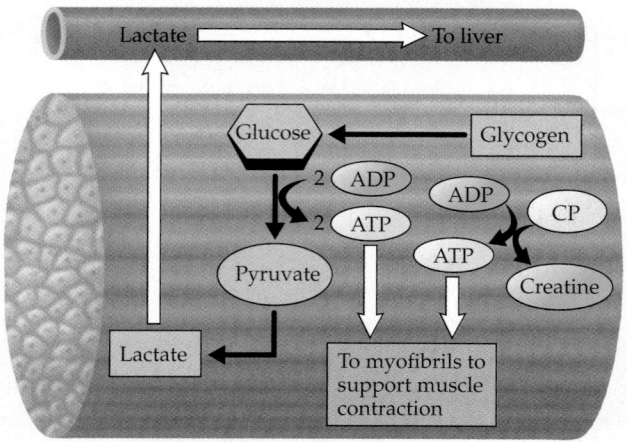

▲ At peak activity, ATP formation relies on creatine phosphate (CP) and glucose from muscle glycogen. Pyruvate is converted to lactate, which enters the bloodstream for transport to the liver, where it is recycled to pyruvate.

22.8 Glycogen Metabolism: Glycogenesis and Glycogenolysis

Learning Objective:

• Explain the pathways for glycogen metabolism and their purpose.

Glycogen, the storage form of glucose in animals, is a branched polymer of glucose. **Glycogenesis** (glycogen synthesis) occurs when glucose concentrations are high. It begins with glucose 6-phosphate and occurs via the three steps shown on the right in Figure 22.8.

• Step 1: *Phosphoglucomutase* isomerizes glucose 6-phosphate to glucose 1-phosphate.

• Step 2: *Pyrophosphorylase* attaches glucose 1-phosphate to uridine triphosphate (UTP) producing uridine diphosphate (UDP)-glucose in a reaction driven by the release of inorganic pyrophosphate. UTP is a high energy compound similar to ATP. UDP serves as a carrier for glucose.

• Step 3: Glycogen synthase adds UDP-glucose to a glycogen chain, lengthening the chain by one glucose unit and freeing UDP in the process.

Glycogenesis The biochemical pathway for synthesis of glycogen, a branched polymer of glucose.

UDP-Glucose, the activated carrier of glucose in glycogen synthesis

Glycogenolysis (glucose release) occurs in the two steps on the left in Figure 22.7. In muscle cells, this occurs when there is an immediate need for energy, while in liver cells, it occurs when blood glucose is low.

Glycogenolysis The biochemical pathway for breakdown of glycogen to free glucose.

◄ **Figure 22.7**
Glycogenolysis and glycogenesis.
Reading from the top down shows the pathway for glycogen synthesis from glucose (glycogenesis). Reading from the bottom up shows the pathway for release of glucose from glycogen (glycogenolysis).

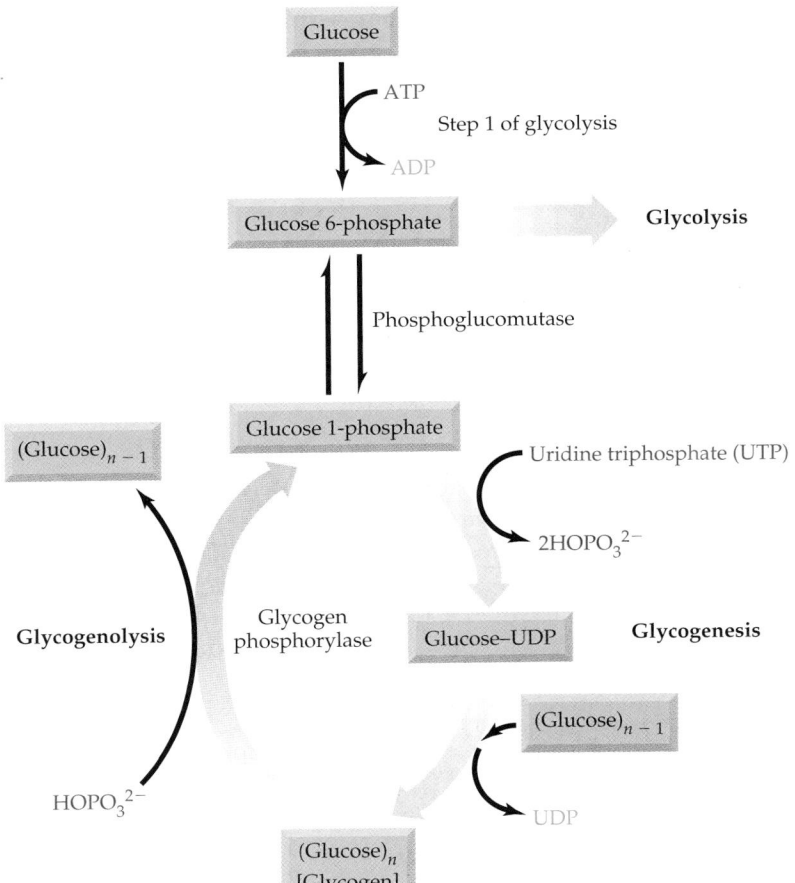

- Step 1: *Glycogen phosphorylase* simultaneously hydrolyzes α-1, 4 glycosidic bonds and sequentially phosphorylates glucose units. The product is glucose 1-phosphate.
- Step 2a: *Phosphoglucomutase* isomerizes glucose 6-phosphate to glucose 1-phosphate. In muscle cells, glucose 1-phosphate immediately enters glycolysis at step 2. This is the reverse of the same reaction in glycogenesis.
- Step 2b: In liver cells, *glucose 6-phosphatase* hydrolyzes glucose 6-phosphate to glucose that moves out of the liver to blood stream to raise blood sugar levels.

PROBLEM 22.17

What is the difference between glycogenesis and glycogenolysis?

PROBLEM 22.18

Why is glycogenesis necessary? Why is glycogenolysis necessary?

22.9 Gluconeogenesis: Glucose Synthesis from Noncarbohydrates

Learning Objective:

- Explain the pathways for synthesis of glucose from noncarbohydrate molecules.

Gluconeogenesis The biochemical pathway for the synthesis of glucose from noncarbohydrates, such as lactate, amino acids, or glycerol.

Glucose is so important for energy production that there are two pathways involved in the synthesis of glucose from noncarbohydrates. The *Cori cycle* converts lactate into pyruvate, the substrate for **gluconeogenesis,** a pathway that makes glucose from noncarbohydrate molecules (lactate, amino acids, and glycerol) beginning with pyruvate. This pathway becomes critical when glucose is not available.

We noted earlier that for metabolic pathways to be favorable, they must be exergonic. As a result, most are not reversible, because the amount of energy required by the reverse, endergonic pathway would be too large to be supplied by cellular metabolism. Glycolysis and gluconeogenesis provide another good example of this relationship and of the way around it.

Cori Cycle

Lactate is a normal product of glycolysis in red blood cells and in muscle cells during vigorous exercise. The bloodstream moves lactate from muscle cells to liver cells; it is oxidized to pyruvate by lactate dehydrogenase. Pyruvate is the substrate for an 11-step series of reactions in the gluconeogenesis pathway; the final product is glucose, which is exported to tissues dependent on glucose but lack the gluconeogenesis pathway. The Cori cycle is essentially a recycling pathway. See Figure 22.8.

Gluconeogenesis

Gluconeogenesis, the synthesis of glucose from noncarbohydrate sources, runs when available glucose from the diet and stored glycogen has been used up. Glucose is the preferred energy source for brain and blood cells and must be supplied. Although some of the steps in gluconeogenesis are the reverse of the identical step in glycolysis, the energy requiring steps in gluconeogenesis use different enzymes than the same steps in glycolysis and vice versa. Steps 1, 3, and 10 in Figure 22.3 illustrate this point. These reactions in glycolysis are too exergonic to be directly reversed. The steps in gluconeogenesis are shown in Figure 22.9 and outlined next.

- Step 1: In an energetically expensive step, *pyruvate carboxylase* adds CO_2 to pyruvate forming oxaloacetate. ATP is changed to ADP in this step.
- Step 2: In a second energetically expensive step, *phosphoenolpyruvate carboxylase* removes CO_2 from oxaloacetate while adding a phosphate group from guanosine

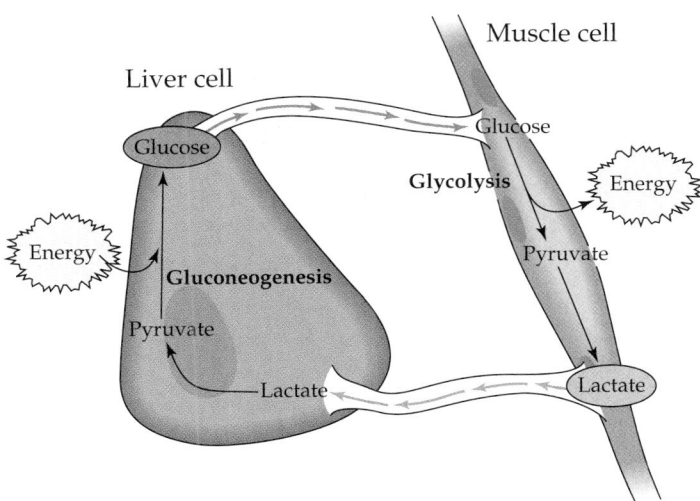

◄**Figure 22.8**
Glucose production during exercise (the Cori cycle).
L-Lactate produced in muscles under anaerobic conditions during exercise is sent to the liver, where it is converted back to glucose. This new glucose can then return via the bloodstream to the muscles, to be stored as glycogen or used for energy production. Gluconeogenesis requires energy, so shifting this pathway to the liver frees the muscles from the burden of having to produce even more energy.

triphosphate (GTP) (similar to ATP) producing phosphoenolpyruvate and guanosine diphosphate (GDP).

- Steps 3–8: In reversible reactions, *the same set of enzymes as found in glycolysis steps 4–9* convert phosphoenolpyruvate to fructose 1,6-bisphosphate via the same intermediates found in glycolysis.

- Step 9: In a one-way reaction, *fructose 1,6-bisphosphatase* hydrolyzes fructose 1,6-bisphosphate to fructose 6-phosphate.

- Step 10: In a one-way reaction, *phosphohexose isomerase* changes fructose 6-phosphate into glucose 6-phosphate.

- Step 11: In a one-way reaction, *glucose 6-phosphatase* hydrolyzes glucose 6-phosphate to glucose.

Glycerol from triacylglycerol catabolism (Section 24.3) is converted to dihydroxyacetone phosphate and enters the gluconeogenesis pathway at step 7 in Figure 22.9 (or step 5 of glycolysis in Figure 22.3). The carbon atoms from certain amino acids (the glucogenic amino acids, Section 27.5) enter gluconeogenesis as either pyruvate or oxaloacetate.

Glycolysis and gluconeogenesis both occur in the cytoplasm of cells. Recall that the citric acid cycle and electron transport system are found in the mitochondria. Glycogenesis and glycogenolysis occur at the surface of glycogen storage granules in the cytoplasm.

PROBLEM 22.19

What two types of reactions convert glycerol to dihydroxyacetone phosphate?

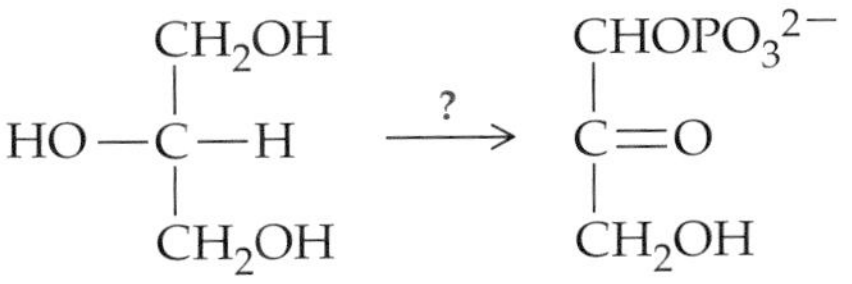

$$
\begin{array}{c}
\text{CH}_2\text{OH} \\
| \\
\text{HO}-\text{C}-\text{H} \\
| \\
\text{CH}_2\text{OH} \\
\text{Glycerol}
\end{array}
\xrightarrow{\ ?\ }
\begin{array}{c}
\text{CHOPO}_3{}^{2-} \\
| \\
\text{C}=\text{O} \\
| \\
\text{CH}_2\text{OH} \\
\text{Dihydroxyacetone} \\
\text{phosphate}
\end{array}
$$

PROBLEM 22.20

What is the purpose of the Cori cycle?

PROBLEM 22.21

Why is gluconeogenesis necessary?

► **Figure 22.9**
Gluconeogenesis.
The pathway begins at the bottom of the figure and moves upwards. Each step in the pathway is numbered. Enzymes shaded in blue are those that differ from the enzymes used in glycolysis to achieve the reverse reaction. For the other steps, gluconeogenesis uses the same enzymes as those used in glycolysis.

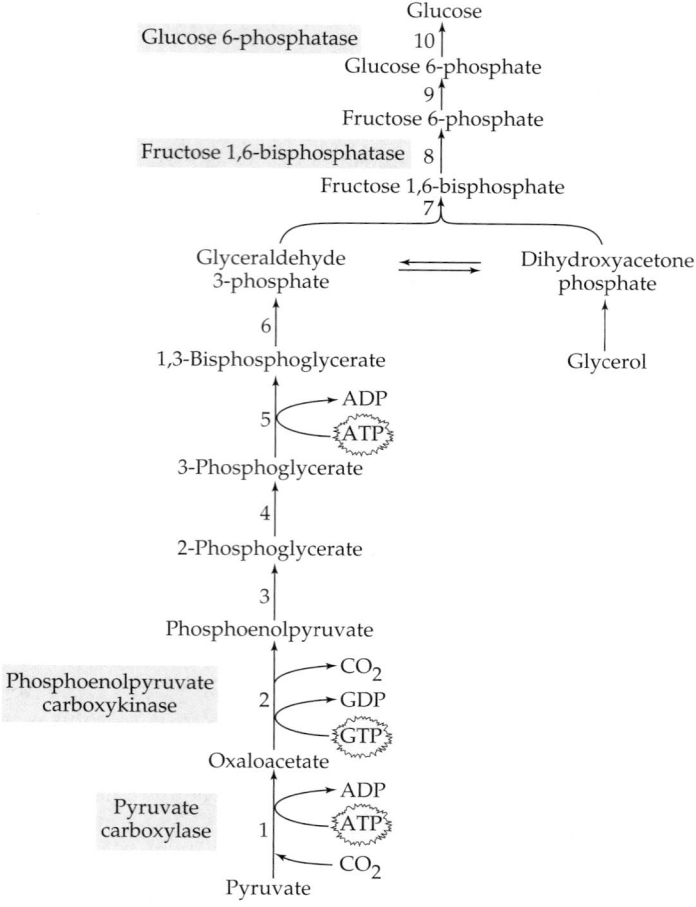

CHEMISTRY IN ACTION

⚕ Diagnosis and Monitoring of Diabetes

Diabetes mellitus is one of the most common metabolic diseases. Although often thought of only as a disease of glucose metabolism, diabetes affects protein and fat metabolism as well, and in some ways the metabolic response resembles starvation. Type I diabetes, an autoimmune disease, is caused by failure of pancreatic β cells to produce insulin. Type II diabetes is caused by "insulin resistance" of target cells; insulin is in good supply but fails to promote the passage of glucose across cell membranes. In both cases, diabetes is not the inability to metabolize glucose but the inability of sufficient glucose to enter cells to be metabolized. A prediabetic condition named metabolic syndrome has been characterized by a set of physical symptoms and blood indicators. Any diabetic as well as a prediabetic with metabolic syndrome is more likely to develop heart disease than nondiabetics. The following table gives typical symptoms, physician observations, and treatment for both types of diabetes.

Diabetes Comparison

	General Symptoms	Type I Diabetes	Type II Diabetes
Physician Observations	Abnormal thirst	Thin	Overweight
	Frequent urination	Losing weight	Gaining weight slowly
	Unusually hungry	Usually under 20 years of age	Usually over 40 years of age
	Injuries heal slowly	Rapid, severe onset	Slow, mild onset
	Persistently tired		
	Dry mouth and itchy skin		
	Blurry vision		
Treatment		Exercise and diet control	Exercise and diet control
		Insulin injections (several times daily)	Oral medications or insulin as needed

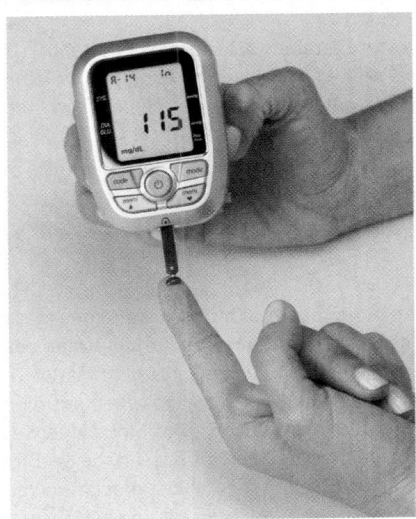

▲ **Glucose blood test.** A tiny drop of blood is absorbed on the test strip in the blood glucose monitor. The results of the test are read in less than 10 seconds by most modern monitors and displayed on an LCD screen.

Glucose measurements are essential in the diagnosis of diabetes mellitus and in the management of diabetic patients, both in a clinical setting and on a day-to-day basis by patients themselves. The *glucose-tolerance test* is among the clinical laboratory tests usually done to pin down a diagnosis of diabetes mellitus. The patient must fast for 10–16 hours, and after a fasting blood sample is drawn, is challenged with a controlled dose sugar drink, and additional blood samples are taken at regular intervals thereafter. The results show an immediate blood glucose rise, followed by a drop in blood glucose. A difference is apparent after 2 hours, when the concentration in a normal individual has dropped to close to the fasting level but that in a diabetic individual remains high. The metabolic syndrome, prediabetic patient has an intermediate response. The fasting glucose level is greater than 100 mg/dL and the challenge response is intermediate between that of the diabetic and nondiabetic patient. A fasting blood glucose concentration of 140 mg/dL or higher and/or a glucose tolerance test concentration that remains above 200 mg/dL beyond 1 hour are considered diagnostic criteria for diabetes. For a firm diagnosis, the glucose tolerance test is usually given more than once. This test does not distinguish between Type I and Type II diabetes. A physician must make that decision based on other information.

An additional test, the A1C test, determines the percent of glycated hemoglobin (glucose covalently bonded to hemoglobin, making it a glycoprotein) present. This value indicates a several month history of blood glucose levels and is used both in diagnosis and in evaluating success and compliance with treatment. Values of 6.5% and higher indicate diabetes; high numbers indicate poor control of the disease.

Individuals with diabetes must monitor their blood glucose levels at home daily, often several times a day. Most tests for glucose rely on detecting a color change that accompanies the oxidation of glucose. Because glucose and its oxidation product, gluconate, are colorless, the oxidation must be tied chemically to the color change of a suitable indicator. Modern methods for glucose detection rely on the action of an enzyme specific for glucose. The most commonly used enzyme is glucose oxidase, and the products of the oxidation are gluconate and hydrogen peroxide (H_2O_2). A second enzyme in the reaction mixture, a peroxidase, catalyzes the reaction of hydrogen peroxide with a dye that gives a detectable color change.

$$\text{Glucose} + O_2 \xrightarrow{\text{Glucose oxidase}} \text{Gluconate} + H_2O_2$$

$$\underset{\text{(colorless)}}{H_2O_2 + \text{Reduced dye}} \xrightarrow{\text{Peroxidase}} \underset{\text{(colored)}}{H_2O_2 + \text{Oxidized dye}}$$

The enzymes needed for the reactions are embedded in the test strip itself and only a miniscule drop of blood is needed. The blood test is desirable because it is specific and quick. It is used to achieve tighter control of blood glucose levels to help those with diabetes live longer, healthier lives.

Remember Maria from the beginning of the chapter? At her follow-up appointment with her physician, her blood tests following a glucose tolerance test showed a classic response for diabetes. The patient history indicated a high probability that she had developed Type II diabetes. She was prescribed exercise and an oral medication designed to improve glucose uptake by cells, and given an appointment with a dietician to help improve her diet. Maria is at increased risk for heart disease because her blood lipids were also elevated, a common complication of Type II diabetes.

CIA Problem 22.9 Briefly describe the enzymatic process used in home glucose monitors for determination of blood glucose levels.

CIA Problem 22.10 How do fasting glucose levels in a diabetic person compare to those in a nondiabetic person?

CIA Problem 22.11 Discuss the differences in the response of a diabetic person compared to those of a nondiabetic person after drinking a glucose solution.

CIA Problem 22.12 If your doctor suspects that you have diabetes, what tests would he or she order to confirm the presence of diabetes?

SUMMARY REVISITING THE CHAPTER LEARNING OBJECTIVES

- **Describe carbohydrate digestion, where it takes place in the body, the enzymes involved, and name the major products of the process.** Carbohydrate *digestion*, the hydrolysis of disaccharides and polysaccharides, begins in the mouth and continues in the stomach and small intestine. The products that enter the bloodstream from the small intestine are monosaccharides—mainly glucose, fructose, and galactose *[see Problems 31–40]*.

- **Identify the pathways by which glucose is first synthesized and then broken down, and describe their interrelationships.** The major catabolic pathway for glucose is *glycolysis*. Pyruvate, the end product of glycolysis, enters the citric acid cycle via acetyl-CoA. An alternative pathway for glucose is *glycogenesis*, the synthesis of glycogen, which is stored mainly in the liver and muscles. Another alternative is the *pentose phosphate pathway*, which provides NADPH and the 5-carbon sugars needed for the synthesis of nucleotides (see Figure 22.2) *[see Problems 23–25, 39, and 40]*.

- **Describe the glycolysis pathway and its products.** Glycolysis (Figure 22.3) is a 10-step pathway that produces two molecules of pyruvate, two molecules of reduced coenzyme (NADH), and two ATP molecules for each molecule of glucose metabolized. Glycolysis begins with phosphorylation (steps 1–3) to form fructose 1,6-bisphosphate, followed by cleavage, and isomerization reactions that produce two molecules of glyceraldehyde 3-phosphate (steps 4–5). Each glyceraldehyde 3-phosphate then proceeds through the energy-generating steps (steps 6–10) in which phosphates are alternately created and then donate their phosphate groups to ADP to yield ATP *[see Problems 22, 26, 30, 41–46, 48, 70–72, and 76]*.

- **Identify where the major monosaccharides enter glycolysis.** Dietary monosaccharides other than glucose enter glycolysis at various points—fructose as fructose 6-phosphate or glyceraldehyde 3-phosphate, galactose as glucose 6-phosphate, and mannose as fructose 6-phosphate *[see Problems 51, 52, 73, 83, and 85]*.

- **Describe the pathways involving pyruvate and their respective outcomes.** Under aerobic conditions, pyruvate is transported into mitochondria and converted to acetyl-CoA for energy generation via the citric acid cycle and oxidative phosphorylation. When there is insufficient oxygen, pyruvate is reduced to lactate, with the production of NAD^+. Production of NAD^+ compensates for the shortage of NAD^+ created by the slowdown of electron transport under anaerobic conditions. Lactate produced in muscle is transported to the liver and is oxidized back to pyruvate. In yeast, pyruvate undergoes *anaerobic fermentation* to yield ethyl alcohol *[see Problems 36, 49, 50, 69, 77, and 84]*.

- **Calculate the energy produced by partial or total oxidation of glucose.** Sum the reactions to determine the total number of ATP, NADH, and $FADH_2$ molecules produced. Use the appropriate multipliers to find the total number of ATP molecules for the reaction *[see Problems 47, 73, 74, and 85]*.

- **Identify the hormones that influence glucose metabolism and describe the changes in metabolism during stress conditions.** *Insulin*, produced when blood glucose concentration rises, accelerates glycolysis and glycogen synthesis to remove glucose from the bloodstream. *Glucagon*, produced when blood glucose concentration drops, accelerates production of glucose in the liver from stored glycogen and from other precursors via the *gluconeogenesis* pathway. Adaptation to stress conditions like fasting and running begins with glucagon mobilizing glucose from storage as glycogen and proceeds to energy production from protein and fat *[see Problems 27, 53–56, 75, and 78–81]*.

- **Explain the pathways for glycogen metabolism and their purpose.** *Glycogenesis* (Figure 22.8), the synthesis of glycogen, puts excess glucose into storage, mainly in muscle and the liver cells. *Glycogenolysis* is the release of stored glucose from glycogen. Glycogenolysis occurs in muscles when there is an immediate need for energy, producing glucose 6-phosphate for intracellular glycolysis. When blood glucose concentration is low, liver cells can convert glucose 6-phosphate to glucose and release it to the bloodstream *[see Problems 38, and 57–60]*.

- **Explain the pathways for synthesis of glucose from noncarbohydrate molecules.** *Gluconeogenesis* (Figure 22.9) maintains glucose levels by synthesizing new glucose from lactate, from certain amino acids derived from proteins, and from glycerol derived from fatty tissue; this pathway, found in liver cells, is part of normal metabolism and is critical during fasting and starvation. The gluconeogenesis pathway uses alternate enzymes for the reverse of the three highly exergonic steps of glycolysis, but otherwise utilizes the same enzymes for reactions that run in reverse of their direction in glycolysis *[see Problems 28, 29, 37, 61–68, 76, and 82]*.

KEY WORDS

Aerobic, *p. 698*	**Digestion**, *p. 691*	**Glycogenolysis**, *p. 705*	**Pentose phosphate pathway,** *p. 692*
Alcoholic fermentation, *p. 699*	**Fermentation**, *p. 699*	**Glycolysis**, *p. 692*	
Anaerobic, *p. 698*	**Gluconeogenesis**, *p. 706*	**Hyperglycemia**, *p. 702*	
	Glycogenesis, *p. 705*	**Hypoglycemia**, *p. 701*	

CONCEPT MAP: GLUCOSE METABOLISM

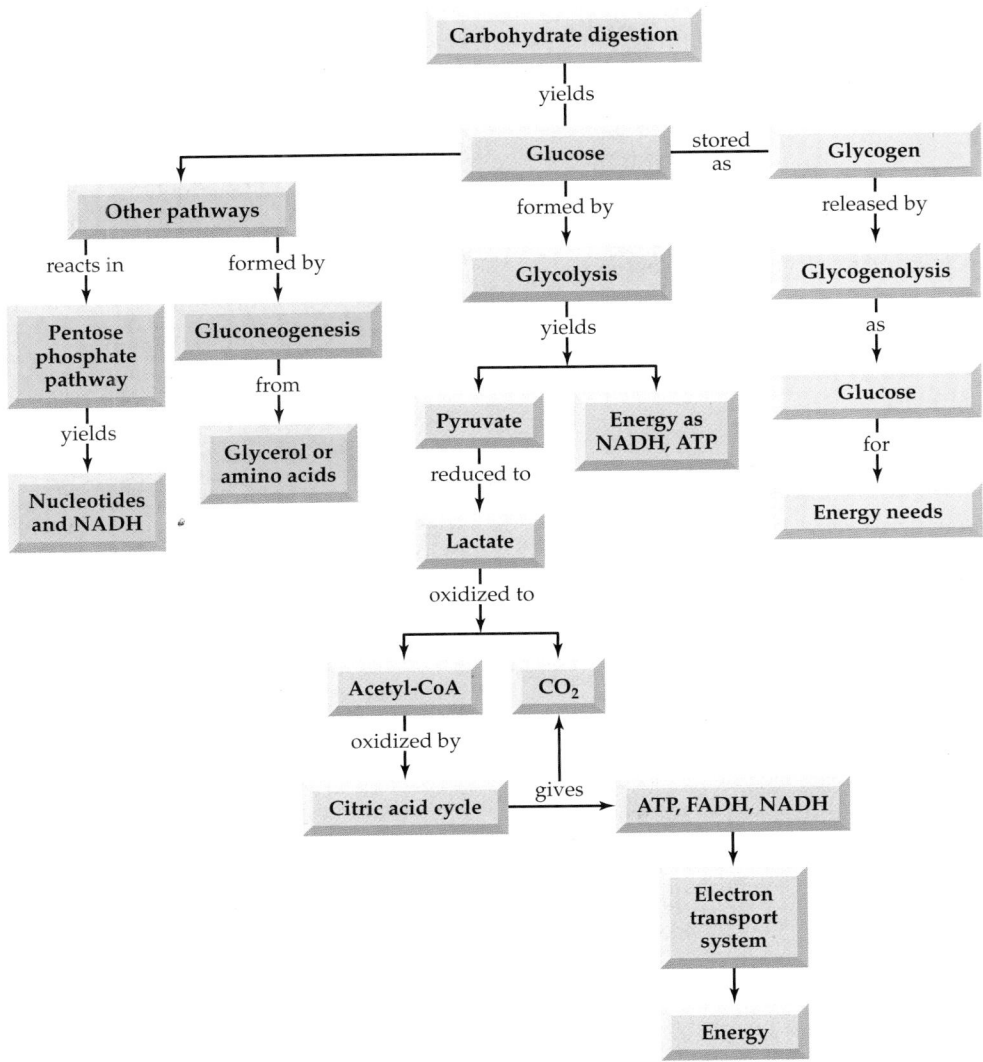

▲ **Figure 22.10 Concept Map.** Glucose is the primary fuel for energy production when pyruvate, the product of glycolysis, is converted to acetyl-CoA and subsequently completely oxidized via the citric acid cycle and oxidative phosphorylation, as seen in Chapter 21. This chapter also explores the relationship between the catabolism and anabolism of glucose. These relationships are shown in the concept map.

⊙⊐ UNDERSTANDING KEY CONCEPTS

22.22 What class of enzymes catalyzes the majority of the reactions involved in carbohydrate digestion?

22.23 Glucose 6-phosphate is in a pivotal position in metabolism. Depending on conditions, glucose 6-phosphate follows one of several pathways. Under what conditions do the following occur?

    (a) Glycolysis

    (b) Hydrolysis to free glucose

    (c) Pentose phosphate pathway

    (d) Glycogenesis

22.24 What "chemical investments" are made to get glycolysis started, and why are they made? What happens in the middle of the pathway to generate two 3-carbon compounds? What are the outcomes of the reactions of these 3-carbon compounds?

22.25 Outline the conditions that direct pyruvate toward the following:

    (a) Entry into the citric acid cycle

    (b) Conversion to ethanol and CO_2

    (c) Conversion to lactate

    (d) Glucose synthesis (gluconeogenesis)

In what tissues or organisms is each pathway present?

22.26 Classify each enzyme of glycolysis into one of the six classes of enzymes. What class of enzymes has the most representatives in glycolysis? Why is this consistent with the goals of glycolysis? Why are ligases *not* represented in glycolysis?

22.27 When blood glucose levels rise following a meal, the following events occur. Arrange these events in the appropriate sequence.

    (a) Glucagon is secreted.

    (b) Glycolysis replenishes ATP supplies.

    (c) Glucose is absorbed by cells.

    (d) The liver releases glucose into the bloodstream.

    (e) Glycogen synthesis (glycogenesis) occurs with excess glucose.

    (f) Blood levels pass through normal to below normal (hypoglycemic).

    (g) Insulin levels rise.

ADDITIONAL PROBLEMS

DIGESTION AND METABOLISM (SECTIONS 22.1 AND 22.2)

22.31 Where does digestion occur in the body, and what kinds of chemical reactions does it involve?

22.32 Complete the following word equation:

$$\text{Lactose} + H_2O \longrightarrow ? + ?$$

Where in the digestive system does this process occur?

22.33 What are the major monosaccharide products produced by digestion of carbohydrates?

22.34 What are the products of digestion of proteins, triacylglycerols, maltose, sucrose, lactose, and starch?

22.35 What do the words *aerobic* and *anaerobic* mean?

22.36 What three products are formed from pyruvate under aerobic, anaerobic, and fermentation conditions?

22.37 Name the substrate and the product of (a) glycolysis and (b) gluconeogenesis.

22.38 Name the substrate and the product of (a) glycogenesis and (b) glycogenolysis.

22.39 What is the major purpose of the pentose phosphate pathway? What cofactor (coenzyme) is used?

22.40 Depending on the body's needs, into what type of compounds is glucose converted in the pentose phosphate pathway?

GLYCOLYSIS (SECTIONS 22.3, 22.4, AND 22.5)

22.41 Where in a liver cell do the following pathways occur?

    (a) Glycolysis

    (b) Gluconeogenesis

    (c) Glycogenesis

    (d) Glycogenolysis

22.42 Which cells, liver, muscle, or brain, use the following pathways?

    (a) Glycolysis

    (b) Gluconeogenesis

    (c) Glycogenesis

    (d) Glycogenolysis

22.28 Name the molecules used for gluconeogenesis. What are the sources of these molecules? Under what conditions would gluconeogenesis occur?

22.29 Fatty acids from stored triacylglycerols (fat) are *not* available for gluconeogenesis. Speculate why we do not have the enzymes to directly convert fatty acids into glucose. Plants (especially seeds) *do* have enzymes to convert fatty acids into carbohydrates. Why are they so lucky?

22.30 The pathway that converts glucose to acetyl-CoA is often referred to as an "aerobic oxidation pathway." (a) Is molecular oxygen involved in any of the steps of glycolysis? (b) Thinking back to Chapter 20, where does molecular oxygen enter the picture?

22.43 Although the catabolism of glucose produces energy, the first step uses energy. Explain why.

22.44 Glycolysis can occur under both aerobic and anaerobic conditions. Why is glycolysis called an anaerobic pathway?

22.45 Which glycolysis reactions are catalyzed by the following enzymes?

    (a) Pyruvate kinase

    (b) Glyceraldehyde 3-phosphate dehydrogenase

    (c) Hexokinase

    (d) Phosphoglycerate mutase

    (e) Aldolase

22.46 Review the 10 steps in glycolysis (Figure 22.3) and then answer the following questions:

    (a) Which steps involve phosphorylation?

    (b) Which step is an oxidation?

    (c) Which step is a dehydration?

22.47 How many moles of ATP are produced by phosphorylation in the following?

    (a) Glycolysis of 1 mol of glucose

    (b) Aerobic conversion of 1 mol of pyruvate to 1 mol of acetyl-CoA

    (c) Catabolism of 1 mol of acetyl-CoA in the citric acid cycle

22.48 For each reaction in Problem 22.47, tell if the ATP formed is produced by oxidative phosphorylation or substrate-level phosphorylation. What is the difference in the two types of ATP formation?

22.49 Why is pyruvate converted to lactate under anaerobic conditions?

22.50 Lactate can be converted into pyruvate by the enzyme lactate dehydrogenase and the coenzyme NAD^+. Write the reaction in the standard biochemical format, using a curved arrow to show the involvement of NAD^+.

22.51 How many moles of CO_2 are produced by the complete catabolism of 1 mol of sucrose?

22.52 How many moles of acetyl-CoA are produced by the complete catabolism of 1 mol of sucrose?

REGULATION OF GLUCOSE METABOLISM AND METABOLISM DURING STRESS (SECTION 22.7)

22.53 Differentiate between the effect of insulin and glucagon on blood sugar concentration.

22.54 Differentiate between blood sugar levels and resulting symptoms in hyperglycemia and hypoglycemia.

22.55 What molecules are used initially during starvation or fasting to produce glucose?

22.56 (Fill in the blank) As starvation continues, acetyl-CoA is converted to _____ to prevent buildup of acetyl-CoA in the cells.

GLYCOGEN CATABOLISM AND ANABOLISM (SECTION 22.8)

22.57 Where is most of the glycogen in the body stored?

22.58 What major site of glycogen storage is not able to release glucose to the bloodstream?

22.59 How is UTP used in the formation of glycogen from glucose?

22.60 Why does glycogenolysis use fewer steps than the reverse process, glycogenesis? Which process uses less energy?

GLUCOSE FROM NONCARBOHYDRATES (SECTION 22.9)

22.61 Name the anabolic pathway for making glucose.

22.62 Name the two molecules that serve as starting materials for glucose synthesis.

22.63 (Fill in the blanks.) Pyruvate is initially converted to _____ in the anabolism of glucose. That molecule in turn is converted to _____.

22.64 Explain why pyruvate cannot be converted to glucose in an exact reverse of the glycolysis pathway.

22.65 Explain how the energy-releasing steps of glycolysis are reversed in gluconeogenesis.

22.66 How many steps in gluconeogenesis are not the exact reversal of the steps in glycolysis? What kind of conversion of substrate to product does each involve? What is the common theme in each of these reactions?

22.67 What is the Cori cycle?

22.68 Explain why the Cori cycle is necessary and when your cells would use this cycle.

CONCEPTUAL PROBLEMS

22.69 Why can pyruvate cross the mitochondrial membrane but no other molecule after step 1 in glycolysis can?

22.70 Look at the glycolysis pathway (Figure 22.3). With what type of reactions are kinase enzymes usually associated?

22.71 Explain why one more ATP is produced when glucose is obtained from glycogen rather than used directly from the blood.

22.72 Why is it important that glycolysis be tightly controlled by the cell?

22.73 How many moles of ATP are generated from the catabolism of fructose (by glycolysis) in (a) liver cells and (b) muscle cells?

22.74 Which of the following conversions would you expect to consume energy and which would you expect to yield energy based on the final oxidation state of the coenzymes involved in each reaction?

   (a) pyruvate $\longrightarrow$ lactate

   (b) pyruvate $\longrightarrow$ acetyl-CoA + CO_2

22.75 Why is it important for muscle cells to export lactate into the bloodstream during heavy exercise?

22.76 Under which physiological condition is the following pathway the predominant one?

   (a) glycolysis

   (b) gluconeogenesis

22.77 Why is it important for the cell that the NADH produced when pyruvate is converted to lactate be converted back to NAD^+?

22.78 What are the characteristics of Type I diabetes?

22.79 What are the characteristics of Type II diabetes?

22.80 Explain the relationship between metabolic syndrome and diabetes.

22.81 Many diabetics suffer blindness due to cataracts. Why is this condition associated with this disease?

GROUP PROBLEMS

22.82 A primary function of liver cells is to synthesize new glucose via gluconeogenesis, while working muscle cells use glucose via glycolysis. Why is this a good physiological strategy for your body?

22.83 In liver cells, galactose is converted to glucose 6-phosphate in a four-step process; it then enters glycolysis. People with the genetic disease galactosemia lack one or more of the enzymes necessary to convert galactose to glucose 6-phosphate; galactose instead is converted to undesirable molecules that damage various organs. This disease can be controlled by a careful diet. What food or foods are a major source of galactose in the diet?

22.84 It is important to avoid air when making wine, so a novice winemaker added yeast to fresh grape juice and placed it in a sealed bottle to avoid air. Several days later, the lid exploded off the bottle. Explain the biochemistry responsible for the exploding lid.

22.85 Is the same net production of ATP observed in the complete oxidation of fructose as is observed in the complete oxidation of glucose? Why or why not?

23

Lipids

CONTENTS

◀◀◀ CONCEPTS TO REVIEW

A. Intermolecular Forces
   (Section 8.2)

B. Cis–Trans Isomerism
   (Section 13.3)

C. Esters and Amides
   (Sections 17.4 and 17.6)

D. Phosphoric Acid Derivatives
   (Section 17.8)

E. Carboxylic Acids
   (Sections 17.1 and 17.2)

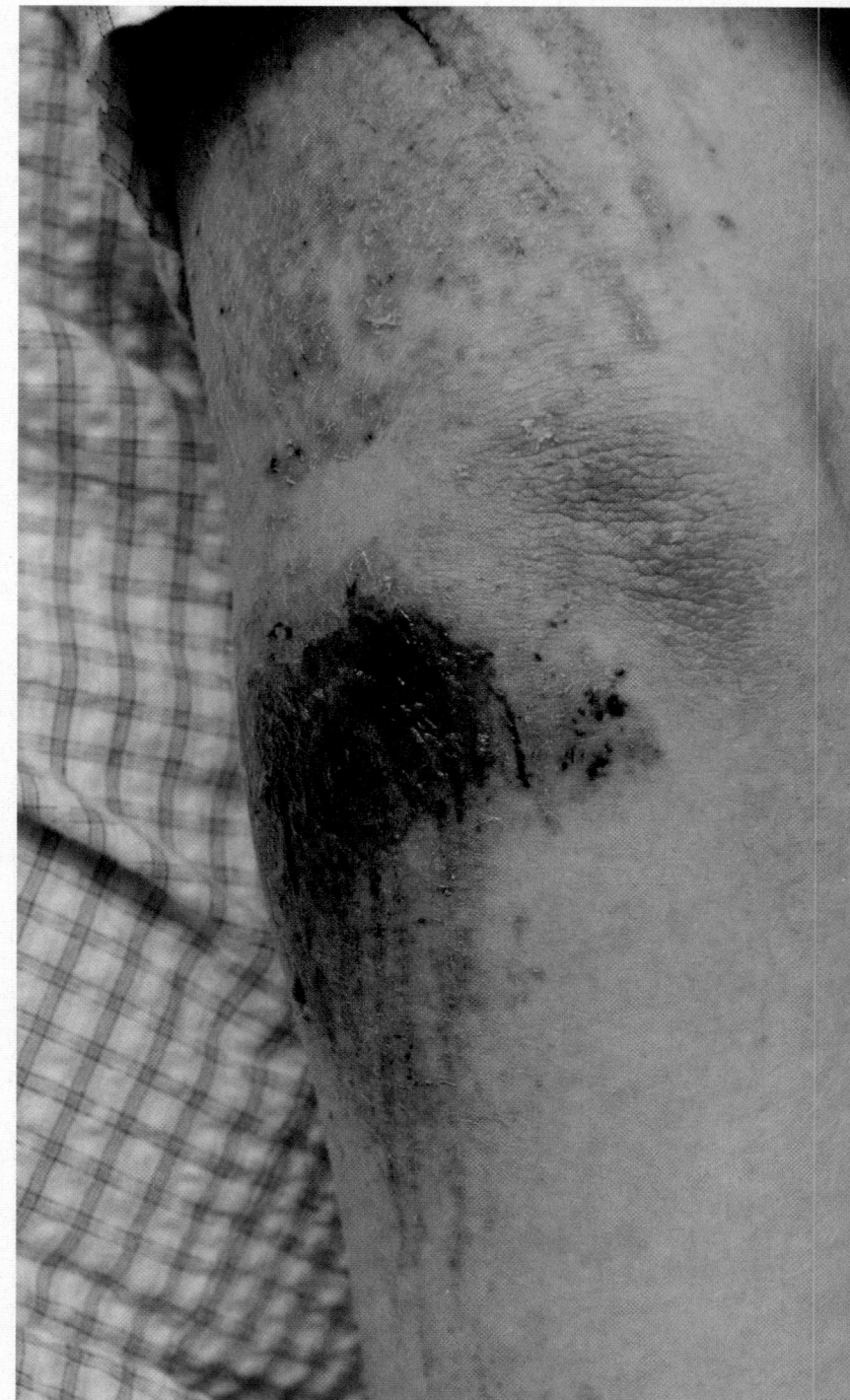

▲ The red, raised but unbroken skin around this abrasion is a local reaction caused by a class of lipids called prostaglandins, a type of eicosanoid.

ipids are less well known than carbohydrates and proteins, yet lipids are just as essential to our diet and well-being. They have three major roles in human biochemistry: (1) Within fat cells *(adipocytes)*, they store energy from metabolism of food. (2) As part of all cell membranes, they keep separate the different chemical environments inside and outside the cells. (3) In the endocrine system and elsewhere, lipids serve as chemical messengers;

steroids and eicosanoids are two such examples. Steroids serve as chemical messengers circulating throughout the body, whereas certain eicosanoids are responsible for the localized minor pain you may experience from scrapes and abrasions from falls, or the redness, heat, and swelling from tangling with a rose bush. One response to alleviate minor pain is to take aspirin to lessen the discomfort because it has analgesic, antipyretic (fever reducing), and anti-inflammatory properties. Why does aspirin, one of the oldest known analgesics, alleviate pain and hasten the disappearance of redness, heat, and swelling of a scrape or cut when other nonsteroidal anti-inflammatory drugs (NSAIDs) do not? The Chemistry in Action "Eicosanoids: Prostaglandins and Leukotrienes" at the end of this chapter has the answer, which lies in a lipid.

23.1 Structure and Classification of Lipids

Learning Objective:

- Describe the chemical structures and general properties of fatty acids, waxes, sterols, fats, and oils.

Lipids are naturally occurring organic molecules that are nonpolar and therefore dissolve in nonpolar organic solvents but not in water. For example, if a sample of plant or animal tissue is placed in a kitchen blender, finely ground, and then treated with ether, any molecule that dissolves in ether is a lipid and any molecule that does not dissolve in ether (including carbohydrates, proteins, and inorganic salts) is not a lipid.

Since **lipids** are defined by solubility in nonpolar solvents (a physical property) rather than by chemical structure, it should not surprise you that there are a great many different kinds and that they serve a variety of functions in the body. In the following examples of lipid structures, note that the molecules contain large hydrocarbon portions and not many polar groups, which accounts for their solubility behavior. Many lipids have hydrocarbon or modified hydrocarbon structures, properties, and behavior. This similarity to hydrocarbons and their derivatives unifies a set of highly diverse molecules into one class.

Figure 23.1 organizes the classes of lipids discussed in this chapter according to their chemical structures. Many lipids are esters or amides of carboxylic acids with long, unbranched hydrocarbon chains, known as **fatty acids.** The fatty acids that contain unbranched hydrocarbon chains are loosely referred to as *straight-chain fatty acids.*

Lipid A naturally occurring molecule from a plant or animal that is soluble in nonpolar organic solvents.

Fatty acid A long-chain carboxylic acid; those in animal fats and vegetable oils often have 12–22 carbon atoms.

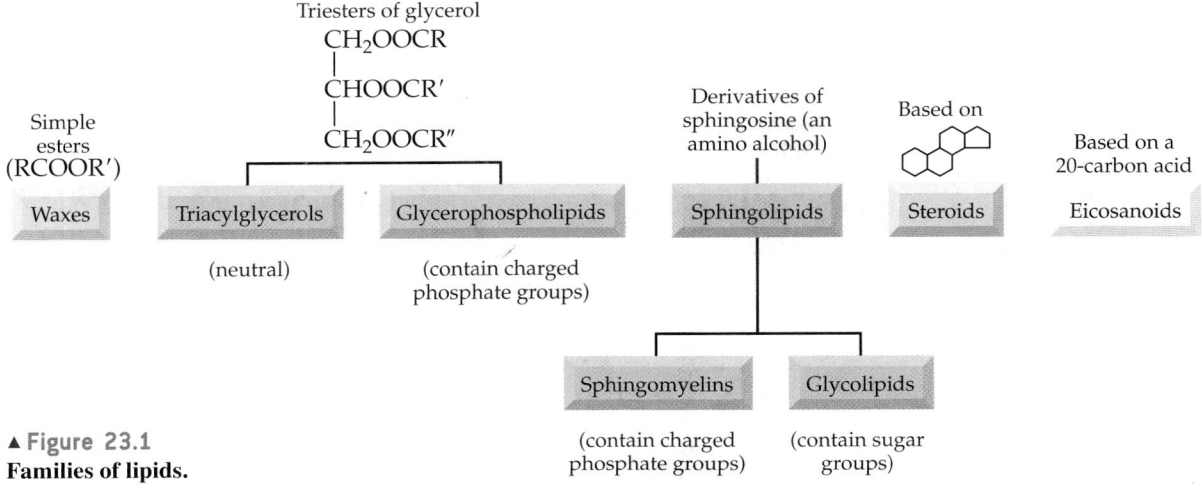

▲ **Figure 23.1**
Families of lipids.

Lipids That Are Esters or Amides of Fatty Acids

- *Waxes* are carboxylic acid esters (RCOOR′) with long, straight hydrocarbon chains in both R groups; they are secreted by sebaceous glands in the skin of animals and perform mostly external protective functions (Section 23.2).

- *Triacylglycerols* are carboxylic acid triesters of glycerol, a three-carbon trialcohol. Triacylglycerols (Sections 23.2–23.3) are found in most dietary fats and oils and are also the fat storage molecules in our body. They are a major source of biochemical energy, a function described in Chapter 24.

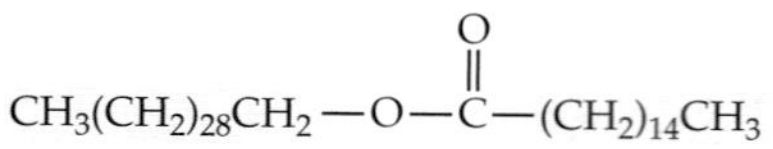

A wax

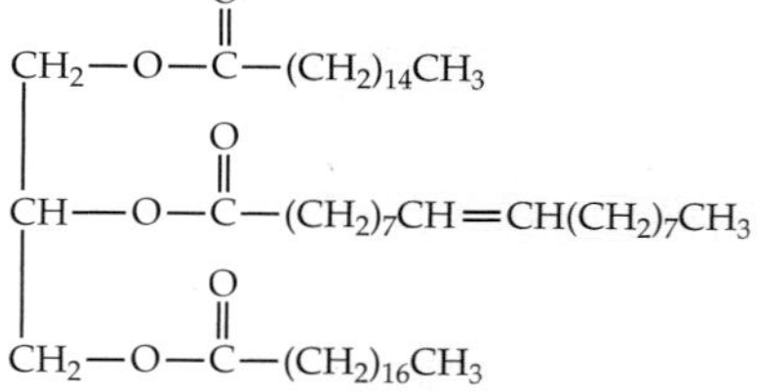

A triacylglycerol

- *Glycerophospholipids* (Section 23.5) are triesters of glycerol that contain charged phosphate-diester groups and are abundant in cell membranes. Together with other lipids, they help to control the flow of molecules into and out of cells.
- *Sphingomyelins* are amides derived from an amino alcohol *(sphingosine)* that also contain charged phosphate-diester groups; they are essential to the structure of cell membranes (Section 23.5) and are especially abundant in nerve cell membranes.
- *Glycolipids* are different amides derived from *sphingosine* that contain polar carbohydrate groups; on cell surfaces the carbohydrate portion is recognized and interacts with intercellular messengers (Section 23.5).

Other Types of Lipids

There are also two groups of lipids that are not esters or amides:

- *Sterols* are a family of molecules that all contain the four-ring steroid nucleus structure. Important sterols are cholesterol, found in cell membranes; bile salts, necessary for fat emulsification in digestion; and sex hormones (Section 23.6).

Eicosanoid A lipid derived from a 20-carbon unsaturated carboxylic acid.

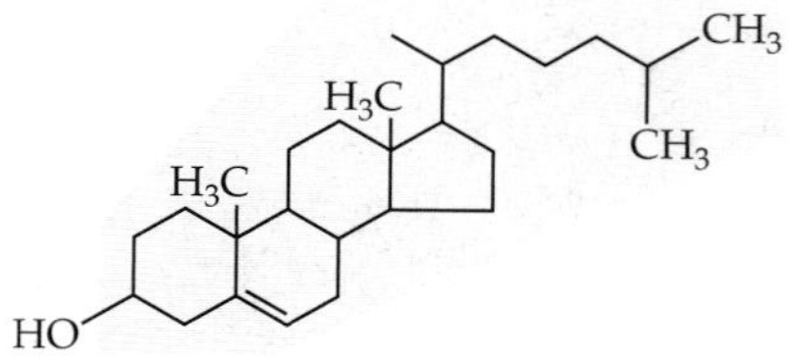

- *Eicosanoids.* The eicosanoids are carboxylic acids that are a special type of localized intercellular chemical messenger (see the Chemistry in Action "Eicosanoids: Prostaglandins and Leukotrienes").

Cholesterol, a sterol

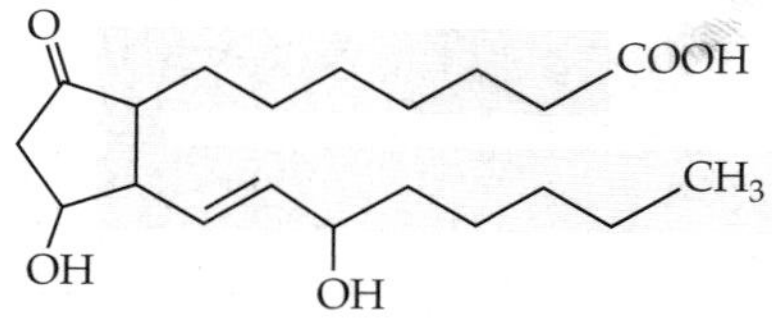

A prostaglandin

Worked Example 23.1 Identifying Lipid Families

Use Figure 23.1 to identify the family of lipids to which each of these molecules belongs.

(a)

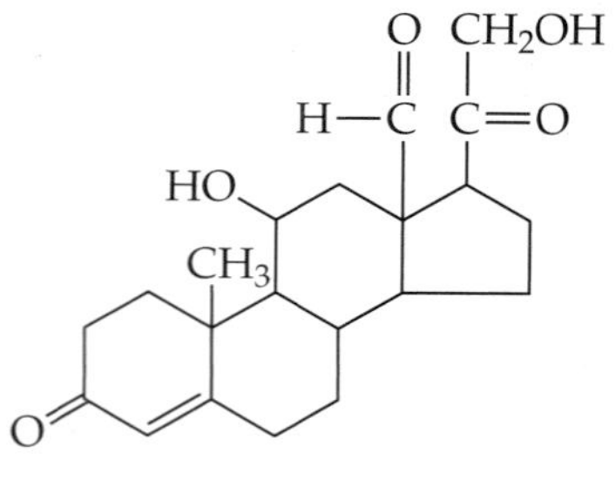

(b)

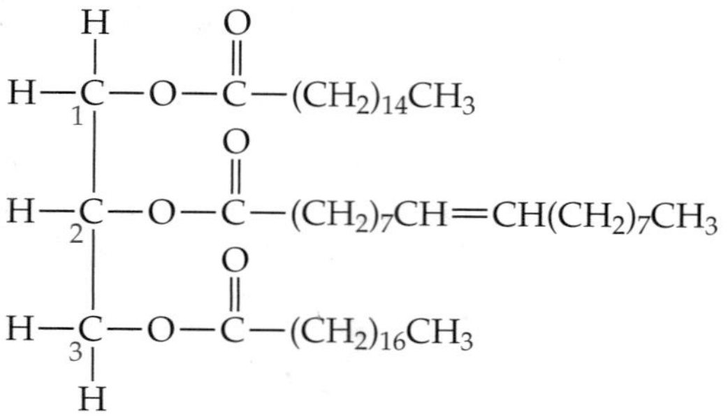

ANALYSIS Inspect the molecules and note their distinguishing characteristics. Molecule (a) has a four-member fused-ring system. Only sterols have this structure. Molecule (b) has three fatty acids esterified to a single backbone molecule—glycerol. Thus, (b) must be a member of the triacylglycerol family.

SOLUTION
Molecule (a) is a sterol, and molecule (b) is a triacylglycerol.

PROBLEM 23.1

Use Figure 23.1 to identify the family of lipids to which each of these molecules belongs.

(a)

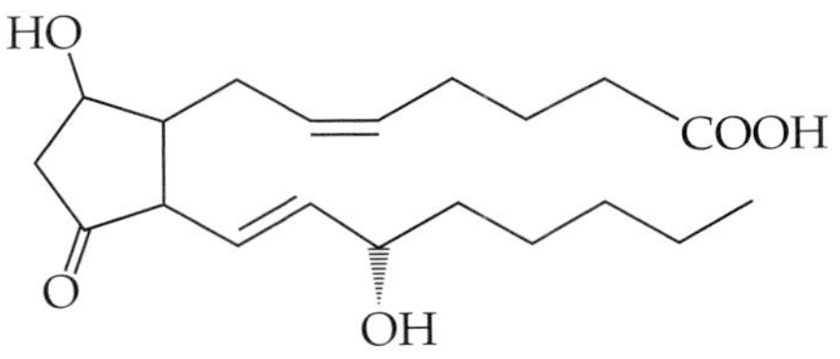

(b)

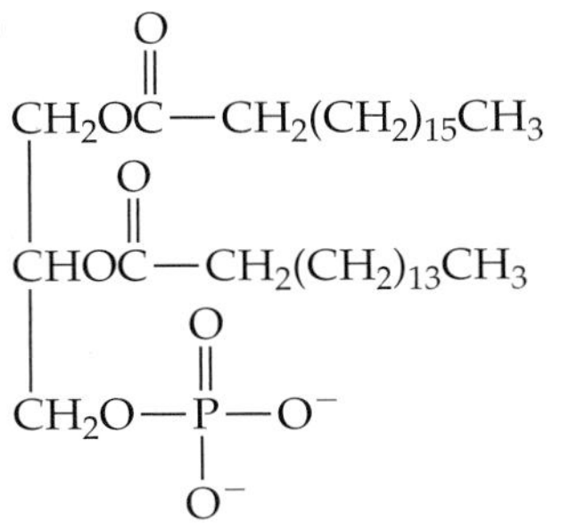

$$CH_2OC-CH_2(CH_2)_{15}CH_3$$
$$CHOC-CH_2(CH_2)_{13}CH_3$$
$$CH_2O-P-O^-$$
$$O^-$$

(c) $CH_3(CH_2)_{16}C-O-CH_2(CH_2)_6CH=CH(CH_2)_6CH_3$

23.2 Fatty Acids and Their Esters

Learning Objective:

• Describe the characteristics of fatty acids and fatty acid esters.

Naturally occurring fats and oils are triesters formed between glycerol and fatty acids. Fatty acids are long, unbranched hydrocarbon chains with a carboxylic acid group at one end. Most have even numbers of carbon atoms. Fatty acids may or may not contain carbon–carbon double bonds. Those containing only carbon–carbon single bonds are known as **saturated fatty acids;** those containing one or more carbon–carbon double bonds are known as **unsaturated fatty acids.** If double bonds are present in naturally occurring fats and oils, the double bonds are usually *cis* rather than *trans*.

◀◀◀ **CONCEPTS TO REVIEW** Recall that an ester, RCOOR′, is formed from a carboxylic acid and an alcohol (Section 17.4).

◀◀◀ In the *cis* configuration, the groups attached to the double-bond carbons are on the same side of the double bond (Section 13.3).

Saturated fatty acid A long-chain carboxylic acid containing only carbon–carbon single bonds.

Unsaturated fatty acid A long-chain carboxylic acid containing one or more carbon–carbon double bonds.

$$CH_3CH_2CH_2CH_2CH_2CH_2CH_2CH_2CH_2CH_2CH_2CH_2CH_2CH_2CH_2C-OH$$

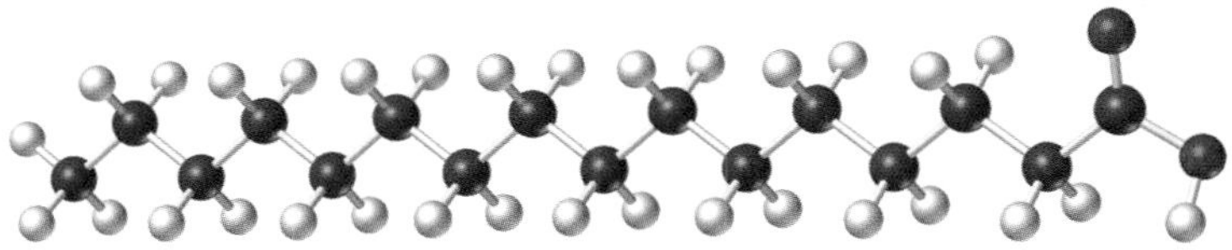

A saturated fatty acid
(palmitic acid)

$$CH_3CH_2CH=CHCH_2CH=CHCH_2CH=CHCH_2CH_2CH_2CH_2CH_2CH_2CH_2C-OH$$

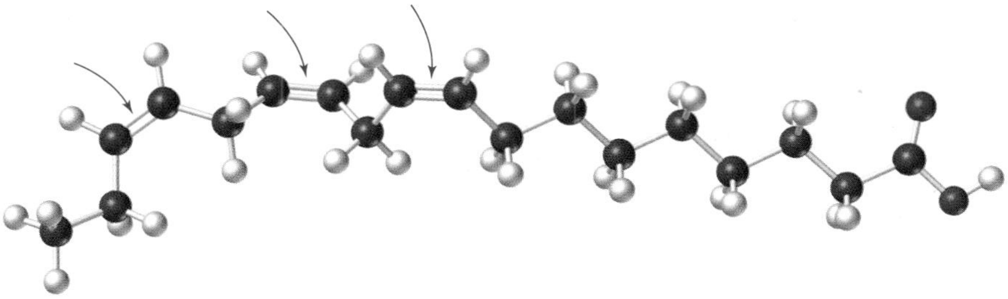

A cis unsaturated fatty acid
(linolenic acid)

Some of the common fatty acids are listed in Table 23.1. Chemists use a shorthand nomenclature for fatty acids that avoids using the common names. This notation uses C for carbon followed by the number of carbon atoms present in the fatty acid, a colon, and the number of unsaturated bonds present. For example, lauric acid, which contains 12 carbon atoms and no double bonds, is represented by C12:0. Oleic acid is *monounsaturated,* that is, it has only one carbon–carbon double bond. The **polyunsaturated fatty acids** have more than one carbon–carbon double bond. The number of double bonds present in a fatty acid is referred to as the **degree of unsaturation.**

Polyunsaturated fatty acid A long-chain carboxylic acid that has two or more carbon–carbon double bonds.

Degree of unsaturation The number of carbon–carbon double bonds in a molecule.

Table 23.1 Structures of Some Common Fatty Acids

Name	Typical Source	Number of Carbons	Number of Double Bonds	Condensed Formula	Condensed Notation	Melting Point (°C)
Saturated						
Lauric	Coconut oil	12	0	$CH_3(CH_2)_{10}COOH$	C12:0	44
Myristic	Butter fat	14	0	$CH_3(CH_2)_{12}COOH$	C14:0	58
Palmitic	Most fats and oils	16	0	$CH_3(CH_2)_{14}COOH$	C16:0	63
Stearic	Most fats and oils	18	0	$CH_3(CH_2)_{16}COOH$	C18:0	70
Unsaturated						
Oleic	Olive oil	18	1	$CH_3(CH_2)_7CH{=}CH(CH_2)_7COOH\,(cis)$	C18:1	4
Linoleic	Vegetable oils	18	2	$CH_3(CH_2)_3(CH_2CH{=}CH)_2(CH_2)_7COOH\,(all\ cis)$	C18:2	−5
Linolenic	Soybean and canola oils	18	3	$CH_3(CH_2CH{=}CH)_3(CH_2)_7COOH\,(all\ cis)$	C18:3	−11
Arachidonic	Animal fat	20	4	$CH_3(CH_2)_4(CH_2CH{=}CH)_4(CH_2)_2COOH\,(all\ cis)$	C18:4	−50

Wax A mixture of monoesters of long-chain carboxylic acids with long-chain alcohols.

Two of the polyunsaturated fatty acids, linoleic and linolenic, are essential in the human diet because the body does not synthesize them, even though these omega-6 and omega-3 fatty acids are needed for the synthesis of other lipids. Infants grow poorly and develop severe skin lesions if fed a diet lacking these acids. Adults usually have sufficient reserves in body fat to avoid such problems. A deficiency in adults can arise, however, after long-term intravenous feeding that contains inadequate essential fatty acids or among those surviving on limited and inadequate diets.

Example of a wax

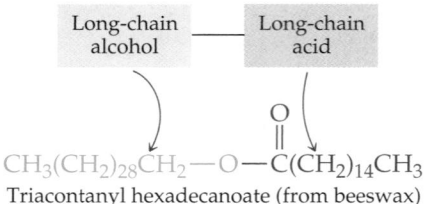

$$CH_3(CH_2)_{28}CH_2-O-\overset{\overset{\textstyle O}{\|}}{C}(CH_2)_{14}CH_3$$

Triacontanyl hexadecanoate (from beeswax)

▲ This grebe is coated with oil spilled by a tanker that sank off Brittany on the northwest coast of France. If the oil is not removed from its feathers, the bird will perish.

Waxes

The simplest fatty acid esters in nature are waxes. A **wax** is a mixture of fatty acids and long-chain alcohol esters. The acids usually have an even number of carbon atoms, generally from 16 to 36 carbons, whereas the alcohols have an even number of carbon atoms ranging from 24 to 36 carbons. For example, a major component in beeswax is the ester formed from a 30-carbon alcohol (triacontanol) and a 16-carbon acid (palmitic acid). The waxy protective coatings on most fruits, berries, leaves, and animal furs have similar structures. Aquatic birds have a water-repellent waxy coating on their feathers. When caught in an oil spill, the waxy coating dissolves in the oil and the birds lose their buoyancy.

Triacylglycerols

Animal fats and vegetable oils are the most plentiful lipids in nature. Although they appear different—animal fats like butter and lard are solid, whereas vegetable oils like corn, olive, soybean, and peanut oil are liquid—their structures are closely related. All fats and oils are composed of triesters of glycerol (1,2,3-propane-triol, also known as glycerin) with three fatty acids. They are named chemically as **triacylglycerols** but are often called **triglycerides.**

Triacylglycerol **(triglyceride)** A triester of glycerol with three fatty acids.

Triacylglycerols

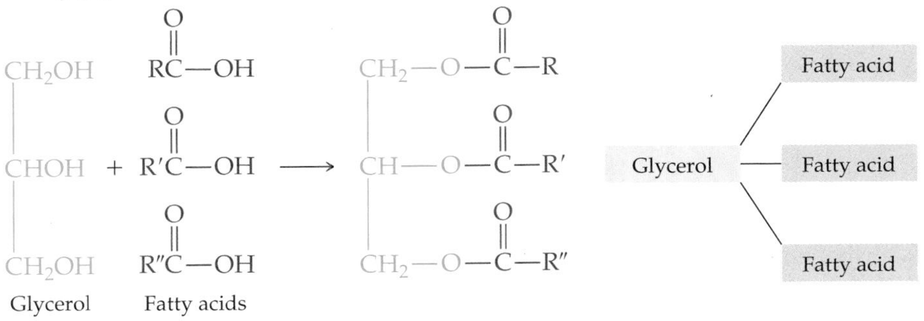

The three fatty acids of any specific triacylglycerol are not necessarily the same, as is the case in the following molecule.

Example of a triacylglycerol

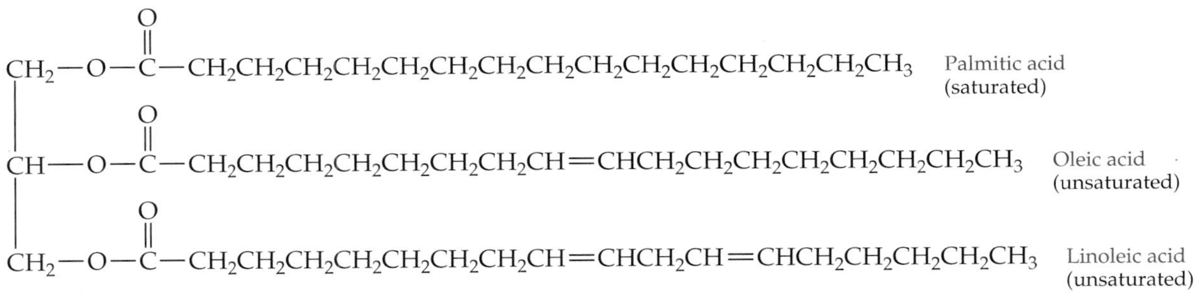

$CH_2-O-\overset{\overset{O}{\|}}{C}-CH_2CH_2CH_2CH_2CH_2CH_2CH_2CH_2CH_2CH_2CH_2CH_2CH_2CH_2CH_3$ Palmitic acid (saturated)

$CH-O-\overset{\overset{O}{\|}}{C}-CH_2CH_2CH_2CH_2CH_2CH_2CH_2CH=CHCH_2CH_2CH_2CH_2CH_2CH_2CH_2CH_3$ Oleic acid (unsaturated)

$CH_2-O-\overset{\overset{O}{\|}}{C}-CH_2CH_2CH_2CH_2CH_2CH_2CH_2CH=CHCH_2CH=CHCH_2CH_2CH_2CH_2CH_3$ Linoleic acid (unsaturated)

Furthermore, the fat or oil from a given natural source is a complex mixture of many different triacylglycerols. Table 23.2 lists the average composition of fats and oils from several different sources. Note particularly that vegetable oils consist almost entirely of unsaturated fatty acids, whereas animal fats contain a much larger percentage of saturated fatty acids. This difference in composition is the primary reason for the different melting points of fats and oils, as explained in the next section.

Table 23.2 Approximate Composition of Some Common Fats and Oils*

Source	Saturated Fatty Acids (%)			Unsaturated Fatty Acids (%)		
	C12:0 Lauric	C14:0 Myristic	C16:0 Palmitic	C18:0 Stearic	C18:1 Oleic	C18:2 Linoleic
Animal Fat						
Lard	—	1	25	15	50	6
Butter	2	10	25	10	25	5
Human fat	1	3	25	8	46	10
Whale blubber	—	8	12	3	35	10
Vegetable Oil						
Corn	—	1	8	4	46	42
Olive	—	1	5	5	83	7
Peanut	—	—	7	5	60	20
Soybean	—	—	7	4	34	53

*Where totals are less than 100%, small quantities of several other acids are present, with cholesterol also present in animal fats.

PROBLEM 23.2

One of the constituents of the carnauba wax used in floor and furniture polish is an ester of a 32-carbon straight-chain alcohol with a C20:0 straight-chain carboxylic acid. Draw the structure of this ester. (Use subscripts to show the numbers of connected CH_2 groups.)

PROBLEM 23.3

Draw the structure of a triacylglycerol whose components are glycerol and three oleic acid acyl groups.

🔑 **KEY CONCEPT PROBLEM 23.4**

(a) Which animal fat has the largest percentage of saturated fatty acids?
(b) Which vegetable oil has the largest percentage of polyunsaturated fatty acids?
(c) Which fat or oil has the largest percentage of the essential fatty acid linoleic acid?

23.3 Properties of Fats and Oils

Learning Objective:

• List the physical properties of fats and oils and explain why they are different.

Oil A mixture of triacylglycerols that is liquid because it contains a high proportion of unsaturated fatty acids.

Fat A mixture of triacylglycerols that is solid because it contains a high proportion of saturated fatty acids.

A saturated fat has only single C–C bonds and appears straight

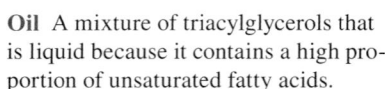

Stearic acid, an 18-carbon saturated fatty acid

Unsaturated fats bend due to cis double bonds

cis double bonds

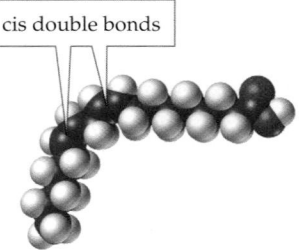

Linoleic acid, an 18-carbon unsaturated fatty acid

Table 23.1 shows that as the number of double bonds in a fatty acid increases, the melting point decreases. For example, the saturated 18-carbon acid (stearic) melts at 70 °C, the monounsaturated 18-carbon acid (oleic) melts at 4 °C, and the diunsaturated 18-carbon acid (linoleic) melts at −5 °C. The same trend also holds true for triacylglycerols: the more highly unsaturated the acyl groups in a triacylglycerol, the lower its melting point. The dissimilarity in melting points between fats and oils is a consequence of this difference. Vegetable **oils** are lower melting because oils generally have a higher proportion of unsaturated fatty acids than animal **fats.**

How do the double bonds make such a significant difference in the melting point? Compare the shapes of a saturated and an unsaturated fatty acid molecules in the margin.

The hydrocarbon chains in saturated acids are uniform in shape with identical angles at each carbon atom, and the chains are flexible, allowing them to nestle together. By contrast, the carbon chains in unsaturated acids have rigid kinks wherever they contain *cis* double bonds. The kinks make it difficult for such chains to fit next to each other in the orderly fashion necessary to form a solid. The more double bonds there are in a triacylglycerol, the harder it is for it to solidify. The shapes of the molecular models in Figure 23.2 further illustrate this concept.

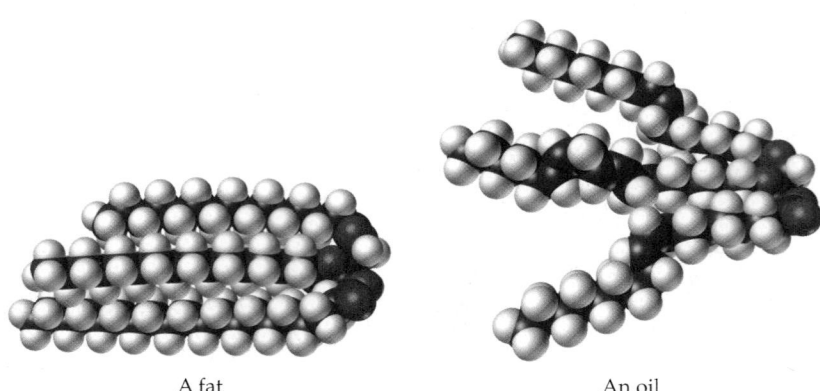

A fat   An oil

▲ **Figure 23.2**
Triacylglycerols from a fat and an oil.

CHEMISTRY IN ACTION

Lipids in the Diet

The major recognizable sources of fats and oils in our diet are butter and margarine, vegetable oils, the visible fat in meat, and chicken skin. In addition, triacylglycerols in meat, poultry, fish, dairy products, and eggs add saturated fats to our diet, along with small quantities of cholesterol. Vegetable oils, such as those in nuts, seeds, and whole-grain cereals, have a higher unsaturated fatty acid content and no cholesterol. Vegetable oils never contain cholesterol because plants do not synthesize cholesterol.

Fats and oils are a popular component of our diet: they taste good, give a pleasant texture to food, and, because they are digested slowly, give a feeling of satisfaction after a meal. The percentage of calories from fats and oils in the average U.S. diet has declined from 40–45%, to around 35%, a number approaching the recommended 30%. Excess energy from dietary fats and oils is mostly stored as fat in adipose tissue.

Concern for the relationships among saturated fats, cholesterol levels, and various diseases—most notably heart disease and cancer (see the Chemistry in Action "Fat Storage, Lipids, and Atherosclerosis," Chapter 24)—caused a reevaluation of the kinds of fats recommended for consumption. The consumption of butter, eggs, beef, and whole milk (all containing relatively high proportions of saturated fat and cholesterol) decreased in response to new nutrition guidelines. This decrease in fat intake is relative, however; at the same time, the total number of calories consumed increased. The increase is attributed to an increase in carbohydrates eaten. So, unfortunately, the change in fat intake did not coincide with a reduction in obesity, which is a weight 20% over the desirable weight for a person's height, sex, and activity level or a body mass index (BMI) of 30 or greater. In fact, concern has been accelerating in recent years over a rise in obesity in the U.S. population and its inevitable association with heart disease and diabetes.

Several organizations, including the U.S. Food and Drug Administration (FDA), recommend a diet with not more than 30% of its calories from fats and oils. In a daily diet of 2200 Cal, which is about right for teenage girls, active women, and sedentary men, 30% from fats and oils is approximately 73 grams, the amount in 6 tablespoons of butter. Men and very active women require more daily calories and can include proportionately more fats in their diets.

▲ A selection of appealing but high-fat foods.

The Nutrition Facts labels (see the Chemistry in Action "Vitamins, Minerals, and Food Labels," Chapter 19) list the calories from fat, grams of fat (which includes all triacylglycerols), and grams of saturated fat in a single serving of a commercially prepared food. The FDA further recommends that not more than 10% of daily calories come from saturated fat and not more than 300 mg of cholesterol be included in the daily diet. For those with the goal of 2200 Cal/day, the limit is 24 g of saturated fats. In order to reduce dietary intake of saturated fats you should choose low-fat varieties of foods and foods that contain different kinds of fats. The foods highest in cholesterol are high-fat dairy products, liver, and egg yolks.

CIA Problem 23.1 Fats and oils are major sources of triacylglycerols. List some other foods that are associated with high-lipid content.

CIA Problem 23.2 According to the FDA, what is the maximum percentage of your daily calories that should come from fats and oils?

CIA Problem 23.3 Which one should you choose for a treat—a small dipped ice cream cone from kiosk A or two oatmeal cookies from kiosk B? Some of the nutrition facts for these choices are listed in the following table. To decide, consider which snack would best help you stay within the nutrition guidelines regarding daily intake of total fat and saturated fat in the diet.

Food	Total Calories	Total Fat (g)	Saturated Fat (g)	% Calories from Fat	Carbohydrates (g)	% Calories from Carbohydrates
Cone	340	17	9	45	42	49
Two Cookies	300	12	2	36	46	61

HANDS-ON CHEMISTRY 23.1

How can you tell if a food contains fat? Use this simple test. Place a small amount of your sample (cookie, cracker, cereal, candy bar, carrot, etc.) on a piece of paper (notebook, newspaper, or napkin). Observe the paper and sample in 15 minute intervals for an hour. What did you see? Did you expect this? Foods containing a lot of fat will leave a large "grease" spot while foods that contain little fat will leave either no greasy spot or a small one.

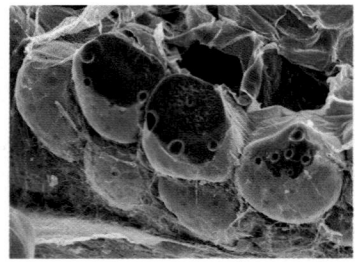

▲ Where the fat goes? Each of these adipose tissue cells holds a globule of fat (magnified more than 500 times).

LOOKING AHEAD ➤ Triacylglycerols from plants and animals are a major component of our diet. In our bodies, they are the depots for energy storage. Therefore, in considering the metabolism of lipids, it is the metabolism of triacylglycerols that is of greatest interest. This topic is discussed in Chapter 24.

Triacylglycerols are uncharged, nonpolar, hydrophobic molecules. When stored in fatty tissue they coalesce, and the interior of an adipocyte (fat cell) is occupied by one large fat droplet with the cell's nucleus pushed to one side. The primary function of triacylglycerols is long-term storage of energy for the organism. In addition, adipose tissue serves to provide thermal insulation and protective padding. Most fatty tissue is located under the skin or in the abdominal cavity, where it cushions the organs.

We are accustomed to the characteristic yellow color and flavors of cooking oils, but these are caused by natural materials carried along during production of the oils from plants; pure oils are colorless and odorless. Overheating, or exposure to air or oxidizing agents, causes decomposition to products with unpleasant odors or flavors, creating what we call a *rancid oil*. Antioxidants such as phenolic compounds are added to prepared foods to prevent oxidation of their oils.

Properties of the Triacylglycerols in Natural Fats and Oils

- Nonpolar and hydrophobic
- No ionic charges
- Solid triacylglycerols (fats)—high proportion of saturated fatty acid chains
- Liquid triacylglycerols (oils)—high proportion of unsaturated fatty acid chains

Worked Example 23.2 Comparing Melting Points

Which of these two fatty acids has the higher melting point?

$$\text{(a) } CH_3(CH_2)_4CH=CHCH_2CH=CHCH_2(CH_2)_6\overset{\displaystyle O}{\overset{\|}{C}}-OH \qquad \text{(b) } CH_3(CH_2)_5CH=CHCH_2(CH_2)_6\overset{\displaystyle O}{\overset{\|}{C}}-OH$$

ANALYSIS First, determine the chain length (number of carbon atoms) and the number of unsaturated bonds present. In general, the more carbon atoms present in a molecule, the higher the melting point. However, the higher the number of unsaturated bonds, the lower the melting point. The degree of unsaturation is more important than the number of carbon atoms when the number of carbon atoms is identical or similar.

SOLUTION
Molecule (a) has 18 carbon atoms and two unsaturated bonds. Molecule (b) has 16 carbon atoms and one unsaturated bond. Although molecule (a) is slightly larger than molecule (b) and would be expected to have a higher melting point, molecule (a) has two double bonds, whereas molecule (b) has only one double bond. Since the degree of unsaturation is more important in these similarly sized molecules, molecule (b) has the higher melting point.

PROBLEM 23.5

Draw the complete structural formula of arachidonic acid (Table 23.1) in a way that shows the *cis* stereochemistry of its four double bonds.

PROBLEM 23.6

Can there be any chiral carbon atoms in triacylglycerols? If so, which ones can be chiral and what determines their chirality?

⚬⚬ KEY CONCEPT PROBLEM 23.7 ————————————————

What noncovalent interactions (covered in Section 8.2) hold lipid molecules together? Are these forces generally weak or strong? Why do lipids not mix readily with water?

23.4 Chemical Reactions of Triacylglycerols

Learning Objective:

- Describe hydrogenation and hydrolysis reactions of triacylglycerols, and, given the reactants, predict the products.

Hydrogenation

The carbon–carbon double bonds in unsaturated fatty acids such as those found in triacylglycerides in vegetable oils can be hydrogenated to yield saturated fats in the same way that any alkene can react with hydrogen to yield an alkane (see Section 13.6). Margarine and solid cooking fats (shortenings) are produced commercially by hydrogenation of vegetable oils to give a product chemically similar to that found in animal fats.

Partial structure of an unsaturated vegetable oil

$$-O-\overset{\overset{\textstyle O}{\|}}{C}-CH_2CH_2CH_2CH_2CH_2CH_2CH_2CH=CHCH_2CH=CHCH_2CH_2CH_2CH_2CH_3$$

$2H_2$ | Pd catalyst

Partial structure of hydrogenated oil

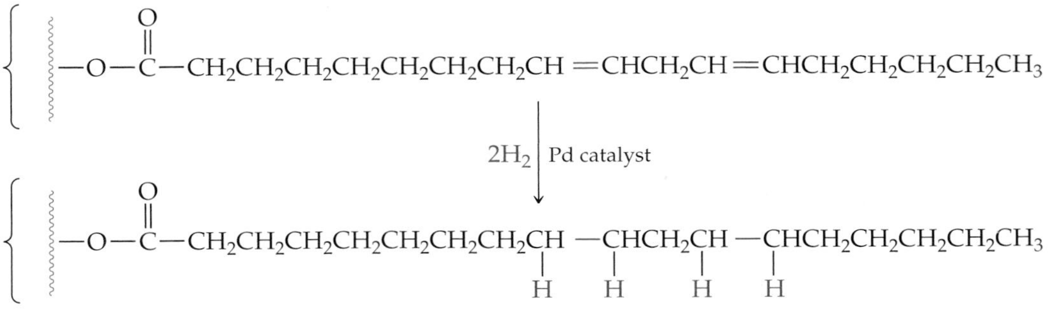

$$-O-\overset{\overset{\textstyle O}{\|}}{C}-CH_2CH_2CH_2CH_2CH_2CH_2CH_2\underset{\underset{\textstyle H}{|}}{CH}-\underset{\underset{\textstyle H}{|}}{CH}CH_2\underset{\underset{\textstyle H}{|}}{CH}-\underset{\underset{\textstyle H}{|}}{CH}CH_2CH_2CH_2CH_2CH_3$$

The extent of hydrogenation varies with the number of double bonds in the unsaturated acids and their locations. In general, the number of double bonds is reduced in a stepwise fashion from three to two to one. By controlling the extent of hydrogenation and monitoring the composition of the product, it is possible to control consistency. In margarine, for example, only about two-thirds of the double bonds present in the starting vegetable oil are hydrogenated. Most of the remaining double bonds, which vary in their locations, are left intact so that the margarine has exactly the right consistency to remain soft in the refrigerator and melt on warm toast. However, partial hydrogenation, to create margarine, results in the rearrangement of *cis* bonds to *trans* bonds in the partially hydrogenated fatty acids. Research indicates consumption of *trans* fats, which do not occur naturally, poses health risks.

PROBLEM 23.8

Write an equation for the complete hydrogenation of triolein, the triacylglycerol with three oleic acid acyl groups for which you drew the structure in Problem 23.3. Name the fatty acid from which the resulting acyl groups are derived.

PROBLEM 23.9

Butter and an equally solid margarine both contain an abundance of saturated fatty acids. What lipid that has been identified as a health hazard is not present in margarine but is present in butter? Conversely, what other lipid that may cause health problems is present in large amounts in some margarines but is present in small amounts in butter as a naturally occurring lipid?

Hydrolysis of Triacylglycerols

Triacylglycerols, like all esters, can be hydrolyzed—that is, they can react with water to form their carboxylic acids and alcohols. In the body, this hydrolysis is catalyzed by enzymes (hydrolases) and is the first reaction in the digestion of dietary fats and oils.

Commercial hydrolysis of fats and oils is usually carried out by strong aqueous bases (NaOH or KOH) and is called *saponification* (pronounced sae-*pon*-if-i-*ka*-tion, from the Latin *sapon*, soap [see Section 17.6]). The initial products of saponification of a fat or oil molecule are one molecule of glycerol and three molecules of fatty acid carboxylate salts:

Strong aqueous base catalyzes fat hydrolysis.

Saponification

$$CH_2-O-\overset{\overset{\textstyle O}{\|}}{C}-R$$
$$CH-O-\overset{\overset{\textstyle O}{\|}}{C}-R' \xrightarrow[H_2O]{NaOH}$$
$$CH_2-O-\overset{\overset{\textstyle O}{\|}}{C}-R''$$

A fat or oil

$$CH_2-OH$$
$$CH-OH \quad +$$
$$CH_2-OH$$

Glycerol

$$R-\overset{\overset{\textstyle O}{\|}}{C}-O^- Na^+$$
$$+$$
$$R'-\overset{\overset{\textstyle O}{\|}}{C}-O^- Na^+$$
$$+$$
$$R''-\overset{\overset{\textstyle O}{\|}}{C}-O^- Na^+$$

Fatty acid salts (soap)

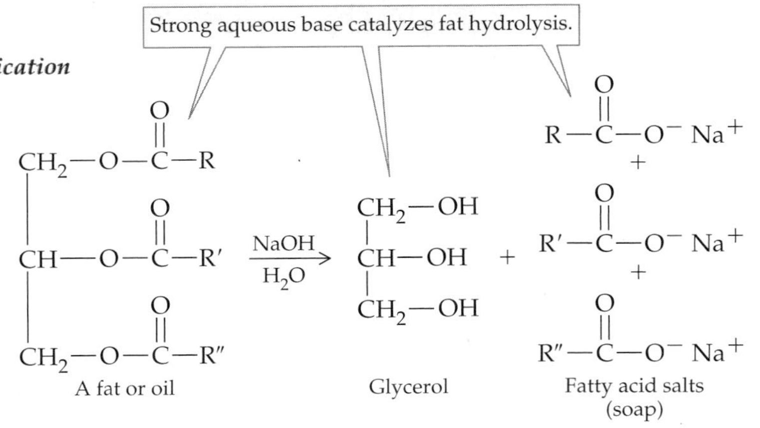

The fatty acid salts produced by base hydrolysis of triacylglycerols are referred to as **soaps.** Soaps can sequester other molecules because the two ends of a soap molecule are so different. The sodium salt end is ionic and therefore hydrophilic (water-loving); it tends to dissolve in water. The long hydrocarbon chain portion of the molecule, however, is nonpolar and therefore hydrophobic (water-fearing). When soap is dispersed in water, the big, organic anions cluster together so that their long, hydrophobic hydrocarbon tails are in contact, creating a nonpolar microenvironment. At the same time, their hydrophilic ionic heads on the surface of the cluster stick out into the water. The resulting spherical clusters are called **micelles** (Figure 23.3). Grease and dirt become coated by the nonpolar tails of the soap molecules and trapped in the center of the micelles as they form. Once suspended within micelles, the grease and dirt can be rinsed away. In exactly the same way soaps sequester greasy dirt, polar lipids form micelles in the bloodstream to transport neutral lipids trapped inside the micelles through the body.

▶ **Figure 23.3**
Soap or detergent molecules in water.
The hydrophilic ionic ends (blue spheres) remain in the water. At the surface of the water, a film forms with the hydrocarbon chains (yellow tails) on the surface. Within the solution, the hydrocarbon chains cluster together at the centers of micelles. Greasy dirt is dissolved in the oily center and carried away. Lipids are transported in the bloodstream in similar micelles, as described in Section 24.2.

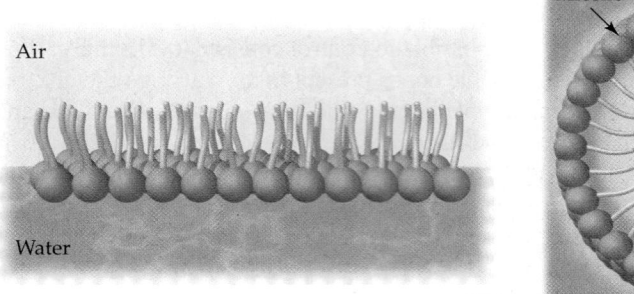
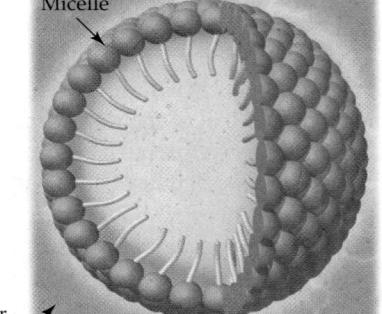

PROBLEM 23.10

Draw a saturated fatty acid salt that could participate in micelle formation. Indicate the hydrophilic head and the hydrophobic tail. Which end will be on the interior of the micelle and which end will be on the exterior of the micelle?

PROBLEM 23.11

Write the complete equation for the hydrolysis of a triacylglycerol in which the fatty acids are two molecules of stearic acid and one of oleic acid (see Table 23.1).

23.5 Phospholipids and Glycolipids

Learning Objective:

• Recognize phospholipids and glycolipids and describe their functions.

Cell membranes separate the aqueous interior of cells from the aqueous environment surrounding the cells. To accomplish this, the membranes establish a hydrophobic barrier between the two watery environments. Lipids are ideal for this function. The three major kinds of cell membrane lipids in animals are *phospholipids, glycolipids,* and *cholesterol.*

Phospholipids

Phospholipids contain a phosphate ester link between phosphoric acid and an alcohol. They are built up from either glycerol (to give *glycerophospholipids*) or from the alcohol sphingosine (to give *sphingomyelins*). The general structures of these lipids and the relationships of their classification are shown in Figure 23.4. Because phospholipids have ionized phosphate groups at one end, they are similar to soap molecules in having ionic, hydrophilic heads and hydrophobic tails (see Figure 23.3). They differ, however, in having *two* tails instead of one.

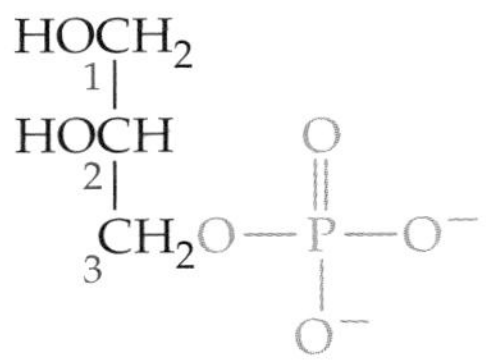

HOCH$_2$
$^1|$
HOCH
$^2|$ O
$_3$CH$_2$O—P—O$^-$
‖
O$^-$

Glycerol 3-phosphate
(alcohol in glycerophospholipids)

Location of
phosphate in
sphingomyelins

CH$_2$OH
$^1|$
H$_2$NCH
$^2|$
HOCH
$^3|$
CH$_3$(CH$_2$)$_{12}$CH=CH
^{4}

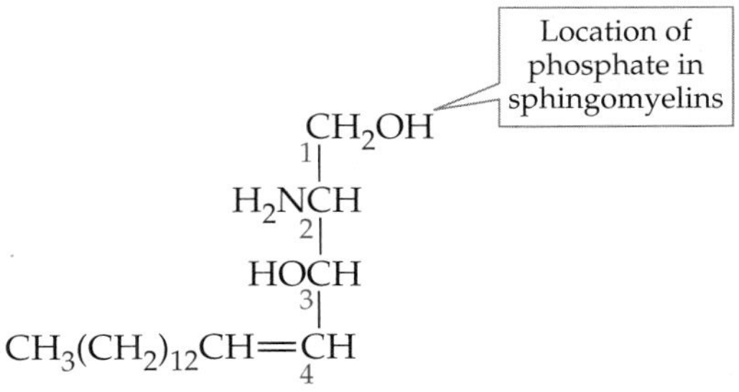

Sphingosine
(alcohol in sphingolipids)

Glycerophospholipids (also known as **phosphoglycerides**) are triesters of glycerol 3-phosphate and are the most abundant membrane lipids. Two of the ester bonds are with fatty acids, which provide the two hydrophobic tails (pink in the general glycerophospholipid structure in Figure 23.4). The fatty acids may be any of the fatty acids normally present in fats or oils. The fatty acid acyl group (R—C=O) bonded to C1 of glycerol is usually saturated, whereas the fatty acyl group at C2 is usually unsaturated. At the third position in glycerophospholipids, there is a phosphate ester group (orange in Figure 23.4). This phosphate has a second ester link to one of several different OH-containing compounds, often ethanolamine, choline, or serine (green in Figure 23.4; see structures in Table 23.3).

Glycerophospholipid (phosphoglyceride) A lipid in which glycerol is linked by ester bonds to two fatty acids and one phosphate, which is in turn linked by another ester bond to an amino alcohol (or other alcohol).

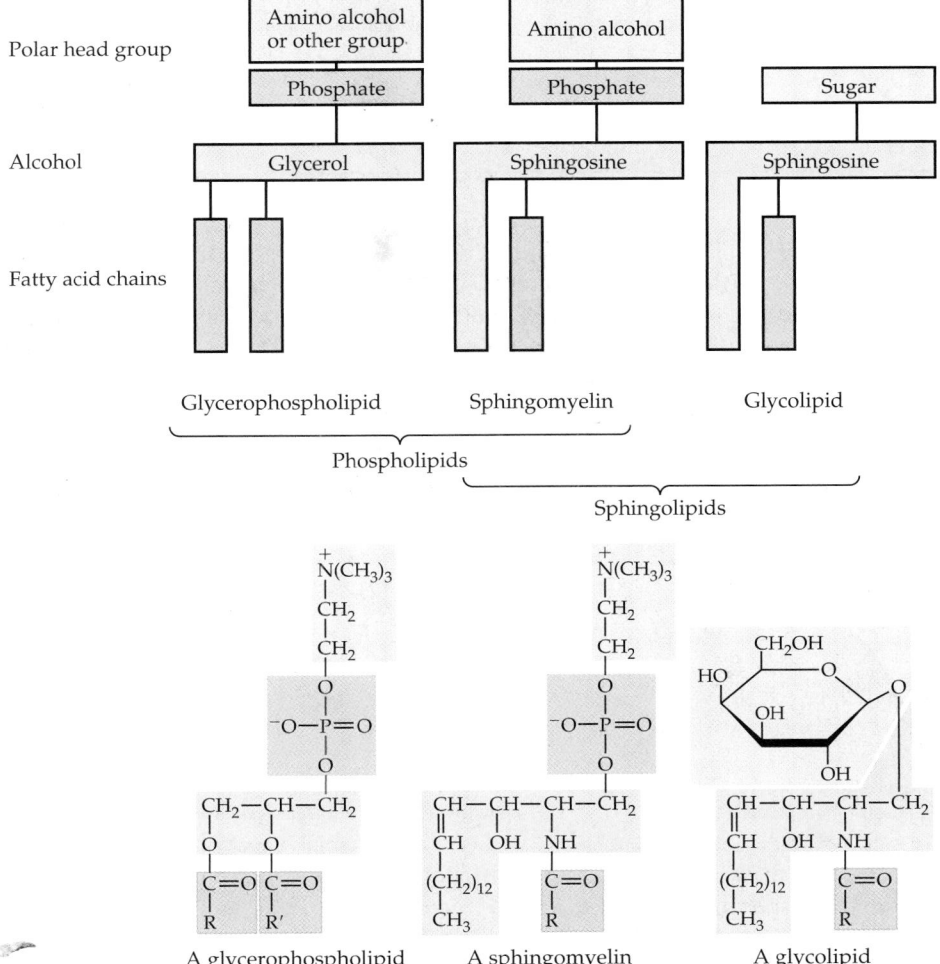

◄ **Figure 23.4**
Membrane lipids.
The top row shows the identity of the components of each class of membrane lipid. The bottom row shows a structural example of each class. Note that all classes have two hydrocarbon tails and polar, hydrophilic head groups. In the sphingolipids (sphingomyelins and glycolipids), one of the two hydrocarbon tails is part of the alcohol sphingosine (blue).

Table 23.3 Some Glycerophospholipids

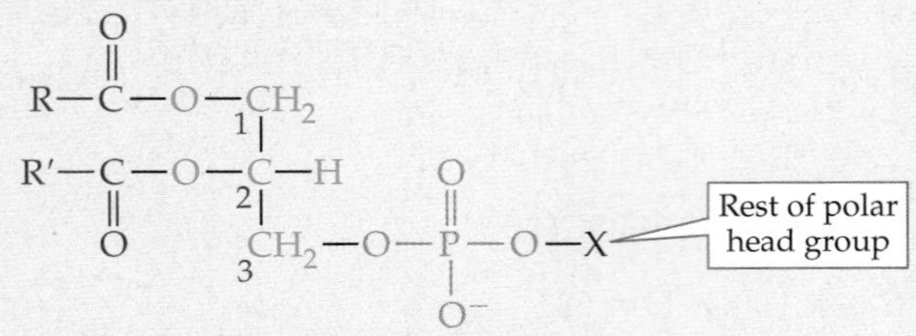

Precursor of X (HO–X)	Formula of X	Name of Resulting Glycerophospholipid Family	Function
Water	—H	Phosphatidate	Basic structure of glycerophospholipids
Choline	$-CH_2CH_2\overset{+}{N}(CH_3)_3$	Phosphatidylcholine	Basic structure of lecithins; most abundant membrane phospholipids
Ethanolamine	$-CH_2CH_2\overset{+}{N}H_3$	Phosphatidylethanolamine	Membrane lipids
Serine	$-CH_2-\overset{\overset{\overset{+}{N}H_3}{|}}{\underset{\underset{COO^-}{|}}{CH}}$	Phosphatidylserine	Present in most tissues; abundant in brain
myo-Inositol	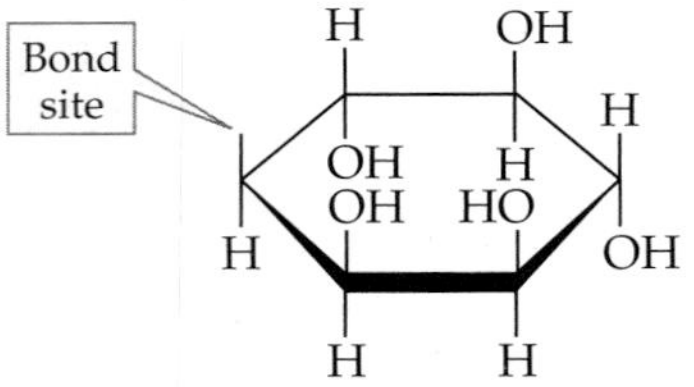	Phosphatidylinositol	Relays chemical signals across cell membranes

The glycerophospholipids are named as derivatives of phosphatidic acids. In the following molecule on the right, for example, the phosphate ester link to the right of the phosphorous atom is the amino alcohol choline, $HOCH_2CH_2N^+(CH_3)_3$. Lipids of this type are known as either *phosphatidylcholines* or *lecithins*. (A substance referred to in the singular as either lecithin or phosphatidylserine, or any of the other classes of phospholipids, is usually a mixture of molecules with different R and R′ tails.) Examples of some other classes of glycerophospholipids are included in Table 23.3.

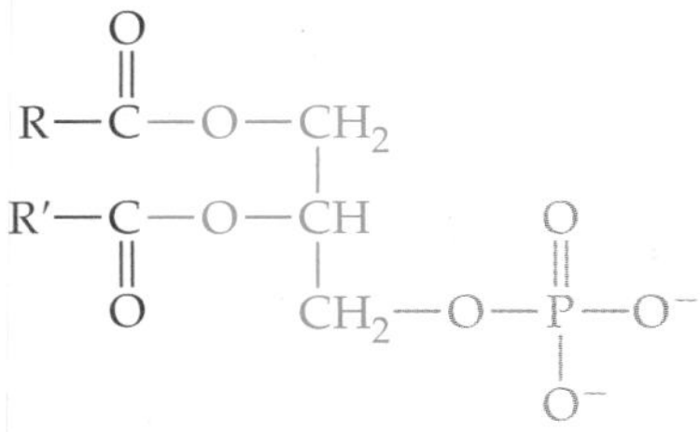

A phosphatidate

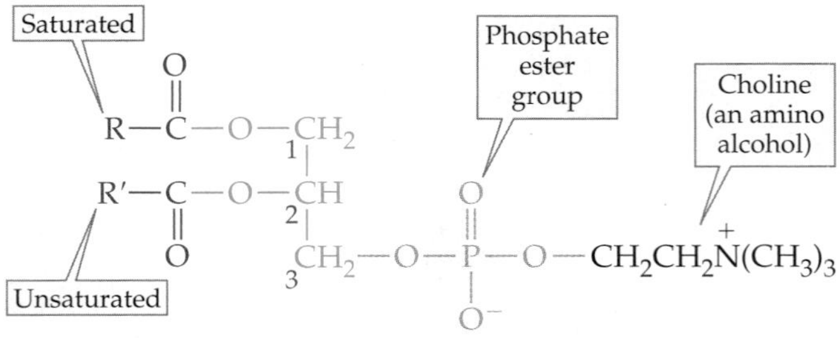

A phosphatidylcholine
(a glycerophospholipid that is a lecithin)

Because of their combination of hydrophobic tails and hydrophilic head groups, the glycerophospholipids are *emulsifying agents*—substances that surround droplets of nonpolar liquids and hold them in suspension in water (see the micelle diagram in Figure 23.3). You will find lecithin, usually obtained from soybean oil, listed as an ingredient in chocolate bars and other foods, where it is added to keep oils from separating out. It is the lecithin in egg yolk that emulsifies the oil droplets in mayonnaise.

In **sphingolipids,** the amino alcohol sphingosine provides one of the two hydrophobic hydrocarbon tails (blue here and in Figure 23.4). The second hydrocarbon tail is from a fatty acid acyl group connected by an amide link to the $-NH_2$ group in sphingosine (red in the following diagram; pink in Figure 23.4).

Fatty acid acyl group

Amide link

Sphingosine

A sphingomyelin (a sphingolipid)

Sphingomyelins are sphingosine derivatives with a phosphate ester group at C1 of sphingosine. The sphingomyelins are major components of the coating around nerve fibers (the *myelin sheath*) and are present in large quantities in brain tissue. A diminished amount of sphingomyelins and phospholipids in brain myelin has been associated with multiple sclerosis. Whether this is a cause or a result of multiple sclerosis is unclear. The orientation of the hydrophilic and hydrophobic regions of a sphingomyelin is shown in Figure 23.5, together with a general representation of this and other types of cell membrane lipids used in drawing cell membranes.

PROBLEM 23.12

Lecithins are often used as food additives to provide emulsification. How do they accomplish this purpose?

PROBLEM 23.13

Identify the products formed by complete hydrolysis of all ester bonds in (a) the phosphatidylcholine on page 726 and (b) the sphingomyelin in Figure 23.5.

Glycolipids

Glycolipids, like sphingomyelins, are derived from sphingosine, a diol with an amine group. They differ from phospholipids by having a carbohydrate group at C1 (orange in the glycolipid in Figure 23.4) instead of a phosphate bonded to an amino alcohol.

Like glycoproteins (see Section 22.8), glycolipids reside in cell membranes with their short carbohydrate chains extending into the fluid surrounding the cells. Here, they function as receptors that, as you will see in Chapter 28, are essential for recognizing chemical messengers, other cells, pathogens, and drugs. The general structures of these lipids and the relationships of their classification are shown at the top in Figure 23.4. Note the overlapping classes of membrane lipids. Glycolipids and sphingomyelins both contain sphingosine and are therefore classified as sphingolipids, whereas glycerophospholipids and sphingomyelins both contain phosphate groups and are therefore classified as phospholipids.

The glycolipid molecule is classified as a *cerebroside*. Cerebrosides, which contain a single monosaccharide, are particularly abundant in nerve cell membranes in the brain, where the monosaccharide is D-galactose. They are also found in other cell membranes, where the sugar unit is D-glucose.

Sphingolipid A lipid derived from the amino alcohol sphingosine.

▲ Lecithin (phosphatidylcholine) is the emulsifying agent in most chocolates.

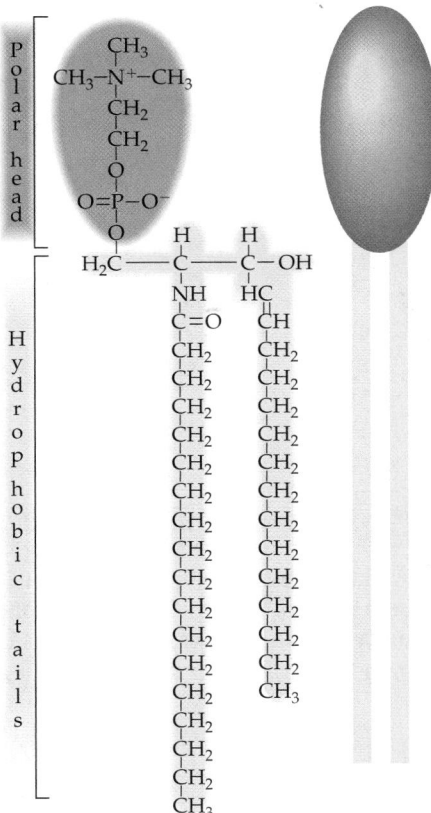

A sphingomyelin

▲ Figure 23.5

A sphingomyelin, showing its polar, hydrophilic head group and its two hydrophobic tails.

The drawing on the right is the representation of phospholipids used in picturing cell membranes. It shows the relative positions of the hydrophilic head and the hydrophobic tails.

Glycolipid A lipid with a fatty acid bonded to the C2—NH₂ group and a sugar bonded to the C1—OH group of sphingosine.

A glycolipid

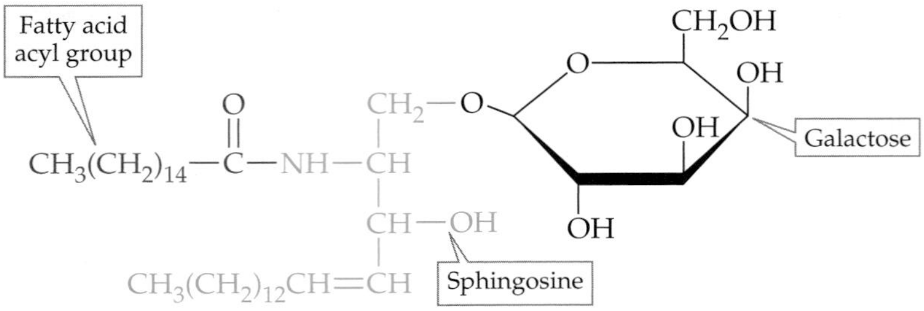

Fatty acid acyl group

$$CH_3(CH_2)_{14}-\overset{\overset{\displaystyle O}{\|}}{C}-NH-\overset{\displaystyle CH}{\underset{\displaystyle \overset{|}{CH-OH}}{|}}$$

CH_2-O-

$CH_3(CH_2)_{12}CH=CH$ | Sphingosine

CH_2OH / OH / OH / OH — Galactose

A glycolipid
(a cerebroside)

Gangliosides are glycolipids in which the carbohydrate is a small polysaccharide (an oligosaccharide) rather than a monosaccharide. Over 60 different gangliosides are known. The oligosaccharides responsible for blood types are ganglioside molecules (see the Chemistry in Action "Cell-Surface Carbohydrates and Blood Type" in Chapter 20).

Tay-Sachs disease, a genetic disorder found mainly in persons of Eastern European Jewish descent, Cajuns, and French Canadians, is the result of a deficiency in the enzyme β-hexosaminidase A, which causes an elevated concentration of a particular ganglioside in the brain. An infant born with this defect suffers mental retardation and liver enlargement and usually dies by age 3. Tay-Sachs is one of a group of sphingolipid storage diseases. Another well-known, fatal disease in this group is Niemann-Pick disease, in which sphingomyelin accumulates due to a deficiency in the enzyme sphingomyelinase. These metabolic diseases result from deficiencies in the supply of enzymes that break down sphingolipids.

Currently there is no known therapy for either Tay-Sachs disease or Niemann-Pick disease. The harmful consequences result from the *storage* of the excess sphingolipids. A more promising outcome may be available for those with Gaucher's disease, the most common lipid storage disease. In Gaucher's patients, fats accumulate in many organs (liver, lungs, and brain) due to a deficiency in the enzyme glucocerebrosidase. Enzyme replacement therapy allows many of these patients to avoid some of the nonneurological effects of Gaucher's disease.

 Worked Example 23.3 Identifying Complex Lipid Components

A class of membrane lipids known as *plasmalogens* has the general structure shown here. Identify the component parts of this lipid and choose the terms that apply to it: phospholipid, glycerophospholipid, sphingolipid, glycolipid. Is it most similar to a phosphatidylethanolamine, a phosphatidylcholine, a cerebroside, or a ganglioside?

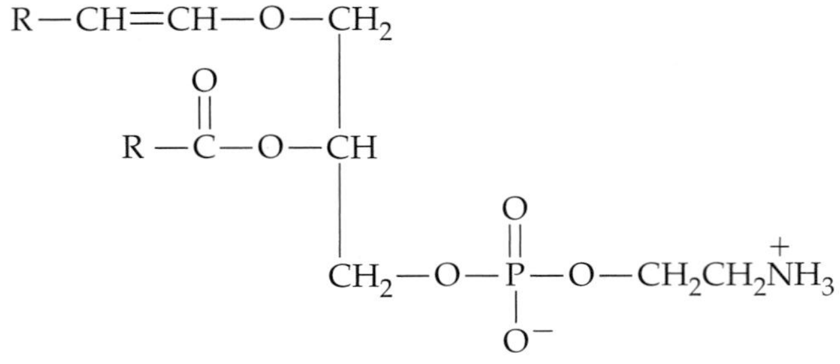

$$R-CH=CH-O-CH_2$$
$$R-\overset{\overset{\displaystyle O}{\|}}{C}-O-CH$$
$$CH_2-O-\overset{\overset{\displaystyle O}{\|}}{\underset{\displaystyle \overset{|}{O^-}}{P}}-O-CH_2CH_2\overset{+}{N}H_3$$

ANALYSIS Compare each part of the molecule with the basic components found in complex lipids and decide which lipid component the part resembles most. The molecule contains a phosphate group and thus is a phospholipid. The glycerol backbone of three carbon atoms bonded to three oxygen atoms is also present, so the compound is a glycerophospholipid, but one in which there is an ether linkage ($-CH_2-O-CH=CHR$) in place of one of the ester linkages. The phosphate group is bonded to ethanolamine ($HOCH_2CH_2NH_2$).

This compound is not a sphingolipid or a glycolipid because it is not derived from sphingosine; for the same reason it is not a cerebroside or a ganglioside. Except for the ether group in place of an ester group, the compound has the same structure as a phosphatidylethanolamine.

SOLUTION
The terms that apply to this plasmalogen are *phospholipids* and *glycerophospholipid*. It has a structure nearly identical to phosphatidylethanolamine, so it is most similar to phosphatidylethanolamine.

PROBLEM 23.14
Draw the structure of the sphingomyelin that contains a myristic acid acyl group. Identify the hydrophilic head group and the hydrophobic tails in this molecule.

PROBLEM 23.15
Draw the structure of the glycerophospholipid that contains a stearic acid acyl group, an oleic acid acyl group, and a phosphate bonded to ethanolamine.

PROBLEM 23.16
Which of the following terms apply to the compound shown below? (Hint: Look at the functional groups and the bonds involved to begin analyzing the compound part by part in comparison to the lipids discussed in this chapter.)

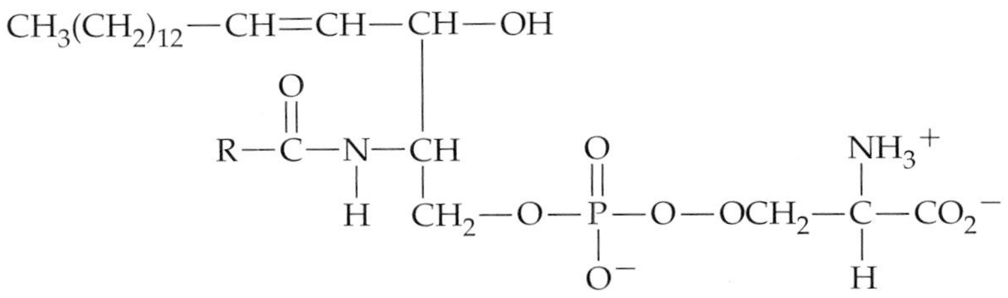

(a) A phospholipid

(b) A steroid

(c) A sphingolipid

(d) A glycerophospholipid

(e) A lipid

(f) A phosphate ester

(g) A ketone

23.6 Sterols

Learning Objective:
• Identify sterols and their derivatives and describe their structures and roles.

All **sterols** have a common central structure composed of the four connected rings, as shown in the margin. Because they are soluble in hydrophobic solvents and not in water, sterols are classified as lipids.

Sterols have many roles throughout both the plant and animal kingdoms. In human biochemistry, the main sterol is cholesterol, which is an important component of cell membranes. The major functions of sterols other than cholesterol are as the bile acids that are essential for the digestion of fats and oils in the diet (Section 24.1) and as hormones.

The steroid nucleus

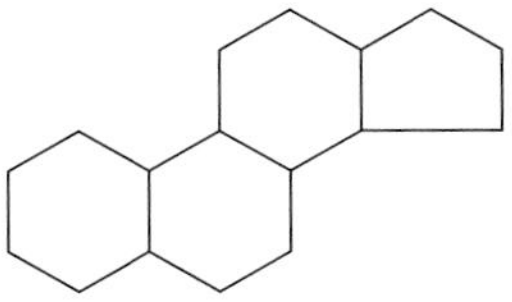

Sterol A lipid whose structure is based on a fused tetracyclic (four-ring) carbon skeleton.

▶▶ Sterols are discussed in their role as hormones in Chapter 28 and their connection to heart disease in the Chemistry in Action "Fat Storage, Lipids, and Atherosclerosis" in Chapter 24.

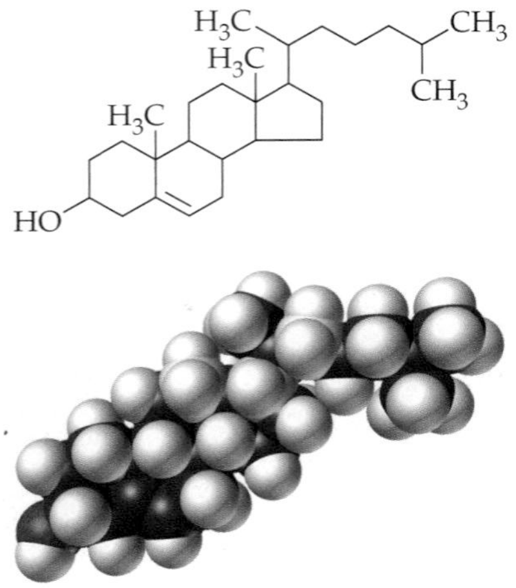

▲ Cholesterol is shown here in the line structure (upper image) and in the space filling structure (lower image).

Cholesterol

Cholesterol has the molecular structure and shape shown in the margin.

Cholesterol is the most abundant animal sterol. The body of a 60 kg person contains about 75 g of cholesterol, which serves two important functions: as a component of cell membranes and as the starting material for the synthesis of all other sterols. "Cholesterol" has become a household word because of its presence in the arterial plaque that contributes to heart disease. Some cholesterol is obtained from the diet, but most of our cholesterol is synthesized in the liver. Even on a strict no-cholesterol diet, an adult's organs can manufacture approximately 800 mg of cholesterol per day.

The molecular model of cholesterol reveals the nearly flat shape of the molecule. Except for its —OH group, cholesterol is hydrophobic. Within a cell membrane, cholesterol molecules are distributed among the hydrophobic tails of the phospholipids. Because cholesterol is more rigid than hydrophobic phospholipid tails, the cholesterol molecules help to maintain the structural rigidity of the membrane. Approximately 25% of liver cell membrane lipid is cholesterol.

Bile Acids

Bile acids are essential for the emulsification of fats during digestion. Synthesized in liver cells from cholesterol and stored in the gall bladder until release into the small intestine is stimulated by a meal, these molecules have a polar end and a nonpolar end. Solubility of bile acids is increased by conjugation with taurine, a cysteine derivative, or glycine. This structural alteration increases solubility and enhances the formation of micelles of bile acids and fats in the digestive system, with the polar heads exposed to the aqueous medium of the small intestine and the nonpolar ends and fats on the interior of the micelle. Formation of micelles is essential for the digestion of dietary fat, as you will see in Chapter 24.

Note the acidic group added to cholesterol in each of the two most common bile acids, cholic acid and chenodeoxycholic acid. In the intestinal tract, these acids are ionized to anions and referred to as *bile* salts.

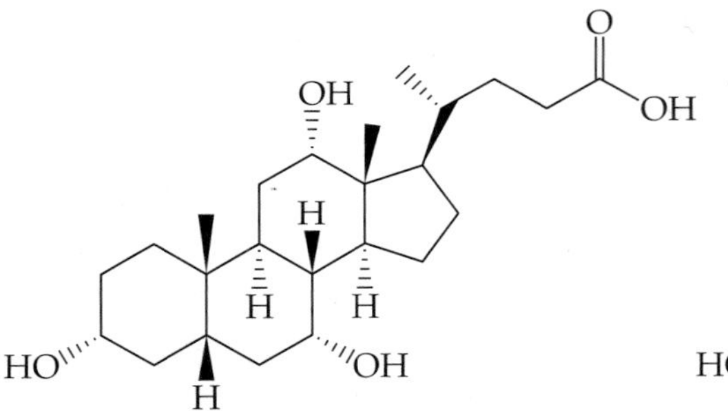

Cholic acid

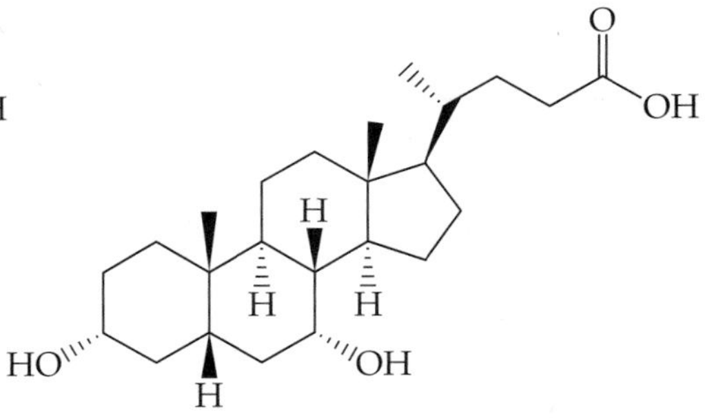

Chenodeoxycholic acid

Steroid Hormones

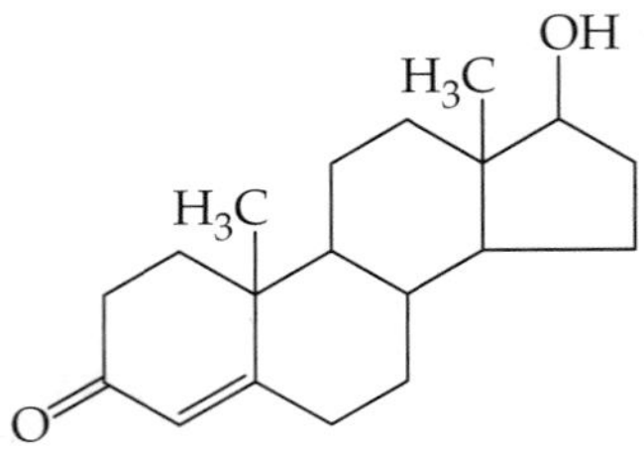

The steroid hormones are divided according to function into three types. *Mineralocorticoids,* such as *aldosterone,* regulate the delicate cellular fluid balance between Na^+ and K^+ ions (hence the "mineral" in their name). The second type, *glucocorticoids,* such as cortisol (also known as *hydrocortisone*) and its close relative cortisone, help to regulate glucose metabolism and inflammation. You have probably used an anti-inflammatory ointment containing hydrocortisone to reduce the swelling and itching of poison ivy or some other skin irritation. The third type of steroid hormones is the family of *sex hormones.* The two most important male sex hormones, or *androgens,* are *testosterone* and *androsterone.* They are responsible for the development of male secondary sex characteristics during puberty and for promoting tissue and muscle growth. *Estrone* and *estradiol,* the female hormones known as *estrogens,* are synthesized from testosterone,

Testosterone
(an androgen)

primarily in the ovaries but also to a small extent in the adrenal cortex. Estrogens govern development of female secondary sex characteristics and participate in regulation of the menstrual cycle. We will learn more about the signaling properties of the sex hormones in Chapter 28. The structures of testosterone and estradiol are shown in the margin. Note the steroid ring system common to these molecules.

In addition to the several hundred known steroids isolated from plants and animals, a great many more have been synthesized in the laboratory in the search for new drugs. You will discover more about steroids as cellular signals in Chapter 28.

Estradiol
(an estrogen)

23.7 Cell Membranes: Structure and Transport

Learning Objectives:

- Identify the membrane lipids and describe their structures and roles.
- Describe the general structure of a cell membrane and its chemical composition.
- Distinguish between passive transport and active transport and between simple diffusion and facilitated diffusion.

Every cell in your body is surrounded by a membrane. Cell membranes keep the interior of the cell separate from the exterior world, selectively permitting ions and molecules to enter or leave the cell. Lipids comprise most of the cell membrane, but proteins are also involved as are carbohydrates bonded either to lipids or proteins.

Membrane Structure

Phospholipids provide the basic structure of cell membranes, where they aggregate in a closed, sheet-like, *double leaflet* structure—the **lipid bilayer** (Figure 23.6). The bilayer is formed by two parallel layers of lipids oriented so that the ionic head groups are exposed to the aqueous environments on either side of the bilayer. The nonpolar tails cluster together in the middle of the bilayer, where they interact and avoid water. Each half of the bilayer is termed a *leaflet*.

The bilayer is a favorable arrangement for phospholipids—it is highly ordered and stable but still flexible. When phospholipids are shaken vigorously with water, they spontaneously form **liposomes**—small spherical vesicles with a lipid bilayer surrounding an aqueous center, as shown in Figure 23.6. Water-soluble substances can be trapped in the center of liposomes, and lipid-soluble substances can be incorporated into the bilayer. Liposomes are potentially useful as carriers for drug delivery because they can fuse with cell membranes and empty their contents into the cell. One approved medical use of liposomes targets systemic fungal infections. Individuals with compromised immune systems due to acquired immunodeficiency syndrome (AIDS) are especially

Lipid bilayer The basic structural unit of cell membranes; composed of two parallel sheets of membrane lipid molecules arranged tail to tail.

Liposome A spherical structure in which a lipid bilayer surrounds a water droplet.

◄ **Figure 23.6**
Aggregation of membrane lipids. The lipid bilayer provides the basic structure of a cell membrane.

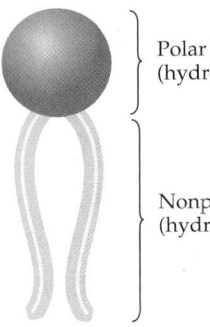

Polar head (hydrophilic)

Nonpolar tail (hydrophobic)

Membrane lipid

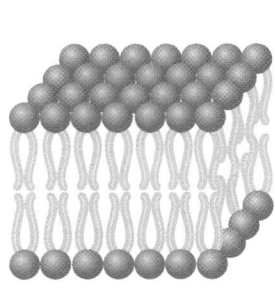

Lipid bilayer

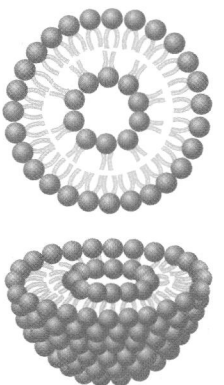

Liposome

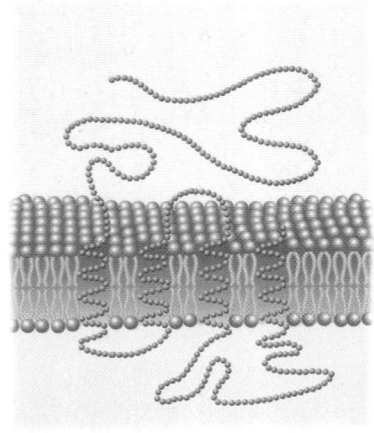

▲ **An example of an integral membrane protein.** The green circles represent amino acids. Many membrane proteins pass in and out of the membrane numerous times.

susceptible to this kind of infection. The liposomes carry amphotericin B, an antibiotic that attacks the fungal cell membrane. By delivering amphotericin to the fungal cells, the liposomal drug diminishes the serious side effects of attack by this antibiotic on kidney cells and cells in other healthy organs. Current medical research includes investigation of liposomes as delivery agents for other drugs.

The overall structure of cell membranes is represented by the *fluid-mosaic model.* The membrane is described as *fluid* because it is not rigid and molecules can move around within it and as a *mosaic* because it contains many kinds of molecules. The components of the cell membrane are shown in Figure 23.7.

Glycolipids and cholesterol are present in cell membranes, and 20% or more of the weight of a membrane consists of protein molecules, many of them glycoproteins (p. 650). *Peripheral proteins* are associated with just one face of the bilayer (i.e., with one leaflet) and are held within the membrane by noncovalent interactions with the hydrophobic lipid tails or the hydrophilic head groups. *Integral proteins* extend completely through the cell membrane and are anchored by hydrophobic regions that extend through the bilayer. In some cases, the hydrophobic amino acid chain may traverse the membrane many times before ending on the exterior of the membrane with a hydrophilic sugar group. The carbohydrate parts of glycoproteins and glycolipids mediate the interactions of the cell with outside agents. Some integral proteins form channels to allow specific molecules or ions to enter or leave the cell.

Because the bilayer membrane is fluid rather than rigid, it is not easily ruptured. The lipids in the bilayer simply flow back together to repair any small hole or puncture. The effect is similar to what is observed in cooking when a thin film of oil or melted butter floats on water in a cooking pot. The film can be punctured and broken, but it immediately flows together when left alone.

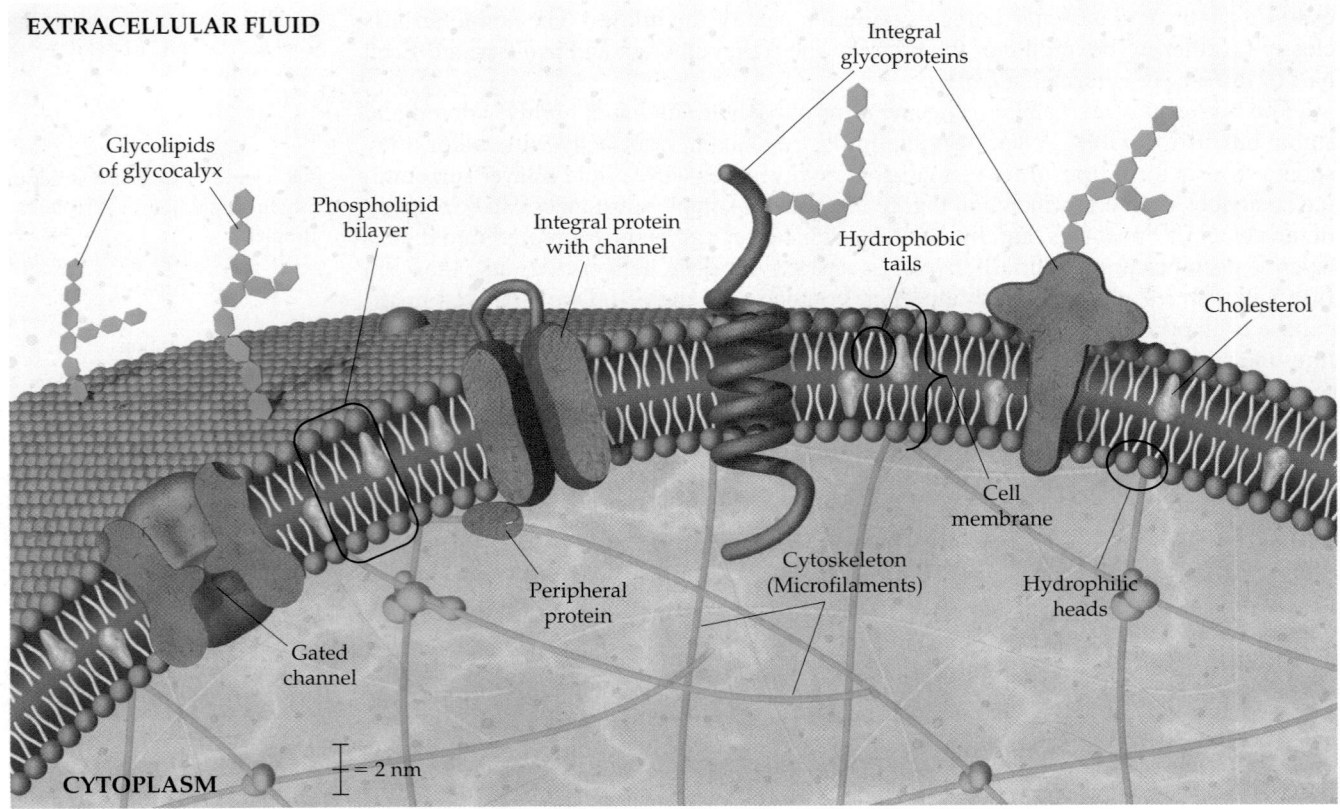

▲ **Figure 23.7**
The cell membrane.
Cholesterol forms part of the membrane, proteins are embedded in the lipid bilayer, and the carbohydrate chains of glycoproteins and glycolipids extend into the extracellular space, where they act as receptors. Integral proteins form channels to the outside of the cell and also participate in transporting large molecules across the membrane.

One consequence of membrane fluidity is the movement of proteins within the membrane. For example, low-density lipoprotein receptors, which are glycoproteins that interact with lipoproteins in the extracellular fluid (discussed in Section 24.2), move sideways within the membrane to form clusters of receptors on the cell surface. The glycoproteins move sideways in the membrane layers continuously, not unlike floating on a pond; this is an energetically neutral motion. However, phospholipids and other membrane components do not flip from the inside leaflet of the membrane to the outside leaflet or vice versa. That is an energetically unfavored action because it would force polar and nonpolar interactions between membrane components.

Two other consequences of bilayer fluidity are that small *nonpolar* molecules can easily enter the cell through the membrane and that some individual lipid or protein molecules can diffuse rapidly from place to place within the membrane.

The fluidity of the membrane varies with the relative amounts of saturated and unsaturated fatty acids in the glycerophospholipids. Such variation is put to use in the adaptation of organisms to their environment. In reindeer, for example, the membranes of cells near the hooves contain a higher proportion of unsaturated fatty acid chains than in other cells. These chains do not pack tightly together. The result is a membrane that remains fluid while the animals stand in snow.

◼▭ KEY CONCEPT PROBLEM 23.17

Integral membrane proteins are not water-soluble. Why? How must these proteins differ from globular proteins?

Transport Across Cell Membranes

The cell membrane must accommodate opposing needs in allowing the passage of molecules and ions into and out of a cell. The membrane surrounding a living cell cannot be impermeable, because nutrients must enter and waste products must leave the cell. However, the membrane cannot be completely permeable, or substances would just move back and forth until their concentrations were equal on both sides—hardly what is required for the maintenance of a constant internal environment in the body or *homeostasis* (see the Chemistry in Action "Homeostasis," Chapter 28, p. 834).

The problem is solved by two modes of passage across the membrane (Figure 23.8). In **passive transport,** substances move across the membrane freely by diffusion from regions of higher concentration to regions of lower concentration. In **active transport,** substances can cross the membrane only when energy is supplied because they must go in the reverse direction—from lower to higher concentration regions.

Passive Transport by Simple Diffusion

Some solutes enter and leave cells by **simple diffusion**—they move by normal molecular motion into areas of lower concentration. Small, nonpolar molecules, such as CO_2 and O_2, and lipid-soluble substances, including steroid hormones, move through the hydrophobic lipid bilayer in this way. Hydrophilic substances similarly pass through the aqueous environment inside channels formed by integral proteins. What passes through the protein channels is limited by the size of the molecules relative to the size of the openings. The lipid bilayer is essentially impermeable to ions and larger polar molecules, which are not soluble in the nonpolar hydrocarbon region.

Passive Transport by Facilitated Diffusion

Like simple diffusion, **facilitated diffusion** is passive transport and requires no energy input. However, in facilitated diffusion solutes are moved across the membrane by proteins. The interaction is similar to that between enzymes and substrates. The molecule to be transported binds to a membrane protein, which changes shape so that

Passive transport Movement of a substance across a cell membrane without the use of energy, from a region of higher concentration to a region of lower concentration.

Active transport Movement of substances across a cell membrane with the assistance of energy (e.g., from ATP).

Simple diffusion Passive transport by the random motion of diffusion through the cell membrane.

Facilitated diffusion Passive transport across a cell membrane with the assistance of a protein that changes shape.

▶ Figure 23.8
**Modes of transport
across cell membranes.**

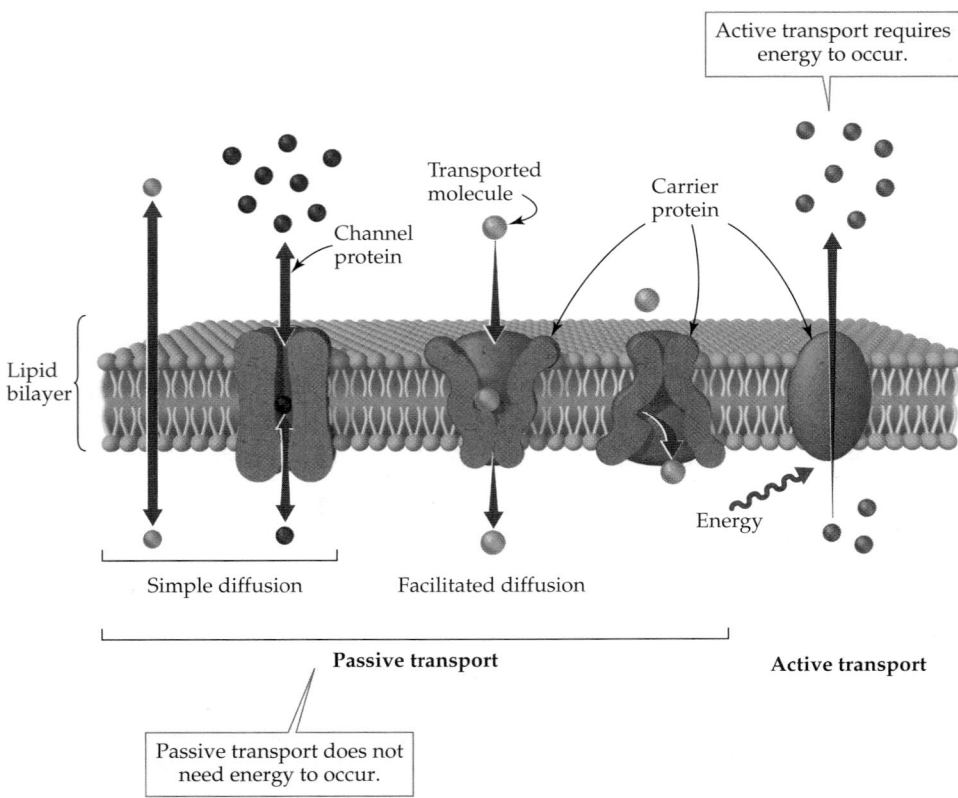

Active transport requires energy to occur.

Transported molecule

Channel protein

Carrier protein

Lipid bilayer

Energy

Simple diffusion

Facilitated diffusion

Passive transport

Active transport

Passive transport does not need energy to occur.

Concentration gradient A difference in concentration within the same system.

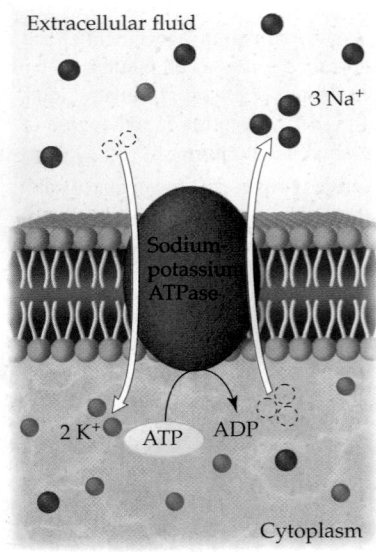

Extracellular fluid

3 Na⁺

Sodium-potassium ATPase

2 K⁺   ATP   ADP

Cytoplasm

▲ Figure 23.9
An example of active transport.
A protein known as sodium–potassium ATPase uses energy from ATP to move Na⁺ and K⁺ ions across cell membranes against their concentration gradients.

the transported molecule is released on the other side of the membrane. Glucose is transported into cells in this fashion.

Active Transport

It is essential to life that the concentrations of some solutes be different inside and outside cells. Such differences are contrary to the natural tendency of solutes to move about until the concentration equalizes. Therefore, maintaining **concentration gradients** (differences in concentration within the same system) requires the expenditure of energy. An important example of active transport is the continuous movement of sodium and potassium ions across cell membranes. This is the only way to maintain homeostasis, which requires low Na^+ concentrations within cells and higher Na^+ concentrations in extracellular fluids, with the opposite concentration ratio for K^+. Energy from the conversion of adenosine triphosphate (ATP) to adenosine diphosphate (ADP) is used to change the shape of an integral membrane protein (an ATPase referred to as the sodium/potassium pump), simultaneously bringing two K^+ ions into the cell and moving three Na^+ ions out of the cell (Figure 23.9).

Properties of Cell Membranes

- Cell membranes are composed of a fluid-like phospholipid bilayer.
- The bilayer incorporates cholesterol, proteins (including glycoproteins), and glycolipids.
- Small nonpolar molecules cross by simple diffusion through the lipid bilayer.
- Small ions and polar molecules diffuse across the membrane via protein pores (*simple diffusion*).
- Glucose and certain other substances (including amino acids) cross with the aid of proteins and without energy input (*facilitated diffusion*).
- Na^+, K^+, and other substances that maintain concentration gradients across the cell membrane cross with expenditure of energy and the aid of proteins (*active transport*).

CHEMISTRY IN ACTION

☦ Eicosanoids: Prostaglandins and Leukotrienes

Have you ever cut yourself, hit your fingers with a hammer, or scratched your skin on thorns while picking blackberries? Did the injured area swell and hurt? If so, that is a response mediated by an **eicosanoid.** This group of compounds, derived from the 20-carbon polyunsaturated fatty acid arachidonic acid and synthesized throughout the body, function as short-lived chemical messengers that act near their points of synthesis ("local hormones").

The *prostaglandins* (named for their discovery in prostate cells) and the *leukotrienes* (named for their discovery in leukocytes) are two classes of eicosanoids that differ somewhat in their structure. The prostaglandins all contain a five-membered ring, which the leukotrienes lack.

Prostaglandins and leukotrienes are synthesized in the body from the 20-carbon unsaturated fatty acid arachidonic acid. Arachidonic acid, in turn, is synthesized from linolenic acid, an essential fatty acid.

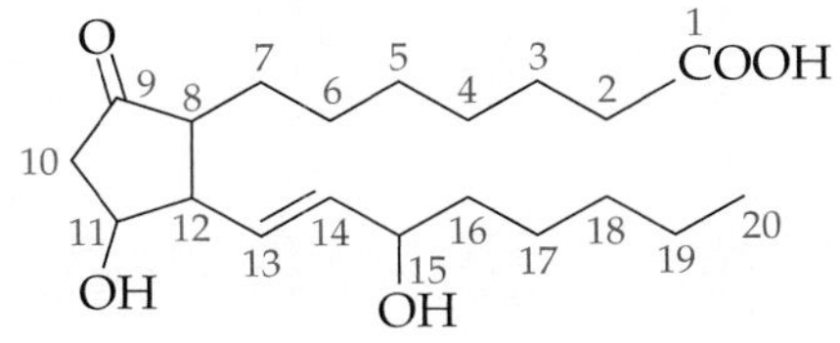

PGE_1, a prostaglandin

The several dozen known prostaglandins have an extraordinary range of biological effects. They can lower blood pressure, influence platelet aggregation during blood clotting, stimulate uterine contractions, and lower the extent of gastric secretions. In addition, they are responsible for some of the pain and swelling that accompany inflammation.

Aspirin's anti-inflammatory and fever-reducing *(antipyretic)* action results in part from its irreversible inhibition of prostaglandin synthesis by transferring its acetyl group to a serine side chain in cyclooxygenase (COX), the enzyme that catalyzes the first step in conversion of arachidonic acid to prostaglandins. This inhibition is also thought to explain the effect of aspirin on combating heart attacks. COX is present in two forms in cells, referred to as COX-1 and COX-2. Aspirin's effect is short lived, so other drugs have been designed to inhibit either one or the other of these enzymes. Of great interest are drugs that block the activity of COX-2, the enzyme responsible for synthesizing prostaglandins involved in inflammation and pain responses in diseases such as arthritis. While basic research seeking alternative COX-2 inhibitors continues, current medical practice prescribes these drugs sparingly and depends on older, better-understood analgesics such as aspirin and acetaminophen to lessen pain and fever.

There is also great medical interest in leukotrienes. Leukotriene release has been found to trigger the asthmatic

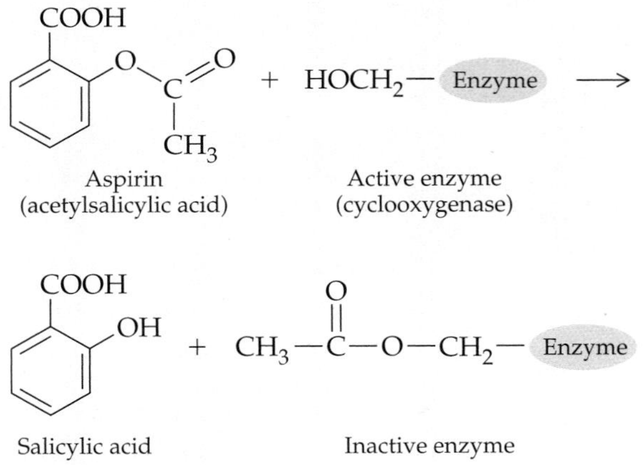

response, severe allergic reactions, and inflammation. Asthma treatment with drugs that inhibit leukotriene synthesis is being studied, although the available drugs are not yet as effective as standard steroid treatments.

As it turns out, the lipid responsible for localized minor pain, heat, and inflammation is a prostaglandin, and the discomfort is effectively treated with aspirin but not other NSAIDs. Unlike other NSAIDs, aspirin irreversibly inhibits COX, the enzyme that catalyzes the first reaction in a pathway that converts arachidonic acid into a prostaglandin.

CIA Problem 23.4 In the eicosanoid shown here, identify all the functional groups. Which groups are capable of hydrogen bonding? Which are most acidic? Is this molecule primarily nonpolar, polar, or something in between?

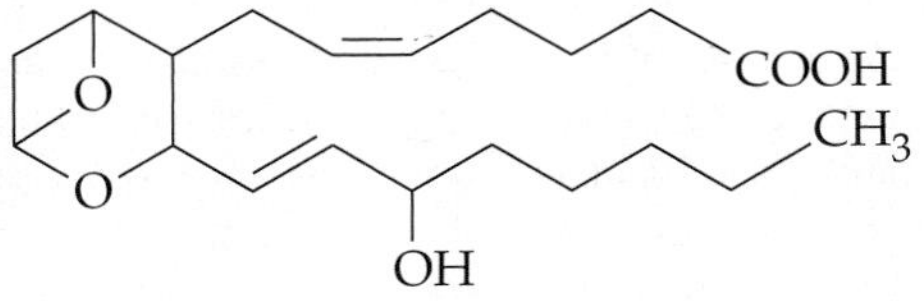

CIA Problem 23.5 The molecule in CIA Problem 23.4 is *Thromboxane A_2*—a lipid involved in the blood-clotting process. To what category of lipids does thromboxane A_2 belong? What fatty acid do you think serves as a biological precursor of thromboxane A_2?

CIA Problem 23.6 How does aspirin disrupt the synthesis of prostaglandins?

CIA Problem 23.7 Why are the eicosanoids often called "local hormones"?

CIA Problem 23.8 List some of the functions prostaglandins serve in the body.

CIA Problem 23.9 Which two of the following would involve a prostaglandin response?

  (a) The itchy bump from a mosquito bite
  (b) A sunburn after spending the day at the beach
  (c) A strep throat caught from your sibling
  (d) The sneezing, stuffy nose, and itchy eyes after working in the rose garden

HANDS-ON CHEMISTRY 23.2

Either alone or with a partner, build a model of a cell membrane. Gather up any arts and crafts supplies you may have and be creative. Suggested supplies are colored paper, cardboard, pipe cleaners (these make good transmembrane proteins), beads, pins with round heads (phospholipid), yarn, balloons, scissors, tape, and glue. Or head for the various types of dry pasta in the grocery store and use different kinds for different membrane structures. Make a key for your model and explain this model to someone not taking this class. Was your explanation understood? How might you improve your explanation? (Hint: Search the web for model ideas if you are stuck.)

PROBLEM 23.18

Does an NO molecule cross a lipid bilayer by simple diffusion? Explain.

PROBLEM 23.19

As noted earlier (Section 22.3), the first step in glycolysis, which occurs within cells, is phosphorylation of glucose to glucose 6-phosphate. Why does this step prevent passive diffusion of glucose back out of the cell?

KEY CONCEPT PROBLEM 23.20

The compositions of the inner and outer surfaces of the lipid bilayer are different. Why do these differences exist and how might they be of use to a living cell?

SUMMARY REVISITING THE LEARNING OBJECTIVES

- **Describe the chemical structures and general properties of fatty acids, waxes, sterols, fats, and oils.** *Fatty acids* are long-chain carboxylic acids. *Waxes* are esters of unbranched fatty acids and alcohols. *Sterols* contain four interconnecting rings. *Fats* and *oils* are *triacylglycerols*—triesters of glycerol and fatty acids. In fats, the fatty acid chains are mostly saturated; in oils, the proportions of unsaturated fatty acid chains vary *(see Problems 26, 27, 77, and 88).*

- **Describe the characteristics of fatty acids and fatty acid esters.** Fatty acids are long-chain alkanes or alkenes with a carboxyl group. They have a polar "head" and a nonpolar "tail" and can aggregate into micelles in water. Fatty acid esters have an alcohol esterified to the carboxyl group on the fatty acid. Esters are neutral in charge *(see Problems 28–35 and 76).*

- **List the physical properties of fats and oils and explain why they are different.** Fats are solid because the saturated hydrocarbon chains pack together neatly; oils are liquids because the kinks at the *cis* double bonds prevent such packing *(see Problems 36–45, 79, and 80).*

- **Describe hydrogenation and hydrolysis reactions of triacylglycerols, and, given the reactants, predict the products.** The principal reactions of triacylglycerols are catalytic *hydrogenation* and *hydrolysis*. Hydrogen adds to the double bonds of unsaturated hydrocarbon chains in oils, thereby thickening the consistency of the oils and raising their melting points. Treatment of a fat or oil with a strong base such as NaOH hydrolyzes the triacylglycerols to give glycerol and salts of fatty acids. Such *saponification* reactions produce soap, a mixture of fatty acid salts *(see Problems, 22, 46–53, 76, and 86).*

- **Recognize phospholipids and glycolipids and describe their functions.** *Phospholipids,* which are either *glycerophospholipids* (derived from glycerol) or *sphingomyelins* (derived from the amino alcohol sphingosine), have charged phosphate-diester groups in their hydrophilic heads. Glycolipids have carbohydrate head groups. These lipids are found in cell membranes *(see Problems 25, 44, and 45).*

- **Identify sterols and their derivatives and describe their structures and roles.** The unifying feature of sterols is a fused four-ring system. Sterols include cholesterol, an important participant in membrane structure. Bile acids and salts, necessary for the emulsification of fats during digestion, are synthesized from cholesterol. The third major group of sterols includes steroid hormones, including the sex hormones, which function as signaling molecules *(see Problems 64–67, 81–85, and 87).*

- **Identify the membrane lipids and describe their structures and roles.** The membrane lipids include *phospholipids* and *glycolipids* (which have hydrophilic, polar head groups and two hydrophobic tails) and cholesterol (a steroid). See the learning objectives earlier for structural descriptions *(see Problems 23, 77, and 83–85).*

- **Describe the general structure of a cell membrane and its chemical composition.** The basic structure of cell membranes is a *bilayer of lipids,* with their hydrophilic heads in the aqueous environment outside and inside the cells, and their hydrophobic tails clustered together in the center of the bilayer. *Cholesterol* molecules fit between the hydrophobic tails and help maintain membrane structure and rigidity. The membrane also contains *glycoproteins* and *glycolipids* (with their carbohydrate segments at the cell surface, where they serve as receptors) as well as *proteins.* Some of the proteins extend through the membrane (*integral proteins*), and others are only partially embedded at one surface (*peripheral proteins*) *(see Problems 24, 17–20, and 68–70).*

- **Distinguish between passive transport and active transport and between simple diffusion and facilitated diffusion.** Small, nonpolar molecules and lipid-soluble substances can cross the lipid bilayer by simply diffusing through it. Ions and hydrophilic substances can move through aqueous fluid-filled channels in membrane proteins. Some substances cross the membrane by binding to an integral protein, which then releases them inside the cell. These modes of crossing are all *passive transport*—they do not require energy because the substances move from regions of higher concentration to regions of lower concentration. Passive transport takes the form of *simple diffusion,* crossing the membrane by passing through it unimpeded, or *facilitated diffusion,* crossing the membrane with the aid of a protein embedded in the membrane. *Active transport,* which requires energy and is carried out by certain integral membrane proteins, moves substances against their *concentration gradients (see Problems 71–75).*

CONCEPT MAP

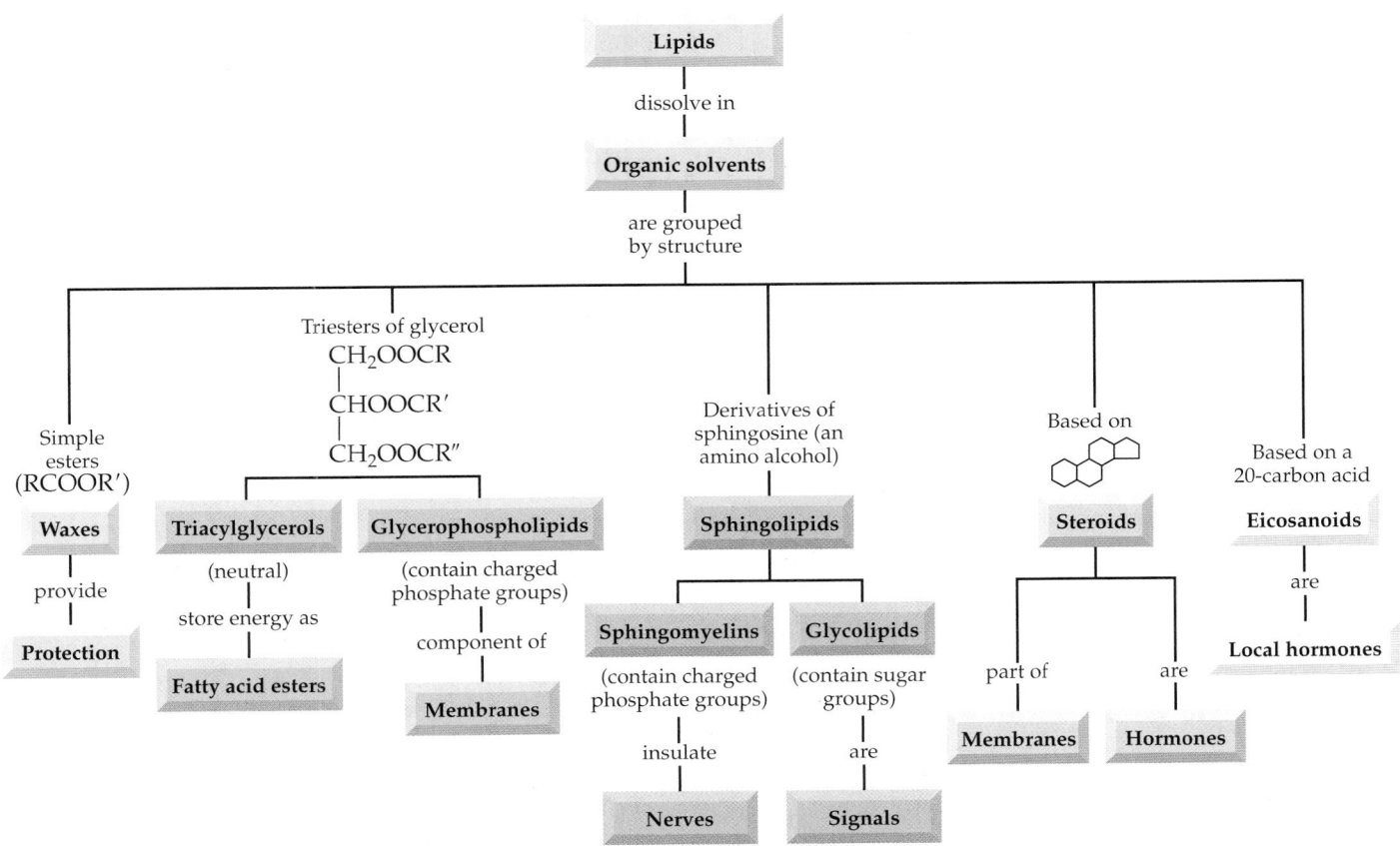

▲ **Figure 23.10 Concept Map.** This lipid concept map connects the disparate categories of lipids and indicates important functions and the importance of lipids in membrane structure.

KEY WORDS

Active transport, *p. 733*
Concentration gradient,
   p. 734
Degree of unsaturation,
   p. 718
Eicosanoid, *p. 716*
Facilitated diffusion, *p. 733*
Fat, *p. 720*

Fatty acid, *p. 715*
Glycerophospholipid
   (phosphoglyceride),
   p. 725
Glycolipid, *p. 727*
Lipid, *p. 715*
Lipid bilayer, *p. 731*
Liposome, *p. 731*

Micelle, *p. 724*
Oil, *p. 720*
Passive transport, *p. 733*
Phospholipid, *p. 724*
Polyunsaturated fatty acid,
   p. 718
Saturated fatty acid, *p. 717*
Simple diffusion, *p. 733*

Soap, *p. 724*
Sphingolipid, *p. 727*
Sterol, *p. 729*
Triacylglycerol
   (triglyceride), *p. 719*
Unsaturated fatty acid,
   p. 717
Wax, *p. 718*

🔑 UNDERSTANDING KEY CONCEPTS

23.21   The fatty acid composition of three triacylglycerols (A, B, and C) is reported below. Predict which one has the highest melting point. Which one do you expect to be liquid (oil) at room temperature? Explain.

	Palmitic Acid	Stearic Acid	Oleic Acid	Linoleic Acid
A	21.4%	27.8%	35.6%	11.9%
B	12.2%	16.7%	48.2%	22.6%
C	11.2%	8.3%	28.2%	48.6%

23.22   Complete hydrogenation of triacylglycerol C in Problem 23.20 yields a triacylglycerol of what fatty acid composition? Would the hydrogenation product of triacylglycerol C be more like the hydrogenation product of triacylglycerol A or B? Explain.

23.23   A membrane lipid was isolated and completely hydrolyzed. The following products were detected: ethanolamine, phosphate, glycerol, palmitic acid, and oleic acid. Propose a structure for this membrane lipid, and name the family (Table 23.3) to which it belongs.

23.24   According to the fluid-mosaic model (Figure 23.7), the cell membrane is held together mostly by hydrophobic interactions. Considering the forces applied, why does the cell membrane not rupture as you move, press against objects, etc.?

23.25   Dipalmitoylphosphatidylcholine (DPPC) is a surfactant on the surface of the alveoli in the lungs. What is the nature of its fatty acid groups? In what arrangement is it likely to exist at the lung surfaces?

ADDITIONAL PROBLEMS

WAXES, FATS, AND OILS (SECTION 23.1)

23.26 What makes a molecule a lipid?

23.27 Name two classes of lipids found in your body.

FATTY ACIDS AND THEIR ESTERS (SECTION 23.2)

23.28 Draw an 18-carbon saturated fatty acid. Is this a "straight-chain" molecule or a "bent" molecule?

23.29 Draw an 18-carbon unsaturated fatty acid that contains two carbon–carbon double bonds, one on carbon 6 and one on carbon 9 (count starting with the carboxyl carbon). Is this a "straight-chain" molecule or a "bent" molecule?

23.30 Differentiate between saturated, monoun-saturated, and polyunsaturated fatty acids.

23.31 Are the carbon–carbon double bonds in naturally occurring fatty acids primarily *cis* or *trans*?

23.32 What is an essential fatty acid?

23.33 Name two essential fatty acids. What are good sources of these fatty acids?

23.34 Which of these fatty acids has the lower melting point? Explain why.

    (a) Linoleic acid   **(b)** Stearic acid

23.35 Which of these fatty acids has the higher melting point? Explain why.

    (a) Linolenic acid   **(b)** Stearic acid

FATS AND OILS (SECTION 23.3)

23.36 What are the chemical and physical differences between fats and oils?

23.37 List typical food sources for oils and fats. Are there similarities or differences in the sources for each?

23.38 Draw the structure of glyceryl trilaurate, which is made from glycerol and three lauric acid molecules.

23.39 There are two isomeric triacylglycerol molecules whose components are glycerol, one palmitic acid unit, and two stearic acid units. Draw the structures of both, and explain how they differ.

23.40 What function does a wax serve in a plant or animal?

23.41 What functions do fats serve in an animal?

23.42 *Spermaceti*, a fragrant substance isolated from sperm whales, was commonly used in cosmetics until it was banned in 1976 to protect the whales from extinction. Chemically, spermaceti is cetyl palmitate, the ester of palmitic acid with cetyl alcohol (the straight-chain 16-carbon alcohol). Draw the structure of spermaceti.

23.43 What kind of lipid is spermaceti—a fat, a wax, or a sterol?

23.44 A major ingredient in peanut butter cup candy is soy lecithin. Draw the structure of lecithin.

23.45 Which kind of lipid is lecithin?

CHEMICAL REACTIONS OF LIPIDS (SECTION 23.4)

23.46 What is the name of the reaction that converts unsaturated fatty acids to saturated fatty acids?

23.47 When a vegetable oil is converted to a soft margarine, a nonnatural product is synthesized. What is this product?

23.48 Is the reaction shown here esterification, hydrogenation, hydrolysis, saponification, or substitution?

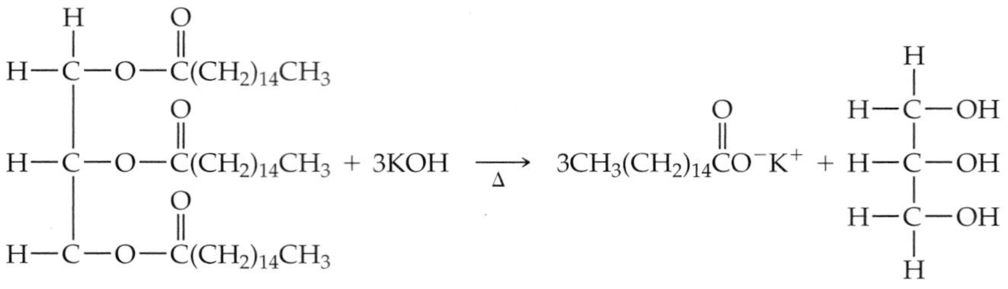

23.49 Draw the structures of all products you would obtain by saponification of the following lipid with aqueous KOH. What are the names of the products?

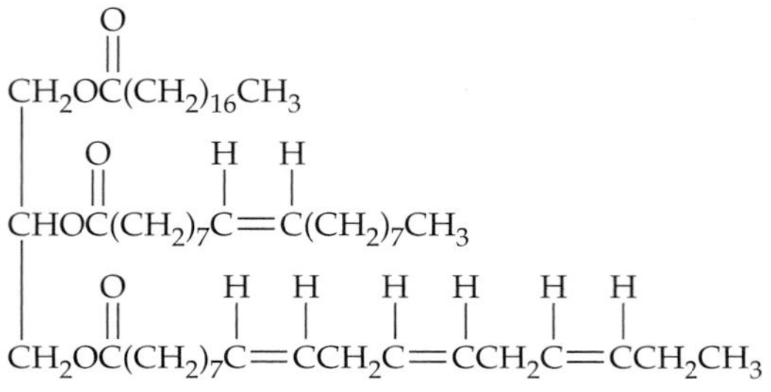

23.50 Draw the structure of the product you would obtain on complete hydrogenation of the triacylglycerol in Problem 23.49. What is its name? Does it have a higher or lower melting temperature than the original triacylglycerol?

23.51 Tell how many different products you would obtain on hydrogenation of the triacylglycerol in Problem 23.49 if:

    (a) One double bond was converted to a single bond

    (b) Two double bonds were converted to single bonds

    (c) Three double bonds were converted to single bonds

    (d) All four double bonds were converted to single bonds

23.52 Dietary guidelines suggest we limit our intake of butter due to the cholesterol content and substitute oils or margarine. The following table shows the major fatty acid distribution for a typical stick of margarine and also for butter. Values are percentages.

Sample	Myristic Acid (C14:0)	Palmitic Acid (C16:0)	Stearic Acid (C18:0)	Oleic Acid (C18:1)	Linoleic Acid (C18:2)
Margarine	0.7	14.1	7.0	60.7	17.0
Butter	12	31	11	24	3

    (a) Which contains more monounsaturated fatty acids?

    (b) Which contains more polyunsaturated fatty acids?

    (c) Which is likely to contain fewer *trans*-fatty acids

23.53 Recently it has been suggested that using oils with more monounsaturated fatty acids (e.g., oleic acid) is better for our health than those with polyunsaturated fatty acids or saturated fatty acids. What are good sources of oils with predominantly monounsaturated fatty acids? (Hint: See Table 23.2.)

PHOSPHOLIPIDS AND GLYCOLIPIDS (SECTION 23.5)

23.54 Describe the difference between a triacylglycerol and a phospholipid.

23.55 Why are glycerophospholipids, rather than triacylglycerols, found in cell membranes?

23.56 How do sphingomyelins and cerebrosides differ structurally?

23.57 Name the two different kinds of sphingosine-based lipids.

23.58 Why are glycerophospholipids more soluble in water than triacylglycerols?

23.59 What are the functions of glycerophospholipids in the human body? Of triacylglycerides in the human body?

23.60 Show the structure of a cerebroside made up of D-galactose, sphingosine, and myristic acid.

23.61 Draw the structure of a sphingomyelin that contains a stearic acid unit.

23.62 Draw the structure of a glycerophospholipid that contains palmitic acid, oleic acid, and the phosphate bonded to propanolamine.

23.63 *Cardiolipin,* a compound found in heart muscle, has the following structure. What products are formed if all ester bonds in the molecule are saponified by treatment with aqueous NaOH?

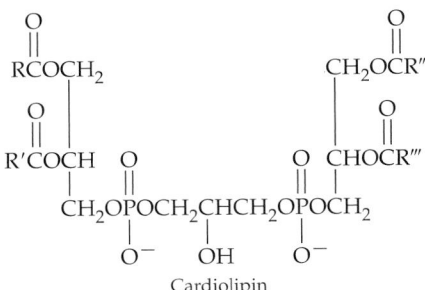
Cardiolipin

STEROLS (SECTION 23.6)

23.64 What is a major function of cholesterol in your body?

23.65 What is the function of the bile acids?

23.66 Name a male sex hormone and a female sex hormone.

23.67 Compare the structures of the sex hormones named in Problem 23.66. What portions of the structures are the same? Where do they differ?

CELL MEMBRANES (SECTION 23.7)

23.68 Explain how a micelle differs from a membrane bilayer.

23.69 Describe the similarities and differences between a liposome and a micelle.

23.70 What constituents besides phospholipids are present in a cell membrane?

23.71 What would happen if cell membranes were freely permeable to all molecules?

23.72 Which process requires energy—passive or active transport? Why is energy sometimes required to move solute across the cell membrane?

23.73 How does facilitated diffusion differ from simple diffusion?

23.74 Based on the information in Section 23.7, how would you expect each of these common metabolites to cross the cell membrane?
(a) NO (nitrous oxide)   (b) Fructose
(c) Ca^{2+}

23.75 Based on the information in Section 23.7, how would you expect each of these common metabolites to cross the cell membrane?
(a) Galactose   (b) CO   (c) Mg^{2+}

CONCEPTUAL PROBLEMS

23.76 Which of the following are saponifiable lipids? (Recall that ester bonds are broken by base hydrolysis.)
(a) Progesterone   (b) Glyceryl trioleate
(c) A sphingomyelin   (d) Prostaglandin E_1
(e) A cerebroside   (f) A lecithin

23.77 Identify the component parts of each saponifiable lipid listed in Problem 23.76.

23.78 Draw the structure of a triacylglycerol made from two molecules of myristic acid and one molecule of linolenic acid.

23.79 Would the triacylglycerol described in Problem 23.78 have a higher or lower melting temperature than the triacylglycerol made from one molecule each of linolenic, myristic, and stearic acids? Why?

23.80 Common names for some triacylglycerols depend on their source. Identify the source. Choices are plant oils (soybean, canola, corn, sunflower, and so on), beef fat, and pork fat.
(a) Tallow   (b) Cooking oil   (c) Lard

23.81 Explain why cholesterol is not saponifiable.

23.82 Draw cholesterol acetate. Is this molecule saponifiable? Explain.

23.83 Which three types of lipids are particularly abundant in brain tissue?

23.84 What is the function of sphingomyelin?

23.85 In what disease is a decrease in sphingomyelin observed?

23.86 If the average molar mass of a sample of soybean oil is 1500 g/mol, how many grams of NaOH are needed to saponify 5.0 g of the oil?

GROUP PROBLEMS

23.87 The concentration of cholesterol in the blood serum of a normal adult is approximately 200 mg/dL. How many grams of cholesterol does a person with a blood volume of 5.75 L have circulating in his or her blood? (You may need to review Chapter 1.)

23.88 Jojoba wax, used in candles and cosmetics, is partially composed of the ester of stearic acid and a straight-chain 22-carbon atom alcohol. Draw the structure of this wax component. Compare this structure with the structure drawn for spermaceti in Problem 23.42. Do you think jojoba wax could replace spermaceti in the cosmetic industry?

24

Lipid Metabolism

CONTENTS

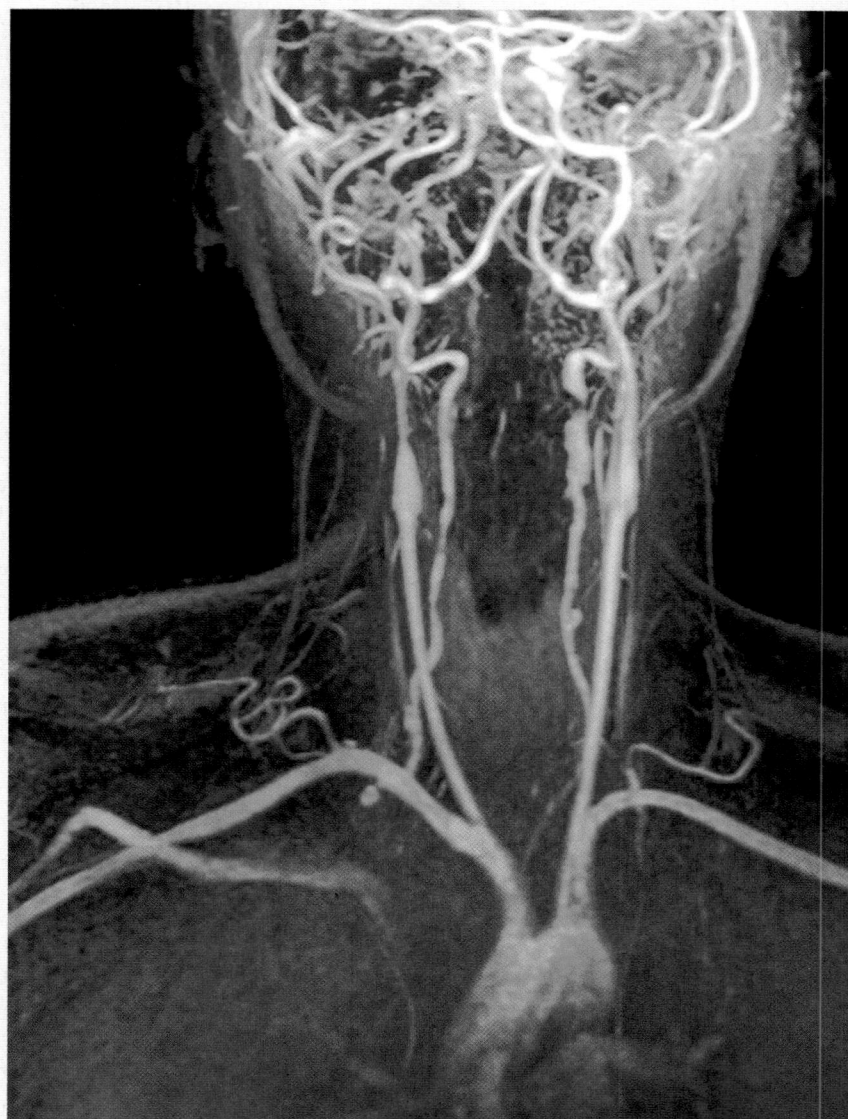

▲ Narrowed portions of blood vessels, generally caused by fatty deposits, are shown in this imaging of blood flow in the head and neck of an adult.

 ◀◀◀ CONCEPTS TO REVIEW

A. Types of Lipids (Section 23.1)

B. Cell Membranes (Section 23.7)

C. Metabolism and Energy Production (Section 21.4)

Carbohydrate metabolism (discussed in Chapter 22) is one of our two major sources of energy. Lipid metabolism, the topic of this chapter, is the other. The majority of the lipids in our diet are triacylglycerols. Surplus carbohydrate energy is also stored as triacylglycerols. Therefore, our focus here is on the metabolism of triacylglycerols, which are stored in fatty tissue and constitute our chief energy reserve. Storage of excess fat raises multiple health concerns.

Consider Malcolm, a middle-aged man who, while working at his desk, is suddenly struck with intense chest pain that radiates down his left arm. Rushed to an emergency room (ER), the ER staff physician orders an electrocardiogram, an enzyme blood panel including troponins, and a blood lipid panel and stabilizes Malcolm. A cardiologist arrives, notes that Malcolm is overweight, and questions him regarding his pain and personal habits such as exercise level, diet, smoking, drug and alcohol use as well as previous medical care. Because the initial test results show elevated lipids and elevated enzymes, a computed tomography (CT) cardiac scan is ordered. The results of this heart imaging will determine the next step in treatment. Throughout this chapter and in the Chemistry in Action "Fat Storage, Lipids, and Atherosclerosis" at the end of the chapter, we'll learn how this cardiac emergency could result from the regular metabolic processes of carbohydrate and fat metabolism.

24.1 Digestion of Triacylglycerols

Learning Objective:

- List the steps in the digestion of dietary triacylglycerols and their transport into the bloodstream.

When eating, any triacylglycerols present pass through the mouth unchanged and enter the stomach (Figure 24.1). The heat and churning action of the stomach break triacyl-glycerols into small droplets, a process that takes longer than the physical breakdown and digestion of other food in the stomach. To ensure that there is time for this breakdown, the presence of triacylglycerols slows down the rate at which the mixture of partially digested food leaves the stomach (a reason foods containing lipids are a pleasing part of the diet is that the stomach feels full for a longer time after a fatty meal). No catabolism of triacylglycerols has taken place yet, only preparation for this step by breaking fats into microscopic droplets.

The pathway of dietary triacylglycerols from the mouth to their ultimate biochemical fate in the body is not as straightforward as that of carbohydrates. Complications arise because triacylglycerols are not water-soluble, but nevertheless must enter an aqueous environment. To be moved around within the body by the blood and lymph systems, they must be dispersed and surrounded by a water-soluble coating, a process that must happen more than once as triacylglycerols travel along their metabolic pathways. During these travels, they are packaged in various types of **lipoproteins,** which consist of droplets of hydrophobic lipids surrounded by phospholipids, proteins, and other molecules with their hydrophilic ends to the outside (Figure 24.2). Lipoproteins are special forms of micelles.

When partially digested food leaves the stomach, it enters the upper end of the small intestine (the *duodenum*), where its arrival triggers the release of *pancreatic lipases*— enzymes for the hydrolysis of lipids. The gallbladder simultaneously releases **bile,** a mixture that is manufactured in the liver and stored in the gallbladder until needed. Among other components, bile contains cholesterol and cholesterol-derived **bile acids,** both of which are sterols, and phospholipids.

By the time dietary triacylglycerols enter the small intestine, they are dispersed as small, greasy, insoluble droplets, and for this reason enzymes in the small intestine cannot attack them. It is the job of the bile acids and phospholipids to emulsify the triacylglycerols by forming micelles similar to soap micelles (see Figure 23.3). The major bile acid is cholic acid, and the structure of its anion closely resembles soaps because it contains both hydrophilic and hydrophobic regions allowing it to act as an emulsifying agent.

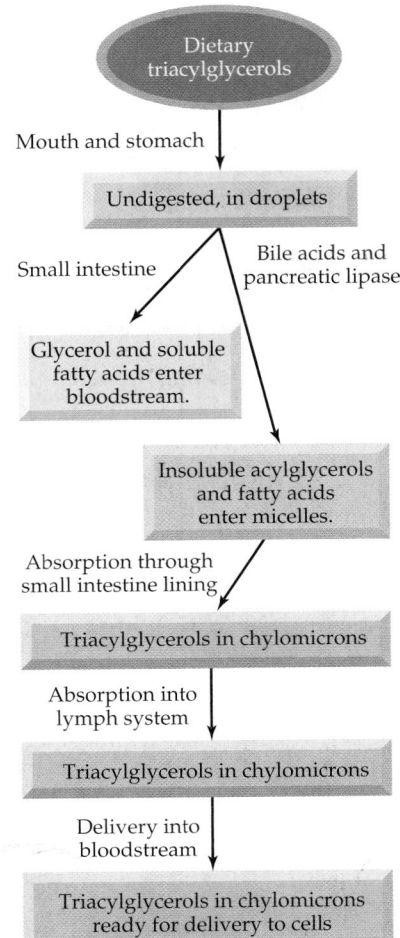

Cholate

Pancreatic lipase partially hydrolyzes the emulsified triacylglycerols, producing mono- and diacylglycerols plus "free" fatty acids and a small amount of glycerol.

◀◀ **CONCEPTS TO REVIEW**
Recall that an *acyl* group is the R—C=O portion of an ester. The acyl groups from fatty acids have relatively long, R chain groups (Section 17.1).

▲ **Figure 24.1**
Digestion of triacylglycerols.

Lipoprotein A lipid–protein complex that transports lipids.

Bile Fluid secreted by the liver and released into the small intestine from the gallbladder during digestion; contains bile acids, cholesterol, phospholipids, bicarbonate ions, and other electrolytes.

Bile acids Sterol acids derived from cholesterol that are secreted in bile.

◀◀ Recall from Section 23.5 that polar phospholipids are the major component of cell membranes.

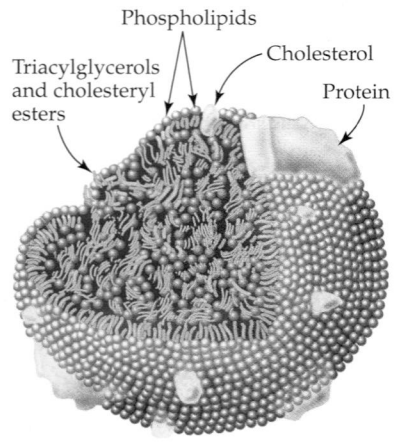

▲ **Figure 24.2**
A Lipoprotein.
A lipoprotein contains a core of neutral lipids, including triacylglycerols and cholesteryl esters. Surrounding the core is a layer of phospholipids in which varying proportions of proteins and cholesterol are embedded.

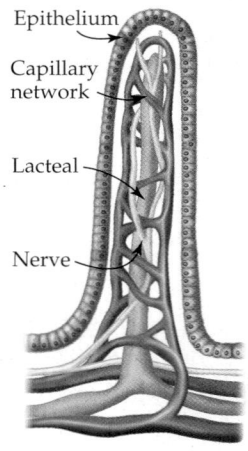

▲ **Figure 24.3**
A villus, site of absorption in the intestinal lining.
A huge number of villi provide the surface at which lipids and other nutrients are absorbed. Small molecules enter the capillary network, and larger lipids enter the lacteals, small vessels of the lymph system.

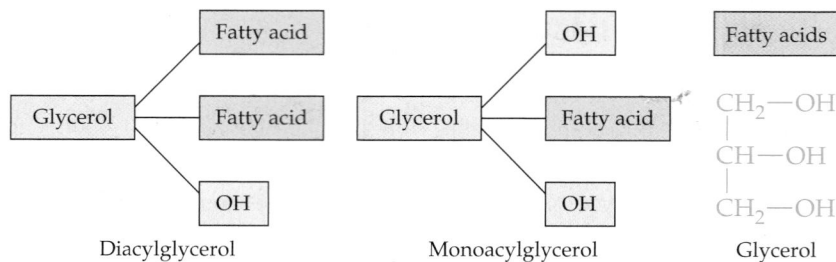

Small fatty acids and glycerol are water-soluble and are absorbed directly by simple diffusion through the surface of the villi that line the small intestine. Once they are inside the villi (Figure 24.3), these molecules diffuse into the capillaries and are carried by the blood to the liver (via the hepatic portal vein). Amino acids and simple sugars also move by simple diffusion into the villi and then the capillary network for transport to the liver by the bloodstream.

The water-insoluble acylglycerols and larger fatty acids are once again emulsified within the intestine. Then, at the intestinal lining they are released from the micelles and absorbed by the cells lining the intestine. Because these lipids, and also cholesterol and partially hydrolyzed phospholipids, must next enter the aqueous bloodstream for transport, they are once again packaged into water-soluble units—in this case, the lipoproteins known as *chylomicrons*. This elaborate process of hydrolysis, absorption, resynthesis, secretion, and transport is necessary for the triacylglycerol components to cross cell membranes and also for their travel through aqueous media. Remember, triacylglycerols and cholesterol must move from food particles in the intestinal system to the cytosol or mitochondria of liver cells and other cells for use in your body.

Chylomicrons are too large to enter the bloodstream through capillary walls. Instead, they are absorbed into the lymphatic system through lacteals, small vessels analogous to capillaries, within the villi (see Figure 24.3). Then, chylomicrons are carried to the thoracic duct (just below the collarbone), where the lymphatic system empties into the bloodstream. At this point, the lipids within these chylomicrons are ready to be used either for energy generation or to be put into storage; once leaving the thoracic duct the chylomicrons are carried directly to the liver, where hepatocytes use the lipid components depending on their own needs and the needs of other cells. The pathways of lipids through the villi and into the transport systems of the bloodstream and the lymphatic system are summarized in Figure 24.4.

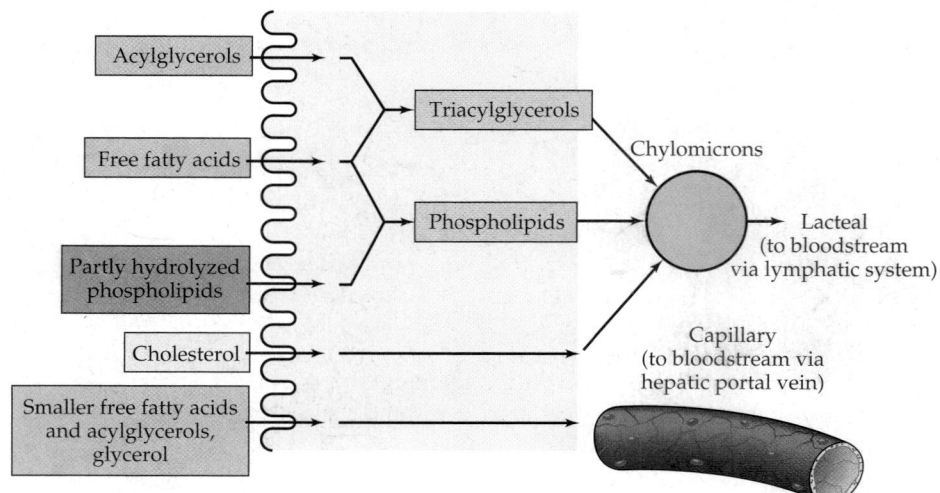

▲ **Figure 24.4**
Pathways of lipids through the villi.

Cholesterol (see structure in margin) and cholate (a bile acid anion, whose structure is shown on p. 731) are sterols with very similar structures. However, the roles they play in the body are different: Cholate is an emulsifier, whereas cholesterol plays an important role in membrane structure. Identify the small differences in their structures that make them well suited to their jobs in the body. Given their similar structures, can the roles of these molecules be reversed?

Cholesterol

24.2 Lipoproteins for Lipid Transport

Learning Objective:

• Name the major classes of lipoproteins, specify the nature and function of the lipids they transport, and identify their destinations.

The lipids used in the body's metabolic pathways have three sources: (1) from the digestive tract as food is broken down; (2) from adipose tissue, where excess lipids have been stored; and (3) from the liver, where lipids are synthesized. Whatever their source, these lipids must eventually be transported in blood, an aqueous medium, as summarized in Figure 24.5.

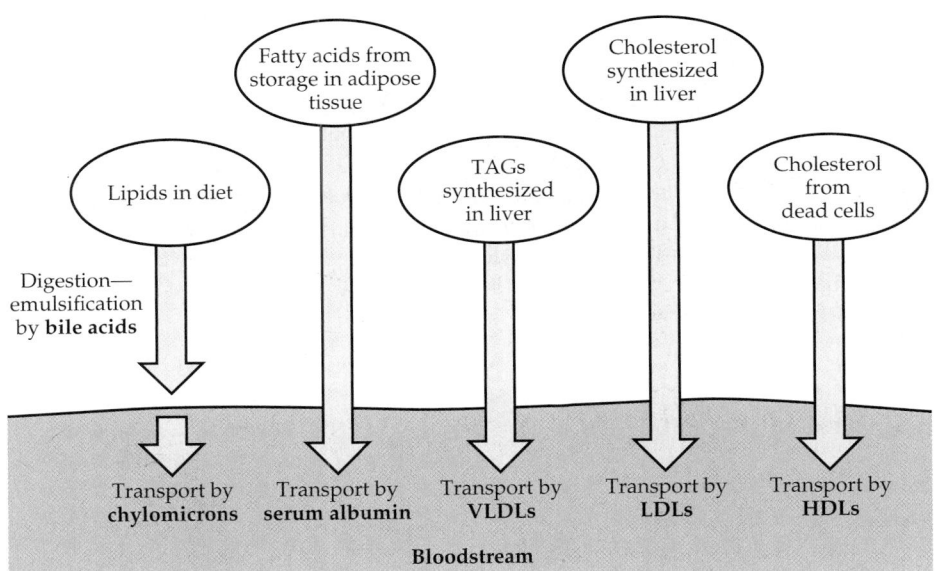

◄ Figure 24.5
Transport of lipids.
Fatty acids released from storage are carried by albumin, which is a large protein. All of the other lipids are carried packaged in various lipoproteins.

To become water-soluble, fatty acids released from adipose tissue associate with albumin, a protein found in blood plasma that binds up to 10 fatty acid molecules per protein molecule. All other lipids are carried by lipoproteins. (The role of lipoproteins in heart disease, where they are of great concern, is discussed in the Chemistry in Action "Fat Storage, Lipids, and Atherosclerosis" on p. 756.)

Because lipids are less dense than proteins, the density of lipoproteins depends on the ratio of lipid to protein. Therefore, lipoproteins are arbitrarily divided into five major types distinguishable by their composition and densities. Chylomicrons, which transport dietary lipids, carry triacylglycerols through the lymphatic system into the blood and thence to the liver for processing. These are the lowest-density lipoproteins (less than 0.95 g/cm^3) because they carry the highest ratio of lipid to protein. The four denser lipoprotein fractions have the following roles:

• *Very low-density lipoproteins (VLDLs)* (0.96–1.006 g/cm^3) carry triacylglycerols from the liver (where they are synthesized) to peripheral tissues for storage or energy generation.

- *Intermediate-density lipoproteins (IDLs)* ($1.007-1.019$ g/cm^3) carry remnants of the VLDLs from peripheral tissues to the liver for use in synthesis.
- *Low-density lipoproteins (LDLs)* ($1.020-1.062$ g/cm^3) transport cholesterol from the liver to peripheral tissues, where it is used in cell membranes or for steroid synthesis (and is also available for formation of arterial plaque).
- *High-density lipoproteins (HDLs)* ($1.063-1.210$ g/cm^3) transport cholesterol *from* dead or dying cells to the liver, where it is converted to bile acids. The bile acids are then available for use in digestion or are excreted via the digestive tract when in excess.

Worked Example 24.1 Digesting and Transporting Fats

Describe how the fat in an ice cream cone gets from the ice cream to a liver cell.

ANALYSIS Dietary fat from animal sources (such as the whole milk often found in ice cream) is primarily triacylglycerols with a small amount of cholesterol present. Cholesterol is not degraded in the digestive system. Fat-digesting enzymes are secreted by the pancreas and delivered via the common duct to the small intestine, along with bile acids. As discussed earlier, only free fatty acids and mono- and diacylglycerols can cross the intestinal cell wall before being passed on to the bloodstream. Smaller molecules such as some free fatty acids and glycerol diffuse across the cell membrane to enter the bloodstream; larger molecules must be delivered there in special packaging, called lipoproteins.

SOLUTION
As the ice cream cone is eaten, it passes through the mouth to the stomach, where mixing occurs. This mixing action promotes the formation of triacylglycerols into small droplets. No enzymatic digestion of lipids occurs in the stomach. When the stomach contents move to the small intestine, bile acids and pancreatic lipases are secreted into the mixture. The bile acids help to emulsify the fat droplets into micelles. Once micelles have formed, lipases hydrolyze the triacylglycerols to mono- and diacylglycerols; the hydrolysis also produces fatty acids. These three hydrolysis products cross into the cells lining the small intestine, are resynthesized into triacylglycerides, and are secreted into the bloodstream in the form of chylomicrons. Chylomicrons travel to the liver and enter cells for processing. The small amount of cholesterol in the ice cream will be directly absorbed, packaged into chylomicrons as well, and sent to the liver.

24.3 Triacylglycerol Metabolism: An Overview

Learning Objective:

- Name the major pathways for the synthesis and breakdown of triacylglycerols and fatty acids, and identify their connections to other metabolic pathways.

Figure 24.6 summarizes the metabolic pathways for triacylglycerols. Triacylglcerols are essential for our well-being as long-term energy storage, insulation for our bodies, and cushioning for our internal organs. These essential molecules are made from any extra glucose or protein we eat as well as from dietary fat as you will see in the metabolic paths discussed here.

Dietary Triacylglycerols

Hydrolysis of dietary triacylglycerols occurs when chylomicrons in the bloodstream encounter lipoprotein lipase anchored in capillary walls as chylomicrons are moving to hepatocytes for processing. The resulting fatty acids then have two possible fates: (1) If energy is in good supply, they are converted back to triacylglycerols for storage in adipose tissue; (2) If cells need energy, the fatty acid carbon atoms are activated by conversion to fatty acyl-CoA and then oxidized to acetyl-CoA, shortening the fatty acyl-CoA molecule by two carbon atoms for each oxidation.

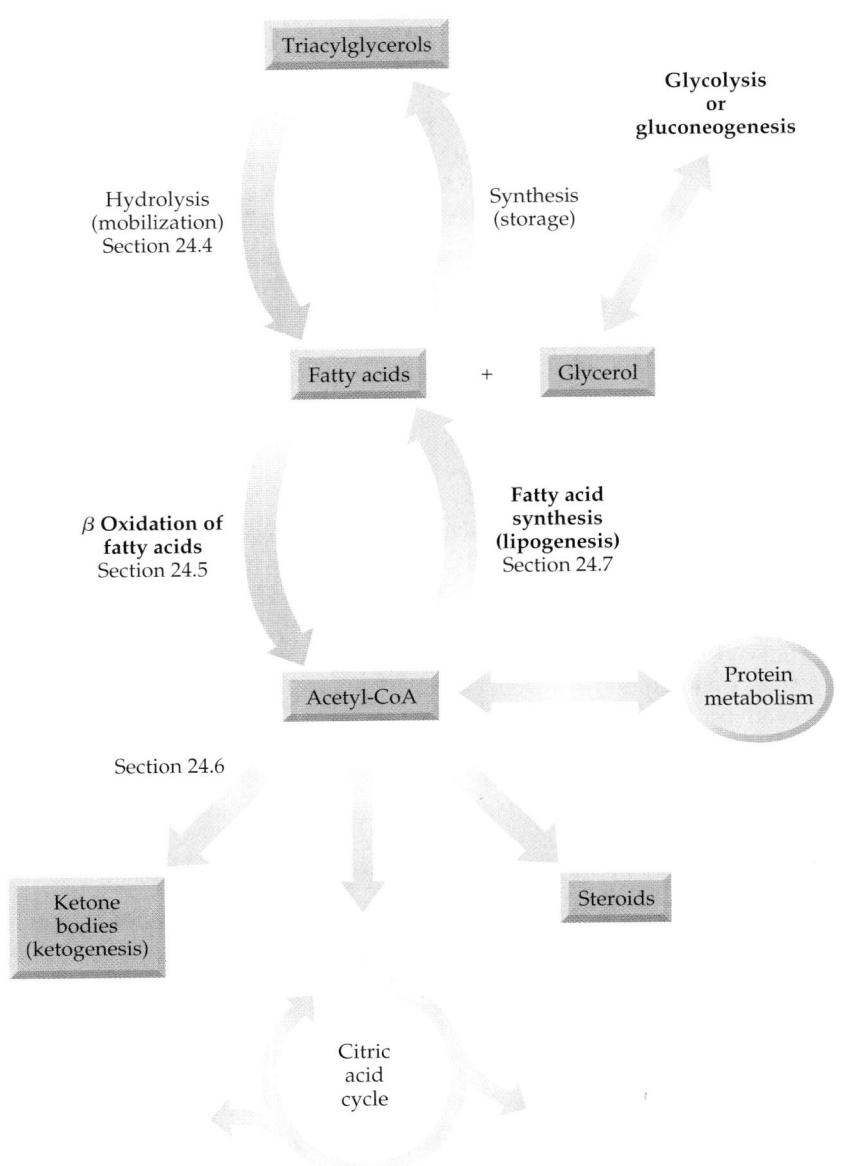

◄ **Figure 24.6**
Metabolism of triacylglycerols.
Pathways that break down molecules (catabolism) are shown in light brown, and synthetic pathways (anabolism) are shown in blue. Connections to other pathways or intermediates of metabolism are shown in green.

The primary metabolic fate of acetyl-CoA is the generation of energy via the citric acid cycle and oxidative phosphorylation (see Figure 21.4). Acetyl-CoA has several important roles in lipid metabolism as well. Acetyl-CoA serves as the starting material for the biosynthesis of fatty acids *(lipogenesis)* in the liver (Section 24.7). In addition, it enters the *ketogenesis* pathway for production of ketone bodies, a source of energy called on when glucose is in short supply (Section 24.6). Acetyl-CoA is also the starting material for the synthesis of cholesterol, from which all other steroids are made.

Triacylglycerols from Adipocytes

When stored triacylglycerols are needed as an energy source, lipases within fat cells are activated by hormone level variation (low insulin and high glucagon, Section 22.7). The stored triacylglycerols are hydrolyzed to fatty acids and glycerol, which are released into the bloodstream. These fatty acids travel in association with *albumins* (blood-plasma proteins) to cells (primarily muscle and liver cells), where they are converted to acetyl-CoA for energy generation.

Glycerol from Triacylglycerols

Glycerol produced from triacylglycerol hydrolysis is carried in the bloodstream to the liver or kidneys, where it is converted to glycerol 3-phosphate and dihydroxyacetone phosphate (DHAP):

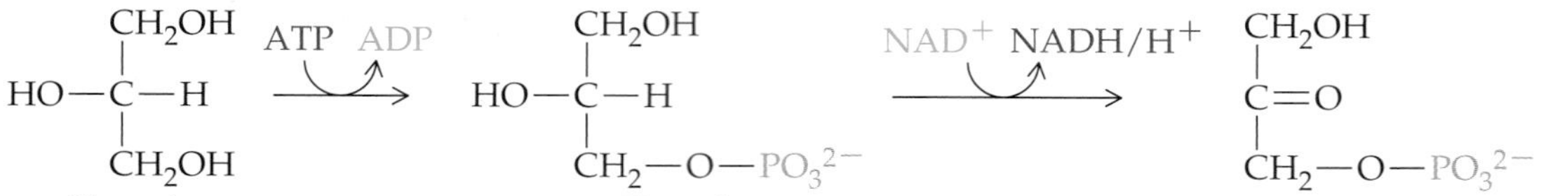

$$
\underset{\text{Glycerol}}{\begin{array}{c} CH_2OH \\ | \\ HO-C-H \\ | \\ CH_2OH \end{array}}
\xrightarrow{\;ATP\;\;ADP\;}
\underset{\substack{\text{Glycerol} \\ \text{3-phosphate}}}{\begin{array}{c} CH_2OH \\ | \\ HO-C-H \\ | \\ CH_2-O-PO_3^{2-} \end{array}}
\xrightarrow{\;NAD^+\;\;NADH/H^+\;}
\underset{\substack{\text{Dihydroxyacetone} \\ \text{phosphate (DHAP)}}}{\begin{array}{c} CH_2OH \\ | \\ C=O \\ | \\ CH_2-O-PO_3^{2-} \end{array}}
$$

DHAP can enter either the glycolysis or gluconeogenesis pathway (see Figure 22.3, step 5 and Figure 22.10, step 7) and is a link between carbohydrate metabolism and lipid metabolism.

The varied possible metabolic destinations of the fatty acids, glycerol, and acetyl-CoA from dietary triacylglycerols are summarized as follows:

Fate of Dietary Triacylglycerols

- *Triacylglycerols* undergo hydrolysis to fatty acids and glycerol.
- *Fatty acids* undergo
  - Resynthesis of triacylglycerols for storage
  - Conversion to acetyl-CoA
- *Glycerol* is converted to glyceraldehyde 3-phosphate and DHAP, which participate in
  - *Glycolysis*—energy generation (Section 22.3)
  - *Gluconeogenesis*—glucose formation (Section 22.9)
  - *Triacylglycerol synthesis*—energy storage (Section 24.4)
- *Acetyl-CoA* participates in
  - *Triacylglycerol synthesis* (Section 24.4)
  - Ketone body synthesis (*ketogenesis,* Section 24.6)
  - Synthesis of sterols and other lipids
  - *Citric acid cycle and oxidative phosphorylation* (Sections 21.7 and 21.8)

PROBLEM 24.2

Examine Figure 22.3 (pp. 694–695) and explain how DHAP can enter the glycolysis pathway and be converted to pyruvate.

PROBLEM 24.3

How are long-chain fatty acids released from triacylglycerides transported through the bloodstream?

24.4 Storage and Mobilization of Triacylglycerols

Learning Objective:

- Explain the reactions by which triacylglycerols are stored and mobilized, and how these reactions are regulated.

Although adipose tissue is the storage depot for triacylglycerols, triacylglycerols do not just sit unused until needed for energy production. The passage of fatty acids in and out of storage in adipose tissue is a continuous process essential to maintaining homeostasis (see the Chemistry in Action "Homeostasis," page 834).

Mobilization (of triacylglycerols)
Hydrolysis of triacylglycerols in adipose tissue and release of fatty acids into the bloodstream.

Triacylglycerol Synthesis

Our bodies regulate the storage and **mobilization** of triacylglycerols through the same hormones that regulate blood glucose concentration, insulin, and glucagon. After a meal, blood glucose levels rise, and glucagon levels drop. Glucose enters cells, and the rate of glycolysis increases. Under these conditions, insulin activates the synthesis of triacylglycerols for storage.

Figure 22.6 shows the effects of insulin and glucagon hormones on metabolism.

The reactants in triacylglycerol synthesis are glycerol 3-phosphate and fatty acid acyl groups carried by coenzyme A. Triacylglycerol synthesis proceeds by transfer of first one and then another fatty acid acyl group from coenzyme A to glycerol 3-phosphate. The reaction is catalyzed by acyl transferase, and the product is phosphatidic acid.

Next, the phosphate group is removed from phosphatidic acid by phosphatidic acid phosphatase to produce 1,2-diacylglycerol. In the presence of acyl transferase, the third fatty acid group is then added to give a triacylglycerol.

As the reaction on page 746 shows, glycerol is one source of glycerol phosphate. But adipocytes do not synthesize glycerol kinase, the enzyme needed to convert glycerol to glycerol 3-phosphate; thus they cannot synthesize glycerol 3-phosphate from glycerol. However, glycerol 3-phosphate can be synthesized from DHAP produced from glyceraldehyde 3-phosphate generated in gluconeogenesis (Figure 22.10). Thus, adipocytes can synthesize triacylglycerols as long as DHAP is available. In adipocytes, this pathway is called *glyceroneogenesis,* and it supplies the DHAP for conversion to glycerol 3-phosphate. Glyceroneogenesis is an abbreviated form of gluconeogenesis (see Figure 22.10), ending with the conversion of DHAP to glycerol 3-phosphate followed by triacylglycerol synthesis.

Triacylglycerol Mobilization

When digestion of a meal is finished, blood glucose levels return to normal; consequently, insulin levels drop and glucagon levels rise. The lower insulin level and higher glucagon level together activate *triacylglycerol lipase,* the enzyme within adipocytes that controls hydrolysis of stored triacylglycerols. If glycerol 3-phosphate is in short supply—an indication that glycolysis is not producing sufficient energy—the fatty acids and glycerol produced by hydrolysis of the stored triacylglycerols are released to the bloodstream for transport to energy-generating cells. Otherwise, the fatty acids and glycerol are cycled back into new triacylglycerides for storage. Dieters on special low-carbohydrate diets are trying to produce this metabolic state in order to "burn fat." An undesirable side effect of these diets is ketosis and the production of ketone bodies (Section 24.6).

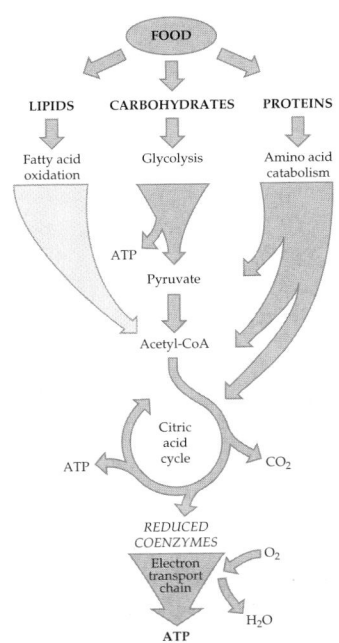

24.5 Oxidation of Fatty Acids

Learning Objectives:

• Describe fatty acid oxidation.
• Calculate the energy yield from fatty acid oxidation.

Once a fatty acid enters the cytosol of a cell that needs energy, three successive processes occur.

1. *Activation* The fatty acid is activated by conversion to fatty acyl-CoA. This activation, which occurs in the cytosol, serves the same purpose as the first few steps in oxidation of glucose by glycolysis. Initially, some energy from adenosine triphosphate (ATP) must be invested in converting the fatty acid to fatty acyl-CoA, a form that breaks down more easily. Since only one phosphate ester bond is broken in the reaction, the activation energy used is for one ATP only.

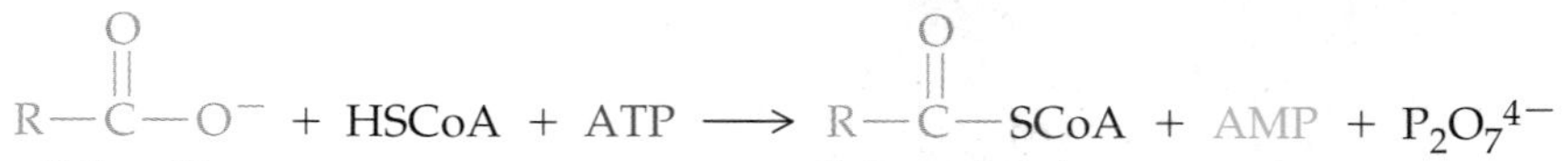

$$\underset{\text{Fatty acid}}{R-\overset{\overset{\displaystyle O}{\|}}{C}-O^-} + \text{HSCoA} + \text{ATP} \longrightarrow \underset{\text{Fatty acyl-CoA}}{R-\overset{\overset{\displaystyle O}{\|}}{C}-\text{SCoA}} + \text{AMP} + P_2O_7{}^{4-}$$

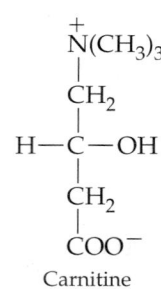

Carnitine

2. *Transport* The fatty acyl-CoA, which cannot cross the mitochondrial membrane by diffusion, is transported by carnitine from the cytosol into the mitochondrial matrix, where energy generation occurs. Carnitine, an amino-oxy acid, undergoes an ester-formation exchange reaction with the fatty acyl-CoA, resulting in a fatty acyl-carnitine ester that moves across the membrane into the mitochondria by facilitated diffusion. There, another ester-formation exchange reaction regenerates the fatty acyl-CoA and carnitine.

$$\text{Fatty acyl-CoA} + \text{Carnitine} \xrightarrow{\overset{\text{Carnitine acyl}}{\text{transferase}}} \text{Fatty acyl-carnitine} + \text{HS-CoA}$$

3. *Oxidation* The fatty acyl-CoA is oxidized by enzymes in the mitochondrial matrix to produce acetyl-CoA, nicotinamide adenine dinucleotide (NADH), and flavin adenine dinucleotide (FADH$_2$). The oxidation occurs by repeating the series of four reactions, which make up the **β-oxidation pathway.** Each repetition of these reactions cleaves a 2-carbon acetyl group from the end of a fatty acid acyl group and produces one acetyl-CoA. This pathway is a *spiral* because the shortened long-chain fatty acyl group must continue to return to the pathway until each pair of carbon atoms is removed.

β-Oxidation pathway A repetitive series of biochemical reactions that degrades fatty acids to acetyl-CoA by removing carbon atoms two at a time.

The β-Oxidation Pathway

The name β oxidation refers to the oxidation of the carbon atom β to the thioester linkage in two steps of the pathway.

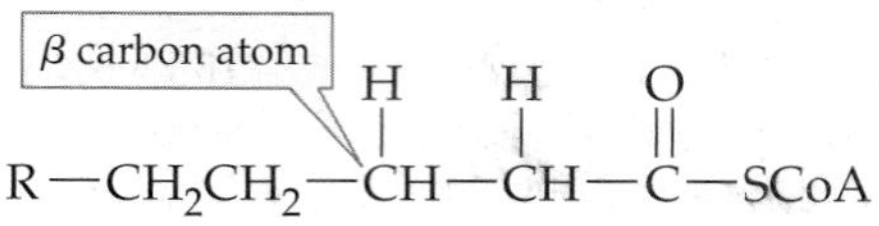

$$R-CH_2CH_2-\overset{\overset{\displaystyle H}{|}}{C}H-\overset{\overset{\displaystyle H}{|}}{C}H-\overset{\overset{\displaystyle O}{\|}}{C}-SCoA$$

β carbon atom

A fatty acyl-CoA

STEP 1: The first β oxidation *Acyl-CoA dehydrogenase* and its coenzyme FAD remove hydrogen atoms from the carbon atoms α and β to the carbonyl group in the fatty acyl-CoA, forming a carbon–carbon double bond. These hydrogen atoms and their electrons are passed directly from $FADH_2$ to coenzyme Q so that the electrons can enter the electron transport chain (Section 21.8).

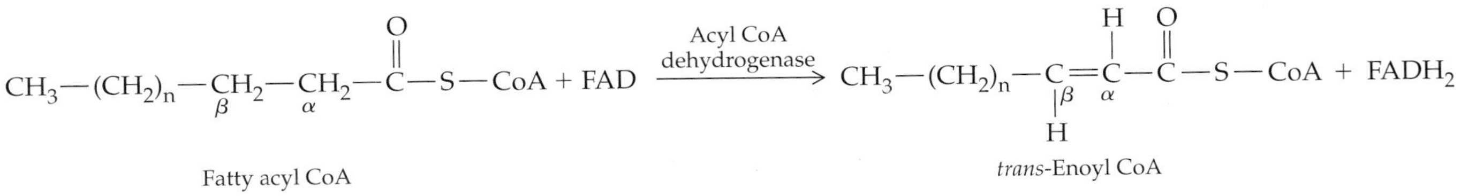

$$CH_3-(CH_2)_n-\underset{\beta}{CH_2}-\underset{\alpha}{CH_2}-\overset{\overset{\textstyle O}{\|}}{C}-S-CoA + FAD \xrightarrow{\substack{\text{Acyl CoA} \\ \text{dehydrogenase}}} CH_3-(CH_2)_n-\underset{\underset{\textstyle H}{|}}{\overset{\overset{\textstyle H}{|}}{\underset{\beta}{C}}}=\underset{\alpha}{C}-\overset{\overset{\textstyle O}{\|}}{C}-S-CoA + FADH_2$$

Fatty acyl CoA   *trans*-Enoyl CoA

STEP 2: Hydration *Enoyl-CoA hydratase* adds a water molecule across the newly created double bond to give an alcohol with the —OH group on the β carbon.

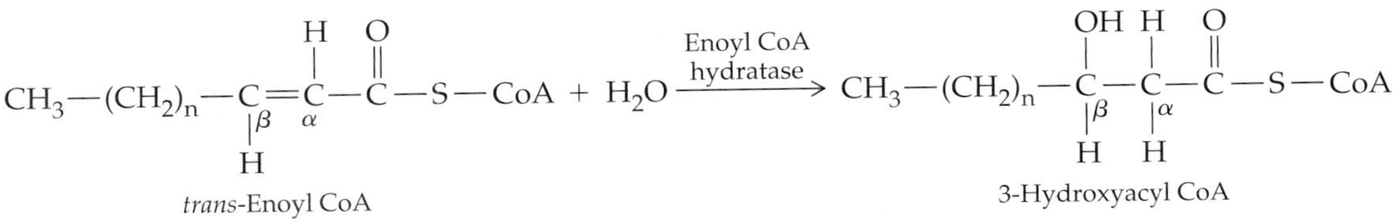

$$CH_3-(CH_2)_n-\underset{\underset{\textstyle H}{|}}{\overset{\overset{\textstyle H}{|}}{\underset{\beta}{C}}}=\underset{\alpha}{C}-\overset{\overset{\textstyle O}{\|}}{C}-S-CoA + H_2O \xrightarrow{\substack{\text{Enoyl CoA} \\ \text{hydratase}}} CH_3-(CH_2)_n-\underset{\underset{\textstyle H}{|}}{\overset{\overset{\textstyle OH}{|}}{\underset{\beta}{C}}}-\underset{\underset{\textstyle H}{|}}{\overset{\overset{\textstyle H}{|}}{\underset{\alpha}{C}}}-\overset{\overset{\textstyle O}{\|}}{C}-S-CoA$$

trans-Enoyl CoA   3-Hydroxyacyl CoA

STEP 3: The second β oxidation The coenzyme NAD^+ is the oxidizing agent for conversion of the β—OH group to a carbonyl group by *β-hydroxyacyl-CoA dehydrogenase*.

$$CH_3-(CH_2)_n-\underset{\underset{\textstyle H}{|}}{\overset{\overset{\textstyle OH}{|}}{\underset{\beta}{C}}}-\underset{\underset{\textstyle H}{|}}{\overset{\overset{\textstyle H}{|}}{\underset{\alpha}{C}}}-\overset{\overset{\textstyle O}{\|}}{C}-S-CoA + NAD^+ \xrightarrow{\substack{\text{3-Hydroxyacyl CoA} \\ \text{dehydrogenase}}} CH_3-(CH_2)_n-\underset{\beta}{\overset{\overset{\textstyle O}{\|}}{C}}-\underset{\underset{\textstyle H}{|}}{\overset{\overset{\textstyle H}{|}}{\underset{\alpha}{C}}}-\overset{\overset{\textstyle O}{\|}}{C}-S-CoA + NADH + H^+$$

3-Hydroxyacyl CoA   β-Ketoacyl CoA

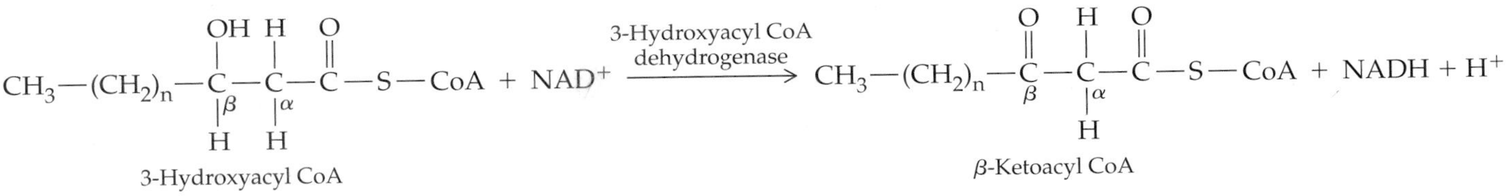

STEP 4: Cleavage to remove an acetyl group An acetyl group is split off by *thiolase (acyl-CoA acetyltransferase)* and attached to a new coenzyme A molecule, leaving behind an acyl-CoA that is two carbon atoms shorter.

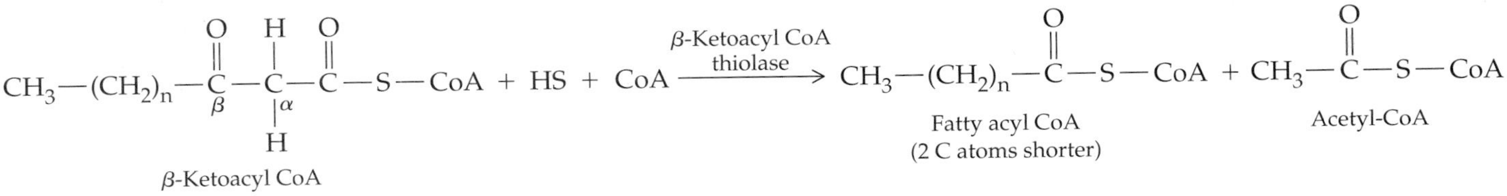

$$CH_3-(CH_2)_n-\underset{\beta}{\overset{\overset{\textstyle O}{\|}}{C}}-\underset{\underset{\textstyle H}{|}}{\overset{\overset{\textstyle H}{|}}{\underset{\alpha}{C}}}-\overset{\overset{\textstyle O}{\|}}{C}-S-CoA + HS + CoA \xrightarrow{\substack{\text{β-Ketoacyl CoA} \\ \text{thiolase}}} CH_3-(CH_2)_n-\overset{\overset{\textstyle O}{\|}}{C}-S-CoA + CH_3-\overset{\overset{\textstyle O}{\|}}{C}-S-CoA$$

β-Ketoacyl CoA   Fatty acyl CoA   Acetyl-CoA
                                            (2 C atoms shorter)

If a fatty acid has an even number of carbon atoms, all of the carbons are transferred to acetyl-CoA molecules by an appropriate number of trips through the β-oxidation spiral. Additional steps are required to oxidize fatty acids with odd numbers of carbon atoms and those with double bonds. Ultimately, all fatty acid carbons are released for further oxidation in the citric acid cycle.

The total energy output from fatty acid catabolism, like that from glucose catabolism, is measured by the total number of ATP molecules produced. For fatty acids, this is the total number of ATP molecules from acetyl-CoA oxidation through the citric acid cycle, including those produced from the reduced coenzymes NADH and $FADH_2$ during oxidative phosphorylation, plus those produced by the reduced coenzymes (NADH and $FADH_2$) during fatty acid oxidation. The following worked examples show how to calculate the energy yield in ATP.

Worked Example 24.2 Spiraling through β Oxidation

How many times does stearic acid $(CH_3(CH_2)_{16}COOH)$ spiral through the β-oxidation pathway to produce acetyl-CoA?

ANALYSIS Each turn of the β-oxidation spiral pathway produces one acetyl-CoA. To determine the number of turns, divide the total number of carbon atoms in the fatty acid, 18 in this case, by two since an acetyl group contains two carbon atoms and they come from the fatty acid. Subtract one turn, since the last turn produces two acetyl-CoA molecules.

SOLUTION
Stearic acid contains 18 carbon atoms; the acetyl group contains two carbon atoms. Therefore, eight β-oxidation turns occur, and nine molecules of acetyl-CoA are produced.

▲ **Fat as a source of water.** A camel's hump is almost entirely fat, which serves as a source of energy and also water. As reduced coenzymes from fatty acid oxidation pass through electron transport to generate ATP, large amounts of water are formed (about one water molecule for each carbon atom in a fatty acid). This water sustains camels during long periods when no drinking water is available.

⊙━ KEY CONCEPT PROBLEM 24.4

In β oxidation, (a) identify the steps that are oxidations and describe the changes that occur; (b) identify the oxidizing agents; (c) identify the reaction that is an addition; (d) identify the reaction that is a substitution.

PROBLEM 24.5

How many molecules of acetyl-CoA are produced by catabolism of the following fatty acids, and how many β oxidations are needed?

   (a) Palmitic acid, $CH_3(CH_2)_{14}COOH$
   (b) Lignoceric acid, $CH_3(CH_2)_{22}COOH$

PROBLEM 24.6

Look back at the reactions of the citric acid cycle (Figure 20.9) and identify the three reactions in that cycle that are similar to the first three reactions of the β oxidation of a fatty acid.

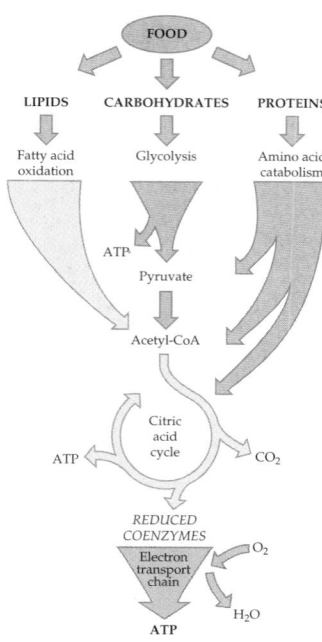

 Worked Example 24.3 Calculating Energy Yield from β Oxidation

How much energy is released as ATP from the complete oxidation of lauric acid $(CH_3(CH_2)_{10}COOH)$?

ANALYSIS Complete oxidation of a molecule includes conversion of any energy released in oxidation pathways, as NADH or $FADH_2$ is also converted to ATP by passage through the electron transport system. To calculate the ATP yield from lauric acid:

- Determine the number of acetyl groups and number of turns of the β-oxidation spiral needed.
- Determine the ATP, NADH, and $FADH_2$ yield from one turn of the β-oxidation spiral.
- Determine the ATP, NADH, and $FADH_2$ yield from oxidation of acetyl-CoA in the citric acid cycle.
- Convert NADH and $FADH_2$ yields to ATP yields from oxidative phosphorylation.
- Adjust β-oxidation ATP yield for number of turns of the spiral.
- Adjust citric acid cycle ATP yield for number of acetyl-CoA molecules oxidized.
- Add the ATP yield and subtract 2 ATP molecules used to prime the start of β oxidation.

SOLUTION
From the citric acid cycle:

$$12 \text{ C atoms}/2 = 6 \text{ acetyl-CoA molecules}$$

$$\frac{12 \text{ ATP molecules}}{\text{acetyl-CoA molecule}} \times 6 \text{ acetyl-CoA molecules} = 72 \text{ ATP molecules}$$

Activation of the fatty acid: $= -2$ ATP molecules

From the 5 β oxidations:

$$\frac{5 \text{ ATP molecules}}{\beta \text{ oxidation}} \times 5\ \beta \text{ oxidations} = 25 \text{ ATP molecules}$$

Summation of the ATP used and produced:

$$Total = (72 - 2 + 25) \text{ ATP molecules} = 95 \text{ ATP molecules}$$

Comparing the amount of ATP produced by fatty acid catabolism with the amount produced by glucose catabolism illustrates why our bodies use triacylglycerols rather than carbohydrates for long-term energy storage. We used lauric acid as our example because it has a molar mass close to that of glucose. Our best estimates show that 1 mol of glucose (180 g) generates 38 mol of ATP, whereas 1 mol of lauric acid (200 g) generates 95 mol of ATP. Thus, fatty acids yield nearly three times more energy per gram as carbohydrates. In terms of nutritional calories (i.e., kilocalories), carbohydrates yield 4 Cal/g (16.7 kJ/g), whereas fats and oils yield 9 Cal/g (37.7 kJ/g).

In addition, stored fats have a greater "energy density" than stored carbohydrates. Because glycogen—the storage form of carbohydrates—is hydrophilic, about 2 g of water are held with each gram of glycogen. The hydrophobic fats do not hold water in this manner.

PROBLEM 24.7
How much energy is released as ATP from the complete oxidation of stearic acid $(CH_3(CH_2)_{16}COOH)$?

24.6 Ketone Bodies and Ketoacidosis

Learning Objective:

• Identify ketone bodies, describe their properties and synthesis, and explain their role in metabolism.

What happens if lipid catabolism produces more acetyl-CoA than the citric acid cycle can handle? This happens when β oxidation of the fatty acids from triacylglcerols produces acetyl-CoA faster than the citric acid cycle can process it. Not only does β oxidation produce several molecules of acetyl-CoA from each molecule of fatty acid, but the enzymes in the β-oxidation pathway catalyze reactions more rapidly than the enzymes in the citric acid cycle do. Consequently, the energy is preserved by conversion of excess acetyl-CoA in liver mitochondria to 3-hydroxybutyrate and acetoacetate. Because it is a β-keto acid and therefore somewhat unstable, acetoacetate undergoes spontaneous, nonenzymatic decomposition to acetone.

Ketone bodies

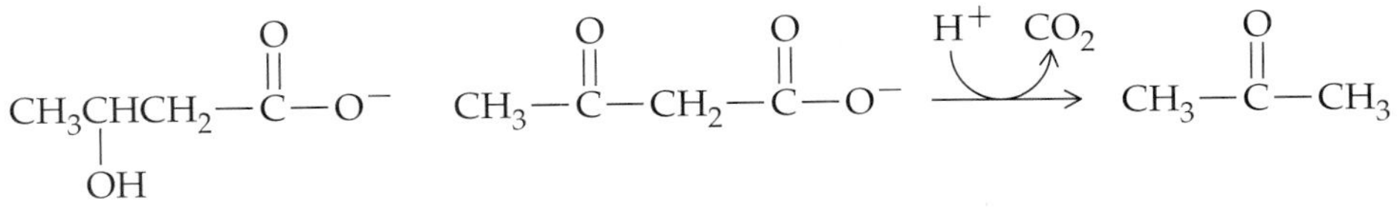

Ketone bodies Compounds produced in the liver that can be used as fuel by muscle and brain tissue; for example, 3-hydroxybutyrate, acetoacetate, and acetone.

Ketogenesis The synthesis of ketone bodies from acetyl-CoA.

These compounds are traditionally known as **ketone bodies,** although one of them, 3-hydroxybutyrate, contains no ketone functional group. Because they are water-soluble, ketone bodies do not need protein carriers to travel in the bloodstream. Once formed, they become available to all tissues in the body.

The formation of the three ketone bodies, a process known as **ketogenesis,** occurs in four enzyme-catalyzed steps plus the spontaneous decomposition of acetoacetate.

Ketogenesis

Steps 1 and 2 of Ketogenesis: Assembly of 6-Carbon Intermediate

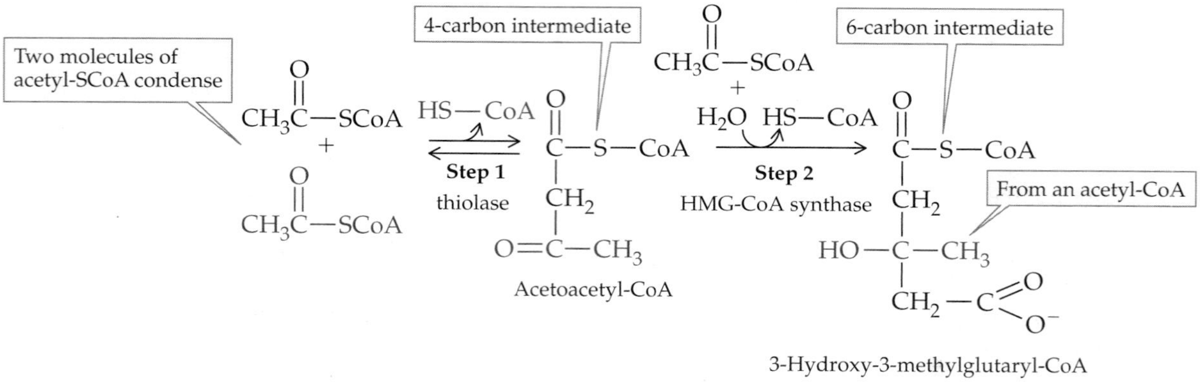

In step 1, the reverse of the final step of β oxidation (step 4 in Figure 24.7), two acetyl-CoA molecules combine in a reaction catalyzed by *thiolase* to produce acetoacetyl-CoA. In step 2, a third acetyl-CoA and a water molecule react with acetoacetyl-CoA to give 3-hydroxy-3-methylglutaryl-CoA (HMG-CoA). The enzyme for this step, *HMG-CoA synthase,* is found only in mitochondria and is specific only for the D isomer of the substrate. The enzyme for the β-oxidation pathway, also found in mitochondria, has the same name but is specific for the L form of HMG-CoA. The pathways are separated by the specificity of the enzymes for their respective substrates.

Steps 3 and 4 of Ketogenesis: Formation of the Ketone Bodies

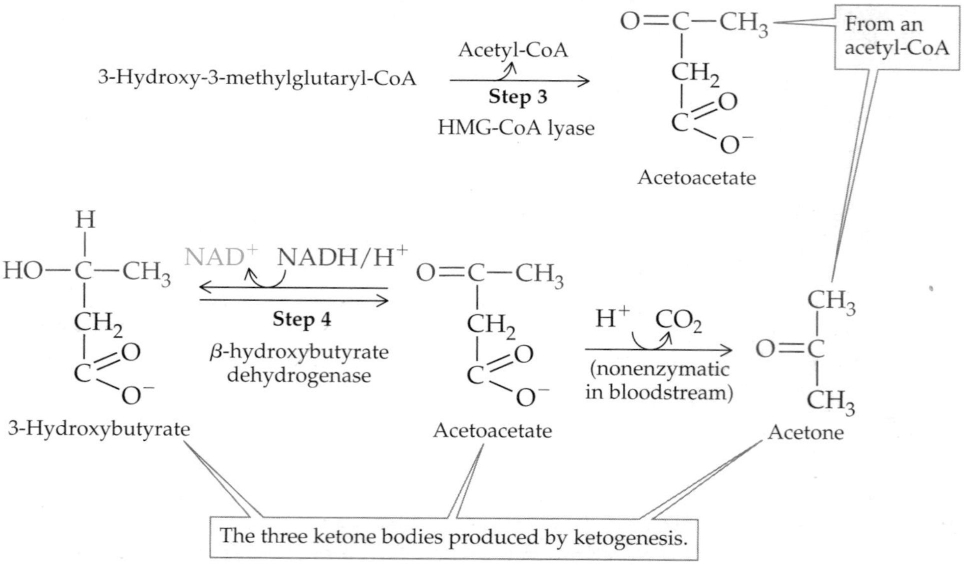

The three ketone bodies produced by ketogenesis.

In step 3, removal of acetyl-CoA from the product of Step 2 by *HMG-CoA lyase* produces the first of the ketone bodies, *acetoacetate.* Acetoacetate is the precursor of the other two ketone bodies produced by ketogenesis, 3-hydroxybutyrate and acetone. In step 4, acetoacetate is reduced to 3-hydroxybutyrate by *3-hydroxybutyrate dehydrogenase.* (Note in the equation for step 4 that 3-hydroxybutyrate and acetoacetate are connected by a reversible reaction. In tissues that need energy, acetoacetate is produced by different enzymes than those used for ketogenesis. Acetyl-CoA can then be produced from the acetoacetate.) As acetoacetate and 3-hydroxybutyrate are synthesized by ketogenesis in liver mitochondria, they are released to the bloodstream. Decomposition of acetoacetate in the bloodstream forms acetone, which is excreted in urine and by exhalation.

CHEMISTRY IN ACTION

The Liver—Clearinghouse for Metabolism

The liver is the largest reservoir of blood in the body and also the largest internal organ, making up about 2.5% of the body's mass. Blood carrying the end products of digestion (glucose, other sugars, amino acids, and so forth) enters the liver through the hepatic portal vein before going into general circulation, so the liver is ideally situated to regulate the concentrations of nutrients and other substances in the blood. The liver is important as the gateway for entry of drugs into the circulation and also contains the enzymes needed to inactivate toxic substances as well.

The liver synthesizes glycogen from glucose, glucose from noncarbohydrate precursors, triacylglycerols from mono- and diacylglycerols, and fatty acids from acetyl-CoA. It also synthesizes cholesterol, bile acids, plasma proteins, and blood-clotting factors. In addition, liver cells catabolize glucose, fatty acids, and amino acids to yield carbon dioxide and energy stored in ATP. The *urea cycle,* which converts nitrogen to urea for excretion, takes place in the liver (Section 25.4).

The liver stores reserves of glycogen, certain lipids and amino acids, iron, and fat-soluble vitamins, in order to release them as needed to maintain homeostasis. In addition, only liver cells have the enzyme needed to convert glucose 6-phosphate from glycogenolysis and gluconeogenesis to glucose.

Given its central role in metabolism, the liver is subject to a number of pathological conditions based on excessive accumulation of various metabolites. For example *cirrhosis,* the development of fibrous tissue that is preceded by excessive triacylglycerol buildup is a serious medical condition. Cirrhosis occurs in alcoholism, uncontrolled diabetes, and metabolic conditions in which the synthesis of lipoproteins from triacylglycerols is blocked.

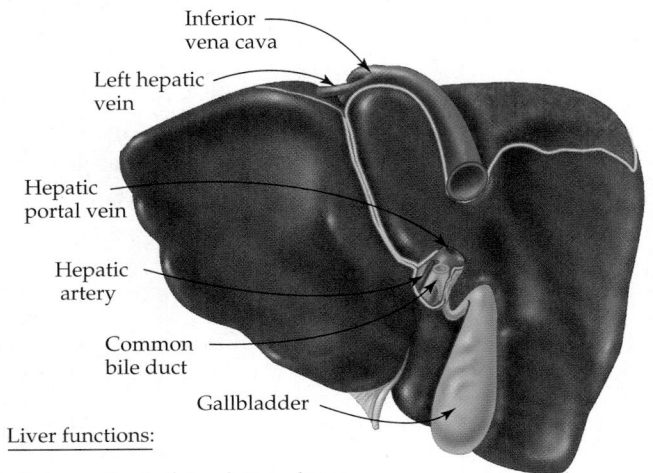

Liver functions:

- Balances level of circulating glucose
- Balances levels of circulating triacylglycerol, fatty acid, and cholesterol
- Removes excess amino acids from circulation; converts their nitrogen to urea for excretion
- Stores reserves of fat-soluble vitamins and iron
- Removes drugs from circulation and breaks them down

▲ Anatomy of the liver. Blood carries metabolites from the digestive system entering the liver through the hepatic portal vein. The gallbladder is the site for storage of bile.

CIA Problem 24.1 Give some reasons why the liver is so vital to proper metabolic function.

CIA Problem 24.2 What is cirrhosis of the liver, and what can trigger it?

CIA Problem 24.3 Why is the liver referred to as the clearinghouse for metabolism in your body?

Under normal conditions, acetoacetate supplies some of the daily energy needs for skeletal muscles, and heart muscles use it in preference to glucose when fatty acids are in short supply. But consider the situation when energy production from glucose is inadequate due to starvation or because glucose is not metabolized normally due to diabetes (Section 22.7). The body responds by providing other energy sources in what can become a precarious balancing act. Under these conditions, ketone body production accelerates because acetoacetate and 3-hydroxybutyrate are converted to acetyl-CoA for oxidation in the citric acid cycle.

During the early stages of starvation, heart and muscle tissues burn larger quantities of acetoacetate, thereby preserving glucose for use in the brain. In prolonged starvation, even the brain switches to ketone bodies to meet up to 75% of its energy needs.

The condition in which ketone bodies are produced faster than they are utilized *(ketosis)* occurs in diabetes. It is indicated by the characteristic odor of acetone (a highly volatile ketone) on the patient's breath and the presence of ketone bodies in the urine *(ketonuria)* and the blood *(ketonemia).*

Ketoacidosis Lowered blood pH due to accumulation of ketone bodies.

Because two of the ketone bodies are carboxylic acids, continued ketosis such as might occur in untreated diabetes leads to the potentially serious condition known as **ketoacidosis**—acidosis resulting from increased concentrations of ketone bodies in the blood. The blood's buffers are overwhelmed and blood pH drops. An individual experiences dehydration due to increased urine flow, labored breathing because acidic blood is a poor oxygen carrier, and depression. Ultimately, if untreated, the condition leads to coma and death.

PROBLEM 24.8

Which of the following classifications apply to the formation of 3-hydroxybutyrate from acetoacetate?

(a) Condensation   **(b)** Hydrolysis

(c) Oxidation   **(d)** Reduction

PROBLEM 24.9

Consider the reactions of ketogenesis.

(a) What role does acetyl-CoA play?

(b) How many acetyl-CoA molecules are used in the production of the ketone bodies?

(c) What is the essential role of ketone bodies during prolonged starvation?

24.7 Biosynthesis of Fatty Acids

Learning Objective:

• Compare the pathways for fatty acid synthesis and oxidation, and describe the reactions of the synthesis pathway.

Lipogenesis The biochemical pathway for synthesis of fatty acids from acetyl-CoA.

Fatty acid biosynthesis from acetyl-CoA, a process known as **lipogenesis,** provides a link between carbohydrate, lipid, and protein metabolism. Because acetyl-CoA is an end product of carbohydrate and amino acid catabolism, using it to make fatty acids allows the body to divert the energy of excess carbohydrates and amino acids into storage as triacylglycerols.

Fatty acid synthesis and catabolism are similar in that they both proceed two carbon atoms at a time and in that they are both recursive, spiral pathways. But, as is usually the case, the biochemical pathway in one direction is not the exact reverse of the pathway in the other direction because the reverse of an energetically favorable pathway is energetically unfavorable. This principle applies to β oxidation of fatty acids and its reverse, lipogenesis. Furthermore, catabolism of fatty acids occurs in the mitochondria and anabolism is located in the cytoplasm. The two pathways are compared in Table 24.1.

Table 24.1 Comparison of Fatty Acid Oxidation and Synthesis

Oxidation	Synthesis
Occurs in mitochondria	Occurs in cytosol
Enzymes different from synthesis	Enzymes different from oxidation
Intermediates carried by coenzyme A	Intermediates carried by acyl carrier protein
Coenzymes: FAD and NAD^+	Coenzyme: NADPH
Carbon atoms removed two at a time	Carbon atoms added two at a time

The stage is set for lipogenesis by two separate reactions: (1) transfer of an acetyl group from acetyl-CoA to a carrier enzyme in the fatty acid synthase complex (S-enzyme-1) and (2) conversion of acetyl-CoA to malonyl-CoA in a reaction that requires the investment of energy from ATP, followed by transfer of the malonyl group to the acyl carrier protein (ACP) and regeneration of coenzyme A.

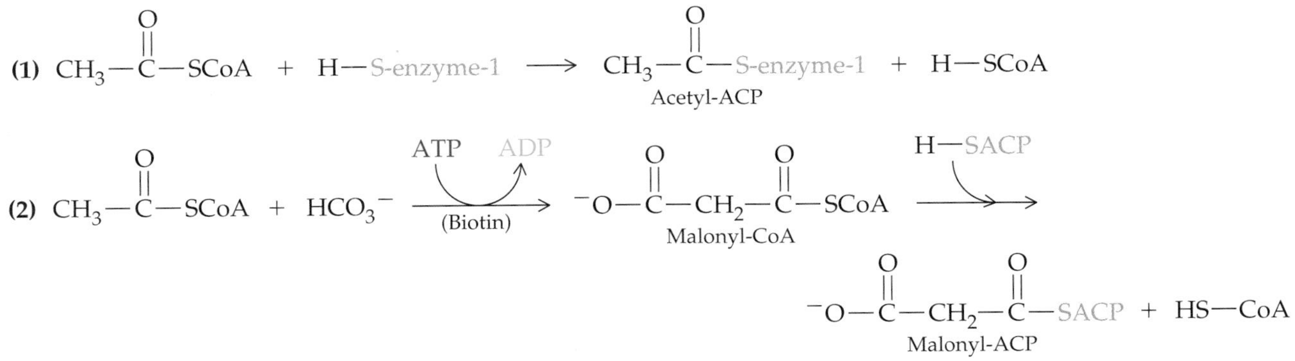

$$
\textbf{(1)} \quad CH_3-\overset{\overset{\displaystyle O}{\|}}{C}-SCoA \;+\; H-S\text{-enzyme-1} \;\longrightarrow\; CH_3-\overset{\overset{\displaystyle O}{\|}}{C}-S\text{-enzyme-1} \;+\; H-SCoA
$$
Acetyl-ACP

$$
\textbf{(2)} \quad CH_3-\overset{\overset{\displaystyle O}{\|}}{C}-SCoA \;+\; HCO_3^- \;\xrightarrow[\text{(Biotin)}]{\;ATP\quad ADP\;}\; {}^-O-\overset{\overset{\displaystyle O}{\|}}{C}-CH_2-\overset{\overset{\displaystyle O}{\|}}{C}-SCoA \;\xrightarrow{\;H-SACP\;}
$$
Malonyl-CoA

$$
{}^-O-\overset{\overset{\displaystyle O}{\|}}{C}-CH_2-\overset{\overset{\displaystyle O}{\|}}{C}-SACP \;+\; HS-CoA
$$
Malonyl-ACP

Fatty acid synthase is a multienzyme complex that contains all six of the enzymes needed for lipogenesis, with a protein called ACP anchored in the center of the complex. Enzyme-1 is also part of the complex. The malonyl group of reaction (2) carries the carbon atoms that will be incorporated two at a time into the fatty acid.

Once malonyl-ACP and the acetyl group on S-enzyme-1 have been readied, a series of four reactions, explained in Figure 24.7, lengthens the growing fatty acid chain by two carbon atoms with each repetition.

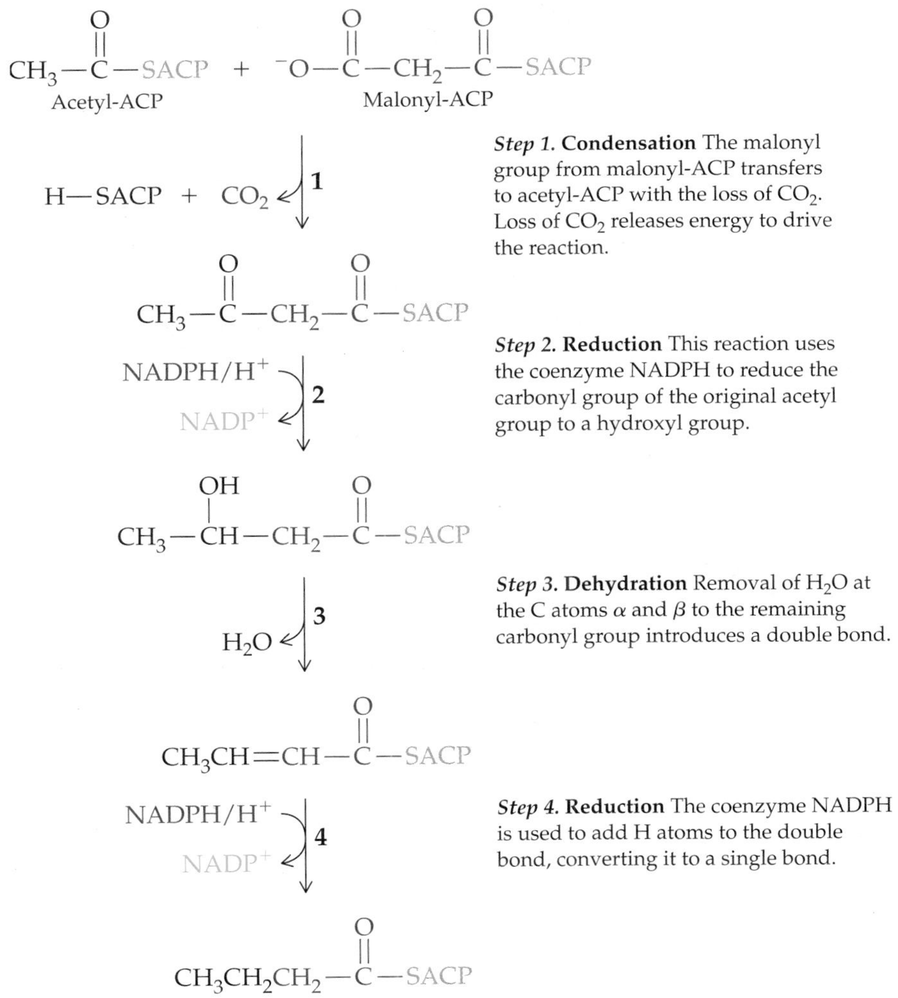

◀ **Figure 24.7**
Chain elongation in the biosynthesis of fatty acids.
The steps shown begin with acetyl-acyl carrier protein (acetyl-ACP), the reactant in the first spiral of palmitic acid synthesis. Each new pair of carbon atoms is carried into the next spiral by a new malonyl-ACP. The growing chain remains attached to the carrier protein from the original acetyl-ACP.

$$
CH_3-\overset{\overset{\displaystyle O}{\|}}{C}-SACP \;+\; {}^-O-\overset{\overset{\displaystyle O}{\|}}{C}-CH_2-\overset{\overset{\displaystyle O}{\|}}{C}-SACP
$$
Acetyl-ACP Malonyl-ACP

$$H-SACP \;+\; CO_2 \;\xleftarrow{\quad 1 \quad}$$

Step 1. **Condensation** The malonyl group from malonyl-ACP transfers to acetyl-ACP with the loss of CO_2. Loss of CO_2 releases energy to drive the reaction.

$$
CH_3-\overset{\overset{\displaystyle O}{\|}}{C}-CH_2-\overset{\overset{\displaystyle O}{\|}}{C}-SACP
$$

$$NADPH/H^+ \quad\rightharpoonup\!\!\!\downarrow\; 2 \qquad NADP^+ \;\leftharpoondown$$

Step 2. **Reduction** This reaction uses the coenzyme NADPH to reduce the carbonyl group of the original acetyl group to a hydroxyl group.

$$
CH_3-\overset{\overset{\displaystyle OH}{|}}{CH}-CH_2-\overset{\overset{\displaystyle O}{\|}}{C}-SACP
$$

$$H_2O \;\xleftarrow{\quad 3 \quad}$$

Step 3. **Dehydration** Removal of H_2O at the C atoms α and β to the remaining carbonyl group introduces a double bond.

$$
CH_3CH=CH-\overset{\overset{\displaystyle O}{\|}}{C}-SACP
$$

$$NADPH/H^+ \quad\rightharpoonup\!\!\!\downarrow\; 4 \qquad NADP^+ \;\leftharpoondown$$

Step 4. **Reduction** The coenzyme NADPH is used to add H atoms to the double bond, converting it to a single bond.

$$
CH_3CH_2CH_2-\overset{\overset{\displaystyle O}{\|}}{C}-SACP
$$

Chain Elongation of Fatty Acid

The result of the first cycle in fatty acid synthesis is the addition of two carbon atoms to an acetyl group to give a 4-carbon acyl group still attached to the carrier protein in fatty acid synthase. The next cycle then adds two more carbon atoms to give a 6-carbon acyl group by repeating the four steps of chain elongation shown here:

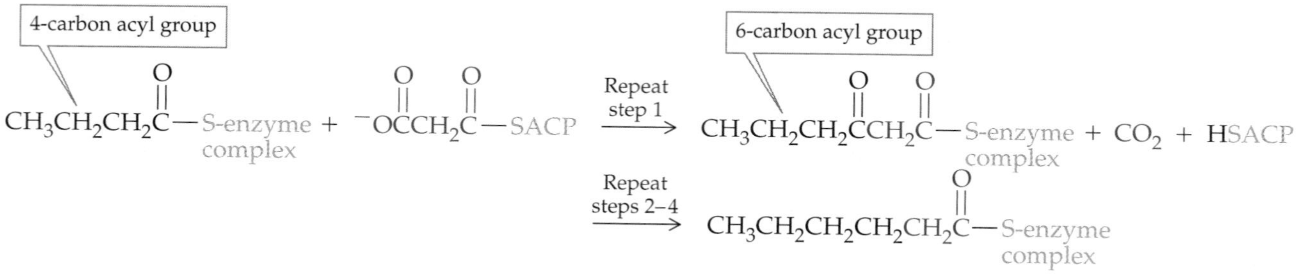

4-carbon acyl group

$$CH_3CH_2CH_2C\!-\!S\text{-enzyme} + \,^-OCCH_2C\!-\!SACP \xrightarrow{\text{Repeat step 1}}$$
complex

6-carbon acyl group

$$CH_3CH_2CH_2CCH_2C\!-\!S\text{-enzyme} + CO_2 + HSACP$$
complex

$$\xrightarrow[\text{steps 2--4}]{\text{Repeat}} CH_3CH_2CH_2CH_2CH_2C\!-\!S\text{-enzyme}$$
complex

CHEMISTRY IN ACTION

✚ Fat Storage, Lipids, and Atherosclerosis

Mammals store excess dietary calories as triacylglycerols in adipocytes (fat cells, found in adipose tissue). Some mammals, like bears and groundhogs, eat to store energy for use during hibernation; others, humans among them, seem simply to eat more calories than necessary when given the opportunity. Your body can do several things with extra calories. It can burn fuel through exercise, use it to create heat, or store it for future use. Our bodies are very efficient at storing the extra calories against future need.

Excessive storage of triacylglycerols is a predictor of serious health problems and is associated with increased risk of developing Type II diabetes, colon cancer, heart disease, and fatty liver disease. For example, those with a body mass index (BMI) of 30 or greater (defined as obese) develop Type II diabetes at a higher rate than those with a normal BMI. The problem is even more acute in obese children. Not only do they risk developing serious health problems at an early age, but children have more fat cells than adults and can make new fat cells, allowing for storage of even more triacylglycerols.

Heart disease is the leading cause of death in many countries. Multiple long-term research projects provide consistent evidence for the connection between heart disease and diets high in saturated fats and cholesterol. Research has also provided strong evidence that high dietary fat is one risk factor for certain types of cancer. Several points are clear.

- A diet rich in saturated animal fats leads to an increase in blood-serum cholesterol.
- A diet lower in saturated fat and higher in unsaturated fat can lower the serum cholesterol level.

▲ These Emperor penguins will survive for months on the energy supplied by the catabolism of stored fat.

- High levels of serum cholesterol are correlated with *atherosclerosis*, a condition in which yellowish waxy deposits (*arterial plaque*) composed of cholesterol and other lipid-containing materials form within the larger arteries. The result of atherosclerosis is an increased risk of coronary artery disease and heart attack brought on by blockage of blood flow to heart muscles or an increased risk of stroke due to blockage of blood flow to the brain.

After seven trips through the elongation spiral, a 16-carbon palmitoyl group is produced and released from the fatty acid synthase. Larger fatty acids are synthesized from palmitoyl-CoA with the aid of specific enzymes in the endoplasmic reticulum.

PROBLEM 24.10

Starting with acetyl-S-enzyme-1 and malonyl-CoA, how many molecules of acetyl-CoA are needed to synthesize an 18-carbon fatty acid (C18:0)? How many molecules of CO_2 are released in this process?

HANDS-ON CHEMISTRY 24.1

The leading cause of death in the United States is cardiac disease. Use the Web to answer these questions.

- What is a heart attack?
- What are the symptoms of a heart attack in men? In women?

- Why is a heart attack dangerous?
- One treatment for heart problems is "bypass surgery." What is this and why is it done?

Other risk factors considered in an overall evaluation of an individual's risk of heart disease include high blood levels of cholesterol coupled with low levels of HDLs, cigarette smoking, high blood pressure, diabetes, obesity, a low level of physical activity, and a family history of early heart disease.

As discussed in Section 24.2, lipoproteins are complex assemblages of lipids and proteins that transport lipids throughout the body. If LDL delivers more cholesterol than is needed to peripheral tissues, and if insufficient HDL is present to remove it, the excess cholesterol is deposited in cells and arteries. Thus, the higher the HDL level, the less the likelihood of deposits and the lower the risk of heart disease. Also, LDL has the harmful potential to trigger inflammation and the buildup of plaque in artery walls. (Remember it this way—*low* LDL is good; *high* HDL is good.)

Many groups recommend that individuals strive for the following cholesterol levels in blood:

Total cholesterol	200 mg/dL or lower
LDL	100 mg/dL or lower
HDL	60 mg/dL or higher

Decreasing saturated fats and cholesterol in the diet, adopting an exercise program, and not smoking constitute the first line of defense for those at risk. For those at high risk or for whom the first-line defenses are inadequate, drugs are available that prevent or slow the progress of coronary artery disease by lowering serum cholesterol levels. Among the drugs are indigestible resins (*cholestyramine* and *colestipol*) that bind bile acids and accelerate their excretion, causing the liver to use up more cholesterol in bile acid synthesis. Another class of effective drugs is the statins (e.g., lovastatin), which inhibit an enzyme crucial to the synthesis of cholesterol.

Remember Malcom from the beginning of the chapter? His blood tests showed significantly elevated cholesterol and triacylglycerides as well as abnormal levels of HDL and LDL. Other tests revealed that he had a heart attack and needed bypass surgery due to large plaque deposits in the arteries leading to his heart. In addition to the heart surgery, Malcolm was given diet and exercise advice to improve his activity level and weight and counseled on smoking cessation. He was prescribed a statin among other medications and given a follow-up appointment for a week after hospital discharge.

CIA Problem 24.4 What diseases are obese people at high risk of developing?

CIA Problem 24.5 What factors contribute to storage of excess energy as triacylglycerols?

CIA Problem 24.6 What are desirable goals for fasting levels of total cholesterol, HDL, and LDL values? What are the differences between the roles of LDL and HDL?

CIA Problem 24.7 What is atherosclerosis?

CIA Problem 24.8 What is arterial plaque? Why is it desirable to have a high HDL value and a relatively low LDL value?

SUMMARY REVISITING THE CHAPTER GOALS

- **List the steps in the digestion of dietary triacylglycerols and their transport into the bloodstream.** *Triacylglycerols* from the diet are broken into droplets in the stomach and enter the small intestine, where they are emulsified by *bile acids* and form micelles. Pancreatic lipases partially hydrolyze the triacylglycerols in the micelles. Small fatty acids and glycerol from triacylglycerol hydrolysis are absorbed directly into the bloodstream at the intestinal surface. Insoluble hydrolysis products are carried to the lining in micelles, where they are absorbed and reassembled into triacylglycerols. These triacylglycerols are then assembled into *chylomicrons* (which are *lipoproteins*) and absorbed into the lymph system for transport to the bloodstream *(see Problems 19–24)*.

- **Name the major classes of lipoproteins, specify the nature and function of the lipids they transport, and identify their destinations.** In addition to chylomicrons, which carry triacylglycerols from the diet into the bloodstream, there are VLDLs *(very low-density lipoproteins)*, which carry triacylglycerols synthesized in the liver to peripheral tissues for energy generation or storage; LDLs *(low-density lipoproteins)*, which transport cholesterol from the liver to peripheral tissues for cell membranes or steroid synthesis; and HDLs *(high-density lipoproteins)*, which transport cholesterol from peripheral tissues back to the liver for conversion to bile acids that are used in digestion or excreted *(see Problems 12, 25–28, 68, 70, and 71)*.

- **Name the major pathways for the synthesis and breakdown of triacylglycerols and fatty acids, and identify their connections to other metabolic pathways.** Dietary triacylglycerols carried by chylomicrons in the bloodstream undergo hydrolysis to fatty acids and glycerol by enzymes in capillary walls. Triacylglycerols in storage are similarly hydrolyzed within adipocytes. The fatty acids from either source undergo β oxidation to acetyl-CoA or resynthesis into triacylglycerols for storage. Acetyl-CoA can participate in resynthesis of fatty acids *(lipogenesis)*, formation of *ketone bodies (ketogenesis)*, steroid synthesis, or energy generation via the citric acid cycle and oxidative phosphorylation. Glycerol can participate in glycolysis, gluconeogenesis, or triacylglycerol synthesis *(see Problems 29, 64, 65, and 72)*.

- **Explain the reactions by which triacylglycerols are stored and mobilized, and how these reactions are regulated.** Synthesis of triacylglycerols for storage is activated by insulin when blood glucose levels are high. The synthesis requires DHAP (from glycolysis or glycerol) for conversion to glycerol 3-phosphate, to which fatty acyl groups are added one at a time to yield triacylglycerols. Hydrolysis of triacylglycerols stored in adipocytes is activated by glucagon when glucose levels drop *(see Problems 13 and 31–34)*.

- **Describe fatty acid oxidation.** Fatty acids are activated (in the cytosol) by conversion to fatty acyl coenzyme A, a reaction that requires the equivalent of two ATPs in the conversion of ATP to adenosine monophosphate (AMP). The fatty acyl-CoA molecules are transported into the mitochondrial matrix and are then oxidized two carbon atoms at a time to acetyl-CoA by repeated trips through the β-oxidation spiral *(see Problems 11, 14–16, 35–42, and 66)*.

- **Calculate the energy yield from fatty acid oxidation.** Energy yield as ATP is calculated by summing the number of ATP molecules generated by β-oxidation freeing the acetyl-CoA groups, oxidation of acetyl-CoA in the citric acid cycle, and oxidative phosphorylation transformation of all NADH and $FADH_2$ molecules into ATP. Subtract the 2 ATP molecules used to prime the catabolism of the fatty acid *(see Problems 17, 43–50, and 69)*.

- **Identify ketone bodies, describe their properties and synthesis, and explain their role in metabolism.** The ketone bodies are 3-hydroxybutyrate, acetoacetate, and acetone. They are produced from two acetyl-CoA molecules. Their production is increased when energy generation from the citric acid cycle cannot keep pace with the quantity of acetyl-CoA available. This occurs during the early stages of starvation and in unregulated diabetes. Ketone bodies are water-soluble and can travel unassisted in the bloodstream to tissues where acetyl-CoA is produced from acetoacetate and 3-hydroxybutyrate. In this way, acetyl-CoA is made available for energy generation when glucose is in short supply *(see Problems 51–55)*.

- **Compare the pathways for fatty acid synthesis and oxidation, and describe the reactions of the synthesis pathway.** Fatty acid synthesis (lipogenesis), like β oxidation, proceeds two carbon atoms at a time in a four-step pathway. The pathways utilize different enzymes and coenzymes. In synthesis, the initial four carbons are transferred from acetyl-CoA to the malonyl carrier protein. Each additional pair of carbons is then added to the growing chain bonded to the carrier protein, with the final three steps of the four-step synthesis sequence the reverse of the first three steps in β oxidation *(see Problems 18 and 56–63)*.

KEY WORDS

β-oxidation pathway, *p. 748*	**Bile acids,** *p. 741*	**Ketone bodies,** *p. 752*	**Mobilization (of**
Bile, *p. 741*	**Ketoacidosis,** *p. 754*	**Lipogenesis,** *p. 754*	**triacylglycerols),** *p. 746*
	Ketogenesis, *p. 752*	**Lipoprotein,** *p. 741*	

CONCEPT MAP

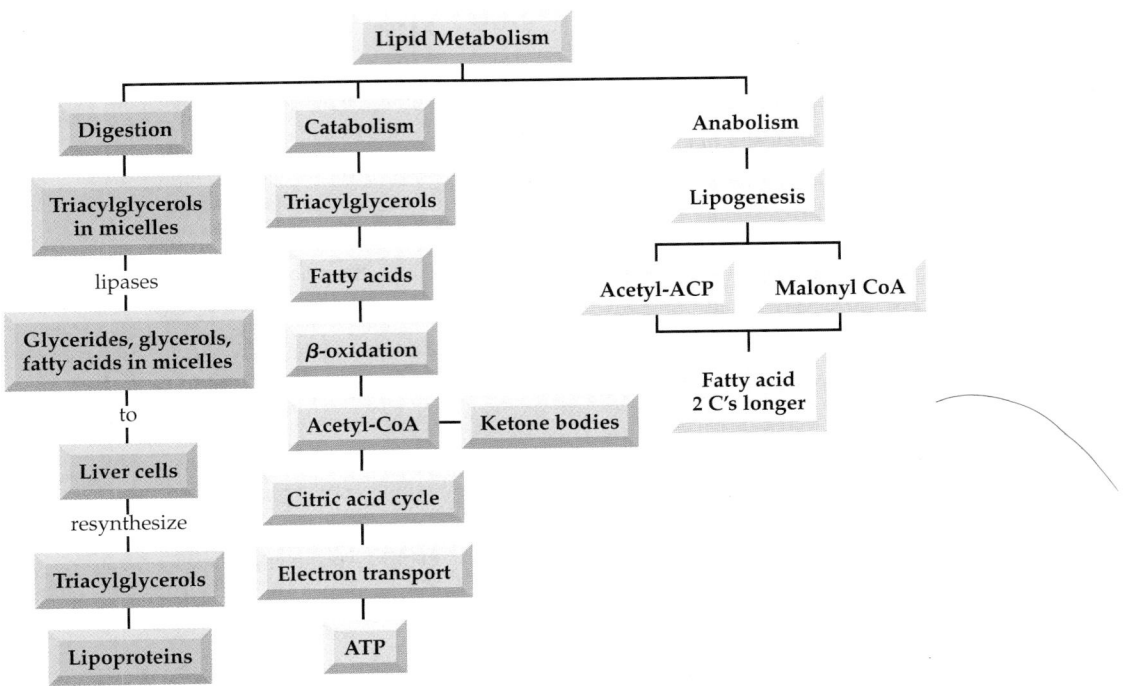

▲ **Figure 24.8 Concept Map.** This map links the digestion and transport of lipids (especially triacylglycerides) to the catabolism products of triacylglycerides and energy yield and to the generation of fatty acids from other molecules.

⊙◉ UNDERSTANDING KEY CONCEPTS

24.11   Oxygen is not a reactant in the β oxidation of fatty acids. Can β oxidation occur under anaerobic conditions? Explain.

24.12   Identify each lipoprotein described here as either chylomicron, HDL, LDL, or VLDL.

    (a) Which lipoprotein has the lowest density? Why?

    (b) Which lipoprotein carries triacylglycerols from the diet?

    (c) Which lipoprotein removes cholesterol from circulation?

    (d) Which lipoprotein contains "bad cholesterol" from a vascular disease risk standpoint?

    (e) Which lipoprotein has the highest ratio of protein to lipid?

    (f) Which lipoprotein carries triacylglycerols from the liver to peripheral tissues? How are triacylglycerols used?

    (g) Which lipoprotein transports cholesterol from the liver to peripheral tissues?

24.13   Lipid metabolism, especially triacylglycerol anabolism and catabolism, is closely associated with carbohydrate (glucose) metabolism. Insulin and glucagon levels in blood are regulated by the glucose levels in blood. Draw lines from the appropriate phrases in column A to appropriate phrases in columns B and C.

A	B	C
High blood glucose	High glucagon / low insulin	Fatty acid and triacylglycerol synthesis
Low blood glucose	High insulin / low glucagon	Triacylglycerol hydrolysis; fatty acid oxidation

24.14   One strategy used in many different biochemical pathways is an initial investment of energy early on and a large payoff in energy at the end of the pathway. How is this strategy utilized in the catabolism of fats?

24.15   When oxaloacetate in liver tissue is being used for gluconeogenesis, what impact does this have on the citric acid cycle? Explain.

24.16   Why is it more efficient to store energy as triacylglycerols rather than as glycogen?

24.17   Explain the rationale for the production of ketone bodies during starvation.

24.18   Compare the differences between β oxidation and fatty acid synthesis (lipogenesis). Are these pathways the reverse of each other?

ADDITIONAL PROBLEMS

DIGESTION OF LIPIDS (SECTION 24.1)

24.19 Why do lipids make you feel full for a long time after a meal?

24.20 Where does digestion of lipids occur?

24.21 What is the purpose of bile acids in lipid digestion?

24.22 Where are bile acids synthesized, and what is the starting molecule?

24.23 Write the equation for the hydrolysis of a triacylglycerol composed of stearic acid, oleic acid, and linoleic acid by pancreatic lipase.

24.24 Lipases break down triacylglycerols by catalyzing hydrolysis. What are the products of this hydrolysis?

LIPID TRANSPORT (SECTION 24.2)

24.25 What are chylomicrons, and how are they involved in lipid metabolism?

24.26 What is the origin of the triacylglycerols transported by very low-density lipoproteins?

24.27 How are the fatty acids from adipose tissue transported?

24.28 How is cholesterol transported around the body? When it leaves the liver, what is its destination and use?

OVERVIEW OF TRIACYLGYCERIDE STORAGE AND METABOLISM (SECTIONS 24.3 AND 24.4)

24.29 The glycerol derived from lipolysis of triacylglycerols is converted into glyceraldehyde 3-phosphate, which then enters into step 6 of the glycolysis pathway. What further transformations are necessary to convert glyceraldehyde 3-phosphate into pyruvate?

24.30 If the conversion of glycerol to glyceraldehyde 3-phosphate releases 1 molecule of ATP, how many molecules of ATP are released during the conversion of glycerol to pyruvate?

24.31 How many molecules of ATP are released in the overall catabolism of glycerol to acetyl-CoA? How many molecules of ATP are released in the complete catabolism of glycerol to CO_2 and H_2O? (Hint: Combine pathways of glycerol to DHAP with glycolysis from DHAP to pyruvate and pyruvate to acetyl-CoA. Remember to account for any NADH and $FADH_2$ produced.)

24.32 How many molecules of acetyl-CoA result from catabolism of 1 molecule of glyceryl trilaurate? (Hint: See Worked Example 24.3 and don't forget glycerol.)

24.33 What is an adipocyte?

24.34 What is the primary function of adipose tissues, and where in the body are they located?

OXIDATION OF FATTY ACIDS (SECTION 24.5)

24.35 Which tissues carry out fatty acid oxidation as their primary source of energy?

24.36 Where in the cell does β oxidation take place?

24.37 What initial chemical transformation takes place on a fatty acid to activate it for catabolism?

24.38 What must take place before an activated fatty acid undergoes β oxidation?

24.39 Why is the stepwise oxidation of fatty acids called β oxidation?

24.40 Why is the sequence of reactions that catabolize fatty acids described as a *spiral* rather than a *cycle*?

24.41 Which coenzymes are required for β oxidation?

24.42 Are these the same coenzymes necessary for fatty acid synthesis?

24.43 How many moles of ATP are produced by one cycle of β oxidation?

24.44 How many moles of ATP are produced by the complete oxidation of 1 mol of myristic acid?

24.45 Arrange these following four molecules in increasing order of their biological energy content (per mole):

(a) Sucrose

(b) Myristic acid, $CH_3(CH_2)_{12}COOH$

(c) Glucose

(d) Capric acid, $CH_3(CH_2)_8COOH$

24.46 Arrange these four molecules in increasing order of their biological energy content per mole:

(a) Mannose

(b) Stearic acid, $CH_3(CH_2)_{16}COOH$

(c) Fructose

(d) Palmitic acid, $CH_3(CH_2)_{14}COOH$

24.47 Show the products of each step in the fatty acid oxidation of hexanoic acid.

(a) $CH_3(CH_2)_4\overset{\displaystyle O}{\overset{\displaystyle \|}{C}}SCoA \xrightarrow[\text{Acetyl-CoA dehydrogenase}]{FAD \quad FADH_2}$?

(b) Product of (a) + $H_2O \xrightarrow[\text{hydratase}]{\text{Enoyl-CoA}}$?

(c) Product of (b) $\xrightarrow[\text{$\beta$-Hydroxyacyl-CoA dehydrogenase}]{NAD^+ \quad NADH/H^+}$?

(d) Product of (c) + HSCoA $\xrightarrow[\text{transferase}]{\text{Acetyl-CoA}}$?

24.48 Write the equation for the final step in the catabolism of any fatty acid with an even number of carbons.

24.49 How many molecules of acetyl-CoA result from complete catabolism of the following compounds?

(a) Myristic acid, $CH_3(CH_2)_{12}COOH$

(b) Caprylic acid, $CH_3(CH_2)_6COOH$

24.50 How many cycles of β oxidation are necessary to completely catabolize myristic and caprylic acids?

KETONE BODY PRODUCTION (SECTION 24.6)

24.51 What three compounds are classified as ketone bodies? Why are they so designated? What process in the body produces them? Why do they form?

24.52 What is ketosis? What condition results from prolonged ketosis? Why is it dangerous?

24.53 What causes acetone to be present in the breath of someone with uncontrolled diabetes?

24.54 Individuals suffering from ketoacidosis have acidic urine. What effect do you expect ketones to have on pH? Why is pH lowered when ketone bodies are present?

24.55 Diets that severely restrict carbohydrate intake often result in ketosis for the dieter. Explain why this occurs.

FATTY ACID ANABOLISM (SECTION 24.7)

24.56 Name the anabolic pathway that synthesizes fatty acids.

24.57 Explain why β oxidation cannot proceed backward to produce triacylglycerols.

24.58 Name the starting material for fatty acid synthesis.

24.59 Why are fatty acids generally composed of an even number of carbons?

24.60 How many rounds of the lipogenesis cycle are needed to synthesize stearic acid, $C_{17}H_{35}COOH$?

24.61 How many molecules of NADPH are needed to synthesize stearic acid, $C_{17}H_{35}COOH$?

24.62 How does the cell keep the processes of fatty acid synthesis and degradation separated?

24.63 Describe two differences in the reactions for fatty synthesis and the reactions for fatty acid degradation.

CONCEPTUAL PROBLEMS

24.64 Consuming too many carbohydrates causes deposition of fats in adipose tissue. How does this happen?

24.65 Why are extra calories consumed as carbohydrates stored as fat and not as glycogen?

24.66 Are any of the intermediates in the β-oxidation pathway chiral? Explain.

24.67 Compare fats and carbohydrates as energy sources in terms of the amount of energy released per mole, and account for the observed energy difference.

24.68 Lipoproteins that transport lipids from the diet are described as exogenous. Those that transport lipids produced in metabolic pathways are described as endogenous. Which of the following lipoproteins transports exogenous lipids and which transports endogenous lipids?

(a) Low-density lipoprotein (LDL)

(b) Chylomicrons

24.69 Behenic acid (C22:0) is present in peanut butter.

(a) How many molecules of acetyl-CoA are produced by β oxidation of behenic acid?

(b) How many molecules of ATP are produced in (a)?

(c) How many molecules of CO_2 are produced by complete oxidation of the acetyl-CoA produced in (a)?

(d) How many molecules of ATP are produced in (c)?

(e) How many total molecules of ATP are produced by the complete oxidation of behenic acid to CO_2?

GROUP PROBLEMS

24.70 High blood-cholesterol levels are dangerous because of their correlation with atherosclerosis and consequent heart attacks and strokes. Is it possible to eliminate all cholesterol from the bloodstream by having a diet that includes no cholesterol? Is it desirable to have no cholesterol at all in your body? Explain your answer.

24.71 In the synthesis of cholesterol, acetyl-CoA is converted to 2-methyl-1,3-butadiene. Molecules of 2-methyl-1,3-butadiene are then joined to give the carbon skeleton of cholesterol. Draw the condensed structure of 2-methyl-1,3-butadiene. How many carbon atoms does cholesterol contain? What minimum number of 2-methyl-1,3-butadiene molecules is required to make one molecule of cholesterol?

24.72 A low-fat diet of pasta, bread, beer, and soda can easily lead to an increase in weight. The increase is stored triacylglycerols in adipocytes. Explain the weight increase and why the excess carbohydrate is stored as fat.

25

Protein and Amino Acid Metabolism

CONTENTS

◀◀◀ CONCEPTS TO REVIEW

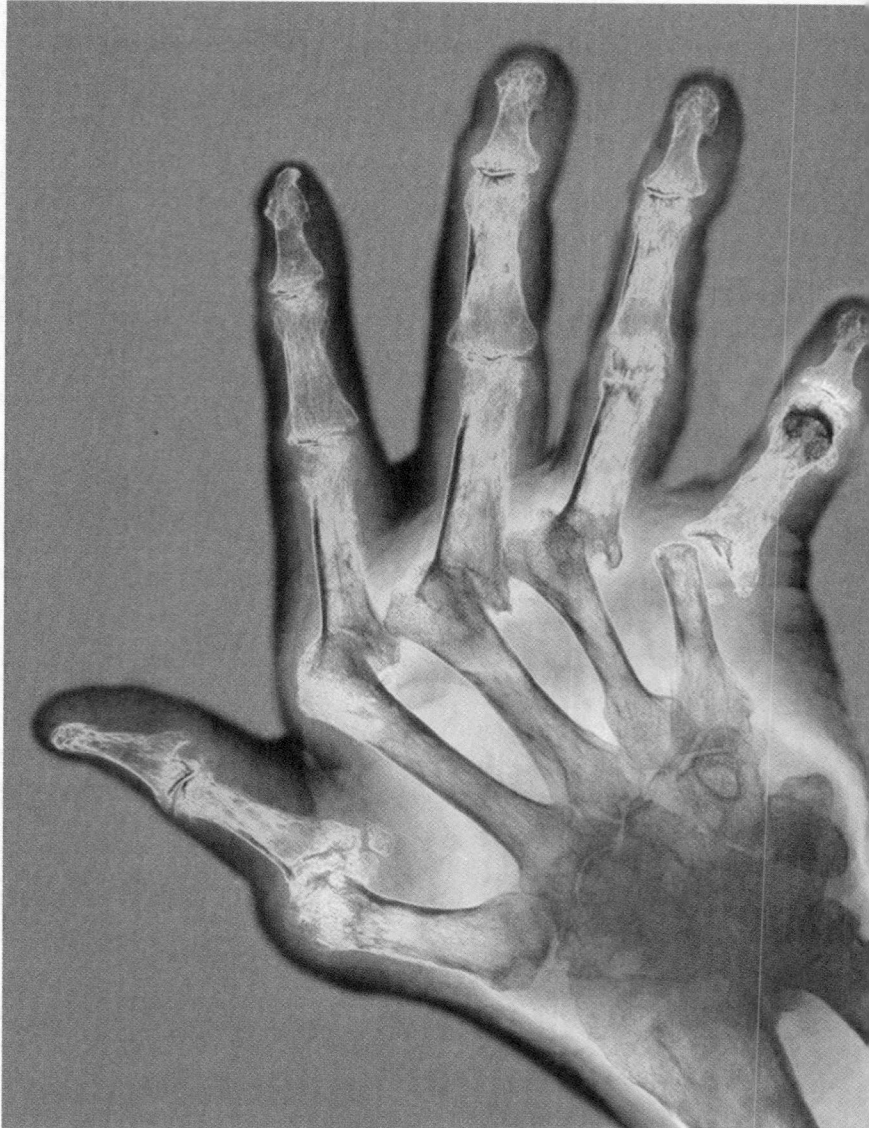

▲ Colored X ray of the deformed hand of a patient suffering from rheumatoid arthritis (RA). Joint damage (shown in red) has caused the fingers to bend abnormally. Decreased serum levels of the essential amino acid histidine is a specific metabolic marker for this disease

The number of extremely complex biomolecules our bodies can synthesize is astounding, yet there are some we need that we do not have the ability to make. These molecules, called essential nutrients, must be obtained daily from the foods we eat. Foremost among these are the nine essential amino acids, which must be obtained via the digestion of protein obtained from external sources. But what would happen if one or more of the essential amino acids was missing from our diet? In that case, any number of amino acid deficiency problems could arise, ranging from anemia and kidney disease to psychotic and schizophrenic behavior. For example, a dietary deficiency of histidine, one of the more debated essential amino acids, may play a role in rheumatoid arthritis (RA), one of the most debilitating diseases known and shown in the photo above. Indeed, decreased histidine levels in blood serum have been used as a specific metabolic marker for RA. The role and additional consequences of deficiencies of the essential amino acids will be discussed in the Chemistry in Action "The Importance of Essential Amino Acids and Effects of Deficiencies" found at the end of this chapter.

We now turn to discuss the metabolic fate of proteins and ultimately the amino acids that they are constructed from. Although we have the biochemical machinery necessary to make almost all of the amino acids we need, the hydrolysis of dietary protein is still our major source for them. Before diving into the discussion of protein and amino acid metabolism, it will be helpful to review the structures of the amino acids and the proteins they form (Chapter 18) as well as the essential function of proteins as enzymes (Chapter 19). The actual biosynthesis of proteins will be examined in Chapter 26, and the examination of body fluids for the diagnosis of disease will be discussed in Chapter 29.

25.1 Digestion of Proteins

Learning Objective:

• List the steps of protein digestion.

Recall from Chapter 18 that proteins are polymers of individual amino acids linked together by connecting the $-NH_2$ group of one amino acid to the $-COOH$ of another, forming peptide bonds ($-CONH-$), which are nothing more than amide bonds. The end result of protein digestion is simple—the hydrolysis of all peptide bonds to produce a collection of amino acids.

◄◄ **CONCEPTS TO REVIEW**
Hydrolysis of amide bonds was discussed in Section 17.6.

Hydrolysis of peptide bonds

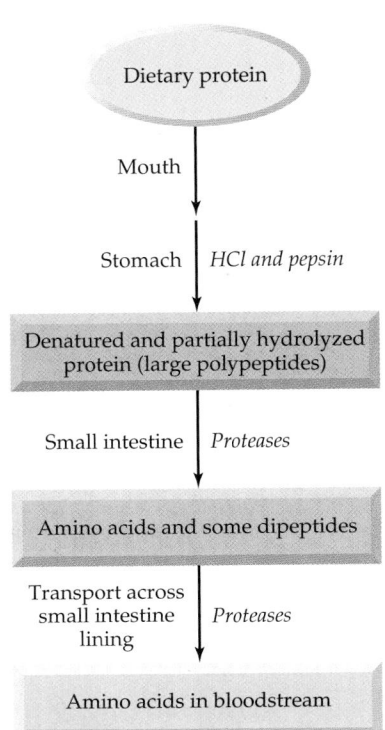

For example,

Alanine

Serine

Phenylalanine

Figure 25.1 summarizes the digestive processes involved in the conversion of protein to amino acids. The breakdown of protein begins in the mouth, where large pieces of food are converted (by chewing) into smaller, more digestible portions. Although no

Dietary protein

Mouth

Stomach | *HCl and pepsin*

Denatured and partially hydrolyzed protein (large polypeptides)

Small intestine | *Proteases*

Amino acids and some dipeptides

Transport across small intestine lining | *Proteases*

Amino acids in bloodstream

▲ **Figure 25.1**
Digestion of proteins.

◄◄ Recall from Section 19.8 that a zymogen (or proenzyme) is a compound that becomes an active enzyme after undergoing a chemical change.

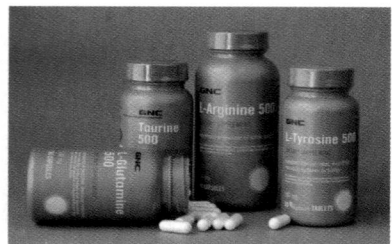

▲ Individual amino acids are promoted for a variety of unproven health benefits. Because amino acids are classified as foods, they need not undergo the stringent testing for purity, safety, and efficacy required for Food and Drug Administration (FDA) approval.

chemical digestion of the protein has begun, this step is necessary to increase the surface area of the food to be digested. The chemical digestion of dietary proteins begins with their denaturation in the strongly acidic environment of the stomach (pH 1–2), where the tertiary and secondary structures of consumed proteins begin to unfold. In addition to hydrochloric acid, gastric secretions include pepsinogen, a zymogen that is activated by acid to give the enzyme pepsin. Unlike most proteins, pepsin is stable and active at pH 1–2. Protein hydrolysis begins as pepsin breaks some of the peptide bonds in the denatured proteins, producing polypeptides.

The polypeptides produced by pepsin then enter the small intestine, where the pH is about 7–8. Pepsin is rendered inactive in this less acidic environment, and a group of pancreatic zymogens is secreted. These activated enzymes (proteases such as trypsin, chymotrypsin, and carboxypeptidase) then take over to further hydrolyze peptide bonds in the partially digested proteins.

The combined action of the pancreatic proteases in the small intestine and other proteases in the cells of the intestinal lining completes the conversion of dietary proteins into free amino acids. After active transport across cell membranes lining the intestine, the amino acids are absorbed directly into the bloodstream.

The active transport of amino acids into cells is managed by several transport systems devoted to different groups of amino acids. For this reason, an excess of one amino acid in the diet can dominate the transport and produce a deficiency of others. This condition usually arises only in individuals taking large quantities of a single amino acid dietary supplement, such as those often sold in health food stores.

HANDS-ON CHEMISTRY 25.1

Nutritional experts have established what are known as Recommended Daily Allowance (RDA) or Dietary Reference Intake (DRI) values for everything from vitamins to sugar. In this exercise you are going to calculate how much protein you should be taking in daily, and then examining some dietary scenarios and the consequences of them. You will need at least three days and an internet connection to fully carry out this activity.

a. Let's begin calculating how much protein you should be eating a day. Begin by getting an accurate body weight for yourself. Convert your weight from pounds to kilograms (this can be done by dividing your weight in pounds by 2.2). The DRI values for protein are 0.8 g of protein per kilogram of body weight for moderately active adults from 19 to 24 years old. Based on this number, calculate how much protein you should be consuming in a day.

b. The protein DRI value increases as a person's average daily activity levels increase. For example, if you are a runner your DRI for protein should be 1.2–1.4 g of protein per kilogram of body weight and up to 1.8 g of protein per kilogram of body weight if you are doing

strength training. Let's assume that in an average day you are fairly active, either through walking, running, exercising, or playing sports. Assuming your DRI is 1.1 g of protein per kilogram of body weight, calculate how much protein you should be consuming in a day if this scenario were to describe you.

c. Now, using a journal, record exactly what you eat for breakfast, lunch, dinner, and snacks in between meals for three days. If you can, try and estimate how much of each item you ate. If you skip a meal, record that as well. Using the internet, see if you can find the grams of protein (if any) in each item you ate. Total that number up for each day and take the average for the three days you recorded. Are you eating too little, too much, or just enough protein based on the numbers in parts a and b?

d. Protein intake is not just about quantity, it is also about quality. As a final exercise, look up what "quality" means with respect to protein. Provide a list of foods that provide "quality protein." How can you personally change your diet to incorporate more quality protein in it?

25.2 Amino Acid Metabolism: An Overview

Learning Objectives:

• Define the amino acid pool and its metabolic role.
• Explain how amino acids are catabolized.

The entire collection of free amino acids throughout the body—the **amino acid pool**—occupies a central position in protein and amino acid metabolism (see the concept map at the end of the chapter; Figure 25.5). All tissues and biomolecules in the body are constantly being degraded, repaired, and replaced—a process known as **turnover.** A healthy adult turns over about 300 g of protein every day, meaning amino acids are continuously entering the pool, not only from digestion but also from the breakdown of old proteins, and are continuously being withdrawn for synthesis of new nitrogen-containing biomolecules.

Each of the 20 amino acids is degraded via its own unique pathway. The important point to remember is that the process is the same for each one.

Amino acid pool The entire collection of free amino acids in the body.

Turnover The continual renewal or replacement of biomolecules; for protein it is defined by the balance between protein synthesis and protein degradation.

◀◀◀ Recall from Section 21.3 that catabolism is the breakdown and anabolism is the synthesis of biomolecules.

General Process for Amino Acid Catabolism

• Removal of the amino group (Section 25.3)
• Use of the removed —NH_2 in the synthesis of new nitrogen compounds (Section 25.3)
• Passage of nitrogen into the urea cycle (Section 25.4)
• Incorporation of the carbon atoms into compounds that can enter the citric acid cycle (Section 25.5)

Our bodies do not store nitrogen-containing compounds, and ammonia is toxic to cells. Therefore, the amino nitrogen from dietary protein has just two possible fates: It must either be incorporated into urea and excreted or be used in the synthesis of new nitrogen-containing compounds; these include the following:

• Nitric oxide (NO, a chemical messenger)
• Hormones
• Neurotransmitters
• Nicotinamide (in coenzymes NAD^+ and $NADP^+$)
• Heme (as part of hemoglobin in red blood cells)
• Purine and pyrimidine bases (for nucleic acids)

LOOKING AHEAD ▶▶ Hormones and neurotransmitters are chemical messengers discussed in Chapter 28; Figure 19.10 highlights the nicotinamide group on NAD^+; view the chemical structure of heme in Figure 21.10; purine and pyrimidines can be seen in Table 26.1.

Nitrogen monoxide (NO) is a particularly interesting molecule: Chemically, it has an odd number of electrons (a *free radical;* Section 13.7) and is therefore very reactive. Biologically, it lowers blood pressure, kills invading bacteria, and enhances memory. NO is synthesized in the linings of blood vessels and elsewhere from oxygen and the amino acid arginine. In blood vessels, NO activates reactions in smooth muscle cells that cause dilation and a resulting decrease in blood pressure. Drugs such as nitroglycerin release NO, which explains their usefulness in treating angina, the pain experienced during exertion by individuals with partially blocked blood vessels.

◀◀◀ NO was discussed in Chapter 4's Chemistry in Action "CO and NO: Pollutants or Miracle Molecules?".

The carbon portion of the amino acid has a much more varied fate. The carbon atoms of amino acids are converted to compounds that can enter the citric acid cycle. They continue through the citric acid cycle (the body's main energy-generating pathway; Section 20.8) to give CO_2 and energy stored in adenosine triphosphate (ATP). About 10–20% of our energy is normally produced in this way from amino acids. If not needed immediately for energy, the carbon-carrying intermediates produced from amino acids enter storage as triacylglycerols (via lipogenesis) or glycogen (via gluconeogenesis and glycogen synthesis). They can also be converted to ketone bodies.

◀◀◀ Lipogenesis and ketone body synthesis were discussed in Chapter 24. Review gluconeogenesis and glycogen synthesis in Chapter 22.

PROBLEM 25.1

Decide whether each of the following statements is true or false. If false, explain why.

(a) The amino acid pool is found mainly in the liver.
(b) Nitrogen-containing compounds can be stored in fatty tissue.
(c) Some hormones and neurotransmitters are synthesized from amino acids.

◐⊃ KEY CONCEPT PROBLEM 25.2

Serotonin is a monoamine neurotransmitter. It is formed in the body from the amino acid tryptophan (Figure 28.6, p. 836). What class of enzyme catalyzes each of the two steps that convert tryptophan to serotonin?

25.3 Amino Acid Catabolism: The Amino Group

Learning Objective:

• Discuss the fate of the nitrogen of an amino acid.

Transamination The interchange of the amino group of an amino acid and the keto group of an α-keto acid.

The first step in amino acid catabolism is removal of the amino group and occurs primarily in the intracellular fluid (cytosol) of liver cells. In this process, known as **transamination,** the amino group of the amino acid and the keto group of an α-keto acid change places.

$$R'-\underset{\underset{NH_3^+}{|}}{CH}-COO^- \; + \; R''-\overset{\overset{O}{||}}{C}-COO^- \quad \underset{}{\overset{\alpha\text{-Transaminase}}{\rightleftharpoons}} \quad R'-\overset{\overset{O}{||}}{C}-COO^- \; + \; R''-\underset{\underset{NH_3^+}{|}}{CH}-COO^-$$

Amino acid 1 $\qquad$ α-Keto acid 1 $\qquad$ α-Keto acid 2 $\qquad$ Amino acid 2

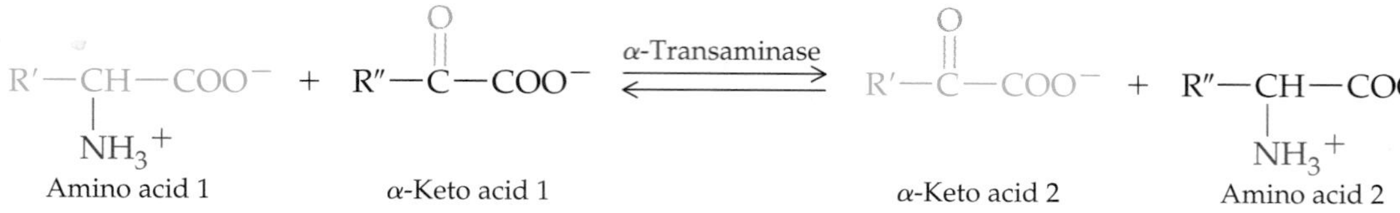

A number of transaminase enzymes are responsible for "transporting" (hence the prefix "trans") an amino group from one molecule to another. Most are specific for α-ketoglutarate as the amino-group acceptor and can remove the $-NH_2$ group (deaminate) from several different amino acids. The α-ketoglutarate is converted to glutamate, and the amino acid is converted to an α-keto acid. For example, alanine is converted to pyruvate by transamination.

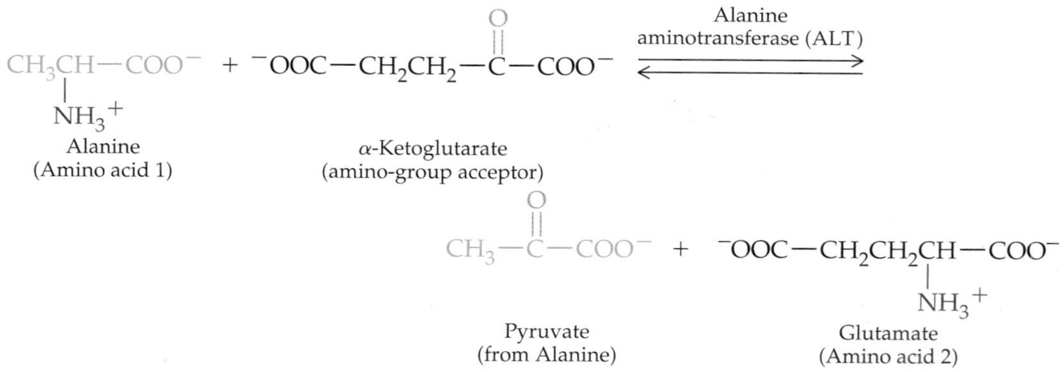

$$CH_3\underset{\underset{NH_3^+}{|}}{CH}-COO^- \; + \; {}^-OOC-CH_2CH_2-\overset{\overset{O}{||}}{C}-COO^- \quad \overset{\text{Alanine}}{\underset{}{\overset{\text{aminotransferase (ALT)}}{\rightleftharpoons}}}$$

Alanine $\qquad\qquad\qquad\qquad$ α-Ketoglutarate
(Amino acid 1) $\qquad\qquad\qquad$ (amino-group acceptor)

$$CH_3-\overset{\overset{O}{||}}{C}-COO^- \; + \; {}^-OOC-CH_2CH_2\underset{\underset{NH_3^+}{|}}{CH}-COO^-$$

Pyruvate $\qquad\qquad\qquad$ Glutamate
(from Alanine) $\qquad\qquad$ (Amino acid 2)

The enzyme for this conversion, alanine aminotransferase (ALT), is especially abundant in the liver, and above-normal ALT concentrations in the blood are taken as an indication of liver damage that has allowed ALT to leak into the bloodstream.

Transamination is a key reaction in many biochemical pathways, where amino acid amino groups and carbonyl groups are interconverted as necessary. This process is reversible and goes easily in either direction, depending on the concentrations of the reactants. In this way, amino acid concentrations are regulated by keeping synthesis and breakdown in balance. For example, the reaction of pyruvate with glutamate (the reverse of the preceding reaction) is the main synthetic route for alanine.

Glutamate from transamination serves as an amino-group carrier and can be used to provide amino groups for the synthesis of new amino acids. Most of the glutamate formed in this way, however, is recycled to regenerate α-ketoglutarate. This process, which occurs in mitochondria, is known as **oxidative deamination.** Here, the glutamate amino group is oxidatively removed as ammonium ion to give back α-ketoglutarate.

Oxidative deamination Conversion of an amino acid $-NH_2$ group to an α-keto group, with removal of NH_4^+.

$$^-OOC-CH_2CH_2CH-COO^- + H_2O \xrightarrow[\substack{\text{Glutamate}\\\text{dehydrogenase}}]{\substack{NAD^+\quad NADH\\(NADP^+)\,(NADPH)}} NH_4^+ + {^-OOC-CH_2CH_2C-COO^-}$$

$$\underset{\underset{\text{Glutamate}}{NH_3^+}}{}\qquad\qquad\qquad\qquad\qquad\qquad\qquad\underset{\alpha\text{-Ketoglutarate}}{\overset{O}{\|}}$$

The ammonium ion formed in this reaction proceeds to the urea cycle where it is eliminated in the urine as urea. The pathway of nitrogen from an amino acid to urea is summarized in Figure 25.2, to the right.

 Worked Example 25.1 Predicting Transamination Products

The blood-serum concentration of the heart-muscle transaminase, aspartate aminotransferase (AST), is used in the diagnosis of heart disease because the enzyme escapes into the serum from damaged heart cells. AST catalyzes transamination of aspartate with α-ketoglutarate. What are the products of this reaction?

ANALYSIS The reaction is the interchange of an amino group from aspartate with the keto group from α-ketoglutarate. We know that α-ketoglutarate always gives glutamate in transamination, so one product is glutamate. The product from the amino acid will have a keto group instead of the amino group; we need to consider various amino acid structures to identify a candidate. Consulting Table 18.3 (which lists the structures of the 20 amino acids), we see that the structure of aspartate (aspartic acid) is as shown here.

$$^-OOC-CH_2\overset{\alpha}{\underset{\underset{NH_3^+}{|}}{CH}}-COO^-$$

Aspartate

Removing the $-NH_3^+$ and $-H$ groups bonded to the α carbon and replacing them by a C$=$O gives the desired α-keto acid, which in this case happens to be oxaloacetate.

$$^-OOC-CH_2-\overset{\overset{O}{\|}}{C}-COO^-$$

Oxaloacetate

SOLUTION
The overall reaction is, therefore,

$$\text{Aspartate} + \alpha\text{-Ketoglutarate} \longrightarrow \text{Oxaloacetate} + \text{Glutamate}$$

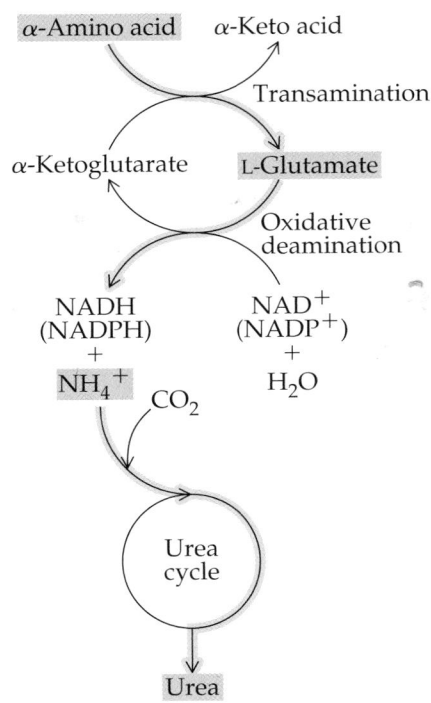

▲ **Figure 25.2**
Pathway of nitrogen from an amino acid to urea.
The nitrogen-bearing compounds and their pathway are highlighted in red.

PROBLEM 25.3

What is the structure of the α-keto acid formed by transamination of the amino acid phenylalanine (Phe)? Refer to Table 18.3 for the structure of Phe.

PROBLEM 25.4

What is the structure of the α-keto acid formed in the following reaction?

$$CH_3-S-CH_2CH_2CH-COO^- \xrightarrow{\quad\overset{\displaystyle\alpha\text{-Ketoglutarate}\quad\text{Glutamate}}{\curvearrowright}\quad} \;?$$
$$\underset{NH_3^+}{|}$$

PROBLEM 25.5

Explain how the conversion of alanine to pyruvic acid (pyruvate) can be identified as an oxidation reaction.

PROBLEM 25.6

Unlike most amino acids, branched-chain amino acids are broken down in tissues other than the liver. Using Table 18.3, identify the three amino acids with branched-chain R groups. For any one of these amino acids, write the equation for its transamination.

25.4 The Urea Cycle

Learning Objective:

• Identify the major reactants and products of the urea cycle.

Ammonia (as well as the ammonium ion, NH_4^+) is highly toxic to living things and must be eliminated in a way that does no harm. Fish are able to excrete ammonia through their gills directly into their watery surroundings where it is immediately diluted and its toxic effects effectively neutralized. Since mammals do not live in an environment where this immediate dilution is possible, they must find other ways to get rid of ammonia. Direct excretion of ammonia in urine is not feasible for mammals, because the volume of water needed to accomplish this safely would cause dehydration. Mammals must first convert ammonia, in solution as ammonium ion, to nontoxic urea via the **urea cycle.**

Urea cycle The cyclic biochemical pathway that produces urea for excretion.

The conversion of ammonium ion to urea takes place in the liver. From there, the urea is transported to the kidneys and transferred to urine for excretion. Like many other biochemical pathways, urea formation begins with an energy investment. Ammonium ion (from oxidative deamination of amino acids), bicarbonate ion (from carbon dioxide produced in the citric acid cycle), and ATP combine to form carbamoyl phosphate. This reaction takes place in the mitochondrial matrix. Two ATPs are invested and one phosphate is transferred to form the carbamoyl phosphate (an energy-rich phosphate ester, like ATP).

$$NH_4^+ \;+\; HCO_3^- \xrightarrow[\substack{\text{Carbamoyl}\\\text{phosphate synthetase I}}]{\overset{\displaystyle 2ATP\quad 2ADP}{\curvearrowright}} \underset{\text{Carbamoyl phosphate}}{H_3\overset{+}{N}-\overset{\displaystyle \overset{O}{\|}}{C}-O-PO_3^{2-}} \;+\; HOPO_3^{2-} \;+\; H_2O$$

Carbamoyl phosphate next reacts in the first step of the four-step urea cycle, shown in Figure 25.3.

STEPS 1 AND 2 OF THE UREA CYCLE: Building Up a Reactive Intermediate The first step of the urea cycle transfers the carbamoyl group, $H_2NC=O$, from carbamoyl phosphate to ornithine, an amino acid not found in proteins, to give citrulline, another nonprotein amino acid. This exergonic reaction introduces the first urea nitrogen into the urea cycle.

In Step 2, a molecule of aspartate combines with citrulline in a reaction driven by conversion of ATP to adenosine monophosphate (AMP) and pyrophosphate $(P_2O_7^{4-})$, followed by the additional exergonic hydrolysis of pyrophosphate. Both nitrogen atoms destined for elimination as urea are now bonded to the same carbon atom in argininosuccinate (red C atom in Figure 25.3).

STEPS 3 AND 4 OF THE UREA CYCLE: Cleavage and Hydrolysis of the Step 2 Product Step 3 cleaves argininosuccinate into two pieces: arginine, an amino acid, and fumarate,

▲ Fish do not need to convert ammonia to urea for elimination because it is quickly diluted in the surrounding water; this is why the water in fish tanks must be constantly monitored to ensure that the ammonia concentration does not reach toxic levels.

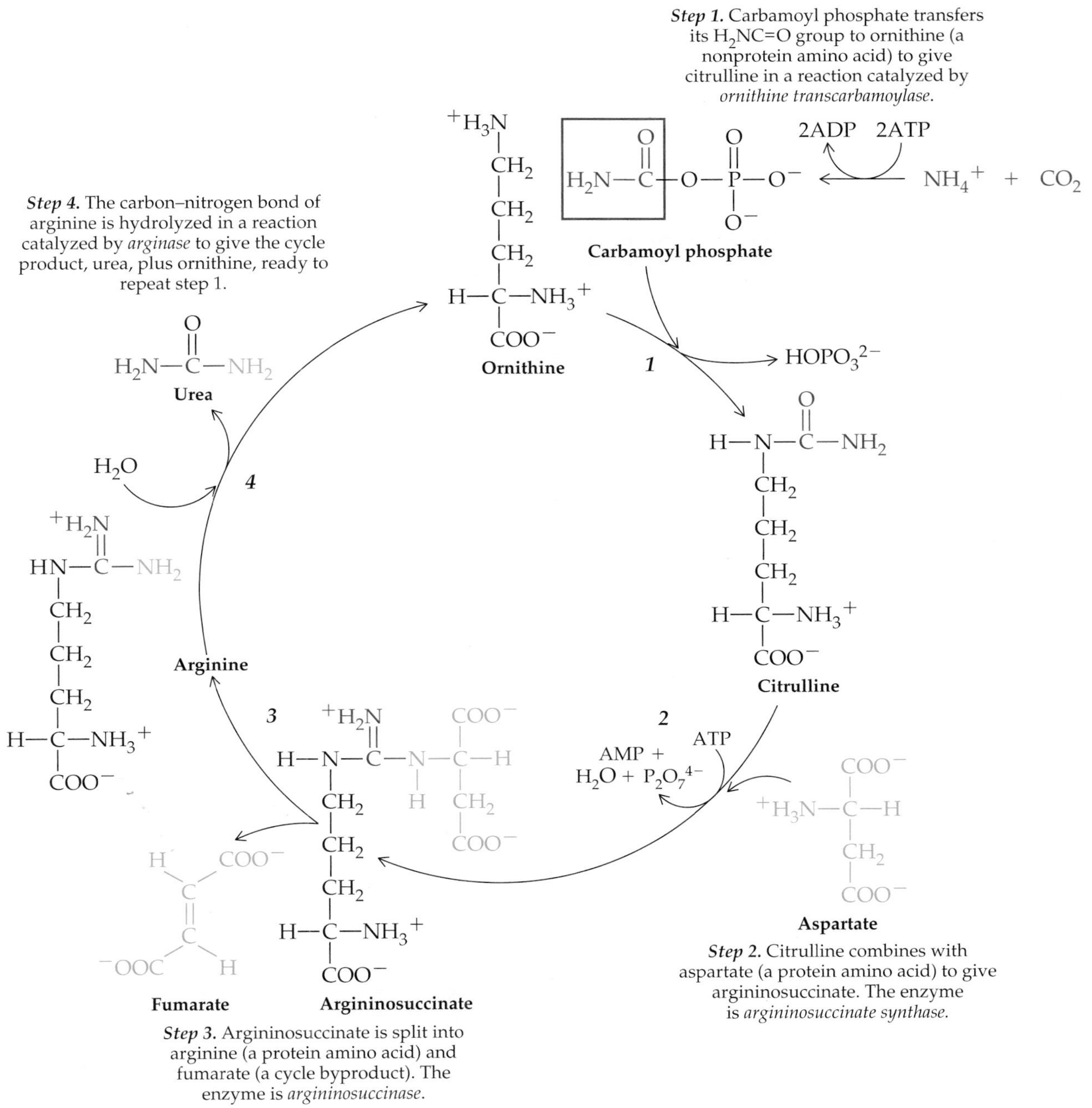
Step 1. Carbamoyl phosphate transfers its H2NC=O group to ornithine (a nonprotein amino acid) to give citrulline in a reaction catalyzed by ornithine transcarbamoylase.
2ADP 2ATP
NH4+ + CO2
Carbamoyl phosphate
Ornithine
HOPO3 2−
1
Citrulline
Step 4. The carbon–nitrogen bond of arginine is hydrolyzed in a reaction catalyzed by arginase to give the cycle product, urea, plus ornithine, ready to repeat step 1.
Urea
H2O
4
Arginine
3
2
ATP
AMP + H2O + P2O7 4−
Aspartate
Step 2. Citrulline combines with aspartate (a protein amino acid) to give argininosuccinate. The enzyme is argininosuccinate synthase.
Fumarate
Argininosuccinate
Step 3. Argininosuccinate is split into arginine (a protein amino acid) and fumarate (a cycle byproduct). The enzyme is argininosuccinase.

▲ **Figure 25.3**
The urea cycle.
The formation of carbamoyl phosphate and Step 1, the formation of citrulline, take place in the mitochondrial matrix. Steps 2–4 take place in the cytosol. The carbamoyl group is shown boxed in red at the top of the figure.

which you may recall is an intermediate in the citric acid cycle (Figure 21.8). Now all that remains, in step 4, is hydrolysis of arginine to give urea and regenerate the reactant in step 1 of the cycle, ornithine.

Net Result of the Urea Cycle

$$HCO_3^- + NH_4^+ + 3ATP + {}^-OOC{-}CH_2{-}\underset{\substack{|\\ NH_3^+}}{CH}{-}COO^- + 2H_2O \longrightarrow$$

Aspartate

$$H_2N{-}\overset{\substack{O\\ \|}}{C}{-}NH_2 + 2ADP + AMP + 4HOPO_3^{2-} + {}^-OOC{-}CH{=}CH{-}COO^-$$

Urea Fumarate

CHEMISTRY IN ACTION

✝ Gout: When Biochemistry Goes Awry

A small amount of our waste nitrogen is excreted in urine and feces as urate rather than urea. Because the urate salt is highly insoluble, any excess of the urate anion causes precipitation of sodium urate, which can lead to the severely painful condition known as gout. Gout has become more common in recent years; the increase is believed to be due to increasing risk factors in the population, such as longer life expectancy and changes in diet. The pain of gout results from a cascade of inflammatory responses to these crystals in the affected tissue. Even though it has been known for a very long time that the symptoms of gout are caused by urate crystals, understanding the many possible causes of the crystal formation is far from complete, even with modern medicine and all its sophisticated technology. Looking at a few of the pathways to gout illustrates some of the many ways that the delicate balance of our biochemistry can be disrupted.

Uric acid is an end product of the breakdown of purine nucleosides, and loss of its acidic H (in red) gives urate ion. Adenosine, for example, undergoes a number of enzymatic steps to produce xanthine, which is eventually converted to uric acid.

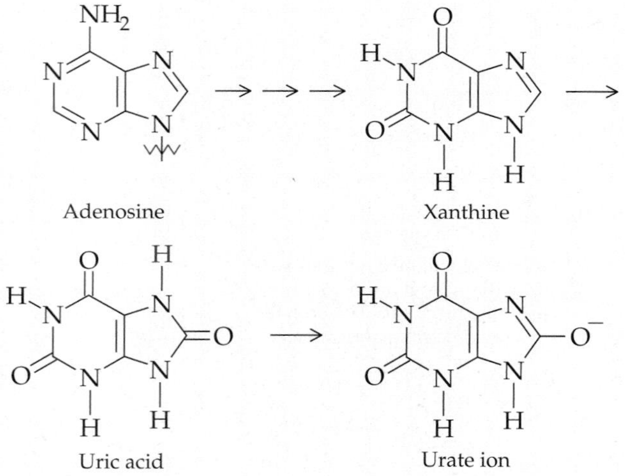

Adenosine   Xanthine

Uric acid   Urate ion

Anything that increases the production of uric acid or inhibits its excretion in the urine is a possible cause of gout. For example, several known hereditary enzyme defects increase the quantity of purines and therefore of uric acid. Sometimes, gouty attacks follow injury or severe muscle exertion. Complicating matters is the observation that the presence of crystals in a joint is not always accompanied by inflammation and pain.

One significant cause of increased uric acid production is accelerated breakdown of ATP, ADP, or the production of AMP. For example, alcohol abuse generates acetaldehyde that must

be metabolized in the kidney by a pathway that requires ATP and produces excess AMP. Inherited fructose intolerance, glycogen-storage diseases, and circulation of poorly oxygenated blood also accelerate uric acid production by this route. With low oxygen, ATP is not efficiently regenerated from ADP in mitochondria, leaving the ADP to be disposed of.

Conditions that diminish excretion of uric acid include kidney disease, dehydration, hypertension, lead poisoning, and competition for excretion from anions produced by ketoacidosis.

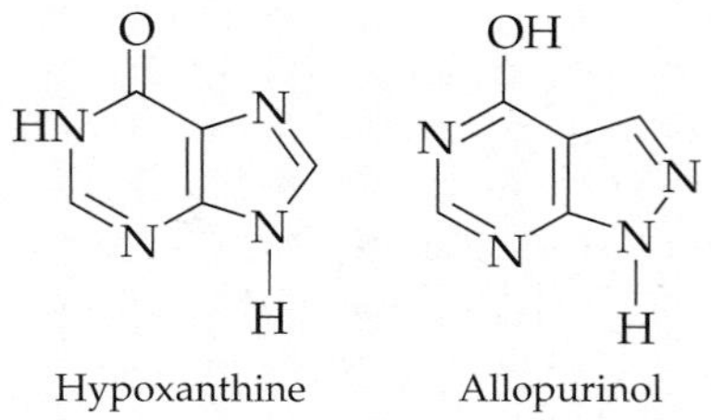

Hypoxanthine   Allopurinol

One treatment for gout relies on allopurinol, a structural analog of hypoxanthine, which is a precursor of xanthine in the formation of urate. Allopurinol inhibits the enzyme for conversion of hypoxanthine and xanthine to urate. Since hypoxanthine and xanthine are more soluble than sodium urate, they are more easily eliminated.

CIA Problem 25.1 Adenosine is known to be converted to xanthine, the direct precursor to uric acid. Starting with adenosine, list all the chemical changes that occurred on its conversion to xanthine.

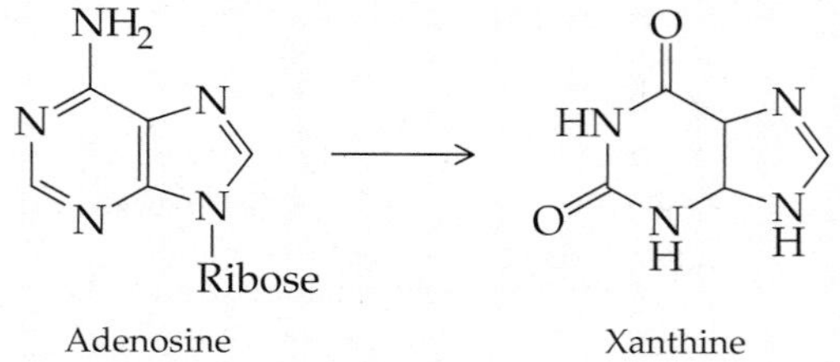

Adenosine   Xanthine

CIA Problem 25.2 Your grandfather complains of pain in his swollen and inflamed big toe, and the doctor indicates that it is caused by gout.

(a) How would you explain to him what gout is and its biochemical cause?

(b) What can you suggest to him to prevent these gouty attacks?

CIA Problem 25.3 Compare the structure of allopurinol with the structures of hypoxanthine and xanthine. Where does allopurinol differ in structure from hypoxanthine?

We can summarize the results of the urea cycle as follows:

- Formation of urea from the carbon of CO_2, NH_4^+, and one nitrogen from the amino acid aspartate, followed by biological elimination through urine
- Breaking of four high-energy phosphate bonds to provide energy
- Production of the citric acid cycle intermediate, fumarate

Hereditary diseases are associated with defects in the enzymes for each step in the urea cycle. The resulting abnormally high levels of ammonia in the blood *(hyperammonemia)* cause vomiting in infancy, lethargy, irregular muscle coordination *(ataxia)*, and mental retardation. Immediate treatment consists of transfusions, blood dialysis *(hemodialysis)*, and use of chemical agents to remove ammonia. Long-term treatment requires a low-protein diet and frequent small meals to avoid protein overload.

PROBLEM 25.7

As Figure 25.3 shows, arginine (a) is converted to ornithine (b) in the last step of the urea cycle. To ultimately enter the citric acid cycle, ornithine undergoes transamination at its terminal amino group to give an aldehyde (c), followed by oxidation to glutamate (d), and conversion to α-ketoglutarate (e). Write the structures of the five molecules (a–e) in the pathway beginning with arginine and ending with α-ketoglutarate. Circle the region of structural change in each.

◉ KEY CONCEPT PROBLEM 25.8

Fumarate from step 3 of the urea cycle may be recycled into aspartate for use in step 2 of the cycle. The sequence of reactions for this process is

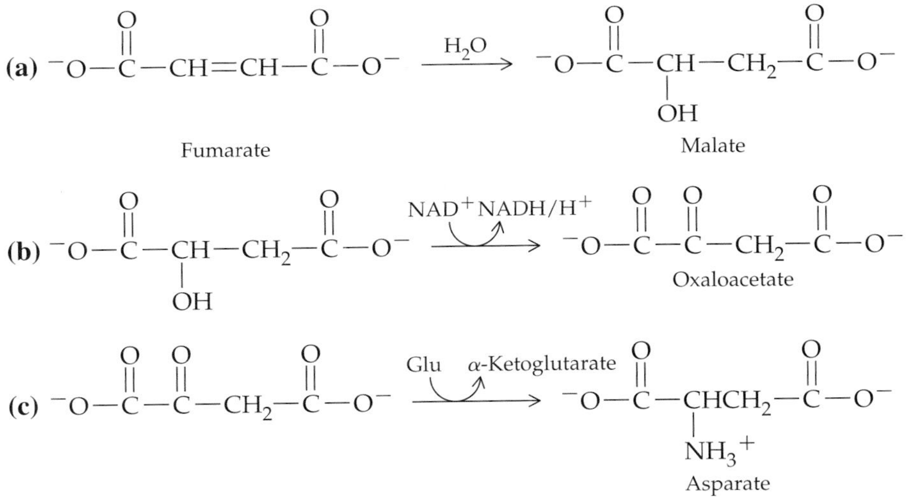

Classify each reaction as one of the following:

(1) Oxidation   (2) Reduction   (3) Transamination
(4) Elimination   (5) Addition

25.5 Amino Acid Catabolism: The Carbon Atoms

Learning Objective:
- Describe the metabolic fate of the carbon atoms in an amino acid.

The carbon atoms of each protein amino acid arrive, by distinctive pathways, at pyruvate, acetyl-CoA, or one of the citric acid cycle intermediates shown in blue type in Figure 25.4. Eventually, all of the amino acid carbon skeletons can be used to generate energy, either by passing through the citric acid cycle and into the gluconeogenesis pathway to form glucose or by entering the ketogenesis pathway to form ketone bodies.

Table 25.1 Glucogenic and Ketogenic Amino Acids

Glucogenic	
Alanine	Glycine
Arginine	Histidine
Aspartate	Methionine
Asparagine	Proline
Cysteine	Serine
Glutamate	Threonine
Glutamine	Valine

Glucogenic and Ketogenic
Isoleucine
Lysine
Phenylalanine
Tryptophan
Tyrosine

Ketogenic
Leucine

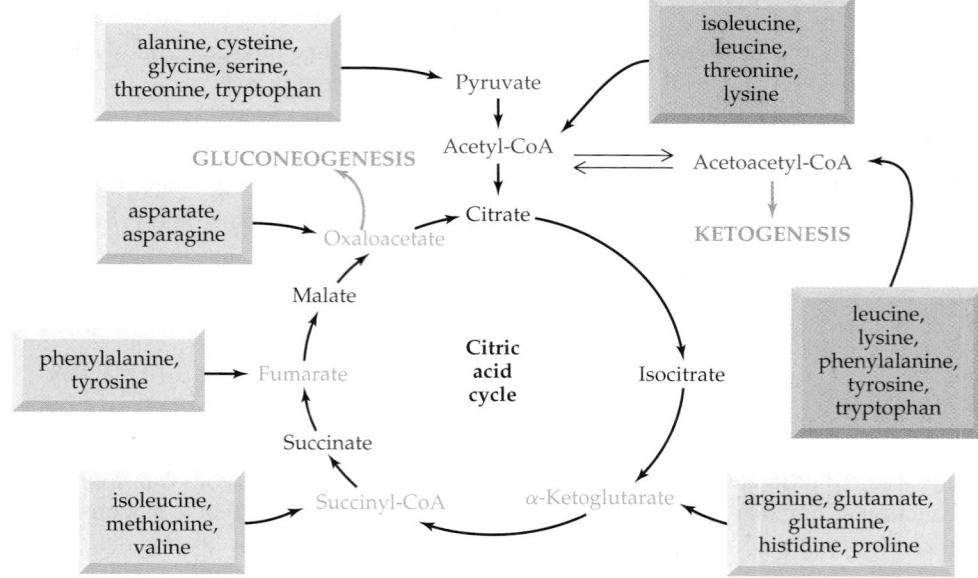

▲ **Figure 25.4**
Fate of amino acid carbon atoms.
The carbon atoms of the amino acids are converted to the seven compounds shown here in red and blue type, each of which is either an intermediate in the citric acid cycle or a precursor to citrate. The amino acids in the blue boxes are glucogenic—they can form glucose via the entry of oxaloacetate into gluconeogenesis. Those in the pink boxes are ketogenic—they are available for ketogenesis.

Those amino acids that are converted to acetoacetyl-CoA or acetyl-CoA then enter the ketogenesis pathway and are called *ketogenic amino acids.*

Those amino acids that proceed by way of oxaloacetate to the gluconeogenesis pathway (Section 22.11) are known as *glucogenic amino acids* (Table 25.1). Both ketogenic and glucogenic amino acids are able to enter fatty acid biosynthesis via acetyl-CoA (Section 24.8).

25.6 Biosynthesis of Nonessential Amino Acids

Learning Objective:

• Define essential and nonessential amino acids, and describe the general scheme of amino acid biosynthesis.

Nonessential amino acid One of 11 amino acids that are synthesized in the body and are therefore not necessary in the diet.

Essential amino acid An amino acid that cannot be synthesized by the body and thus must be obtained from the diet.

Humans are able to synthesize about half of the 20 amino acids found in proteins. These are known as the **nonessential amino acids** because they do not have to be supplied by our diet. The remaining amino acids—the **essential amino acids** (Table 25.2)—are synthesized only by plants and microorganisms. Humans must obtain the essential amino acids from food (see the Chemistry in Action "Proteins in the Diet" in Chapter 18). Meats contain all of the essential amino acids. The foods that do not have all of them are described as having *incomplete amino acids,* and dietary deficiencies of the essential amino acids can lead to a number of health problems (see the Chemistry in Action "The Importance of Essential Amino Acids and Effects of Deficiencies," p. 774). Food combinations that together contain all of the amino acids are *complementary* sources of protein. It is interesting to note that we synthesize the nonessential amino acids in pathways containing only one to three steps, whereas synthesis of the essential amino acids by other organisms is much more complicated, requiring many more steps and a substantial energy investment.

All of the nonessential amino acids derive their amino groups from glutamate. As you have previously seen, this is the molecule that picks up

Table 25.2 Essential Amino Acids

Amino Acids Essential for Adults		
Histidine	Lysine	Threonine
Isoleucine	Methionine	Tryptophan
Leucine	Phenylalanine	Valine

Some Foods with Incomplete Amino Acids
Grains, nuts, and seeds: High in methionine, low in lysine
Legumes: High in lysine, low in methionine
Corn: High in methionine, low in lysine and tryptophan

Some Examples of Complementary Sources of Protein	
Peanut butter on bread	Nuts and soybeans
Rice and beans	Black-eyed peas and corn bread
Beans and corn	

ammonia in amino acid catabolism and carries it into the urea cycle. Glutamate can also be made from NH_4^+ and α-ketoglutarate by **reductive amination,** the reverse of oxidative deamination (Section 25.3). The same glutamate dehydrogenase enzyme carries out the reaction.

Reductive amination Conversion of an α-keto acid to an amino acid by reaction with NH_4^+.

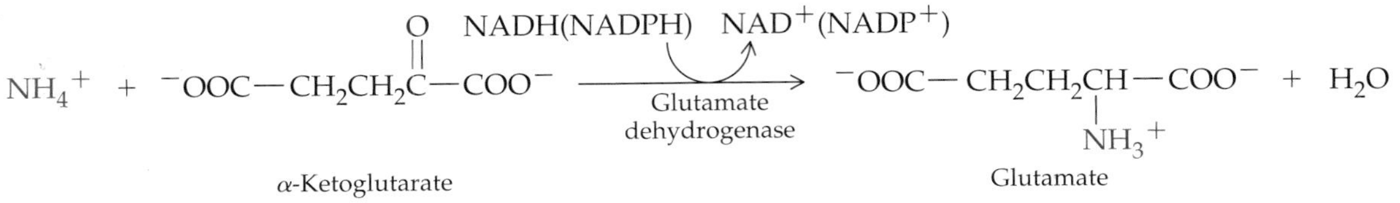

$$NH_4^+ + {}^-OOC-CH_2CH_2\overset{O}{\underset{||}{C}}-COO^- \xrightarrow[\text{dehydrogenase}]{\overset{\text{NADH(NADPH)} \quad \text{NAD}^+(\text{NADP}^+)}{\curvearrowright}}{\text{Glutamate}} {}^-OOC-CH_2CH_2\underset{\underset{NH_3^+}{|}}{CH}-COO^- + H_2O$$

α-Ketoglutarate   Glutamate

Glutamate also provides nitrogen for the synthesis of other nitrogen-containing compounds, including the purines and pyrimidines that are part of DNA.

◀◀◀ Recall that the structures and roles of NADH, NADPH, NAD^+, and $NADP^+$ were discussed in Chapter 21.

The following four common metabolic intermediates, which you have seen play many roles, are the precursors for synthesis of the nonessential amino acids.

Precursors in synthesis of nonessential amino acids

$$CH_3\overset{O}{\underset{||}{C}}-COO^- \qquad {}^-OOC-\overset{O}{\underset{||}{C}}CH_2-COO^- \qquad {}^-OOC-CH_2CH_2\overset{O}{\underset{||}{C}}-COO^- \qquad {}^{-2}O_3POCH_2\underset{\underset{OH}{|}}{CH}-COO^-$$

Pyruvate   Oxaloacetate α-Ketoglutarate   3-Phosphoglycerate

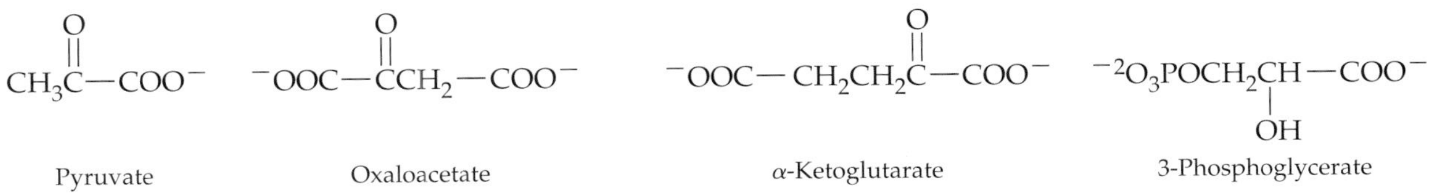

Glutamine is made from glutamate, and asparagine is made by reaction of glutamine with aspartate.

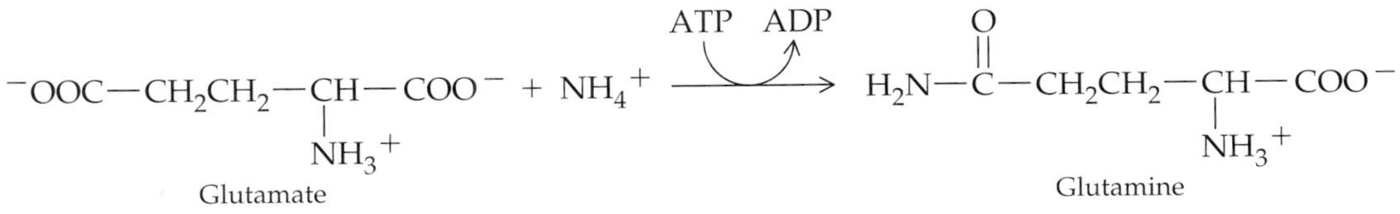

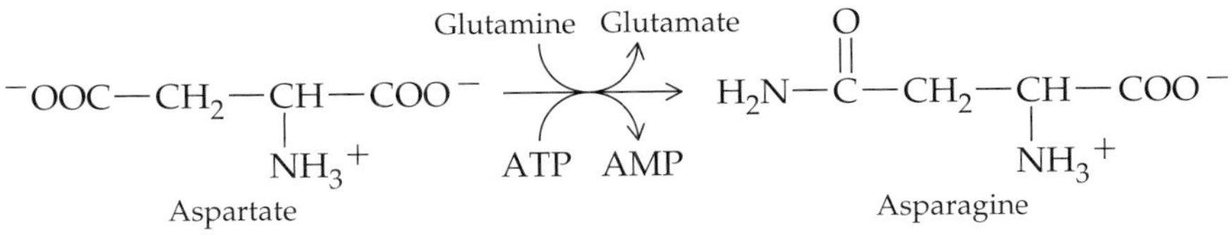

$$^-OOC-CH_2CH_2-\underset{\underset{NH_3^+}{|}}{CH}-COO^- + NH_4^+ \xrightarrow{\overset{\text{ATP} \quad \text{ADP}}{\curvearrowright}} H_2N-\overset{O}{\underset{||}{C}}-CH_2CH_2-\underset{\underset{NH_3^+}{|}}{CH}-COO^-$$

Glutamate   Glutamine

$$^-OOC-CH_2-\underset{\underset{NH_3^+}{|}}{CH}-COO^- \xrightarrow[\text{ATP} \quad \text{AMP}]{\overset{\text{Glutamine} \quad \text{Glutamate}}{\curvearrowright}} H_2N-\overset{O}{\underset{||}{C}}-CH_2-\underset{\underset{NH_3^+}{|}}{CH}-COO^-$$

Aspartate   Asparagine

The amino acid tyrosine is classified as nonessential because we can synthesize it from phenylalanine, an essential amino acid.

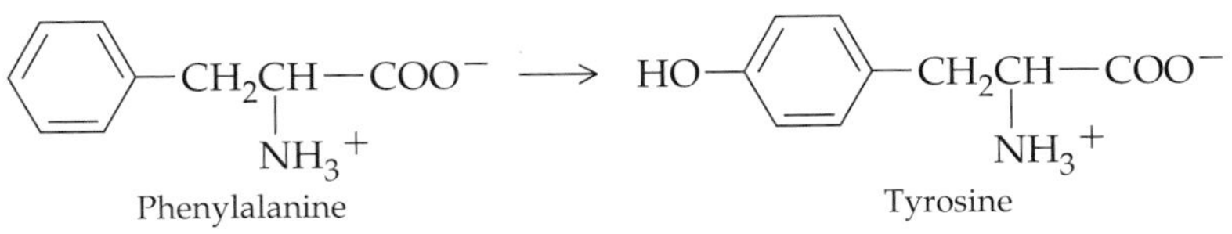

$$\text{(benzene ring)}-CH_2\underset{\underset{NH_3^+}{|}}{CH}-COO^- \longrightarrow HO-\text{(benzene ring)}-CH_2\underset{\underset{NH_3^+}{|}}{CH}-COO^-$$

Phenylalanine   Tyrosine

Whatever the classification, we have a high nutritional requirement for phenylalanine, and several metabolic diseases are associated with defects in the enzymes needed to convert it to tyrosine and other metabolites. The best known of these diseases is phenylketonuria (PKU), the first inborn error of metabolism for which the biochemical cause was recognized. In 1947, it was found that failure to convert phenylalanine to tyrosine causes PKU.

PKU results in elevated blood-serum and urine concentrations of phenylalanine, phenylpyruvate, and several other metabolites produced when the body diverts phenylalanine to metabolism by other pathways. Undetected PKU causes mental retardation by the second month of life. Estimates are that, prior to the 1960s, 1% of those institutionalized for mental retardation were PKU victims. Widespread screening of newborn infants is the only defense against PKU and similar treatable metabolic disorders that take their toll early in life. In the 1960s a test for PKU was introduced, and virtually all hospitals in the United States now routinely screen for it. Treatment consists of a diet low in phenylalanine, which is maintained in infants with special formulas and in older individuals by eliminating meat and using low-protein grain products. Individuals with PKU must be on alert for foods sweetened with aspartame (e.g., Nutrasweet), which is a derivative of phenylalanine.

PROBLEM 25.9

Classify each of the essential amino acids as being either glucogenic, ketogenic, or both.

◯━ KEY CONCEPT PROBLEM 25.10 ──────────────────────────

In the pathway for synthesis of serine,

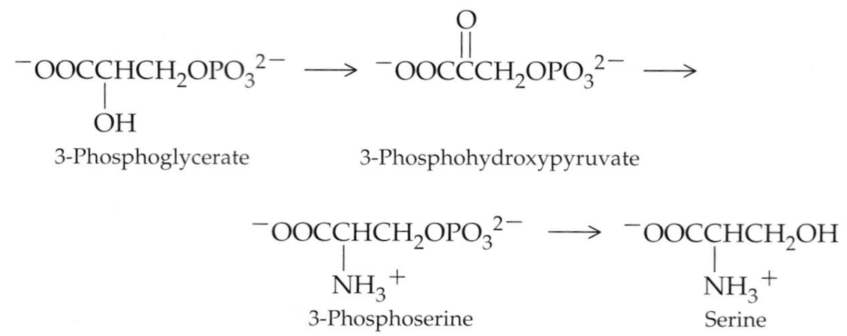

$$^-OOCCHCH_2OPO_3{}^{2-} \longrightarrow {}^-OOCCCH_2OPO_3{}^{2-} \longrightarrow$$

$$\underset{\text{3-Phosphoglycerate}}{\overset{|}{OH}} \qquad \underset{\text{3-Phosphohydroxypyruvate}}{\overset{\overset{O}{\|}}{}}$$

$$^-OOCCHCH_2OPO_3{}^{2-} \longrightarrow {}^-OOCCHCH_2OH$$

$$\underset{\text{3-Phosphoserine}}{\overset{|}{NH_3{}^+}} \qquad \underset{\text{Serine}}{\overset{|}{NH_3{}^+}}$$

identify which step of the reaction is a(n)

(a) transamination   **(b)** hydrolysis   **(c)** oxidation

CHEMISTRY IN ACTION

✚ The Importance of Essential Amino Acids and Effects of Deficiencies

Regardless of the amazing numbers of biomolecules our bodies can synthesize, there are some we cannot make. These molecules, called "essential" nutrients, must be harvested daily from the foods we eat. Although there are no known essential carbohydrates, there are essential fatty acids and essential amino acids. The two essential fatty acids, linoleic and linolenic acid were discussed in Section 23.2. Let's now turn our attention to the amino acids.

The amino acids can nutritionally be placed into one of three groups: nonessential (Ala, Asn, Asp, and Glu), conditional (Arg, Cys, Gln, Tyr, Gly, Pro, and Ser), and essential (or indispensible) amino acids. Our bodies can make both the nonessential and conditional amino acids, even if we don't get them from the

food we eat. Conditional amino acids are so named because in healthy individuals they are normally produced in sufficient quantities; however, in times of illness and physiological stress (like growth or tissue healing) dietary intake is necessary to achieve sufficient levels. The essential amino acids, on the other hand, cannot be prepared with the biochemical machinery we possess and must therefore be obtained through diet. Table 25.2 lists some dietary sources of these indispensible amino acids.

There are nine essential amino acids: histidine, isoleucine, leucine, lysine, methionine, phenylalanine, threonine, tryptophan, and valine. There is little discussion among scientists regarding the amino acids on this list; however, the classification of histidine as essential is argued by some biochemists, who wish to place it as a conditional amino acid. Although essential in growing children, histidine is generally considered nonessential for healthy adults, who are quite capable of synthesizing enough to meet their normal biochemical requirements except under physiological requirements imposed by certain stress or disease situations.

Nutritional biochemists seek to understand what physiological fate will befall someone whose diet is deficient in one of the essential amino acids. This challenging research requires tight controls over the food given to the animal models under study. For example, to determine the effect of a valine deficiency on a mouse, researchers must ensure that its diet contains very little (if any) valine, while not lacking in

any other nutrient. Studies like this, as well as observations in humans, have given rise to a number of conclusions concerning the functions of individual essential amino acids and the effects a deficiency may cause. For example, as we learned in the beginning of the chapter, low blood serum values of the amino acid histidine have been consistently found in people suffering from RA. While no direct cause and effect relationship has yet been established, it has given scientists new directions to explore in the possible prevention and treatment of this debilitating disease.

Amino Acid(s)	Role and Effect of Deficiency
Histidine	• Essential in growing children and repair of tissues. • Conditionally essential in adult diet during old age and in those suffering from degenerative diseases. • Deficiency can cause pain in bony joints and has been shown to lead to cataract formation in animals. • Deficiency also has a possible link to RA.
Isoleucine, Leucine, Valine	• All three essential for the production and maintenance of body proteins. • Difficult to assess the true effects of the deficiency of any of these three amino acids. • Leucine is especially important in controlling the net synthesis of protein. • Leucine deficiency may severely limit regeneration of protein and may affect healing after surgery. • Leucine and valine have been reported to increase mental alertness. • Valine deficiency has been reported to cause sensitivity to touch and sound.
Lysine	• Generally considered the most important of the essential amino acids. • Plays a role in absorption of calcium; formation of collagen for bones, cartilage, and connective tissues; and the production of antibodies, hormones, and enzymes. • Deficiency can lead to a poor appetite, reduction in body weight, anemia, and a reduced ability to concentrate. • Deficiency has also been associated with pneumonia, kidney disease (nephritis), and acidosis, as well as with malnutrition and rickets in children (due to the decreased calcium absorption).
Methionine	• Metabolically a primary source of sulfur. • Only necessary when cysteine intake is limited. • May play a role in lowering cholesterol and reducing liver fat, protecting kidneys, and promoting hair growth. • Deficiency may ultimately lead to chronic rheumatic fever in children, hardening of the liver (cirrhosis), and nephritis.
Phenylalanine	• The primary source of aromatic rings needed for a whole array of biomolecules, most notably the neurotransmitters (Section 28.4). • Deficiency can lead to behavioral changes such as psychotic and schizophrenic behavior (presumably due to its being needed for the synthesis of tyrosine, dopamine, and epinephrine).
Threonine	• Key in the formation of collagen, elastin, and tooth enamel. • Suggested to be essential in the prevention and treatment of mental illness. • Deficiency can result in irritability in children.
Tryptophan	• Considered to be a natural relaxant, it has been used to help relieve insomnia. • Often recommended for the treatment of migraines and mild depression (as it is the metabolic starting material for serotonin); sometimes called "nature's Prozac." • Deficiency can lead to serotonin deficiency syndrome, which in turn can lead to a broad array of emotional and behavioral problems such as depression, premenstrual syndrome (PMS), anxiety, alcoholism, insomnia, violence, aggression, and suicide.

CIA Problem 25.4 What is meant by a conditional amino acid?

CIA Problem 25.5 What medical conditions might arise if your diet was found to be low in methionine?

CIA Problem 25.6 What essential amino acid has been called "nature's Prozac"? What are some of the symptoms seen if deficiencies of it occur?

CONCEPT MAP: PROTEIN AND AMINO ACID METABOLISM

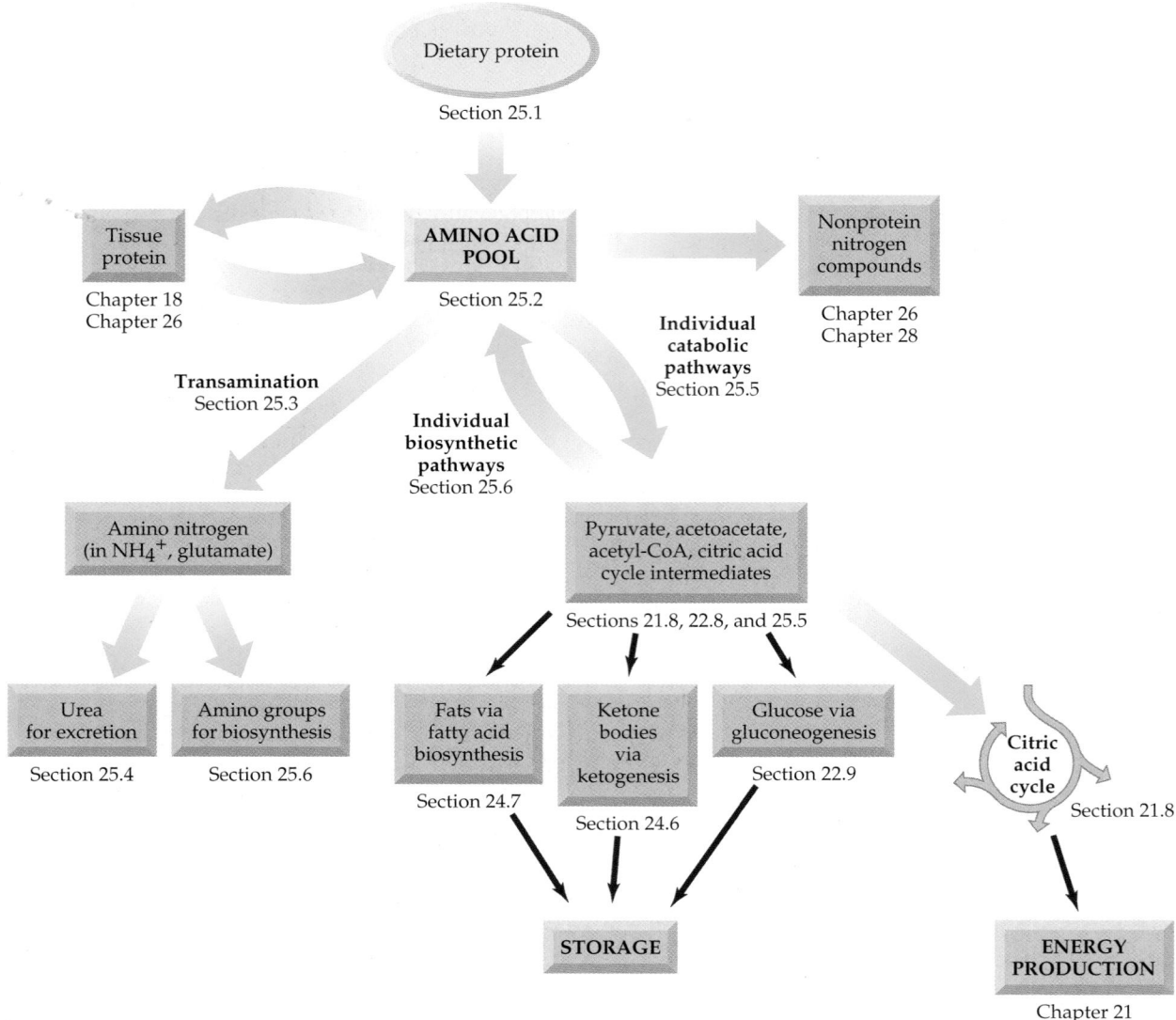

▲ **Figure 25.5 Concept Map.** This concept map shows how amino acids move in and out of the amino acid pool, and what their possible metabolic fates are.

SUMMARY REVISITING THE CHAPTER LEARNING OBJECTIVES

- **List the steps of protein digestion.** Protein digestion begins in the stomach and continues in the small intestine. The result is virtually complete hydrolysis to yield free amino acids. The active transport of amino acids into cells lining the intestine is managed by several transport systems devoted to different groups of amino acids. The amino acids enter the bloodstream after active transport where they enter the amino acid pool (see Problems 11, 12, 17, 18, 47, 48, and 50).

- **Define the amino acid pool and its metabolic role.** The amino acid pool represents the entire collection of free amino acids throughout

the body. Amino acids are constantly entering the amino acid pool from dietary protein or broken-down body protein. The body does not store nitrogen compounds, using this pool for biosynthesis of nitrogen-containing biomolecules (see Problems 17–20, 48, and 50).

- **Explain how amino acids are catabolized.** Each amino acid is catabolized by a distinctive pathway, but the general sequence involves: (i) removal of the amino group; (ii) use of the removed —NH_2 in the synthesis of new nitrogen compounds or the ammonium ion; (iii) passage of nitrogen into the urea cycle; and

(iv) incorporation of the carbon atoms into compounds that can enter the citric acid cycle *(see Problems 21–30 and 51).*

- **Discuss the fate of the nitrogen of an amino acid.** For almost all amino acids, the amino group is removed by *transamination* (the transfer of an amino group from an amino acid to a keto acid), usually to form glutamate. Then, the amino group of glutamate is removed as ammonium ion by *oxidative deamination.* The ammonium ion is destined for the *urea cycle.* The transamination process can also be used to synthesize new amino acids from appropriate keto acids *(see Problems 31, 33, 34, 36, and 43).*

- **Identify the major reactants and products of the urea cycle.** Ammonium ion (from amino acid catabolism) and bicarbonate ion (from carbon dioxide) react to produce carbamoyl phosphate, which enters the urea cycle. The first two steps of the urea cycle produce a reactive intermediate in which both of the nitrogens that will be part of the urea end product are bonded to the same carbon atom. Then arginine is formed and split by hydrolysis to yield urea, which will be excreted. The net result of the urea cycle is reaction of ammonium ion with aspartate to give urea and fumarate *(see Problems 31–34, 42, and 46).*

- **Describe the metabolic fate of the carbon atoms in an amino acid.** The carbon atoms from amino acids are incorporated into compounds that can enter the *citric acid cycle.* Amino acids are classified as either glucogenic or ketogenic depending on how they enter the citric acid cycle. Ketogenic amino acids are those that are converted to acetoacetyl-CoA or acetyl-CoA; glucogenic amino acids are those that are eventually converted to oxaloacetate. These carbon compounds formed are then available for conversion to fatty acids or glycogen for storage or for synthesis of ketone bodies *(see Problems 14, 16, 29, 30, 44, 45, and 49).*

- **Define essential and nonessential amino acids, and describe the general scheme of amino acid biosynthesis.** *Essential amino acids* must be obtained in the diet because our bodies do not synthesize them. They are made only by plants and microorganisms, and their synthetic pathways are complex. Our bodies do synthesize the so-called *nonessential amino acids.* Their synthetic pathways are quite simple and generally begin with pyruvate, oxaloacetate, α-ketoglutarate, or 3-phosphoglycerate. The nitrogen is commonly supplied by glutamate *(see Problems 35–41, 47, 51, and 53).*

KEY WORDS

Amino acid pool, *p. 765*
Essential amino acid, *p. 772*

Nonessential amino acid, *p. 772*
Oxidative deamination, *p. 767*

Reductive amination, *p. 773*
Transamination, *p. 766*

Turnover, *p. 765*
Urea cycle, *p. 768*

⊙ UNDERSTANDING KEY CONCEPTS

25.11   In the diagram shown here, fill in the sources for the amino acid pool.

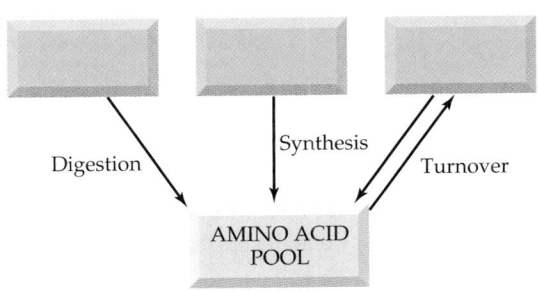

25.12   What are the fates of the carbon and nitrogen atoms in a catabolized amino acid?

25.13   A treatment for hyperammonemia (excess NH_4^+ in the blood) is to administer pyruvate. What two enzymes are necessary to detoxify the ammonium ion in the presence of pyruvate? What is the product?

25.14   Three metabolites that can result from the breakdown of the carbon skeleton of amino acids are ketone bodies, acetyl-CoA, and glucose. Briefly describe how each of these metabolites can be produced from amino acid catabolism.

25.15   Define what an "essential" nutrient is and explain how it differs from a "nonessential" nutrient.

25.16   In the liver, the relative activity of ornithine transcarbamylase is high, that of argininosuccinate synthetase is low, and that of arginase is high. Why is it important that ornithine transcarbamylase activity be high in the liver? What might be the consequence if arginase activity is low or defective?

ADDITIONAL PROBLEMS

AMINO ACID POOL (SECTIONS 25.1 AND 25.2)

25.17   Where is the body's amino acid pool?

25.18   In what part of the digestive tract does the digestion of proteins begin?

25.19   What glycolytic intermediates are precursors to amino acids?

25.20   What citric acid cycle intermediates are precursors to amino acids?

AMINO ACID CATABOLISM (SECTIONS 25.3 AND 25.5)

25.21   What is meant by transamination?

25.22   Pyruvate and oxaloacetate can be acceptors for the amino group in transamination. Write the structures for the products formed from transamination of these two compounds.

25.23   What is the structure of the α-keto acid formed from transamination of the following amino acids?

   (a) Glutamic acid   **(b)** Alanine

25.24   What is the structure of the α-keto acid formed from transamination of the following amino acids (Refer to Table 18.3)?

   (a) Isoleucine   **(b)** Valine

25.25   In general, how does oxidative deamination differ from transamination?

25.26   What coenzymes are associated with oxidative deamination?

25.27   Write the structure of the α-keto acid produced by oxidative deamination of the following amino acids (Refer to Table 18.3):

   (a) Leucine   **(b)** Tryptophan

25.28   What other product is formed in oxidative deamination besides an α-keto acid?

25.29   What is a ketogenic amino acid? Give three examples.

25.30   What is a glucogenic amino acid? Give three examples.

UREA CYCLE (SECTION 25.4)

25.31   Why does the body convert NH_4^+ to urea for excretion?

25.32   What is the source of carbon in the formation of urea?

25.33   From what two amino acids do the nitrogens in urea arise? (Hint: See Figure 25.3.)

25.34   Where does aspartate enter the urea cycle and what compound does it eventually leave as? What metabolic cycle does this compound then enter?

AMINO ACID BIOSYNTHESIS (SECTION 25.6)

25.35   How do essential and nonessential amino acids differ from each other in the number of steps required for their synthesis in organisms that synthesize both?

25.36   Which amino acid serves as the source of nitrogen for synthesis of the other amino acids?

25.37   If you were diagnosed as having a diet low in lysine, what foods might you include in your diet to alleviate this problem?

25.38   How is tyrosine biosynthesized in the body? What disease prevents this biosynthesis, thereby making tyrosine an essential amino acid for those who have this condition?

25.39   PKU is an abbreviation for what disorder? What are the symptoms of PKU? How can PKU be treated for a nearly normal life?

25.40   Diet soft drinks that are sweetened with aspartame carry a warning label for phenylketonurics. Why?

25.41   Which of the following biomolecules contain nitrogen?

   (a) Glycogen (Chapter 22)

   (b) Nitric oxide (Chapter 4)

   (c) Collagen (Chapter 18)

   (d) Epinephrine (Chapter 28)

   (e) Stearic acid (Chapter 23)

   (f) Fructose (Chapter 20)

CONCEPTUAL PROBLEMS

25.42   What energy source is used in the formation of urea?

25.43   Write the equation for the transamination reaction that occurs between phenylalanine and pyruvate.

25.44   **(a)** Name the four compounds within the citric acid cycle that the carbon skeletons of the glucogenic amino acid enter as.

   (b) Which of these four compounds arise exclusively from aromatic amino acids?

25.45   Can an amino acid be both glucogenic and ketogenic? Explain why or why not.

25.46   Where in the body does the conversion of ammonium ion to urea occur? Where is the urea that is formed ultimately transported?

25.47   Considering all of the metabolic processes we have studied, why do we say that the biochemistry of the body is dynamic?

25.48   Two major differences between the amino acid pool and the fat and carbohydrate pools in the body center on storage and on energy. Discuss these major differences.

25.49   When some of the carbons of glutamate are converted to glycogen, what is the order of the following compounds in that pathway?

   (a) Glucose   **(b)** Glutamate

   (c) Glycogen   **(d)** Oxaloacetate

   (e) α-Ketoglutarate   **(f)** Phosphoenolpyruvate

25.50 The pancreatic proteases are synthesized and stored as zymogens. They are activated after the pancreatic juices enter the small intestine. Why is it essential that these enzymes be synthesized and stored in their inactive forms?

25.51 What is the general scheme by which amino acids are catabolized?

25.52 The net reaction for the urea cycle shows that three ATPs are hydrolyzed; however, the total energy "cost" is four ATPs. Explain why this is true.

25.53 Why might it be a bad idea to take large quantities of a single amino acid dietary supplement?

GROUP PROBLEMS

25.54 Write down what foods you had for lunch and dinner yesterday. Try and determine what essential amino acids were present in the foods you ate. Were there any that were missing?

25.55 Pretend that you were deficient in all of the essential amino acids. Have you and your group draw up with a diet plan for one day (breakfast, lunch, and dinner) that would ensure you were getting all of the essential amino acids over the course of that day.

25.56 Determine how many ATPs you would make if you consumed a tetrapeptide comprised of leucine, histidine, valine, and lysine. Have each member of your group take one of the four amino acids and determine the number of ATPs their amino acid would make and combine them to get the total.

26

Nucleic Acids and Protein Synthesis

CONTENTS

◀◀◀ CONCEPTS TO REVIEW

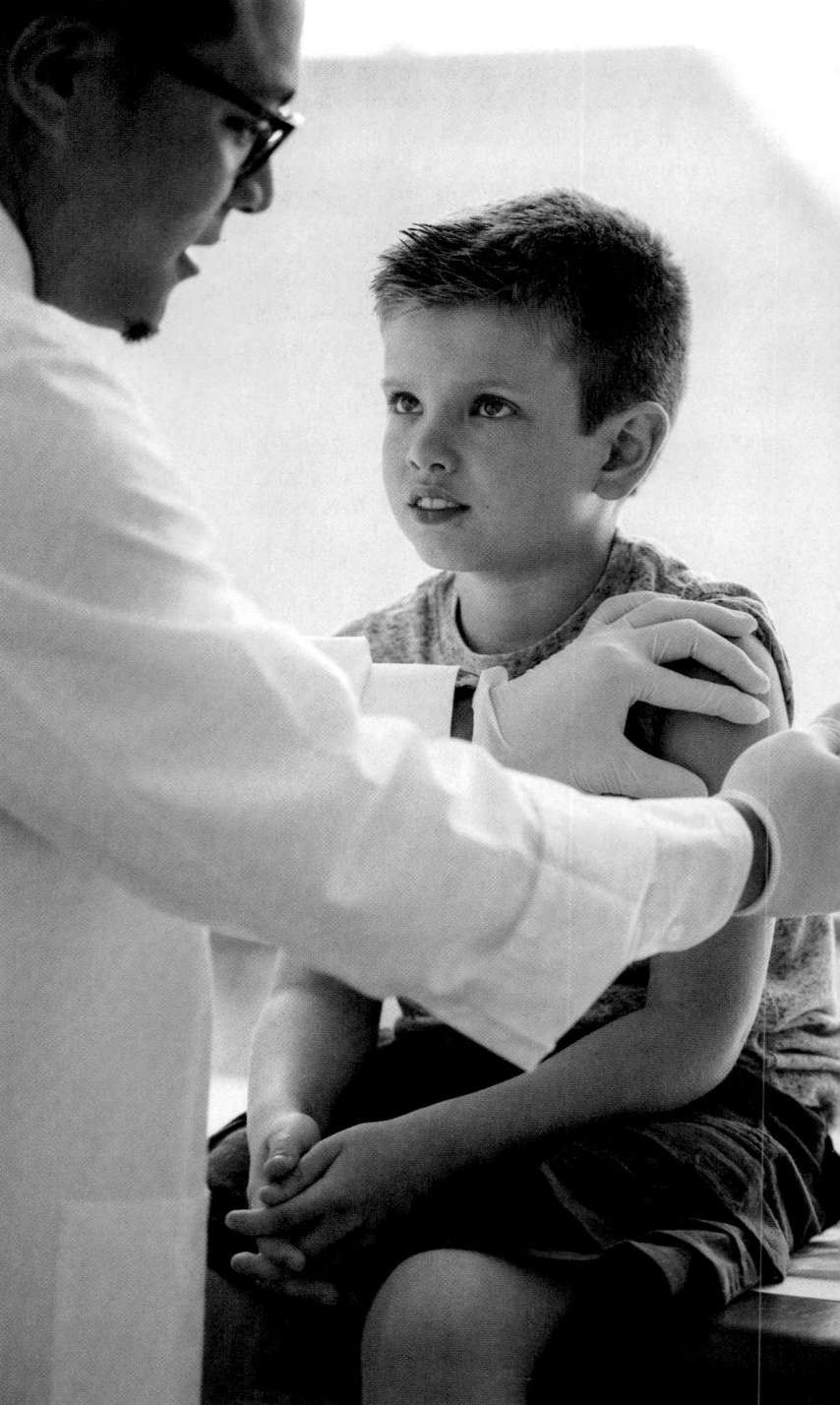

▲ Vaccinations educate the immune system so that it can rapidly kill disease-causing viruses such as influenza, measles, and many others preventing serious illnesses.

Flu is caused by the influenza virus, of which there are three major types—A, B, and C (all of which humans are susceptible to)—with many subtypes of each one. As you will learn in the Chemistry in Action "Influenza: Variations on a Theme" later in this chapter, influenza A and B are infectious. If enough people are affected, an epidemic can occur. Symptoms of a viral infection like the flu include fever, cough, sore throat, runny nose, headache, tiredness, muscle or bone aches, or in more severe cases, vomiting, diarrhea, or stomach pain; however, humans can get a flu shot to prevent illness from types A and B influenza.

Viruses, just like humans, have either deoxyribonucleic acids (DNA) or ribonucleic acids (RNA), which use a host cell (our bodies) for replication. The influenza vaccine prevents the virus from replicating in our bodies by introducing inactivated strains of the influenza virus into the body. The flu shot provides the necessary molecules to strengthen our immune system to combat the effects of the influenza infection. In other words, the vaccine is engineered to provide immunity to influenza A and/or B, but because the nucleic acids that make up the DNA and RNA of the influenza virus change rapidly, annual flu shots are recommended.

Nucleic acids are the basic molecular structures present in DNA and RNA, which ultimately form the blueprint for our genetic information. We will learn more about nucleic acids in this chapter and how our genetic information is duplicated, transferred, and expressed through protein synthesis. Protein synthesis also helps maintain all of our normal body functions, such as inhalation and exhalation of the lungs, food digestion, and energy generation.

26.1 DNA, Chromosomes, and Genes

Learning Objective:

- Explain the role of chromosomes, genes, and DNA, and describe their basic function in the human body.

When a cell is not actively dividing, its nucleus is occupied by *chromatin,* which is a compact, orderly tangle of **deoxyribonucleic acid (DNA),** the carrier of genetic information, twisted around organizing proteins known as *histones.* During cell division, chromatin becomes even more compact and organizes itself into **chromosomes.** Each chromosome contains a different DNA molecule, and all of the DNA is duplicated so that each new cell receives a complete copy.

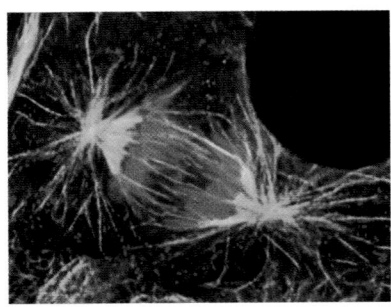

▲ Chromosomes (red) during cell division.

deoxyribonucleic acid (DNA) The nucleic acid that stores genetic information; a polymer of deoxyribonucleotides.

Chromosome A complex of proteins and DNA; visible during cell division.

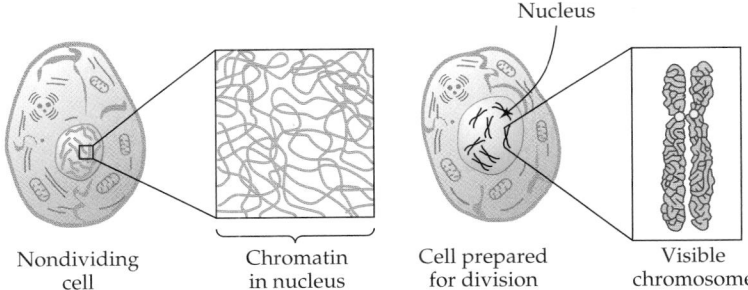

Nondividing cell — Chromatin in nucleus — Cell prepared for division — Visible chromosome

Nucleus

Each DNA molecule, in turn, is composed of many **genes**—individual segments of the DNA molecule containing the instructions that direct the synthesis of a single polypeptide. Interestingly, not all genes coded for by an organism's DNA are expressed as protein. As we will see later in this chapter, some genes code for *functional RNA* molecules.

Interestingly, organisms differ widely in their numbers of chromosomes. A horse, for example, has 64 chromosomes (32 pairs), a cat has 38 chromosomes (19 pairs), a mosquito has 6 chromosomes (3 pairs), and a corn plant has 20 chromosomes (10 pairs). A human has 46 chromosomes (23 pairs).

Gene Segment of DNA that directs the synthesis of a single polypeptide.

LOOKING AHEAD ▶▶ The complete map of the genetic information passed along during cell division is now available for numerous organisms, including humans. This amazing development of the human genome will be further explored in Chapter 27.

26.2 Composition of Nucleic Acids

Learning Objective:

- Describe, identify, and draw the components of nucleosides and nucleotides.

Like proteins and carbohydrates, nucleic acids are polymers. Proteins are polypeptides, carbohydrates are polysaccharides, and **nucleic acids** are *polynucleotides.* Each **nucleotide** has three parts: a five-membered cyclic monosaccharide, a

Nucleic acid A polymer of nucleotides.

Nucleotide A five-carbon sugar bonded to a heterocyclic nitrogen base and a phosphate group; the monomer for nucleic acids.

A nucleotide

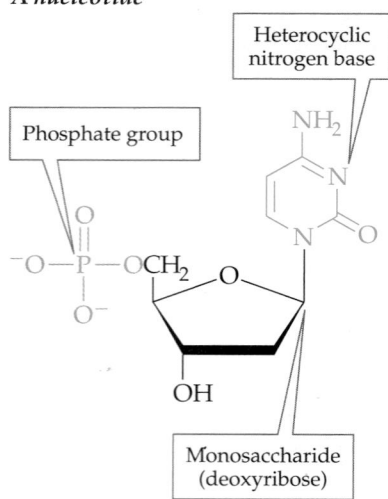

nitrogen-containing cyclic compound known as a *nitrogenous base,* and a phosphate group ($-OPO_3^{2-}$).

There are two classes of nucleic acids, DNA and **ribonucleic acid (RNA),** where several types of RNA exist. The function of one type of RNA is to put the information stored in DNA to use. Other types of RNA assist in the conversion of the message a specific RNA carries into protein. Before we discuss how the nucleic acids fulfill their functions, we need to understand how their component parts are joined together and how DNA and RNA differ from each other.

The Sugars

The difference between DNA and RNA is found in the sugar portion of the molecules. In RNA, the sugar is D-ribose, except hereafter simply referred to as ribose, as indicated by the name *ribonucleic acid.* In DNA, the sugar is 2-*deoxy*ribose, giving *deoxyribonucleic acid.* The prefix 2-*deoxy-* means that an oxygen atom is missing from the C2 position of ribose.

The Bases

There are five different kinds of nitrogenous bases found in DNA and RNA. They are all derived from two parent compounds, purine and pyrimidine, and, each has its unique one-letter code (A, G, C, T, U). The five nitrogenous bases are shown in Table 26.1, along with the two parent bases; notice the functional groups in each. The nitrogenous bases that are purine derivatives, adenine and guanine, contain two fused nitrogen-containing rings. The bases that are pyrimidine derivatives—cytosine, thymine, and uracil—contain only one nitrogen-containing ring. Notice that adenine, guanine, and cytosine are in DNA and RNA, whereas thymine is present in DNA and uracil is present in RNA.

ribonucleic acid (RNA) Nucleic acids responsible for putting the genetic information to use in protein synthesis; a polymer of ribonucleotides. Includes messenger (mRNA), transfer (tRNA), and ribosomal RNA (rRNA).

Nucleoside A five-carbon sugar bonded to a heterocyclic nitrogenous base; like a nucleotide but with no phosphate group.

Table 26.1 Bases in DNA and RNA

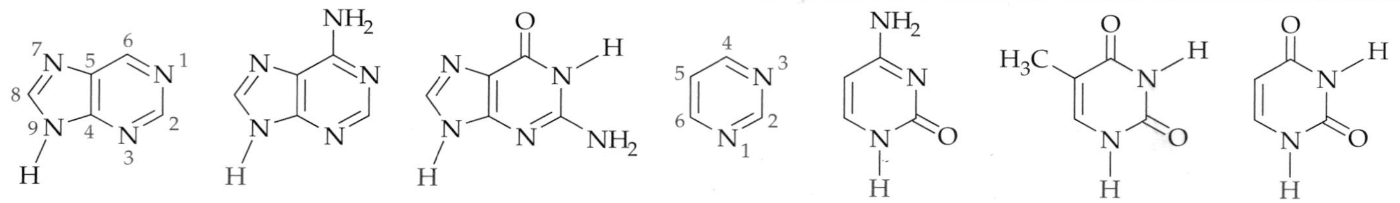

Purine Bases in Nucleic Acids			Pyrimidine Bases in Nucleic Acids			
Purine (Parent)	Adenine (A) (DNA, RNA)	Guanine (G) (DNA, RNA)	Pyrimidine (Parent)	Cytosine (C) (DNA, RNA)	Thymine* (T) (DNA)	Uracil (U) (RNA)

Thymine occurs in a few cases of RNA.

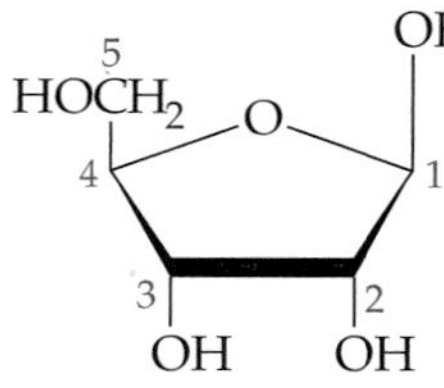

D-Ribose (in RNA)

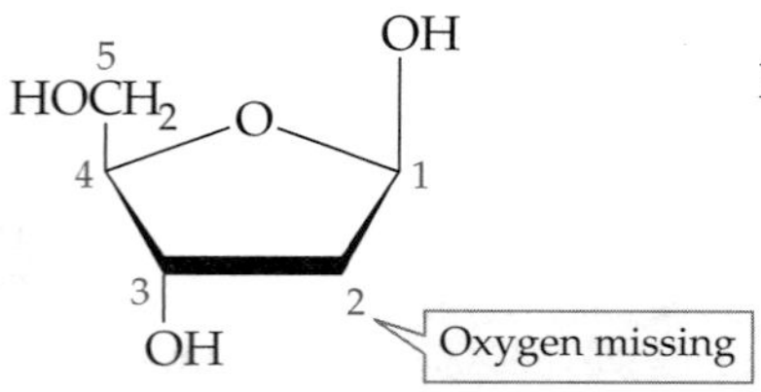

Sugar + Base = Nucleoside

A molecule composed of either ribose or deoxyribose and one of the five nitrogenous bases found in DNA and/or RNA is called a **nucleoside.** The combination of ribose and adenine, for example, gives the nucleoside known as adenosine, which you should recognize as the parent molecule of adenosine triphosphate (ATP) (Section 21.4, p. 667).

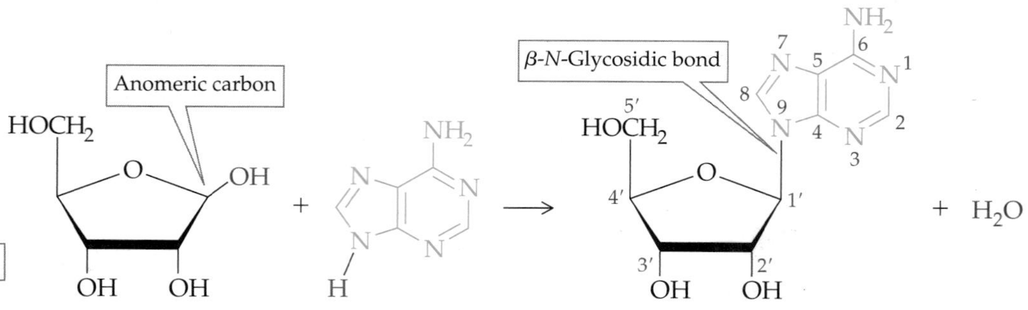

2-Deoxy-D-ribose (in DNA)

Oxygen missing

Anomeric carbon

Ribose

Adenine

β-N-Glycosidic bond

Adenosine (a nucleoside)

$+ H_2O$

The sugar and base are connected by a bond between one of the nitrogen atoms in the base and the anomeric carbon atom (the one bonded to two oxygen atoms) of the sugar. This bond is a β-*N*-glycosidic bond. Notice that this linkage (the 1′ position of the sugar to the nine-position nitrogen atom of the adenine) is closely related to an acetal (Section 15.7).

In each of the nucleic acid bases in Table 26.1, the hydrogen atom lost in nucleoside formation is shown in red.

Nucleoside names are the nitrogenous base name modified by the suffix -*osine* for the purine bases (as we just saw for adenosine) and the suffix -*idine* for the pyrimidine bases. No prefix is used for nucleosides containing ribose, but the prefix *deoxy*- is added for those that contain deoxyribose. Therefore the four nucleosides found in RNA are named adenosine, guanosine, cytidine, and uridine, and the four found in DNA are named deoxyadenosine, deoxyguanosine, deoxycytidine, and deoxythymidine.

To distinguish between atoms in the sugar ring of a nucleoside and atoms in the base ring (or rings), numbers without primes are used for atoms in the base ring (or rings), and numbers with primes are used for atoms in the sugar ring.

> ◀◀◀ **CONCEPTS TO REVIEW** Recall from Chapter 20 that a glycosidic bond is the bond between the anomeric carbon atom of a sugar and an —OR or —NR group. β Bonds point above the sugar ring, and α bonds point below it.

Worked Example 26.1 Naming a Nucleic Acid Component from Its Structure

Is the compound shown here a nucleoside or a nucleotide? Identify its sugar and base components, and name the compound.

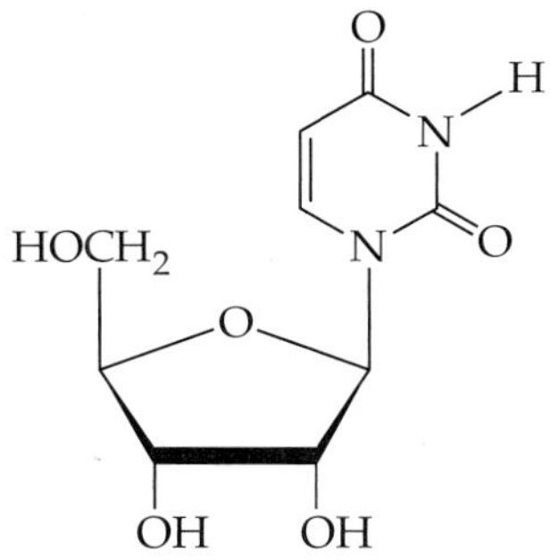

ANALYSIS The compound contains a sugar, recognizable by the oxygen atom in the ring and the —OH groups. It also contains a nitrogenous base, recognizable by the nitrogen-containing ring. The sugar has an —OH in the 2′ position and is therefore ribose (if it were missing the —OH in the 2′ position, it would be a *deoxy*ribose). Checking the base structures in Table 26.1 shows that this is uracil, a pyrimidine base, requiring its name to end in -*idine*.

SOLUTION
The compound is a nucleoside, and its name is uridine.

⊙⊐ KEY CONCEPT PROBLEM 26.1

Name the nucleoside shown here. Copy the structure, and number the C and N atoms (refer to Table 26.1).

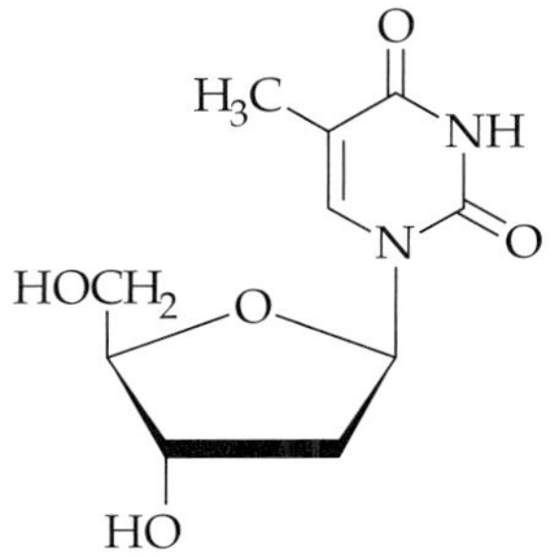

PROBLEM 26.2

Write the molecular formulas for the sugars D-ribose and 2-deoxy-D-ribose. Exactly how do they differ in composition? Can you think of one chemical property that might differ slightly between the two?

Nucleoside + Phosphate = Nucleotide

Nucleotides are the building blocks of nucleic acids; they are the monomers of the DNA and RNA polymers. Each nucleotide is a 5′-monophosphate ester of a nucleoside.

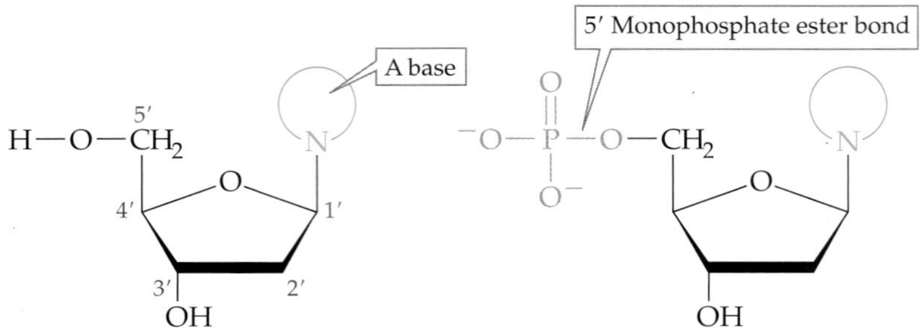

A deoxyribonucleoside   A deoxyribonucleotide

Nucleotides are named by adding 5′-*monophosphate* at the end of the name of the nucleoside. The nucleotides corresponding, for example, to adenosine and deoxycytidine are thus adenosine 5′-monophosphate (AMP) and deoxycytidine 5′-monophosphate (dCMP). Nucleotides that contain ribose are classified as **ribonucleotides** and those that contain 2-deoxy-D-ribose are known as **deoxyribonucleotides** (and are designated by leading their abbreviations with a lower case "d"). For example,

Ribonucleotide A nucleotide that contains D-ribose—monophosphate examples are AMP, uridine monophosphate (UMP), cytidine monophosphate (CMP), and guanosine monophosphate (GMP).

Deoxyribonucleotide A nucleotide that contains 2-deoxy-D-ribose (monophosphate examples are dAMP, dTMP, dCMP, and dGMP).

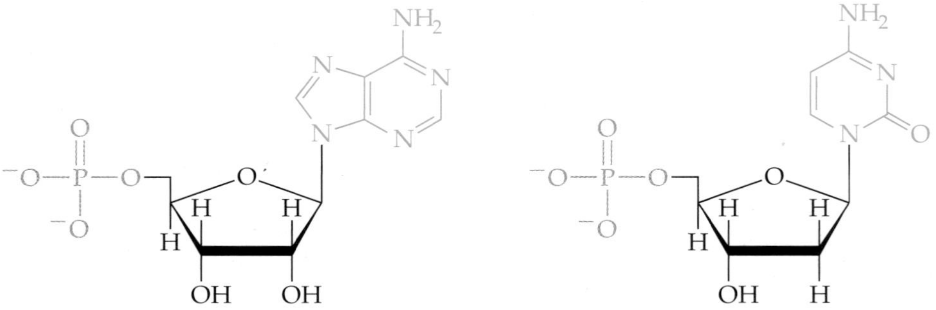

Adenosine 5′-monophosphate (AMP)
(a ribonucleotide)

Deoxycytidine 5′-monophosphate (dCMP)
(a deoxyribonucleotide)

Phosphate groups can be added to any of the nucleotides to form diphosphate or triphosphate esters. As illustrated by *ATP*, these esters are named with the nucleoside name plus *diphosphate* or *triphosphate*. In preceding chapters, you learned that the biochemical energy from the conversion of ATP to adenosine diphosphate (ADP) can be coupled to another less favorable reaction (Section 21.5).

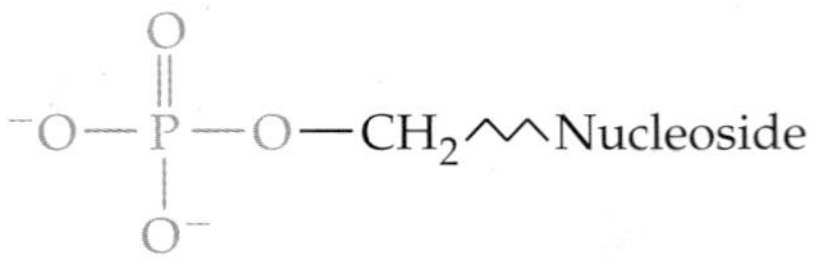

Nucleoside monophosphate 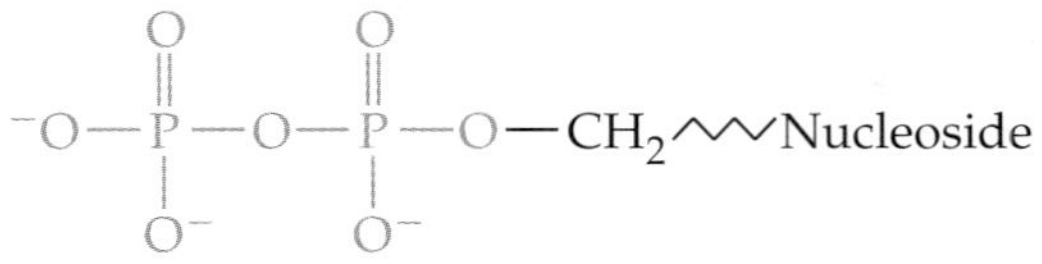   Nucleoside diphosphate

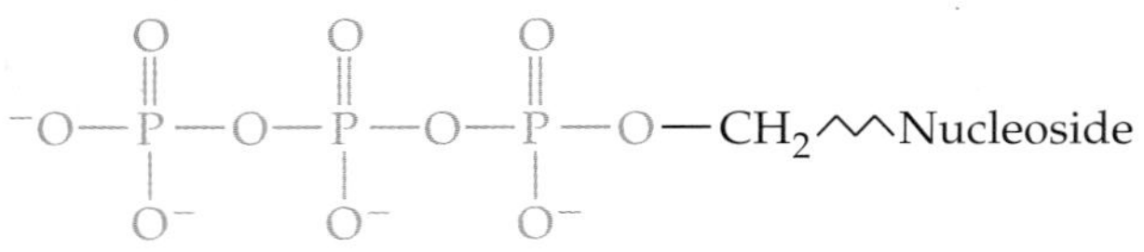

Nucleoside triphosphate

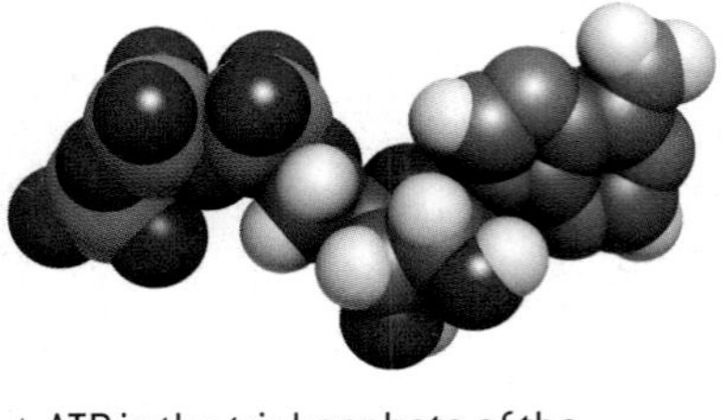

▲ ATP is the triphosphate of the adenosine nucleotide; brown is phosphorus, red is oxygen, and blue is nitrogen.

Summary—Nucleoside, Nucleotide, and Nucleic Acid Composition

Nucleoside
- A sugar and a base

Nucleotide
- A sugar, a base, and a phosphate group ($-OPO_3^{2-}$)

DNA
- A polymer of deoxyribonucleotides
- The sugar is 2-deoxy-D-ribose
- The bases are A, G, C, and *T*

RNA
- A polymer of ribonucleotides
- The sugar is D-ribose
- The bases are A, G, C, and *U*

Worked Example 26.2 Drawing a Nucleic Acid Component from Its Name

Draw the structure of the nucleotide represented by dTMP.

ANALYSIS Referencing Table 26.1 the "T" in dTMP is thymine, "M" is for mono- and "P" is for phosphate. The prefix "d" stands for *deoxy-* on the ribose sugar 2' carbon. Since nitrogen base in this nucleotide is thymine, whose structure is shown in Table 26.1. This base must be bonded (by replacing the H that is red in Table 26.1) to the 1' position of the deoxyribose. Lastly, there must be a phosphate group in the 5' position of the deoxyribose.

SOLUTION
The structure is

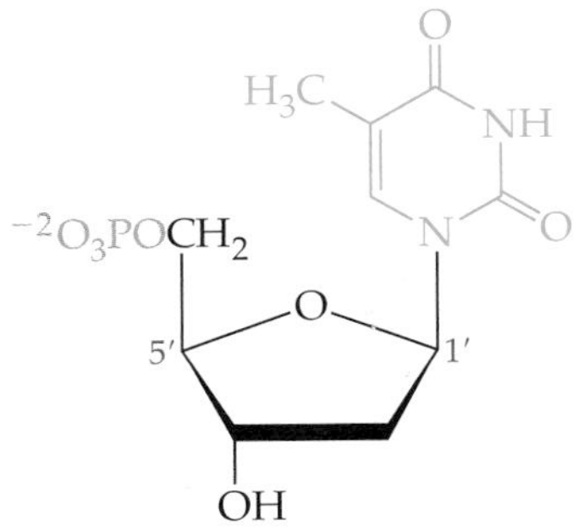

◖◗ KEY CONCEPT PROBLEM 26.3

Draw the structure of 2'-deoxyadenosine 5'-monophosphate, dAMP, and use the primed-unprimed format to number all the atoms in the rings.

PROBLEM 26.4

Draw the structure of the triphosphate of guanosine, a triphosphate that, like ATP, provides energy for certain reactions (see reaction 5 of the citric acid cycle in Section 21.7).

PROBLEM 26.5

Write the full names of dUMP, UMP, CDP, AMP, and ATP.

26.3 The Structure of Nucleic Acid Chains

Learning Objective:

• Describe and identify nucleic acid chains in DNA and RNA.

Keep in mind that nucleic acids are polymers of nucleotides. The nucleotides in DNA and RNA are connected by phosphate diester linkages between the —OH group on C3′ of the sugar ring of one nucleotide and the phosphate group on C5′ of the next nucleotide.

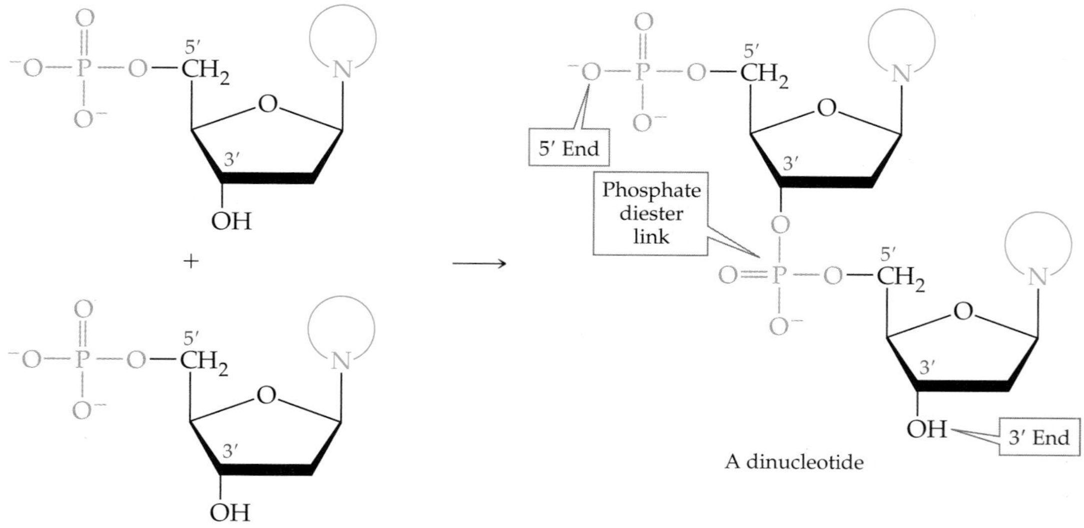

A nucleotide chain commonly has a free phosphate group on a 5′ carbon at one end (known as the 5′*end*) and a free —OH group on a 3′ carbon at the other end (the 3′ *end*), as illustrated in the dinucleotide just above and in the trinucleotide in Figure 26.1. Additional nucleotides join by forming additional phosphate diester linkages between these groups until the polynucleotide chain of a DNA molecule is formed.

Just as the structure and function of a protein depend on the sequence in which the amino acids are connected (see Section 18.7), the structure and function of a nucleic acid depend on the sequence in which the nucleotides are connected. With a nucleic acid, however, we have a second detail to consider: Structure and function both depend on the *direction* in which the nucleic acid is read by enzymes involved in making gene products. Like proteins, nucleic acids have backbones that do not vary in composition. The differences between different proteins and between different nucleic acids result from the *order* of the groups bonded to the backbone—amino acid side chains in proteins and bases in nucleic acids.

Comparison of protein and nucleic acid backbones and side chains

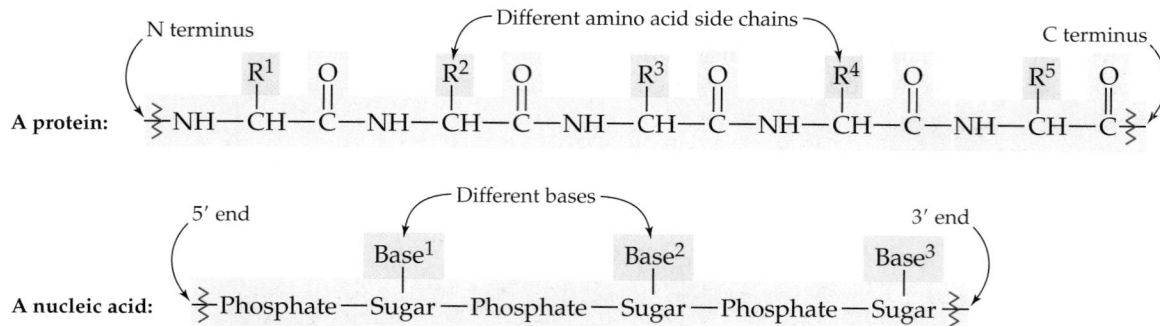

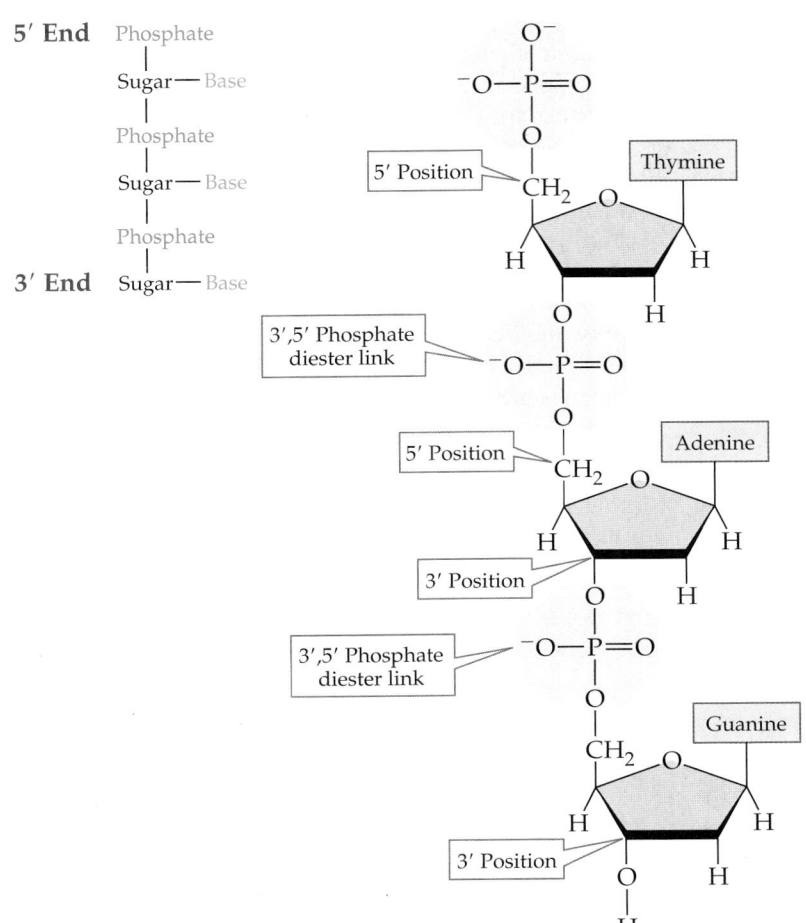

5' End   Phosphate
         |
         Sugar——Base
         |
         Phosphate
         |
         Sugar——Base
         |
         Phosphate
         |
3' End   Sugar——Base

◄ **Figure 26.1**
A deoxytrinucleotide.
In all polynucleotides, as shown here, there is a phosphate group at the 5' end; there is a sugar —OH group at the 3' end; and the nucleotides are connected by 3', 5'-phosphate diester links.

The sequence of nucleotides in a nucleic acid chain is read by starting at the 5' end and identifying the bases in the order of occurrence. Rather than writing the full name of each nucleotide or each base, one-letter abbreviations of the bases are commonly used to designate the order in which they are attached to the sugar–phosphate backbone: A for adenine, G for guanine, C for cytosine, T for thymine, and U for uracil in RNA. The trinucleotide in Figure 26.1, for example, would be represented by T-A-G or TAG.

PROBLEM 26.6

Name the bases in the pentanucleotide with the sequence G-A-U-C-A. Does this come from RNA or DNA? Explain.

PROBLEM 26.7

Draw the full structure of the DNA dinucleotide C-T. Identify the 5' and 3' ends of this dinucleotide.

26.4   Base Pairing in DNA: The Watson–Crick Model

Learning Objective:

• Interpret the structure of DNA, and write complementary sequences.

Analysis of the nitrogenous bases in many DNA samples from many different species revealed that in any given species, the amounts of adenine and thymine were always equal, and the amounts of cytosine and guanine were always equal (A = T and G = C). It was also found that the proportions of each (A/T:G/C) vary from one species to another. For example, human DNA contains 30% each of adenine and thymine and 20% each of guanine and cytosine, whereas the bacterium *Escherichia coli* contains 24% each of adenine and thymine and 26% each of guanine and cytosine. Note that in both cases, A and T are present in equal amounts and G and C are present in equal amounts. This observation, known as Chargaff's rule (named for Erwin Chargaff, who discovered these base ratios in 1950), suggests that the bases occur in discrete pairs. Why should this be?

In 1953, James Watson and Francis Crick proposed a structure for DNA that not only accounts for the pairing of bases but also accounts for the storage and transfer of genetic information. According to the Watson–Crick model, a DNA molecule consists of *two* polynucleotide strands coiled around each other in a helical, screw-like fashion. The sugar–phosphate backbone is on the *outside* of this right-handed **double helix,** and the heterocyclic bases are on the *inside,* so that a base on one strand points directly toward a base on the second strand. The double helix resembles a twisted ladder, with the sugar–phosphate backbone making up the sides and the paired bases, the rungs.

Double helix Two strands coiled around each other in a screw-like fashion; in most organisms the two polynucleotides of DNA form a double helix.

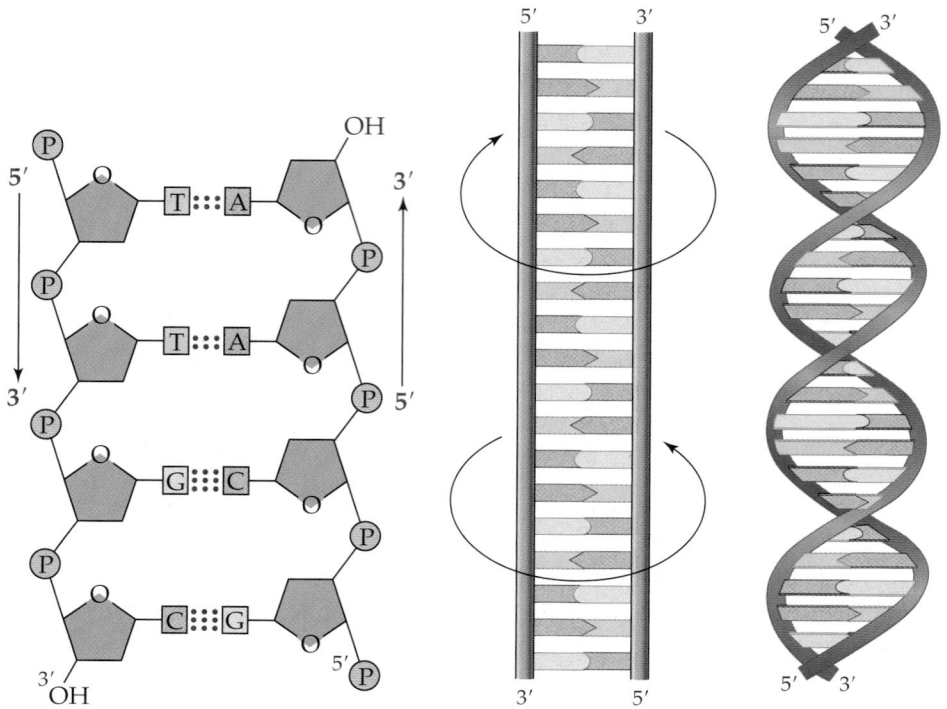

The two strands of the DNA double helix run in opposite directions—one in the 5′ to 3′ direction, the other in the 3′ to 5′ direction (the strands are said to be *antiparallel* to each other). The stacking of the hydrophobic bases in the interior and the alignment of the hydrophilic sugars and phosphate groups on the exterior provide stability to the structure. Hydrogen bonding also enhances DNA stability. Each pair of bases in the center of the double helix is connected by hydrogen bonding. As shown in Figure 26.2, adenine and thymine (A-T) form two hydrogen bonds to each other, and cytosine and guanine (C-G) form three hydrogen bonds to each other. Although individual hydrogen bonds are not especially strong, the thousands upon thousands along a DNA chain collectively contribute to stability of the double helix.

▶ **Figure 26.2**
Base pairing in DNA.
Hydrogen bonds (red dots) of similar lengths connect the pairs of bases; thymine with adenine and cytosine with guanine.

Thymine–Adenine

Cytosine–Guanine

The pairing of the bases linearly ordered along the two polynucleotide strands of the DNA double helix is described as *complementary.* Wherever a thymine occurs in one strand, an adenine falls opposite it in the other strand; wherever a cytosine occurs in one strand, a guanine falls opposite it on the other strand. This **base pairing** explains why A and T occur in equal amounts in double-stranded DNA, as do C and G.

The DNA double helix is shown in Figure 26.3. Both its strength and its shape depend on the fit and hydrogen bonding of the bases. As you will see, base pairing is also the key to understanding how DNA functions.

Base pairing The pairing of bases connected by hydrogen bonding (G-C and A-T), as in the DNA double helix.

Adenine Cytosine Guanine Thymine

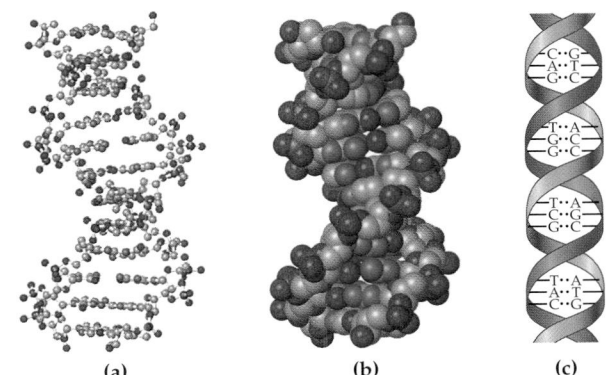

(a)   (b)   (c)

◀ **Figure 26.3**
A segment of DNA.
(a) In this model, notice that the base pairs are nearly perpendicular to the sugar–phosphate backbones. (b) A space-filling model of the same DNA segment. (c) An abstract representation of the DNA double helix and base pairing.

Worked Example 26.3 Writing Complementary Nucleic Acid Sequences

What sequence of bases on one strand of DNA (reading in the 3′ to 5′ direction) is complementary to the sequence 5′ T-A-T-G-C-A-G 3′ on the other strand?

ANALYSIS Remembering that A always bonds to T and C always bonds to G, go through the original 5′ to 3′ sequence, replacing each A by T, each T by A, each C by G, and each G by C. Keep in mind that when a 5′ to 3′ strand is matched in this manner to its complementary strand, the complementary strand will be oriented 3′ to 5′ when read from left to right. (If the direction in which a base sequence is written is not specified, you can assume it follows the customary 5′ to 3′ direction when read left to right.)

SOLUTION

Original strand	5′ T-A-T-G-C-A-G 3′
Complementary strand	3′ A-T-A-C-G-T-C 5′

PROBLEM 26.8

Write the complementary sequence of bases for each DNA strand shown next.

(a) 5′T-A-T-A-C-T-G 3′   **(b)** 5′G-A-T-C-G-C-T-C-T 3′

PROBLEM 26.9

Draw the structures of adenine and uracil (which replaces thymine in RNA), and show the hydrogen bonding that occurs between them.

PROBLEM 26.10

Is a DNA molecule neutral, negatively charged, or positively charged? Explain.

🔄 KEY CONCEPT PROBLEM 26.11

(a) DNA and RNA, like proteins, can be denatured to produce unfolded or uncoiled strands. Heating DNA to what is referred to as its "melting temperature" denatures it (the two strands of the double helix become separated). Why does a longer strand of DNA have a higher melting temperature than a shorter one? (b) The DNA melting temperature also varies with base composition. Would you expect a DNA with a high percentage of G-C base pairs to have a higher or lower melting point than one with a high percentage of A-T base pairs? How do you account for your choice?

26.5 Nucleic Acids and Heredity

Learning Objective:

• Describe how genetic information is duplicated, transferred, and expressed.

Your heredity is determined by the DNA in the fertilized egg from which you grew. A sperm cell carrying DNA from your father united with an egg cell carrying DNA from your mother. Their combination produced the full complement of chromosomes and genes that you carry through life. Each of your 23 pairs of chromosomes contains one DNA molecule copied from that of your father and one DNA molecule copied from that of your mother. Most cells in your body contain copies of these originals. (The exceptions are red blood cells, which have no nuclei and no DNA, and egg or sperm cells, which have 23 single DNA molecules, rather than pairs.)

Cell division is an ongoing process—no single cell has a life span equal to that of the organism in which it is found. Therefore, every time a cell divides, its DNA must be copied. The double helix of DNA and complementary base pairing make this duplication possible. Because of how bases pair, each strand of the double helix is a blueprint for the other strand. However, there are two remaining questions: How do nucleic acids carry the information that determines our inherited traits, and, how is stored information interpreted and put into action?

Genetic information is conveyed not just in the numbers and kinds of bases in DNA, but in the *sequence* of bases along the DNA strands; any mistakes in either copying or reading a given DNA sequence can lead to changes in the DNA code (called mutations), which may have disastrous consequences for the resulting daughter cells. Every time a cell divides, the information is passed along to the daughter cells, which ultimately pass this genetic information to their daughter cells. Within cells, the genetic information encoded in the DNA directs the synthesis of proteins, a process known as the *expression* of genes.

The duplication, transfer, and expression of genetic information occur as the result of three fundamental processes: *replication, transcription,* and *translation.*

Replication The process by which copies of DNA are made when a cell divides.

Transcription The process by which the information in DNA is read and used to synthesize RNA.

Translation The process by which RNA directs protein synthesis.

• **Replication** (Section 26.6) is the process by which a replica, or identical copy, of DNA is made when a cell divides, so that each of the two daughter cells has the same DNA (Figure 26.4).
• **Transcription** (Section 26.8) is the process by which the genetic messages contained in DNA are read and copied. The products of transcription are specific RNAs, which carry the instructions stored by DNA out of the nucleus and to the sites of protein synthesis.
• **Translation** (Section 26.10) is the process by which the genetic messages carried by RNA are decoded and used to build proteins.

In the following sections, we will look at these important processes. Replication, transcription, and translation must proceed with great accuracy and require participation by many auxiliary molecules to ensure the integrity (or fidelity) of the genetic information. Many enzymes working in harmony with one another, coupled with energy-supplying nucleoside triphosphates (NTPs), play essential roles. Our next goal in this chapter is to present a simple overview of how the genetic information is duplicated and put to work, as the full elucidation of these processes is still in progress.

26.6 Replication of DNA

Learning Objective:

• Explain the process of DNA replication.

DNA replication begins in the nucleus with partial unwinding of the double helix; this process involves enzymes known as *helicases.* The unwinding occurs simultaneously in many specific locations known as *origins of replication* (Figure 26.4). The DNA strands separate, exposing the bases and effectively forming a "bubble" in which the replication process can begin. At either end of the bubble, where double-stranded DNA and single-stranded DNA meet, are branch points known as *replication forks.* A set of multisubunit enzymes called DNA polymerases move into position on the separated strands—their

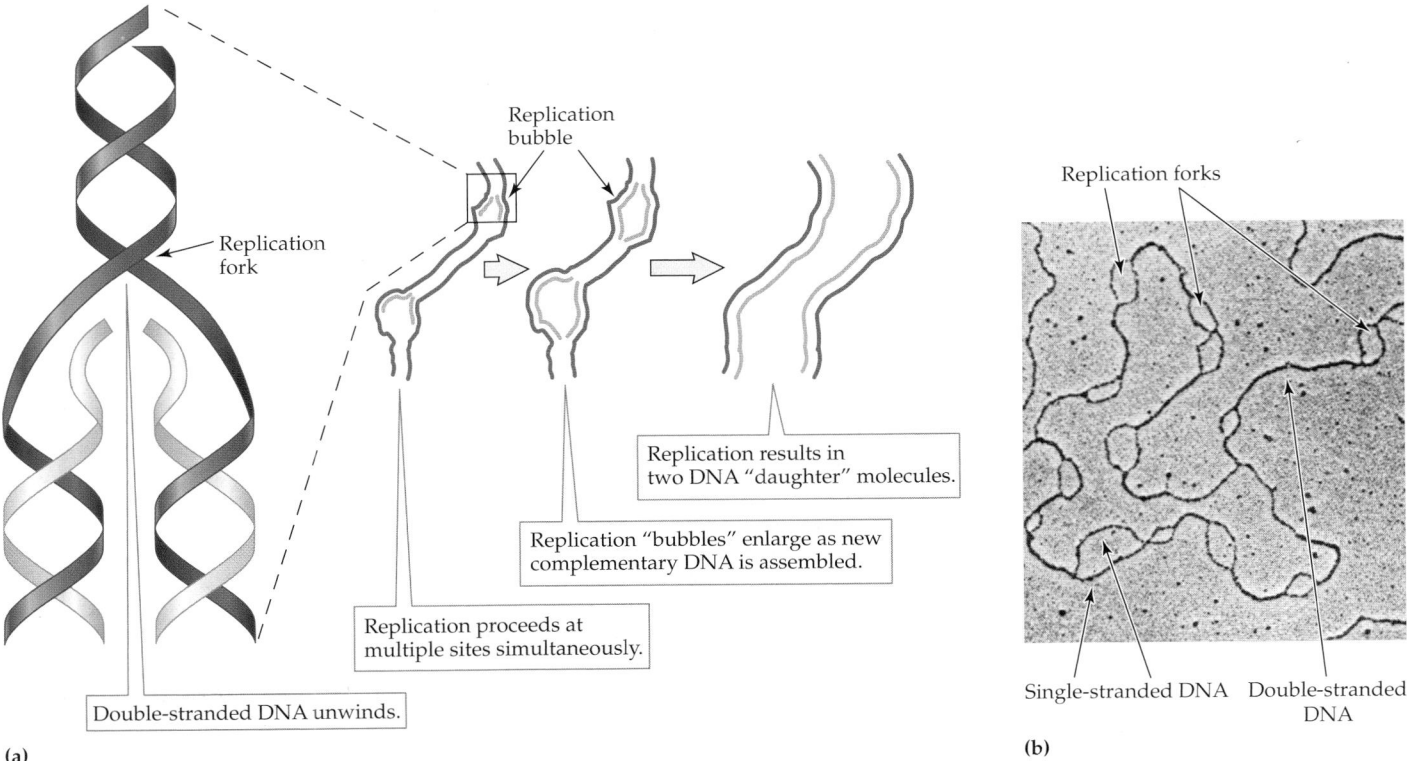

(a)

(b)

▲ **Figure 26.4**
DNA replication sites.
(a) Replication initiates at sites where the DNA unwinds, exposing single strands. This occurs in multiple locations simultaneously. (For simplicity, only one replication fork is shown.) (b) Electron micrograph of DNA. As DNA unwinds at multiple sites, single-stranded DNA is exposed and replication forks form at the junctions between single- and double-stranded DNA.

function is to facilitate transcription of the exposed single-stranded DNA. The NTPs carrying each of the four bases are available in the vicinity. One by one, the triphosphates move into place by forming hydrogen bonds with the bases exposed on the DNA template strand. A can only form hydrogen bonds with T, and G can only form hydrogen bonds with C. DNA polymerase then catalyzes covalent bond formation between the 5′ phosphate group of the arriving NTP and the 3′—OH at the end of the growing polynucleotide strand, as the two extra phosphate groups are removed.

Bond formation in DNA replication

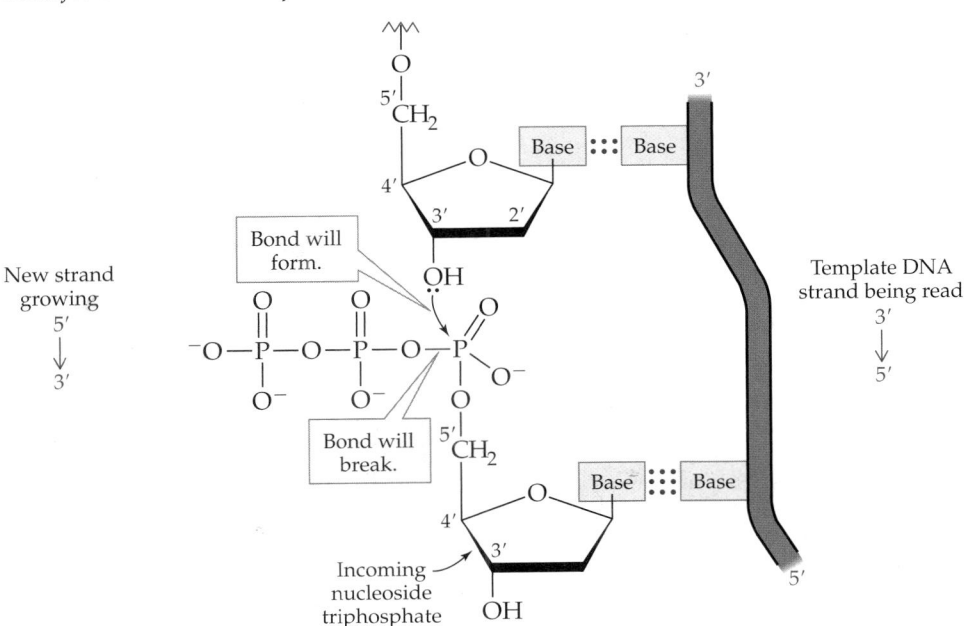

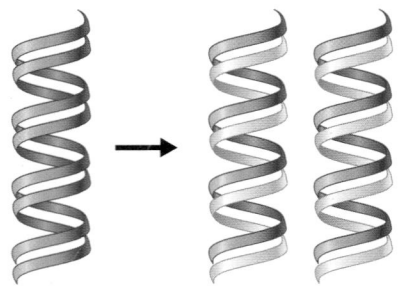

▲ Semiconservative replication produces a pair of DNA double helixes in which one strand (dark green) is the original strand and the other (light green) is the strand that has been copied from the original.

DNA polymerase catalyzes the reaction between the 5′ phosphate on an incoming nucleotide and the free 3′—OH on the growing DNA strand. Therefore, the template strand can only be read in the 3′ to 5′ direction, and the new DNA strand can grow only in the 5′ to 3′ direction.

Since each new strand is complementary to its template strand, two identical copies of the DNA double helix are produced during replication. In each new double helix, one strand is the template and the other is the newly synthesized strand. We describe the result as *semiconservative* replication (one of the two parent strands is conserved in each of the two new DNA molecules).

Note in Figure 26.5 that the incoming NTP is added to the 3′ end of the new strand. In other words, new DNA is synthesized in the 5′ to 3′ direction as the polymerase travels along the template strand in the 3′ to 5′ direction. Because the original DNA strands are antiparallel, only one new strand, known as the *leading strand,* is able to grow continuously as the point of replication (the *replication fork*) moves along. For the leading strand the DNA polymerase, traveling along the template in the 3′ to 5′ direction, is moving in the *same* direction as the replication fork. On the other strand, movement of the DNA polymerase along the template strand in the 3′ to 5′ direction means that the DNA polymerase is moving in the *opposite direction* as the replication fork. As a consequence, this other strand, called the *lagging strand,* is replicated in short segments called *Okazaki fragments* (after the Japanese scientist who discovered them). The directions of growth are shown in Figure 26.5, where the leading strand is the continuously growing strand of the new DNA and the lagging strand is the one composed of the short Okazaki fragments. To form the lagging strand from the Okazaki fragments, these short DNA segments are joined together by the action of an enzyme known as *DNA ligase.*

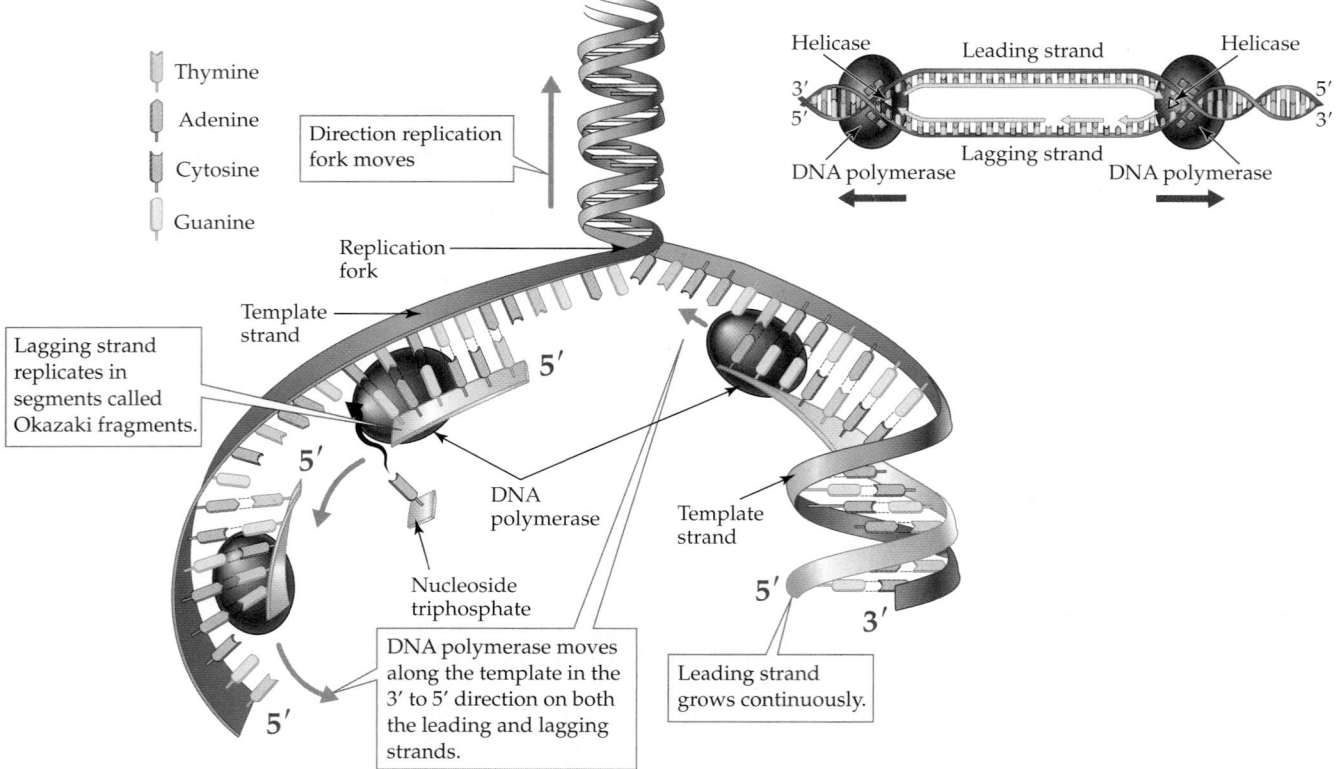

▲ **Figure 26.5**
DNA replication.
(a) Because the new polynucleotide chain must grow in the 5′ to 3′ direction, the leading strand (shown at the right, in light green) grows continuously toward the replication fork while the lagging strand (at the left in light green) grows in segments as the fork moves. The segments are later joined by a DNA ligase enzyme. (b) DNA polymerases at each replication fork travel along the DNA as more and more of it unwinds. The DNA polymerases are responsible for copying of the single-stranded DNA, generating new strands that grow in the 5′ to 3′ direction. One single strand, the leading strand, is copied continuously; the other single strand, called the lagging strand, is copied in segments.

The total number of base pairs in a human cell—the human **genome**—is 3 *billion* base pairs. The complete copying process in human cells takes several hours. To replicate a huge molecule such as human DNA at this speed requires not one, but many replication forks, producing many segments of DNA strands that are ultimately joined to produce a faithful copy of the original.

Genome All of the genetic material in the chromosomes of an organism; its size is given as the number of base pairs.

PROBLEM 26.12

What are Okazaki fragments? What role do they serve in DNA metabolism?

PROBLEM 26.13

What is the difference between DNA polymerase and DNA ligase?

26.7 Structure and Function of RNA

Learning Objective:

• List the types of RNA, their locations in the cell, and their functions.

RNA is similar to DNA—both are sugar–phosphate polymers and both have nitrogen-containing bases attached—but there are important differences (Table 26.2). We have already seen that RNA and DNA differ in composition (Section 26.2): The sugar in RNA is ribose rather than deoxyribose, and the base uracil in RNA pairs up with adenine rather than with thymine. RNA and DNA also differ in size and structure—RNA strands are not as long as DNA molecules. The RNAs are almost always single-stranded molecules (as distinct from DNA, which is almost always double-stranded); RNA molecules also often have complex folds, sometimes folding back on themselves to form double helices in some regions.

Table 26.2 Comparison of DNA and RNA

	Sugar	Bases	Shape and Size	Function
DNA	Deoxyribose	Adenine Guanine Cytosine Thymine	Paired strands in double helix; 50 million or more nucleotides per strand	Stores genetic information
RNA	Ribose	Adenine Guanine Cytosine Uracil	Single-stranded with folded regions; <100 to about 50,000 nucleotides per RNA	*mRNA*—Encodes a copy of genetic information ("blueprints" for protein synthesis) *tRNA*—Carries amino acids for incorporation into protein *rRNA*—Component of ribosomes (sites of protein synthesis)

There are also different kinds of RNA, each type with its own unique function in the flow of genetic information, whereas DNA has only one function—storing genetic information. Working together, the three types of RNA make it possible for the encoded information carried by DNA to be put to use in the synthesis of proteins.

• **Ribosomal RNAs** Outside the nucleus but within the cytoplasm of a cell are the **ribosomes**—small granular organelles where protein synthesis takes place. (Their location in the cell is shown in Figure 21.2, p. 663.) Each ribosome is a complex consisting of about 60% **ribosomal RNA (rRNA)** and 40% protein, with a total molecular mass of approximately 5,000,000 amu.
• **Messenger RNAs** The **messenger RNAs (mRNA)** carry information transcribed from DNA. They are formed in the cell nucleus and transported out to the ribosomes, where proteins will be synthesized. They are polynucleotides of varying length that carry the same code for proteins as does the DNA.
• **Transfer RNAs** The **transfer RNAs (tRNA)** are smaller RNAs that deliver amino acids one by one to protein chains growing at ribosomes. Each tRNA carries only one amino acid.

Ribosome The structure in the cell where protein synthesis occurs; composed of protein and rRNA.

Ribosomal RNA (rRNA) The RNA that is complexed with proteins in ribosomes.

Messenger RNAs (mRNA) The RNA that carries code transcribed from DNA and directs protein synthesis.

Transfer RNA (tRNA) The RNA that transports amino acids into position for protein synthesis.

26.8 Transcription: RNA Synthesis

Learning Objective:

• Explain the process of transcription, and write complementary strands through mRNA.

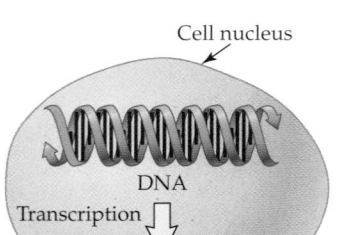

Cell nucleus

DNA

Transcription

mRNA

RNAs are synthesized in the cell nucleus. Before leaving the nucleus, all types of RNA molecules are modified in various ways that enable them to perform their different functions. We focus here on mRNA (in eukaryotes) because its synthesis (transcription) is the first step in transferring the information carried by DNA into protein synthesis.

In transcription, as in replication, a small section of the DNA double helix unwinds, the bases on the two strands are exposed, and one by one the complementary nucleotides are attached. rRNA, tRNA, and mRNA are all synthesized in essentially the same manner. Only one of the two DNA strands is transcribed during RNA synthesis. The DNA strand that is transcribed is the *template strand;* its complement in the original helix is the *informational strand.* The mRNA molecule is complementary to the template strand, which makes it an exact RNA duplicate of the DNA informational strand, with the exception that a U replaces each T in the DNA strand. The relationships are illustrated by the following short DNA and mRNA segments:

DNA informational strand	5′ ATG CCA GTA GGC CAC TTG TCA 3′	
DNA template strand	3′ TAC GGT CAT CCG GTG AAC AGT 5′	
mRNA	5′ AUG CCA GUA GGC CAC UUG UCA 3′	

The transcription process, shown in Figure 26.6, begins when RNA polymerase, an enzyme that synthesizes RNA, recognizes a control segment in DNA that precedes the nucleotides to be transcribed. *The genetic code,* which we will discuss in Section 26.9, consists of triplets of consecutive bases known as *codons.* The nucleotide triplets carried by mRNA code for amino acids to be assembled into proteins (Section 26.10). The sequence of nucleic

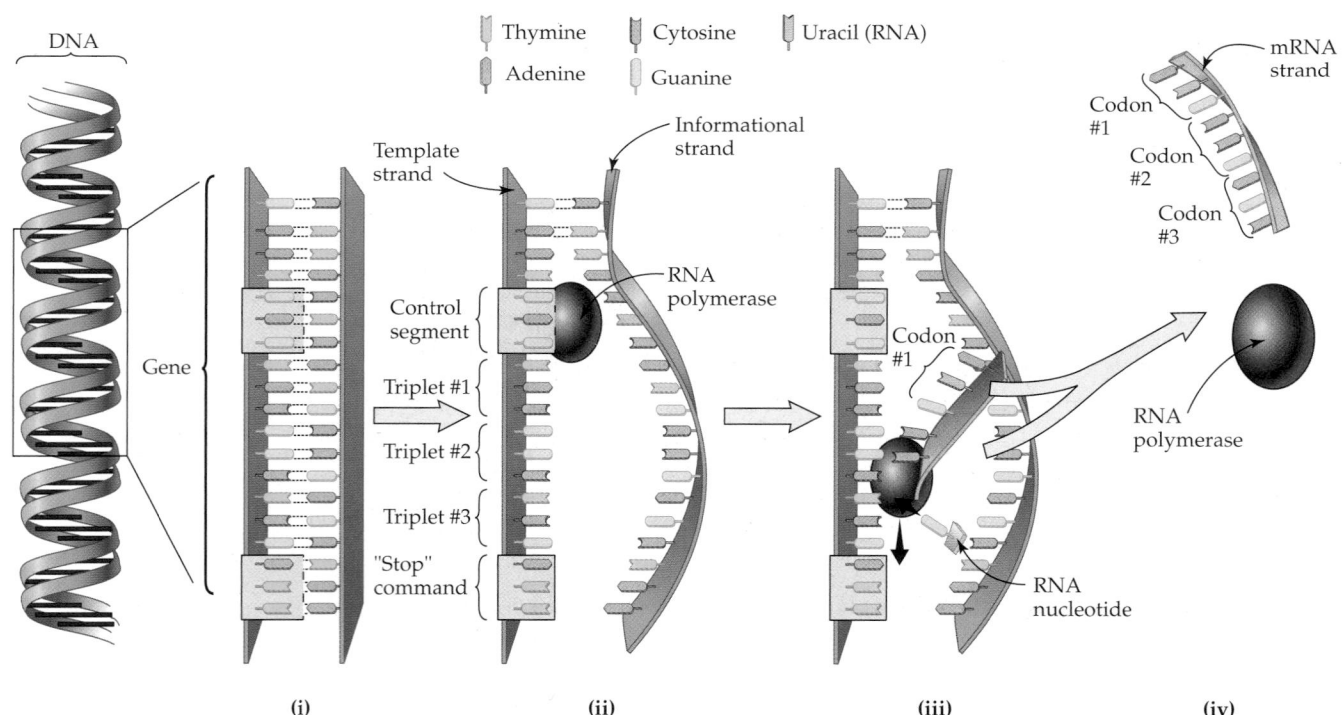

▲ **Figure 26.6**

Transcription of DNA to produce mRNA.
The transcription shown here produces a hypothetical three-codon mRNA. From left to right, (i) the DNA unwinds; (ii) the RNA polymerase connects with the control, or start, segment on the template strand; (iii) the mRNA is assembled as the polymerase moves along the template strand; and (iv) transcription ends when the polymerase reaches the stop command, releasing both the new mRNA strand and RNA polymerase.

acid code that corresponds to a complete protein is known as a *gene*. RNA polymerase moves down the DNA segment to be transcribed, adding complementary nucleotides one by one to the growing RNA strand as it goes. Transcription ends when the RNA polymerase reaches a termination sequence that signals the end of the sequence to be copied.

At the end of transcription, the mRNA molecule contains a matching base for every base that was on the informational DNA strand, from the site of transcription initiation to the site of transcription termination. The code for a gene is contained in one or more small sections of DNA called an **exon** (exons carry code that is *ex*pressed). The code for a given gene may be interrupted by a sequence of bases called an **intron** (a section that *in*tervenes or *in*terrupts) and then resumed farther down the chain in another exon. Introns are sections of DNA that do not code for any part of the protein to be synthesized. The initial mRNA strand (the "primary transcript"), like the DNA from which it was synthesized, contains both exons and introns and is known as **heterogeneous nuclear RNA (hnRNA)**. In the final mRNA molecule released from the nucleus, the intron sections have been cut out and the remaining pieces (consisting of the exons) are spliced together through the action of a structure known as a *spliceosome*.

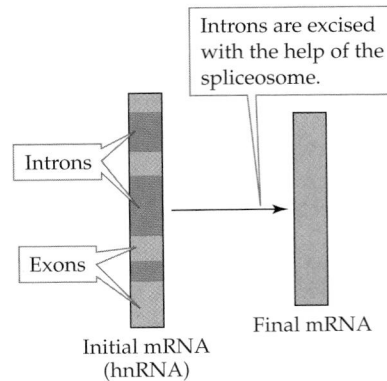

Introns are excised with the help of the spliceosome.

Introns

Exons

Initial mRNA (hnRNA)

Final mRNA

Exon A nucleotide sequence in a gene that codes for part of a protein.

Intron A nucleotide sequence in mRNA that does not code for part of a protein; removed before mRNA proceeds to protein synthesis.

Heterogeneous nuclear RNA (hnRNA) The initially synthesized mRNA strand containing both introns and exons.

Worked Example 26.4 Writing Complementary DNA and RNA Strands from Informational DNA Strands

The nucleotide sequence in a segment of a DNA informational strand is given here. What is the nucleotide sequence in the complementary DNA template strand? What is the sequence transcribed from the template strand into mRNA?

5'AAC GTT CCA ACT GTC 3'

ANALYSIS Recall:
1. In the informational and template strands of DNA, the base pairs are A-T and C-G.
2. Matching base pairs along the informational strand gives the template strand written in the 3' to 5' direction.
3. The mRNA strand is identical to the DNA informational strand except that it has a U wherever the informational strand has a T.
4. Matching base pairs along the template strand produces the mRNA strand written in the 5' to 3' direction.

SOLUTION
Applying these principles gives

DNA informational strand	5'AAC GTT CAA ACT GTC 3'
DNA template strand	3'TTG CAA GTT TGA CAG 5'
mRNA	5'AAC GUU CAA ACU GUC 3'

PROBLEM 26.14

What is the function of the spliceosome in hnRNA?

PROBLEM 26.15

What mRNA base sequences are complementary to the following DNA template sequences? Be sure to label the 5' and 3' ends of the complementary sequences.
   (a) 5'CAT GCT CTA CAG 3'   **(b)** 3'TAT TAG CGA CCG 5'

26.9 The Genetic Code

Learning Objective:

- Interpret mRNA codons from the genetic code, and write the primary sequence of a protein.

Codon A sequence of three ribonucleotides in the mRNA chain that codes for a specific amino acid; also a three-nucleotide sequence that is a stop codon and stops translation.

Genetic code The sequence of nucleotides, coded in triplets (codons) in mRNA, that determines the sequence of amino acids in protein synthesis.

The ribonucleotide sequence in an mRNA chain is like a coded sentence that spells out the order in which amino acid residues should be joined to form a protein. Each "word" consists of a triplet of ribonucleotides, or **codon,** in the mRNA sentence, which in turn corresponds to a specific amino acid. That is, a series of codons spells out a sequence of amino acids. For example, the series uracil-uracil-guanine (UUG) on an mRNA transcript is a codon directing incorporation of the amino acid leucine into a growing protein chain. Similarly, the sequence guanine-adenine-uracil (GAU) codes for aspartate.

Of the 64 possible three-base combinations in RNA, 61 code for specific amino acids and 3 code for chain termination (the *stop codons*). The "meaning" of each codon—the **genetic code** universal to all but a few living organisms—is given in Table 26.3. Note that most amino acids are specified by more than one codon and that codons are always written in the 5′ to 3′ direction.

Table 26.3 Codon Assignments of Base Triplets in mRNA

First Base (5′ end)	Second Base	Third Base (3′ end)			
		U	C	A	G
U	U	Phe	Phe	Leu	Leu
	C	Ser	Ser	Ser	Ser
	A	Tyr	Tyr	Stop	Stop
	G	Cys	Cys	Stop	Trp
C	U	Leu	Leu	Leu	Leu
	C	Pro	Pro	Pro	Pro
	A	His	His	Gln	Gln
	G	Arg	Arg	Arg	Arg
A	U	Ile	Ile	Ile	Met
	C	Thr	Thr	Thr	Thr
	A	Asn	Asn	Lys	Lys
	G	Ser	Ser	Arg	Arg
G	U	Val	Val	Val	Val
	C	Ala	Ala	Ala	Ala
	A	Asp	Asp	Glu	Glu
	G	Gly	Gly	Gly	Gly

The relationship between the DNA informational and template strand segments illustrated earlier is repeated here along with the protein segment for which they code.

DNA informational strand	5′ATG CCA GTA GGC CAC TTG TCA 3′
DNA template strand	3′TAC GGT CAT CCG GTG AAC AGT 5′
mRNA	5′AUG CCA GUA GGC CAC UUG UCA 3′
Protein	Met Pro Val Gly His Leu Ser

Notice that the 5′ end of the mRNA strand codes for the *N*-terminal amino acid, whereas the 3′ end of the mRNA strand codes for the *C*-terminal amino acid. (Remember, proteins are written *N*-terminal to *C*-terminal, reading left to right.)

Worked Example 26.5 Translating RNA into Protein

In Worked Example 26.4, we derived the mRNA sequence of nucleotides shown. What is the sequence of amino acids coded for by the mRNA sequence?

$$5'AAC \ GUU \ CAA \ ACU \ GUC \ 3'$$

ANALYSIS The codons must be identified by consulting Table 26.3. They are

$$5'AAC \ GUU \ CAA \ ACU \ GUC \ 3'$$
$$Asn \ \ Val \ \ Gln \ \ Thr \ \ Val$$

SOLUTION
Written out in full, the protein sequence is

asparagine-valine-glutamine-threonine-valine

HANDS-ON CHEMISTRY 26.1

In this activity, you will assemble an unwound section of DNA and then build a complementary section of mRNA (see Figure 26.6). Then, by using Table 26.3, you will determine the amino acids for the primary structure of a tripeptide (very small protein).

In this exercise, you will use colored drinking straws to represent nucleotides. If possible, select a package of drinking straws with five colors. If only four colors are possible, then one end of a color can be marked with a pen.

1. Cut each straw into four pieces. Follow the color code in Figure 26.6: T = blue, A = red, C = purple, G = green, and U = gray by matching the straw colors if possible. (If matching the Figure 26.6 colors is not possible, just assign each straw color a nucleoside; T, A, C, G, and for U use the color for T but mark it with a pen).

2. Look at Figure 26.6, part i. The template strand is on the left and the informational strand is on the right. In part ii, the control segment and stop command are highlighted. You will assemble the DNA from the control segment to the stop command. The template strand will begin with GAGTACGGCTCGATT. Remember, the mRNA complementary sequence is the same as the informational strand but uracil is present in mRNA and thymine is present in DNA. Take the pieces of straws

(the nucleotides), and put them in the order of the template strand in Figure 26.6, part i.

3. Next, put the pieces of straw that are complementary to the template strand to make the informational strand. Then, squeeze and fold one piece of the straw and connect it to its complementary base. This will represent the hydrogen bonding between the bases for the DNA template and informational strands.

4. Next, you must put the mRNA sequence in order. Since mRNA carries the codons needed for proteins, determine which straws are needed for the mRNA sequence from the template strand. Then, using Table 26.3, write down the amino acids you need from the codons in the mRNA. Do the straw colors for the mRNA matchup with the mRNA in Figure 26.6, part iv? How many amino acids do you need for the protein that is encoded in the DNA? Notice that in the mRNA the control segment and stop command are not represented.

5. Refer back to Problem 26.15. Assemble the template and informational strands for each part of Problem 26.15. Determine which colored straws are needed for the mRNA and determine which amino acids will be synthesized into a protein.

CHEMISTRY IN ACTION

Influenza: Variations on a Theme

Flu is caused by the influenza virus, where influenza A and B viruses cause human flu epidemics almost every winter. In the United States, these seasonal epidemics can cause illness in 10–20% of the human population and are associated with an average of 36,000 deaths and 114,000 hospitalizations per year.

Viruses are submicroscopic infectious agents that can replicate only inside living cells. Thousands of viruses are known, each of which can infect a particular plant or animal cell. Virus particles consist of only a few biomolecules: some nucleic acid (either DNA or RNA, which can be either single-stranded or double-stranded) and a protein coating (capsid) made of just a few proteins. Some viral classes also have a lipid coating over the capsid. How can something so small and with so few components cause the flu?

A virus particle cannot make copies of itself without a host cell providing the necessary cellular machinery. Once a virus enters a living cell, it takes over the host cell and forces it to produce virus copies, which then leave the host and spread the infection to other cells causing symptoms of the flu. To prevent illnesses from types A and B influenza, we can get a flu shot. However, the other influenza infection called type C causes a mild respiratory illness and are not thought to cause epidemics. Flu shots do not protect against type C influenza. Unfortunately, one shot does not protect you from influenza for life; you have to be re-immunized yearly because the influenza virus mutates rapidly, especially the protein coat. Since influenza viruses are ubiquitous, flu can cause either an epidemic or a pandemic. A disease that quickly and severely affects a large number of people and then subsides is an epidemic. A pandemic is a widespread epidemic that may affect entire continents or even the world. Both have occurred.

Can animals get the flu? The answer is yes. Many subtypes of influenza A viruses are also found in a variety of animals, including ducks, chickens, pigs, whales, horses, and seals. Birds are susceptible to all known subtypes of the influenza A virus and serve as reservoirs.

Influenza viruses that infect birds are called avian influenza viruses; first identified in Italy more than 100 years ago, these viruses occur naturally among birds worldwide. Wild birds, most notably migratory waterfowl such as wild ducks, carry the viruses in their intestines. Avian influenza is very contagious among birds. If infection does occur, domesticated birds, such as chickens, ducks, and turkeys, are particularly susceptible to infection, which either makes them very sick or kills them.

Humans also are susceptible to influenza A viruses, but avian influenza viruses do not usually infect humans due to subtype differences. However, several cases of human infection with avian influenza viruses have occurred since 1997. These viruses may be transmitted to humans directly from birds, from an environment contaminated by avian virus, or through an intermediate host, such as a pig. Because pigs are susceptible to infection by both avian and human viruses, they can serve as a "mixing vessel" for the scrambling of genetic material from

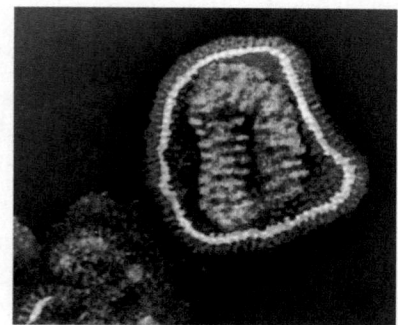

▲ A transmission electron micrograph of negatively stained influenza A virus particles.

human and avian viruses, resulting in the emergence of a novel viral subtype. For example, if a pig is infected with a human influenza virus and an avian influenza virus at the same time, the viruses can re-assort genes and produce a new virus that has most of the genes from the human virus but surface proteins from the avian virus. This process is known as an antigenic shift. This is how a new virus is formed—a virus against which humans will have little or no immunity and that may result in sustained human-to-human transmission and ultimately an influenza epidemic. Conditions favorable for the emergence of antigenic shift have long been thought to involve humans living in close proximity to domestic poultry and pigs. However, recent events suggest humans themselves can serve as the "mixing vessel." This scenario has frightening consequences; so frightening that the Centers for Disease Control and Prevention (CDC) considers the control of avian influenza to be a top priority. Luckily, the bird flu outbreak in 2006 was limited, although serious, and the swine flu pandemic of 2009 was not as virulent a strain as was first thought. That particular influenza A virus mixed genes from human, avian, and swine viruses, resulting in a novel virus to which humans had no immunity. The 2009 viral strain has some genetic similarities to an older influenza virus that had an alarmingly high mortality rate.

Scientists continue to monitor viral sub-strain shifts and drug companies prepare seasonal influenza vaccine based on predictions of what the next season's predominant viral strains will be. Work is also moving forward on a universal vaccine so that you can avoid the yearly shot and be immunized against influenza like you are against other common viral diseases such as measles.

CIA Problem 26.1 How do viruses differ from living organisms?

CIA Problem 26.2 What symptoms might a person have when infected with influenza A? influenza B? influenza C?

CIA Problem 26.3 Using a variety of sources, research which influenza types and strains are being implemented into the flu shot?

CIA Problem 26.4 Why is it difficult to develop a universal influenza vaccine?

PROBLEM 26.16

List possible codon sequences for the following amino acids.
  (a) Val   **(b)** Phe   **(c)** Asn   **(d)** Gly   **(e)** Met

PROBLEM 26.17

Identify the amino acid for which the codon GAG codes, and what other codon could encode for this same amino acid?

PROBLEM 26.18

What amino acids do the following sequences code for?
  (a) AUC   **(b)** GCU   **(c)** CGA   **(d)** AAG

PROBLEM 26.19

A hypothetical tripeptide Leu-Leu-Leu could be synthesized by the cell. What three different base triplets in mRNA could be combined to code for this tripeptide?

26.10   Translation: tRNA and Protein Synthesis

Learning Objective:

• Identify the initiation, elongation, and termination steps in translation for protein synthesis.

How are the messages carried by mRNA translated and how does the translation process result in the synthesis of proteins? Protein synthesis occurs at ribosomes, which are located outside the nucleus in the cytoplasm of cells. First, mRNA binds to the ribosome; then, amino acids, which are available in the cytosol, are delivered one by one by tRNA molecules to be joined into a specific protein by the ribosomal "machinery." All of the RNA molecules required for translation were synthesized from DNA by transcription in the nucleus and moved to the cytosol for translation.

Every cell contains more than 20 different tRNAs, each designed to carry a specific amino acid, even though they are all similar in overall structure. A tRNA molecule is a single polynucleotide chain held together by regions of base pairing in a partially helical structure something like a cloverleaf (Figure 26.7a). In three dimensions, a tRNA molecule is L-shaped, as shown in Figures 26.7b and c.

At one end of the L-shaped tRNA molecule, an amino acid is bonded to its specific tRNA by an ester linkage between the —COOH of the amino acid and an —OH group on the last ribose at the 3′ end of the tRNA chain. Individual synthetase enzymes are responsible for connecting each amino acid with its partner tRNA in an energy-requiring reaction. This reaction is referred to as *charging* the tRNA. Once charged, the tRNA is ready to be used in the synthesis of new protein.

At the other end of the tRNA, "L" is a sequence of three nucleotides called an **anticodon** (Figure 26.7). The anticodon of each tRNA is complementary to an mRNA codon—*always the one designating the particular amino acid that the tRNA carries.* For example, the tRNA carrying the amino acid leucine, which is coded for by 5′ CUG 3′ in mRNA, has the complementary sequence 3′ GAC 5′ as its anticodon on the tRNA. This is how the genetic message of nucleotide triplets, the codons, is translated into the sequence of amino acids in a protein. When the tRNA anticodon pairs off with its complementary mRNA codon, leucine is delivered to its proper place in the growing protein chain. The three stages in protein synthesis are *initiation, elongation,* and *termination.* These stages in translation are illustrated in Figure 26.8 and described in detail in the following sections.

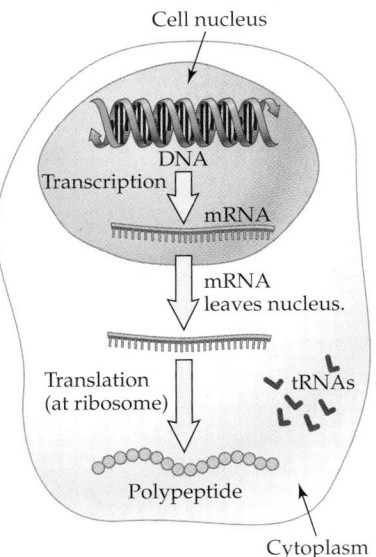

▲ Overview of protein synthesis. The codons of mature mRNA are translated in the ribosomes, where tRNAs deliver amino acids to be assembled into proteins (polypeptides).

Anticodon A sequence of three ribo-nucleotides on tRNA that recognizes the complementary sequence (the codon) on mRNA.

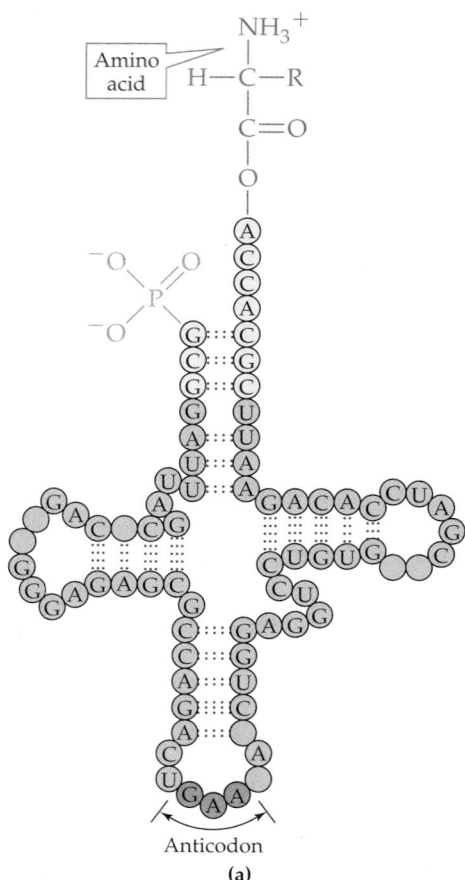

(a)

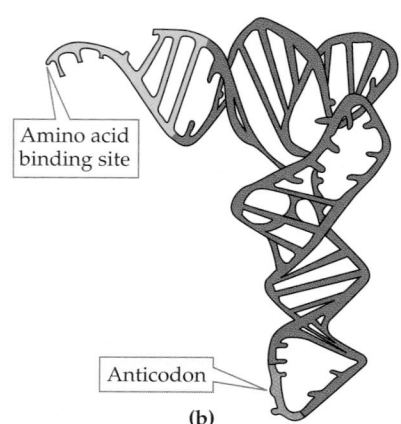

Amino acid binding site

Anticodon

(b)

▲ **Figure 26.7**
Structure of tRNA.
(a) Schematic, flattened tRNA molecule. The cloverleaf-shaped tRNA contains an anticodon triplet on one "leaf" and a covalently bonded amino acid at its 3′ end. The example shown is a yeast tRNA that codes for phenylalanine. All tRNAs have similar structures. The nucleotides not identified (blank circles) are slightly altered analogs of the four normal ribonucleotides. (b) The three-dimensional shape (the tertiary structure) of a tRNA molecule. Note how the anticodon is at one end and the amino acid is at the other end.

Ribozyme RNA that acts as an enzyme.

Translation Initiation

Each ribosome in a cell is made up of two subunits of markedly different sizes, called, logically enough, the *small subunit* and the *large subunit*. Each subunit contains protein enzymes and rRNA. Protein synthesis begins with the binding of an mRNA to the small subunit of a ribosome, joined by the first tRNA. The first codon on the 5′ end of mRNA, an AUG, acts as a "start" signal for the translation machinery and codes for a methionine-carrying tRNA. Initiation is completed when the large ribosomal subunit joins the small one and the methionine-bearing tRNA occupies one of the two binding sites on the united ribosome. Not all proteins have methionine at one end. If it is not needed, the methionine from chain initiation is removed by *posttranslational modification* before the new protein goes to work.

Translation Elongation

Next to the first binding site on the ribosome is a second binding site where the next codon on mRNA is exposed and the tRNA carrying the next amino acid will be attached. All available tRNA molecules can approach and try to fit, but only one with the appropriate anticodon sequence can bind. Once the tRNA with amino acid 2 arrives, a **ribozyme** in the large subunit catalyzes formation of the new peptide bond and breaks the bond linking amino acid 1 to its tRNA. These energy-requiring steps are fueled by the hydrolysis of guanosine triphosphate (GTP) to guanosine diphosphate (GDP). The first tRNA then leaves the ribosome, and the entire ribosome shifts one codon (three positions) along the mRNA chain. As a result, the second binding site is opened up to accept the tRNA carrying the next amino acid.

The three elongation steps now repeat:

- The next appropriate tRNA binds to the ribosome.
- Peptide bond formation attaches the newly arrived amino acid to the growing chain, and the tRNA carrying it is released.
- Ribosome position shifts to free the second binding site for the next tRNA.

A single mRNA can be "read" simultaneously by many ribosomes. The growing polypeptides increase in length as the ribosomes move down the mRNA strand.

Translation Termination

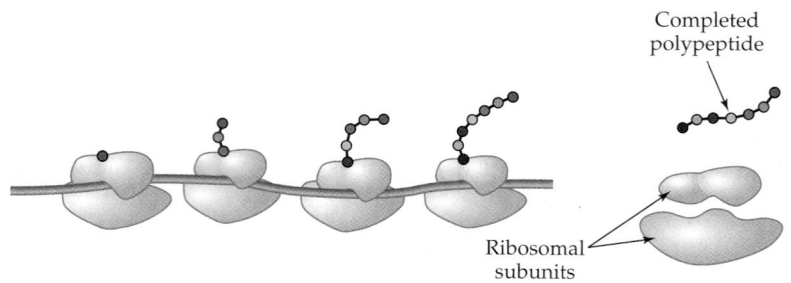

Completed polypeptide

Ribosomal subunits

When synthesis of the protein is completed, a "stop" codon signals the end of translation. An enzyme called a *releasing factor* then catalyzes cleavage of the polypeptide chain from the last tRNA; the tRNA and mRNA molecules are released from the ribosome, and the two ribosome subunits separate. This step also requires energy from GTP. Overall, to add one amino acid to the growing polypeptide chain requires four molecules of GTP, excluding the energy needed to charge the tRNA.

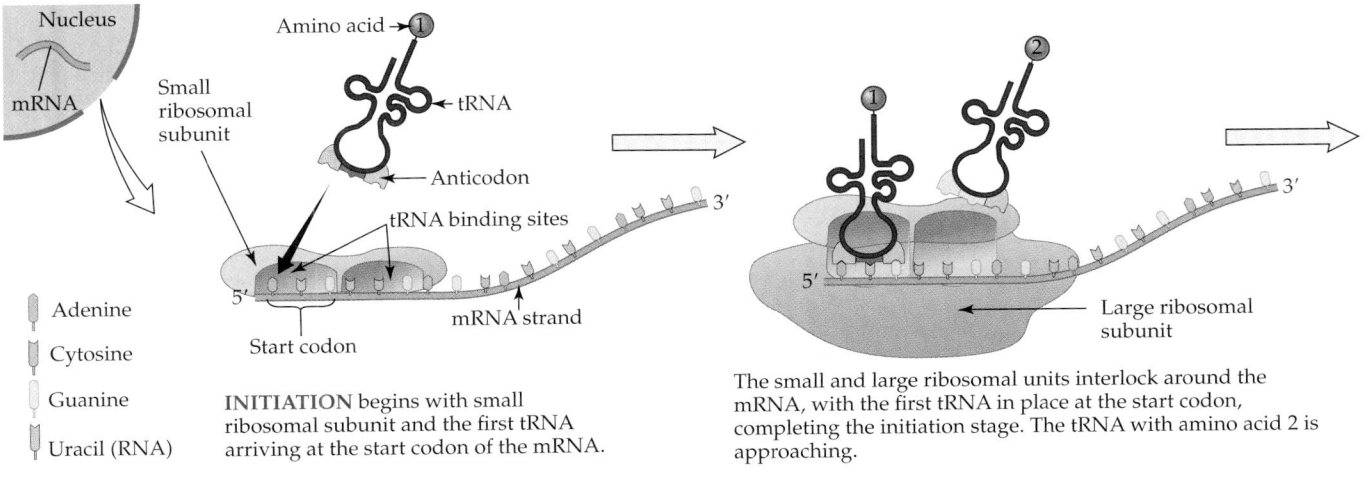

INITIATION begins with small ribosomal subunit and the first tRNA arriving at the start codon of the mRNA.

The small and large ribosomal units interlock around the mRNA, with the first tRNA in place at the start codon, completing the initiation stage. The tRNA with amino acid 2 is approaching.

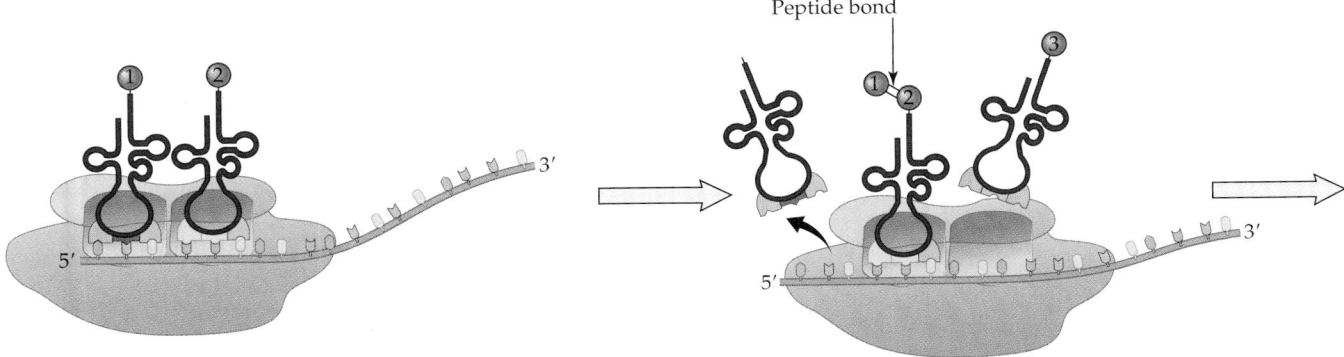

ELONGATION begins as the tRNA with amino acid 2 binds to its codon at the second site within the ribosome.

A peptide bond forms between amino acid 1 and 2, the first tRNA is released, the ribosome moves one codon to the right, and the tRNA with amino acid 3 is arriving.

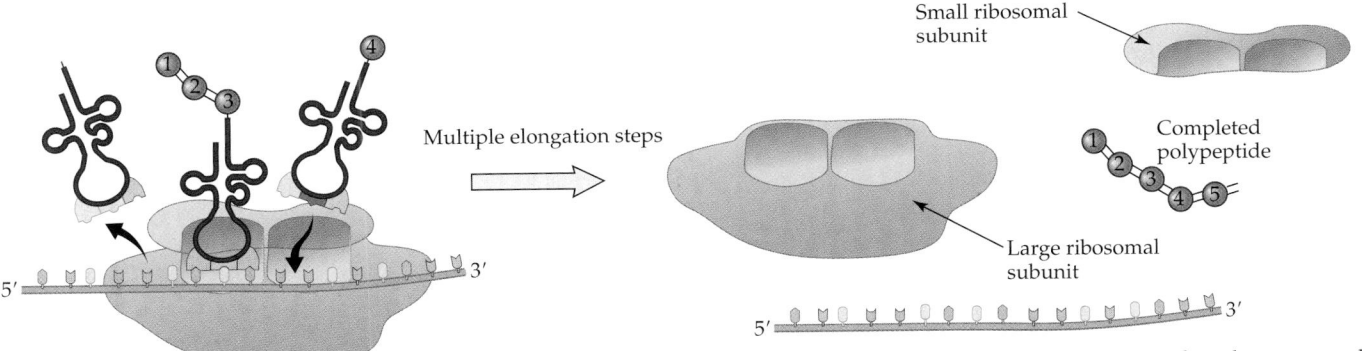

Elongation continues with three amino acids in the growing chain and the fourth one arriving with its tRNA.

TERMINATION occurs after the elongation steps have been repeated until the stop codon is reached. The ribosomal units, the mRNA, and the polypeptide separate.

▲ **Figure 26.8**
Translation: The initiation, elongation, and termination stages in protein synthesis.

PROBLEM 26.20

What amino acid sequence is coded for by the mRNA base sequence CUC-AUU-CCA-UGC-GAC-GUA?

PROBLEM 26.21

What anticodon sequences of tRNAs match the mRNA codons in Problem 25.20?

SUMMARY REVISITING THE CHAPTER LEARNING OBJECTIVES

- **Explain the role of chromosomes, genes, and DNA, and describe their basic function in the human body.** Chromosomes are molecular packages that contain all the information necessary for an organism to duplicate. Within chromosomes are genes that encode the synthesis of specific proteins primary structure or other functional molecules. Genes have a molecular makeup of DNA, which are very large molecules that contain genetic information (see Problems 28–31).

- **Describe, identify, and draw the components of nucleosides and nucleotides.** Nucleic acids are polymers of nucleotides. Each nucleotide contains a sugar, a base, and a phosphate group. The sugar is D-ribose in RNAs and 2-deoxy-D-ribose in DNAs. The C5—OH of the sugar is bonded to the phosphate group, and the anomeric carbon of the sugar is connected by an N-glycosidic bond to one of five heterocyclic nitrogen bases (Table 26.1). A nucleoside contains a sugar and a base but not the phosphate group (see Problems 32–35).

- **Describe and identify nucleic acid chains in DNA and RNA.** In DNA and RNA, the nucleotides are connected by phosphate diester linkages between the 3'—OH group of one nucleotide and the 5' phosphate group of the next nucleotide. DNA and RNA both contain adenine, guanine, and cytosine; thymine occurs in DNA and uracil occurs in RNA (see Problems 36–41).

- **Interpret the structure of DNA, and write complementary sequences.** The DNA in each chromosome consists of two polynucleotide strands twisted together in a double helix. The sugar–phosphate backbones are on the outside, and the bases are in the center of the helix. The bases on the two strands are complementary—opposite every thymine is an adenine, opposite every guanine is a cytosine. The base pairs are connected by hydrogen bonds (two between T and A; three between G and C). Because of the base pairing, the DNA strands are antiparallel: One DNA strand runs in the 5' to 3' direction and its complementary partner runs in the 3' to 5' direction (see Problems 42–46).

- **Describe how genetic information is duplicated, transferred, and expressed.** Human heredity is the combination of a full complement of chromosomes and genes. These 23 pairs of chromosomes are DNA molecules copied from the fertilized egg. However, in an ongoing process when a cell divides, the genetic information can be passed on to daughter cells. This genetic information not only depends on the number and kinds of bases in the DNA but also on sequences of the bases in the DNA. Through processes called replication, transcription, and translation, gene expression can occur through the encoded DNA (see Problems 47 and 50).

- **Explain the process of DNA replication.** Replication (Figure 26.5) requires DNA polymerases and deoxyribonucleoside triphosphates.

The DNA helix partially unwinds and the enzymes move along the separated DNA strands, synthesizing a new strand with bases complementary to those on the unwound DNA strand being copied. The enzymes move only in the 3' to 5' direction along the template strand (and thus new DNA strands only grow in the 5' to 3' direction), so that one strand is copied continuously and the other strand is copied in segments as the replication fork moves along. In each resulting double helix, one strand is the original template strand and the other is the new copy (see Problems 48 and 49).

- **List the types of RNA, their locations in the cell, and their functions.** mRNA carries the genetic information out of the nucleus to the ribosomes in the cytosol, where protein synthesis occurs. tRNAs circulate in the cytosol, where they bond to amino acids that they then deliver to ribosomes for protein synthesis. rRNAs are incorporated into ribosomes (see Problems 50 and 51).

- **Explain the process of transcription, and write complementary strands through mRNA.** In transcription (Figure 26.6), one DNA strand serves as the template and the other, the informational strand, is not copied. Nucleotides carrying bases complementary to the template bases between a control segment and a termination sequence are connected one by one to form mRNA. The primary transcript mRNA (or hnRNA) is identical to the matching segment of the informational strand but with uracil replacing thymine. Introns, which are base sequences that do not code for amino acids in the protein, are cut out before the final transcript mRNA leaves the nucleus (see Problems 52–55).

- **Interpret mRNA codons from the genetic code, and write the primary sequence of a protein.** The genetic information is read as a sequence of codons—triplets of bases in DNA that give the sequence of amino acids in a protein. Of the 64 possible codons (Table 26.3), 61 specify amino acids and three are stop codons (see Problems 56–67).

- **Identify the initiation, elongation, and termination steps in translation for protein synthesis.** Each tRNA has at one end an anticodon consisting of three bases complementary to those of the mRNA codon that specifies the amino acid it carries. Initiation of translation (Figure 26.8) is the coming together of the large and small subunits of the ribosome, an mRNA, and the first amino acid–bearing tRNA connected at the first of the two binding sites in the ribosome. Elongation proceeds as the next tRNA arrives at the second binding site, its amino acid is bonded to the first one, the first tRNA leaves, and the ribosome moves along so that once again there is a vacant second site. These steps repeat until the stop codon is reached. The termination step consists of separation of the two ribosome subunits, the mRNA, and the protein (see Problems 68 and 69).

KEY WORDS

Anticodon, p. 799	Exon, p. 795	Nucleic acid, p. 781	RNA (ribonucleic acid), p. 782
Base pairing, p. 789	Gene, p. 781	Nucleoside, p. 782	
Chromosome, p. 781	Genetic code, p. 796	Nucleotide, p. 781	Transcription, p. 790
Codon, p. 796	Genome, p. 793	Replication, p. 790	Transfer RNA (tRNA), p. 793
Deoxyribonucleotide, p. 784	Heterogeneous nuclear RNA (hnRNA), p. 795	Ribonucleotide, p. 784	Translation, p. 790
DNA (deoxyribonucleic acid), p. 781	Intron, p. 795	Ribosome, p. 793	
Double helix, p. 788	Messenger RNA (mRNA), p. 793	Ribosomal RNA (rRNA), p. 793	
		Ribozyme, p. 800	

CONCEPT MAP

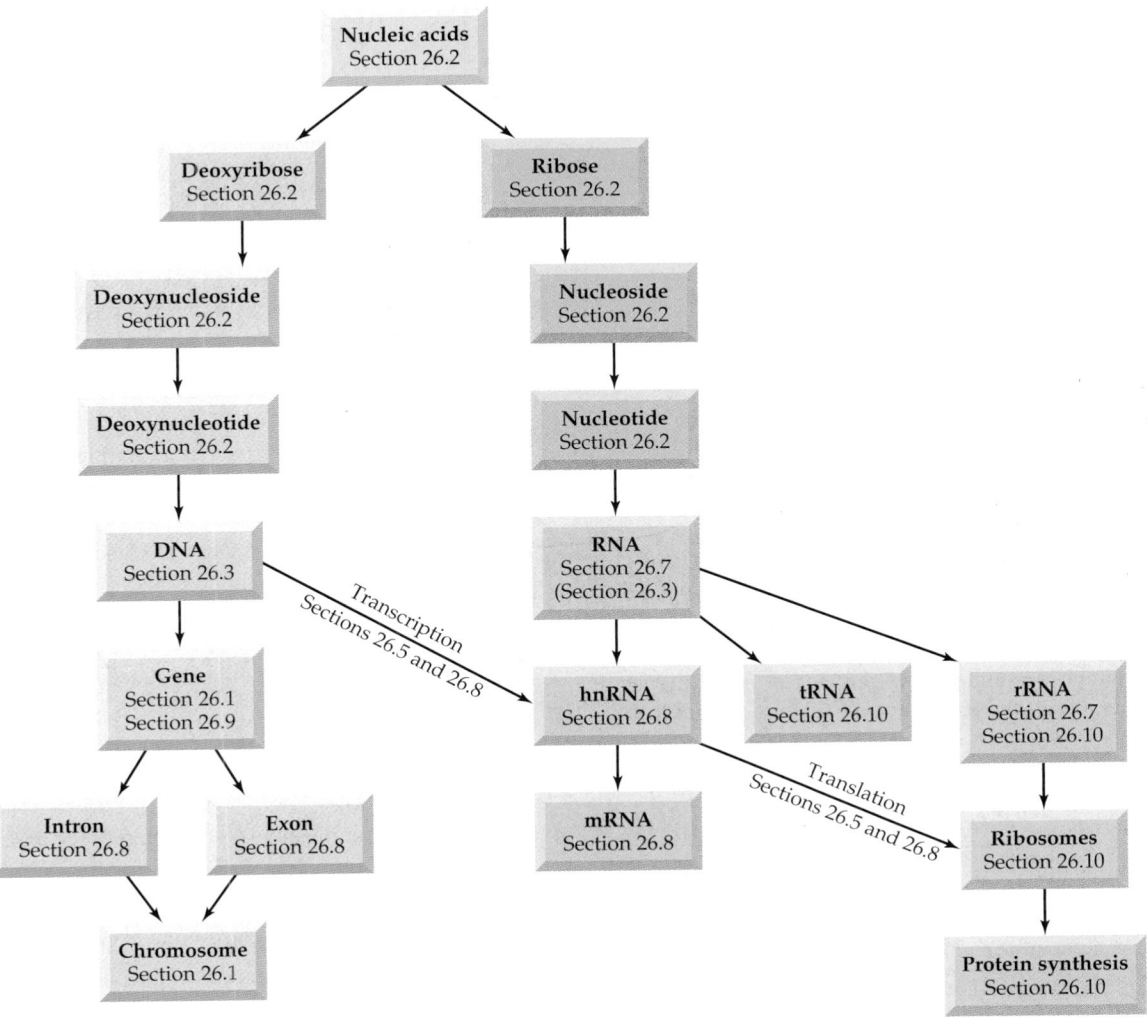

▲ **Figure 26.9 Concept Map.** This concept map shows the molecular structures in DNA and RNA as well as the process for protein synthesis.

◉━ UNDERSTANDING KEY CONCEPTS ──────

26.22 Combine the following structures to create a ribonucleotide. Show where water is removed to form an *N*-glycosidic linkage and where water is removed to form a phosphate ester. Draw the resulting ribonucleotide structure, and name it.

26.23 Copy the diagram to the right and use dotted lines to indicate where hydrogen bonding occurs between the complementary strands of DNA. What is the sequence of each strand of DNA drawn (remember that the sequence is written from the 5′ to 3′ end)?

26.24 Copy the following simplified drawing of a DNA replication fork:

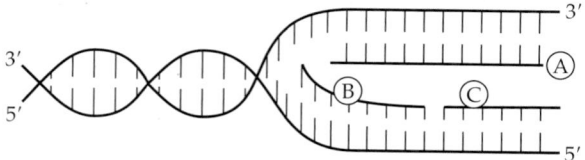

(a) On the drawing, indicate the direction of synthesis of the new strand labeled A and the location of DNA polymerase on the strand.

(b) On the drawing, indicate the direction of synthesis of the new strand labeled B and the location of DNA polymerase on the strand.

(c) How will strand C and strand B be connected?

26.25 What groups are found on the exterior of the DNA double helix? In the nucleus, DNA strands are wrapped around proteins called histones. Would you expect histones to be neutral, positively charged, or negatively charged? Based on your answer, which amino acids do you expect to be abundant in histones and why?

26.26 In addition to RNA polymerase, transcription of DNA for the synthesis of mRNA requires (a) a control segment of DNA (also called an initiation sequence), (b) an informational strand of DNA, (c) a template strand of DNA, and (d) an end of the sequence (termination sequence). Determine the direction of RNA synthesis on the RNA strand in the following diagram. Draw in the locations of elements (a)–(d).

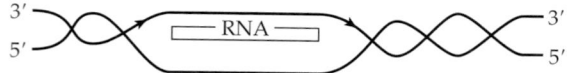

26.27 Gln-His-Pro-Gly is the sequence of a molecule known as progenitor thyrotropin-releasing hormone (pro-TRH). If we were searching for pro-TRH genes, we would need to know what sequence of bases in DNA we should be looking for. Use the following boxes to indicate answers to parts (a)–(d).

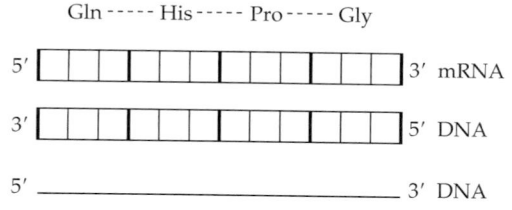

(a) What RNA sequence could code for these four amino acids?

(b) What double-stranded DNA sequence (gene) could code for these amino acids?

(c) Which strand of DNA is the template strand, and which is the informational strand?

(d) How many possible DNA sequences are there?

ADDITIONAL PROBLEMS

DNA, CHROMOSOMES, AND GENES (SECTION 26.1)

26.28 What is the difference between a gene and a chromosome?

26.29 What are the two major components of chromatin?

26.30 What genetic information does a single gene contain?

26.31 How many chromosomes are present in a human cell?

STRUCTURE AND FUNCTION OF NUCLEIC ACIDS (SECTIONS 26.2 AND 26.3)

26.32 For the following molecule:

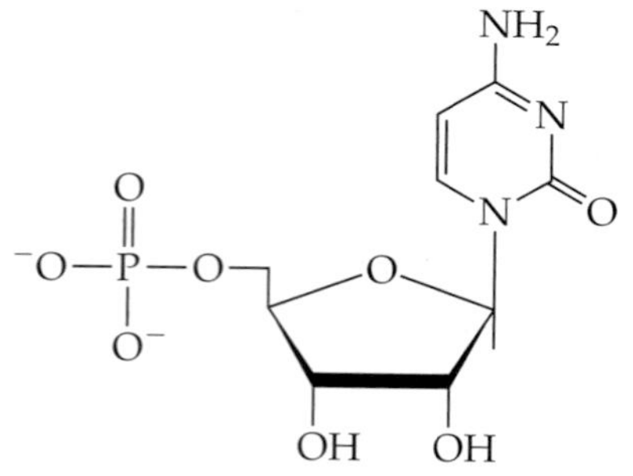

(a) Label the three nucleic acid building blocks it contains.

(b) Draw a box around the nucleoside portion of the molecule.

(c) Draw a circle around the nucleotide portion of the molecule.

26.33 What are the sugars in DNA and RNA, and how do they differ?

26.34 (a) What are the four major heterocyclic bases in DNA?

(b) What are the four major heterocyclic bases in RNA?

(c) Structurally, how do the heterocyclic bases in RNA differ from those in DNA? (See Table 26.1.)

26.35 What are the two structural types of bases in DNA and RNA? Which bases correspond to each type?

26.36 Draw structures to show how the phosphate and sugar components of a nucleic acid are joined. What kind of linkage forms between the sugar and the phosphate?

26.37 Draw structures to show how the sugar and heterocyclic base components of a nucleic acid are joined. What small molecule is formed?

26.38 What is the difference between the 3′ end and the 5′ end of a polynucleotide?

26.39 Are polynucleotides synthesized 3′ to 5′ or 5′ to 3′?

26.40 Draw the complete structure of uridine 5′-phosphate, one of the four major ribonucleotides.

26.41 Draw the complete structure of the RNA dinucleotide U-C. Identify the 5′ and 3′ ends of the dinucleotide.

BASE PAIRING (SECTION 26.4)

26.42 (a) What is meant by the term *base pairing*?

(b) Which bases pair with which other bases?

(c) How many hydrogen bonds does each base pair have?

26.43 What kind of intermolecular attraction holds the DNA double helix together?

26.44 What does it mean to speak of bases as being *complementary*?

26.45 The DNA from sea urchins contains about 32% A and about 18% G. What percentages of T and C would you expect in sea urchin DNA? Explain.

26.46 If a double-stranded DNA molecule is 22% G, what is the percentage of A, T, and C? Explain.

NUCLEIC ACIDS, REPLICATION OF DNA, AND STRUCTURE AND FUNCTION OF RNA (SECTIONS 26.5–26.7)

26.47 How are replication, transcription, and translation similar? How are they different?

26.48 Why is more than one replication fork needed when human DNA is duplicated?

26.49 Why do we say that DNA replication is semiconservative?

26.50 What are the three main kinds of RNA, and what are their functions?

26.51 Rank the following in order of size: tRNA, DNA, mRNA.

TRANSCRIPTION: RNA SYNTHESIS (SECTION 26.8)

26.52 The segment of DNA that encompasses a gene typically contains *introns* and *exons*. Define each of these terms.

26.53 What are some possible roles introns might have? What roles do exons have?

26.54 Transcribed RNA is complementary to which strand of DNA?

26.55 What is a codon and on what kind of nucleic acid is it found?

THE GENETIC CODE AND TRANSLATION (SECTIONS 26.9 AND 26.10)

26.56 What is an anticodon, and on what kind of nucleic acid is it found?

26.57 Which amino acid(s) have the most codons? Which amino acid(s) have the fewest codons? Can you think of a reason why multiple codons code for certain amino acids but other amino acids are coded for by very few codons?

26.58 Look at Table 26.3 and find codons for the following amino acids:

  (a) Val   **(b)** Arg   **(c)** Ser

26.59 What amino acids are specified by the following codons?

  (a) C-C-C   **(b)** G-C-G   **(c)** U-U-A

26.60 What anticodon sequences are complementary to the codons listed in Problem 26.59? (Remember that the anticodons are opposite in direction to the codons, so label the 3′ and 5′ ends!)

26.61 What anticodon sequences are complementary to the codons for the amino acids given in Problem 26.58? (Remember that the anticodons are opposite in direction to the codons, so label the 3′ and 5′ ends!)

26.62 If the sequence T-A-C-C-C-T appears on the informational strand of DNA, what sequence appears opposite it on the template strand? Label your answer with 3′ and 5′ ends.

26.63 Refer to Problem 26.62. What sequence appears on the mRNA molecule transcribed from the DNA sequence T-A-C-C-C-T? Label your answer with 3′ and 5′ ends.

26.64 Refer to Problems 26.62 and 26.63. What dipeptide is synthesized from the informational DNA sequence T-A-C-C-C-T?

26.65 What tetrapeptide is synthesized from the informational DNA sequence G-T-C-A-G-T-A-C-G-T-T-A?

26.66 Metenkephalin is a small peptide found in animal brains that has morphine-like properties. Give an mRNA sequence that could code for the synthesis of metenkephalin: Tyr-Gly-Gly-Phe-Met. Label your answer with 3′ and 5′ ends.

26.67 Refer to Problem 26.66. Give a double-stranded DNA sequence that could code for metenkephalin. Label your answer with 3′ and 5′ ends.

26.68 What is the general shape and structure of a tRNA molecule?

26.69 There are different tRNAs for each amino acid. What is one major way to differentiate among the tRNAs for each amino acid?

CONCEPTUAL PROBLEMS

26.70 A normal hemoglobin protein has a glutamic acid at position 6; in sickle-cell hemoglobin, this glutamic acid has been replaced by a valine. List all the possible mRNA codons that could be present for each type of hemoglobin. Can a single base change result in a change from Glu to Val in hemoglobin?

26.71 Insulin is synthesized as preproinsulin, which has 81 amino acids. How many heterocyclic bases must be present in the informational DNA strand to code for preproinsulin (assuming no introns are present)?

26.72 Human and horse insulin are both composed of two polypeptide chains with one chain containing 21 amino acids and the other containing 30 amino acids. Human and horse insulin differ at two amino acids: position 9 in one chain (human has serine and horse has glycine) and position 30 on the other chain (human has threonine and horse has alanine). How must the DNA differ to account for this? Identify the 5′ and 3′ ends of the four trinucleotide complementary DNA sequences.

26.73 If the initiation codon for proteins is AUG, how do you account for the case of a protein that does not include methionine as its first amino acid?

26.74 Suppose that 22% of the nucleotides of a DNA molecule are deoxyadenosine and during replication the relative amounts of available deoxynucleoside triphosphates are 22% dATP, 22% dCTP, 28% dGTP, and 28% dTTP. What deoxynucleoside triphosphate is limiting to the replication? Explain.

GROUP PROBLEMS

26.75 Imagine that you are part of a research team investigating new cures for HIV/AIDS. Discuss the HIV infection and locate stages in the infection that might be problematic to drug designs and cure.

26.76 Describe how the avian influenza virus is transmitted to humans. (See the Chemistry in Action "Influenza: Variations on a Theme," p. 798.)

26.77 Find 10 subtypes of influenza A, then divide the subtypes up. For each subtype, determine which species would be most infected by the subtype. In addition, find out if the subtype can be transmitted to another species.

26.78 The influenza virus H1N1 can infect both humans and other animals. Use the Internet to collect information that allows you to describe some of the similarities and some of the differences between the H1N1 virus and the virus responsible for avian influenza. (See the Chemistry in Action "Influenza: Variations on a Theme," p. 798.)

27

Genomics

CONTENTS

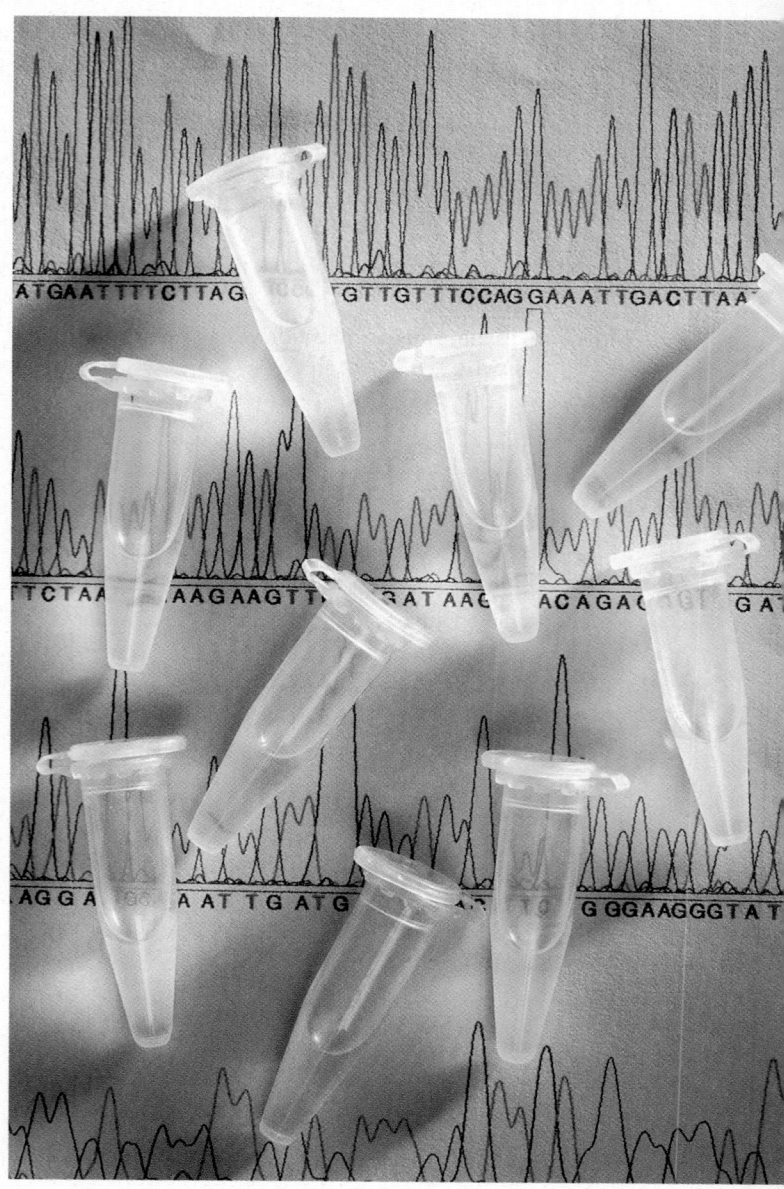

▲ The sequencing of DNA samples has led to advances in everything from medicine to criminal investigation.

◀◀◀ CONCEPTS TO REVIEW

A. Structure, Synthesis, and Function of DNA
(Sections 26.2 and 26.3)

B. Base Pairing and Heredity
(Sections 26.4 and 26.5)

C. Replication of DNA
(Section 26.6)

D. Transcription, Translation, and the Genetic Code
(Sections 26.8–26.10)

Imagine this: A "perfect" crime has been committed and all the investigators can find is a drop of the criminal's blood, or a cigarette butt, or some other trace evidence. Yet from that trace evidence they are able to get a deoxyribonucleic acid (DNA) sample and identify, catch, and convict the criminal. This "DNA fingerprinting" has arisen from the scientific revolution that research on DNA has provided. But how is DNA fingerprinting actually done, and why is it so important in criminal forensics? You will read about this in the Chemistry in Action "DNA Fingerprinting" found at the end of this chapter.

Scientifically, the crowning achievement of DNA research has been the complete and accurate mapping of the human genome. Creation of this map has been compared to such landmark achievements as harnessing nuclear power and flight into outer space. In significance for individual human beings, there has never been anything like it. In this chapter, we will examine how the human genome was mapped, the variations in the content of the DNA in each chromosome, how DNA can be manipulated, and ways in which genomic information can be put to use.

27.1 Mapping the Human Genome

Learning Objective:

• Describe how a genome is mapped.

Genomics has a simple and straightforward definition: It is the study of whole sets of genes and their functions. For example, the study of bacterial genomics not only gives us a better understanding of how bacteria cause disease, but has also led to new treatments. The analysis of plant genomics is allowing the production of agricultural crops with enhanced value and utility, whereas the genomic study of farm animals is leading to improvements in animal health. Humans ultimately benefit from these studies, and applying the techniques learned will eventually lead to improvements in our own health. All work in genomics begins with developing a genetic map for the organism being studied.

Genomics The study of whole sets of genes and their functions.

How to Map a Genome

What exactly is a genetic "map," and how is it established? While it is easy to think of it as a "turn-by-turn" set of directions one might get from a global positioning system (GPS), in reality a genetic map is more like a map you get when you visit a large amusement park. You may see the scary mansion in one corner of the map, the thrill rides in another, the kiddie-ride area in another, and so on, with all the paths that lead to them shown. The typical map of this type is made up of landmarks and their location with respect to each other. A genetic map is no different, with one huge exception: We do not know exactly what many of the landmarks represent. For example, one genetic landmark (or *marker*) might represent a gene for eye color, or it might simply be a specific pattern of repeating nucleotides. So, in effect, a genomic map is a physical representation of all the landmarks in a genome and where they are with respect to one another.

▲ A sample of DNA ready for analysis.

Mapping the genes on a eukaryotic chromosome is no easy feat. When you consider that the nucleotides that code for proteins (the *exons*) are interrupted by noncoding nucleotides (the *introns*) (see Section 26.8), it should be clear what mapping challenges exist for any organism whose genome contains only a few dozen genes. These challenges are greatly magnified for the human genome, which contains between twenty and twenty-five *thousand* genes! Another challenge to consider is that there is neither spacing between "words" in the genetic code nor any "punctuation." Using the English language as an analogy, try to find a meaningful phrase in the following:

sfdggmaddrydkdkdkrrrsjfljhadxccctmctmaqqqoumlittgklejagkjghjoailambrsslj

The phrase is "mary had a little lamb":

sfdg**g**m**addr**y**dkdkdkrrrsjflj**had**xccctmctmaqqqoum**littgklejagk**jghjoai**lambr**sslj

Now consider how hard finding meaning would be if the phrase you were looking for was in an unfamiliar language! It has been estimated that the string of Cs, Gs, Ts, and As that make up the human genome would fill 75,490 pages of standard-size type in a newspaper like *The New York Times.*

Two organizations led the effort to map the human genome: the Human Genome Project (HGP; a collection of 20 groups at not-for-profit institutes and universities) and Celera Genomics (a commercial biotechnology company). These two groups used different approaches to taking DNA apart, analyzing its base sequences, and reassembling the information. The HGP created a series of maps of finer and finer resolution (think of a satellite map program such as Google Earth, where you can progress from a satellite photo of the United States to a map of your state to a map of the city where you live to the street you live on and, ultimately, to a picture of the house you live in). Celera followed a seemingly random approach in which they fragmented DNA and then relied on instrumental and computer-driven techniques to establish the sequence (think of breaking a piece of glass into thousands of shards and then piecing them back together). It was believed that data obtained via the combination of these two approaches would speed up the enormous task of sequencing the human genome.

In October 2004, the HGP reported that 99% of the gene-containing parts of the genome were sequenced and declared to be 99.999% accurate. Additionally, the mapped sequence reportedly identifies correctly almost all known genes (99.74% of them, to be exact). At a practical level, this "gold-standard" sequence data allows researchers to rely on highly accurate sequence information, priming new biomedical research.

The strategy utilized by the HGP for generating the complete map is shown in Figure 27.1. Pictured at the top is a type of chromosome drawing, known as an ideogram (pronounced *id-ee-uh-gram*), for human chromosome 21. The light- and dark-blue shadings represent the location of banding visible in electron micrographs, first discussed in Section 26.6. Chromosome 21 is the smallest human chromosome, with 37 million base pairs (abbreviated 37 Mb) and was the second chromosome to be mapped (chromosome 22 was the first).

The first step is to generate a *genetic map*. A genetic map shows the physical location of *markers,* identifiable DNA sequences (some within genes, some within noncoding DNA) that are known to be inherited. In the human genome, the markers were an average of 1 million nucleotides apart. This is known as a genetic map because the order and locations of the markers are established by genetic studies of inheritance in related individuals.

The next map, the *physical map,* refines the distance between markers to about 100,000 base pairs. The physical map includes markers identified by a variety of experimental methods, most notably the use of *restriction enzymes* (discussed in Section 27.4).

▶ **Figure 27.1**
Human Genome Project mapping strategy.

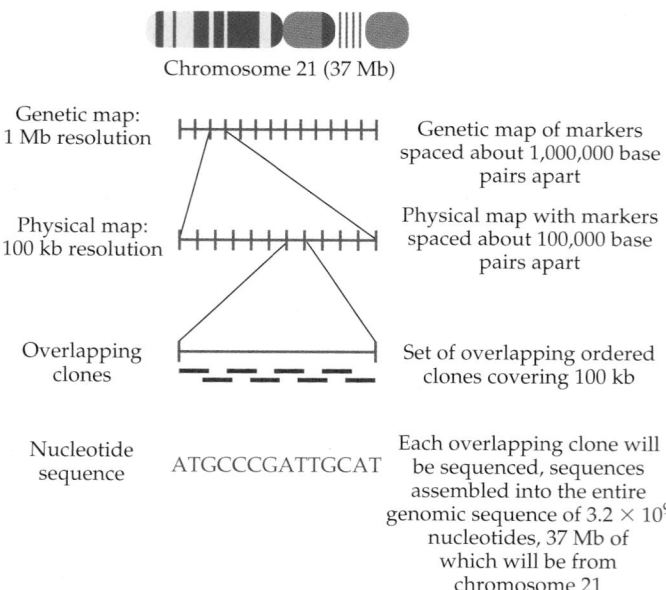

Chromosome 21 (37 Mb)

Genetic map:
1 Mb resolution — Genetic map of markers spaced about 1,000,000 base pairs apart

Physical map:
100 kb resolution — Physical map with markers spaced about 100,000 base pairs apart

Overlapping clones — Set of overlapping ordered clones covering 100 kb

Nucleotide sequence — ATGCCCGATTGCAT — Each overlapping clone will be sequenced, sequences assembled into the entire genomic sequence of 3.2×10^9 nucleotides, 37 Mb of which will be from chromosome 21

Clones Identical copies of organisms, cells, or DNA segments from a single ancestor.

To proceed to a map of finer resolution, a chromosome was cut into large segments and multiple copies of the segments were produced. The segment copies are called **clones,** a term that refers to identical copies of organisms, cells, or in this case, DNA segments. The overlapping clones, which covered the entire length of the chromosome, were arranged to produce the final level of the map (see Figure 27.1).

Each clone was cut into fragments containing 500 base pairs, and the order of bases in each fragment was determined. In the final step, all the different 500 base-pair sequences are assembled into a completed nucleotide map of the chromosome.

The approach taken by Celera Genomics was much bolder. In what has come to be known as their "shotgun approach," Celera broke the human genome into fragments without identifying the origin of any given fragment. The fragments were copied many times to generate many clones of each area of the genome; ultimately, they were cut into 500-base-long pieces and modified with fluorescently labeled bases that could be sequenced by high-speed machines. The resulting sequences were reassembled by identifying overlapping ends. At Celera, this monumental reassembly task was carried out using the world's largest nongovernmental supercomputing center.

PROBLEM 27.1

Decode the following sequence of letters to find an English phrase made entirely out of three-letter words. (Hint: First look for a word you recognize and then work forward and backward from there.)

uouothedtttrrfatnaedigopredsldjflsjfxxratponxbvateugfaqqthenqeutbadpagfratmeabrrx

27.2 DNA and Chromosomes

Learning Objective:

• Identify the genetic roles of telomeres, centromeres, exons and introns, and noncoding DNA.

Let us now examine the major regions and structural variations in the DNA folded into each chromosome. Understanding how DNA is structured should provide insight into the biotechnology revolution ushered in by the HGP.

Telomeres and Centromeres

At both ends of every linear chromosome are specialized regions of DNA called **telomeres.** Each telomere in human DNA is a long, noncoding series of a repeating sequence of nucleotides, $(TTAGGG)_n$. Telomeres act as "endcaps," or "covers," protecting the ends of the chromosome from accidental damage. Telomeres also prevent the DNA ends from fusing to the DNA in other chromosomes or to DNA fragments.

Another chromosomal region that contains large repetitive base sequences that do not code for proteins is the **centromere.** As the DNA in each chromosome is duplicated in preparation for cell division, the two copies remain joined together at a constricted point in the middle of the chromosome; this is the centromere. The duplicated chromosomes bound together at the centromere are known as *sister chromatids.*

Because of the repetitive nature of their sequences, neither telomeres nor centromeres were sequenced in the mapping projects described in Section 27.1.

Each new cell starts life with a long stretch of telomeric DNA on each of its chromosome ends, with over 1000 copies of the repeating group; in humans and other mammals this sequence is usually TTAGGG. Some of this repeating sequence is lost with each cell division, so that as the cell ages, the telomere gets shorter and shorter. A very short telomere is associated with the stage at which a cell stops dividing (known as *senescence).* Continuation of shortening beyond this stage is associated with DNA instability and cell death.

Telomerase is the enzyme responsible for adding telomeres to DNA. It is active during embryonic development. In adults, telomerase is only active in the germ cells destined to become egg and sperm. Under normal, healthy conditions, telomerase is not active in other adult cells (the *somatic* cells). There is widespread speculation that telomere-shortening plays a role in the natural progression of human aging. Some support for this concept comes from experiments with mice whose telomerase activity has been destroyed ("knocked out" in genetic research vernacular). These mice age prematurely, and if they become pregnant, their embryos do not survive.

What would happen if telomerase remains active in a cell rather than declining in activity with age? With the length of its telomeres constantly being replenished by telomerase, the cell would not age and instead would continue to divide. Continuing division is one characteristic of cancer cells; in fact, the majority of cancer cells are known to contain active telomerase, which is thought to confer immortality on these

◀◀◀ CONCEPTS TO REVIEW In Chapter 18, we saw how electrophoresis is used as a technique to separate proteins by charge or size (Chemistry in Action "Protein Analysis by Electrophoresis"). Gel electrophoresis is also routinely used with DNA to separate DNA molecules by size.

Telomeres The ends of chromosomes; in humans, telomeres contain long series of repeating groups of nucleotides.

Centromeres The central regions of chromosomes.

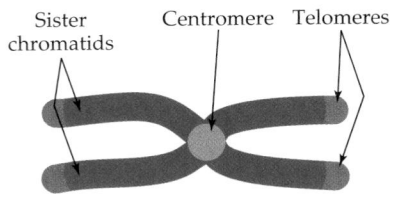

Sister chromatids Centromere Telomeres

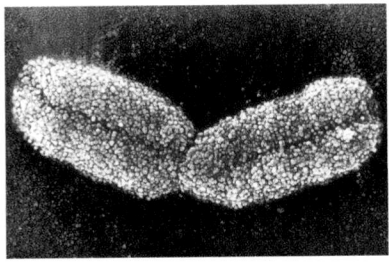

▲ Top: A duplicated chromosome immediately prior to cell division showing the locations of the telomeres and the centromere. Bottom: Color-enhanced electron microscope image showing the constriction of the centromere during metaphase.

tumor cells. Where this activity stands in relation to the presence of cancer-causing genes and environmental factors is not yet understood because neither amplification nor mutation of the telomerase gene has been identified in tumors; it is simply active when normally it would not be. As a result, a causal role for telomerase in tumor formation has yet to be established. Current research suggests that it is the genes responsible for regulating telomerase expression that are altered in cancer cells. As you might suspect, there are ongoing experiments on the consequences of telomerase inactivation on cancer cells. Additionally, scientists are examining the role that telomerase might play in achieving a sort of human "immortality," at least from a cellular standpoint.

Noncoding DNA

In addition to the noncoding telomeres, centromeres, and introns along a chromosome, there are noncoding promoter sequences, which are regulatory regions of DNA that determine which of its genes are turned on. All of your cells (except red blood cells) contain all of your genes, but only the genes needed by any individual cell will be activated in that cell. As of 2014, researchers have confirmed the existence of approximately 19,000 protein-coding genes in the human genome (versus the 100,000 genes originally estimated to exist); this number keeps shrinking as more research is done. This current data suggests that only about 1.5% of all DNA in the human genome actually codes for protein. It is interesting to note that the human genome has much more noncoding DNA (once referred to as "junk" DNA) than do the genomes known for other organisms. This evidence raises the question of the role played by the vast amount of noncoding DNA present in our genome. The question arises out of the observation that genome size does not correlate with organismal complexity, with one example being that many plants have larger genomes than humans. Some scientists have suggested that the segments of noncoding DNA are needed to accommodate the folding of DNA within the nucleus, others think these segments may have played a role in evolution, while still others argue that the segments are functional but the functions are not yet understood. The function of noncoding DNA remains to be discovered; meanwhile the debate over its role continues to this day.

Genes

In learning about transcription (Section 26.8), you saw that the nucleotides of a single gene are not consecutive along a stretch of DNA but have coding (expressed) segments (the *exons*) that alternate with noncoding (interruption) segments (the *introns*). As an example, consider a "small," 2900-nucleotide sequence found in a much simpler organism (corn) that codes for the enzyme triose phosphate isomerase.

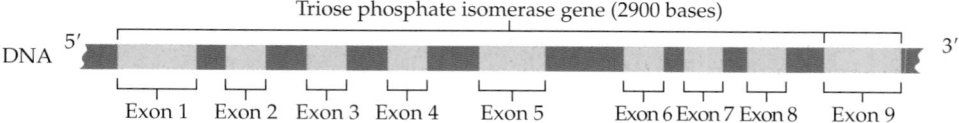

This gene consists of nine exons (in yellow) that account for 759 of the 2900 nucleotides (26%), with the eight introns (in green) accounting for the remaining bases. Now consider a more complex genome such as ours, where only 1–2% of genetic material is coding sequence. Take, for example, chromosome 22. It is one of the smaller human chromosomes and was the first to have all of its nonrepetitive DNA sequenced and mapped. Chromosome 22 is of medical interest because it carries genes known to be associated with the immune system as well as disorders such as congenital heart disease, schizophrenia, leukemia, various cancers, and many other genetically related conditions. The chromosome map identified 49 million bases containing approximately 693 genes, with an average of eight exons and seven introns per gene. The map also revealed several hundred previously unknown genes. With the signal (exon) to noise (intron) ratio being so low (meaning more noise to hide the signal) in the human genome, it will be challenging to completely identify all the coding sequences present.

27.3   Mutations and Polymorphisms

Learning Objectives:

- Describe a mutation and what can result from one.
- Define polymorphisms and SNPs, and explain the significance of the locations of SNPs.

▲ An error in nucleic acid composition that occurs once in 3–4 million lobsters is responsible for the beautiful color of this crustacean.

The base-pairing mechanism of DNA replication and ribonucleic acid (RNA) transcription provides an extremely efficient and accurate method for preserving and using genetic information, but it is not perfect. Occasionally, an error occurs, resulting in the incorporation of an incorrect base at some point.

An occasional error during the transcription of a messenger RNA (mRNA) molecule may not create a serious problem, since large numbers of mRNA molecules are continually being produced. An error that occurs perhaps one out of a million times would hardly be noticed in the presence of many correct mRNAs. If an error occurs during the replication of a DNA molecule, however, the consequences can be far more damaging. Each chromosome in a cell contains only *one* kind of DNA, and if this template is miscopied during replication, then the error is passed on when the cell divides.

An error in base sequence that is carried along during DNA replication is called a **mutation.** Mutation commonly refers to variations in DNA sequence found in a very small number of individuals of a species. Some mutations result from spontaneous and random events. Others are induced by exposure to a **mutagen**—an external agent that can cause a mutation. Viruses, chemicals, and ionizing radiation can all be mutagenic.

Mutation A rare DNA variant; an error in base sequence that is carried along in DNA replication and passed on to the offspring.

Mutagen A substance that causes mutations.

The biological effects of incorporating an incorrect amino acid into a protein range from negligible to catastrophic, depending on both the nature and location of the change. There are thousands of known human hereditary diseases. Some of the more common ones are listed in Table 27.1. Mutations, or sometimes the combination of several mutations, can also produce vulnerability to certain diseases, which may or may not develop in an individual.

Table 27.1 Some Common Hereditary Diseases, Their Causes, and Their Prevalence

Name	Nature and Cause of Defect	Prevalence in Population
Phenylketonuria (PKU)	Brain damage in infants caused by the defective enzyme phenylalanine hydroxylase	1 in 40,000
Albinism	Absence of skin pigment caused by the defective enzyme tyrosinase	1 in 20,000
Tay-Sachs disease	Mental retardation caused by a defect in production of the enzyme hexosaminidase A	1 in 6000 (Ashkenazi Jews); 1 in 100,000 (General population)
Cystic fibrosis	Bronchopulmonary, liver, and pancreatic obstructions by thickened mucus; defective gene and protein identified	1 in 3000
Sickle-cell anemia	Anemia and obstruction of blood flow caused by a defect in hemoglobin	1 in 185 (African Americans)

Polymorphisms are also variations in the nucleotide sequence of DNA within a given population. Most polymorphisms are simply differences in the DNA sequence between individuals due to geographical and ethnic differences and are part of the biodiversity exhibited by life on earth. While the vast majority of polymorphisms recorded have neither advantageous nor deleterious effects, some do and have been shown to give rise to various disease states. The locations of polymorphisms responsible for some inherited human diseases are shown in Figure 27.2.

Polymorphism A variation in DNA sequence within a population.

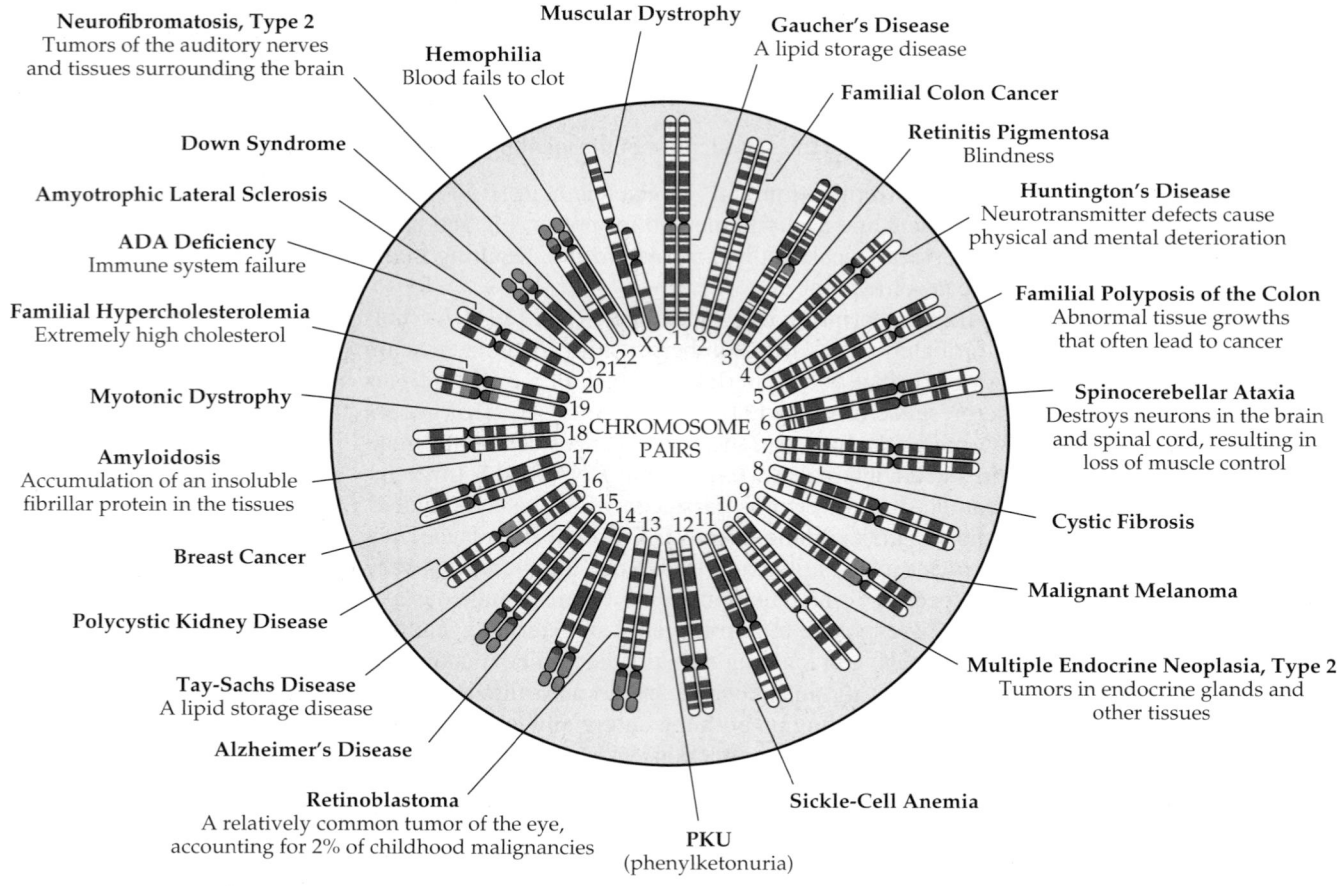

▲ **Figure 27.2**
A human chromosome map.
Regions on each chromosome that have been identified as responsible for inherited diseases are indicated.

HANDS-ON CHEMISTRY 27.1

Table 27.1 shows five common hereditary diseases, but there are many more. In this exercise you are going to choose one of the diseases listed next and research various aspects of it. This exercise may be assigned as a class project, if your instructor wishes, by assigning a group of students to each disease and having 5–10 minute classroom presentations on their findings. You will need an internet connection to do this activity.

a. Choose one of the following genetic disorders to study:
- Angelman syndrome
- Canavan disease
- Charcot–Marie–Tooth disease
- Cri du chat
- Klinefelter syndrome
- Prader–Willi syndrome
- Becker's muscular dystrophy
- Hemochromatosis

(If done as a class project, your instructor may choose which to assign.)

b. For the disorder you have chosen, determine the following:
1. History (including other names it may be known by)
2. Prevalence in the population of your country and worldwide
3. Genetic mutation and where the mutation is found
4. Symptoms and treatment
5. Prognosis
6. Current research, including gene therapy if applicable.

c. Finally, pretend you are a physician, a nurse, or a genetic counselor. Write a short paragraph outlining what and how you would tell the parents of a child who you had diagnosed with the disorder. Remember, the person you are going to talk to may have NEVER taken this class!

Single-Nucleotide Polymorphism and Disease

The replacement of one nucleotide by another in the same location along the DNA sequence is known as a **single-nucleotide polymorphism** (**SNP,** pronounced "snip"). In other words, two different nucleotides at the same position along two defined stretches of DNA are SNPs. A SNP is expected to occur in at least 1% of a specific population and therefore provides a link to a genetic characteristic of that population.

The biological effects of SNPs can be wide ranging, from being negligible to being normal variations such as those in eye or hair color, to being genetic diseases. *SNPs are the most common source of variations between individual human beings.* Most genes carry one or more SNPs, and in different individuals most SNPs occur in the same location.

Imagine that the sequence A-T-G on the informational strand of DNA is replaced with the sequence A-C-G (an SNP); now the mRNA produced will have the codon sequence A-C-G rather than the intended sequence A-U-G. Because A-C-G codes for threonine, whereas A-U-G codes for methionine, threonine will be inserted into the corresponding protein during translation. Furthermore, every copy of the protein will have the same variation. The seriousness of the outcome depends on the function of the protein and the effect of the amino acid change on its structure and activity.

In addition to producing a change in the identity of an amino acid, a SNP might specify the same amino acid (e.g., changing GUU to GUC, both of which code for valine) or it might terminate protein synthesis by introducing a stop codon (like changing CGA to UGA).

Industrial and academic scientists are compiling a catalog of SNPs. Their frequency is roughly one SNP for about every 300 nucleotides, with many of them in coding regions. Knowing their exact locations may one day help doctors to predict an individual's risk of developing a disease.

We have described the single amino acid change that results in sickle-cell anemia. It took years of research to identify the SNP responsible for that disease. Had a computerized catalog of SNPs been available at the time, it might have been found in a few hours. Another known SNP is associated with the risk of developing Alzheimer's disease. Not all SNPs create susceptibility to diseases; for example, there is also one that imparts a resistance to human immunodeficiency virus (HIV) and acquired immunodeficiency syndrome (AIDS). Most SNPs have neither advantageous nor deleterious effects on the organism.

The SNP catalog, although far from complete, has been valuable from the start. It has been used to locate SNPs responsible for 30 abnormal conditions, including total color blindness, one type of epilepsy, and susceptibility to the development of breast cancer. For example, examination of the DNA from prostate cancer patients showed that cataloged SNPs occur in four combinations in these people. The next step is to hunt down the role of each of those four genetic variations in the disease. It is hoped that this information will inspire the development of new treatments for diseases. As of June 2015, the SNP catalog maintained by the National Human Genome Research Institute contains over 147 *million* SNP entries and correlation to diseases is growing at an ever increasing pace (one estimate is over 14,000 diseases have been correlated to SNPs).

The cataloging of SNPs has ushered in the era of genetic medicine. Ultimately, the SNP catalog may allow physicians to predict for an individual the potential age at which inherited diseases will become active, their severity, and their reactions to various types of treatment. The therapeutic course will be designed to meet the distinctive genomic profile of the person.

Single-nucleotide polymorphism (SNP) Common single base-pair variation in DNA.

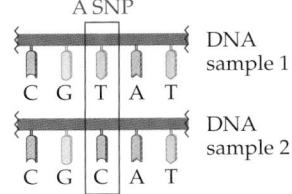

The mutation leading to sickle-cell anemia is described in the Chemistry in Action "What Is Sickle-Cell Anemia?" found in Chapter 18.

CHEMISTRY IN ACTION

The Polymerase Chain Reaction

Before the 1980s, studying DNA involved the frustration of working with very small, hard-to-obtain samples. Everyone wished there was a way to copy DNA, to make millions of copies of a sample. As a result, scientists focused on making this wish a reality. The outcome was the development and automation of the *polymerase chain reaction (PCR)*, which today can be carried out easily in any molecular biology lab. PCR is so common and so simple a technique that it is routinely taught and carried out in undergraduate lab courses.

The goal of PCR is to produce many copies of a specific segment of DNA. The DNA might be part of a genome study, it might be from a crime scene or a fossil, or it might be from a specimen preserved as a medical record. The raw materials required for the reaction are a DNA sample that contains the nucleotide sequence to be amplified, *primers* (short synthetic oligonucleotides with bases complementary to the sequences flanking the sequence of interest), the deoxyribonucleoside triphosphates that carry the four DNA bases, and a DNA polymerase enzyme that will create a copy of the DNA between the primers.

The reaction is carried out in three steps:

STEP 1: Heating of the DNA sample to cause the helix to unravel into single strands:

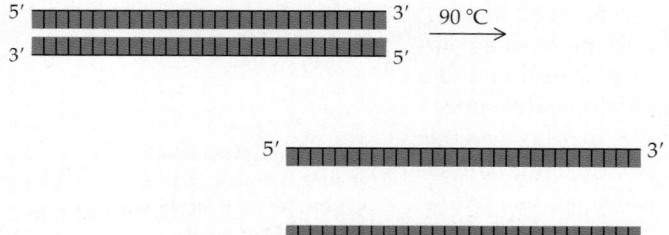

STEP 2: Addition of primers complementary to the DNA flanking the single-stranded DNA sequence to be amplified. It is necessary to create double-stranded DNA at the point where copying is to start, because DNA polymerase needs a free existing 3' end to which it adds nucleotides. The primers indicate this starting point:

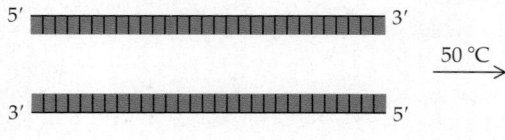

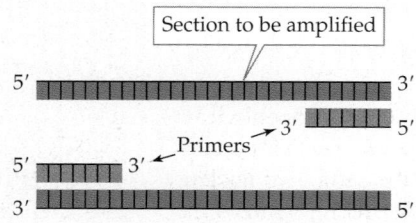

STEP 3: Extension of the primers by DNA polymerase to create double-stranded DNA identical to the original. The DNA polymerase adds nucleotides to the ends of the primers so that the new DNA segment includes the primer DNA:

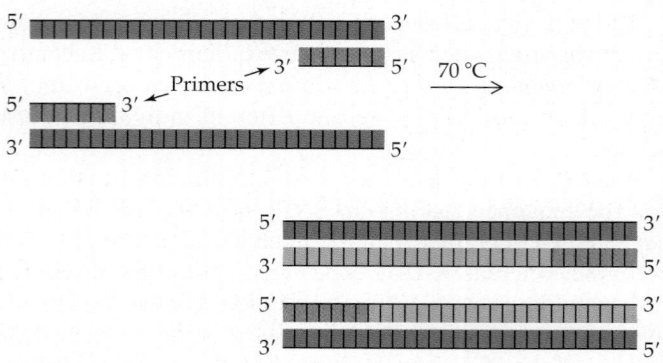

The reactants are combined in a closed container and the temperature cycled from about 90 °C for step 1, to about 50 °C for step 2, and to about 70 °C for step 3. The temperature cycle requires only a few minutes and can be repeated over and over again for the same mixture. The first cycle produces two molecules of DNA; the second produces four molecules; and so on, with doubling at each cycle. Just 25 amplification cycles yield over 30 million copies of the original DNA segment.

Automation of the PCR was made possible by the discovery of a heat-stable polymerase *(Taq polymerase)* isolated from a bacterium that lives in hot springs. Because the enzyme survives the temperature needed for separating the DNA strands, it is not necessary to add fresh enzymes for each three-step cycle.

CIA Problem 27.1 What is the purpose of the PCR?

CIA Problem 27.2 Briefly describe how the PCR works.

CIA Problem 27.3 In automated PCR experiments, why is *Taq* polymerase used instead of the DNA polymerase found in humans?

Worked Example 27.1 Determining the Effect of Changes in DNA on Proteins

The severity of a mutation in a DNA sequence that changes a single amino acid in a protein depends on the type of amino acid replaced and the nature of the new amino acid. (a) What kind of change would have little effect on the protein containing the alternative amino acid? (b) What kind of change could have a major effect on the protein that contains the alternative amino acid? Give an example of each type of mutation.

ANALYSIS The result of exchanging one amino acid for another depends on the change in the nature of the amino acid side chains. To speculate on the result of such a change requires us to think again about the structure of the side chains, which are shown in Table 18.3. The question to consider is whether the mutation introduces an amino acid with such a different side chain character that it is likely to alter the structure and function of the resulting protein.

SOLUTION

(a) Exchange of an amino acid with a small nonpolar side chain for another with the same type of side chain (e.g., glycine for alanine) or exchange of amino acids with very similar side chains (say, serine for threonine) might have little effect.

(b) Conversion of an amino acid with a nonpolar side chain to one with a polar, acidic, or basic side chain could have a major effect because the side-chain interactions that affect protein folding may change (see Figure 18.4). Some examples of this type include exchanging threonine, glutamate, or lysine for isoleucine. In hemoglobin, a single replacement of glutamic acid (a hydrophilic, acidic amino acid) with a valine (a hydrophobic, neutral amino acid) leads to sickle-cell anemia.

KEY CONCEPT PROBLEM 27.2

Consider that a SNP alters the base sequence in an mRNA codon by changing UGU to UGG (see Table 26.3). Speculate on the significance of this change.

27.4 Recombinant DNA

Learning Objective:

• Describe recombinant DNA and its uses.

In this section, we describe a technique for manipulating, altering, and reproducing pieces of DNA. The technique requires the creation of **recombinant DNA**—DNA that joins two or more DNA segments not found together in nature. Progress in all aspects of genomics has built upon information gained in the application of recombinant DNA. The two other techniques that play major roles in DNA studies are the PCR and electrophoresis. PCR is a method by which large quantities of identical pieces of DNA can be synthesized (see the Chemistry in Action "The Polymerase Chain Reaction"). Electrophoresis, which can be carried out simultaneously on large numbers of samples, separates proteins or DNA fragments according to their size (see the Chemistry in Action "Protein Analysis by Electrophoresis" in Chapter 18).

Using recombinant DNA technology, it is possible to cut a gene out of one organism and splice it into (*recombine* it with) the DNA of a second organism. Bacteria provide excellent hosts for recombinant DNA. Bacterial cells, unlike the cells of higher organisms, contain part of their DNA in small circular pieces called *plasmids,* each of which carries just a few genes. Plasmids are extremely easy to isolate, several copies of each plasmid may be present in a cell, and each plasmid replicates through the normal base-pairing pathway. The ease of isolating and manipulating plasmids plus the rapid replication of bacteria create ideal conditions for production of recombinant DNA and the proteins whose synthesis it directs in bacteria.

To prepare a plasmid for insertion of a foreign gene, the plasmid is cut open with a bacterial enzyme, known as a *restriction endonuclease* or *restriction enzyme,* that recognizes a specific sequence in a DNA molecule and cleaves between the same two nucleotides in that sequence. For example, the restriction endonuclease *Eco*RI recognizes the sequence G-A-A-T-T-C and cuts between G and A. This restriction enzyme makes its cut at the same spot in the sequence of both strands of the double-stranded DNA when read

Recombinant DNA DNA that contains two or more DNA segments not found together in nature.

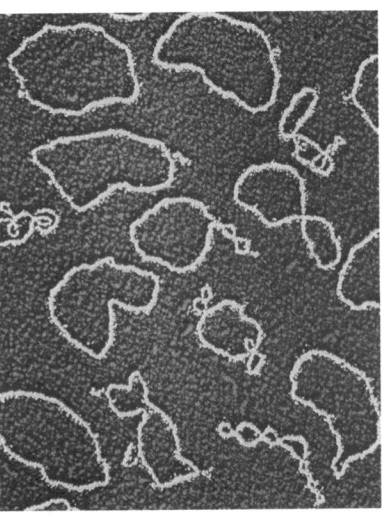
▲ Plasmids from the bacterium *Escherichia coli,* hosts for recombinant DNA.

in the same 5′ to 3′ direction. As a result, the cut is offset so that both DNA strands are left with a few unpaired bases on each end. These groups of unpaired bases are known as *sticky ends* because they are available to match up with complementary base sequences.

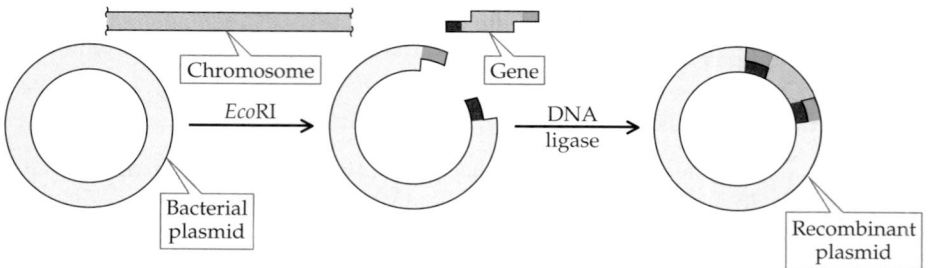

Recombinant DNA is produced by cutting the two DNA segments to be combined with the same restriction endonuclease. The result is DNA fragments with sticky ends that are complementary to each other.

Consider a gene fragment that has been cut from human DNA and is to be inserted into a plasmid. The gene and the plasmid are both cut with the same enzyme, one that produces sticky ends. Thus, the sticky ends on the gene fragment are complementary to the sticky ends on the opened plasmid. The two are mixed in the presence of DNA ligase, an enzyme that joins them together by re-forming their phosphodiester bonds and reconstitutes the now-altered plasmid.

Once the altered plasmid is made, it is inserted back into a bacterial cell, where the normal processes of transcription and translation take place to synthesize the protein encoded by the inserted gene. Since bacteria multiply rapidly, there are soon a large number of them, all containing the recombinant DNA and all manufacturing the protein encoded by the recombinant DNA. Huge numbers of the bacteria can be put to work as a protein factory.

As ideal as this strategy sounds, there are tremendous technical hurdles that have to be overcome before a protein manufactured in this way can be used commercially. One hurdle is getting the recombinant plasmid back into a bacterium. Another is finding a host organism that does posttranslationally modify the protein you are trying to make; for example, yeast cells are known to attach carbohydrates to various amino acids in a protein, rendering the protein inactive. The most serious hurdle of all is isolation of the protein of interest from unwanted endotoxins. *Endotoxins* are potentially toxic natural compounds (usually structural components released when bacteria are lysed) found inside the host organism. Because the presence of even small amounts of endotoxins can lead to serious inflammatory responses, rigorous purification and screening protocols are necessary before the protein can be used in humans.

Despite the aforementioned obstacles, proteins manufactured in this manner have already reached the marketplace, and many more are on the way. Human insulin was the first such protein to become available. Others now include human growth hormone used for children who would otherwise be abnormally small and blood-clotting factors for hemophiliacs. A major advantage of this technology is that large amounts of these proteins can be made, thus allowing their practical therapeutic use.

PROBLEM 27.3

A restriction enzyme known as *Bgl*II cuts DNA in the place marked below.

$$5′-A–//-G-A-T-C-T-3′$$

Draw the complementary 3′ to 5′ strand and show where it is cut by the same enzyme.

PROBLEM 27.4

A restriction enzyme known as *EcoR*I cuts DNA in the place marked below.

$$5'-G-/\!/-A-A-T-T-C-3'$$

Draw the complementary 3' to 5' strand and show where it is cut by the same enzyme.

PROBLEM 27.5

Are the following base sequences "sticky" (complementary) or not? All sequences are written 5' to 3'.

(a) A-C-G-G-A and T-G-C-C-T   (b) G-T-G-A-C and C-A-T-G-G

(c) G-T-A-T-A and A-C-G-C-G

27.5   Genomics: Using What We Know

Learning Objective:

• Identify the possible applications of genomic mapping.

To see where genomics may be headed, Table 27.2 provides descriptions of some of its applications. These descriptions are not quite definitions; many of these fields are so new that their scope is viewed differently by different individuals. We stand at the beginning of a revolution. Let us examine in a little more depth three developments that have arisen from this work.

1. Genetically Modified Plants and Animals

The development of new varieties of plants and animals has been proceeding for centuries as the result of natural accidents and occasional success in the hybridization of known varieties. Now, the mapping and study of plant and animal genomes can greatly accelerate our ability to generate crop plants and farm animals with desirable characteristics and lacking undesirable ones.

Some genetically modified crops have already been planted in large quantities in the United States. Each year millions of tons of corn are destroyed by a caterpillar (the European corn borer) that does its damage deep inside the corn stalk and out of reach of pesticides. To solve this problem, a bacterial gene (from *Bacillus thuringiensis,* Bt) has been transplanted into corn. The gene causes the corn to produce a toxin that kills the caterpillars. In 2000, one-quarter of all corn planted in the United States was Bt corn. Tests are under way with genetically modified coffee beans that are caffeine-free, potatoes that absorb less fat when they are fried, and "golden rice," a yellow rice that provides the vitamin A desperately needed in poor populations where insufficient vitamin A causes death and blindness.

Will genetically modified plants and animals intermingle with natural varieties and cause harm to them? Should food labels state whether the food contains genetically modified ingredients? Might unrecognized harmful substances enter the food supply? These are hotly debated questions and have led to the establishment of the Non-GMO Project, where the GMO stands for genetically modified organism. The goal of this project is to offer consumers a non-GMO choice for organic and natural products that are produced without genetic engineering or recombinant DNA technologies. Many foods found in stores are labeled "Non-GMO."

Genetic modifications can also be used to produce previously unseen beauty. Consider the blue rose, a flower that is currently produced by dyeing white roses. Suntory Limited, in a joint venture with Florigene, has recently been able to successfully implant into roses a gene from petunias that leads to the synthesis of blue pigments; these roses are currently being grown in test batches in Japan. Even more exciting is the expectation that the introduction of blue pigments into roses will lead to an explosion in the variety of possible rose colors available to the average consumer.

▲ "Golden rice" has been genetically modified to provide vitamin A.

Table 27.2 Genomics-Related Fields of Study

Biotechnology

A collective term for the application of biological and biochemical research to the development of products that improve the health of humans, other animals, and plants.

Bioinformatics

The use of computers to manage and interpret genomic information and to make predictions about biological systems. Applications of bioinformatics include studies of individual genes and their functions, drug design, and drug development.

Functional genomics

Use of genome sequences to solve biological problems.

Comparative genomics

Comparison of the genome sequences of different organisms to discover regions with similar functions and perhaps similar evolutionary origins.

Proteomics

Study of the complete set of proteins coded for by a genome or synthesized within a given type of cell, including the quest for an understanding of the role of each protein in healthy or diseased conditions. This understanding has potential application in drug design and is being pursued by more than one commercial organization.

Pharmacogenomics

The genetic basis of responses to drug treatment. Goals include the design of more effective drugs and an understanding of why certain drugs work in some patients but not in others.

Pharmacogenetics

The matching of drugs to individuals based on the content of their personal genome in order to avoid administration of drugs that are ineffective or toxic and focus on drugs that are most effective for that individual.

Toxicogenomics

A newly developing application that combines genomics and bioinformatics in studying how toxic agents affect genes and in screening possibly harmful agents.

Genetic engineering

Alteration of the genetic material of a cell or an organism. The goals may be to make the organism produce new substances or perform new functions. Examples are introduction of a gene that causes bacteria to produce a desired protein or allows a crop plant to withstand the effects of a pesticide that repels harmful insects.

Gene therapy

Alteration of an individual's genetic makeup with the goal of curing or preventing a disease.

Bioethics

The ethical implications of how knowledge of the human genome is used.

2. Gene Therapy

Gene therapy, to put it simply, is the use of DNA to treat disease. It is based on the premise that a disease-causing gene within an individual's cells can be corrected or replaced by inserting a functional, healthy gene into the cells. The most clear-cut expectations for gene therapy lie in treating *monogenic* diseases, those that result from defects in a single gene.

The focus has been on using nonpathogenic viruses as *vectors,* the agents that deliver therapeutic quantities of DNA directly into cell nuclei. The expectation was that this method could result in lifelong elimination of an inherited disease, and many studies have been undertaken. Unfortunately, expectations remain greater than achievements thus far. Investigations into the direct injection of "naked DNA" have begun, with one early report of success in encouraging blood vessel growth in patients with inadequate blood supply to their hearts. The Food and Drug Administration (FDA) has, as of 2014, not yet approved any human gene therapy product for sale, although over 2000 clinical trials are currently approved or under way. While currently gene therapy is still experimental, vigorous research into this area continues as new approaches continue to be examined.

3. Personal Genomic Survey

One outcome of the genome mapping project is that the cost of genetic mapping and testing has decreased dramatically, from about $1000 in 2007 to around $100 in 2014, making it available to the average consumer. Suppose that prior to diagnosis and treatment for a health problem that your entire genome could be surveyed. It is possible that the choice of drugs could be directed toward those that would be most effective for you. It is no secret that not everyone reacts in the same manner to a given medication. Perhaps a patient lacks an enzyme needed for a drug's metabolism, or has a monogenic defect, a flaw in a single gene that is the direct cause of the disease. Such a patient might, at some time in the future, be a candidate for gene therapy.

In cancer therapy, there may be advantages in understanding the genetic differences between a patient's normal cells and tumor cells. Such knowledge could assist in chemotherapy, where the goal is the use of an agent that kills the tumor cells but does the least possible amount of harm to noncancerous cells.

Another possible application is the genetic screening of infants. The immediate use of gene therapy might eliminate the threat of a monogenically based disease, or perhaps a lifestyle adjustment would be in order for an individual with one or more SNPs that predict a susceptibility to heart disease, diabetes, or some other disease that results from combinations of genetic and environmental influences. In addition, an individual's genetic map would be available for the rest of his or her life; they may even carry a wallet card encoded with their genetic information. With this knowledge, however, also come ethical dilemmas that have made this use of genomics a hotly debated topic.

Bioethics

Finally, one area of major concern that has arisen from the genomics revolution is that of the ethical and social implications this groundbreaking work has brought to the fore. The ELSI program of the National Human Genome Research Institute was formed to examine and comment on these concerns. ELSI deals with the Ethical, Legal, and Social Implications of human genetic research. The scope of ELSI is broad and thought-provoking. It deals with many questions such as the following:

- Who should have access to personal genetic information and how will it be used?
- Who should own and control genetic information?
- Should genetic testing be performed when no treatment is available?
- Are disabilities diseases? Do they need to be cured or prevented?
- Preliminary attempts at gene therapy are exorbitantly expensive. Who will have access to these therapies? Who will pay for their use?
- Should we re-engineer the genes we pass on to our children?

If you are interested in the ELSI program, their web page is an excellent resource (www.genome.gov/ELSI).

PROBLEM 27.6

Classify the following activities according to the fields of study listed in Table 27.2.

(a) Identification of genes that perform identical functions in mice and humans.

(b) Creation of a variety of wheat that will not be harmed by an herbicide that kills weeds that threaten wheat crops.

(c) Screening of an individual's genome to choose the most appropriate pain-killing medication for that person.

(d) Computer analysis of base-sequence information from groups of people with and without a given disease to discover where the disease-causing polymorphism lies.

CHEMISTRY IN ACTION

DNA Fingerprinting

A crime scene does not always yield fingerprints. It may, instead, yield samples of blood, semen, or bits of hair. As we learned at the beginning of the chapter, DNA analysis of such samples provides a new kind of "fingerprinting" for identifying criminals or proving suspects innocent.

DNA fingerprinting relies on finding variations between two or more DNA samples; for example, DNA isolated from a crime scene can be examined to determine if its variations match those of a suspect or a victim. The naturally occurring variability of the base sequence in DNA is like a fingerprint. It is the same in all cells from a given individual and is sufficiently different from that of other individuals that it can be used for identification.

In the human genome, there are regions of noncoding DNA that contain repeating nucleotide sequences. The repetitive patterns used in DNA fingerprinting are known as *variable number tandem repeats (VNTRs)*. As the name suggests, a VNTR is a short DNA sequence that is repeated multiple times in a tandem array (end to end to end). The key feature that makes VNTRs useful in fingerprinting is that *for any given VNTR, the number of copies of the repeated sequence varies between individuals.* One person may have a sequence repeated 15 times, whereas another may have the sequence repeated 40 times. For statistical significance, lab technicians examine several of the known VNTRs across multiple chromosomes to create a DNA fingerprint. The probability of a DNA-fingerprint match with someone other than the correct individual is estimated at 1 in 1.5 billion.

There are two common techniques used for DNA fingerprinting today: the restriction fragment length polymorphism (RFLP) approach and the PCR method.

RFLP relies on use of a restriction endonuclease (an enzyme used to cut DNA) that recognizes and cuts sequences on either side of a given VNTR. The general procedure is as follows:

- Digest the DNA sample with the restriction endonuclease.
- Separate the resulting DNA fragments according to their size by gel electrophoresis.
- Transfer the fragments to a nylon membrane (a *blotting* technique).
- Treat the blot with a radioactive DNA probe complementary to the repeating VNTR sequence, so that the probe binds the fragment containing the VNTR sequence.
- Identify the locations of the now-radioactive fragments by exposing an X-ray film to the blot. (The film result of this procedure is known as an *autoradiogram*.)

An autoradiogram resembles a bar code, with dark bands arrayed in order of increasing molecular size of the DNA fragments. To compare the DNA of different individuals, the DNA samples are run in parallel columns on the same electrophoresis gel. In this way, the comparison is validated by having been run under identical conditions. While this method is very accurate, it requires a significant amount of DNA and can take

two to four weeks to carry out; it is used primarily for genetic screening.

A more recent method for DNA fingerprinting involves the use of PCR (see the Chemistry in Action "The Polymerase Chain Reaction," p. 814). In this method, one can use primers directed toward regions of the DNA that are known to contain variations; these can then be copied using PCR. This amplification process is repeated about 30 times (about four minutes per cycle) so that in two hours more than 1 billion copies are produced. These fragments can then be separated according to size by gel electrophoresis, stained using a blue dye that binds to DNA, and compared against other samples. Unlike the RFLP method, the PCR system, from amplification to analysis, can be carried out in about 24 hours. It can be performed on small amounts of DNA, and even on DNA that has begun to degrade, and is successful with almost every sample. This method has become the primary technique used in crime scene forensic analysis.

How useful is DNA fingerprinting? The following illustration shows hypothetical DNA-fingerprint patterns of six members of a family, where three of the children share the same mother and father and the fourth has been adopted. As you can see, even individuals in the same family will have distinguishably different DNA fingerprints; only identical twins have identical DNA fingerprints. There are always some similarities in the DNA patterns of offspring and their parents, making such fingerprints valuable in proving or disproving paternity.

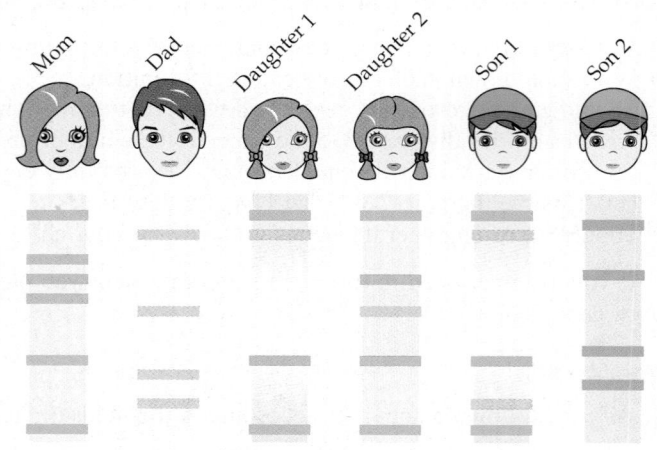

CIA Problem 27.4 In 2011, the population of the world was estimated to be about 7 billion. How many people in the world could theoretically have the same DNA fingerprint?

CIA Problem 27.5 State the five basic steps of DNA fingerprinting using the RFLP method. Why do you think the PCR method is of more use in crime scene investigations?

CIA Problem 27.6 What is a VNTR? What is its significance for DNA fingerprinting?

SUMMARY   REVISITING THE CHAPTER GOALS

- **Describe how a genome is mapped.** The HGP, an international consortium of not-for-profit institutions, along with Celera Genomics, a for-profit company, have working drafts of the human genome. With the exception of large areas of repetitive DNA, the DNA base sequences of all chromosomes have been examined. The HGP utilized a series of progressively more detailed maps to create a collection of DNA fragments with known location. Celera began by randomly fragmenting all of the DNA without first placing it within the framework of a map. In both groups the fragments were cloned, labeled, ordered, and the individual sequences assembled by computers. The results of the two projects are generally supportive of each other. There are about 3 billion base pairs and about 19,000 genes in the human genome. The bulk of the genome consists of noncoding, repetitive sequences. About 200 of the human genes are identical to those in bacteria *(see Problems 7, 8, and 14–20).*

- **Identify the genetic roles of telomeres, centromeres, exons and introns, and noncoding DNA.** Telomeres, which fall at the ends of chromosomes, are regions of noncoding, repetitive DNA that protect the ends from accidental changes. At each cell division, the telomeres are shortened, with significant shortening associated with senescence and death of the cell. Telomerase, the enzyme that lengthens telomeres, is typically inactivated in adult cells but can become reactivated in cancer cells. Centromeres are the constricted regions of chromosomes that form during cell division and also carry noncoding DNA. Exons are the protein-coding regions of DNA and the noncoding regions separating the exons that make up a gene are the introns. The exons, when strung together, make up the genes that direct protein synthesis. The repetitive, noncoding segments of DNA are of either no function or unknown function *(see Problems 9 and 21–25).*

- **Describe a mutation and what can result from one.** A mutation is an error in the base sequence of DNA that is passed along during replication. Mutations arise by random error during replication but may also be caused by ionizing radiation, viruses, or chemical agents *(mutagens).* Mutations can cause inherited diseases and increase the tendency to acquire others *(see Problems 10, 26, 27, 32–35, and 47–52).*

- **Define polymorphisms and SNPs, and explain the significance of the locations of SNPs.** A polymorphism is a variation in DNA that is found within a population. A SNP is the replacement of one nucleotide by another. The result might be the replacement of one amino acid by another in a protein, no change because the new codon specifies the same amino acid, or the introduction of a "stop codon." Many inherited diseases are known to be caused by SNPs, but they can also be beneficial or neutral. Understanding the location and effect of SNPs is expected to lead to new therapies *(see Problems 28–32, 50, and 52).*

- **Describe recombinant DNA and its uses.** Recombinant DNA is produced by joining DNA segments that do not normally occur together. A gene from one organism is inserted into the DNA of another organism. Recombinant DNA techniques can be used to create large quantities of a particular protein. The gene of interest is inserted into bacterial plasmids (small, extrachromosomal circular DNA). Bacteria carrying these plasmids then serve as factories for the synthesis of large quantities of the encoded protein *(see Problems 11 and 36–41).*

- **Identify the possible applications of genomic mapping.** Mapping the human genome holds major promise for applications in health and medicine. Drugs can be precisely chosen based on a patient's own DNA, thereby avoiding drugs that are ineffective or toxic for that individual. Perhaps one day inherited diseases will be prevented or cured by gene therapy. By genetic modification of crop plants and farm animals, the productivity, marketability, and health benefits of these products can be enhanced. Progress in each of these areas is bound to be accompanied by controversy and ethical dilemmas *(see Problems 12 and 42–46).*

KEY WORDS

Clones, *p. 808*	**Mutation,** *p. 811*	**Single-nucleotide**	**Telomeres,** *p. 809*
Centromeres, *p. 809*	**Polymorphism,** *p. 811*	**polymorphism (SNP),**	
Genomics, *p. 807*	**Recombinant DNA,**	*p. 813*	
Mutagen, *p. 811*	*p. 815*		

UNDERSTANDING KEY CONCEPTS

27.7   What steps are necessary in the mapping of the human genome, as outlined by the Human Genome Project?

27.8   Clearly, all humans have variations in their DNA sequences. How is it possible to sequence the human genome if every individual is unique? How was the diversity of the human genome addressed?

27.9   List the four types of noncoding DNA (see Section 27.2). Give the function of each, if it is known.

27.10   In general, what are the differences between mutations and polymorphisms?

27.11   What is recombinant DNA? How can it be used to produce human proteins in bacteria?

27.12   Identify some major potential benefits of the applications of genomics and some major negative outcomes.

ADDITIONAL PROBLEMS

THE HUMAN GENOME MAP (SECTION 27.1)

27.13 What is genomics?

27.14 How did the private corporation Celera Genomics approach the sequencing of the human genome? What was the advantage of this approach?

27.15 How did the competition that developed between the groups developing the human genome map benefit the HGP?

27.16 Approximately what portion of the human genome is composed of repeat sequences?

27.17 Approximately how many base pairs were identified in the human genome working drafts?

27.18 Among the results of the genome working drafts, (a) were any human genes found to be identical to genes in bacteria and (b) what was learned about the number of proteins produced by a given gene?

27.19 What is the most surprising result found thus far in the human genome studies?

27.20 You may have heard of Dolly, the cloned sheep grown from an embryo created in a laboratory. But in the context of DNA mapping, what are clones and what essential role do they play?

CHROMOSOMES, MUTATIONS, AND POLYMORPHISMS (SECTIONS 27.2 AND 27.3)

27.21 What is thought to be the primary purpose of telomeres?

27.22 How is the age of a cell predicted by its telomeric sequences?

27.23 What is the role of the enzyme telomerase? In what kind of cell is it normally most active and most inactive?

27.24 What is the centromere?

27.25 What is a mutagen?

27.26 Why is a mutation of a base in a DNA sequence much more serious than a mutation in a transcribed mRNA sequence?

27.27 What are the two general and common ways that mutations occur in a DNA sequence?

27.28 What is a SNP?

27.29 How are SNPs linked to traits in individual human beings?

27.30 List some potential biological effects of SNPs.

27.31 What would be a medical advantage of having a catalog of SNPs?

27.32 Does a single base-pair substitution in a strand of DNA always result in a new amino acid in the protein coded for by that gene? Why or why not?

27.33 What determines the significance of a change in the identity of an amino acid in a protein?

27.34 Compare the severity of DNA mutations that produce the following changes in mRNA codons (Consult Table 26.3 for help):

(a) UCA to UCG   (b) UAA to UAU

27.35 Compare the severity of DNA mutations that produce the following changes in mRNA codons:

(a) GCU to GCC   (b) ACU to AUU

RECOMBINANT DNA (SECTION 27.4)

27.36 Why are bacteria excellent hosts for recombinant DNA experiments?

27.37 What is an advantage of using recombinant DNA to make proteins such as insulin, human growth hormone, or blood-clotting factors?

27.38 How can DNA fragments be separated by size?

27.39 In the formation of recombinant DNA, a restriction endonuclease cuts a bacterial plasmid to give sticky ends. The DNA segments that are to be added to the plasmid are cleaved with the same restriction endonuclease. What are sticky ends and why is it important that the target DNA and the plasmid it will be incorporated into have complementary sticky ends?

27.40 Give the sequence of unpaired bases that would be sticky with the following sequences:

(a) GGTAC   (b) ACCCA   (c) GTGTC

27.41 Are the following base sequences sticky or not sticky? Each piece is written 5′ to 3′.

(a) TTAGC and GCTAA

(b) CGTACG and CCTTCG

USING GENOMICS (SECTION 27.5)

27.42 What is pharmacogenomics and how might it benefit patient care?

27.43 Genetic engineering and gene therapy are similar fields within genomics. What do they have in common and what distinguishes them?

27.44 Provide two examples of genetically engineered crops that are improvements over their predecessors.

27.45 Imagine that you become a parent in an age when a full genetic workup is available for every baby. What advantages and disadvantages might there be to having this information?

27.46 Why is the field of bioethics so important in genomics?

CONCEPTUAL PROBLEMS

27.47 What is a monogenic disease?

27.48 What is the role of a vector in gene therapy?

27.49 Write the base sequence that would be sticky with the sequence T-A-T-G-A-C-T.

27.50 If the DNA sequence A-T-T-G-G-C-C-T-A on an informational strand mutated and became A-C-T-G-G-C-C-T-A, what effect would the mutation have on the sequence of the protein produced?

27.51 What is a restriction endonuclease?

27.52 In the DNA of what kind of cell must a mutation occur for the genetic change to be passed down to future generations?

GROUP PROBLEMS

27.53 Discuss the advantages and drawbacks to having your own personal genomic map. Have half the members of your group take the pro side and the others take the con side of the discussion.

27.54 One of the most actively pursued areas in genomics is that of gene therapy. Have each member of your group research and then discuss the current state of research and development into gene therapy for a disease of their choosing. Some suggestions are Parkinson's disease, Huntington's disease, prostate and pancreatic cancers, and muscular dystrophy.

27.55 Do a keyword search for "unlocking life's code" and see if you can find a timeline for the human genome. Have each member of your group choose a decade and discuss the important strides made during it.

28

Chemical Messengers: Hormones, Neurotransmitters, and Drugs

CONTENTS

◄◄◄ CONCEPTS TO REVIEW

▲ Unwittingly surfing with sharks may result in high anxiety due to the hormone epinephrine.

Imagine you are on a hike, enjoying the scenery when all of the sudden a mother bear appears with her cubs; or, you are paddling out on the ocean to catch a big wave while surfing when a shark approaches your surfboard. Imagine walking casually into class when you abruptly realize there is an important exam that you forgot to study for. In each case, your body initially had a metabolic level where your internal biochemical conditions were in a relaxed state, a condition called homeostasis. However, once fear, stress, or anxiety set in, you are likely to feel shaky, your body's response to an increase in epinephrine.

Epinephrine is one example of a hormone your body produces to signal dangerous or stressful situations. Similar responses occur throughout your body on a daily basis to signal an abundance of situations. How do these rapid, body-wide responses happen? Furthermore, how does the biochemistry in our body maintain a constant internal environment despite these responses?

There are thousands of enzymatic reactions in our bodies that maintain balance for our normal internal biochemistry in response to our external environment. Many metabolic reactions work hard and constantly to maintain body temperature, produce chemicals for energy, eliminate waste products, sustain normal metabolic processes, transport nutrients to various cells, and even stabilize oxygen concentrations.

Two systems share the major responsibility for regulating body chemistry—the *endocrine system* and the *nervous system*. The endocrine system depends on *hormones,* chemical messengers that circulate in the bloodstream. The nervous system relies primarily on a much faster means of communication—electrical impulses in nerve cells, triggered by its own chemical messengers, the *neurotransmitters.* Neurotransmitters carry signals from one nerve cell to another and also from nerve cells to their targets, the ultimate recipients of the messages.

If the normal internal environment is compromised in the situation of fear, or, more complex situations such as severe illness, many drugs act by mimicking, modifying, or opposing the action of chemical messengers. To help maintain our biochemistry when normal processes are disturbed, outside medical intervention might assist in restoring the balance of the many biochemical reactions.

28.1 Messenger Molecules

Learning Objective:

- Describe the origins, pathways, and actions of hormones.

Chemical messengers control and coordinate your body's vital functions. Whether the messengers are hormones that arrive via the bloodstream or neurotransmitters released by nerve cells, such messengers ultimately connect with a *target.* The message is delivered by interaction between the chemical messenger and a **receptor** at the target. The receptor then acts like a light switch, causing some biochemical response to occur—the contraction of a muscle, for example, or the secretion of another biomolecule.

Noncovalent attractions draw messengers and receptors together, much as a substrate is drawn into the active site of an enzyme (Sections 18.8 and 19.4). These attractions hold the messenger and receptor together long enough for the message to be delivered but without any permanent chemical change to the messenger or the receptor. The results of this interaction are chemical changes within the target cell.

Hormones are the chemical messengers of the endocrine system. Endocrine glands and tissues in various parts of the body produce these molecules, often at distances far from their ultimate site of action. Because of this, hormones must travel through the bloodstream to their targets, and the responses they produce can require anywhere from seconds to hours to begin. The action or actions they elicit, however, may last a long time and can be wide-ranging. A single hormone will often affect many different tissues and organs—any cell with the appropriate receptors is a target. Insulin, for example, is a hormone secreted by the pancreas in response to elevated blood glucose levels. At target cells throughout the body, insulin accelerates uptake and utilization of glucose; in muscles it accelerates formation of glycogen, a glucose polymer that is metabolized when muscles need quick energy; and in fatty tissue it stimulates storage of triacylglycerols.

The chemical messengers of the nervous system are a set of molecules referred to as **neurotransmitters.** The electrical signals of the nervous system travel along nerve fibers, taking only a fraction of a second to reach their highly specific destinations. Most nerve cells, however, do not make direct contact with the cells they stimulate. A neurotransmitter must carry the message across the tiny gap separating the nerve

Receptor A molecule or portion of a molecule with which a hormone, neurotransmitter, or other biochemically active molecule interacts to initiate a response in a target cell.

◀◀◀ **CONCEPTS TO REVIEW** Figure 18.3 shows the various types of noncovalent forces that govern the shape of protein molecules. These same types of interactions mediate substrate–enzyme binding, as described in Section 19.4.

Hormone A chemical messenger secreted by cells of the endocrine system and transported through the bloodstream to target cells with appropriate receptors, where it elicits a response.

Neurotransmitter A chemical messenger that travels between a neuron and a neighboring neuron or other target cell to transmit a nerve impulse.

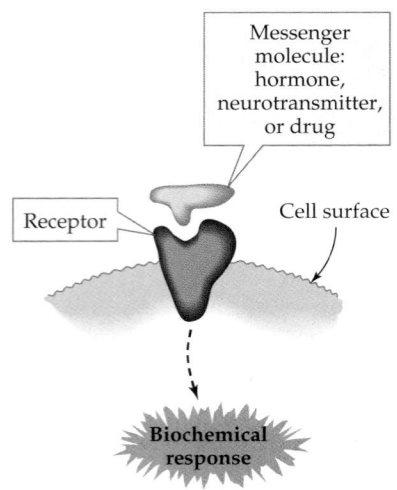

▲ A general representation of the interaction between a messenger molecule and a cellular receptor.

Endocrine system A system of specialized cells, tissues, and ductless glands that secretes hormones and shares with the nervous system the responsibility for maintaining constant internal body conditions and responding to changes in the environment.

cell from its target. Because neurotransmitters are released in very short bursts and are quickly broken down or reabsorbed by the nerve cell, their effects are short-lived. The nervous system is organized so that nearly all of its vital switching, integrative, and information-processing functions depend on neurotransmitters. Neurotransmitters are typically synthesized and released very close to their site of action.

PROBLEM 28.1

While thinking about how a messenger molecule and receptor molecule interact, list three possible intermolecular forces that involve noncovalent interations.

28.2 Hormones and the Endocrine System

Learning Objectives:

- Distinguish between the different types of hormonal control.
- List the different chemical types of hormones and give examples of each.

The **endocrine system** includes all cells that secrete hormones into the bloodstream. Some of these cells are found in organs that also have non-endocrine functions (e.g., the pancreas, which also produces digestive enzymes); others occur in glands devoted solely to hormonal control (e.g., the thyroid gland). It is important to note, however, that hormones do not carry out chemical reactions. Hormones are simply messengers that alter the biochemistry of a cell by signaling the inhibition or activation of an existing enzyme, by initiating or altering the rate of synthesis of a specific protein, or in other ways.

The major endocrine glands are the thyroid gland, the adrenal glands, the ovaries and testes, and the pituitary gland (found in the brain). The hypothalamus, a section of the brain just above the pituitary gland, controls the endocrine system. It communicates with other tissues in the following three ways:

- *Direct neural control* A nervous system message from the hypothalamus initiates release of hormones by the adrenal gland. For example,

$$\text{Hypothalamus} \xrightarrow{\text{Nerve message}} \text{Adrenal gland} \longrightarrow \text{Epinephrine}$$

Epinephrine is targeted to many cells; it increases heart rate, blood pressure, and glucose availability.
- *Direct release of hormones* Hormones move from the hypothalamus to the posterior pituitary gland, where they are stored until needed. For example,

$$\text{Hypothalamus} \longrightarrow \text{Antidiuretic hormone}$$

Antidiuretic hormone, which is stored in the posterior pituitary gland, targets the kidneys and causes retention of water and elevation of blood pressure.
- *Indirect control through release of regulatory hormones* In the most common control mechanism, *regulatory hormones* from the hypothalamus stimulate or inhibit the release of hormones by the anterior pituitary gland. Many of these pituitary hormones in turn stimulate release of still other hormones by their own target tissues. For example,

$$\text{Hypothalamus} \xrightarrow{\text{Releasing factor}} \text{Pituitary gland} \longrightarrow$$

$$\text{Thyrotropin (a regulatory hormone)} \longrightarrow$$

$$\text{Thyroid gland} \longrightarrow \text{Thyroid hormones}$$

Thyroid hormones are targeted to cells throughout the body; they affect oxygen availability, blood pressure, and other endocrine tissues.

Chemically, hormones are of three major types: (1) amino acid derivatives, such as epinephrine; (2) polypeptides, which range from just a few amino acids to several hundred amino acids; and (3) steroids, which are lipids with the distinctive molecular structure based on four connected rings common to all sterols (see Section 23.6).

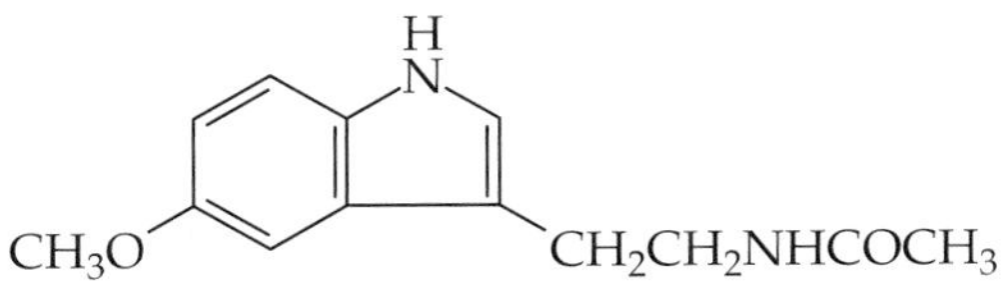

Melatonin, an amino acid derivative
(regulates day–night cycle)

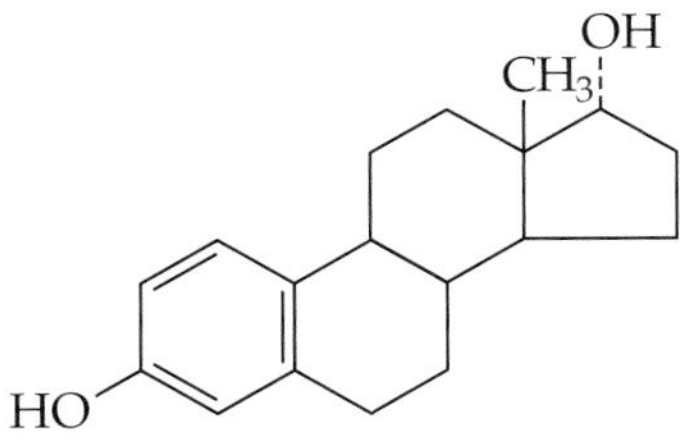

Estradiol, a steroid
(an estrogen that acts in ovulation)

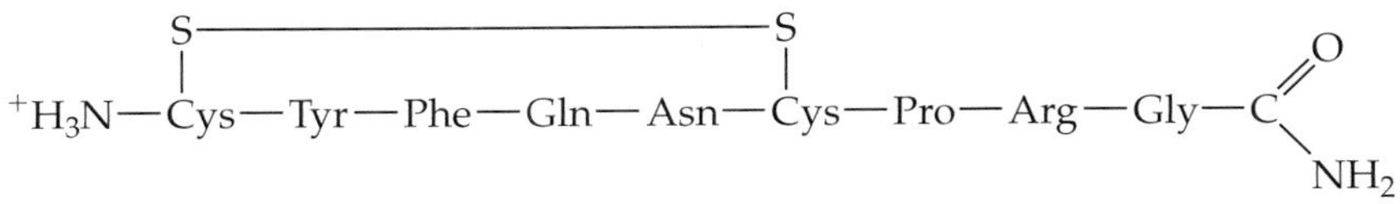

Vasopressin, a polypeptide
(controls urine volume)

Table 28.1 gives examples of the targets and actions of each type of hormone.

Table 28.1 Examples of Each Chemical Class of Hormones

Chemical Class	Hormone Examples	Source	Target	Major Action
Amino acid derivatives	Epinephrine and norepinephrine	Adrenal medulla	Most cells	Release glucose from storage; increase heart rate and blood pressure
	Thyroxine	Thyroid gland	Most cells	Influence energy use, oxygen consumption, growth, and development
Polypeptides (regulatory hormones)	Adrenocorticotropic hormone	Anterior pituitary	Adrenal cortex	Stimulate release of glucocorticoids (steroids), which control glucose metabolism
	Growth hormone	Anterior pituitary	Peripheral tissues	Stimulate growth of muscle and skeleton
	Follicle-stimulating hormone, luteinizing hormone (LH)	Anterior pituitary	Ovaries and testes	Stimulate release of steroid hormones
	Vasopressin	Posterior pituitary	Kidneys	Cause retention of water, elevation of blood volume and blood pressure
	Thyrotropin	Anterior pituitary	Thyroid gland	Stimulates release of thyroid hormones
Steroids	Cortisone and cortisol (glucocorticoids)	Adrenal cortex	Most cells	Counteract inflammation; control metabolism when glucose must be conserved
	Testosterone; estrogen, progesterone	Testes; ovaries	Most cells	Control development of secondary sexual characteristics, maturation of sperm and eggs

Upon arrival at its target cell, a hormone must deliver its signal to create a chemical response inside the cell. The signal enters the cell in ways determined by the chemical nature of the hormone (Figure 28.1). Because the cell is surrounded by a membrane composed of hydrophobic molecules, only nonpolar, hydrophobic molecules can move across it on their own. The steroid hormones are nonpolar, so they can enter the cell directly by diffusion; this is one of the ways a hormone delivers its message. Once within the cell's cytoplasm, a steroid hormone encounters a receptor molecule that carries it to its target, DNA in the nucleus of the cell. The result is some change in production of a protein governed by a particular gene.

▶ **Figure 28.1**
Interaction of hormones and receptors at the cellular level.
Steroid hormones are hydrophobic and can cross the cell membrane to find receptors inside the cell. Amine and polypeptide hormones are hydrophilic and, because they cannot cross the cell membrane, act via second messengers.

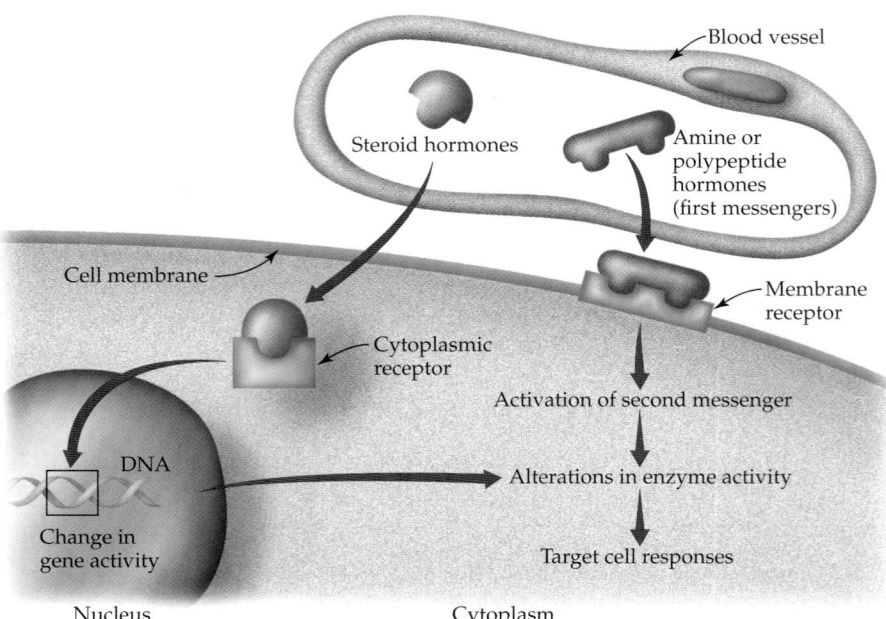

In contrast, the polypeptide and amine hormones are water-soluble molecules and cannot cross the hydrophobic cell membranes. Rather than entering cells, they deliver their messages by bonding noncovalently with receptors on cell surfaces. The result is release of a **second messenger** within the cell. There are several different second messengers, and the specific sequence of events varies. In general, three membrane-bound proteins participate in release of the second messenger: (1) the receptor and (2) a *G protein* (a member of the guanine nucleotide-binding protein family) that transfer the message to (3) an enzyme. First, interaction of the hormone with its receptor causes a change in the receptor (much like the effect of an allosteric regulator on an enzyme; Section 19.7). This stimulates the G protein to activate an enzyme that participates in release of the second messenger.

Second messenger Chemical messenger released inside a cell when a hydrophilic hormone or neurotransmitter interacts with a receptor on the cell surface.

▶ **Worked Example 28.1**   Classifying Hormones Based on Structure

Classify the following hormones as an amino acid derivative, a polypeptide, or a steroid.

(a)

(b)

(c) ^+H_3N—His—Ser—Glu— ••• Thr—COO$^-$

ANALYSIS Hormones that are amino acid derivatives are recognized by the presence of amino groups. Those that are polypeptides are composed of amino acids. Steroids are recognizable by their distinctive four-ring structures.

SOLUTION
Compound (a) is a steroid, (b) is an amino acid derivative, and (c) is a polypeptide.

PROBLEM 28.2

Look at the structure of epinephrine in Section 28.3. Is it a steroid, an amino acid derivative, or a polypeptide?

PROBLEM 28.3

Review the structure of thyroxine in Section 28.4. Which amino acid could be biochemically altered to synthesize thyroxine? Review the amino acid structures in Chapter 18 for assistance.

PROBLEM 28.4

Review the structure of thyrotropin-releasing hormone (TRH) in Section 28.4. This chemical messenger has one chiral carbon, which happens to be an alpha carbon of an amino acid. Which amino acid is part of TRH?

28.3 How Hormones Work: Epinephrine and Fight-or-Flight

Learning Objective:

• Explain the sequence of events in epinephrine's action as a hormone.

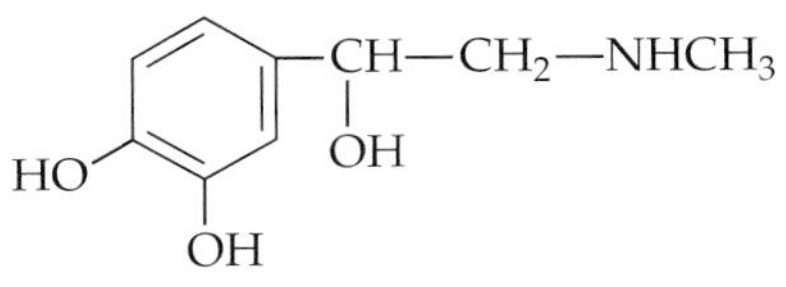

Epinephrine (pronounced ep-pin-*eff*-rin), also known as *adrenaline,* is often called the *fight-or-flight hormone* because it is released from the adrenal glands when we need an instant response to danger.

Epinephrine
(adrenaline)

We have all felt the rush of epinephrine that accompanies a near-miss accident or a sudden loud noise. The main function of epinephrine in a "startle" reaction is a dramatic increase in the availability of glucose as a source of energy to deal with whatever stress is immediate. The time elapsed from initial stimulus to glucose release into the bloodstream is only a few seconds.

Epinephrine acts via *cyclic adenosine monophosphate (cyclic AMP, or cAMP),* an important second messenger. The sequence of events in this action, shown in Figure 28.2 and described next, illustrates one type of biochemical response to a change in an individual's external or internal environment.

• Epinephrine, a hormone carried in the bloodstream, binds to a receptor on the surface of a cell.
• The hormone–receptor complex activates a nearby G protein embedded in the interior surface of the cell membrane.
• GDP (guanosine diphosphate) associated with the G protein is exchanged for GTP (guanosine triphosphate) from the cytosol.
• The G protein–GTP complex activates *adenylate cyclase,* an enzyme that also is embedded in the interior surface of the cell membrane.
• Adenylate cyclase catalyzes production within the cell of the second messenger—*cyclic AMP*—from adenosine triphosphate (ATP), as shown in Figure 28.3.
• Cyclic AMP initiates reactions that activate glycogen phosphorylase, the enzyme responsible for release of glucose from storage. (Interaction of other hormones with their specific receptors results in initiation by cyclic AMP of other reactions.)
• When the emergency has passed, cyclic AMP is converted back to ATP.

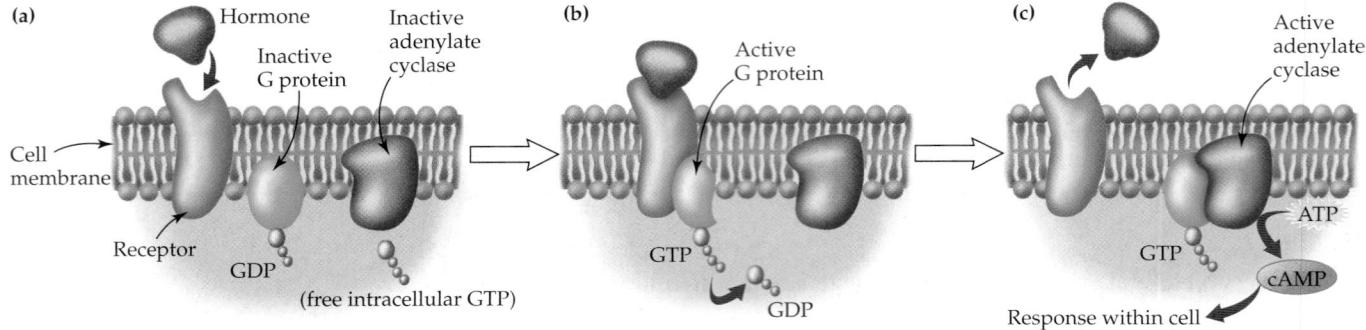

▲ **Figure 28.2**
Activation of cyclic AMP as a second messenger.
(a) The hormone receptor, inactive G protein, and inactive adenylate cyclase enzyme reside in the cell membrane.
(b) On formation of the hormone–receptor complex, an allosteric change occurs in the G protein, resulting in the GDP of
the G protein being replaced by a free intracellular GTP. (c) The active G protein–GTP complex activates adenylate cyclase,
causing production of cyclic AMP inside the cell, where it initiates the action called for by the hormone.

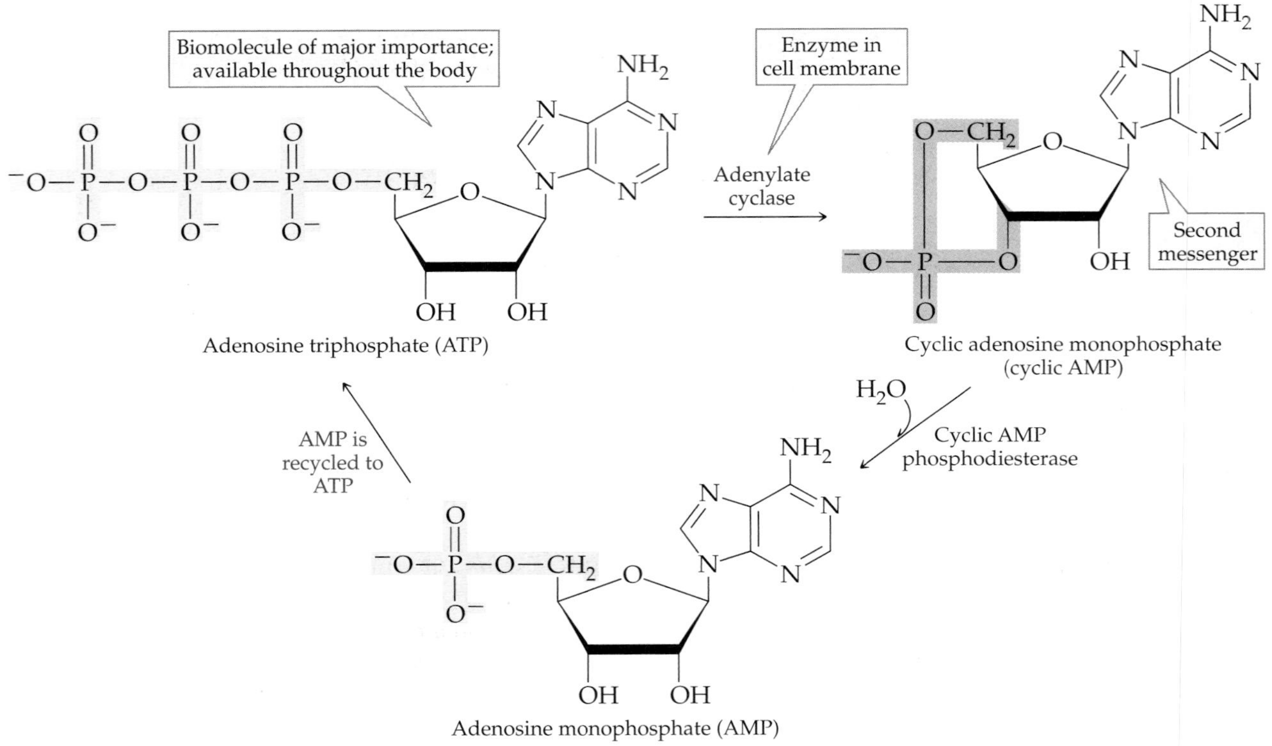

▲ **Figure 28.3**
Production of cyclic AMP as a second messenger.
The reactions shown take place within the target cell after epinephrine or some other chemical messenger interacts with a receptor on the cell surface. (The major role of ATP in providing energy for biochemical reactions was
discussed in Section 21.4.)

In addition to making glucose available, epinephrine reacts with other receptors to increase blood pressure, heart rate, and respiratory rate; decrease blood flow to the digestive
system (digestion is not important during an emergency); and counteract spasms in the
respiratory system. The resulting combined and rapid effects make epinephrine the most
crucial drug for treatment of *anaphylactic shock*. Anaphylactic shock is the result of a
severe allergic reaction, perhaps to a bee sting, a drug, or even to something seemingly
as benign as peanuts; it is an extremely serious medical emergency. The major symptoms
include a severe drop in blood pressure due to blood vessel dilation and difficulty breathing
due to bronchial constriction. Epinephrine directly counters these symptoms. Individuals
who know they are susceptible to these life-threatening allergic responses carry epinephrine with them at all times (typically in the form of an autoinjector known as an "EpiPen").

PROBLEM 28.5

A phosphorus-containing anion is removed from ATP in its conversion to cyclic AMP, as shown in Figure 28.3. The anion is often abbreviated as PP_i. Which of the following anions is represented by PP_i?

(a) $P_3O_{10}^{5-}$ (b) $P_2O_7^{4-}$ (c) PO_4^{3-} (d) $H_2PO_4^-$

KEY CONCEPT PROBLEM 28.6

Caffeine and theobromine (from chocolate) act as stimulants. They work by altering the cAMP signal. Refer to Figure 28.3 and decide how these molecules might interact with an enzyme in the cAMP pathway to enhance the effect of cAMP.

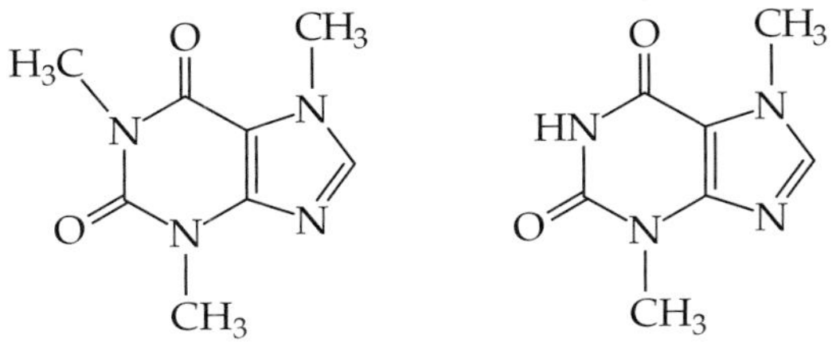

Caffeine

Theobromine

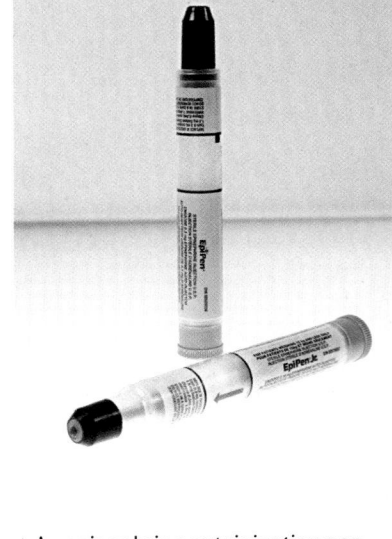

▲ An epinephrine autoinjection pen. Such devices are carried by individuals at risk of an anaphylactic reaction to an allergen.

28.4 Amino Acid Derivatives, Polypeptides, and Steroid Hormones

Learning Objective:

• Explain the functions of the three major types of hormones: amino acid derivatives, polypeptides, and steroids.

Amino Acid Derivatives

The biochemistry of the brain is an active area of research. As our understanding of chemical messages in the brain grows, the traditional distinctions between hormones and neurotransmitters are vanishing. Several amino acid derivatives classified as hormones because of their roles in the endocrine system are also synthesized in neurons and function as neurotransmitters in the brain. (Because a barrier—the *blood–brain barrier*—limits entry into the brain of chemicals traveling in the bloodstream, the brain cannot rely on a supply of chemical messengers synthesized elsewhere; see the Chemistry in Action "The Blood–Brain Barrier," Chapter 29.) Epinephrine, the fight-or-flight hormone, is one of the amino acid derivatives that is both a hormone and a neurotransmitter. The pathway for the synthesis of epinephrine is shown in Figure 28.4; several other chemical messengers are also formed in this pathway.

Thyroxine, another amino acid derivative, is also a hormone. It is one of two iodine-containing hormones produced by the thyroid gland, and our need for dietary iodine is due to these hormones. Unlike other hormones derived from amino acids, thyroxine is a nonpolar compound that can cross cell membranes and enter cells, where it activates the synthesis of various enzymes. When dietary iodine is insufficient, the thyroid gland compensates by enlarging in order to produce more thyroxine. Thus, a greatly enlarged thyroid gland (a goiter) is a symptom of iodine deficiency. In developed countries, where iodine is added to table salt, goiter is uncommon. In some regions of the world, however, iodine deficiency is a common and serious problem that results not only in goiter but also in severe mental retardation in infants (*cretinism*).

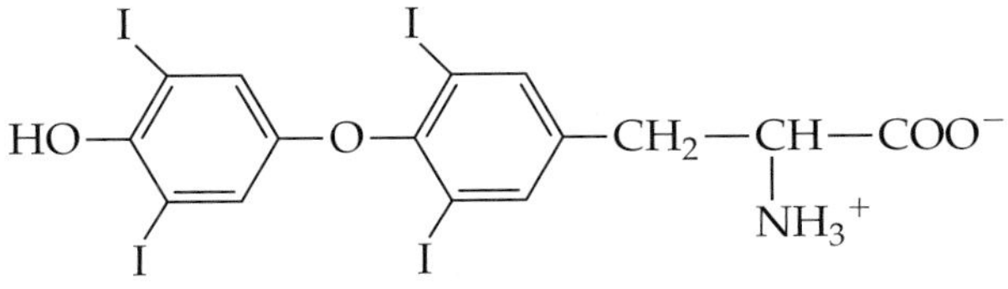

Thyroxine

Polypeptides

Polypeptides are the largest class of hormones. They range widely in molecular size and complexity, as illustrated by two hormones that control the thyroid gland, *TRH* and *thyroid-stimulating hormone (TSH)*. TRH, a modified tripeptide, is a regulatory

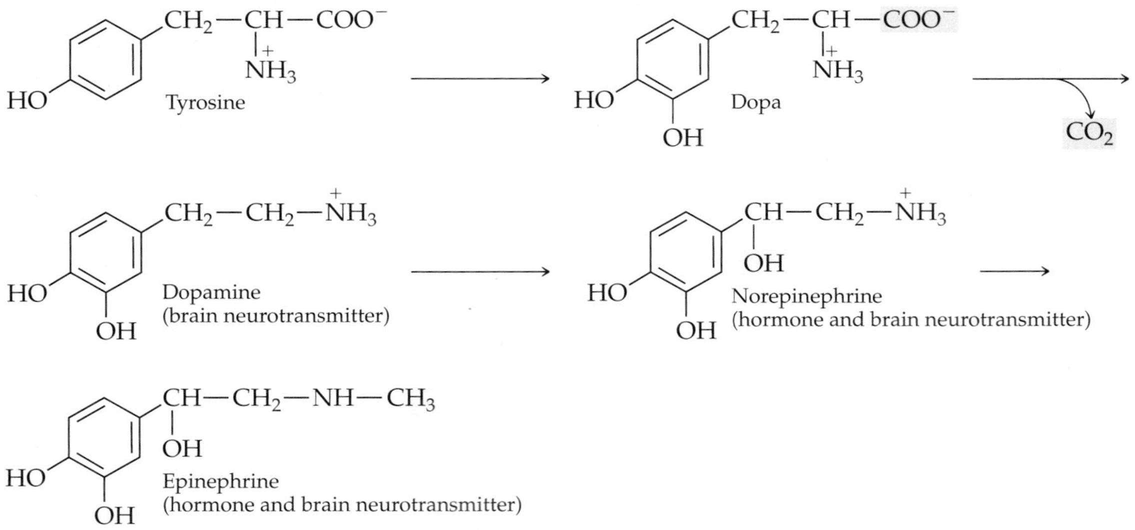

▲ Figure 28.4
Synthesis of chemical messengers from tyrosine.
The changes in each step are highlighted in gold (yellow) for substitution reactions and green for respiratory (elimination) reactions.

hormone released by the hypothalamus. At the pituitary gland, TRH activates release of TSH, a protein that has 208 amino acid residues in two chains. TSH in turn triggers release of amino acid derivative hormones from the thyroid gland.

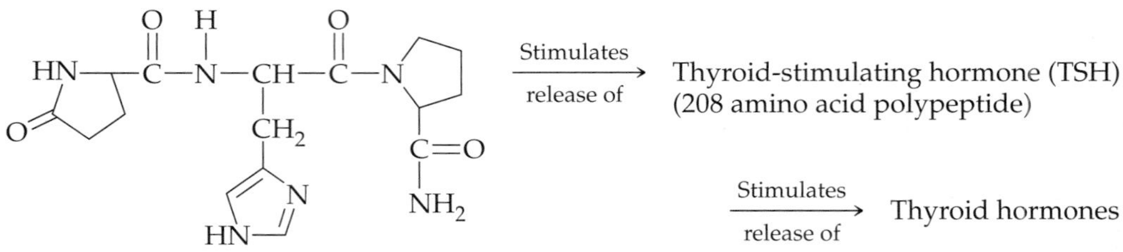

Insulin, a protein containing 51 amino acids, is released by the pancreas in response to high concentrations of glucose in the blood. It stimulates cells to take up glucose to either generate or store energy.

◀◀ Because of its importance in glucose metabolism and diabetes mellitus, the function of insulin as a hormone is described in Chapter 22 as part of the discussion of glucose metabolism.

PROBLEM 28.7

Examine the TRH structure and identify the three amino acids from which it is derived. The *N*-terminal amino acid has undergone ring formation, and the carboxyl group at the *C*-terminal end has been converted to an amide.

⬤⬤ KEY CONCEPT PROBLEM 28.8

Look at the structure of thyroxine shown earlier in this section. Is thyroxine, an amino acid derivative, hydrophobic or hydrophilic? Explain.

Steroid Hormones

Sterols have a central structure composed of the four connected rings as you saw in Chapter 23. Because sterols are soluble in hydrophobic solvents, they are classified as lipids. Sterol hormones, referred to as steroids, are divided into three types according to function: mineralcorticoids, glucocorticoids (Section 23.6), and the sex hormones that are responsible for male and female hormonal and physical characteristics.

The two most important male sex hormones, or androgens, are testosterone and androsterone. These steroids are responsible for the development of male secondary sex characteristics during puberty and for promoting tissue and muscle growth.

Male sex hormones (androgens)

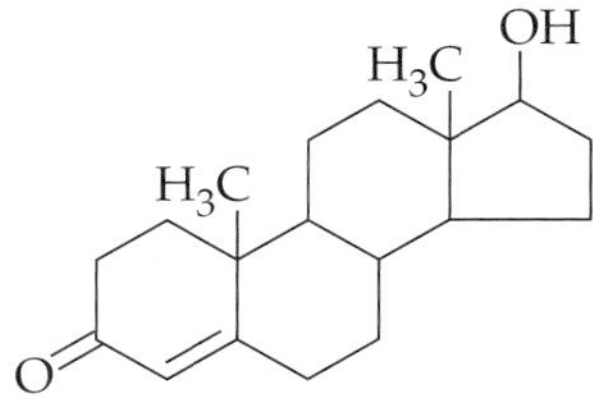

Testosterone

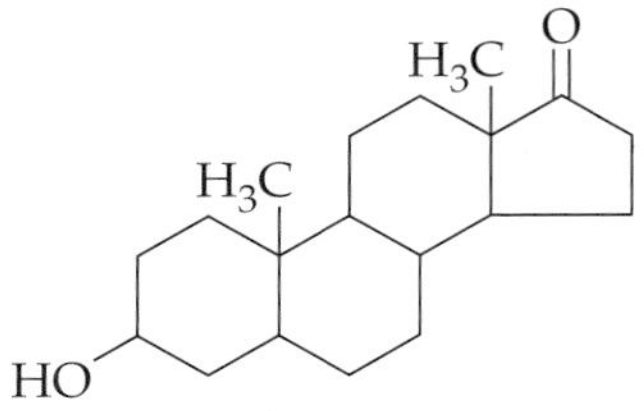

Androsterone

Estrone and *estradiol*, the female steroid hormones known as *estrogens,* are synthesized from testosterone, primarily in the ovaries but also to a small extent in the adrenal cortex. Estrogens govern development of female secondary sex characteristics and participate in regulation of the menstrual cycle. The ovaries release *progestins,* principally *progesterone,* during the second half of the menstrual cycle and prepare the uterus for implantation of a fertilized ovum should conception occur.

Female sex hormones

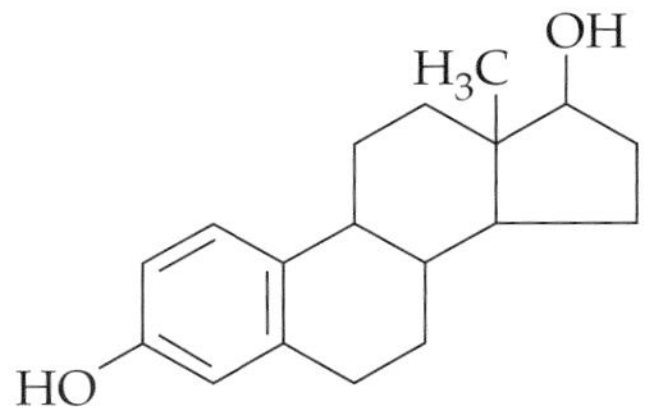

Estradiol
(an estrogen)

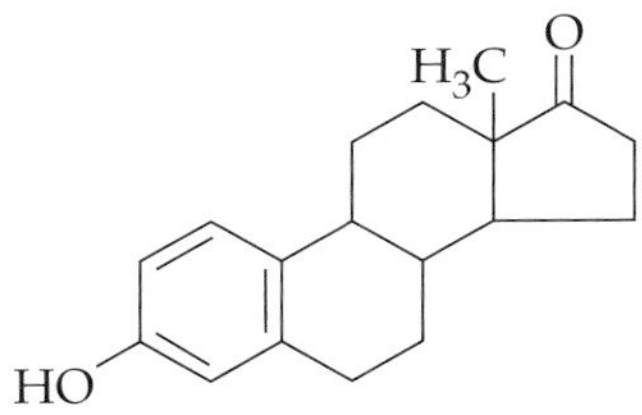

Estrone
(an estrogen)

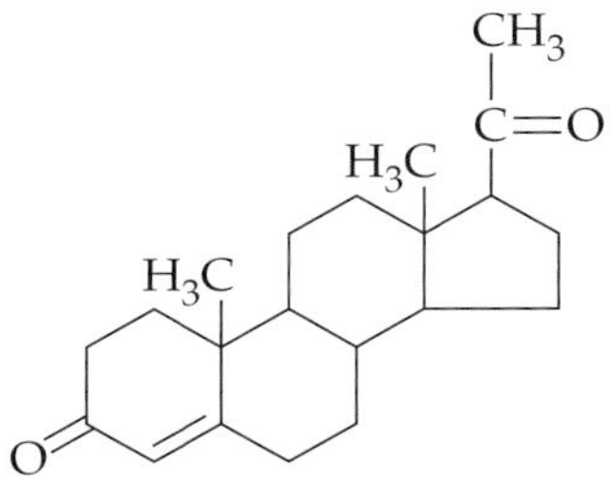

Progesterone
(a progestin)

In addition to the several hundred known steroids isolated from plants and animals, others have been synthesized in the laboratory in the search for new drugs. Most birth control pills are a mixture of the synthetic estrogen *ethynyl estradiol* and the synthetic progestin *norethindrone.* These steroids function by tricking the body into a false pregnant state, making it temporarily infertile. The compound known as *RU-486,* or *mifepristone,* is effective as a "morning after" pill. It prevents pregnancy by binding strongly to the progesterone receptor, thereby blocking implantation in the uterus of a fertilized egg cell.

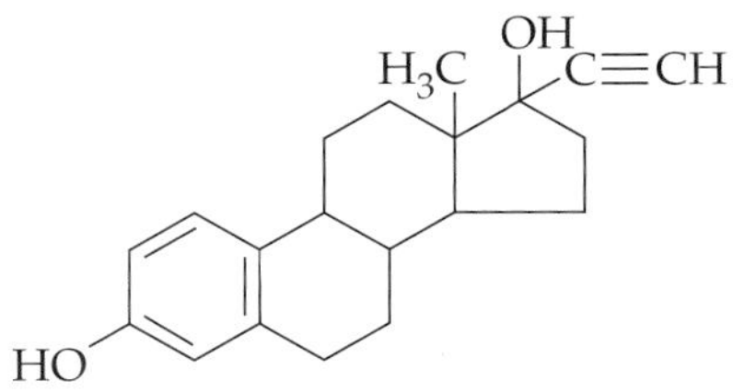

Ethynyl estradiol
(a synthetic estrogen)

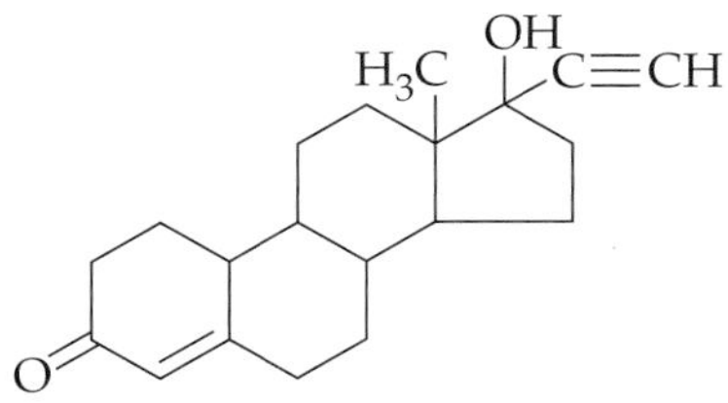

Norethindrone
(a synthetic progestin)

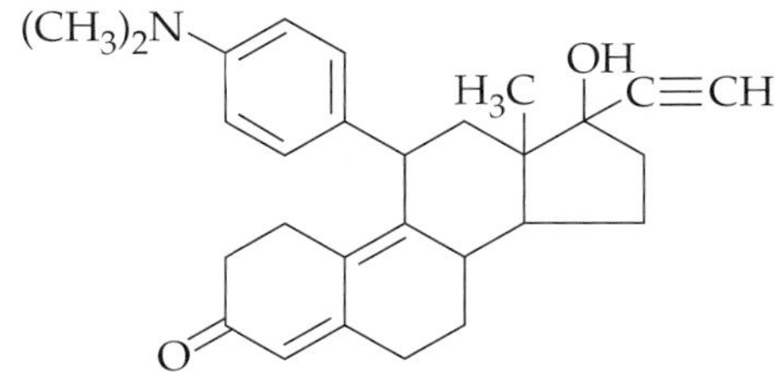

RU-486
(Mifepristone)

Anabolic steroids, which have the ability to increase muscle mass and consequently strength, are drugs that resemble androgenic (male) hormones, such as testosterone. These steroids have been used by bodybuilders for decades to change their body shape to a more muscular, bulky form; some professional and semiprofessional athletes (both men and women) have used them in the hope of gaining weight, strength, power, speed, endurance, and aggressiveness. Unfortunately, many serious side effects can arise from this abuse of anabolic steroids. Stunted bone growth in adolescents, liver, prostate, and kidney

CHEMISTRY IN ACTION

Homeostasis

Homeostasis—the maintenance of a constant internal environment in the body—is as important to the study of living things as atomic structure is to the study of chemistry. The phrase "internal environment" is a general way to describe all the conditions within cells, organs, and body systems. Conditions such as body temperature, the availability of chemical compounds that supply energy, and the disposal of waste products must remain within specific limits for an organism to function properly. Throughout our bodies, sensors track the internal environment and send signals to restore proper balance if the environment changes. If oxygen is in short supply, for example, a signal is sent that makes us breathe harder. When we are cold, a signal is sent to constrict surface blood vessels and prevent further loss of heat.

At the chemical level, homeostasis regulates the concentrations of ions and many different organic compounds so that they stay near normal levels. The predictability of the concentrations of such substances is the basis for *clinical chemistry*—the chemical analysis of body tissues and fluids. In the clinical lab, various tests measure concentrations of significant ions and compounds in blood, urine, feces, spinal fluid, or other samples from a patient's body. Comparing the lab results with "norms" (average concentration ranges in a population of healthy individuals) shows which body systems are struggling, or possibly failing, to maintain homeostasis. To give just one example, urate (commonly known as uric acid) is an anion that helps to carry waste nitrogen from the body. A uric acid concentration higher than the normal range of about 2.5–7.7 mg/dL in blood can indicate the onset of gout or signal possible kidney malfunction.

A copy of a clinical lab report for a routine blood analysis is shown in the following figure. (Fortunately, this individual has no significant variations from normal.) The metal names in the report refer to the various cations, and the heading "Phosphorus" refers to the phosphate anion.

CIA Problem 28.1 One of the responsibilities of the endocrine system is maintenance of homeostasis in the body. Briefly explain what is meant by the term *homeostasis*.

CIA Problem 28.2 What is the goal of the measurements of clinical chemistry?

Test	Result	Normal Range
Albumin	4.3 g/dL	3.5–5.3 g/dL
Alk. Phos.*	33 U/L	25–90 U/L
BUN*	8 mg/dL	8–23 mg/dL
Bilirubin T.*	0.1 mg/dL	0.2–1.6 mg/dL
Calcium	8.6 mg/dL	8.5–10.5 mg/dL
Cholesterol	227 mg/dL	120–250 mg/dL
Chol., HDL*	75 mg/dL	30–75 mg/dL
Creatinine	0.6 mg/dL	0.7–1.5 mg/dL
Glucose	86 mg/dL	65–110 mg/dL
Iron	101 mg/dL	35–140 mg/dL
LDH*	48 U/L	50–166 U/L
SGOT*	23 U/L	0–28 U/L
Total protein	5.9 g/dL	6.2–8.5 g/dL
Triglycerides	75 mg/dL	36–165 mg/dL
Uric Acid	4.1 mg/dL	2.5–7.7 mg/dL
GGT*	23 U/L	0–45 U/L
Magnesium	1.7 mEq/L	1.3–2.5 mEq/L
Phosphorus	2.6 mg/dL	2.5–4.8 mg/dL
SGPT*	13 U/L	0–26 U/L
Sodium	137.7 mEq/L	135–155 mEq/L
Potassium	3.8 mEq/L	3.5–5.5 mEq/L

▲ **A clinical lab report for routine blood analysis.** The abbreviations marked with asterisks are for the following tests (alternative standard abbreviations are in parentheses): Alk. Phos., alkaline phosphatase (ALP); BUN, blood urea nitrogen; Bilirubin T., total bilirubin; Chol., HDL, cholesterol, high-density lipoproteins; LDH, lactate dehydrogenase; SGOT, serum glutamic oxaloacetic transaminase (AST); GGT, γ-glutamyl transferase; SGPT, serum glutamic pyruvic transaminase (ALT).

CIA Problem 28.3 In humans, approximately 12% of all genes are regulatory genes necessary to maintain homeostasis within cells. Health checkups often include a blood panel; common compounds measured include blood glucose and triacylglycerols. Based on your knowledge of metabolism, why would these compounds be included in the blood test? What might that have to do with regulatory genes?

cancer, high blood pressure, aggressive behavior, liver damage, irregular heartbeat, and nosebleeds (arising out of blood coagulation disorders) are but a few of the short and long-term side effects of these agents. Today, most organized amateur and professional sports have banned the use of these and other "performance-enhancing" drugs.

Despite bans, "roids" are still used by some athletes. Baseball, track, wrestling, and cycling have all investigated the use of anabolic steroids, with prominent athletes stripped of their honors. It is legal to use steroids to treat injuries in racehorses, but treatment must stop a month prior to a race. Trainers still abuse this rule. To enforce the ban on anabolic steroids, athletes (human and animal) are subjected to random drug screening, but some athletes attempt to get around the screenings by using *designer steroids*—steroids that cannot be detected with current screening methods, such as tetrahydrogestrinone (THG), trenbolone (used by cattle ranchers to increase the size of cattle), and gestrinone (used to treat endometriosis in women), because identification depends on knowing the compound's structure. However, analysis of a synthetic steroid to determine its structure is easily done, thwarting athletes' plans.

Designer Anabolic Steroids

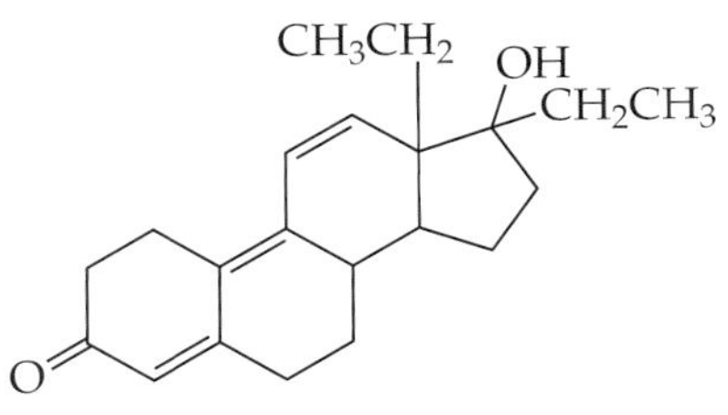

Tetrahydrogestrinone
(THG)

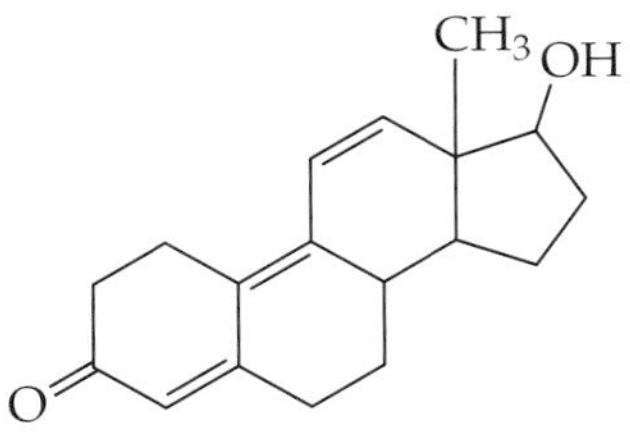

Trenbolone

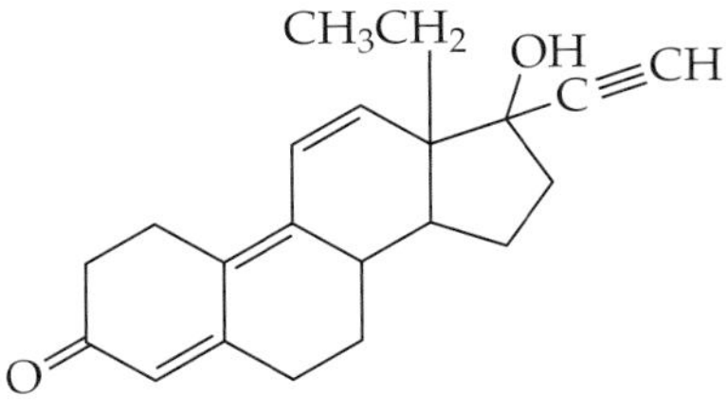

Gestrinone

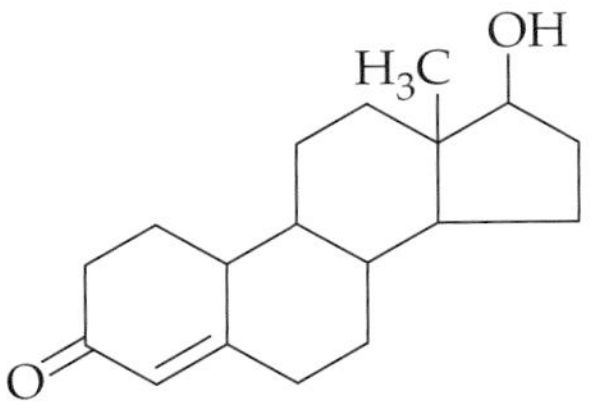

Nandrolone
(an anabolic steroid)

PROBLEM 28.9

Nandrolone is an anabolic, or tissue-building, steroid sometimes taken by athletes seeking to build muscle mass (it is banned by the International Olympic Committee as well as other athletic organizations). Among its effects is a high level of androgenic activity. Which of the androgens shown on page 833 does it most closely resemble? How does it differ from that androgen?

28.5   Neurotransmitters

Learning Objective:

• Describe the origins, pathways, and actions of neurotransmitters.

Neurotransmitters are the chemical messengers of the nervous system. Released by nerve cells *(neurons),* they transmit signals to neighboring target cells, such as other nerve cells, muscle cells, or endocrine cells. Structurally, nerve cells that rely on neurotransmitters typically have a bulb-like body connected to a long, thin stem called an *axon* (Figure 28.5). Short, tentacle-like appendages, the *dendrites,* protrude from the bulbous end of the neuron, and numerous filaments protrude from the axon at the opposite end. The filaments lie close to the target cell, separated only by a narrow gap—the **synapse.**

A nerve impulse is transmitted along a nerve cell by variations in electrical potential caused by the exchange of positive and negative ions across the cell membrane. Chemical transmission of the impulse between a nerve cell and its target occurs when neurotransmitter molecules are released from a *presynaptic neuron,* cross the synapse, and bind to receptors on the target cell. When the target is another nerve cell, it is called a *postsynaptic neuron,* where receptors on the postsynaptic neuron's dendrites receive the neurotransmitter, as shown in Figure 28.5. Once neurotransmitter–receptor binding has occurred, the message has been delivered. The postsynaptic neuron then transmits the nerve impulse down its own axon until a neurotransmitter delivers the message to the next neuron or other target cell.

Neurotransmitter molecules are synthesized in the presynaptic neurons and stored there in small pockets, known as *vesicles,* from which they are released as needed. After a neurotransmitter has done its job, it must be *rapidly* removed from the synaptic cleft so that the postsynaptic neuron is ready to receive another impulse. Removal occurs in one of two ways. Either a chemical change catalyzed by an enzyme available in the synaptic cleft inactivates the neurotransmitter or, alternatively, the neurotransmitter is returned to the presynaptic neuron and placed in storage until it is needed again.

Most neurotransmitters are amines synthesized from amino acids. Figure 28.4 shows the synthesis of dopamine, norepinephrine, and epinephrine from tyrosine. Figure 28.6 shows the synthesis of serotonin and melatonin from tryptophan. Some neurotransmitters act directly by causing changes in adjacent cells as soon as they

Synapse The place where the tip of a neuron and its target cell lie adjacent to each other.

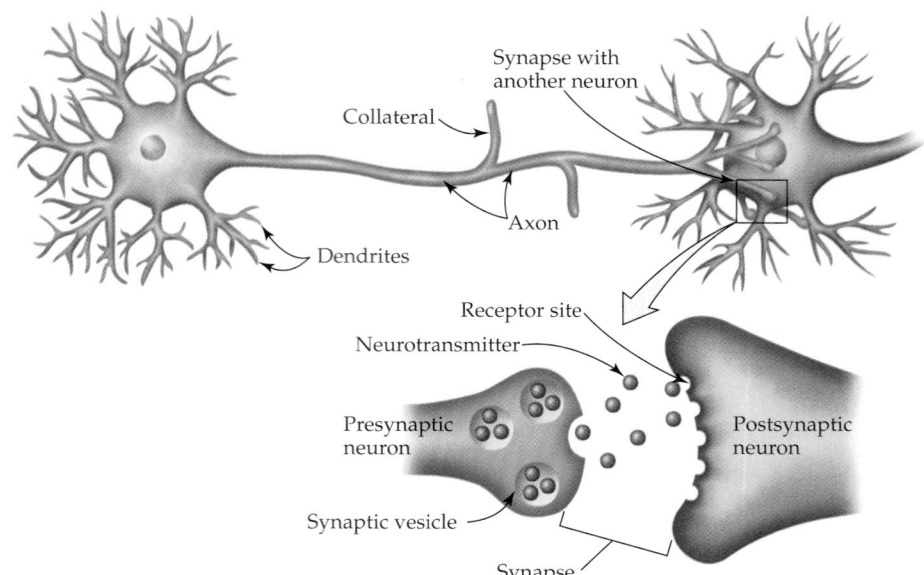

▶ **Figure 28.5**
A nerve cell and transmission of a nerve signal by neurotransmitters. Transmission occurs between neurons when a neurotransmitter is released by the presynaptic neuron, crosses the synapse, and fits into a receptor on the postsynaptic neuron or other target cell.

connect with their receptors. Others rely on second messengers, often cyclic AMP, the same second messenger utilized by hormones. Individual neurotransmitters are associated with emotions, drug addiction, pain relief, and other brain functions, as we shall see in the following sections.

PROBLEM 28.10

Which of the following transformations of amines in Figure 28.6 is (1) an acetylation, (2) a methylation, and (3) a decarboxylation?

(a) 5-Hydroxytryptophan to serotonin

(b) Serotonin to N-acetylserotonin

(c) N-Acetylserotonin to melatonin

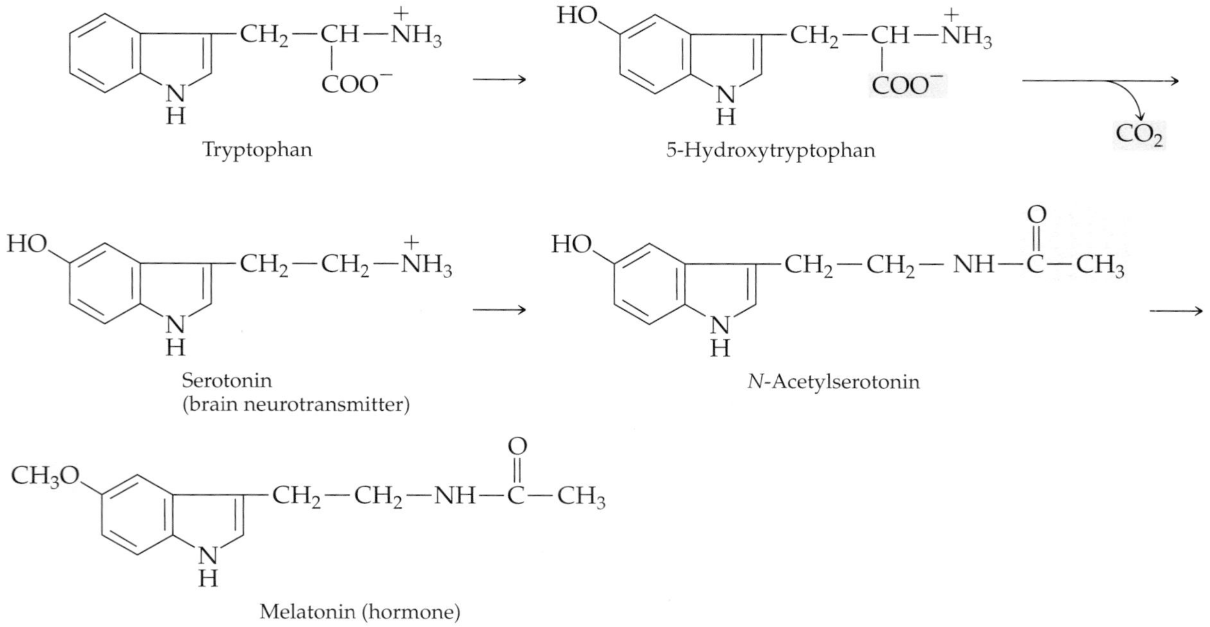

▲ **Figure 28.6**
Synthesis of chemical messengers from tryptophan.
The changes in each step are highlighted in yellow for substitution reactions and in green for elimination reactions.

28.6 How Neurotransmitters Work: Acetylcholine, Its Agonists and Antagonists

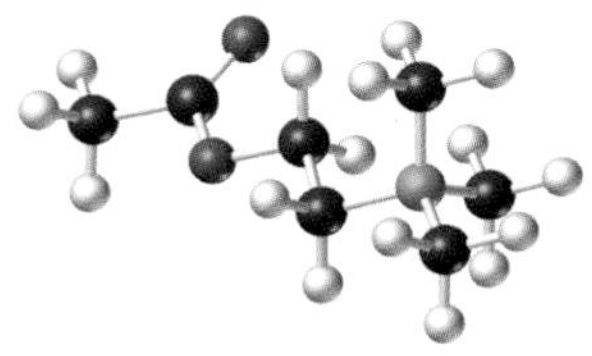

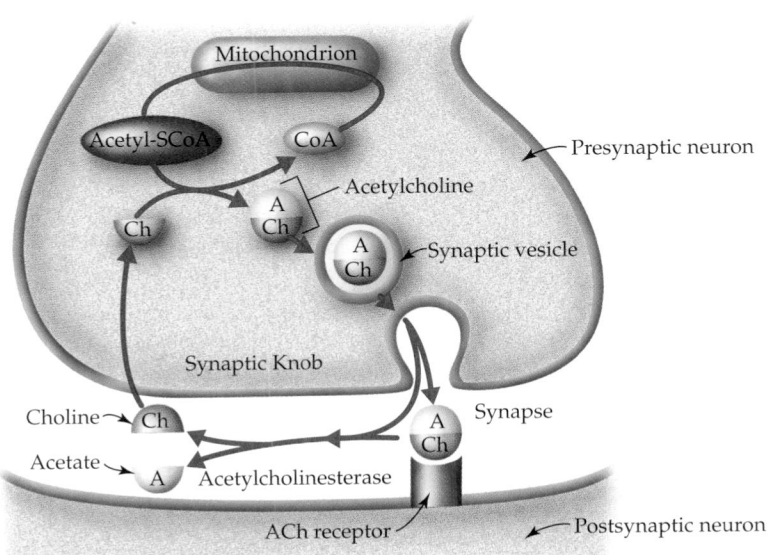

Acetylcholine

Learning Objective:

- Outline the sequence of events in acetylcholine's action as a neurotransmitter and give examples of its agonists and antagonists.

Acetylcholine in Action

Acetylcholine is a neurotransmitter responsible for the control of skeletal muscles. It is also widely distributed in the brain, where it plays a role in the sleep–wake cycle, learning, memory, and mood. *Cholinergic nerves* rely on acetylcholine as their neurotransmitter.

Acetylcholine is synthesized in presynaptic neurons and stored in their vesicles. The rapid sequence of events in Figure 28.7 shows the action of acetylcholine communicating between nerve cells, and the sequence is as follows:

- A nerve impulse arrives at the presynaptic neuron.
- Vesicles move to the cell membrane, fuse with it, and release their acetylcholine molecules (several thousand molecules from each vesicle).
- Acetylcholine crosses the synapse and binds to receptors on the postsynaptic neuron, causing a change in membrane permeability to ions.
- This change in the permeability to ions of the postsynaptic neuron initiates the nerve impulse in that neuron.
- After the message is delivered, acetylcholinesterase present in the synaptic cleft catalyzes the decomposition of acetylcholine.

Acetylcholine A vertebrate neurotransmitter that is most commonly found in muscle neurons.

$$CH_3-\overset{\overset{\displaystyle O}{\|}}{C}-O-CH_2-CH_2-\overset{+}{N}(CH_3)_3 \xrightarrow[\text{H}_2\text{O}]{\text{Acetylcholinesterase}} CH_3COO^- + HO-CH_2-CH_2-\overset{+}{N}(CH_3)_3$$

Acetylcholine (ACh)   Acetate   Choline

- Choline is absorbed back into the presynaptic neuron, where new acetylcholine is synthesized.

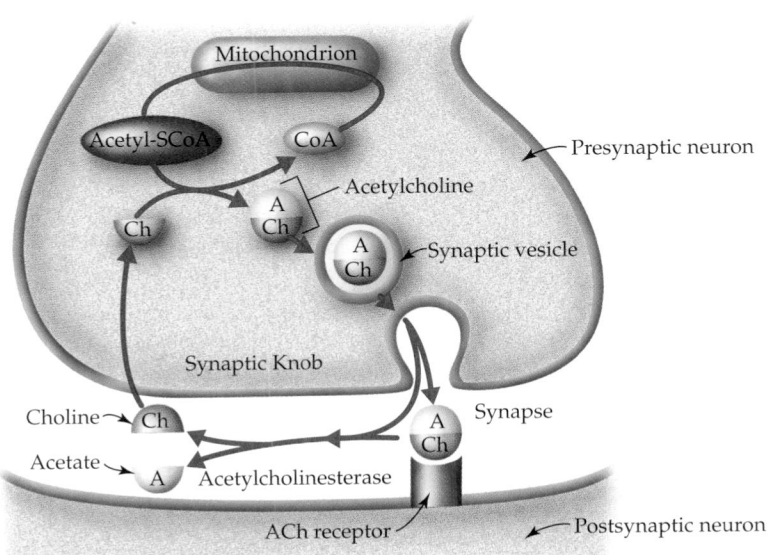

◄ **Figure 28.7**
Acetylcholine release and re-uptake. Acetylcholine is stored in vesicles in the presynaptic neuron. After it is released into the synapse and connects with its receptor, it is broken down by hydrolysis into acetate and choline in a reaction catalyzed by acetylcholinesterase. The choline is taken back into the synaptic knob and reused to synthesize acetylcholine, which is then stored in the vesicles until needed.

Drugs and Acetylcholine

Many drugs act at acetylcholine synapses, where the tip of a neuron that releases acetylcholine and its target cell lie adjacent to each other. A **drug** is any molecule that alters normal functions when it enters the body from an external source. The action is at the molecular level, and it can be either therapeutic or poisonous. To have an effect, many drugs must connect with a receptor just as a substrate must bind to an enzyme or as a hormone or neurotransmitter must bind to a receptor. In fact, many drugs are designed to mimic a given hormone or neurotransmitter and in so doing elicit either an enhanced or attenuated effect.

Pharmacologists classify some drugs as **agonists**—substances that act to produce or prolong the normal biochemical response of a receptor. Other drugs are classified as **antagonists**—substances that block or inhibit the normal response of a receptor. Many agonists and antagonists compete with normal signaling molecules for interaction with the receptor, just as inhibitor molecules compete with substrate for the active site in an enzyme. To illustrate the ways in which drugs can affect our biochemical activity, we next describe the action of a group of drugs. These drugs are all members of the same family in the sense that their biochemical activity occurs at acetylcholine synapses in the central nervous system. Figure 28.7 shows the locations of their actions and Table 28.2 describes examples of the acetylcholine drug family.

Drug Any substance that alters body function when it is introduced from an external source.

Agonist A substance that interacts with a receptor to cause or prolong the receptor's normal biochemical response.

Antagonist A substance that blocks or inhibits the normal biochemical response of a receptor.

◀ Alkaloids are naturally occurring, nitrogen-containing compounds isolated from plants; usually basic, bitter, and poisonous (see Section 16.7).

Table 28.2 Acetylcholine Drug Family (therapeutic or poisonous)

Name (drug mechanism)	Origin	Drug Action
Botulinum toxin (antagonist)	The botulinum toxin is found in *Clostridium botulinum* that are located in soil. One type of exposure to the toxin is through improperly canned food.	The toxin binds irreversibly to the presynaptic neuron, where acetylcholine would be released. It prevents this release, frequently causing death due to muscle paralysis.
Black widow spider (agonist)	Venom from bite	The synapse is flooded with acetylcholine, resulting in muscle cramps and spasms.
Organophosphorus insecticides (antagonists)	These are synthesized in the laboratory. Some examples include parathion, diazinon, and malathion.	All of the organophosphorus insecticides prevent acetylcholinesterase from breaking down acetylcholine within the synapse. As a result, the nerves are overstimulated, causing a variety of symptoms including muscle contraction and weakness, lack of coordination, and at high doses, convulsions.
Nicotine (agonist) (Chapter 16)	A general nicotine alkaloid source is found in the leaves nicotiana nightshade plants, which are used for manufacturing tobacco.	Nicotine at low doses is a stimulant because it activates acetylcholine receptors. The sense of alertness and well-being produced by inhaling tobacco smoke is a result of this effect. At high doses, nicotine is an antagonist. It irreversibly blocks the acetylcholine receptors and can cause their degeneration.
Atropine (antagonist)	Atropine, found naturally in a variety of nightshade plants, is an alkaloid that is poisonous at high doses.	At controlled doses, its therapeutic uses include acceleration of abnormally slow heart rate, paralysis of eye muscles during surgery, and relaxation of intestinal muscles in gastrointestinal disorders. Most importantly, it is a specific antidote for acetylcholinesterase poisons such as organophosphorus insecticides. By blocking activation of the receptors, it counteracts the excess acetylcholine created by acetylcholinesterase inhibitors.
Tubocurarine (antagonist)	Tubocurarine is a purified alkaloid from curare, a mixture of chemicals extracted from a plant found in South America.	Tubocurarine competes with acetylcholine at receptors. It is used to paralyze patients in conjunction with anesthesia drugs prior to surgery.

PROBLEM 28.11

Propranolol (trade name Inderal) is an antagonist for certain epinephrine receptors and is a member of the class of drugs known as beta blockers (because they block what are known as beta receptors). Circle the functional groups in propranolol and name them. Compare the structure of propranolol with the structure of epinephrine and describe the differences.

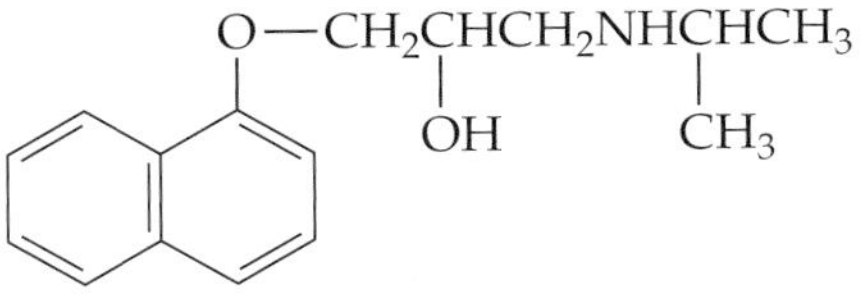

$$O—CH_2CHCH_2NHCHCH_3$$

Propranolol
(Inderal)

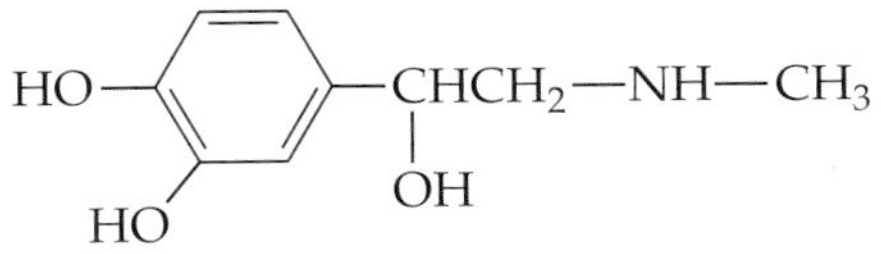

$$HO——CHCH_2—NH—CH_3$$

Epinephrine
(adrenaline)

PROBLEM 28.12

The LD_{50} values (lethal dose in mg/kg, for rats) for the three organophosphorus insecticides listed in this section are parathion, 3–13 mg/kg; diazinon, 250–285 mg/kg; and malathion, 1000–1375 mg/kg. (a) Find the molecular structures using the Internet. (b) Which would you choose for use in your garden and why? (c) Thinking about hydrophobic and hydrophilic, which is most dangerous for mammals to ingest? Why?

KEY CONCEPT PROBLEM 28.13

Some drugs are classified as agonists, whereas others are classified as antagonists.

(a) Sumatripan, sold as Imitrex, is effective in treating migraine headaches. It acts as an agonist at the serotonin receptor. Explain the effect Imitrex has on the serotonin receptor.

(b) Ondansetron, sold as Zofran, acts on a subclass of serotonin receptors to inhibit nausea and vomiting; it is frequently prescribed to patients in chemotherapy. It acts as an antagonist at these receptors. Explain the effect Zofran has on these receptors.

28.7 Histamines, Antihistamines, and Important Neurotransmitters

Learning Objective:

• Describe the neurotransmitters and types of drugs that play roles in allergies, mental depression, and drug addiction.

Histamine and Antihistamines

Histamine is the neurotransmitter responsible for the symptoms of the allergic reaction familiar to hay fever sufferers or those who are allergic to animals. It is also the chemical that causes an itchy bump when an insect bites you. In the body, histamine is produced by decarboxylation of the amino acid histidine.

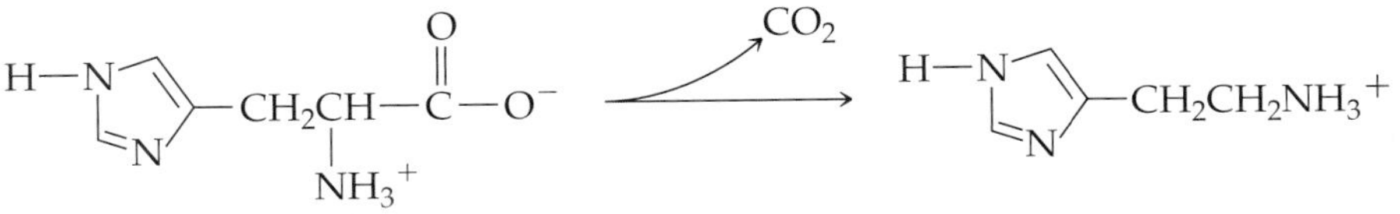

$$H—N—CH_2CH—\overset{O}{\overset{\|}{C}}—O^- \xrightarrow{CO_2} H—N—CH_2CH_2NH_3{}^+$$

Histidine

Histamine

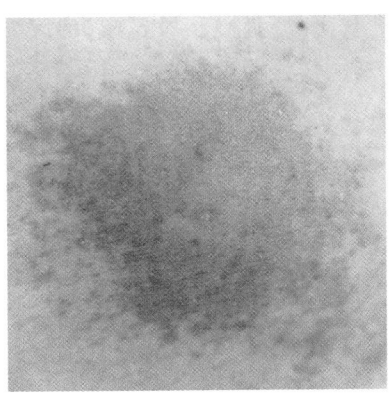

▲ The swelling and inflammation surrounding this insect bite are due to a histamine response.

The *antihistamines* are a family of drugs that counteract the effect of histamine because they are histamine-receptor antagonists. They competitively block the attachment of histamine to its receptors. Members of this family all have in common a disubstituted ethylamine side chain, usually with two *N*-methyl groups. As illustrated by the following examples, the R′ and R″ groups at the other end of the molecule tend to be bulky and aromatic.

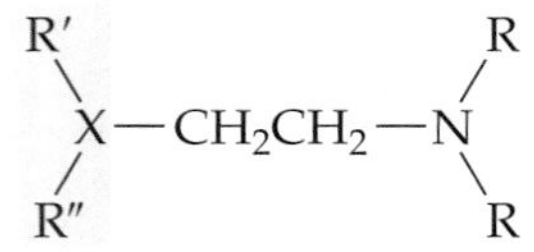

General antihistamine structure

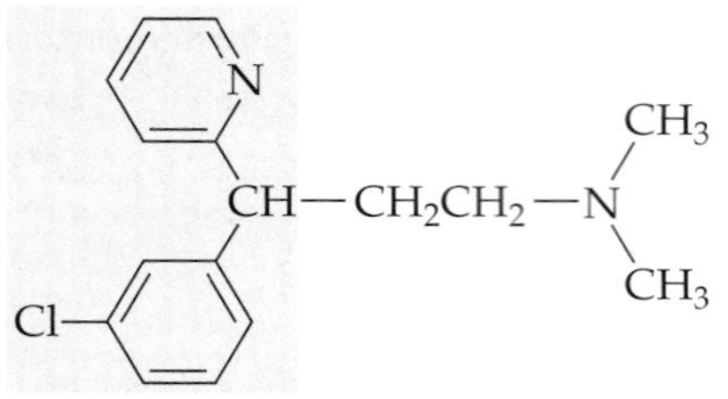

Chlorpheniramine
(an antihistamine)

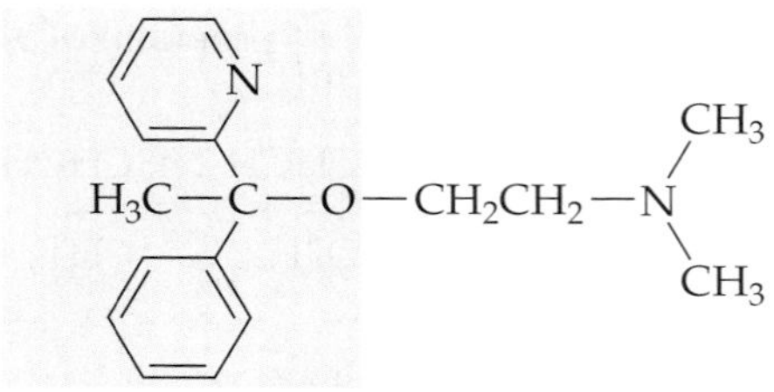

Doxylamine
(an antihistamine)

Histamine also activates secretion of acid in the stomach. After synthesis of about 200 different compounds with systematic variations on the histamine structure, a histamine antagonist was developed. The result was *cimetidine,* widely publicized as a treatment for heartburn under its trade name Tagamet. Today, many other histamine antagonists exist, including ranitidine, sold under its trade name Zantac.

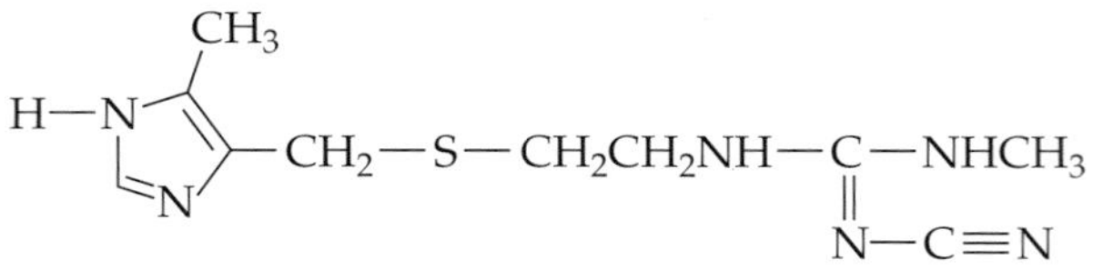

Cimetidine
(Tagamet)

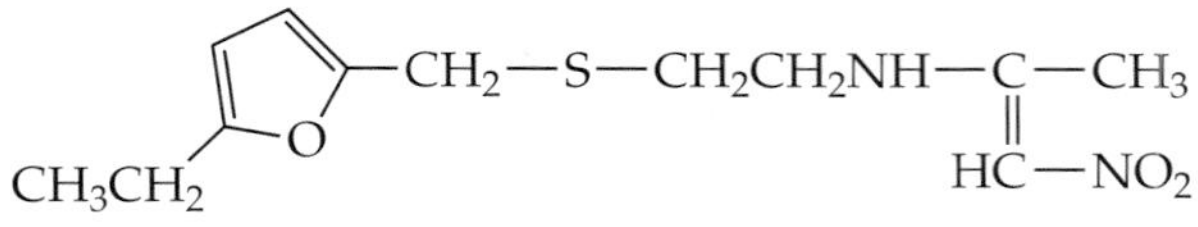

Ranitidine
(Zantac)

Serotonin, Norepinephrine, and Dopamine

Serotonin, norepinephrine, and dopamine could be called the "big three" of neurotransmitters. Regular news reports appear as discoveries about them accumulate. Collectively, serotonin, norepinephrine, and dopamine are known as *monoamines.* Figures 28.4 and 28.6 show their biochemical syntheses. All are active in the brain and all are associated with mood, fear and pleasure, mental illness, and drug addiction.

The connection between major depression and a deficiency of serotonin, norepinephrine, and dopamine is well-established. The evidence comes from the different modes of action of three families of drugs used to treat depression: amitriptyline, phenelzine, and fluoxetine. Each in its own way increases the concentration of the neurotransmitters at synapses.

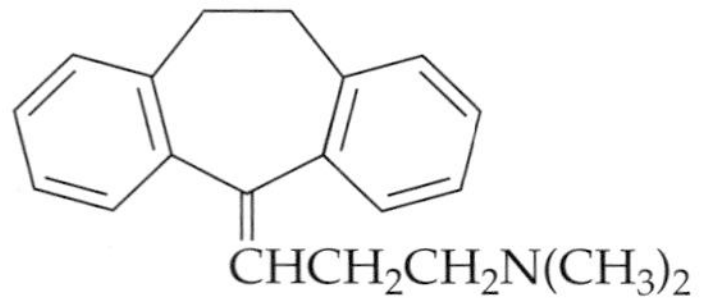

Amitriptyline, a tricyclic antidepressant
(Elavil)

Phenelzine, an MAO inhibitor
(Nardil)

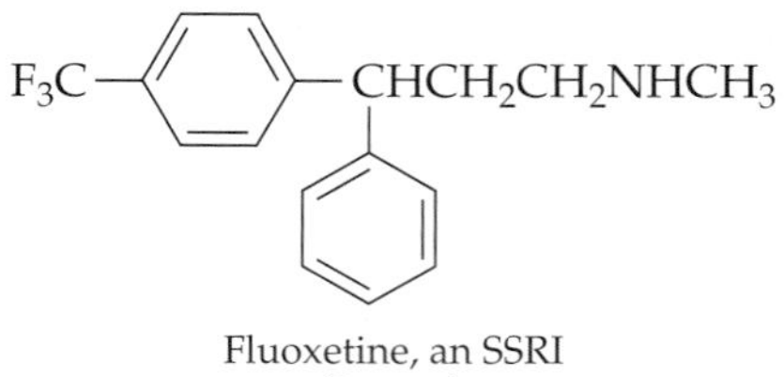

Fluoxetine, an SSRI
(Prozac)

- Amitriptyline is representative of the *tricyclic antidepressants,* which were the first generation of these drugs. The tricyclics prevent the re-uptake of serotonin and norepinephrine from within the synapse. Serotonin is important in mood-control pathways and functions more slowly than other neurotransmitters; slowing its re-uptake often improves mood in depressed patients.
- Phenelzine is a *monoamine oxidase (MAO) inhibitor,* one of a group of medications that inhibit the enzyme that breaks down monoamine neurotransmitters. This inhibition of *MAO* allows the concentrations of monoamines at synapses to increase.

- Fluoxetine represents the newest class of antidepressants, the *selective serotonin re-uptake inhibitors (SSRI)*. They are more selective than the tricyclics because they inhibit only the re-uptake of serotonin. Fluoxetine (Prozac) has rapidly become the most widely prescribed drug for all but the most severe forms of depression. Most antidepressants cause unpleasant side effects; fluoxetine does not, a major benefit.

It is important to note that the relief of depression symptoms by these drugs is not evidence that the chemical basis of depression is fully understood nor that increasing neurotransmitter concentration is the only action of these drugs. The brain still holds many secrets. The use of fluoxetine for conditions other than depression illustrates the complex and not yet fully understood relationships between neurotransmitter activity and behavior. It is used to treat obsessive compulsive disorder, bulimia, obesity, panic disorder, body dysmorphic disorder, teen depression, and premenstrual dysphoric disorder (formerly known as PMS). New uses for this class of drugs are constantly being explored.

Dopamine and Drug Addiction

Dopamine plays a role in the brain in processes that control movement, emotional responses, and the experiences of pleasure and pain. It interacts with five different kinds of receptors in different parts of the brain. An oversupply of dopamine is associated with schizophrenia, and an undersupply results in the loss of fine motor control in Parkinson's disease (see the Chemistry in Action "The Blood–Brain Barrier," Chapter 29). Dopamine also plays an important role in the brain's reward system. An ample supply of brain dopamine produces the pleasantly satisfied feeling that results from a rewarding experience—a "natural high." Herein lies the role of dopamine in drug addiction: the more the dopamine receptors are stimulated, the greater the high.

Experiments show that cocaine blocks re-uptake of dopamine from the synapse, and amphetamines accelerate release of dopamine. Studies have linked increased brain levels of dopamine to alcohol and nicotine addiction as well. The higher-than-normal stimulation of dopamine receptors by drugs results in tolerance. In the drive to maintain constant conditions (see the Chemistry in Action "Homeostasis," p. 834), the number of dopamine receptors decreases and the sensitivity of those that remain decreases. Consequently, brain cells require more and more of a drug for the same result, a condition that contributes to addiction.

Marijuana also creates an increase in dopamine levels in the same brain areas where dopamine levels increase after administration of heroin or cocaine. The most-active ingredient in marijuana is tetrahydrocannabinol (THC). The use of marijuana medically for chronic pain relief has become a controversial topic in recent years, as questions about its benefits and drawbacks are debated.

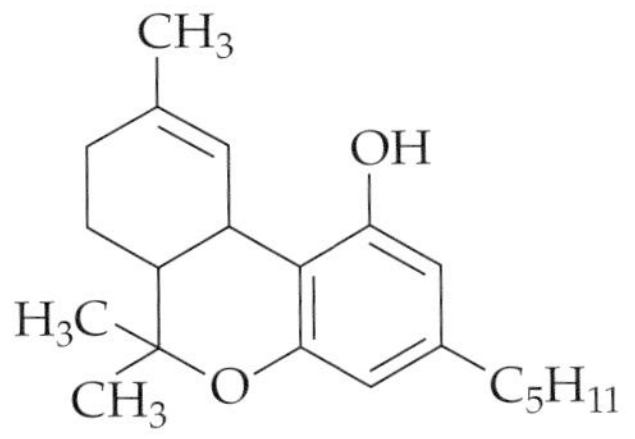

Tetrahydrocannabinol (THC)

🔲 KEY CONCEPT PROBLEM 28.14

Identify the functional groups present in THC. Is the molecule likely to be hydrophilic or hydrophobic? Would you expect THC to build up in fatty tissues in the body, or would it be readily eliminated in the urine?

Worked Example 28.2 Predicting Biological Activity Based on Structure

The relationship between the structure of a molecule and its biochemical function is an essential area of study in biochemistry and the design of drugs. Terfenadine (Seldane) was one of the first of the new generation of "nondrowsy" antihistamines (it was removed from the market due to potential heart toxicity). Based solely on what you have learned so far, suggest which of its structural features make it an antihistamine.

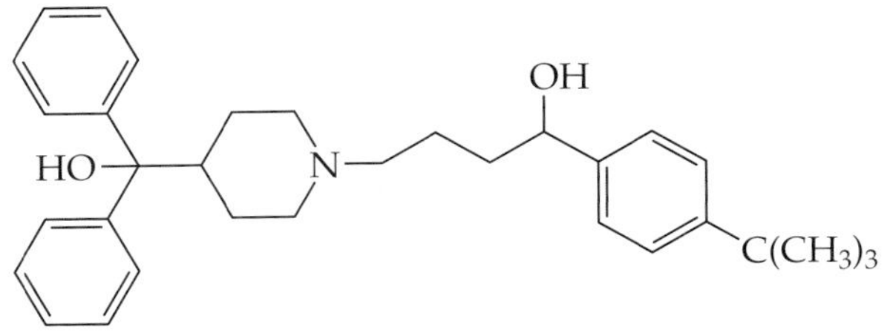

Terfenadine

—continued on next page

—continued from previous page

ANALYSIS Members of the antihistamine family have in common the general structure shown here: an X group (usually a CH) to which two aromatic groups (noted as *aryl* in the drawing) are attached. The X is also attached to a disubstituted nitrogen by a carbon chain.

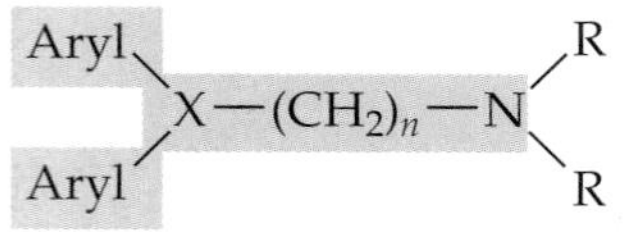

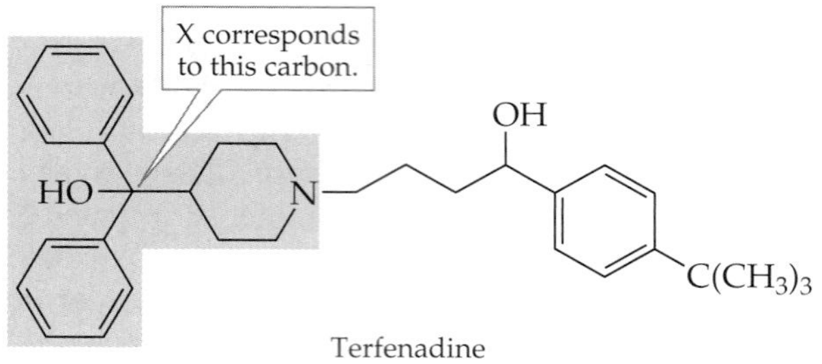

Terfenadine

SOLUTION
Since terfenadine contains the same basic structure as a general antihistamine, its biological function should be similar.

KEY CONCEPT PROBLEM 28.15

Predict which of the following compounds is an antihistamine and which is an antidepressant.

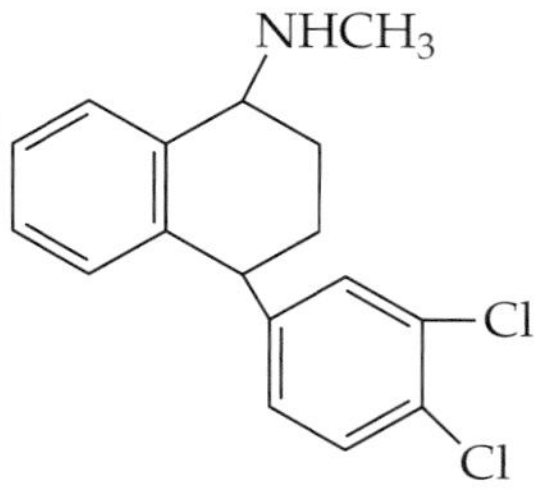

Neuropeptides and Pain Relief

Studies of morphine and other opium derivatives in the 1970s revealed that these addictive but effective pain-killing substances act via their own specific brain receptors, raising some interesting questions: Why are there brain receptors for chemicals from a plant? Could it be that there are animal neurotransmitters that act at the same receptors?

The two pentapeptides, *Met-enkephalin* and *Leu-enkephalin* (Met and Leu stand for the carboxy terminal amino acids, Section 18.3), were discovered to exert morphine-like suppression of pain when injected into the brains of experimental animals.

Met-enkephalin: Tyr-Gly-Gly-Phe-**Met**

Leu-enkephalin: Tyr-Gly-Gly-Phe-**Leu**

The structural similarity between Met-enkephalin and morphine, highlighted in the following figure, supports the concept that both interact with the same receptors, which are located in regions of the brain and spinal cord that act in the perception of pain.

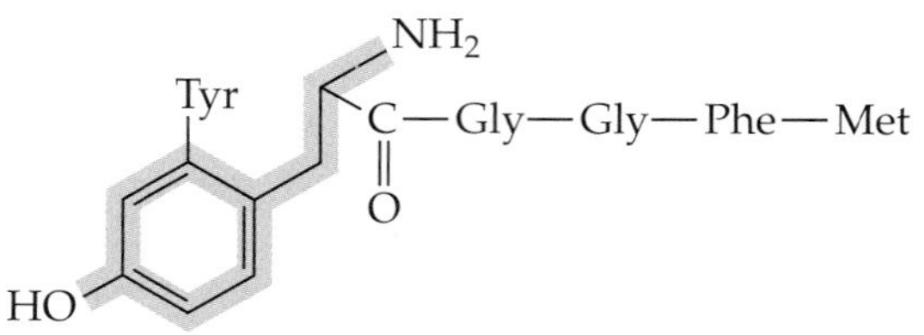

Met-enkephalin 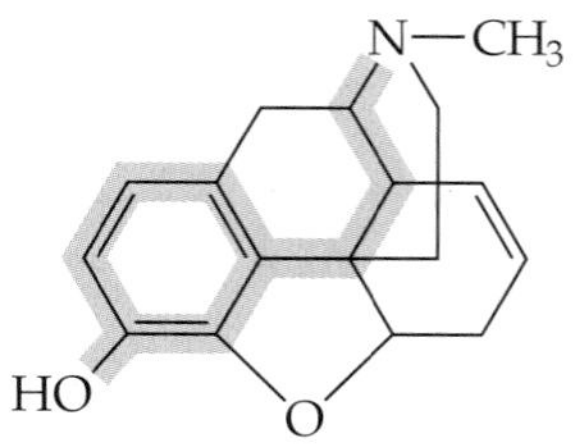   Morphine

Subsequently, about a dozen natural pain-killing polypeptides that act via the opiate receptors, classified as *endorphins,* have also been found. A 31-amino acid polypeptide that ends with the same 5-amino acid sequence as Met-enkephalin is one such endorphin and is a more potent pain suppressor than morphine.

HANDS-ON CHEMISTRY 28.1

In this exercise, you will track various biochemical responses during simple activities and may be able to identify some hormones and neurotransmitters discussed in this chapter like serotonin (a neurotransmitter molecule involved in mood or the sleep–wake cycle) or epinephrine (the flight-or-fight molecule that activates the secondary messenger cAMP).

For a few days, you will keep a log that correlates activity or inactivity to alertness.

1. On day one, right before class, record your alertness, mood, and how long it lasts. Also, rank your bodily functions using the following defined scale. Then, if you get a break during class, record your alertness, mood, and bodily functions again using the same scale.
2. Before class on day two, take a five minute walk and record your mood, alertness, and bodily functions. If the class takes a break, repeat the bodily function recording.
3. On day three, repeat day two but walk a little longer and record your alertness, mood, and bodily functions.
4. On day four, repeat day three but walk even longer, and record your alertness, mood, and bodily functions.

Use the following scale to record your bodily functions each day, where 1 = excellent, 2 = above average, 3 = average, 4 = below average, 5 = terrible, and 6 = no change.

Concentration	1	2	3	4	5	6
Heart rate	1	2	3	4	5	6
Cold hands	1	2	3	4	5	6
Quality of sleep	1	2	3	4	5	6
Frustration	1	2	3	4	5	6
Nausea	1	2	3	4	5	6
Headache	1	2	3	4	5	6
Change of appetite	1	2	3	4	5	6
Breathing	1	2	3	4	5	6

Now that you have collected some data; reflect on which hormones might be elevated or lowered and why. Some generalizations might be if you have a headache or if your heart rate, breathing, and concentration levels are different than normal, there could be increased levels of epinephrine or norepinephrine. If your quality of sleep or appetite is affected, serotonin might be involved. In addition, cortisol has been known to give a feeling of nausea or cold hands.

If you are comfortable, discuss your findings with a classmate. Some points of discussion might be: Did your concentration levels change at all on a day you didn't get good sleep, or, did your mood improve at all after taking a walk? Did you notice your heart rate spike when you were frustrated? Can you conclude any patterns or connections that you observed?

SUMMARY REVISITING THE LEARNING OBJECTIVES

- **Describe the origins, pathways, and actions of hormones.** *Hormones* are the chemical messengers of the *endocrine system.* Under control of the hypothalamus, they are released from various locations, many in response to intermediate, regulatory hormones. Hormones travel in the bloodstream to target cells, where they connect with receptors that initiate chemical changes within cells *(see Problems 22–27).*

- **Distinguish between the different types of hormonal control.** There are three basic types of hormonal control that allow communication between the endocrine system and other tissues: direct neural control, direct release of the hormone, and indirect control through the release of regulatory hormones. In direct neural control, a nervous system message from the hypothalamus initiates release of hormones by the adrenal gland. Direct release of the hormones involves their movement from the hypothalamus to the posterior pituitary gland, where they are stored until needed. Lastly, regulatory hormones from the hypothalamus stimulate or inhibit the release of hormones by the anterior pituitary gland. Many of these pituitary hormones in turn stimulate release of still other hormones by their own target tissues *(see Problems 28–31).*

- **List the different chemical types of hormones and give examples of each.** Hormones are *polypeptides, steroids,* or *amino acid derivatives* (Table 28.2). Many are polypeptides, which range widely in size and include small molecules such as vasopressin and oxytocin, larger ones like insulin, and all of the regulatory hormones. Steroids have a distinctive four-ring structure and are classified as lipids because they are hydrophobic. All of the sex hormones are steroids *(see Problems 32–35).*

- **Explain the sequence of events in epinephrine's action as a hormone.** Epinephrine, the fight-or-flight hormone, acts via a cell-surface receptor and a G protein that connects with an enzyme, both of which are embedded in the cell membrane. The enzyme adenylate cyclase transfers the message to a *second messenger,* a cyclic AMP, which acts within the target cell *(see Problems 36–45).*

- **Explain the functions of the three major types of hormones: amino acid derivatives, polypeptides, and steroids.** Hormones that are amino acid derivatives are *synthesized* from amino acids (Figures 28.4 and 28.6). Epinephrine and norepinephrine act as hormones throughout the body and also act as neurotransmitters in the brain. Polypeptide hormones are the largest class of hormones. Steroid hormones are classified as mineralcorticoids, glucocorticoids, or sex hormones. All three types are synthesized from the endocrine system *(see Problems 46–57).*

- **Describe the origins, pathways, and actions of neurotransmitters.** *Neurotransmitters* are synthesized in presynaptic neurons and stored there in vesicles for release when needed. They travel across a *synaptic cleft* to *receptors* on adjacent target cells. Some act directly via their receptors; others utilize cyclic AMP or other second messengers. After their message is delivered, neurotransmitters are either broken down rapidly or taken back into the presynaptic neuron so that the receptor is free to receive further messages *(see Problems 58–67).*

● **Outline the sequence of events in acetylcholine's action as a neurotransmitter and give examples of its agonists and antagonists.**
Acetylcholine is released from the vesicles of a presynaptic neuron and connects with receptors that initiate continuation of a nerve impulse in the postsynaptic neuron. It is broken down in the synaptic cleft by acetylcholinesterase to form choline, which is returned to the presynaptic neuron and converted back to acetylcholine. *Agonists,* such as nicotine at low doses, activate acetylcholine receptors and are stimulants. *Antagonists,* such as tubocurarine or atropine, which block activation of the receptors, are toxic in high doses, but at low doses are useful as muscle relaxants *(see Problems 68–70).*

● **Describe the neurotransmitters and types of drugs that play roles in allergies, mental depression, drug addiction, and pain relief.**
Histamine, an amino acid derivative, causes allergic symptoms. *Antihistamines* are antagonists with a general structure that resembles histamines but with bulky groups at one end. Monoamines (serotonin, norepinephrine, and dopamine) are brain neurotransmitters; a deficiency of any of these molecules is associated with mental depression. *Drugs* that increase their activity include *tricyclic antidepressants* (e.g., amitriptyline), *MAO inhibitors* (e.g., phenelzine), and *SSRI* (e.g., fluoxetine). An increase of dopamine activity in the brain is associated with the effects of most addictive substances. A group of neuropeptides acts as opiate receptors to counteract pain; all may be addictive *(see Problems 71–82).*

KEY WORDS

Acetylcholine, *p. 837*
Agonist, *p. 838*
Antagonist, *p. 838*

Drug, *p. 838*
Endocrine system, *p. 826*
Hormone, *p. 825*

Neurotransmitter, *p. 825*
Receptor, *p. 825*
Second messenger, *p. 828*

Synapse, *p. 835*

CONCEPT MAP

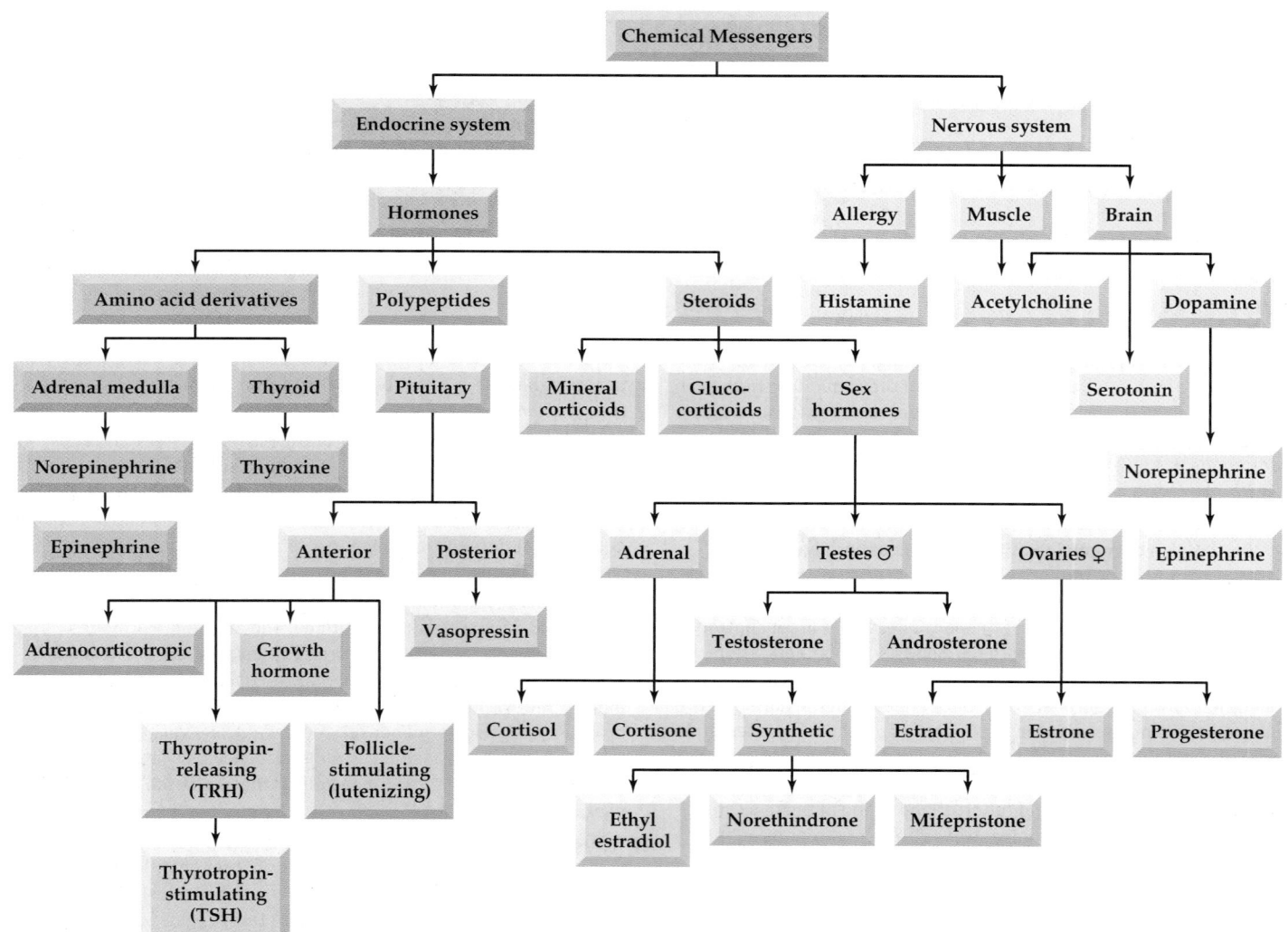

▲ **Figure 28.8 Concept Map.** This concept map shows the categorization of different types of hormones and neurotransmitters.

UNDERSTANDING KEY CONCEPTS

28.16   In many species of animals, at the onset of pregnancy, LH is released; it promotes the synthesis of progesterone—a major hormone in maintaining the pregnancy.

(a) Where is LH produced, and to what class of hormones does it belong?

(b) Where is progesterone produced, and to what class of hormones does it belong?

(c) Do progesterone-producing cells have LH receptors on their surface, or does LH enter the cell to carry out its function?

(d) Does progesterone bind to a cell-surface receptor, or does it enter the cell to carry out its function? Explain.

28.17   The "rush" of epinephrine in response to danger causes the release of glucose in muscle cells so that those muscles can carry out either "fight-or-flight." Very small amounts of the hormone produced in the adrenal gland cause a powerful response. To get such a response, the original signal (epinephrine) must be amplified many times. At what step in the sequence of events (Section 28.3) would you predict that the signal is amplified? Explain. How might that amplification take place?

28.18   Diabetes occurs when there is a malfunction in the uptake of glucose from the bloodstream into the cells. Your friend's youngest brother was just diagnosed with type I diabetes, and she has asked you the following questions. How would you answer them?

(a) What hormone is involved, and what class is it?

(b) Where is the hormone released?

(c) How is this hormone transported to the cells that need it to allow glucose to enter?

(d) Would you expect the hormone to enter the cell to carry out its function? Explain.

28.19   Give two mechanisms by which neurotransmitters exert their effects.

28.20   When an impulse arrives at the synapse, the synaptic vesicles open and release neurotransmitters into the cleft within a thousandth of a second. Within another ten thousandth of a second, these molecules have diffused across the cleft and bound to receptor sites in the effector cell. In what two ways is transmission across a synapse terminated so that the neuron's signal is concluded?

28.21   What is the significance of dopamine in the addictive effects of cocaine, amphetamines, and alcohol?

ADDITIONAL PROBLEMS

CHEMICAL MESSENGERS (SECTION 28.1)

28.22   What do the terms *chemical messenger, target tissue,* and *hormone receptor* mean?

28.23   What is a hormone? What is the function of a hormone? How is the presence of a hormone detected by its target?

28.24   What is the main difference between a hormone and a vitamin?

28.25   What is the main difference between a hormone and a neurotransmitter?

28.26   Is a hormone changed as a result of binding to a receptor? Is the receptor changed as a result of binding the hormone? What are the binding forces between hormone and receptor?

28.27   How is hormone binding to its receptor more like an allosteric regulator binding to an enzyme than a substrate binding to an enzyme?

HORMONES AND THE ENDOCRINE SYSTEM (SECTION 28.2)

28.28   What is the purpose of the body's endocrine system?

28.29   Name as many endocrine glands as you can.

28.30   List the three major classes of hormones.

28.31   Give two examples of each of the three major classes of hormones.

28.32   What is the structural difference between an enzyme and a hormone?

28.33   What is the relationship between enzyme specificity and tissue specificity for a hormone?

28.34   Describe in general terms how a peptide hormone works.

28.35   Describe in general terms how a steroid hormone works.

HOW HORMONES WORK: EPINEPHRINE (SECTION 28.3)

28.36   In what gland is epinephrine produced and released?

28.37   Under what circumstances is epinephrine released?

28.38   How does epinephrine reach its target tissues?

28.39   What is the main function of epinephrine at its target tissues?

28.40   In order of their involvement, name the three membrane-bound proteins involved in transmitting the epinephrine message across the cell membrane.

28.41   What is the "second messenger" inside the cell that results from the epinephrine message? Is the ratio of epinephrine molecules to second messenger less than 1:1, 1:1, or greater than 1:1? Explain.

28.42   What role does the second messenger play in a cell stimulated by epinephrine?

28.43   What enzyme catalyzes hydrolysis of the second messenger to terminate the message? What is the product called? (Hint: Consult Figure 28.2.)

28.44   Epinephrine is used clinically in the treatment of what life-threatening allergic response? (Hint: Think about the use of the EpiPen.)

28.45 People susceptible to anaphylactic shock due to insect stings or certain food allergies must be prepared to treat themselves in case of exposure. How are they prepared and what must they do?

HORMONES (SECTION 28.4)

28.46 Give an example of a polypeptide hormone. How many amino acids are in the hormone? Where is the hormone released? Where does the hormone function? What is the result of the hormone message?

28.47 Give an example of a steroid hormone. What is the structure of the hormone? Where is the hormone released? Where does the hormone function? What is the result of the hormone message?

28.48 What do the three major classes of steroid hormones have in common?

28.49 What molecules are the steroid hormones derived from? How does that make the physical properties of steroid hormones different from the other hormones?

28.50 Name the two primary male sex hormones.

28.51 Name the three principal female sex hormones.

28.52 Until relatively recently, the use of androgens by athletes was a common, legal practice. What are the advantages of using androgens during athletic training and competition?

28.53 The use of androgens during athletic training and competition has been banned in national and international sports. What are the disadvantages of using androgens during athletic training and competition?

28.54 List two hormones that also function as neurotransmitters.

28.55 Explain why epinephrine can act as both a neurotransmitter and a hormone without "crossover" between the two functions.

28.56 Identify the class to which each of these following hormones belongs:

(a) 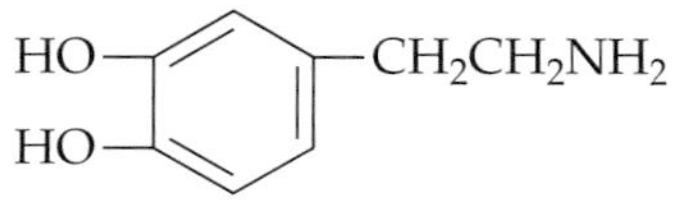 HO—⟨phenyl⟩—$CH_2CH_2NH_2$, HO—

(b) Insulin

(c)

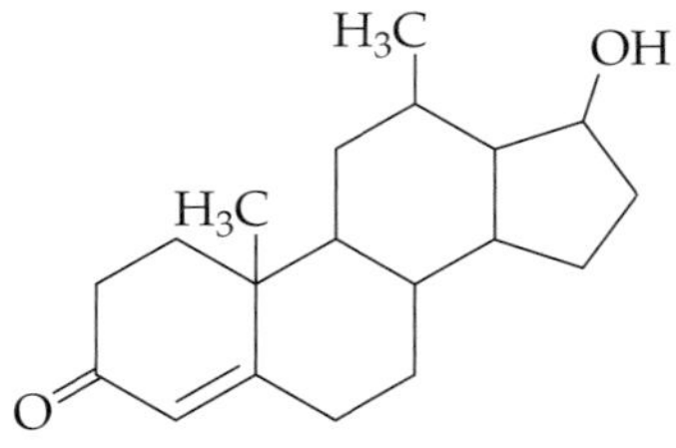

28.57 Identify the class to which each of these following hormones belongs:

(a) Glucagon

(b)

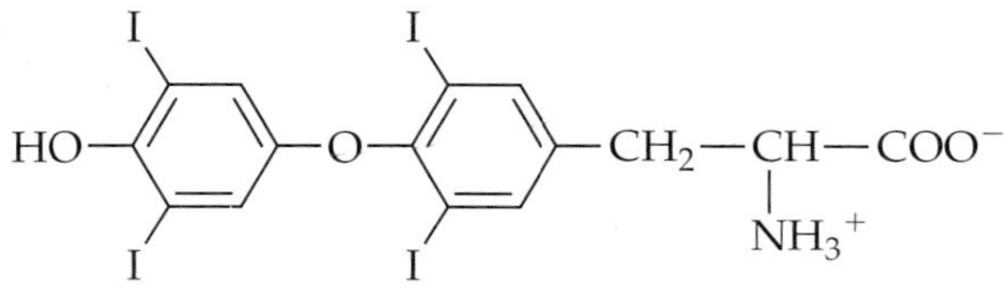

HO—⟨ring⟩(I, I)—O—⟨ring⟩(I, I)—CH_2—CH—COO^- with NH_3^+

Thyroxine

(c)

H_3C OH

HO

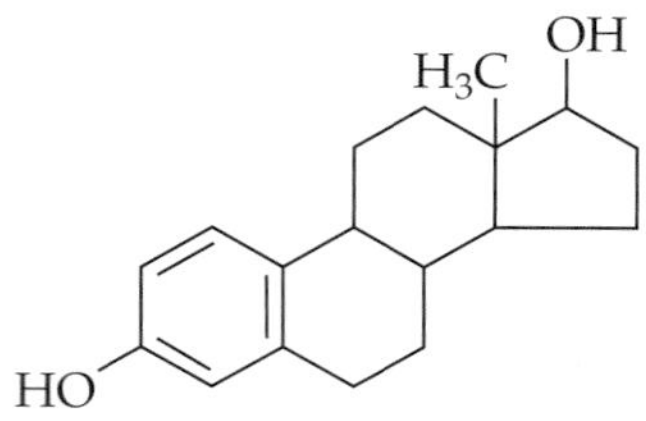

Estradiol

NEUROTRANSMITTERS (SECTION 28.5)

28.58 What is a synapse, and what role does it play in nerve transmission?

28.59 What is an axon, and what role does it play in nerve transmission?

28.60 List three cell types that might receive a message transmitted by a neurotransmitter.

28.61 What kinds of cellular or organ actions would you expect to be influenced by neurotransmitters?

28.62 Describe in general terms how a nerve impulse is passed from one neuron to another.

28.63 What are the two methods for removing the neurotransmitter once its job is done?

28.64 List the three steps in chemical transmission of the impulse between a nerve cell and its target.

28.65 Write an equation for the reaction that is catalyzed by acetylcholinesterase.

28.66 Why are enkephalins sometimes called *neurohormones*?

28.67 Outline the six steps in cholinergic nerve transmission.

CHEMICAL MESSENGERS AND DRUGS (SECTION 28.6)

28.68 Describe the difference between drugs that are agonists and those that are antagonists.

28.69 Give an example of a drug that acts as an agonist for acetylcholine receptors and one that acts as an antagonist for these receptors.

28.70 Give an example of a drug from each family in Problem 28.69.

HISTAMINES, ANTIHISTAMINES, AND IMPORTANT NEUROTRANSMITTERS, NEUROPEPTIDES, AND PAIN RELIEF (SECTION 28.7)

28.71 Give examples of two histamine antagonists that have very different tissue specificities and functions.

28.72 Name three families of drugs used to treat depression.

28.73 Name the "big three" monoamine neurotransmitters.

28.74 What is the impact and mode of action of cocaine on dopamine levels in the brain?

28.75 What is the impact and mode of action of amphetamines on dopamine levels in the brain?

28.76 How is the THC of marijuana similar in action to heroin and cocaine?

28.77 Why do we have brain receptors that respond to morphine and other opium derivatives from plants?

28.78 In schizophrenia, the neurons affected by dopamine are overstimulated. This condition is treated with drugs like chlorpromazine (Thorazine), which bind to the affected receptors and inhibit the dopamine signal. Does chlorpromazine act as an agonist or antagonist?

28.79 Methamphetamine "highs" often are accompanied by behavioral changes that resemble schizophrenia. Does methamphetamine act as an agonist or antagonist?

28.80 What are endorphins? Where in the body are they found?

28.81 Enkephalins and endorphins are referred to as "nature's opiates." Explain this saying.

28.82 Why might it be an advantage for an animal to produce its own pain-suppressing molecules?

CONCEPTUAL PROBLEMS

28.83 Suppose you are hiking in the Alaskan wilderness when your path crosses that of a bear. What hormone is responsible for your immediate response?

28.84 How do curare-treated arrows work?

28.85 What characteristics in their mechanism of action does thyroxine share with the steroid hormones?

28.86 List and describe the functions of the three types of proteins involved in transmission of a hormone signal.

28.87 The cyclic AMP (second messenger) of signal transmission is very reactive and breaks down rapidly after synthesis. Why is this important to the signal-transmission process?

28.88 We say that there is signal amplification in the transmission process. Explain how signal amplification occurs and what it means for transmission of the signal to the sites of cellular activity.

28.89 Compare the structures of the sex hormones testosterone and progesterone. What portions of the structures are the same? Where do they differ?

28.90 When you compare the structures of ethynyl estradiol to norethindrone, where do they differ? Where is ethynyl estradiol similar to estradiol? Where is norethindrone similar to progesterone?

28.91 Identify the structural changes that occur in the first two steps in the conversion of tyrosine to epinephrine (Figure 28.4). To what main classes and subclasses of enzymes do the enzymes that catalyze these reactions belong?

28.92 Look at the structures of the two male sex hormones shown on page 833. Identify the type of functional group change that interconverts testosterone and androsterone. To which class of chemical reactions does this change belong?

28.93 Look at the structures of the three female sex hormones shown on page 833. Identify the type of functional group change that interconverts estradiol and estrone. To which class of chemical reactions does this change belong?

GROUP PROBLEMS

28.94 Anandamides have been isolated from brain tissues and appear to be the natural ligand for the receptor that also binds THC. Anandamides have also been discovered in chocolate and cocoa powder. How might the craving for chocolate be explained?

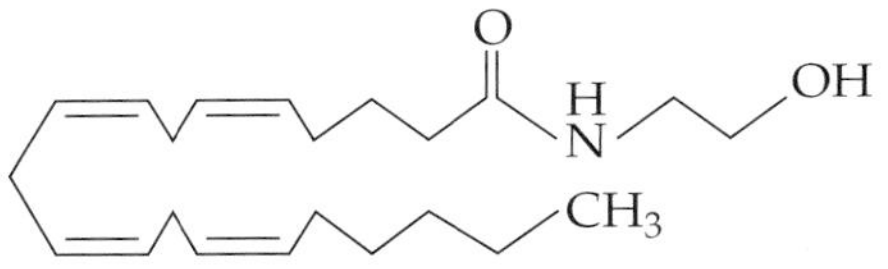

An anandamide structure

28.95 The phosphodiesterase that catalyzes hydrolysis of cyclic AMP is inhibited by caffeine. What overall effect would caffeine have on a signal that is mediated by cAMP?

29

Body Fluids

CONTENTS

◀◀◀ CONCEPTS TO REVIEW

A. Solutions
   (Sections 9.1, 9.2, and 9.9)

B. Osmosis and Osmotic Pressure
   (Section 9.10)

C. Dialysis
   (Section 9.11)

D. pH
   (Sections 10.5 and 10.6)

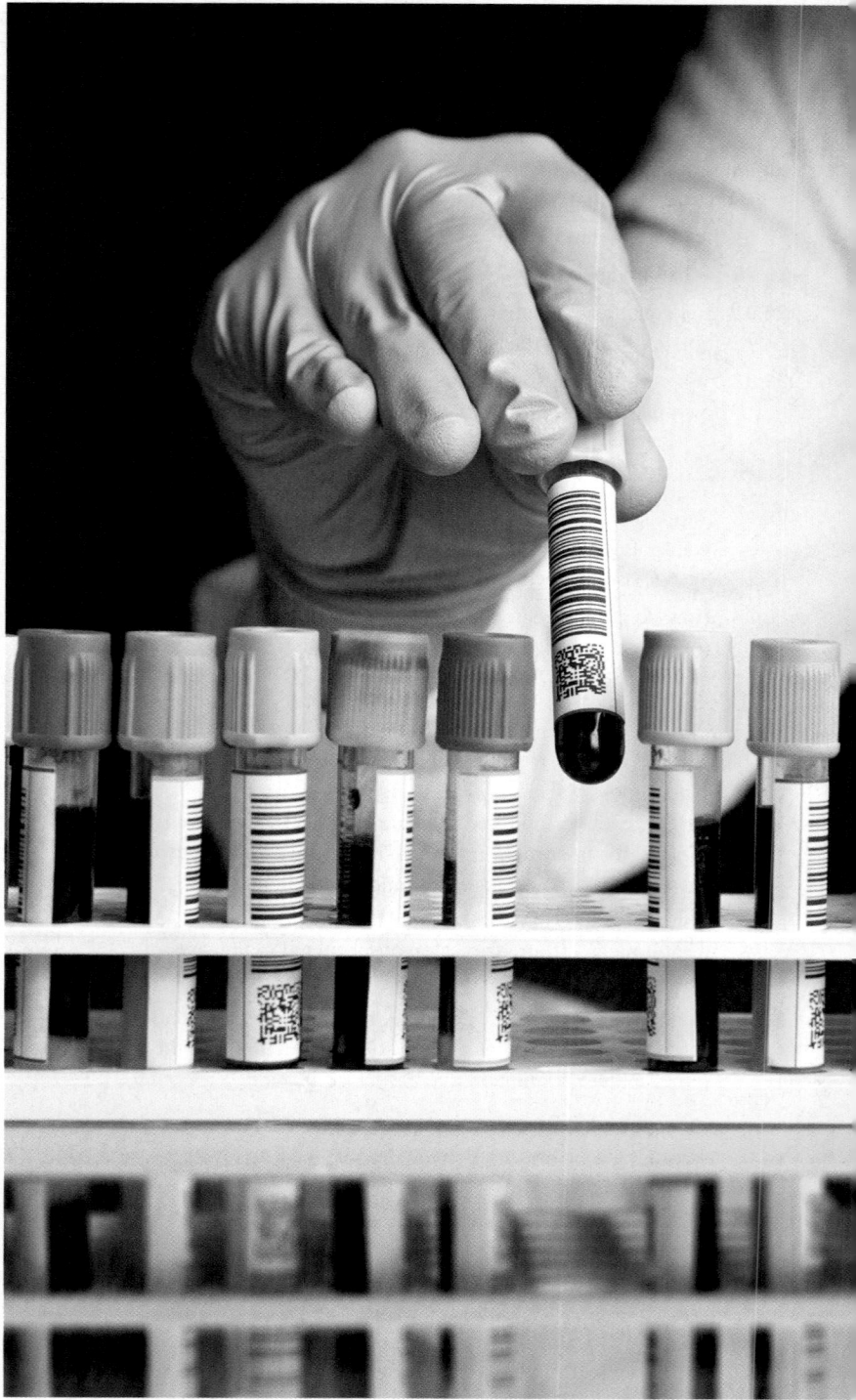

▲ An annual blood test can alert your doctor to medical problems before they become life-threatening.

When you were young, going to the doctor's office was something you did when you were sick, and if you had blood drawn it was because your physician was looking for the cause of your illness. As we get older, the need to see a doctor once a year for an annual checkup becomes more important as a preventative measure, and with that comes blood work. But what exactly is your doctor screening for, and why? Blood is the one fluid that touches every part of your body, and in it are clues to the health of your heart, kidneys, liver, and other organs. In the Chemistry in Action "What's in a Blood Test?," we will examine what is being looked at in a typical blood panel and what variations from normal can mean. For example, why are calcium levels being measured in a comprehensive metabolic panel (CMP)? Or what is a lipid panel screening looking for? Or what is the purpose of a fasting blood glucose analysis?

We have chosen to discuss body fluids last in your text because just about every aspect of chemistry you have studied so far applies to them. Electrolytes, nutrients and waste products, metabolic intermediates, and chemical messengers flow through your body in blood and in lymph fluid and exit as waste in the urine and feces. The chemical compositions of blood and urine mirror chemical reactions throughout the body. Fortunately, samples of these fluids are easily collected and studied. Many advances in understanding biological chemistry have been based on information obtained from analysis of blood and urine. As a result, studies of blood and urine chemistry provide information essential for the diagnosis and treatment of disease.

29.1 Body Water and Its Solutes

Learning Objective:

- Describe the major categories of body fluids, their composition, and the exchange of solutes between them.

The water content of the human body averages about 60% (by weight). Physiologists describe body water as occupying two different "compartments"—the *intracellular* and the *extracellular* compartments. We have looked primarily at the chemical reactions occurring in the **intracellular fluid** (the fluid inside cells), which includes about two-thirds of all body water (Figure 29.1). We now turn our attention to the remaining one-third of body water, the **extracellular fluid,** which includes mainly **blood plasma** (the fluid portion of blood) and **interstitial fluid** (the fluid that fills the spaces between cells).

To be soluble in water, a substance must be an ion, a gas, a small polar molecule, or a large molecule having many polar, hydrophilic or ionic groups on its surface. All four types of solutes are present in body fluids. The majority are inorganic ions and ionized biomolecules (mainly proteins); this is depicted in Figure 29.2. Although these fluids have different compositions, their **osmolarities** are the same; that is, they have the same number of moles of dissolved solute particles (ions or molecules) per liter. The osmolarity is kept in balance by the passage of water across cell membranes by osmosis, which occurs in response to osmolarity differences.

Inorganic ions, known collectively as *electrolytes* (Section 9.8), are major contributors to the osmolarity of body fluids and they move about as necessary to maintain charge balance. Water-soluble proteins make up a large proportion of the solutes in blood plasma and intracellular fluid; 100 mL of blood contains about 7 g of protein. Blood proteins are used to transport lipids and other molecules, and they play essential roles in blood clotting (Section 29.5) and the immune response (Section 29.4). The blood gases (oxygen and carbon dioxide), along with glucose, amino acids, and the nitrogen-containing by-products of protein catabolism, are the major small molecules in body fluids.

Blood travels through peripheral tissue in a network of tiny, hair-like capillaries that connect the arterial and venous parts of the circulatory system (Figure 29.3). This is where nutrients and end products of metabolism are exchanged between blood and interstitial fluid. Water and many small solutes move freely across the capillary walls in response to differences in fluid pressure and concentration (see Figure 29.3).

Solutes that can cross membranes freely (passive diffusion) move from regions of high solute concentration to regions of low solute concentration. On the arterial ends of capillaries, blood pressure is higher than interstitial fluid pressure and solutes and water are pushed into interstitial fluid. On the venous ends of the capillaries, blood pressure is lower, and water and solutes from the surrounding tissues are able to reenter the blood plasma. Except for protein content, blood plasma and interstitial fluid are similar in composition (Figure 29.2).

Intracellular fluid Fluid inside cells.

Extracellular fluid Fluid outside cells.

Blood plasma Liquid portion of the blood: An extracellular fluid.

Interstitial fluid Fluid surrounding cells: An extracellular fluid.

Osmolarity Amount of dissolved solute per volume of solution.

◀◀ **CONCEPTS TO REVIEW** The concept of hydrophilic and hydrophobic groups was discussed in Section 14.3, and the idea of ionized biomolecules was discussed in the Chemistry in Action "Medications, Body Fluids, and the 'Solubility Switch,'" found in Chapter 17.

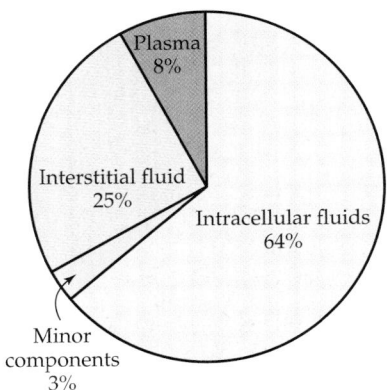

▲ **Figure 29.1**

Distribution of body water.

About two-thirds of body water is intracellular—within cells. The extracellular fluids include blood plasma, fluids surrounding cells (interstitial), and such minor components as lymph, cerebrospinal fluid, and the fluid that lubricates joints (synovial fluid).

◀◀ In osmosis, water moves across a semipermeable membrane from the more dilute solution to the more concentrated solution (see Section 9.10).

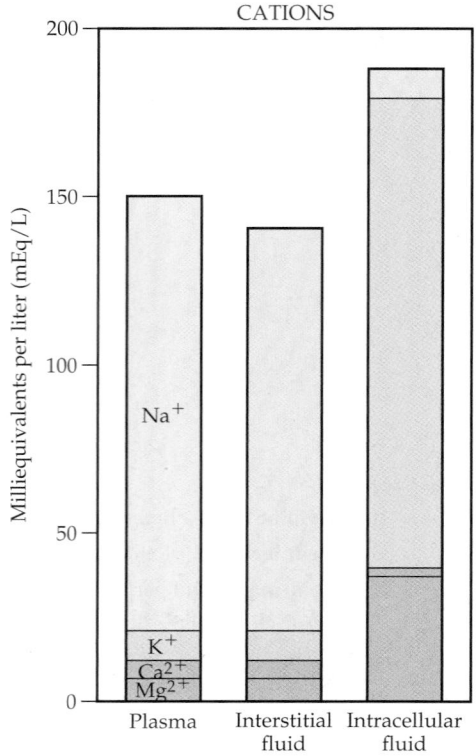

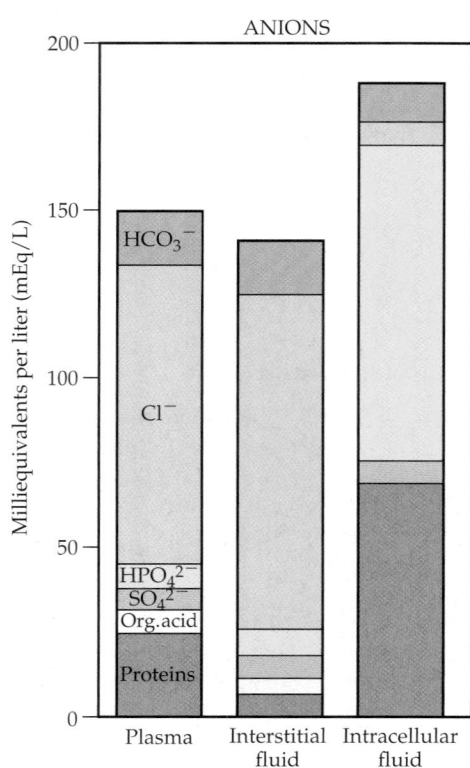

▲ **Figure 29.2**

The distribution of cations and anions in body fluids.

Outside cells, Na^+ is the major cation and Cl^- is the major anion. Inside cells, K^+ is the major cation and HPO_4^{2-} is the major anion. Note that at physiological pH, proteins are negatively charged.

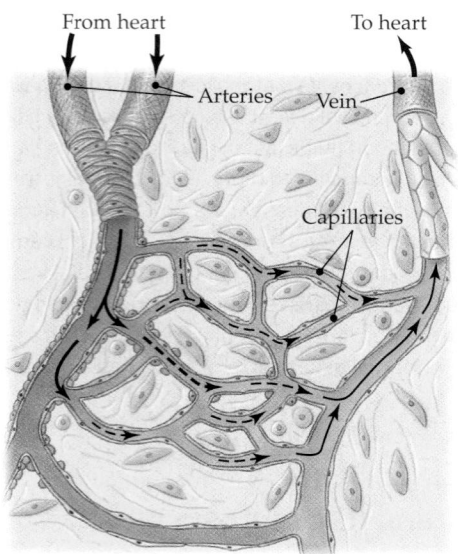

▲ **Figure 29.3**

The capillary network.

Solute exchange between blood and interstitial fluid occurs across capillary walls.

Additionally, peripheral tissue is networked with lymph capillaries (Figure 29.4). The lymphatic system collects excess interstitial fluid, debris from cellular breakdown, and proteins and lipid droplets too large to pass through capillary walls. Interstitial fluid and the substances that accompany it into the lymphatic system are referred to as *lymph,* and the walls of lymph capillaries are constructed so that lymph cannot return to the surrounding tissue. Ultimately, lymph enters the bloodstream at the thoracic duct.

Exchange of solutes between the interstitial fluid and the intracellular fluid occurs by crossing cell membranes. Here, major differences in concentration are maintained by active transport (transport requiring energy) *against* concentration gradients (from regions of *low* concentration to regions of *high* concentration) and by the impermeability of cell membranes to certain solutes, notably the sodium ion (Figure 29.5). Sodium ion concentration is high in extracellular fluids and low in intracellular fluids, whereas potassium ion concentrations are just the reverse: high inside cells and low outside cells (see Figure 29.2).

🔑 KEY CONCEPT PROBLEM 29.1

The drug cisplatin is used to treat various forms of cancer in humans. As with many other drugs, the difficult part in designing the cisplatin molecule was to have a structure that ensures transport into the cell. The equilibrium reaction that takes place in the body when cisplatin is administered is

$$\begin{bmatrix} Cl & \diagdown & NH_3 \\ & Pt & \\ Cl & \diagup & NH_3 \end{bmatrix} (aq) + H_2O(l) \rightleftharpoons \begin{bmatrix} Cl & \diagdown & NH_3 \\ & Pt & \\ H_2O & \diagup & NH_3 \end{bmatrix}^+ (aq) + Cl^-(aq)$$

Cisplatin   Monoaquacisplatin

Which form of cisplatin would you expect to exist inside the cell (where chloride concentrations are small)? Which form of cisplatin would you expect to exist outside the cell (where chloride concentrations are high)? Which form—cisplatin or monoaquacisplatin—enters the cell most readily? Why?

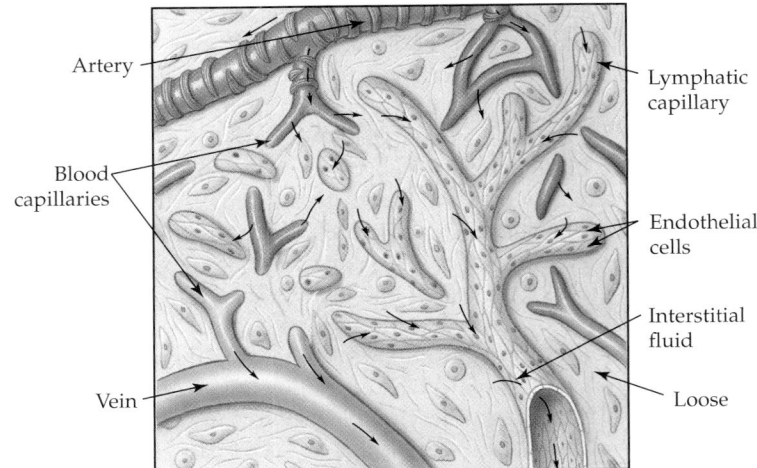

◄**Figure 29.4**
Blood and lymph capillaries.
The arrows show the flow of fluids in and out of the various components of peripheral tissue.

◄**Figure 29.5**
Exchange among body fluids.
Water exchanges freely in most tissues, with the result that the osmolarities of blood plasma, interstitial fluid, and intracellular fluid are the same. Large proteins cross neither capillary walls nor cell membranes, leaving the interstitial fluid protein concentration low. Concentration differences between interstitial fluid and intracellular fluid are maintained by active transport of Na^+ and K^+.

29.2   Fluid Balance

Learning Objective:

• Discuss how fluid balance is maintained.

Preserving fluid balance—a constant amount of fluid in the body—is crucial in maintaining physiological homeostasis. One way to accomplish this is by ensuring that daily intake and output of water are roughly equal as shown in Table 29.1.

What are the physiological effects if this delicate balance is not maintained—a question especially important to endurance athletes. During the course of a typical event, especially when performed in the heat, much fluid loss occurs with minimal fluid intake to counter it. Shown in Table 29.2, this typically results in a loss of body mass during the event and makes it easy to monitor performance versus fluid loss.

Exercise physiologists consider 4% body mass loss and above to be the "danger zone." In fact, the sports drink Gatorade was developed in 1965 for just this reason. Doctors at the University of Florida developed the original formula to solve a serious problem for

Table 29.1 Adult Human Daily Average Water Intake/Output

Water Intake (mL/day)		Water Output (mL/day)	
Drinking water	1200	Urine	1400
Water from food	1000	Skin	400
Water from metabolic oxidation of food	300	Lungs	400
		Sweat	100
		Feces	200
Total	2500		2500

Table 29.2 Effects of Body Mass Loss during Athletic Endurance Events

Body Mass Loss (%)	Symptoms and Performance
0	Normal heat regulation and performance
1	Thirst is stimulated, heat regulation during exercise is altered, performance begins to decline
2–3	Further decrease in heat regulation, increased thirst, worsening performance
4	Exercise performance cut by 20–30%
5	Headache, irritability, "spaced-out" feeling, fatigue
6	Weakness, severe loss of thermoregulation
7	Collapse is likely unless exercise is stopped

the school's football team—dehydration. This formula was so successful that by 1968, Gatorade had become the official sports drink of the National Football League and today commands a major share of the sports-drink market, with gross sales of over $800 million per year. One can see why research into hydration strategies has led to the plethora of "sports drinks" that are now available in your local supermarket. See the Chemistry in Action "Electrolytes, Fluid Replacement, and Sports Drinks" on p. 274.

Physiologically, the intake of water and electrolytes is regulated, but not closely. However, the output of these substances *is very* closely controlled. Both the intake and output of water are controlled by hormones. Receptors in the hypothalamus monitor the concentration of solutes in blood plasma, and as little as a 2% change in osmolarity can cause an adjustment in hormone secretion. For example, when a rise in blood osmolarity indicates an increased concentration of solutes and therefore a shortage of water, secretion of *antidiuretic hormone* (ADH; also known as *vasopressin*) increases. One key role of the kidneys is to keep water and electrolytes in balance by increasing or decreasing the amounts eliminated. In the kidneys, ADH causes a decrease in the water content of the urine. At the same time, osmoreceptors in the hypothalamus and baroreceptors in the heart and blood vessels activate the thirst mechanism, triggering increased water intake.

ADH is so tightly regulated that both oversecretion and undersecretion of this hormone can lead to serious disease states. Excess secretion can lead to what physicians refer to as the *syndrome of inappropriate ADH secretion (SIADH)*. Two of the many causes of SIADH are regional low blood volume arising from decreased blood return to the heart (caused by, for example, asthma, pneumonia, pulmonary obstruction, or heart failure) and misinterpretation by the hypothalamus of osmolarity (due, for example, to central nervous system disorders, barbiturates, or morphine). When ADH secretion is too high, the kidney excretes too little water, the water content of body compartments increases, and serum concentrations of electrolytes drop to dangerously low levels.

The reverse problem, inadequate secretion of ADH, is often a result of injury to the hypothalamus and causes *diabetes insipidus*. In this condition (unrelated to diabetes mellitus), up to 15 L of dilute urine is excreted each day. Administration of synthetic hormone can control the problem.

HANDS-ON CHEMISTRY 29.1

Sports drinks and sports energy bars have become an important part of the athletics scene. With claims of better energy, better performance, and faster recovery, these hydrating sports drinks and snack bars have moved from athletic field into the consumer marketplace. But are the claims that these companies make warranted? In this exercise, you will examine what is in these products and what the science behind them is. You will need to have an internet connection to fully carry out this activity. For this exercise, disregard the so-called energy shots or energy drinks so popular on college campuses today.

a. The American College of Sports Medicine (ACSM) (www.acsm.org) has done extensive studies on selecting and effectively using sports drinks and energy bars; use the ACSM as your primary source of information. First off, begin by looking at exactly what a sports drink is. What is typically found in one? What are the ingredients purported to do? What considerations should be made in selecting one? Would simply drinking water be just as good?

b. Now, consider sports energy bars. What is found in a typical energy bar? What considerations should be made in selecting one? Most energy bars have a high glycemic index. What does this mean and why is it so attractive for an energy bar to have a high index?

c. Finally, based on what you discovered in parts a and b, do you think it is wise for an average person to consume sports drinks and energy bars on a regular basis? Why or why not? By average we mean someone who is not a runner or an endurance athlete; someone who is moderately active, perhaps like yourself.

29.3 Blood

Learning Objective:

• Describe the composition and functions of blood.

Blood flows through the body in the circulatory system, which in the absence of trauma or disease, is essentially a closed system. About 55% of blood is plasma, which contains the proteins and other solutes shown in Figure 29.6; the remaining 45% is a mixture of red blood cells (**erythrocytes;** RBCs), platelets, and white blood cells (**leukocytes;** WBCs).

The plasma and cells together make up **whole blood,** which is what is usually collected for clinical laboratory analysis. The whole blood sample is collected directly into evacuated tubes that contain an anticoagulant to prevent clotting (which would normally occur within 20–26 minutes at room temperature). Typical anticoagulants include heparin (which interferes with the action of enzymes needed for clotting) and citrate or oxalate ion (either of which form precipitates with calcium ion, which is also needed for blood clotting, thereby removing it from solution). Plasma is separated from blood cells by spinning the sample in a centrifuge, which causes the blood cells to clump together at the bottom of the tube, leaving the plasma at the top.

Erythrocytes Red blood cells (RBCs); transporters of blood gases.

Leukocytes White blood cells (WBCs).

Whole blood Blood plasma plus blood cells.

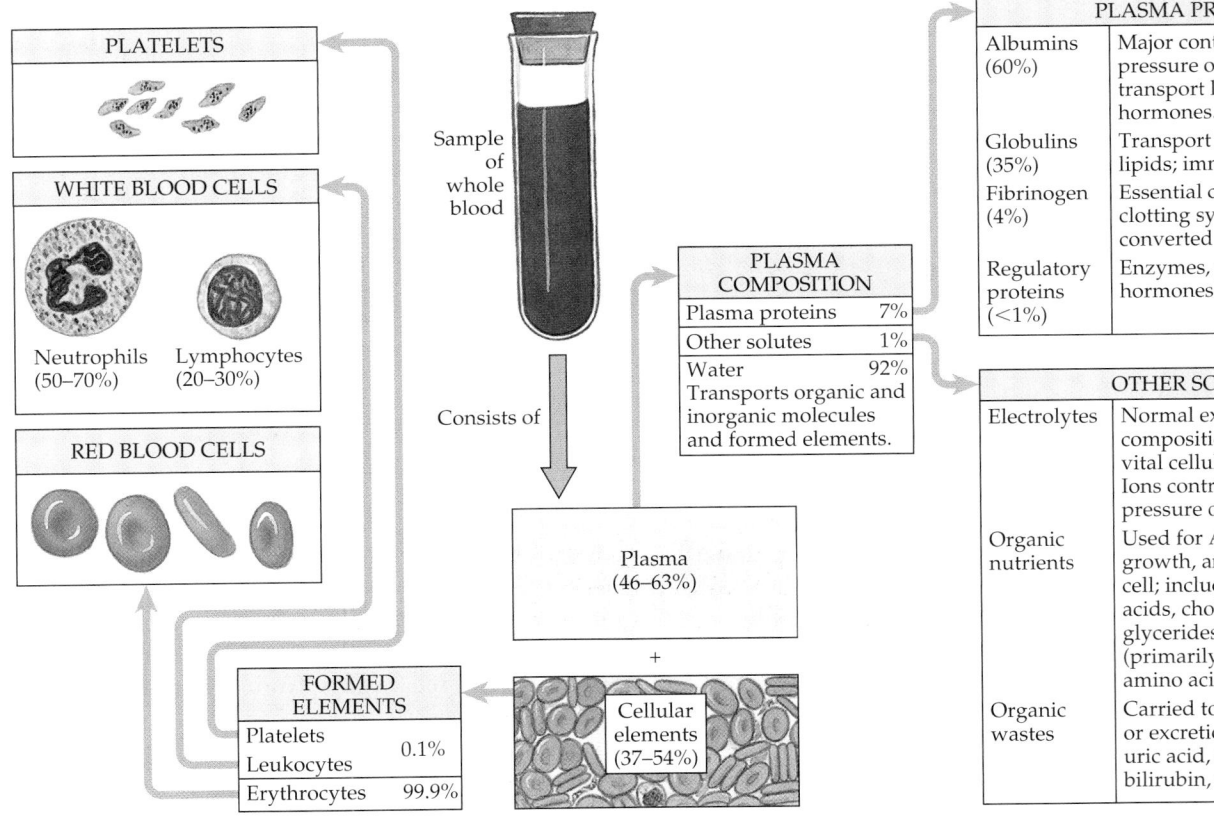

▲ **Figure 29.6**
The composition of whole blood.

Many laboratory analyses are performed on **blood serum,** the fluid remaining after blood has completely clotted. Blood serum composition is not the same as that of blood plasma—as we'll see in Section 29.5, blood clots are not simply clumps of cells, but also include networks of protein that originated from the plasma. When a serum sample is desired, whole blood is collected in the presence of an agent that hastens clotting. Thrombin, a natural component of the clotting system, is often used for this purpose. Centrifugation separates the clot and cells to leave behind the serum.

Blood serum Fluid portion of blood remaining after clotting has occurred.

Major Components of Blood

- **Whole blood**
    Blood plasma—fluid part of blood containing water-soluble solutes
    Blood cells —RBCs (carry gases)
    —WBCs (part of immune system)
    —platelets (help to initiate blood clotting)
- **Blood serum**—fluid portion of plasma left after blood has clotted

Table 29.3 summarizes the functions of the major protein and cellular components of blood. These functions fall into three categories.

Table 29.3 Protein and Cellular Components of Blood

Blood Component	Function
Proteins	
Albumins	Transport lipids, hormones, drugs; major contributor to plasma osmolarity
Globulins	
Immunoglobulins (γ-globulins, antibodies)	Identify antigens (microorganisms and other foreign invaders) and initiate their destruction
Transport globulins	Transport lipids and metal ions
Fibrinogen	Forms fibrin, the basis of blood clots
Blood cells	
RBCs (erythrocytes)	Transport O_2, CO_2, and H^+
WBCs (leukocytes)	
Lymphocytes	Defend against specific pathogens and foreign substances (T cells and B cells)
Phagocytes	Carry out phagocytosis—engulf foreign invaders (neutrophils, eosinophils, and monocytes)
Basophils	Release histamine during inflammatory response of injured tissue
Platelets	Help to initiate blood clotting

Major Functions of Blood

- **Transport** The circulatory system is the body's equivalent of an interstate high-way network, transporting materials from where they enter the system to where they are used or disposed of. Oxygen and carbon dioxide are carried to and from by RBCs. Nutrients are carried from the intestine to the sites of their catabolism. Waste products of metabolism are carried to the kidneys. Hormones from endocrine glands are delivered to their target tissues.
- **Regulation** Blood redistributes body heat as it flows along, thereby participating in the regulation of body temperature. It also picks up or delivers water and electrolytes as they are needed. In addition, blood buffers are essential to the maintenance of acid-base balance.
- **Defense** Blood carries the molecules and cells needed for two major defense mechanisms: (1) the immune response, which destroys foreign invaders, and (2) blood clotting, which prevents loss of blood and begins the healing of wounds.

CHEMISTRY IN ACTION

⚕ The Blood–Brain Barrier

Nowhere in human beings is the maintenance of a constant internal environment more important than in the brain. Because of the fluctuations in blood concentrations of hormones, amino acids, neurotransmitters, and potassium that occur elsewhere in the body, the brain must be rigorously isolated from variations in blood composition.

How can the brain receive nutrients from the blood in capillaries and yet be protected? The answer lies in the unique structure of the *endothelial cells* that form the walls of brain capillaries. Unlike the cells in most other capillaries, those in brain capillaries form a series of continuous tight junctions so that nothing can pass between them. To reach the brain, therefore, a substance must cross this blood–brain barrier (BBB) by crossing the endothelial cell membranes. The BBB serves as internal protection for the brain just as the skull serves as the brain's external protection. Scientists have come to the realization that the BBB is itself a vital organ and have begun calling it the neurovascular unit. Finding ways to breach this barrier will undoubtedly lead to new cures for many diseases, from brain cancers to Alzheimer's disease.

Consider glucose, the main source of energy for brain cells. It must have a way to cross the barrier. Also, certain amino acids the brain cannot manufacture must be recognized and brought across the cell membranes; all of this indicates that specific transporters must exist to move substances in and out of the brain. Glycine is another example of a substance that must cross the barrier. As a small amino acid that is a potent neurotransmitter, an asymmetric (one-way) transport system exists for it. Glycine inhibits rather than activates transmission of nerve signals, and its concentration must be held at a lower level in the brain than in the blood. To accomplish this, there is a glycine transport system in the cell membrane closest to the brain, but no matching transport system on the other side. Thus, glycine can be transported out of the brain but not into it.

The brain is also protected by a "metabolic" BBB. In this case, a compound that gets into an endothelial cell is converted within the cell to a metabolite that is unable to enter the brain. A striking demonstration of the metabolic brain barrier is provided by *dopamine,* a neurotransmitter, and L-*dopa,* a metabolic precursor of dopamine.

L-Dopa can both enter and leave the brain because it is recognized by one of these transport systems. However, the brain is protected from an excess of L-dopa entering by its conversion to dopamine within the endothelial cells of the BBB. Like glycine, dopamine, which is also produced from L-dopa within the brain, can leave the brain but cannot enter it. The dopamine deficiency that occurs in Parkinson's disease is therefore treated by administration of L-dopa.

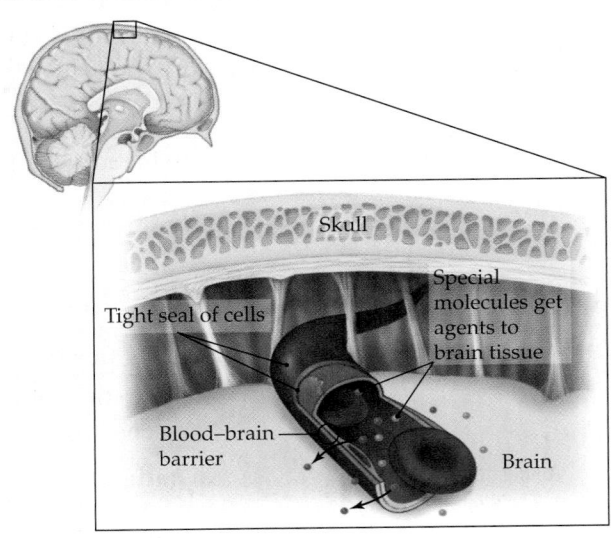

▲ The blood–brain barrier.

Since crossing the endothelial cell membrane is the route into the brain, substances soluble in the membrane lipids readily breach the BBB. Think about heroin, which differs from morphine in having two nonpolar acetyl groups where the morphine has polar hydroxyl groups (Table 16.2). The resulting difference in lipid solubility allows heroin to enter the brain much more efficiently than morphine. Once inside the brain, enzymes remove the acetyl groups to produce morphine, and in doing so, trap it in the brain. For a long time, scientists believed that the BBB was an inviolable wall that should not be meddled with; now finding ways to breach the BBB is of major concern to medicinal chemists. For example, brain tumors are currently treated with either radiation or surgery, as the chemical agents used to typically treat cancer cannot cross the BBB. Researchers have begun to examine *chimeric therapeutics,* materials that are half drug (which do not cross the BBB) and half "molecular Trojan horse" (genetically engineered proteins that do cross the BBB). This strategy has been shown to work in mice, but human trials are still off in the future. As our understanding of this crucial barrier unfolds, we can expect many advances in the treatment of diseases of the brain that thus far have been treatable by only the most invasive of techniques.

CIA Problem 29.1 What is meant by an asymmetric transport system? Give one specific example of such a system.

CIA Problem 29.2 What type of substance is likely to breach the BBB? Would ethanol be likely to cross this barrier? Why or why not?

CIA Problem 29.3 What is the metabolic BBB?

CIA Problem 29.4 Heroin is better able to cross the BBB than morphine. Looking at the structures of these two molecules (refer to Table 16.2), circle the areas where they differ and why this explains the difference between the potencies of heroin and morphine as analgesics.

$$\text{(L-Dopa)} \quad \longrightarrow \quad \text{(Dopamine)} + CO_2$$

L-Dopa: $CH_2-CH-NH_3^+$ with $C-O^-$ / $\|$ / O group

Dopamine: $CH_2-CH_2-NH_3^+$

PROBLEM 29.2

Match each term in the (a)–(e) group with its definition from the (i)–(v) group.

(a) Interstitial fluid
(b) Whole blood

(c) Blood serum
(d) Intracellular fluid

(e) Blood plasma

(i) Fluid that remains when blood cells are removed
(ii) Fluid, solutes, and cells that together flow through veins and arteries
(iii) Fluid that fills spaces between cells
(iv) Fluid that remains when blood clotting agents are removed from plasma
(v) Fluid within cells

29.4 Plasma Proteins, White Blood Cells, and Immunity

Learning Objective:

• Explain the roles of the blood components that participate in inflammation and the immune response.

Antigen A substance foreign to the body that triggers the immune response.

Inflammatory response A nonspecific defense mechanism triggered by antigens or tissue damage.

Immune response Defense mechanism of the immune system dependent on the recognition of specific antigens, including viruses, bacteria, toxic substances, and infected cells; either cell-mediated or antibody-mediated.

Antibody (immunoglobulin) Glycoprotein molecule that identifies antigens.

An **antigen** is any molecule or portion of a molecule recognized by the body as a foreign invader. An antigen might be a molecule never seen before by the body or a molecular segment recognized as an invader (for example, a protein on the surface of a bacterium or virus). Antigens can also be small molecules, known as *haptens* that are only recognized as antigens after they have bonded to carrier proteins. Haptens include some antibiotics, environmental pollutants, and allergens from plants and animals.

The recognition of an antigen can initiate three different responses. The first, the **inflammatory response,** is a nonspecific, localized response to a given antigen. The two remaining types of **immune response** (cell-mediated response and antibody-mediated response) do depend on recognition of *specific* invaders (such as viruses, bacteria, toxic substances, or infected cells; Figure 29.7). At the molecular level, the invading antigen is detected by an interaction very much like that between an enzyme and its substrate. Noncovalent attraction allows a spatial fit between the antigen and a defender that is specific to that antigen. The *cell-mediated immune response* depends on WBCs known as *T cells.* The *antibody-mediated immune response* depends on **antibodies** (or **immunoglobulins**) produced by the WBCs known as *B cells.*

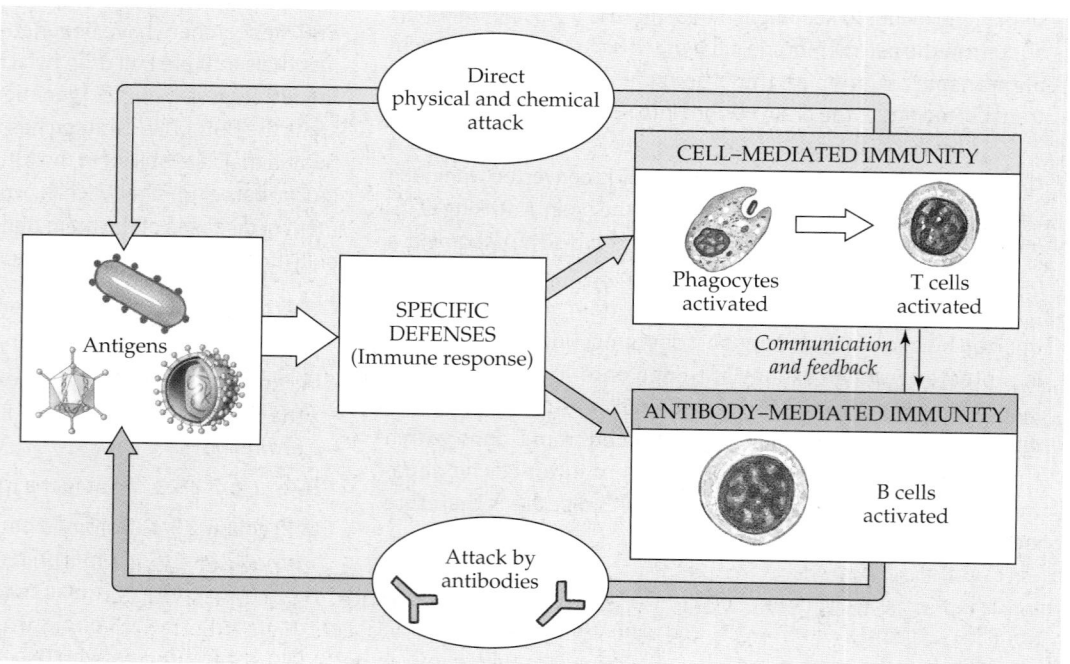

▲ Figure 29.7
The immune response.
The attack on antigens occurs by cell-mediated and antibody-mediated immune responses.

Both inflammation and the immune responses require normal numbers of WBCs to be effective (5–10 million WBCs per milliliter). If the WBC count falls below 1000 per milliliter of blood, any infection can be life-threatening. The devastating results of WBC destruction in acquired immunodeficiency syndrome (AIDS) is an example of this condition.

Inflammatory Response

Cell damage due to infection or injury initiates **inflammation,** a nonspecific defense mechanism that produces swelling, redness, warmth, and pain. For example, the swollen, painful, red bump that develops around a splinter in your finger is an inflammation (generally known as a *wheal-and-flare reaction*). Chemical messengers released at the injured site direct the inflammatory response. One such messenger is histamine, which is synthesized from the amino acid histidine and is stored in cells throughout the body. Histamine release is also triggered by an allergic response.

Inflammation Result of the inflammatory response; includes swelling, redness, warmth, and pain.

$$\text{HN} \underset{\text{N}}{\overset{}{\diagdown}} \text{—CH}_2\text{CH—NH}_3{}^+ \quad \xrightarrow[\text{decarboxylase}]{\text{Histidine}} \quad \text{HN} \underset{\text{N}}{\overset{}{\diagdown}} \text{—CH}_2\text{CH}_2\text{—NH}_3{}^+ \; + \; CO_2$$

Histidine (with C—O⁻, C=O below)   Histamine

Histamine sets off dilation of capillaries and increases the permeability of capillary walls. The resulting increased blood flow into the damaged area reddens and warms the skin, and swelling occurs as plasma carrying blood-clotting factors and defensive proteins enters the intercellular space. At the same time, WBCs cross capillary walls to attack invaders.

Bacteria or other antigens at the inflammation site are destroyed by WBCs known as *phagocytes,* which engulf invading cells and destroy them by enzyme-catalyzed hydrolysis reactions. Phagocytes also emit chemical messengers that help to direct the inflammatory response. An inflammation caused by a wound will heal completely only after all infectious agents have been removed, with dead cells and other debris absorbed into the lymph system.

Cell-Mediated Immune Response

The cell-mediated immune response is under the control of several kinds of *T lymphocytes* or *T cells.* The cell-mediated immune response principally guards against abnormal cells and bacteria or viruses entering the normal cells; it also guards against the invasion of some cancer cells and causes the rejection of transplanted organs.

A complex series of events begins when a T cell recognizes an antigenic cell. The result of these events is production of *cytotoxic,* or *killer,* T cells that can destroy the invader (e.g., by releasing a toxic protein that kills the antigenic invaded perforating cell membranes) and *helper* T cells, which enhance the body's defenses against the invader. Thousands of *memory* T cells are also produced; they remain on guard and will immediately generate the appropriate killer T cells if the same pathogen reappears.

Antibody-Mediated Immune Response

The WBCs known as *B lymphocytes* or *B cells,* with the assistance of T cells, are responsible for the antibody-mediated immune response. Unlike T cells, which identify only antigenic cells, B cells identify antigens adrift in body fluids. A B cell is activated when it first binds to an antigen and then encounters a helper T cell that recognizes the same antigen. This activation can take place anywhere in the body, but it often occurs in lymph nodes, tonsils, or the spleen, which have large concentrations of lymphocytes.

Once activated, B cells divide to form plasma cells that secrete antibodies specific to the antigen. The antibodies are immunoglobulins. The body contains up to 10,000

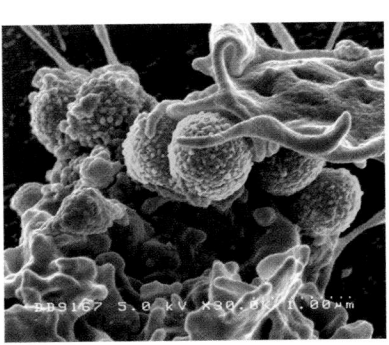

▲ A lymphocyte reaches out to snare several *Staphylococcus aureus* bacteria (highlighted in green).

different immunoglobulins at any given time, and we have the capacity to make more than 100 million others. The immunoglobulins are glycoproteins composed of two "heavy" polypeptide chains and two "light" polypeptide chains joined by disulfide bonds, as shown in Figure 29.8. The variable regions are sequences of amino acids that will bind a specific antigen. Once synthesized, antibodies spread out to find their antigens.

▶ **Figure 29.8**
Structure of an immunoglobulin, which is an antibody.
(a) The regions of an immunoglobulin. The disulfide bridges that hold the chains together are shown in orange. (b) Molecular model of an immunoglobulin; the heavy chains are gray and blue and both light chains are red.

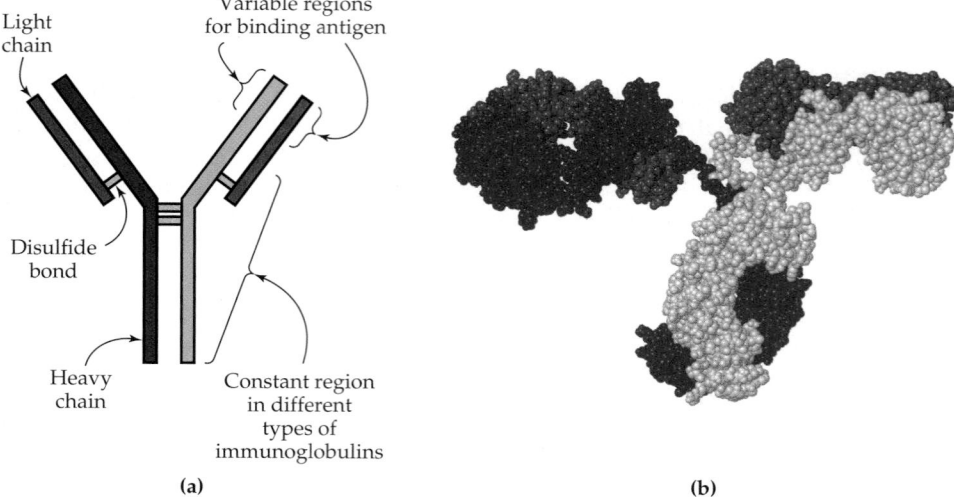

(a)

(b)

Formation of an antigen–antibody complex (Figure 29.9) inactivates the antigen by one of several methods. The complex may, for example, attract phagocytes, or it may block the mechanism by which the invader connects with a target cell.

▶ **Figure 29.9**
Antigen–antibody complexes.
(a) Antigens bind to antigenic-determinant sites on the surface of, for example, a bacterium. (b) Because each antibody has two binding sites, the interaction of many antigens and antibodies creates a large immune complex.

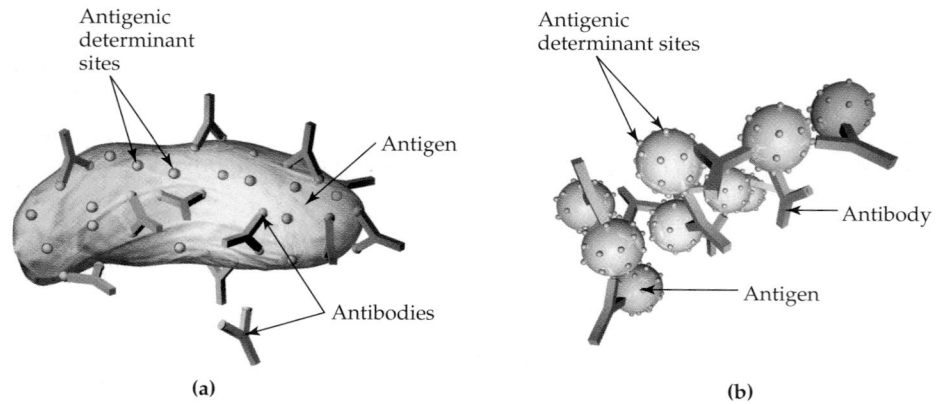

(a)

(b)

Activated B-cell division also yields memory cells that remain on guard and quickly produce more plasma cells if the same antigen reappears. The long-lived B and T memory cells are responsible for long-term immunity to diseases after the first illness or after a vaccination.

Several classes of immunoglobulins have been identified. *Immunoglobulin G antibodies* (known as *gamma globulins*), for example, protect against viruses and bacteria. Allergies and asthma are caused by an oversupply of *immunoglobulin E*. Numerous disorders result from the mistaken identification of normal body constituents as foreign and the overproduction of antibodies to combat them. These **autoimmune diseases** include attack on connective tissue at joints in rheumatoid arthritis, attack on pancreatic islet cells in some forms of diabetes mellitus, and a generalized attack on nucleic acids and blood components in systemic lupus erythematosus.

Autoimmune disease Disorder in which the immune system identifies normal body components as antigens and produces antibodies to them.

29.5 Blood Clotting

Learning Objective:

• List the steps involved in blood clotting.

A blood clot consists of blood cells trapped in a mesh of the insoluble fibrous protein known as **fibrin.** Clot formation is a multiple-step process requiring participation of 12 clotting factors; calcium ion is one of the clotting factors. Others, most of which are glycoproteins, are synthesized in the liver by pathways that require vitamin K as a coenzyme. Therefore, a deficiency of vitamin K, the presence of a competitive inhibitor of vitamin K, or a deficiency of a clotting factor can cause excessive bleeding, sometimes from even minor tissue damage. Hemophilia is a disorder caused by an inherited genetic defect that results in the absence of one or more of the clotting factors. Hemophilia occurs in 1 in 10,000 individuals, with 80–90% of people with hemophilia being male.

The body's mechanism for halting blood loss from even the tiniest capillary is referred to as **hemostasis.** The first events in hemostasis are (1) constriction of surrounding blood vessels and (2) formation of a plug composed of the blood cells known as *platelets* at the site of tissue damage.

Next, a **blood clot** is formed in a process that is triggered by two pathways: (1) The *intrinsic pathway* begins when blood makes contact with the negatively charged surface of the fibrous protein collagen, which is exposed at the site of tissue damage. Clotting is activated in exactly the same manner when blood is placed in a glass tube, because the surface of the glass has a negative charge. (2) The *extrinsic pathway* begins when damaged tissue releases an integral membrane glycoprotein known as *tissue factor.*

The result of either pathway is a cascade of reactions that is initiated when an inactive clotting factor (a zymogen, Section 19.8) is converted to its active form by cleavage of specific polypeptide sequences on its surface. Commonly, the newly activated enzyme then catalyzes the activation of the next factor in the cascade. The two pathways merge and, in the final step of the common pathway, the enzyme *thrombin* catalyzes cleavage of small polypeptides from the soluble plasma protein fibrinogen. Negatively charged groups in these polypeptides make fibrinogen soluble and keep the molecules apart. Once these polypeptides are removed, the resulting insoluble fibrin molecules immediately associate with each other by noncovalent interactions. Then they are bound into fibers by formation of amide cross-links between lysine and glutamine side chains in a reaction catalyzed by another of the clotting factors.

Fibrin Insoluble protein that forms the fiber framework of a blood clot.

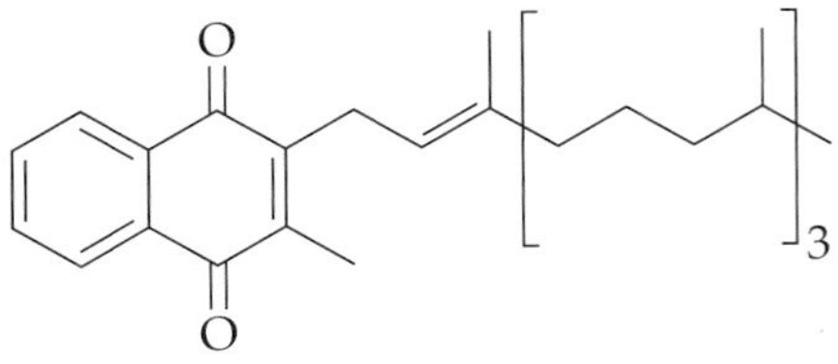

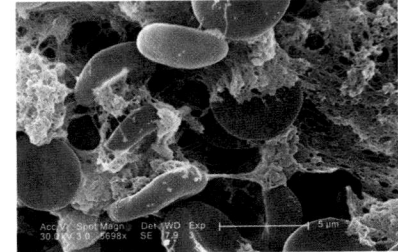

Vitamin K
(Phylloquinone)

Hemostasis The stopping of bleeding.

Blood clot A network of fibrin fibers and trapped blood cells that forms at the site of blood loss.

▲ Colorized electron micrograph of a blood clot. RBCs can be seen enmeshed in the fibrin network.

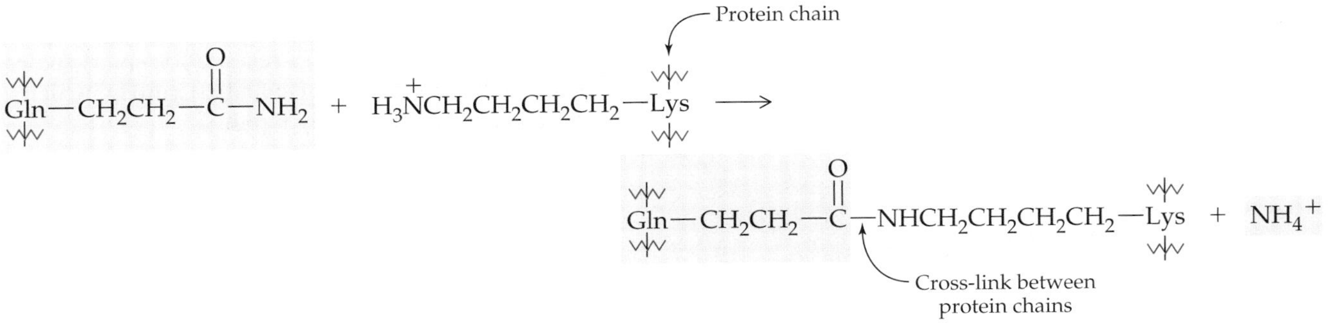

Gln—CH₂CH₂—C(=O)—NH₂ + H₃N⁺CH₂CH₂CH₂CH₂—Lys ⟶

Protein chain

Gln—CH₂CH₂—C(=O)—NHCH₂CH₂CH₂CH₂—Lys + NH₄⁺

Cross-link between protein chains

Once the clot has done its job of preventing blood loss and binding together damaged surfaces as they heal, the clot is broken down by hydrolysis of its peptide bonds.

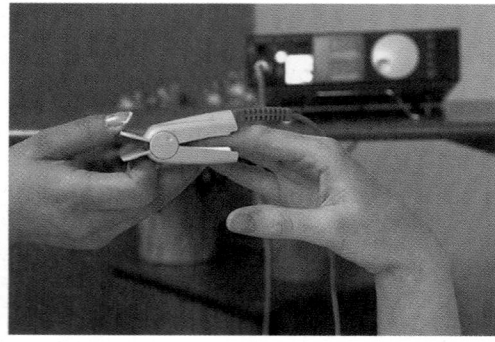

▲ **Figure 29.10**
A pulse oximetry sensor for continuous monitoring of blood oxygen.
One side of the sensor contains two light-emitting diodes (LEDs), one that emits in the visible red range (better absorbed by dark-red deoxygenated blood) and one that emits in the infrared range (better absorbed by oxygenated blood, which is bright red). On the opposite side of the sensor, a photodetector measures the light that passes through and sends the signal to an instrument that computes the percent oxygen saturation of the blood and also records the pulse. Normal oxygen saturation is 95–100%. Below 85%, tissues are at risk, and below 70% is typically life-threatening.

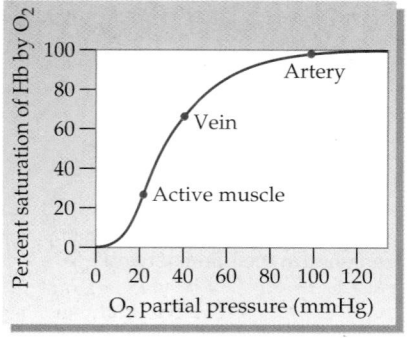

▲ **Figure 29.11**
Oxygen saturation of hemoglobin at normal physiological conditions.
Oxygen pressure is about 100 mmHg in arteries and 20 mmHg in active muscles. Note the large release of oxygen as the partial pressure drops from 40 mmHg to 20 mmHg.

29.6 Red Blood Cells and Blood Gases

Learning Objective:

• Explain the relationships among O_2 and CO_2 transport and acid-base balance.

RBCs, or erythrocytes, have one major purpose: to transport blood gases. Erythrocytes in mammals have no nuclei or ribosomes and cannot replicate themselves. In addition, they have no mitochondria or glycogen and must obtain glucose from the surrounding plasma. Their enormous number—about 250 million in a single drop of blood—and their large surface area provide for rapid exchange of gases throughout the body. Because they are small and flexible, erythrocytes can squeeze through the tiniest capillaries one at a time.

Of the protein in an erythrocyte, 95% is hemoglobin, the transporter of oxygen and carbon dioxide. Hemoglobin (Hb) is composed of four polypeptide chains with the quaternary structure shown earlier in Figure 18.5. Each protein chain has a central heme molecule in a crevice in its nonpolar interior, and each of the four hemes can combine with one O_2 molecule.

Oxygen Transport

The iron(II) ion, Fe^{2+}, sits in the center of each heme molecule and is the site to which O_2 binds through one of oxygen's unshared electron pairs. In contrast to the cytochromes of the respiratory chain, where iron cycles between Fe^{2+} and Fe^{3+}, heme iron must remain in the reduced Fe^{2+} state to maintain its oxygen-carrying ability. Hemoglobin (Hb) carrying four oxygens (oxyhemoglobin) is bright red. Hemoglobin that has lost one or more oxygens (deoxyhemoglobin) is dark red-purple, which accounts for the darker color of venous blood. Dried blood is brown, because exposure to atmospheric oxygen has oxidized the iron (think of rust). The color of arterial blood carrying oxygen is used in a clinically valuable method for monitoring oxygenation (known as *pulse oximetry,* Figure 29.10).

At normal physiological conditions, the percentage of heme molecules that carry oxygen, known as the *percent saturation,* is dependent on the partial pressure of oxygen in surrounding tissues (Figure 29.11). The shape of the curve indicates that binding of oxygen to heme is allosteric in nature (see Section 19.7). Each O_2 that binds causes changes in the hemoglobin quaternary structure that enhance binding of the next O_2, and releasing each oxygen enhances release of the next. As a result, oxygen is more readily released to tissue where the partial pressure of oxygen is low. The average oxygen partial pressure in peripheral tissue is 40 mmHg, a pressure at which Hb remains 75% saturated by oxygen, leaving a large amount of O_2 in reserve for emergencies. Note, however, the rapid drop in the curve between 40 mmHg and 20 mmHg, which is the oxygen pressure in tissue where metabolism is occurring rapidly.

Carbon Dioxide Transport, Acidosis, and Alkalosis

Oxygen and carbon dioxide are the "blood gases" transported by erythrocytes. By way of the bicarbonate ion/carbon dioxide buffer, the intimate relationships among H^+ and HCO_3^- concentrations and O_2 and CO_2 partial pressures are essential to maintaining electrolyte and acid-base balance.

$$\underbrace{CO_2(aq) + H_2O(l)}_{\text{Controlled by the lungs}} \rightleftharpoons H_2CO_3(aq) \rightleftharpoons \underbrace{HCO_3^-(aq) + H^+(aq)}_{\text{Controlled by the kidneys}}$$

In a clinical setting, "monitoring blood gases" usually refers to measuring the pH of blood as well as the gas concentrations. Carbon dioxide from metabolism in peripheral cells diffuses into interstitial fluid and then into capillaries, where it is transported in the blood three ways: (1) as dissolved $CO_2(aq)$, (2) bonded to Hb, or (3) as HCO_3^- in solution. About 7% of the CO_2 produced dissolves in blood plasma. The rest enters erythrocytes, where some of it binds to the protein portion of hemoglobin by reaction with the nonionized amino acid $—NH_2$ groups present.

$$Hb—NH_2 + CO_2 \rightleftharpoons Hb—NHCOO^- + H^+$$

Most of the CO_2 is rapidly converted to bicarbonate ion within erythrocytes, which contain a large concentration of carbonic anhydrase. The resulting water-soluble HCO_3^- ion can leave the erythrocyte and travel in the blood to the lungs, where it will be converted back to CO_2 for exhalation. To maintain electrolyte balance, a Cl^- ion enters the erythrocyte for every HCO_3^- ion that leaves, and the process is reversed when the blood reaches the lungs.

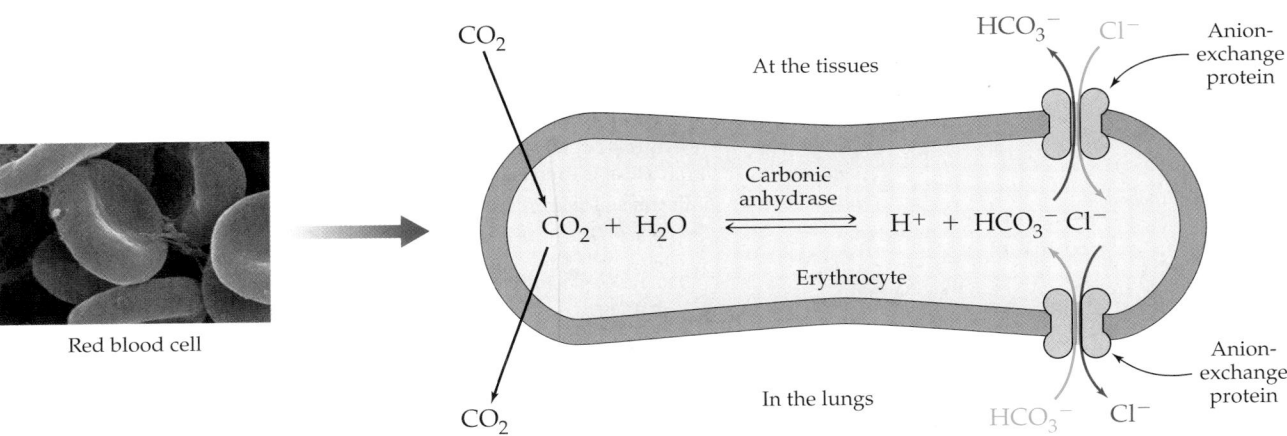

Red blood cell

A cell-membrane protein controls this ion exchange, which is passive, as the ions move from higher to lower concentrations.

Without some compensating change, the result of hemoglobin reacting with CO_2 and the action of carbonic anhydrase would be an unacceptably large increase in acidity. To cope with this, hemoglobin responds by reversibly binding hydrogen ions.

$$Hb \cdot 4O_2 + 2H^+ \rightleftharpoons Hb \cdot 2H^+ + 4O_2$$

The release of oxygen is enhanced by allosteric effects when the hydrogen ion concentration increases, and oxygen is held more firmly when the hydrogen ion concentration decreases.

The changes in the oxygen saturation curve with CO_2 and H^+ concentrations and with temperature are shown in Figure 29.12. The curve shifts to the right, indicating decreased affinity of Hb for O_2, when the H^+ and CO_2 concentrations increase, and when the temperature increases. These are exactly the conditions in muscles that are working hard and need more oxygen. The curve shifts to the left, indicating increased affinity of Hb for oxygen, under the opposite conditions of decreased H^+ and CO_2 concentrations and lower temperature.

Homeostasis requires a blood pH between 7.35 and 7.45. A pH outside this range results in either **acidosis** or **alkalosis**.

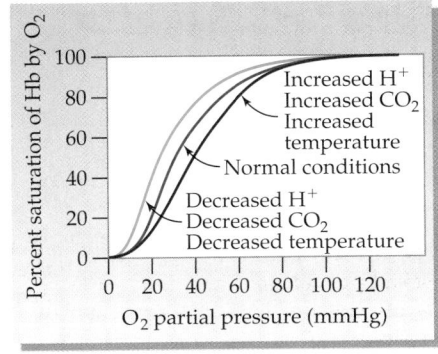

▲ **Figure 29.12**
Changes in oxygen affinity of hemoglobin with changing conditions.
The normal curve of Figure 29.11 is shown in red here.

Acidosis The abnormal condition associated with a blood plasma pH below 7.35; may be respiratory or metabolic.

Alkalosis The abnormal condition associated with a blood plasma pH above 7.45; may be respiratory or metabolic.

Acidosis	Normal	Alkalosis
Blood pH Below 7.35	Blood pH 7.35–7.45	Blood pH Above 7.45

The wide variety of conditions that cause acidosis or alkalosis can be divided between respiratory malfunctions and metabolic malfunctions. Table 29.4 gives examples of each. *Respiratory* disruption of acid-base balance can result when carbon dioxide generation by metabolism and carbon dioxide removal at the lungs are out of balance. *Metabolic* disruption of acid-base balance can result from abnormally high acid generation or failure of buffer systems and kidney function to regulate bicarbonate concentration.

Table 29.4 Causes of Acidosis and Alkalosis

Type of Imbalance	Causes
Respiratory acidosis	CO_2 buildup due to: Decreased respiratory activity (hypoventilation) Cardiac insufficiency (e.g., congestive failure, cardiac arrest) Deterioration of pulmonary function (e.g., asthma, emphysema, pulmonary obstruction, pneumonia)
Respiratory alkalosis	Loss of CO_2 due to: Excessive respiratory activity (hyperventilation, due, for example, to high fever, nervous condition)
Metabolic acidosis	Increased production of metabolic acids due to: Fasting or starvation Untreated diabetes Excessive exercise Decreased acid excretion in urine due to: Poisoning Renal failure Decreased plasma bicarbonate concentration due to: Diarrhea
Metabolic alkalosis	Elevated plasma bicarbonate concentration due to: Vomiting Diuretics Antacid overdose

⊙ KEY CONCEPT PROBLEM 29.3

Carbon dioxide dissolved in body fluids has a pronounced effect on pH.
(a) Does pH go up or down when carbon dioxide dissolves in these fluids? Does this change indicate higher or lower acidity?
(b) What does a blood gas analysis measure?

PROBLEM 29.4

Classify the following conditions as a cause of respiratory or metabolic acidosis or alkalosis (consult Table 29.4).
(a) Emphysema (b) Kidney failure
(c) Overdose of an antacid

PROBLEM 29.5

Classify the following conditions as a cause of respiratory or metabolic acidosis or alkalosis (consult Table 29.4).
(a) Severe panic attack (b) Congestive heart failure
(c) Running a marathon

29.7 The Kidney and Urine Formation

Learning Objective:

• Describe the transfer of water and solutes during urine formation.

The kidneys bear the major responsibility for maintaining a constant internal environment in the body. By managing the elimination of appropriate amounts of water, electrolytes, hydrogen ions, and nitrogen-containing wastes, the kidneys respond to changes in health, diet, and physical activity.

About 25% of the blood pumped from the heart goes directly to the kidneys, where the functional units are the *nephrons* (Figure 29.13). Each kidney contains over a million of them. Blood enters a nephron at a *glomerulus* (at the top in Figure 29.13), a tangle of capillaries surrounded by a fluid-filled space. **Filtration,** the first of three essential kidney functions, occurs here. The pressure of blood pumped into the glomerulus directly from the heart is high enough to push plasma and all its solutes except large proteins across the capillary membrane into the surrounding fluid, the **glomerular filtrate.** The filtrate flows from the capsule into the tubule that makes up the rest of the nephron, and the blood enters the network of capillaries intertwined with the tubule.

About 125 mL of filtrate per minute enters the kidneys, and they produce 180 L of filtrate per day. This filtrate contains not only waste products but also many solutes the body cannot afford to lose, such as glucose and electrolytes. Since we excrete only about 1.4 L of urine each day, you can see that another important function of the kidneys is **reabsorption**—the recapture of water and essential solutes by moving them out of the tubule.

Reabsorption alone, however, is not sufficient to provide the kind of control over urine composition that is needed. More of certain solutes must be excreted than are present in the filtrate. This situation is dealt with by **secretion**—the transfer of solutes *into* the kidney tubule.

Reabsorption and secretion require the transfer of solutes and water among the filtrate, the interstitial fluid surrounding the tubule, and blood in the capillaries. Table 29.5 lists some of the substances reabsorbed or secreted. Solutes cross the tubule and capillary membranes by passive diffusion in response to concentration or ionic charge differences or by active transport. Water moves in response to differences in the osmolarity of the fluids on the two sides of the membranes. Solute and water movement is also controlled by hormone-directed variations in the permeability of the tubule membrane.

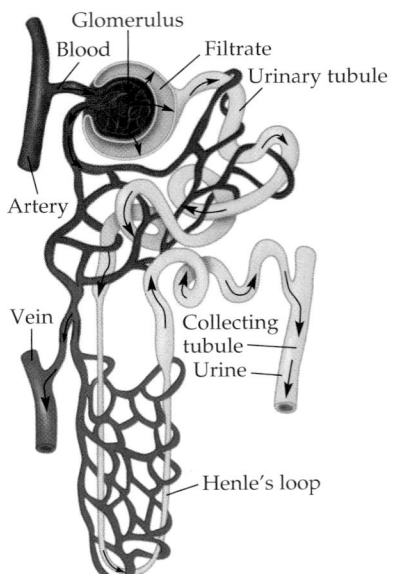

▲ **Figure 29.13**
Structure of a nephron.
Water moves out of the urinary tubule and the collecting tubule. The concentration of solutes in urine is established as they move both in and out along the tubules.

Filtration (kidney) Filtration of blood plasma through a glomerulus and into a kidney nephron.

Glomerular filtrate Fluid that enters the nephron from the glomerulus; filtered blood plasma.

Reabsorption (kidney) Movement of solutes out of filtrate in a kidney tubule.

Secretion (kidney) Movement of solutes into filtrate in a kidney tubule.

Table 29.5 Reabsorption and Secretion in Kidney Tubules

Reabsorbed	Secreted
Ions	Ions
Na^+, Cl^-, K^+, Ca^{2+}, Mg^{2+}, PO_4^{3-}, SO_4^{2-}, HCO_3^-	K^+, H^+, Ca^{2+}
Metabolites	Wastes
Glucose	Creatinine
Amino acids	Urea
Proteins	Ammonia
Vitamins	Various organic acids and bases (including uric acid)
	Miscellaneous
	Neurotransmitters
	Histamine
	Drugs (penicillin, atropine, morphine, numerous others)

29.8 Urine Composition and Function

Learning Objective:

• Describe the composition of urine.

Urine contains the products of glomerular filtration, minus the substances reabsorbed in the tubules, plus the substances secreted in the tubules. The actual concentrations of these substances in urine at any time are determined by the amount of water being excreted, which can vary significantly with water intake, exercise, temperature, and state of health. (For identical quantities of solutes, concentration *decreases* when the quantity of solvent water *increases,* and concentration *increases* when the quantity of water *decreases.*)

About 50 g of solids in solution are excreted every day—about 20 g of electrolytes and 30 g of nitrogen-containing wastes (urea and ammonia from amino acid catabolism, creatinine from breakdown of creatine phosphate in muscles, and uric acid from purine catabolism). Normal urine composition is usually reported as the quantity of each solute excreted per day, and laboratory urinalysis often requires collection of all urine excreted during a 24-hour period.

The following paragraphs briefly describe a few of the mechanisms that control the composition of urine.

Acid-Base Balance

Respiration, buffers, and excretion of hydrogen ions in urine combine to maintain acid-base balance. Metabolism normally produces an excess of hydrogen ions; a portion of these must be excreted each day to prevent acidosis. Very little free hydrogen ion exists in blood plasma, and therefore very little enters the glomerular filtrate. Instead, the H^+ to be eliminated is produced by the reaction of CO_2 with water in the cells lining the tubules of the nephrons:

$$CO_2 + H_2O \xrightarrow{\text{Carbonic anhydrase}} H^+ + HCO_3^-$$

To bloodstream
To filtrate

The HCO_3^- ions return to the bloodstream, and the H^+ ions enter the filtrate. Thus, the more hydrogen ions there are to be excreted, the more bicarbonate ions are returned to the bloodstream.

The urine must carry away the necessary quantity of H^+ without becoming excessively acidic. To accomplish this, the H^+ is tied up by reaction with HPO_4^{2-} absorbed at the glomerulus or by reaction with NH_3 produced in the tubule cells by deamination of glutamate:

$$H^+ + HPO_4^{2-} \longrightarrow H_2PO_4^-$$
$$H^+ + NH_3 \longrightarrow NH_4^+$$

When acidosis occurs, the kidney responds by synthesizing more ammonia, thereby increasing the quantity of H^+ eliminated.

A further outcome of H^+ production in tubule cells is the net reabsorption of the HCO_3^- that entered the filtrate at the glomerulus. The body cannot afford to lose its primary buffering ion, HCO_3^-. If HCO_3^- were to be lost, the body would have to produce more; the result would be production of additional acid from carbon dioxide by reaction with water. Instead, H^+ secreted into the filtrate combines with HCO_3^- in the filtrate to produce CO_2 and water:

$$H^+ + HCO_3^- \longrightarrow CO_2 + H_2O$$

In the filtrate
To bloodstream

Upon returning to the bloodstream, the CO_2 is reconverted to HCO_3^-.

CHEMISTRY IN ACTION

✤ What's in Your Blood Test?

Along with your annual physical, your doctor will almost certainly order that routine blood work be done either before or right after they see you. If you have ever looked at the lab orders, you are sure to have come across a myriad of confusing abbreviations, such as CBC, or CMP, WBC with differential, or LP. What exactly has your doctor ordered and why?

As we learned in the beginning of the chapter, because blood is one of the body fluids that touches every part of your body, including the major organs, it is the "biochemical superhighway" of the body and in it are clues to what is happening in areas that are not easily accessed by your physician. These clues come in the form of the levels of chemical species present. The quantity of a given

chemical in the blood is determined either directly or indirectly using automated analyzers that rely on premixed reagents and automatic division of a fluid sample into small portions for each test. As a result, there are certain tests (or 'screens') that are commonly run. Almost all routine blood work will request a chemistry panel (either a basic (BMP) or comprehensive (CMP) metabolic panel), a complete blood count (CBC), and some sort of lipid panel (LP). Depending on age, sex, or previous medical conditions, your physician may order other tests be done as well. The following table shows the most common things being looked for in a blood test and why. Normal ranges have been left out because some are dependent on the laboratory doing the test, some on age and sex, while others are still being revised.

Most Common Blood Tests Run during a Typical Annual Physical

Test	Classification	What Test Tells You
Serum glucose[1]	General test	Abnormal levels can be a sign of diabetes or prediabetes; requires fasting for 8–12 hours prior.
Calcium[2] Serum calcium[2]	General test Protein tests	Abnormal calcium levels in the blood may be a sign of kidney problems, bone disease, thyroid disease, cancer, malnutrition, or another disorder.
Sodium[1] Potassium[1] Chloride[1] Carbon dioxide[1] (CO_2)	Electrolyte tests	Abnormal electrolyte levels may be a sign of dehydration, kidney disease, liver disease, heart failure, high blood pressure, or other disorders.
Human serum albumin[2]	Protein tests	Produced in the liver, it is the most abundant protein in blood plasma. Low levels can indicate liver disease, kidney damage, or malnutrition. Elevated levels can indicate dehydration.
Bilirubin	Liver function	A breakdown product of old blood cells; found in bile. High levels can indicate liver or gall bladder disease.
RBC count Mean corpuscular volume (MCV or MPV)	CBC	RBCs carry oxygen from your lungs to the rest of your body. Abnormal RBC levels may be a sign of anemia, dehydration, bleeding, or another disorder. MCV is a measure of the average size of the RBCs and abnormal MCV levels may be a sign of anemia.
WBC count WBC with differential	CBC	WBCs are part of your immune system, which fights infections and diseases. Abnormal WBC levels may be a sign of infection, blood cancer, or an immune system disorder.
Hemoglobin (Hgb)	CBC	An iron-rich protein in RBCs that carries oxygen. Abnormal levels may be a sign of anemia or other blood disorders. Excess glucose due to diabetes can raise the level of hemoglobin A1c.
Total cholesterol	Lipid panel	Measures all of the cholesterol in all the lipoprotein particles. High levels correlate to higher risk of heart attack and stroke.
High-density lipoprotein cholesterol (HDL-C)	Lipid panel	Measures the cholesterol in HDL particles; often called "good cholesterol" because it removes excess cholesterol and carries it to the liver for removal. High levels correlate to lower risk of heart attack and stroke.
Low-density lipoprotein cholesterol (LDL-C)	Lipid panel	Calculates the cholesterol in LDL particles; often called "bad cholesterol" because it deposits excess cholesterol in walls of blood vessels, which can contribute to atherosclerosis. High levels correlate to higher risk of heart attack and stroke.
Triglycerides	Lipid panel	Measures all the triglycerides in all the lipoprotein particles; most is in the very low-density lipoproteins (VLDL). High levels correlate to higher risk of heart attack and stroke.

[1]Done in BMP and CMP; [2]Done in CMP only

It is important to note that the actual numbers obtained, and where they fall within currently accepted normal ranges, is crucial. It is also key to note that these typical blood tests act simply as first indicators; for example, your doctor may look at your blood glucose level and note that it is too high; this does not mean that you have diabetes, but it does suggest further testing. You need to talk to your doctor after your blood test and have them explain to you what each value means, and if out of range, what can be done to bring it back into range. Your annual blood test can be your first step in preventing disease.

CIA Problem 29.5 Which tests might indicate a patient was suffering from dehydration? Or anemia?

CIA Problem 29.6 Why do blood tests play such an important part in assessing the overall health of a patient?

CIA Problem 29.7 One of the more advanced blood tests used to screen for lipids is the Vertical Auto Profile (VAP) test. Using the internet, determine what this test is and why it believed to be a better indicator of cardiovascular health than a standard lipid panel.

In summary, acid-base reactions in the kidneys have the following results:

- Secreted H^+ is eliminated in the urine as NH_4^+ or $H_2PO_4^-$.
- Secreted H^+ combines with filtered HCO_3^-, producing CO_2 that returns to the bloodstream and again is converted to HCO_3^-.

Fluid and Na$^+$ Balance

The amount of water reabsorbed is dependent on the osmolarity of the fluid passing through the kidneys, the ADH–controlled permeability of the collecting duct membrane, and the amount of Na^+ actively reabsorbed. Increased sodium reabsorption means higher interstitial osmolarity, greater water reabsorption, and decreased urine volume. In the opposite condition of decreased sodium reabsorption, less water is reabsorbed and urine volume increases. "Loop diuretic" drugs such as furosemide (trademarked as Lasix), which is used in treating hypertension and congestive heart failure, act by inhibiting the active transport of Na^+ out of the region of the urinary tubule called Henle's loop. Caffeine acts as a diuretic in a similar way.

The reabsorption of Na^+ is normally under the control of the steroid hormone aldosterone. The arrival of chemical messengers signaling a decrease in total blood plasma volume accelerates the secretion of aldosterone. The result is increased Na^+ reabsorption in the kidney tubules accompanied by increased water reabsorption.

SUMMARY REVISITING THE LEARNING OBJECTIVES

- **Describe the major categories of body fluids, their general composition, and the exchange of solutes between them.** Body fluids are either intracellular or extracellular. *Extracellular fluid* includes *blood plasma* (the fluid part of blood) and *interstitial fluid*. *Blood serum* is the fluid remaining after blood has clotted. Solutes in body fluids include blood gases, electrolytes, metabolites, and proteins. Solutes are carried throughout the body in blood and lymph. Exchange of solutes between blood and interstitial fluid occurs at the network of blood and lymph capillaries in peripheral tissues. Exchange of solutes between interstitial fluid and intracellular fluid occurs by passage across cell membranes *(see Problems 6, 13–15, 18, 19, 23, 26, 27, and 55–59)*.

- **Discuss how fluid balance is maintained.** To maintain physiological homeostasis, the daily intake of water must roughly equal that of the daily output of water; this is approximately 2500 mL per day for an average adult. If output is greater than intake (as in the case of endurance athletes), body mass will be lost; 4% or greater body mass loss is considered to be dangerous. Output of water and electrolytes are very closely controlled by hormones. A shortage of water causes secretion of ADH. In the kidney, ADH causes a decrease in the water content of the urine, while thirst receptors in the hypothalamus, the heart, and blood vessels trigger increased water intake *(see Problems 6, 12, 20, 21, 23, 26–29, 53, 57, and 61)*.

- **Describe the composition and functions of blood.** The principal functions of blood are (1) transport of solutes and blood gases, (2) regulation, such as regulation of heat and acid-base balance, and (3) defense, which includes the *immune response* and *blood clotting*. In addition to plasma and proteins, blood is composed of RBCs (*erythrocytes*), which transport blood gases; WBCs (*leukocytes*), for defense functions; and *platelets*, which participate in blood clotting (Table 29.3) *(see Problems 7, 8, 15–17, 22, 25–28, and 61)*.

- **Explain the roles of the blood components that participate in inflammation and the immune response.** The presence of an *antigen* (a substance foreign to the body) initiates (1) the inflammatory response, (2) the cell-mediated immune response, and (3) the antibody-mediated immune response. The *inflammatory response* is initiated by histamine and accompanied by the destruction of invaders by *phagocytes*. The *cell-mediated response* is effected by *T cells* that can, for example, release a toxic protein that kills invaders. The *antibody-mediated response* is effected by *B cells*, which generate *antibodies (immunoglobulins)*, proteins that complex with antigens and destroy them *(see Problems 8–11, 18, 19, and 29–36)*.

- **List the steps involved in blood clotting.** A blood clot is a multistep process that is triggered either by an intrinsic pathway that begins when blood makes contact with the protein collagen or by an extrinsic pathway that begins when damaged tissue releases a membrane glycoprotein known as tissue factor. The result of either pathway is a cascade of reactions in which a series of zymogens are activated, ultimately resulting in the formation of a clot composed of the insoluble fibrous protein *fibrin* and platelets *(see Problems 7, 37–40, and 56)*.

- **Explain the relationships among O_2 and CO_2 transport and acid-base balance.** Oxygen is transported attached to Fe^{2+} ions in hemoglobin. The percent saturation of hemoglobin with oxygen (Figure 29.12) is governed by the partial pressure of oxygen in surrounding tissues and allosteric variations in hemoglobin structure. Carbon dioxide is transported in blood as a solute, attached to hemoglobin, or in solution as bicarbonate ion. In peripheral tissues, carbon dioxide diffuses into RBCs, where it is converted to bicarbonate ion. Acid-base balance is controlled as hydrogen ions generated by bicarbonate formation are bound by hemoglobin. At the lungs, oxygen enters the cells, and bicarbonate and hydrogen ions leave. A blood pH outside the normal range of 7.35–7.45 can be caused by respiratory or metabolic imbalance, resulting in the potentially serious conditions of *acidosis* or *alkalosis* (see Problems 12, 41–52, and 60).

● **Describe the transfer of water and solutes during urine formation.** The first essential kidney function is *filtration,* in which plasma and most of its solute cross capillary membranes and enter the *glomerular filtrate.* Water and essential solutes are then reabsorbed, whereas additional solutes for elimination are secreted into the filtrate (see Problems 12, 20, 53, 54, and 60).

● **Describe the composition of urine.** Urine is composed of the products of filtration, minus the substances reabsorbed, plus any secreted substances. It is composed of water, nitrogen-containing wastes, and electrolytes (including $H_2PO_4^-$ and NH_4^+) that are excreted to help maintain acid-base balance. The balance between water and Na^+ excreted or absorbed is governed by the osmolarity of fluid in the kidney, the hormone aldosterone, and various chemical messengers (see Problems 12, 20, 53, 57, and 60).

KEY WORDS

Acidosis, *p. 861*
Alkalosis, *p. 861*
Antibody (immunoglobulin), *p. 856*
Antigen, *p. 856*
Autoimmune disease, *p. 858*
Blood clot, *p. 859*
Blood plasma, *p. 849*

Blood serum, *p. 853*
Erythrocytes, *p. 853*
Extracellular fluid, *p. 849*
Fibrin, *p. 859*
Filtration (kidney), *p. 863*
Glomerular filtrate, *p. 863*
Hemostasis, *p. 859*
Immune response, *p. 856*

Inflammation, *p. 857*
Inflammatory response, *p. 856*
Interstitial fluid, *p. 849*
Intracellular fluid, *p. 849*
Leukocytes, *p. 853*
Osmolarity, *p. 849*

Reabsorption (kidney), *p. 863*
Secretion (kidney), *p. 863*
Whole blood, *p. 853*

UNDERSTANDING KEY CONCEPTS

29.6 Body fluids occupy two different compartments, either inside the cells or outside the cells.

(a) What are body fluids found inside the cell called?

(b) What are body fluids found outside the cell called?

(c) What are the two major subclasses of fluids found outside the cells?

(d) What major electrolytes are found inside the cells?

(e) What major electrolytes are found outside the cells?

29.7 In the diagram shown here, fill in the blanks with the names of the principal components of whole blood.

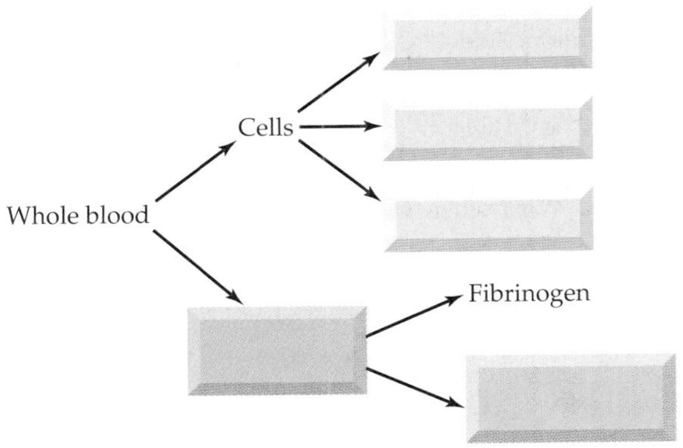

29.8 Fill in the blanks to identify some of the major functions of blood

(a) Blood carries _____ from lungs to tissues.

(b) Blood carries _____ from the tissues to lungs.

(c) Blood transports _____ from the digestive system to the tissues.

(d) Blood carries _____ from the tissues to the site of excretion.

(e) Blood transports _____ from the endocrine glands to their site of binding.

(f) Blood transports defensive agents such as _____ to destroy foreign material and to prevent blood loss.

29.9 List four symptoms of inflammation.

29.10 Explain how the chemical messenger histamine is biosynthesized and how it elicits each symptom of inflammation.

29.11 What type of WBCs are involved in a cell-mediated immune response? In an antibody-mediated immune response? (see Figure 29.7).

29.12 How does the composition of urine help to maintain a healthy physiological acid-base balance?

ADDITIONAL PROBLEMS

BODY FLUIDS

29.13 What are the three principal body fluids and the approximate percentage of total body water accounted for by each?

29.14 What characteristics are needed for a substance to be soluble in body fluids?

29.15 Give an example of a substance found in tissues that is not soluble in blood. How are components that are not normally soluble in blood transported?

29.16 What effects do the differences in pressure between arterial capillaries, interstitial fluids, and venous capillaries have on solutes crossing cell membranes?

29.17 How does blood pressure compare with the interstitial fluid pressure in arterial capillaries? With the interstitial fluid pressure in venous capillaries?

29.18 What is the purpose of the lymphatic system?

29.19 Where in the body does the lymph enter the bloodstream?

29.20 What is vasopressin?

29.21 What happens when excess secretion of ADH occurs? State two causes of this.

29.22 What is the difference between blood plasma and blood serum?

29.23 At what percent of body mass loss is collapse very likely to occur?

29.24 What are the three main types of cells found in blood?

29.25 What is the major function of each of the three types of blood cells?

29.26 What are electrolytes?

29.27 What are the major cations found in interstitial fluid?

29.28 What are the major cations found in intracellular fluid?

29.29 What is an antigen?

29.30 The recognition of an antigen can elicit three types of responses. What are they?

29.31 How are specific immune responses similar to the enzyme–substrate interaction (Section 19.4)?

29.32 What class of plasma proteins is involved in the antibody-mediated immune response?

29.33 What kinds of cells are associated with the antibody-directed immune response, and how do they work?

29.34 In the cell-mediated immune response, there are three types of T cells produced. What are they, and what is the function of each?

29.35 T cells are often discussed in conjunction with the disease AIDS, in which a virus destroys these cells. How do T cells work to combat disease?

29.36 What are memory cells, and what is their role in the immune response?

29.37 What is a blood clot? What is it composed of?

29.38 What vitamin and what mineral are specifically associated with the clotting process?

29.39 Describe the intrinsic pathway in blood clotting.

29.40 Why, do you suppose, are many of the enzymes involved in blood clotting secreted by the body as zymogens?

29.41 How many O_2 molecules can be bound by each hemoglobin tetramer?

29.42 What must be the charge of the iron in hemoglobin for it to perform its function?

29.43 What color is deoxyhemoglobin? Why?

29.44 How does the degree of saturation of hemoglobin vary with the partial pressure of O_2 in the tissues?

29.45 Oxygen has an allosteric interaction with hemoglobin. What are the results of this interaction as oxygen a) binds to and b) is released from hemoglobin?

29.46 What are the three ways of transporting CO_2 in the body?

29.47 Use Figure 29.11 to estimate the partial pressure of O_2 at which hemoglobin is 50% saturated with oxygen under normal conditions. Dry air at sea level is about 21% oxygen. What would be the percentage saturation of your hemoglobin under these conditions?

29.48 When an actively metabolizing tissue produces CO_2, the H^+ concentration of blood increases. Explain how this happens using a chemical equation.

29.49 Do the following conditions cause hemoglobin to release more O_2 to the tissues or to absorb more O_2?

(a) Raising the temperature

(b) Increased production of CO_2

(c) Increasing the H^+ concentration

29.50 What are the two types of acidosis? How do they differ? (Hint: See Table 29.4.)

29.51 Ketoacidosis is a condition that can arise in an individual with diabetes due to excessive production of ketone bodies. Is this condition classified as metabolic acidosis or respiratory acidosis? Explain.

29.52 What are the two types of alkalosis? How do they differ? (Hint: See Table 29.4.)

29.53 Kidneys are often referred to as filters that purify the blood. What other two essential functions do the kidneys perform to help maintain homeostasis?

29.54 Write the reactions by which HPO_4^{2-} and HCO_3^- absorb excess H^+ from the urine before elimination.

CONCEPTUAL PROBLEMS

29.55 What is the chemical basis for ethanol's solubility in blood?

29.56 Nursing mothers are able to impart some immunity to their infants. Why do you think this is so?

29.57 Many people find they retain water after eating salty food, evidenced by swollen fingers and ankles. Explain this phenomenon in terms of how the kidneys operate.

29.58 How does active transport differ from osmosis?

29.59 When is active transport necessary to move substances through cell membranes?

29.60 Discuss the importance of the CO_2/HCO_3^- equilibrium in blood and in urine.

29.61 We have discussed homeostasis throughout this text. But what is *hemostasis*? Is it related to homeostasis?

29.62 When people panic, cry, or have a high fever, they often begin to hyperventilate. Hyperventilation is abnormally fast or deep respiration, which results in the loss of carbon dioxide from the blood. Explain how hyperventilation changes the blood chemistry. Why can breathing into a paper bag alleviate hyperventilation?

GROUP PROBLEMS

29.63 Have each member of your group choose an energy drink. Search the internet and determine what ingredients are present, and what each does. Compare your results; what do you find they have in common? What are their major differences?

29.64 Referring to Table 16.2, which compounds would you expect to cross the BBB the easiest? Which would be the hardest to cross? Have each member of the group choose a compound and provide a chemical rationale for their answer.

29.65 Certain common medications you might take require a doctor to monitor your liver function. Search the internet to find a list of these. Have each member of the group choose a drug and provide what it is used for.

Scientific Notation

What Is Scientific Notation?

The numbers that you encounter in chemistry are often either very large or very small. For example, there are about 33,000,000,000,000,000,000,000 H_2O molecules in 1.0 mL of water, and the distance between the H and O atoms in an H_2O molecule is 0.000 000 000 095 7 m. These quantities are more conveniently written in *scientific notation* as 3.3×10^{22} molecules and 9.57×10^{-11} m, respectively. In scientific notation (also known as *exponential notation*), a quantity is represented as a number between 1 and 10 multiplied by a power of 10. In this kind of expression, the small raised number to the right of the 10 is the exponent.

Number	Exponential Form	Exponent
1,000,000	1×10^6	6
100,000	1×10^5	5
10,000	1×10^4	4
1,000	1×10^3	3
100	1×10^2	2
10	1×10^1	1
1		
0.1	1×10^{-1}	−1
0.01	1×10^{-2}	−2
0.001	1×10^{-3}	−3
0.000 1	1×10^{-4}	−4
0.000 01	1×10^{-5}	−5
0.000 001	1×10^{-6}	−6
0.000 000 1	1×10^{-7}	−7

Numbers greater than 1 have *positive* exponents, which tell how many times a number must be *multiplied* by 10 to obtain the correct value. For example, the expression 5.2×10^3 means that 5.2 must be multiplied by 10 three times:

$$5.2 \times 10^3 = 5.2 \times 10 \times 10 \times 10 = 5.2 \times 1000 = 5200$$

Note that doing this means moving the decimal point three places to the right:

$$5200.$$
$$123$$

The value of a positive exponent indicates *how many places to the right the decimal point must be moved* to give the correct number in ordinary decimal notation.

Numbers less than 1 have *negative* exponents, which tell how many times a number must be *divided* by 10 (or multiplied by one-tenth) to obtain the correct value. Thus, the expression 3.7×10^{-2} means that 3.7 must be divided by 10 two times:

$$3.7 \times 10^{-2} = \frac{3.7}{10 \times 10} = \frac{3.7}{100} = 0.037$$

Note that doing this means moving the decimal point two places to the left:

$$0.037$$
$$21$$

The value of a negative exponent indicates *how many places to the left the decimal point must be moved* to give the correct number in ordinary decimal notation.

Representing Numbers in Scientific Notation

How do you convert a number from ordinary notation to scientific notation? If the number is greater than or equal to 10, shift the decimal point to the *left* by n places until you obtain a number between 1 and 10. Then, multiply the result by 10^n. For example, the number 8137.6 is written in scientific notation as 8.1376×10^3:

$$8137.6 = 8.1376 \times 10^3$$

Shift decimal point to the left by 3 places to get a number between 1 and 10.

Number of places decimal point was shifted to the left.

When you shift the decimal point to the left by three places, you are in effect dividing the number by $10 \times 10 \times 10 = 1000 = 10^3$. Therefore, you must multiply the result by 10^3 so that the value of the number is unchanged.

To convert a number less than 1 to scientific notation, shift the decimal point to the *right* by n places until you obtain a number between 1 and 10. Then, multiply the result by 10^{-n}. For example, the number 0.012 is written in scientific notation as 1.2×10^{-2}:

$$0.012 = 1.2 \times 10^{-2}$$

Shift decimal point to the right by 2 places to get a number between 1 and 10.

Number of places decimal point was shifted to the right.

When you shift the decimal point to the right by two places, you are in effect multiplying the number by $10 \times 10 = 100 = 10^2$. Therefore, you must multiply the result by 10^{-2} so that the value of the number is unchanged ($10^2 \times 10^{-2} = 10^0 = 1$).

The following table gives some additional examples. To convert from scientific notation to ordinary notation, simply reverse the preceding process. Thus, to write the number 5.84×10^4 in ordinary notation, drop the factor of 10^4 and move the decimal point 4 places to the *right* ($5.84 \times 10^4 = 58{,}400$). To write the number 3.5×10^{-1} in ordinary notation, drop the factor of 10^{-1} and move the decimal point 1 place to the *left* ($3.5 \times 10^{-1} = 0.35$). Note that you don't need scientific notation for numbers between 1 and 10 because $10^0 = 1$.

Number	Scientific Notation
58,400	5.84×10^4
0.35	3.5×10^{-1}
7.296	$7.296 \times 10^0 = 7.296 \times 1$

Mathematical Operations with Scientific Notation

Addition and Subtraction in Scientific Notation

To add or subtract two numbers expressed in scientific notation, both numbers must have the same exponent. Thus, to add 7.16×10^3 and 1.32×10^2, first write the latter number as 0.132×10^3 and then add:

$$
\begin{array}{r}
7.16 \ \times 10^3 \\
+0.132 \times 10^3 \\
\hline
7.29 \ \times 10^3
\end{array}
$$

The answer has three significant figures. (Significant figures are discussed in Section 1.8.) Alternatively, you can write the first number as 71.6×10^2 and then add:

$$7.16 \times 10^2$$
$$+\; 1.32 \times 10^2$$
$$\overline{72.9 \;\; \times 10^2 = 7.29 \times 10^3}$$

Subtraction of these two numbers is carried out in the same manner.

$$7.16 \;\; \times 10^3 \qquad\qquad 7.16 \times 10^2$$
$$-0.132 \times 10^3 \quad \text{or} \quad -1.32 \times 10^2$$
$$\overline{7.03 \;\; \times 10^3} \qquad\qquad \overline{70.3 \times 10^2 = 7.03 \times 10^3}$$

Multiplication in Scientific Notation

To multiply two numbers expressed in scientific notation, multiply the factors in front of the powers of 10 and then add the exponents. For example,

$$(2.5 \times 10^4)(4.7 \times 10^7) = (2.5)(4.7) \times 10^{4+7} = 12 \times 10^{11} = 1.2 \times 10^{12}$$
$$(3.46 \times 10^5)(2.2 \times 10^{-2}) = (3.46)(2.2) \times 10^{5+(-2)} = 7.6 \times 10^3$$

Both answers have two significant figures.

Division in Scientific Notation

To divide two numbers expressed in scientific notation, divide the factors in front of the powers of 10 and then subtract the exponent in the denominator from the exponent in the numerator. For example,

$$\frac{3 \times 10^6}{7.2 \times 10^2} = \frac{3}{7.2} \times 10^{6-2} = 0.4 \times 10^4 = 4 \times 10^3 \;(\text{1 significant figure})$$
$$\frac{7.50 \times 10^{-5}}{2.5 \times 10^{-7}} = \frac{7.50}{2.5} \times 10^{-5-(-7)} = 3.0 \times 10^2 \;(\text{2 significant figures})$$

Scientific Notation and Electronic Calculators

With a scientific calculator you can carry out calculations in scientific notation. You should consult the instruction manual for your particular calculator to learn how to enter and manipulate numbers expressed in an exponential format. On most calculators, you enter the number $A \times 10^n$ by (i) entering the number A, (ii) pressing a key labeled EXP or EE, and (iii) entering the exponent n. If the exponent is negative, you press a key labeled $+/-$ before entering the value of n. (Note that you do not enter the number 10.) The calculator displays the number $A \times 10^n$ with the number A on the left followed by some space and then the exponent n. For example,

$$4.625 \times 10^2 \quad \text{is displayed as} \quad 4.625\; 02$$

To add, subtract, multiply, or divide exponential numbers, use the same sequence of keystrokes as you would in working with ordinary numbers. When you add or subtract on a calculator, the numbers need not have the same exponent; the calculator automatically takes account of the different exponents. Remember, though, that the calculator often gives more digits in the answer than the allowed number of significant figures. It's sometimes helpful to outline the calculation on paper, as in the preceding examples, to keep track of the number of significant figures.

PROBLEM A.1

Perform the following calculations, expressing the results in scientific notation with the correct number of significant figures. (You don't need a calculator for these.)

(a) $(1.50 \times 10^4) + (5.04 \times 10^3)$

(b) $(2.5 \times 10^{-2}) - (5.0 \times 10^{-3})$

(c) $(6.3 \times 10^{15}) \times (10.1 \times 10^3)$

(d) $(2.5 \times 10^{-3}) \times (3.2 \times 10^{-4})$

(e) $(8.4 \times 10^4) \div (3.0 \times 10^6)$

(f) $(5.530 \times 10^{-2}) \div (2.5 \times 10^{-5})$

ANSWERS

(a) 2.00×10^4 (b) 2.0×10^{-2} (c) 6.4×10^{19}

(d) 8.0×10^{-7} (e) 2.8×10^{-2} (f) 2.2×10^3

PROBLEM A.2

Perform the following calculations, expressing the results in scientific notation with the correct number of significant figures. (Use a calculator for these.)

(a) $(9.72 \times 10^{-1}) + (3.4823 \times 10^2)$

(b) $(3.772 \times 10^3) - (2.891 \times 10^4)$

(c) $(1.956 \times 10^3) \div (6.02 \times 10^{23})$

(d) $3.2811 \times (9.45 \times 10^{21})$

(e) $(1.0015 \times 10^3) \div (5.202 \times 10^{-9})$

(f) $(6.56 \times 10^{-6}) \times (9.238 \times 10^{-4})$

ANSWERS

(a) 3.4920×10^2 (b) -2.514×10^4 (c) 3.25×10^{-21}

(d) 3.10×10^{22} (e) 1.925×10^{11} (f) 6.06×10^{-9}

Conversion Factors

Length   SI Unit: Meter (m)

1 meter = 0.001 kilometer (km)

= 100 centimeters (cm)

= 1.0936 yards (yd)

1 centimeter = 10 millimeters (mm)

= 0.3937 inch (in.)

1 nanometer = 1×10^{-9} meter

1 Angstrom ($\mathring{A}$) = 1×10^{-10} meter

1 inch = 2.54 centimeters

1 mile = 1.6094 kilometers

Volume   SI Unit: Cubic meter (m³)

1 cubic meter = 1000 liters (L)

1 liter = 1000 cubic centimeters (cm³)

= 1000 milliliters (mL)

= 1.056710 quarts (qt)

1 cubic inch = 16.4 cubic centimeters

Temperature   SI Unit: Kelvin (K)

0 K = −273.15 °C

= −459.67 °F

°F = (9/5)°C + 32°; °F = (1.8 × °C) + 32°

°C = (5/9)(°F − 32°); °C = $\dfrac{(°F − 32°)}{1.8}$

K = °C + 273.15°

Mass   SI Unit: Kilogram (kg)

1 kilogram = 1000 grams (g)

= 2.205 pounds (lb)

1 gram = 1000 milligrams (mg)

= 0.03527 ounce (oz)

1 pound = 453.6 grams

1 atomic mass unit = 1.66054×10^{-24} gram

Pressure   SI Unit: Pascal (Pa)

1 pascal = 9.869×10^{-6} atmosphere

1 atmosphere = 101,325 pascals

= 760 mmHg (Torr)

= 14.70 lb/in² (psi)

Energy   SI Unit: Joule (J)

1 joule = 0.23901 calorie (cal)

1 calorie = 4.184 joules

1 Calorie (nutritional unit) = 1000 calories

= 1 kcal

Answers to Selected Problems

Short answers are given for in-chapter problems, Understanding Key Concepts problems, and even-numbered end-of-chapter problems. Explanations and full answers for all problems are provided in the accompanying Study Guide and Full Solutions Manual.

Chapter 1

1.1 solid   **1.2** mixture (heterogeneous): **(a), (d)**; pure (element): **(b), (c)**
1.3 physical: **(a)**; chemical: **(b), (c), (d)**   **1.4** chemical change; on the left: pure substance; on the right: mixture   **1.5** **(a)** 2 **(b)** 1 **(c)** 6 **(d)** 5 **(e)** 4 **(f)** 3   **1.6** **(a)** 1 nitrogen atom, 3 hydrogen atoms **(b)** 1 sodium atom, 1 hydrogen atom, carbon atom, 3 oxygen atoms **(c)** 8 carbon atoms, 18 hydrogen atoms **(d)** 6 carbon atoms, 8 hydrogen atoms, 6 oxygen atoms   **1.7** **(a)** 0.01 m **(b)** 0.1 g **(c)** 1000 m **(d)** 0.000 001 s **(e)** 0.000 000 001 g   **1.8** **(a)** 3 **(b)** 4 **(c)** 5 **(d)** exact   **1.9** 32.3 °C; three significant figures   **1.10** **(a)** 5.8×10^{-2} g **(b)** 4.6792×10^4 m **(c)** 6.072×10^{-3} cm **(d)** 3.453×10^2 kg
1.11 **(a)** 48,850 mg **(b)** 0.000 008 3 m **(c)** 0.0400 m   **1.12** **(a)** 6.3000×10^5 **(b)** 1.30×10^3 **(c)** 7.942×10^{11} **1.13** **(a)** 2.30 g **(b)** 188.38 mL **(c)** 0.009 L **(d)** 1.000 kg   **1.14** **(a)** 50.9 mL **(b)** 0.078 g **(c)** 11.9 m **(d)** 51 mg **(e)** 103
1.15 **(a)** 454 g **(b)** 2.5 L **(c)** 105 qt   **1.16** 795 mL   **1.17** 2.5 mL   **1.18** **(a)** 10.6 mg/kg **(b)** 36 mg/kg   **1.19** 331.0 K   **1.20** 102 °F
1.21 7,700 cal   **1.22** 0.21 cal/g·°C   **1.23** float; density = 0.637 g/cm³   **1.24** 8.392 mL   **1.25** more dense   **1.26** gases: helium (He), neon (Ne), argon (Ar), krypton (Kr), xenon (Xe), radon (Rn); coinage metals: copper (Cu), silver (Ag), gold (Au)   **1.27** Red: vanadium, sources: magnetite, fossil fuels, and bauxite, uses: steel alloys, emeralds, superconducting magnet, and ceramics; Green: boron, sources: borate minerals, including borax and kernite, uses: laundry aid, silly putty, glass, semiconductors, and insecticides; Blue: bromine, sources: Earth's crust and sea water, uses: flame retardant, gasoline additive, and pesticides   **1.28** Americium   **1.29** **(a)** 0.978 **(b)** three **(c)** less dense   **1.30** The smaller cylinder is more precise because the gradations are smaller.   **1.31** 3 1/8 in.; 8.0 cm   **1.32** start: 0.11 mL stop: 0.25 mL volume: 0.14 mL   **1.33** higher in chloroform   **1.34** Physical change doesn't alter the identity of the substance; a chemical change alters the chemical identity   **1.36** physical: **(a), (d)**; chemical **(b), (c), (e)** **1.38** Changes in state: melting, boiling, condensation, and freezing. Melting: a solid is heated to a liquid. Boiling: a liquid is heated to a gas. Condensation: a gas is cooled to a liquid. Freezing: a liquid is cooled to a solid.   **1.40** No, as butane is a liquid at 25 °F   **1.42** **(a)** gasoline—(i) and (iii) **(b)** iodine—(ii) and (v) **(c)** water—(iii) and (vi) **(d)** air—(i) and (iv) **(e)** blood—(i) and (iii) **(f)** sodium bicarbonate—(ii) and (vi) **(g)** gaseous ammonia—(iv) and (vi) **(h)** silicon—(ii) and (v)   **1.44** **(a)** reactants: sodium (solid), water (liquid); products: hydrogen (gas), sodium hydroxide (aqueous) **(b)** compounds: water, sodium hydroxide; element: sodium, hydrogen   **1.46** **(a)** I, use: preventing goiter **(b)** Cr, use: harden steel **(c)** Tc, use: biomedical imaging **(d)** As, use: pesticides **(e)** Ba, uses: paint and biomedical imaging   **1.48** **(a)** Br **(b)** Mn **(c)** C **(d)** K   **1.50** Carbon, hydrogen, nitrogen, and oxygen; 10 atoms   **1.52** $C_{13}H_{18}O_2$ **1.54** A physical quantity consists of a number and a unit.   **1.56** **(a)** cubic centimeter **(b)** decimeter **(c)** millimeter **(d)** nanoliter **(e)** milligram **(f)** cubic meter   **1.58** 10^9 pg, 3.5×10^4 pg   **1.60** **(a)** 9.457×10^3 **(b)** 7×10^{-5} **(c)** 2.000×10^{10} **(d)** 1.2345×10^{-2} **(e)** 6.5238×10^2 **1.62** **(a)** 6 **(b)** 3 **(c)** 3 **(d)** 4 **(e)** 1 to 5 **(f)** 2 or 3   **1.64** **(a)** 7,926 mi, 7,900 mi, 7,926.38 mi **(b)** $7.926 381 \times 10^3$ mi   **1.66** **(a)** 12.1 g **(b)** 96.19 cm **(c)** 263 mL **(d)** 20.9 mg   **1.68** **(a)** 0.3614 cg **(b)** 0.0120 mL **(c)** 0.0144 mm **(d)** 60.3 ng **(e)** 1.745 dL **(f)** 1.5×10^3 cm   **1.70** **(a)** 97.8 kg **(b)** 0.133 mL **(c)** 0.46 ng **(d)** 2.99 mm   **1.72** **(a)** 62.1 mi/hr **(b)** 91.1 ft/s   **1.74** **(a)** 6×10^{-4} cm **(b)** 2×10^3 cells/cm;   **1.76** 10 g   **1.78** 6×10^{10} cells
1.80 537 cal = 0.537 kcal   **1.82** 0.092 cal/g · °C
1.84 Hg: 76 °C; Fe: 40.7 °C   **1.86** 0.179 g/cm³
1.88 11.4 g/cm³   **1.90** 159 mL   **1.92** freezing point = 491.67 °R; boiling point = 671.67 °R   **1.94** 3.12 in; 7.92 cm; Discrepancies are due to rounding errors and changes in significant figures.   **1.96** **(a)** 3.5×10^5 cal $(1.46 \times 10^6 \text{ J})$; **(b)** 9.86 °C   **1.98** 3.9×10^{-2} g/dL iron, 8.3×10^{-3} g/dL calcium, 2.24×10^{-1} g/dL cholesterol

1.100 7.8×10^6 mL/day   **1.102** 0.13 g   **1.104** 4.4 g; 0.0097 lb   **1.106** 2200 mL   **1.108** 2.2 tablespoons   **1.110** iron   **1.112** At the crossover point, °F = °C.

$$°F = \left(\frac{1.8 \; °F}{°C} \times °C \right) + 32 \; °F \quad \text{If } °C = °F, °F = 1.8 \; °F + 32°.$$

The crossover temperature is °F = °C = −40°.   **1.114** $C_2H_3Cl_3O_2$—four different elements; carbon—two, hydrogen—three, chlorine—three, oxygen—two   **1.116** 1.26×10^{11} L; production of fertilizers

Chapter 2

2.1 **(a)** Re **(b)** Sr **(c)** Te   **2.2** The answers agree.   **2.3** **(a)** $^{79}_{35}\text{Br}$, $^{81}_{35}\text{Br}$ **(b)** 79.986 amu; slight difference with the periodic table at 79.904 amu   **2.4** $^{35}_{17}\text{Cl}$, $^{37}_{17}\text{Cl}$ **2.5** group 3A, period 3   **2.6** silver, calcium   **2.7** nitrogen (2), phosphorus (3), arsenic (4), antimony (5), bismuth (6)   **2.8** The metalloids are along the black zigzag line, beginning in column 3A. They are found between the metals and the nonmetals.   **2.9** **(a)** Titanium, transition metal groups **(b)** Tellurium, main group **(c)** Selenium, main group **(d)** Scandium, transition metal groups **(e)** Astatine, main group, halogens **(f)** Argon, main group, noble gas   **2.10** **(a)** nonmetal, main group, noble gas **(b)** metal, main group **(c)** nonmetal, main group **(d)** metal, transition element   **2.11** **(a)** Li, Na, K, Rb **(b)** F, O, C, Li **(c)** F, Cl, Br, I   **2.12** **(a)** Rb, K, Na, Li **(b)** F, O, Li, C **(c)** F, Cl, Br, I   **2.13** **(a)** Na-23, Group 1A, third period, metal; **(b)** O-18, Group 6A, sixth period, nonmetal   **2.14** 12, magnesium   **2.15** sulfur; main group (6A); nonmetal; last electron found in a $3p$ orbital.
2.16 **(a)** $1s^2 2s^2 2p^2$ **(b)** $1s^2 2s^2 2p^6 3s^2 3p^3$ **(c)** $1s^2 2s^2 2p^6 3s^2 3p^5$ **(d)** $1s^2 2s^2 2p^6 3s^2 3p^6 4s^1$ **2.17** $4p^3$, all are unpaired   **2.18** gallium   **2.19** **(a)** $1s^2 2s^2 2p^5$; [He] $2s^2 2p^5$ **(b)** $1s^2 2s^2 2p^6 3s^2 3p^1$; [Ne] $3s^2 3p^1$ **(c)** $1s^2 2s^2 2p^6 3s^2 3p^6 4s^2 3d^{10} 4p^3$; [Ar] $4s^2 3d^{10} 4p^3$ **2.20** group 2A   **2.21** group 7A; shell 1 = 2 electrons, shell 2 = 8 electrons, shell 3 = 7 electrons; $1s^2 2s^2 2p^6 3s^2 3p^5$ **2.22** group 6A, $ns^2 np^4$
2.23 $\cdot\overset{..}{\text{X}}\cdot$ **2.24** $:\overset{..}{\text{Rn}}:$ $\cdot\overset{.}{\text{Pb}}\cdot$ $:\overset{..}{\text{Xe}}:$ $\cdot\text{Ra}\cdot$ **2.25** red = 700 − 780 nm; blue = 400 − 480 nm; blue = higher energy

2.26

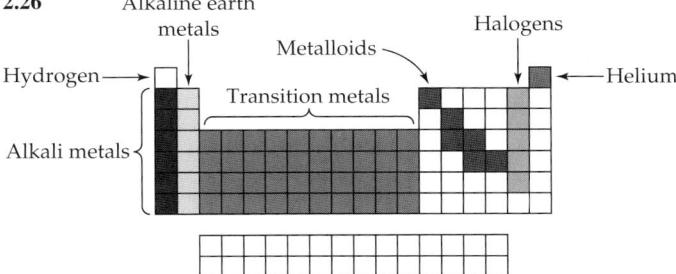

2.27 red: gas (fluorine); blue: atomic number 79 (gold); green: (calcium); beryllium, magnesium, strontium, barium, and radium are similar.

2.28

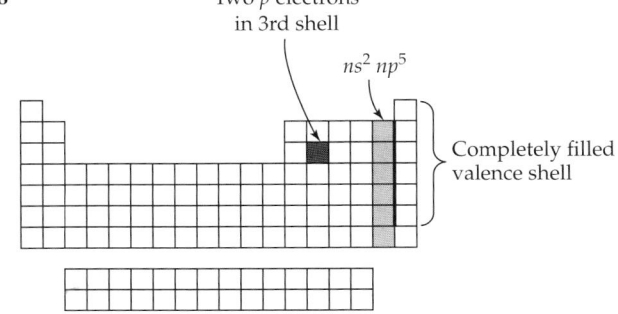

2.29 selenium   **2.30** $1s^2 2s^2 2p^6 3s^2 3p^6 4s^2 3d^{10} 4p^3$ **2.32** Atoms of different elements differ in the number of protons and electrons they have.
2.34 **(a)** 16.0 amu **(b)** 78.9 amu   **2.36** 16.0 g   **2.38** 6.022×10^{23} atoms
2.40 Protons and neutrons are found in a dense central region called the nucleus. Electrons move about the nucleus in large, specifically defined regions called orbitals.

2.42

Isotope	(a) $^{27}_{13}Al$	(b) $^{28}_{14}Si$	(c) $^{11}_{5}B$	(d) $^{115}_{47}Ag$
Number of protons	13	14	5	47
Number of neutrons	14	14	6	68
Number of electrons	13	14	5	47

2.44 (a) fluorine—19 (b) neon—19 (c) fluorine—21 (d) magnesium—21
2.46 (a) $^{120}_{50}Sn$ (b) $^{56}_{26}Fe$ (c) $^{226}_{88}Ra$ **2.48** 63.55 amu **2.50** Eight electrons are needed to fill the $3s$ and $3p$ subshells. **2.52** Am, metal **2.54** (a, b) transition metals (c) $3d$ **2.56** (a) Rb: (i), (v), (vii) (b) W: (i), (iv) (c) Ge: (iii), (v) (d) Kr: (ii), (v), (vi) **2.58** selenium **2.60** sodium, potassium, rubidium, cesium, francium **2.62** 2 **2.64** 2, 8, 18 **2.66** 3, 4, 5 **2.68** 10, neon **2.70** (a) two paired, two unpaired (b) four paired, one unpaired (c) two unpaired **2.72** 2, 1, 2, 1, 3, 3 **2.74** 2 **2.76** beryllium, $2s$; arsenic, $4p$ **2.78** (a) 8 (b) 4 (c) 2 (d) 1 (e) 3 (f) 7 **2.80** neon, argon, krypton, xenon, radon **2.82** 119 **2.84** (a) $5p$ (b) $3d$ (c) $4p$ (d) $3p$ **2.86** Sr, metal, group 2A, period 5, 38 protons **2.88** 2, 8, 18, 18, 4; metal **2.90** (a) The $4s$ subshell fills before $3d$ (b) The $2s$ subshell fills before $2p$. (c) Silicon has 14 electrons: $1s^2\,2s^2\,2p^6\,3s^2\,3p^2$ (d) The $3s$ electrons have opposite spins. **2.92** Electrons will fill or half-fill a d subshell instead of filling an s subshell of a higher shell. **2.94** $7p$ **2.96** (a) Co-60: 33 neutrons, 27 protons, 27 electrons (there are lots of possible answers for radioactive isotopes) (b) Os-190: 114 neutrons, 76 protons, 76 electrons (c) Tc-99: 56 neutrons, 43 protons, 43 electrons **2.98** (a) The peaks and valleys tend to correlate with the different groups of the periodic table. (b) Electronegativity, ionization energy, electron affinity, etc.

Chapter 3

3.1 Mg^{2+} is a cation. **3.2** S^{2-} is an anion. **3.3** O^{2-} is an anion. **3.4** Potassium ($1s^2\,2s^2\,2p^6\,3s^2\,3p^6\,4s^1$) can gain the argon configuration by losing 1 electron. **3.5** Aluminum must lose 3 electrons to form Al^{3+}. **3.6** $X\!:\,+\,\cdot\dot{Y}\cdot\,\longrightarrow\,X^{2+}\,+\,:\ddot{Y}\!:^{2-}$ **3.7** Fe^{2+}, $1s^2\,2s^2\,2p^6\,3s^2\,3p^6\,3d^6$ **3.8** (a) $Se + 2\,e^- \rightarrow Se^{2-}$ (b) $Ba \rightarrow Ba^{2+} + 2\,e^-$ (c) $Br + e^- \rightarrow Br^-$ **3.9** 1.0 g of $Na^+ = 312.5$ mL; 1.0 g of $Cl^- = 285.7$ mL **3.10** similar but slightly smaller ionization energies **3.11** (a) B (b) Ca (c) Sc **3.12** (a) H (b) S (c) Cr **3.13** (a) copper(II) ion (b) fluoride ion (c) magnesium ion (d) sulfide ion **3.14** (a) Ag^+ (b) Fe^{2+} (c) Cu^+ (d) Te^{2-} **3.15** Na^+, sodium ion; K^+, potassium ion; Ca^{2+}, calcium ion; Cl^-, chloride ion **3.16** (a) nitrate ion (b) cyanide ion (c) hydroxide ion (d) hydrogen phosphate ion **3.17** Group 1 A: Na^+, K^+; Group 2A: Ca^{2+}, Mg^{2+}; transition metals: Fe^{2+}; halogens: Cl^- **3.18** (a) MgI_2 (b) Al_2O_3 (c) $Fe_3(PO_4)_2$ (d) $Cr_2(SO_4)_3$ **3.19** $(NH_4)_2CO_3$ **3.20** $Al_2(SO_4)_3$, $Al(CH_3CO_2)_3$ **3.21** blue: K_2S; red: $BaBr_2$; green: Al_2O_3 **3.22** silver(I) sulphide **3.23** (a) tin (IV) oxide (b) calcium cyanide (c) sodium carbonate (d) copper (I) sulfate (e) barium hydroxide (f) iron (II) nitrate **3.24** (a) Li_3PO_4 (b) $CuCO_3$ (c) $Al_2(SO_3)_3$ (d) CuF (e) $Fe_2(SO_4)_3$ (f) NH_4Cl **3.25** Ca_3N_2 **3.26** Strongest—NaCl; weakest—RbCl; smaller cations have stronger bonds **3.27** acids: (a), (d); bases (b), (c) **3.28** (a) HCl (b) H_2SO_4

3.29

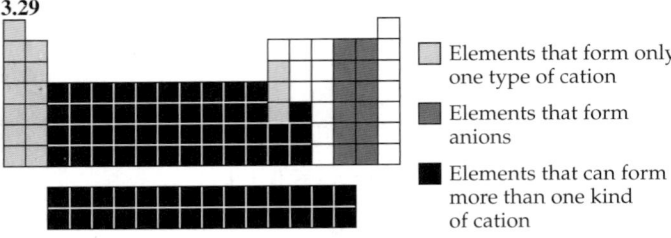

Elements that form only one type of cation

Elements that form anions

Elements that can form more than one kind of cation

All of the other elements form neither anions nor cations readily.

3.30

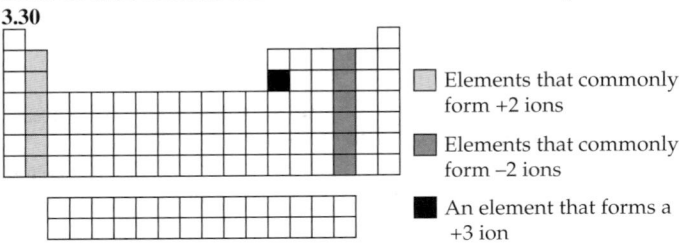

Elements that commonly form +2 ions

Elements that commonly form –2 ions

An element that forms a +3 ion

3.31 (a) O^{2-} (b) Na^+ (c) Ca^{2+} (d) Fe^{2+} **3.32** (a) sodium atom (larger) (b) Na^+ ion (smaller) **3.33** (a) chlorine atom (smaller) (b) Cl^- anion (larger) **3.34** iron (II) chloride or ferrous chloride, $FeCl_2$; iron (III) chloride or ferric chloride, $FeCl_3$; iron (II) oxide or ferrous oxide, FeO; iron (III) oxide or ferric oxide, Fe_2O_3; lead (II) chloride, $PbCl_2$; lead (IV) chloride, $PbCl_4$; lead (II) oxide, PbO; lead (IV) oxide, PbO_2 **3.35** (a) ZnS (b) $PbBr_2$ (c) CrF_3 (d) Al_2O_3 **3.36** Cr_2O_3 chromium (III) oxide **3.38** Ion charges are determined by the element's position on the periodic table relative to the noble gases (which have an octet of electrons). **3.40** Se^{2-} **3.42** (a) Sr (b) Br **3.44** (a) $1s^2\,2s^2\,2p^6\,3s^2\,3p^6\,4s^2\,3d^{10}\,4p^6$ (b) $1s^2\,2s^2\,2p^6\,3s^2\,3p^6\,4s^2\,3d^{10}\,4p^6$ (c) $1s^2\,2s^2\,2p^6\,3s^2\,3p^6$ (d) $1s^2\,2s^2\,2p^6\,3s^2\,3p^6\,4s^2\,3d^{10}\,4p^6\,5s^2\,4d^{10}\,5p^6$ (e) $1s^2\,2s^2\,2p^6$ **3.46** (a) $Ca \rightarrow Ca^{2+} + 2\,e^-$ (b) $Au \rightarrow Au^+ + e^-$ (c) $F + e^- \rightarrow F^-$ (d) $Cr \rightarrow Cr^{3+} + 3e^-$ **3.48** true: (d); false: (a), (b), (c) **3.50** (a) O (b) Li (c) Zn (d) N **3.52** none **3.54** Cr^{2+}: $1s^2\,2s^2\,2p^6\,3s^2\,3p^6\,3d^4$; Cr^{3+}: $1s^2\,2s^2\,2p^6\,3s^2\,3p^6\,3d^3$ **3.56** greater **3.58** (a) sulfide ion (b) tin (II) ion (c) strontium ion (d) magnesium ion (e) gold (I) ion **3.60** (a) Se^{2-} (b) O^{2-} (c) Ag^+ **3.62** (a) OH^- (b) HSO_4^- (c) $CH_3CO_2^-$ (d) MnO_4^- (e) OCl^- (f) NO_3^- (g) CO_3^{2-} (h) $Cr_2O_7^{2-}$ **3.64** (a) $Al_2(SO_4)_3$ (b) Ag_2SO_4 (c) $ZnSO_4$ (d) $BaSO_4$

3.66

	S^{2-}	Cl^-	PO_4^{3-}	CO_3^{2-}
Copper(II)	CuS	$CuCl_2$	$Cu_3(PO_4)_2$	$CuCO_3$
Ca^{2+}	CaS	$CaCl_2$	$Ca_3(PO_4)_2$	$CaCO_3$
NH_4^+	$(NH_4)_2S$	NH_4Cl	$(NH_4)_3PO_4$	$(NH_4)_2CO_3$
Ferric ion	Fe_2S_3	$FeCl_3$	$FePO_4$	$Fe_2(CO_3)_3$

3.68 copper(II) sulfide, copper(II) chloride, copper(II) phosphate, copper(II) carbonate; calcium sulfide, calcium chloride, calcium phosphate, calcium carbonate; ammonium sulfide, ammonium chloride, ammonium phosphate, ammonium carbonate; iron(III) sulfide, iron(III) chloride, iron(III) phosphate, iron(III) carbonate **3.70** (a) magnesium carbonate (b) calcium acetate (c) silver(I) cyanide (d) sodium dichromate **3.72** $Ca_3(PO_4)_2$ **3.74** An acid gives H^+ ions in water; a base gives OH^- ions. **3.76** (a) $H_2CO_3 \rightarrow 2H^+ + CO_3^{2-}$ (b) $HCN \rightarrow H^+ + CN^-$ (c) $Mg(OH)_2 \rightarrow Mg^{2+} + 2\,OH^-$ (d) $KOH \rightarrow K^+ + OH^-$ **3.78** H^- has the helium configuration, $1s^2$ **3.80** (a) CrO_3 (b) VCl_5 (c) MnO_2 (d) MoS_2 **3.82** (a) Cu_3PO_4 copper(I)phosphate (b) Na_2SO_4 sodium sulfate (c) MnO_2 manganese (IV) oxide (d) $AuCl_3$ gold (III) chloride (e) $Pb(CO_3)_2$ lead (IV) carbonate (f) Ni_2S_3 nickel (III) sulfide

3.84

Ion	Protons	Electrons	Neutrons
(a) $^{16}O^{2-}$	8	10	8
(b) $^{89}Y^{3+}$	39	36	50
(c) $^{133}Cs^+$	55	54	78
(d) $^{81}Br^-$	35	36	46

3.86 (a) Mn^{4+} (b) Cu^+ (c) Ti^{4+} **3.88** Ca^{2+} (monoatomic); $C_6H_{11}O_7^-$ (polyatomic) **3.90** stannous fluoride, SnF_2

Chapter 4

4.1 $:\!\ddot{I}\!:\!\ddot{I}\!:$; xenon **4.2** (a) P 3, H 1 (b) Se 2, H 1 (c) H 1, Cl 1 (d) Si 4, F 1 **4.3** (a) CH_2Cl_2 (b) BH_3 (c) NI_3 (d) $SiCl_4$

4.4

$$\begin{array}{c}
\quad H\quad :\!\ddot{O}\!: \\
\quad |\quad\quad || \\
H\!-\!C\!-\!C\!-\!\ddot{O}\!-\!H \\
\quad | \\
\quad H
\end{array}$$

4.5

(purine/caffeine ring structure with CH_3, N, C, O, H_3C substituents)

4.6

$$:\!\ddot{F}\!-\!\overset{:\ddot{F}:}{\underset{:\ddot{F}:}{B}}\quad + \quad \overset{H}{\underset{H}{:N\!-\!H}} \quad \longrightarrow \quad :\!\ddot{F}\!-\!\overset{:\ddot{F}:}{\underset{:\ddot{F}:}{B}}\!-\!\overset{H}{\underset{H}{N}}\!-\!H$$

Coordinate covalent bond

4.7 $AlCl_3$ is a covalent compound, and Al_2O_3 is ionic.

4.8

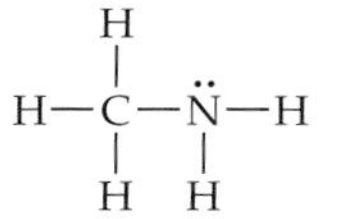

$$H-\underset{\underset{H}{|}}{\overset{\overset{H}{|}}{C}}-\underset{}{\overset{..}{N}}-H$$

4.9 (a) $H-\underset{\underset{H}{|}}{\overset{\overset{H}{|}}{C}}-\overset{..}{\underset{..}{O}}-H$ (b) $:N\equiv C-\underset{\underset{H}{|}}{\overset{\overset{H}{|}}{C}}-H$ (c) $:\overset{..}{\underset{..}{Cl}}:$ $:\overset{..}{N}-\overset{..}{\underset{..}{Cl}}:$ $:\overset{..}{\underset{..}{Cl}}:$

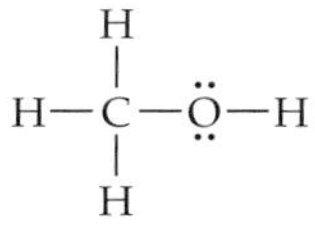

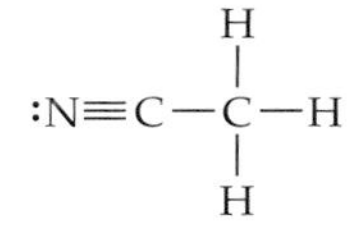

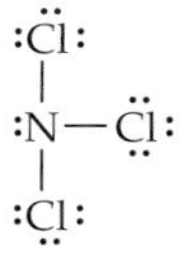

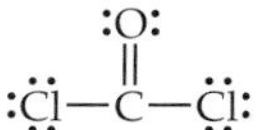

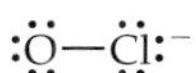

4.10 (a) $:\overset{..}{\underset{}{O}}:$ $:\overset{..}{\underset{..}{Cl}}-\overset{||}{C}-\overset{..}{\underset{..}{Cl}}:$ (b) $:\overset{..}{\underset{..}{O}}-\overset{..}{\underset{..}{Cl}}:^{-}$

(c) $H-\overset{..}{\underset{..}{O}}-\overset{..}{\underset{..}{O}}-H$ (d) $:\overset{..}{\underset{..}{Cl}}-\overset{..}{\underset{..}{S}}-\overset{..}{\underset{..}{Cl}}:$

4.11 $:\overset{..}{\underset{}{O}}:$ $:\overset{..}{\underset{..}{O}}-\overset{||}{N}-\overset{..}{\underset{..}{O}}-H$

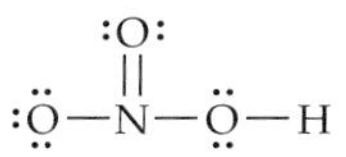

4.12 (a) $C_6H_{10}O_2$ (b)

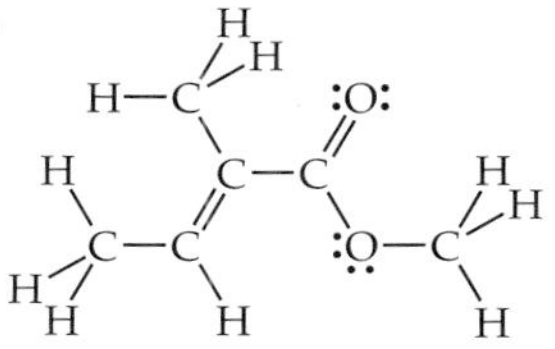

4.13 $:\overset{..}{O}=\overset{..}{O}-\overset{..}{\underset{..}{O}}:$ Oxygen normally has two bonds. Ozone is reactive as one oxygen atom has a single bond.

4.14 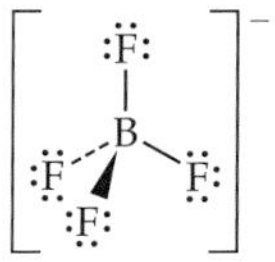
$$\left[:\overset{..}{\underset{..}{F}}: \quad \overset{|}{\underset{\overset{..}{\underset{..}{F}}:}{B}} \quad :\overset{..}{\underset{..}{F}}: \right]^{-} \quad \text{tetrahedral}$$

4.15 chloroform, $CHCl_3$—tetrahedral; dichloroethylene—planar

4.16 Both are bent.

4.17 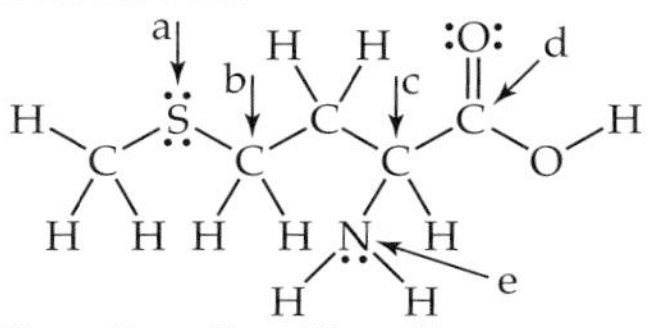
(a) bent
(b) tetrahedral
(c) tetrahedral
(d) trigonal planar
(e) pyramidal

4.18 $H = P < S < N < O$

4.19 (a) polar covalent (b) ionic (c) nonpolar covalent (d) polar covalent

$\overset{\delta+}{I}-\overset{\delta-}{Cl}$ $\overset{\delta+}{P}-\overset{\delta-}{Br}$

4.20
$$\overset{H}{\underset{H}{>}}C=\overset{..}{\underset{}{O}} \quad \overset{\delta+ \quad \delta-}{}$$

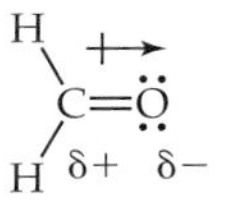

4.21 The carbons are tetrahedral; the oxygen is bent, the molecule is polar.

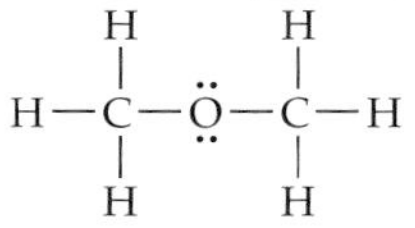

$$H-\underset{\underset{H}{|}}{\overset{\overset{H}{|}}{C}}-\overset{..}{\underset{..}{O}}-\underset{\underset{H}{|}}{\overset{\overset{H}{|}}{C}}-H$$

4.22
$$\overset{\delta+}{Li} \\ \overset{\delta-}{|} \\ C \\ H \diagup \diagdown H \\ H$$

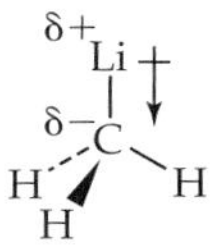

4.23 (a) disulfur dichloride (b) iodine monochloride (c) iodine trichloride
4.24 (a) SeF_4 (b) P_2O_5 (c) BrF_3 **4.25** (a) tetrahedral (b) pyramidal (c) trigonal planar   **4.26** (c) is square planar   **4.27** (a) $C_8H_9NO_2$
(b)

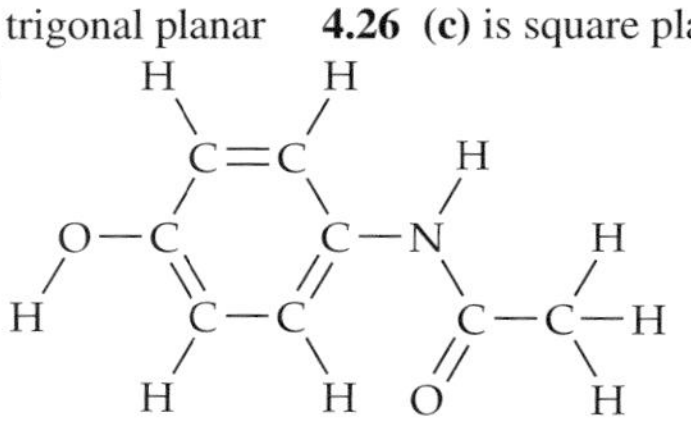

(c) All carbons are trigonal planar except the —CH_3 carbon. Nitrogen is pyramidal.

4.28

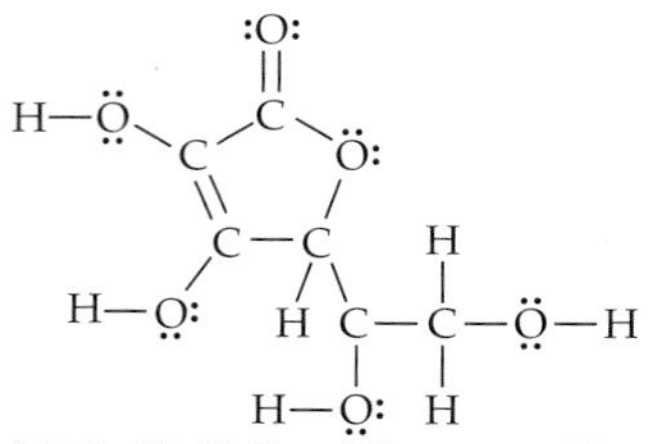

4.29 (a) $C_{13}H_{10}N_2O_4$ (b)

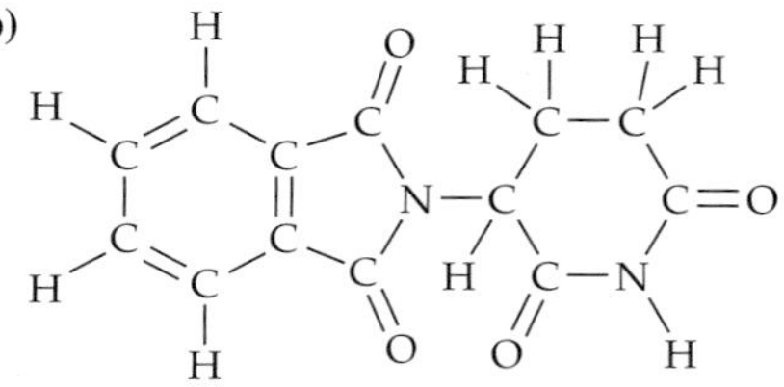

(c) Double-bonded carbon atoms are trigonal planar. The three carbon atoms with four single bonds are tetrahedral. The nitrogen atoms are pyramidal.

4.30 $:\overset{..}{\underset{}{O}}: \leftarrow$ electron rich

electron poor $\rightarrow$

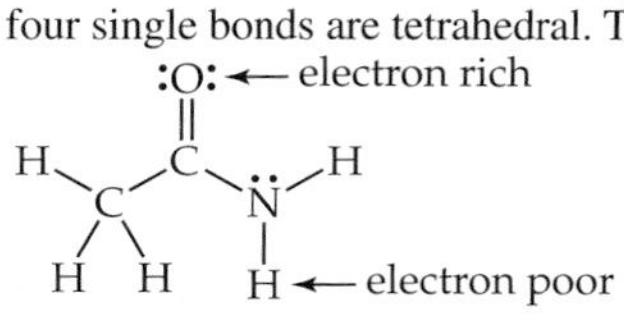

4.32 In a coordinate covalent bond, both electrons in the bond come from the same atom.   **4.34** covalent bonds: (b); ionic bonds: (a), (c), (d), (e)   **4.36** Two covalent bonds.   **4.38** (b), (c)   **4.40** $SnCl_4$ **4.42** The N—O bond   **4.44** (a) A molecular formula shows the numbers and kinds of atoms; a structural formula shows how the atoms are bonded to one another. (b) A structural formula shows the bonds between atoms; a condensed structure shows atoms but not bonds. (c) A lone pair of valence electrons is not shared in a bond; a shared pair of electrons is shared between two atoms.   **4.46** (a) 10; triple bond (b) 18; double bond between N, O (c) 24; double bond between C, O (d) 20   **4.48** too many hydrogens
4.50 (a) $H-\overset{..}{\underset{..}{O}}-N=\overset{..}{\underset{..}{O}}$ (b)   (c) $H-\overset{..}{\underset{..}{F}}:$

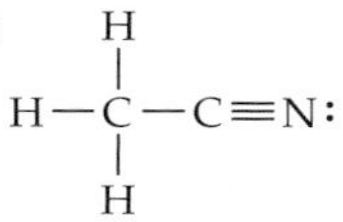

4.52 (a) $CH_3CH_2CH_3$ (b) $H_2C=CHCH_3$ (c) CH_3CH_2Cl **4.54** CH_3COOH
4.56 (a) $H-\overset{..}{\underset{..}{O}}-N=\overset{..}{\underset{..}{O}}$ (b) $:\overset{..}{\underset{}{O}}:$ (c)

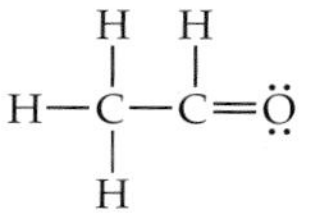

4.58 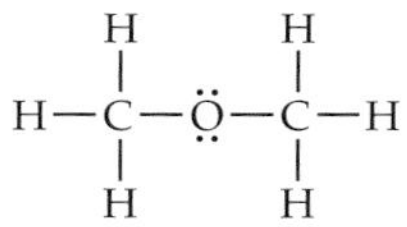
$$H-\underset{\underset{H}{|}}{\overset{\overset{H}{|}}{C}}-\overset{..}{\underset{..}{O}}-\underset{\underset{H}{|}}{\overset{\overset{H}{|}}{C}}-H \quad \text{Dimethyl ether}$$

4.60 $H-\overset{..}{\underset{\underset{H}{|}}{N}}-\overset{..}{\underset{..}{O}}-H$

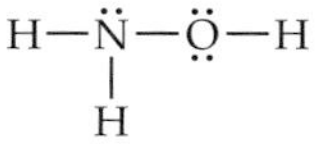

4.62 (a) $\left[\begin{array}{c} :\overset{..}{\underset{}{O}}: \\ H-\overset{||}{C}-\overset{..}{\underset{..}{O}}: \end{array} \right]^{-}$ (b) $\left[\begin{array}{c} :\overset{..}{\underset{}{O}}: \\ :\overset{..}{\underset{..}{O}}-\overset{||}{S}-\overset{..}{\underset{..}{O}}: \end{array} \right]^{2-}$ (c) $\left[:\overset{..}{\underset{..}{S}}-C\equiv N: \right]^{-}$

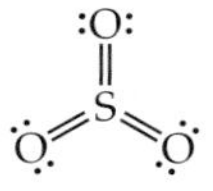

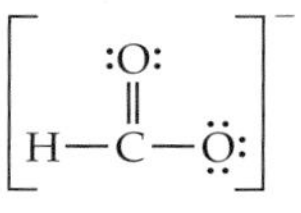

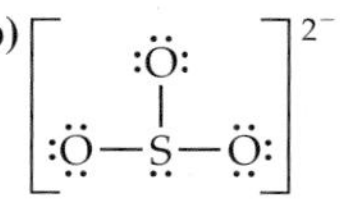

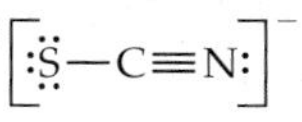

(d) $\left[\begin{array}{c} :\overset{..}{\underset{}{O}}: \\ :\overset{..}{\underset{..}{O}}-\overset{|}{P}-\overset{..}{\underset{..}{O}}: \\ :\overset{..}{\underset{..}{O}}: \end{array} \right]^{3-}$ (e) $\left[:\overset{..}{\underset{..}{O}}-\overset{..}{\underset{..}{Cl}}-\overset{..}{\underset{..}{O}}: \right]^{-}$

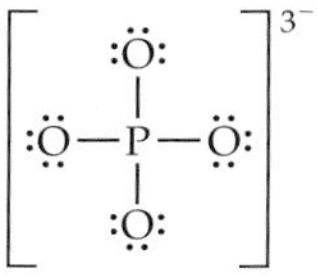

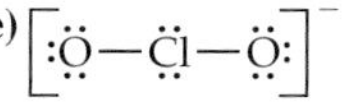

4.64 tetrahedral; pyramidal; bent   **4.66** (a), (b) tetrahedral (c), (d) trigonal planar (e) pyramidal   **4.68** All are trigonal planar, except for the —CH_3 carbon, which is tetrahedral.   **4.70** It should have low electronegativity, like other alkali metals.   **4.72** $Cl > C > Cu > Ca > Cs$

4.74 (a) δ^- δ^+ **(e)** δ^+ δ^- **4.76** $PH_3 < HCl < H_2O < CF_4$
O—Cl   C—O

4.78 (a) $\overset{\longleftrightarrow}{H—Cl}$ **(b)** (c) **(d)** nonpolar
polar

polar   polar

4.80 S—H bonds are nonpolar.   **4.82 (a)** selenium dioxide **(b)** xenon tetroxide **(c)** dinitrogen pentasulfide **(d)** triphosphorus tetraselenide
4.84 (a) $SiCl_4$ **(b)** NaH **(c)** SbF_5 **(d)** OsO_4
4.86 (a)

(b) The C=O carbons are trigonal planar; the other carbons are tetrahedral.
(c) The C=O bonds are polar.
4.88 (a) C forms four bonds. **(b)** N forms three bonds. **(c)** S forms two bonds. **(d)** COS: C has four bonds; O and S typically have two bonds each.
4.90 (a)

(b) tetrahedral

(c) contains a coordinate covalent bond **(d)** has 19 p and 18 e^-
4.92 (a) calcium chloride **(b)** tellurium dichloride **(c)** boron trifluoride **(d)** magnesium sulfate **(e)** potassium oxide **(f)** iron(III) fluoride **(g)** phosphorus trifluoride
4.94

4.96

4.98 (a)   **(b)**

4.100 (i) Oxygen, iodine, hydrogen; nonmetals can bond to themselves. **(ii)** Oxygen, phosphorus, iodine, and hydrogen; nonmetals form covalent bonds. **(iii)** Potassium and cesium; metals form up ionic bonds. **(iv)** Oxygen, phosphorus, iodine, and hydrogen; nonmetals are found in covalent and ionic bonds.
4.102

Chapter 5
5.1 $3O_2 \rightarrow 2O_3$ **5.2 (a)** $Ca(OH)_2 + 2HCl \rightarrow CaCl_2 + 2H_2O$
(b) $4Al + 3O_2 \rightarrow 2Al_2O_3$ **(c)** $2CH_3CH_3 + 7O_2 \rightarrow 4CO_2 + 6H_2O$
(d) $2AgNO_3 + MgCl_2 \rightarrow 2AgCl + Mg(NO_3)_2$ **5.3** $2A + B_2 \rightarrow A_2B_2$
5.4 Soluble: **(b), (d)**; insoluble: **(a), (c), (e)**   **5.5**
(a) $NiCl_2(aq) + (NH_4)_2S(aq) \rightarrow NiS(s) + 2NH_4Cl(aq)$; precipitation
(b) $2AgNO_3(aq) + CaBr_2(aq) \rightarrow Ca(NO_3)_2(aq) + 2AgBr(s)$
5.6 (a) $2CsOH(aq) + H_2SO_4(aq) \rightarrow Cs_2SO_4(aq) + 2H_2O(l)$
(b) $Ca(OH)_2(aq) + 2CH_3CO_2H(aq) \rightarrow Ca(CH_3CO_2)_2(aq) + 2H_2O(l)$
(c) $NaHCO_3(aq) + HBr(aq) \rightarrow NaBr(aq) + CO_2(g) + H_2O(l)$
5.7 (a) precipitation **(b)** redox **(c)** acid-base neutralization
5.8 (a) oxidized reactant (reducing agent): Fe; reduced reactant (oxidizing agent): Cu^{2+} **(b)** oxidized reactant (reducing agent): Mg; reduced reactant (oxidizing agent): Cl_2; **(c)** oxidized reactant (reducing agent): Al; reduced reactant (oxidizing agent): Cr_2O_3 **5.9** $2K(s) + Br_2(l) \rightarrow 2KBr(s)$; oxidizing agent: Br_2; reducing agent: K **5.10 (a)** V(III) **(b)** Sn(IV)
(c) Cr(VI) **(d)** Cu(II) **(e)** Ni(II) **5.11 (a)** not redox
(b) Na oxidized from 0 to +1; H reduced from +1 to 0

(c) C oxidized from 0 to +4; O reduced from 0 to -2 **(d)** C oxidized from +2 to +4; O reduced from 0 to -2 **(e)** not redox **(f)** S oxidized from +4 to +6; Mn reduced from +7 to +2 **5.12 (b)** oxidizing agent: H_2; reducing agent: Na **(c)** oxidizing agent: O_2; reducing agent: C **(d)** oxidizing agent: O_2; reducing agent: CO **(f)** oxidizing agent: MnO_4^-; reducing agent: SO_2 **5.13 (a)** $Zn(s) + Pb^{2+}(aq) \rightarrow Zn^{2+}(aq) + Pb(s)$
(b) $OH^-(aq) + H^+(aq) \rightarrow H_2O(l)$
(c) $2Fe^{3+}(aq) + Sn^{2+}(aq) \rightarrow 2Fe^{2+}(aq) + Sn^{4+}(aq)$
5.14 (a) redox **(b)** neutralization **(c)** redox **5.15 (a)** Zn oxidized from 0 to +2; Pb reduced from +2 to 0; oxidizing agent: Pb in $Pb(NO_3)_2$; reducing agent: Zn **(c)** Sn oxidized from +2 to +4; Fe reduced from +3 to +2; oxidizing agent: Fe in $FeCl_3$; reducing agent: Sn in $SnCl_2$ **5.16 (d)** **5.17 (c)**
5.18 reactants: **(d)**; products: **(c)** **5.19 (a)** box 1 **(b)** box 2 **(c)** box 3
5.20 $2Ag^+ + CO_3^{2-}; 2Ag^+ + CrO_4^{2-}$ **5.21 (a)** $CaCl_2$ **(b)** Na_2SO_4
(c) $CaSO_4$, spectator ions: Na^+ and Cl^- **5.22** In a balanced equation, the numbers and kinds of atoms are the same on both sides of the reaction arrow.
5.24 (a) $HCl(aq) + CaCO_3(s) \rightarrow CO_2(g) + CaCl_2(aq) + H_2O(l)$
(b) $2K(s) + Br_2(l) \rightarrow 2KBr(s)$
(c) $C_3H_8(g) + 5O_2(g) \rightarrow 3CO_2(g) + 4H_2O(l)$
5.26 (a) $2C_2H_6(g) + 7O_2(g) \rightarrow 4CO_2(g) + 6H_2O(g)$
(b) balanced **(c)** $2Mg(s) + O_2(g) \rightarrow 2MgO(s)$
(d) $2K(s) + 2H_2O(l) \rightarrow 2KOH(aq) + H_2(g)$
5.28 (a) $Hg(NO_3)_2(aq) + 2LiI(aq) \rightarrow 2LiNO_3(aq) + HgI_2(s)$
(b) $I_2(s) + 5Cl_2(g) \rightarrow 2ICl_5(s)$
(c) $4Al(s) + 3O_2(g) \rightarrow 3Al_2O_3(s)$
(d) $CuSO_4(aq) + 2AgNO_3(aq) \rightarrow Ag_2SO_4(s) + Cu(NO_3)_2(aq)$
(e) $2Mn(NO_3)_3(aq) + 3Na_2S(aq) \rightarrow Mn_2S_3(s) + 6NaNO_3(aq)$
5.30 (a) $2C_4H_{10}(g) + 13O_2(g) \rightarrow 8CO_2(g) + 10H_2O(l)$
(b) $C_2H_6O(g) + 3O_2(g) \rightarrow 2CO_2(g) + 3H_2O(l)$
(c) $2C_8H_{18}(g) + 25O_2(g) \rightarrow 16CO_2(g) + 18H_2O(l)$
5.32 $4HF + SiO_2 \rightarrow SiF_4 + 2H_2O$ **5.34 (a)** redox **(b)** neutralization
(c) precipitation **(d)** neutralization
5.36 (a) $Ba^{2+}(aq) + SO_4^{2-}(aq) \rightarrow BaSO_4(s)$
(b) $Zn(s) + 2H^+(aq) \rightarrow Zn^{2+}(aq) + H_2(g)$ **5.38** precipitation:
(a), (d), (e); redox: **(b), (c)** **5.40** $Ba(NO_3)_2$
5.42 (a) $2NaBr(aq) + Hg_2(NO_3)_2(aq) \rightarrow Hg_2Br_2(s) + 2NaNO_3(aq)$
(d) $(NH_4)_2CO_3(aq) + CaCl_2(aq) \rightarrow CaCO_3(s) + 2NH_4Cl(aq)$
(e) $2KOH(aq) + MnBr_2(aq) \rightarrow Mn(OH)_2(s) + 2KBr(aq)$
(f) $3Na_2S(aq) + 2Al(NO_3)_3(aq) \rightarrow Al_2S_3(s) + 6NaNO_3(aq)$
5.44 (a) $2Au^{3+}(aq) + 3Sn(s) \rightarrow 3Sn^{2+}(aq) + 2Au(s)$
(b) $2I^-(aq) + Br_2(l) \rightarrow 2Br^-(aq) + I_2(s)$
(c) $2Ag^+(aq) + Fe(s) \rightarrow Fe^{2+}(aq) + 2Ag(s)$
5.46 (a) $Sr(OH)_2(aq) + FeSO_4(aq) \rightarrow SrSO_4(s) + Fe(OH)_2(s)$
(b) $S^{2-}(aq) + Zn^{2+}(aq) \rightarrow ZnS(s)$ **5.48** Most easily oxidized: metals on left side; most easily reduced: groups 6A and 7A **5.50** oxidation number increases: **(b), (c)**; oxidation number decreases **(a), (d)**
5.52 (a) Co: +3 **(b)** Fe: +2 **(c)** U: +6 **(d)** Cu: +2 **(e)** Ti: +4
(f) Sn: +2 **5.54 (a)** oxidized: S; reduced: O **(b)** oxidized: Na; reduced: Cl **(c)** oxidized: Zn; reduced: Cu **(d)** oxidized: Cl; reduced: F
5.56 (a) $N_2O_4(l) + 2N_2H_4(l) \rightarrow 3N_2(g) + 4H_2O(g)$
(b) $CaH_2(s) + 2H_2O(l) \rightarrow Ca(OH)_2(aq) + 2H_2(g)$
(c) $2Al(s) + 6H_2O(l) \rightarrow 2Al(OH)_3(s) + 3H_2(g)$
5.58 oxidizing agents: N_2O_4, H_2O; reducing agents: N_2H_4, CaH_2, Al
5.60 $Li_2O(s) + H_2O(g) \rightarrow 2LiOH(s)$; not a redox reaction
5.62 (a) x neutralization
(b) $3AgNO_3(aq) + FeCl_3(aq) \rightarrow 3AgCl(s) + Fe(NO_3)_3(aq)$; precipitation **(c)** $(NH_4)_2Cr_2O_7(s) \rightarrow Cr_2O_3(s) + 4H_2O(g) + N_2(g)$; redox **(d)** $Mn_2(CO_3)_3(s) \rightarrow Mn_2O_3(s) + 3CO_2(g)$; redox
5.64

Compound	Oxidation Number of Metal	Compound	Oxidation Number of Metal
(a) MnO_2	+4	**(b)** CrO_2	+4
Mn_2O_3	+3	CrO_3	+6
$KMnO_4$	+7	Cr_2O_3	+3

5.66 $Fe^{3+}(aq) + 3NaOH(aq) \rightarrow Fe(OH)_3(s) + 3Na^+(aq)$;
$Fe^{3+}(aq) + 3OH^-(aq) \rightarrow Fe(OH)_3(s)$
5.68 $2Bi^{3+}(aq) + 3S^{2-}(aq) \rightarrow Bi_2S_3(s)$
5.70 $CO_2(g) + 2NH_3(g) \rightarrow NH_2CONH_2(s) + H_2O(l)$

5.72 (a) reactants: I $= -1$, Mn $= -4$; products: I $= 0$, Mn $= +2$
(b) reducing agent: NaI; oxidizing agent: MnO_2 **5.74** (a) $Mg(OH)_2$
(b) $Mg(OH)_2(s) + 2\ HCl(aq) \rightarrow MgCl_2(aq) + H_2O(l)$

Chapter 6

6.1 (a) 206.0 amu (b) 232.0 amu **6.2** 1.71×10^{21} molecules **6.3** 0.15 g
6.4 111.0 amu **6.5** 0.217 mol; 4.6 g **6.6** 5.00 g weighs more
6.7 $3.0 \times 10^3 \mu$mols **6.8** (a) $Ni + 2HCl \rightarrow NiCl_2 + H_2$; 4.90 mol
(b) 6.00 mol **6.9** $6CO_2 + 6H_2O \rightarrow C_6H_{12}O_6 + 6O_2$; 90.0 mol CO_2
6.10 (a) 39.6 mol (b) 13.8 g **6.11** (a) 0.0272 mol (b) 0.0272 mol WO_3;
0.0816 mol H_2 (c) 6.31 g WO_3; 0.165 g H_2 **6.12** 44.7 g; 57.0%
6.13 47.3 g **6.14** A_2 **6.15** $C_5H_{11}NO_2S$; MW = 149.1 amu
6.16 (a) $A_2 + 3B_2 \rightarrow 2AB_3$ (b) 2 mol AB_3; 0.67 mol AB_3
6.17 10 AB ($2B_2$ left over) **6.18** Blue is the limiting reagent, yield:
73% **6.19** 22 g, 31 g **6.20** One mole of a substance is an amount
equal to its formula weight in grams. One mole of a molecular com-
pound contains 6.022×10^{23} molecules. **6.22** 1.204×10^{24} Na^+ ions;
6.022×10^{23} SO_4^{2-} ions **6.24** 2.43×10^{23} atoms Ca
6.26 (a) 100.1 g/mol (b) 60.0 g/mol (c) 62.0 g/mol
6.28 (a) 6.022×10^{23} atoms; 12.0 g (b) 6.022×10^{23} atoms; 12.0 g
(c) 1.204×10^{23} atoms; 24.0 g **6.30** 2.78×10^{-3} mol aspirin
6.32 (a) 342.3 g/mol (b) 84.0 g/mol (c) 74.0 g/mol (d) 350.1 g/mol
6.34 (a) 26 g (b) 6.3 g (c) 5.6 g (d) 26 g
6.36 (a) $N_2(g) + O_2(g) \rightarrow 2NO(g)$ (b) 7.50 mol N_2 (c) 7.62 mol NO
(d) 0.125 mol O_2 **6.38** 58.3 g/mol (b) 0.0070 mol in one teaspoon
6.40 (a) $N_2H_4(g) + 3O_2(g) \rightarrow 2NO_2(g) + 2H_2O(g)$
(b) 15.5 mol O_2 (c) 496 g O_2 **6.42** (a) $2Mg(s) + O_2(g) \rightarrow 2MgO(s)$
(b) 16.5 g O_2; 41.5 g MgO (c) 38.0 g Mg; 63.0 g MgO
6.44 1.97×10^3 mol CO **6.46** 19 mol Fe **6.48** 69 g B_2H_2
6.50 (a) O_2 (b) 71.9 kg NO_2 (c) 82.5% **6.52** (a) 4.57 g NH_3 (b) 38 g
cisplatin **6.54** 89.6% **6.56** (a) 0.463 g H_2 (b) redox reaction; H^+ is
reduced (oxidizing agent); Zn is oxidized (reducing agent)
6.58 (a) $Cu(s) + 4H^+(aq) + 2NO_3^-(aq) \rightarrow Cu^{2+}(aq) + 2NO_2(g) +$
$2H_2O(l)$ (b) yes, 35.0 g HNO_3 can dissolve 8.82 g Cu
6.60 31.1 qt ethanol **6.62** 0.406 mol NaOCl
6.64 (a) $3NO_2(g) + H_2O(l) \rightarrow 2HNO_3(aq) + NO(g)$
(b) 59.3 g HNO_3 (c) 73.9% **6.66** 23.9 g $AgNO_3$ **6.68** 132 kg Li_2O
6.70 (a) 1000 mg/day (b) 4.14 g calcium citrate
6.72 (a) $C_{24}H_{36}O_5$; 404 g/mol (b) 2.5×10^{-5} mol lovastatin
6.74 (a) recommend daily dose: 90 mg for a man and 75 mg for a woman;
500 mg/tablet (b) men = 555%; women = 666%

Chapter 7

7.1 (a) potential (b) kinetic (c) potential (d) kinetic (e) potential (f) kinetic
7.2 (a) N_2 (b) CO **7.3** (a) $\Delta H = +652$ kcal/mol (2720 kJ/mol)
(b) endothermic **7.4** (a) endothermic (b) 200 kcal; 836 kJ (c) 74.2 kcal;
310 kJ **7.5** 91 kcal; 380 kJ **7.6** 303 kcal/mol; 6.4 kcal/g
7.7 (a) increase (b) decrease (c) decrease **7.8** (a) positive (b) spontaneous at all temperatures **7.9** Relatively slow. Activation energy is relatively
large; ΔG is negative. **7.10** Increase the temperature, add a catalyst, and
increase the concentration of reagents.
7.11 (a) $K = \dfrac{[NO_2]^2}{[N_2O_4]}$ (b) $K = \dfrac{[H_2O]^2}{[H_2S]^2[O_2]}$ (c) $K = \dfrac{[Br_2][F_2]^5}{[BrF_5]^2}$
7.12 (a) products strongly favored (b) reactants strongly favored (c) prod-
ucts somewhat favored **7.13** $K = 29.0$
7.14 (a) $K = \dfrac{[AB]^2}{[A_2][B_2]}$; $K = \dfrac{[AB]^2}{[A_2][B]^2}$ (b) $K = 0.11$; $K = 0.89$
7.15 reaction favored by high pressure and low temperature **7.16** (a) favors
reactants (b) favors product (c) favors product **7.17** 0.401 mol glucose
7.18 ΔH is positive; ΔS is positive; ΔG is negative **7.19** ΔH is negative;
ΔS is negative; ΔG is negative **7.20** (a) $2A_2 + B_2 \rightarrow 2A_2B$ (b) ΔH is
negative; ΔS is negative; ΔG is negative **7.21** (a) blue curve represents
faster reaction (b) red curve is spontaneous **7.22** (a) positive
(b) nonspontaneous at low temperature; spontaneous at high temperature
7.24 Differences in bond energies between the products and reactants =
heat of reaction or enthalpy change
7.26 (a) ΔH is negative. $H_2O(l) \rightarrow H_2O(s) + 1.44$ kcal
(b) -15.1 kJ (c) -2.6 kcal (d) $+1.44$ kcal/mol

7.28 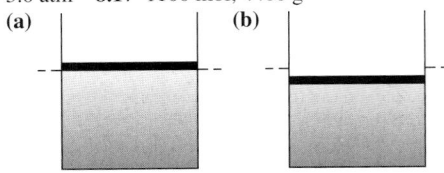 (b) 78 kcal and 330 kJ
7.30 (a) $2C_8H_{18} + 25O_2 \rightarrow 16CO_2 + 18H_2O + $ heat
(b) ΔH is negative. (c) 2.28×10^4 kJ/1 mol C_8H_{18}
(d) 0.0824 mol C_8H_{18}; 9.39 g C_8H_{18} (d) 3.40×10^3 kJ
7.32 Decreases in (a), (b), (c), (f); increases in (d), (e)
7.34 Exothermic release heat (negative ΔH); exergonic is spontaneous
(negative ΔG) **7.36** Endothermic with a large increase in entropy
7.38 (a) decreases (b) spontaneous at low temperatures until the
temperature results in $\Delta H = T\Delta S$ **7.40** (a) negative (b) spontaneous at
low temperatures and nonspontaneous at high temperatures, depending on
the temperature **7.42** $E_{act} = +5$ kcal/mol **7.44** causes more
collisions **7.46** also reduces the activation energy of the reverse reaction
by 5.0 kcal/mol **7.48** (a) nonspontaneous (b) no, as the reaction is nonspontaneous at all temperatures **7.50** Catalysts only change the activation
energy and not the equilibrium constant.
7.52 (a) $K = \dfrac{[H_2S]^2}{[S_2][H_2]^2}$ (b) $K = \dfrac{[HCl]^2}{[H_2S][Cl_2]}$ (c) $K = \dfrac{[BrCl]^2}{[Br_2][Cl_2]}$
(d) $K = \dfrac{[CO][H_2]}{[H_2O]}$ **7.54** (a) $K = \dfrac{[CO_2]^2}{[CO]^2[O_2]}$ (b) 1.3×10^3; products
7.56 (a) 0.062 mol/L (b) 2.1 mol/L **7.58** reactants
7.60 (a) exothermic (b) products (c) no effect for (1) and (5); shifts left for
(2) and (3); shifts right for (4) **7.62** (a) reactants (b) products (c) no effect
7.64 increases **7.66** (a) increases (b) decreases (c) increases (d) no
change **7.68** (a) exothermic (b) -7.7 kcal, -32 kJ **7.70** (a) CO
removes Hb so less Hb is available to react with O_2 (b) shifts equilibrium
to the right **7.72** (a) 5.40 kcal needed (b) 22.6 kJ released
7.74 (a) $2CH_3OH(l) + 3O_2(g) \rightarrow 2CO_2(g) + 4H_2O(g)$ (b) -322 kcal
(c) -1140 kJ **7.76** (a) -108 kJ (b) -18.8 kcal **7.78** Snack food:
SunChips—210 Cal (a) Running—590 Cal/hour; biking—590 Cal/hour;
swimming—510 Cal/hour (b) 21 minutes running or biking; 25 minutes
swimming (Note: The exact number of minutes depends on the type of snack.)
7.80 (a) -23 kcal; -104 kJ; exothermic (b) increase either N_2 or H_2;
remove NH_3; cool the reaction; increase pressure or decrease volume
(c) high pressures; intermediate temperatures; removing liquefied NH_3

Chapter 8

8.1 (a) disfavored by ΔH; favored by ΔS
(b) $\Delta H = -9.72$ kcal/mol $(-40.6$ kJ/mol$)$;
$\Delta S = -2.61$ cal/$(mol \cdot K)$ $[-109$ J/$(mol \cdot K)]$ **8.2** (a) decrease
(b) increase **8.3** (a), (c) **8.4** (a) London forces (b) hydrogen bonds, dipole–
dipole forces, London forces (c) dipole–dipole forces, London forces
8.5 220 mmHg; 4.25 psi; 2.93×10^4 Pa **8.6** 2.2 atm; 1700 mmHg;
220,000 Pa **8.7** 749 torr; 986 atm **8.8** 1000 mmHg
8.9 450 L **8.10** 1.3 L, 18 L **8.11** 637 °C; -91 °C
8.12 33 psi **8.13** 352 L **8.14** balloon (a)
8.15 4.46×10^3 mol; 7.14×10^4 g CH_4; 1.96×10^5 g CO_2
8.16 5.0 atm **8.17** 1100 mol; 4400 g
8.18 (a)   (b)

8.19 9.3 atm He; 0.19 atm O_2; about the same.
8.20 75.4% N_2, 13.2% O_2, 5.3% CO_2, 6.2% H_2O **8.21** 35.0 mmHg
8.22 $P_{He} = 500$ mmHg; $P_{Xe} = 250$ mmHg **8.23** 1.93 kcal, 14.3 kcal
8.24 102 kJ **8.25** ether, isopropyl alcohol, ammonia, and water; increases
with strength of intermolecular forces

8.26 (a)   (b)   (c)

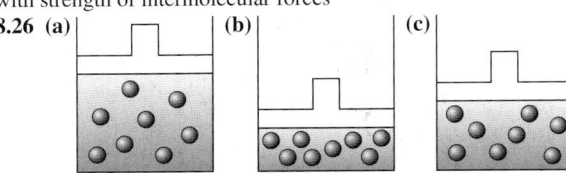

(a) volume increases by 50% (b) volume decreases by 50% (c) volume
unchanged

8.27 (b); (c)   8.28 (c)
8.29

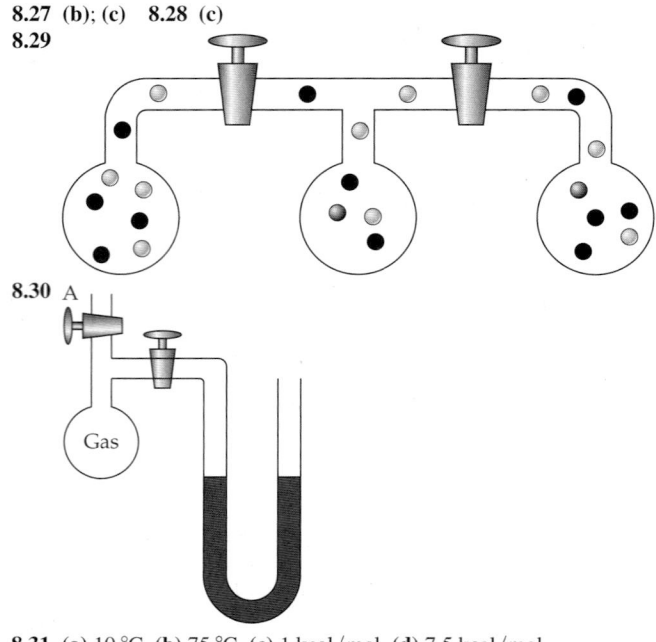

8.30 A

8.31 (a) 10 °C **(b)** 75 °C **(c)** 1 kcal/mol **(d)** 7.5 kcal/mol
8.32 (a)   **(b)**

(c)

8.33 red = 360 mmHg; yellow = 120 mmHg; total pressure = 720 mmHg   **8.34 (a)** all molecules **(b)** molecules with polar covalent bonds **(c)** molecules with —OH or —NH bonds and HF
8.36 Ethanol forms hydrogen bonds.   **8.38** One atmosphere is equal to exactly 760 mmHg.   **8.40** (1) A gas consists of tiny particles moving at random with no forces between them. (2) The amount of space occupied by the gas particles is small. (3) The average kinetic energy of the gas particles is proportional to the Kelvin temperature. (4) Collisions between particles are elastic.   **8.42 (a)** 760 mmHg **(b)** 1310 mmHg **(c)** 5.7×10^3 mm Hg **(d)** 711 mmHg **(e)** 0.314 mmHg   **8.44** 930 mmHg; 1.22 atm   **8.46** V varies inversely with P when n and T are constant.   **8.48** 101 mL   **8.50** 1.75 L
8.52 V varies directly with T when n and P are constant.   **8.54** 364 K = 91 °C   **8.56** 220 mL   **8.58** P varies directly with T when n and V are constant.   **8.60** 1.2 atm   **8.62** 493 K = 220 °C   **8.64** 68.4 mL   **8.66 (a)** P increases by factor of 4 **(b)** P decreases by factor of 4   **8.68** Because gas particles are so far apart and have no interactions, their chemical identity is unimportant.   **8.70** 2.7×10^{22} molecules/L; 1.4 g   **8.72** 11.8 g   **8.74** 15 kg
8.76 $PV = nRT$ **8.78** Cl_2 has fewer molecules but weighs more.
8.80 370 atm; 5400 psi   **8.82** 2.2×10^4 mmHg   **8.84** 22.3 L
8.86 the pressure contribution of one component in a mixture of gases
8.88 93 mmHg   **8.90** the partial pressure of the vapor above the liquid
8.92 Increased pressure raises a liquid's boiling point; decreased pressure lowers it.   **8.94 (a)** 29.2 kcal **(b)** 173 kcal   **8.96** Atoms in a crystalline solid have a regular, orderly arrangement.
8.98 4.82 kcal   **8.100** As temperature increases, molecular collisions become more violent.   **8.102** 0.13 mol; 4.0 L   **8.104** 590 g/day
8.106 0.589 mol; 17.0 g/mol   **8.108** 6×10^{15} L; 1×10^8 atoms/L
8.110 (a) $2C_8H_{18} + 25O_2 \rightarrow 16CO_2 + 18H_2O$ **(b)** 1.1×10^{11} kg CO_2**(c)** 5.6×10^{13} L CO_2 **8.112 (a)** 3.5 atm **(b)** 0.7 atm O_2; 2.8 atm N_2
8.114 (a) As pressure increases, the ice melts slightly, allowing for ice skating. **(b)** No, as pressure increases, CO_2 stays as a solid. (This assumes that the temperature is low enough to keep CO_2 as a solid.)   **8.115** Atmospheric CO_2 levels would remain constant.

Chapter 9

9.1 (a) heterogeneous mixture **(b)** homogeneous solution **(c)** homogeneous colloid **(d)** homogeneous solution   **9.2 (c), (d)   9.3** unsaturated; Cooling would reduce the solubility of KBr, causing some to precipitate from solution.
9.4 5.6 g/100 mL   **9.5** 6.8×10^{-5} g/100 mL   **9.6** 231 g   **9.7** Place 38 mL acetic acid in flask and dilute to 500.0 mL.   **9.8** 0.0086% (m/v)
9.9 (a) 20 g **(b)** 60 mL H_2O **9.10** 1.6 ppm   **9.11** Pb: 0.015 ppm, 0.0015 mg; Cu: 1.3 ppm, 0.13 mg   **9.12** 0.927 M **9.13 (a)** 0.061 mol
(b) 0.67 mol   **9.14** 0.48 g   **9.15 (a)** 0.0078 mol **(b)** 0.39 g   **9.16** 39.1 mL
9.17 750 L   **9.18 (a)** 39.1 g; 39.1 mg **(b)** 79.9 g; 79.9 mg **(c)** 12.2 g; 12.2 mg
(d) 48.0 g; 48.0 mg **(e)** 9.0 g; 9.0 mg **(f)** 31.7 g; 31.7 mg   **9.19** 9.0 mg
9.20 (a) 2.0 mol ions; **(b)** 2.0 °C   **9.21** weak electrolyte   **9.22 (a)** Red curve is a pure solvent; blue curve is a solution. **(b)** solvent bp = 62 °C; solution bp = 69 °C **(c)** 2 M   **9.23** −1.9 °C   **9.24** 3 ions/mol
9.25 (a) 0.70 osmol **(b)** 0.30 osmol   **9.26 (a)** 0.090 M Na^+; 0.020 M K^+; 0.110 M Cl^-; 0.11 M glucose **(b)** 0.33 osmol
9.27

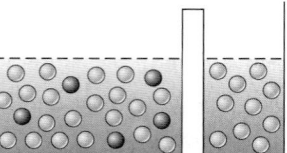 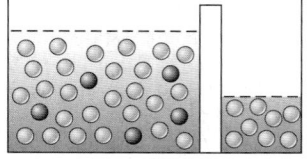

Before equilibrium   At equilibrium

9.28 HCl completely dissociates into ions; acetic acid dissociates only slightly.   **9.29** upper curve: HF; lower curve: HBr   **9.30 (a)   9.31 (d)**
9.32 homogeneous: mixing is uniform; heterogeneous: mixing is nonuniform   **9.34** polarity   **9.36 (b), (d)   9.38 (a)** 15.3 g/100 mL **(b)** 14.6 mols NH_3 in 1 L   **9.40** Concentrated solutions can be saturated or not; saturated solutions can be concentrated or not.   **9.42** Molarity is the number of moles of solute per liter of solution.   **9.44 (a)** 157.5 mL **(b)** 3.596 M
9.46 Dissolve 1.5 g NaCl in water to a final volume of 250 mL.
9.48 (a) 7.7% (m/v) **(b)** 3.9% (m/v)   **9.50 (a)** 0.054 mol **(b)** 0.25 mol
9.52 230 mL, 1600 mL   **9.54** 10 ppm   **9.56 (a)** 3.6 g **(b)** 15 g **(c)** 120 g
9.58 0.38 mL   **9.60 (a)** 4.80×10^{-3} mol **(b)** 240 mL   **9.62** 333 mL
9.64 5.0% (m/v) NaCl   **9.66** 375 mL   **9.68** NaCl—strong electrolyte; glucose—nonelectrolyte   **9.70** 19 mEq/L   **9.72 (a)** 5.0 g **(b)** 2.9 g
(c) 9.56 g **(d)** 21 g   **9.74** 5 mg   **9.76** 0.300 M KCl   **9.78** 100.65 °C
9.80 NaCl has the same osmolarity; distilled water has a lower osmolarity
9.82 neither solution, as they have the same osmotic pressure
9.84 ~2.0 g   **9.86** 0.25 g $CaCl_2$; 4.6 mEq Ca^{2+} **9.88 (a)** 1.30×10^{-4} mol
(b) 0.00520 M or 5.20 mM **(c)** 66 mL   **9.90** 1.9 ppm
9.92   **(b)** 3.05 mol/L

$$\overset{H}{\underset{H}{\overset{|}{N}}} - H \cdots \cdots \overset{:\ddot{O}:}{\underset{H}{|}} \diagdown H$$

9.94 (a) 46.7 mL **(b)** 1.63 g   **9.96 (a)** CO_2 is the most soluble, and then O_2, N_2, and the least soluble is CO. **(b)** Increased pressures of air or oxygen will force N_2 and CO out of the body.
9.98 (a) NaCl: 0.147 M; KCl: 0.0040 M; $CaCl_2$: 0.0030 M **(b)** 0.31 osmol; essentially isotonic; cells are unharmed
9.100 (a) $CaCO_3(s) + CO_2(aq) + H_2O(l) \rightarrow Ca(HCO_3)_2(aq)$; Calcium carbonate is insoluble, but its solubility increases in water that is saturated in dissolved CO_2 due to the formation of soluble bicarbonate. **(b)** At higher temperatures, the solubility of CO_2 decreases, which shifts the equilibrium in (a) to the left, resulting in the formation of the calcium carbonate (scale).

Chapter 10

10.1 (a), (b)   10.2 (a), (c)   10.3 (a) H_2S **(b)** HPO_4^{2-} **(c)** HCO_3^-
(d) NH_3 **10.4** acids: HF, H_2S; bases: HS^-, F^-; conjugate acid-base pairs: H_2S and HS^-, HF and F^- **10.5 (a)** NH_4^+ **(b)** H_2SO_4 **(c)** H_2CO_3
10.6 (a) F^- **(b)** OH^- **10.7** $HPO_4^{2-} + OH^- \rightleftharpoons H_2O + PO_4^{3-}$; conjugate acid-base pairs: H_2O and OH^-, HPO_4^{2-} and PO_4^{3-}; forward reaction is favored   **10.8** $HF + NH_3 \rightleftharpoons F^- + NH_4^+$; conjugate acid-base pairs: HF and F^-, NH_3 and NH_4^+; favored in forward direction
10.9 The —NH_3^+ hydrogens are most acidic.   **10.10** benzoate
10.11 (a) basic, $[OH^-] = 3.2 \times 10^{-3}$ M
(b) acidic, $[OH^-] = 2.5 \times 10^{-12}$ M **10.12 (a)** 11.51 **(b)** 2.40

10.13 **(a)** $[H_3O^+] = 1 \times 10^{-13}\,M;\ [OH^-] = 0.1\,M$
(b) $[H_3O^+] = 1 \times 10^{-3}\,M;\ [OH^-] = 1 \times 10^{-11}\,M$
(c) $[H_3O^+] = 1 \times 10^{-8}\,M;\ [OH^-]\ 1 \times 10^{-6}\,M$ **(b)** is most acidic;
(a) is most basic **10.14** $0.010\,M$ HNO_2; weaker acid
10.15 **(a)** acidic; $[H_3O^-] = 3 \times 10^{-7}\,M;\ [OH^-] = 3 \times 10^{-8}\,M$
(b) basic; $[H_3O^+] = 1 \times 10^{-8}\,M;\ [OH^-] = 1 \times 10^{-6}\,M$
(c) acidic; $[H_3O^+] = 2 \times 10^{-4}\,M;\ [OH^-] = 5 \times 10^{-11}\,M$
(d) acidic; $[H_3O^+] = 3 \times 10^{-4}\,M;\ [OH^-] = 3 \times 10^{-11}\,M$; order
$b < a < c < d$ **10.16** **(a)** 8.28 **(b)** 5.05 **10.17** 2.60 **10.18** **(a)** 0.079 Eq
(b) 0.338 Eq **(c)** 0.14 Eq **10.19** **(a)** 0.26 N **(b)** 1.13 N **(c)** 0.47 N
10.20 $Al(OH)_3 + 3HCl \rightarrow AlCl_3 + 3H_2O;$
$Mg(OH)_2 + 2HCl \rightarrow MgCl_2 + 2H_2O$
10.21 **(a)** $2HCO_3^-(aq) + H_2SO_4(aq) \rightarrow 2H_2O(l) + 2CO_2(g) + SO_4^{2-}$
(b) $CO_3^{2-}(aq) + 2HNO_3(aq) \rightarrow H_2O(l) + CO_2(g) + 2NO_3^-(aq)$
10.22 $H_2SO_4(aq) + 2NH_3(aq) \rightarrow (NH_4)_2SO_4(aq)$
10.23 $CH_3CH_2NH_2 + HCl \rightarrow CH_3CH_2NH_3^+Cl^-$ **10.24** **(a)** neutral
(b) basic **(c)** basic **(d)** acidic **10.25** 3.38 **10.26** 9.45
10.27 bicarbonate/carbonic acid = 10/1 **10.28** 9.13 **10.29** 0.730 M
10.30 133 mL **10.31** **(a)** $2.41 \times 10^{-3}\,M;\ 4.83 \times 10^{-3}$ Eq **(b)** 0.225 M
10.32 $2.23 \times 10^{-4}\,M$; pH = 3.65 **10.33** **(a)** box 2 **(b)** box 3 **(c)** box 1
10.34 The O—H hydrogen in each is most acidic.; acetic acid
10.35 **(a)** box 1 **(b)** box 2 **(c)** box 1 **10.36** **(a)** box 3 **(b)** box 1
10.37 0.67 M **10.38** HBr dissociates completely into H^+ and Br^- ions.
10.40 KOH dissociates completely into K^+ and OH^- ions.
10.42 A monoprotic acid can donate one proton; a diprotic acid can donate
two; HCl, H_2SO_4. **10.44** (a), (e) **10.46** **(a)** acid **(b)** base **(c)** neither
(d) acid **(e)** neither **(f)** acid **10.48** **(a)** CH_2ClCO_2H **(b)** $C_5H_5NH^+$
(c) $HSeO_4^-$ **(d)** $(CH_3)_3NH^+$ **10.50** The equilibrium constant
for the dissociation of an acid. $K_a = \dfrac{[H_3O^+][A^-]}{[HA]}$ **10.52** pH is defined
as the negative logarithm of the molar H_3O^+ concentration.
10.54 $[H_3O^+] = 1.32 \times 10^{-3}$; 1.3%
10.56 $HSO_4^- < HF < HCOOH < H_2CO_3 < NH_4^+$ **10.58** 6×10^{-6};
weak acid **10.60** 2×10^{-6} to 8×10^{-8}
10.62

	10.57	10.58	10.59	10.60	10.61
pOH	6.1	8.8	7.2–10.0	6.9–8.2	12.3; 1.7

10.64

	$[OH^-]$	pOH
(a) Egg white	4×10^{-7}	6.40
(b) Apple cider	2.0×10^{-11}	10.70
(c) Ammonia	4.3×10^{-3}	2.36
(d) Vinegar	2.5×10^{-12}	11.60

Most acidic   vinegar, apple cider, egg white, ammonia   *Least acidic*

10.66 $[H_3O^+] = 1.2 \times 10^{-2}$; $[OH^-] = 8.3 \times 10^{-13}$; pH = 1.92
10.68 **(a)** $HCl(aq) + PO^{3-}(aq) \rightleftharpoons HPO_4^{2-}(aq) + Cl^-(aq)$
     stronger acid   stronger base   weaker acid   weaker base
(b) $CN^-(aq) + HSO_4^-(aq) \rightleftharpoons HCN(aq) + SO_4^{2-}(aq)$
     stronger base   stronger acid   weaker acid   weaker base
(c) $HClO_4(aq) + NO_2^-(aq) \rightleftharpoons HNO_2(aq) + ClO_4^-(aq)$
     stronger acid   stronger base   weaker acid   weaker base
(d) $HF(aq) + CH_3O^-(aq) \rightleftharpoons CH_3OH(aq) + F^-(aq)$
     stronger acid   stronger base   weaker acid   weaker base
10.70 **(a)** $LiOH(aq) + HNO_3(aq) \longrightarrow H_2O(l) + LiNO_3(aq)$
(b) $BaCO_3(aq) + 2HI(aq) \longrightarrow H_2O(l) + CO_2(g) + BaI_2(aq)$
(c) $H_3PO_4(aq) + 3KOH(aq) \longrightarrow 3H_2O(l) + K_3PO_4(aq)$
(d) $Ca(HCO_3)_2(aq) + 2HCl(aq) \longrightarrow$
                          $2H_2O(l) + 2CO_2(g) + CaCl_2(aq)$
(e) $Ba(OH)_2(aq) + H_2SO_4(aq) \longrightarrow 2H_2O(l) + BaSO_4(s)$
10.72 **(a)** acidic **(b)** neutral **(c)** basic **(d)** basic **10.74** A buffer contains
a weak acid and its anion. The acid neutralizes any added base, and the
anion neutralizes any added acid.
10.76 **(a)** pH = $pK_a + \log\dfrac{[CH_3CO_2^-]}{[CH_3CO_2H]} = 4.74 + \log\dfrac{[0.100]}{[0.100]} = 4.74$

(b) $CH_3CO_2^-\ Na^+ + H_3O^+ \rightarrow CH_3CO_2H + Na^+; CH_3CO_2H + OH^- \rightarrow$
$CH_3CO_2^- + H_2O$ **10.78** 9.19 **10.80** 9.07 **10.82** An equivalent for
an acid/base is the amount necessary to produce one mole H^+/OH^- ions.
10.84 **(a)** 1 Eq/mol **(b)** 3 Eq/mol **(c)** 1 Eq/mol **(d)** 2 Eq/mol
10.86 25 mL; 50 mL **10.88** **(a)** 0.50 Eq **(b)** 0.084 Eq **(c)** 0.25 Eq
10.90 0.13 M; 0.26 N **10.92** 0.22 M **10.94** 0.0750 M
10.96 pH = 7 (neutral) as both reactions involve a strong acid and a strong
base **10.98** **(a)** 0.613 mol **(b)** pH = −0.39 **10.100** 250 mg
10.102 Both have the same amount of acid; HCl has higher $[H_3O^+]$ and
lower pH. **10.104** 0.70 N; 0.35 M **10.106** **(a)** NH_4^+, acid; OH^-, base;
NH_3, conjugate base; H_2O, conjugate acid **(b)** 5.56 g
10.108 **(a)** $Na_2O(aq) + H_2O(l) \longrightarrow 2NaOH(aq)$
(b) 13.0 **(c)** 5.00 L **10.110** **(a)** ammonium carbonate, $(NH_4)_2CO_3$
(b) formation of ammonium carbonate: $2NH_3 + CO_2 \rightarrow NH_2CO_2NH_4$
$NH_2CO_2NH_4 + H_2O \rightarrow (NH_4)_2CO_3$ decomposition of ammonium
carbonate into NH_3, which is the "active component":
$(NH_4)_2CO_3 \rightarrow NH_4HCO_3 + NH_3$

Chapter 11
11.1 $^{218}_{84}Po$ **11.2** $^{226}_{88}Ra$ **11.3** $^{89}_{38}Sr \rightarrow {}^{0}_{-1}e + {}^{89}_{39}Y$
11.4 **(a)** $^{3}_{1}H \rightarrow {}^{0}_{-1}e + {}^{3}_{2}He$ **(b)** $^{210}_{82}Pb \rightarrow {}^{0}_{-1}e + {}^{210}_{83}Bi$ **(c)** $^{20}_{9}F \rightarrow {}^{0}_{-1}e + {}^{20}_{10}Ne$
11.5 **(a)** $^{38}_{20}Ca \rightarrow {}^{0}_{1}e + {}^{38}_{19}K$ **(b)** $^{118}_{54}Xe \rightarrow {}^{0}_{1}e + {}^{118}_{53}I$
(c) $^{79}_{37}Rb \rightarrow {}^{0}_{1}e + {}^{79}_{36}Kr$ **11.6** **(a)** $^{62}_{30}Zn + {}^{0}_{-1}e \rightarrow {}^{62}_{29}Cu$
(b) $^{110}_{50}Sn + {}^{0}_{-1}e \rightarrow {}^{110}_{49}In$ **(c)** $^{86}_{36}Kr + {}^{0}_{-1}e \rightarrow {}^{81}_{35}Br$
11.7 $^{120}_{49}In \rightarrow {}^{0}_{-1}e + {}^{120}_{50}Sn$ **11.8** 13% **11.9** 5.0 L
11.10 (a), (b)

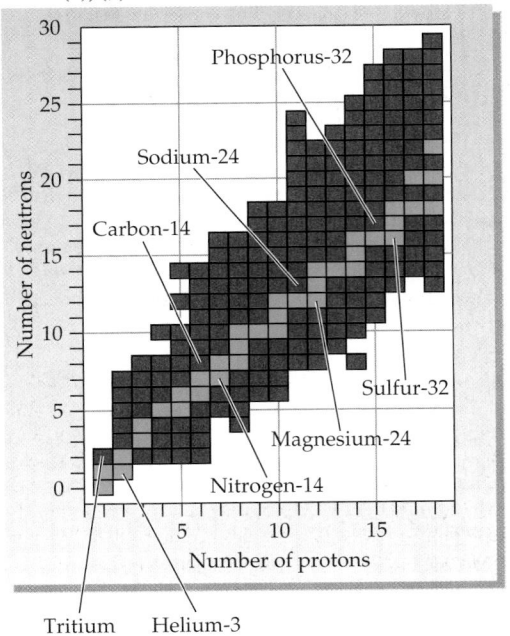

(b) $^{3}_{1}H \rightarrow {}^{0}_{-1}e + {}^{3}_{2}He;\ {}^{14}_{6}C \rightarrow {}^{0}_{-1}e + {}^{14}_{7}N;\ {}^{24}_{11}Na \rightarrow {}^{0}_{-1}e + {}^{24}_{12}Mg;$
$^{32}_{15}P \rightarrow {}^{0}_{-1}e + {}^{32}_{16}S$ **11.11** 3 days **11.12** 13 m **11.13** 175 μCi
11.14 0.002 rem; 12,500 X-rays **11.15** $^{237}_{93}Np$
11.16 $^{241}_{95}Am + {}^{4}_{2}He \rightarrow 2\,{}^{1}_{0}n + {}^{243}_{97}Bk$ **11.17** $^{40}_{18}Ar + {}^{1}_{1}H \rightarrow {}^{1}_{0}n + {}^{40}_{19}K$
11.18 $^{235}_{92}U + {}^{1}_{0}n \rightarrow 2\,{}^{1}_{0}n + {}^{137}_{52}Te + {}^{97}_{40}Zr$
11.19 $^{238}_{92}U + {}^{1}_{0}n \rightarrow {}^{239}_{92}U \rightarrow {}^{0}_{-1}e + {}^{239}_{93}Np \rightarrow {}^{0}_{-1}e + {}^{239}_{94}Pu$ **11.20** $^{3}_{2}He$
11.21 2 half-lives **11.22** $^{28}_{12}Mg \rightarrow {}^{0}_{-1}e + {}^{28}_{13}Al$
11.23

11.24 $^{14}_{6}C$; unstable **11.25** The shorter arrows represent β emission;
longer arrows represent α emission.
11.26 $^{241}_{94}Pu \rightarrow {}^{241}_{95}Am \rightarrow {}^{237}_{93}Np \rightarrow {}^{233}_{91}Pa \rightarrow {}^{233}_{92}U$
11.27 $^{148}_{69}Tm \rightarrow {}^{0}_{1}e + {}^{148}_{68}Er$ or $^{148}_{69}Tm + {}^{0}_{-1}e \rightarrow {}^{148}_{68}Er$ **11.28** 3.5 years

11.29 Inconsistent with nuclear decay because time between 100% → 50% (5 days) is different than time between 50% → 25% (8 days). **11.30** It emits radiation by decay of an unstable nucleus. **11.32** A nuclear reaction changes the identity of the atoms, is unaffected by temperature or catalysts, and often releases a large amount of energy. A chemical reaction does not change the identity of the atoms, is affected by temperature and catalysts, and involves relatively small energy changes. **11.34** by breaking bonds in DNA **11.36** A neutron decays to a proton and an electron. **11.38** The number of nucleons and the number of charges is the same on both sides. **11.40** α emission: Z decreases by 2 and A decreases by 4; β emission: Z increases by 1 and A is unchanged **11.42** Radioactive decay of an unstable nucleus occurs spontaneously. In fission, radioactive decay is induced by bombardment of and reaction of a nucleus with neutrons. **11.44** (a) $^{35}_{17}Cl$ (b) $^{24}_{11}Na$ (c) $^{90}_{39}Y$ **11.46** (a) $^{109}_{47}Ag$ (b) $^{10}_{5}B$ **11.48** (a) $4^{1}_{0}n$ (b) $^{146}_{57}La$ **11.50** $^{198}_{80}Hg + ^{1}_{0}n \rightarrow ^{198}_{79}Au + ^{1}_{1}H$; a proton **11.52** $^{228}_{90}Th$ **11.54** Half of a sample decays in that time. **11.56** (a) 2.3 half-lives (b) 0.0063 g **11.58** 0.8 ng; 2×10^{-3} ng **11.60** The inside walls of a Geiger counter tube are negatively charged, and a wire in the center is positively charged. Radiation ionizes argon gas inside the tube, which creates a conducting path for current between the wall and the wire. **11.62** In a scintillation counter, a phosphor emits a flash of light when struck by radiation, and the flashes are counted. **11.64** more than 25 rems **11.66** 1.9 mL **11.68** (a) 4.7 rem (b) 1.9 rem **11.70** no filter—α radiation; plastic—β radiation; foil—γ radiation; based on penetrating power of decay particles **11.72** Nuclear decay is an intrinsic property of a nucleus and is not affected by external conditions or chemical conversion of the compound containing the radioactive nucleus. **11.74** 112 cpm **11.76** (a) β emission (b) Mo-98 **11.78** (a) $^{238}_{94}Pu \rightarrow ^{4}_{2}He + ^{234}_{92}U$ (b) for radiation shielding **11.80** Their cells divide rapidly. **11.82** advantages: few harmful by-products, fuel is inexpensive; disadvantage: needs a high temperature **11.84** (a) $^{253}_{99}Es + ^{4}_{2}He \rightarrow ^{256}_{101}Md + ^{1}_{0}n$ (b) $^{250}_{98}Cf + ^{11}_{5}B \rightarrow ^{257}_{103}Lr + 4^{1}_{0}n$ **11.86** six α particles and four β particles **11.88** 3; 4 **11.90** (a) A stable isotope of boron is attached to compounds that seek out tumors in the body. (b) Protons strike either Be-7 or Li-7 within a small nuclear reactor. This results in a neutron beam that is externally directed toward the patient's tumor. (c) $^{10}_{5}B + ^{1}_{0}n \rightarrow ^{11}_{5}B$; $^{11}_{5}B \rightarrow ^{4}_{2}He + ^{7}_{3}Li + E$; Both the alpha particle and lithium ions are produced in the area of the tumor and due to their limited penetration depth (approximately the diameter of one cell), they deposit their energy directly into the tumor cells.

Chapter 12

12.1 (a) 2 alcohols (b) 2 carboxylic acids (c) alcohol, carboxylic acid (d) aromatic ring, amine, carboxylic acid **12.2** (a) CH_3CH_2CHO (b) CH_3COCH_3 (c) $CH_3CH_2CO_2H$ **12.3** (a) $CH_3CH_2CH_2CH_2CH_2CH_2CH_3$ (b) $CH_3CH_2CH_2CH_2CH_2CH_2CH_2CH_2CH_3$

12.4

$CH_3CH_2CH_2CH_2CHCH_3$ with CH_3 on C

$CH_3CH_2CH_2CHCH_2CH_3$ with CH_3 on C

12.5 (a) $CH_3CH_2CH_2CH_2CH_3$ Pentane (b) $CH_3CHCH_2CH_3$ with CH_3; 2-Methylbutane

(c) CH_3CCH_3 with CH_3 above and CH_3 below; 2,2-Dimethylpropane

12.6 (a) **(b)**

(c)

12.7 (a) $CH_3CH_2C-CHCH_2CH_3$ with H_3C and Cl on top carbon and CH_2CHCH_3 / CH_3 branch **(b)** $CH_3C-CH-CCH_3$ with H_3C CH_3 and H_3C CH_3 on top and CH_2CH_3 branch

12.8 (a) CH_3CH_2O **(b)** CH_3COCH_3 **(c)** $CH_3CH_2CO_2H$

12.9 Structures (a) and (c) are identical and are isomers of (b). **12.10** (a) same (b) different (c) same **12.11**

p = primary
s = secondary
t = tertiary
q = quaternary

12.12 (a) 3-methylheptane **(b)** 4-isopropylheptane **12.13 (a)**

$CH_3CH_2CH_2CHCH_2CH_3$ with $P CH_3$; labels p s s t s p

(b) $CH_3CH_2CH_2CH_2CHCHCH_2CH_3$ with $P CH_3$ (t) and $P CH_3$; labels p s s s t s p

(c) $CH_3CHCH_2CCH_3$ with $P CH_3$ $P CH_3$ on top, q $P CH_3$ below; labels p t s p

12.14 (a) $CH_3CH_2CHCH_3$ with CH_3; labeled t; 2-Methylbutane **(b)** CH_3CHCCH_3 with H_3C CH_3 on top and CH_3 below; labels t q; 2,3,3-Trimethylbutane

12.15 (a) 2,2-dimethylpentane **(b)** 2,3,3-trimethylpentane **12.16** $CH_4 + 2O_2 \rightarrow CO_2 + 2H_2O$ **12.17**

12.18 (a) 1-ethyl-4-methylcyclohexane **(b)** 1-ethyl-3-isopropylcyclopentane **12.19 (a)** **(b)**

12.20 (a) numbering of methyl groups; 1,3,4-trimethylcyclohexane **(b)** wrong parent; cyclopentylcyclohexane **(c)** combine like substituents; 1,3-diethyl-2-methylcyclopentane **12.21** propylcyclohexane **12.22 (a)** **(b)**

12.23 (a) double bond, ketone, ether **(b)** double bond, amine, carboxylic acid **12.24 (a)** 2,3-dimethylpentane **(b)** 2,5-dimethylhexane **12.25 (a)** 1,1-dimethylcyclopentane **(b)** isopropylcyclobutane

12.26 The methyl groups are on the same side of the ring in one structure and on opposite sides in the other. **12.28** groups of atoms that have a characteristic reactivity; chemistry of compounds is determined by their functional groups **12.30** A polar covalent bond is a covalent bond in which electrons are shared unequally. **12.32** (a) (i) amine; (ii) amide; (iii) ester; (iv) aldehyde (b) (v) ketone; (vi) aromatic ring; (vii) alcohol; (viii) carboxylic acid

12.34 (a)

$CH_3CH_2CH_2CH_2CH$ (with =O)
Aldehyde

(b) $CH_3CH_2CH_2C-OCH_2CH_3$ (with =O)
Ester

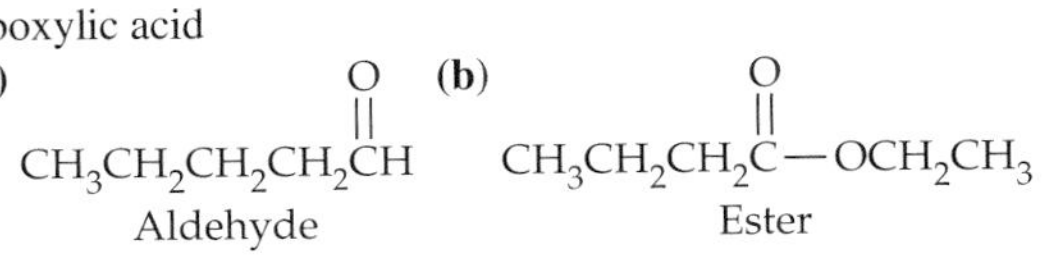

(c) $HS-CH_2CH_2C-NH_2$ (with =O)
Amide, thiol

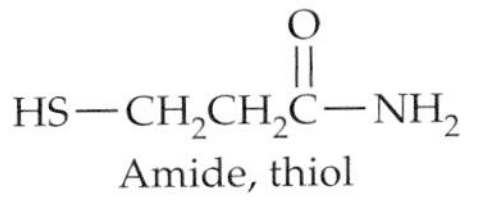

Note: There are other possibilities for (a)–(c).

12.36 They must have the same molecular formula but different structures.

12.38 (a), (b) A primary carbon is bonded to one other carbon; a secondary carbon is bonded to two other carbons; a tertiary carbon is bonded to three other carbons; and a quaternary carbon is bonded to four other carbons.

(c)

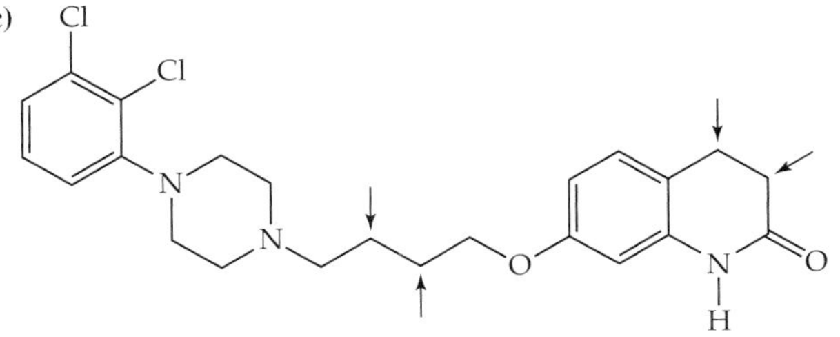

12.40 (a) 2,3-dimethylbutane (b) 1,2-dimethylcyclohexane, 1,3-dimethylcyclohexane, 1,4-dimethylcyclohexane

12.42 (a)

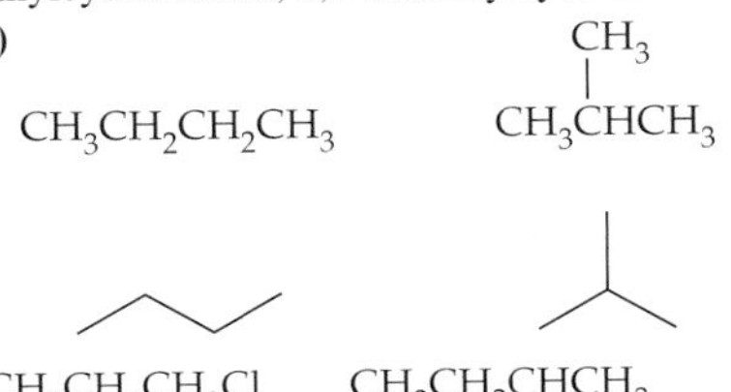

$CH_3CH_2CH_2CH_3$

CH_3CHCH_3 with CH_3

(b) $CH_3CH_2CH_2CH_2Cl$ $CH_3CH_2CHCH_3$ with Cl

CH_3CHCH_2Cl with CH_3 CH_3CCH_3 with CH_3 and Cl

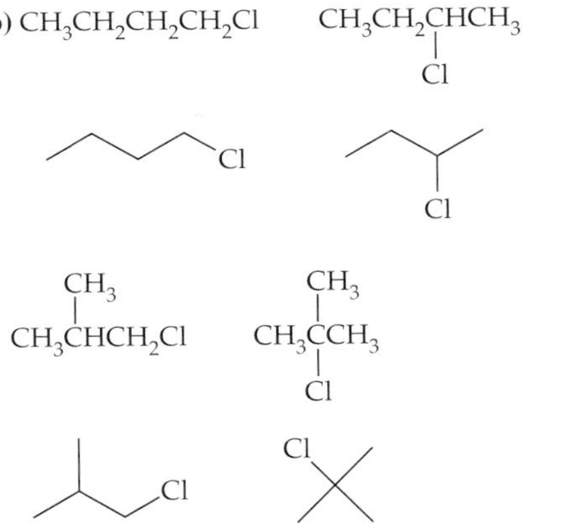

(c) $CH_3CH_2OCH_2CH_3$ $CH_3CH_2CH_2OCH_3$ CH_3CHOCH_3 with CH_3

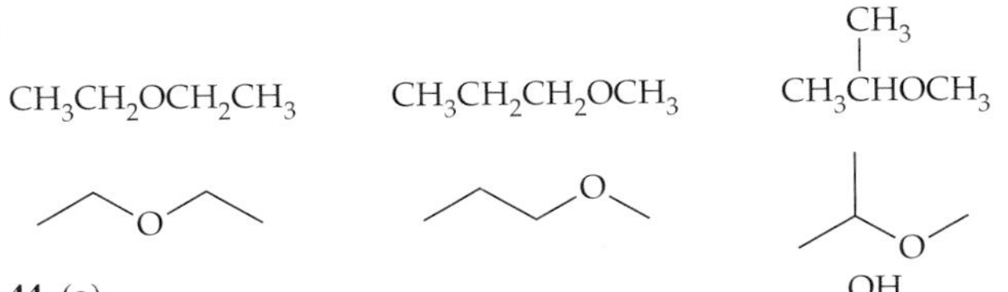

12.44 (a)

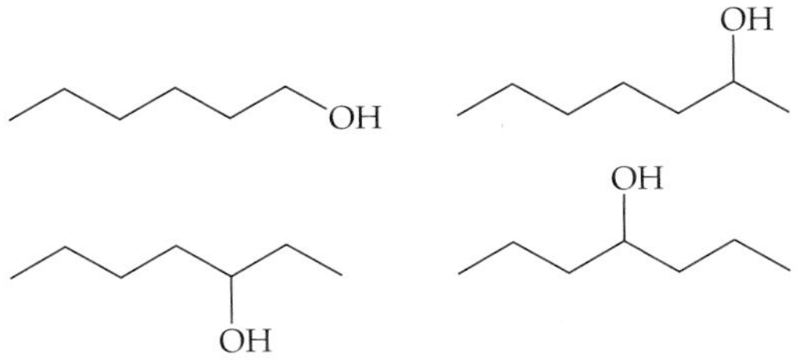

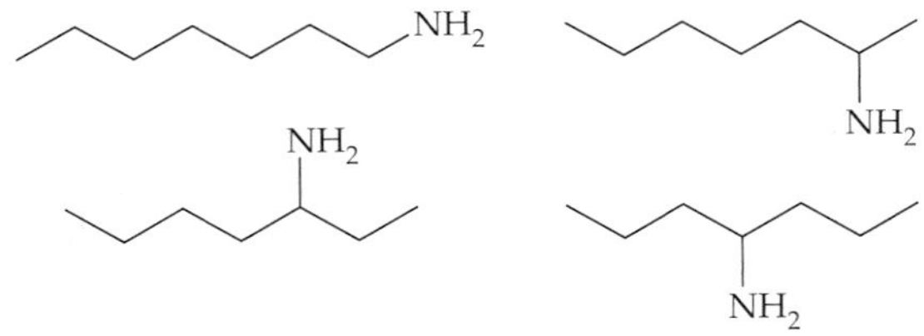

12.46 identical: (a); isomers: (b), (d), (e); unrelated: (c) **12.48** All have a carbon with five bonds. **12.50** (a) 4-ethyl-3-methyloctane (b) 5-isopropyl-3-methyloctane (c) 2,2,6-trimethylheptane (d) 4-isopropyl-4-methyloctane (e) 2,2,4,4-tetramethylpentane (f) 4,4-diethyl-2-methylhexane (g) 2,2-dimethyldecane

12.52 (a)

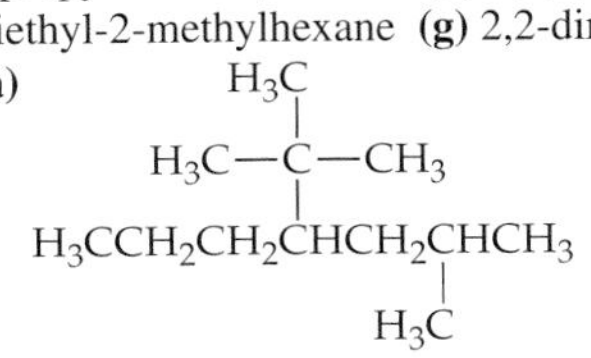

$H_3C-C-CH_3$ (with H_3C) $H_3CCH_2CH_2CHCH_2CHCH_3$ (with H_3C)

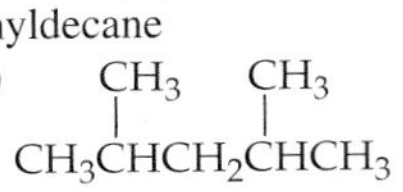

(b) $CH_3CHCH_2CHCH_3$ (with two CH_3)

(c) $CH_3CH_2CHCCH_2CH_2CH_2CH_3$ (with H_3C, CH_2CH_3, CH_2CH_3)

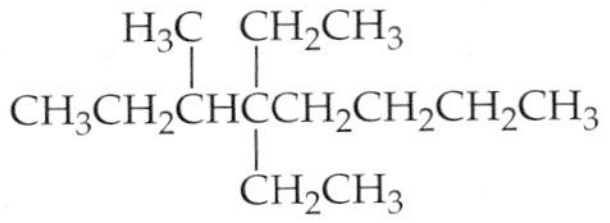

(d) structure with H_3C, CH_3, HC, CH_3, H_3C, CH_2

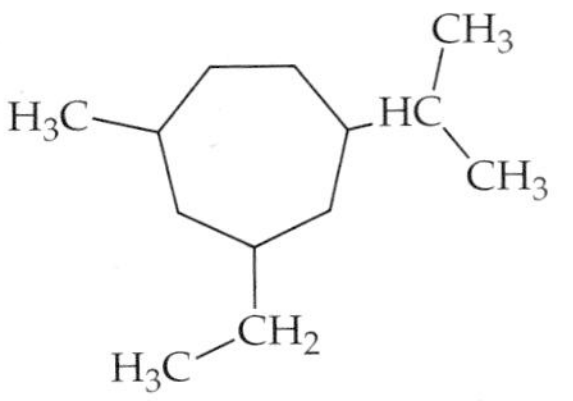

(e) cyclopentane with CH_3, CH_3, H_3C

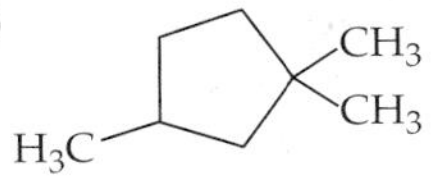

12.54 (a) 1-ethyl-3-methylcyclobutane (b) 1,1,3,3-tetramethylcyclopentane (c) 1-ethyl-3-propylcyclohexane (d) 4-butyl-1,1,2,2-tetramethylcyclopentane **12.56** (a) 2,2-dimethylpentane (b) 2,4-dimethylpentane (c) isobutylcyclobutane **12.58** heptane, 2-methylhexane, 3-methylhexane, 2,2-dimethylpentane, 2,3-dimethylpentane, 2,4-dimethylpentane, 3,3-dimethylpentane, 3-ethylpentane, 2,2,3-trimethylbutane

12.60 $C_3H_8 + 5O_2 \rightarrow 3CO_2 + 4H_2O$

12.62

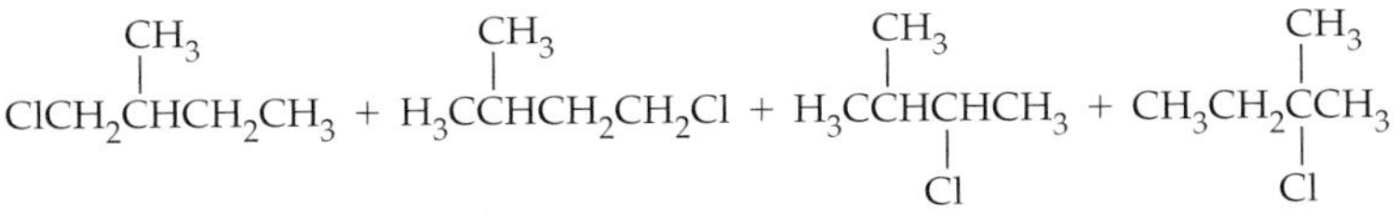

$ClCH_2CHCH_2CH_3$ (with CH_3) + $H_3CCHCH_2CH_2Cl$ (with CH_3) + $H_3CCHCHCH_3$ (with CH_3 and Cl) + $CH_3CH_2CCH_3$ (with CH_3 and Cl)

12.64 (a) ketone, alkene, alcohol (b) amide, carboxylic acid, sulfide, amine

(c)

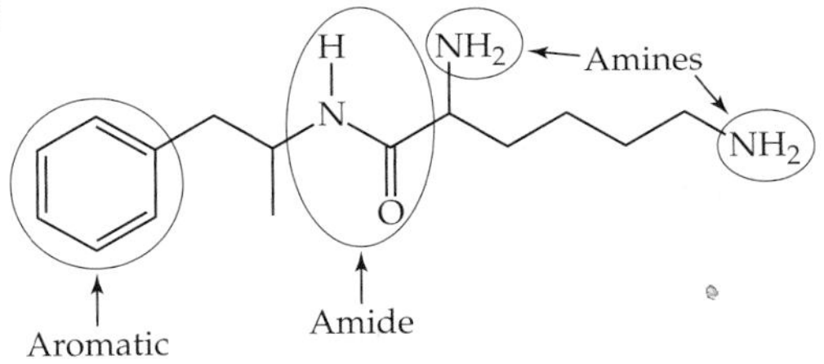

Amines

Aromatic   Amide

Therapeutic properties: treats ADHD in adults and children aged 6 years or older; treats moderate to serve binge eating disorder in adults **12.66** two tertiary carbons **12.68** Nonpolar solvents dissolve nonpolar substances. **12.70** pentane; greater London forces, due to its rod-like shape **12.72** (a) and (d) **12.74** Remove eye make-up, remove chewing gum from wood, shine patent-leather shoes, soften dry skin, lengthen the life of your perfume, soothe shoe blisters, remove a stuck ring, relieve razor burn, protect a new tattoo, soothe pets cracked paw pads, remove candle wax, loosen a stiff bike chain, etc. **12.76** No, isomers cannot be converted without breaking bonds.

Chapter 13

13.1 (a) 2-methyl-3-heptene (b) 2-methyl-1,5-hexadiene (c) 3-methyl-3-hexene (d) 3-ethyl-6-methyl-4-octyne **13.2** (a)

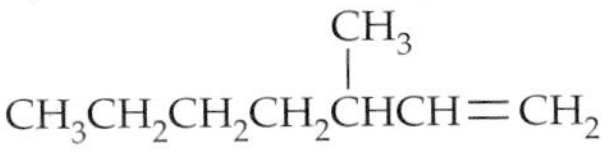

$CH_3CH_2CH_2CH_2CHCH=CH_2$ (with CH_3)

(b) $H_3C-C-C\equiv C-CH_3$ (with two CH_3)

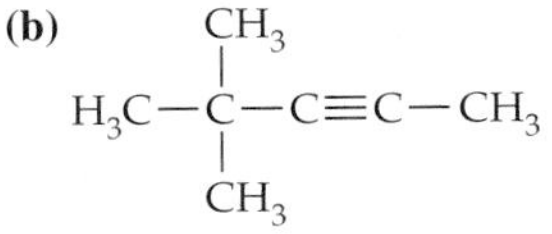

(c)

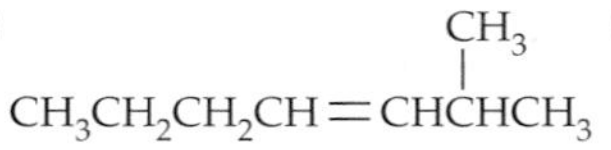

CH₃
$CH_3CH_2CH_2CH=CHCHCH_3$

(d) 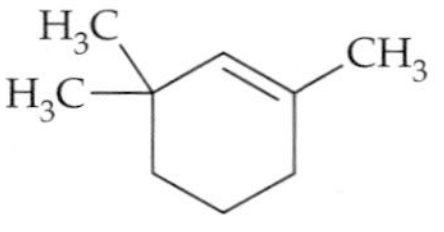 H₃C / H₃C — CH₃ (cyclohexene structure)

13.3 (a) 2,3-dimethyl-1-pentene (b) 2,3-dimethyl-2-hexene
13.4 (a) and (c)
13.5

cis-3,4-Dimethyl-3-hexene

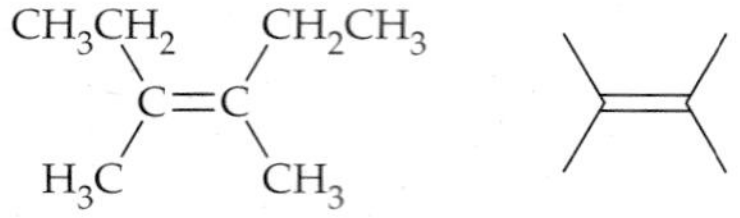

CH₃CH₂   CH₂CH₃
     C=C
H₃C   CH₃

trans-3,4-Dimethyl-3-hexene

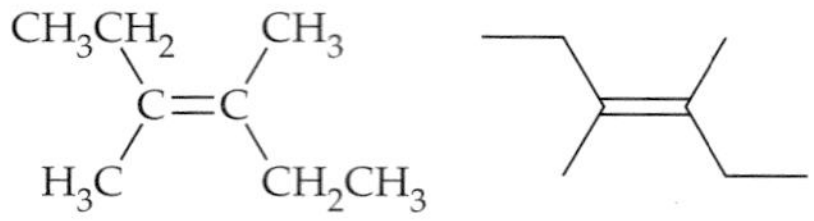

CH₃CH₂   CH₃
     C=C
H₃C   CH₂CH₃

13.6 (a) cis-4-methyl-2-hexene (b) trans-5,6-dimethyl-3-heptene
13.7 (a) substitution (b) addition (c) elimination   **13.8** (a) addition
(b) elimination
13.9 (a) 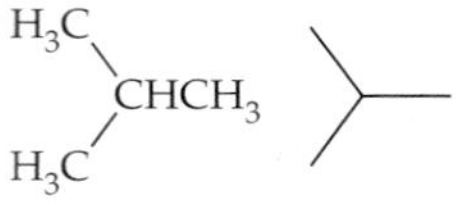 H₃C
              CHCH₃
        H₃C

(b) CH₃CH₂CH₂CH₃

(c) CH₃CH₂CH₂CH₂CH₂CH₂CH₃ (d)

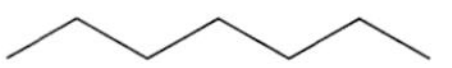

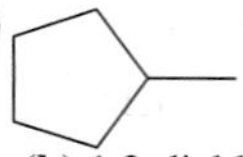

13.10 (a) 1,2-dibromo-2-methylpropane (b) 1,2-dichloropentane
(c) 4,5-dichloro-2,4-dimethylheptane (d) 1,2-dibromocyclopentane
13.11

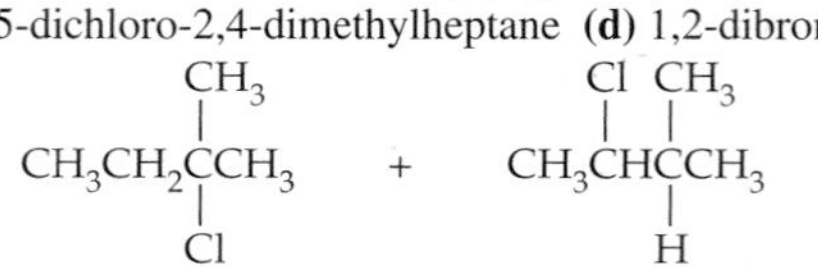

        CH₃   Cl CH₃
CH₃CH₂CCH₃   +   CH₃CHCHCH₃
        Cl   H

     Major   Minor

13.12 (a) 1-chloro-1-methylcyclopentane (b) 2-bromobutane (c) 2-chloro-2,4-
dimethylpentane   **13.13** (a) Major product; H bonds to double-bond carbon
with more H atoms (b) Minor product; H bonds to double-bond carbon with
less H atoms to form this product   **13.14** 2-bromo-2,4-dimethylhexane
13.15 (a), (b)

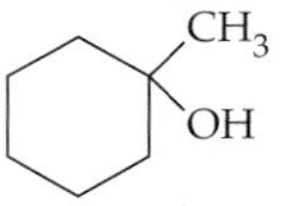

        CH₃
        OH
(cyclohexane structure)

Major product for both
(c) 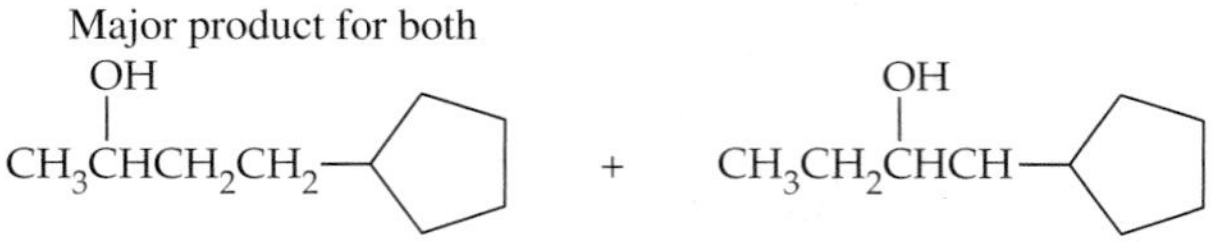   OH   OH
CH₃CHCH₂CH₂—(cyclopentane)   +   CH₃CH₂CHCH—(cyclopentane)

13.16 (a) 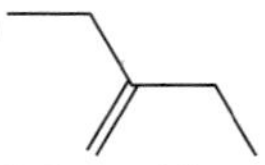   (b)

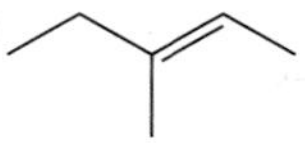

Both formed in roughly equal amounts.
13.17

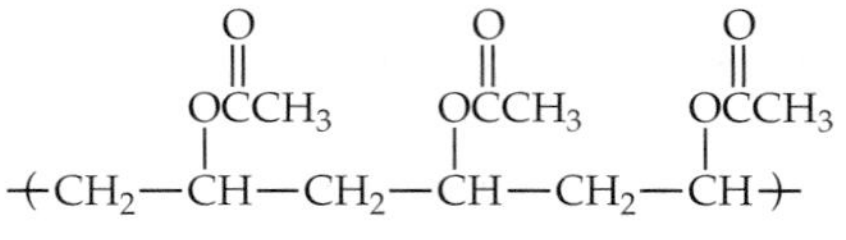

        O   O   O
        ‖   ‖   ‖
        OCCH₃   OCCH₃   OCCH₃
+CH₂—CH—CH₂—CH—CH₂—CH+

13.18

    ⌈ F F F F ⌉
    | | | | | |
    — C—C—C—C —
    | | | | | |
    ⌊ F Cl F Cl ⌋

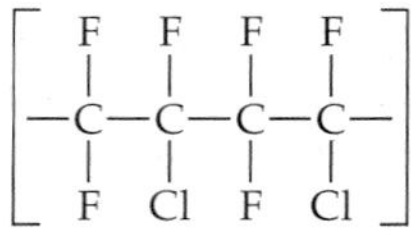

13.19 (a) 3-ethylphenol or m-ethylphenol (b) 3-chlorotoluene or
m-chlorotoluene (c) 1-ethyl-3-isopropylbenzene
13.20 (a) 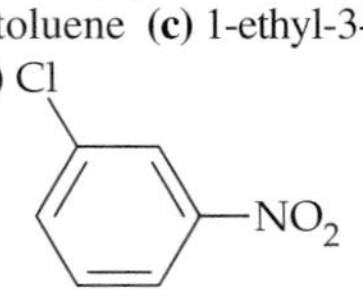 Cl   (b) 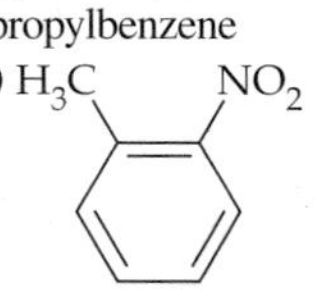 H₃C   NO₂

(benzene ring with NO₂)   (benzene ring with NO₂)

(c) 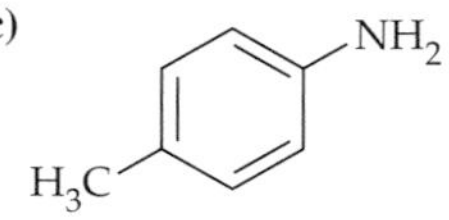   NH₂ (d) 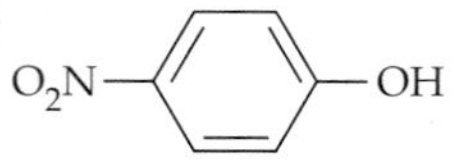 O₂N—(benzene)—OH

(toluene ring with NH₂)

H₃C

13.21 (a) o-isopropylphenol (b) p-bromoaniline
13.22 (a)

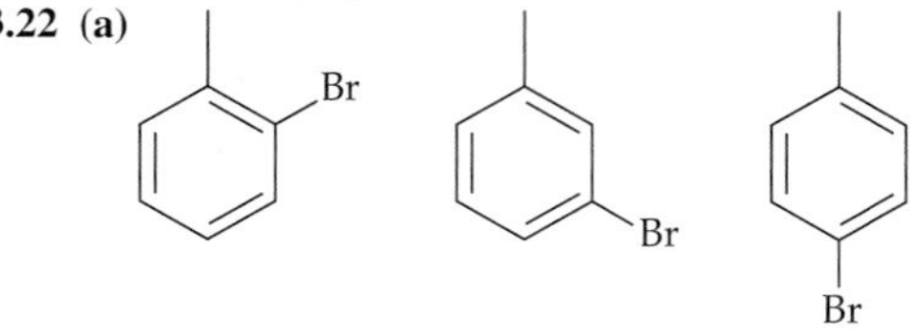

(toluene with Br ortho) (toluene with Br meta) (toluene with Br para)

(b)

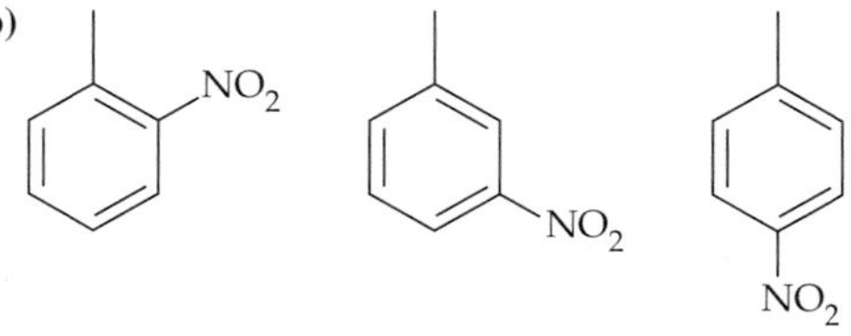

(toluene with NO₂ ortho) (toluene with NO₂ meta) (toluene with NO₂ para)

(c)

(toluene with SO₃H ortho) (toluene with SO₃H meta) (toluene with SO₃H para)

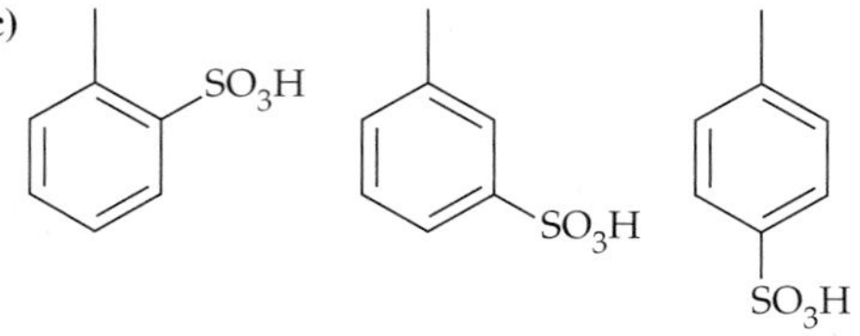

13.23 o-, m-, and p-bromophenol
13.24 (a) 2,5-dimethyl-2-heptene

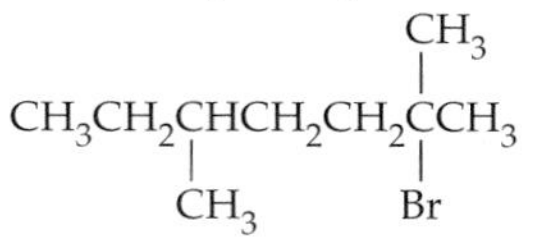

                        CH₃
                        |
CH₃CH₂CHCH₂CH₂CCH₃   CH₃CH₂CHCH₂CH₂CCH₃
        | | | |
        CH₃   Br   CH₃   OH

     Major product 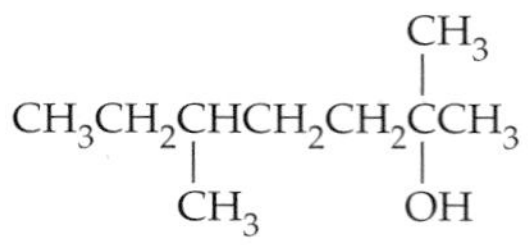   Major product

(b) 3,3-dimethylcyclopentene

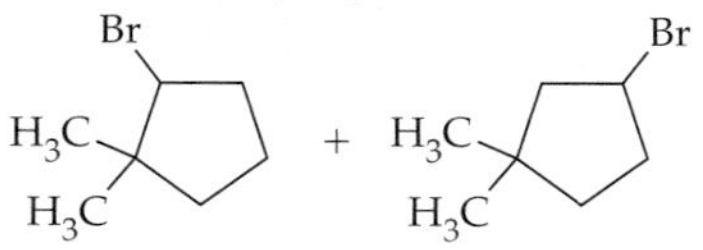

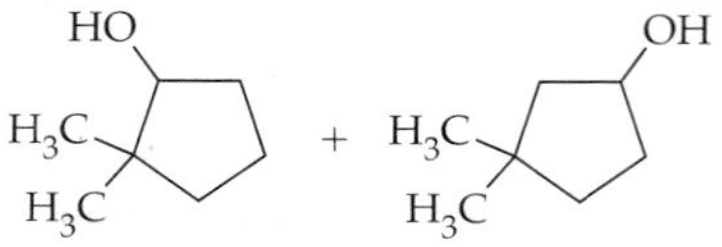

        Br   Br
H₃C—(cyclopentane)   +   H₃C—(cyclopentane)
H₃C   H₃C

                HO   OH
        H₃C—(cyclopentane)   +   H₃C—(cyclopentane)
        H₃C   H₃C

13.25 (a) 4,4-dimethyl-1-hexyne (b) 2,7-dimethyl-4-octyne
13.26 (a) m-isopropylphenol (b) o-bromobenzoic acid
13.27 (a)

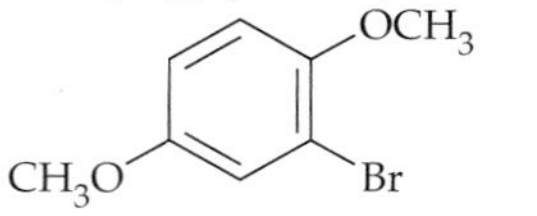

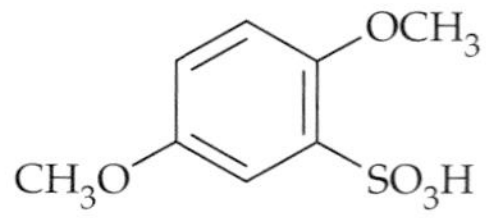

        OCH₃   OCH₃
CH₃O—(benzene)—Br   CH₃O—(benzene)—SO₃H

(b)

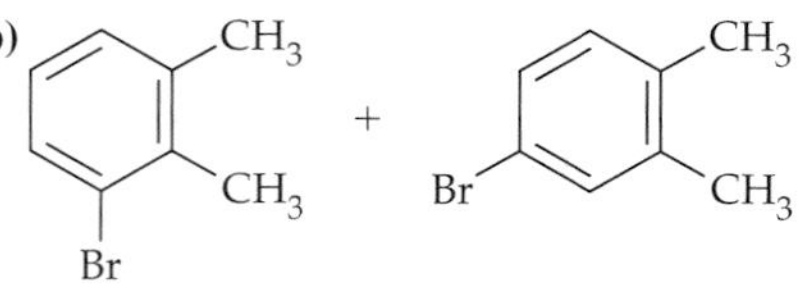

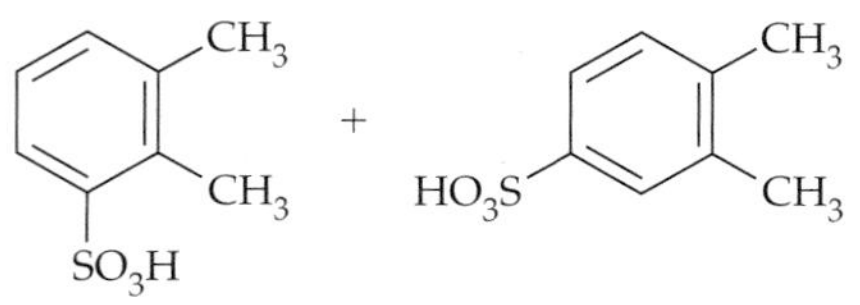

        CH₃   CH₃
(benzene)—CH₃   +   Br—(benzene)—CH₃
Br

Br

        CH₃   CH₃
(benzene)—CH₃   +   HO₃S—(benzene)—CH₃
SO₃H

13.28 (a) 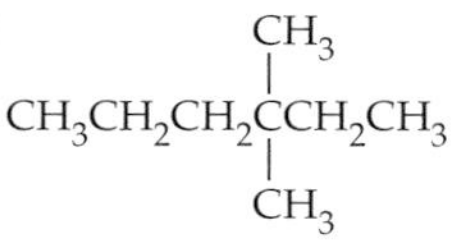   CH₃   (b)   CH₃
                        | |
CH₃CH₂CH₂CCH₂CH₃   CH₃CHCH₂CH₂CH₂CH₂CHCH₃
                        | |
                        CH₃   CH₃

     3,3-dimethylhexane   2,7-dimethyloctane

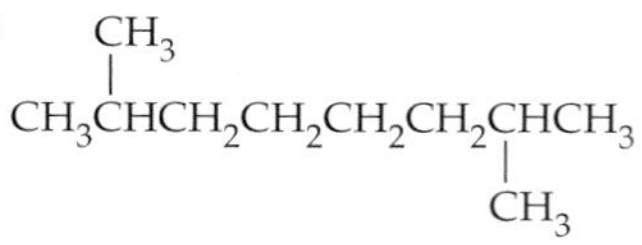

13.29

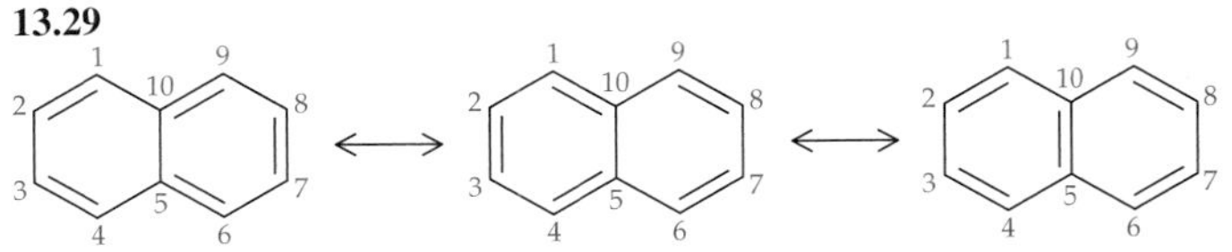

(naphthalene resonance structures)

13.30 (a) saturated: carbon atoms have four single bonds; unsaturated: carbon–carbon multiple bonds **(b)**

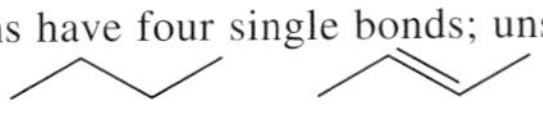

13.32 alkene: *–ene*: alkyne: *–yne*: aromatic: *–benzene*

13.34 (a)

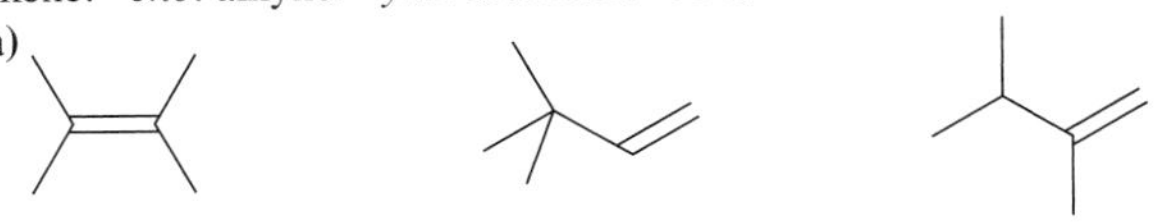

(b)

$CH_3CH_2CH_2C{\equiv}CH$ $CH_3CH_2C{\equiv}CCH_3$ $CH_3CHC{=}CH$ (with CH_3)

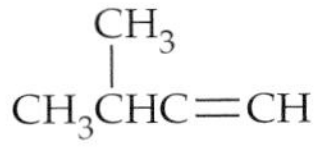

(c)

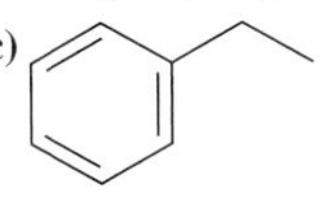

(d)

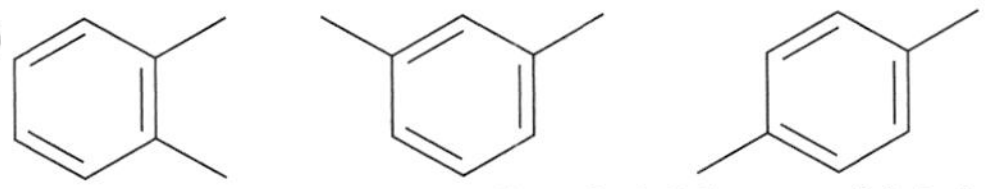

13.36 (a) 2-pentene **(b)** 2,5-dimethyl-3-hexyne **(c)** 3,4-diethyl-3-hexene **(d)** 2,4-dimethyl-2,4-hexadiene **(e)** 3,6-dimethylcyclohexene **(f)** 4-ethyl-1,2-dimethylcyclopentene

13.38 (a) CH_3CH_2, H / C=C / H, CH_3 **(b)** CH_3CH_2, CH_3 / C=C / H_3C, CH_2CH_3

(c) $H_2C{=}CHC{=}CH_2$ (with CH_3)   **(d)** $CH_3CH_2CH_2$, H / C=C / H, CH_2CH_3

(e) O_2N—⟨ ⟩—CH_3 **(f)** Cl, OH on benzene ring   **(g)** cyclobutane with two methyls

(h) $CH_3CH_2CH_2CHCH{=}CHCCH_2CH_3$ (with CH_3 and CH_2CH_3, CH_2CH_3)

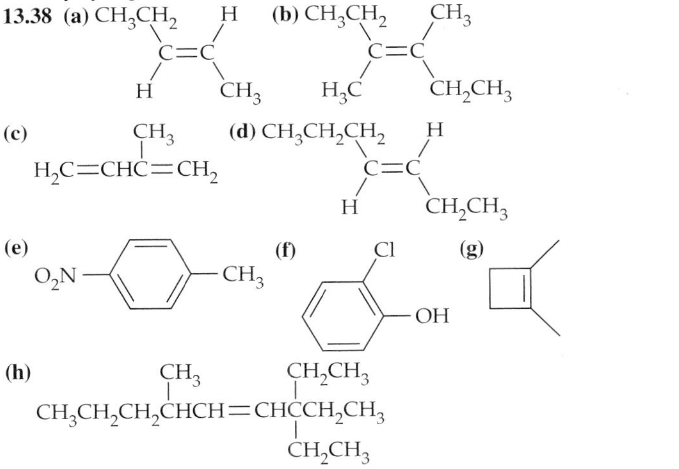

13.40 1-hexyne, 2-hexyne, 3-hexyne, 3-methyl-1-pentyne, 4-methyl-1-pentyne, 4-methyl-2-pentyne, 3,3-dimethyl-1-butyne

13.42

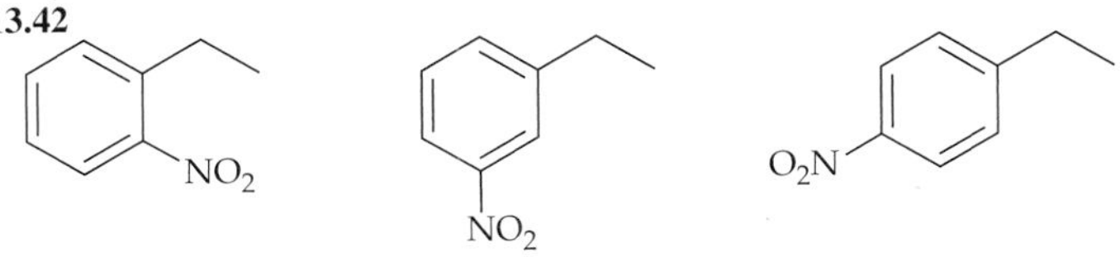

o-Ethylnitrobenzene   *m*-Ethylnitrobenzene   *p*-Ethylnitrobenzene

13.44 Each double bond carbon must be bonded to two different groups.

13.46 (a)   **(b)**

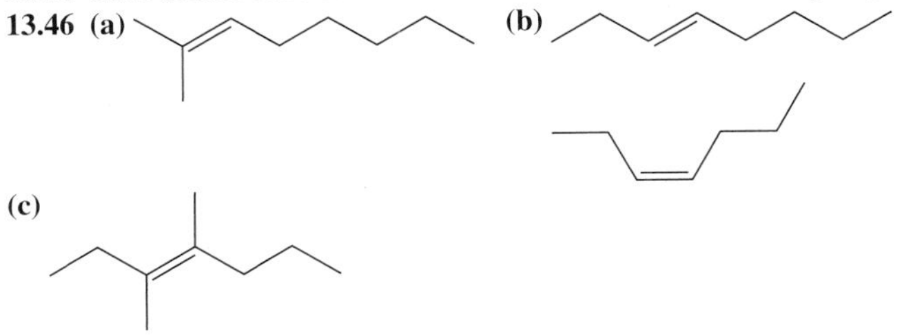

(c)

13.48 (a) $CH_3CH_2CH_2$, CH_2CH_3 / C=C / H, H   **(b)** CH_3CH (with CH_3), CH_3 / C=C / H, H

(c) CH_3, CHCH$_3$ / H, C=C / CH_3CH (with CH_3), H

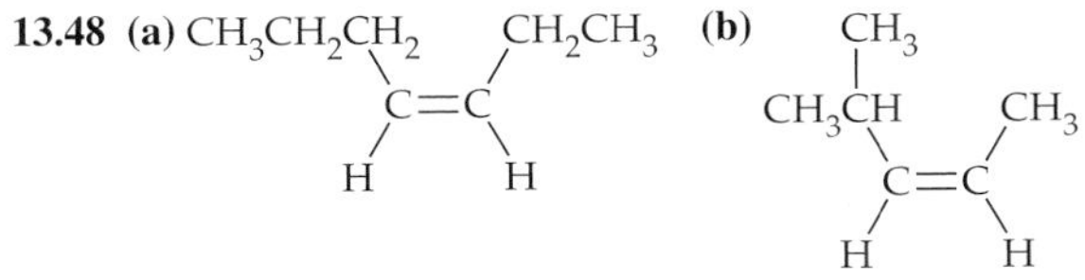

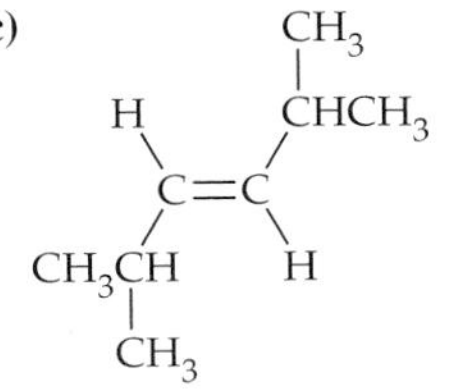

13.50 (a) identical **(b)** identical   **13.52** substitution: two reactants exchange parts to give two products; addition: two reactants add to give one product   **13.54** rearrangement   **13.56 (a)** substitution **(b)** rearrangement

13.58 (a) $CH_3CH_2CH_2CH_3$ **(b)** 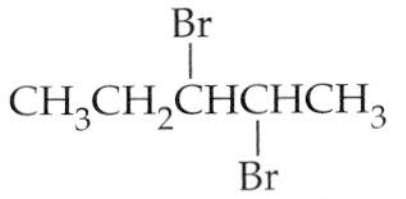 $CH_3CH_2CHCHCH_3$ (with Br, Br)

(c) 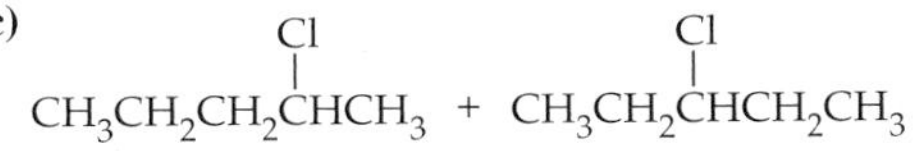 $CH_3CH_2CH_2CHCH_3$ (Cl) + $CH_3CH_2CHCH_2CH_3$ (Cl)

(d)  $CH_3CH_2CH_2CHCH_3$ (OH) + $CH_3CH_2CHCH_2CH_3$ (OH)

13.60 (a) 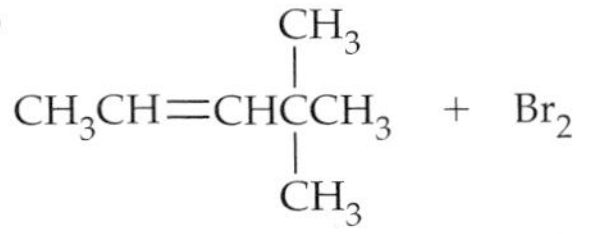 $CH_3CH{=}CHCCH_3$ (with CH_3, CH_3) + Br_2 **(b)** $CH_3CH{=}CH_2 + H_2$

(c) $CH_3CH{=}CHCH_3$ or $H_2C{=}CHCH_2CH_3$ + HBr
(d)  cyclopentene + H_2O **(e)** 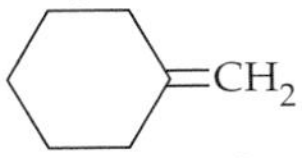 cyclohexane ${=}CH_2$ + Cl_2

13.62 $CH_3CH_2CH_2CH{=}CHBr$ + $CH_3CH_2CH_2C{=}CH_2$ (with Br)

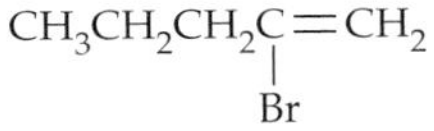

13.64 $H_2C{=}CCl_2$

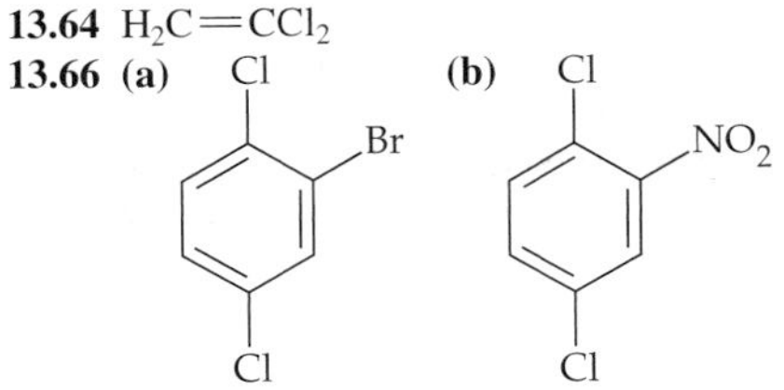

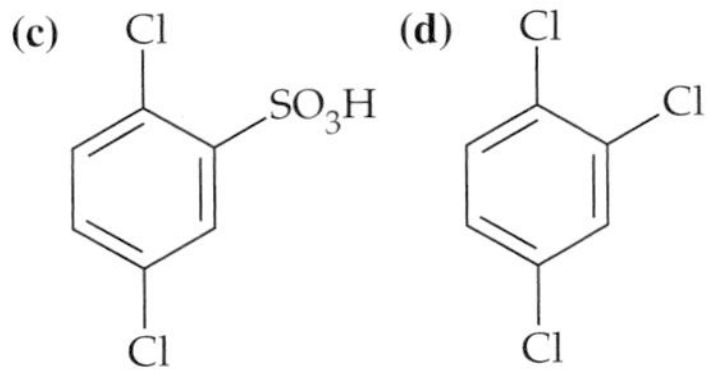

13.66 (a) Cl, Br, Cl on benzene   **(b)** Cl, NO_2, Cl on benzene

(c) Cl, SO_3H, Cl on benzene   **(d)** Cl, Cl, Cl on benzene

13.68 O_2N—benzene with NO_2, CH_3, NO_2 TNT

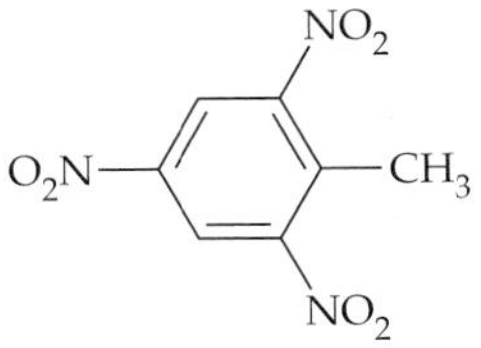

13.70 (a) 5-methyl-2-hexene **(b)** 4-methyl-2-heptyne **(c)** 2,3-dimethyl-1-butene **(d)** 1,2,4-trinitrobenzene **(e)** 3,4-dimethylcyclohexene **(f)** 3-methyl-1,3-pentadiene   **13.72** Br_2 reacts only with cyclohexene.

13.74 Cl—⟨ ⟩—Cl   **13.76** benzene with OH, $CHCH_2C{-}H$ (with O)

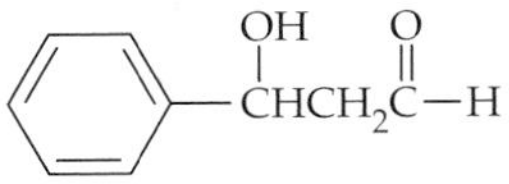

13.78

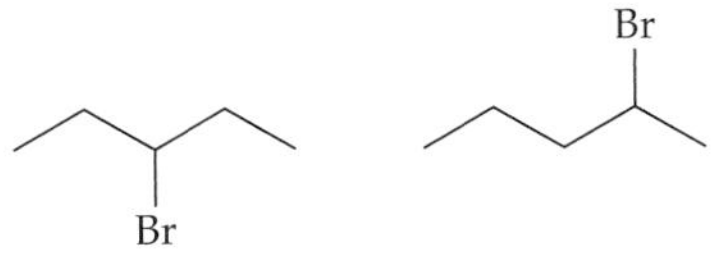

Both ends of the double bond have the same number of hydrogens, and both products can form.

13.80

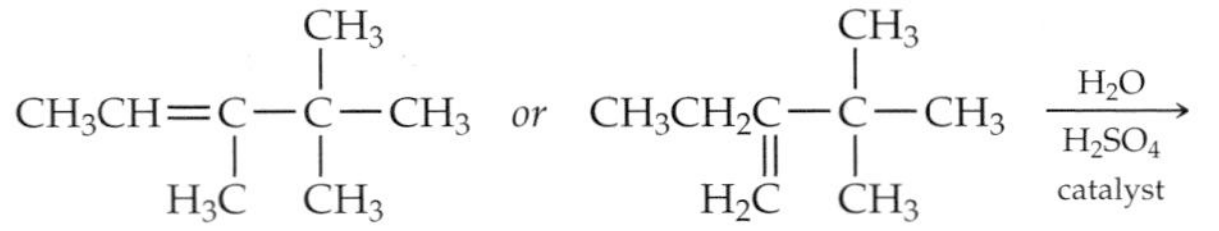

$$CH_3CH=C-C-CH_3 \quad or \quad CH_3CH_2C-C-CH_3 \xrightarrow[\text{catalyst}]{\underset{H_2SO_4}{H_2O}}$$

13.82 A trans double bond is too strained to exist in a small ring like cyclohexene, but a large ring is more flexible and can include a trans double bond:

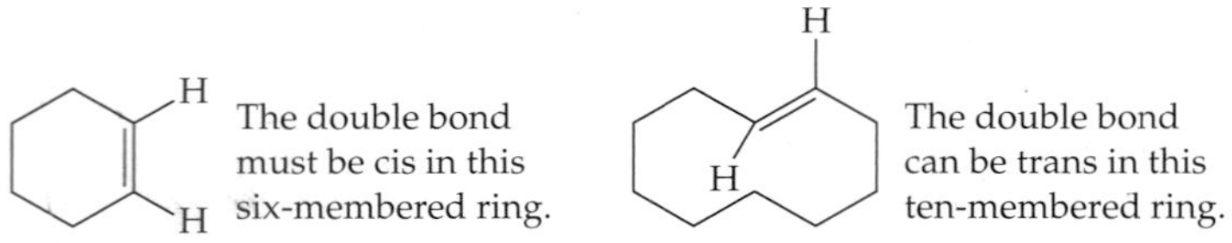

The double bond must be cis in this six-membered ring.

The double bond can be trans in this ten-membered ring.

13.84

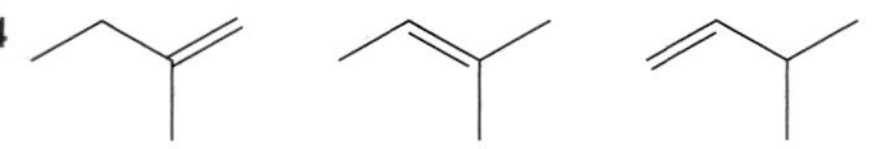

Chapter 14

14.1 (a) alcohol (b) alcohol (c) phenol (d) alcohol (e) ether (f) ether
14.2 The ether oxygen can accept hydrogen bonds from water.
14.3 (a) HO Primary alcohol (b) HO Tertiary alcohol
(c) Secondary alcohol (d) OH Secondary alcohol
(e) OH Secondary alcohol

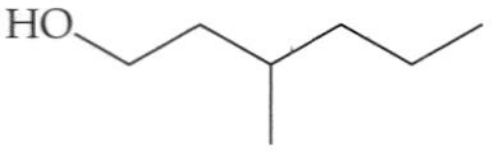

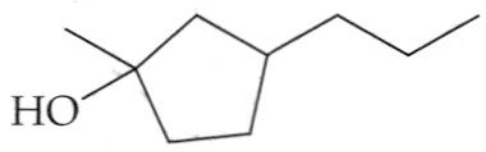

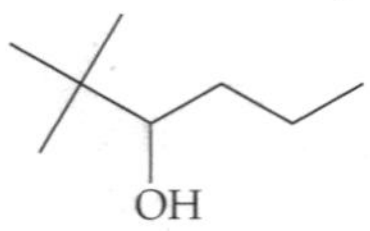

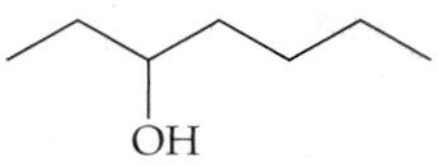

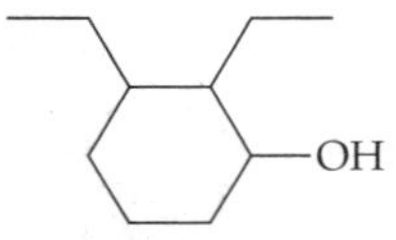

14.4 (a) 2-methyl-2-propanol (*tert*-butyl alcohol), tertiary (b) 3-methyl-2-pentanol, secondary (c) 5-chloro-2-ethyl-1-hexanol, primary (d) 1,2-cyclopentanediol, secondary **14.5** See 14.3 and 14.4. **14.6** highest (d), (b), (a), (c) lowest
14.7
(a) OH ← Hydrophilic, Hydrophobic
(b) Hydrophobic OH Hydrophilic (c) Hydrophobic OH Hydrophilic OH Hydrophilic
water soluble (b) and (c); insoluble (a)
14.8 (a) propene (b) cyclohexene (c) 4-methyl-1-pentene (minor) and 4-methyl-2-pentene (major) **14.9** (a) 2-methyl-2-butanol or 3-methyl-2-butanol (b) 1,2-dimethylcyclopentanol (c) 1,2-diphenylethanol
14.10 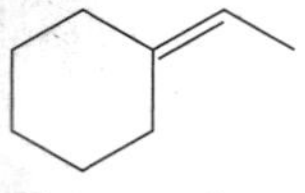
Major product 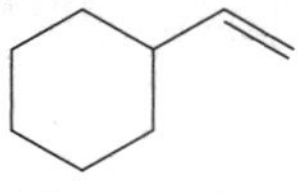   Minor product
14.11 (a) 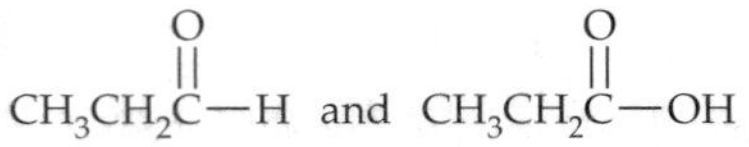
$$CH_3CH_2C-H \text{ and } CH_3CH_2C-OH$$
(b) 
$$CH_3CCH_2CH_2CH_3$$
(c)
$$CCH_3$$

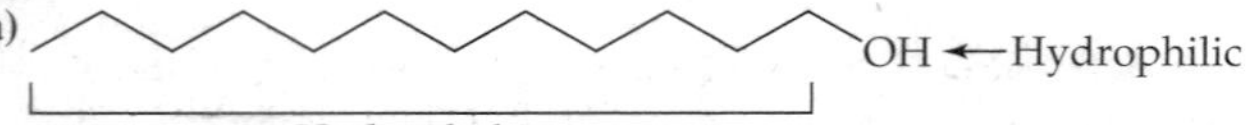

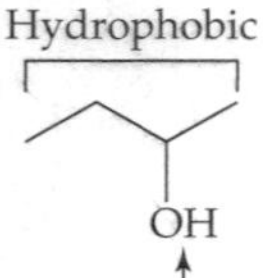

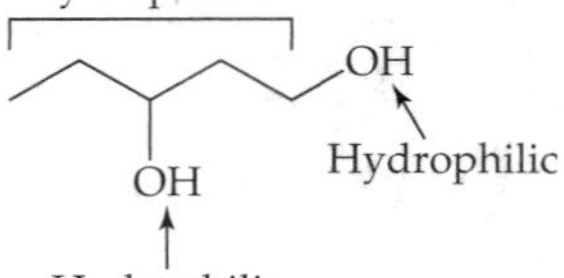

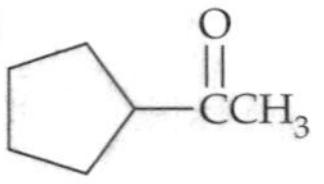

14.12 (a) 2-propanol (b) cycloheptanol (c) 3-methyl-1-butanol
14.13 (a) 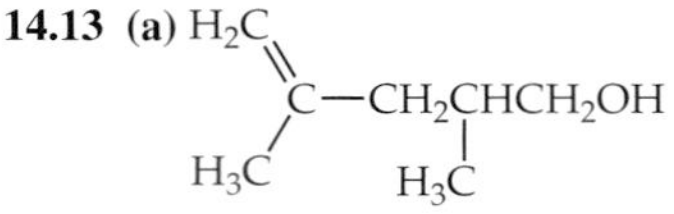
$$H_2C \\ C-CH_2CHCH_2OH \\ H_3C \quad H_3C$$
(b) 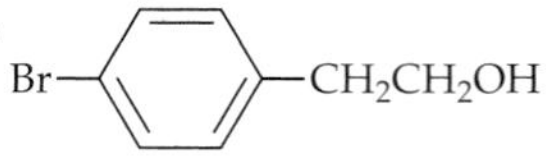
Br—⬡—CH₂CH₂OH
14.14 (a) 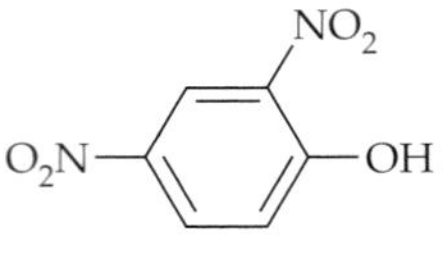
NO₂, O₂N—⬡—OH
(b) 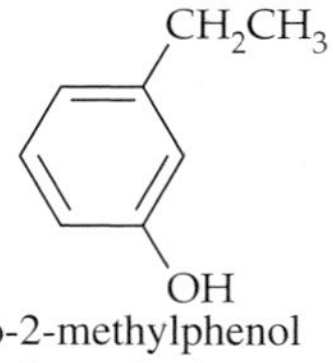
CH₂CH₃ ⬡ OH
14.15 (a) 2,4-dibromophenol (b) 3-iodo-2-methylphenol
14.16 (a) 1,2-dimethoxypropane (b) *p*-methoxynitrobenzene (*p*-nitroanisole) (c) *tert*-butyl methyl ether **14.17** (a) CH₃CH₂CH₂S—SCH₂CH₂CH₃
(b) (CH₃)₂CHCH₂CH₂S—SCH₂CH₂CH(CH₃)₂ **14.18** (a) 1-chloro-1-ethylcyclopentane (b) 3-bromo-5-methylheptane **14.19** 2-Aminobutane has a carbon with four different groups bonded to it. **14.20** chiral: (b), (c)
14.21 (a) 5-methyl-3-hexanol (b) *m*-methoxytoluene (c) 3-methylcyclohexanol
14.22
$$CH_3CH=C-⬡ + CH_3CH_2C-⬡ + H_2O \\ CH_3 \qquad\qquad CH_2$$
Major   Minor
14.23 (CH₃)₂CHCH₂CH₂CHO, (CH₃)₂CHCH₂CH₂CO₂H
14.24 (a) SH (b) S
14.25 (a) HO H CH₃ (b) CH₃ H₃C—C=C—CH₂OH H
(c) Br—⬡—CH₂OH

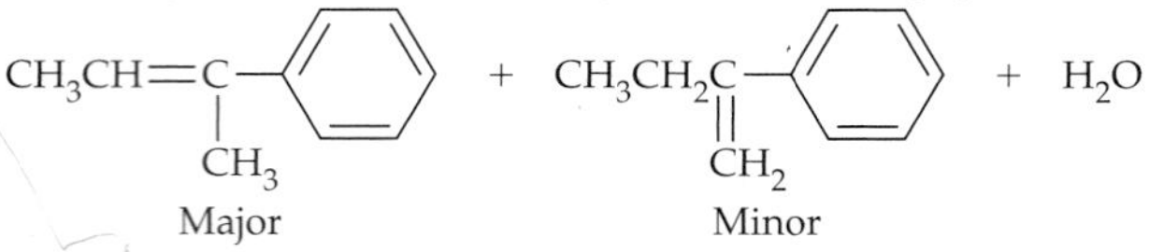

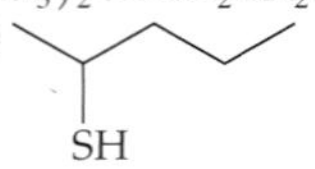

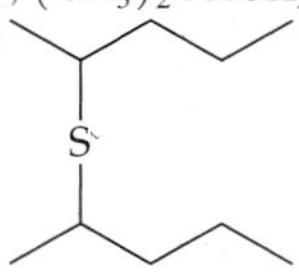

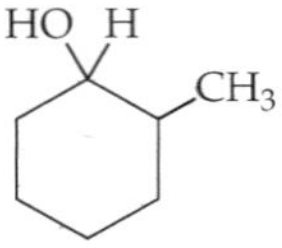

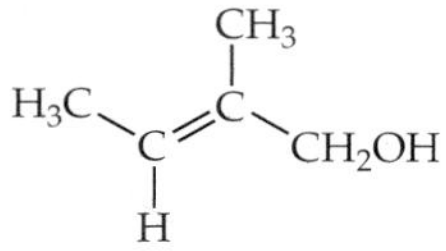

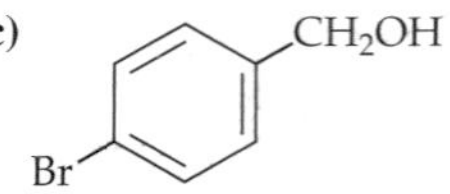

14.26 Alcohols have an —OH group bonded to an alkane-like carbon atom; ethers have an oxygen atom bonded to two carbon atoms; and phenols have an —OH group bonded to a carbon of an aromatic ring.
14.28 Alcohols form hydrogen bonds. **14.30** alcohol, ether, ketone, carbon–carbon double bond **14.32** (a) 2-methyl-2-propanol (*tert*-butyl alcohol) (b) 2-methyl-1-propanol (c) 1,2,4-butanetriol (d) 2-methyl-2-phenyl-1-propanol (e) 3-methylcyclohexanol (f) 3-ethyl-3-methyl-2-hexanol
14.34 (a) 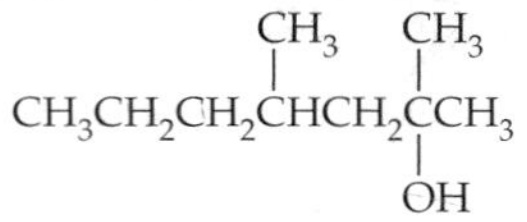
$$CH_3 \quad CH_3 \\ CH_3CH_2CH_2CHCH_2CCH_3 \\ \qquad\qquad OH$$
(b) 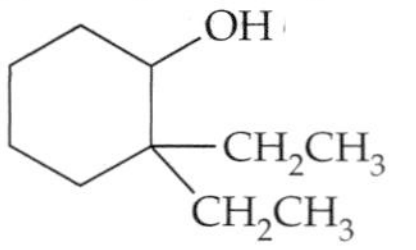
OH ⬡ CH₂CH₃ CH₂CH₃
(c) 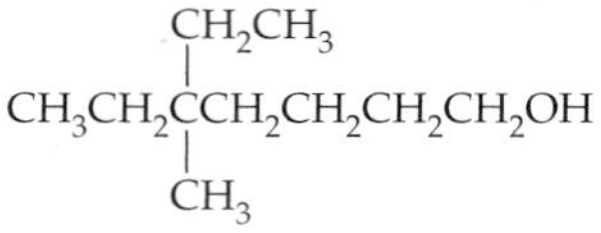
$$CH_2CH_3 \\ CH_3CH_2CCH_2CH_2CH_2CH_2OH \\ CH_3$$
(d) 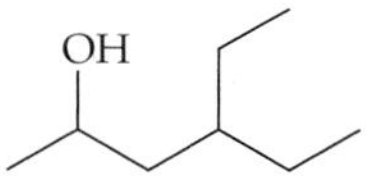
OH
(e) HO ⬡ O
(f)
$$OH \quad CH_2CH_3 \\ CH_3CHCH_2CH_2CCH_2CH_2OH \\ \qquad CH_2CH_3$$

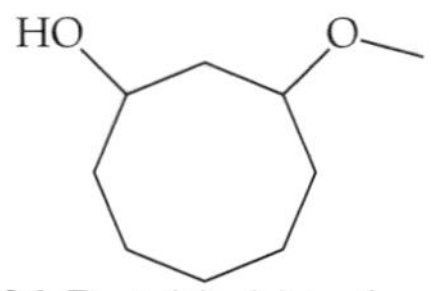

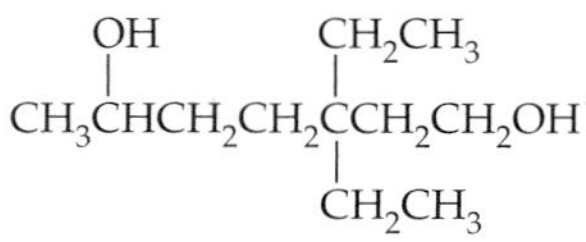

14.36 Part (a): (a) tertiary (b) primary (c) primary, secondary (d) primary (e) secondary (f) secondary
Part (b): (a) Hydrophilic (b) Hydrophilic

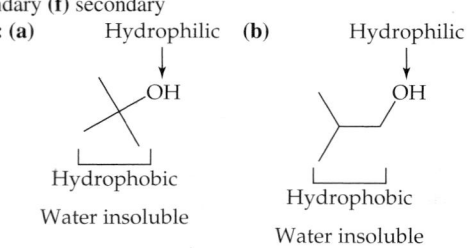

OH Hydrophobic Water insoluble   OH Hydrophobic Water insoluble

(c)

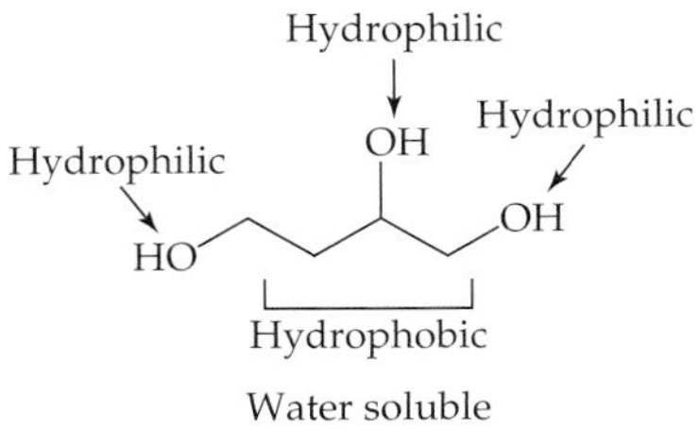

Hydrophilic

Hydrophilic   Hydrophilic

OH

HO   OH

Hydrophobic

Water soluble

(d)   Hydrophilic

OH

Hydrophobic

Water insoluble

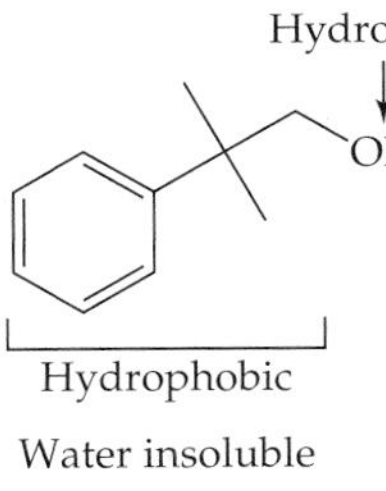

(e)   Hydrophilic

OH

Hydrophobic

Water insoluble

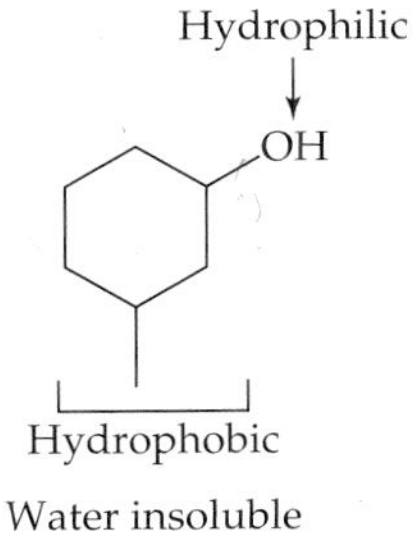

(f)   Hydrophilic

OH

Hydrophobic

Water insoluble

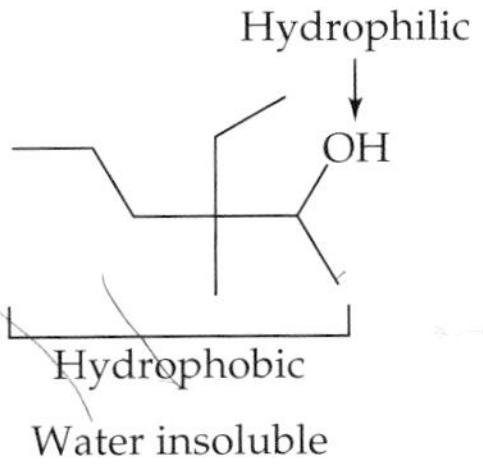

14.38 lowest **(a)** < **(c)** < **(b)** highest, due to molar mass and/or ability to hydrogen bond   **14.40** a ketone   **14.42** a carboxylic acid
14.44 Phenols dissolve in aqueous NaOH; alcohols don't.
14.46 (a)   OH
—CH₂CH₃
CH₂CH₃

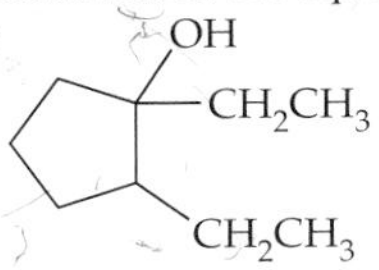

(b)   HO   or   OH

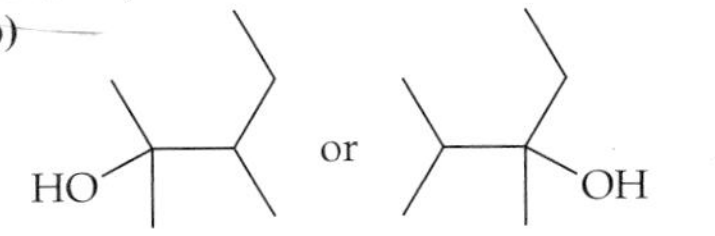

(c)   OH
CH₃CH₂CH₂CH₂CCH₃ or CH₃CH₂CH₂CHCHCH₃
C₆H₅   C₆H₅

(d)   OH
CCH₃ or CHCH₂OH
CH₃   CH₃

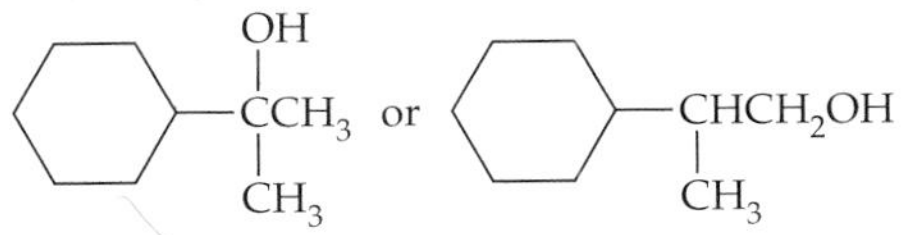

(e) HOCH₂CH₂CH₂CH₂CH₂OH
14.48 (a)
O
—CH₂C   and   —CH₂C
H   OH

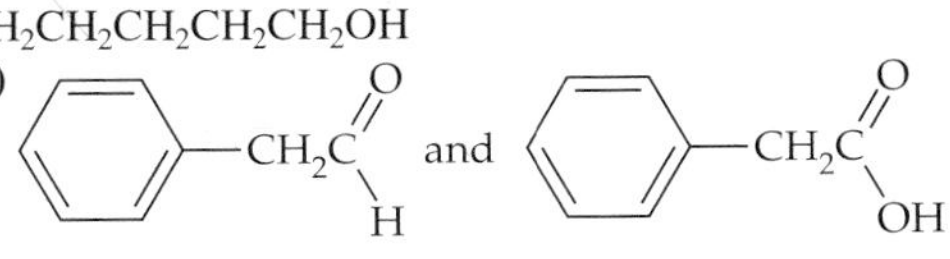

(b) O   **(c)** O
CH₃CH₂CCH₃   CH₃CH₂CCCH₃
O

(d) NR **(e)** NR

(f)
O
CCH₂CH₃

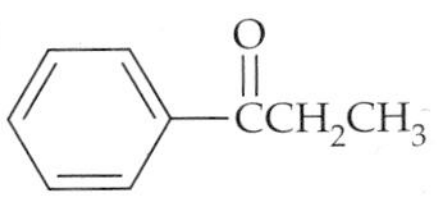

14.50 odor
14.52
O   O
HOCCHCH₂S—SCH₂CHCOH
NH₂   NH₂

14.54 Alcohols can form hydrogen bonds; thiols and alkyl chlorides can't.
14.56 (a) right- or left-handedness with two different mirror images
(b) superimposable mirror images with no handedness **(c)** a carbon atom bonded to four different groups **(d)** mirror-image forms of a chiral molecule

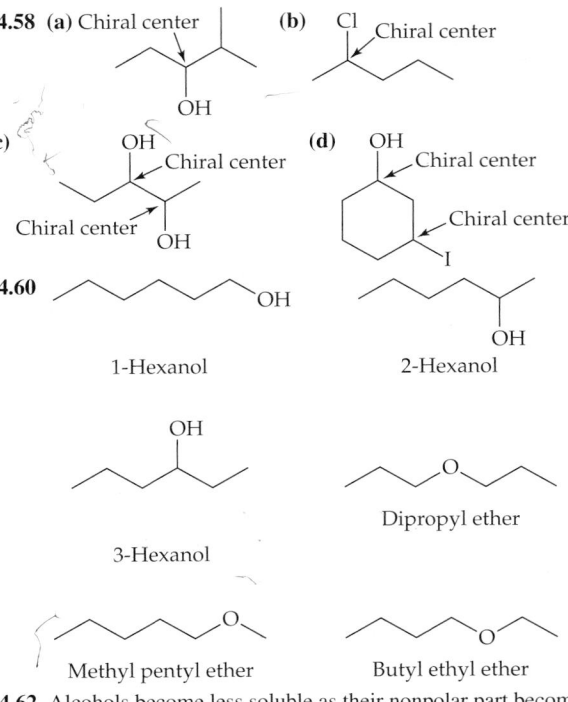

14.58 (a) Chiral center   **(b)** Cl Chiral center
OH

(c) OH Chiral center   **(d)** OH Chiral center
Chiral center OH   Chiral center
I

14.60   OH   OH

1-Hexanol   2-Hexanol

OH

Dipropyl ether

3-Hexanol

O

Methyl pentyl ether   Butyl ethyl ether

14.62 Alcohols become less soluble as their nonpolar part becomes larger.
14.64 An antiseptic kills microorganisms on living tissue; a disinfectant is used on nonliving matter.   **14.66** achiral: **(a)**, **(d)**
chiral:
(b)   **(c)**   OH
Chiral carbon   Chiral carbon
OH   Chiral carbon OH

(e) OH Chiral carbon   **(f)** OH
Chiral carbon

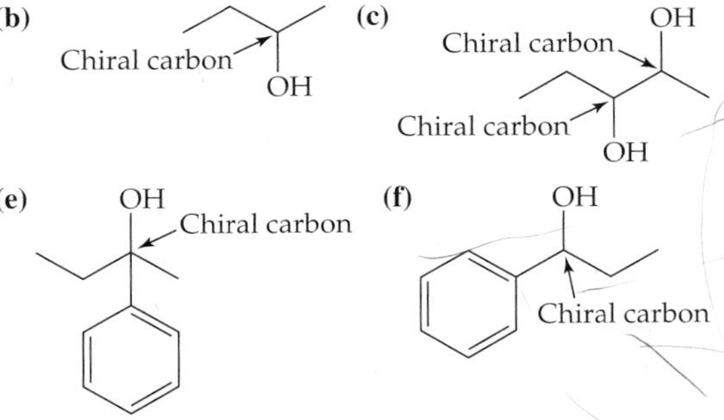

14.68 (a) *p*-dibromobenzene **(b)** 1,2-dibromo-1-butene **(c)** *m*-propylanisole
(d) 1,1-dibromocyclopentane **(e)** 2,4-dimethyl-2,4-pentanediol
(f) 4-methyl-2,4,5-heptanetriol **(g)** 4-bromo-6,6-dimethyl-2-heptyne
(h) 1-chloro-2-iodocyclobutane   **14.70** 3,7-dimethyl-2,6-octadiene-1-ol
CH₃   CH₃   O
CH₃C=CHCH₂CH₂C=CHC—H

14.72 $C_2H_6O + 3 O_2 \rightarrow 2 CO_2 + 3 H_2O$
14.74

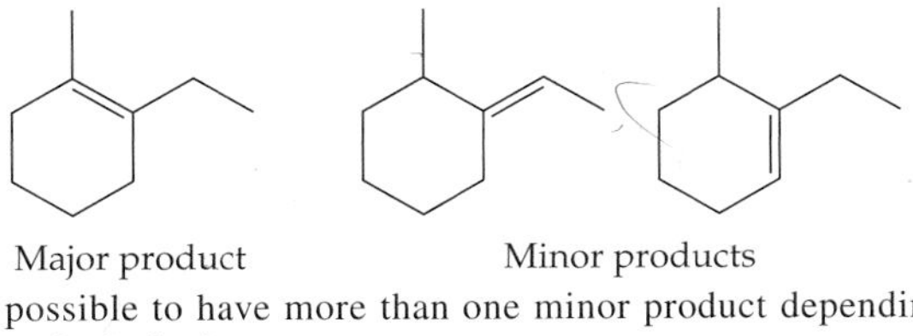

Major product   Minor products

*It is possible to have more than one minor product depending on the amount of substitution.

Chapter 15
15.1 (a)   (CH₂)₆COOH   OH
O   (CH₂)₄CH₃
Ketone
OH

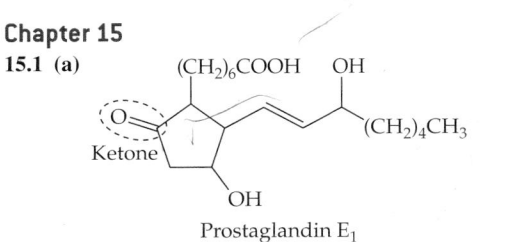

Prostaglandin E₁

(b)

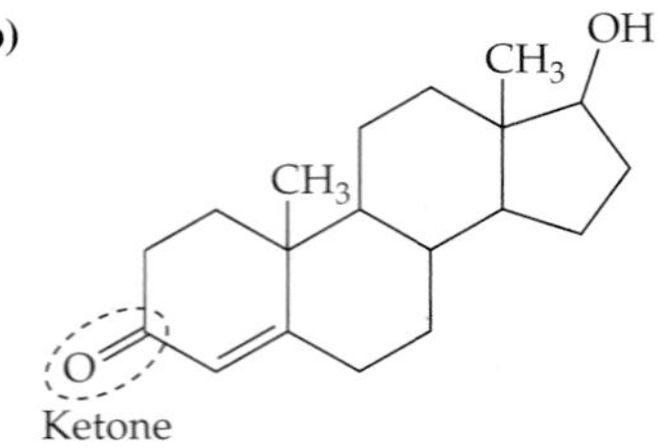

Testosterone

Ketone

CH₃ OH

(c) CH₃O

Aldehyde

HO   CHO

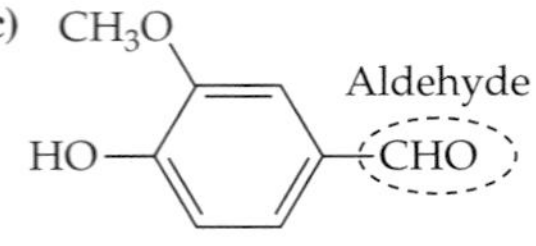

Vanillin

(d) C₄H₉COCH₃
Ketone

(e) C₄H₉CHO
Aldehyde

15.2 (d)

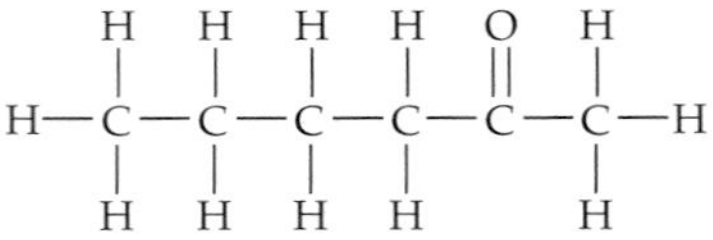

$$H-\overset{H}{\underset{H}{C}}-\overset{H}{\underset{H}{C}}-\overset{H}{\underset{H}{C}}-\overset{H}{\underset{H}{C}}-\overset{O}{C}-\overset{H}{\underset{H}{C}}-H$$

(e)

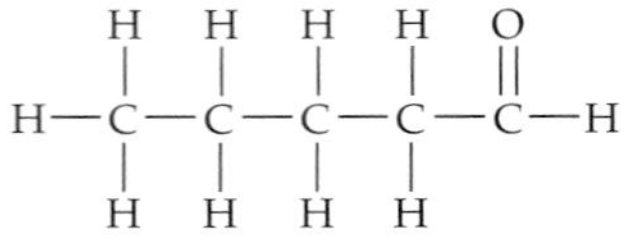

$$H-\overset{H}{\underset{H}{C}}-\overset{H}{\underset{H}{C}}-\overset{H}{\underset{H}{C}}-\overset{H}{\underset{H}{C}}-\overset{O}{C}-H$$

15.3 (a)

CH₃CH₂CH₂CH₂CH₂CH₂CH₂CH

O

(b)

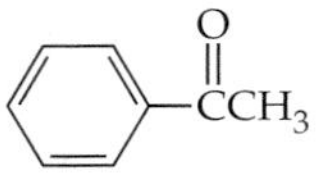

O
║
CCH₃

(c)

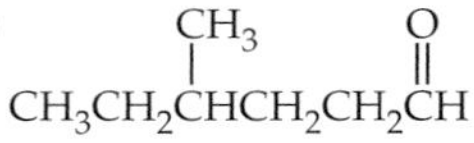

CH₃
|
CH₃CH₂CHCH₂CH₂CH

O

(d)

H₃C   O
| ║
CH₃C—CCH₃
|
CH₃

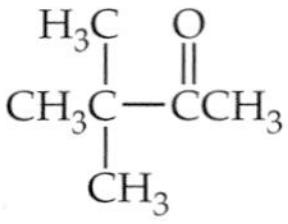

15.4 (a) pentanal **(b)** 3-pentanone **(c)** 4-methylhexanal **(d)** 4-heptanone

(a) **(b)** 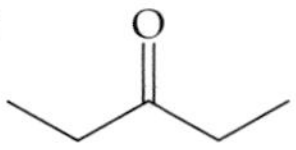 **(c)** 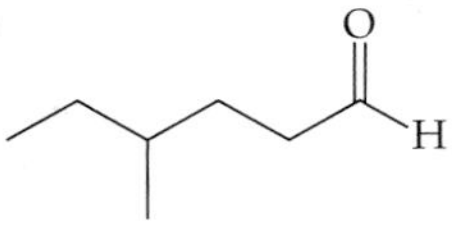 **(d)**

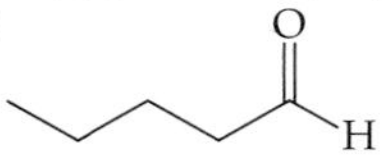

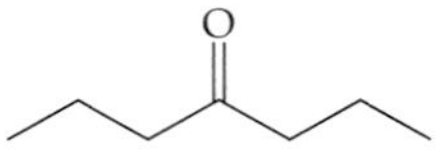

15.5 (a)

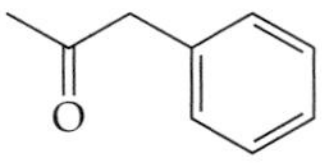

Methyl benzyl ketone

(b)

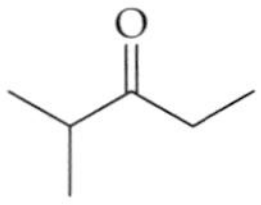

Ethyl isopropyl ketone

(c)

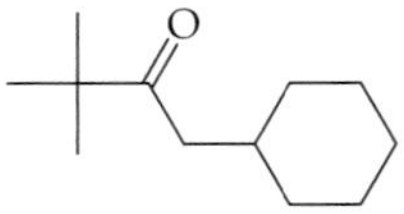

Tert-butyl cyclohexyl ketone

15.6 (left)

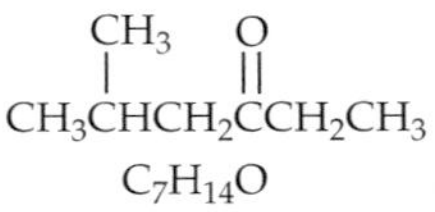

CH₃ O
| ║
CH₃CHCH₂CCH₂CH₃
C₇H₁₄O
5-Methyl-3-hexanone
(A ketone)

(right)

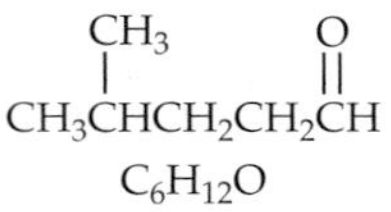

CH₃ O
| ║
CH₃CHCH₂CH₂CH
C₆H₁₂O
4-Methylpentanal
(An aldehyde)

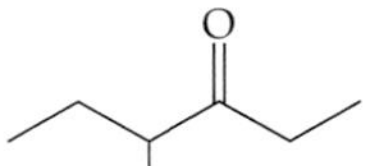

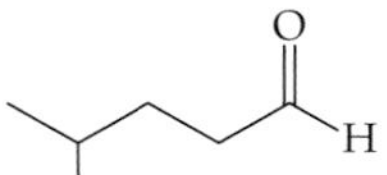

15.7 (a) polar, insoluble **(b)** polar, soluble **(c)** nonpolar, insoluble **(d)** polar, insoluble   **15.8** Alcohols form hydrogen bonds, which raise their boiling points. Aldehydes and ketones have higher boiling points than alkanes because they are polar.

15.9 (a)

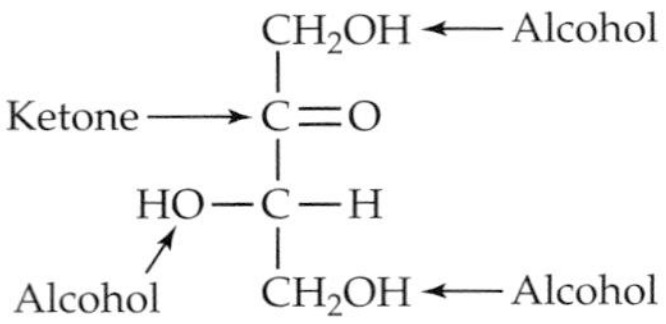

CH₂OH ← Alcohol
Ketone → C=O
HO—C—H
Alcohol ↗   CH₂OH ← Alcohol

(b)

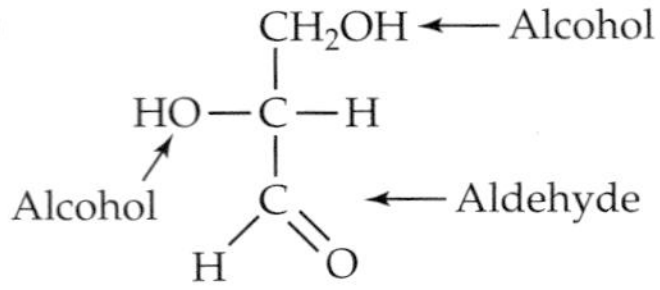

CH₂OH ← Alcohol
HO—C—H
Alcohol ↗   C ← Aldehyde
‖
O   H

(c)

CH₂CHO
Aldehyde

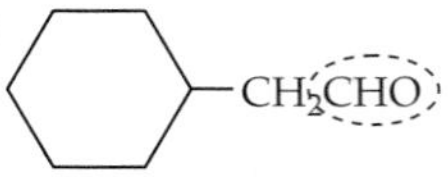

(d) H₂NCH₂CH₂COCH₃

Amine   Ketone

15.10 (a) (i) positive, (ii) positive **(b)** (i) negative, (ii) negative
(c) (i) positive, (ii) positive **(d)** (i) negative, (ii) positive

15.11 (a)

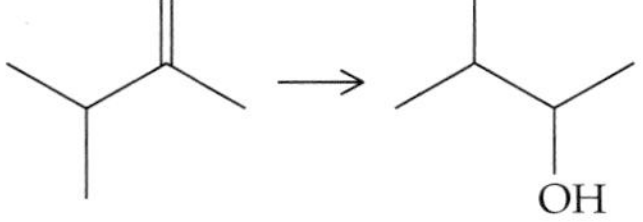

O   OH

→

(b)

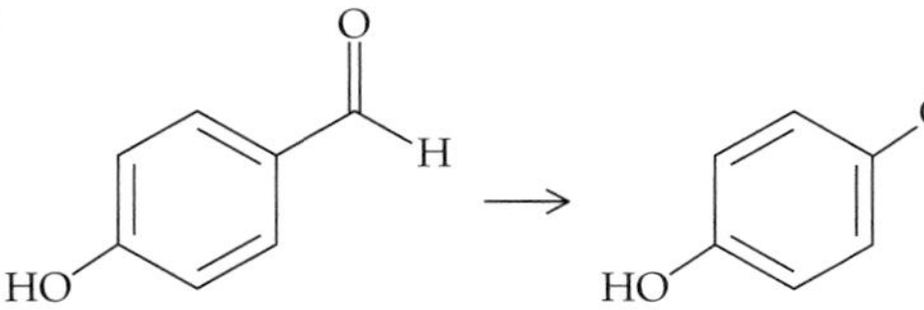

O   CH₂OH
‖
H

→

HO   HO

(c)

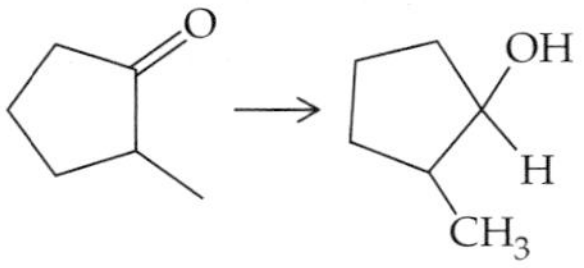

O   OH
| |
H

→

CH₃   CH₃

15.12 (a)

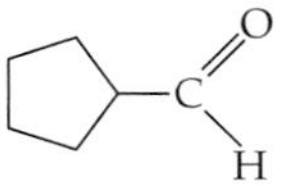

O
‖
C
|
H

(b)

O
‖
Ph
H

(c)

O   O
‖   ‖
C—CH₂—C
| |
H   H

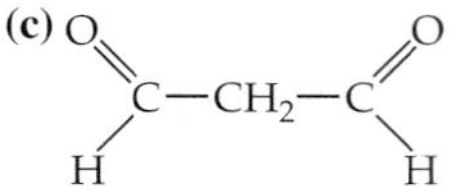

15.13 (a) hemiacetal **(b)** neither **(c)** neither **(d)** hemiacetal
15.14 (a) Ketal; **(b)** Acetal;

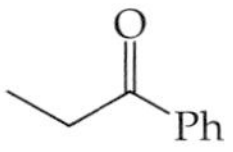

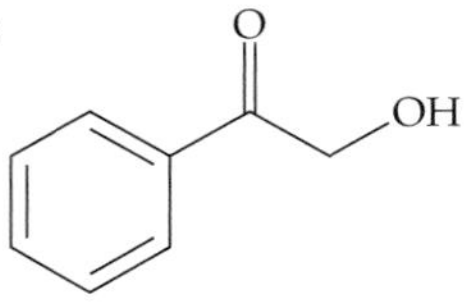

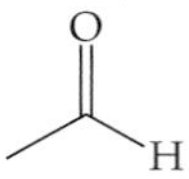

O   O
‖   ‖
OH   H

(c) Ketal;

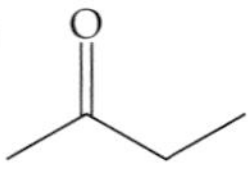

O
‖

15.15 (a)

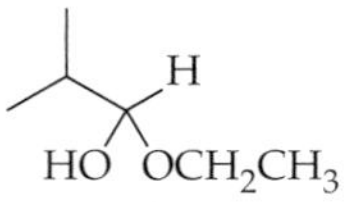

H
|
HO   OCH₂CH₃

(b)

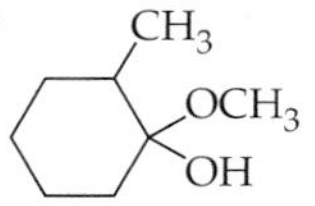

CH₃
OCH₃
OH

15.16 (a)

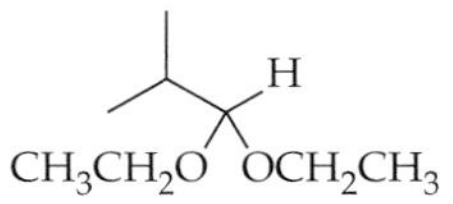

H
|
CH₃CH₂O   OCH₂CH₃

(b)

CH₃
OCH₃
OCH₃

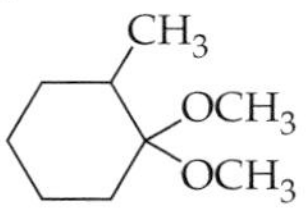

15.17 (a) hemiacetal **(b)** acetal **(c)** ketal **(d)** hemiketal
15.18 (a)

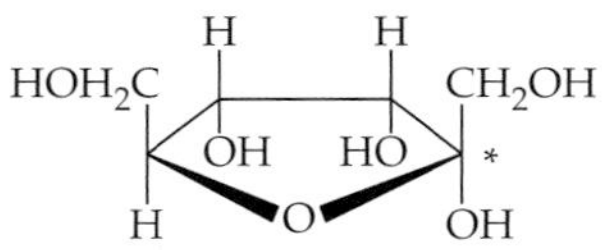

H   H
HOH₂C   CH₂OH
OH   HO   *
H   O   OH

Tagatose
Hemiketal

(b)

CH₂OH
HO   O   OH
H   *
H   HO   H
OH   H

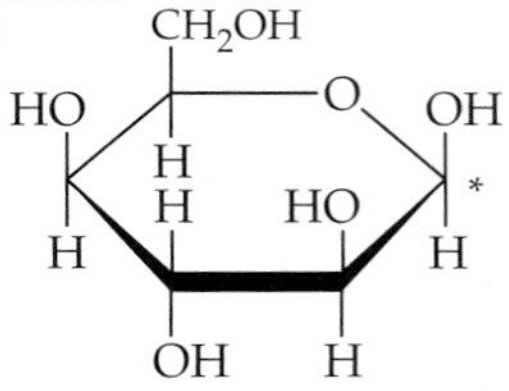

Idose
Hemiacetal

15.19 (a)

[benzene ring]—CH$_2$CCH$_2$CH$_3$ (C=O) + 2 CH$_3$OH

(b) CH$_3$CH$_2$CHO + 2 CH$_3$CH$_2$CH$_2$OH

(c) O
HCH + 2 CH$_3$CH$_2$CH$_2$OH

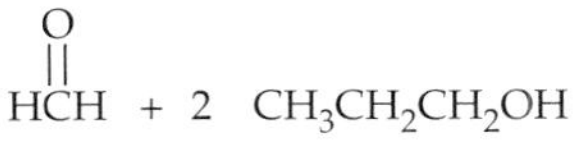

15.20 (a) Hydride adds to the carbonyl carbon, because the polar C=O carbon has a partial positive charge. **(b)** The arrow to the right represents reduction, and the arrow to the left represents oxidation.

15.21 Aldehydes can be oxidized to carboxylic acids. Tollens' reagent differentiates an aldehyde from a ketone.

15.22

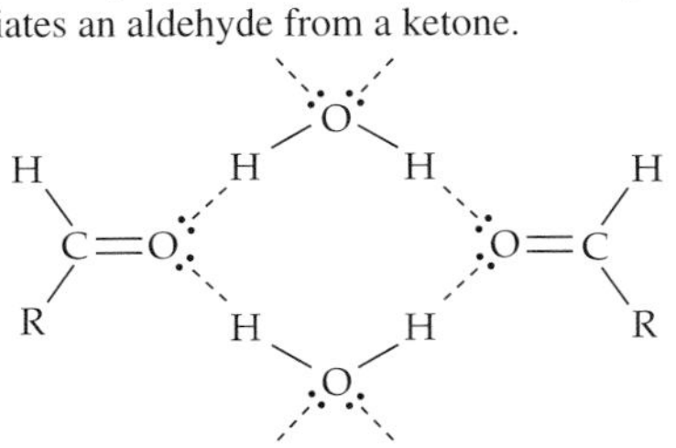

15.23 (a) Under acidic conditions, an alcohol adds to the carbonyl group of an aldehyde to form a hemiacetal, which is unstable and further reacts to form an acetal.

(b)

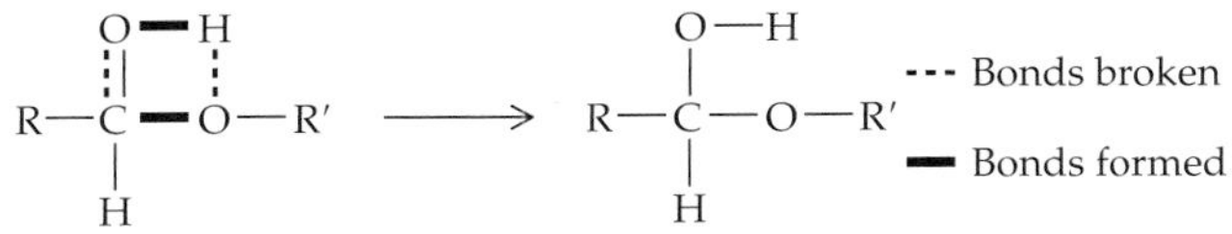

R—C(O—H)(O—R')(H) ⟶ R—C(O—H)(O—R')(H)   --- Bonds broken   — Bonds formed

15.24 In solution, glucose exists as a cyclic hemiacetal because this structure is more stable and it protects the reactive aldehyde functional group from oxidation to the carboxylic acid.   **15.25** In addition to the two oxygens, an acetal carbon of a ketone is bonded to two carbons. The acetal carbon of an aldehyde is bonded to a carbon and a hydrogen.

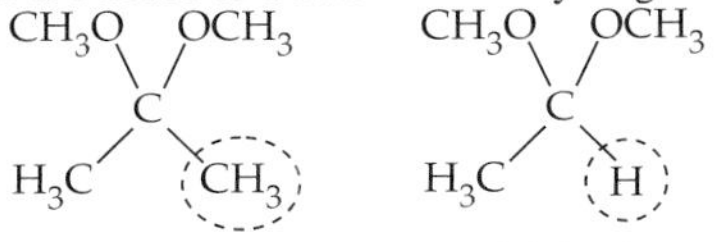

CH$_3$O OCH$_3$ / C / H$_3$C (CH$_3$) — Ketone   CH$_3$O OCH$_3$ / C / H$_3$C (H) — Aldehyde

15.26 (a) O
CH$_3$CHCH$_2$CHCH$_2$CH$_2$CH$_2$

(b) O
CH$_3$CH$_2$CH$_2$CH   or   H$_3$CCHCH (CH$_3$)

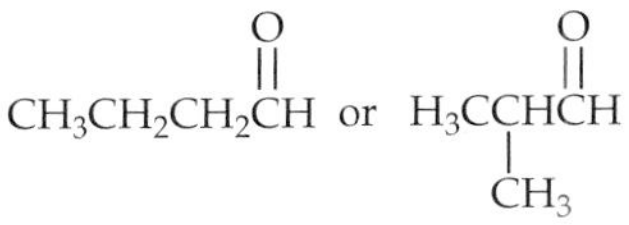

(c) CH$_3$CH$_2$CHCHH (Br)   **(d)** O
HOCH$_2$CH$_2$CCH$_3$

15.28 Structure **(c)** has an aldehyde group, and structures **(a)**, **(b)**, and **(f)** have ketone groups.

15.30 (a) O
CH$_3$CH$_2$CHCHCH (CH$_3$)   **(b)** Cl O
CH$_2$CH$_2$CHCH (OH)

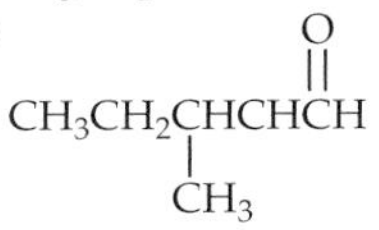

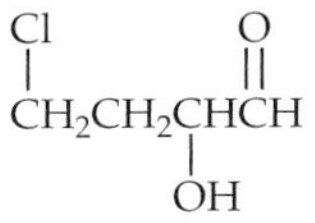

(c) H$_3$C—[benzene]—CH (=O)   **(d)** [cycloheptanone with CH$_2$CH$_3$]

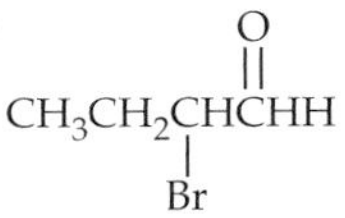

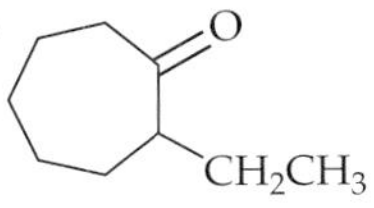

(e) [cyclopropyl]—CCH$_3$ (=O)   **(f)** [benzene]—CCH$_3$ (=O)

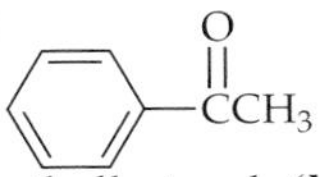

15.32 (a) 2,2-dimethylbutanal **(b)** 2-hydroxy-2-methylpentanal **(c)** 3-methylbutanal **(d)** 4-methyl-3-hexanone **(e)** 3-hydroxy-2-methylcyclohexanone **15.34** For **(a)**, a ketone can't occur at the end of a carbon chain. For **(b)**, the methyl group receives the lowest possible number. For **(c)**, numbering must start at the end of the carbon chain closer to the carbonyl group.

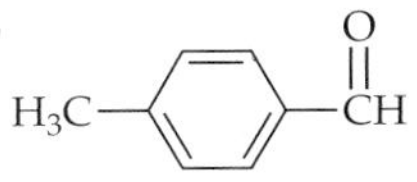

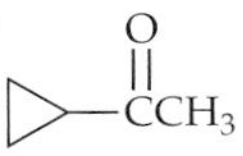

15.36
[HO, O—CH$_3$ hemiacetal structure]

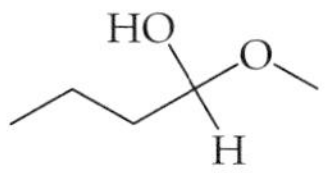

15.38 Tollens' reagent: (b) and (c); Benedict's reagent: (b) and (c). (a) reacts with neither

15.40 (a) H$_3$C—[benzene]—CHO   **(b)** CHO
CH$_3$CH$_2$CHCH$_2$CHCH$_3$ (CH$_3$)

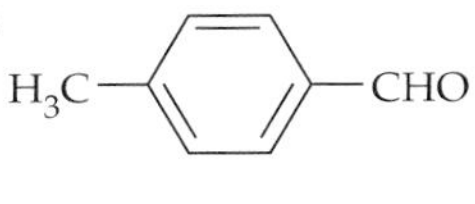

(c) CH$_3$CH=CHCHO

15.42 (a) OH
CH$_3$CH$_2$COCH$_2$CH$_2$CH$_3$ (CH$_3$)   Hemiketal   **(b)** OH
CH$_3$CH$_2$CH$_2$COCH(CH$_3$)$_2$ (H)   Hemiacetal

(c) O
CH$_3$CH$_2$CH$_2$CH + CH$_3$CH$_2$OH + CH$_3$OH

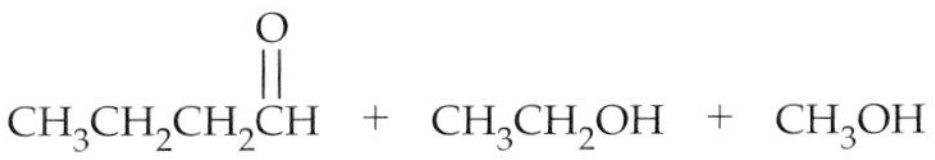

(d) H$_3$C
C=O + HOCH$_2$CH$_2$OH
H$_3$C

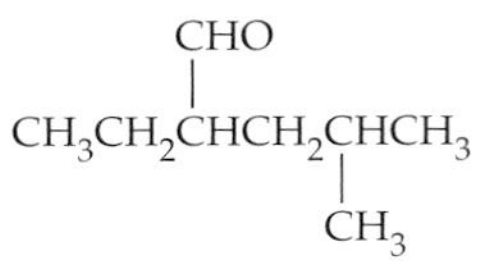

15.44 O   OH
HCCH$_2$CH$_2$CH$_2$CHCH$_3$ 5-Hydroxyhexanal

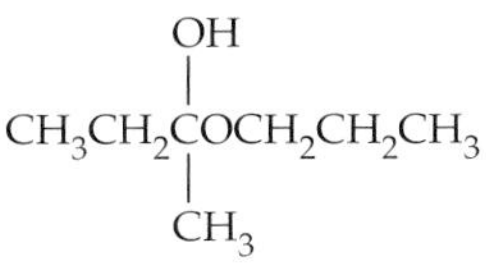

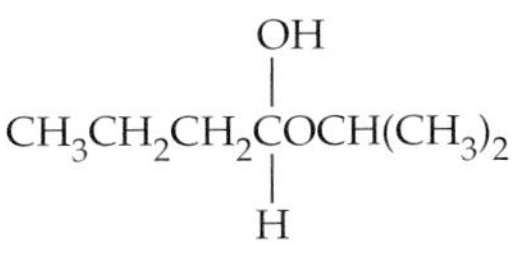

15.46 HOCH$_2$CH$_2$CH$_2$OH and HCHO (formaldehyde).

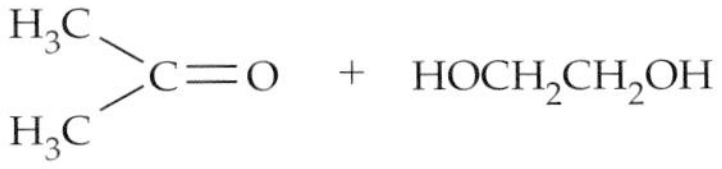

15.48

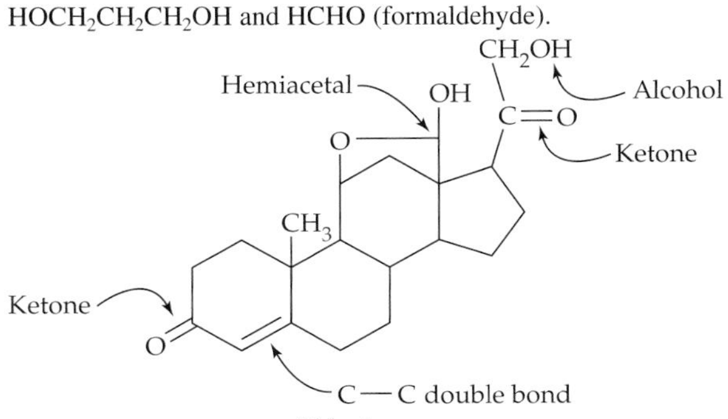

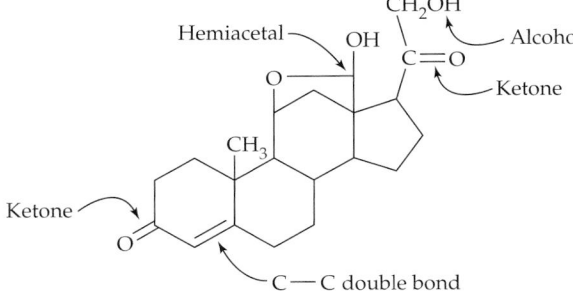

Hemiacetal — Alcohol — Ketone — Ketone — C—C double bond
Aldosterone

15.50 *p*-methoxybenzaldehyde   **15.52** Aldehydes are easily oxidized while ketones are not.   **15.54 (a)** 2-methyl-3-pentanone **(b)** 1,5-hexadiene **(c)** *m*-bromotoluene **(d)** 4,5,5-trimethyl-3-hexanone

15.56 (a) NO$_2$
O$_2$N—[benzene]—CCH$_3$ (O)   **(b)** OH [cyclopentanone with HO]   **(c)** CH$_3$
CH$_3$C—CH$_3$ (OCH$_3$)

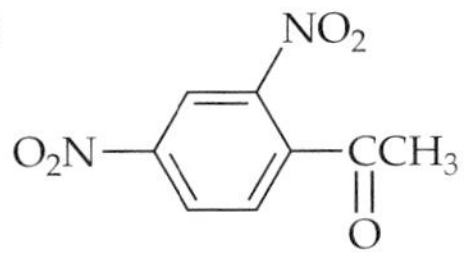

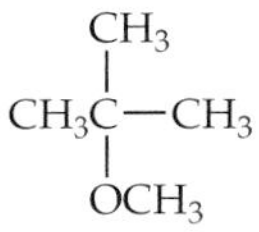

(d) CH$_3$
CH$_3$CH—CH—CHCH$_3$ (CH$_3$, OH, CH$_3$)

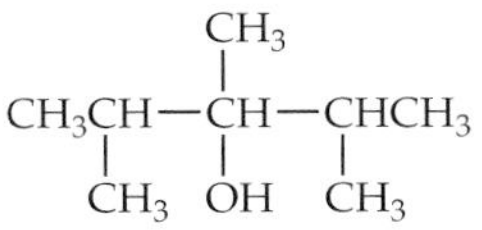

15.58 (a) CH$_3$CH$_2$CH(CH$_3$)$_2$ **(b)** O
(CH$_3$)$_2$CHCCH$_3$

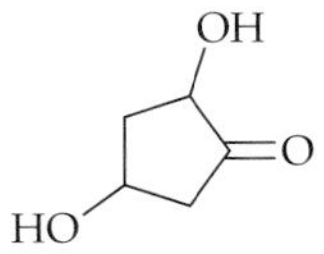

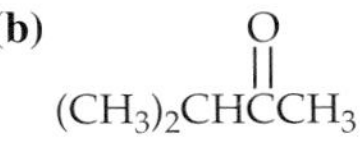

(c) HOCH$_2$CH$_2$CH$_2$CH$_3$ **(d)** HO H
[benzene]—C—O—isopropyl

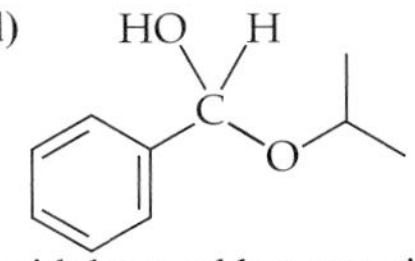

15.60 Tollens' reagent reacts with hexanal but not with 3-hexanone.
15.62 2-Heptanone is less soluble in water because it has a longer hydrocarbon chain.
15.64 (a) [sugar ring structure]   **(b)** [sugar ring structure]

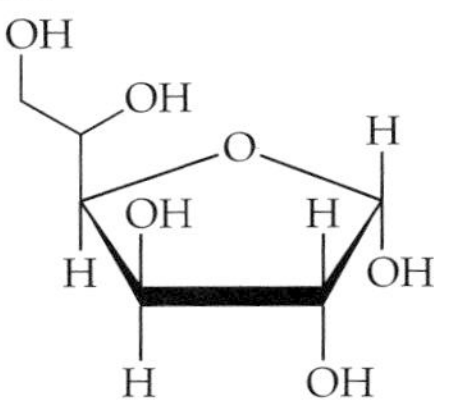

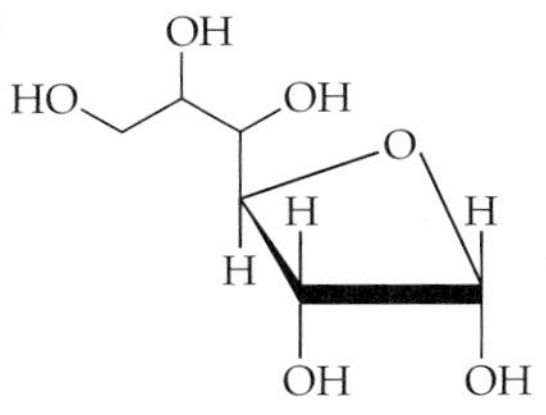

15.66

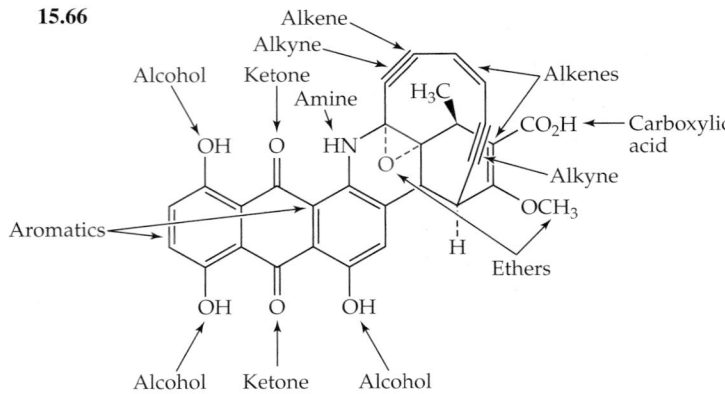

Chapter 16

16.1 (a) primary **(b)** secondary **(c)** primary **(d)** secondary **(e)** tertiary
16.2 (a) tripropylamine **(b)**N-ethyl-N-methylcyclopentylamine
(c) N-isopropylaniline
16.3 (a) CH₃CH₂CH₂CH₂CH₂CH₂CH₂CH₂NH₂
(b)

$$CH_3CH_2CH_2CH_2CH_2\overset{\overset{CH_3}{|}}{N}H$$

(c)

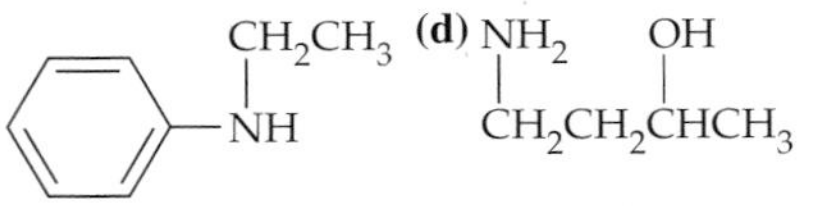

$$\text{(phenyl)}\overset{\overset{CH_2CH_3}{|}}{N}H$$

(d) NH₂   OH

CH₂CH₂CHCH₃

16.4 (a) primary **(b)** secondary **(c)** secondary **(d)** primary
16.5 The ion for carbon groups permanently bound to the nitrogen atom.

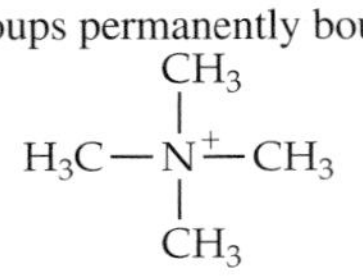

$$H_3C - \overset{\overset{CH_3}{|}}{\underset{\underset{CH_3}{|}}{N^{\pm}}} - CH_3$$

16.6 CH₃CH₂CH₂CH₂NHCH₂CH₃   ⟋⟍⟋N⟍   *N*-ethylbutylamine;

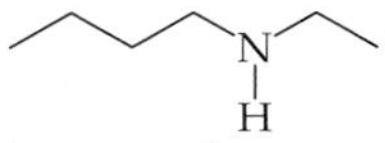

It is a secondary amine since the N has two carbon groups bound directly to it.   **16.7** Compound **(a)** is lowest boiling (it cannot hydrogen bond with itself); **(b)** is highest boiling (strongest hydrogen bonds).
16.8 (a)   **(b)**

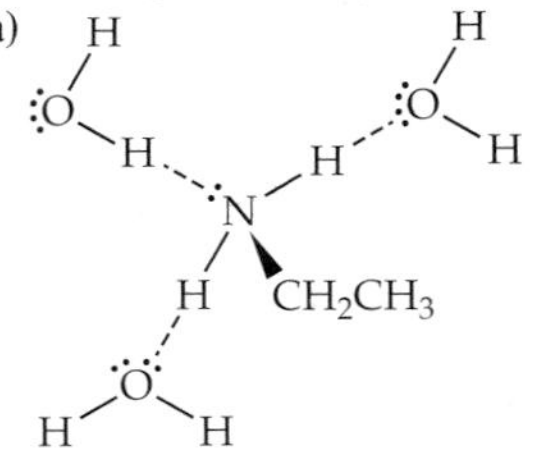

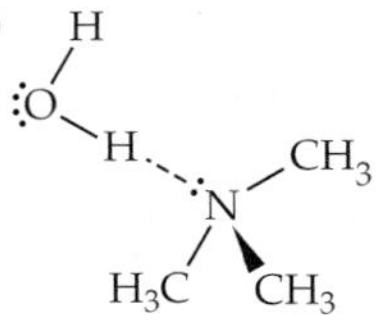

16.9 (a) methylamine, ethylamine, dimethylamine, trimethylamine
(b) pyridine **(c)** aniline   **16.10 (a)** pyrimidine: C₄H₄N₂ **(b)** purine: C₅H₄N₄
16.11 (a) and **(d)**
16.12
(a)

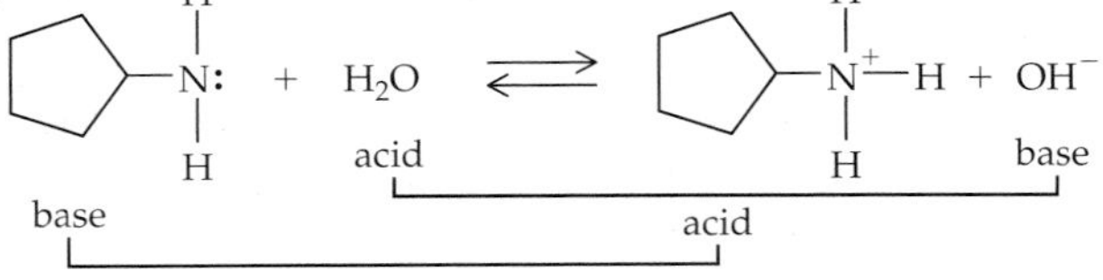

cyclopentyl-N: + H₂O ⇌ cyclopentyl-N⁺-H + OH⁻
          acid   base
base ————————————— acid

(b)

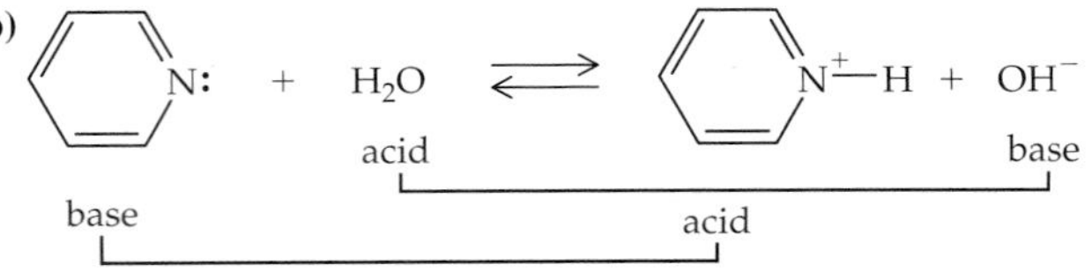

pyridine-N: + H₂O ⇌ pyridine-N⁺-H + OH⁻
          acid   base
base ————————————— acid

16.13 (a) CH₃CHNH₂CH₃⁺Br⁻(aq) **(b)** (phenyl)—NH₃⁺Cl⁻(aq)

with CH₃ branch

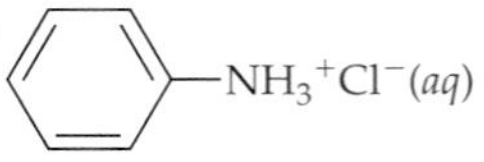

(c) piperidinium-N⁺H₂ Cl⁻(aq)   **(d)** (CH₃)₃CNH₂ + H₂O(l) + Na⁺(aq)

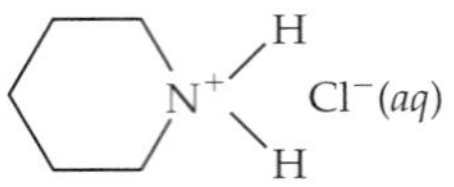

16.14 (a) N-methylisopropylammonium bromide **(b)** anilinium chloride
(c) piperidinium chloride   **16.15 (a)** ethylamine **(b)** triethylamine
16.16 (a)

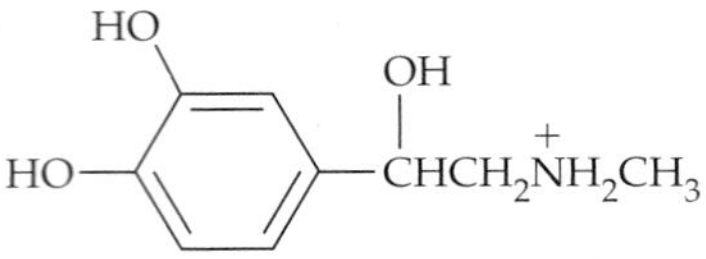

HO—, OH (catechol ring) —CHCH₂NH₂CH₃⁺

(b)

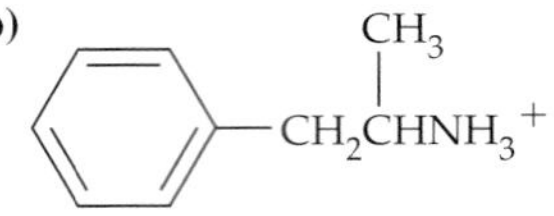

(phenyl)—CH₂CHNH₃⁺ with CH₃

16.17–16.18 (a)

$$CH_3CH_2CH_2CH_2\overset{\overset{CH_2CH_3}{|}}{\underset{\underset{CH_2CH_3}{|}}{N}}H^+Br^-$$

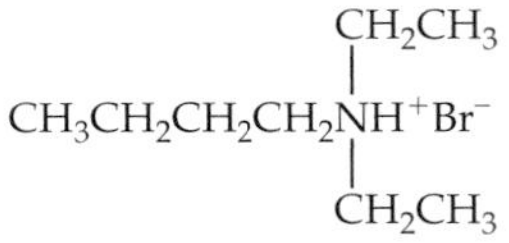

Butyldiethylammonium bromide
or N,N–Diethylbutylammonium bromide
salt of a tertiary amine

(b)   (CH₃CH₂CH₂CH₂)₄N⁺OH⁻

Tetrabutylammonium hydroxide
salt of a quaternary amine

(c)   CH₃CH₂CH₂NH₃⁺I⁻   **(d)**

Propylammonium iodide
salt of a primary amine

$$CH_3\overset{\overset{CH_3}{|}}{\underset{\underset{CH_3}{|}}{CH}}NH_2^+Cl^-$$

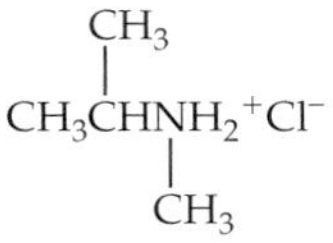

Isopropylmethylammonium chloride
salt of a secondary amine

16.19 CH₃CH₂CH₂CH₂NH₃⁺Cl⁻(aq) + NaOH(aq) →
CH₃CH₂CH₂CH₂NH₂ + H₂O(l) + NaCl(aq)
16.20 Benadryl has the general structure. In Benadryl, R = —CH₃ and
R′ = R″ = C₆H₅—.
16.21

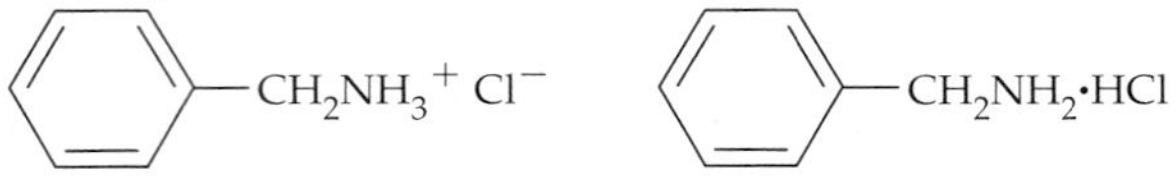

(phenyl)—CH₂NH₃⁺ Cl⁻   (phenyl)—CH₂NH₂·HCl

Benzylammonium chloride

16.22 (a) (CH₃CH₂)₃N + H₂O + LiBr
(b)

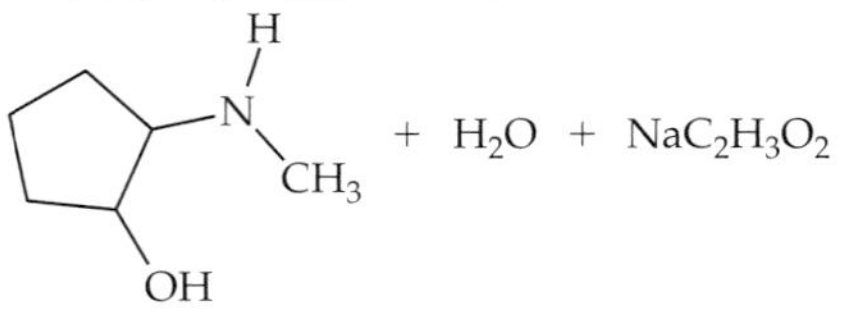

cyclopentyl ring with N—CH₃ and OH + H₂O + NaC₂H₃O₂

(c)

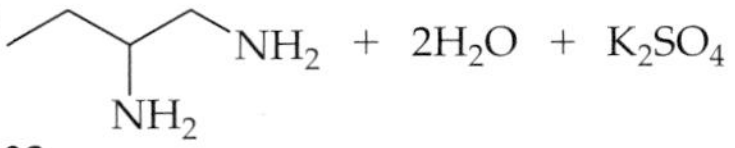

⟋⟍ with NH₂ and NH₂ + 2H₂O + K₂SO₄

16.23

pyrrolidine-N⁺(CH₃)— q —CH₂CH₂NHCH₂—(pyridine)   Provides and accepts a hydrogen bond
                          s   a   ← Accepts a hydrogen bond

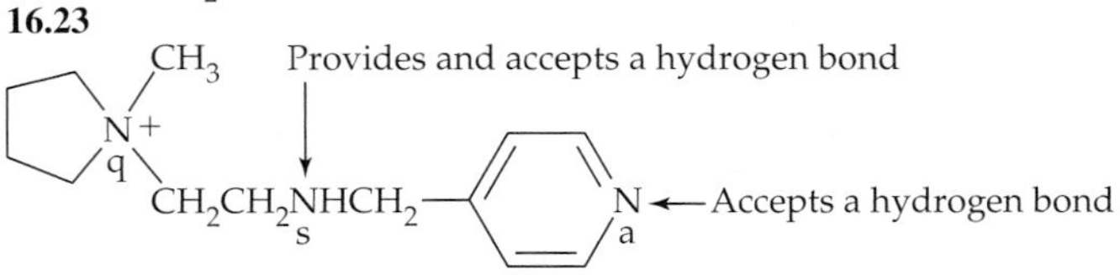

16.24 (a) Both amine groups can participate in hydrogen bonding.
(b) Lysine is water-soluble because it can form hydrogen bonds with water.

16.25 (a)

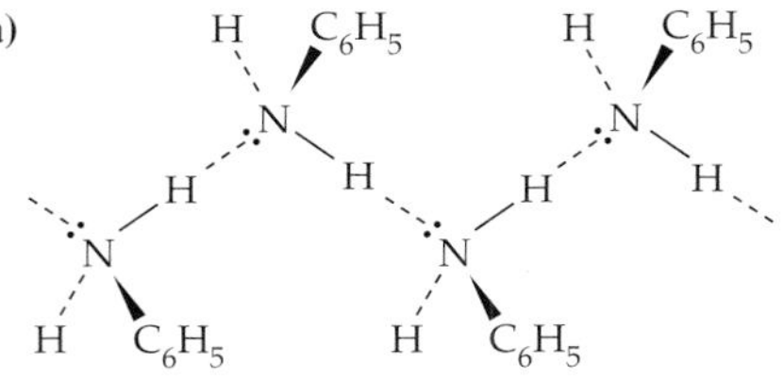

(b)

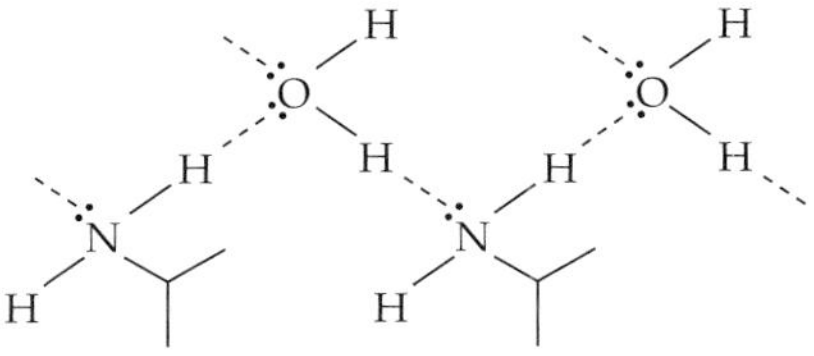

(c)

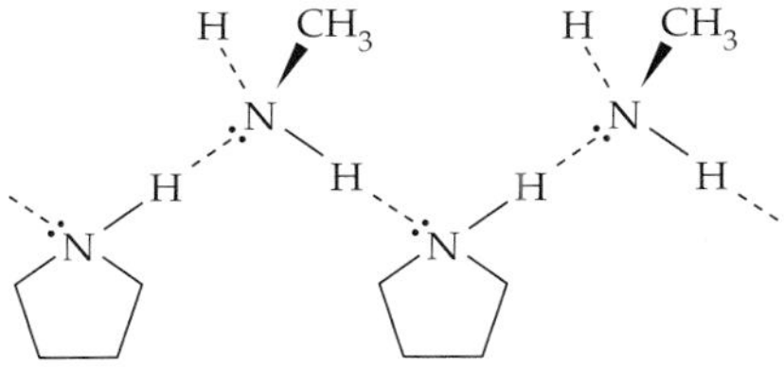

16.26

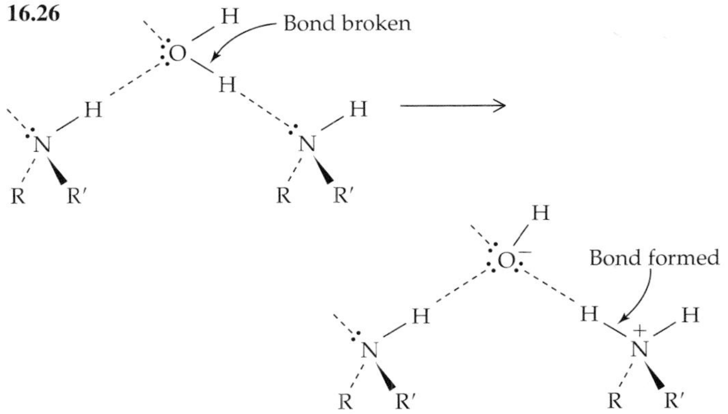

Bond broken

Bond formed

16.27 strongest base: $(CH_3)_2NH$ weakest base: $C_6H_5NH_2$

16.28 (a)

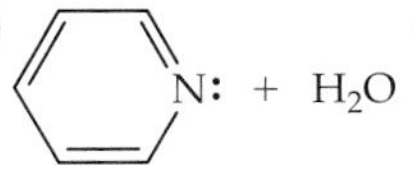

$N: + H_2O$

(b) $(CH_3)_2CHNH_3^+ + OH^-$

(c) $(CH_3CH_2)_3\overset{+}{N}H \ Br^-$ **(d)**

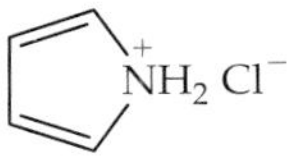

16.30 (a)

$CH_3CH_2CH_2CH_2CH_2\overset{H}{\underset{}{N}}CH_3$

(b)

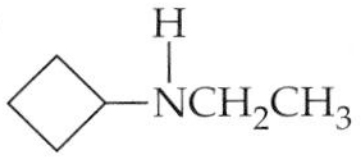

(c)

$CH_3CH_2CH_2$—⟨benzene⟩—NH_2

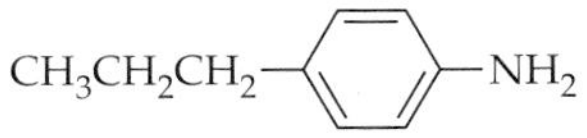

16.32 (a) N-ethylcyclopentylamine (secondary) **(b)** cycloheptylamine (primary) **16.34** diethylamine **16.36 (a)** N-methyl-2-butylammonium nitrate (salt of a secondary amine).

(b)

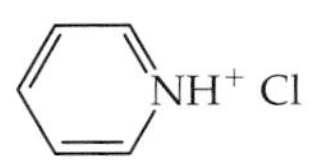

$NH^+ \ Cl$

(salt of a heterocyclic amine)

(c)

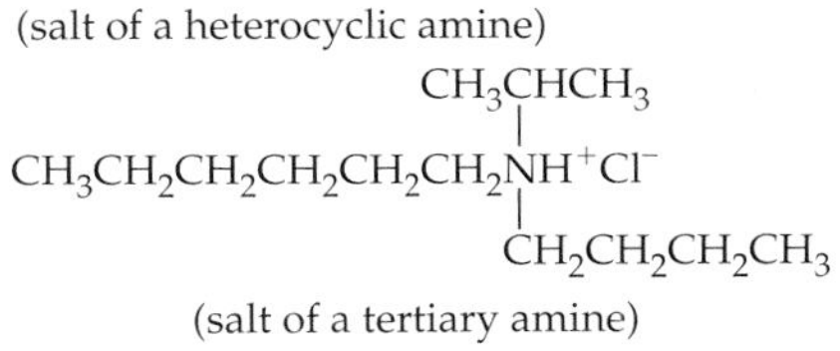

$CH_3\overset{|}{CHCH_3}$

$CH_3CH_2CH_2CH_2CH_2CH_2\overset{|}{N}H^+Cl^-$

$\overset{|}{CH_2CH_2CH_2CH_3}$

(salt of a tertiary amine)

16.38

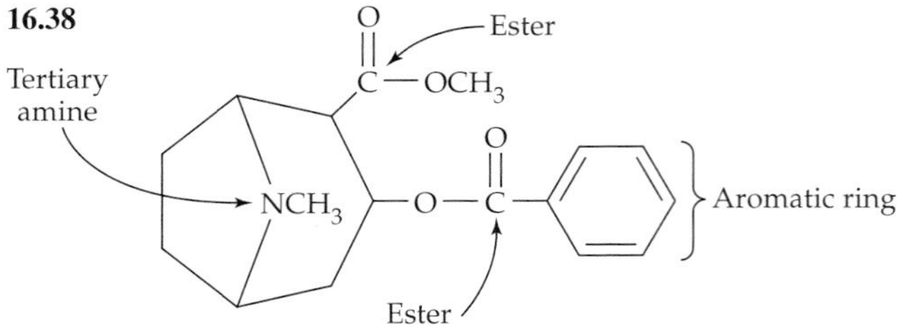

Tertiary amine

Ester

Ester

Aromatic ring

Cocaine

16.40 (a)

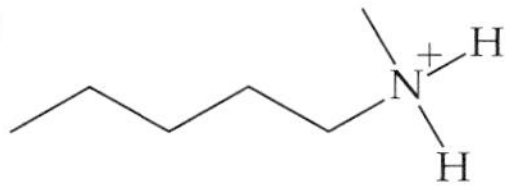

(b)

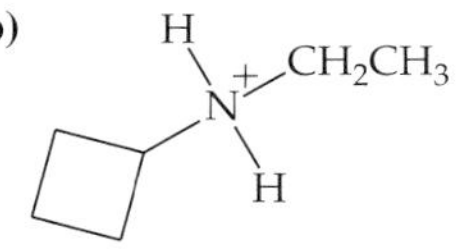

(c)

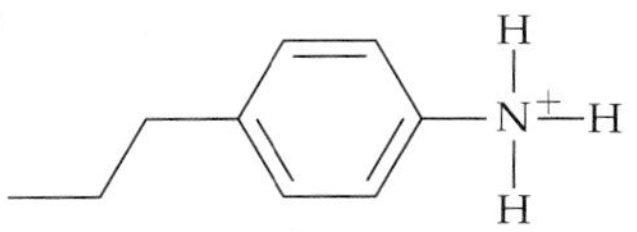

16.42 (a)

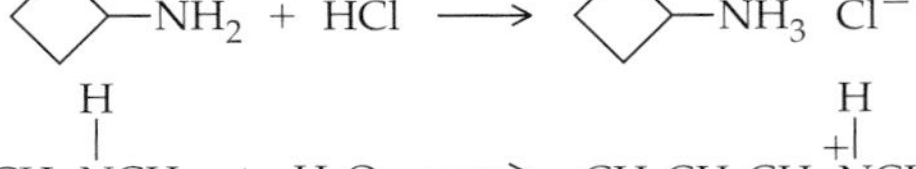

$—NH_2 + HCl \longrightarrow$ $—\overset{+}{N}H_3 \ Cl^-$

(b)

$CH_3CH_2CH_2\overset{H}{\underset{}{N}}CH_3 + H_2O \rightleftharpoons CH_3CH_2CH_2\overset{H}{\underset{H}{\overset{+}{N}}}CH_3 + OH^-$

(c)

$+ \ NaOH \longrightarrow$

$+ \ H_2O$
$+ \ NaBr$

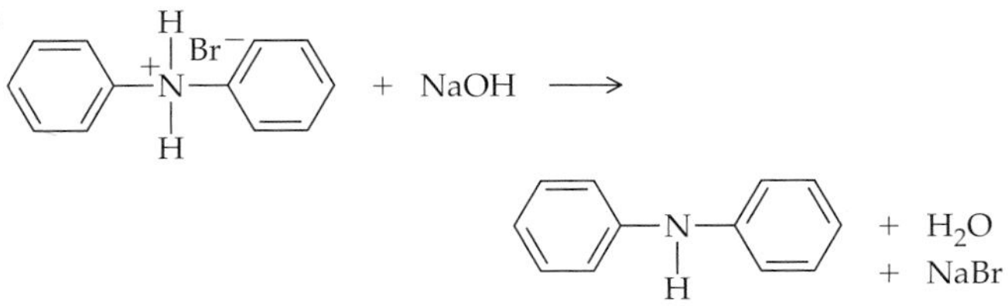

16.44 Choline doesn't react with HCl because its nitrogen isn't basic.

16.46

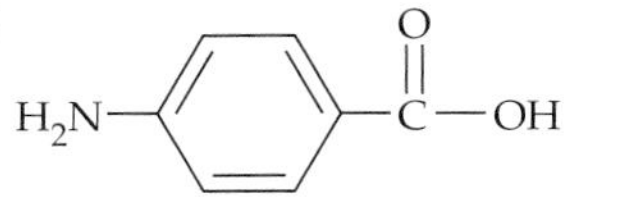

H_2N—⟨benzene⟩—$\overset{O}{\underset{}{C}}$—OH

PABA

16.48

Amide

Amine

Alcohol

Amine

Ether

Amine

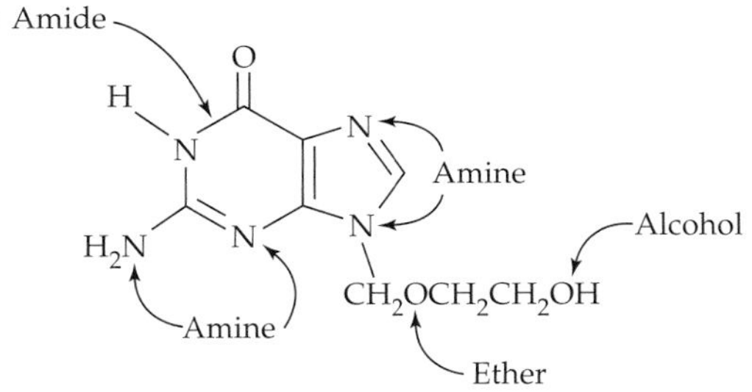

Acyclovir—related to purine

16.50 amines: foul-smelling, somewhat basic, lower boiling (weaker hydrogen bonds); Alcohols: pleasant-smelling, not basic, higher boiling (stronger hydrogen bonds) **16.52 (a)** 6-methyl-2-heptene **(b)** p-isopropylphenol **(c)** dibutylamine **16.54** Molecules of hexylamine can form hydrogen bonds to each other, but molecules of triethylamine can't. **16.56** The nitrogen atom is not part of the ring. **16.58 (a)** N-ethylcyclohexylamine **(b)** anilinium bromide **(c)** N-methylethylamine **16.60** Decylamine and ethylamine are both primary amines and can form hydrogen bonds but ethylamine has a smaller hydrocarbon region so it would be more soluble.

Chapter 17

17.1 carboxylic acid: **(c)**; amides: **(a)**, **(f)**, **(h)**; ester: **(d)**; none: **(b)**, **(e)**, **(g)**
17.2 (a)

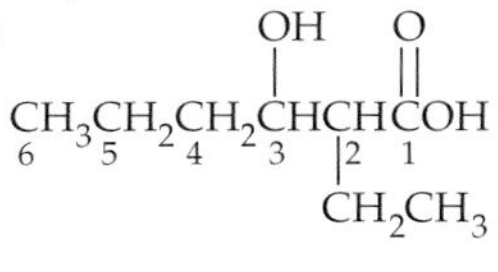

(b)

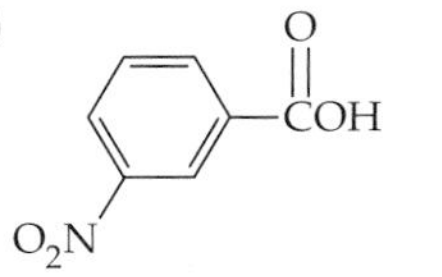

17.3

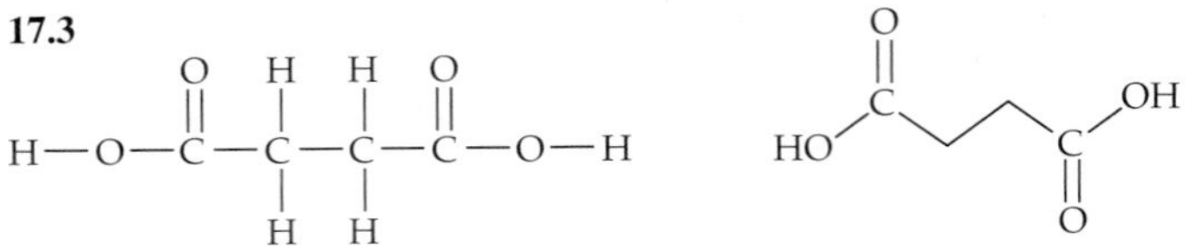

17.4

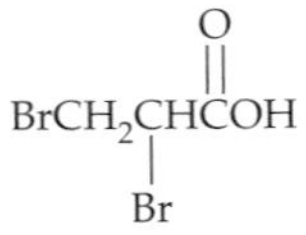

BrCH₂CHCOH   2,3-Dibromopropanoic acid
    |
    Br

17.5 (a)

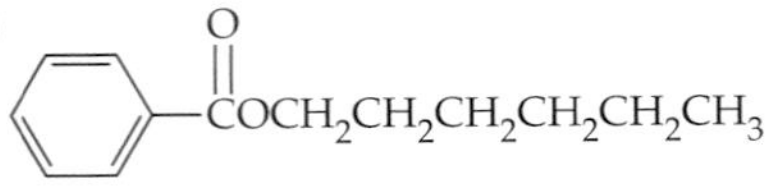

(b)    **(c)**

17.6 CH_3COOH is highest boiling (most H-bonding). $CH_3CH_2CH_3$ is lowest boiling (nonpolar).   **17.7 (a)** C_3H_7COOH is more soluble (smaller —R group). **(b)** $(CH_3)_2CHCOOH$ is more soluble (carboxylic acid).

17.8 (a)

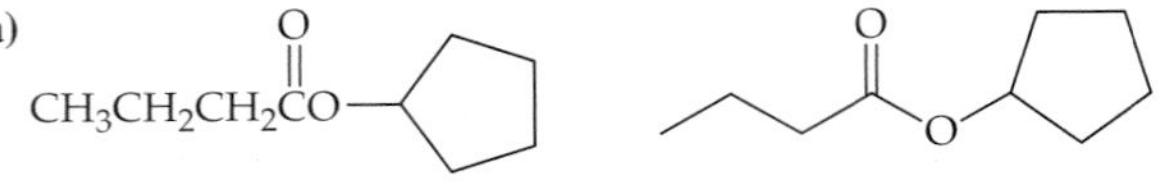

(b)

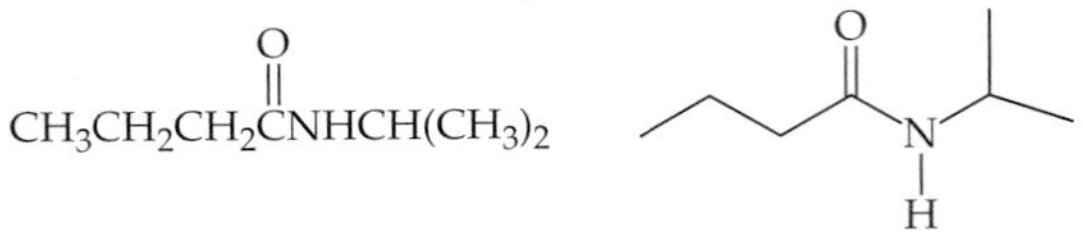

(c)

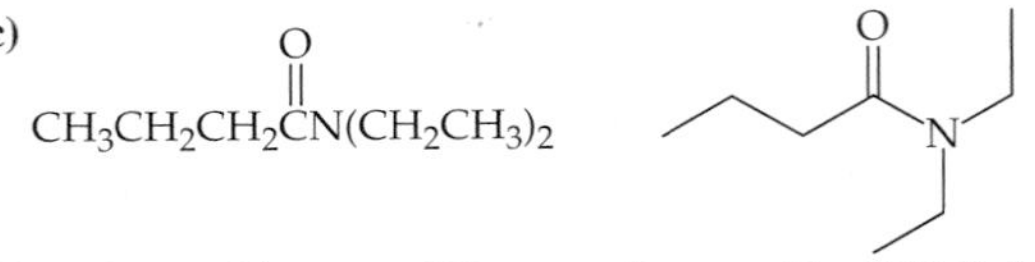

(d) cyclopentyl butyrate; *N*-isopropylbutyramide; *N,N*-diethylbutyramide
17.9 (a) 2-bromo-*N*-methylbutanamide **(b)** *N*-ethyl-*N*-methylbenzamide
(c) 3-hydroxy-2-methylpropanamide
17.10 (a)   **(b)**

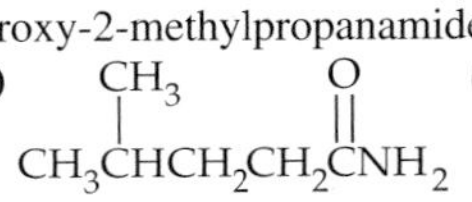

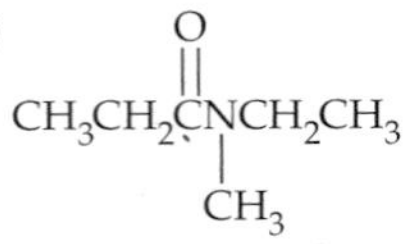

17.11

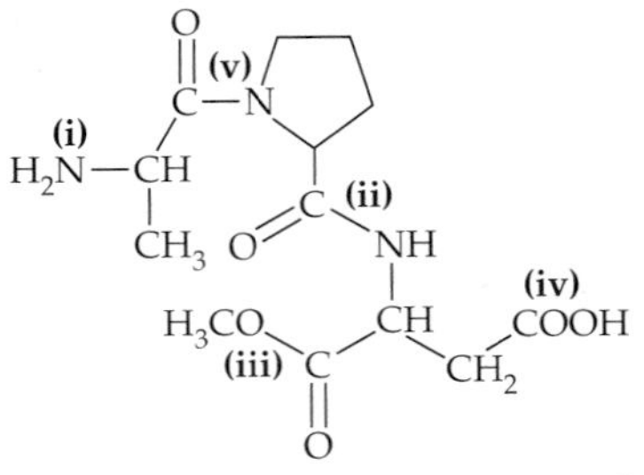

17.12 (a) (ii) **(b)** (i) **(c)** (iii) **(d)** (i) **(e)** (i) **(f)** (iii)
17.13 (a)   **(b)**

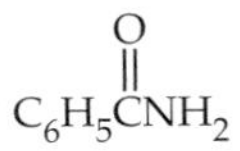

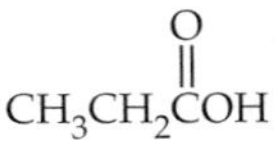

Amide (C₇H₇NO)   Carboxylic acid (C₃H₆O₂)

(c)

$CH_3\overset{O}{\overset{||}{C}}OCH_2CH_3$

Ester (C₄H₈O₂)

17.14 (a)   HO   O

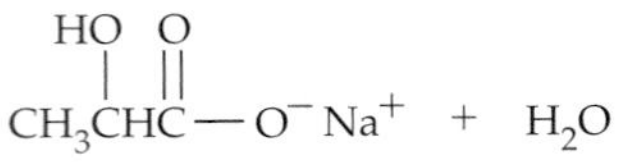

(b)

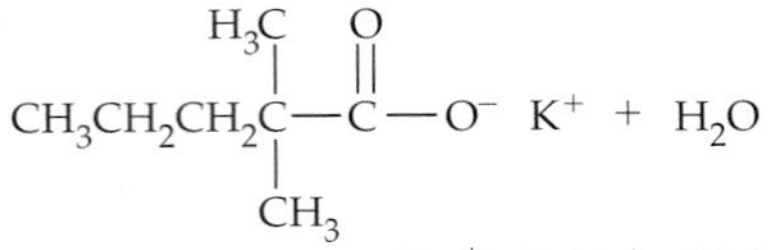

17.15 (a) 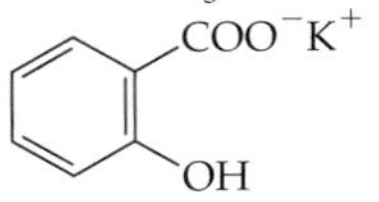 **(b)** $Na^+\ ^-OOCCOO^-Na^+$

17.16 CH_3COO^- $^-OOCCH_2CH_2CH_2COO^-$
17.17

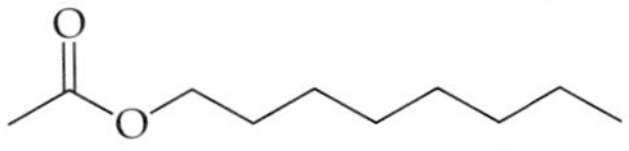

Octyl actetate (octyl methanoate)

17.18 $HCOOCH_2CH(CH_3)_2$
17.19 (a)

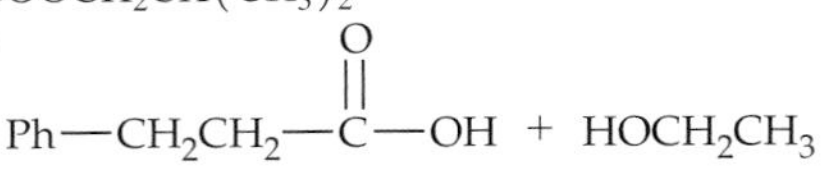

$Ph-CH_2CH_2-\overset{O}{\overset{||}{C}}-OH\ +\ HOCH_2CH_3$

(b)

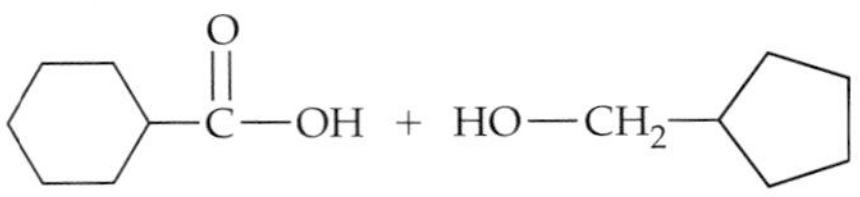

17.20 (a) 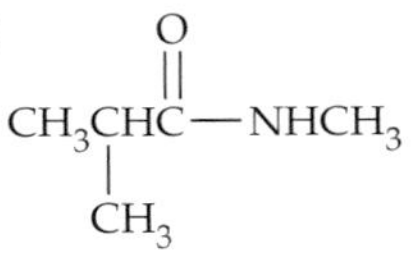   **(b)**

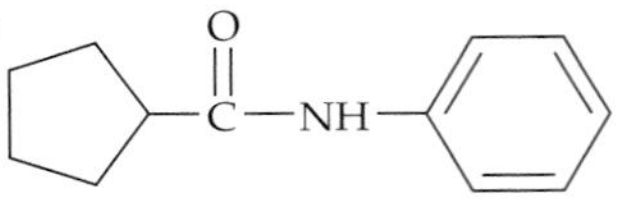

17.21 (a) ether, aromatic, amide
(b)

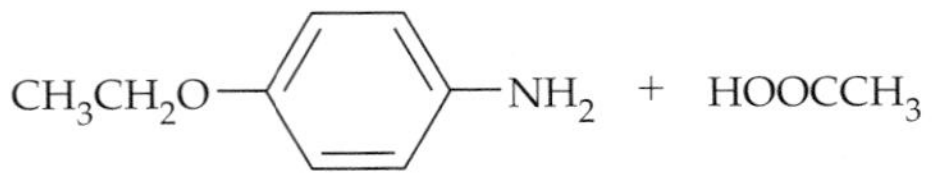

CH_3CH_2O—⟨⟩—NH_2 + $HOOCCH_3$

17.22 Moisture in the air hydrolyzes the ester bond, producing acetic acid as one of the products.

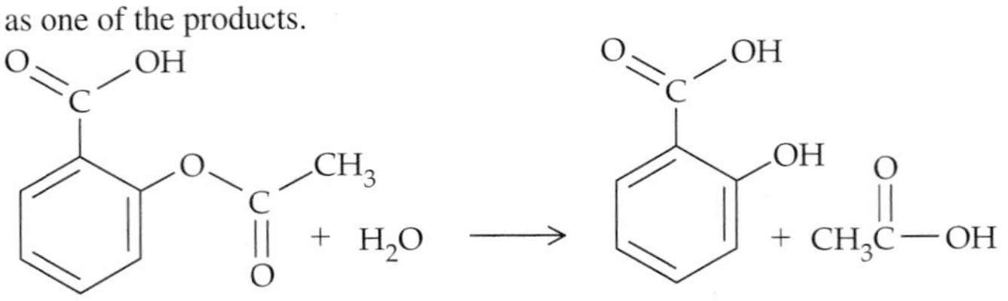

17.23 (a) benzoic acid + 2-propanol **(b)** phenol + cyclopentanecarboxylic acid **(c)** ethanol and propanoic acid   **17.24 (a)** 2-butenoic acid + methylamine **(b)** *p*-nitrobenzoic acid + dimethylamine
17.25

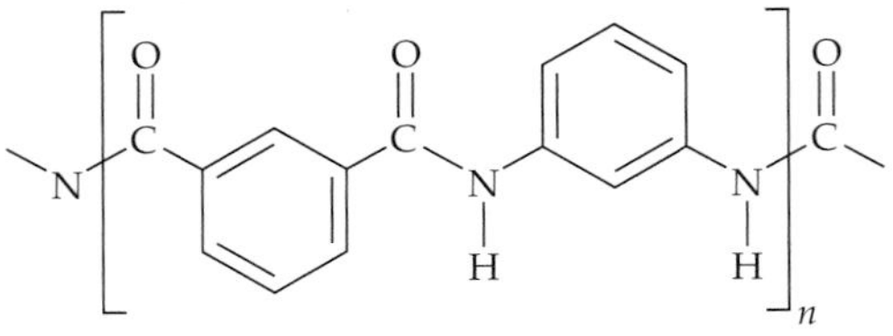

Nomex

17.26 (a)

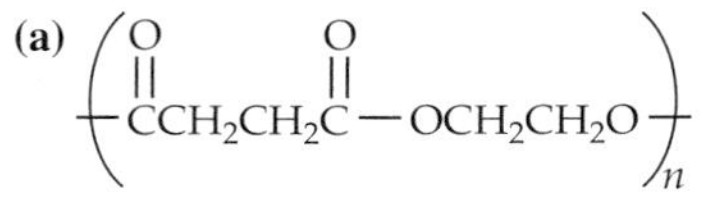

$$\left(\!\!\begin{array}{c}O \quad\quad\quad O \\ \| \quad\quad\quad\quad \| \\ -CCH_2CH_2C-OCH_2CH_2O-\end{array}\!\!\right)_{\!n}$$

(b)

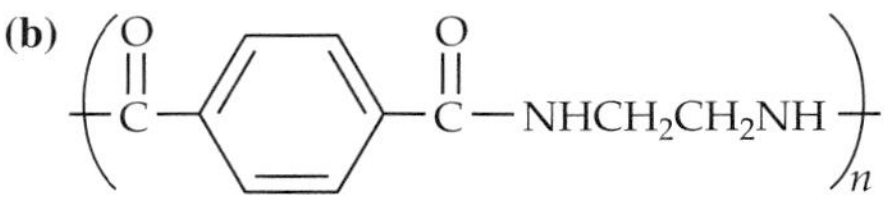

$$\left(\!\!\begin{array}{c}O \quad\quad\quad\quad O \\ \| \quad\quad\quad\quad\quad \| \\ -C-\!\!\!\bigcirc\!\!\!-C-NHCH_2CH_2NH-\end{array}\!\!\right)_{\!n}$$

17.27

$$\begin{array}{c}O \quad\quad CH_3 \\ \| \quad\quad\quad | \\ HO-P-OCHCH_3 \\ | \\ OH\end{array}$$

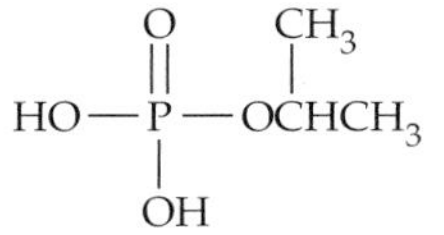

17.28 (a) amide + $H_2O \rightarrow CH_3COOH + NH_3$
(b) phosphate monoester + $H_2O \rightarrow CH_3CH_2OH + HOPO_3^{2-}$
(c) carboxylic acid ester + $H_2O \rightarrow CH_3CH_2COOH + HOCH_3$
17.29

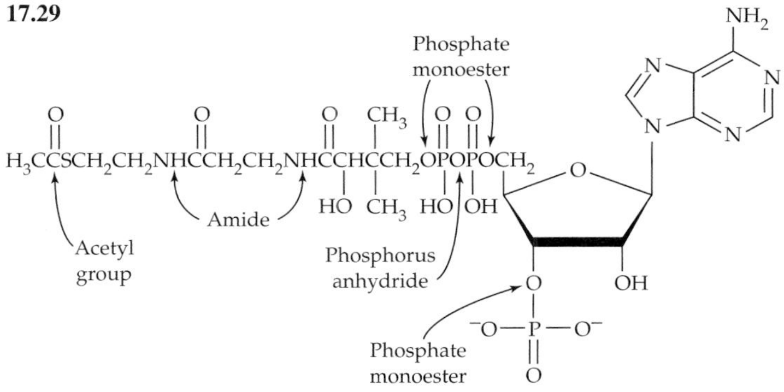

(structural formula: acetyl group, amide, phosphorus anhydride, phosphate monoester, adenine ribose nucleotide structure)

17.30 (a) At pH = 7.4, pyruvate and lactate are anions.
(b)

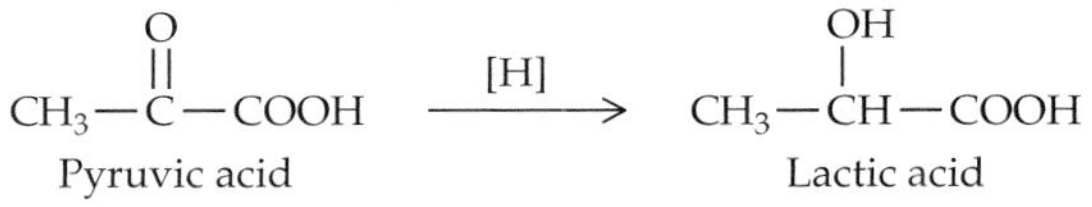

$$\begin{array}{ccc}O \\ \| \\ CH_3-C-COOH & \xrightarrow{[H]} & \begin{array}{c}OH \\ | \\ CH_3-CH-COOH\end{array}\end{array}$$

Pyruvic acid   Lactic acid

(c) Pyruvate and lactate have similar solubilities in water.

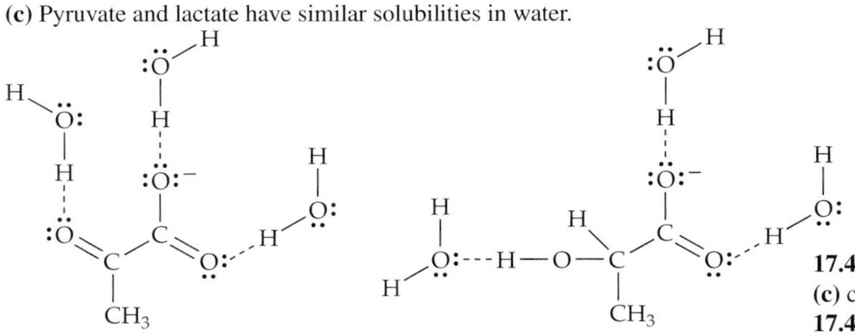

(hydrogen-bonding structural diagrams of pyruvate/lactate with water)

17.31 (a) H_2O + acid or base
(b)

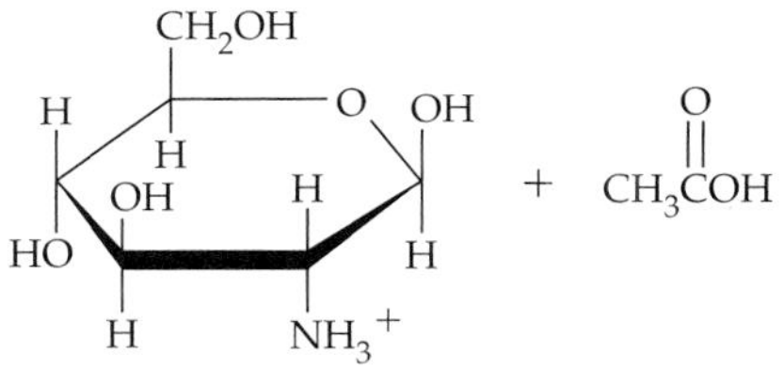

(cyclic sugar structure with CH₂OH, OH, NH₃⁺) + $CH_3\overset{O}{\overset{\|}{C}}OH$

17.32 (a) a phosphate ester linkage
(b)

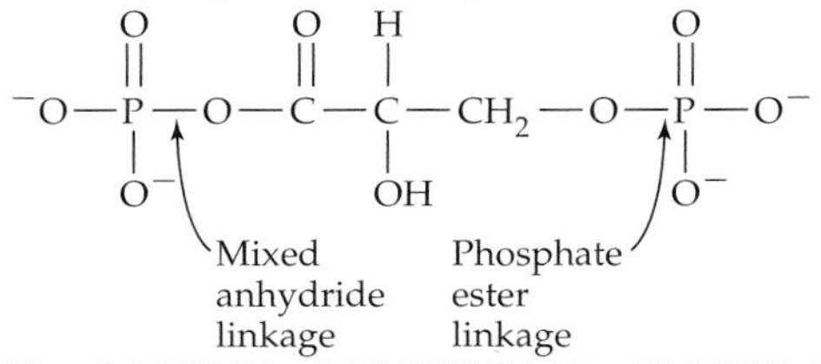

$$\begin{array}{c}O \quad\quad O \quad H \quad\quad\quad O \\ \| \quad\quad\quad \| \quad | \quad\quad\quad\quad \| \\ {}^-O-P-O-C-C-CH_2-O-P-O^- \\ | \quad\quad\quad\quad | \quad\quad\quad\quad\quad\quad | \\ O^- \quad\quad\quad OH \quad\quad\quad\quad\quad O^-\end{array}$$

Mixed anhydride linkage   Phosphate ester linkage

17.33 $^-OOCCOO^-$ $^-OOCCH_2COO^-$ $^-OOCCH_2CH_2COO^-$
　　　oxalate　　　　malonate　　　　　succinate
$^-OOCCH_2CH_2CH_2COO^-$ $^-OOCCH_2CH_2CH_2CH_2COO^-$
　　glutarate　　　　　　　　　adipate
$^-OOCCH_2CH_2CH_2CH_2CH_2COO^-$
　　pimelate

17.34 (a)

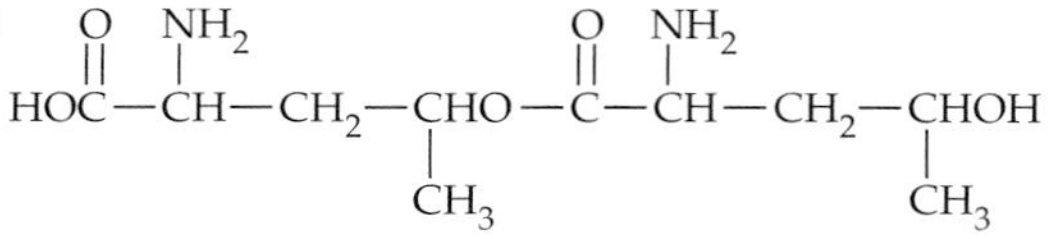

$$\begin{array}{c}O \quad NH_2 \quad\quad\quad\quad\quad\quad O \quad NH_2 \\ \| \quad | \quad\quad\quad\quad\quad\quad\quad \| \quad | \\ HOC-CH-CH_2-CHO-C-CH-CH_2-CHOH \\ \quad\quad | \quad\quad\quad\quad\quad\quad\quad\quad\quad\quad | \\ \quad\quad CH_3 \quad\quad\quad\quad\quad\quad\quad\quad\quad CH_3\end{array}$$

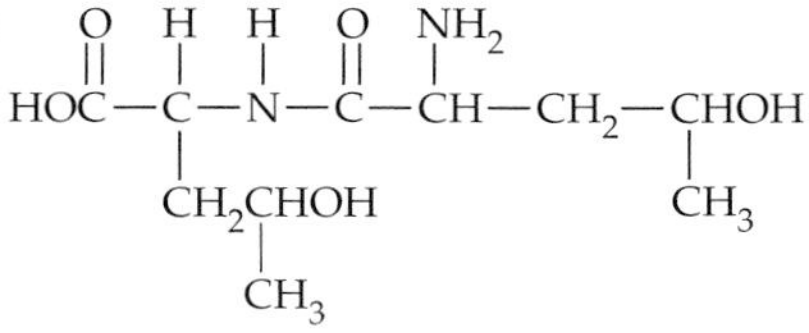

(b)

$$\begin{array}{c}O \quad H \quad H \quad O \quad NH_2 \\ \| \quad | \quad | \quad \| \quad | \\ HOC-C-N-C-CH_2-CHOH \\ \quad\quad | \quad\quad\quad\quad | \quad\quad\quad\quad | \\ \quad CH_2CHOH \quad\quad\quad CH_3 \\ \quad\quad\quad | \\ \quad\quad\quad CH_3\end{array}$$

(c)

(lactam ring structure with H₂N, CHCH₃)

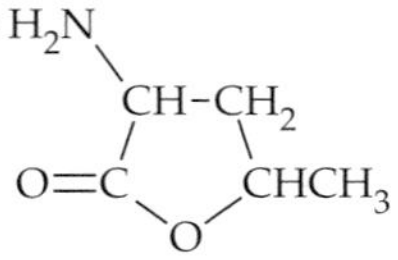

17.35 (a)
(i)

$$\begin{array}{c}:\!O\!:--- \\ \| \\ H-C \\ | \\ :\!O\!-H--- \\ \ddot{}\end{array}$$

Formic acid

(ii)

$$\begin{array}{c}O \\ \| \\ H-C \\ \quad\quad OCH_3\end{array}$$

Methyl formate

(iii)

$$\begin{array}{c}:\!O\!:--- \\ \| \\ H-C \\ \quad :N-H--- \\ \quad\quad | \\ \quad ---H\end{array}$$

Formamide

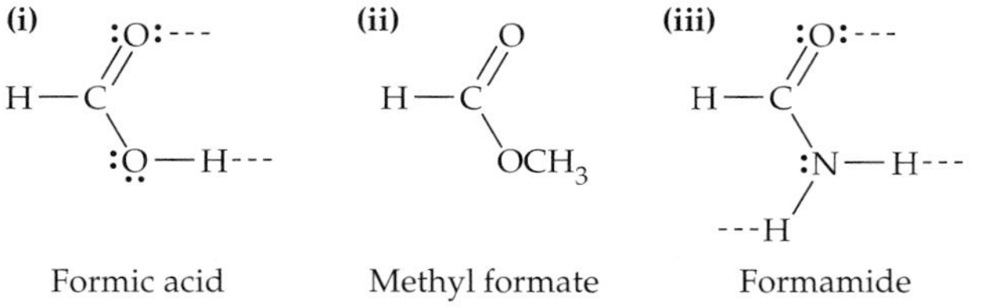

(b) Methyl acetate is lowest boiling (no hydrogen bonds); acetamide is highest boiling.

17.36

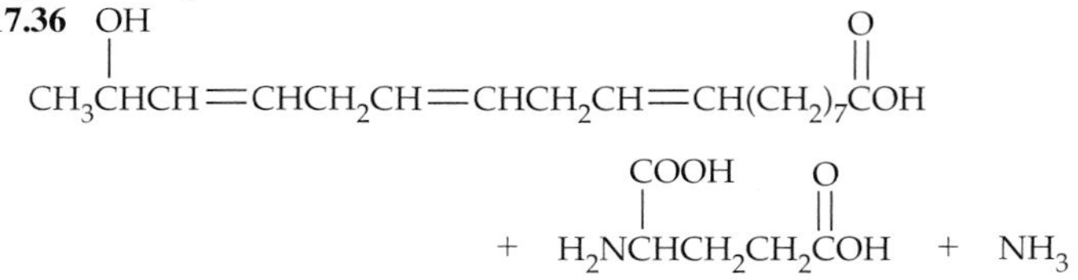

$$\begin{array}{c}OH \\ | \\ CH_3CHCH=CHCH_2CH=CHCH_2CH=CH(CH_2)_7\overset{O}{\overset{\|}{C}}OH\end{array}$$

$$+ \quad \begin{array}{c}COOH \quad\quad O \\ | \quad\quad\quad\quad \| \\ H_2NCHCH_2CH_2COH\end{array} \quad + \quad NH_3$$

17.37 (a) *N*-ethyl acetamide **(b)** methyl 2-chlorocyclopentanecarboxylate **(c)** ethyl pentanoate **(d)** *N*-ethyl-*N*-methylformamide

17.38

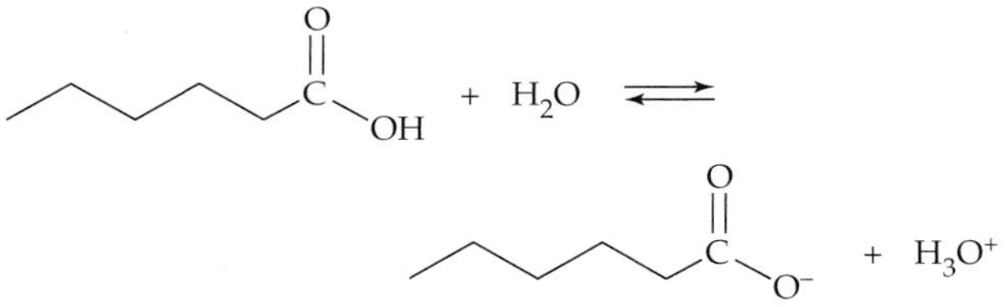

(hexanoic acid structure) $+ \ H_2O \rightleftharpoons$

(hexanoate anion structure) $+ \ H_3O^+$

17.40

$$CH_3CH_2CH_2COOH \quad\quad \begin{array}{c}CH_3 \\ | \\ CH_3CHCOOH\end{array}$$

Butanoic acid   2-Methylpropionic acid

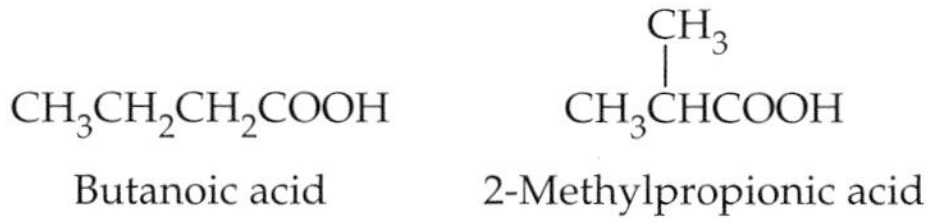

17.42 (a) 3-hydroxy-4-methylpentanoic acid **(b)** nonanoic acid **(c)** cyclohexanecarboxylic acid **(d)** *p*-aminobenzoic acid
17.44 (a) potassium 3-ethylpentanoate **(b)** ammonium benzoate **(c)** calcium propanoate

17.46 (a)

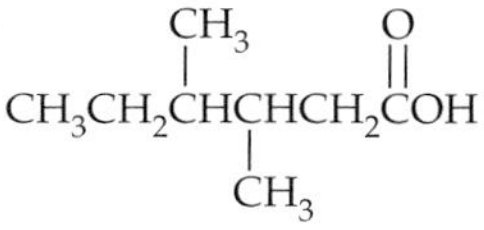

$$\begin{array}{c}CH_3 \quad\quad\quad O \\ | \quad\quad\quad\quad\quad \| \\ CH_3CH_2CHCHCH_2COH \\ \quad\quad\quad | \\ \quad\quad\quad CH_3\end{array}$$

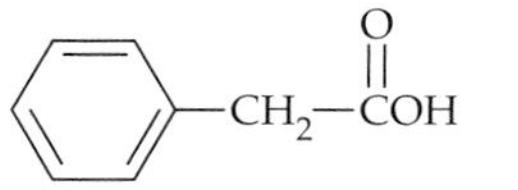

(b)

(benzene ring)$-CH_2-\overset{O}{\overset{\|}{C}}OH$

(c)

(benzene ring with O₂N, O₂N, COH substituents)

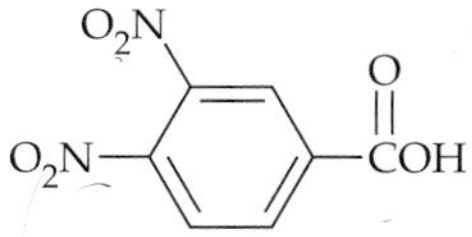

(d)

$$CH_3CH_2CH_2C\overset{O}{\overset{\|}{}}O^- \ {}^+NH(CH_2CH_3)_3$$

17.48

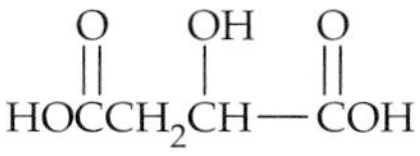

$$\begin{array}{c}O \quad\quad OH \quad\quad O \\ \| \quad\quad | \quad\quad\quad \| \\ HOCCH_2CH-COH\end{array}$$

17.50

$$\begin{array}{c}NH_4^+ \ {}^-O-\overset{O}{\overset{\|}{C}} \quad\quad H \\ \quad\quad\quad\quad C=C \\ \quad\quad H \quad\quad\quad \overset{O}{\underset{\|}{C}}-O^- \ NH_4^+\end{array}$$

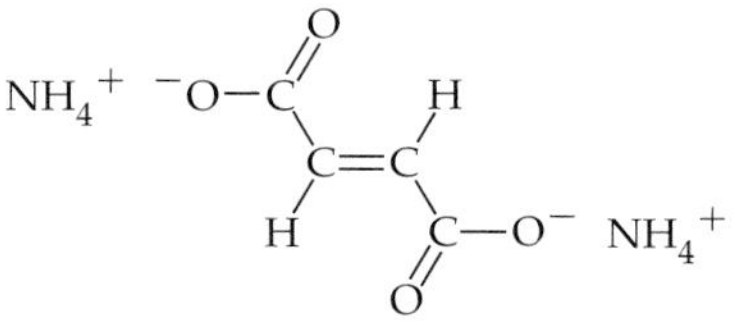

17.52 (a) $CH_3CH_2CH_2CH_2CONH_2$　　$CH_3CH_2CONHCH_2CH_3$
　　　Pentanamide　　　　　　　　*N*-Ethylpropanamide

$$HCON(CH_2CH_3)_2$$
N,*N*-Diethylformamide

(b) $CH_3CH_2CH_2CH_2COOCH_3$ $CH_3CH_2COOCH_2CH_2CH_3$
Methyl pentanoate   Propyl propanoate

$HCOOCH_2CH_2CH_2CH_2CH_3$
Pentyl formate

17.54 (a) 3-methylbutyl acetate **(b)** methyl 4-methylpentanoate
(c) **(d)**

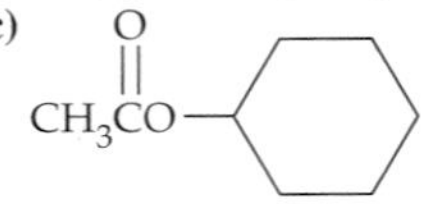

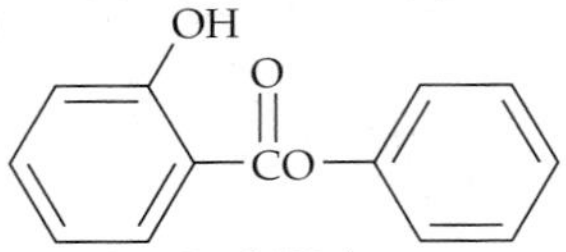

17.56 (a) $CH_3COOH + HOCH_2CH_2CH(CH_3)_2$
(b) $(CH_3)_2CHCH_2CH_2COOH + HOCH_3$
(c)

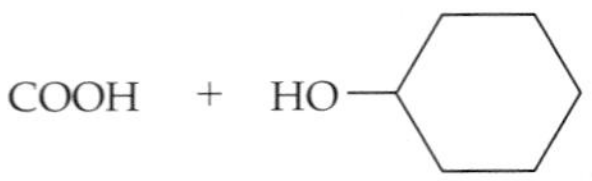

(d)

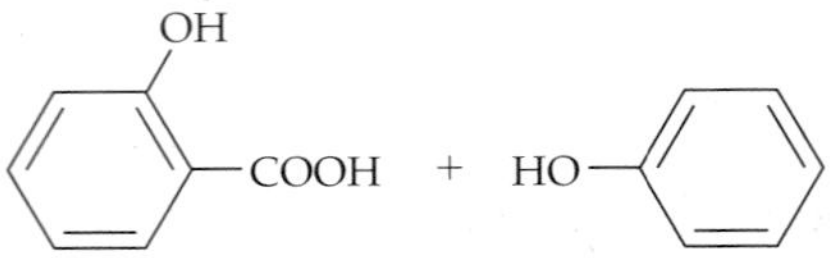

17.58 (a) 2-ethylbutanamide **(b)** N-phenylbenzamide
(c) **(d)**

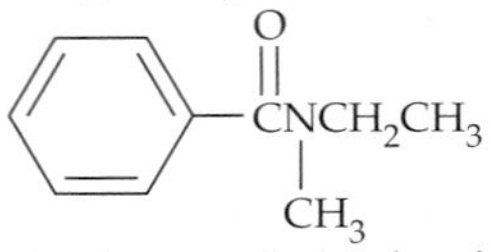

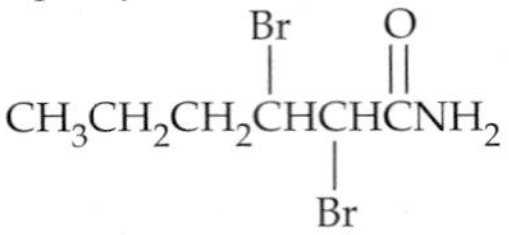

17.60 (a) 2-ethylbutanoic acid + ammonia **(b)** benzoic acid + aniline
(c) benzoic acid + N-methylethylamine **(d)** 2,3-dibromohexanoic acid + ammonia

17.62

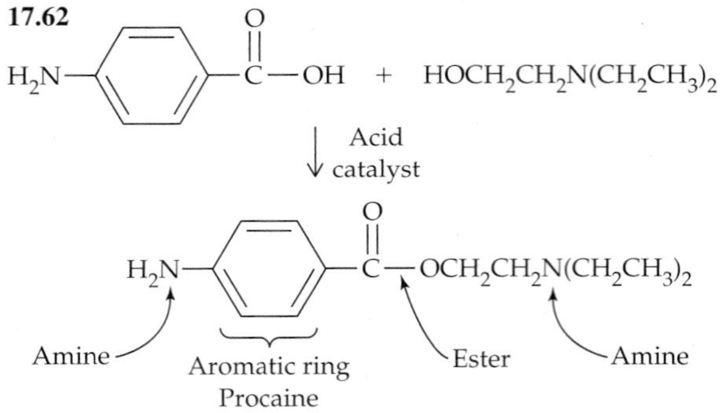

17.64 $HOCH_2CH_2CH_2COOH$
17.66

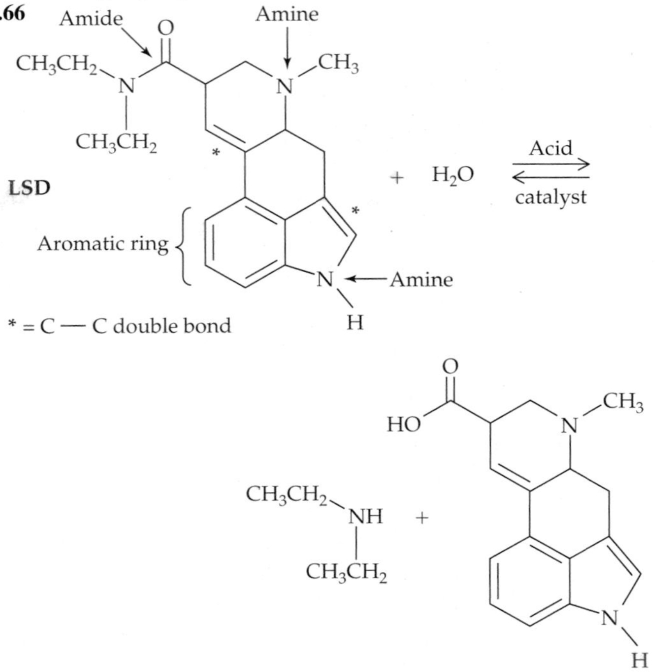

17.68

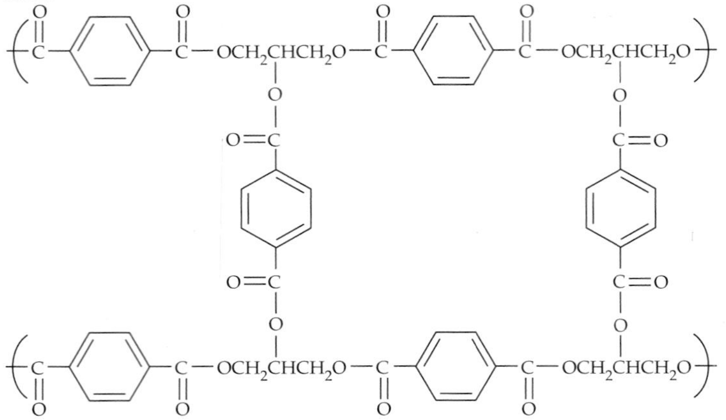

17.70 Dihydroxyacetone and hydrogen phosphate anion.
17.72

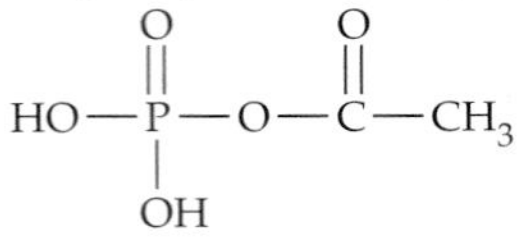

17.74 A cyclic phosphate diester is formed when a phosphate group forms an ester with two hydroxyl groups in the same molecule.
17.76 N, N-dimethylformamide is lowest boiling because it doesn't form hydrogen bonds. Propanamide is highest boiling because it forms the most hydrogen bonds.   **17.78** Both propanamide and methyl acetate are water-soluble because they can form hydrogen bonds with water. Propanamide is higher boiling because molecules of propanamide can form hydrogen bonds with each other.

17.80 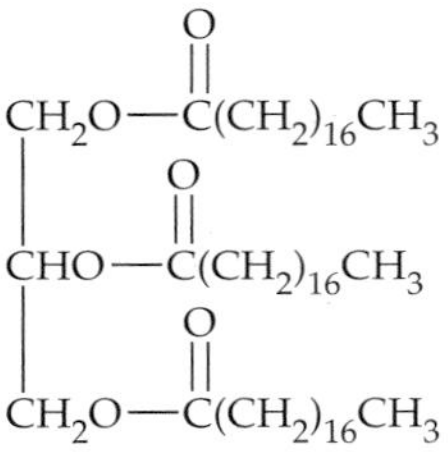
Glyceryl tristearate

17.82
(a)   Ester   Alcohol   Carboxylic acid

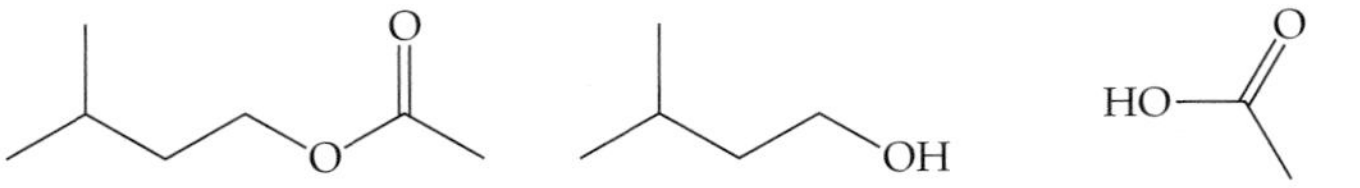

(b)
(Other possible structures for peach flavoring as well) 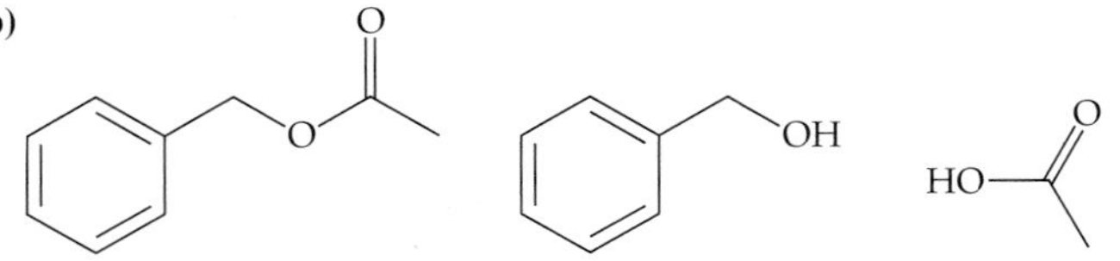

(c) 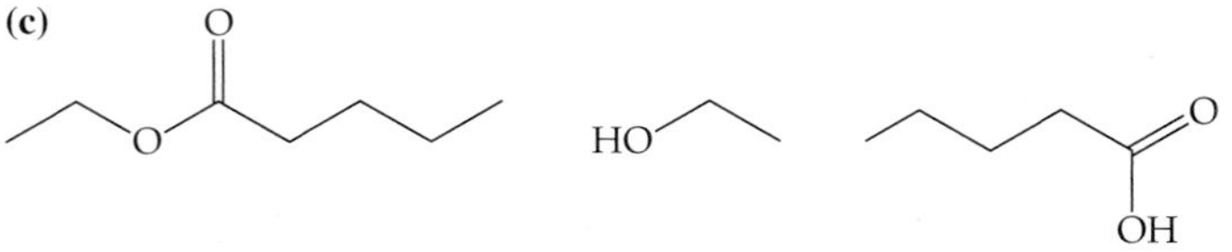
(Other possible structures for apple flavoring as well)

(d) 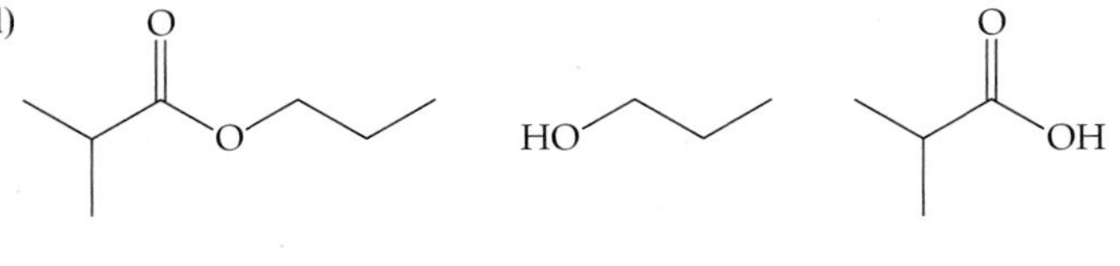
(Other possible structures for rum flavoring as well)

17.84 Four possible Beta-lactams; however, there are lots of other examples.

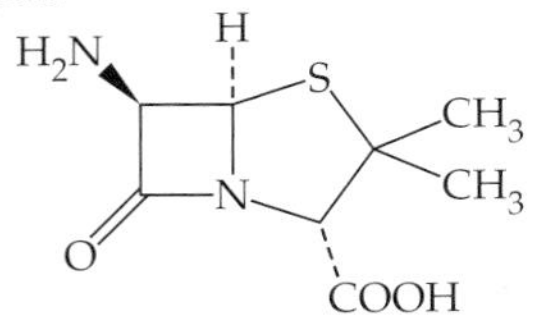

Penicillin: amides, sulfide, carboxylic acid

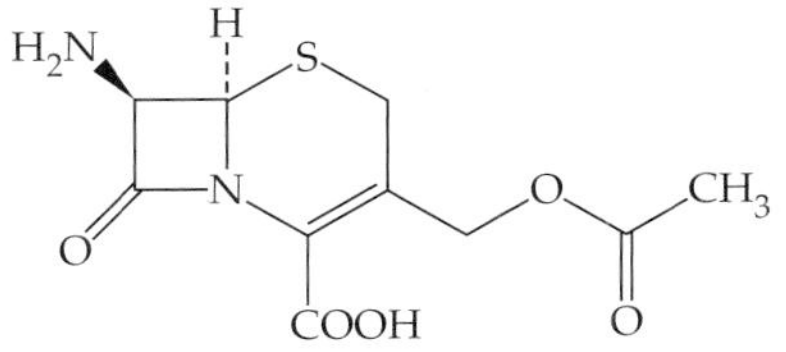

Cephalosporin: amide, amine, sulfide, carboxylic acid, alkene, ester

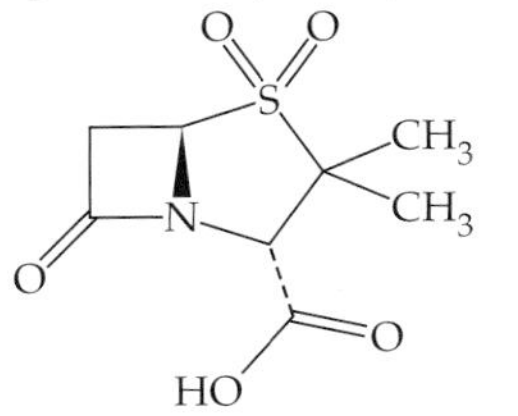

Sulbactam: amide, carboxylic acid

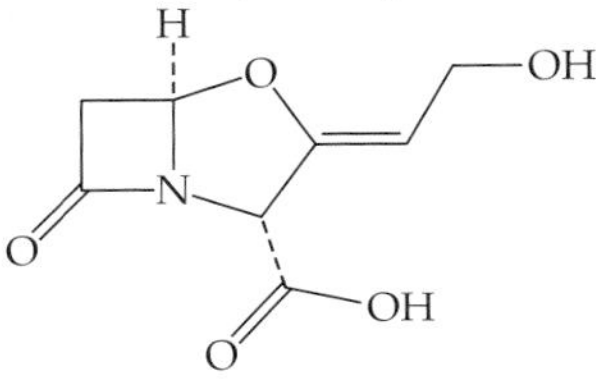

Clavulanate: amide, ether, alkene, alcohol, carboxylic acid
Common: All contain a cyclobutane and a second ring; amide within the cyclobutane, carboxylic acid

Chapter 18

18.1 enzyme **18.2** hormones
18.3 Amine / Carboxylic acid

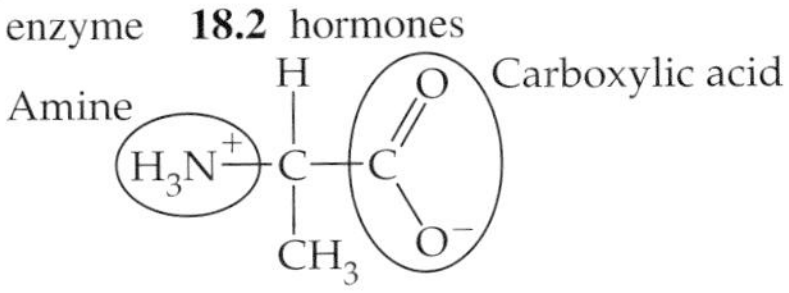

Ala, A, Nonpolar

18.4 Amino group → Carboxylic acid group / "R" group / Valine

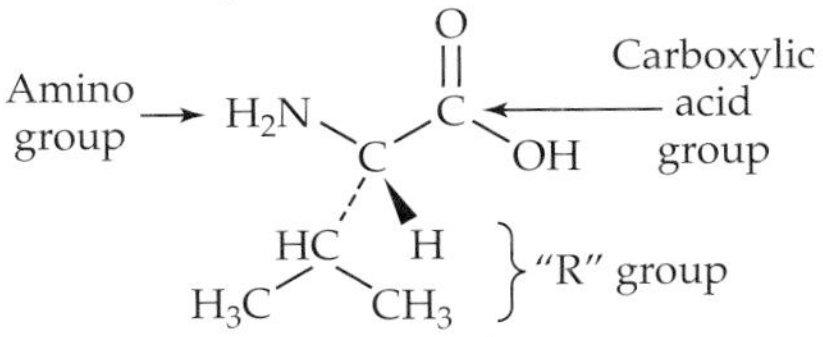

18.5 α-amino acids: **(a), (d)** **18.6** aromatic ring: phenylalanine, tyrosine, tryptophan; contain sulfur: cysteine, methionine alcohols: serine, threonine, tyrosine (phenol); alkyl side chain: alanine, valine, leucine, isoleucine
18.7

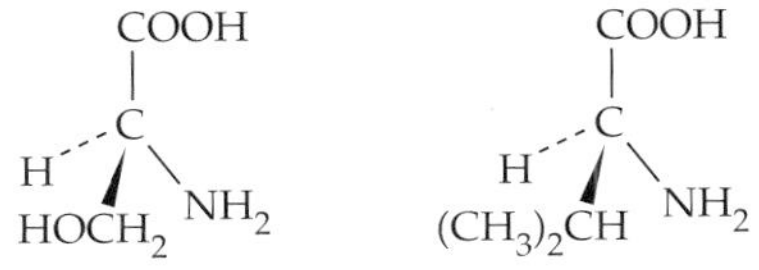

Serine   Valine

(a) The serine side chain has a polar hydroxyl group; the valine side chain has a nonpolar isopropyl group. **(b)** serine—hydrophilic; valine—hydrophobic **18.8** aspartic acid; Side chain contains a polar carboxyl group.

18.9 tryptophan; Side chain contains nonpolar aromatic rings.
18.10

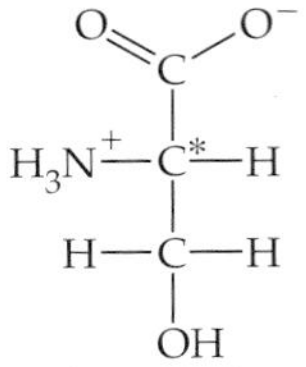

Chiral as the starred carbon is bonded to four different groups.
18.11

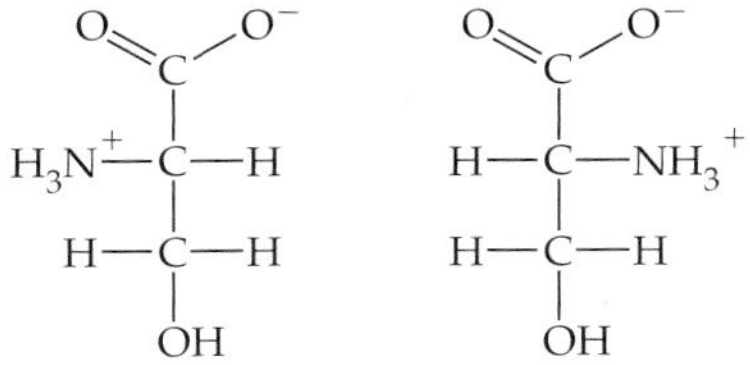

L-serine   D-serine

18.12

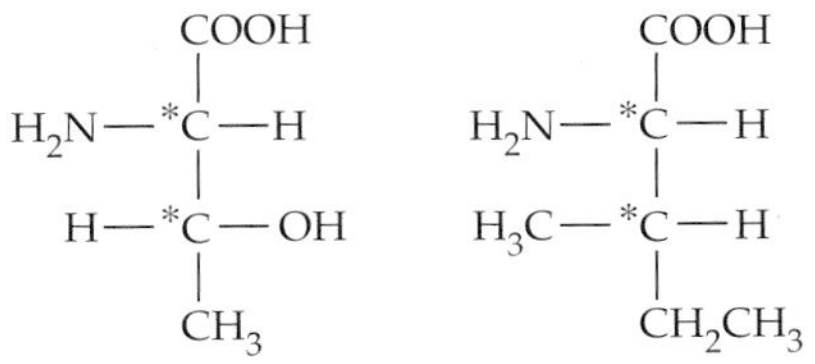

Threonine   Isoleucine

18.13

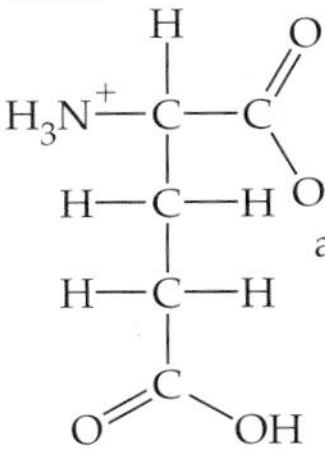

at low pH 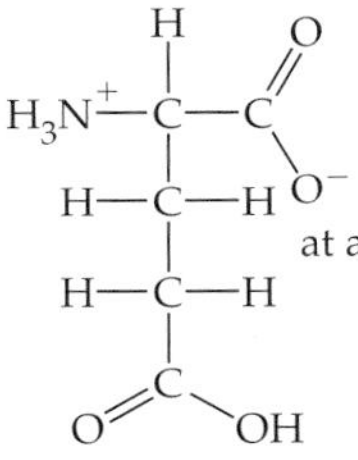   at an intermediate pH

Zwitterion

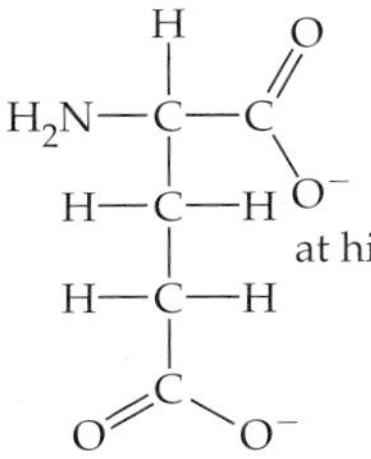

at high pH

18.14 In the zwitterionic form of an amino acid, the $-NH_3^+$ group is an acid, and the $-COO^-$ group is a base.
18.15

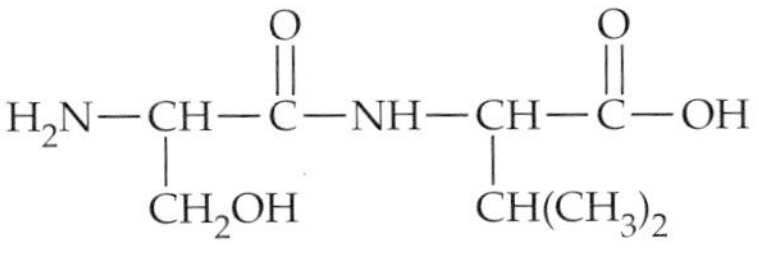

Serine   Valine

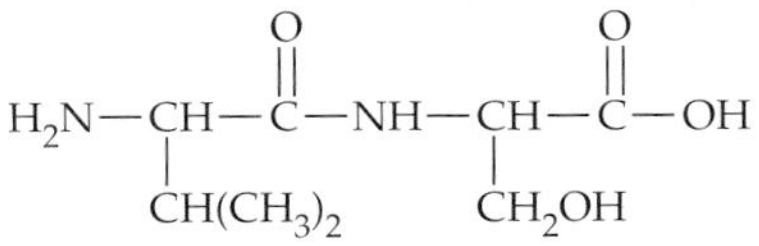

Valine   Serine

18.16 **(a)** Gly—Ser—Tyr   Tyr—Ser—Gly   Ser—Tyr—Gly
Gly—Tyr—Ser   Tyr—Gly—Ser   Ser—Gly—Tyr
(b)

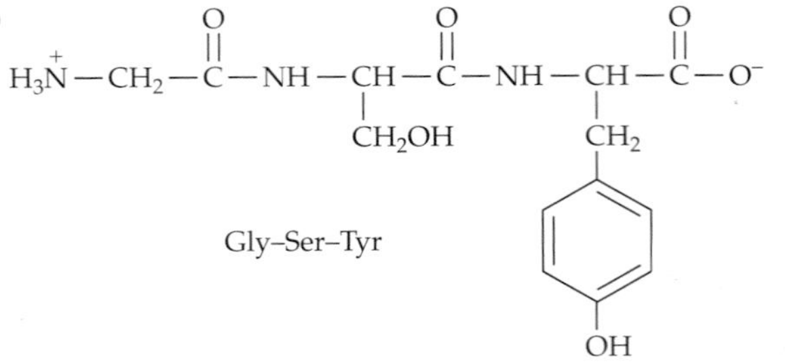

Gly–Ser–Tyr

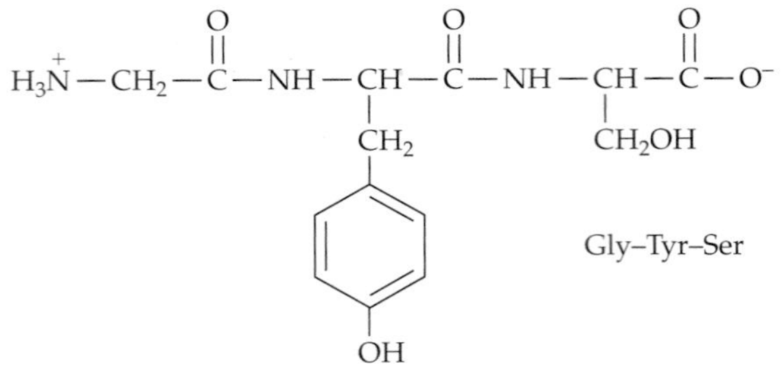

Gly–Tyr–Ser

18.17 lle—Arg—Val   Arg—lle—Val   Val—Arg—lle
lle—Val—Arg   Arg—Val—lle   Val—lle—Arg
18.18 **(a)** Leu-Asp (nonpolar, polar) **(b)** Tyr-Ser-Lys (all polar) **18.19** seven peptide bonds **18.20** **(a)** six atoms **(b)** two amino acid units; the electrons of the carbonyl are shared with the C-N bond, making it rigid like a double bond **18.21** 24 **18.22** Protein function depends on the order of the amino acids **18.23** 11 backbone atoms **18.24** **(a)** hydrogen bonding **(b)** Hydrogen bonding takes place between an amide hydrogen and an amide carbonyl oxygen on an adjacent chain. **18.25** **(a)** globular or fibrous **(b)** fibrous **18.26** Outer surface consists of largely hydrophobic amino acids side chains **18.27** **(b)** Asn, Ser **(c)** Thr, Tyr

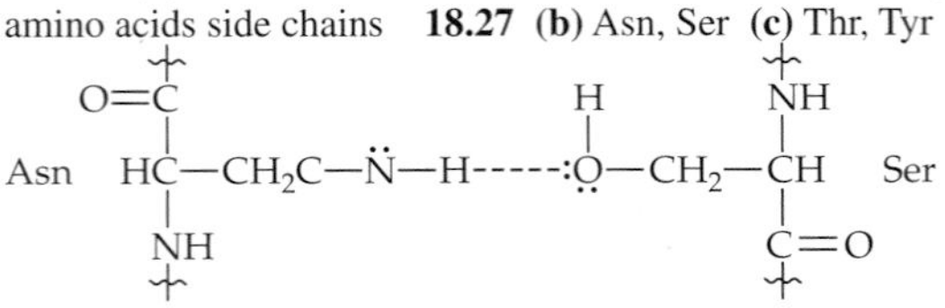

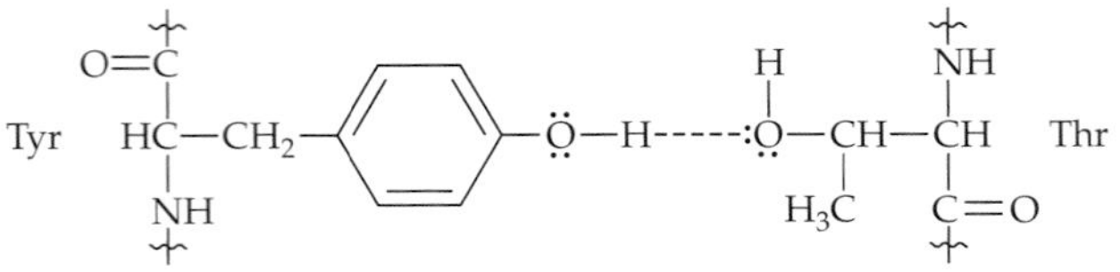

Asn

Tyr

18.28 **(a)** hydrogen bond **(b)** hydrophobic interaction **(c)** salt bridge **(d)** hydrophobic interaction **18.29** **(a)** Tyr, Asp, Ser **(b)** Ala, lle, Val, Leu **18.30** **(a)** lipoproteins **(b)** metalloproteins **(c)** phosphoproteins **(d)** glycoproteins **(e)** hemoproteins **(f)** nucleoprotiens **18.31** In α-keratin, pairs of α-helixes twist together into small fibrils that are twisted into larger bundles. In tropocollagen, three coiled chains wrap around each other to form a triple helix. **18.32** Three fragments; Ala-Phe-Lys, Cys-Gly-Asp-Arg, Leu-Leu-Phe-Gly-Ala **18.33** No fragments, only 12 individual amino acids; acid hydrolysis cleaves all peptide bonds and is not selective **18.34** At low pH, the groups at the end of the polypeptide chain exist as $-NH_3^+$ and $-COOH$. At high pH, they exist as $-NH_2$ and $-COO^-$. In addition, side chain functional groups may be ionized as follows: **(a)** no change **(b)** Arg positively charged at low pH; neutral at high pH **(c)** Tyr neutral at low pH, negatively charged at high pH **(d)** Glu, Asp neutral at low pH, negatively charged at high pH **(e)** no change **(f)** Cys neutral at low pH, negatively charged at high pH. **18.35** **(a)** 1, 4 **(b)** 2, 4 **(c)** 2

18.36

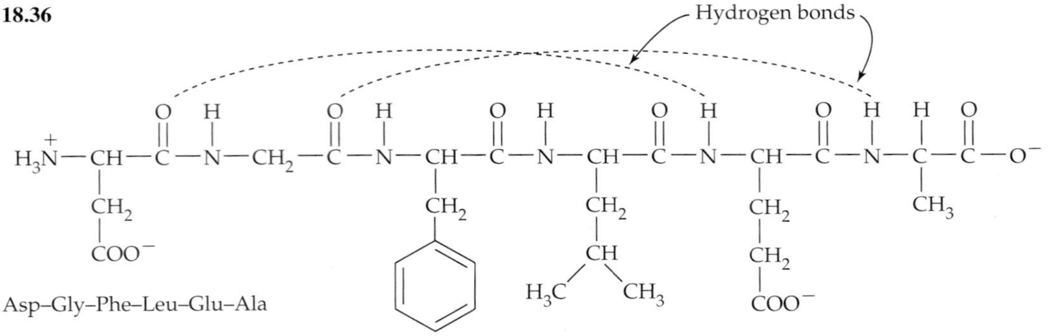

Asp–Gly–Phe–Leu–Glu–Ala

18.37 *Fibrous Proteins*: structural proteins, water-insoluble, contain many Gly and Pro residues, contain large regions of α-helix or β-sheet, few side-chain interactions. Examples: Collagen, α-Keratin, Fibroin. *Globular Proteins*: enzymes and hormones, usually water-soluble, contain most amino acids, contain smaller regions of α-helix and β-sheet, complex tertiary structure. Examples: Ribonuclease, hemoglobin, insulin. **18.38** **(a)** Leu, Phe, Ala, or any other amino acid with a nonpolar side chain. **(b), (c)** Asp, Lys, Thr, or any other amino acid with a polar side chain.

18.39

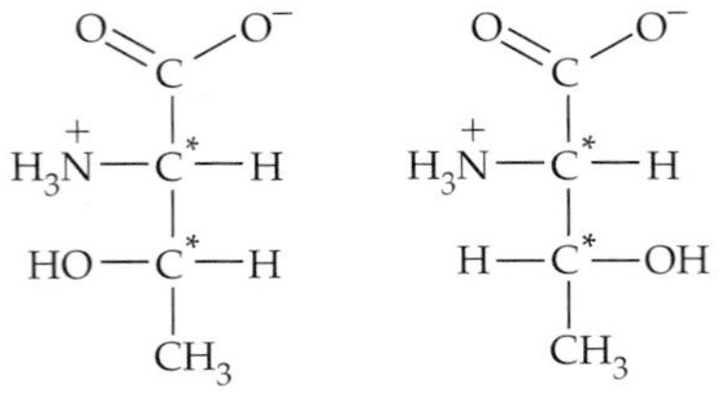

The upper chiral carbon is responsible for the *d, l* configuration.

18.40

Type of Protein	Function	Example
Enzymes:	Catalyze biochemical reactions	Ribonuclease
Hormones:	Regulate body functions	Insulin
Storage proteins:	Store essential substances	Myoglobin
Transport proteins:	Transport substances through body fluids	Serum albumin
Structural proteins:	Provide shape and support	Collagen
Protective proteins:	Defend the body against foreign matter	Immunoglobulins
Contractile proteins:	Do mechanical work	Myosin and actin

18.42 (a)

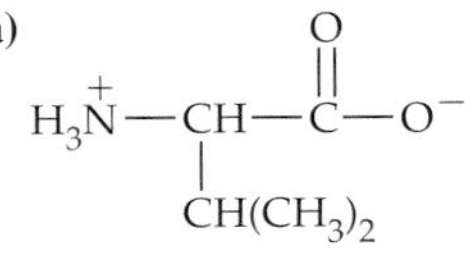

$$H_3\overset{+}{N}-CH-\overset{O}{\overset{\|}{C}}-O^-$$
$$\qquad\quad |$$
$$\qquad\quad CH(CH_3)_2$$

(b)

$$H_3\overset{+}{N}-CH-\overset{O}{\overset{\|}{C}}-O^-$$
$$\qquad\quad |$$
$$\qquad\quad CH_2OH$$

(c)

$$H_3\overset{+}{N}-CH-\overset{O}{\overset{\|}{C}}-O^-$$
$$\qquad\quad |$$
$$\qquad\quad CH_2CH_2C=O$$
$$\qquad\qquad\qquad\quad |$$
$$\qquad\qquad\qquad\quad O^-$$

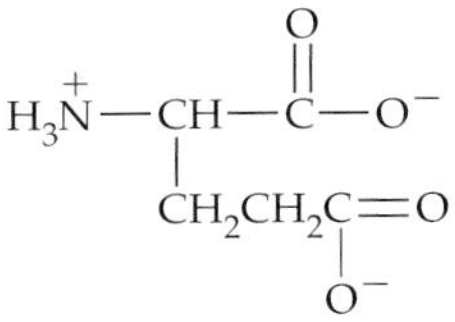

18.44 (a)

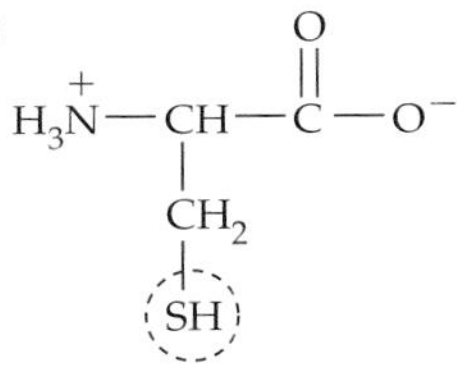

$$H_3\overset{+}{N}-CH-\overset{O}{\overset{\|}{C}}-O^-$$
$$\qquad\quad |$$
$$\qquad\quad CH_2$$
$$\qquad\quad |$$
$$\qquad\quad (SH)$$

Cysteine (Cys)

(b)

$$H_3\overset{+}{N}-CH-\overset{O}{\overset{\|}{C}}-O^-$$
$$\qquad\quad |$$
$$\qquad\quad CH_2$$
$$\qquad\quad |$$
(benzene ring with OH)

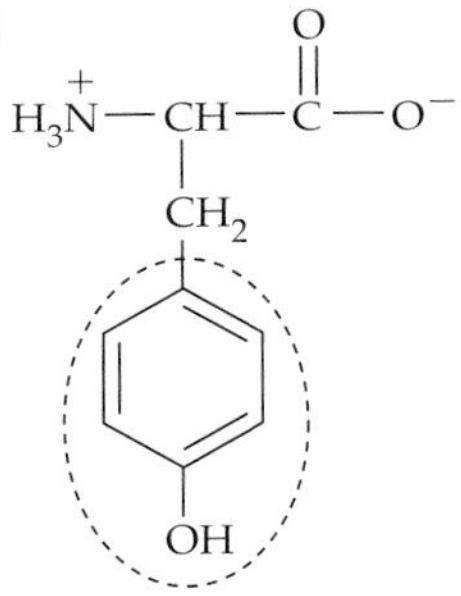

Tyrosine (Tyr)

18.46 A chiral object is handed. Examples: glove, scissors.

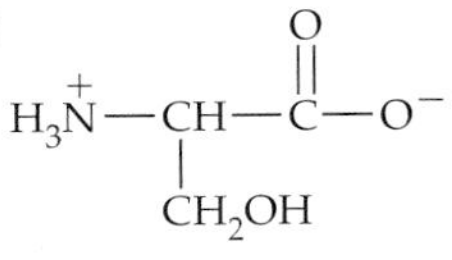

18.48

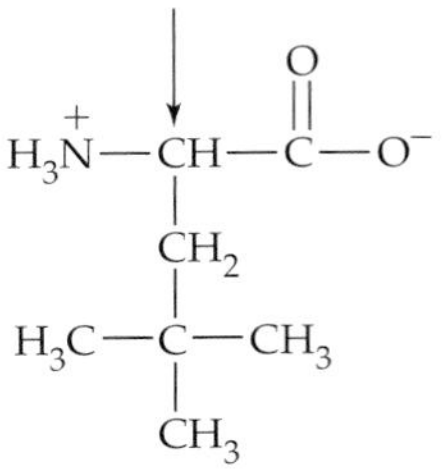

$$H_3\overset{+}{N}-\overset{\downarrow}{CH}-\overset{O}{\overset{\|}{C}}-O^-$$
$$\qquad\quad |$$
$$\qquad\quad CH_2$$
$$\qquad\quad |$$
$$H_3C-\overset{|}{C}-CH_3$$
$$\qquad\quad |$$
$$\qquad\quad CH_3$$

18.50 hydrophobic; side chain is nonpolar   **18.52** neutral: (a), (c); positive charge: (b)   **18.54** (a), (c) low pH; (b) high pH

18.56 (a)

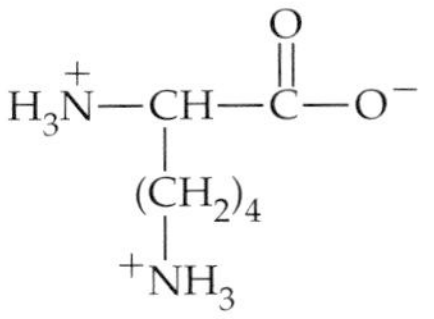

$$H_3\overset{+}{N}-CH-\overset{O}{\overset{\|}{C}}-O^-$$
$$\qquad\quad |$$
$$\qquad\quad (CH_2)_4$$
$$\qquad\quad |$$
$$\qquad\quad \overset{+}{N}H_3$$

at pH = 7
(neutral pH)

(b)

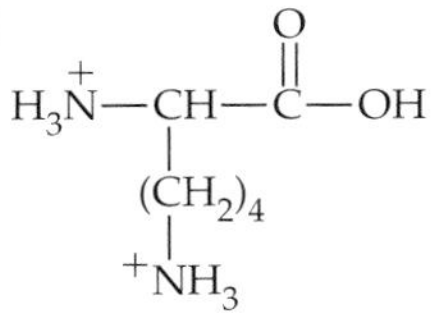

$$H_3\overset{+}{N}-CH-\overset{O}{\overset{\|}{C}}-OH$$
$$\qquad\quad |$$
$$\qquad\quad (CH_2)_4$$
$$\qquad\quad |$$
$$\qquad\quad \overset{+}{N}H_3$$

at pH = 3
(low pH)

(c)

$$H_3\overset{+}{N}-CH-\overset{O}{\overset{\|}{C}}-O^-$$
$$\qquad\quad |$$
$$\qquad\quad (CH_2)_4$$
$$\qquad\quad |$$
$$\qquad\quad NH_2$$

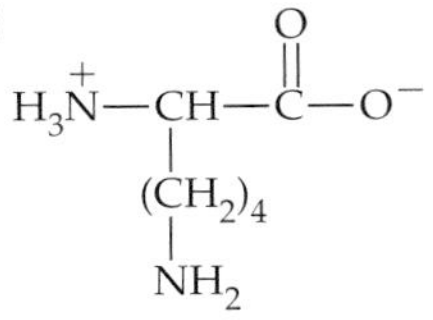

at pH = 9.7 (pI)
(high pH)

18.58 At its isoelectric point, a protein is electrically neutral which makes it insoluble in water. When a protein is charged, it is more soluble.

18.60 Val—Met—Leu, Met—Val—Leu, Leu—Met—Val, Val—Leu—Met, Met—Leu—Val, Leu—Val—Met.

18.62 N-terminal   C-terminal

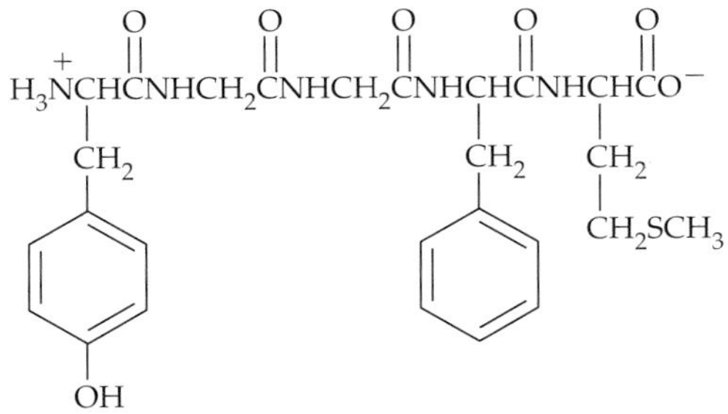

$$H_3\overset{+}{N}CHCNHCH_2CNHCH_2CNHCHCNHCHCO^-$$

(with side chains: CH_2–(benzene ring with OH); CH_2–(benzene ring); CH_2; CH_2SCH_3)

18.64 *N*-terminal: Val—Gly—Ser—Ala—Asp C-terminal

18.66 *primary structure:* The sequence of connection of amino acids in a protein.

18.68 (a)

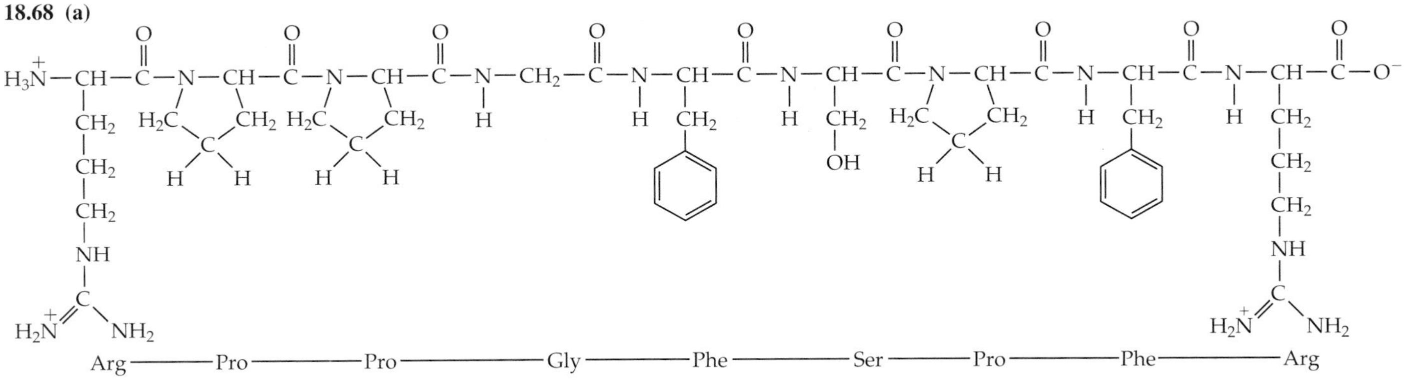

$$H_3\overset{+}{N}-CH-\overset{O}{\overset{\|}{C}}-N-CH-\overset{O}{\overset{\|}{C}}-N-CH-\overset{O}{\overset{\|}{C}}-N-CH_2-\overset{O}{\overset{\|}{C}}-N-CH-\overset{O}{\overset{\|}{C}}-N-CH-\overset{O}{\overset{\|}{C}}-N-CH-\overset{O}{\overset{\|}{C}}-N-CH-\overset{O}{\overset{\|}{C}}-N-CH-\overset{O}{\overset{\|}{C}}-O^-$$

Arg———Pro———Pro———Gly———Phe———Ser———Pro———Phe———Arg

(b) Proline rings introduce kinks and bends and prevent hydrogen bonds from forming.

18.70 *secondary structure:* The orientation of segments of the protein chain into a regular pattern, such as an α-helix or a β-sheet, by hydrogen bonding between backbone atoms. **18.72** Stabilized by hydrogen bonds between the carbonyl oxygen of the polypeptide backbone and the amide hydrogen four amino acids later **18.74** α-keratins: wool, hair and fingernails; fibrous **18.76** (a) disulfide bonds (b) hydrophobic (c) salt bridge (d) hydrogen bonding **18.78** Hydrophilic residues interact with aqueous environment and hydrophobic residues fold into the interior away from the aqueous environment **18.80** A simple protein is composed only of amino acids. A conjugated protein consists of a protein associated with one or more nonprotein molecules. **18.82** Disulfide bonds stabilize tertiary structure. **18.84** (a) *primary structure:* The sequence of connection of amino acids in a protein. (b) *secondary structure:* The orientation of segments of the protein chain into a regular pattern, such as an α-helix or a β-sheet, by hydrogen bonding between backbone atoms. (c) *tertiary structure:* The coiling and folding of the entire protein chain into a three-dimensional shape as a result of interactions between amino acid side chains. (d) *quaternary structure:* The aggregation of several protein chains to form a larger structure. **18.86** In *hydrophobic interactions,* hydrocarbon side chains cluster in the center of proteins and make proteins spherical. Examples: Phe, lle. *Salt bridges* bring together distant parts of a polypeptide chain. Examples: Lys, Asp. **18.88** 2 **18.90** A protein with a non-amino acid unit; myoglobin **18.92** When a protein is denatured, its nonprimary structure is disrupted, and loss of function occurs. **18.94** Protein digestion = hydrolysis of peptide bonds to form amino acids. Protein denaturation = disruption of secondary, tertiary, or quaternary structure without disrupting peptide bonds. **18.96** Canned pineapple has been heated to inactivate enzymes. **18.98** hydrophobic interactions: (e), (f), (g), (h); hydrogen bonding: (a), (c), (d); salt bridges: (d); covalent bonding: (b) **18.100** Methionine is a sulfide and not a thiol; only thiols can form disulfide bridges. **18.102** on the outside of a globular protein: Glu, Ser. on the outside of a fibrous protein: Ala, Val. On the outside of neither: Leu, Phe. **18.104** Asp is similar in size and function to Glu. **18.106** Enzymes would hydrolyze insulin. **18.108** A combination of grains, legumes, and nuts in each meal provides all of the essential amino acids. **18.110** Nonpolar amino acids, leucine and phenylalanine, are on the inside away from water. Polar amino acids, glutamate and glutamine, are on the outside as they can interact with water.

18.112 Arg, Asp, Asn, Glu, Gln, His, Lys, Ser, Thr, Tyr

Chapter 19

19.1 kinase **19.2** Enzymes are specific for one of two enantiomers; since lactate is found as both D and L, there must be two forms of LDH. **19.3** (a) NAD⁺, coenzyme A, FAD; (b) The remaining cofactors are minerals. **19.4** (a) catalyzes the removal of two —H from an alcohol, (b) catalyzes the transfer of an amino group from aspartate to a second substrate, (c) catalyzes the synthesis of tyrosine–tRNA from tyrosine and its tRNA, coupled with ATP hydrolysis, (d) catalyzes the isomerization of a phosphohexose. **19.5** (a) urease (b) cellulase **19.6** transferase. It catalyzes the transfer of a phosphoryl group to a hexose. **19.7** Water adds to fumarate (substrate) to give L-malate (product). **19.8** reaction (a) **19.9** Acidic, basic, and polar side chains take part in catalytic activity. All types of side chains hold the enzyme in the active site. **19.10** Substrate molecules are bound to all of the active sites. (a) no effect

(b) increases the rate **19.11** higher at 35°C in both cases **19.12** The rate is much greater at pH = 2. **19.13** molecule (b), because it resembles the substrate **19.14** a product that resembles the substrate **19.15** (a) E1 (b) no **19.16** (a) competitive inhibition (b) covalent modification or feedback control (c) zymogen form present (d) genetic control **19.17** (a) needs a cofactor (b) needs a cofactor (c) does not require a cofactor **19.18** (a) niacin (B₃) (b) pantothenic acid (B₅) **19.19** vitamin A—fat-soluble as a long hydrocarbon chain; vitamin C—water-soluble as polar hydroxyl groups **19.20** retinal—aldehyde; retinoic acid—carboxylic acid. **19.21** enzyme cofactors; antioxidants; aid in absorption of calcium and phosphate ions; aid in synthesis of visual pigments and blood clotting factors. **19.22** vitamins C and E, β-carotene; These vitamins scavenge damaging free radicals. **19.23** copper, selenium; Both have a biological function and are toxic only in excess.

19.24

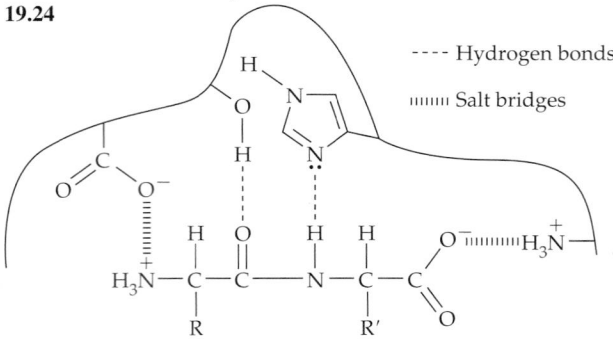

19.25 (a) oxidoreductase (b) dehydrogenase (c) L-lactate (d) pyruvate (e) L-lactate dehydrogenase **19.26** No. An enzyme usually catalyzes the reaction of only one isomer. D-Lactate might be a competitive inhibitor. **19.27** NAD⁺ is an oxidizing agent and includes the vitamin niacin. **19.28** (a) Rate increases when [substrate] is low, but maximum rate is soon reached; maximum rate is always lower than maximum rate of uninhibited reaction. (b) Rate increases. **19.29** (a) Addition or removal of a covalently bonded group changes the activity of an enzyme (b) Hormones control the synthesis of enzymes. (c) Binding of the regulator at a site away from the catalytic site changes the shape of the enzyme. (d) Feedback inhibition occurs when the product of a series of reactions serves as an inhibitor for an earlier reaction. **19.30** (a) feedback inhibition (b) irreversible inhibition (c) genetic control (d) noncompetitive inhibition **19.31** from left to right: aspartate (acidic), serine, glutamine, arginine (basic), histidine (basic). **19.32** (a) riboflavin (B₂) (b) pantothenic acid (B₅) (c) niacin (B₃) **19.34** (b) **19.36** (a) removal of two H atoms from a substrate to form a double bond (b) replacement of a carboxyl group by H (c) hydrolysis of ester groups in lipids **19.38** (a) amylase (b) peroxidase (c) DNAse **19.40** An enzyme is a large three-dimensional molecule with a catalytic site into which a substrate can fit. Enzymes are specific in their action because only one or a few molecules have the appropriate shape and functional groups to fit into the catalytic site. **19.42** (a) hydrolase (b) lyase (c) oxidoreductase **19.44** (a) bonding together of two substrate molecules (b) transfer of a methyl group between substrates (c) reduction of a substrate **19.46** hydrolase **19.48** Lock-and-key: An enzyme is rigid (lock) and only one specific substrate (key) can fit in the active site. Induced fit: An enzyme can change its shape to accommodate the substrate and to catalyze the reaction. **19.50** No. Protein folding can bring the residues close to each other. **19.52** In the stomach, an enzyme must be active at an acidic pH. In the intestine, an enzyme needs to be active at a higher pH and need not be active at pH = 1.5. **19.54** At a high substrate concentration relative to enzyme concentration, the rate of reaction triples if the concentration of enzyme is tripled. **19.56** (a) (b) lowers rate and may denature the enzyme (c) denatures the enzyme and stops reaction **19.58** *Uncompetitive inhibition*: Inhibitor binds reversibly and noncovalently away from the active site and changes the shape of the site to make it difficult for the enzyme to catalyze reactions. *Competitive inhibition*: Inhibitor binds reversibly and noncovalently at the active site and keeps the substrate from entering. *Irreversible inhibition*: Inhibitor irreversibly forms a covalent bond at the active site and destroys the catalytic ability of the enzyme. **19.60** diagram B

19.62 (1) displacing an essential metal from an active site; (2) bonding to a cysteine residue (irreversible) **19.64** Papain catalyzes the hydrolysis of peptide bonds and partially digests the proteins in meat. **19.66** One site is for catalysis, and one site is for regulation. **19.68** The end product of a reaction series is an inhibitor for an earlier step. **19.70** A zymogen is an enzyme synthesized in a form different from its active form because it might otherwise harm the organism. **19.72** Trypsin and chymotrypsin must be inactive so they do not digest the pancreas. **19.74** Vitamins are small, essential organic molecules that must be obtained from food. **19.76** Vitamin C is excreted, but Vitamin A is stored in fatty tissue. **19.78** Bone is composed of both calcium and phosphorus.

19.80

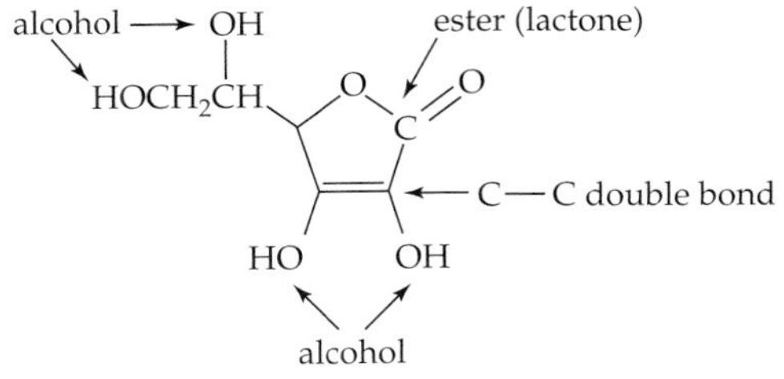

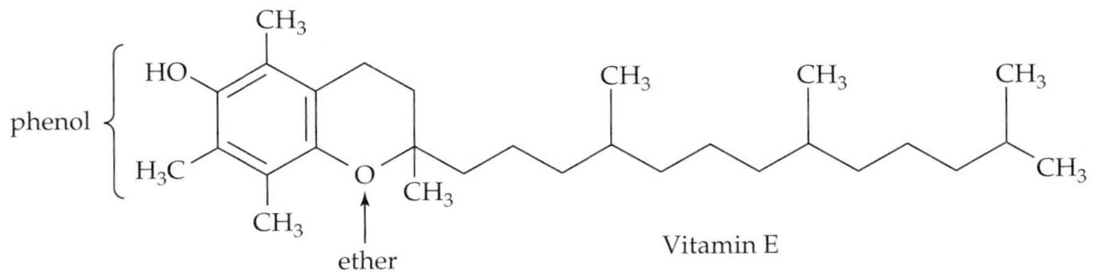

19.82 Blanching denatures enzymes to slow deterioration of food quality in frozen foods. **19.84** Amount of energy needed for a reaction to occur or for effective collisions; determines the rate of reaction **19.86** This problem requires an explaination. A brief explanation was included here. **(a)** rate decreases; not enough energy for a reaction to occur **(b)** rate decreases; enzyme denatures **(c)** rate decreases; enzyme denatures **(d)** rate decreases; enzyme denatures **(e)** rate increases/doubles; more substrate to react with the enzymes (assuming not at saturation) **(f)** rate decreases by half; less substrate to react with **19.88** 9.3 L apple juice **19.90** Look for Arg, His, and Lys (basic amino acids) in the polypeptide, and break the bond between the basic amino acid and the amino acid to its right. (There are three fragments.)

Leu—Gly—Arg ⫮ Ile—Met—His ⫮ Tyr—Trp—Ala

↓ Trypsin

Leu—Gly—Arg + Ile—Met—His + Tyr—Trp—Ala

Chapter 20

20.1 **(a)** aldopentose **(b)** ketotriose **(c)** aldotetrose

20.2

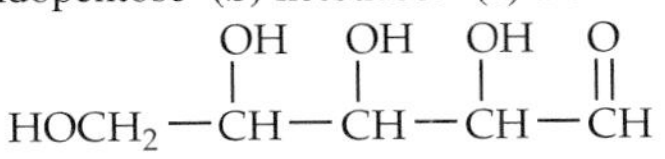

An aldopentose

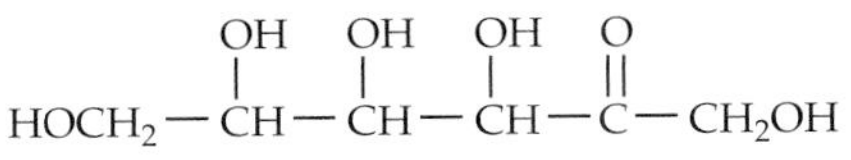

A ketohexose

20.3 The bottom carbon is not chiral. The orientations of the hydroxyl groups bonded to the chiral carbons must be shown in order to indicate which stereoisomer is pictured. **20.4** **(d)** **20.5** 32 stereoisomers

20.6 **(a)**

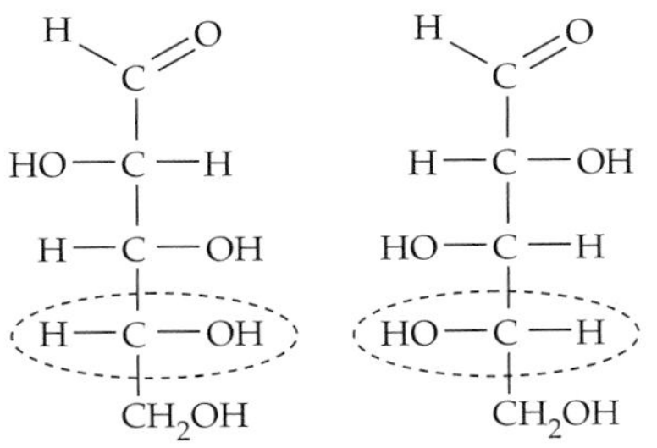

A D-aldopentose An L-aldopentose

(b)

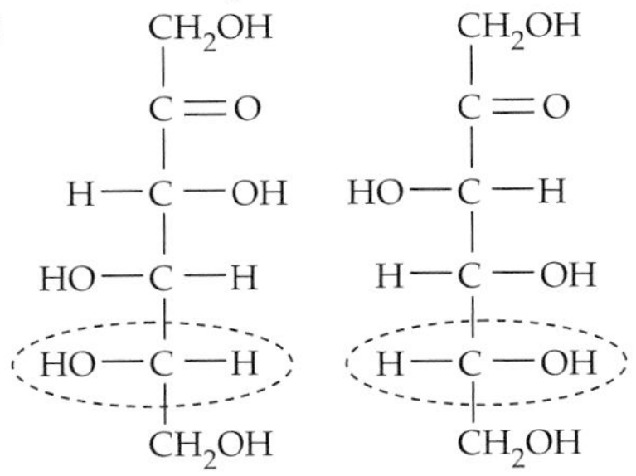

An L-ketohexose A D-ketohexose

20.7

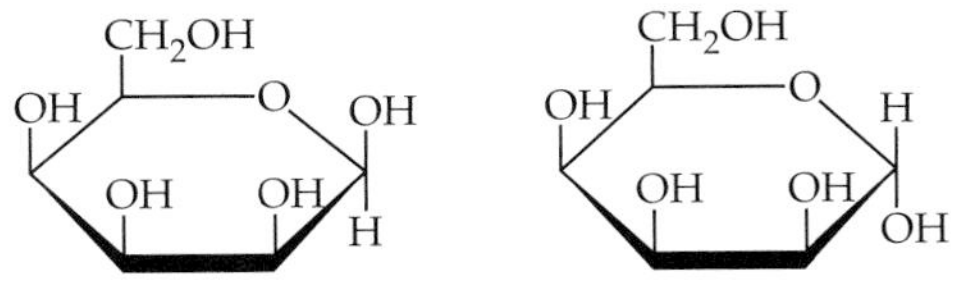

β-anomer α-anomer

20.8

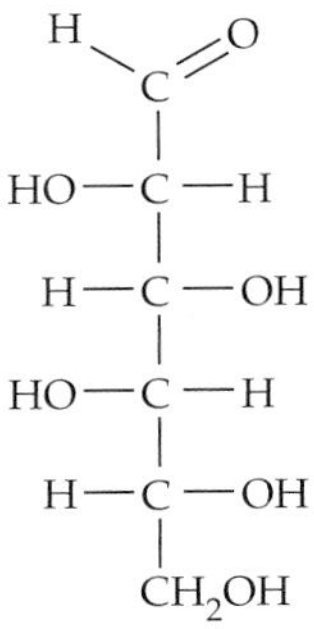

D-Idose

20.9 **(a)**

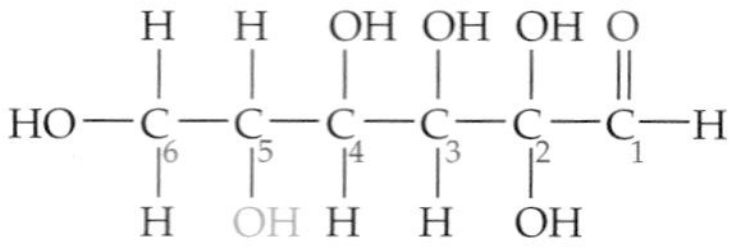

(b)

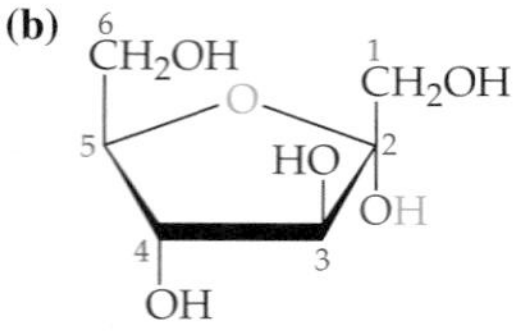

20.10 **(a)** Rings **1** and **4** (5 carbons) are amino sugars **(b)** Ring **3** (4 carbons) is an unmodified sugar **(c)** Ring **2** (6 carbons) is a nonsugar.

20.11

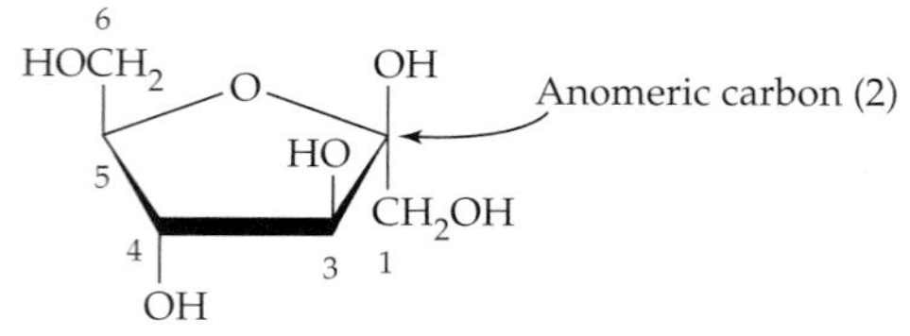

β-anomer

20.12 **(a)**

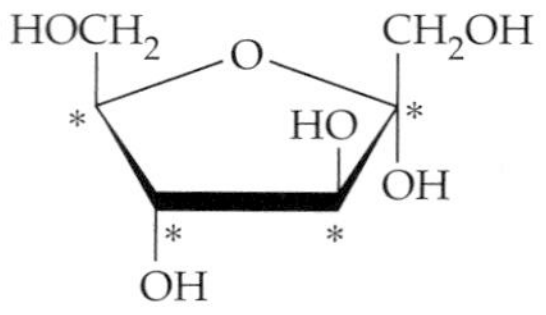

(b)

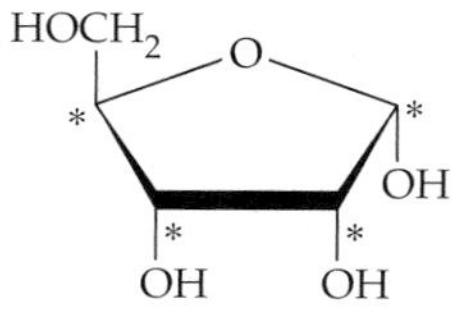

(c)

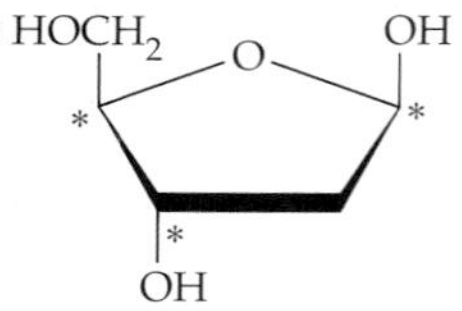

20.13 **(a)** an α anomer **(b)** carbon 6 **(c)** Groups that are below the plane of the ring in D-galactose are above the plane of the ring in L-fucose. Groups that are above the plane of the ring in D-galactose are below the plane of the ring in L-fucose. **(d)** yes

20.14 Both are acetals.

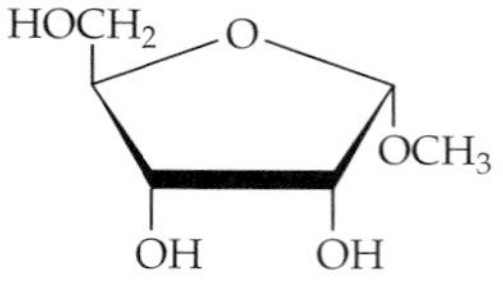

Methyl α-D-riboside

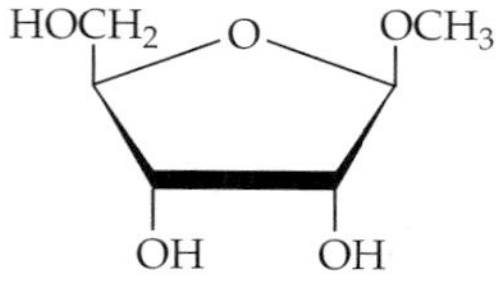

Methyl β-D-riboside

20.15 a β-1,4 glycosidic link **20.16** β-D-Glucose + β-D-Glucose **20.17** **(a)** maltose; fermenting grain **(b)** sucrose; sugar beets **(c)** lactose; milk **20.18** **(a)** On C5, there is a —CH_2OH group in glucose and a —COO^- in β-D-glucuronate. **(b)** On C2, there is a —OH group in glucose and a —NH_2 in β-D-glucosamine. **(c)** On C2, there is a —OH group in glucose and a —NH_2COCH_3 in *N*-acetyl-β-D-glucosamine. **20.19** glutamine, asparagine **20.20** Starch (polysaccharide) $\xrightarrow{\text{Amylase}}$ Maltose (disaccharide) $\xrightarrow{\text{Maltase}}$ Glucose (monosaccharide)

20.21 **(a)** diastereomers, anomers **(b)** enantiomers **(c)** diastereomers

20.22 **(a)** **(b)**

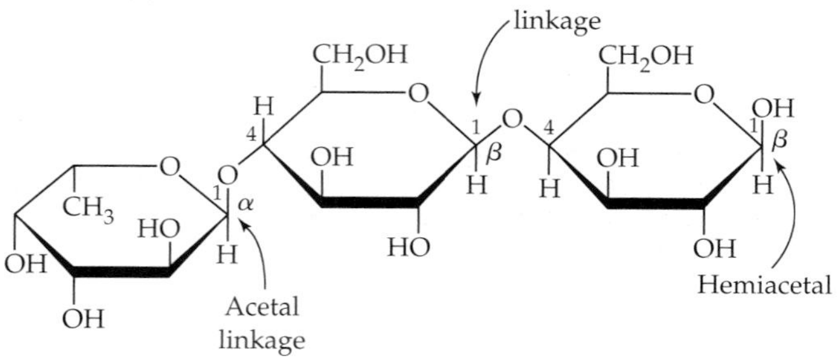

A α-anomer — B β-anomer — C β-anomer

(c) α-1,4 linkage between C4 of B and C1 of A **(d)** β-1,4 linkage between C4 of C and C1 of B **20.23** **(a)** **(b)** No monosaccharides are identical, and none are enantiomers. **(c)** **(d)**

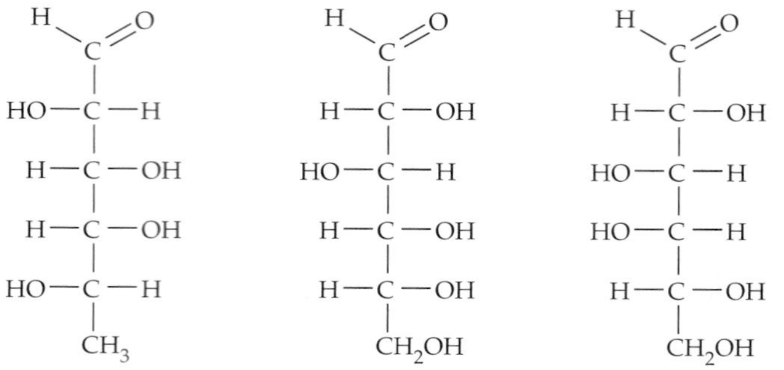

L-Fucose — D-Glucose — D-Galactose

20.24 Monosaccharide C is oxidized. Identification of the carboxylic acid also identifies the terminal monosaccharide.

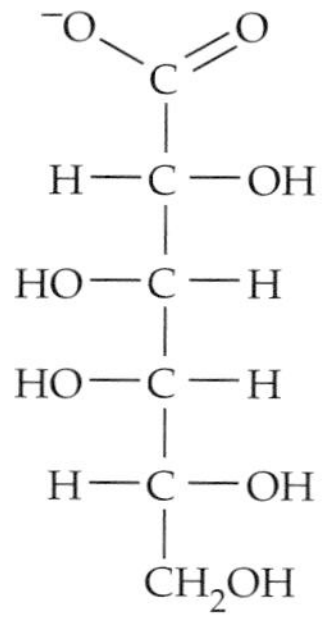

20.25 No

20.26

Polysaccharide	Linkage	Branching?
Cellulose	β-1,4	no
Amylose	α-1,4	no
Amylopectin	α-1,4	yes: α- 1,6 branches occur ~ every 25 units
Glycogen	α-1,4	yes: even more α- 1,6 branches than in amylopectin

20.27 Glucose is in equilibrium \with its open-chain aldehyde form, which reacts with an oxidizing agent. **20.28** A carbohydrate is a polyhydroxylated aldehyde or ketone that belongs to one of the biologically most important classes of compounds. **20.30** An aldose contains an aldehyde and a ketose contains a ketone. **20.32** **(a)** two **(b)** two **(c)** three **(d)** three

20.34

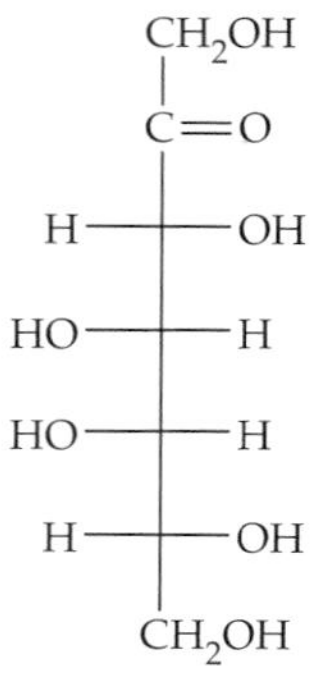

A ketoheptose

20.36 glucose—foods like fruits and vegetables; galactose—brain tissue and a component of lactose; fructose—honey and fruits; ribose—nucleic acids **20.38** Enantiomers are stereoisomers that are nonsuperimposable mirror images.

20.40

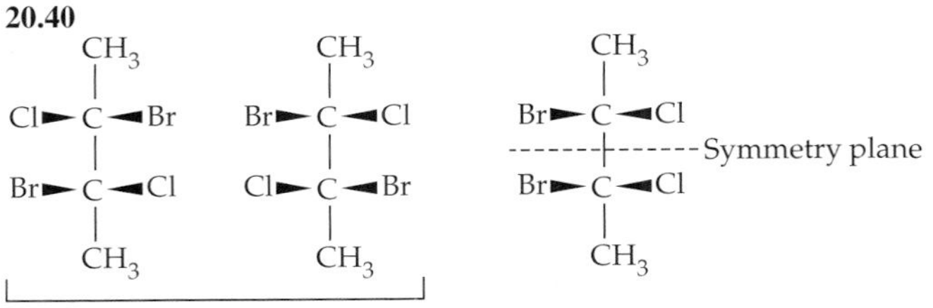

Enantiomers

The third stereoisomer has a symmetry plan and is not chiral so there is no enantiomer.   **20.42** **(a)** Fructose rotates light to the left to a greater degree than glucose. **(b)** The sign of rotation of the fructose–glucose mixtures is inverted or opposite the sign of rotation of sucrose.   **20.44** A sugar that gives a positive reaction when treated with an oxidizing agent (Tollens' reagent or Benedict's reagent).   **20.46** Mutarotation occurs when either a pure anomer or a mixture of anomers is dissolved in water. If the rotation of plane-polarized light is measured, the degree of rotation, as well as the ratio of anomers, changes until it reaches a constant value. At this point, an equilibrium mixture of both anomers is present in the solution. Mutarotation is not a general characteristic of all chiral compounds.   **20.48** In the β form of the carbohydrate, the —OH group attached to C1 is on the same side as the —CH_2OH group on C5. In the α form, the —OH group attached to C1 is on opposite sides of the —CH_2OH group on C5.

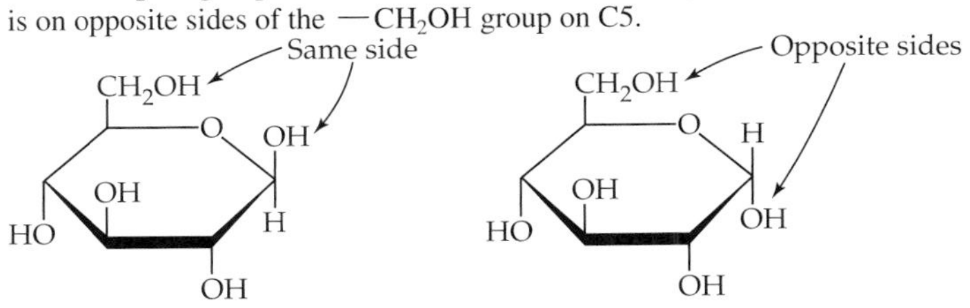

A β-anomer

An α-anomer

20.50

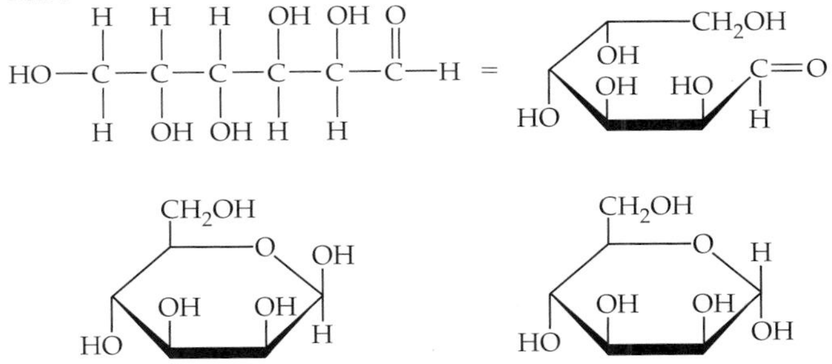

β-D-Mannose

α-D-Mannose

20.52

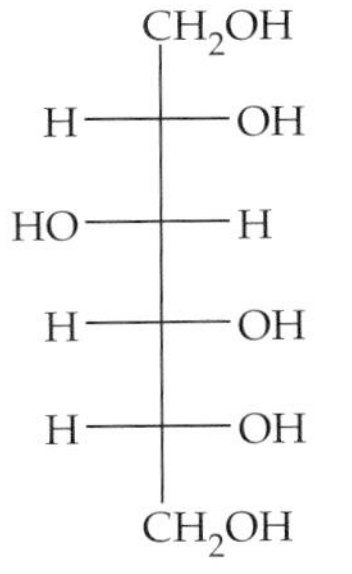

Sorbitol

20.54

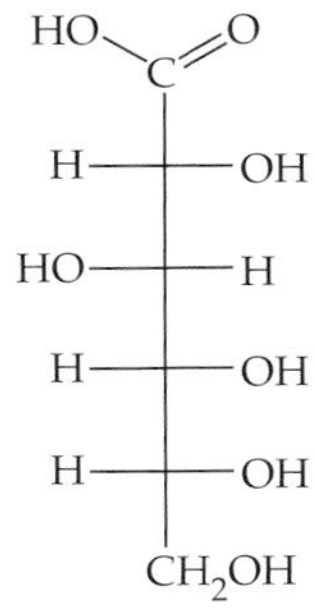

Gluconic acid

20.56 In a hemiacetal, an —OH group and an —OR group are bonded to a carbon atom that was previously a carbonyl carbon. In an acetal, the carbon is bonded to two —OR groups.

20.58

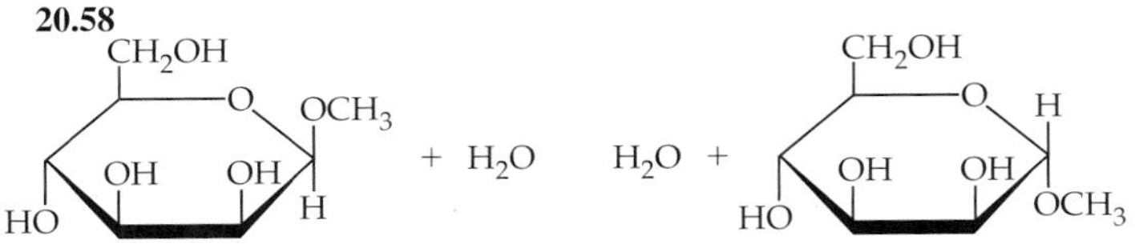

Methyl β-D-mannoside

Methyl α-D-mannoside

20.60 maltose: fermenting grains, two glucose units; lactose: milk, galactose, and glucose; sucrose: plants, glucose, and fructose   **20.62** Amylose, a major component of the human diet, consists of α-D-glucose units linked by α-1,4 glycosidic bonds. Cellulose, a structural material in plants, consists of β-D-glucose units linked by β-1,4 glycosidic bonds. **20.64** **(c)**   **20.66** Two β-D-glucose units   **20.68** Two α-D-glucose units **20.70** Glycogen has many more branches and is significantly larger than amylopectin.   **20.72** heparin: α-D-glucuronate and β-D-glucosamine; hyaluronate: α-D-glucuronate and N-acetyl-β-D-glucosamine; chondroitin 6-sulfate: α-D-glucuronate and N-acetyl-β-D-glucosamine   **20.74** Diastereomers because they are not mirror images.

20.76

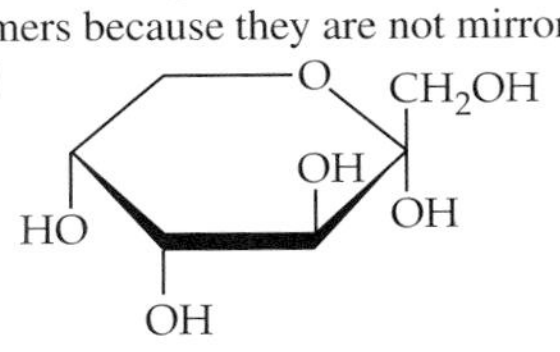

α-D-Fructose

20.78

$HOCH_2CCH_2OH$

1,3-dihydroxyacetone has no optical isomers, as it is not chiral **20.80** Lactose intolerance is an inability to digest lactose; symptoms include bloating, cramps, and diarrhea.

20.82

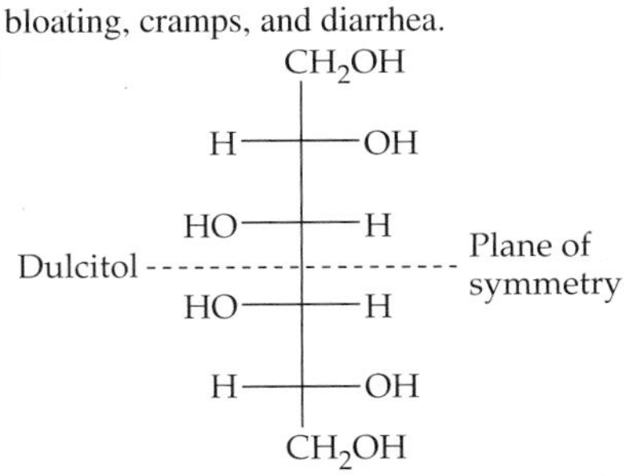

Dulcitol ---- Plane of symmetry

Dulcitol is optically inactive because it has a plane of symmetry and thus doesn't have an enantiomer.   **20.84** fructose: fruit; lactose: milk; amylose: wheat starch   **20.86** Enzymes produced by the bacteria in yogurt predigest most of the lactose, making it possible for lactose-intolerant people to eat yogurt without symptoms.   **20.88** 170 kcal (710 kJ)

Chapter 21

21.1 Both pathways produce the same amount of energy.
21.2 (a) exergonic: oxidation of glucose; endergonic: photosynthesis
(b) sunlight **21.3** (a)

Carbohydrates $\xrightarrow{\text{digestion}}$ Glucose, Sugars $\xrightarrow{\text{glycolysis}}$ Pyruvate → Acetyl-CoA $\xrightarrow[\text{cycle}]{\text{citric acid}}$ Reduced coenzymes $\xrightarrow[\text{transport}]{\text{electron}}$ ATP

(b) pyruvate, acetyl-CoA, citric acid cycle intermediates.
21.4

$$H_3C-\overset{\overset{O}{\|}}{C}-O-\overset{\overset{O}{\|}}{\underset{\underset{O^-}{|}}{P}}-O^- + H_2O \longrightarrow$$

$$H_3C-\overset{\overset{O}{\|}}{C}-O^- + \ ^-O-\overset{\overset{O}{\|}}{\underset{\underset{OH}{|}}{P}}-O^- + H^+$$

21.5 Energy is produced only when it is needed.
21.6

$$HOCH_2CHCH_2OH \xrightarrow[\text{ADP}]{\text{ATP}} HOCH_2CHCH_2O-\overset{\overset{O}{\|}}{\underset{\underset{O^-}{|}}{P}}-O^-$$
(with OH on the second carbon)

21.7 If a process is exergonic, its exact reverse is endergonic and can't occur unless it is coupled with an exergonic reaction in a different pathway.
21.8 favorable ($\Delta G = -3.0$ kcal/mol; -12.3 kJ/mol).
21.9 (b), (c), (d) FAD has five heterocyclic rings (three in the ADP part, and two in the site of reaction on the left).
21.10 (a)

$$^-OOC-\overset{\overset{(H)-O}{|}}{\underset{\underset{(H)}{|}}{C}}-\overset{\overset{COO^-}{|}}{CH}-CH_2COO^-$$

$$^-OOC-\overset{\overset{(H)}{|}}{CH}-\overset{\overset{(H)}{|}}{CH}-COO^-$$

$$^-OOC-CH_2-\overset{\overset{O-(H)}{|}}{\underset{\underset{(H)}{|}}{C}}-COO^-$$

(b) oxidoreductases **21.11** citric acid, isocitric acid **21.12** steps 3, 4, 6, 8
21.13 Succinic dehydrogenase catalyzes the removal of two hydrogens from succinate to yield fumarate, and FAD is the coenzyme associated with dehydrogenations. **21.14** citrate (tertiary); isocitrate (secondary); malate (secondary) **21.15** isocitrate **21.16** Steps 1–4 correspond to the first stage, and steps 5–8 correspond to the second stage. **21.17** mitochondrial matrix **21.18** *Similarities:* Both involve the reaction of glucose, oxygen, carbon dioxide, and water; both take place in organelles (chloroplasts, mitochondria); both involve large, metal ion–containing molecules (chlorophyll, heme); both involve electron transfer; both involve similar coenzymes. *Differences*: photosynthesis captures energy, whereas electron transport releases energy; photosynthesis requires light, whereas oxidative phosphorylation doesn't. **21.19** O_2. Movement of H^+ from a region of high $[H^+]$ to a region of low $[H^+]$ releases energy that is used in ATP synthesis.
21.20 (a) succinyl phosphate $+ H_2O \longrightarrow$ Succinate $+ HOPO_3^{2-} + H^+$
(b) $ADP + HOPO_3^{2-} + H^+ \longrightarrow$
$$ATP + H_2O \ \ \Delta G = +7.3 \text{ kcal/mol } (+30.5 \text{ kJ/mol})$$
21.21 (a) Stage 1 (digestion) (b) Stage 4 (ATP synthesis) (c) Stage 2 (glycolysis) (d) Stage 3 (citric acid cycle). **21.22** Endergonic; coupled reactions **21.23** NAD^+ accepts hydride ions; hydrogen ions are released to the mitochondrial matrix and ultimately combine with reduced O_2 to form H_2O.
21.24 (a) step A (NAD^+) (b) step B (c) product of A (d) oxidoreductase **21.25** step 1: lyase; step 2: isomerase; step 3: oxidoreductase; step 4: oxidoreductase, lyase; step 5: ligase; step 6: oxidoreductase; step 7: lyase; step 8: oxidoreductase **21.26** Metals are better oxidizing and reducing agents. Also, they can accept and donate electrons in one-electron increments. **21.28** An endergonic reaction requires energy, and an exergonic reaction releases energy. **21.30** Enzymes affect only the rate of

a reaction not the size or sign of ΔG. **21.32** exergonic: (a), (b); endergonic: (c). Reaction (b) proceeds farthest toward products. **21.34** prokaryote: (b), (e); eukaryote: (a), (b), (c), (d) **21.36** Organelles are subcellular structures that perform specialized tasks within the cell. **21.38** Cristae, the folds of the inner mitochondrial membrane, provide extra surface area for electron transport and ATP production to take place. **21.40** Metabolism refers to all reactions that take place inside cells. Digestion is the process of breaking food into small organic molecules prior to cellular absorption.
21.42 acetyl-CoA **21.44** An ATP molecule transfers a phosphoryl group to another molecule in exergonic reactions.
21.46 $\Delta G = -4.5$ kcal/mol (-18.8 kJ/mol). **21.48** not favorable (positive ΔG) **21.50** (a) NAD^+ is reduced, (b) NAD^+ is an oxidizing agent, (c) NAD^+ participates in the oxidation of a secondary alcohol to a ketone, (d) $NADH/H^+$ (e)

$$H-\overset{|}{\underset{|}{C}}-OH \xrightarrow[\quad\quad]{NAD^+ \ \ NADH/H^+} \overset{|}{\underset{|}{C}}=O$$

21.52 mitochondria **21.54** Both carbons are oxidized to CO_2. **21.56** three NADH, one $FADH_2$. **21.58** step 3 (isocitrate → α-ketoglutarate), step 4 (α-ketoglutarate → succinyl-SCoA) and step 8 (malate → oxaloacetate) transfer energy as NADH. **21.60** One complete citric acid cycle produces four reduced coenzymes, which enter the electron transfer chain and ultimately generate ATP. **21.62** H_2O, ATP, oxidized coenzymes **21.64** (a) FAD = flavin adenine dinucleotide; (b) CoQ = coenzyme Q; (c) $NADH/H^+$ = reduced nicotinamide adenine dinucleotide, plus hydrogen ion; (d) Cyt c = Cytochrome c **21.66** NADH, coenzyme Q, cytochrome c **21.68** The citric acid cycle would stop. **21.70** In oxidative phosphorylation, reduced coenzymes are oxidized, and ADP is phosphorylated. **21.72** H^+ ions pass through a channel that is part of the ATP synthase enzyme, where they release energy that drives oxidative phosphorylation. **21.74** Oxygen consumption increases because the proton gradient from ATP production dissipates. **21.76** Avoids the production of large amounts of heat, allows for storage of energy, controls the rate of metabolism, and allows energetically favorable steps to be coupled with energetically unfavorable reactions. **21.78** The isomer with a *cis* double bond cannot act as a substrate for the enzyme. **21.80** Electrons from the oxidation of reduced coenzymes are used to reduce O_2, which eventually forms H_2O. **21.82** Energy from combustion is released to the surroundings as heat and is wasted. Energy from metabolic oxidation is released in several steps and is stored in each step so that is available for use in other metabolic processes. **21.84** No. Step 5 produced GTP, which is converted to ATP. **21.86** Cells store energy as polymers, which can be hydrolyzed as needed for energy. **21.88** Oxygen debt occurs because the increased metabolic rate due to running consumes oxygen in the electron-transport chain. Panting is the body's attempt to resupply tissues with oxygen.

Chapter 22

22.1 (a) glycogenesis (b) glycogenolysis (c) gluconeogenesis
22.2 glycogenesis, pentose phosphate pathway, glycolysis **22.3** (a) steps 6 and 7 (b) steps 9 and 10 **22.4** Isomerizations: steps 2, 5, 8
22.5

$$
\begin{array}{c}
H-\overset{\overset{O}{\diagup\!\!\diagdown}}{C} \\
| \\
H-C-OH \\
| \\
HO-C-H \\
| \\
H-C-OH \\
| \\
H-C-OH \\
| \\
CH_2OPO_3^{2-}
\end{array}
\rightleftharpoons
\begin{array}{c}
CH_2OH \\
| \\
C=O \\
| \\
HO-C-H \\
| \\
H-C-OH \\
| \\
H-C-OH \\
| \\
CH_2OPO_3^{2-}
\end{array}
$$

22.6 (a) pyruvate (b) step 6: glyceraldehyde 3-phosphate is oxidized; NAD^+ is the oxidizing agent.

22.7

$HOCH_2$ ... O ... OH / HO ... CH_2OH / OH

ATP → ADP

$CH_2OPO_3{}^{2-}$ ... O ... OH / HO ... CH_2OH / OH

Fructose 6-phosphate enters glycolysis at step 3.

Fructose 6-phosphate enters glycolysis at step 3.   **22.8** Glucose and galactose differ in configuration at C4.   **22.9** (a) The energy is lost as heat. (b) The reverse of fermentation is very endothermic; loss of CO_2 drives the reaction to completion in the forward direction.   **22.10** in preparation of bread, yogurt, cheese, beer, and wine   **22.11** (a) acetyl-CoA under aerobic conditions (b) lactate under anaerobic conditions (c) glucose by gluconeogenesis, which occurs only in liver cells   **22.12** 80 ATP molecules **22.13** 38 moles of ATP   **22.14** Insulin decreases; blood glucose decreases, the level of glucagon increases. Glucagon causes the breakdown of liver glycogen and the release of glucose. As glycogen is used up, the level of free fatty acids and ketone bodies increases.

22.15

CH_2OH
H—C—OH
HO—C—H
H—C—OH
H—C—OH
CH_2OH
Sorbitol

Sorbitol can not form a cyclic acetal because it does not have a carbonyl group.

22.16 (a) The increase in $[H^+]$ drives the equilibrium shown in Section 22.9 to the right, causing the production of CO_2. (b) Le Châtelier's principle   **22.17** Glycogenesis is the pathway to synthesize glycogen from glucose molecules while glycogenolysis is the pathway that breaks down glycogen, resulting in free glucose.   **22.18** Glycogenesis occurs when glucose levels are high in order to store glucose molecules for later use. Glycogenolysis occurs when there is an immediate need for energy in muscle cells or when blood glucose levels are low.   **22.19** phosphorylation, oxidation   **22.20** the pathway for making glucose from lactate, amino acids, or glycerol   **22.21** critical during fasting and early stages of starvation to provide glucose for energy production; without gluconeogenesis, death occurs   **22.22** hydrolases   **22.23** (a) when the supply of glucose is adequate and the body needs energy (b) when the body needs free glucose (c) when ribose 5-phosphate or NADPH are needed (d) when glucose supply is adequate, and the body doesn't need to use glucose for energy production **22.24** Phosphorylations of glucose and fructose 6-phosphate produce important intermediates that repay the initial energy investment. Fructose 1,6-bisphosphate is cleaved into two three-carbon compounds, which are converted to pyruvate.   **22.25** (a) when the body needs energy, in mitochondria (b) under anaerobic conditions, in yeast (c) under anaerobic conditions, in muscle, red blood cells (d) when the body needs free glucose, in the liver   **22.26** step 1: transferase; step 2: isomerase; step 3: transferase; step 4: lyase; step 5: isomerase; step 6: oxidoreductase, transferase; step 7: transferase; step 8: isomerase; step 9: lyase; step 10: transferase; transferases (because many reactions involve phosphate transfers); Ligases are associated with reactions that synthesize molecules, not with reactions that break down molecules.   **22.27** (g), (c), (b), (e), (f), (a), (d) **22.28** Sources of compounds for gluconeogenesis: pyruvate, lactate, citric acid cycle intermediates, many amino acids. Gluconeogenesis takes place when glucose levels are low.   **22.29** Germinating seeds need to synthesize carbohydrates from fats; humans obtain carbohydrates from food.

22.30 (a) No (b) Molecular oxygen appears in the last step of the electron transport chain, where it combines with water, H^+ and electrons (from electron transport) to form H_2O.   **22.32** glucose + galactose; in the lining of the small intestine

22.34

Type of Food Molecules	Products of Digestion
Proteins	Amino acids
Triacylglycerols	Glycerol and fatty acids
Sucrose	Glucose and fructose
Lactose	Glucose and galactose
Starch, maltose	Glucose

22.36 acetyl-CoA; lactate; ethanol + CO_2 **22.38** glycogenesis: synthesis of glycogen from glucose; glycogenolysis: breakdown of glycogen to form glucose   **22.40** ribose 5-phosphate, glycolysis intermediates   **22.42** (a) all organs (b) liver (c), (d) muscle, liver   **22.44** None of the steps of glycolysis require oxygen.   **22.46** (a) steps 1, 3, 6, 7, 10 (b) step 6 (c) step 9 **22.48** (a) substrate-level phosphorylation: 2 mol ATP; oxidative phosphorylation (ideal): 6 ATP (b) oxidative phosphorylation: 3 mol ATP (c) substrate-level phosphorylation: 1 mol ATP; oxidative phosphorylation: 11 mol ATP. Substrate-level phosphorylation is formation of ATP as a by-product of a reaction; oxidative phosphorylation is formation of ATP as a by-product of electron transport.

22.50

CH_3CH(OH)—C(=O)—O^- → CH_3C(=O)—C(=O)—O^-
Lactate NAD^+ → $NADH/H^+$ Pyruvate
Lactate dehydrogenase

22.52 4 mol acetyl-CoA   **22.54** *hypoglycemia:* low blood sugar; weakness, sweating, rapid heartbeat, confusion, coma, death; *hyperglycemia:* high blood sugar; increased urine flow, low blood pressure, coma, death   **22.56** ketone bodies   **22.58** muscle cells   **22.60** Glycogenolysis uses less energy because it is a hydrolysis reaction.   **22.62** pyruvate, lactate   **22.64** Several steps in the reverse of glycolysis are energetically unfavorable.   **22.66** steps 1, 3, 10 of glycolysis; all involve phosphate transfers **22.68** When muscle glucose is depleted and oxygen is in short supply   **22.70** phosphoryl group transfers   **22.72** Glucose obtained from the hydrolysis of glycogen is phosphorylated by reaction with inorganic phosphate ion and enters the glycolysis pathway as glucose 6-phosphate. Thus, one less ATP is needed (at step 1), and one more ATP is produced.   **22.74** (a) consumes energy (b) yields energy   **22.76** (a) when glucose is abundant and the body needs energy (b) when glucose is in short supply, as in starvation or fasting   **22.78** Symptoms include excessive thirst, frequent urination, high concentrations of glucose in the urine and blood, and weight loss.   **22.80** Metabolic syndrome resembles a prediabetic state and is a predictor for diabetes as blood sugar levels are slightly elevated, blood pressure is slightly high, and glucose tolerance is slightly impaired.   **22.82** Muscle tissue needs a steady supply of glucose, and the compounds needed for glucose synthesis by gluconeogenesis are present in the liver.   **22.84** In the absence of oxygen, pyruvate from catabolism of glucose in wine was fermented by yeast enzymes to ethanol and CO_2, which increased the pressure in the bottle and popped the cork.

Chapter 23

23.1 (a) eicosanoid (b) glycerophospholipid (c) wax

23.2

$CH_3(CH_2)_{18}C$(=O)—$OCH_2(CH_2)_{30}CH_3$

23.3

CH_2OC(=O)$(CH_2)_7CH$=$CH(CH_2)_7CH_3$
$CHOC$(=O)$(CH_2)_7CH$=$CH(CH_2)_7CH_3$
CH_2OC(=O)$(CH_2)_7CH$=$CH(CH_2)_7CH_3$

23.4 (a) butter (b) soybean oil (c) soybean oil

23.5

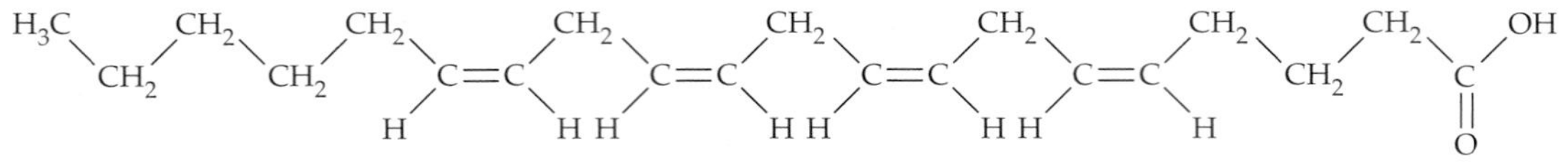

23.6 When two different fatty acids are bonded to C1 and C3 of glycerol, C2 is chiral.   **23.7** London forces; weak; Hydrogen bonds between water molecules are stronger than London forces.   **23.8** The resulting acyl groups are from stearic acid.

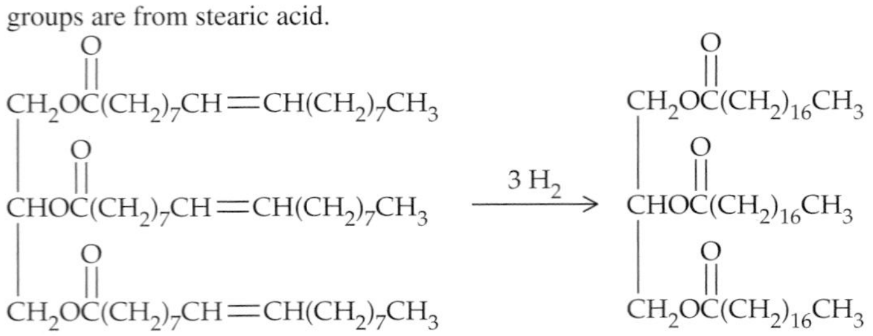

23.9 in butter: cholesterol; in margarine: *trans* fatty acids
23.10

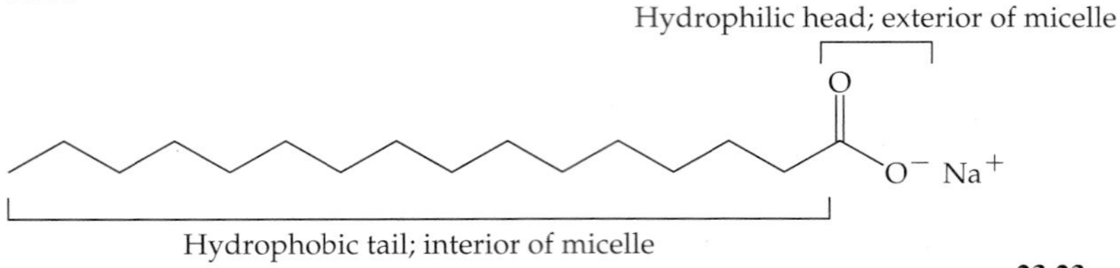

Hydrophilic head; exterior of micelle

Hydrophobic tail; interior of micelle

23.11

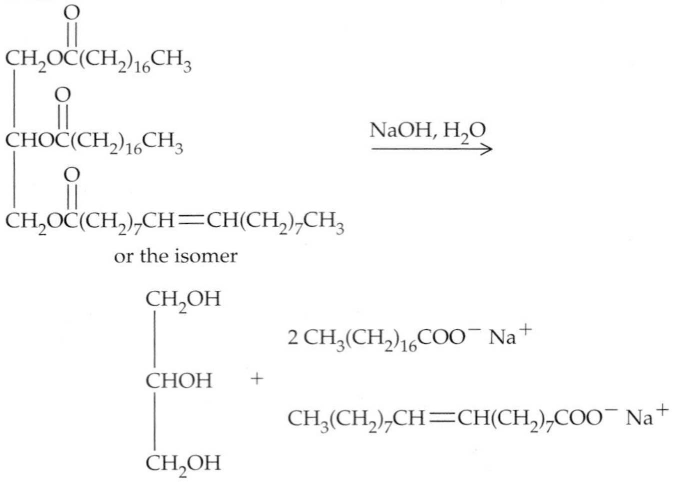

or the isomer

23.12 Lecithins emulsify fats in the same way as soaps dissolve grease: The fats are coated by the nonpolar part of a lecithin, and the polar part of lecithins allows fats to be suspended in aqueous solution.   **23.13 (a)** glycerol, phosphate ion, choline, $RCOO^-Na^+$, $R'COO^-Na^+$ **(b)** sphingosine, phosphate ion, choline, sodium palmitate
23.14

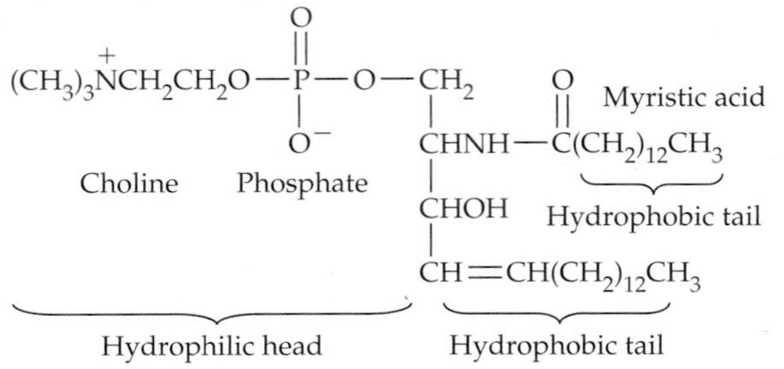

23.15

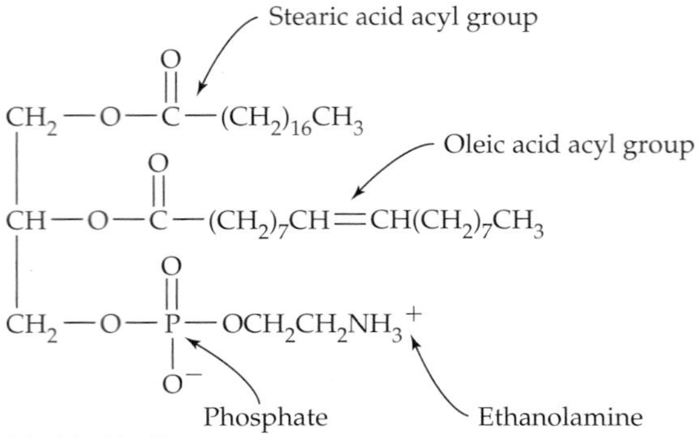

23.16 (a), (c), (e), (f)
23.17 They must be hydrophobic, contain many amino acids with nonpolar side chains, and must be folded so that the hydrophilic regions face outward.   **23.18** yes   **23.19** Glucose 6-phosphate has a charged phosphate group and can't pass through the hydrophobic lipid bilayer.   **23.20** The surfaces are in different environments and serve different functions.   **23.21** A has the highest melting point. B and C are probably liquids at room temperature.
23.22 12.2% palmitic acid, 87.5% stearic acid; more like C
23.23

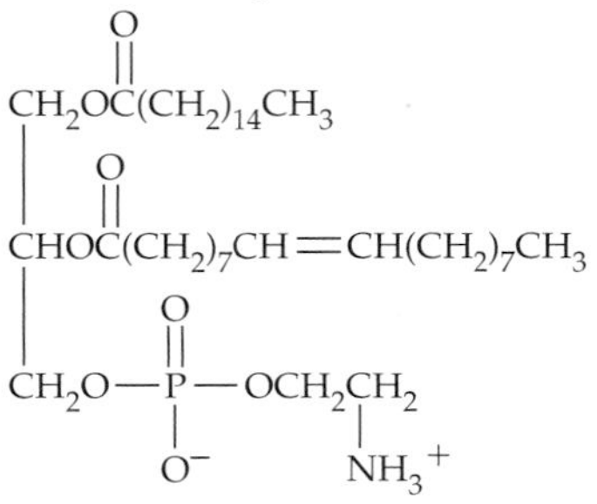

A glycerophospholipid

23.24 Because the membrane is fluid, it can flow together after an injury.   **23.25** C_{16} saturated fatty acids. The polar head lies in lung tissue, and the hydrocarbon tails protrude into the alveoli.
23.26 A lipid is a naturally occurring molecule that dissolves in nonpolar solvents.   **23.28** $CH_3(CH_2)_{16}COOH$: straight chain   **23.30** *Saturated fatty acids* are long-chain carboxylic acids that contain no carbon–carbon double bonds. *Monounsaturated fatty acids* contain one carbon–carbon double bond. *Polyunsaturated fatty acids* contain two or more carbon–carbon double bonds.   **23.32** An essential fatty acid can't be synthesized by the human body and must be part of the diet.   **23.34 (a)** The double bonds in an unsaturated fatty acid (linolenic acid) make it harder for them to be arranged in a crystal.   **23.36** fats: saturated and unsaturated fatty acids, solids; oils: mostly unsaturated fatty acids, liquids.
23.38

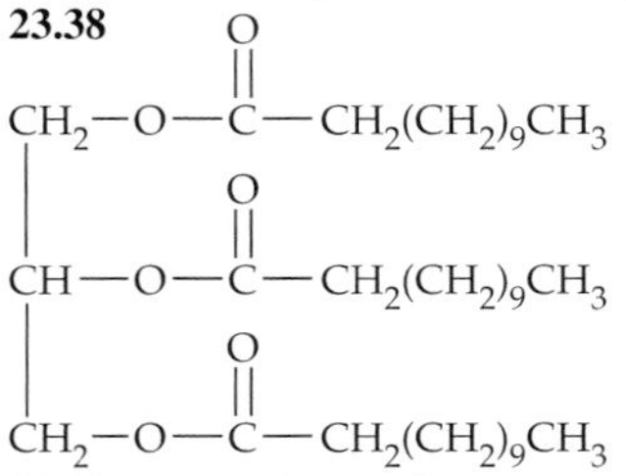

23.40 a protective coating
23.42

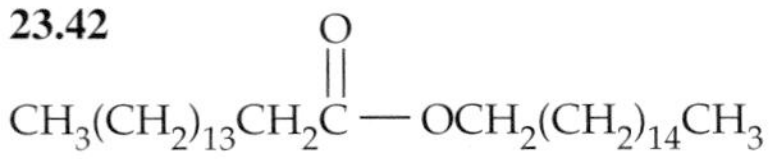

Cetyl palmitate

23.44

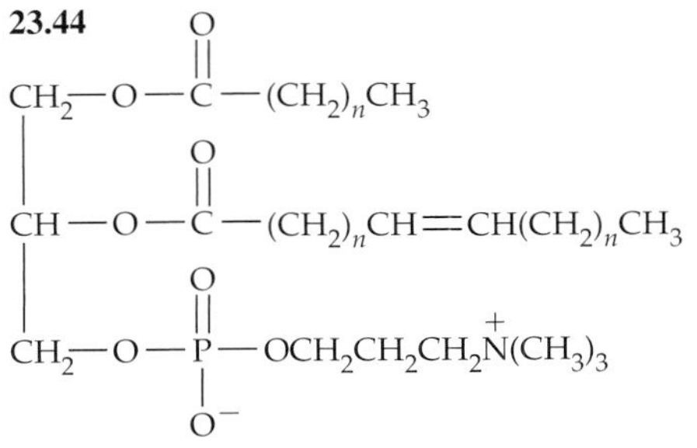

23.60

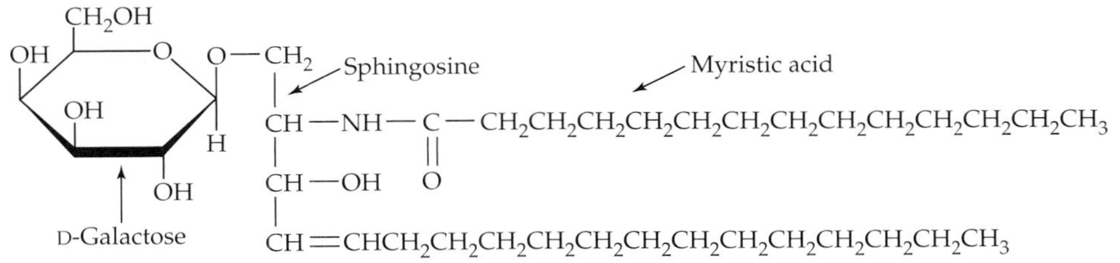

A cerebroside

23.62

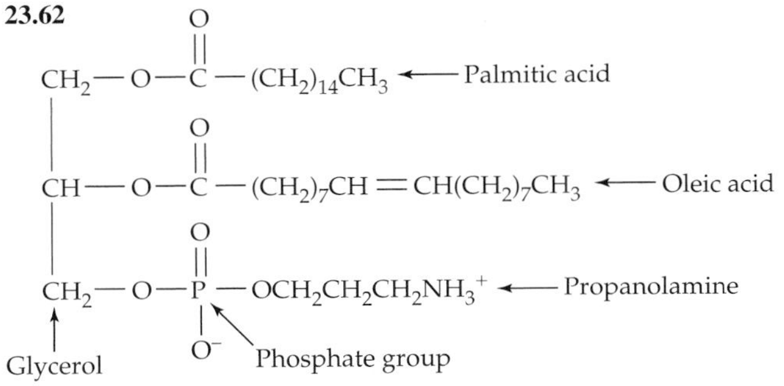

A glycerophospholipid

23.64 Cholesterol is a component of cell membranes and is the starting material for the synthesis of all other steroids. **23.66** *male sex hormones*: androsterone, testosterone *female sex hormones*: estrone, estradiol, progesterone **23.68** In a soap micelle, the polar hydrophilic heads are on the exterior, and the hydrophobic tails cluster in the center. In a membrane bilayer, hydrophilic heads are on both the exterior and interior surfaces of the membrane, and the region between the two surfaces is occupied by hydrophobic tails. **23.70** glycolipids, cholesterol, proteins **23.72** Active transport requires energy because it is a process in which substances are transported across a membrane in a direction opposite to their tendency to diffuse. **23.74** (a) simple diffusion (b) facilitated diffusion (c) active transport **23.76** (b), (c), (e), (f)

23.78

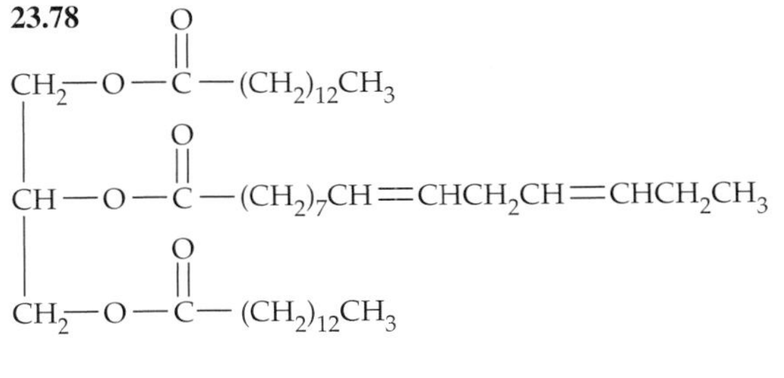

or

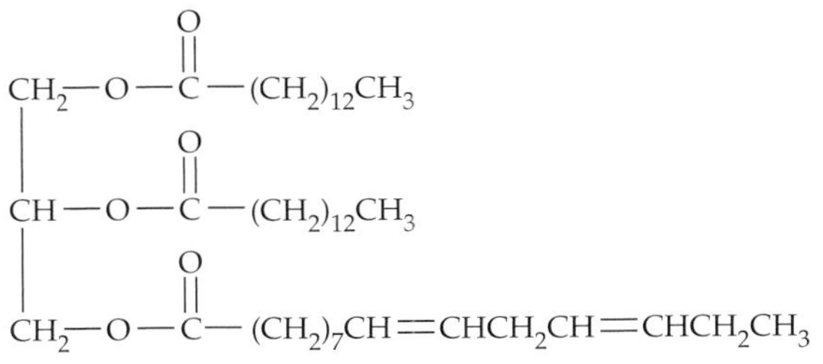

23.46 hydrogenation **23.48** saponification **23.50** The product is shown in Problem 23.8. It has a higher melting point. **23.52** Margarine contains more mono- and polyunsaturated fats but is also more likely to contain *trans* fats. **23.54** Glycerophospholipids have polar heads (point outward) and nonpolar tails that cluster to form the membrane. Triacylglycerols don't have polar heads. **23.56** A sphingomyelin and a cerebroside are similar in that both have a sphingosine backbone. The difference between the two occurs at C1 of sphingosine. A sphingomyelin has a phosphate group bonded to an amino alcohol at C1; a cerebroside has a glycosidic link to a monosaccharide at C1. **23.58** Glycerophospholipids have an ionic phosphate group that is solvated by water.

23.80 (a) beef fat (b) plant oil (c) pork fat **23.82** It is saponifiable.
23.84 coatings for nerve fibers and are present in brain tissue
23.86 0.40 g NaOH
23.88

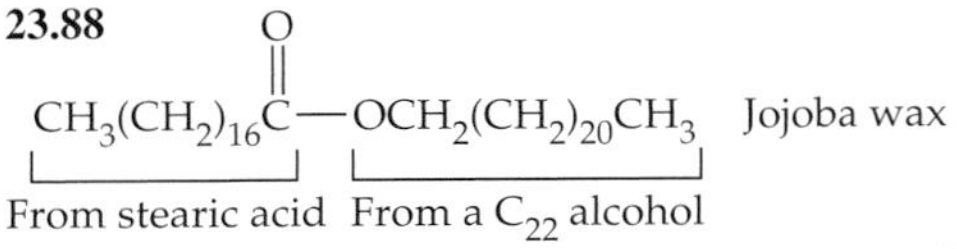

Jojoba wax is the ester formed by a C_{22} alcohol and a C_{18} carboxylic acid. Spermaceti is the ester formed by a C_{18} alcohol and a C_{16} carboxylic acid. It might be possible to substitute jojoba wax as long as the greater mass and higher melting point do not alter the cosmetic product.

Chapter 24

24.1 Cholate has four polar groups on its hydrophilic side that allow it to interact with an aqueous environment; its hydrophobic side interacts with triacylglycerides. Cholate and cholesterol can't change roles.
24.2 Dihydroxyacetone phosphate is isomerized to glyceraldehyde 3-phosphate, which enters glycolysis. **24.3** Free fatty acids travel with albumins (blood-plasma proteins). **24.4** (a), (b) step 1; a C=C double bond is introduced; FAD is the oxidizing agent. step 3; an alcohol is oxidized to a ketone; NAD^+ is the oxidizing agent. (c) step 2; water is added to a carbon–carbon double bond. (d) step 4; HSCoA displaces acetyl-CoA, producing a chain-shortened acyl-SCoA fatty acid. **24.5** (a) 8 acetyl-CoA, 7 β oxidations (b) 12 acetyl-CoA, 11 β oxidations **24.6** step 6, step 7, step 8 **24.7** 146 ATP molecules **24.8** (d) **24.9** (a) Acetyl-CoA provides the acetyl groups used in synthesis of ketone bodies (b) three (c) The body uses ketone bodies as an energy source during starvation. **24.10** seven additional acetyl-CoA; eight additional CO_2 **24.11** Oxygen is needed to reoxidize reduced coenzymes, formed in β oxidation, that enter the electron transport chain. **24.12** (a) chylomicrons; because they have the greatest ratio of lipid to protein (b) chylomicrons (c) HDL (d) LDL (e) HDL (f) VLDL; used for storage or energy production (g) LDL **24.13** high blood glucose $\rightarrow$ high insulin/low glucagon $\rightarrow$ fatty acid and triacylglycerol synthesis: low blood glucose $\rightarrow$ low insulin/high glucagon $\rightarrow$ triacylglycerol hydrolysis; fatty acid oxidation **24.14** Formation of a fatty acyl-CoA is coupled with conversion of ATP to AMP and pyrophosphate. This energy expenditure is recaptured in β oxidation. **24.15** Less acetyl-CoA can be catabolized in the citric acid cycle, and acetyl-CoA is diverted to ketogenesis. **24.16** Catabolism of fat provides more energy per gram than does catabolism of glycogen, and thus fats are a more efficient way to store energy. **24.17** Ketone bodies can be metabolized to form acetyl-CoA, which provides energy. **24.18** No. Although both these processes add or remove two carbon units, one is not the reverse of the other. The two processes involve different enzymes, coenzymes, and activation steps. **24.20** small intestine **24.22** liver from cholesterol **24.24** pancreatic lipase: mono- and diacylglycerols, fatty acids, and glycerol; lipoprotein lipase: fatty acids and glycerol **24.26** liver

24.28 transported by LDLs to peripheral tissue, where it is used in cell membranes and to synthesize sterols   **24.30** six ATP molecules   **24.32** 190 acetyl-CoA molecules   **24.34** storage and mobilization of triacylglycerols; located under the skin and in the abdominal cavity   **24.36** mitochondrial matrix   **24.38** The activated fatty acid must be transported from the cytosol into the mitochondrial matrix.   **24.40** The sequence is a spiral because the same reaction series is repeated on a two-carbon-shortened fatty acid until the original acid is consumed. In a cycle, the product of the final step is a reactant in the first step.   **24.42** no; the coenzyme NADPH replaces NAD⁺ and FAD.   **24.44** 112 moles ATP per mole of myristic acid   **24.46** fructose, mannose, palmitic acid, stearic acid

24.48

$$CH_3\overset{O}{\overset{||}{C}}CH_2\overset{O}{\overset{||}{C}}SCoA \xrightarrow[\text{Acetyl-CoA transferase}]{HSCoA} 2\ CH_3\overset{O}{\overset{||}{C}}SCoA$$

24.50 caprylic acid: three cycles; myristic acid: six cycles   **24.52** Ketosis is a condition in which ketone bodies accumulate in the blood faster than they can be metabolized. Since two of the ketone bodies are carboxylic acids, they lower the pH of the blood, producing the condition known as ketoacidosis. Symptoms of ketoacidosis include dehydration, labored breathing, and depression; prolonged ketoacidosis may lead to coma and death.   **24.54** Ketones have little effect on pH, but the two other ketone bodies are acidic, and they lower the pH of urine.   **24.56** lipogenesis   **24.58** acetyl-CoA   **24.60** eight rounds   **24.62** Fatty acid synthesis takes place in the cytosol; fatty acid degradation takes place in mitochondria.   **24.64** The excess acetyl-CoA from catabolism of carbohydrates is stored as fat. The body can't resynthesize carbohydrate from acetyl-CoA.   **24.66** The alcohol intermediate is chiral.   **24.68 (a)** endogenous **(b)** exogenous   **24.70** The body synthesizes cholesterol when no cholesterol is present in the diet. The body needs cholesterol for membrane function and for synthesis of steroid hormones.   **24.72** The excess carbohydrates pass through glycolysis and ends up as acetyl-CoA. Since the body doesn't need extra energy, acetyl-CoA enters lipogenesis to form fatty acids, which are stored as triacylglycerols in adipocytes, leading to weight gain.

Chapter 25

25.1 (a) false **(b)** true **(c)** true   **25.2** oxidoreductase; lyase

25.3

25.4 4-Hydroxy-α-ketopentanoate

$$H_3CSCH_2CH_2\overset{O}{\overset{||}{C}}-\overset{O}{\underset{||}{C}}-O^-$$

25.5 by the loss of two hydrogens to either NAD⁺ or NADP⁺   **25.6** valine, leucine, isoleucine

$$CH_3\underset{\underset{|}{H_3C}}{\overset{\overset{NH_3^+}{|}}{CH}}CHCOO^- + {}^-OOCCH_2CH_2\overset{O}{\overset{||}{C}}COO^-$$

Valine + α-Ketoglutarate

↓

$$CH_3\underset{\underset{|}{H_3C}}{\overset{O}{\overset{||}{C}}}CHCOO^- + {}^-OOCCH_2CH_2\overset{NH_3^+}{\overset{|}{C}}HCOO^-$$

α-Keto-3-methylbutanoate + Glutamate

25.7 (a) (b) (c) (d) (e) [structures]

25.8 (a) 5 **(b)** 1 **(c)** 3   **25.9** glucogenic: Histidine, Threonine, Methionine, Valine; ketogenic: Leucine; both: Isoleucine, Lysine, Phenylalanine, Tryptophan   **25.10** 3-phosphoglycerate → 3-phosphohydroxypyruvate (oxidation); 3-phosphohydroxypyruvate → 3-phosphoserine (transamination); 3-phosphoserine → serine (hydrolysis)

25.11

25.12 (1) Catabolism of an amino acid begins with a transamination reaction that removes the amino nitrogen. (2) The resulting α-keto acid, which contains the carbon atoms, is converted to a common metabolic intermediate. (3) The amino group of glutamate (from the amino acid) is removed by oxidative deamination. (4) The amino nitrogen is transformed to urea in the urea cycle and is excreted.   **25.13** glutamate dehydrogenase; alanine aminotransferase. Alanine is the product.   **25.14** The carbon atoms from ketogenic amino acids can be converted to ketone bodies or to acetyl-SCoA. The carbon atoms from glucogenic amino acids can be converted to compounds that can enter gluconeogenesis and can form glucose, which can enter glycolysis and also yield acetyl-CoA.   **25.15** All amino acids are necessary for protein synthesis. The body can synthesize only some of them; the others must be provided by food and are thus essential in the diet.   **25.16** to quickly remove ammonia from the body; buildup of urea and shortage of ornithine   **25.18** digestion begins in the stomach   **25.20** oxaloacetate and α-ketoglutarate

25.22

$$\underset{\alpha\text{-Amino acid}}{\overset{NH_3^+}{\overset{|}{R}CHCOO^-}} + \underset{\text{Pyruvate}}{CH_3\overset{O}{\overset{||}{C}}COO^-} \underset{\alpha\text{-Aminotransferase}}{\rightleftharpoons} \underset{\alpha\text{-Keto acid}}{R\overset{O}{\overset{||}{C}}COO^-} + \underset{\text{Alanine}}{CH_3\overset{NH_3^+}{\overset{|}{C}}HCOO^-}$$

$$\underset{\alpha\text{-Amino acid}}{\overset{NH_3^+}{\overset{|}{R}CHCOO^-}} + \underset{\text{Oxaloacetate}}{{}^-OOCCH_2\overset{O}{\overset{||}{C}}COO^-} \underset{\alpha\text{-Aminotransferase}}{\rightleftharpoons} \underset{\alpha\text{-Keto acid}}{R\overset{O}{\overset{||}{C}}COO^-} + \underset{\text{Aspartate}}{{}^-OOCCH_2\overset{NH_3^+}{\overset{|}{C}}HCOO^-}$$

25.24 (a)

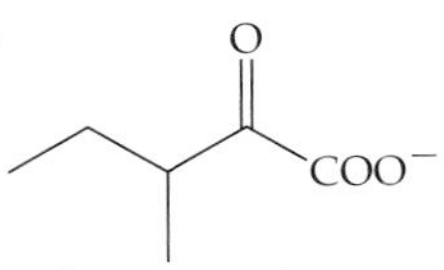

(b)

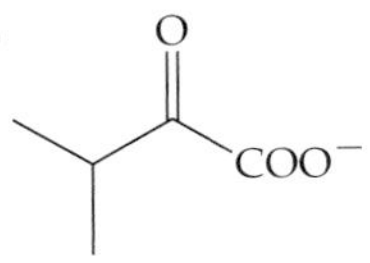

25.26 NAD$^+$ or NADP$^+$ **25.28** ammonium ion **25.30** Catabolized to pyruvate or citric acid cycle intermediates and is able to enter gluconeogenesis. Examples: alanine, glycine, serine. **25.32** carbamoyl phosphate **25.34** Enters the urea cycle at step 2 and leaves in step 3 as fumarate, which can enter the citric acid cycle. **25.36** glutamate **25.38** Biosynthesized by hydroxylation of phenylalanine; phenylketonuria **25.40** Aspartame is a dipeptide that contains phenylalanine, which must be severely restricted in phenylketonurics **25.42** Three molecules of ATP **25.44 (a)** succinyl-SCoA, fumarate, oxaloacetate, pyruvate **(b)** fumarate **25.46** liver; transported to the kidneys, where it is excreted in urine **25.48** storage: fats and carbohydrates are stored in the body while amino acids are not; energy: surplus amino acids must be converted to fats or carbohydrates to be an energy source; fats and carbohydrates that are not stored are catabolized. **25.50** The activated forms of the proteases would hydrolyze the proteins in the lines of the pancreas; in the inactive form, they can be safely stored. **25.52** One of the ATPs in the urea cycle is hydrolyzed to AMP, which is the equivalent of spending two ATPs. **25.54** Answer depends on what foods were consumed. Refer to Figure 25.2. Essential amino acids: histidine, lysine, threonine, isoleucine, methionine, tryptophan, leucine, phenylalanine, valine. Complete protein sources: meat and dairy product; Incomplete protein sources: grains, nuts, seeds, legumes, corn **25.56** leucine: 12 ATPs; histidine: 9 ATPs; valine: 3 ATPs; lysine: 12 ATPs; total ATPs: 36 ATPs

Chapter 26
26.1

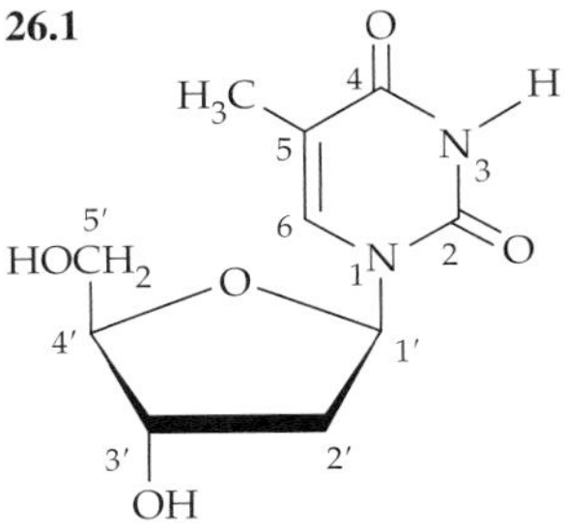

2′-Deoxythymidine

26.2 D-Ribose ($C_5H_{10}O_5$) has one more oxygen atom than 2-deoxy-D-ribose ($C_5H_{10}O_4$), and thus can form more hydrogen bonds.
26.3

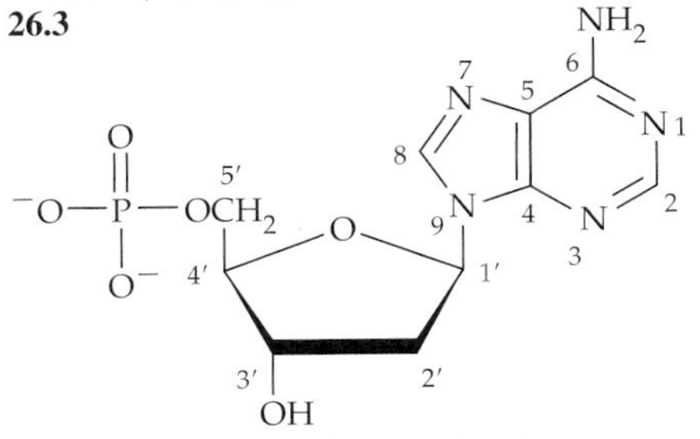

2′-Deoxyadenosine 5′-monophosphate
26.4

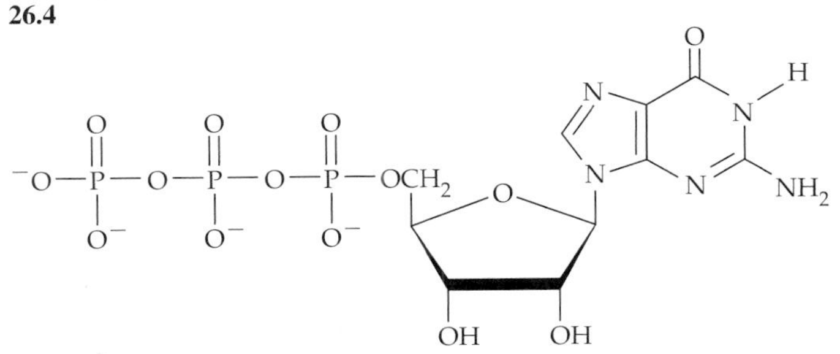

Guanosine 5′-triphosphate (GTP)

26.5 dUMP—2′-deoxyuridine 5′-monophosphate; UMP—uridine 5′-monophosphate; CDP—cytidine 5′-diphosphate; AMP—adenosine 5′-monophosphate; ATP—adenosine 5′-triphosphate **26.6** guanine–adenine–uracil–cytosine–adenine. The pentanucleotide comes from RNA because uracil is present.
26.7

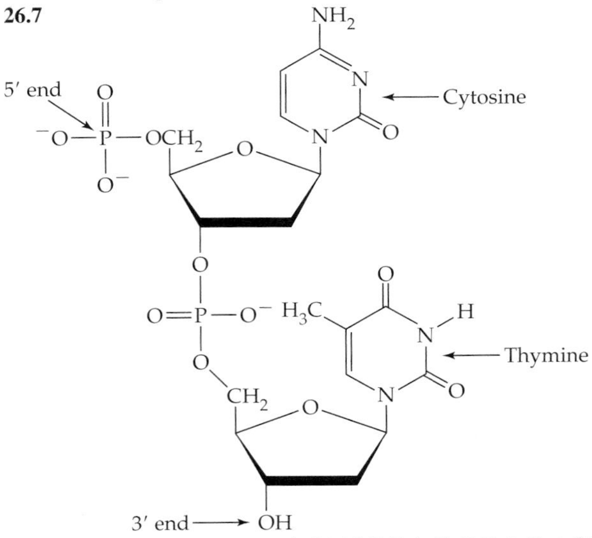

26.8 (a) 3′ A-T-A-T-G-A-C 5′ **(b)** 3′ C-T-A-G-C-G-A-G-A 5′
26.9

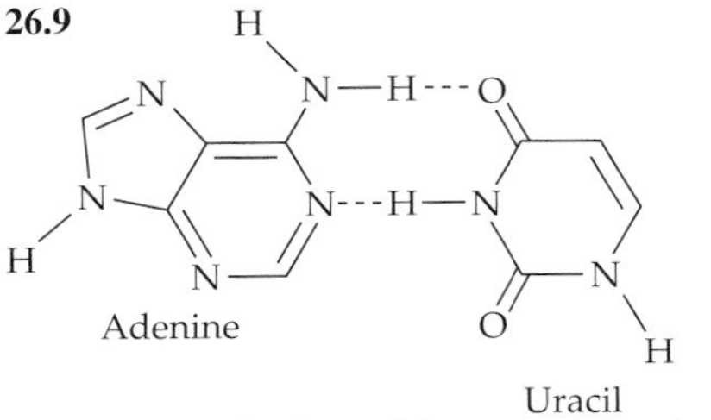

26.10 negatively charged (because of the phosphate groups)
26.11 (a) A longer strand has more hydrogen bonds. **(b)** A chain with a higher percent of G/C pairs has a higher melting point, because it has more hydrogen bonds. **26.12** Okazaki fragments are segments of DNA synthesized by using the lagging strand as a template. The fragments are later joined by a DNA ligase enzyme. **26.13** DNA polymerase facilitates transcription of the single-stranded DNA while DNA ligase joins short DNA strands (Okazaki fragments) together in the lagging strand. **26.14** In spliceosomes, introns are removed and the exons are spliced together to yield mRNA. **26.15 (a)** 3′ G-U-A-C-G-A-G-A-U-G-U-C 5′ **(b)** 5′ A-U-A-A-U-C-G-C-U-G-G-C 3′
26.16 (a) GUU GUC GUA GUG **(b)** UUU UUC **(c)** AAU AAC **(d)** GGU GGC GGA GGG **(e)** AUG **26.17** The sequence GAG codes for glutamic acid as does the sequence GAA. **26.18 (a)** Ile **(b)** Ala **(c)** Arg **(d)** Lys **26.19** Six mRNA triplets can code for Leu: UUA, UUG, CUU, CUC, CUA, CUG if no codons are duplicated. Among the possible combinations:

5′ UUAUUGCUU 3′ 5′ UUAUUGCUC 3′ 5′ UUAUUGCUA 3′
5′ UUAUUGCUG 3′ 5′ UUACUUCUC 3′ 5′ UUACUUCUA 3′

26.20–26.21
mRNA
sequence: 5′ CUC—AUU—CCA—UGC—GAC—GUA 3′
amino acid
sequence: L e u—I l e—P r o—C y s—A s p—V a l
tRNA
anticodons: 3′ GAG UAA GGU ACG CUG CAU 5′

26.22

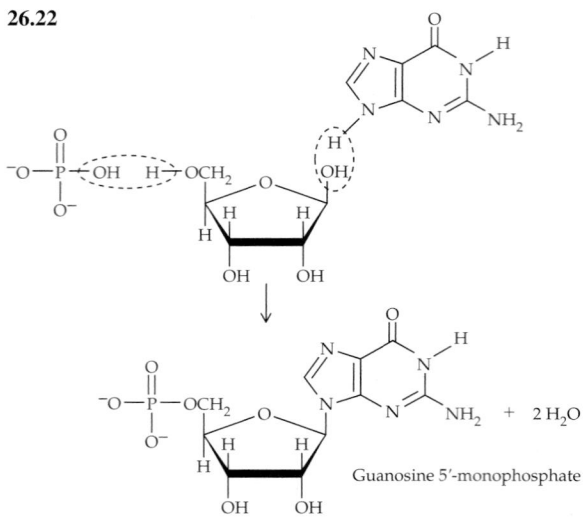

Guanosine 5'-monophosphate

26.23

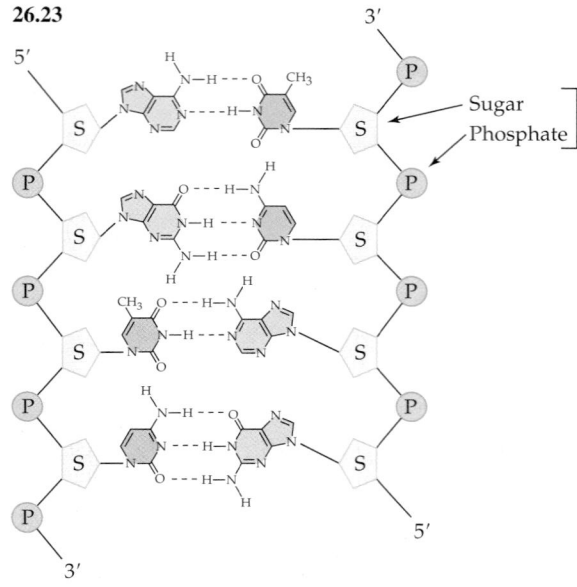

sequence of the left chain: 5' A-G-T-C 3'
sequence of the right chain: 5' G-A-C-T 3'

26.32

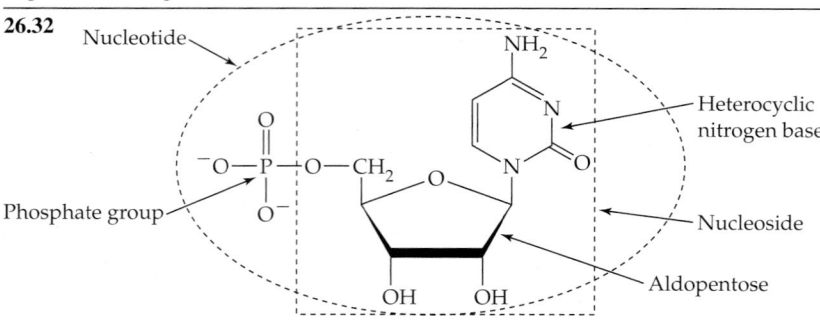

26.34 **(a)** adenine, cytosine, guanine, and thymine **(b)** adenine, cytosine, guanine, and uracil **(c)** Adenine, cytosine, and guanine are common to DNA and RNA. Thymine differs from uracil in having a methyl at position 5 of the pyrimidine ring.

26.24

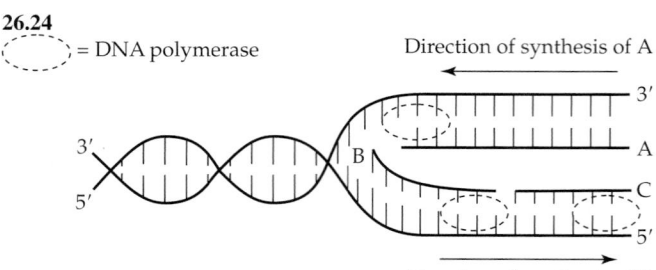

26.25 The sugar-phosphate backbone is found on the outside of the DNA double helix. Histones are positively charged; they contain groups such as Lys, Arg, and His.

26.26

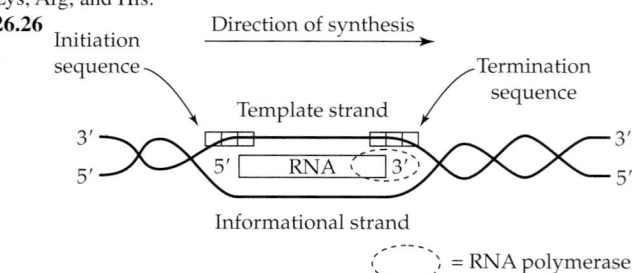

26.27 More than one codon can code for each amino acid. Only one possibility is shown.

(a) 5' | C | A | A | C | A | C | C | C | C | G | G | G | 3' mRNA

(b) 3' | G | T | T | G | T | G | G | G | G | C | C | C | 5' DNA template strand

(c) 5' | C | A | A | C | A | C | C | C | C | G | G | G | 3' DNA informational strand

(d) 65 possible sequences

26.28 A chromosome is an enormous molecule of DNA. A gene is a part of the chromosome that codes for a single protein needed by a cell.

26.30 A gene carries the DNA code needed to synthesize a specific polypeptide.

26.36

Bond between phosphate group and C5 of sugar

Phosphate group

Ribose

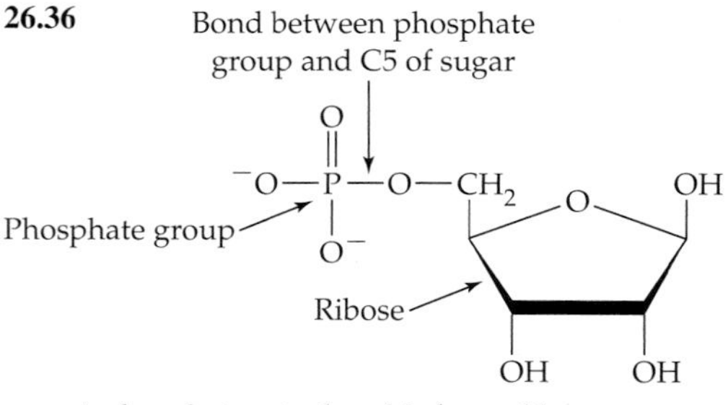

A phosphate ester bond is formed between the phosphate group and the sugar.

26.38 The 5′ end of a nucleotide is a phosphate group bonded to carbon 5 of ribose. The 3′ end is an —OH group bonded to carbon 3 of ribose.
26.40 Uridine 5′-monophosphate

26.42 (a) Base pairing is the hydrogen-bonded pairing of two complementary heterocyclic bases in the double helix of DNA and during replication, transcription, and translation. (b) Adenine pairs with thymine (or uracil in RNA) and guanine pairs with cytosine. (c) Adenine and thymine (or uracil) form two hydrogen bonds. Cytosine and guanine form three hydrogen bonds.
26.44 They always occur in pairs: They always H bond with each other.
26.46 22% G, 22% C, 28% A, 28% T
$(\%G = \%C; \%A = \%T: \%T + \%A + \%C + \%G = 100\%)$
26.48 to increase the speed of replication of DNA **26.50** *Messenger RNA (mRNA)* carries the genetic message from DNA to ribosomes. *Ribosomal RNA (rRNA)* complexes with protein to form ribosomes, where protein synthesis takes place. *Transfer RNA (tRNA)* transports specific amino acids to the ribosomes, where they are incorporated into proteins. **26.52** Exons are sequences of DNA that code for part of a specific protein. Introns are sequences of DNA that are found between exons and whose function is unclear; they are spliced from mRNA before protein synthesis. **26.54** template strand **26.56** An anticodon is a sequence of three nucleotides that is complementary to a sequence on a codon; tRNA
26.58

Amino Acid	Codons (5′ → 3′)					
(a) Val	GUU	GUC	GUA	GUG		
(b) Arg	CGU	CGC	CGA	CGG	AGA	AGG
(c) Ser	UCU	UCC	UCA	UCG	AGU	AGC

26.60 (a) 3′-GGG-5′ (b) 3′-CGC-5′ (c) 3′-AAU-5′ **26.62** template strand: 3′-ATG-GGA-5′ **26.64** Tyr-Pro
26.66
Metenkephalin: mRNA (5′ → 3′) Tyr—Gly—Gly—Phe—Met Stop
UAU–GGU–GGU–UUU–AUG–UAA
UAC GGC GGC UUC UAG
GGG GGG UGA
GGA GGA
26.68 A tRNA molecule is cloverleaf shaped. The tRNA anticodon triplet is on one "leaf," and an amino acid bonds covalently to the 3′ end.
26.70 The two mRNA codons for Glu are GAA and GAG. Of the four codons for Val (GUU, GUC, CUA, and GUG), the last two differ from the Glu codons by one base. Thus, a change in one base can result in a change from Glu to Val.
26.72
Position 9: Horse amino acid = Gly Human amino acid = Ser
mRNA codons (5′ → 3′):
GGU GGC GGA GGG UCU UCC UCA UCG AGU AGC

DNA bases (template strand 3′ → 5′):
<u>CCA</u> <u>CCG</u> CCT CCC AGA AGG AGT AGC <u>TCA</u> <u>TCG</u>

The underlined horse DNA base triplets differ from their human counterparts (also underlined) by only one base.

Position 30: Horse amino acid = Ala Human amino acid = Thr
mRNA codons (5′ → 3′):
GCU GCC GCA GCG ACU ACC ACA ACG

DNA bases (template strand 3′ → 5′):
CGA CGG CGT CGC TGA TGG TGT TGC

Each group of three DNA bases from horse insulin has a counterpart in human insulin that differs from it by only one base. It is possible that horse insulin DNA differs from human insulin DNA by only two bases out of 159!
26.74 dCTP **26.76** Avian flu viruses may be transmitted to humans from domesticated birds, which have been infected by migratory waterfowl. The virus can also be transmitted from an intermediate host, such as swine.
26.78 Influenza A viruses are described by a code that describes the hemagglutinins (H) and the neuraminidases (N) in the virus. The H1N1 virus was responsible for the 1918 influenza pandemic, and the H5N1 virus is present in avian flu. Since these viruses can undergo antigenic shift in host animals, there is concern when infected birds and animals harbor influenza viruses.

Chapter 27

27.1 "the fat red rat ate the bad rat" **27.2** As a result of the SNP, the base sequence codes for Trp, instead of Cys. This change would probably affect the functioning of the protein. **27.3** 3′-T-C-T-A-G-//-A- 5′
27.4 3′-C-T-T-A-A-//-G- 5′ **27.5** (a) sticky (b), (c) not sticky
27.6 (a) comparative genomics (b) genetic engineering (c) pharmacogenetics (d) bioinformatics **27.7** (1) A genetic map, which shows the location of markers one million nucleotides apart, is created. (2) Next, comes a physical map, which refines the distance between markers to 100,000 base pairs. (3) The chromosome is cleaved into large segments of overlapping clones. (4) The clones are fragmented into 500 base pieces, which are sequenced. **27.8** The variations are only a small part of the genome; the rest is identical among humans. A diverse group of individuals contributed DNA to the project. **27.9** *telomeres* (protect the chromosome from damage, involved with aging), *centromeres* (involved with cell division), *promoter sequences* (determine which genes will be replicated), *introns* (function unknown) **27.10** Differences: A mutation is an error that is transferred during replication and affects only a few people; a polymorphism is a variation in sequence that is common within a population.
27.11 Recombinant DNA contains two or more DNA segments that do not occur together in nature. The DNA that codes for a specific human protein can be incorporated into a bacterial plasmid using recombinant DNA technology. The plasmid is then reinserted into a bacterial cell, where its protein-synthesizing machinery makes the desired protein. **27.12** Major benefits of genomics: creation of disease-resistant and nutrient-rich crops, gene therapy, and genetic screening. Major negative outcomes: misuse of an individual's genetic information and prediction of a genetic disease for which there is no cure. **27.14** Celera broke the genome into many unidentified fragments. The fragments were multiplied and cut into 500 base pieces, which were sequenced. A supercomputer was used to determine the order of the bases. This approach allowed for faster sequencing of the human genome. **27.16** 50% **27.18** (a) Approximately 200 genes are shared between bacteria and humans. (b) A single gene may produce several proteins. **27.20** The clones used in DNA mapping are identical copies of DNA segments from a single individual. In mapping, it is essential to have a sample large enough for experimental manipulation. **27.22** The youngest cells have long telomeres, and the oldest cells have short telomeres. **27.24** It is the constriction that determines the shape of a chromosome during cell division. **27.26** Error in the mRNA sequence affects only one molecule of RNA; an error in the DNA sequence can be copied into all subsequent DNA molecules during replication. **27.28** A single-nucleotide polymorphism (SNP) is the replacement of one nucleotide by another at the same location in a DNA strand. **27.30** Changes in hair and eye color, sickle-cell anemia, epilepsy, total color blindness, Alzheimer's disease, breast cancer, resistance to diseases like AIDS. **27.32** Not always as some amino acids are coded by several different base sequences.
27.34

	Normal Codon	Codes For	Mutated Codon	Codes For
(a)	UCA	Ser	UCG	SER
(b)	UAA	Stop	UAU	Tyr

In (a), the mutated mRNA codes for the same amino acid as the nonmutated mRNA, and thus the mutation has no effect. In (b), the mutated mRNA replaces a "stop" codon with a Tyr codon; instead of stopping protein synthesis, mRNA continues adding amino acids to the polypeptide chain. Mutation (b) is much more serious that mutation (a).

27.36 DNA of bacterial cells occurs in plasmids, which carry only a few genes. Plasmids are easy to isolate, several copies of each plasmid are within a bacterial cell, and the DNA of plasmids replicates rapidly. **27.38** electrophoresis **27.40** (a) CCATG (b) TGGGT (c) CACAG **27.42** Pharmacogenomics is the study of the genetic basis of responses to drug treatment. Pharmacogenomics helps doctors prescribe the most effective medicine for a patient, based on the patient's genetic makeup. **27.44** corn, soybeans **27.46** Bioethics studies ethical issues such as ownership and access to genetic information, implications of genetic testing, prevention of genetic disability, and use of gene therapy. **27.48** A vector is the agent used to carry therapeutic quantities of DNA directly into cell nuclei. **27.50** The mutation would substitute Thr (hydrophilic side chain) for Ile (hydrophobic side chain), which will affect the tertiary structure of the protein. **27.52** germ cell (sperm or egg) **27.54** Some of the current developments in gene therapy; there is additional research in each of these diseases that is not provided here.

Parkinson's disease: Gene therapy reprograms the brain cells to produce dopamine, which helps control motor function.

Huntington's disease: Switch the gene mutation that causes Huntington's disease off in individual brain regions in mice; gene variant that influences when Huntington's disease breaks out early or later on has also been identified.

Prostate cancer: Stimulate the body's own immune system to attack the tumor, possibly preventing surgery for prostate cancer; product of a gene known as *EZH2* could determine how aggressive the cancer is.

Pancreatic cancer: Identification of genes that can increase a person's risk of developing pancreatic cancer; developing tests for detecting gene changes that are not due to inherited genes in pancreatic cancer precancerous conditions.

Muscular dystrophy: Identification of a gene sequence that is essential for helping muscle tissues function; creation of an experimental drug in children designed to cover the gene mutation so that the mutation is skipped resulting in a functional protein

Chapter 28

28.1 Hydrogen bonding, hydrophobic interactions, and ionic attractions or salt bridges **28.2** Amino acid derivative **28.3** Tyrosine **28.4** His **28.5** (b) **28.6** The molecules resemble the heterocyclic part of cAMP, and they might act as inhibitors to the enzyme that inactivates cAMP. **28.7** Glu-His-Pro **28.8** Hydrophobic because the hydrophobic part of the structure is larger than the polar, hydrophilic part. **28.9** Testosterone has a —CH$_3$ group between the first two rings; nandrolone doesn't. Otherwise, their structures are identical. **28.10** (a) 3 (b) 1 (c) 2 **28.11** Similarities: Both structures have aromatic rings, secondary amine groups, and alcohol groups. Differences: Propranolol has an ether group and a naphthalene ring system; epinephrine has two phenol hydroxyl groups; the compounds have different side-chain carbon skeletons. **28.12** (a) Malathion: it's the least toxic. (b) Parathion is most toxic (smallest LD$_{50}$). **28.13** (a) prolongs the effect of serotonin (b) blocks the response at the receptor **28.14** phenol hydroxyl group, ether, carbon–carbon double bond, aromatic ring. Tetrahydrocannabinol (THC) is hydrophobic and is likely to accumulate in fatty tissue. **28.15** (a) antihistamine (b) antidepressant **28.16** (a) polypeptide hormone (produced in the anterior pituitary gland) (b) steroid hormone (produced in ovaries) (c) Progesterone-producing cells have LH receptors. (d) Progesterone is lipid-soluble and can enter cells. **28.17** Adenylate cyclase can produce a great many molecules of cAMP, which phosphorylate kinase enzymes. These enzymes can cause the breakdown of gycogen to yield glucose. **28.18** (a) insulin (polypeptide hormone) (b) pancreas (c) in the bloodstream (d) Insulin doesn't enter cells directly because it can't pass through cell membranes. Instead, it binds with a cell surface receptor. **28.19** binding to receptors; activating second messengers **28.20** Enzymatic inactivation; reuptake by presynaptic neuron. **28.21** These substances increase dopamine levels in the brain. The brain responds by decreasing the number and sensitivity of dopamine receptors. Thus, more of the substance is needed to elevate dopamine levels, leading to addiction. **28.22** *A chemical messenger* is a molecule that travels from one part of the body to another location, where it delivers a signal or

acts to control metabolism. The *target tissue* is the cell or group of cells whose activity is regulated by the messenger. A hormone receptor is the molecule with which the chemical messenger interacts if it is a hormone. **28.24** A vitamin is usually an enzyme cofactor, whereas a hormone regulates enzyme activity. **28.26** Neither a hormone nor its receptor is changed as a result of binding to each other. The binding forces between hormone and receptor are noncovalent. **28.28** The endocrine system manufactures and secretes hormones. **28.30** polypeptide hormones, steroid hormones, amino acid derivatives **28.32** Enzymes are proteins; hormones may be polypeptides, proteins, steroids, or amino acid derivatives. **28.34** Polypeptide hormones travel through the bloodstream and bind to cell receptors, which are on the outside of a cell. The receptors cause production within cells of "second messengers" that activate enzymes. **28.36** the adrenal medulla **28.38** through the bloodstream **28.40** In order of involvement; the hormone receptor, G protein, and adenylate cyclase. **28.42** It initiates reactions that release glucose from storage. Termination occurs when phosphodiesterase converts cAMP to AMP. **28.44** anaphylaxis **28.46** Insulin contains 51 amino acids, is released from the pancreas, and acts at cells, causing them to take up glucose. **28.48** Mineralocorticoids (aldosterone), glucocorticoids (cortisone), and sex hormones (testosterone, estrone) all have the four-fused-ring skeleton. **28.50** androsterone, testosterone **28.52** Androgens increase muscle mass and strength. **28.54** epinephrine, norepinephrine, dopamine **28.56** (a) amino acid derivative (b) polypeptide hormone (c) steroid hormone **28.58** A synapse is the gap between two nerve cells that neurotransmitters cross to transmit their message. **28.60** nerve cell, muscle cell, endocrine cell **28.62** A nerve impulse arrives at the presynaptic end of a neuron. The nerve impulse stimulates the movement of a vesicle, containing neurotransmitter molecules, to the cell membrane. The vesicle fuses with the cell membrane and releases the neurotransmitter, which crosses the synaptic cleft to a receptor site on the postsynaptic end of a second neuron. After reception, the cell transmits an electrical signal down its axon and passes on the impulse. Enzymes then deactivate the neurotransmitter so that the neuron can receive the next impulse. Alternatively, the neurotransmitter may be returned to the presynaptic neuron. **28.64** (1) Neurotransmitter molecules are released from a presynaptic neuron. (2) Neurotransmitter molecules bind to receptors on the target cell. (3) The neurotransmitter is deactivated. **28.66** They are secreted in the central nervous system and have receptors in brain tissue. **28.68** Agonists prolong the response of a receptor. Antagonists block the response of a receptor. **28.70** agonists— nicotine; antagonists—atropine **28.72** *Tricyclic antidepressant:* Elavil *MAO inhibitor:* Nardil *SSRI:* Prozac **28.74** Cocaine increases dopamine levels by blocking reuptake. **28.76** THC increases dopamine levels in the same brain areas where dopamine levels increase after administration of heroin and cocaine. **28.78** antagonist **28.80** Endorphins are polypeptides with morphine-like activity. They are produced by the pituitary gland and have receptors in the brain. **28.82** If an animal produced its own pain-suppressing molecule, it would have an advantage in escaping from prey while injured. **28.84** Curare acts as an antagonist to acetylcholine at receptors. **28.86** The *hormone receptor* recognizes the hormone and sets into motion the series of reactions that result in the response of the cell to hormonal stimulation. The hormone–receptor complex interacts with the *G protein* and causes it to bind GTP. The G protein mediates the reaction between the receptor and adenylate cyclase. The G protein–GTP complex activates adenylate cyclase, which catalyzes the formation of the second messenger, cyclic AMP. Cyclic AMP initiates the reactions that the hormone is designed to stimulate. **28.88** Signal amplification is the process in which a small signal induces a response much larger in magnitude than the original signal. For hormones, this amplification begins with the activation of the G-protein; one hormone–receptor complex can activate many G-protein–GTP complexes. Each G-protein–GTP complex, in turn, can activate many molecules of adenylate cyclase, which can stimulate production of many molecules of cyclic AMP. The importance of signal amplification is that a small amount of hormone can cause a very large response. **28.90** Ethynyl estradiol and norethindrone differ only in the ring on the far left: The ring is a phenol in ethynyl estradiol and is an enone in norethindrone. Ethynyl estradiol and estradiol differ only in the five-membered ring: A —C≡CH group is present in ethynyl estradiol and absent in estradiol. Norethindrone is similar to progesterone in all but two respects: Progesterone has a methyl group between the first two rings and has an acetyl group in the five-membered ring, instead of the two groups of norethindrone. **28.92** Testosterone can be converted to androsterone by reduction of the ketone group and the double bond in the first ring and by oxidation of the hydroxyl group in the five-membered ring. These reactions are reductions and oxidations. **28.94** The craving for chocolate might be explained by the stimulation of dopamine receptors by anandamides, producing feelings of satisfaction similar to those produced by THC. The effect of chocolate consumption may be a milder version of marijuana's effects.

Chapter 29

29.1 in the cell: the charged form; outside the cell: the uncharged form The uncharged form enters the cell more readily. **29.2 (a)** iii **(b)** ii **(c)** iv **(d)** v **(e)** i **29.3 (a)** pH goes down; more acidic **(b)** $[O_2]$, $[CO_2]$, $[pH]$ **29.4 (a)** respiratory acidosis **(b)** metabolic acidosis **(c)** metabolic alkalosis **29.5 (a)** respiratory alkalosis **(b)** respiratory acidosis **(c)** metabolic acidosis **29.6 (a)** intracellular fluid **(b)** extracellular fluid **(c)** blood plasma, interstitial fluid **(d)** K^+, Mg^{2+}, HPO_4^{2-} **(e)** Na^+, Cl^-
29.7

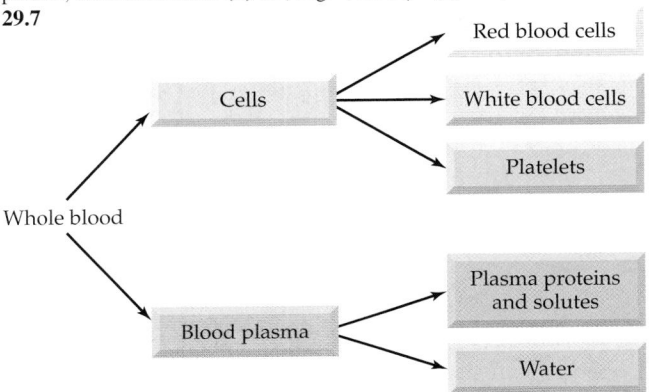

29.8 (a) O_2 **(b)** CO_2 **(c)** nutrients **(d)** waste products **(e)** hormones **(f)** white blood cells, platelets **29.9** swelling, redness, warmth, pain **29.10** Histamine is synthesized by the enzymatic decarboxylation of histidine. Histamine dilates capillaries, increasing blood flow that reddens and warms the skin. Blood-clotting factors and defensive proteins cause pain and swelling. **29.11** *cell-mediated immune response*: T cells; *antibody-mediated immune response*: under control of B cells, assisted by T cells **29.12** Excess hydrogen ions are excreted by reaction with NH_3 or HPO_4^{2-}. H^+ ions also combine with bicarbonate, producing CO_2 that returns to the bloodstream. **29.14** characteristics: ion, a gas, a small molecule, or a molecule with many polar or ionic groups on its surface **29.16** The difference in blood pressure between arterial capillaries and interstitial fluid pushes solutes and water into interstitial fluid. The difference in blood pressure between interstitial fluid and venous capillaries draws solutes and water into venous capillaries. **29.18** Collects excess interstitial fluid, cellular debris, proteins, and lipid droplets and ultimately returns them to the bloodstream. **29.20** antidiuretic hormone **29.22** Blood plasma is the fluid portion of blood that contains water-soluble solutes. Blood serum is the fluid that remains after blood has completely clotted. **29.24** erythrocytes (red blood cells), platelets, and white blood cells.

29.26 Electrolytes produce ions in water and conducts electricity. They maintain water balance, blood pH, muscle function, and more. **29.28** K^+, Mg^{2+} **29.30** inflammation, cell-mediated immune response, antibody-mediated immune response **29.32** immunoglobulins **29.34** Killer T cells destroy the invader; helper T cells enhance defenses; memory T cells can produce new killer T cells if needed. **29.36** Memory cells "remember" an antigen and are capable of producing antibodies to it for a long time. **29.38** Vitamin K, Ca^{2+} **29.40** They are released as zymogens in order to avoid undesirable clotting in noninjured tissues. **29.42** $+2$ **29.44** If pO_2 is below 10 mm Hg, hemoglobin is unsaturated. If pO_2 is greater than 100 mm Hg, hemoglobin is completely saturated. Between these pressures, hemoglobin is partially saturated. **29.46** a dissolved gas, bound to hemoglobin, bicarbonate ion
29.48
$$CO_2 + H_2O \underset{}{\overset{Carbonic\ anhydrase}{\rightleftharpoons}} HCO_3^- + H^+$$
29.50 *Respiratory acidosis* occurs when there is buildup of CO_2 in the blood. *Metabolic acidosis* is due to increased production of metabolic acids. **29.52** *Respiratory alkalosis* occurs when there is a loss of CO_2. *Metabolic alkalosis* occurs when there is elevated plasma bicarbonate concentration.
29.54 $H^+ + HCO_3^- \rightleftharpoons CO_2 + H_2O$
$H^+ + HPO_4^{2-} \rightleftharpoons H_2PO_4^-$
29.56 A nursing mother's antibodies can be passed to her baby in breast milk. **29.58** Active transport is the movement of solutes from regions of low concentration to regions of high concentration, a process that requires energy. Osmosis is the movement of water through a semipermeable membrane from a dilute solution to a more concentrated solution, a process that requires no energy. **29.60** In the blood, CO_2 from metabolism reacts to form $HCO_3^- + H^+$. The H^+ is bound to hemoglobin, which releases O_2, and is carried to the lungs. There, the H^+ is released and O_2 is bound to hemoglobin. In the urine, CO_2 reacts to form HCO_3^- and H^+. The HCO_3^- returns to the bloodstream, and the H^+ is neutralized by reaction with HPO_4^{2-} or NH_3. Whenever excess HCO_3^- accumulates in blood or urine, it can react with H^+ to form $H_2O + CO_2$. **29.62** When blood CO_2 level drops, the following reaction occurs to restore CO_2 supply:
$$H^+ + HCO_3^- \rightarrow H_2CO_3 \rightarrow CO_2 + H_2O.$$
This reaction uses up H^+ ions and leads to alkalosis. Breathing into a paper bag recaptures the expired CO_2 and restores the blood CO_2 level. **29.64** easiest to cross blood–brain barrier: Coniine, Atropine, Codeine, Heroin; hardest to cross blood–brain barrier: Solanine, Reserpine, Morphine; chemical rationale: *Coniine* has a structure similar to nicotine, as it is almost completely nonpolar and relatively small. *Atrophine* has very few polar groups on its surface, making it relatively nonpolar and able to cross the blood–brain barrier. In comparison to some of the other molecules, it is relatively small. *Solanine* has a large nonpolar surface; however, it is larger than some of the other molecules. This could slow down its rate of movement. *Reserpine* also has a large nonpolar surface with a small number of polar groups. However, it is the largest of the molecules listed in Table 16.1, which should slow down its rate of movement. *Morphine, codeine,* and *heroin* have similar structures and size. Except *morphine* has two alcohol groups, making the surface more polar, while *codeine* has one alcohol and an ether, and *heroin* has two esters, making it the least polar on the surface. Therefore, of this group of drugs, *heroin* can most easily pass the blood–brain barrier.

Glossary

1,4 Link A glycosidic link between the hemiacetal hydroxyl group at C1 of one sugar and the hydroxyl group at C4 of another sugar.

Acetal A compound that has two ether-like —OR groups bonded to the same carbon atom of what was once an aldehyde.

Acetyl coenzyme A (acetyl-CoA) Acetyl-substituted coenzyme A—the common intermediate that carries acetyl groups into the citric acid cycle.

Acetyl group A $CH_3C=O$ group.

Acetylcholine A vertebrate neurotransmitter that is most commonly found in muscle neurons.

Achiral The opposite of chiral, having superimposable mirror images and thus no right- or left-handedness.

Acid A substance that provides H^+ ions in water.

Acid dissociation constant (K_a) The equilibrium constant for the dissociation of an acid (HA), equal to $[H^+][A^-]/[HA]$.

Acidosis The abnormal condition associated with a blood plasma pH below 7.35; may be respiratory or metabolic.

Acid-base indicator A dye that changes color depending on the pH of a solution.

Activation (of an enzyme) Any process that initiates or increases the action of an enzyme.

Activation energy (E_{act}) The amount of energy necessary for a reaction to occur; it determines the reaction rate.

Active site A pocket in an enzyme with the specific shape and chemical makeup necessary to bind a substrate.

Active transport Movement of substances across a cell membrane with the assistance of energy (for example, from ATP).

Actual Yield The amount of product actually formed in a reaction.

Acyl group An $RC=O$ group.

Addition reaction A general reaction type in which a substance X—Y adds to the multiple bond of an unsaturated reactant to yield a saturated product that has only single bonds.

Addition reaction, aldehydes and ketones Addition of an alcohol or other compound to the carbon-oxygen double bond to give a carbon-oxygen single bond.

Adenosine triphosphate (ATP) The principal energy-carrying molecule; removal of a phosphoryl group to give ADP releases free energy.

Aerobic In the presence of oxygen.

Agonist A substance that interacts with a receptor to cause or prolong the receptor's normal biochemical response.

Alcohol A compound that has an —OH group bonded to a saturated, alkane-like carbon atom, R—OH.

Alcoholic fermentation The anaerobic breakdown of glucose to ethanol plus carbon dioxide by the action of yeast enzymes.

Aldehyde A compound that has a carbonyl group bonded to at least one hydrogen, RCHO.

Aldose A monosaccharide that contains an aldehyde carbonyl group.

Alkali metal An element in group 1A of the periodic table.

Alkaline earth metal An element in group 2A of the periodic table.

Alkaloid A naturally occurring nitrogen-containing compound isolated from a plant; usually basic, bitter, and often poisonous.

Alkalosis The abnormal condition associated with a blood plasma pH above 7.45; may be respiratory or metabolic.

Alkane A hydrocarbon that has only single bonds.

Alkene A hydrocarbon that contains a carbon-carbon double bond.

Alkoxide ion The anion resulting from the removal of the H from an alcohol, RO^-.

Alkoxy group An —OR group.

Alkyl group The part of an alkane that remains when a hydrogen atom is removed.

Alkyl halide A compound that has an alkyl group bonded to a halogen atom, R—X.

Alkyne A hydrocarbon that contains a carbon-carbon triple bond.

Allosteric control An interaction in which the binding of a regulator at one site on a protein affects the protein's ability to bind another molecule at a different site.

Allosteric enzyme An enzyme whose activity is controlled by the binding of an activator or inhibitor at a location other than the active site.

Alpha (α) particle A helium nucleus (He^{2+}), emitted as α-radiation.

Alpha- (α-) amino acid An amino acid in which the amino group is bonded to the carbon atom next to the —COOH group.

Alpha- (α-) helix Secondary protein structure in which a protein chain forms a right-handed coil stabilized by hydrogen bonds between peptide groups along its backbone.

Amide A compound that has a carbonyl group bonded to a nitrogen atom group, $RCONR_2'$, where the R' groups may be alkyl groups or hydrogen atoms.

Amine A compound that has one or more organic groups bonded to nitrogen; primary, RNH_2; secondary, R_2NH; or tertiary, R_3N.

Amino acid A molecule that contains both an amino functional group and a carboxyl functional group.

Amino acid pool The entire collection of free amino acids in the body.

Amino group The —NH_2 functional group.

Amino-terminal (N-terminal) amino acid The amino acid with the free —NH_3^+ group at the end of a protein.

Ammonium ion A positive ion formed by addition of hydrogen to ammonia or an amine (may be primary, secondary, or tertiary).

Ammonium salt An ionic compound composed of an ammonium cation and an anion; an amine salt.

Amorphous solid A solid whose particles do not have an orderly arrangement.

Amphoteric Describing a substance that can react as either an acid or a base.

Anabolism Metabolic reactions that build larger biological molecules from smaller pieces.

Anaerobic In the absence of oxygen.

Anion A negatively charged ion.

Anomeric carbon atom The hemiacetal C atom in a cyclic sugar; the C atom bonded to an —OH group and an O in the ring.

Anomers Cyclic sugars that differ only in positions of substituents at the hemiacetal carbon (the anomeric carbon); the α form has the —OH on the opposite side from the —CH_2OH; the β form has the —OH on the same side as the —CH_2OH.

Antagonist A substance that blocks or inhibits the normal biochemical response of a receptor.

Antibody (immunoglobulin) Glycoprotein molecule that identifies antigens.

Anticodon A sequence of three ribonucleotides on tRNA that recognizes the complementary sequence (the codon) on mRNA.

Antigen A substance foreign to the body that triggers the immune response.

Antioxidant A substance that prevents oxidation by reacting with an oxidizing agent.

Aromatic The class of compounds containing benzene-like rings.

Artificial radioisotope A radioactive isotope not found in nature.

Artificial transmutation The change of one atom into another brought about by a nuclear bombardment reaction.

Aryl halide A compound that has an aromatic group bonded to a halogen atom, Ar-X.

Atom The smallest and simplest particle of an element.

Atomic mass unit (amu) A unit for describing the mass of an atom; 1 amu = 1/12 the mass of a carbon-12 atom.

Atomic number (Z) The number of protons in the nucleus of an atom of a given element.

Atomic theory A set of assumptions proposed by English scientist John Dalton to explain the chemical behavior of matter.

Atomic weight The weighted average mass of an element's atoms.

ATP synthase The enzyme complex in the inner mitochondrial membrane where hydrogen ions cross the membrane and ATP is synthesized from ADP.

Autoimmune disease Disorder in which the immune system identifies normal body components as antigens and produces antibodies to them.

Avogadro's law The volume of a gas is directly proportional to its molar amount at a constant temperature and pressure (V/n = constant, or $V_1/n_1 = V_2/n_2$).

Avogadro's number (N_A) The number of units in 1 mole of anything; 6.02×10^{23}.

Balanced equation A chemical equation in which the numbers and kinds of atoms are the same on both sides of the reaction arrow.

Base A substance that provides OH^- ions in water.

Base pairing The pairing of bases connected by hydrogen bonding (G-C and A-T), as in the DNA double helix.

Beta- (β-) Oxidation pathway A repetitive series of biochemical reactions that degrades fatty acids to acetyl-SCoA by removing carbon atoms two at a time.

Beta (β) particle An electron (e^-), emitted as β radiation.

Beta- (β-) Sheet Secondary protein structure in which adjacent protein chains either in the same molecule or in different molecules are held in place by hydrogen bonds along the backbones forming a flat, sheet-like structure.

Bile Fluid secreted by the liver and released into the small intestine from the gallbladder during digestion; contains bile acids, cholesterol, phospholipids, bicarbonate ions, and other electrolytes.

Bile acids Steroid acids derived from cholesterol that are secreted in bile.

Binary compound A compound formed by combination of two different elements.

Blood clot A network of fibrin fibers and trapped blood cells that forms at the site of blood loss.

Blood plasma Liquid portion of the blood: an extracellular fluid.

Blood serum Fluid portion of blood remaining after clotting has occurred.

Boiling point (bp) The temperature at which liquid and gas are in equilibrium.

Bond angle The angle formed by three adjacent atoms in a molecule.

Bond dissociation energy The amount of energy that must be supplied to break a bond and separate the atoms in an isolated gaseous molecule.

Bond length The optimum distance between nuclei in a covalent bond.

Boyle's law The pressure of a gas at constant temperature is inversely proportional to its volume ($PV =$ constant, or $P_1V_1 = P_2V_2$).

Branched-chain alkane An alkane that has a branching connection of carbons.

Brønsted-Lowry acid A substance that can donate a hydrogen ion, H^+, to another molecule or ion.

Brønsted-Lowry base A substance that can accept H^+ from an acid.

Buffer A combination of substances that act together to prevent a drastic change in pH; usually a weak acid and its conjugate base.

Carbohydrate A member of a large class of naturally occurring polyhydroxy ketones and aldehydes.

Carbonyl compound Any compound that contains a carbonyl group $C=O$.

Carbonyl group A functional group that has a carbon atom joined to an oxygen atom by a double bond, $C=O$.

Carbonyl-group substitution reaction A reaction in which a new group replaces (substitutes for) a group attached to a carbonyl-group carbon in an acyl group.

Carboxyl group The —COOH functional group.

Carboxyl-terminal (C-terminal) amino acid The amino acid with the free —COO$^-$ group at the end of a protein.

Carboxylate anion The anion that results from ionization of a carboxylic acid, RCOO$^-$.

Carboxylic acid A compound that has a carbonyl group bonded to a carbon atom and an —OH group, RCOOH.

Carboxylic acid salt An ionic compound containing a cation and a carboxylate acid anion.

Catabolism Metabolic reaction pathways that break down food molecules and release biochemical energy.

Catalyst A substance that speeds up the rate of a chemical reaction but is itself unchanged.

Cation A positively charged ion.

Cellular protein A protein found inside cells.

Centromeres The central regions of chromosomes.

Chain reaction A reaction that, once started, is self-sustaining.

Change of state The conversion of a substance from one state to another—for example, from a liquid (l) to a gas (g).

Charles's law The volume of a gas at constant pressure is directly proportional to its Kelvin temperature ($V/T =$ constant, or $V_1/T_1 = V_2/T_2$).

Chemical change A change in the chemical makeup of a substance.

Chemical compound A pure substance that can be broken down into simpler substances by chemical reactions.

Chemical equation An expression in which symbols and formulas are used to represent a chemical reaction.

Chemical equilibrium A state in which the rates of forward and reverse reactions are the same.

Chemical formula A notation for a chemical compound using element symbols and subscripts to show how many atoms of each element are present.

Chemical reaction A process in which the identity and composition of one or more substances are changed.

Chemistry The study of the nature, properties, and transformations of matter.

Chiral Having right- or left-handedness with two *different* mirror-image forms.

Chiral carbon atom (chirality center) A carbon atom bonded to four different groups; also referred to as a chiral center or stereocenter.

Chromosome A complex of proteins and DNA; visible during cell division.

Cis-trans isomers Alkenes that have the same connections between atoms but differ in their three-dimensional structures because of the way that groups are attached to different sides of the double bond.

Citric acid cycle The series of biochemical reactions that breaks down acetyl groups to produce energy carried by reduced coenzymes and carbon dioxide.

Clones Identical copies of organisms, cells, or DNA segments from a single ancestor.

Codon A sequence of three ribonucleotides in the messenger RNA chain that codes for a specific amino acid; also the three nucleotide sequence (a stop codon) that stops translation.

Coefficient A number placed in front of a formula to balance a chemical equation.

Coenzyme An organic molecule that acts as an enzyme cofactor.

Cofactor A nonprotein part of an enzyme that is essential to the enzyme's catalytic activity; a metal ion or a coenzyme.

Colligative property A property of a solution that depends only on the number of dissolved particles, not on their chemical identity.

Colloid A homogeneous mixture that contains particles that range in diameter from 2 to 500 nm.

Combined gas law The product of the pressure and volume of a gas is proportional to its temperature ($PV/T =$ constant, or $P_1V_1/T_1 = P_2V_2/T_2$).

Combustion A chemical reaction that produces a flame, usually because of burning with oxygen.

Competititve (enzyme) inhibition Enzyme regulation in which an inhibitor competes with a substrate for binding to the enzyme active site.

Concentration A measure of the amount of a given substance in a mixture.

Concentration gradient A difference in concentration within the same system.

Condensed structure A shorthand way of drawing structures in which $C—C$ and $C—H$ bonds are understood rather than shown.

Configurations Stereoisomers that *cannot* be converted into one another by rotation around a single bond.

Conformation The specific three-dimensional arrangement of atoms in a molecule achieved specifically through rotations around carbon–carbon single bonds.

Conformers Molecular structures having identical connections between atoms where the interconversion of $C—C$ bond rotations results only in a different spatial arrangement of atoms.

Conjugate acid The substance formed by addition of H^+ to a base.

Conjugate acid-base pair Two substances whose formulas differ by only a hydrogen ion, H^+.

Conjugate base The substance formed by loss of H^+ from an acid.

Conjugated protein A protein that incorporates one or more non-amino acid units in its structure.

Constitutional isomers Compounds with the same molecular formula but different connections among their atoms; also known as structural isomers.

Conversion factor An expression of the numerical relationship between two units.

Coordinate covalent bond The covalent bond that forms when both electrons are donated by the same atom.

Cosmic rays A mixture of high-energy particles—primarily of protons and various atomic nuclei—that shower the earth from outer space.

Covalent bond A bond formed by sharing electrons between atoms.

Critical mass The minimum amount of radioactive material needed to sustain a nuclear chain reaction.

Crystalline solid A solid whose atoms, molecules, or ions are rigidly held in an ordered arrangement.

Cycloalkane An alkane that contains a ring of carbon atoms.

Cycloalkene A cyclic hydrocarbon that contains a double bond.

Cytoplasm The region between the cell membrane and the nuclear membrane in a eukaryotic cell.

Cytosol The fluid part of the cytoplasm surrounding the organelles within a cell. It contains dissolved proteins and nutrients.

***d*-Block element** A transition metal element that results from the filling of *d* orbitals.

D-Sugar Monosaccharide with the —OH group on the chiral carbon atom farthest from the carbonyl group pointing to the right in a Fischer projection.

Dalton's law The total pressure exerted by a mixture of gases is equal to the sum of the partial pressures exerted by each individual gas.

Decay series A sequential series of nuclear disintegrations leading from a heavy radioisotope to a nonradioactive product.

Degree of unsaturation The number of carbon-carbon double bonds in a molecule.

Dehydration The loss of water from an alcohol to yield an alkene.

Denaturation The loss of secondary, tertiary or quaternary protein structure due to disruption of noncovalent interactions and/or disulfide bonds that leaves peptide bonds and primary structure intact.

Density The physical property that relates the mass of an object to its volume; mass per unit volume.

Deoxyribonucleotide A nucleotide containing 2-deoxy-D-ribose.

Diabetes mellitus A chronic condition due to either insufficient insulin or failure of insulin to activate crossing of cell membranes by glucose.

Diastereomers Stereoisomers that are not mirror images of each other.

Digestion A general term for the breakdown of food into small molecules.

Dilution factor The ratio of the initial and final solution volumes (V_1/V_2).

Dipole A difference in charge ($+$ or $-$) associated with one end of a covalent bond compared with the other, or one end of a molecule compared with another.

Dipole-dipole force The attractive force between positive and negative ends of polar molecules.

Disaccharide A carbohydrate composed of two monosaccharides.

Dissociation The splitting apart of an acid in water to give H^+ and an anion.

Disulfide A compound that contains a sulfur-sulfur bond, RS-SR.

Disulfide bond (in protein) An S-S bond formed between two cysteine side chains; can join two peptide chains together or cause a loop in a peptide chain.

DNA (deoxyribonucleic acid) The nucleic acid that stores genetic information; a polymer of deoxyribonucleotides.

Double bond A covalent bond formed by sharing two electron pairs.

Double helix Two strands coiled around each other in a screwlike fashion; in most organisms the two polynucleotides of DNA form a double helix.

Drug Any substance that alters body function when it is introduced from an external source.

Eicosanoid A lipid derived from a 20-carbon unsaturated carboxylic acid.

Electrolyte A substance that produces ions and therefore conducts electricity when dissolved in water.

Electron A negatively charged subatomic particle.

Electron affinity The energy released on adding an electron to a single atom in the gaseous state.

Electron capture A process in which the nucleus captures an inner-shell electron from the surrounding electron cloud, thereby converting a proton into a neutron.

Electron configuration The specific arrangement of electrons in an atom's shells and subshells.

Electron shell A grouping of electrons in an atom according to energy.

Electron subshell A grouping of electrons in a shell according to the shape of the region of space they occupy.

Electron-dot (Lewis) symbol An atomic symbol with dots placed around it to indicate the number of valence electrons.

Electron-transport chain The series of biochemical reactions that passes electrons from reduced coenzymes to oxygen and is coupled to ATP formation.

Electronegativity The ability of an atom to attract electrons in a covalent bond.

Element A fundamental substance that cannot be broken down chemically into any simpler substance.

Elimination reaction A general reaction type in which a saturated reactant yields an unsaturated product by losing groups from two adjacent atoms.

Enantiomers (optical isomers) The two mirror-image forms of a chiral molecule.

Endergonic A nonspontaneous reaction or process that absorbs free energy and has a positive ΔG.

Endocrine system A system of specialized cells, tissues, and ductless glands that secretes hormones and shares with the nervous system the responsibility for maintaining constant internal body conditions and responding to changes in the environment.

Endothermic A process or reaction that absorbs heat and has a positive ΔH.

Energy The capacity to do work or supply heat.

Enthalpy A measure of the amount of energy associated with substances involved in a reaction.

Enthalpy change (ΔH) An alternative name for heat of reaction.

Entropy (S) A measure of the amount of molecular disorder in a system.

Entropy change (ΔS) A measure of the increase in disorder ($\Delta S = +$) or decrease in disorder ($\Delta S = -$) as a chemical reaction or physical change occurs.

Enzyme A protein or other molecule that acts as a catalyst for a biological reaction.

Equilibrium constant (K) Value obtained at a given temperature from the ratio of the concentrations of products and reactants, each raised to a power equal to its coefficient in the balanced chemical equation.

Equivalent For ions, the amount equal to 1 mol of charge.

Equivalent of acid Amount of an acid that contains 1 mole of H^+ ions.

Equivalent of base Amount of base that contains 1 mole of OH^- ions.

Erythrocytes Red blood cells (RBCs); transporters of blood gases.

Essential amino acid An amino acid that cannot be synthesized by the body and thus must be obtained in the diet.

Ester A compound that has a carbonyl group bonded to an $-OR'$ group, RCOOR'.

Esterification The reaction between an alcohol and a carboxylic acid to yield an ester plus water.

Ether A compound that has an oxygen atom bonded to two organic groups, R$-$O$-$R.

Ethyl group The $-CH_2CH_3$ alkyl group.

Exergonic A spontaneous reaction or process that releases free energy and has a negative ΔG.

Exon A nucleotide sequence that is part of a gene and codes for part of a protein.

Exothermic A process or reaction that releases heat.

Extracellular fluid Fluid outside cells.

f-Block element An inner transition metal element that results from the filling of f orbitals.

Facilitated diffusion Passive transport across a cell membrane with the assistance of a protein that changes shape.

Factor-label method A problem-solving procedure in which equations are set up so that unwanted units cancel and only the desired units remain.

Fat A mixture of triacylglycerols that is solid because it contains a high proportion of saturated fatty acids.

Fatty acid A long-chain carboxylic acid; those in animal fats and vegetable oils often have 12–22 carbon atoms.

Feedback control Regulation of an enzyme's activity by the product of a reaction later in a pathway.

Fermentation The production of energy under anaerobic conditions.

Fibrin Insoluble protein that forms the fiber framework of a blood clot.

Fibrous protein A tough, insoluble protein whose protein chains form fibers or sheets.

Filtration (kidney) Filtration of blood plasma through a glomerulus and into a kidney nephron.

Fischer projection Structure that represents chiral carbon atoms as the intersections of two lines, with the horizontal lines representing bonds pointing out of the page and the vertical lines representing bonds pointing behind the page. For sugars, the aldehyde or ketone is at the top.

Formula unit The formula that identifies the smallest neutral unit of an ionic compound.

Formula weight The sum of the atomic weights of the atoms in one formula unit of any compound, whether molecular or ionic.

Free-energy change (ΔG) A measure of the change in free energy as a chemical reaction or physical change occurs.

Free radical An atom or molecule with an unpaired electron.

Functional group An atom or group of atoms within a molecule that has a characteristic structure and chemical behavior.

Functional group isomer Isomers having the same chemical formula but belonging to different chemical families due to differences in bonding.

Gamma (γ) radiation Radioactivity consisting of high-energy light waves.

Gas A substance that has neither a definite volume nor a definite shape.

Gas constant (R) The constant R in the ideal gas law, $PV = nRT$.

Gas laws A series of laws that predict the influence of pressure (P), volume (V), and temperature (T) on any gas or mixture of gases.

Gay-Lussac's law For a fixed amount of gas at a constant voume, pressure is directly proportional to the Kelvin temperature ($P/T = $ constant, or $P_1/T_1 = P_2/T_2$).

Gene Segment of DNA that directs the synthesis of a single polypeptide.

Genetic (enzyme) control Regulation of enzyme activity by control of the synthesis of enzymes.

Genetic code The sequence of nucleotides, coded in triplets (codons) in mRNA, that determines the sequence of amino acids in protein synthesis.

Genome All of the genetic material in the chromosomes of an organism; its size is given as the number of base pairs.

Genomics The study of whole sets of genes and their functions.

Globular protein A water-soluble protein whose chain is folded in a compact shape with hydrophilic groups on the outside.

Glomerular filtrate Fluid that enters the nephron from the glomerulus; filtered blood plasma.

Gluconeogenesis The biochemical pathway for the synthesis of glucose from non-carbohydrates, such as lactate, amino acids, or glycerol.

Glycerophospholipid (phosphoglyceride) A lipid in which glycerol is linked by ester bonds to two fatty acids and one phosphate, which is in turn linked by another ester bond to an amino alcohol (or other alcohol).

Glycogenesis The biochemical pathway for synthesis of glycogen, a branched polymer of glucose.

Glycogenolysis The biochemical pathway for breakdown of glycogen to free glucose.

Glycol A dialcohol, or diol having the two —OH groups on adjacent carbons.

Glycolipid A lipid with a fatty acid bonded to the C2—NH_2 and a sugar bonded to the C1—OH group of sphingosine.

Glycolysis The biochemical pathway that breaks down a molecule of glucose into two molecules of pyruvate plus energy.

Glycoprotein A protein that contains a short carbohydrate chain.

Glycoside A cyclic acetal formed by reaction of a monosaccharide with an alcohol, accompanied by loss of H_2O.

Glycosidic bond Bond between the anomeric carbon atom of a monosaccharide and an —OR group.

Group One of the 18 vertical columns of elements in the periodic table.

Guanosine diphosphate (GDP) An energy-carrying molecule that can gain or lose a phosphoryl group to transfer energy.

Guanosine triphosphate (GTP) An energy-carrying molecule similar to ATP; removal of a phosphoryl group to give GDP releases free energy.

Half-life ($t_{1/2}$) The amount of time required for one-half of a radioactive sample to decay.

Halogen An element in group 7A of the periodic table.

Halogenation (alkene) The addition of Cl_2 or Br_2 to a multiple bond to give a 1,2-dihalide product.

Halogenation (aromatic) The substitution of a halogen group (—X) for a hydrogen on an aromatic ring.

Heat A measure of the transfer of thermal energy.

Heat of fusion The quantity of heat required to completely melt 1 gram of a substance once it has reached its melting point.

Heat of reaction (ΔH) The difference between the energy of bonds broken in the reactants and the energy of bonds formed in the products.

Heat of vaporization The quantity of heat needed to completely vaporize 1 gram of a liquid once it has reached its boiling point.

Hemiacetal A compound with both an alcohol-like —OH group and an ether-like —OR group bonded to the carbon atom that was at one time the aldehyde carbonyl carbon.

Hemiketal A compound with both an alcohol-like —OH group and an ether-like —OR group bonded to the carbon atom that was at one time the ketone carbonyl carbon.

Hemostasis The stopping of bleeding.

Henderson-Hasselbalch equation The logarithmic form of the K_a equation for a weak acid, used in applications involving buffer solutions.

Henry's law The solubility of a gas in a liquid is directly proportional to its partial pressure over the liquid at constant temperature.

Heterocycle A ring that contains nitrogen or some other atom in addition to carbon.

Heterogeneous mixture A nonuniform mixture that has regions of different composition.

Heterogeneous nuclear RNA (hnRNA) The initially synthesized mRNA strand containing both introns and exons.

Homogeneous mixture A uniform mixture that has the same composition throughout.

Hormone A chemical messenger secreted by cells of the endocrine system and transported through the bloodstream to target cells with appropriate receptors where it elicits a response.

Hydration The addition of water to a multiple bond to give an alcohol product.

Hydrocarbon An organic compound that contains only carbon and hydrogen.

Hydrogen bond The attraction between a hydrogen atom bonded to an electronegative atom (O, N, or F) and another nearby electronegative N or O atom.

Hydrogenation The addition of H_2 to a multiple bond to give a saturated product.

Hydrohalogenation The addition of HCl or HBr to a multiple bond to give an alkyl halide product.

Hydrolysis A reaction in which a bond or bonds are broken and the H— and —OH of water add to the atoms of the broken bond or bonds.

Hydronium ion The H_3O^+ ion, formed when an acid reacts with water.

Hydrophilic Water-loving; a hydrophilic substance dissolves in water.

Hydrophobic Water-fearing; a hydrophobic substance does not dissolve in water.

Hyperglycemia Higher-than-normal blood glucose concentration.

Hypertonic Having an osmolarity greater than the surrounding blood plasma or cells.

Hypoglycemia Lower-than-normal blood glucose concentration.

Hypotonic Having an osmolarity less than the surrounding blood plasma or cells.

Ideal gas A gas that obeys all the assumptions of the kinetic-molecular theory.

Ideal gas law A general expression relating pressure, volume, temperature, and amount for an ideal gas: $PV = nRT$.

Immune response Defense mechanism of the immune system dependent on the recognition of specific antigens, including viruses, bacteria, toxic substances, and infected cells; either cell-mediated or antibody-mediated.

Induced-fit model A model of enzyme action in which the enzyme has a flexible active site that changes shape to best fit the substrate and catalyze the reaction.

Inflammation Result of the inflammatory response: includes swelling, redness, warmth, and pain.

Inflammatory response A nonspecific defense mechanism triggered by antigens or tissue damage.

Inhibition (of an enzyme) Any process that slows or stops the action of an enzyme.

Inner transition metal element An element in one of the 14 groups shown separately at the bottom of the periodic table.

Intermolecular force A force that acts between molecules or discrete atoms and holds them close to one another. Also called van der Waals forces.

Interstitial fluid Fluid surrounding cells: an extracellular fluid.

Intracellular fluid Fluid inside cells.

Intron A nucleotide sequence in mRNA that does not code for part of a protein; removed before mRNA proceeds to protein synthesis.

Ion An electrically charged atom or group of connected atoms.

Ion-product constant for water (K_w) The product of the H_3O^+ and OH^- molar concentrations in water or any aqueous solution ($K_w = [H_3O^+][OH^-] = 1.00 \times 10^{-14}$).

Ionic bond The electrical attractions between ions of opposite charge in an ionic compound.

Ionic compound A compound that contains ionic bonds.

Ionic equation An equation in which ions are explicitly shown.

Ionic solid A crystalline solid held together by ionic bonds.

Ionization energy The energy required to remove one valence electron from a single atom in the gaseous state.

Ionizing radiation A general name for high-energy radiation of all kinds.

Irreversible (enzyme) inhibition Enzyme deactivation in which an inhibitor forms covalent bonds to the active site, permanently blocking it.

Isoelectric point (pI) The pH at which a sample of an amino acid has equal number of + and − charges.

Isomers Compounds with the same molecular formula but different structures.

Isopropyl group The branched-chain alkyl group —$CH(CH_3)_2$.

Isotonic Having the same osmolarity.

Isotopes Atoms with identical atomic numbers but different mass numbers.

Ketal A compound that has two ether-like —OR groups bonded to the same carbon atom of what was once a ketone.

Ketoacidosis Lowered blood pH due to accumulation of ketone bodies.

Ketogenesis The synthesis of ketone bodies from acetyl-CoA.

Ketone A compound that has a carbonyl group bonded to two carbons in organic groups that can be the same or different, $R_2C = O$, RCOR′.

Ketone bodies Compounds produced in the liver that can be used as fuel by muscle and brain tissue; 3-hydroxybutyrate, acetoacetate, and acetone.

Ketose A monosaccharide that contains a ketone carbonyl group.

Kinetic energy The energy of motion of an object in motion.

Kinetic-molecular theory (KMT) of gases A group of assumptions that explain the behavior of gases.

L-Sugar Monosaccharide with the —OH group on the chiral carbon atom farthest from the carbonyl group pointing to the left in a Fischer projection.

Law of conservation of energy Energy can be neither created nor destroyed in any physical or chemical change.

Law of conservation of mass Matter is neither created nor destroyed in any physical or chemical change.

Le Châtelier's principle When a stress is applied to a system in equilibrium, the equilibrium shifts to relieve the stress.

Leukocytes White blood cells (WBCs).

Lewis base A compound containing an unshared pair of electrons.

Lewis structure A molecular representation that shows both the connections among atoms and the locations of lone-pair valence electrons.

Limiting reagent The reactant that runs out first in a chemical reaction.

Line structure Also known as line-angle structure; a shorthand way of drawing structures in which carbon and hydrogen atoms are not explicitly shown. Instead, a carbon atom is understood to be wherever a line begins or ends and at every intersection of two lines, and hydrogens are understood to be wherever they are needed to have each carbon form four bonds.

Lipid A naturally occurring molecule from a plant or animal that is soluble in nonpolar organic solvents.

Lipid bilayer The basic structural unit of cell membranes; composed of two parallel sheets of membrane lipid molecules arranged tail to tail.

Lipogenesis The biochemical pathway for synthesis of fatty acids from acetyl-CoA.

Lipoprotein A lipid-protein complex that transports lipids.

Liposome A spherical structure in which a lipid bilayer surrounds a water droplet.

Liquid A substance that has a definite volume but that assumes the shape of its container.

Lock-and-key model A model of enzyme action in which the enzyme is a rigid lock that exactly fits the substrate, the key for the reaction.

London dispersion force The short-lived attractive force due to the constant motion of electrons within molecules.

Lone pair A pair of electrons that is not used for bonding.

Main group element An element in one of the two groups on the left or the six groups on the right of the periodic table.

Markovnikov's rule In the addition of HX to an alkene, the major product arises from the H attaching to the double-bond carbon that

has the larger number of H atoms *directly* attached to it and the X attaching to the carbon that has the smaller number of H atoms attached.

Mass A measure of the amount of matter in an object.

Mass/mass percent concentration [(m/m)%] Concentration expressed as the number of grams of solute per 100 grams of solution.

Mass number (A) The total number of protons and neutrons in an atom.

Mass/volume percent concentration [(m/v)%] Concentration expressed as the number of grams of solute per 100 mL of solution.

Matter The physical material that makes up the universe; anything that has mass and occupies space.

Melting point (mp) The temperature at which solid and liquid are in equilibrium.

Metabolism The sum of all of the chemical reactions that take place in an organism.

Messenger RNA (mRNA) The RNA that carries the code transcribed from DNA and directs protein synthesis.

Metal A malleable element with a lustrous appearance that is a good conductor of heat and electricity.

Metalloid An element whose properties are intermediate between those of a metal and a nonmetal.

Methyl group The —CH_3 alkyl group.

Methylene Another name for a —CH_2 unit.

Micelle A spherical cluster formed by the aggregation of soap or detergent molecules so that their hydrophobic ends are in the center and their hydrophilic ends are on the surface.

Miscible Mutually soluble in all proportions.

Mitochondrial matrix The space surrounded by the inner membrane of a mitochondrion.

Mitochondrion (plural, mitochondria) An egg-shaped organelle where small molecules are broken down to provide the energy for an organism.

Mixture A blend of two or more substances, each of which retains its chemical identity.

Mobile protein A protein found in body fluids such as blood.

Mobilization (of triacylglycerols) Hydrolysis of triacylglycerols in adipose tissue and release of fatty acids into the bloodstream.

Molar mass The mass in grams of one mole of a substance, numerically equal to the molecular weight.

Molarity (M) Concentration expressed as the number of moles of solute per liter of solution.

Mole The amount of a substance whose mass in grams is numerically equal to its molecular or formula weight.

Molecular compound A compound that consists of atoms joined by covalent bonds to form molecules rather than ions.

Molecular formula A formula that shows the numbers and kinds of atoms in one molecule of a compound.

Molecular weight The sum of the atomic weights of the atoms in a molecule.

Molecule A group of atoms held together by covalent bonds.

Monomer A small molecule that is used to prepare a polymer.

Monosaccharide (simple sugar) A carbohydrate with 3–7 carbon atoms.

Mutagen A substance that causes mutations.

Mutarotation Change in rotation of plane-polarized light resulting from the equilibrium between cyclic anomers and the open-chain form of a sugar.

Mutation An error in base sequence that is carried along in DNA replication and passed on to the offspring.

Native protein A protein with the shape (secondary, tertiary, and quaternary structure) in which it exists naturally in living organisms.

Natural radioisotope Radioactive isotopes that occur naturally and are found in the Earth's crust.

Net ionic equation An equation that does not include spectator ions.

Neurotransmitter A chemical messenger that travels between a neuron and a neighboring neuron or other target cell to transmit a nerve impulse.

Neutralization reaction The reaction of an acid with a base.

Neutron An electrically neutral subatomic particle.

Nitration The substitution of a nitro group (—NO_2) for a hydrogen on an aromatic ring.

Noble gas An element in group 8A of the periodic table.

Noncovalent forces Forces of attraction other than covalent bonds that can act between molecules or within molecules.

Nonelectrolyte A substance that does not produce ions when dissolved in water.

Nonessential amino acid One of 11 amino acids that are synthesized in the body and are therefore not necessary in the diet.

Nonmetal An element that is a poor conductor of heat and electricity.

Normal boiling point The boiling point at a pressure of exactly 1 atmosphere.

Normality (N) A measure of acid (or base) concentration expressed as the number of acid (or base) equivalents per liter of solution.

Nuclear decay The spontaneous emission of a particle from an unstable nucleus.

Nuclear fission When heavy nuclei fragment into lighter nuclei.

Nuclear fusion When lighter nuclei combine to form a heavier nuclide.

Nuclear reaction A reaction that changes an atomic nucleus, usually causing the change of one element into another.

Nucleic acid A polymer of nucleotides.

Nucleon A general term for both protons and neutrons.

Nucleoside A 5-carbon sugar bonded to a heterocyclic nitrogenous base; like a nucleotide but with no phosphate group.

Nucleotide A 5-carbon sugar bonded to a heterocyclic nitrogen base and a phosphate group; monomer for nucleic acids.

Nucleus The dense, central core of an atom that contains protons and neutrons.

Nuclide The nucleus of a specific isotope of an element.

Octet rule The tendency of atoms to gain or lose electrons to achieve a stable, noble gas configuration, that is, a completely filled subshell containing eight electrons.

Oil A mixture of triacylglycerols that is liquid because it contains a high proportion of unsaturated fatty acids.

Orbital A region of space within an atom where an electron in a given subshell can be found.

Orbital diagram A representation of the electron distribution into orbitals, in which orbitals are indicated by a line or a box, and electrons in each orbital are represented as arrows.

Organic chemistry The study of carbon compounds.

Osmolarity (osmol/L) The sum of the molarities of all dissolved particles (osmol) in 1 liter of solution.

Osmosis The passage of solvent through a semipermeable membrane separating two solutions of different concentration.

Osmotic pressure The amount of external pressure that must be applied to the more concentrated solution to halt the passage of solvent molecules across a semipermeable membrane.

Oxidation The loss of one or more electrons by an atom.

Oxidation number A number that indicates whether an atom is neutral, electron-rich, or electron-poor.

Oxidation-reduction (redox), reaction A reaction in which electrons are transferred from one atom to another.

Oxidative deamination Conversion of an amino acid $-NH_2$ group to an α-keto group, with removal of NH_4^+.

Oxidative phosphorylation The synthesis of ATP from ADP using energy released in the electron-transport chain.

Oxidizing agent A reactant that causes an oxidation by taking electrons from another reactant.

p-Block element A main group element that results from the filling of p orbitals.

p Function The negative common logarithm of some variable, $pX = -(\log X)$.

Partial pressure The contribution of a given gas in a mixture to the total pressure.

Parts per billion (ppb) Number of parts of solute (in mass or volume) per one billion parts of solution.

Parts per million (ppm) Number of parts of solute (in mass or volume) per one million parts of solution.

Passive transport Movement of a substance across a cell membrane without the use of energy, from a region of higher concentration to a region of lower concentration.

Pathway A series of enzyme-catalyzed chemical reactions that are connected by their intermediates, that is, the product of the first reaction is the reactant for the second reaction, and so on.

Pentose phosphate pathway The biochemical pathway that produces ribose (a pentose), NADPH, and other sugar phosphates from glucose; an alternative to glycolysis.

Peptide bond An amide bond that links two amino acids together.

Percent yield The percentage of the theoretical yield actually obtained from a chemical reaction.

Period One of the seven horizontal rows of elements in the periodic table.

Periodic table A tabular format listing all known elements where the atomic number (top),

symbol for the element (middle), and atomic mass (bottom) are given in each box that represents the element.

pH A measure of the acid strength of a solution; the negative common logarithm of the H_3O^+ concentration.

Phenol A compound that has an $-OH$ group bonded directly to an aromatic, benzene-like ring, $Ar-OH$.

Phenyl The C_6H_5- group.

Phosphate ester A compound formed by reaction of an alcohol with phosphoric acid; may be a monoester, $ROPO_3H_2$; a diester, $(RO)_2PO_3H$; or a triester, $(RO)_3PO$; also may be a di- or triphosphate.

Phospholipid A lipid that has an ester link between phosphoric acid and an alcohol (glycerol or sphingosine).

Phosphoryl group The $-PO_3^{2-}$ group in organic phosphates.

Phosphorylation Transfer of a phosphoryl group, $-PO_3^{2-}$, between organic molecules.

Physical change A change that does not affect the chemical makeup of a substance or object.

Physical quantity A physical property that can be measured.

Polar covalent bond A bond in which the electrons are attracted more strongly by one atom than by the other.

Polyatomic ion An ion that is composed of more than one atom.

Polymer A large molecule formed by the repetitive bonding together of many smaller molecules.

Polymorphism A variation in DNA sequence within a population.

Polysaccharide (complex carbohydrate) A carbohydrate that is a polymer of monosaccharides.

Polyunsaturated fatty acid A long-chain fatty acid that has two or more carbon-carbon double bonds.

Positron A "positive electron," which has the same mass as an electron but a positive charge.

Potential energy Energy that is stored because of position, composition, or shape.

Precipitate An insoluble solid that forms in solution during a chemical reaction.

Pressure The force per unit area pushing against a surface.

Primary (1°) carbon atom A carbon atom with one other carbon attached to it.

Primary protein structure The sequence in which amino acids are linked by peptide bonds in a protein.

Product A substance that is formed as the result of a chemical reaction and is written on the right side of the reaction arrow in a chemical equation.

Property A characteristic useful for identifying a substance or object.

Propyl group The straight-chain alkyl group $-CH_2CH_2CH_3$.

Protein A large biological molecule made of many amino acids linked together through amide (peptide) bonds.

Proton A positively charged subatomic particle.

Pure substance A substance that has uniform chemical composition throughout.

Quaternary ammonium ion A positive ion with four organic groups bonded to the nitrogen atom.

Quaternary ammonium salt An ionic compound composed of a quaternary ammonium ion and an anion.

Quaternary (4°) carbon atom A carbon atom with four other carbons attached to it.

Quaternary protein structure The way in which two or more protein chains aggregate to form large, ordered structures.

Radioactivity The spontaneous emission of radiation from a nucleus.

Radioisotope A radioactive isotope.

Radionuclide The nucleus of a radioactive isotope.

Reabsorption (kidney) Movement of solutes out of filtrate in a kidney tubule.

Reactant A substance that undergoes change in a chemical reaction and is written on the left side of the reaction arrow in a chemical equation.

Reaction mechanism A description of the individual steps by which old bonds are broken and new bonds are formed in a reaction.

Reaction rate A measure of how rapidly a reaction occurs; determined by E_{act}.

Rearrangement reaction A general reaction type in which a molecule undergoes bond reorganization to yield an isomer.

Receptor A molecule or portion of a molecule with which a hormone, neurotransmitter, or other biochemically active molecule interacts to initiate a response in a target cell.

Recombinant DNA DNA that contains segments from two different species.

Reducing agent A reactant that causes a reduction of another reactant by giving up electrons to it.

Reducing sugar A carbohydrate that reacts in basic solution with a mild oxidizing agent.

Reduction The gain of one or more electrons by an atom.

Reductive deamination Conversion of an α-keto acid to an amino acid by reaction with NH_4^+.

Regular tetrahedron A geometric figure with four identical triangular faces.

Replication The process by which copies of DNA are made when a cell divides.

Residue (amino acid) An amino acid unit in a polypeptide.

Resonance The phenomenon where the true structure of a molecule is an average among two or more conventional Lewis structures that differ only in the placement of double bonds.

Restricted rotation The limited ability of a molecule to rotate around a given bond.

Reversible reaction A reaction that can go in either the forward direction or the reverse direction, from products to reactants or reactants to products.

Ribonucleotide A nucleotide containing D-ribose.

Ribosomal RNA (rRNA) The RNA that is complexed with proteins in ribosomes.

Ribosome The structure in the cell where protein synthesis occurs; composed of protein and rRNA.

Ribozyme RNA that acts as an enzyme.

RNA (ribonucleic acids) The nucleic acids responsible for putting the genetic information to use in protein synthesis; polymers of ribonucleotides. Includes messenger (mRNA), transfer (tRNA), and ribosomal RNA (rRNA).

Rounding off A procedure used for deleting non-significant figures.

s-Block element A main group element that results from the filling of an *s* orbital.

Salt An ionic compound formed from reaction of an acid with a base.

Saponification The reaction of an ester with aqueous hydroxide ion to yield an alcohol and the metal salt of a carboxylic acid.

Saturated A molecule in which each carbon atom has the maximum number of single bonds possible (four).

Saturated fatty acid A long-chain carboxylic acid containing only carbon-carbon single bonds.

Saturated solution A solution that contains the maximum amount of dissolved solute at equilibrium.

Scientific Method Systematic process of observation, hypothesis, and experimentation to expand and refine a body of knowledge.

Scientific notation A number expressed as the product of a number between 1 and 10, times the number 10 raised to a power.

Second messenger Chemical messenger released inside a cell when a hydrophilic hormone or neurotransmitter interacts with a receptor on the cell surface.

Secondary (2°) carbon atom A carbon atom with two other carbons attached to it.

Secondary protein structure Regular and repeating structural patterns (e.g., α-helix, β-sheet) created by hydrogen bonding between backbone atoms in neighboring segments of protein chains.

Secretion (kidney) Movement of solutes into filtrate in a kidney tubule.

Shell (electron) A grouping of electrons in an atom according to energy.

SI units Units of measurement defined by the International System of Units. Examples include kilograms, meters, and kelvins.

Side chain (amino acid) The group bonded to the carbon next to the carboxyl group in an amino acid; different in different amino acids.

Significant figures The number of meaningful digits used to express a value.

Simple diffusion Passive transport by the random motion of diffusion through the cell membrane.

Simple protein A protein composed of only amino acid residues.

Single bond A covalent bond formed by sharing one electron pair.

Single-nucleotide polymorphism (SNP) Common single-base-pair variation in DNA.

Soap The mixture of salts of fatty acids formed on saponification of animal fat.

Solid A substance that has a definite shape and volume.

Solubility The maximum amount of a substance that will dissolve in a given amount of solvent at a specified temperature.

Solute A substance dissolved in a solvent.

Solution A homogeneous mixture that contains particles the size of a typical ion or small molecule.

Solvation The clustering of solvent molecules around a dissolved solute molecule or ion.

Solvent The substance in which another substance (the solute) is dissolved.

Specific gravity The density of a substance divided by the density of water at the same temperature.

Specific heat The amount of heat that will raise the temperature of 1 g of a substance by 1 °C.

Specificity (enzyme) The limitation of the activity of an enzyme to a specific substrate, specific reaction, or specific type of reaction.

Spectator ion An ion that appears unchanged on both sides of a reaction arrow.

Sphingolipid A lipid derived from the amino alcohol sphingosine.

Spontaneous process A process or reaction that, once started, proceeds on its own without any external influence.

Standard molar volume The volume of one mole of an ideal gas at standard temperature and pressure (22.4 L).

Standard temperature and pressure (STP) Standard conditions for a gas, defined as 0 °C (273 K) and 1 atm (760 mmHg) pressure.

State of matter The physical state of a substance as a solid, a liquid, or a gas.

Stereochemistry The study of the relative three-dimensional spatial arrangement of the atoms in a molecule.

Stereoisomers Isomers that have the same molecular and structural formulas, but different spatial arrangements of their atoms.

Sterol A lipid whose structure is based on a fused tetracyclic (four-ring) carbon skeleton.

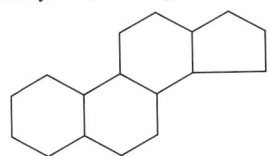

Straight-chain alkane An alkane that has all its carbons connected in a row.

Strong acid An acid that gives up H^+ easily and is essentially 100% dissociated in water.

Strong base A base that has a high affinity for H^+ and holds it tightly.

Strong electrolyte A substance that ionizes completely when dissolved in water.

Structural formula A molecular representation that shows the connections among atoms by using lines to represent covalent bonds.

Subatomic particles Three kinds of fundamental particles from which atoms are made: protons, neutrons, and electrons.

Subshell (electron) A grouping of electrons in a shell according to the shape of the region of space they occupy.

Substituent An atom or group of atoms attached to a parent compound.

Substitution reaction A general reaction type in which an atom or group of atoms in a molecule is replaced by another atom or group of atoms.

Substrate A reactant in an enzyme catalyzed reaction.

Sulfonation The substitution of a sulfonic acid group ($-SO_3H$) for a hydrogen on an aromatic ring.

Supersaturated solution A solution that contains more than the maximum amount of dissolved solute; a nonequilibrium situation.

Synapse The place where the tip of a neuron and its target cell lie adjacent to each other.

Telomeres The ends of chromosomes; in humans, contain long series of repeating groups of nucleotides.

Temperature The measure of the amount of heat energy in an object.

Tertiary (3°) carbon atom A carbon atom with three other carbons attached to it.

Tertiary protein structure The way in which an entire protein chain is coiled and folded into its specific three-dimensional shape.

Theoretical yield The amount of product formed assuming complete reaction of the limiting reagent.

Thiol A compound that contains an $-SH$ group, $R-SH$.

Titration A procedure for determining the total acid or base concentration of a solution.

Transamination The interchange of the amino group of an amino acid and the keto group of an α-keto acid.

Transcription The process by which the information in DNA is read and used to synthesize RNA.

Transfer RNA (tRNA) The RNA that transports amino acids into position for protein synthesis.

Transition metal element An element in one of the 10 smaller groups near the middle of the periodic table.

Translation The process by which RNA directs protein synthesis.

Transmutation The change of one element into another.

Triacylglycerol (triglyceride) A triester of glycerol with three fatty acids.

Triple bond A covalent bond formed by sharing three electron pairs.

Turnover The continual renewal or replacement of biomolecules; for protein it is defined by the balance between protein synthesis and protein degradation.

Turnover number The maximum number of substrate molecules acted upon by one molecule of enzyme per unit time.

Uncompetitive (enzyme) inhibition Enzyme regulation in which an inhibitor binds reversibly to the enzyme-substrate complex, blocking the binding of the second substrate to the active site.

Unit A defined quantity used as a standard of measurement.

Unsaturated A molecule that contains one or more carbon–carbon multiple bonds.

Unsaturated fatty acid A long-chain car-boxylic acid containing one or more carbon-carbon double bonds.

Urea cycle The cyclic biochemical pathway that produces urea for excretion.

Valence electron An electron in the outermost, or valence, shell of an atom.

Valence shell The outermost electron shell of an atom.

Valence-shell electron-pair repulsion (VSEPR) model A method for predicting molecular shape by noting how many electron charge clouds surround atoms and assuming that the clouds orient as far away from one another as possible.

Vapor The gas molecules in equilibrium with a liquid.

Vapor pressure The partial pressure of gas molecules in equilibrium with a liquid.

Vicinal Referring to groups on adjacent carbons.

Vitamin An organic molecule, essential in trace amounts that must be obtained in the diet because it is not synthesized in the body.

Volume/volume percent concentration [(v/v)%] Concentration expressed as the number of milliliters of solute dissolved in 100 mL of solution.

Wax A mixture of esters of long-chain carboxylic acids with long-chain alcohols.

Weak acid An acid that gives up H^+ with difficulty and is less than 100% dissociated in water.

Weak base A base that has only a slight affinity for H^+ and holds it weakly.

Weak electrolyte A substance that is only partly ionized in water.

Weight A measure of the gravitational force that the earth or other large body exerts on an object.

Whole blood Blood plasma plus blood cells.

X rays Electromagnetic radiation with an energy somewhat less than that of γ rays.

Zwitterion A neutral dipolar ion that has one + charge and one − charge.

Zymogen A compound that becomes an active enzyme after undergoing a chemical change.

Credits

Text and Art Credits

Cover: Adapted from CVS, http://www.cvs.com/drug/felodipine.

Chapter 10: 309, National Atmospheric Deposition Program (NRSP-3). 2015. NADP Program Office, Illinois State Water Survey, 2204 Griffith Dr., Champaign, IL 61820.

Chapter 11: 346, Data from UBM Medica, LLC.

Chapter 14: 467, From the article "Alcohol Use in Pregnancy," Centers for Disease Control and Prevention (CDC), (2014 April 17). www.cdc.gov/ncbddd/fasd/alcohol-use.html.

Chapter 19: 615, Based on Frederic H. Martini, Fundamentals of Anatomy and Physiology, 4th edition (Prentice Hall, 1998).; **616,** Based on Frederic H. Martini, Fundamentals of Anatomy and Physiology, 4th edition (Prentice Hall, 1998).

Photo Credits

Cover: Sebastian Kaulitzk/SPL/AGE Fotostock.

Chapter 1: 2, David Madison/Getty Images; **3,** Richard Megna/Fundamental Photographs; **7,** Kalcutta/Shutterstock; **11 (all),** Richard Megna/Fundamental Photographs; **12,** Rainer Walter Schmie/Fotolia; **14,** Centers for Disease Control and Prevention (CDC); **16,** Richard Megna/Fundamental Photographs; **18,** Pearson Education, Inc.; **19,** artkamalov/Shutterstock; **20,** Pearson Education, Inc.; **22,** Pearson Education, Inc.; **23,** Alamy; **26,** Pearson Education, Inc.; **27,** Richard Megna/Fundamental Photographs; **29,** Todd Bennett/KRT/Newscom; **32,** Shutterstock; **33 top,** BD; **33 bottom,** Ivica Drusany/Shutterstock; **37,** Pearson Education, Inc.

Chapter 2: 42, toysf400/Shutterstock; **44,** Actionpics/Fotolia; **45 left,** Image originally created by IBM Corporation; **45 right,** Lawrence Berkeley National Laboratory; **51(a) bottom,** Science Source; **51(b) bottom,** Peter Sobolev/Shutterstock; **51(a) middle,** Andraž Cerar/Shutterstock; **51(b) middle,** Leeuwtje/Getty Images; **51(c) middle,** Ben Mills; **51(a) top,** Norov Dmitriy/Getty Images; **51(b) top,** Ben Mills; **51(c) top,** Shutterstock; **53,** Richard Megna/Fundamental Photographs; **55,** Wellcome Image Library/Custom Medical Stock Photo; **56,** Michael Neary/Getty Images; **66,** Tyler Olson/Shutterstock.

Chapter 3: 72, Sciepro/Science Photo Library/Getty Images; **73,** Pearson Education, Inc.; **81,** Phase4Photography/Fotolia; **85 top (both),** Richard Megna/Fundamental Photographs; **85 bottom,** NASA; **91 top,** Richard Megna/Fundamental Photographs; **91 bottom,** Ezinne Achinivu, Ph.D.; **94,** Spencer Sutton/Science Source.

Chapter 4: 100, Wuttichok Painichiwarapun/Shutterstock; **102,** OJO Images Ltd/Alamy; **116,** Eye of Science/Science Source; **121,** Grieze/Fotolia; **128 top,** Zia Shusha/Fotolia; **128 bottom,** Coprid/Fotolia.

Chapter 5: 136 top, Zephyr/Science Source; **136 bottom,** MC/EB/Reuters; **140,** Thinkstock/Getty Images; **141,** Richard Megna/Fundamental Photographs; **142,** Evan Lorne/Shutterstock; **146 (both),** Peticolas/Megna/Fundamental Photographs; **150,** Arnd Wiegmann AKW/DG/THI/Reuters; **151,** Dmitry Kutlayev/Getty Images.

Chapter 6: 162, Robyn Mackenzie/Getty Images; **164,** Richard Megna/Fundamental Photographs; **177,** Delmas Lehman/Shutterstock.

Chapter 7: 184, Ted Kinsman/Science Source; **187,** Richard Megna/Fundamental Photographs; **191,** Joshua Alan Manchester/Newscom; **192,** GeoStock/Getty Images; **193 left,** Aaron Amat/Shutterstock; **193 right,** Samuel Perry/Shutterstock; **199,** Philipus/Alamy; **201,** Igor Stepovik/Shutterstock; **208,** Reuters Photographer/Reuters.

Chapter 8: 216, Bananaef/Fotolia; **224,** NASA Johnson Space Center; **228,** Cornishman/Getty Images; **230,** Laura Stone/Shutterstock; **240,** Richard MegnaFundamental Photographs; **241 top,** MedicImage/Alamy; **241 middle,** Alexei Zaycev/Getty Images; **241 bottom,** Marcel/Fotolia; **242 top left,** Jens Mayer/Shutterstock; **242 top right,** Jonny Kristoffersson/Getty Images.

Chapter 9: 254, Hero Images/Getty Images; **257,** Pearson Education, Inc.; **258,** Charles Thatcher/Getty Images; **260,** Richard Megna/Fundamental Photographs; **264,** Andrew Peacock/Getty Images; **265 (all),** Richard Megna/Fundamental Photographs; **273 (both),** Richard Megna/Fundamental Photographs; **274,** John Tlumacki/The Boston Globe/Getty Images; **280 (all),** Sam Singer; **283 top,** Custom Medical Stock Photo Custom Medical Stock Photo/Newscom; **283 bottom,** Syda Productions/Shutterstock.

Chapter 10: 290, Bob Pardue/Medical Lifestyle/Alamy; **296,** Pearson Education, Inc.; **299,** Gastrolab/Science Source; **304 bottom center,** Richard Megna/Fundamental Photographs; **304 bottom right,** Pearson Education, Inc.; **305,** Photongpix/iStock/Getty Images; **308,** Rmax/Getty Images; **312,** Pearson Education, Inc.; **319 top left,** Richard Megna/Fundamental Photographs; **319 top middle,** Richard Megna/Fundamental Photographs; **319 top right,** David Ballantine; **321,** Sam Edwards/Getty Images.

Chapter 11: 328, Science Source; **338,** SPL/Science Source; **339,** Fermilab; **343 top,** Stanford Dosimetry, LLC; **343 bottom,** Snowleopard1/E+/Getty Images; **345,** Tony Freeman/PhotoEdit; **346,** Stephen Uber/E+/Getty Images; **347,** Astier/BSIP SA/Alamy.

Chapter 12: 356, Metinkiyak/iStock/Getty Images; **359,** Xinhua News Agency/Newscom; **383,** Tetra Images/Alamy; **394,** Alamy.

Chapter 13: 402, Steve Gschmeissner/Getty Images; **404 top,** Jakub Krechowicz/Fotolia; **404 bottom,** National Oceanic and Atmospheric Administration (NOAA); **418 (both),** Richard Megna/Fundamental Photographs; **424,** Pearson Education, Inc.; **427,** small frog/Getty Images.

Chapter 14: 440, Andriy Petrenko/Fotolia; **445,** Riverwalker/Fotolia; **457,** Rod Planck/Photo Researchers, Inc./Science Source; **458,** Prisma Archivo/Alamy; **460,** Bill McMullen/Getty Images; **467,** Dmitry Lobanov/Fotolia.

Chapter 15: 474, Inga Spence/Alamy; **478,** Jack Goldfarb/Design Pics/Getty Images; **482 top,** Richard Megna/Fundamental Photographs; **482 bottom,** Richard Megna/Fundamental Photographs; **495,** Karen Faljyan/Shutterstock.

Chapter 16: 502, Legend_tp/Shutterstock; **514,** Pearson Education, Inc.

Chapter 17: 522, Fundamental Photographs; **536,** Andrei Rybachuk/Shutterstock; **542,** Pearson Education, Inc.

Chapter 18: 554, NMSB/Custom Medical Stock Photo; **566 left,** Swalls/Getty Images; **566 right,** Centers for Disease Control and Prevention (CDC); **568,** Centers for Disease Control and Prevention (CDC); **571 top,** Larry Ye/Shutterstock; **571 bottom,** Nata/Shutterstock; **576 (both),** Pearson Education, Inc.; **578,** Pearson Education, Inc.; **579 (both),** Pearson Education, Inc.; **582,** Vladimir Glazkov/iStock/Getty Images.

Chapter 19: 590, Olegpchelov/Fotolia; **592,** Ted Foxx/Alamy; **614,** voylodyon/Shutterstock; **616,** marlee/Shutterstock.

Chapter 20: 626, Wavebreakmedia/Shutterstock; **632,** Sergey Kolesnikov/iStock/Getty Images; **644 top,** Lew Robertson/Corbis; **644 middle,** Pearson Education, Inc.; **644 bottom,** Olga Langerova/

Index

Functional Groups of Importance in Biochemical Molecules

Functional Group	Structure	Type of Biomolecule
Amino group	$-NH_3^+$, $-NH_2$	Alkaloids and neurotransmitters; amino acids and proteins (Sections 16.1, 16.3, 16.6, 18.3, 18.7, 28.6)
Hydroxyl group	$-OH$	Monosaccharides (carbohydrates) and glycerol: a component of triacylglycerols (lipids) (Sections 14.1, 14.2, 20.1, 23.2)
Carbonyl group	$-\overset{\overset{\displaystyle O}{\|\|}}{C}-$	Monosaccharides (carbohydrates); in acetyl group (CH_3CO) used to transfer carbon atoms during catabolism (Sections 16.1, 17.4, 20.4, 20.8, 21.4)
Carboxyl group	$-\overset{\overset{\displaystyle O}{\|\|}}{C}-OH$, $-\overset{\overset{\displaystyle O}{\|\|}}{C}-O^-$	Amino acids, proteins, and fatty acids (lipids) (Sections 17.1, 18.3, 18.7, 23.2)
Amide group	$-\overset{\overset{\displaystyle O}{\|\|}}{C}-\overset{\overset{\displaystyle}{}}{N}-$	Links amino acids in proteins; formed by reaction of amino group and carboxyl group (Sections 17.1, 17.4, 18.7)
Carboxylic acid ester	$-\overset{\overset{\displaystyle O}{\|\|}}{C}-O-R$	Triacylglycerols (and other lipids); formed by reaction of carboxyl group and hydroxyl group (Sections 17.1, 17.4, 23.2)
Phosphates: mono-, di-, tri-	$-\overset{}{C}-O-\overset{\overset{\displaystyle O}{\|\|}}{\underset{\underset{\displaystyle O^-}{\|}}{P}}-O^-$ $-\overset{}{C}-O-\overset{\overset{\displaystyle O}{\|\|}}{\underset{\underset{\displaystyle O^-}{\|}}{P}}-O-\overset{\overset{\displaystyle O}{\|\|}}{\underset{\underset{\displaystyle O^-}{\|}}{P}}-O^-$ $-\overset{}{C}-O-\overset{\overset{\displaystyle O}{\|\|}}{\underset{\underset{\displaystyle O^-}{\|}}{P}}-O-\overset{\overset{\displaystyle O}{\|\|}}{\underset{\underset{\displaystyle O^-}{\|}}{P}}-O-\overset{\overset{\displaystyle O}{\|\|}}{\underset{\underset{\displaystyle O^-}{\|}}{P}}-O^-$	ATP and many metabolism intermediates (Sections 17.6, 21.4, and throughout metabolism sections)
Hemiacetal group, Hemiketal group	$-\overset{\overset{\displaystyle}{\|}}{\underset{\underset{\displaystyle OR}{\|}}{C}}-OH$	Cyclic forms of monosaccharides; formed by a reaction of carbonyl group with hydroxyl group (Sections 15.7, 20.3)
Acetal group, Ketal group	$-\overset{\overset{\displaystyle}{\|}}{\underset{\underset{\displaystyle OR}{\|}}{C}}-OR$	Connects monosaccharides in disaccharides and larger carbohydrates; formed by reaction of carbonyl group with hydroxyl group (Sections 15.7, 20.3, 20.5)
Thiols Sulfides Disulfides	$-SH$ $-S-$ $-S-S-$	Found in amino acids cysteine, methionine; structural components of proteins (Sections 14.8, 18.3, 18.8, 18.10)